# The Geology of Central Europe
# Volume 2: Mesozoic and Cenozoic

**Geological Society books refereeing procedures**

The Society makes every effort to ensure that the scientific and production quality of its books matches that of its journals. Since 1997, all book proposals have been refereed by specialist reviewers as well as by the Society's Books Editorial Committee. If the referees identify weaknesses in the proposal, these must be addressed before the proposal is accepted.

Once the book is accepted, the Society Book Editors ensure that the volume editors follow strict guidelines on refereeing and quality control. We insist that individual papers can only be accepted after satisfactory review by two independent referees. The questions on the review forms are similar to those for *Journal of the Geological Society.* The referees' forms and comments must be available to the Society's Book Editors on request.

Although many of the books result from meetings, the editors are expected to commission papers that were not presented at the meeting to ensure that the book provides a balanced coverage of the subject. Being accepted for presentation at the meeting does not guarantee inclusion in the book.

More information about submitting a proposal and producing a book for the Society can be found on its web site: www.geolsoc.org.uk.

It is recommended that reference to all or part of this book should be made in one of the following ways:
McCann, T. (ed.) 2008. *The Geology of Central Europe. Volume 2: Mesozoic and Cenozoic.* Geological Society, London.
Froitzheim, N., Plasienka, D. & Schuster, R. 2008. Alpine tectonics of the Alps and Western Carpathians. *In*: McCann, T. (ed.) *The Geology of Central Europe. Volume 2: Mesozoic and Cenozoic.* Geological Society, London, 1141–1232.

# The Geology of Central Europe
# Volume 2: Mesozoic and Cenozoic

EDITED BY

T. McCANN

Bonn University, Germany

2008

Published by

The Geological Society

London

## THE GEOLOGICAL SOCIETY

The Geological Society of London (GSL) was founded in 1807. It is the oldest national geological society in the world and the largest in Europe. It was incorporated under Royal Charter in 1825 and is Registered Charity 210161.

The Society is the UK national learned and professional society for geology with a worldwide Fellowship (FGS) of over 9000. The Society has the power to confer Chartered status on suitably qualified Fellows, and about 2000 of the Fellowship carry the title (CGeol). Chartered Geologists may also obtain the equivalent European title, European Geologist (EurGeol). One fifth of the Society's fellowship resides outside the UK. To find out more about the Society, log on to www.geolsoc.org.uk.

**The Geological Society Publishing House** (Bath, UK) produces the Society's international journals and books, and acts as European distributor for selected publications of the American Association of Petroleum Geologists (AAPG), the Indonesian Petroleum Association (IPA), the Geological Society of America (GSA), the Society for Sedimentary Geology (SEPM) and the Geologists' Association (GA). Joint marketing agreements ensure that GSL Fellows may purchase these societies' publications at a discount. The Society's online bookshop (accessible from www.geolsoc.org.uk ) offers secure book purchasing with your credit or debit card.

To find out about joining the Society and benefiting from substantial discounts on publications of GSL and other societies worldwide, consult www.geolsoc.org.uk, or contact the Fellowship Department at: The Geological Society, Burlington House, Piccadilly, London W1J 0BG: Tel. +44 (0)20 7434 9944; Fax +44 (0)20 7439 8975; E-mail: enquiries@geolsoc.org.uk.

For information about the Society's meetings, consult *Events* on www.geolsoc.org.uk. To find out more about the Society's Corporate Affiliates Scheme, write to enquiries@geolsoc.org.uk

Published by The Geological Society from:
The Geological Society Publishing House, Unit 7, Brassmill Enterprise Centre, Brassmill Lane, Bath BA1 3JN, UK

(*Orders*: Tel. +44 (0)1225 445046
Fax +44 (0)1225 442836)
Online bookshop: www.geolsoc.org.uk/bookshop



**British Library Cataloguing in Publication Data**
A catalogue record for this book is available from the British Library.

ISBN 978-1-86239-264-9 (hardback)
ISBN 978-1-86239-265-6 (paperback)

Typeset by Keytec Tyesetting Ltd, Bridport, UK
Printed by MPG Books Ltd, Bodmin, UK

**Distributors**

*North America*

For trade and institutional orders:
The Geological Society, c/o AIDC, 82 Winter Sport Lane, Williston, VT 05495, USA
*Orders*: Tel +1 800-972-9892
Fax +1 802-864-7626
Email gsl.orders@aidcvt.com

For individual and corporate orders:
AAPG Bookstore, PO Box 979, Tulsa, OK 74101-0979, USA
*Orders*: Tel +1 918-584-2555
Fax +1 918-560-2652
Email *bookstore@aapg.org*
Website http://bookstore.aapg.org

*India*

Affiliated East-West Press Private Ltd, Marketing Division, G-1/16 Ansari Road, Darya Ganj, New Delhi 110 002, India
*Orders*: Tel. +91 11 2327-9113/2326-4180
Fax +91 11 2326-0538
E-mail affiliat@vsnl.com

# Contents of Volume 2


Acknowledgements vii

Contributing authors ix

13. **Triassic.** S. Feist-Burkhardt, A. E. Götz, J. Szulc, R. Borkhataria, M. Geluk, J. Haas, J. Hornung, P. Jordan, O. Kempf, J. Michalík, J. Nawrocki, L. Reinhardt, W. Ricken, H.-G. Röhling, T. Rüffer, Á. Török & R. Zühlke 749

14. **Jurassic.** G. Pieńkowski, M. E. Schudack, P. Bosák, R. Enay, A. Feldman-Olszewska, J. Golonka, J. Gutowski, G.F.W. Herngreen, P. Jordan, M. Krobicki, B. Lathuiliere, R. R. Leinfelder, J. Michalík, E. Mönnig, N. Noe-Nygaard, J. Pálfy, A. Pint, M. W. Rasser, A. G. Reisdorf, D. U. Schmid, G. Schweigert, F. Surlyk, A. Wetzel & T. E. Wong 823

15. **Cretaceous.** S. Voigt, M. Wagreich, F. Surlyk, I. Walaszczyk, D. Uličný, S. Čech, T. Voigt, F. Wiese, M. Wilmsen, B. Niebuhr, M. Reich, H. Funk, J. Michalík, J. W. M. Jagt, P. J. Felder & A. S. Schulp 923

16. **Permian to Cretaceous tectonics.** M. Scheck-Wenderoth, P. Krzywiec, R. Zühlke, Y. Maystrenko & N. Froitzheim 999

17. **Palaeogene and Neogene.** M. W. Rasser, M. Harzhauser, O. Y. Anistratenko, V. V. Anistratenko, D. Bassi, M. Belak, J.-P. Berger, G. Bianchini, S. Čičić, V. Ćosović, N. Doláková, K. Drobne, S. Filipescu, K. Gürs, Š. Hladilová, H. Hrvatović, B. Jelen, J. R. Kasiński, M. Kováč, P. Kralj, T. Marjanac, E. Márton, P. Mietto, A. Moro, A. Nagymarosy, J. H. Nebelsick, S. Nehyba, B. Ogorelec, N. Oszczypko, D. Pavelić, R. Pavlovec, J. Pavšič, P. Petrová, M. Piwocki, M. Poljak, N. Pugliese, R. Redžepović, H. Rifelj, R. Roetzel, D. Skaberne, L. Sliva, G. Standke, G. Tunis, D. Vass, M. Wagreich & F. Wesselingh 1031

18. **Alpine tectonics of the Alps and Western Carpathians.** N. Froitzheim, D. Plašienka & R. Schuster 1141

19. **Alpine tectonics north of the Alps.** K. Reicherter, N. Froitzheim, M. Jarosiński, J. Badura, H.-J. Franzke, M. Hansen, C. Hübscher, R. Müller, P. Poprawa, J. Reinecker, W. Stackebrandt, T. Voigt, H. von Eynatten & W. Zuchiewicz 1233

20. **Quaternary.** T. Litt, H.-U. Schmincke, M. Frechen & C. Schlüchter 1287

21. **Fossil fuels, ore and industrial minerals.** H. G. Dill, R. F. Sachsenhofer, P. Grecula, T. Sasvári, L. A. Palinkaš, S. Borojević-Šoštarić, S. Strmić-Palinkaš, W. Prochaska, G. Garuti, F. Zaccarini, D. Arbouille & H.-M. Schulz (Mineral and Energy Resources of Central Europe (map 1:2 500 000). CD on inside back cover) 1341

Index Ii

# Contents of Volume 1


Acknowledgements vii

Contributing authors ix

1. **Introduction and overview.** T. McCann 1

2. **Precambrian.** U. Linnemann, R. L. Romer, C. Pin, P. Aleksandrowski, Z.Buła, T. Geisler, V. Kachlik, E. Krzemińska, S. Mazur, G. Motuza, J. B. Murphy, R. D. Nance, S. A. Pisarevsky, B. Schulz, J. Ulrich, J. Wiszniewska, J. Żaba & A. Zeh 21

3. **Cadomian tectonics.** U. Linnemann, R. D'Lemos, K. Drost, T. Jeffries, A. Gerdes, R. L. Romer, S. D. Samson & R. A. Strachan 103

4. **Cambrian.** G. Geyer, O. Elicki, O. Fatka & A. Żylińska 155

5. **Ordovician.** T. Servais, J. Dzik, O. Fatka, T. Heuse, M. Vecoli & J. Verniers 203

6. **Silurian.** J. Verniers, J. Maletz, J. Kříž, Ž. Žigaitė, F. Paris, H. P. Schönlaub & R. Wrona 249

7. **Caledonian tectonics.** C. M. Krawczyk, T. McCann, L. R. M. Cocks, R. England, J. McBride & S. Wybraniec 303

8. **Devonian.** Z. Bełka & M. Narkiewicz 383

9. **Carboniferous.** T. McCann, S. Skompski, E. Poty, M. Dusar, A. Vozárová, J. Schneider, A. Wetzel, K. Krainer, K. Kornpihl, A. Schäfer, M. Krings, S. Oplustil & J. Tait 411

10. **Permian.** T. McCann, H. Kiernowski, K. Krainer, A. Vozárová, T. Peryt, S. Oplustil, H. Stollhofen, J. Schneider, A.Wetzel, F. Boulvain, M. Dusar, Á. Török, J. Haas, J. Tait & F. Körner 531

11. **Variscan tectonics.** U. Kroner, J.-L. Mansy, S. Mazur, P. Aleksandrowski, H. P. Hann, H. Huckriede, F. Lacquement, J. Lamarche, P. Ledru, T. C. Pharaoh, H. Zedler, A. Zeh & G. Zulauf 599

12. **Palaeozoic magmatism.** M. J. Timmerman 665

Index Ii

# Acknowledgements

The idea of publishing a reference work on Central European geology, written in English, by research-active experts from a range of European countries, was initially conceived in 2004. From this idea to final completion was a long road! Manuscripts began to arrive in 2005, were refereed and revised during 2006, with the completed work submitted to the Geological Society in May 2007. A mammoth work such as this involves the efforts of many, many people. I would, therefore, like to first thank the co-ordinators of the individual chapters for their work in steering to completion each of their manuscripts. These co-ordinators built up expert teams of contributing authors who wrote on specific areas or topics, and I would also like to thank each individual, in turn, for their excellent work.

A work such as this, however, could not have been completed without the published scientific papers of the many hundreds, if not thousands, of individual authors working over the last century or so. Many of these studies were carried out at a time when Central Europe, both politically and economically, was a very different region from the one we know today. Working in sometimes difficult circumstances, these authors have contributed to our knowledge and understanding of the evolution of this complex area. Without the detailed studies of these many scientists, any overview such as this would have been impossible, and I would, therefore, like to acknowledge our collective debt to these many workers.

Finally, I would like to acknowledge the support and guidance of Angharad Hills of the Geological Society Publishing House as well as the superlative editorial skills of Sally Oberst and her colleague Jessica Pollitt in bringing this work to fruition.

The editor gratefully acknowledges the work of the following referees:

Richard Aldridge
Marek Awdankiewicz
Thilo Bechstädt
David Blundell
Christoph Breitkreuz
Tim Brewer
Robin Cocks
Juergen Ehlers
Mary Ford
Sven-Oliver Franz
Hans-Joachim Franzke
Bernhard Fügenschuh
Andrew Gale
Reinhard Gast
Reinhard Gaupp
Alice Giannetti
Phil Gibbard
Ken Glennie
David Harper
Adrian Hartley
Jeremy Inglis
Ian Jarvis
Peter Konigshof
Phil Leat
Cherry Lewis
Ralf Littke
Jerzy Nawrocki
Franz Neubauer
Onno Oncken
Alan Owen
Christophe Pascal
Holger Paulick
Andreas Peterek
Niels Poulsen
Cecilio Quesada
Bettina Reitenbacher
David Rickard
Fred Rögl
Reinhard Schaeffer
Andreas Siemes
Randell Stephenson
Rob Strachan
Jaromir Ulrych
Mario Valdivia-Manchego
Cees van Staal
Geoff Warrington
Paul Wignall
John Winchester
Thomas Will
Gernold Zulauf

## Contributing authors

**Paweł Aleksandrowski**
*Institute of Geological Sciences, University of Wrocław, Wrocław, Poland (e-mail: palex@ing.uni.wroc.pl)*
**Olga Y. Anistratenko**
*Institute of Geological Sciences of NAS Ukraine, Kiev, Ukraine (e-mail: nistrat@rambler.ru or anistrat@izan.kiev.ua)*
**Vitaliy V. Anistratenko**
*Schmalhausen Institute of Zoology of NAS Ukraine, Kiev, Ukraine (e-mail: anistrat@izan.kiev.ua or nistrat@rambler.ru)*
**Didier Arbouille**
*IHS Energy 24, Geneva, Switzerland (e-mail: didier.arbouille @ihsenergy.com)*
**Janusz Badura**
*Polish Geological Institute, Wroclaw, Poland (e-mail: janusz.badura@pgi.gov.pl)*
**Davide Bassi**
*Dipartimento di Scienze della Terra, Università degli Studi di Ferrara, Ferrara, Italy (e-mail: bsd@unife.it)*
**Mirko Belak**
*Croatian Geological Survey, Zagreb, Croatia (e-mail: mbelak@ hgi-cgs.hr)*
**Zdzislaw Bełka**
*Institute of Geology, Adam Mickiewicz University, Poznań, Poland (e-mail: zbelka@amu.edu.pl)*
**Jean-Pierre Berger**
*Institut de Géologie, Université de Fribourg, Fribourg, Switzerland (e-mail: jean-pierre.berger@unifr.ch)*
**Gianluca Bianchini**
*Dipartimento di Scienze della Terra, Università degli Studi di Ferrara, Ferrara, Italy (e-mail: bncglc@unife.it)*
**Ravi Borkhataria**
*Institute of Geosciences, University of Tübingen, Tübingen, Germany. Current address: Shell International Exploration and Production B.V., Rijswijk, The Netherlands (e-mail: ravi. borkhataria@shell.com)*
**Sibila Borojević-Šoštarić**
*Department of Geology, University of Zagreb, Zagreb, Croatia (e-mail: sborojsost@geol.pmf.hr)*
**Pavel Bosák**
*Institute of Geology, Academy of Sciences of the Czech Republic, Prague, Czech Republic (e-mail: bosak@gli.cas.cz)*
**Frédéric Boulvain**
*Département de Géologie, Université de Liège, Liège, Belgium (e-mail: fboulvain@eulg.ac.be)*
**Zbigniew Buła**
*Polish Geological Institute, Sosnowiec, Poland (e-mail: zbigniew.bula@pgi.gov.pl)*
**Stanislav Čech**
*Czech Geological Survey, Prague, Czech Republic (e-mail: stanislav.cech@geology.cz)*
**Safet Čičić**
*Mining & Civil Engineering Faculty, University of Tuzla, Tuzla, Bosnia Herzegovina.*
**L. Robin M. Cocks**
*Natural History Museum, London UK (e-mail: r.cocks@nhm. ac.uk)*
**Vlasta Ćosović**
*Department of Geology, University of Zagreb, Zagreb, Croatia (e-mail: vcosovic@geol.pmf.hr)*
**Harald G. Dill**
*Federal Institute for Geosciences and Natural Resources, Hanover, Germany (e-mail: h.dill@bgr.de)*
**Richard S. D'Lemos**
*Crustal Dynamics Group, Oxford Brookes University, Oxford, UK. Present address: Somerton, Oxfordshire, UK (e-mail: richard@dlemos2.wanadoo.co.uk)*
**Nela Doláková**
*Institute of Geological Sciences, Masaryk University, Brno, Czech Republic (e-mail: nela@sci.muni.cz)*
**Katica Drobne**
*Institute of Palaeontology ZRC-SAZU, Ljubljana, Slovenia (e-mail: katica@zrc-sazu.si)*
**Kerstin Drost**
*Museum für Mineralogie und Geologie, Dresden, Germany (e-mail: kerstin.drost@snsd.smwk.sachsen.de)*
**Michiel Dusar**
*Geological Survey of Belgium, Brussels, Belgium (e-mail: michiel.dusar@naturalsciences.be)*
**Jerzy Dzik**
*Instytut Paleobiologii PAN, Warsaw, Poland (e-mail: dzik@twarda. pan.pl)*
**Olak Elicki**
*Institut für Geologie, TU Bergakademi Freiberg, Freiberg/Sachsen, Germany (e-mail: elicki@geol.tu-freiberg.de)*
**Raymond Enay**
*UFR des Sciences de la Terre, Université Claude Bernard Lyon 1, Villeurbanne, France (e-mail: raymond.enay@univ-lyon1.fr)*
**Richard England**
*Department of Geology, University of Leicester, Leicester, UK (e-mail: rwe5@leicester.ac.uk)*
**Oldrich Fatka**
*Department of Paleontology, Faculty of Science, Charles University, Prague, Czech Republic (e-mail: fatka@natur.cuni.cz)*
**Susanne Feist-Burkhardt**
*Natural History Museum, London, UK (e-mail: s.feist-burkhardt @nhm.ac.uk)*
**Peter J. Felder**
*Université de Liège, Paléontologie, Liège, Belgium (e-mail: sjeuf.felder@wanadoo.nl)*
**Anna Feldman-Olszewska**
*Polish Geological Institute, Warsaw, Poland (e-mail: anna. feldman-olszewska@pgi.gov.pl)*
**Sorin Filipescu**
*Department of Geology, Babes-Bolyai University, Cluj-Napoca, Romania (e-mail: sorin@bioge.ubbcluj.ro)*
**Hans-Joachim Franzke**
*Institute for Geology and Paleontology, Technische Universität, Clausthal-Zellerfeld, Germany (e-mail: hans.joachim.franzke@ tu-clausthal.de)*
**Manfred Frechen**
*Leibniz Institute for Applied Geoscience (GGA-Institut), Hanover, Germany (e-mail: manfred.frechen@gga-hannover.de)*
**Nikolaus Froitzheim**
*Geologisches Institut, University of Bonn, Bonn, Germany (e-mail: niko.froitzheim@uni-bonn.de)*
**Hanspeter Funk**
*Seminarstraße 26, Baden, Switzerland (e-mail: h.funk@ hispeed.ch)*

**Giorgio Garuti**
*Department of Earth Sciences, University of Modena and Reggio Emilia, Modena, Italy (e-mail: garutig@unimore.it)*
**Thorsten Geisler**
*Institut für Mineralogie, Universität Münster, Münster, Germany (e-mail: tgeisler@nwz.uni-muenster.de)*
**Mark Geluk**
*Shell International Exploration and Production B.V., Rijswijk, The Netherlands (e-mail: mark.geluk@shell.com)*
**Axel Gerdes**
*Institut für Geowissenschaften, Mineralogie, Johann Wolfgang Goethe-Universität, Frankfurt/Main, Germany (e-mail: gerdes @em.uni-frankfurt.de)*
**Gerd Geyer**
*Institut für Paläontologie, Universität Würzburg, Würzburg, Germany (e-mail: gerd.geyer@mail.uni-wuerzburg.de)*
**Jan Golonka**
*University of Science and Technology, Kraków, Poland (e-mail: jan_golonka@yahoo.com)*
**Annette Götz**
*Institute for Applied Geosciences, Darmstadt University of Technology, Schnittspahnstrasse 9, D-64287 Darmstadt, Germany (e-mail: goetz@energycenter.tu-darmstadt.de)*
**P. Grecula**
*Geological Survey of Slovak Republic, Kosice, Slovakia (e-mail: grecula@gssr-ke.sk)*
**Karl Gürs**
*Landesamt für Natur und Umwelt Schleswig-Holstein, Flintbek, Germany (e-mail: kguers@lanu.landsh.de)*
**Jacek Gutowski**
*Polish Geological Institute, Warsaw, Poland (e-mail: jacek. gutowski@pgi.gov.pl)*
**János Haas**
*Geological, Geophysical & Space Science Research Group of the Hungarian Academy of Sciences, Eötvös Loránd University, Budapest, Hungary (e-mail: haas@ludens.elte.hu)*
**Horst Peter Hann**
*Institut für Geologie und Paläontologie, Universität Tübingen, Tübingen, Germany (e-mail: horst.hann@uni-tuebingen.de)*
**Martin Hansen**
*Hydro Oil & Energy, Research Centre Bergen, Norway (e-mail: martin.bak.hansen@hydro.com)*
**Mathias Harzhauser**
*Naturhistorisches Museum in Wien, Vienna, Austria (e-mail: mathias.harzhauser@nhm-wien.ac.at)*
**G.F.W. Herngreen**
*Kenniscentrum Biogeologie (UU/TNO), Utrecht University, Utrecht, The Netherlands (e-mail: g.f.w.herngreen@bio.uu.nl)*
**Thomas Heuse**
*Thüringer Landesanstalt für Umwelt und Geologie, Geologischer Landesdienst, Jena, Germany (e-mail: t.heuse@TLUGJena. Thueringen.de)*
**Šarka Hladilová**
*Institute of Geological Sciences, Masaryk University, Brno, Czech Republic (e-mail: sarka@sci.muni.cz)*
**Jens Hornung**
*Institute for Applied Geosciences, Darmstadt University of Technology, Darmstadt, Germany (e-mail: hornung@geo. tu-darmstadt.de)*
**Hazim Hrvatović**
*Geological Survey of Bosnia and Herzegovina, Iiidza-Sarajevo, Bosnia Herzegovina (e-mail: hharish@bih.net.ba)*
**Christian Hübscher**
*Institut für Geophysik, Universität Hamburg, Hamburg, Germany (e-mail: christian.huebscher@zmaw.de)*
**Hermann Huckriede**
*Thüringer Landesanstalt für Umwelt und Geologie (Außenstelle Weimar), Jena, Germany (e-mail: h.huckriede@tlugjena. thueringen.de)*
**John W.M. Jagt**
*Natuurhistorisch Museum Maastricht, Maastricht, The Netherlands (e-mail: john.jagt@maastricht.nl)*
**Marek Jarosiński**
*Polish Geological Institute, Warszawa, Poland (e-mail: mjar@pgi.gov.pl)*
**Teresa Jeffries**
*Natural History Museum, London, UK (e-mail: t.jeffries@nhm. ac.uk)*
**Bogomir Jelen**
*Geoloski zavod Slovenije, Ljubljana, Slovenia (e-mail: bogomir. jelen@guest.arnes.si)*
**Peter Jordan**
*Institute of Geology and Palaentology, University of Basel, Basel, Switzerland (e-mail: peter.jordan@tiscali.ch)*
**Václav Kachlík**
*Department of Geology and Paleontology, Faculty of Science, Charles University, Prague, Czech Republic (e-mail: kachlik@natur.cuni.cz)*
**Jacek Robert Kasiński**
*Polish Geological Insititute, Warsaw, Poland. (e-mail: jacek. kasinski@pgi.gov.pl)*
**Oliver Kempf**
*Landesgeologie, swisstopo, Seftigenstr. 264, CH-3084 Wabern Switzerland (e-mail: oliver.kempf@swisstopo.ch)*
**Hubert Kiersnowski**
*Polish Geological Institute, Warsaw, Poland (e-mail: hubert. kiersnowski@pgi.gov.pl)*
**Frank Körner**
*Geologisches Insitut, University of Bonn, Bonn, Germany (e-mail: koerner@uni-bonn.de)*
**Kristijan Kornpihl**
*Integrated Exploration Systems, Aachen, Germany (e-mail: k.kornpihl@ies.de)*
**Michal Kováč**
*Department of Geology and Paleontology, Comenius University, Bratislava, Slovakia (e-mail: kovacm@fns.uniba.sk)*
**Karl Krainer**
*Geologie und Paläontologie, Universität Innsbruck, Innsbruck, Austria (e-mail: karl.krainer@uibk.ac.at)*
**Polona Kralj**
*Geological Survey of Slovenia, Ljubljana, Slovenia (e-mail: polona.kralj@geo-zs.si)*
**Charlotte Krawczyk**
*Leibnitz Institute for Applied Geosciences (GGA), Hannover, Germany (e-mail: lotte@gga-hannover.de)*
**Michael Krings**
*Department für Geo- und Umweltwissenschaften an der LMU München, München, Germany (e-mail: m.krings@lrz-uni-muenchen)*
**Jiří Kříž**
*Czech Geological Survey, Prague, Czech Republic (e-mail: jiri.kriz@geology.cz)*
**Michał Krobicki**
*University of Science and Technology, Kraków, Poland (e-mail: krobicki@geol.agh.edu.pl)*
**Uwe Kroner**
*Institut für Geologie, TU Bergakademie Freiberg, Freiberg, Germany (e-mail: uwe.kroner@geo.tu-freiberg.de)*
**Ewa Krzemińska**
*Polish Geological Institute, Warsaw, Poland (e-mail: ewa. krzeminska@pgi.gov.pl)*
**Piotr Krzywiec**
*Polish Geological Institute, Warsaw, Poland (e-mail: piotr. krzywiec@pgi.gov.pl)*

**Frédéric Lacquement**
*Bureau de Recherches Géologiques et Minières, Orleáns, France (e-mail: f.lacquement@brgm.fr)*

**Juliette Lamarche**
*Centre de Sédimentologie-Paléontologie, Université de Provence Aix-Marseille 1, Marseille, France (e-mail: jula@up.univ-mrs.fr)*

**Bernard Lathuiliere**
*UMR CNRS 7566, Géologie et Gestion des Ressources Minérales et Energétiques (G2R), Université de Nancy I, Vandoeuvre-lès-Nancy, France (e-mail: bernard.lathuiliere@g2r.u-nancy.fr)*

**Patrick Ledru**
*BRGM/Research Division 3, Orléans, France (e-mail: p.ledru @brgm.fr)*

**Reinhold R. Leinfelder**
*Museum für Naturkunde, Humboldt-Universität Berlin, Berlin, Germany (e-mail: leinfelder@museum.hu-berlin.de)*

**Ulf Linnemann**
*Museum für Mineralogie und Geologie, Dresden, Germany (e-mail: ulf.linnemann@snsd.smwk.sachsen.de)*

**Thomas Litt**
*Institut für Paläontologie, Universität Bonn, Bonn, Germany (e-mail: t.litt@uni-bonn.de)*

**John McBride**
*Brigham Young University, Provo, Utah, UT, USA (e-mail: john_mcbride@byu.edu)*

**Tom McCann**
*Geologisches Insitut, University of Bonn, Bonn, Germany (e-mail: tmccann@uni-bonn.de)*

**Jörg Maletz**
*Department of Geology, University at Buffalo, SUNY, Buffalo, NY, USA (e-mail: jorgm@buffalo.edu)*

**Tihomir Marjanac**
*Department of Geology, University of Zagreb, Zagreb, Croatia (e-mail: marjanac@geol.pmf.hr)*

**Emö Márton**
*Eötvös Loránd Geophysical Institute of Hungary, Budapest, Hungary (e-mail: paleo@elgi.hu or h11000mar@helka.iif.hu)*

**Yuriy Maystrenko**
*GeoForschungsZentrum Potsdam, Potsdam, Germany (e-mail: yuram@gfz-potsdam.de)*

**Stanisław Mazur**
*Institute of Geological Sciences, University of Wrocław, Wrocław, Poland (e-mail: smazur@ing.uni.wroc.pl)*

**Jozef Michalík**
*Slovak Academy of Science, Bratislava, Slovakia (e-mail: geolmich@savba.sk)*

**Paolo Mietto**
*Dipartimento di Geoscienze, Università di Padova, Padova, Italy (e-mail: paolo.mietto@unipd.it)*

**Eckhard Mönnig**
*Naturkunde-Museum Coburg, Coburg, Germany (e-mail: e.moennig@naturkunde-museum-coburg.de)*

**Gediminas Motuza**
*Department of Geology and Mineralogy, Faculty of Natural Sciences, Vilnius, Lithuania (e-mail: gediminas.motuza@gf.vu.lt)*

**Alan Moro**
*Department of Geology, University of Zagreb, Zagreb, Croatia (e-mail: amoro@geol.pmf.hr)*

**Rainer Müller**
*Institute for Geology and Palaeontology, Technische Universität, Clausthal-Zellerfeld, Germany (e-mail: rainer.mueller@ tu-clausthal.de)*

**J. Brendan Murphy**
*Department of Earth Sciences, St. Francis Xavier University, Antigonish, NS, Canada (e-mail: bmurphy@stfx.ca)*

**András Nagymarosy**
*Department of Physical and Historical Geology, Eötvös Loránd University, Budapest, Hungary (e-mail: gtorfo@ludens.elte.hu)*

**R. Damian Nance**
*Department of Geological Sciences, Ohio University, Athens, OH, USA (e-mail: nance@ohio.edu)*

**Marek Narkiewicz**
*Polish Geological Institute, Warsaw, Poland (e-mail: marek. narkiewicz@pgi.gov.pl)*

**Jerzy Nawrocki**
*Paleomagnetic Laboratory, Polish Geological Institute, Warsaw, Poland (e-mail: jerzy.nawrocki@pgi.gov.pl)*

**James H. Nebelsick**
*Institute of Geosciences, University of Tübingen, Tübingen, Germany (e-mail: nebelsick@uni-tuebingen.de)*

**Slavomír Nehyba**
*Masaryk University, Institute of Geological Sciences, Brno, Czech Republic (e-mail: slavek@sci.muni.cz)*

**Birgit Niebuhr**
*GeoZentrum Nordbayern, Fachgruppe Paläoumwelt, FAU Universität Erlangen-Nürmberg, Erlangen, Germany (e-mail: niebuhr@pal.uni-erlangen.de)*

**Nanna Noe-Nygaard**
*Department of Geography and Geology, Copenhagen, Denmark (e-mail: nannan@geol.ku.dk)*

**Bojan Ogorelec**
*Geological Survey of Slovenia, Ljubljana, Slovenia (e-mail: bojan.ogorelec@geo-zs-si)*

**Stanislav Oplustil**
*Institute of Geology and Palaeontology, Charles University, Praha, Czech Republic (e-mail: oplustil@natur.cuni.cz)*

**Nestor Oszczypko**
*Institute of Geological Sciences, Jagiellonian University, Kraków, Poland (e-mail: nestor@geos.ing.uj.edu.pl)*

**József Pálfy**
*Hungarian Academy of Sciences, Hungarian Natural History Museum, Budapest, Hungary (e-mail: palfy@nhmus.hu)*

**Ladislav A. Palinkaš**
*Department of Geology, University of Zagreb, Zagreb, Croatia (e-mail: lpalinkas@geol.pmf.hr)*

**Florentin Paris**
*Géosciences Rennes, UPR 4661 CNRS, Université de Rennes, Renne, France (e-mail: florentin.paris@univ-rennes1.fr)*

**Davor Pavelić**
*Faculty of Mining, Geology and Petroleum Engineering, University of Zagreb, Zagreb, Croatia (e-mail: dpavelic@yahoo. com)*

**Rajko Pavlovec**
*Department of Geology, University of Ljubljana, Ljubljana, Slovenia (e-mail: rajko.pavlovec@ntf.uni-lj.si)*

**Jernej Pavšič**
*Department of Geology, University of Ljubljana, Ljubljana, Slovenia (e-mail: jernej.pavsic@ntf.uni-lj.si)*

**Tadeusz Peryt**
*Polish Geological Institute, Warsaw, Poland (e-mail: tadeusz. peryt@pgi.gov.pl)*

**Pavla Tomanová Petrová**
*Czech Geological Survey, Brno, Czech Republic (e-mail: pavla. petrova@geology.cz)*

**Timothy C. Pharaoh**
*British Geological Survey, Keyworth, UK (e-mail: tcp@bgs. ac.uk)*

**Grzegorz Pieńkowski**
*Polish Geological Institute, Warsaw, Poland (e-mail: grzegorz. pienkowski@pgi.gov.pl)*

**Christian Pin**
*Département des Sciences de la Terre, CNRS & Université Blaise Pascal, Clermont-Ferrand, France (e-mail: c.pin@opgc.univ-bpclermont.fr)*
**Anna Pint**
*Institut für Geologische Wissenschaften, Freie Universität Berlin, Berlin, Germany (e-mail: annapint@web.de)*
**Sergei A. Pisarevsky**
*Tectonics Special Research Centre, University of Western Australia, Crawley, WA, Australia (e-mail: spisarevsky@tsrc.uwa.edu.au)*
**Marcin Piwocki**
*Polish Geological Institute, Warsaw, Poland (e-mail: marcin.piwocki@pgi.gov.pl)*
**Dušan Plašienka**
*Department of Geology and Paleontology, Comenius University, Bratislava, Slovakia*
**Marijan Poljak**
*Geoloski zavod Slovenije, Ljubljana, Slovenia (e-mail: marijan.poljak@geo-zs.si)*
**Paweł Poprawa**
*Polish Geological Institute, Warszawa, Poland (e-mail: pawel.poprawa@pgi.gov.pl)*
**Edouard Poty**
*Département de Géologie, Université de Liège, Liège, Belgium (e-mail: e.poty@ulg.ac.be)*
**W. Prochaska**
*Department of Applied Geosciences and Geophysics, University of Leoben, Leoben, Austria (e-mail: walter.prochaska@unileoben.ac.at)*
**Nevio Pugliese**
*Dipartimento di Scienze Geologiche Ambientali e Marine, Università di Trieste, Trieste, Italy (e-mail: pugliese@univ.trieste.it)*
**Michael W. Rasser**
*Staatliches Museum für Naturkunde, Stuttgart, Germany (e-mail: rasser.smns@naturkundemuseum-bw.de)*
**Rejhana Redžepović**
*Mining Geology & Civil Engineering Faculty, Universtiy of Tuzla, Tuzla, Bosnia Herzegovina (e-mail: rredzepovic@yahoo.com)*
**Mike Reich**
*Geowissenschaftliches Zentrum der Universität Göttingen (GZG), Museum, Sammlungen & Geopark, Göttingen, Germany (e-mail: mreich@gwdg.de)*
**Klaus Reicherter**
*Institut für Neotektonik und Georisiken, RWTH Aachen, Aachen, Germany (e-mail: k.reicherter@nug.rwth-aachen.de)*
**John Reinecker**
*Geological Institute, Tübingen University, Tubingen, Germany (email: reinecker@uni-tuebingen.de)*
**Lutz Reinhardt**
*Federal Institute for Geosciences and Natural Resources, Hanover, Germany (e-mail: l.reinhardt@bgr.de)*
**Achim G. Reisdorf**
*Institute of Geology and Palaeontology, University of Basel, Basel, Switzerland (e-mail: achim.reisdorf@unibas.ch)*
**Werner Ricken**
*Department of Geology and Mineralogy, University of Cologne, Cologne, Germany (e-mail: wricken@uni-koeln.de)*
**Helena Rifelj**
*Geoloski zavod Slovenije, Ljubljana, Slovenia (e-mail: helena.rifelj@geo-zs.si)*
**Reinhard Roetzel**
*Geological Survey of Austria, Vienna, Austria (e-mail: reinhard.roetzel@geologie.ac.at)*
**Heinz-Gerd Röhling**
*State Authority for Mining, Energy and Geology, Geological Survey of Lower Saxony and Bremen, Hannover, Germany (e-mail: heinz-gerd.roehling@lbeg.niedersachsen.de)*
**Rolf L. Romer**
*GeoForschungsZentrum Potsdam, Potsdam, Germany (e-mail: romer@gfz-potsdam.de)*
**Thomas Rüffer**
*Halle (Saale), Germany (e-mail: thomas.rueffer@t-online.de)*
**Reinhard F. Sachsenhofer**
*Department of Applied Geosciences and Geophysics, University of Leoben, Leoben. Austria (e-mail: reinhard.sachsenhofer@mu-leoben.at)*
**Scott D. Samson**
*Department of Earth Sciences, Syracuse University, Syracuse, NY, USA (e-mail: sdsamson@syr.edu)*
**Tibor Sasvári**
*Faculty of Mining, Ecology, Process Control and Geotechnologies, Technical University of Košice, Košice, Slovakia (e-mail: tibor.sasvari@tuke.sk)*
**Andreas Schäfer**
*Geologisches Institut, University of Bonn, Bonn, Germany (e-mail: schaefer@uni-bonn.de)*
**Magdalena Scheck-Wenderoth**
*GeoForschungsZentrum Potsdam, Potsdam, Germany (e-mail: leni@gfz-potsdam.de)*
**Christian Schlüchter**
*Institut für Geologie der Universität Bern, Bern, Switzerland (e-mail: christian.schluechter@geo.unibe.ch)*
**Dieter U. Schmid**
*Department für Geo- und Umweltwissenschaften/GeoBio-Center an der Ludwig-Maximilians-Universität München, München, Germany (e-mail: d.schmid@lrz.uni-muenchen.de)*
**Hans-Ulrich Schmincke**
*Leibniz Institut für Meereswissenschaften IFM-GEOMAR, Kiel, Germany (e-mail: hschmincke@ifm-geomar.de)*
**Jörg Schneider**
*Department of Palaeontology, Universität Freiberg, Freiberg, Germany (e-mail: schneidj@geo.tu-freiberg.de)*
**Hans Peter Schönlaub**
*Kötschach 350, A9640 Kötschach-Mauthen, Austria (e-mail: schoenlaub@aon.at)*
**Michael E. Schudack**
*Institut für Geologische Wissenschaften, Freie Universität Berlin, Berlin, Germany (e-mail: schudack@zedat.fu-berlin.de)*
**Anne S. Schulp**
*Natuurhistorisch Museum Maastricht, Maastricht, The Netherlands (e-mail: mail@nhmmaastricht.nl)*
**Bernhard Schulz**
*Institut für Geologie und Mineralogie, Erlangen, Germany. (e-mail: bschulz@geol.uni-erlangen.de)*
**Hans-Martin Schulz**
*GeoForschungsZentrum Potsdam, Potsdam, Germany (e-mail: schulzhm@gfz-potsdam.de)*
**Ralf Schuster**
*Geologische Bundesanstalt, Vienna, Austria (e-mail: ralf.schuster@geologie.ac.at)*
**Günter Schweigert**
*Staatliches Museum für Naturkunde, Stuttgart, Germany (e-mail: schweigert.smns@naturkundemuseum-bw.de)*
**Thomas Servais**
*Géosystèmes, UMR8157 du CNRS, Université des Sciences et Technologies de Lille, Villeneuve d'Ascq, France (e-mail: thomas.servais@univ-lille1.fr)*
**Dragomir Skaberne**
*Geoloski zavod Slovenije, Ljubljana, Slovenia (e-mail: dragomir.skaberne@geo-zs.si)*

**Stanislaw Skompski**
*Institute of Geology, Warsaw University, Warsaw, Poland (e-mail: skompski@uw.edu.pl)*
**L'ubomír Sliva**
*Department of Geology and Paleontology, Comenius University, Bratislava, Slovakia (e-mail: sliva@fns.uniba.sk)*
**Werner Stackebrandt**
*Landesamt für Geowissenschaften und Rohstoffe Brandenburg, Kleinmachnow, Germany (e-mail: werner.stackebrandt@lbgr-brandenburg.de)*
**Gerda Standke**
*Sächsisches Landesamt für Umwelt und Geologie, Dresden, Germany (e-mail: gerda.standke@smul.sachsen.de)*
**Harald Stollhofen**
*Geologisches Institut der RWTH, Aachen, Germany (e-mail: stollhofen@geol.rwth-aachen.de)*
**Robin A. Strachan**
*School of Earth and Environmental Sciences, University of Portsmouth, Portsmouth, UK (e-mail: rob.strachan@port.ac.uk)*
**Sabina Strmić-Palinkaš**
*Department of Geology, University of Zagreb, Zagreb, Croatia (e-mail: sabina.strmic@inet.hr)*
**Finn Surlyk**
*Department of Geography and Geology, Copenhagen, Denmark (e-mail: finns@geol.ku.dk)*
**Joachim Szulc**
*Institute of Geological Science, Jagiellonian University, Kraków, Poland (e-mail: szulc@geos.ing.uj.edu.pl)*
**Jennifer Tait**
*School of Geosciences, University of Edinburgh, Edinburgh, UK (e-mail: jenny.tait@ed.ac.uk)*
**Martin Timmerman**
*Institut für Geowissenschaften, Universität Potsdam, Potsdam, Germany (e-mail: timmer@geo.uni-potsdam.de)*
**Ákos Török**
*Department of Construction Materials and Engineering Geology, Budapest University of Technology and Economics, Budapest, Hungary (e-mail: torokakos@mail.bme.hu)*
**Giorgio Tunis**
*Dipartimento di Scienze Geologische Ambientali e Marine, Università di Trieste, Trieste, Italy (e-mail: tunis@univ.trieste.it)*
**David Uličný**
*Geophysical Institute of the Academy of Sciences of the Czech Republic, Boční 11/1401, 14131 Prague 4, Czech Republic (e-mail: ulicny@ig.cas.cz)*
**Jens Ulrich**
*Museum für Mineralogie und Geologie, Dresden, Germany. (e-mail: jens.ulrich@snsd.smwk.sachsen.de)*
**Dionýz Vass**
*Dionyz Stur Institute of Geology, Bratislava, Slovakia*
**Marco Vecoli**
*Géosystèmes, UMR 8157 du CNRS, Université des Sciences et Technologies de Lille, Villeneuve d'Ascq, France (e-mail: marco-vecoli@univ-lille1.fr)*
**Jacques Verniers**
*Department of Geology and Pedology, Ghent University, Ghent, Belgium (e-mail: jacques.verniers@ugent.be)*
**Silke Voigt**
*IfM-Geomar, Germany (e-mail: svoigt@ifm-geomar.de)*
**Thomas Voigt**
*Institut für Geowissenschaften, Universität Jena, Jena, Germany (e-mail: thomas.voigt@uni-jena.de)*
**Hilmar von Eynatten**
*Geowissenschaftliches Zentrum der Universität Göttingen, Göttingen, Germany (e-mail: hilmar.von.eynatten@geo.uni-goettingen.de)*
**Anna Vozárová**
*Department of Mineralogy and Petrology, Comenius University Bratislava, Bratislava, Slovakia. (e-mail: vozarova@fns.uniba.sk)*
**Michael Wagreich**
*Centre for Earth Sciences, University of Vienna, Vienna, Austria (e-mail: michael.wagreich@univie.ac.at)*
**Ireneusz Walaszczyk**
*Institute of Geology, University of Warsaw, Warsaw, Poland (e-mail: i.walszczyk@uw.edu.pl)*
**Frank Wesselingh**
*Naturalis – National Museum of Natural History, Leiden, The Netherlands (e-mail: wesselingh@naturalis.nl)*
**Andreas Wetzel**
*Geologisch-Paläontologisches Institut, Universität Basel, Basel, Switzerland (e-mail: andreas.wetzel@unibas.ch)*
**Frank Wiese**
*Fachrichtung Paläontologie, FU Berlin, Berlin, Germany (e-mail: frwiese@snafu.de)*
**Markus Wilmsen**
*GeoZentrum Nordbayern, Fachgruppe Paläoumwelt, FAU Erlangen-Nürmberg, Erlangen, Germany (e-mail: markus.wilmsen@pal.uni-erlangen.de)*
**Janina Wiszniewska**
*Polish Geological Institute, Warsaw, Poland (e-mail: janina.wiszniewska@pgi.gov.pl)*
**Theo E. Wong**
*TNO-NITG, Utrecht, The Netherlands (e-mail: theoewong@yahoo.co.uk)*
**Ryszard Wrona**
*Instytut Paleobiologii PAN, Warsaw, Poland (e-mail: wrona@twarda.pan.pl)*
**Stanislaw Wybraniec**
*Polish Geological Institute, Warsaw, Poland (e-mail: swyb@pgi.waw.pl)*
**Jerzy Żaba**
*Faculty of Earth Sciences, University of Silesia, Sosnowiec, Poland (e-mail: jzaba@ultra.cto.us.edu.pl)*
**Federica Zaccarini**
*Department of Applied Geosciences and Geophysics, University of Leoben, Leoben, Austria (e-mail: fedezac@tsc4.com)*
**Hubert Zedler**
*Regierungspräsidium Freiburg, Landesamt für Geologie, Rohstoffe und Bergbau, Freiburg im Breisgau, Germany (e-mail: hubert.zedler@rpf.bwl.de)*
**Armin Zeh**
*Mineralogisches Institut der Universität Würzburg, Würzburg, Germany (e-mail: armin.zeh@mail.uni-wuerzburg.de)*
**Živilė Žigaitė**
*Department of Geology and Mineralogy, Vilnius University, Vilnius, Lithuania (e-mail: zivile.zigaite@gf.vu.lt)*
**Ulf Zimmermann**
*Staatliche Naturhistorische Sammlungen Dresden, Dresden, Germany (e-mail: ulf.linnemann@snsd.smwk.sachsen.de)*
**Witold Zuchiewicz**
*Faculty of Geology, Geophysics & Environmental Protection, University of Science and Technology, Krakow, Poland (e-mail: witoldzuchiewicz@geol.agh.edu.pl)*
**Rainer Zühlke**
*Institute of Geology and Paleontology, Ruprecht Karl University, Heidelberg, Germany (e-mail: zuehlke@uni-hd.de)*
**Gernold Zulauf**
*Institut für Geowissenschaften, Frankfurt, Germany (e-mail: g.zulauf@em.uni-frankfurt.de)*
**Anna Żylińska**
*Institute of Geology, University of Warsaw, Warsaw, Poland (e-mail: anna.zylinska@uw.edu.pl)*

# 13 Triassic

SUSANNE FEIST-BURKHARDT, ANNETTE E. GÖTZ, JOACHIM SZULC (co-ordinators), RAVI BORKHATARIA, MARK GELUK, JÁNOS HAAS, JENS HORNUNG, PETER JORDAN, OLIVER KEMPF, JOZEF MICHALÍK, JERZY NAWROCKI, LUTZ REINHARDT, WERNER RICKEN, HEINZ-GERD RÖHLING, THOMAS RÜFFER, ÁKOS TÖRÖK & RAINER ZÜHLKE

The Triassic period spans 51.4 million years between 251.0 ± 0.4 and 199.6 ± 0.6 Ma (Ogg 2004). It was a phase of major change after the initial breakup of Pangaea and the severe mass extinction event at the end of the Permian. The following sections focus on the two classical Triassic domains in Central Europe: the intracratonic Germanic Basin, sometimes called the Central European Basin, and the northwestern Tethys Sea. The descriptions of Triassic sequences in the Netherlands, Germany, Poland, Slovakia, Hungary, Austria, Italy and Switzerland provide a regional overview of the palaeogeographical settings, sedimentological and palaeontological features and facies evolution in time and space.

The Triassic System was established in Central Europe more than 170 years ago by the German mining engineer Friedrich August von Alberti in 1834. He combined the three stratigraphic units 'Bunter Sandstein', 'Muschelkalch' (Füchsel 1761) and 'Keuper' (Keferstein 1824) into one lithologically and palaeontologically defined formation (Alberti 1834). The German term 'Trias' (see Hagdorn & Nitsch 1999) reflects the trinity of the system in its type region with clastic red-beds (Buntsandstein), carbonates and evaporites (Muschelkalk) and clay/sandstone deposits (Keuper).

Only one decade later, parts of the 'Alpenkalk', which are limestone formations from the Northern and Southern Alps, were correlated with deposits of the 'Germanic Triassic' on the basis of age-diagnostic index fossils (Buch 1845; Hauer 1846). These early works were followed by detailed palaeontological and sedimentological studies that developed a chronostratigraphic framework for the depositional series of the 'Alpine Triassic'.

The long research history of the Triassic System in Central Europe provides a well-established bio- and lithostratigraphic framework (Bachmann *et al.* 1999) that is the basis for regional and global correlation and high-resolution sequence stratigraphy. A genetic interpretation of the depositional sequences already exists for many areas, including parts of the Germanic and Alpine realms. This is the case for the German and Polish parts of the Germanic Basin (Aigner *et al.* 1999; Szulc 2000) as well as for the Alpine successions of the Northern Calcareous Alps, the Southern Alps (Rüffer & Zühlke 1995), and the Transdanubian Range (Haas & Budai 1999). In other regions, which were part of the northwestern Tethys shelf during Triassic times, sequence patterns are still under discussion, for example the Western Carpathians (Jaglarz & Szulc 2003) and the Hungarian Tisza Mega-unit (Török 2000), which are important areas for correlation of the Tethyan and Germanic realms (Götz *et al.* 2003). The southwestern seaway of the Germanic Basin in present-day Switzerland (Feist-Burkhardt *et al.* 2008) requires further investigations in terms of facies evolution and sequence patterns in order to provide a better understanding of the interaction of an open ocean and its peripheral basin.

Over the last decade, numerous works have dealt with the genetic interpretation of Triassic depositional sequences and provided a preliminary sequence stratigraphic framework for the Germanic and Alpine realm (e.g. Aigner & Bachmann 1992; Rüffer & Zühlke 1995; Gianolla *et al.* 1998). These data were complemented by studies on the eustatic evolution of both palaeogeographic settings and the interaction of the Tethys Ocean and its northern periphery basin (Szulc 2000). A compiled framework is given in Figure 13.1. Future work will need to refine and extend this scheme. New stratigraphical methods such as magnetostratigraphy (Nawrocki 1997; Szurlies 2004) and high-resolution cyclostratigraphy (Zühlke 2004) will improve regional and global correlation (see discussion in Bachmann & Kozur 2004).

## The Permian–Triassic boundary (J.H., A.E.G.)

The end of the Permian was marked by the most severe extinction in the Phanerozoic with an estimated loss of more than 90% of marine species and a similar loss in the continental biota. This crisis led to a fundamental reorganization of the post-Palaeozoic ecosystems and precluded a swift recovery of flora and fauna (Raup 1979; Erwin 1994; Yin *et al.* 1996; Erwin *et al.* 2002; Krull *et al.* 2004). Scenarios proposed to explain this mass extinction event include global climate change caused by the volcanic (i.e. Siberian trap eruptions) contribution to atmospheric $CO_2$ (Campbell *et al.* 1992; Wignall 2001), methane release (Erwin 1993; Krull & Retallack 2000), transgression of anoxic oceanic bottom water onto the shelves (Wignall & Hallam 1992), a bolide impact (Kaiho *et al.* 2001; Becker *et al.* 2001, 2004) and hypoxia (Huey & Ward 2005). Geochronological data suggest a relatively rapid event or series of events (Rampino *et al.* 2000; Mundil *et al.* 2001).

In the latest Permian the Germanic Realm was part of the Pangaea supercontinent (Laurussia). The Tisza Mega-unit that constitutes the basement of the southern part of the Pannonian Basin, the Central and Inner Western Carpathian units, the Northern Calcareous Alps, the western part of the Southern Alps, and the southwestern part of the Transdanubian Range were located close to the western termination of Palaeo-Tethys, at the

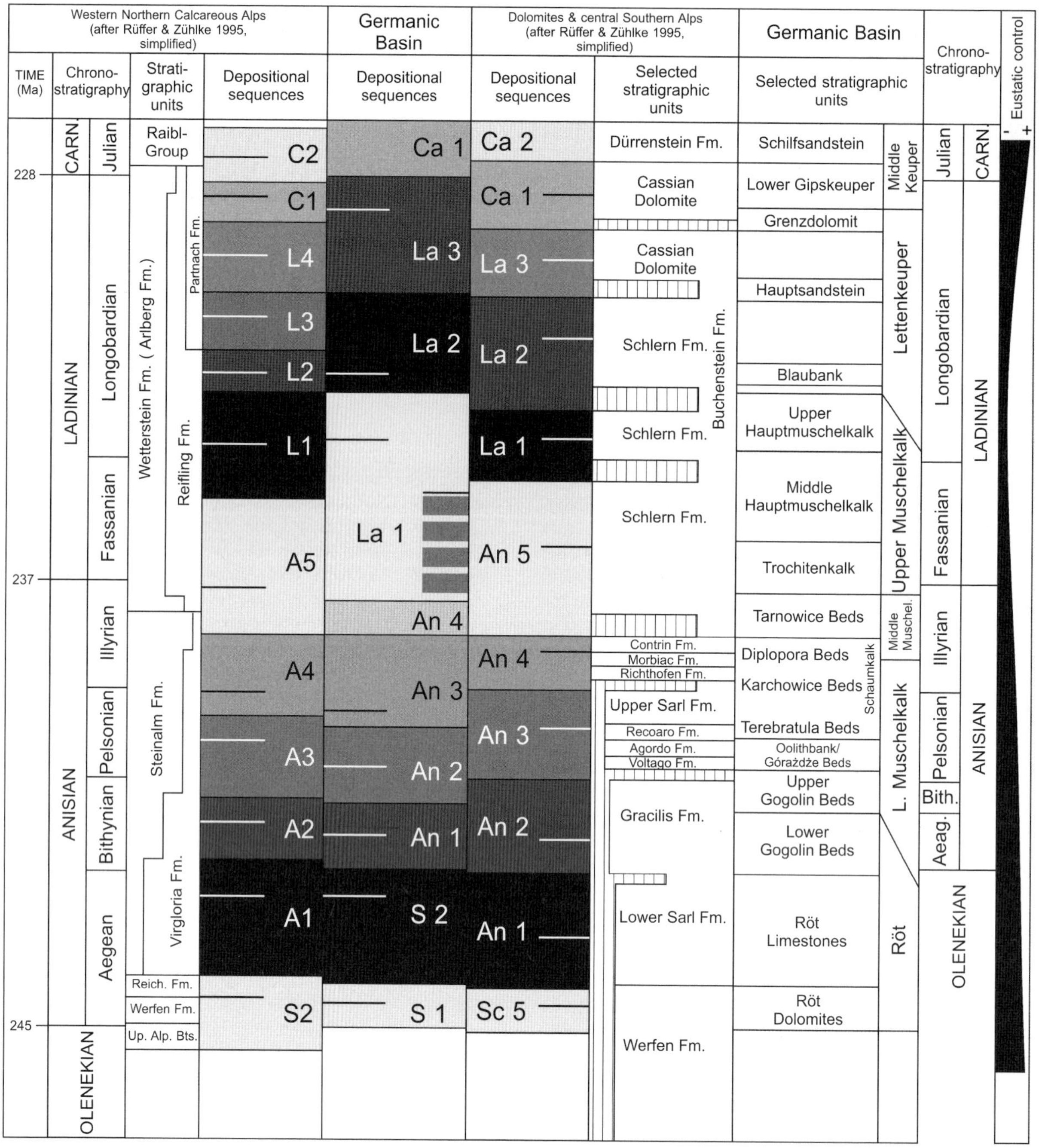


**Fig. 13.1.** Comparative setting of the third-order depositional sequences of the western Tethys and northern Peri-Tethys basins (after Szulc 2000).

foot of the Variscan ranges and partly in the coastal belt. The eastern part of the Southern Alps, the northeastern part of the Transdanubian Range and the Bükk Mountains in Hungary were situated on the broad ramp system of the Palaeo-Tethys (Ziegler 1988; Haas *et al.* 1995*a*; Gawlick *et al.* 1999; Dercourt *et al.* 2000).

In Lombardy, in the western part of the Southern Alps, the Upper Permian is represented by the alluvial Val Gardena (Gröden) Sandstone. It is directly overlain by a marine Lower Triassic succession of dolomitized oolite that is followed by the dolomarl/dolomite succession of the Werfen Formation (Assereto *et al.* 1973; Brandner & Mostler 1982; Broglio Loriga *et al.* 1983, 1988). This transgressional sequence is similar to that in the Balaton Highland area in the southwestern part of the Transdanubian Range (Broglio Loriga *et al.* 1990).

In the Western Dolomites, the Upper Permian is made up of the evaporitic/dolomitic Fiamazza facies of the Bellerophon Formation that is overlain by the oolitic grainstone/packstone of the Tesero Member and the marl/limestone succession of the Mazzin Member of the Werfen Formation. The last occurrence of Permian foraminifers and brachiopods is in the 2 to 5 m thick Tesero Member (Broglio Loriga *et al.* 1988; Posenato 2001). In the Bulla section, the first appearance of the boundary-diagnostic conodont species *Hindeodus parvus* is 1.3 m above the base of the Tesero Member (Peri & Farabegoli 2003).

A very similar facies succession was encountered in cores

from the northeastern part of the Transdanubian Range, Hungary. The Upper Permian Dinnyés Dolomite is made up of lagoonal–sabkha cycles. Based on the disappearance of rich Permian foraminifera, calcareous algae and sporomorph assemblages and the appearance of the Triassic sporomorphs, the boundary was recognized within the oolite bed at the base of the Alcsútdoboz Limestone (Góczán *et al.* 1987; Haas *et al.* 1988*a*). Within the boundary interval, a significant negative $\delta^{13}C$ isotope shift was encountered but no definite peak was found (Haas *et al.* 2006*a*).

In the Eastern Dolomites and Carnic Alps, uppermost Permian shallow-marine limestone (the Badiota facies of the Bellerophon Formation) is overlain by the Tesero Member (Massari 1988). In a core drilled on the Gartnerkofel, Carnic Alps, Austria, a significant negative $\delta^{13}C$ shift was recorded from the boundary interval (Holser *et al.* 1989). Similar successions are known from western Slovenia where the Žažar Formation, an equivalent of the Badiota facies (Ramovš 1982; Buser *et al.* 1988; Dolenec & Ramovš 1998; Dolenec *et al.* 2003), is overlain by a thin oolitic boundary layer and grey laminated dolomite and limestone; a significant negative $\delta^{13}C$ anomaly was recorded at the horizon of the abrupt disappearance of Upper Permian fossils (Dolenec & Ogorelec 2001). This situation shows affinity with that in the Bükk Mountains of northern Hungary (Hips & Pelikán 2002; Haas *et al.* 2004*b*). However, similarity with the Upper Permian–Lower Triassic succession of the Bükk Mountains is even more pronounced in the Jadar Block, Dinarides, Serbia, that was probably located in the neighbourhood of the Bükk unit at that time (Pešić *et al.* 1988; Filipović *et al.* 2003).

The sections in the Bükk Mountains provide information on the effects of the Permian–Triassic boundary event(s) in a deeper outer-ramp setting. The latest Permian Nagyvisnyó Formation was deposited in the euphotic zone, but below the fair-weather wave base. Coeval drastic reduction in the skeletal carbonate production on the outer-ramp, and the enhanced soil erosion that may have resulted from a basic change in the hinterland vegetation, resulted in the deposition of silty marls. The lower part of the 1 m thick boundary shale bed contains a small amount of fine bioclasts, thin-shelled bivalves and brachiopods (Posenato *et al.* 2005). However, a second drastic event which is marked by a significant negative $\delta^{13}C$ peak in the upper part of the shale bed, resulted in the extinction of most of the survivors of the first event (Haas *et al.* 2004*b*, 2006*b*). After this crisis a microbial carbonate factory developed, leading to the production of laminated, stromatolitic carbonates in the middle to outer ramp zone (Hips & Haas 2006).

In Germany and Poland, clastic sediments were deposited in latest Permian to early Triassic times in fluvio-lacustrine environments of a large intracratonic basin, intermittently influenced by marine ingressions (Lepper & Röhling 1998; Beutler & Szulc 1999). Within this interval, which lacks index fossils, Nawrocki (1997), Nawrocki *et al.* (2003) and Szurlies *et al.* (2003) located the Permian–Triassic boundary by means of magnetostratigraphy. The position of the boundary has been recently confirmed by a significant negative $\delta^{13}C$ shift (Hiete 2004).

There is general agreement that the Permian–Triassic boundary in the Germanic Basin is situated within the Lower Buntsandstein succession (Ecke 1986). In some regions the boundary between the Zechstein and the Buntsandstein is marked by an angular unconformity near the base of the Lower Buntsandstein. In other regions, e.g. in NW Poland, the transition is more gradual and depends on the replacement of the evaporitic sediments with more clastic ones (Pienkowski 1991). Conventionally the lower boundary of the Buntsandstein in NW Germany is defined at the base of the first intercalations of oolitic sandstones above the so-called Zechstein Übergangsfolge ('Zechstein transitional sequence') at the base of the Calvörde Folge. The lower boundary of the Zechstein Übergangsfolge is defined by the last occurrence of anhydrites, carbonates or halites of the Zechstein. Depending on the palaeogeographical position the clastic Übergangsfolge overlies different subunits of the uppermost Zechstein saliferous cycle.

The Zechstein–Buntsandstein boundary is similar in the Polish part of the basin where it overlies the Rewal Formation, which is equivalent to the German Zechstein Übergangsfolge.

In the Netherlands there is a slight difference: the Zechstein–Buntsandstein boundary is placed at the base of the Upper Bröckelschiefer, which is considered to form the basal transgressive unit of the Lower Buntsandstein (Van Adrichem Boogaert & Kouwe 1993; Geluk & Röhling 1997). This unit rests, with a minor hiatus, on the various subunits of the underlying upper Zechstein.

In Denmark and in the UK sector of the basin, the Zechstein–Buntsandstein boundary is placed at a level equivalent to the base of the Zechstein Übergangsfolge, at the downward change from the clastic sediments here assigned to the Bröckelschiefer, to evaporites assigned to the Zechstein. As such it lies considerably lower than the boundaries in Germany and the Netherlands (Geluk 2005). The clastic sequence overlying the anhydrite- and halite-bearing Zechstein in the Danish and UK successions is assigned an early Triassic age (Cameron *et al.* 1992; Johnson *et al.* 1994; Fisher & Mudge 1998; Goldsmith *et al.* 2003).

Comparing the European and the Chinese boundary sections, representing the Western and the Eastern Palaeo-Tethys realms respectively, definite similarities can be recognized in the lithological and palaeontological features and in the succession of the phenomena. The biotic decline prior to the final disappearance of the Permian taxa, the abundance of pyrite in the boundary interval, and the appearance of calcimicrobial disaster facies were found in the two regions in the same succession (Wignall & Hallam 1996; Kershaw *et al.* 2002; Haas *et al.* 2004*b*). The negative $\delta^{13}C$ isotope shift within the boundary interval and the negative peak at the horizon of the second biotic decline are characteristic isotope signatures of the Permian–Triassic boundary. A review of the Permian–Triassic boundary in Germanic successions is given by Bachmann & Kozur (2004).

## Climate evolution in the Tethys area and its controls (J.S.)

During almost the entire Triassic, Central Europe was situated within the subtropical convergence zone. The shift into a more moderate climatic zone took place towards the end of the Triassic (Kent & Tauxe 2005). The subtropical position imposed dry climatic conditions which dominated the region. However, humid intervals have also been recognized within the Triassic succession of Central Europe; these were caused by factors such as changes in ocean–land configuration, volcanism, tectonotopographical changes and extraterrestrial controls.

Palaeomagnetic data (see below) indicate that in Early and Mid-Triassic times the Meso-European area lay between 15 and 25° north of the equator. Such a position, along with the continent–ocean configuration, imposed subtropical trade winds as the dominant air-mass circulation system over the NW Tethys and Peri-Tethys area (Fig. 13.2) and should have resulted in low rainfall. However, the scarcity of evaporites in the Lower and Middle Buntsandstein red-bed sediments and their Alpine equivalents (Werfen Formation and Alpine Buntsandstein), as well as the existence of a well-developed braided river network, indicate

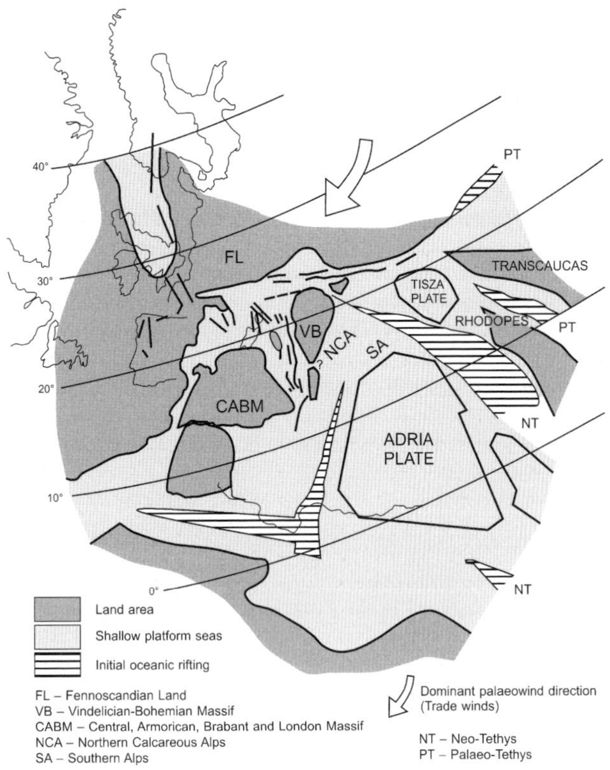


**Fig. 13.2.** Palaeogeographical map of the Western Tethys domain in Middle Triassic times (from Szulc 2000).

more humid conditions, as can be inferred from the subtropical position of the area. This contradiction can be resolved if the strong influence of monsoon circulation, involving substantial rainfall during winter seasons (Kutzbach & Gallimore 1989; van der Zwan & Spaak 1992), is considered. It is likely that development of the braided river system was enhanced by the paucity of rooted plants following the Permian–Triassic extinctions (Ward *et al.* 2000).

Monsoonal impact decreased in late Olenekian and Anisian times when the restricted facies of the Reichenhall and Gutenstein Formations and the Röt and Middle Muschelkalk sulphates and halite formed. Some floral data (Orłowska-Zwolińska 1985; van der Zwan & Spaak 1992) indicate that the concurrent transgression and expansion of marine basins, both in the Tethyan and the Germanic domains, may have moderated the severe dry climate, at least in the coastal belts.

On the other hand, sedimentological studies indicate that the region suffered heavy subtropical storm activity (Marsaglia & Klein 1983; Aigner 1985; Michalík *et al.* 1992; Török 1993*a, b*; Jaglarz & Szulc 2003). The climate changed from the Fassanian onward, and the Upper Muschelkalk and Lower Keuper (Lettenkeuper) deposits of the Germanic Basin formed under relatively humid and warm climates (van der Zwan & Spaak 1992; Szulc 2000).

The Germanic 'wet' facies have their equivalents in the Southern Alps (Livinallongo Formation, Buchenstein Formation, Wengen Formation), in the Northern Calcareous Alps (Reifling Formation, Partnach Formation) and in the Carpathians (Nemesvamos Member in the Balaton area, Kantavar Beds of the Mecsek Mountains, Carpathian Keuper in the Tatra Mountains) and in many other Tethyan basins. Irrespective of the depositional setting, all of these units display high bituminous contents, a lack of evaporites, and are commonly associated with igneous rocks.

Pluvial phenomena coincided with particularly intense volcanism in all of the Alpine basins. Volcanism produced huge amounts of silicate dust and gaseous outpourings that resulted in a drastic increase in runoff and caused subtropical cyclonic circulation over the entire western Tethys domain (Szulc 2000). Furthermore, the increased cloudiness may have resulted in substantial cooling of the Earth's surface (Polack *et al.* 1976; Rampino *et al.* 1988). In conclusion, volcanic activity during the Late Anisian–Ladinian forced pluvialization and caused a substantial decrease in annual mean temperature over the whole Western Tethys domain.

The next arid phase, in early Carnian times, is recorded by evaporitic sediments of the Germanic Basin (Lower Gipskeuper) and by dolomites formed in shallow basins in the Tethyan domain (Cassian Formation). The mid-Carnian was characterized by the re-establishment of a humid climate, as indicated by sedimentological and palaeontological data (Simms & Ruffell 1990). Pluvialization resulted in fluvial activity, forming the braided/anastomosing river network of the Schilfsandstein in the Germanic Basin and resulting in vigorous clastic sedimentation in the Alpine basins (Raibl Formation, Lunzer Formation, Val Sabia Formation). The pluvialization is ascribed either to monsoon activity (Simms & Ruffell 1990; Parrish 1999) or to the greenhouse effect related to volcanism (Veevers 1989). It seems that the monsoonal circulation was hindered at this time by the Cimmerides mountain range that bounded the area in the south and trapped the wet air masses of the winter monsoon that moved from the Tethys toward the north and west. Therefore, it seems more plausible to explain the mid-Carnian humid phase as a result of volcanism developed in southern Alpine basins (Garzanti 1985) and also reported from the North Sea area (Fisher & Mudge 1990; Köppen & Carter 2000).

Sedimentation typical of dry climatic conditions characterizes the late Carnian and early Norian. Evaporite-bearing red-bed sediments are dominant in the Germanic Basin (Upper Gipskeuper, Rote Wand) and the very thick and uniform dolomitic succession of the Hauptdolomit on the shallow shelf of the Tethys Ocean.

During mid- and late Norian times, the climate underwent continual amelioration as indicated by the gradual disappearance of evaporites and their replacement by ephemeral and/or perennial fluvial sediments (Steinmergelkeuper) in the Germanic Basin. This gradual climatic change probably reflects the drift of the stable European block into a higher palaeolatitude zone (40–45°) outside the subtropical dry belt.

This trend continued during the Rhaetian as indicated by the presence of well-sorted fluvial quartz sandstones, and siltstones with coal seams and much plant debris. This particularly concerns the Germanic Basin but is also recorded in the Alpine basins into which land-derived clastic sediments were transported and contributed to the mixed clastic/carbonate sediments of the Kössen Formation in the Alps and the Tomanowa Formation in the Tatra Mountains.

## Sea-level changes and cyclostratigraphy (J.S.)

In spite of the intense tectonic activity (see below) the main eustatic pulses in the Triassic are generally well recorded in both the Tethys and the Peri-Tethys basins. Significant progress in sequence stratigraphy and magnetostratigraphy has improved the potential and reliability of dating and correlation of the most pronounced transgressive–regressive pulses recognized in the area. Of particular importance are the Lower and Middle Triassic in which sequence stratigraphic frameworks from the Alpine and Germanic basins display good correlation at the third-order sedimentary sequence level (Aigner & Bachmann 1992; Rüffer & Zühlke 1995; Gianolla & Jacquin 1998; Gianolla *et al.* 1998; Szulc 1999; Beutler & Szulc 1999) (Fig. 13.1). Correlation is particularly good in the Germanic and southern Alpine basins, whereas the Northern Alps differ in the Lower Triassic interval (Rüffer & Zühlke 1995). More discrepancies are found in the Upper Triassic successions since the Germanic Basin was dominated by continental sedimentation until Rhaetian times.

In addition to third-order depositional cycles, higher frequency cycles (fourth- and fifth-order) have also been studied in the Triassic of Central Europe. Most of these high-frequency cycles are ascribed to Milankovitch orbital rhythms of different periodicities (Geluk & Röhling 1997; Reinhardt & Ricken 2000*b*; Szurlies *et al.* 2003; Götz 2004; Bachmann & Kozur 2004; see below). However, the assumed orbitally driven cycles have not been verified by means of radiometric age dating. Milankovitch cyclicity was originally considered to be responsible for the high-frequency sedimentary cycles in the Middle Triassic carbonates of the Dolomites (Goldhammer *et al.* 1987), but this has been disproved by radiometric age data (Mundil *et al.* 2003). Therefore, for the time being, the Triassic cycles should be treated with caution; more far-reaching inferences may be premature and speculative. Caution is especially needed because the basins discussed (the Germanic Basin in particular) have been strongly influenced by synsedimentary tectonism (see below), which may have overprinted the climatic signals.

## General tectonic setting (J.S.)

### *Peri-Tethys domain*

Despite its peripheral position towards the Tethys spreading centre, the Germanic Basin was also affected by syndepositional tectonism during Triassic times. Generally, two main systems governed the tectonic evolution of the Germanic Basin in the Triassic. The first, mainly in the eastern and southern parts of the basin, was controlled by reactivated Variscan structures, including the Teisseyre-Tornquist Line (TTL), the Cracow-Odra-Hamburg Fault Belt (COHF), the Elbe Fault (EF), the Silesian-Moravian Fault (SMF) and the Saxothuringian Lineament (STL). The second was developed in the NW part of the basin and was related to the North Sea rifting belt (Fig. 13.3).

Evidence of synsedimentary tectonics is recognized from the Lower and Middle Buntsandstein throughout the Peri-Tethys area. Several phases of block tectonics resulted in basin-wide unconformities. The very pronounced Volpriehausen unconformity, for instance, forms the boundary between the Lower and Middle Buntsandstein in the northwestern part of the basin.

Basin-wide tectonic activity characterized the Middle Buntsandstein interval, when intensive block faulting resulted in two regional unconformities, termed the Detfurth and Hardegsen discordances. The latter can be correlated from the Netherlands and northern Germany to central Poland. At the same time, the subsidence rate of the Mid-Polish Trough (MPT), superimposed upon the Teisseyre-Tornquist Lineament, increased threefold when compared to the rate for the Lower Buntsandstein (Szyperko-Teller 1997).

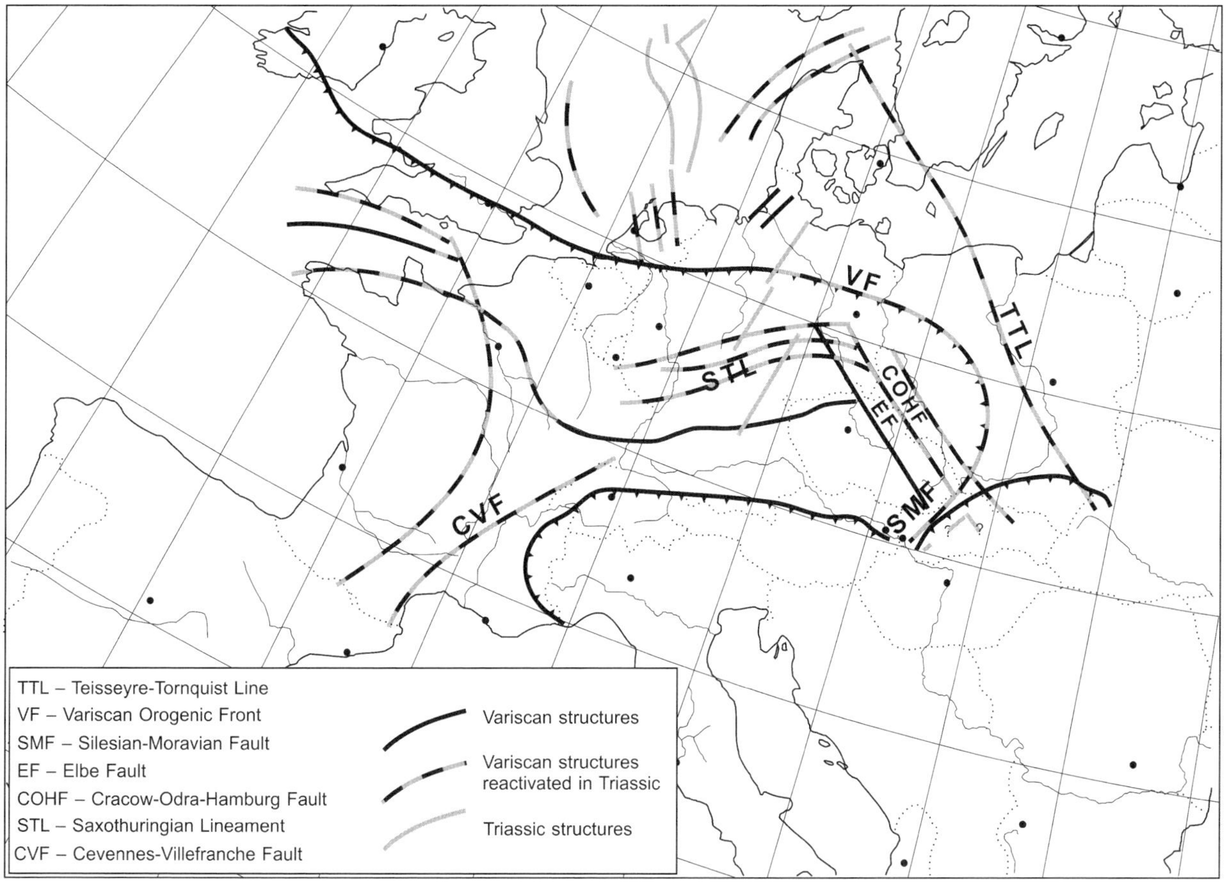


**Fig. 13.3.** Principal tectonic lineaments active in Europe in Triassic times (from Szulc 2000).

Apart from these unconformities, there is much direct evidence of syndepositional crustal mobility in the region. Most of the structures are small synsedimentary faults and dilation cracks that developed within the Triassic deposits and sometimes also affected older basement rocks (Glazek & Roniewicz 1976; Schüler *et al.* 1989). Seismically induced disturbances, such as liquefaction and fluidization, are common features in Buntsandstein clastic sediments (J. Szulc, personal observation).

In Olenekian times a new structural framework began to form in the NW part of the Germanic Basin (Germany, the Netherlands and Denmark). This system consisted of a series of north–south orientated grabens belonging to the initial Proto-Atlantic–North Sea extensional system (see below). The rifts became increasingly active over time and played a particularly important role as depocentres in the Late Triassic (see below).

Seismically induced synsedimentary deformations are common in the marine Muschelkalk carbonates (Szulc 1993; Dualeh 1995; Götz 1996; Voigt & Linnemann 1996; Rüffer 1996) and indicate that the Germanic Basin was also tectonically active in the Mid-Triassic. Given the distribution of the tectonically controlled sedimentary and deformational structures, it appears that most are grouped in belts linked to the ancestral, mostly Variscan faults and lineaments mentioned above (i.e. TTL, COHF, EF, SMF, STL). During Mid-Triassic times, these inherited structures were reactivated and influenced the sedimentary processes and tectonic subsidence within the regions concerned. At the same time, rifting in the North Sea tensional system became more intense, forming localized subsidence centres in the NW part of the basin.

Isopach and lithofacies patterns for the Muschelkalk illustrate migration of the depocentres of the Germanic Basin in Mid-Triassic times (Szulc 2000). During the late Olenekian–Pelsonian (Röt to Lower Muschelkalk) the subsidence centre followed the SMF–COHF–STL fault network (Fig. 13.4A). The second phase (Middle Muschelkalk) was a turning point, because the depocentre began to shift to the western system encompassing the southern STL. This subsidence centre dominated during the third phase of basin evolution (Upper Muschelkalk (Fig. 13.4B) to Lower Keuper).

The three phases noted above differ in their tectonic regime (Szulc 2000). The first phase was related to transtensional tectonics developed along the southern margin of the basin from the Holy Cross Mountains through Upper and Lower Silesia to Thuringia. Strike-slip movement was the dominant crustal motion during this phase. The second phase featured less crustal mobility, while the third phase was characterized by a moderate tensional regime in the western area and vigorous compression (transpression) in the eastern area. Compression finally also encompassed the western basin and resulted in a regional angular unconformity (Muschelkalk–Keuper boundary; Wolburg 1969) traceable across the entire Germanic Basin. The transpression also initiated intense halokinesis in the MPT and the NW German rifts where localized, rapidly subsiding centres developed (Frisch & Kockel 1999; Krzywiec 2004).

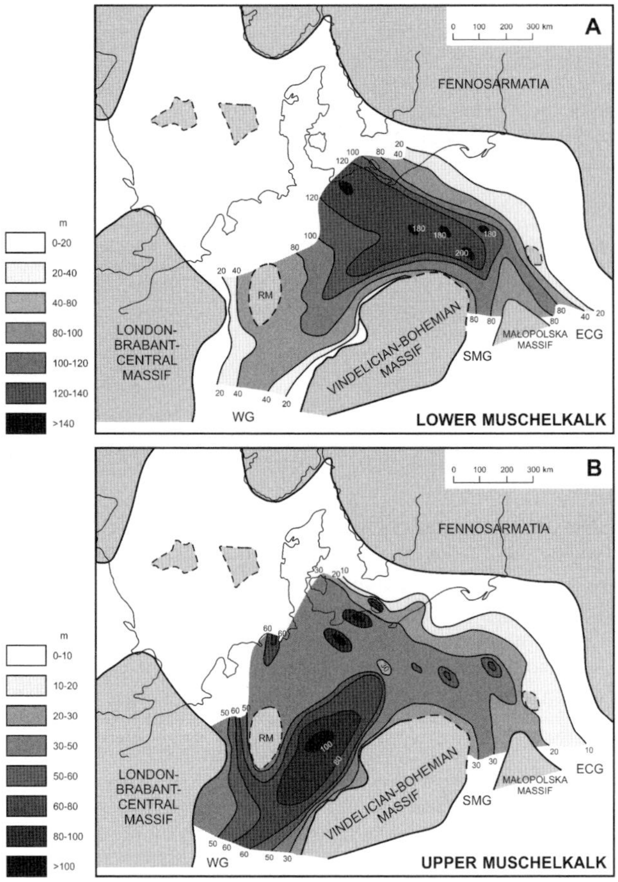


**Fig. 13.4.** Isopach maps of the Middle Triassic sediments in the southern and central parts of the Germanic Basin (from Szulc 2000). (**A**) Lower Muschelkalk (Anisian); (**B**) Upper Muschelkalk (Ladinian). Abbreviations: ECG, East Carpathian Gate; RM, Rhenish Massif; SMG, Silesian-Moravian Gate; WG, Western Gate.

The Late Triassic commenced with relatively weak tectonism, as suggested by the very generally uniform facies pattern, particularly well illustrated by the Grenzdolomit deposits (Figs 13.5E & 13.6). More intense subsidence is seen only in the MPT (Szyperko-Teller 1997).

Strong crustal movements recommenced in Carnian times (Lower Gipskeuper) when intensive rifting occurred in the North Sea Basin and NW Germany (Frisch & Kockel 1999). No such movements affected the southern and eastern sub-basins. Only during the deposition of the Schilfsandstein did rifting occur across the whole basin leading to conspicuous upwarping of the northern Peri-Tethys area. Given the concurrent up and down block movements within the basin, one may assume translatory motion as the dominant tectonic mechanism for this time. The

**Fig. 13.5.** Palaeofacies maps of the Germanic Basin for selected intervals from the Olenekian to Carnian (updated from Szulc 2000) (RM, Rhenish Massif). (**A**) During the maximum flooding event of the first Scythian depositional sequence (S1), Lower Röt. Olenekian. (**B**) During the maximum flooding event of the third Anisian depositional sequence (An3), Terebratula Beds. Pelsonian. Dashed line marks the extent of crinoids. Occurrence of crinoids delineates normal marine environment. (**C**) During the late highstand of the third Anisian depositional sequence (An3), uppermost Diplopora Beds; Orbicularis Beds. Illyrian. Dashed line marks the extent of halite. (**D**) During the maximum flooding stage of the first Ladinian depositional sequence (La1), *cycloides* Bank. Fassanian. Dashed line marks the extent of the brachiopod *Coenothyris cycloides*. (**E**) During the maximum flooding stage of the third Ladinian depositional sequence (La3), Grenzdolomit. Longobardian. (**F**) During the highstand stage of the third Ladinian depositional sequence (La3), Lower Gipskeuper. Longobardian–Julian.

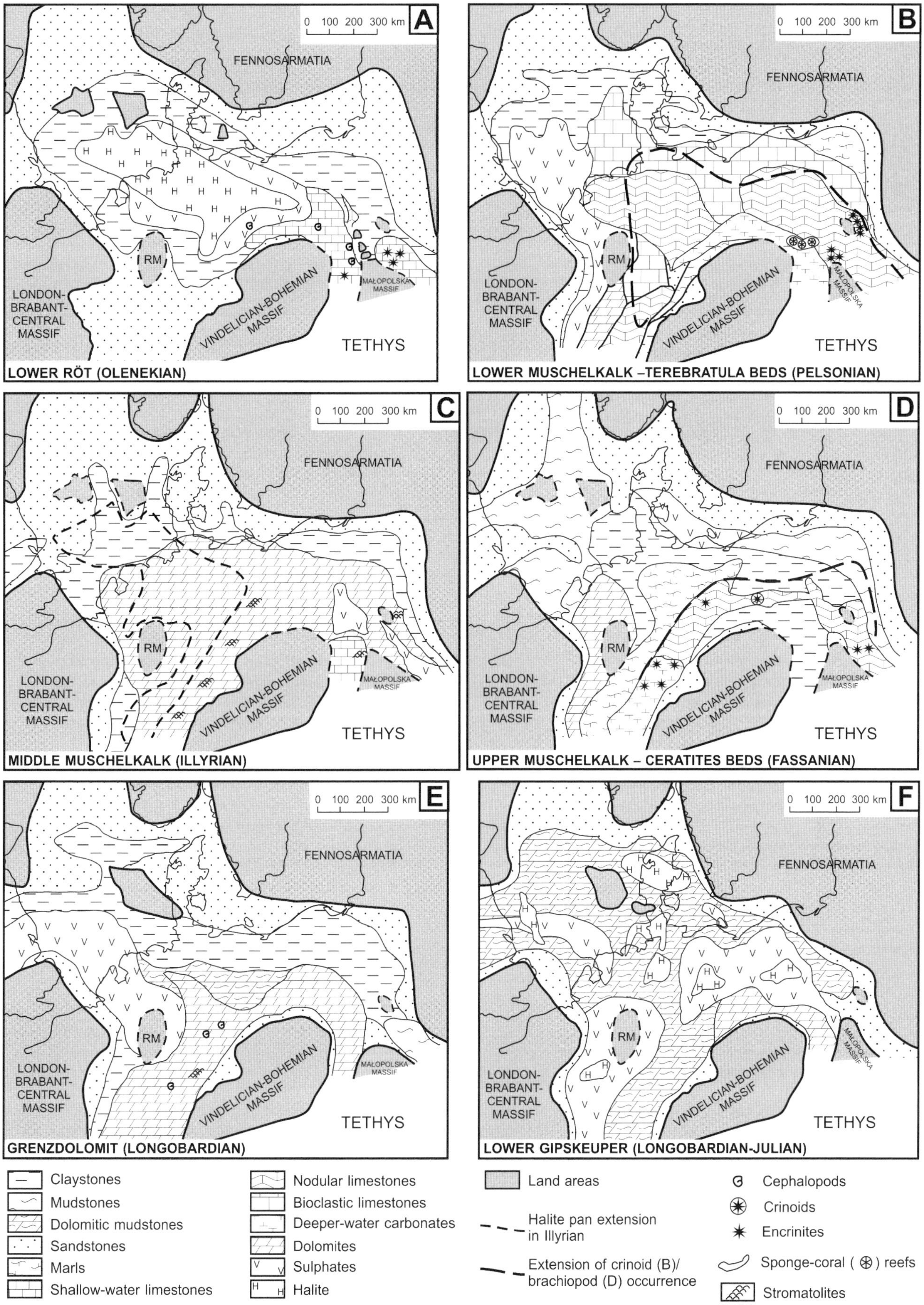
A
0 100 200 300 km
FENNOSARMATIA
RM
LONDON-BRABANT-CENTRAL MASSIF
VINDELICIAN-BOHEMIAN MASSIF
MAŁOPOLSKA MASSIF
TETHYS
LOWER RÖT (OLENEKIAN)
B
0 100 200 300 km
FENNOSARMATIA
RM
LONDON-BRABANT-CENTRAL MASSIF
VINDELICIAN-BOHEMIAN MASSIF
MAŁOPOLSKA MASSIF
TETHYS
LOWER MUSCHELKALK –TEREBRATULA BEDS (PELSONIAN)
C
0 100 200 300 km
FENNOSARMATIA
RM
LONDON-BRABANT-CENTRAL MASSIF
VINDELICIAN-BOHEMIAN MASSIF
MAŁOPOLSKA MASSIF
TETHYS
MIDDLE MUSCHELKALK (ILLYRIAN)
D
0 100 200 300 km
FENNOSARMATIA
RM
LONDON-BRABANT-CENTRAL MASSIF
VINDELICIAN-BOHEMIAN MASSIF
MAŁOPOLSKA MASSIF
TETHYS
UPPER MUSCHELKALK – CERATITES BEDS (FASSANIAN)
E
0 100 200 300 km
FENNOSARMATIA
RM
LONDON-BRABANT-CENTRAL MASSIF
VINDELICIAN-BOHEMIAN MASSIF
MAŁOPOLSKA MASSIF
TETHYS
GRENZDOLOMIT (LONGOBARDIAN)
F
0 100 200 300 km
FENNOSARMATIA
RM
LONDON-BRABANT-CENTRAL MASSIF
VINDELICIAN-BOHEMIAN MASSIF
MAŁOPOLSKA MASSIF
TETHYS
LOWER GIPSKEUPER (LONGOBARDIAN-JULIAN)
Claystones
Mudstones
Dolomitic mudstones
Sandstones
Marls
Shallow-water limestones
Nodular limestones
Bioclastic limestones
Deeper-water carbonates
Dolomites
Sulphates
Halite
Land areas
Halite pan extension in Illyrian
Extension of crinoid (B)/ brachiopod (D) occurrence
Cephalopods
Crinoids
Encrinites
Sponge-coral ( ⊛ ) reefs
Stromatolites

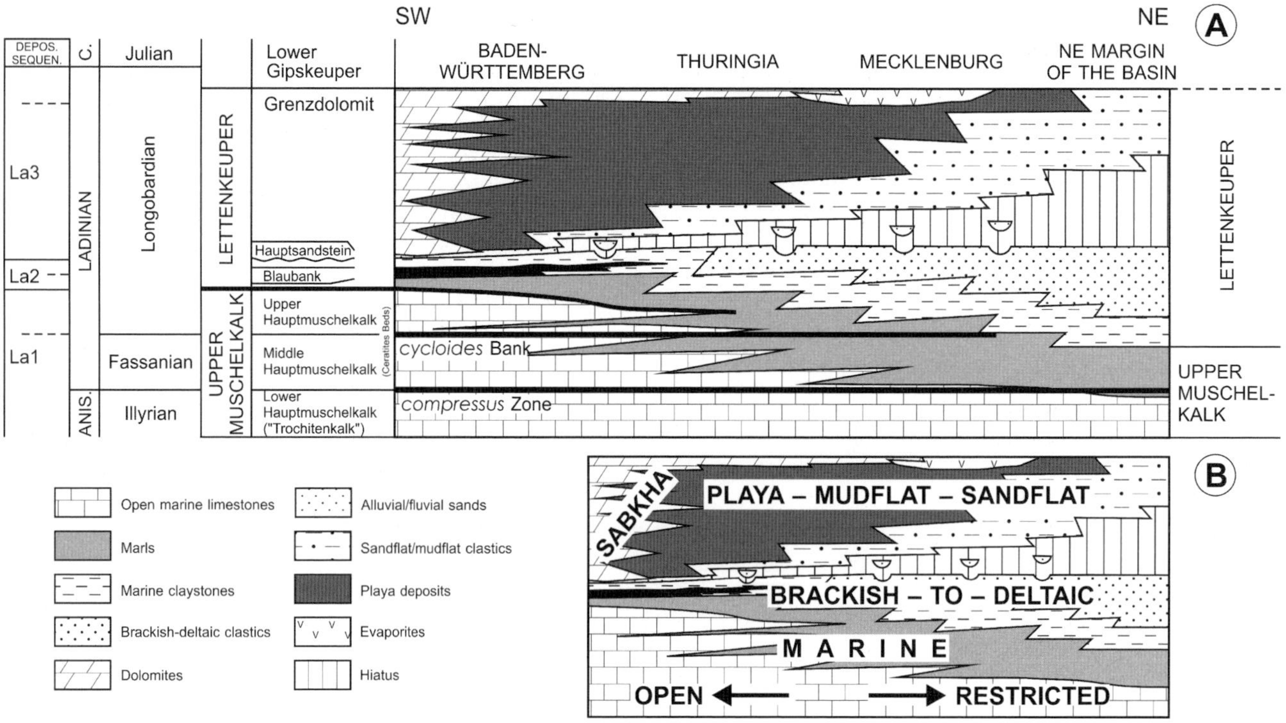


**Fig. 13.6.** (**A**) Sequence-stratigraphic framework of the Upper Muschelkalk–Lower Keuper (late Illyrian–early Carnian) of the western Germanic Basin. Heavy line between Upper Muschelkalk and Lettenkeuper marks the regional angular unconformity in SW Germany. (**B**) Environmental interpretation of the lithofacies distribution from (**A**) (from Szulc 2000).

typical Schilfsandstein anastomosing fluvial channels were superimposed upon the graben network (Dittrich 1989), while the uplifted blocks were eroded, resulting in prominent local unconformities.

Intense tectonic activity in Norian times produced an unconformity between the Middle and Upper Keuper successions. It would appear that these movements were also related to strike-slip motion. The translatory sense of faulting is especially well documented by the flower-like pattern of faults in the Upper Triassic of the Foresudetic area. The Steinmergelkeuper sediments post-date these movements in both the German and the Polish part of the Germanic Basin (Deczkowski & Gajewska 1977; Frisch & Kockel 1999). Finally, some additional, tectonically induced unconformities have been defined in the Rhaetian sequences in Germany (Röhling & Beutler 1993).

## *Tethys Domain*

A detailed reconstruction of the tectonic evolution of the Alpine region, as provided for the non-orogenic Germanic Basin, is not possible because of post-Triassic diastrophism. Nonetheless, even the incomplete data indicate a close relationship between the tectonic evolution of the two areas, in particular in the Mid-Triassic (Szulc 2000).

In the Germanic Basin almost incessant tectonic reorganization is already evident in the Early Triassic, while at the same time in the Alpine basins, tectonic movements were absent or subdued (Gaetani *et al.* 1998). In the Alpine basins the first phase of intense deformation took place as late as the Mid-Triassic (Bechstädt *et al.* 1978; Brandner 1984). Additionally, intense tectonic activity affected only the southern Alpine basins whereas the northern Alpine and Carpathian basins were relatively passive areas (Brandner 1984).

The Mid-Triassic tectonic history of the Germanic Basin (in particular its southern parts) corresponds well with the structural evolution of the southern Alpine basins. The Aegean–Pelsonian phase of transtensional tectonics, expressed in the Germanic Basin in the form of stacked seismites (Szulc 2000), correlates well with complex block movements which have a strong strike-slip component (Montenegro Phase of Brandner 1984) recognized in the southern Alpine domains and on the Tisza Plate (Bechstädt *et al.* 1978; Brandner 1984; Konrád 1998). Additionally, the second, tectonically 'quiet' phase during Illyrian times in the Germanic Basin was accompanied by a weaker deformation phase in the southern Alpine basins (Bechstädt *et al.* 1976; Martini *et al.* 1986).

The Ladinian–Carnian phase, represented by a transpressive regime in the northern Peri-Tethys, was accompanied by very intense transtension, crustal thinning and volcanism in the Neo-Tethys area (Bechstädt *et al.* 1976; Martini *et al.* 1986; Mégard-Galli & Faure 1988; Krainer & Lutz 1995). Brandner (1984) termed it the 'Labinian' tectonic phase and related it to intensification of seafloor spreading within the Tethys belt. At the same time, to the east, the Palaeo-Tethys Ocean closed as the Cimmerian Block began to collide with Europe (Sengör 1984).

These important tectonic events occurred in Mid-Triassic times within Tethys and on its northern periphery, implying a very similar tectonic regime in the two regions. Szulc (2000) suggested that this reflects the same driving mechanism controlling the structural evolution of the two domains. Thus, the tectonic movement sourced in the Tethys spreading centre(s) was transmitted to the northern Peri-Tethys along rejuvenated Variscan dislocations.

This driving mechanism (i.e. the 'Tethyan' control) is particularly apparent in the southeastern part of the Germanic Basin, suggesting a close (direct?) structural link between that area and the Tethyan rift belt. This link is confirmed by the close similarity in the faunal composition of palaeocommunities in Silesia and the Southern Alps. Therefore, it seems very likely that the Silesian seaway and the Southern Alpine basin were influenced by the same master fault system (Fig. 13.2).

These connections are less clear for the Late Triassic, although some important tectonic events, such as the Carnian movements (topographical rejuvenation and Schilfsandstein deposition) or the mid-Norian strike-slip faulting in the Germanic Basin, were penecontemporaneous with intensive periods of deformation recognized in the Southern Alps (Gaetani *et al.* 1998) and in the Northern Calcareous Alps (Szulc 2003*a*).

Direct connections between the SW Germanic Basin and Tethys are not evident since they were substantially modified by the intermediate domains of the South East Basin (Southern France), the Pre-Alps and the Western Alps (Baud & Mégard-Galli 1975; Debelmas 1986).

## Palaeomagnetism (J.N.)

Palaeomagnetic data suggest that the European plate, as part of Laurussia and the megacontinent Pangaea, continued to drift northward during the Triassic, its central part moving from subtropical to moderate palaeolatitudes. Continental playa/lacustrine and epicontinental marine environments were common in Triassic Laurussia. Indeed, the red-beds which are frequently encountered in the deposits of these environments favour palaeomagnetic and magnetostratigraphic studies. In contrast, the poor fossil content of these rocks does not allow their precise stratigraphic correlation. Magnetostratigraphy, therefore, appears to be the most promising method to overcome correlation problems since in the Tethyan and Boreal areas considerable progress has been made in the calibration of magnetozones with detailed biostratigraphic zonation. This polarity record, calibrated by magnetobiostratigraphic correlations of several well-dated tie points, provides a framework for modern geological timescales.

### *Palaeomagnetic data and Triassic palaeogeography*

The good quality Late Permian to Early Jurassic palaeomagnetic poles from the area of stable Europe (i.e. Europe without Iberia and the Alpine domain) are listed in Table 13.1. The Triassic part of the stable European apparent polar wander path (APWP; Fig. 13.7A) was constructed using only these selected poles. The calculation and smoothing of the APWP was performed using the GMAP plotting package (Torsvik & Smethurst 1999).

The smoothing procedures involve the spherical spline method and the following splining parameters have been used: tension factor = 200, time resolution = 2.5 Ma. The shift of the Triassic virtual palaeomagnetic pole is characteristic for stable Europe and is very distinct. Its latitudinal and longitudinal movements reach about 20° and 50°, respectively.

Palaeomagnetic data indicate that stable Europe, as part of Laurussia, moved about 25° to the north through the Triassic period, and rotated anticlockwise by *c.* 30° (Fig. 13.7B). However, as proven by Van der Voo & Torsvik (2001), a precise location of the Late Palaeozoic–Early Mesozoic palaeocontinents cannot be inferred from a pure geocentric axial dipole field (GAD) model. There are many examples of discrepancies between palaeomagnetic inclinations and generally accepted tectonic conclusions. Because of this, Van der Voo & Torsvik (2001) proposed an octupole contribution to the total geomagnetic field that produces different models for Late Permian–Early Triassic Pangaea. They demonstrated that the GAD model implies a Pangaea C-type configuration (Smith & Livermore 1991), a 10% octupole contribution produces a Pangaea B-type configuration (Irving 1977) and a 20% octupole contribution (G3 = 0.2) allows a Pangaea A-type configuration (Van der Voo *et al.* 1976). Palaeogeographic reconstructions of Pangaea A-type configuration for the Triassic timespan are presented in Figure 13.7. It is apparent that the Triassic palaeolatitudes of Central Europe taken from a GAD model differ by about 6–10° from those calculated with a contribution from an octupole field.

### *Magnetostratigraphy*

Magnetostratigraphic studies of Triassic strata have been carried out in many places in the world. Results of studies in North America (e.g. Ogg & Steiner 1991; Kent & Olsen 1999) and Europe (e.g. Muttoni *et al.* 1997; Nawrocki 1997; Katinas 1997; Gallet *et al.* 1998; Nawrocki & Szulc 2000; Scholger *et al.* 2000; Szurlies *et al.* 2003; Hounslow & McIntosh 2003; Channell *et al.* 2003; Szurlies 2004; Hounslow *et al.* 2004) indicate that Triassic rocks have mixed polarity. The sequence of Triassic magnetozones has been calibrated against a detailed biostratigraphic zonation, in both the Boreal and Tethyan areas, and the biomagnetostratigraphic record from these domains was corre-

**Table 13.1.** *Selected Late Permian–Early Jurassic palaeomagnetic poles used for construction of the Stable European apparent polar wander path*

| Rocks | $P_{long.}$ | $P_{lat.}$ | Palaeomagnetic age (Ma) | References |
|---|---|---|---|---|
| Volga region red beds, Russia | 163°E | 47°N | 251–263 | Boronin & Petrov (1986) |
| Lower Buntsandstein sediments, Germany | 166°E | 51°N | 250–252 | Szurlies *et al.* (2003) |
| Lower/Middle Buntsandstein sediments, Holy Cross Mts, Poland | 155°E | 49°N | 248–252 | Nawrocki *et al.* (2003) |
| Sherwood Sandstone Group, UK | 139°E | 53°N | 228–249 | Hounslow & McIntosh (2003) |
| Muschelkalk sediments, Poland | 143°E | 52°N | 235–245 | Nawrocki & Szulc (2000) |
| Heming limestones, France | 141°E | 53°N | 235–240 | Théveniaut *et al.* (1992) |
| Gipskeuper sediments, W Germany | 131°E | 49°N | 222–228 | Edel & Duringer (1997) |
| Cevennes sediments, France | 124°E | 62°N | 204–228 | Henry *et al.* (2001) |
| Rhaetian sediments, France, Germany | 112°E | 50°N | 200–204 | Edel & Duringer (1997) |
| Paris Basin sediments, France | 105°E | 51°N | 190–200 | Yang *et al.* (1996) |
| Normandy limestones, France | 118°E | 69°N | 183–190 | Fabre (1986) |
| Normandy limestones, France | 100°E | 72°N | 175–183 | Fabre (1986) |

$P_{long.}$ = longitude of north palaeomagnetic pole
$P_{lat.}$ = latitude of north palaeomagnetic pole

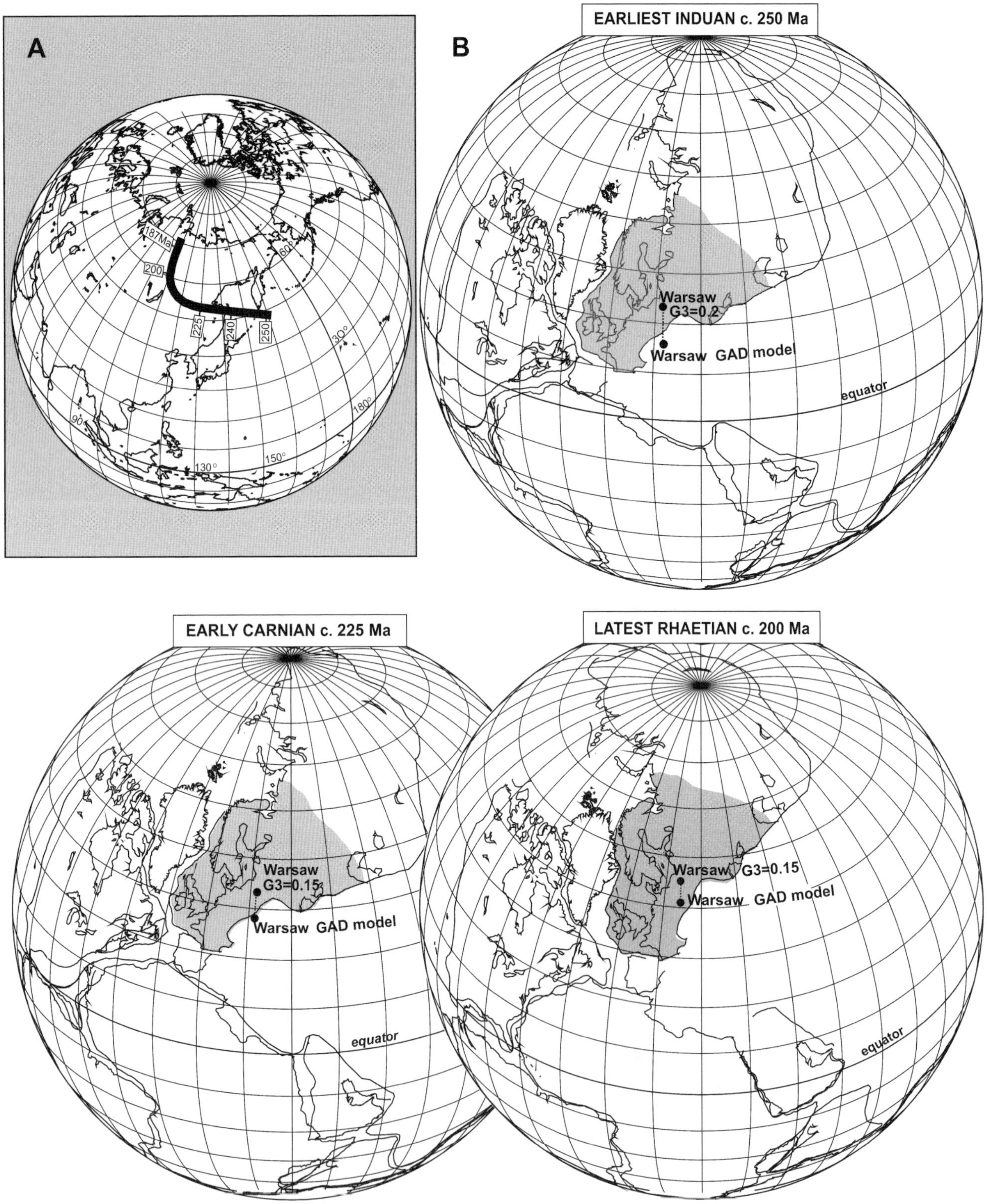


**Fig. 13.7.** (**A**) Triassic–Early Jurassic apparent polar wander path (APWP) for stable Europe (for construction details see text). (**B**) Palaeogeographic reconstructions of palaeocontinents for the Triassic period prepared according to palaeomagnetic data gathered in the GMAP computer package (Torsvik & Smethurst 1994) and adjusted using the method of Van der Voo & Torsvik (2001) assuming a 20% or 15% octupole contribution (G3) to a pure geocentric axial dipole field (GAD). The location of the city of Warsaw according to the GAD model is shown. The area of stable Europe is coloured in grey.

lated with the polarity patterns obtained from several epicontinental basin sections, where sediments are very poor in age-diagnostic fossils. Figure 13.8 shows the magnetostratigraphic correlation of the most complete Triassic sections from Europe and North America.

In the Central European Basin (= Germanic Basin), the basic feature of correlation of the Early Triassic strata is related to the assumption that the long normal polarity zone of the lowermost Buntsandstein (Nawrocki 1997; Szurlies *et al.* 2003) corresponds to that detected in Boreal and Tethyan sections (e.g. Ogg & Steiner 1991; Scholger *et al.* 2000). The next higher magnetozones recognized in the Buntsandstein also fit with the Lower Triassic polarity pattern of the Tethys and Boreal areas. The Griesbachian–Dienerian age of the Lower Buntsandstein and the lower part of Middle Buntsandstein, as well as the Smithian age of the upper part of Middle Buntsandstein would appear to be supported by the magnetostratigraphic correlation (Nawrocki 1997; Szurlies 2004). This correlation also shows that the entire Röt succession in the southern Polish basin should be included in the Olenekian stage (Nawrocki & Szulc 2000).

While the precise location of the Permian–Triassic boundary in the Central European Basin is still not clear, in the stratotype section at Meishan (China, Zhejiang province) it is located within bed 27, which has reversed polarity (Yin *et al.* 2001). This reversed polarity record can be correlated with the magnetozone recognized in the Rewal Formation or in the lower part of the Bröckelschiefer Formation (see Nawrocki 2004) in the Central European Basin (Fig. 13.8). A slightly higher stratigraphic position for this boundary, i.e. in the lowermost Buntsandstein, as postulated by Szurlies *et al.* (2003), cannot be excluded, but requires a reversed polarity horizon to be found within the basal Triassic normal polarity zone. On the other hand, the accuracy of the palaeomagnetic studies of the Meishan section is not undisputed and the reliability of these data needs to be verified.

Magnetostratigraphic correlations of the Muschelkalk sequences of the Polish part of the northern Peri-Tethys with the Tethyan sections of southern Europe indicate that these rocks were deposited during latest Olenekian–Early Fassanian time (Nawrocki & Szulc 2000). Normal marine sedimentation ceased in the Polish basin as early as the Late Fassanian. The equivalents of the Muschelkalk sediments were found in the epicontinental basins of western Europe. According to the palaeomagnetic data of Hounslow & McIntosh (2003), the Otter Sandstone Formation of the Wessex Basin can be correlated with most of the Polish Muschelkalk, i.e. Aegean to early Fassanian (Fig. 13.8).

The Upper Triassic magnetostratigraphic data from the Central European Basin are very incomplete. Moreover, the Upper Triassic sedimentary record of the Central European Basin cannot be regarded as continuous. Only the Lower Keuper strata of the Central European Basin are well characterized magnetos-

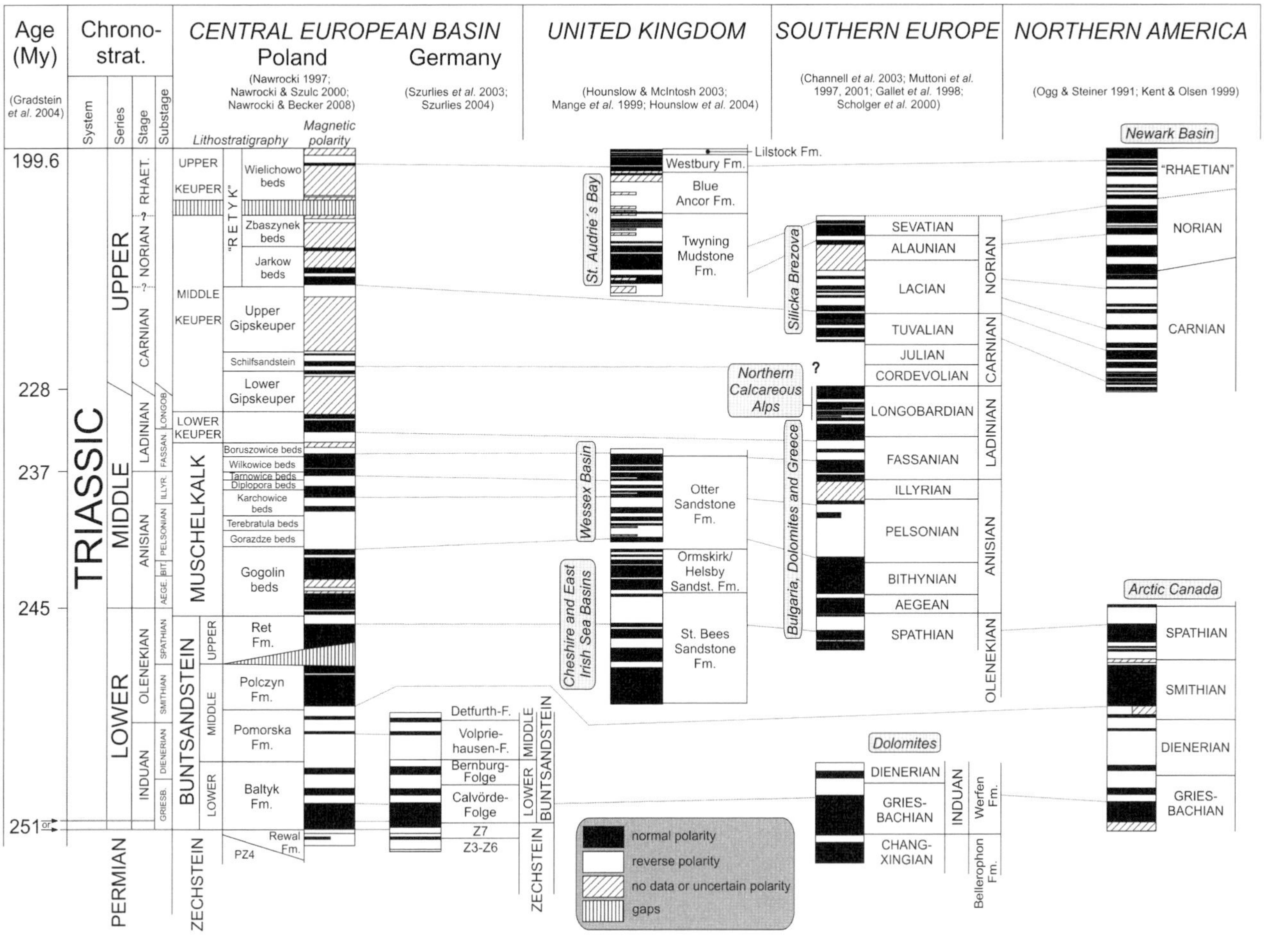


**Fig. 13.8.** The polarity stratigraphy and correlation of selected Triassic sections from Europe and North America.

tratigraphically (Nawrocki & Becker 2008). These rocks are equivalents of the Late Fassanian and Early Longobardian (Fig. 13.8).

An almost complete polarity pattern has been obtained from Tethyan sections of the Upper Triassic. The magnetic stratigraphy and conodont biostratigraphy from the Upper Carnian to Upper Norian limestones exposed at Slicka Berezova (Slovakia) were correlated to other Tethyan sections and the continental succession in the Newark Basin (USA) (Channell *et al.* 2003). This correlation implies that the Norian–Rhaetian boundary lies within the Newark polarity zone E17r at *c.* 207 Ma and the Carnian–Norian boundary lies close to the base of the Newark polarity zone E7r at *c.* 226 Ma. According to Channell *et al.* (2003) this implies durations for the Norian and Rhaetian stages of 19 Ma and 7 Ma, respectively. This time estimate is based on a well-recognized cyclostratigraphy of the Newark section (Kent & Olsen 1999). It should be stressed, however, that any estimation of time based on cyclostratigraphy must be treated with caution. The very distinct cyclicity observed in many Triassic sections can be controlled by both climatic and tectonic factors. More reliable time estimates may be possible after separation of astronomically tuned climatic cycles from tectonic ones.

The magnetostratigraphy from St. Audrie's Bay, UK, provides strong evidence that the Newark Supergroup magnetostratigraphy is very representative of the Upper Triassic magnetic field over the E14r to E20r interval (Hounslow *et al.* 2004). The data from St. Audrie's Bay allow some improvement in the resolution of the stage and substage assignments of the Newark Supergroup magnetostratigraphic polarity pattern.

## Germanic realm: sedimentary basins

### *Stratigraphy and biostratigraphy (A.E.G., S.F.B.)*

The most powerful biostratigraphic tool in the Germanic Triassic is palynology. It is applicable in both continental and marine environments, and can be used for correlation between the Germanic and Alpine realms. A biostratigraphical subdivision and correlation of the mainly non-marine deposits of Buntsandstein and Keuper is only possible with palynomorphs.

Heunisch (1999) provided a generalized palynostratigraphical subdivision of the Germanic Basin into 20 units (Fig. 13.9), based on the original works of authors in different geographical areas and stratigraphical units, e.g. Germany (Mädler 1964; Klaus 1964; Schulz 1966; Lund 1977), western Netherlands, North Sea and southern England (Visscher & Commissaris 1968; Geiger & Hopping 1968; Fisher 1972) and Poland (Orłowska-Zwolińska 1977, 1983, 1985). Palynostratigraphical correlation between the Germanic and Alpine realms, while still difficult, is improving with the increasing number of detailed studies in both areas. In the Alpine region, pioneering palynological work by Klaus (1960) has been followed by a series of important studies (e.g. Morbey 1975; van der Eem 1983; Brugman 1986; Blendinger 1988; Roghi 2004; Kustatscher *et al.* 2006). Visscher & Brugman (1981) provided palynological data for correlating the Alpine and Germanic successions. Palynomorph assemblages of the Germanic Keuper deposits and the correlation of Upper Triassic palynostratigraphic zones of the Germanic and Alpine realms have been compiled and discussed in Schulz & Heunisch (2005) while the Keuper macroflora of the Germanic Basin and the stratigraphic use of Upper Triassic plant remains has been detailed by Kelber (2005).

Recently, palynofacies analysis has been used as a tool for basin-wide correlation and high-resolution sequence stratigraphic interpretation in the Middle Triassic of the Germanic realm (Götz & Feist-Burkhardt 2000; Rameil *et al.* 2000; Feist-Burkhardt *et al.* 2008) as well as for the correlation of depositional sequences of the northwestern Tethys shelf area with the northern Peri-Tethyan Basin (Götz *et al.* 2003, 2005). Stratigraphic and spatial variations in the distribution of sedimentary organic matter reflect changes in a depositional system related to relative sea-level fluctuations, and can be used to detect eustatic signals at the scale of third-order and high-frequency cyclicity. The analysis of significant palynofacies parameters within sedimentary series (e.g. the relative abundance of marine plankton, the ratio of continental to marine particles, the ratio of opaque to translucent phytoclasts, and particle size and shape) enables the characterization of transgressive and highstand deposits and the recognition of maximum flooding zones and sequence boundaries in terms of sequence stratigraphy.

In the marine sediments of the Middle Triassic, ammonoid biostratigraphy provides the most detailed stratigraphic framework attainable within the Germanic Triassic. Fourteen ceratite biozones are recognized in the Upper Muschelkalk (Hagdorn 1991*b*; Urlichs 1993). These correlate with isochronous marker beds of key sections in southern Germany and are, therefore, used as chronozones for basin-wide correlation (Fig. 13.10). Since most of the Germanic ceratites are endemic species (Urlichs 1999), their use for wider correlation is limited. However, some index ammonoids (e.g. *Balatonites*, *Acrochordiceras*, *Judicarites*, *Nevadites*) can be used to correlate Muschelkalk deposits with Alpine successions (Brack *et al.* 1999).

Hagdorn & Simon (1993) discussed the use of ecostratigraphic marker beds for basin-wide correlation within the Upper Muschelkalk. Distinct bioclastic beds comprising exotic stenohaline sessile epibionts, such as crinoids (e.g. *Holocrinus doreckae*), articulate brachiopods (e.g. *Coenothyris cycloides*) or bivalves (e.g. *Chlamys (Praechlamys) reticulata*), record temporary faunal immigration from outside of the Germanic Basin. Ideally, these exotic elements occur in one bed only, thus providing reliable marker horizons (Fig. 13.10), the isochrony of which is indicated by biostratigraphic data from ammonoids.

Conodonts are the most important marine microfossil group used for correlation of the marine sediments of the Germanic and Tethyan realms (Fig. 13.10). Kozur (1974*a*) proposed the first conodont zonation for the central part of the Germanic Basin, including the data of earlier works by Tatge (1956), Hirschmann (1959) and Kozur (1968, 1972, 1973). Subsequently, conodont assemblages from different areas of the western basin were detailed by Rafek (1977), Demonfaucon (1982), Nolte (1989), Götz (1995) and Fuchs & Zwenger (1995). Conodont assemblages from the Polish part of the Germanic Basin were described by Trammer (1971, 1972, 1975), Zawidzka (1975), Kedżierski & Szulc (1996) and Narkiewicz (1999). More recently, the conodont appearance and distribution patterns within the semi-closed Middle Triassic Muschelkalk basin have been analysed with respect to relative sea-level changes (Narkiewicz & Szulc 2004). Muschelkalk biostratigraphy has been improved by investigations on crinoids and echinoids, and this would appear to be a useful tool for correlation with the Alpine realm (Hagdorn & Gluchowski 1993).

Vertebrate footprints (Haubold 1999; Diedrich 2000) and skeletal remains (Schoch & Wild 1999*a, b, c*) may be used for biostratigraphy in marginal settings. Marine reptile faunas as well as tetrapod assemblages described by Hagdorn & Rieppel (1999) and Lucas (1999) suggest new possibilities in Triassic biostratigraphy.

Other fossil groups including conchostracans (Kozur 1999),

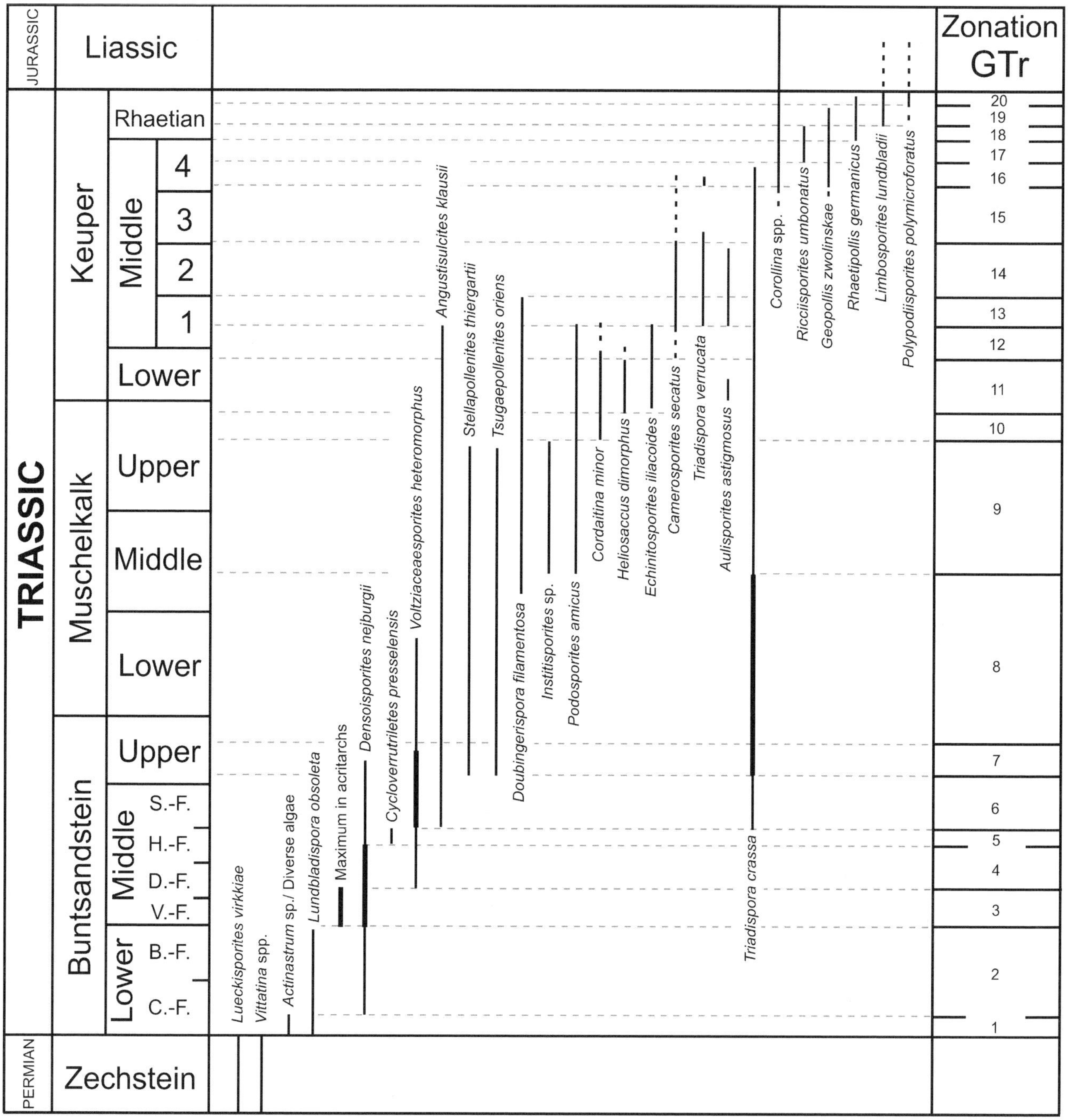


**Fig. 13.9.** Palynostratigraphy of the Germanic Triassic after Heunisch (1999).

ostracods (Kozur 1974*a*; Beutler 1988), foraminifers (Gazdzicki *et al.* 1975) and megaspores (Fuglewicz 1980; Wierer 1997) are of limited biostratigraphical value and are mostly used for local correlation.

Some of the problems of correlating the stratigraphic sucessions between the Germanic and the Alpine realms are discussed by Brack *et al.* (1999) and Kozur (1999, 2003).

*Lower Triassic (Lower and Middle Buntsandstein) (M.G., J.S., H.G.R.)*

The mass extinction at the end of the Permian created difficulties for the stratigraphical study of the Lower Triassic of the Germanic realm. The paucity of fossils in general, and the lack of index fossils in particular, make correlation very difficult, affecting as it does both chronostratigraphy and lithostratigraphy. The most effective correlation tool available is palynostratigraphy. Other fossils, such as conchostracans, ostracods and molluscs that occur only sporadically and are facies dependent, afford only relatively low biostratigraphic resolution. The relative lack of fossil remains means that the subdivision of the Lower Triassic is traditionally based on lithostratigraphy. However, due to the relatively strong lateral facies changes, mainly related to diachronous tectonic activity, lithostratigraphical correlation of the Lower Triassic sections from different parts of the basin can

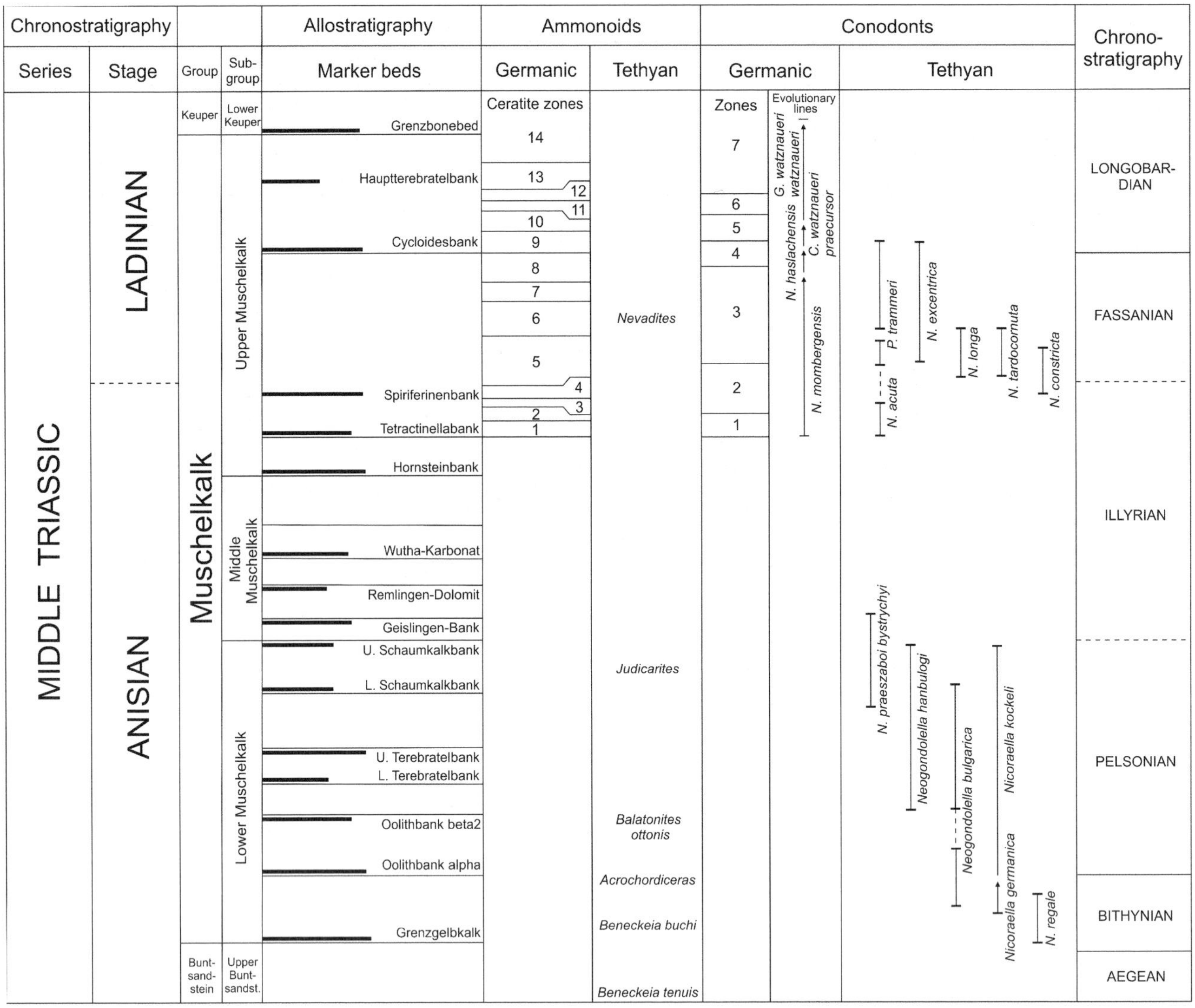


**Fig. 13.10.** Middle Triassic biostratigraphy of the Germanic and Tethyan realms. Ceratite zones after Hagdorn (1991*a*): 1, *atavus*; 2, *pulcher*; 3, *robustus*; 4, *compressus*; 5, *evolutus*; 6, *spinosus*; 7, *postspinosus*; 8, *enodis*; 9, *sublaevigatus*; 10, *praenodosus*; 11, *nodosus*; 12, *weyeri*; 13, *dorsoplanus*; 14, *semipartitus*. Conodont zones after Kozur (1974*a*), conodont lineages after Narkiewicz & Szulc (2004): 1, *Neogondolella mombergensis*, *Chirodella dinodoides*; 2, *Neogondolella mombergensis*; 3, *Neogondolella media*; 4, *Neogondolella haslachensis*; 5, *Neogondolella haslachensis*, *Celsigondolella watznaueri praecursor*; 6, *Celsigondolella watznaueri praecursor*, *Celsigondollela watznaueri watznaueri*; 7, *Celsigondolella watznaueri watznaueri*.

be difficult. Moreover, the scarcity of modern sedimentological studies of the Buntsandstein impedes the application of sequence stratigraphy to overcome correlation problems. Some recent studies on high-frequency sedimentary cyclicity have been limited in their application since the study areas are restricted (Geluk & Röhling 1997; Szurlies *et al.* 2003). Some progress in stratigraphical resolution of the Lower Triassic has, however, resulted from magnetostratigraphical studies (see above), and this may be the most promising method for further refinement of Buntsandstein stratigraphy.

Traditionally, the Buntsandstein is considered to be one stratigraphic entity with the rank of a group. It can be subdivided into three subgroups: the Lower Buntsandstein, comprising fine clastics with prominent carbonate oolitic beds; the Middle Buntsandstein in which coarser clastics alternate with oolites and claystones; and the Upper Buntsandstein (Röt), composed of evaporites, carbonates and fine-grained clastic sediments (Fig. 13.11). This tripartite division is apparent throughout the Germanic Basin, but subdivisions of these units show significant differences throughout the basin. The Lower Buntsandstein in the central and northwestern part of the Germanic Basin is divided into the Calvörde Folge and Bernburg Folge that correspond to the Baltyk Formation in the Polish sub-basin. The Middle Buntsandstein in the western part of the basin is subdivided by means of tectonically controlled unconformities, and in Germany consists of the Volpriehausen Folge, the Detfurth Folge, the Hardegsen Folge and the Solling Folge. The unconformities that separate these formations are not so obvious (or may be absent) in the Polish part of the basin since its tectonic evolution was not quite synchronous. However, the Volpriehausen unconformity, which separates the Lower and Middle Buntsandstein, is recognizable in both areas, and the Hardegsen unconformity is more pronounced in Poland (Nawrocki 1997).

Palynomorph assemblages of the Lower Buntsandstein and the

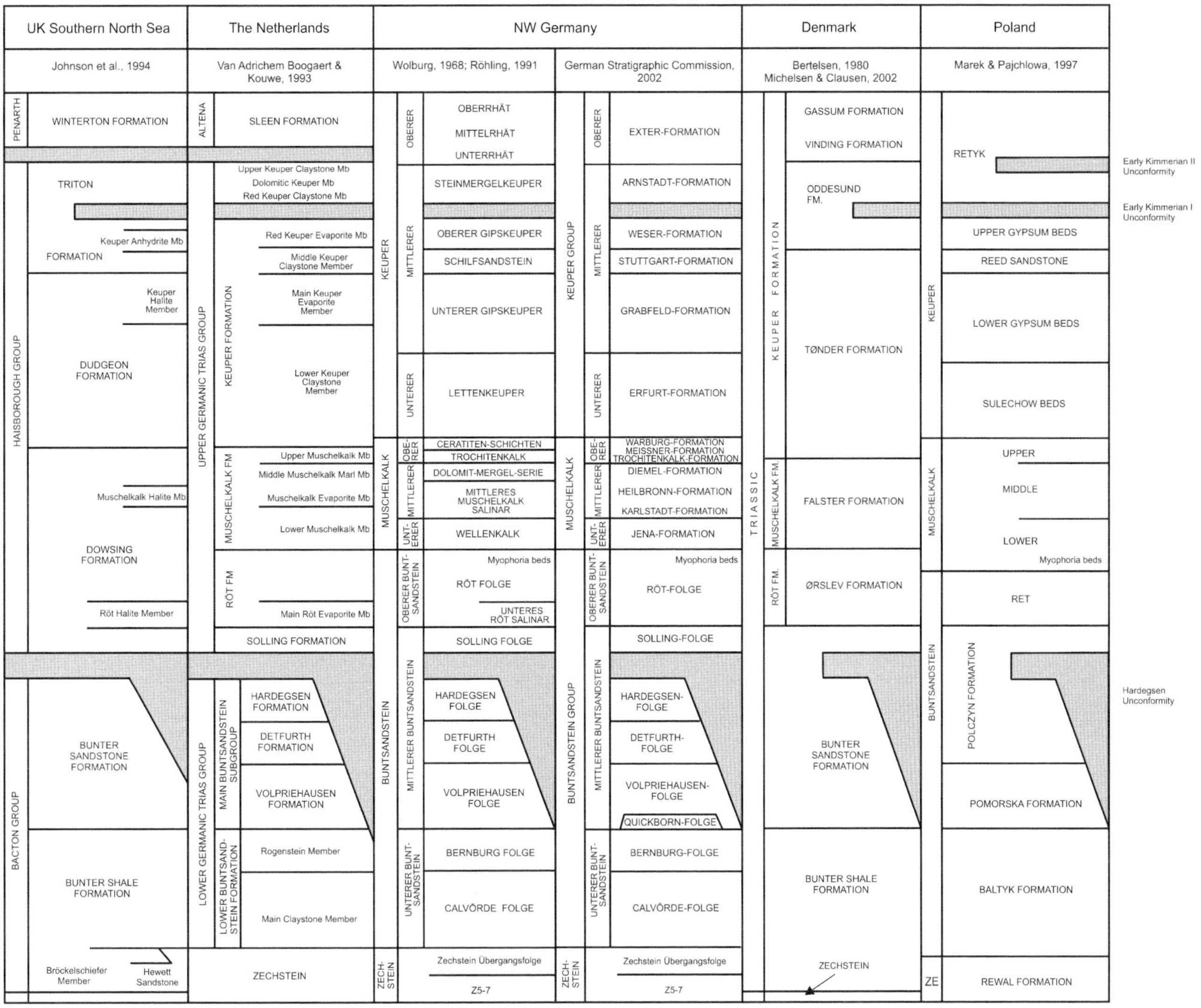


**Fig. 13.11.** Lithostratigraphic units of the Triassic in the southern North Sea, the Netherlands, NW Germany, Denmark and Poland. Compiled by Geluk (2005, updated).

lower part of the Middle Buntsandstein (Volpriehausen Folge and Detfurth Folge, Pomorska Formation) are dominated by lycopsid spores (mostly *Lundbladispora obsoleta* and *Densoisporites nejburgii*). Abundant acritarchs indicate marine influences in the Volpriehausen–lower Detfurth succession in Germany (Reitz 1985; Ecke 1986) and in the Pomorska Formation in Poland (Szyperko-Teller 1997). A significant change in palynomorph assemblages occurs in the Solling Folge (Germany) and the Polczyn Formation (Poland) where the spore *Cycloverrutriletes presselensis* and the conifer pollen *Voltziaceaesporites heteromorphus* become the dominant elements of the miospore spectrum. The Upper Buntsandstein displays a renewed increase in the numbers of marine palynomorphs, related to the onset of the Middle Triassic transgression. Thus, the stratigraphic changes in the Buntsandstein palynomorph assemblages are strongly controlled by environment. Recently it has been pointed out that many of the spore taxa occurring in the Lower Triassic (such as *L. obsoleta*, *D. nejburgii*, *C. presselensis*, and others) may in fact be reworked from Palaeozoic sediments and do not represent the autochthonous flora. Evidence for the possible reworking of these spores is compiled and summarized in Utting *et al.* (2004) along with a discussion of the consequences for biostratigraphy and for the interpretation of Early Triassic climate and palaeoenvironments after the Permian–Triassic extinction event.

*Uppermost Lower and Middle Triassic (Röt–Muschelkalk–Grenzdolomit) (J.S.)*

The Röt–Grenzdolomit succession is a particularly important part of the Germanic Triassic because of its well-established and reliable stratigraphical framework based on bio- and magnetostratigraphical zonations. The lithostratigraphy of the Middle Triassic in Poland and Germany is illustrated in Figure 13.12.

The predominantly fossiliferous marine sediments of this succession provide a firm base for biostratigraphy. Age-diagnostic fossils include miospores, conodonts, echinoderms, ammonoids, bivalves and brachiopods occuring in the Röt, the Lower and Upper Muschelkalk and in the Grenzdolomit marine carbonates. The only fossil-poor intervals are the evaporitic Middle Muschelkalk and the brackish to fluvial clastic sediments of the Lower Keuper.

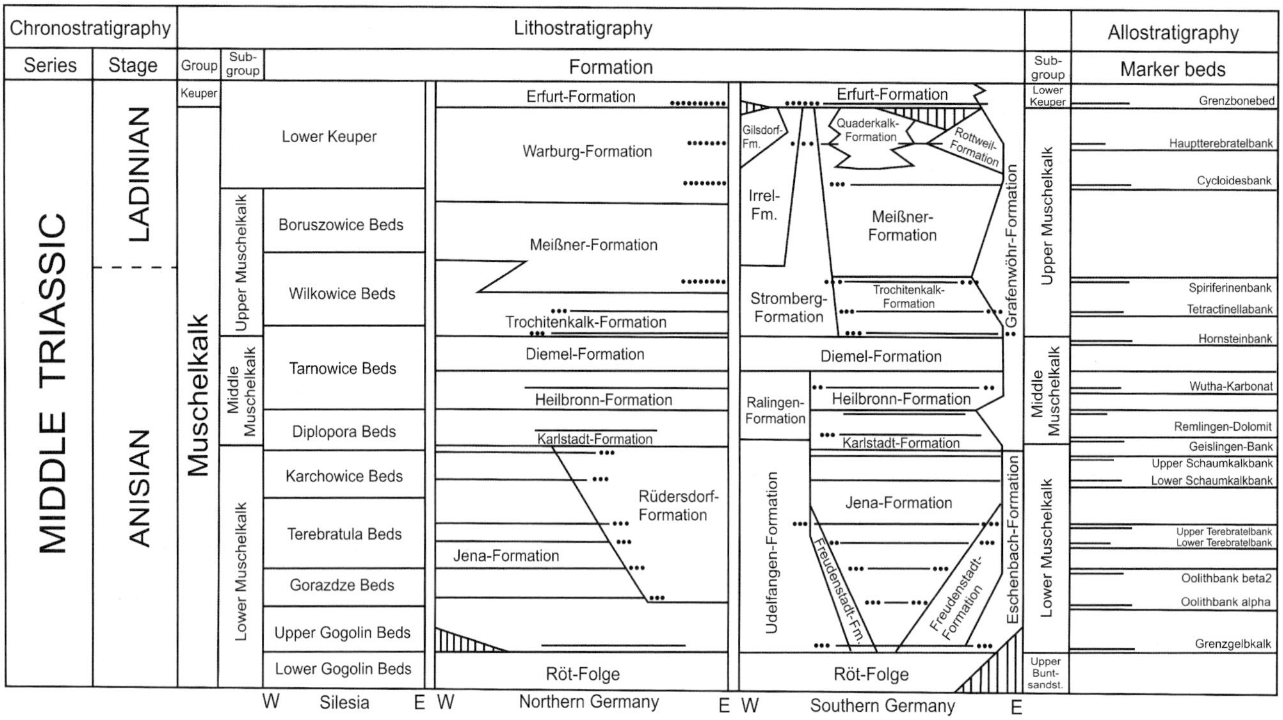


**Fig. 13.12.** Lithostratigraphy of the Middle Triassic of the Germanic Basin after Szulc (2000) and Hagdorn (2004).

Conodonts are the most important fossils for age determination of the Muschelkalk deposits, and provide the basis for a zonal scheme used for chronostratigraphic correlation (Kozur 1968, 1999; Trammer 1975; Zawidzka 1975). The conodonts include Tethyan forms, prevalent in the southeastern part of the Germanic Basin, and endemic forms which are dominant in the western sub-basin. The Tethyan conodonts enabled biostratigraphical zonation of the Muschelkalk in Poland (Narkiewicz 1999) and its correlation with the Anisian–Ladinian of the Alpine basins (Fig. 13.10). The endemic conodonts serve as a local correlation tool, and are especially important for the German Upper Muschelkalk, which has been subdivided into seven conodont zones (Kozur 1972).

Ammonoids are represented by Tethyan and endemic (ceratites) forms. Evolutionary lineages of the latter group have been used for subdivision of the Upper Muschelkalk (Hagdorn 1991*a*; Urlichs 1993). Some Tethyan index ammonites (e.g. *Balatonites*, *Acrochordiceras*, *Judicarites*, *Nevadites*), which are more common in the eastern sub-basin, have long been used for correlation of the Muschelkalk with the Alpine Triassic (Rassmus 1915; Assmann 1926, Brack *et al.* 1999). The ammonoids are also stratigraphically important for the periods of restricted marine conditions. For example, *Beneckeia tenuis* occurs in the Lower Röt (late Olenekian) transgressive deposits, extending from Upper Silesia to Thuringia, and may indicate connections of the Germanic area with the Palaeo-Tethys (Szulc 2000), whereas the ceratites found in the Grenzdolomit carbonates (late Ladinian–early Carnian) of SW Germany reflect open communication with the Proto-Atlantic (Urlichs 1999).

Studies on Triassic echinoderms (Hagdorn & Gluchowski 1993) have shown that these organisms are valuable for correlation within the Tethyan domain and as palaeoenvironmental indicators. The same role is played by brachiopods, especially those common in the Tethyan and Peri-Tethyan domains (e.g. *Decurtella decurtata*, *Tetractinella trigonella*, *Punctospirella fragilis*). Finally, the shallow-marine sediments can be fairly well dated by means of dasycladacean remains (Pia 1930; Kotanski 1994) which occur in Illyrian facies that lack any other age-diagnostic fossils.

The brackish and continental Triassic sediments are dated with palynomorphs (Heunisch 1999) which owe their stratigraphic importance to their presence in both the marine and continental environments and are useful as palaeoenvironmental indicators (see below).

Distinctive and contrasting lithofacies changes from late Olenekian to early Carnian times enabled Alberti (1834) to establish a clear and consistent lithostratigraphical subdivision that appeared to be applicable throughout the Germanic domain. The succession encompasses the evaporite-bearing marine carbonates and fine clastics of the Röt, the marine bioclastic limestones of the Lower and Upper Muschelkalk, the intermittent evaporitic Middle Muschelkalk, the brackish/fluvial clastics of Lower Keuper, and the shallow-marine dolomitic deposits of the Grenzdolomit.

However, as noted above, the lithostratigraphical framework was difficult to establish due to the facies diachroneity throughout the basin. Refinement of the lithostratigraphy, and basin-wide correlation of the lithostratigraphical units were facilitated by progress in terms of the biostratigraphy (see above) and by the application of sequence stratigraphy (Aigner & Bachmann 1992), calibrated by magnetostratigraphy (Nawrocki & Szulc 2000; Szulc 2000). This integrated approach has enabled unequivocal chronostratigraphical correlation of the lithostratigraphical units with their Tethyan counterparts (Ogg 2004; Lehrmann *et al.* 2006) (Fig. 13.1).

A new lithostratigraphical scheme has been introduced for the German Triassic by the German Stratigraphic Commission (Deutsche Stratigraphische Kommission 2002). A similar scheme has been prepared recently for the Polish Triassic (Wagner *et al.* 2008).

*Upper Triassic (J.Ho., L.R., O.K., W.R.)*
The Germanic Keuper group (Ladinian to Rhaetian) is subdivided into three lithostratigraphical units (Fig. 13.13). In stratigraphic order these include the brackish/fluvial Lower Keuper (k1) at the base, the Middle Keuper (k2–k6.1), characterized by a rapidly increasing terrestrial influence, and the marine/deltaic Upper Keuper (k6.2 and k6.3). These subdivisions follow the nomenclature of the German Stratigraphic Commission (Deutsche Stratigraphische Kommission 2005) for the southern basin margin. Local terminologies exist in the east and west, but these are well correlated (e.g. Haunschild & Salger 1978; Beutler 1998; Deutsche Stratigraphische Kommission 2002, 2005; Nitsch 2005).

During deposition of the Lower Keuper (Erfurt Formation, k1) the Germanic Basin was connected to the Tethyan realm via marine gateways in the south and east, from which marine ingressions advanced towards the basin centre (e.g. Ziegler 1990). Offshore to nearshore siliciclastics (of northern provenance) and carbonates (predominantly in the south) interdigitated in the overall regressive Lower Keuper (Pöppelreiter 1999).

The succeeding Middle Keuper comprises five distinct units (k2–k6.1). The lowest unit, the marine/evaporitic Grabfeld Formation (k2), is composed of sulphates (up to 50%), dolomites and dolomitic claystones, which formed in a playa/sabkha environment bordering a terrestrial plain, composed of arkosic sandstones and claystones (e.g. Nitsch 1996). This unit is overlain by the (partly) deeply incised fluvial/deltaic/estuarine Stuttgart Formation (k3) in which mostly fine-grained, well-

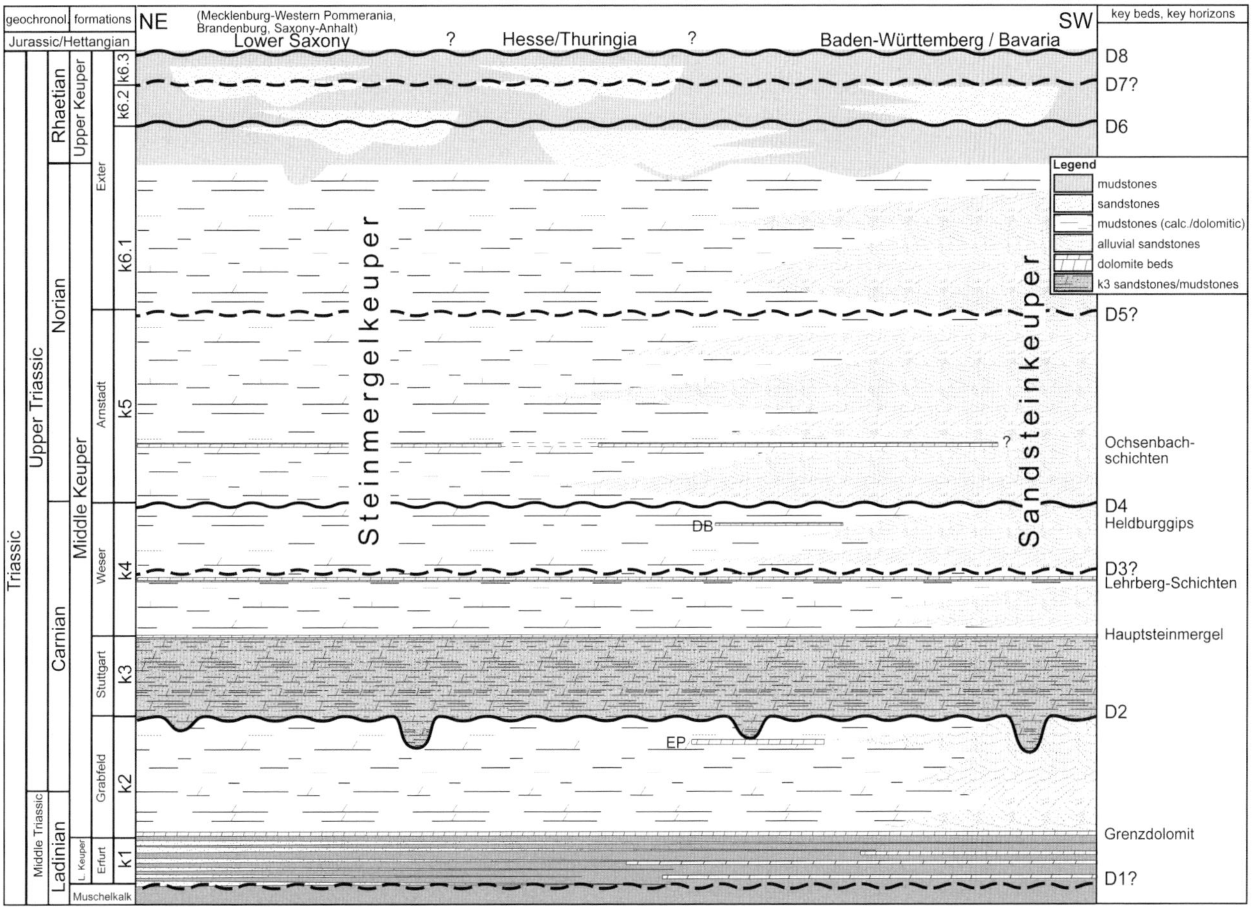


**Fig. 13.13.** Simplified sketch of the Keuper basin fill from Baden-Württemberg/Bavaria, Hesse/Thuringia to Lower Saxony (section roughly from NE to SW). Geochronology follows Deutsche Stratigraphische Kommission (2005). Stratigraphic data are based on Brenner & Villinger (1981), Duchrow (1984), Haunschild (1985), Dittrich (1989), Seidel (1995, 2003), Laemmlen (1996), Nitsch (1996), Seegis (1997), Beutler (1998), Ricken *et al.* (1998), Pöppelreiter (1999), Reinhardt (2000), Gehrmann & Aigner (2002) and Seeling & Kellner (2002). Basin-wide correlation is only provided by a few marker horizons such as the Lehrbergschichten. Orbital control on sedimentation, however, may provide a new correlation tool for other important horizons in the Germanic Keuper Basin. *Description of formations.* k1, Erfurt Fm: shallow marine, estuarine, and tidal sediments; mostly fine-grained mudstones with intercalated dolomite beds of basin-wide extent. Important horizon: Grenzdolomit. k2, Grabfeld Fm: shallow-marine sediments; sabkha develops into continental playa system. Sediments are mostly fine grained, with sulphate deposits (massive gypsum deposits) and halite in more central positions. Important horizon: Engelhofer Platte (EP). k3, Stuttgart Fm: fluvial and shallow marine (tidal influence); sediments are fine-grained sandstones and dark-coloured mudstones. Important horizon: Hauptsteinmergel. k4, Weser Fm: coarse marginal alluvial system grades basinward into playa system with mostly fine-grained sediments intercalated with stratigraphically important gypsum and dolomite beds. Important horizons: Lehrbergschichten (freshwater lake), Doppelbank (DB), Heldburggips. k5, Arnstadt Fm: coarse marginal alluvial system grades basinward into playa system, of mostly fine-grained sediments with stratigraphically important dolomite beds, minor gypsum and a few limestones. Important horizon: Ochsenbachschichten. k6, Exter Fm: fluvial, limnic and shallow-marine fine-grained sediments and sandstones.

sorted sandstones interdigitate with claystones and siltstones, and can be attributed to a basin-wide fluvial system that included channels and associated floodplains (e.g. Wurster 1964*a, b*; Beutler *et al.* 1999; Ricken *et al.* 1998; Köppen 1997). Estuarine environments are also documented (e.g. Gehrmann & Aigner 2002). The sandstone had a northern and northeastern provenance (i.e. Scandinavia; e.g. Köppen & Carter 2000) and the fluvial system expanded across the entire Germanic Basin from north to south and into the Tethyan realm (Lunz Sandstone; Rüffer 1999), thus forming an excellent marker horizon. The Stuttgart Formation has been interpreted in sequence stratigraphic terms as an incised valley-fill formed during sea-level/base-level lowstand and initial rise (e.g. Aigner & Bachmann 1992; Aigner *et al.* 1999). The channel belts were partly tectonically controlled (Dittrich 1989). The overlying, mostly terrestrial formations, include the Weser Formation (k4), the Arnstadt Formation (k5) and the lower part of the Exter Formation (k6.1) which accumulated in a proximal setting along the southern basin margin. Together, these constitute the 'Sandsteinkeuper' subgroup (k4–k6.1). Distally, to the north, this passes laterally into the 'Steinmergelkeuper' subgroup (k4–k6.1) (see Fig. 13.13). All of these formations comprise down-dip fining and thinning arkosic sandstones from an alluvial plain, which merge basinwards into dolomitic claystones and siltstones, and dolomites of a playa lake environment (e.g. Hornung 1999). A few regionally occurring dolomite beds may be of marine origin, as suggested by fauna and isotopic compositions (Reinhardt & Ricken 2000*a*). The provenance of the siliciclastic deposits (k4–k6.1) was in a hinterland area to the east and SE of the SW Germanic Keuper Basin (i.e. the granitic basement of the Bohemian Massif and Vindelician High).

Renewed marine conditions were signalled by the deposition of marine/deltaic sandstones of the upper Middle and Upper Keuper (Exter Formation, k6.1 to k6.3). Transgression commenced in the north and was almost coeval with the base of the lower Exter Formation (k6.1), and resulted in the deposition of deltaic and estuarine/fluvial clays and sandstones in the north of the basin (Duchrow 1984). To the south, deposition of the Sandsteinkeuper subgroup (k4–k6.1) persisted. The succeeding middle Exter Formation (k6.2) was entirely deposited in a shallow epeiric, marginal basin which connected the Tethys Ocean in the south to the North Sea in the north. From the centre of this seaway to the east, narrow facies belts of marine, coastal, deltaic and fluvial/limnic claystones and sandstones developed (Gaupp 1991; Freudenberger 1996; Bloos 1979; Schröder 1982; Ziegler 1990). During deposition of the uppermost Exter Formation (k6.3) terrestrial conditions reoccurred, indicated by a rapid change to coastal and limnic facies successions across the entire basin (Duchrow 1968; Aeppler 1974).

Regional unconformities are recognized within the Keuper (e.g. D2 at the base of k3, D4 at the base of k5, and D6 at the base of k6.2; Beutler 1998). Based on these unconformities, a basin-wide correlation of the Middle Keuper has been proposed (Bachmann *et al.* 1999). The relatively uniform, large-scale subsidence pattern across the region resulted in a layer-cake stratification (Aigner 1985). Numerous authors have worked on this interval (for further details see Deutsche Stratigraphische Kommission 2005).

*Dynamic stratigraphy of the SW German Keuper Basin (upper Middle Keuper)*

During deposition of the upper Middle Keuper (k4 to k6.1), an extended low-relief continental playa (Reinhardt & Ricken 2000*a*), bordered by an alluvial plain, existed in the southeastern part of the Germanic Basin (Fig. 13.5). In this land-locked area, distal conglomerates and arkosic sandstones of a marginal alluvial plain (Aigner *et al.* 1995) graded basinwards into sandstones, siltstones and mudstones that interfinger with dolomitic mudstones and dolomites of the playa system in the basin centre (Fig. 13.13). Deposition occurred under (semi)arid to subhumid conditions (e.g. Hornung & Aigner 2002*b*) at low latitudes (*c.* 20–25°N (Edel & Duringer 1997), 214 Ma/19°N (Kent & Tauxe 2005)) and was characterized by a clastic supply of entirely granitic provenance from the east (i.e. Bohemian Massif) and SE (i.e. Vindelician High; Fig. 13.5). Both source areas were of low relief, probably less than 1000 m in elevation, as suggested by sediment budget analyses (Kempf *et al.* 2002). Sediment accumulation rates were low (*c.* 20 mm/ka) as were gradients (0.02 to 0.2 m/km; Brenner & Villinger 1981).

Climate was characterized by the strong pressure contrast between the Tethys Ocean and the surrounding landmass of Pangaea, resulting in the Pangaean megamonsoon (Loope *et al.* 2004; Parrish 1993; Kutzbach & Gallimore 1989) that brought large amounts of moisture northwards from the tropical Tethyan Sea far into the adjacent continent (see above). Since Milankovitch cycles directly affect the Earth's insolation rate, they also control monsoonal precipitation intensity (e.g. Fairbridge 1986; Clemens *et al.* 2003). Kutzbach (1994) modelled the influence of Milankovitch cycles on Pangaean climate and monsoonal circulation strength, and concluded that the Germanic Keuper Basin was situated in a seasonal semiarid steppe climate governed by orbitally forced Pangaean megamonsoonal precipitation.

Age determination for the Keuper sediments is problematic due to the absence of radiometric data and the scarcity of biostratigraphically useful fossil data. Menning (1995) and Menning *et al.* (2005) determined the age and duration of the Keuper formations in an interpretive way only, so the age correlations presented in Fig. 13.13 should be regarded as preliminary. Fossil remains present in the Keuper strata allow, however, detailed palaeoclimatic and palaeoenvironmental reconstruction. Palaeoecological information is provided by plant material, including palynomorphs (e.g. pollen grains, spores; Kelber & Hansch 1995), and by large numbers of invertebrates that represent only a few species (e.g. bivalves, gastropods; Seegis 1999), which indicate restricted evaporitic environments. The continental Keuper deposits are also important for the study of vertebrate evolution, especially of the earliest turtles found in Mid-Keuper strata of SW Germany (e.g. Hopf & Martens 1992; Schoch & Wild 1999*b*).

Relative age determination in these deposits is possible using dolomite–mudstone couplets from the playa system (e.g. Olsen *et al.* (1996) and Olsen & Kent (1996) for the Newark Basin, USA). The deposition of these cyclic sediments has been interpreted as resulting directly from intensity changes in the Pangaean megamonsoon. Evolutionary spectral analysis (ESA) revealed a predominant and basin-wide Milankovitch signal of precession and eccentricity (Hambach *et al.* 1999; Reinhardt & Ricken 2000*a*). Since these signals occur on a basinal scale, climate is considered as the major factor controlling depositional evolution (Reinhardt & Ricken 2000*b*; Hornung & Aigner 2002*b*). Whereas fault activity significantly influenced sedimentation in the Paris Basin in the west (Bourquin *et al.* 1997), in SW Germany tectonic activity was weak and mostly due to intraplate stress relief (e.g. Krimmel 1980; Beutler 1998). A weak tectonic signal in the region can be best deduced from regional erosional unconformities (e.g. D2–D6 of Beutler 1998; see Fig. 13.13).

*Sedimentary cycles, regional correlation and sequence stratigraphy*

The basic cycle in the Keuper playa system comprises a dolomitic mudstone/dolomite couplet resulting from alternating relatively dry/wet periods, respectively, in the overall semiarid setting (Fig. 13.14). Dolomite bed alteration increased from the central playa towards the playa margin, showing teepee-like structures and partial erosion due to subaerial exposure (Reinhardt & Ricken 2002*a*). Changes in evaporation strength on a seasonal scale are also a prerequisite for the formation of the primary dolomite triggered by bacterial activity (Wright 1999; Reinhardt 2000). Hierarchically organized lower-order cycles are traceable basin-wide from the central playa to the stacked fluvial units of the alluvial plain (Fig. 13.14; meso-scale of Hornung 1999; Hornung & Aigner 1999, 2002*b*, 2004). The meso-scale cycles of the alluvial plain (Fig. 13.15) are typically 5–15 m thick and characterized by erosional surfaces representing down-cutting, sediment bypass, channel-lags and coarse-grained sandstones of braided and meandering river deposits topped by suspension load deposits, which may show an intense pedogenic overprint (pedoturbation and calcrete formation). Two to three stacked meso-scale cycles form a macro-scale cycle, and at least one overall mega-scale cycle is recognized (see Fig. 13.15).

The cycle hierarchy of the playa deposits allowed the estimation of the minimum duration of the upper Middle Keuper (k4–k6.1) at different scales by evolutionary spectral analysis. Geochemical and geophysical proxies, such as K/Al, $\delta^{18}O/\delta^{13}C$, magnetic susceptibility or spectrophotometry were used (e.g. Hambach *et al.* 1999; Reinhardt 2000; Vollmer 2005) since these allow monitoring of megamonsoon intensity variations through time. Magnetic susceptibility and spectrophotometry sensitively reflect palaeoredox conditions throughout the basin (Hambach *et al.* 1999). K/Al ratios derived from XRF-analyses yielded a reliable proxy for changing chemical and physical weathering intensity in the hinterland, complemented by covariance trends of oxygen and carbon stable isotopes that reflect varying water volumes in the playa lake (Reinhardt & Ricken 2000*a*). ESA analysis revealed distinct power maxima, possibly representing Milankovitch orbital

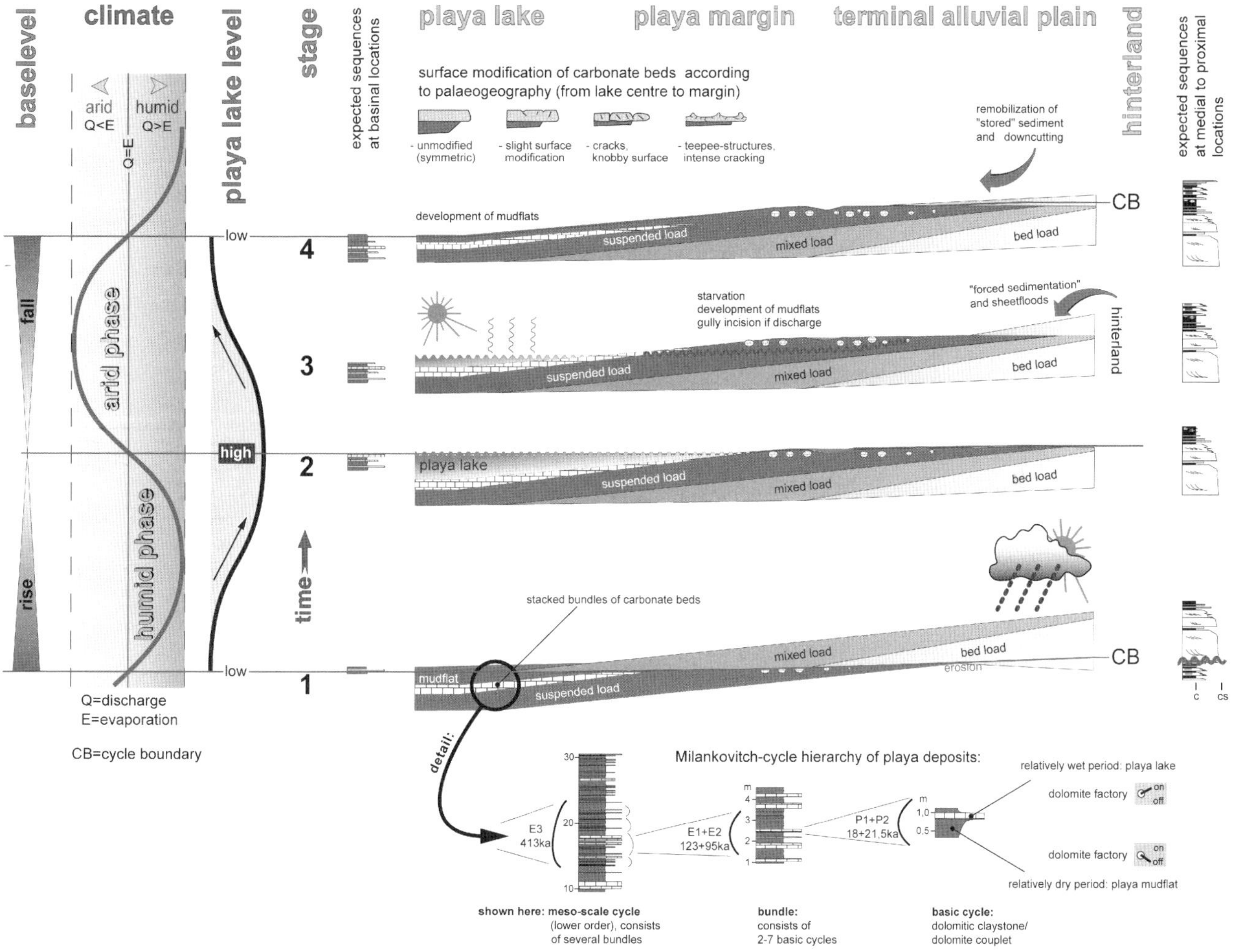


**Fig. 13.14.** Dynamic stratigraphic model for the SW German Keuper Basin in relation to climate and fluctuating base level. Expected depositional sequences are shown for distal and medial to proximal locations. Note possible carbonate bed alterations according to palaeogeography and subaerial exposure. Time (onward from bottom to top) covers a full meso-scale cycle (after Reinhardt & Ricken 2000*a*; *c.* 100 to 400 ka: range of eccentricity cycles E1+E2 and E3, respectively). Meso-scale (lower-order) cycles, which are traceable basin-wide from the central playa to the stacked fluvial units of the alluvial plain, are formed by a set of bundles, which are composed of two to seven basic cycles. The basic cycle of the playa system is a dolomitic mudstone/dolomite bed couplet, which resulted from alternating relatively dry/wet periods and may represent the 20 ka precession signal (P1+P2). Note different vertical scale. Compilation after data from Hornung (1999), Hornung & Aigner (1999, 2002*a*, *b*), Reinhardt (2000), and Reinhardt & Ricken (2000*a*, *b*). See text for a detailed description of the model.

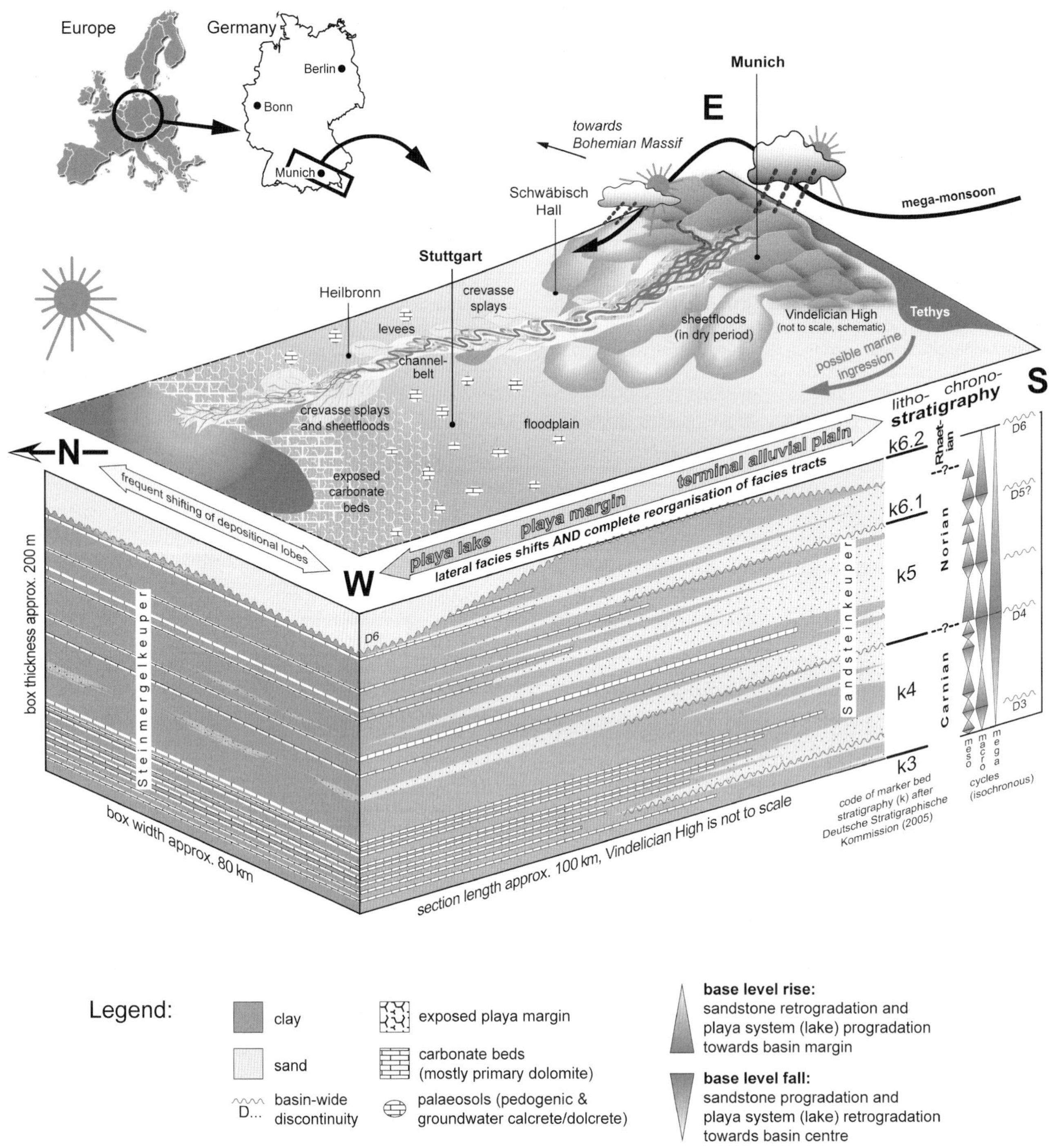


**Fig. 13.15.** Top layer shows palaeogeographical reconstruction and depositional environments of SW Germany during the Upper Triassic Middle Keuper in the SW part of the Germanic Basin. The playa/terminal alluvial plain system is approximately scaled (see box). The discharge area of the Vindelician High is schematic and not to scale (north–south extent of the Vindelician High is *c.* 150 km from Munich to the Tethyan realm). Facies belts prograde and retrograde due to variations in megamonsoonal strength. Significant changes of wet and dry periods entirely reorganized the facies patterns, due to a major change of depositional processes such as 'forced sedimentation' (e.g. sheet floods in dry periods). Possible marine ingressions in some distinct horizons may have occurred during k5. Cross-section reveals that lithostratigraphy (following LGRB 2004) is guided by the interfingering of fluvial sand tongues with clay and carbonate beds of the playa system, due to facies pro- and retrogradation (Deutsche Stratigraphische Kommission 2005.). Several basin-wide unconformities are present (D3–D6). The triangles illustrate stratigraphical base-level changes (see text), which represent an isochronous sequence-stratigraphic framework. Reconstruction is based on the palaeogeography of Ziegler (1990) and data from Beutler (1998), Hornung (1999), Hornung & Aigner (1999, 2002*a*, *b*), Aigner *et al.* (1999), Reinhardt (2000), Reinhardt & Ricken (2000*a*, *b*), Kempf *et al.* (2002) and Deutsche Stratigraphische Kommission (2005).

cycles, predominantly at 100–400 ka (E1+2 and E3 eccentricity cycles at meso-scale; see Fig. 13.14). The duration of the upper Middle Keuper units k4 to k6.1 is *c.* 16 Ma, assuming that the 400-ka eccentricity cycles are the dominant frequencies in the resulting evolutionary spectrum (Hambach *et al.* 1999; Reinhardt 2000). However, this approach has to be treated with caution and yields only a minimum duration, because of a possible incompleteness of the stratigraphic record due to erosional gaps or non-deposition. Nevertheless, basin-wide sedimentary cyclicity is most likely to be externally controlled and can thus be used to establish a sequence stratigraphic framework (see above).

Sequence stratigraphic interpretations of the Germanic Triassic were first carried out by Aigner & Bachmann (1992) for SW Germany and by Bourquin & Guillocheau (1996) for the Paris Basin; the latter authors also established a regional correlation between the two sub-basins. The stratigraphic correlation of the upper Middle Keuper (k4–k6.1) is here based on the interpretation of the stratigraphic base level (Figs 13.14 and 13.15; Wheeler 1964; Homewood *et al.* 1992; Cross & Lessenger 1997, 1998; Aigner *et al.* 1999, and discussion therein), which is defined as the relationship between available accommodation space (A) and sediment supply (S). Increasing A/S ratio results in base-level rise (upward-pointing triangle), whereas decreasing A/S ratio represents a base-level fall (downward-pointing triangle). Turnaround points were used for regional correlation, since they could be identified in all sedimentary successions and are considered to be isochronous at the regional scale.

*Dynamic stratigraphic model for the SW German Middle Keuper*

A general dynamic stratigraphic model can be proposed for the depositional system of the Middle Keuper (k4–k6.1) of SW Germany (Fig. 13.14). The model relates lateral and vertical facies successions to climate-induced base-level cycles. A low playa-lake level (due to a previous arid phase) under increasing discharge led to regional erosion at the basin margins and sand progradation into the basin (stage 1, transition from arid to humid phase). Carbonate was produced during a high playa-lake level (stage 2, humid phase and transition to arid phase) both in the lake and on land (calcretes and dolocretes). Falling playa-lake level due to arid climatic conditions resulted in local erosion (incision of gullies) and forced sedimentation when sediment supply was high (stage 3, arid phase). Finally, during stage 4 (change from arid to humid phase), sediment was remobilized and redeposited.

This depositional model emphasizes the significance of climate and sediment supply as the major controls on denudation and sedimentation in the SW German Keuper Basin. Base-level/playa-lake level changes correlate with climatic changes, although these fluctuations occurred out of phase. Based on this model, the most humid climatic conditions are contemporaneous with the most rapid rise in playa-lake levels (and *vice versa*), and base-level turnarounds are concurrent with changing climatic conditions (touching triangles). Thus, local base-level change can be considered to be dominantly controlled by regional climate.

## *Basin evolution: Germany and Poland (M.G., J.S., H.G.R.)*

*Buntsandstein*

**Basin palaeotopography and tectonic framework.** The Triassic Germanic Basin was situated on the northern margin of the westward expanding Tethys Ocean. In the Early Triassic (Lower Buntsandstein) the basin arrangement followed the Zechstein configuration. The basin extended over more than 1500 km from the British Isles in the west to Poland in the east. The thickness of the complete Buntsandstein succession ranges between 500 and 1200 m, but occasionally reaches up to 4000 m in the graben structures of northwestern Germany (Röhling 1991). From the North Sea rift system the Germanic Basin was bounded by a range of highs, the Mid-North Sea High, the Ringkøbing-Fyn High and the Rügen Swell. These were separated from each other by a series of north–south trending grabens (Central Graben, Horn Graben) which maintained communication between the North Sea and the German and Polish parts of the basin via the depression of the Danish Basin (Figs 13.16 & 13.17). The north–south orientated grabens extended to the south through the Weser Graben, the Glückstadt Graben, the Solling Trough and the Hessian Depression. The Danish Basin passed into the Polish Trough through the Storebælt Gate (Bertelsen 1980).

The eastern part of the Germanic Basin was dominated by the Mid-Polish Trough that was the main depocentre controlled by the older Teisseyre-Tornquist Line (Figs 13.3 & 13.17). Another depocentre was superimposed upon the reactivated Cracow-Odra-Hamburg Fault Zone (Fig. 13.3). The Polish sector of the Buntsandstein basin was subdivided into a northern and a southern part, separated by a high encompassing the Sudetes Mountains, and the Małopolska and Lublin massifs (i.e. the easternmost segment of the Vindelician-Bohemian Massif) (Fig. 13.18). To the south of this high was situated a triangular basin, the Cracow-Tarnow Depression. This basin was inclined gently to the south and subsequently was in connection with the Tethys Ocean.

The Germanic Basin was enclosed by older, mostly Variscan massifs: the Alemannic-Vindelician-Bohemian Massif to the south, the London (Anglo)-Brabant Massif and the Gallic High to the west, and the Fennoscandian (Fennosarmatian) Land to the north and east (Figs 13.5, 13.16 & 13.17). These massifs served as source areas of clastic sediments and were flanked by prograding alluvial fans. Other, intrabasinal highs such as the Rhenish Massif, the Eichsfeld-Altmark Swell, the Rügen Swell and the East Netherlands Swell, were subordinate source areas.

The distribution of sedimentary facies in the Lower Triassic was controlled mainly by continuous thermal subsidence and pulsed rifting, both of which led to fluctuations of the erosional base level and dominant fining-upward cycles in the Buntsandstein sediments.

The presence of unconformities and the thickness variation pattern reflect the subdivision of the basin in structural highs and lows. In contrast to the lows, the highs are characterized by condensed sedimentation and an incomplete stratigraphic record. Indeed, the most pronounced unconformities affect not only the highs and marginal areas but are visible also in the basin centre. As previously noted, these unconformities define the boundaries between the basic lithostratigraphic units of the Buntsandstein in the Germanic Basin.

The majority of the fluvial sediments that accumulated in the depocentres in the western central part of the Germanic Basin was transported from the south by a SSW–NNE trending ephemeral river system. The main distributary system followed the Hessian Depression, flanked by the Rhenish Massif to the west and the Eichsfeld-Altmark Swell to the east, and the Trier Embayment to the west of the Rhenish Massif. Minor sediment influx reached the central part of the basin via the Thuringia-Westbrandenburg Depression to the east of the Eichsfeld-Altmark Swell. The proximal facies of the southern belt are characterized by coarse clastic wedges and conglomerates deposited by a braided river system with local aeolian influence. These facies grade northwards into finer sediments deposited in a playa flat or

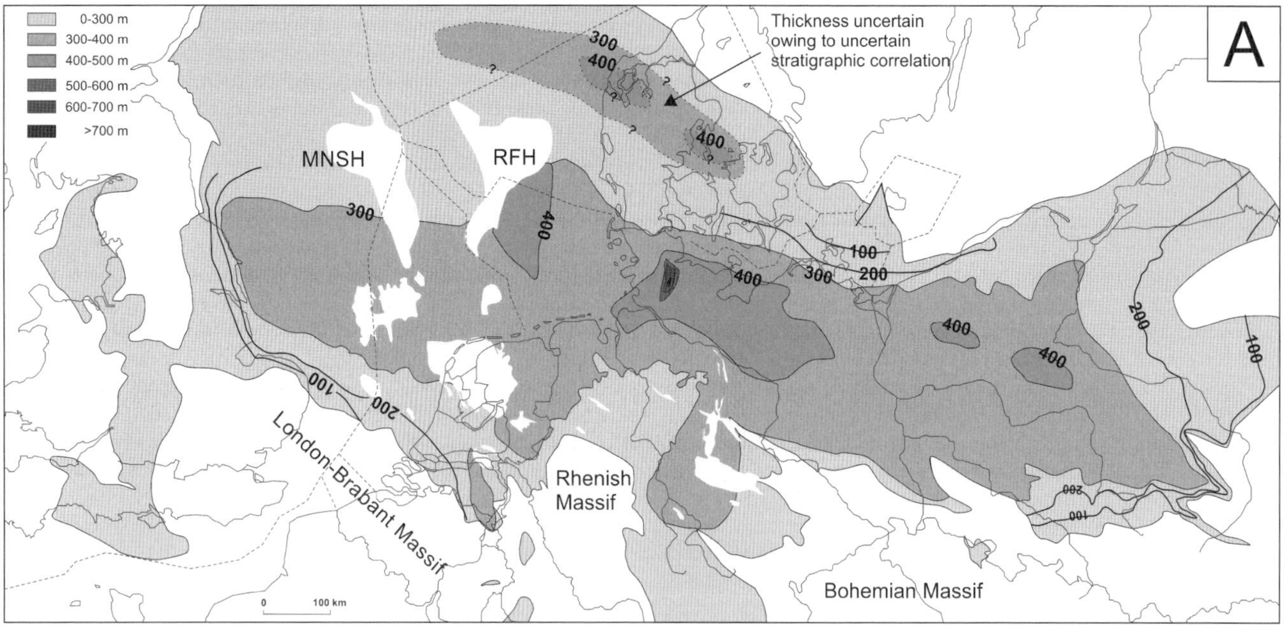


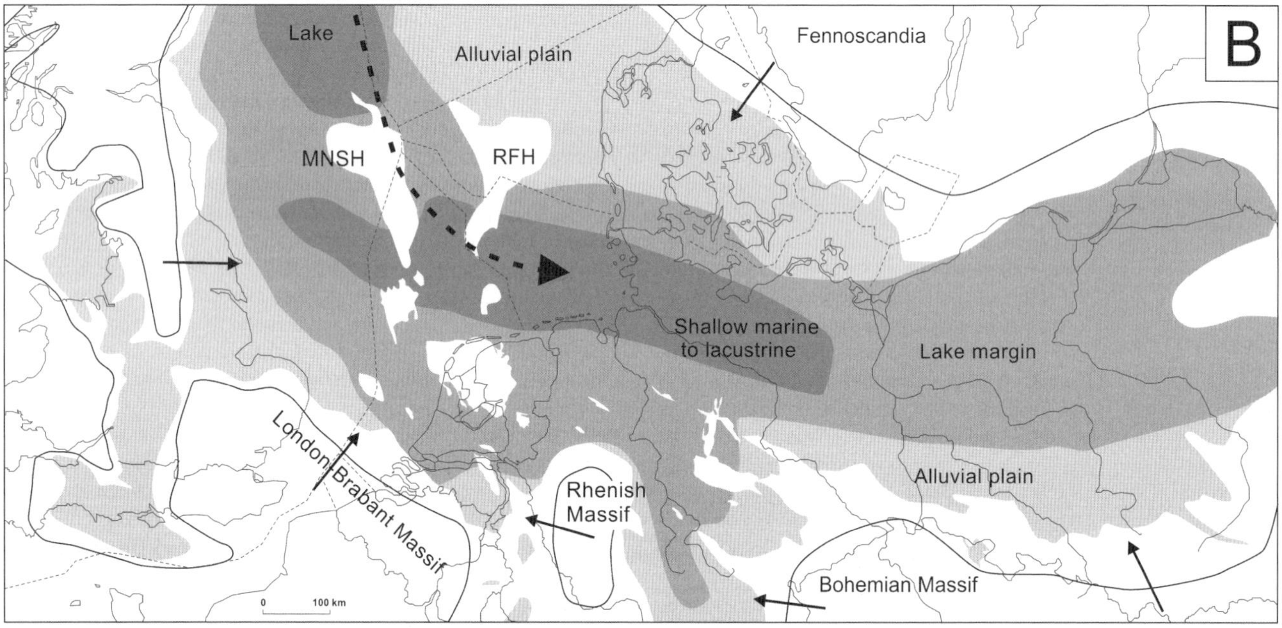


**Fig. 13.16.** (**A**) Present-day distribution and isopach map of the Lower Buntsandstein (latest Permian–Induan). Note the uniform thickness over large areas. Differential subsidence of the Glückstadt Graben began. Compiled by Geluk (2005) after Cameron *et al.* (1992), Dadlez *et al.* (1998), Geluk (1999), Baldschuhn *et al.* (2001) and Goldsmith *et al.* (2003). Additional well data from Hoth *et al.* (1993). (**B**) Present-day distribution and facies map of the Lower Buntsandstein. Compiled by Geluk (2005) after Jubitz *et al.* (1987), Ziegler (1990), Cameron *et al.* (1992), Warrington & Ivimey-Cook (1992), Dadlez *et al.* (1998), Geluk (1999), Baldschuhn *et al.* (2001) and Goldsmith *et al.* (2003). Thin arrows indicate clastic influx; the dashed thick arrow marine incursion. Solid lines represent the reconstructed basin outline. Abbreviations: MNSH, Mid North Sea High; RFH, Ringkøbing-Fyn High.

shallow-marine setting. In the Polish part of the basin the main fluvial transport system followed the axis of the Mid-Polish Trough.

**Marine deposits (J.S.).** One of the most controversial aspects of the Lower Triassic of the Germanic Basin concerns the possible marine influences in the Lower and Middle Buntsandstein successions.

Obvious marine features are particularly common in the lower part of the Middle Buntsandstein (Volpriehausen Folge to lower

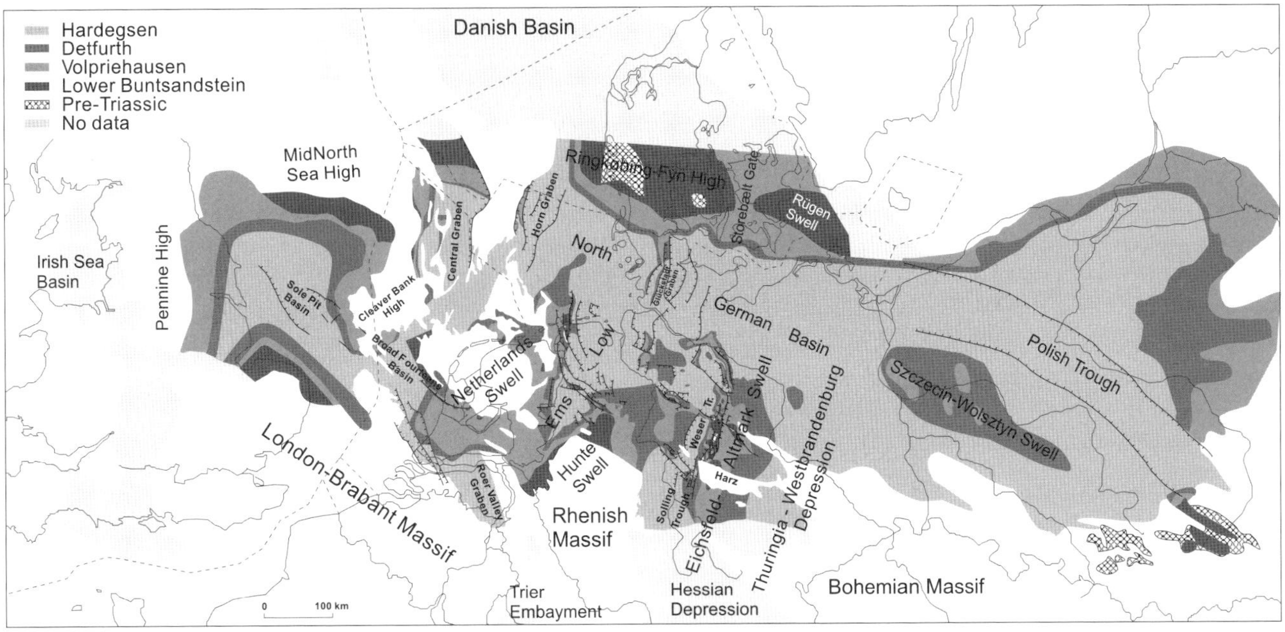


**Fig. 13.17.** Subcrop map of the Hardegsen Unconformity and basin morphology in the Early Triassic. Note the SSW–NNE trending swells in Germany. Compiled by Geluk (2005) after Geluk & Röhling (1999), Beutler & Schüler (1978), Warrington & Ivimey-Cook (1992), Marek & Pajchlowa (1997) and Goldsmith *et al.* (2003). Additional well data from Hoth *et al.* (1993).

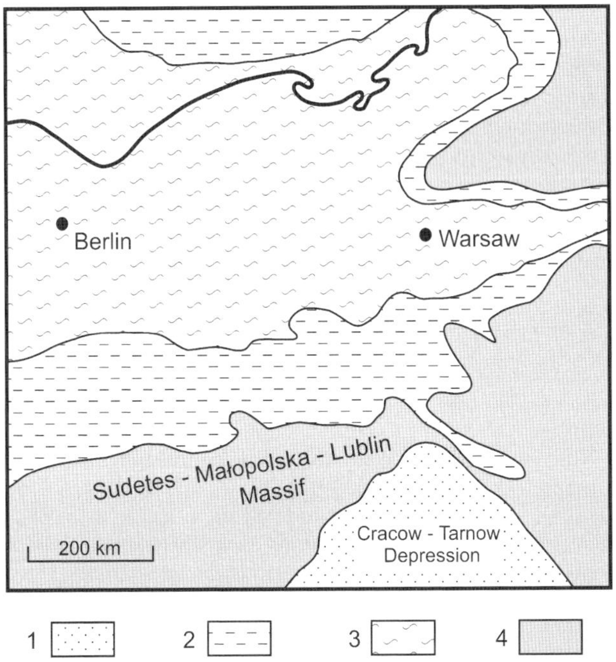


**Fig. 13.18** Lower Buntsandstein facies distribution in the Polish part of the Germanic Basin. Key: 1, continental coarse-grained clastic sediments; 2, continental fine-grained clastic sediments; 3, limnic-shallow marine muddy deposits; 4, land areas (from Szulc 2000).

Detfurth Folge, Pomorska Formation) where sedimentological and palaeontological data provide unequivocal evidence for marine sedimentary environments. In this interval marine acritarchs are common and ubiquitous in the area between western Germany (Reitz 1985; Ecke 1986) and eastern Poland (Szyperko-Teller 1997). Moreover, the acritarchs are accompanied by marine bivalves, such as *Avicula murchisoni*, which is common across the entire basin, and Tethyan foraminifers (*Trocholina ventroplana*) known from SE Poland. Ichnofossils also indicate shallow marine conditions at this interval (Lepper & Uchman 1995).

In contrast to the Middle Buntsandstein, marine influence is less evident in the Lower Buntsandstein although acritarchs are quite common, in both the Polish and German parts of the basin (Reitz 1985; Ecke 1986; Pienkowski 1991). Furthermore, in central Poland nodosarid foraminifers have also been found, suggesting marine conditions (Pienkowski 1991). The common occurrence of glauconite further supports the inference of a marine origin for all of these sediments.

The main problem with the presence of marine sediments in the Germanic Basin is where the early Triassic transgression came from. Considering the basin evolution, there is no doubt that a marine seaway, the East Carpathian Gate, provided communication with the Tethys as early as mid-Induan times (Szulc 2000). However, in earliest Triassic times this marine gateway was most certainly closed and, thus, it is difficult to explain the origin of the marine incursions at this time. The most probable communication route was from the Boreal Sea via the North Sea rift system. The transgression might have progressed through a complex network of grabens related to vigorous early Triassic extension of the Viking–Central graben system (Roberts *et al.* 1995). This phase of rifting was coeval with a global transgression, which has also been recorded in the Boreal realm (Jacobsen & van Veen 1984; Mørk *et al.* 1989, 1992; Skjold *et al.* 1998; Wignall *et al.* 1998; Seidler *et al.* 2004) and in the Tethyan basins (Gianolla & Jacquin 1998). This evidence would suggest that marine incursion occurred across the northern part of the peneplained Buntsandstein basin. Unfortunately, it is difficult to reconstruct the incursion route in detail because very few wells have penetrated the deepest graben fills (Roberts *et al.* 1995) and post-Triassic erosion removed Triassic deposits in the southern North Sea Basin (Fisher & Mudge 1998). Despite this, the most probable transgression pathway was through the Viking–Central grabens, to Lower Saxony, western Poland and the Mid-Polish Trough.

The Lower and Middle Buntsandstein of Central Europe have a significant content of oolitic and stromatolitic carbonates (Paul 1982). These have been interpreted as either marine (Usdowski 1962; Peryt 1975; Beutler & Szulc 1999) or lacustrine (Paul 1999; Szurlies *et al.* 2003, Korte & Kozur 2005) in origin. However, the co-occurrence of acritarchs, dwarf and vermetoidal gastropods, foraminifers and spirorbids, and the ubiquitous association of glauconite, suggests a marine origin for these oolitic and stromatolitic limestones. Additional evidence comes from clastic–oolitic cycles found by Roman (2003) in the Middle Buntsandstein of western Poland. A typical cycle is several metres thick and comprises glauconite-bearing oolitic limestones succeeded by marls and fine-grained clastic sediments rich in acritarchs. Such a succession is typical of marine environments where glauconite-rich oolites represent a transgressive phase (Amorosi 1995) and the subsequent fine-grained clastic sediments formed during the stabilized highstand phase. A longer-term transgression event may also be inferred from a laterally migrated thick oolitic bar (retrogradation/progradation?) observed by Radzinski (1999) in the Lower Buntsandstein of the Southern Brandenburg–Lower Saxony area. Similar oolitic and stromatolitic carbonates are recorded from Early Triassic marine environments in other parts of the world (e.g. Broglio Loriga *et al.* 1990; Schubert & Bottjer 1992; Lehrmann 1999; Baud *et al.* 2003).

The stable isotope signatures of the Lower Buntsandstein carbonates of Central Germany (Korte & Kozur 2005) are very similar to coeval deposits from the Alps. The dominance of chemically and microbially bound carbonates in these successions is typical for periods subsequent to mass extinction events, when skeletal organisms were decimated (Burchette & Wright 1992).

**Lower Buntsandstein.** A general feature of the Lower Buntsandstein (Fig. 13.16) sediments is a southward proximal trend, which can be observed across the entire Germanic Basin. In Induan times, the basin was closed to the south (i.e. separated from the Tethys) where elevated Variscan massifs were the source of alluvial and fluvial deposits that filled up the southern part of the basin. Further to the north, fluviatile deposits were replaced by finer-grained mudflat and playa sediments, and finally, in the northern and eastern parts (the Netherlands, Lower Saxony, Mecklenburg, East Brandenburg, northwestern and central Poland), by lacustrine and shallow-marine clastic sediments with oolitic and stromatolitic limestones. Facies distribution and isopach patterns would appear to indicate that marine influences originated from the Boreal Sea (see the discussion above) through the North Sea graben system (Roberts *et al.* 1995). The Germanic Basin and the Tethys Ocean were completely separate from each other at this time.

The Lower Buntsandstein can be correlated across the Germanic Basin without major difficulty. Its distribution and thickness variations indicate that sedimentation followed a basement structural pattern that had already existed during Late Permian times. The main depocentres were located in the Southern North Sea, the North German sub-basins and the Polish Trough where over 400 m of sediments accumulated (Fig. 13.16A). The succession thins out towards the bordering highs.

The Lower Buntsandstein of the Germanic Basin comprises two fining-upward cycles, the Calvörde Folge and the Bernburg Folge. Several higher-order sedimentary sequences consisting of fining-upward cycles with a thickness of up to several tens of metres have been distinguished in the NW part of the basin by Geluk & Röhling (1997), who interpreted them as orbitally driven Milankovitch cycles with a periodicity of about 100 000 years.

The Polish sector of the Buntsandstein basin was divided into a northern and a southern part separated by the Sudetes-Małopolska-Lublin Massif (Fig. 13.18). The evolution of the two sub-basins differed, particularly in early–mid-Induan times. The Lower Buntsandstein (Baltyk Formation) in the northern part comprises fine-grained clastics with a high concentration of oolitic carbonates. At the same time, coarse-grained, fluvial sedimentation was dominant in the southern part (Cracow-Tarnow Depression) (Szyperko-Teller & Moryc 1988).

**Middle Buntsandstein.** With the onset of the Middle Buntsandstein (Fig. 13.19) in the late Induan, the situation in Poland changed and Tethyan foraminifers first appeared in the Cracow-Tarnow Depression (Glowacki & Senkowiczowa 1969; Milewska & Moryc 1981). This basin provided a link with the area of the subsiding East Carpathian marine gateway.

The 'boreal' marine facies persisted in NW Poland and northern Germany with ongoing fine-grained clastic and oolitic sedimentation, whereas the northernmost part became progradationally filled with deltaic and fluvial sands (Drawsko Sandstone Member) (Szyperko-Teller 1982) that were transported from the north and NE (mostly from the Fennoscandian Land) (Fig. 13.19B). The same direction of transport also dominated the next cycle when a marine transgression finally broke through the southern high and extended far to the NW (Trzebiatow Member of the Pomorska Formation), as indicated by the occurrence of a marine fauna (e.g. *Avicula murchisoni*). The overlying Middle Buntsandstein succession in Poland displays a similar trend in basin evolution. The northern and western parts underwent pronounced shallowing (Polczyn Formation) whereas coastal sabkha, brackish and shallow-marine environments dominated in the southern part (Szyperko-Teller & Moryc 1988). In the Middle Buntsandstein of the northern and NW parts of the Polish sub-basin, periods of intense erosion are marked by significant stratigraphic gaps (Nawrocki 1997). The most pronounced hiatus (sedimentary and erosional) occurs at the top of the Middle Buntsandstein in northern Poland (Szyperko-Teller 1997) and forms a well-defined boundary with the overlying Upper Buntsandstein.

The lower part of the Middle Buntsandstein in the North German and Dutch sub-basins (i.e. the Volpriehausen Folge and Detfurth Folge) comprises a sedimentary facies assemblage similar to the Lower Buntsandstein. Each formation commences with fluvial sandstones which are overlain by alternating fine-grained clastic/oolitic beds that formed in playa flats or shallow-marine environments. Such a succession is typical of third-order depositional sequences (Aigner & Bachmann 1992). Distinctive high-frequency cyclicity (Geluk & Röhling 1997) reflects short marine incursions (Roman 2003). The appearance of *Avicula murchisoni* within the upper part of the Volpriehausen Folge enables it to be correlated with the upper part of the Pomorska Formation in the Polish sub-basin, as well as defining the maximum extent of the Tethyan influence.

The succeeding unit, the Hardegsen Folge, comprises playa flats and lacustrine sediments that show a gradually increasing proportion of coarser clastic, fluvial deposits. The latter dominate the uppermost Middle Buntsandstein (Solling Folge) throughout the Germanic Basin. This trend, as well as the very pronounced

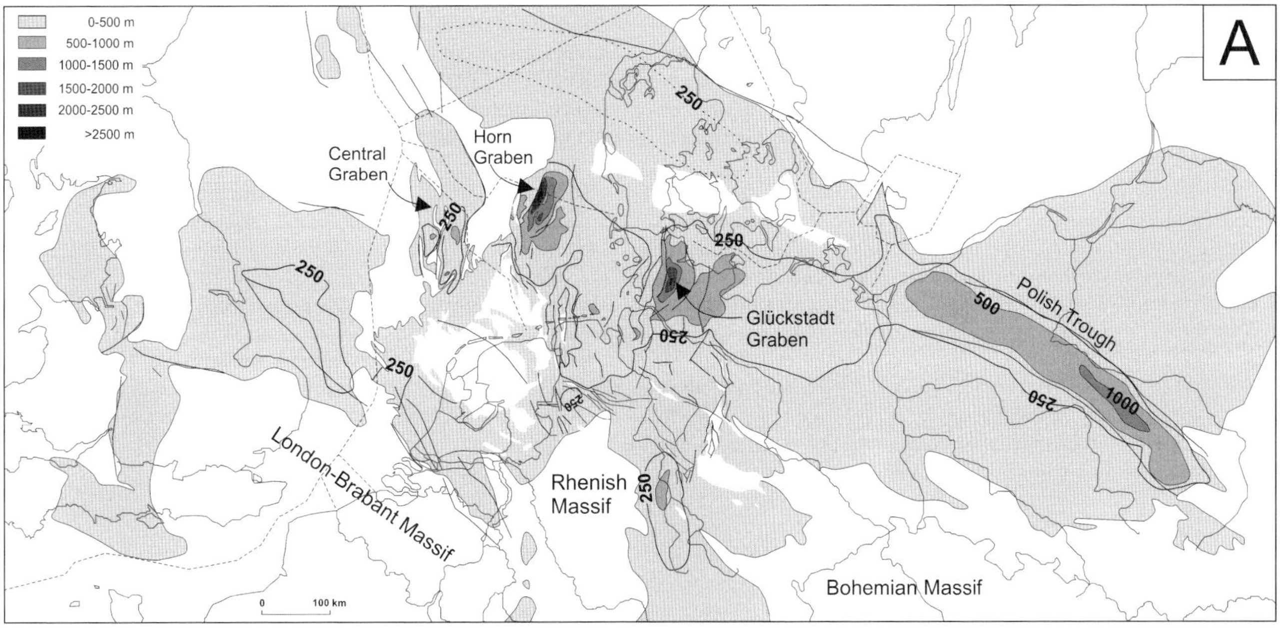


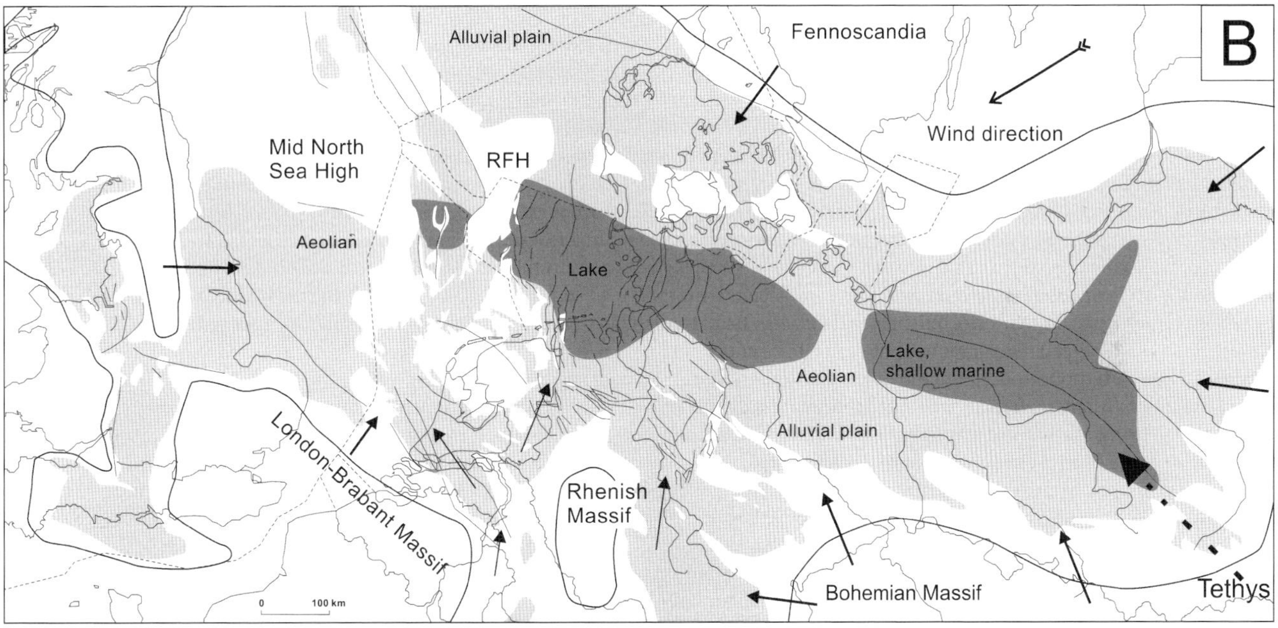


**Fig. 13.19.** (**A**) Present-day distribution and isopach map of the Middle Buntsandstein (excluding Solling Folge). The map highlights strong subsidence of the Central, Horn and Glückstadt grabens and the Polish Trough. In the remainder of the area the thickness varies from <50 to 500 m. Compiled by Geluk (2005) after Cameron *et al.* (1992), Dadlez *et al.* (1998), Geluk (1999), Baldschuhn *et al.* (2001), Goldsmith *et al.* (2003) and well data from Hoth *et al.* (1993). (**B**) Present-day distribution and facies map of the Middle Buntsandstein. Extensive, sandy alluvial plains bordered a lake which occupied the deepest parts of the basin. The facies shown is approximately for the Volpriehausen Sandstone. The thick dashed arrow marked 'Tethys' represents marine ingression; thin arrows the approximate orientation of fluvial systems and clastic influx. The prevailing wind direction was from the NE. Solid lines represent the reconstructed basin outline. Black lines represent active faults. Compiled by Geluk (2005) after Cameron *et al.* (1992), Warrington & Ivimey-Cook (1992) and Dadlez *et al.* (1998). RFH, Ringkøbing-Fyn High.

basin-wide complex and diachronous unconformities (particularly the Hardegsen unconformity; Krämer & Kunz 1969; Rettig 1996; Nawrocki 1997; Geluk & Röhling 1997; Radies *et al.* 2005), reflects the general tectonically controlled uplift of the Germanic Basin in Olenekian times. The intense deformation also created a patchwork arrangement of the sedimentary facies that makes reconstruction and correlation of the different segments of the Germanic Basin difficult.

**Upper Buntsandstein (Röt).** The Upper Buntsandstein sedimentary succession (Fig. 13.20) is apparently bipartite. This is related to the two transgressions recorded throughout the Germanic Basin. Due to the preceding period of regional uplift of the northern segment of the basin, the Boreal Sea and the Germanic Basin were completely separated from each other and transgressions came from the Tethys Ocean, via the Silesian-Moravian Gate. The East Carpathian area was also controlled by open marine influences, but the marine influx did not extend beyond the western foreland of the Holy Cross Mountains (Senkowiczo-

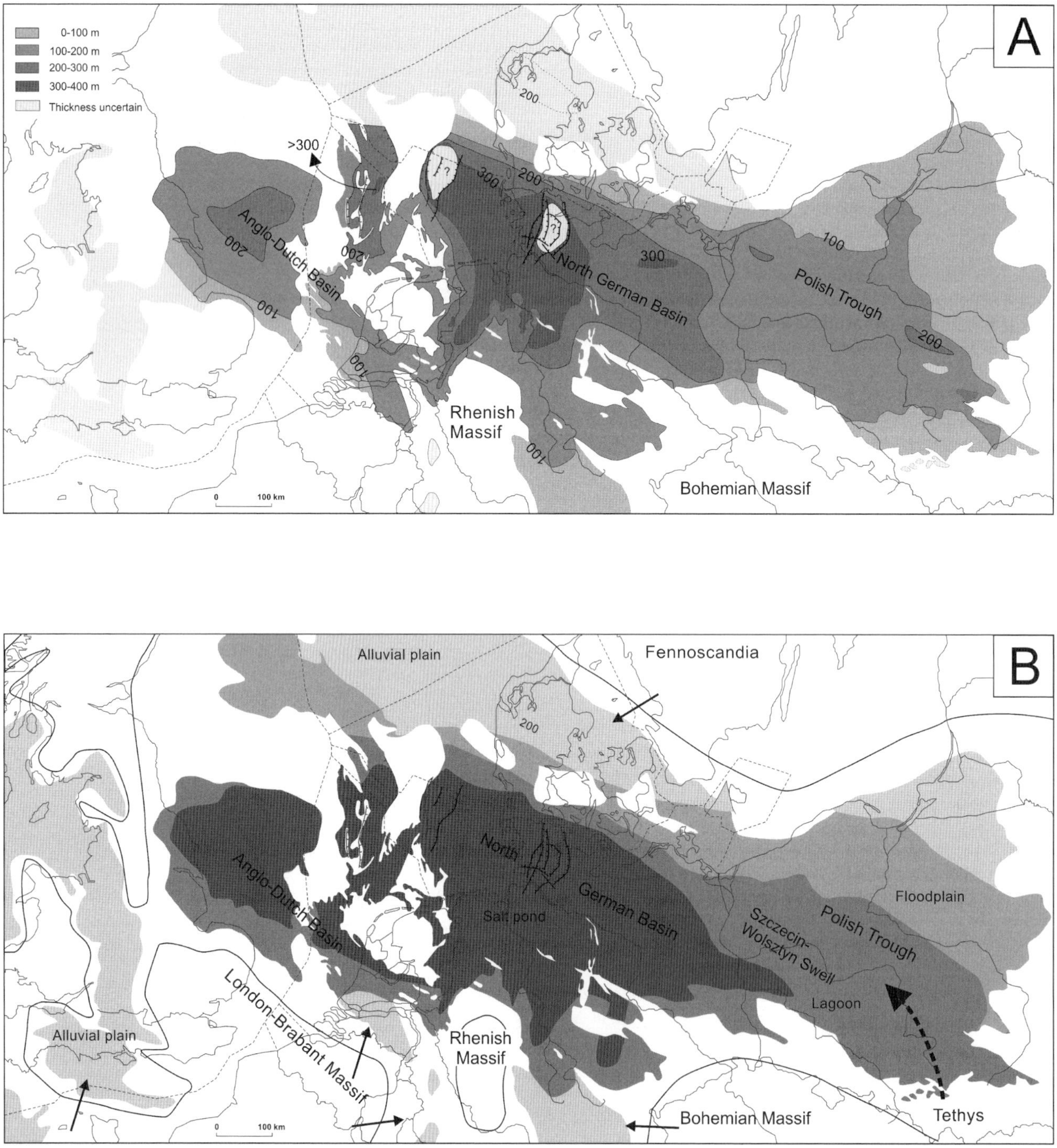


**Fig. 13.20.** (**A**) Present-day distribution and isopach map of the Röt (Early Anisian). Compiled by Geluk (2005) after Wolburg (1969), Bertelsen (1980), Cameron *et al.* (1992), Dadlez *et al.* (1998), Geluk (1999), Baldschuhn *et al.* (2001) and Goldsmith *et al.* (2003). Additional well data from Hoth *et al.* (1993). In the areas with light grey shading the thickness is uncertain. (**B**) Present-day distribution and facies map of the Röt (Early Anisian). The arrow marked 'Tethys' indicates marine ingression. Smaller arrows represent clastic influx. Solid lines represent the reconstructed basin outline. Compiled by Geluk (2005) after Wolburg (1969), Bertelsen (1980), Cameron *et al.* (1992), Warrington & Ivimey-Cook (1992), Dadlez *et al.* (1998), Geluk (1999), Kedżierski (2000) and Goldsmith *et al.* (2003).

wa 1966). The future western marine gateway (i.e. 'Burgundy Gate') was at this time a land area with fluvial and lacustrine sedimentation (Szulc 2000).

The Upper Buntsandstein (Röt) deposits encompass two third-order depositional sequences (Fig. 13.21) (Szulc 1999). The first of these is very well developed in Upper Silesia where it commences with fine-grained clastics followed by dolomites, sulphates and bioclastic limestones. The carbonates contain relatively rich assemblages of gastropods and bivalves; *Costatoria costata* coquinas are dominant. Limestone beds in the upper part of the succession contain numerous cephalopods (*Beneckeia tenuis*) that record the first maximum flooding event (Fig. 13.21).

This distribution of fossils, in particular *Costatoria costata* and *Beneckeia tenuis,* provides evidence for diachroneity of the Upper Buntsandstein (Röt) facies across the Germanic Basin (Szulc 2000) (Fig. 13.21). Moreover, the distribution of *Beneckeia tenuis* records the migration pathway and marine progress fairly well. Cephalopods entered the Germanic Basin through the Silesian-Moravian Gate and migrated NW through Lower Silesia and into Thuringia and Württemberg along the Saxothuringian subsidence centre.

Stenohaline crinoids in the Silesian-Moravian and East Carpathian seaway areas (Moryc 1971) indicate stabilized normal marine conditions in those regions. The basinward migration of these faunas was, however, hampered by bathymetric and chemical barriers to the NW.

The distribution of the various sedimentary facies indicates that the main depocentre was situated between western Poland and eastern England (Fig. 13.5A). Sedimentation in this area was dominated by evaporites (halite and gypsum), whereas carbonates occur only as sporadic intercalations. The evaporitic facies grades into clastic mudflat and sandflat deposits at the western and northwestern basin margins. The distribution of the Upper Buntsandstein (Röt) salt indicates that the halite deposition extended to the southern flank of the Mid-North Sea High–Ringkøbing-Fyn High–Rügen Swell. The evaporitic lower Röt attains its greatest thickness in the lows and axial parts of the basin; for example, in the Ems Low (up to 175 m) and in the Central Graben (over 200 m) (Cameron *et al.* 1992; Geluk & Röhling 1997).

The facies distribution pattern is typical of a semiclosed, evaporitic basin. Marine incursions were from the Tethys Ocean via the Silesian-Moravian Gate, while the other sides of the basin were closed (Fig. 13.5A). Normal marine water flowing from the SE accumulated in the depocentre and underwent evaporation, leading to halite/gypsum precipitation. The sedimentary characteristics of the evaporites in the basin, such as the lamination of halite and the presence of thin alternations of sulphates and dolomitic veneers, indicate that halite precipitated at the surface of a moderately shallow basin, forming thick (>150 m) salt deposits.

The thickness of the deposits ranges from 25 m at the Silesian-Moravian Gate, 50 m in Lower Silesia, to >150 m in the halite-depositing centres. The isopach and facies patterns show that the main subsidence centre was located along the Cracow-Odra-Hamburg Fault (cf. Figs 13.3 and 13.20). A secondary, SW–NE trending depocentre followed the Variscan Saxothuringian Lineament. The most marked, albeit localized, subsidence affected the grabens of the North Sea rift system.

The contrast in thickness and facies characteristics between the Silesian-Moravian Gate domain and the depocentre in the NW of the Germanic Basin indicates that southern Silesia was a relatively stable, elevated area, directly influenced by Tethyan waters (Fig. 13.22). This area was split into a series of narrow

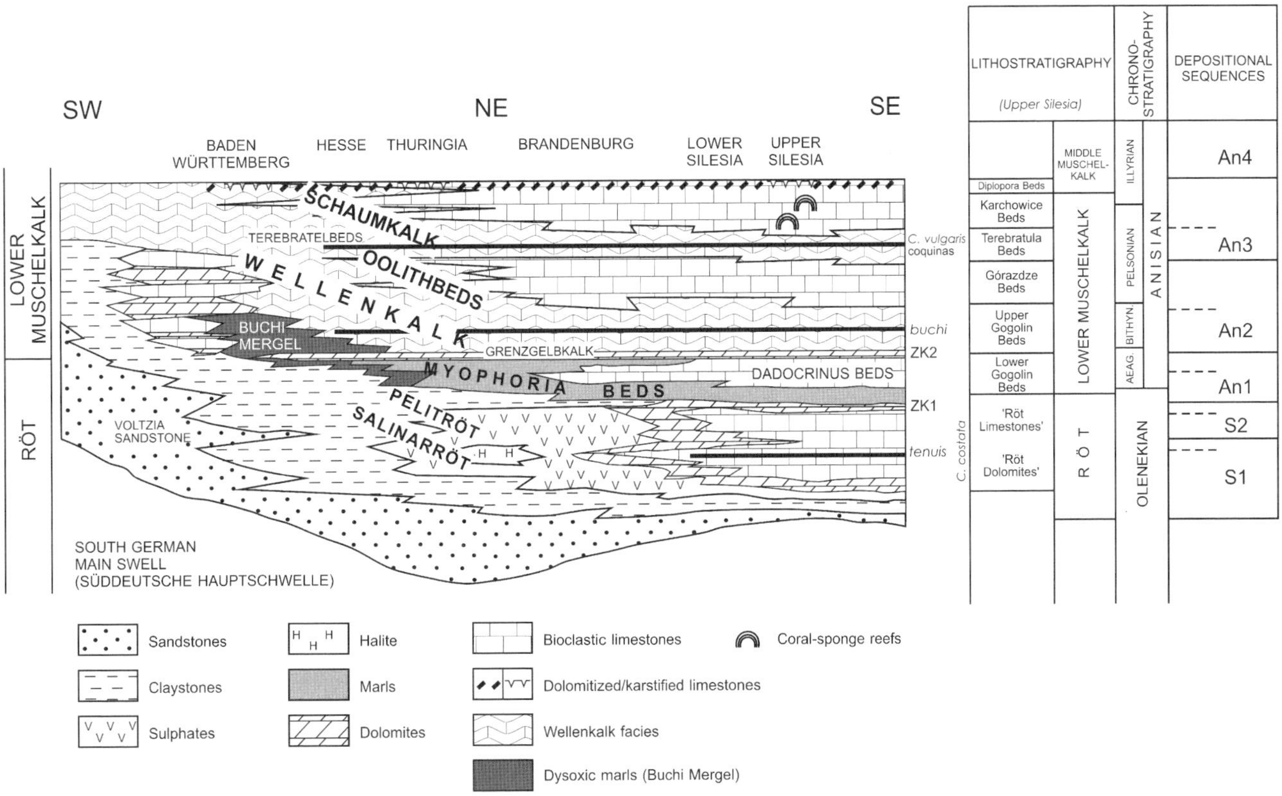


**Fig. 13.21.** Sequence stratigraphy of Röt to Lower Muschelkalk of the Germanic Basin (Olenekian–Anisian) (from Szulc 2000).

grabens and horsts and, thus, the Silesian-Moravian Gate formed a network system of straits, rather than a broad uniform seaway (Szulc 2000).

After the initial Upper Buntsandstein (Röt) transgression, sea level stabilized and the Germanic Basin began to fill progradationally during the following highstand phase. As a result, the basin shallowed and became emergent. Subsequent erosion led to the formation of the intra-Röt unconformity (Geluk & Röhling 1997). In the areas close to the Tethys Ocean (i.e. the East Carpathian and Silesian-Moravian gates) marine carbonate sedimentation persisted, but limestones were replaced by dolomites and, due to elevated salinity, most of the normal marine organisms are not found.

The second transgression in the Germanic Basin generally encompassed the same area as the first one. The lithofacies pattern shows a similar distribution, except that halite deposition was restricted to localized areas in central and northern Germany (Beutler & Schüler 1979). Carbonate sedimentation was again dominant in the areas of the Silesian-Moravian and East Carpathian gates, while basinward both dolomites and sulphates were deposited. To the west and SW (Thuringia-Hesse-Baden) carbonates were replaced by red-bed clastics with subordinate sulphates (Fig. 13.21). In the continental facies of SW Germany a number of shorter cycles (parasequences) are very well expressed by palaeosol horizons that can be correlated from the Pfalz to the Odenwald regions (Richter-Bernburg 1974). The thickest upper Röt successions formed in the rapidly subsiding northwestern rifts (Central Graben, Horn Graben, Glückstadt Graben).

*Muschelkalk (J.S.)*

**Basin palaeotopography and tectonic framework.** The established Olenekian trends in the evolution of the Germanic Basin continued in Mid-Triassic times. The basin became a typical peripheral sea of the Tethys Ocean from which it was separated by peneplained Variscan blocks, with connection provided by tectonically controlled depressions serving as marine gateways (Fig. 13.5B). Those to the east, i.e. the East Carpathian and Silesian-Moravian gates, were already open during Olenekian times, whereas the one to the west (i.e. 'Burgundy Gate' or 'Western Gate') formed as late as the mid-Anisian.

The position of these marine gateways as well as basin topography were mainly controlled by inherited Variscan structures (Szulc 1999). The reactivation of these older structures affected sedimentary processes and resulted in a limited modification of eustatic fluctuations due to regional and/or local tectonic activity.

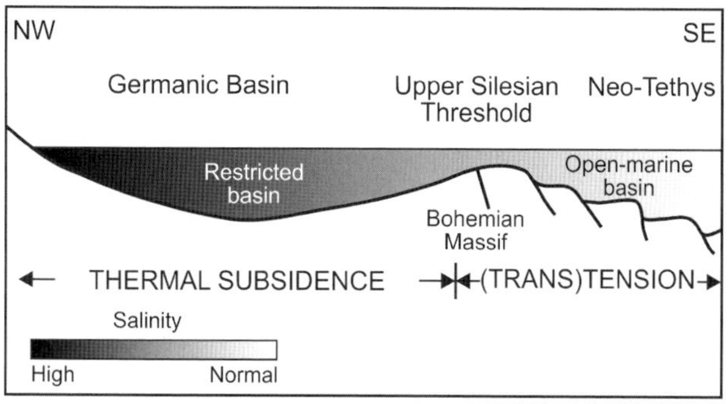


**Fig. 13.22.** Model of the basin dynamics and circulation regime in the northern Peri-Tethys Basin in Olenekian–Ladinian times (from Szulc 2000).

Facies distribution across the basin is markedly diachronous, and this is the most outstanding feature of the Peri-Tethys evolution during Mid-Triassic times (Fig. 13.21). This diachroneity was essentially caused by earlier transgression and final regression in the eastern (Polish) part of the Peri-Tethys area. It reflects a relocation of the connection pathways, following the westward shift of the Tethys spreading centre during the Mid-Triassic. This shift also explains the earlier uplift and separation of the eastern basin that resulted from the closing of the oldest, most easterly branches of the Tethys rifts (Palaeo-Tethys). The tectonic motion initiated within the spreading centre was translated into the rift periphery by reactivated older faults; the Silesian-Moravian Gate was superimposed on the Silesian-Moravian Fault and the East Carpathian Gate was controlled by the SE segment of the Teisseyre-Tornquist Line.

As in the Early Triassic, the southern parts of the Germanic Basin (Silesia, Holy Cross Mountains, SW Germany) were influenced by the Tethys rifts whereas northern Germany and the North Sea sub-basins were controlled by the North Sea rift system. The other, major part of the Germanic Basin was dominated by thermal subsidence (Fig. 13.22).

Relocation of the dominant communication path coincided with displacement of the depocentre. As indicated by the isopach patterns (Fig. 13.4A) during late Olenekian–mid-Anisian times (Röt–Lower Muschelkalk) the main depocentre was situated in the eastern part of the Germanic Basin and followed the Mid-Polish Trough where up to 200 m of carbonates were deposited. In the late Anisian and Ladinian (Middle and Upper Muschelkalk) the main depocentre moved westwards to the actively subsiding Hessian Depression, where the Upper Muschelkalk is up to 100 m thick (Fig. 13.4B). Significant subsidence also occurred in the North German–Dutch grabens, where the thickness of the Upper Muschelkalk exceeds 100 metres.

**Lower Muschelkalk (Anisian to early Illyrian).** In Anisian times the circulation pattern of the Muschelkalk Sea resembled that of the Röt semiclosed basin. During almost the entire Anisian, fully marine conditions prevailed in the eastern part of the Germanic Basin while the western part was affected by restricted circulation typical of a semiclosed, evaporitic basin (Fig. 13.22). The marine incursions resulted from the opening of the eastern marine gateways (i.e. East Carpathian and Silesian-Moravian gates) and advanced gradually westwards. Four such transgressive events have been recognized in the Lower Muschelkalk succession and have been interpreted as third-order depositional sequences (Szulc 1999) (Fig. 13.21). Their boundaries are defined by emersion horizons (mostly karst surfaces) while the maximum flooding zones are characterized by a particularly high proportion of Tethyan immigrants within the faunal palaeocommunities (Szulc 2000; Narkiewicz & Szulc 2004). During the highstand phases bioclastic and oolitic carbonates (Schaumkalk, Oolithbänke, Górazdze Beds) or reef buildups (Karchowice Beds) formed.

The most prominent Anisian maximum flooding surface occurred during the Pelsonian (third Anisian sequence, An3; Fig. 13.21) and is evidenced by palaeobiological, geochemical and sedimentological data (Aigner & Bachmann 1992; Szulc 1993; Götz & Feist-Burkhardt 2000). This was a period when very large numbers of Tethyan brachiopods, bivalves, echinoderms, conodonts and dasycladales invaded the Germanic area (Szulc 2000), indicating that communication between the Germanic Basin and the Tethys Ocean had reached its climax at this time.

Open marine conditions in the Silesian area favoured the development of one of the oldest known *in situ* Mesozoic coral/

sponge reefs. Reefs and other palaeoecological and geochemical indicators (Szulc 2000) suggest that in Anisian times Silesia belonged to the Tethyan domain rather than to the epicontinental Germanic province.

This transgression advanced very quickly, resulting in environmental uniformity over vast areas and enabling the explosive appearance and ubiquitous occurrence of the brachiopod *Coenothyris vulgaris*, which charaterizes the so-called Terebratula Beds (Terebratelbänke) over much of the Germanic Basin.

Rapid transgression, together with local tectonic subsidence, led to the development of starved basin conditions. This phase was characterized by the deposition of dark, poorly fossiliferous nodular limestones of the Reifling type.

Following the maximum phase of the Anisian transgression, the eastern sub-basin filled up with reefal, bioclastic and oolitic sediments. Eventual emergence was marked by dolomitization and karstification of the limestones signalling the onset of the regressive succession of the Middle Muschelkalk (Diplopora-Tarnowice Beds, Orbicularis Beds, and/or Geislingen Bank).

**Middle Muschelkalk (early to mid-Illyrian).** During the Middle Muschelkalk regression the Germanic Basin underwent substantial reorganization. The main depocentre was situated in the Hessian Depression which was the area of maximum subsidence. This new depocentre was filled with up to 100 m of halite that interfingers laterally with sulphate- and dolomite-rich sediments toward the basin margins. In the perilittoral zone, stretching from Baden-Württemberg, through Hesse, Franconia, Thuringia and Silesia to the Holy Cross Mountains, unusual sponge/microbial stromatolites formed (Szulc 1997; Hagdorn *et al.* 1999) (Fig. 13.5C).

The circulation system in the western sub-basin resembled that of the Röt semiclosed evaporitic basin, but the Tethyan waters overstepped the Vindelician High and extended into central and northern Germany through the Hessian Depression.

Several alternating shallowing and deepening cycles have been recognized in the evaporitic complex, but two third-order cycles are particularly pronounced. These are well developed in the SW part of the Germanic Basin where two sulphate and/or halite packages are separated by a dolomite horizon (Geyer & Gwinner 1986). Rothe (1993) has demonstrated that the sulphates and halite formed subaqueously during relative deepening of the basin, but that the carbonates show features of subaerial exposure. Together with the substantial thickness of the evaporites (>70 m), this indicates a restricted, but permanent, influx of marine waters from the Tethys Ocean into the western sub-basin, even during the regressive phase of the Middle Triassic. As indicated by post-evaporitic features, such as halite pseudomorphs, collapse breccias or some residual deposits, the primary extent of halite deposition was more widespread than the present-day occurrence suggests (Simon 1988; Gaupp *et al.* 1998).

In the Silesian and southeastern Polish sub-basin carbonate deposition predominated. This suggests that a significant, normal marine influx persisted near the eastern gates in Illyrian times. In northern Germany, the Middle Muschelkalk locally attains thicknesses greater than 200 m in deep but restricted grabens (Gärtner & Röhling 1993).

**Upper Muschelkalk (late Illyrian to Ladinian).** The basin reorganization that commenced in Illyrian times continued during the deposition of the Upper Muschelkalk. As shown by the isopachs (Fig. 13.4B), the main depocentre was located in the Hessian Depression where the thickness of the Upper Muschelkalk attains 100 m (i.e. two to three times the thickness recorded elsewhere in the Germanic Basin). The observed facies distribution is closely linked to the distribution of structurally controlled highs and lows within the Germanic Basin. Deep-water carbonates were deposited in the deeper, actively subsiding areas, while marls and fine clastic sediments accumulated in the shallower areas (Fig. 13.5D).

Deposition of the Upper Muschelkalk was coeval with the Ladinian transgression and occurs throughout the Germanic Basin. Upper Muschelkalk sediments comprise bioclastic or oolitic limestones overlain by deep ramp marl/limestone deposits (Hauptmuschelkalk) in Germany, and by nodular black limestones in the Mid-Polish Trough. Facies patterns and geochemical and palaeontological data (Hagdorn & Simon 1993; Szulc 2000; Narkiewicz & Szulc 2004) indicate that at this time all three of the marine seaways (i.e. the Western Gate to the west, and the Silesian-Moravian and East Carpathian gates to the east) were open in late Illyrian–Longobardian times. Normal marine carbonates were replaced gradually by prograding shallow marine limestones and dolomites in the Germanic Basin (Aigner 1985). To the east and north of SW Germany the proportion of marls increases, while marly sediments dominate in the Polish sub-basin (Fig. 13.6). According to conodont and ammonoid data (Assmann 1944; Senkowiczowa 1962; Kozur 1974*b*; Trammer 1975; Zawidzka 1975; Urlichs 1999; Narkiewicz & Szulc 2004), normal marine sedimentation in the Polish sub-basin terminated three conodont zones and six ceratite zones earlier than in SW Germany. In the latter area it ended at the Fassanian/Longobardian boundary (Fig. 13.10).

Mass occurrences of *Coenothyris cycloides*, that extend from SW Germany to the Holy Cross Mountains, define the maximum flooding zone of the Upper Muschelkalk in general, while also marking the end of normal marine conditions and the onset of brackish Lower Keuper facies in the Polish sub-basin (cf. Fig. 13.6). Although normal marine organisms retreated from the Polish sub-basin, an impoverished Muschelkalk-type marine fauna persisted in the Lower Keuper of Upper Silesia (Assmann 1926).

Palynological, conodont and ceratite data allow the lower and middle Lower Keuper beds in Poland to be dated as Longobardian and correlated with the Upper Hauptmuschelkalk of SW Germany (Orłowska-Zwolińska 1983). This facies diachroneity has been confirmed by magnetostratigraphy (Nawrocki & Szulc 2000). The diachronous development of Keuper facies in the eastern and western parts of the Germanic Basin was caused by intense uplift in the east (Szulc 2000). This upwarp resulted in an increase in clastic supply in uppermost Muschelkalk–Lower Keuper times and, ultimately, in emersion and the development of a local stratigraphic hiatus encompassing the late Ladinian interval (Fig. 13.6).

### *Keuper (J.S.)*

**Stratigraphy of the Upper Triassic.** The Upper Triassic stratigraphy of the Germanic Basin is based on the dominant lithologies which generally reflect alternating shallow-marine and continental environments and/or fluctuations between arid and humid climatic conditions. The general lithostratigraphical framework is broadly uniform throughout the basin. However, the scarcity of age-diagnostic fossils impedes detailed bio- and chronostratigraphic work and magnetostratigraphic data are still very scarce. High levels of stratigraphical resolution and detailed basin-wide correlations are, therefore, difficult to achieve. For these reasons the lithostratigraphical framework of the uppermost part of the Upper Triassic in Poland is complex, with many local names (Marek & Pajchlowa 1997). In contrast, the other main lithostratigraphical units, i.e. the Lower Keuper, Lower and Upper Gipskeuper or the Schilfsandstein, are common in both Germany and Poland (Fig. 13.11).

**Basin palaeotopography and setting.** Basin configuration in the Late Triassic did not differ significantly from that of the Mid-Triassic. The Germanic Basin was bounded by the Variscan massifs, and the active depocentres were located in the same areas as the Mid-Polish Trough, the Hessian Depression and the North Sea rift system (Figs 13.5, 13.23–13.25). Several smaller subsidence centres (particularly in the Polish sub-basin; Gajewska 1997) were controlled by strike-slip faults and, hence, can be considered as secondary depocentres. The overall basin topography resulted in a facies pattern where fine-grained sediments (either marine or terrestrial) accumulated in the depocentres, while coarser deposits (mostly sandstones) were laid down adjacent to the basin-bounding massifs (in particular the Bohemian Massif). Therefore, the facies deposited within the basin centres have their sandy proximal equivalents at the basin margins: for instance, the Benker Sandstein is the marginal facies of the Lower Gipskeuper, the Blasensandstein and Coburg Sandstein are the marginal facies of the Upper Gipskeuper, and the Stubensandstein is the marginal facies equivalent of the Steinmergelkeuper (Fig. 13.13).

**Lower Keuper: Lettenkeuper (late Ladinian).** In the mid-Ladinian a tectonically forced regression affected the southwestern part of the Germanic Basin. Emersion and erosion resulted in the development of a very pronounced angular unconformity which marks the Middle–Upper Triassic boundary in Germany (Aigner & Bachmann 1992).

The overlying transgressive deposits are fossiliferous fine-grained clastic sediments and dolomites, displaying condensation phenomena (Hagdorn & Reiff 1988). To the north (e.g. in Mecklenburg and northern Poland) the marine deposits were gradually replaced by sandstones and mudstones of brackish and deltaic origin, and finally by continental mudflat deposits (Fig. 13.6). The transgression developed only in depocentres in the area of the Mid-Polish Trough and the Foresudetic Depression, as indicated by the presence of dark grey sandstones with an impoverished marine fauna.

The SE marginal area of the Germanic Basin was emergent. Alluvial sediments deposited in local depressions are interpreted as incised valley systems (Szulc 2000). In Upper Silesia emersion continued up to the Grenzdolomit transgression (late Ladinian–early Carnian).

The upper part of the Lower Keuper is characterized by a regressive trend and erosional activity which is marked across vast areas of the Germanic Basin (Fig. 13.6). Fluvial, sandy sediments (Hauptsandstein) overlying the erosional unconformity, were mostly transported from Fennosarmatia (Paul & Ahrendt 1998). In the south, the uplifted Upper Silesian block provided a local source area for alluvial deposits. The fluvial deposits are overlain directly by fine-grained clastic marine sediments and carbonates (dolomites). Limestones and dolomites dominate in Baden-Württemberg and in Silesia, i.e. in the entrances to the Western and Silesian-Moravian gates. North of these marine seaways, the carbonates pass into mudflat and sandflat deposits (Fig. 13.5E). The transgression climaxed with the so-called Grenzdolomit assemblage that has been identified by Aigner & Bachmann (1992) as a maximum flooding surface (Fig. 13.6). The appearance of cephalopods in SW Germany (Müller 1970; Urlichs 1999) and the onlap of the fossil-rich Grenzdolomit carbonates onto the uplifted Silesian block confirm this interpretation (Assmann 1926; Szulc 2000). The Grenzdolomit transgression was similar in extent to that of the Muschelkalk; the basin at this time, however, was much shallower than its Muschelkalk predecessor.

**Middle Keuper: Lower Gipskeuper (late Ladinian to early Carnian).** The Grenzdolomit transgressive deposits are succeeded by evaporitic/clastic sediments of the Lower Gipskeuper sabkha system. These display a relatively constant thickness and facies distribution throughout the Germanic Basin (Figs 13.5F & 13.23A). Sulphate precipitation predominated, but halite was deposited in local subsidence centres in north and east Germany and central Poland. In terms of sequence stratigraphy, the Lower Gipskeuper represents the highstand systems tract of the sequence beginning with the Grenzdolomit transgressive systems tract deposits. An impoverished opportunistic fauna, including myophorids and linguloids (Beutler 1998; Szyperko-Teller 1997), provides further evidence for the occurrence of very restricted marine and sabkha environments. Finally, the fine clastic sediments of a southward prograding mudflat replaced the evaporite-bearing sabkha deposits.

**Middle Keuper: Schilfsandstein (mid Carnian).** Tectonically controlled topographical rejuvenation and climate-related pluvialization in Carnian times resulted in an increase in fluvial activity and clastic sedimentation across the entire Germanic Basin. The fluvial Schilfsandstein facies is interpreted as having been deposited in a complex and extensive braided river network that transported sandy material southwards from the area of the Fennoscandian Land (Fig. 13.23B).

As indicated by petrographical and zircon fission track data, the Schilfsandstein fluvial system bypassed the southern marine gateways and continued onto the Tethys shelf margin where clastic sediments were deposited, partly forming the Raibl and Lunzer Sandstein deltaic formations (Köppen & Carter 2000). Intensive fluviatile erosion resulted in the Schilfsandstein resting discordantly on various older Triassic and even Palaeozoic formations (Schröder 1977; Beutler & Häusser 1981). Only in the central part of the Mid-Polish Trough was erosion less severe, and laminated, fine-grained lacustrine clastic sediments were deposited.

The Schilfsandstein unit can be subdivided into three parts. The lower and upper parts are dominated by sandstones while the middle part is mainly composed of siltstones. The topmost part of the Schilfsandstein unit consists of dolomitic mudstones and grey marls with intercalations of pink anhydrite suggesting a gradual increase in aridity.

**Middle Keuper: Upper Gipskeuper (late Carnian to early Norian).** As noted above, the sediments of the topmost Schilfsandstein record an increase in aridity. This trend continued and resulted in evaporitic sedimentation of the overlying Upper Gipskeuper. The unit is dominated by sulphates and siltstones deposited in peneplained mudflat/playa environments. The scarcity of fossil remains (including plants) suggests harsh and stressful palaeoenvironmental conditions. The facies pattern of this unit resembles that of the Lower Gipskeuper (Fig. 13.24A). In northern Germany halite formed in inland playas controlled by local subsidence. Some thicker carbonate sequences (Lehrberg Beds; Fig. 13.13) in the lower part of the unit formed in more perennial, lacustrine basins that filled the Swabian-Hessian Depression.

The Heldburg Gips sulphate complex (Fig. 13.13) is several

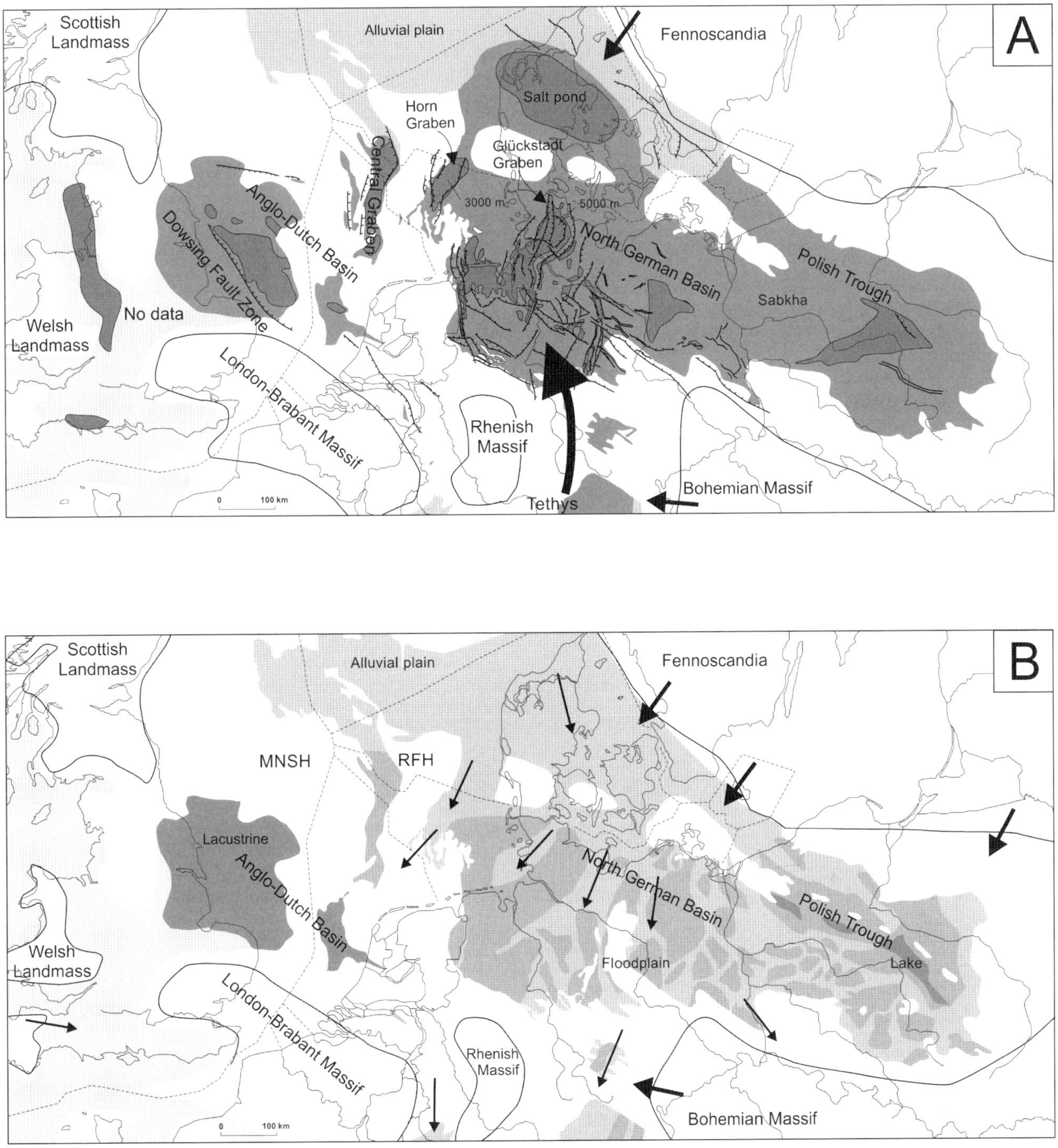


**Fig. 13.23.** (**A**) Present-day distribution and facies map of the Lower Gipskeuper (Early Carnian). Compiled by Geluk (2005) after Wolburg (1969), Beutler & Schüler (1978), Cameron *et al.* (1992), Rheinhardt (1993), Beutler (1995), Marek & Pajchlowa (1997), Dadlez *et al.* (1998), Geluk (1999), Pöppelreiter (1999), Baldschuhn *et al.* (2001), Warrington & Ivimey-Cook (1992) and Goldsmith *et al.* (2003). Active faults are indicated. Solid lines represent the reconstructed basin outline. Thick arrow indicates marine ingression, thinner arrows sediment influx. (**B**) Present-day distribution and facies map of the Schilfsandstein (Carnian). The main sediment supply originated from Fennoscandia. After Wurster (1964*a*), Beutler & Häusser (1981), Beutler & Schüler (1987), Jubitz *et al.* (1988), Cameron *et al.* (1992), Warrington & Ivimey-Cook (1992), Beutler (1998), Dadlez *et al.* (1998), Geluk (1999), Baldschuhn *et al.* (2001) and Goldsmith *et al.* (2003). Solid lines represent the reconstructed basin outline. Arrows indicate sediment influx. Abbreviations: MNSH, Mid-North Sea High; RFH, Ringkøbing-Fyn High.

metres thick and occurs in the uppermost part of the Upper Gipskeuper in northern Germany and in Thuringia, and forms another distinct horizon. To the east (i.e. in the Polish sub-basin) the massive Heldburg Gips splits into many thinner horizons that interfinger with thin-bedded claystones resulting in a cyclical succession. Similar high-frequency sedimentary cycles are visible throughout the basin and probably reflect fluctuations between arid and semiarid climatic conditions.

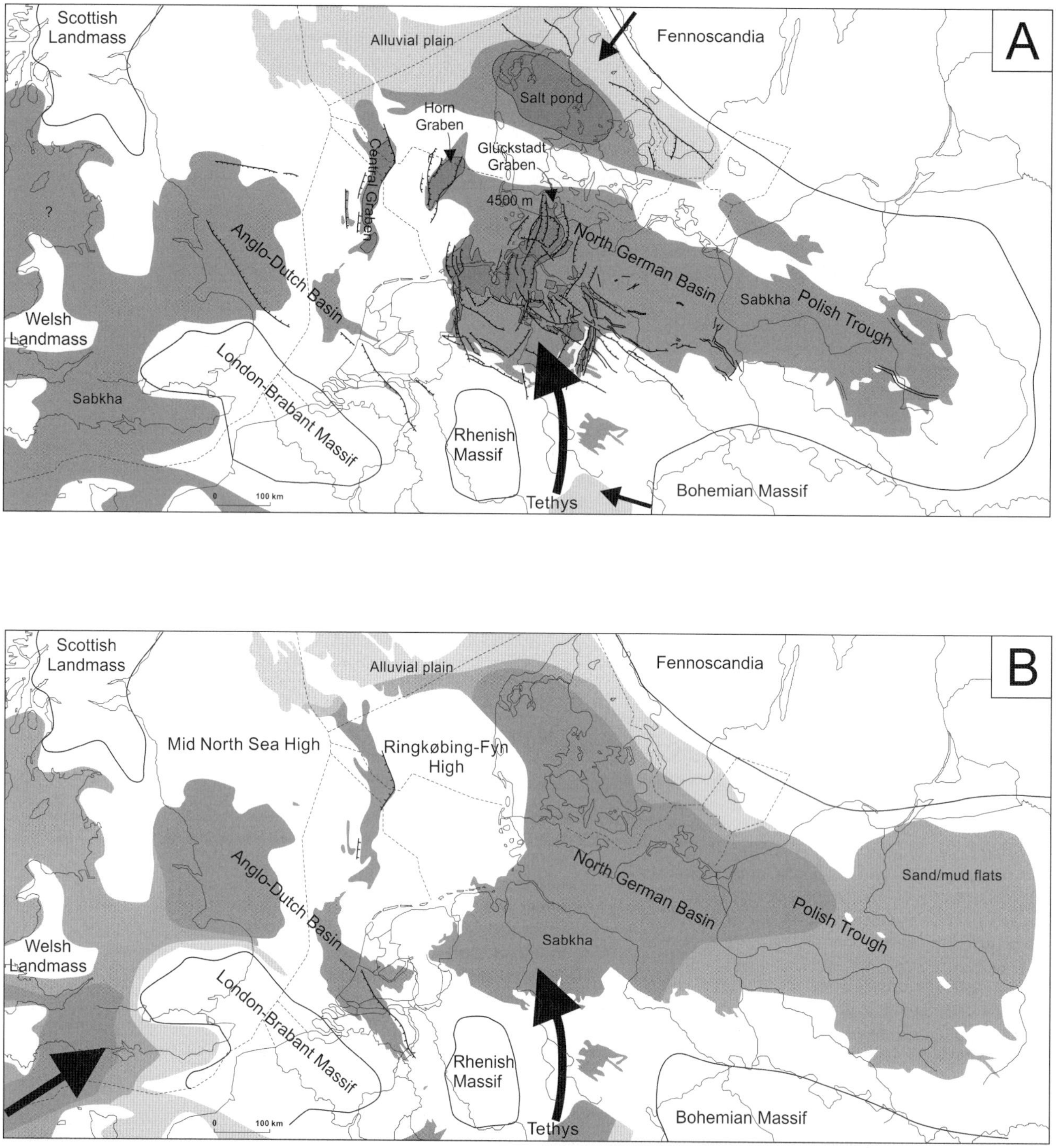


**Fig. 13.24.** (**A**) Present-day distribution and facies map of the Upper Gipskeuper (latest Carnian). Compiled by Geluk (2005) after Wolburg (1969), Beutler & Schüler (1978), Cameron *et al.* (1992), Warrington & Ivimey-Cook (1992), Rheinhardt (1993), Beutler (1995), Marek & Pajchlowa (1997), Dadlez *et al.* (1998), Geluk (1999), Pöppelreiter (1999), Baldschuhn *et al.* (2001) and Goldsmith *et al.* (2003). Solid lines represent the reconstructed basin outline. Thick arrow indicates marine ingression, thinner arrows sediment influx. (**B**) Present-day distribution and facies map of the Steinmergelkeuper (Norian). After Wolburg (1969), Beutler & Schüler (1978), Cameron *et al.* (1992), Warrington & Ivimey-Cook (1992), Rheinhardt (1993), Beutler (1995), Marek & Pajchlowa (1997), Dadlez *et al.* (1998), Geluk (1999), Pöppelreiter (1999), Baldschuhn *et al.* (2001) and Goldsmith *et al.* (2003). Solid lines represent the reconstructed basin outline. Thick arrows indicate marine ingressions.

According to palynological data (Orłowska-Zwolińska 1983) the upper part of the Upper Gipskeuper is of Norian age.

**Middle Keuper: Steinmergelkeuper (middle to late Norian).** The Steinmergelkeuper overlies a prominent basin-wide unconformity that resulted from intense tectonic activity as well as increasing fluvial-related erosion driven by gradual pluvialization. Amelioration of climatic conditions in mid- to late Norian times caused a gradual decrease in evaporite precipitation and their gradual replacement by mottled, marly mudstones fre-

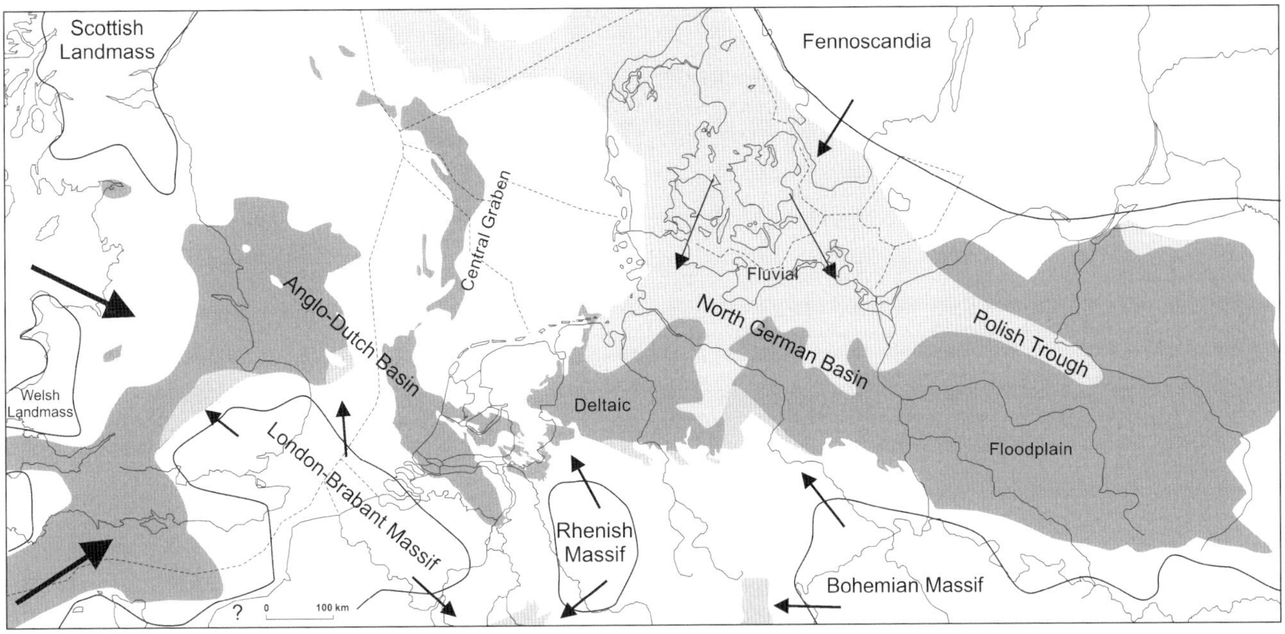


**Fig. 13.25.** Present-day distribution and facies map of the Rhaetian. Compiled by Geluk (2005) after Ziegler (1990), Cameron *et al.* (1992), Warrington & Ivimey-Cook (1992), Beutler (1998), Dadlez *et al.* (1998), Geluk (1999) and Baldschuhn *et al.* (2001). Solid lines represent the reconstructed basin outline. Thick arrows indicate marine ingressions. Thinner arrows indicate sediment influx; different grey shading is related to provenance.

quently containing palaeosols and ephemeral stream deposits (Fig. 13.24B). Typical of the unit are alternating red and green and/or grey fine-grained clastic sediments and dolomitic intercalations. The alternation is ascribed to orbitally controlled climatic fluctuations which resulted in cyclic variation between lacustrine and mudflat environments. Pluvialization led to the gradual re-establishment of vascular plants which, in turn, favoured the development of tetrapods and the appearance of the first dinosaurs (*Plateosaurus*) in SW Germany and in Silesia (Schoch & Wild 1999*b*; Dzik *et al.* 2000).

Within the basin fill there is evidence of localized resedimentation. For example, in the eastern part of the Germanic Basin ephemeral streams reworked the previously deposited muddy sediments and redeposited them in almost the same place. Such recycling is evidenced by pedogenic nodules that after reworking and sieve fractionation formed specific residual 'conglomeratic' deposits (Szulc 2005), erroneously identified in the Polish lithostratigraphy as an individual correlation horizon termed the 'Lisow Breccia'.

One of the most intriguing questions regarding the Norian succession is the problem of possible marine incursions suggested by Dadlez & Kopik (1963) on the basis of the isolated occurrences of foraminifers in central and NE Poland. The problem lies in the questionable communication links of this region with the marine basins. According to facies distribution patterns (Deczkowski 1997), no influx from either the North Sea rifts or from the south (i.e. from the Tethys) was possible at this time. On the other hand, the poor stratigraphic constraints on the Upper Keuper sediments in Poland make this a difficult problem to resolve.

**Upper Keuper: Rhaetian.** The climate-related pluvialization that began in the mid-Norian intensified during the later Triassic. Sediments are dominantly fluvial and lacustrine, comprising organic-rich clastic deposits (Fig. 13.25). Extensive vegetation led to the accumulation of plant debris and the development of coal seams or even coal layers accompanied by siderite and pyrite encrustations. Humid conditions also resulted in the weathering and decay of feldspar minerals, so that the Rhaetian quartz sandstones are readily distinguished from the feldspar-bearing clastic sediments of the Lower and Middle Keuper.

The Rhaetian is separated from the Steinmergelkeuper by a distinctive unconformity (Beutler 1998). The unconformity was caused by fluviatile erosion. Additional gaps in sedimentation also resulted from weathering processes acting on the Steinmergelkeuper clayey sediments. For instance, in western Poland the humid climate caused intense kaolinization of the exposed Norian claystones up to 20 m below the palaeosurface (J. Szulc, personal observation).

In addition to the change in climatic conditions and the resultant sedimentary style, the Rhaetian also differs in containing sediments deposited during the first marine incursion that came from the west (i.e. from the Proto-Atlantic Ocean). These marine deposits were concentrated in the western part of the basin and passed eastwards through brackish to limnic and fluvial facies.

Several transgressive pulses have been recorded in the Germanic Basin. However, the most pronounced transgression occurred in the Mid-Rhaetian and gave rise to open marine conditions which are indicated by a marine fauna. This unit is named the Contorta Beds, after the most characteristic bivalve, *Rhaetavicula contorta*.

The Rhaetian succession initiated the transgressive system which is typical of the succeeding lowest Jurassic stage.

### *Basin evolution: The Netherlands (M.G., R.B.)*

Reconstruction of the depositional history of the Triassic in the Netherlands is hindered by the fact that, owing to strong Late Jurassic to Early Cretaceous uplift and ensuing deep erosion, complete successions are only preserved in isolated concealed basins. In the northeastern part of the Netherlands and the Dutch

Central Graben these show a clear affinity with the classic Germanic Triassic; in the eastern and southern onshore areas, deep intra-Triassic erosion occurred in relation to the Early Cimmerian phase, and the Norian or even Rhaetian deposits rest directly upon the Muschelkalk or Röt (Geluk 1999, 2005; Fig. 13.25).

Compared to the central and eastern parts of the Germanic Basin, the Triassic succession in the SW and west of the Netherlands contains more sandstones in the Lower Triassic (up to the Röt, after this the coarse-grained influx from the south wanes). The Lower Muschelkalk succession is comparable to that in Germany, but the Upper Muschelkalk contains more fine-grained clastic material. The Keuper sediments (if present) are mainly red-coloured, anhydrite-bearing and fine grained. The thickness of the complete Triassic in the onshore area is some 1000–1200 m, and in the Dutch Central Graben up to 2500 m (Fig. 13.26).

The deposition of the Triassic was governed initially by the inherited Permian basin configuration, at a palaeolatitude of around 20°N. Following the regression, which marks the end of the deposition of the Zechstein, continental conditions returned to the basin. Mainly fine-grained sediments were deposited in an extensive playa-lake setting, except in the southern onshore part of the Netherlands, where coarser clastics were already being deposited in the Roer Valley Graben by ephemeral braided rivers during Induan times. The deposition of the Lower Buntsandstein was governed by climatic Milankovich cycles of various magnitudes. These cycles resulted in basin-wide base-level variations (Geluk & Röhling 1997, 1999). A succession of laterally persistent, fining-upward cycles was deposited in a playa lake environment. In the central parts of the Netherlands a subtle, mostly submerged swell developed. Carbonate oolites formed during fair-weather periods around, and on top of, this high in a manner comparable with that proposed by Voigt & Gaupp (2000) for the Thuringian Basin in Germany. During storms, redeposition of the oolites occurred over a large area around the swell corresponding with parts of the Permian Texel-IJsselmeer High and older Carboniferous structures.

A major fluvial system in the southeastern Netherlands supplied clastics from the Armorican Massif, the Massif Central and the Vosges Mountains during the Early to Mid-Triassic (Ziegler 1990). Additional clastics originated from the London (Anglo)-Brabant Massif (Geluk *et al.* 1996). During the Olenekian, uplift of the hinterlands, possibly in combination with extensional tectonics and more humid climatic conditions, resulted in a sharp increase in the amount of clastic material transported into the basin. In response to humid periods in the hinterland, an ephemeral fluvial system transported clastics northwards through the Roer Valley Graben and the West Netherlands Basin (Geluk *et al.* 1996); a second fluvial system was situated in the Ems Low. In more central parts of the basin, redeposition of fluvial sands was widespread during dry periods (Fontaine *et al.* 1993). During phases of low clastic influx (e.g. during dry periods) playa environments expanded towards the margins of the basin. The repetition of these processes resulted in the cyclic alternation in the Main Buntsandstein Subgroup. The larger cycles, represented, for example, by the Volpriehausen and Detfurth formations, are tectonically driven; the high-resolution sequences within these formations are climate-driven (Van der Zwan & Spaak 1992; Geluk & Röhling 1997).

Several pulses of extension resulted in the fragmentation of the former Southern Permian Basin into smaller rift structures. Accommodation space in these rifts changed through time, shifting from the Roer Valley Graben into the Dutch Central Graben and the Ems Low during the Olenekian (Geluk & Röhling 1999). Thickening of the subgroup towards the London-Brabant Massif suggests the presence of a growth fault at the southern margin of the West Netherlands Basin. The Lower Volpriehausen Sandstone and the Lower Detfurth Sandstone are fluvial to aeolian in the southern areas (Ames & Farfan 1996) and the Ems Low, and mainly aeolian in the Dutch Central Graben (Fontaine *et al.* 1993). Extensional tectonics during deposition of the Main Buntsandstein Subgroup resulted in rapid subsidence of the Dutch Central, Horn and Glückstadt grabens, and contemporaneous uplift of a number of NNE–SSW trending swells in the Netherlands. On these highs, erosion removed much of the initial cover of the Main Buntsandstein (Fig. 13.27).

Lacustrine deposits of the Solling Formation covered the relief created by the Hardegsen Unconformity. The upper part of the Solling Formation is a typical post-rift deposit, covering all structural elements in a sheet-like way. The lower part, however, was partly contemporaneous with rifting, as reflected by sand-filled fault-bounded grabens in the northern Dutch offshore areas.

In Early Anisian times, a connection was established with the Tethys Ocean *via* the Silesian-Moravian Gateway, allowing marine water to enter the basin. This resulted in the deposition of a transgressive megasequence, which prograded westwards (Ziegler 1990). Temporary interruption of this connection with the ocean resulted in the deposition of the Röt evaporites. The remainder of the Röt Formation was deposited in a shallow, brackish lagoon, which received the last influx of clastics from southern sources (Geluk *et al.* 1996). This formation was deposited under an extensional tectonic regime, with the Dutch Central Graben as the main area of differential subsidence. A number of faults (e.g. the Mid-Netherlands Fault Zone) became active, dissecting previous Early Triassic structures (e.g. Netherlands Swell).

The Muschelkalk Formation was deposited during a period of maximum transgression, when clastic deposition was confined to the basin margins, and the sea covered most intrabasinal highs. In the Netherlands, situated in the western parts of this large basin and remote from the marine gateways, the carbonate facies is more restricted and the Muschelkalk is distinctly thinner in comparison with the succession in Germany. In the western and southern Netherlands, the carbonates grade laterally into (anhydritic) claystones, representing the coastal-plain to inner-ramp sediments at the basin margin (Borkhataria 2004). Their deposition took place in a shallow, storm-swept epeiric sea. As a result of Late Anisian tectonic movements, the connection with Tethys was briefly interrupted and evaporites were deposited (Middle Muschelkalk). In conjunction with minor extensional activity, thick salt layers accumulated in the Dutch Central Graben and smaller grabens in the Dutch onshore area (Geluk 1999; Geluk *et al.* 2000; Borkhataria 2004). The infilling of these grabens took place gradually during deposition of the Middle Muschelkalk, explaining the facies variations which range from carbonates and anhydrites to salt (Borkhataria 2004).

Uplift of the Fennoscandian Shield during the Early Ladinian resulted in the supply of clastic material to the basin from the NE (Bertelsen 1980; Beutler & Schüler 1987; Ziegler 1990). This renewed clastic influx ended carbonate deposition, and marks the base of the Keuper Formation, which prograded eastwards and southwards with time (Szulc 2000). The transition from Muschelkalk to Keuper deposition in the Netherlands can be considered almost contemporaneous (Geluk 2005). During deposition of the Keuper, the Netherlands received mainly fine-grained sediments, transported a great distance from the Fenno-

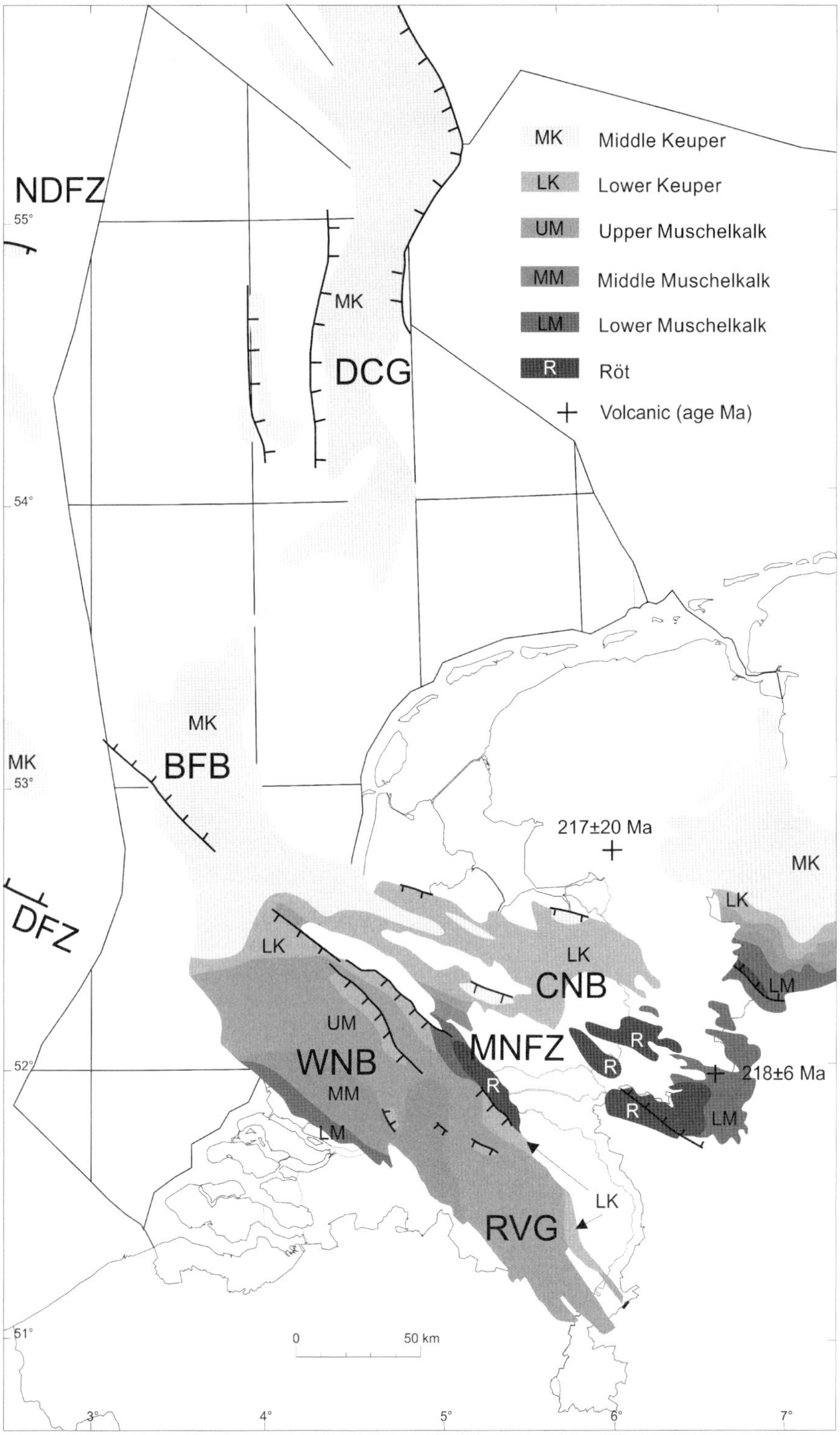


**Fig. 13.26.** Subcrop map of the Early Kimmerian unconformity (e.g. base Steinmergelkeuper or base Rhaetian). Abbreviations: BFB, Broad Fourteens Basin; CNB, Central Netherlands Basin; DCG, Dutch Central Graben; DFZ, Dowsing Fault Zone: MNFZ, Mid-Netherlands Fault Zone; NDFZ, North Dogger Fault Zone; RVG, Roer Valley Graben; WNB, West Netherlands Basin. After Geluk (1999, 2005).

scandian Shield. The Lower Keuper and the equivalent of the Schilfsandstein are predominantly fine-grained, and were deposited mainly in the western parts of the Netherlands in shallow, brackish to normal-marine conditions. In Carnian times, extensional tectonics created rapidly subsiding grabens such as the Dutch Central Graben and the Ems Low where thick evaporite sequences were deposited. In these grabens, basement fault movement triggered widespread salt diapirism, as indicated by

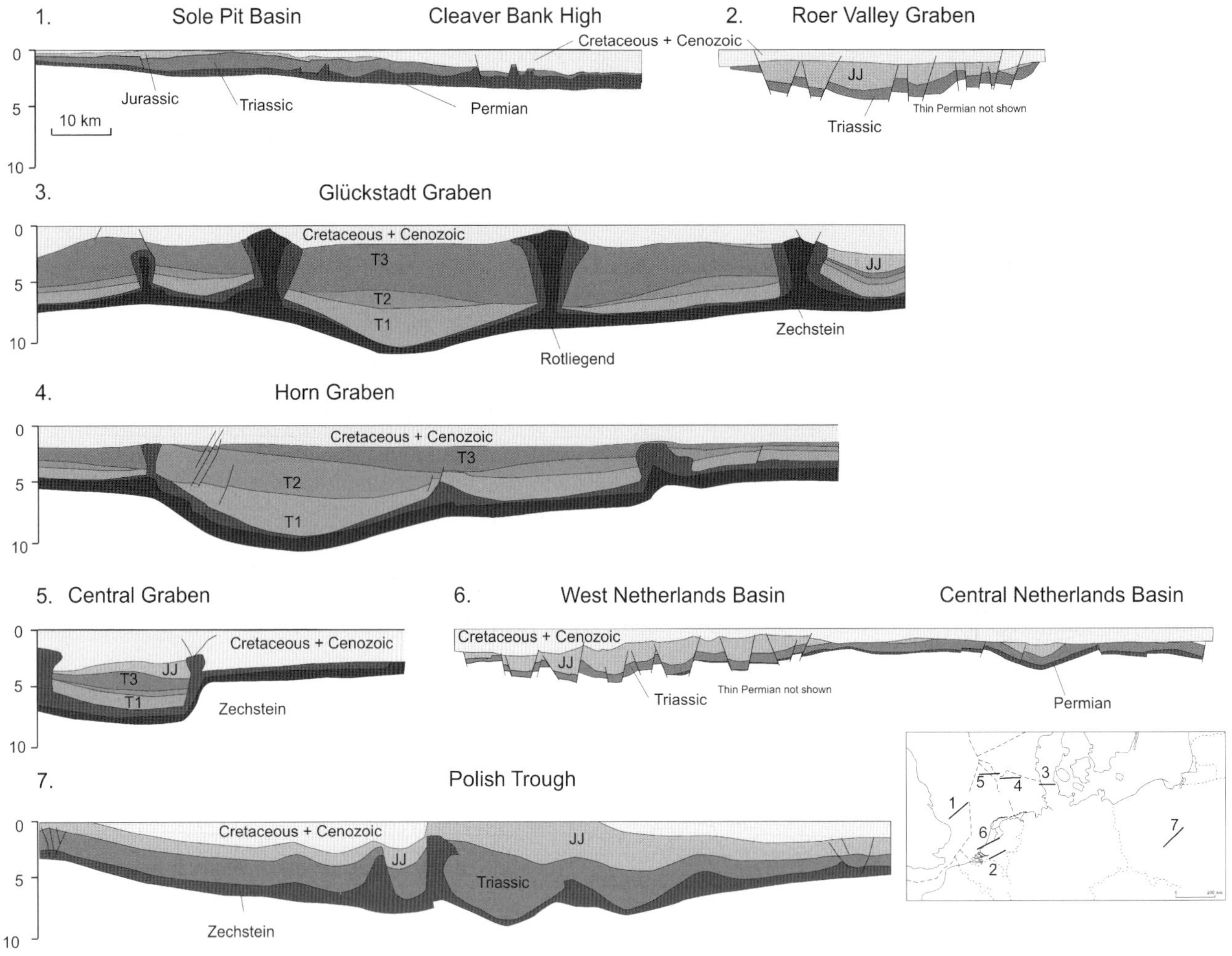


**Fig. 13.27.** Geological cross-sections of various main Triassic basins discussed in the text. Abbreviations: JJ, Jurassic; T1, Lower and Main Buntsandstein; T2, Solling, Röt and Muschelkalk; T3, Keuper. Note the difference in scale between these basins, with the thick Triassic successions in the Glückstadt and Horn grabens. Further note the diapiric Rotliegend salts in the former graben. Modified after Cameron *et al.* (1992), Kockel (1995), Baldschuhn *et al.* (2001), Krzywiec (2004) and NITG (2004). Depth in kilometres; vertical exaggeration ×2.

thick Keuper successions in rim synclines. Contemporaneous uplift of the London-Brabant Massif and surrounding areas resulted in widespread erosion. Following the cessation of tectonic activity, sedimentation resumed in Norian times, and the Red Keuper Claystone and Dolomitic Keuper, equivalent to the Steinmergelkeuper (Fig. 13.11), were deposited unconformably upon older Triassic rocks. These units, however, do not extend into the eastern Netherlands, where deltaic deposits of the Sleen Formation covered the relief.

### *Basin evolution: Southern Denmark (A.E.G.)*

In southern Denmark the Triassic deposits show the classic Germanic tripartite succession (Bertelsen 1980). Lower Triassic continental red-beds (Bunter Shale, Bunter Sandstone and Ørslev formations) are successively overlain by the Middle Triassic carbonates and evaporites (Falster Formation) and the Upper Triassic red-beds and evaporites of the Tønder and Oddesund formations. These pass upwards into marine carbonates, claystones and sandstones of the uppermost Triassic to lower Jurassic (Vinding and Gassum formations) (Fig. 13.11).

Michelsen & Clausen (2002) presented a revised lithostratigraphic scheme based on new Danish well sections which have been used for high-resolution correlation within the southern North Sea and northern Germany. In accordance with Bertelsen (1980), the Danish Lower Triassic lacustrine and fluvial deposits are subdivided into the Bunter Shale and Bunter Sandstone formations. The Danish Lower to Middle Triassic lacustrine to restricted-marine sediments are included in the Röt Formation, replacing the Ørslev Formation (*sensu* Bertelsen 1980). Middle Triassic shallow-marine carbonates and evaporites are included in the Muschelkalk Formation, which replaces the Falster Formation (*sensu* Bertelsen 1980). The uppermost Middle Triassic and Upper Triassic continental series are included in the Keuper Formation, representing the former Tønder, Oddesund, Gassum and Vinding formations (*sensu* Bertelsen 1980).

The basal evaporite layer of the Ørslev (Röt) Formation correlates with the Röt Salinar in northern Germany (Beutler & Schüler 1987). Another evaporitic unit, corresponding to the Middle Muschelkalk evaporites of the central Germanic Basin, occurs in the Falster (Muschelkalk) Formation. The uppermost sandstone unit of the Tønder (Keuper) Formation is a stratigraphic equivalent of the Schilfsandstein (Beutler & Schüler 1987).

## *Basin evolution: Switzerland (P.J.)*

The Swiss Jura Mountains comprise the 'Folded Jura' and the 'Tabular Jura' which form the western and northern margins of Switzerland (Fig. 13.28). The Folded Jura is the inner part of the arcuate Jura fold-and-thrust belt (Trümpy 1980). Middle to Late Triassic evaporites served as décollement horizons for the detachment of the Mesozoic cover that commenced in the Late Miocene (Laubscher 1961, 1975; Jordan 1992; Becker 2000). Consequently, no sediments older than Middle or Late Triassic are exposed in the Folded Jura. Outcrops of Triassic sediments are restricted to the easternmost part of the Jura Boundary Thrust in northern Switzerland. The outcrop stratigraphic record is complemented by some borehole information from both the Swiss and French parts of the Jura Mountains and from the Molasse Basin. Some information is also available from hydrocarbon exploration wells in the Central and West Jura Mountains, but these are, with a few exceptions (e.g. BRGM 1964, 1965, 1975), only poorly documented. The drilling programme of the National Cooperative for the Disposal of Radioactive Waste (NAGRA) supplied numerous cores from the northern part of Switzerland that contain Triassic sediments. These cores represent key sections for the interpretation of the palaeogeographical evolution of the northern Peri-Tethyan realm during Triassic times (Feist-Burkhardt *et al.* 2008).

The Triassic of the Swiss Tabular Jura extends from Switzerland northeastwards into the Rhine–Danube area and the foreland of the Swabian Alb. To the north, Triassic deposits are known from relicts of the Black Forest sedimentary cover which is bounded by the Upper Rhine Graben (e.g. the Dinkelberg area) (Fischer *et. al.* 1971).

In Triassic times, the area of Switzerland represented the southwestern embayment of the Germanic Basin, and at certain times formed its connection to the Tethys (Western Gate). Due to its marginal position close to the Bohemian-Vindelician High, the Gallic High and the Aar Massif–Black Forest High, local peculiarities have developed (Trümpy 1980) (see below).

*Buntsandstein Group (Early Triassic, ?Induan to Olenekian)*
Sediments of the Buntsandstein Group crop out in the Swiss Tabular Jura and adjacent parts of France and Germany. They consist predominantly of coarse-grained red sandstones, conglomerates and mudstones with red silica crusts, and are interpreted as having been deposited in a fluvial system (Geyer & Gwinner 1968). The rivers originated on the Gallic High to the NE. Initial sediment transport pathways paralleled the Rhine Graben and extended into Switzerland only in the Basel and Ajoie areas. Subsequent deposition ('Middle Buntsandstein') did not progress significantly further south. Only in its final phase, characterized by the occurrence of micaceous shale and several palaeosol layers, did sediments extend as far as the present Molasse Basin (Ortlam 1974). The maximum onlap of the Bohemian-Vindelician High is documented by the mostly dark red shales and fine-grained sandstones of the Röt succession. Nodular dolomites in the uppermost part of this unit are the first indicator of marine influence in the area. The total thickness of the Buntsandstein Group ranges from zero in the SE to 100 m in the Basel area and some 300 m in the adjacent French and German areas (Boigk & Schöneich 1974; Müller *et al.* 1984).

*Muschelkalk Group (Middle Triassic, Anisian to Ladinian)*
This predominantly marine succession is subdivided into the Wellengebirge (Lower Muschelkalk), Anhydritgruppe (Middle Muschelkalk) and Hauptmuschelkalk (Upper Muschelkalk) formations (Fig. 13.29). The first of these, the Wellengebirge

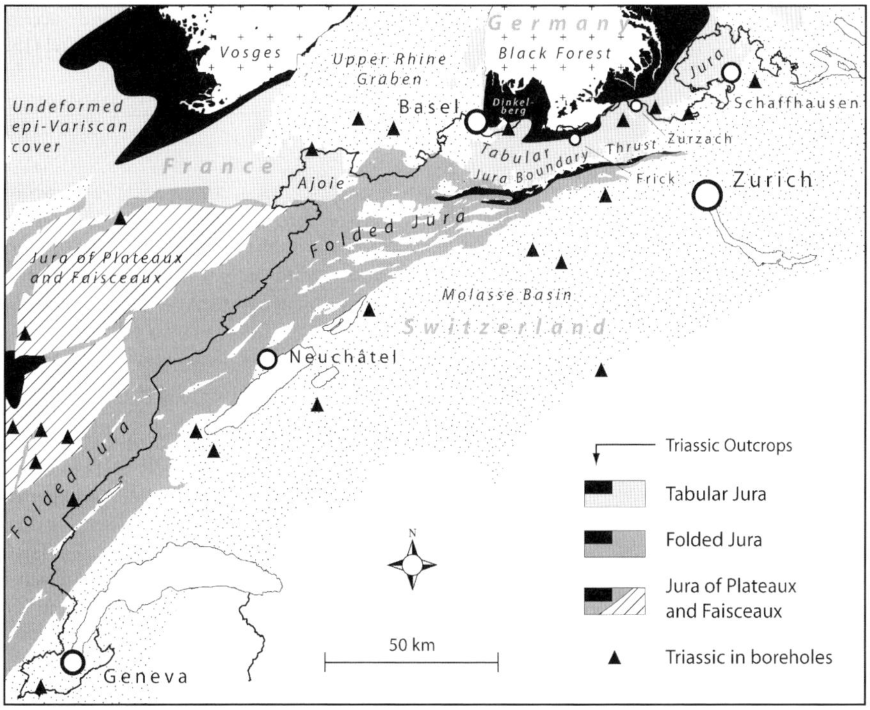


**Fig. 13.28.** Setting of the Folded and Tabular Jura in northwestern Switzerland. The extent of Triassic rock outcrops is exaggerated for better visibility.

(flaser-bedded limestone) Formation consists of dolomites, limestones, marly limestones and marls that accumulated in a shallow epicontinental sea in the southwestern Peri-Tethyan realm (Szulc 2000). Rocks of this formation crop out only in the Tabular Jura and adjacent German areas, while the depocentre is located in central to southern Germany (Schwarz 1975). In the Swiss part, the formation attains a maximum thickness of *c.* 50 m, decreasing towards the Vindelician High in the SE. The sediments record a transgression in early Anisian times, with maximum flooding in the Pelsonian coincident with a connection to the Tethys Ocean. Subsequent regression during the Illyrian marked the onset of basin restriction (Schwarz 1975; Dronkert *et al.* 1990; Götz & Feist-Burkhardt 1999). The sediments differ from the predominantly dolomitic, so-called Freudenstadt facies in adjacent southern Germany, in that the dolomite is restricted to the basal 'Liegender Dolomit' (Becker *et al.* 1997) which includes light-coloured, partly nodular dolomite and limestone with intercalated shales. This is overlain by up to 40 m of fossiliferous, partly silty or sandy clay-marlstones (Buchimergel) with intercalating marlstones and shales. Some of the fossils are concentrated in tempestites (Becker *et al.* 1997). Rare occurrences of the ceratite *Beneckeia* cf. *buchi* at the base, which coincide with the maximum sea-level rise (Götz & Feist-Burkhardt 2000), indicate an Anisian age (Peters *et al.* 1990). The overlying Orbicularismergel consists of dark-coloured, partly bituminous marls. The Wellengebirge Formation includes several metalliferous horizons (e.g. galenite, sphalerite, pyrite, chalcopyrite and marcasite), including the Bleiglanzbank (Hofmann 1979).

During deposition of the Anhydritgruppe Formation, the future Jura area was a sub-basin at the southwestern end of the elongate hypersaline Germanic Basin. The main Swiss depocentre was located in the Neuchâtel area where sediment thickness reached a maximum of *c.* 200 m (Sommaruga 1997; Becker 2000; Fig. 13.30). As the chemistry of the Muschelkalk salt cannot be distinguished from that of other marine salt deposits, a continuous saltwater or brine influx from the Tethys has been suggested (Dronkert *et al.* 1990). The Anhydritgruppe comprises a megacycle which commences with sulphates and passes from pure to impure rock salt (halite), to sulphates, and sulphate/marl intercalations, ending with dolomite. Up to ten small-scale shallowing-upward cycles can be distinguished (Widmer 1991). The halite deposits were also subjected to syndepositional leaching and redeposition (Dronkert *et al.* 1990). Thus, the halite content may vary over very short distances, from more than 70% to almost 0% of the total thickness, with the absent halite being replaced by breccias. An alternative explanation for these changes in thickness is syndepositional tectonics (Hauber 1980). Between Basel and Zurzach, the Muschelkalk halite deposits are exploited by brine extraction.

The Hauptmuschelkalk Formation (Fig. 13.29) constitutes the second marine cycle of the Triassic (Merki 1961; Dronkert *et al.* 1990). The thickness of the formation reaches a maximum of 70 m. Its three units, the Trochitenkalk, Plattenkalk and Trigonodusdolomit members (Fig. 13.29), represent a transgressive–regressive sequence. Indeed, the name Trochitenkalk relates to the characteristic intercalations, often composed entirely of the barrel-shaped ossicles (*Trochites*) of the crinoid *Encrinus*. The crinoids mainly grew on shell fragments and, following storm events, were later buried under carbonate mud. The fauna of the typically greyish limestone represents a rich biocoenosis in a shallow-marine setting below fair-weather wave base. The Plattenkalk Member comprises a succession of micritic limestones, shales and some biocalcarenites, rich in crinoids and, in the upper part, oolites, and was deposited during the maximum flooding phase; siliceous nodules are abundant. The shale content

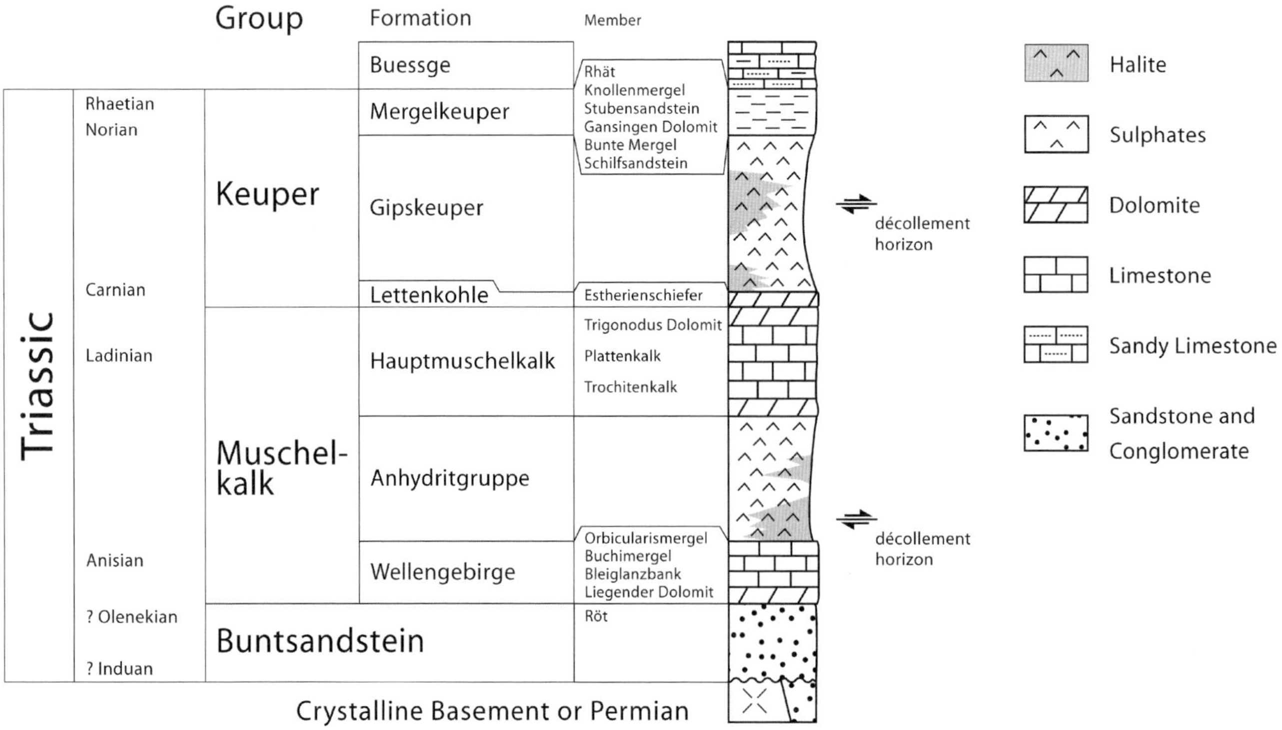


**Fig. 13.29.** Schematic stratigraphic column of the Triassic in the Swiss Jura.

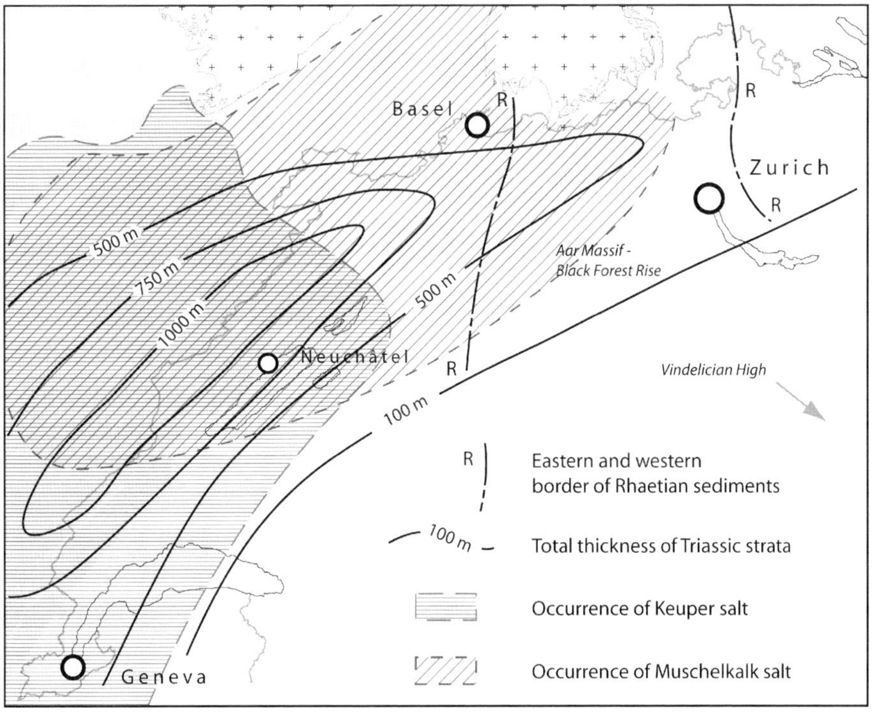


**Fig. 13.30.** Total thickness of Triassic rocks and occurrence of halite in the Middle (Muschelkalk) and Late Triassic (Keuper) according to Sommaruga (1997) and Becker (2000). There is a striking concurrence between the Triassic halite basin and the extent of the Neogene Jura Fold-and-Thrust Belt. Maximum amount of décollement and shortening correspond with maximum thickness of Triassic strata. Halite and anhydrite have served as the main décollement horizons of the thin-skinned Jura Fold-and-Thrust Belt (Jordan 1992, 1994). The isolated basin of low strength evaporite rocks in the foreland enabled the significant leap ahead of tectonic movement ('Fernschub'; Laubscher 1961) resulting in the formation of the Folded Jura as an outlier of Alpine orogeny.

increases towards the north and NE. In some regions, the Plattenkalk Member is affected by diagenetic or post-diagenetic dolomitization. Rare occurrences of *Ceratites* cf. *nodosus* indicate a Ladinian age (Merki 1961) and are the origin for the synonym 'Nodosuskalk' for the Plattenkalk Member. The boundary between the Trochitenkalk and the Plattenkalk members is rather arbitrary. Merki (1961) suggested a glauconite-bearing layer found in some outcrops as the boundary marker. The Trigonodusdolomit Member (regarded as a formation by some authors) consists of primary and secondary dolomite. The secondary dolomite at the base shows many similarities to the underlying Plattenkalk, such as the rhythmic stratification of shale and carbonate with siliceous nodules and some fossiliferous horizons. The dolomite is partly bituminous. Some oolites are found at the base and at the top of this unit. In the subsurface and in outcrops, vuggy dolomite (*Rauhwacke*) is abundant (Müller *et. al.* 1984). A typical feature of the Trigonodusdolomit Member is the presence of cubic cavities that give rise to the member's alternative name 'Zellendolomit'. The thickness of the Trigonodusdolomit Member varies between 10 and 40 m.

*Keuper Group (Late Triassic, Carnian to Rhaetian)*

The Keuper includes marine and terrestrial sediments deposited in an arid climate. It is subdivided into the Lettenkohle, Gipskeuper and Mergelkeuper formations (Fig. 13.29), with the Gipskeuper Formation making up some two-thirds or more of the overall thickness. The name 'Lettenkohle' is misleading as there are no coal measures worth mentioning at this level in the Swiss Jura. In fact, it consists of up to 5 m of dolomite and includes a thin layer of salt marsh to brackish lagoonal sediments, known as the Estherienschiefer. These laminated silty mudstones are rich in fossils, including fish, small crustaceans ('*Estheria*' sp., probably of Carnian age) and plants (Wurster 1968).

The overlying, up to 400 m thick, succession comprises three or four large-scale regressive shallowing-upward cycles. The first two cycles are rich in evaporites and constitute the Gipskeuper Formation. In the eastern Jura, where rock salt (halite) is absent and clay abundant, the sediments are thought to have formed under marginal marine to terrestrial sabkha conditions (Dronkert *et. al.* 1990). In the central and western Jura, the presence of rock salt at the base of the two cycles indicates a marine connection, at least at the beginning of the cycles (Figs 13.29 & 13.30). The centre of the Keuper evaporite basin is located in the western French Jura close to the Bresse Graben (Debrand-Passard *et al.* 1984; Sommaruga 1997). In the upper part of the 75 to 85 m thick Gipskeuper Formation in the eastern Jura, Dronkert *et al.* (1990) recognized at least 27 small-scale regressive cycles. In the lower part, the cycles are less clear and often incomplete.

The third Keuper formation, the Mergelkeuper Formation (Fig. 13.29), is heterogeneous. Evaporite minerals are almost absent and (dolomitic) marlstone prevails. A fluvial system, which spread from Scandinavia down to the western Alps, is represented by the basal Schilfsandstein Member, which consists of channelized greywacke-type sandstones, transported from the NE (Wurster 1964*a*), and overbank and lagoonal sediments (siltstones, and dolomitic marls). The name is derived from the abundant *Equisetites* remains, which are leaves of an extinct horsetail which were formerly mistaken for reeds. From the 'Neue Welt' site close to Basel, a rich macro- and microflora has been reported (Schmassmann 1953; Kräusel & Leschik 1956). The thickness of the formation is very variable, even at a small scale, and ranges from a few metres to 20 m.

Dolomitic marls become dominant in the overlying member, the Bunte Mergel. In the eastern Jura, the Mergelkeuper succession, up to 30 m thick, is interrupted by the Gansingen Dolomite (Fig. 13.29), a marine dolomite, with sporadic fossils, that records a Carnian transgression and probably correlates to the 'Dolomie moëlon' of the western Jura (Trümpy 1980). In places, conglomerates composed of clasts of reworked dolomite are found overlying the Gansingen Dolomite. Many remains of the early herbivorous dinosaur *Plateosaurus*, including a complete skeleton, have been found in the upper part of this member near the village of Frick (Galton 1986; Sander 1992).

In Switzerland, the Stubensandstein Member, a prominent succession of sandstones in SW Germany, is only found in the eastern Swiss Tabular Jura, where its thickness is reduced to 4 m or less. Together with the conglomerates and shales of the succeeding Knollenmergel Member, these sediments document a fluvial system, which was sourced from the Bohemian-Vindelician High in the east.

A thin (2 to 22 m thick) unit of claystone and sandstone with bonebeds containing remains of marine and terrestrial fossils, including teeth of early mammals (Büchi *et al.* 1965; Erni 1926; Tanner 1978; Kindlimann 1985) is known as the Rhät (Fig. 13.29). Rhaetian sediments are missing on the Aar Massif–Black Forest Rise (Fig. 13.30) due to the lack of sedimentation or later erosion (Erni 1926; Hofmann 1981; Etzold & Schweizer 2005; Pieńkowski *et al.* 2008).

## Tethyan realm: stratigraphy and basin development

### *Northern Calcareous Alps (Austria, Germany) (T.R.)*

The Northern Calcareous Alps, situated approximately between the Swiss–Austrian border in the west and Vienna in the east, form part of the Alpine foldbelt. They cover an area of *c.* 500 by 60 km in Austria and Bavaria and comprise a Triassic sedimentary succession including continental red-beds and marginal marine siliciclastics through mixed carbonate/clastic deposits and shallow-water carbonates to basin carbonates (Fig. 13.31). Middle and Upper Triassic platform carbonates are, because of their thickness and wide distribution, the dominant landscape-forming rocks of the Northern Calcareous Alps.

The position of the Northern Calcareous Alps in Triassic times, between epicontinental central and western Europe and the more easterly and southerly Tethyan areas, makes this a key area for understanding the relationship between the Tethys Ocean and the continent when Pangaea started to break apart.

#### *Induan and Olenekian: clastic, carbonate and evaporite ramp*

Analysis of sedimentary structures, lithofacies and palaeocurrent directions of the Early Triassic Lower Alpine Buntsandstein sandstones indicates that they were deposited in a braided river system, with the main source areas of the siliciclastics being to the north and also probably to the west. Rare occurrences of gypsum, increased carbonate content, bimodal current directions and trace fossils suggest a marginal marine influence in the uppermost Lower Alpine Buntsandstein of the central and eastern part of the Northern Calcareous Alps (Stingl 1987). Onlap by fluvial deposits of the Upper Alpine Buntsandstein transgression resulted in the establishment of fluvial-dominated estuaries, which were, in turn, superseded by the clastic and clastic/carbonate deposits of shallow-marine to tidal flat environments (Werfen Formation).

The shallow-marine Werfen facies followed the prograding Tethys from the east and south to the west and north (Fig. 13.31). Therefore, the diachronous Werfen transgression was not related to any particular third-order sea-level rise, but to rifting within (Neo-)Tethys (Hirsch 1992). In contrast to the eastern part of the Northern Calcareous Alps, where the Werfen facies accumulated throughout the Early Triassic, marine deposition in the western part began only during the Olenekian. Most of the Olenekian to early Anisian Reichenhall Formation (Fig. 13.31) consists of generally unfossiliferous carbonates, sometimes bituminous and with a sparse macrofauna. The occurrence of gypsiferous vuggy dolomites, and the sulphur isotopic composition of interbedded anhydrites, suggests a restricted marine depositional environment with episodic evaporitic conditions (Spötl & Burns 1991).

Stratigraphically significant fossils are lacking and no biostratigraphic data have been obtained from the Alpine Buntsandstein. Using conodonts and other microfossils, Mostler & Rossner (1984) dated beds in the Werfen Formation as Spathian (Late Olenekian). The top of the Reichenhall Formation has been placed by most authors at the Olenekian–Anisian boundary, although an early Anisian age cannot be excluded.

#### *Anisian: carbonate ramp deposits*

During Anisian times a wide shelf area with peritidal deposits was established. These comprise mainly the pure calcareous homoclinal ramp deposits of the Steinalm Formation and strongly bioturbated shelf deposits of the Virgloria Formation, the latter consisting of carbonates with a low clastic content. In late Anisian times, the clastic input gradually diminished and eventually disappeared, resulting in the predominance of the Steinalm Formation with respect to the Virgloria Formation (Fig. 13.31). Hardly any terrigenous clastic material reached the extensive ramp setting during the Illyrian. Compared to the Southern Alps, the succession is rather uniform, a distinction expressed in the different number of lithostratigraphic units in both areas (Fig. 13.31). The Steinalm Formation comprises inner to outer ramp deposits, including shallow intraramp basin sediments (Rüffer & Bechstädt 1998). Due to a virtual absence of early diagenesis, along with the predominance of micritic facies in all of the depositional areas, an unstable muddy substrate evolved. Encrusters prevailed in shallow-marine environments; organisms capable of building reefs were completely absent. In the Northern Calcareous Alps neither reef-building organisms nor high-energy shoals were present during Anisian times (development of the first reefs may have begun in the late *Avisianum* zone of the latest Illyrian). Tempestites were intercalated with typically mud-supported carbonates, especially during the final stage of the evolution of the homoclinal ramp.

Whereas biostratigraphic data are not available for the early Anisian, the late Anisian successions are fairly well dated by conodonts that occur within transgressive sequences (e.g. the Pelsonian transgression is characterized by the conodonts *Gondolella bifurcata* and *Nicoraella kockeli*). During this transgression, open-marine pelagic conditions extended as far as the Northern Calcareous Alps. The resulting deposits (Hallstatt Formation) which were, at most, only slightly influenced by both shallow-marine platforms and the terrigenous input, occur throughout the Triassic, mainly in the southern and easternmost parts of the depositional area of the Northern Calcareous Alps (Fig. 13.31).

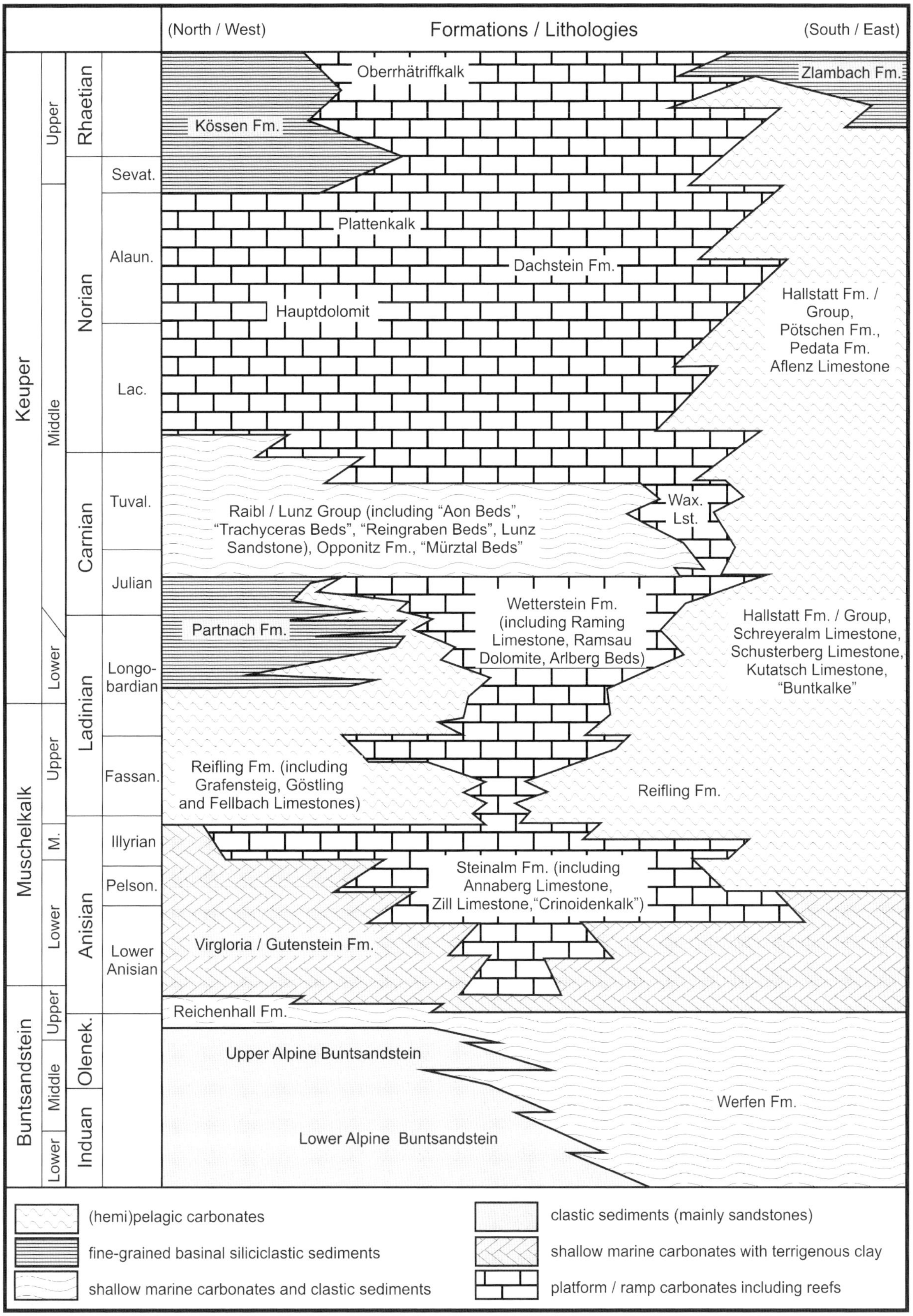


**Fig. 13.31.** Formations, depositional environments and lithological units in the Triassic of the Northern Calcareous Alps.

*Latest Anisian to Early Carnian: rimmed platforms and basin to platform transitions*

The Anisian homoclinal ramp was drowned (Reifling event; Schlager & Schöllnberger 1974) in late Illyrian times. In some areas, carbonate production recovered after a short initial lag phase (incipient drowning), and distally steepened ramps (lower Wetterstein Formation) evolved gradually, but quickly from the Anisian homoclinal ramp (Fig. 13.31). Thus, on the one hand, the gradual deepening of the outer ramp led to the formation of a deep ramp slope, while on the other, high-energy shoals and buildups separated the increasingly restricted lagoons from the more open-marine mid-ramp.

In the Northern Calcareous Alps, no indication of fragmentation of Anisian platforms by synsedimentary tectonics has been recognized. Late Anisian and Fassanian rates of subsidence had the same order of magnitude (20–30 mm/ka, according to almost all existing timescales). A distinct increase in subsidence during Late Fassanian to Mid-Longobardian times (some 50–300 mm/ka) resulted in the transformation from distally steepened ramps to rimmed platforms. Sedimentation in the Northern Calcareous Alps was controlled mainly by the instability of the Tethys realm, leading to increased rates of subsidence. Indeed, these were several times more rapid than during other Triassic stages. Extensive platform development, with aggradation and progradation, characterized this interval and resulted in increasingly large platforms and the accumulation of platform deposits over 1000 m thick (Wetterstein Formation). No basinal intercalations separated the platform succession, but in Late Ladinian times terrigenous clastics (Partnach Formation) appeared within the basins for the first time since the Olenekian (Fig. 13.31).

Conodonts occur widely, and biostratigraphic control is, therefore, good for this interval. A number of studies provide data on other microfossils and ammonoids (e.g. Krystyn 1978; Mandl 1984; Rüffer 1995). Conodont associations within the basinal Reifling Formation allow fairly precise dating of the transgressions during this interval. The most important transgression across the late Anisian to Early Carnian platforms occurred in the late Illyrian, when basinal sediments of the Reifling Formation replaced much of the rimmed platforms (Fig. 13.31).

*Carnian: mixed carbonate–clastic shelf deposits*

In Carnian times (*Aonoides* subzone), terrigenous clastics of the Raibl/Lunz Group abruptly covered carbonate platforms as well as carbonate- and mudstone-filled basins (Fig. 13.31). The Raibl Group consists of three repetitive carbonate-clastic sequences, clearly separated into carbonate- and clastic-dominated units each of which (often including single marker beds) can be correlated for hundreds of kilometres (Bechstädt & Schweizer 1991). The carbonate units mostly represent restricted marginal marine, tidal and evaporitic environments. The clastic units were mainly deposited on the inner and outer shelf areas.

*Late Carnian to Early Rhaetian: shallow-marine carbonates*

In the western Northern Calcareous Alps, the Raibl Lunz Group was capped by *c.* 2000 to 2500 m of shallow-marine deposits that form a continuous sedimentary record of mainly Norian age (Hauptdolomit Formation), and range in facies from oolitic and bioclastic mounds of a barrier bar complex to lagoonal and tidal-flat deposits (Fruth & Scherreiks 1982). Towards the east and south, the Hauptdolomit Formation is overlain and replaced by platform margin deposits of the Dachstein Formation (Fig. 13.31), for example in the Lofer area, where Fischer (1964) established the relationship between high-frequency cyclicity and fluctuations in eustatic sea level. Facies of the Dachstein Formation range from slope through central platform and back margin. In the southern part of the central and eastern Northern Calcareous Alps, basinal facies of the Hallstatt Formation developed adjacent to carbonate platforms (Fig. 13.31). No high-resolution biostratigraphic data are available from the lagoonal and tidal-flat deposits of the Hauptdolomit Formation. The overlying Kössen Formation (Wiedmann 1974; Krystyn 1988; Golebiowski 1989; Holstein 2004) is well dated and can be used to constrain the upper limit of sedimentation.

*Rhaetian: carbonate platforms and mixed clastic–carbonate intraplatform basins*

In contrast to the uniform Norian deposits, the Rhaetian is characterized by the development of various carbonate platforms and mixed carbonate–clastic basins. The platform carbonates, which had been established with the deposition of the Dachstein Formation sediments, persisted into the Rhaetian, while platform-margin carbonates evolved in the northern areas (Oberrhätriffkalk). These platform carbonates pass laterally into an intraplatform basin to the north (late Norian and Rhaetian Kössen Formation; Fig. 13.31). This basin contains mixed carbonate and clastic deposits, which have been used for biostratigraphy (Wiedmann 1974; Krystyn 1988; Golebiowski 1989; Kachroo 1989) and sequence stratigraphy (Fritsch & Hüssner 1996). Terrigenous clastic input originated from northern to northwestern areas and decreased towards the south.

## *Southern Alps (Italy, Switzerland) (R.Z.)*

The Southern Alps cover an area of 600 km (east to west) by 50–150 km (north to south) (Fig. 13.32). They are bounded by the Insubric or Periadriatic Lineament (to the north and west) and by a south-vergent thrust system against the Tertiary Po and Venetian basins to the south. To the east, the Southern Alps continue into the Dinarides. Based on stratigraphic/structural features the Southern Alps can be subdivided into three parts: (1) the western Southern Alps (Ticino, Lombardian Alps, Lago Maggiore to Giudicaria Lineament); (2) the central Southern Alps (Etsch/Adige Valley and Dolomites, Giudicaria Lineament to River Piave); and (3) the eastern Southern Alps (Carnian and Julian Alps, east of the River Piave).

Marked facies variations in time and space, as well as differential subsidence/uplift characterize the development of the Triassic basin in the area. As a result of these variations, the basin fill includes a large number of lithostratigraphic units (Fig. 13.33) of regional extent, albeit with inconsistent naming. While many units have been widely described in the literature, not all of them are formally defined. In the trilingual region of South Tyrol (central Southern Alps) Italian and German names have been used for type localities and lithostratigraphic units. Therefore, this overview will provide names in both languages, e.g. Livinallongo/Buchenstein Formation (Italian/German).

In Triassic times, the Southern Alps were situated on the passive continental margin of Gondwana bordering the western Tethys (Gaetani 2000). However, during the Mid- and early Late Triassic, in particular, the region was affected by transtensive–transpressive tectonics and volcanism. Post-Variscan deposition in the Southern Alps commenced in the Permian. At the Permian–Triassic boundary, marine depositional environments prevailed except in the westernmost parts of the Southern Alps. Although the main structural subdivision of the Southern Alpine basin occurred in the Early Jurassic, with the opening of the Ligurian Ocean (Thierry 2000), structural compartmentalization began in the early Mid-Triassic. Varying thickness trends and

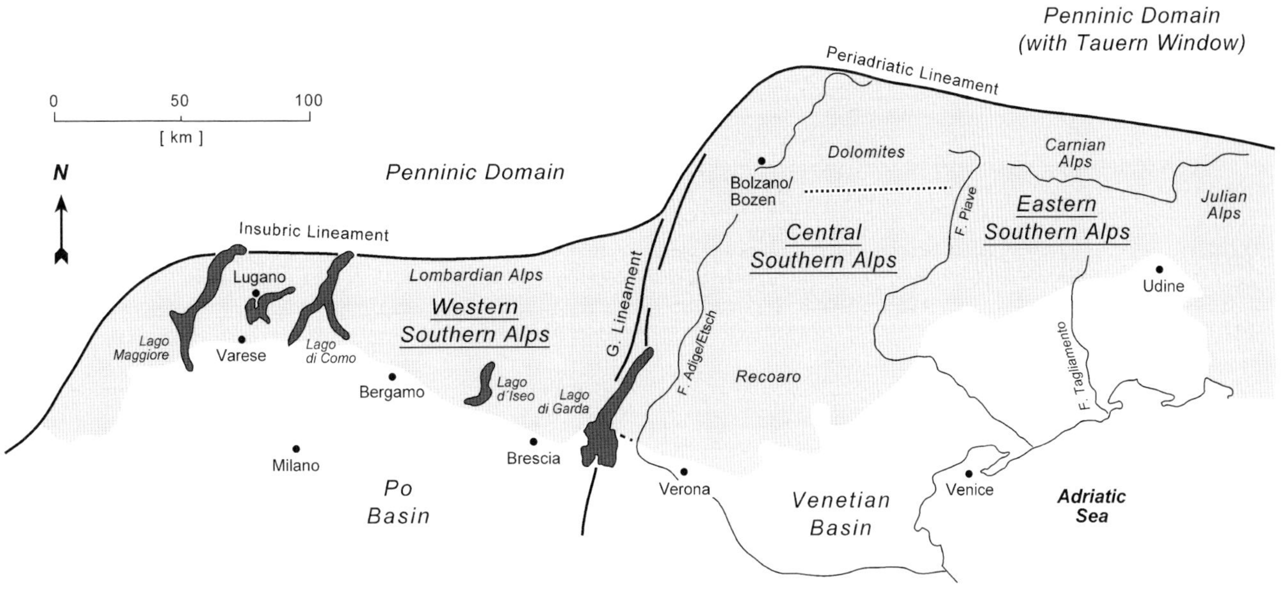


**Fig. 13.32.** Simplified map of the Southern Alps. G. Lineament, Giudicaria Lineament. Dotted line, basin transect of Figure 13.34.

depositional environments defined the initial Lombardian Basin (western Southern Alps), Trento Platform (central Southern Alps) and the Belluno Trough (SW part of the eastern Southern Alps).

Both the western and central Southern Alps have been studied in detail. Indeed, two Triassic stages – the Ladinian and the Carnian – have their type areas in the Southern Alps. From the nineteenth century, basic concepts in geology were developed in the region, for example the concept of 'reefs' (carbonate platforms) with clinoforms, interfingering with time-equivalent basins (Mojsisovics 1879). In more recent times, stratigraphic information from the central Southern Alps has been used for the Triassic segment in eustatic sea-level charts (Haq *et al.* 1988; Hardenbol *et al.* 1998). Standard models on the controls of carbonate deposition have been based on case studies of Middle Triassic carbonate platforms in the central Southern Alps (Goldhammer *et al.* 1993; Preto *et al.* 2004; Zühlke 2004). Additionally, a number of basin fill studies have focused on the Triassic (Gaetani *et al.* 1998; Gianolla *et al.* 1998; Neri & Stefani 1998; Rüffer & Zühlke 1995; Zühlke 2000; Emmerich *et al.* 2005*a*) and these form the main basis for this overview.

*Induan, Olenekian (Scythian)*

Early Triassic successions show a stepwise transgression of the western Tethys from east to west. In the eastern and central Southern Alps, the Werfen Formation conformably overlies subtidal to peritidal deposits of the late Permian Bellerophon Formation. In the western Southern Alps, the Servino Formation onlaps an erosional unconformity at the top of the Late Permian alluvial Verrucano Formation (Fig. 13.33). The time gap involved in this unconformity increases to the west. In the central and eastern Southern Alps, the early Triassic basin fill attains thicknesses of up to 550–650 m and is dominated by mixed

**Fig. 13.33.** (pp. 792–793) Litho-, biochrono- and sequence stratigraphic framework of the Southern Alps. The figure includes lithostratigraphic units and biostratigraphic boundaries at the zone and subzone level which have not been generally defined yet. *Column A*: third-order sequences in the Southern Alps. *Columns B–D*: basin fill and formations in the western, central and eastern Southern Alps (schematic). *Columns E1–3*: biostratigraphic framework of the Triassic in the Tethyan realm. Column E1: subzones and zones after Mietto & Manfrin (1995), Hardenbol *et al.* (1998) and Mietto *et al.* (2003). Column E2: subzones and zones after Broglio Loriga *et al.* (1990; bivalve and ammonoid biostratigraphy, Induan to Olenekian), Brack & Rieber (1993), Brack *et al.* (1996) and Muttoni *et al.* (2004; ammonoid biostratigraphy, Anisian to Carnian). Column E3: Triassic (sub)stages. *Columns F1–2*: chronostratigraphic framework of the Triassic. Column F1: absolute ages (in Ma BP) according to Gradstein *et al.* (1995) and Hardenbol *et al.* (1998) (in full scale). Column F2: absolute ages (in Ma BP) according to Gradstein *et al.* (2004) (not to scale). There are currently four clusters of radiometric ages which constrain the Triassic time scale (Permian–Triassic boundary, base of *Nevadites/Secedensis* Zone, top of *Reticulatus/Suessi* Zone, Triassic/Jurassic boundary). A further cluster covers the *Secedensis* to *Archelaus* Zone (e.g. Mundil *et al.* 1996, 2003). However, most Triassic (sub)stage boundaries are interpolated using scaling from cyclostratigraphy, graphical correlation and other estimates (see Gradstein *et al.* 2004). *Legend*: Column A: unbroken lines, third-order sequence boundaries with absolute ages according to the timescale of Gradstein *et al.* (1995), based on Rüffer & Zühlke (1995) and Gianolla *et al.* (1998). Column B: vertical lines, depositional and/or erosional gaps; Low. Serv. Fm., Lower Servino Formation; Bell. Fm., Bellano Formation; D.M. Fm., Dosso dei Morti Formation; C. Fm., Camorelli Formation; C.R., 'Calcare Rosso'; C.M.B., 'Calcare Metallifero Bergamasco'. Column C: V.Leogra /P.d.Peres Hz., Val Leogra and Piz da Peres Horizons; Schlernp. Fm., Schlernplateau Formation. Column D: P.d.Peres Hz., Piz da Peres Horizon; Ug./Tu. Fm., Ugovizza Formation (base) and Tuglia Formation (top); R. Gel. Fm., Rio Gelovitz Formation; Ug./Po. Fm., Ugovizza Formation (base) and Pontebba Formation (top); R.F.V., Rio Freddo Volcanics. Columns E1–E3: *Spiniger & Plurif. & Prah.*, *Spiniger & Pluriformis & Prahlada*; *Longobard.*, *Longobardicum*; *D.* cf. *canad.*, *Daxatina* cf. *canadensis*; *Neoprotrach.*, *Neoprotrachyceras*; *Paracera.*, *Paraceratites*; *Eoprotrachy.*, *Eoprotrachyceras*, *Quinquep.*, *Quinquepunctatus*; *C. wangi-griesb.*, *Claraia wangi-griesbachi*; *C. clarai*, *Claraia clarai*; *C. aurita*, *Claraia aurita*; *E. multiformis*, *Eumorphotis multiformis*; *E. hinnitidea*, *Eumorphotis hinnitidea*; *T. cas.*, *Tirolites cassianus*; *E. kittli*, *Eumorphotis kittli*; *E. tell.*, *Eumorphotis telleri*; *D. dal.*, *Dinarites dalmatinus*; *C. cost.*, *Costatoria costata*. Columns F1–F2: absolute ages indicated refer to stage and substage boundaries in the timescales of Gradstein *et al.* (1995, 2004).

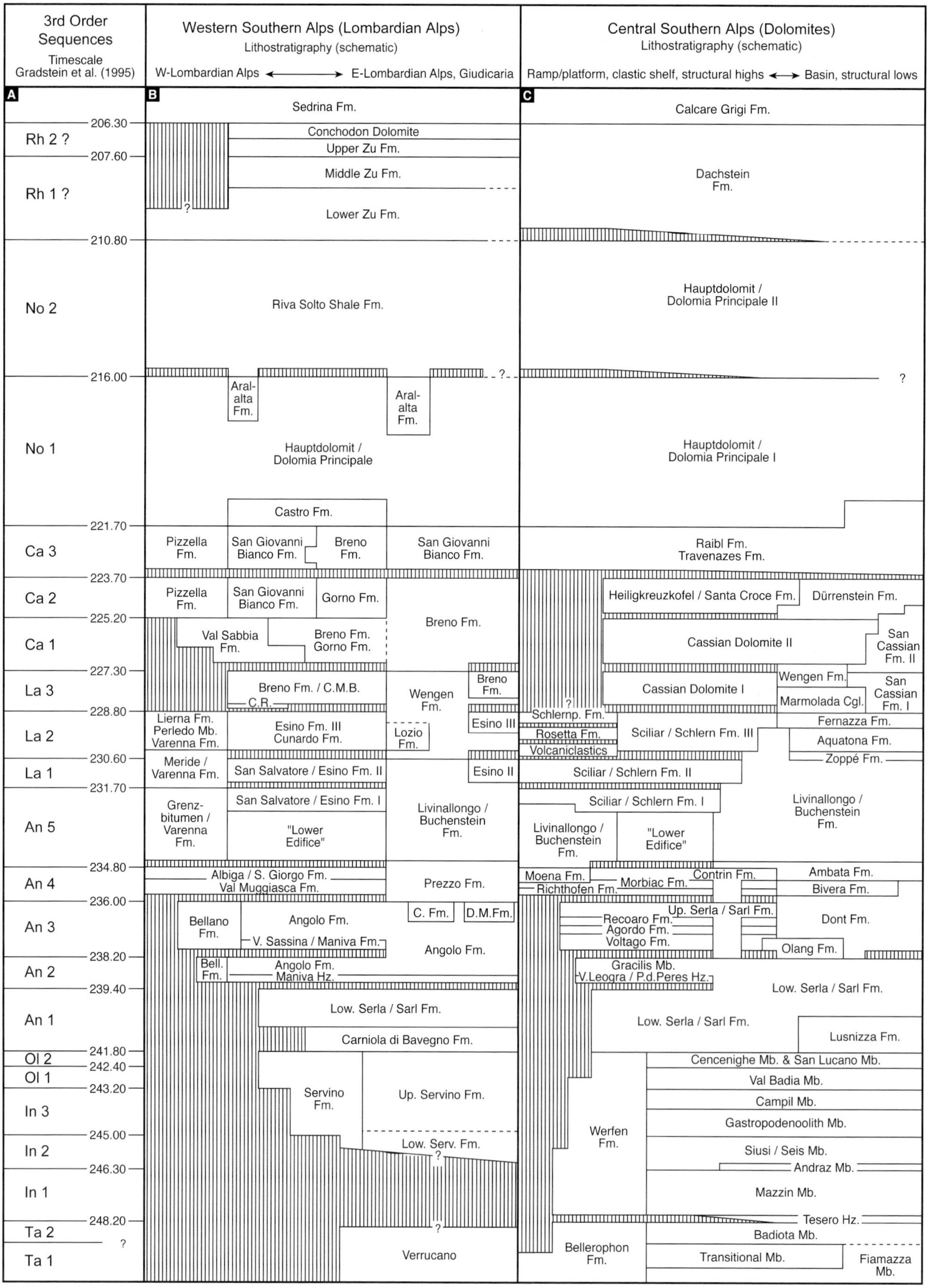
3rd Order Sequences
Timescale Gradstein et al. (1995)
Western Southern Alps (Lombardian Alps)
Lithostratigraphy (schematic)
W-Lombardian Alps ⟵⟶ E-Lombardian Alps, Giudicaria
Central Southern Alps (Dolomites)
Lithostratigraphy (schematic)
Ramp/platform, clastic shelf, structural highs ⟵⟶ Basin, structural lows
A
B
C
206.30
207.60
210.80
216.00
221.70
223.70
225.20
227.30
228.80
230.60
231.70
234.80
236.00
238.20
239.40
241.80
242.40
243.20
245.00
246.30
248.20
Rh 2 ?
Rh 1 ?
No 2
No 1
Ca 3
Ca 2
Ca 1
La 3
La 2
La 1
An 5
An 4
An 3
An 2
An 1
Ol 2
Ol 1
In 3
In 2
In 1
Ta 2
Ta 1
?
Sedrina Fm.
Conchodon Dolomite
Upper Zu Fm.
Middle Zu Fm.
Lower Zu Fm.
Riva Solto Shale Fm.
Aral-alta Fm.
Aral-alta Fm.
Hauptdolomit / Dolomia Principale
Castro Fm.
Pizzella Fm.
San Giovanni Bianco Fm.
Breno Fm.
San Giovanni Bianco Fm.
Pizzella Fm.
San Giovanni Bianco Fm.
Gorno Fm.
Breno Fm.
Val Sabbia Fm.
Breno Fm. Gorno Fm.
Breno Fm. / C.M.B.
C.R.
Wengen Fm.
Breno Fm.
Lierna Fm. Perledo Mb. Varenna Fm.
Esino Fm. III Cunardo Fm.
Lozio Fm.
Esino III
Meride / Varenna Fm.
San Salvatore / Esino Fm. II
Esino II
Grenz-bitumen / Varenna Fm.
San Salvatore / Esino Fm. I
"Lower Edifice"
Livinallongo / Buchenstein Fm.
Albiga / S. Giorgo Fm.
Val Muggiasca Fm.
Prezzo Fm.
Bellano Fm.
Angolo Fm.
C. Fm.
D.M.Fm.
V. Sassina / Maniva Fm.
Angolo Fm.
Bell. Fm.
Angolo Fm.
Maniva Hz.
Low. Serla / Sarl Fm.
Carniola di Bavegno Fm.
Servino Fm.
Up. Servino Fm.
Low. Serv. Fm.
Verrucano
Calcare Grigi Fm.
Dachstein Fm.
Hauptdolomit / Dolomia Principale II
Hauptdolomit / Dolomia Principale I
Raibl Fm. Travenazes Fm.
Heiligkreuzkofel / Santa Croce Fm.
Dürrenstein Fm.
Cassian Dolomite II
San Cassian Fm. II
Cassian Dolomite I
Wengen Fm.
Marmolada Cgl.
San Cassian Fm. I
Schlernp. Fm.
Rosetta Fm.
Volcaniclastics
Sciliar / Schlern Fm. III
Fernazza Fm.
Aquatona Fm.
Zoppé Fm.
Sciliar / Schlern Fm. II
Sciliar / Schlern Fm. I
Livinallongo / Buchenstein Fm.
"Lower Edifice"
Livinallongo / Buchenstein Fm.
Moena Fm.
Morbiac Fm.
Contrin Fm.
Ambata Fm.
Richthofen Fm.
Bivera Fm.
Up. Serla / Sarl Fm.
Recoaro Fm.
Agordo Fm.
Voltago Fm.
Dont Fm.
Olang Fm.
Gracilis Mb.
V.Leogra / P.d.Peres Hz.
Low. Serla / Sarl Fm.
Low. Serla / Sarl Fm.
Lusnizza Fm.
Cencenighe Mb. & San Lucano Mb.
Val Badia Mb.
Campil Mb.
Gastropodenoolith Mb.
Werfen Fm.
Siusi / Seis Mb.
Andraz Mb.
Mazzin Mb.
Tesero Hz.
Badiota Mb.
Bellerophon Fm.
Transitional Mb.
Fiamazza Mb.

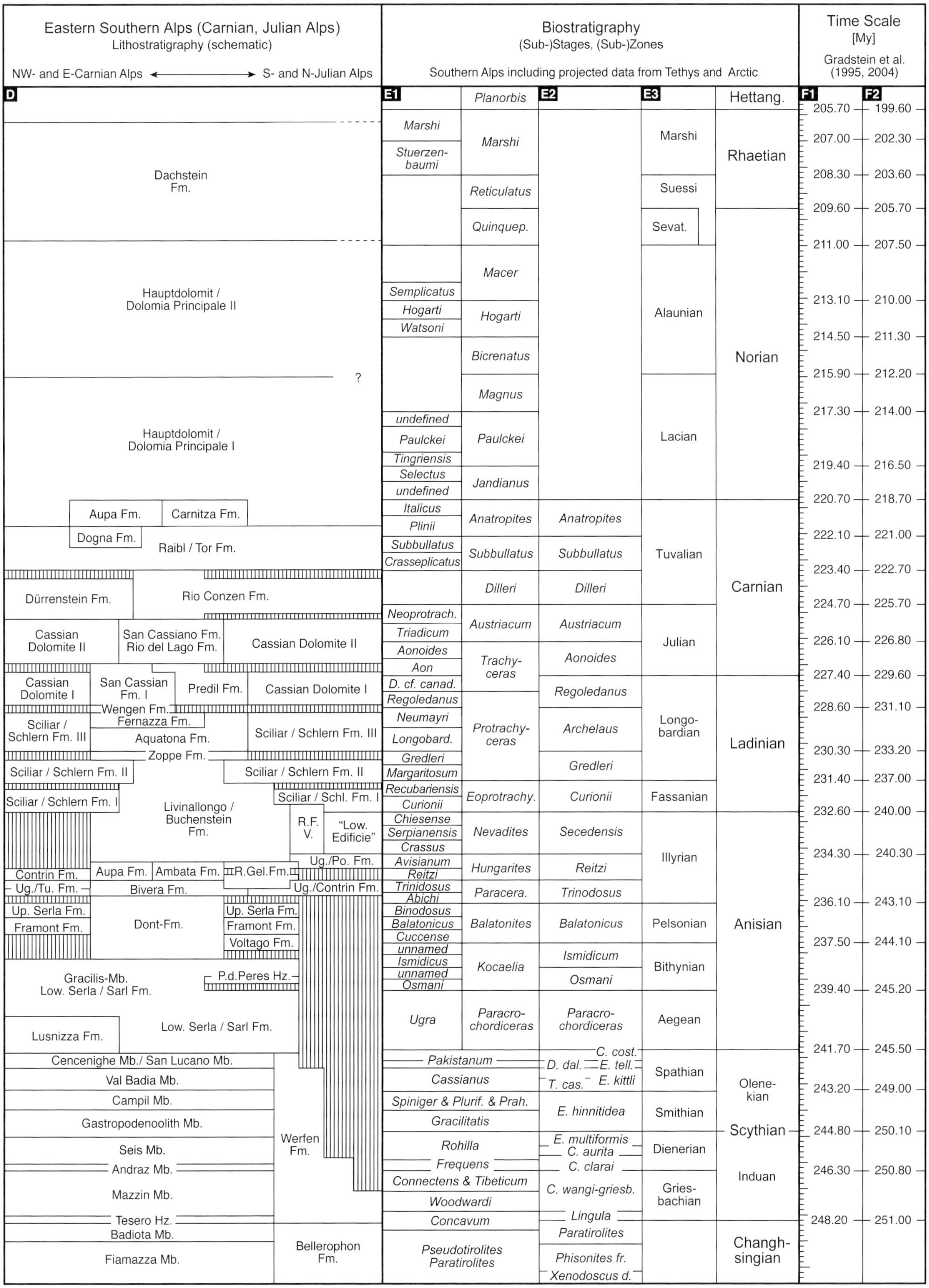
Eastern Southern Alps (Carnian, Julian Alps)
Lithostratigraphy (schematic)
NW- and E-Carnian Alps ←→ S- and N-Julian Alps
Biostratigraphy
(Sub-)Stages, (Sub-)Zones
Southern Alps including projected data from Tethys and Arctic
Time Scale
[My]
Gradstein et al.
(1995, 2004)
D
E1
E2
E3
F1
F2
Dachstein Fm.
Hauptdolomit / Dolomia Principale II
?
Hauptdolomit / Dolomia Principale I
Aupa Fm.
Carnitza Fm.
Dogna Fm.
Raibl / Tor Fm.
Dürrenstein Fm.
Rio Conzen Fm.
Cassian Dolomite II
San Cassiano Fm. Rio del Lago Fm.
Cassian Dolomite II
Cassian Dolomite I
San Cassian Fm. I
Predil Fm.
Cassian Dolomite I
Wengen Fm.
Fernazza Fm.
Sciliar / Schlern Fm. III
Aquatona Fm.
Sciliar / Schlern Fm. III
Zoppe Fm.
Sciliar / Schlern Fm. II
Sciliar / Schlern Fm. II
Sciliar / Schlern Fm. I
Livinallongo / Buchenstein Fm.
Sciliar / Schl. Fm. I
R.F. V.
"Low. Edificie"
Ug./Po. Fm.
Contrin Fm.
Aupa Fm.
Ambata Fm.
R.Gel.Fm.
Ug./Tu. Fm.
Bivera Fm.
Ug./Contrin Fm.
Up. Serla Fm.
Dont-Fm.
Up. Serla Fm.
Framont Fm.
Framont Fm.
Voltago Fm.
Gracilis-Mb. Low. Serla / Sarl Fm.
P.d.Peres Hz.
Lusnizza Fm.
Low. Serla / Sarl Fm.
Cencenighe Mb./ San Lucano Mb.
Val Badia Mb.
Campil Mb.
Gastropodenoolith Mb.
Seis Mb.
Andraz Mb.
Mazzin Mb.
Tesero Hz.
Badiota Mb.
Fiamazza Mb.
Werfen Fm.
Bellerophon Fm.
Planorbis
Marshi
Marshi
Stuerzenbaumi
Reticulatus
Quinquep.
Macer
Semplicatus
Hogarti
Hogarti
Watsoni
Bicrenatus
Magnus
undefined
Paulckei
Paulckei
Tingriensis
Selectus
Jandianus
undefined
Italicus
Anatropites
Anatropites
Plinii
Subbullatus
Subbullatus
Subbullatus
Crasseplicatus
Dilleri
Dilleri
Neoprotrach.
Austriacum
Austriacum
Triadicum
Aonoides
Aonoides
Aon
Trachyceras
D. cf. canad.
Regoledanus
Regoledanus
Neumayri
Protrachyceras
Archelaus
Longobard.
Gredleri
Gredleri
Margaritosum
Recubariensis
Eoprotrachy.
Curionii
Curionii
Chiesense
Serpianensis
Nevadites
Secedensis
Crassus
Avisianum
Hungarites
Reitzi
Reitzi
Trinidosus
Paracera.
Trinodosus
Abichi
Binodosus
Balatonicus
Balatonites
Balatonicus
Cuccense
unnamed
Ismidicus
Kocaelia
Ismidicum
unnamed
Osmani
Osmani
Ugra
Paracrochordiceras
Paracrochordiceras
Pakistanum
C. cost.
D. dal.
E. tell.
Cassianus
T. cas.
E. kittli
Spiniger & Plurif. & Prah.
E. hinnitidea
Gracilitatis
Rohilla
E. multiformis
C. aurita
Frequens
C. clarai
Connectens & Tibeticum
C. wangi-griesb.
Woodwardi
Concavum
Lingula
Paratirolites
Pseudotirolites Paratirolites
Phisonites fr.
Xenodoscus d.
Hettang.
Marshi
Rhaetian
Suessi
Sevat.
Alaunian
Norian
Lacian
Tuvalian
Carnian
Julian
Longobardian
Ladinian
Fassanian
Illyrian
Pelsonian
Anisian
Bithynian
Aegean
Spathian
Olenekian
Smithian
Scythian
Dienerian
Induan
Griesbachian
Changhsingian
205.70 199.60
207.00 202.30
208.30 203.60
209.60 205.70
211.00 207.50
213.10 210.00
214.50 211.30
215.90 212.20
217.30 214.00
219.40 216.50
220.70 218.70
222.10 221.00
223.40 222.70
224.70 225.70
226.10 226.80
227.40 229.60
228.60 231.10
230.30 233.20
231.40 237.00
232.60 240.00
234.30 240.30
236.10 243.10
237.50 244.10
239.40 245.20
241.70 245.50
243.20 249.00
244.80 250.10
246.30 250.80
248.20 251.00

carbonate–clastic ramps. In the western Southern Alps, the thickness increases from west (30 m) to east (>300 m). Basin fill is dominated by clastic ramps interbedded with some carbonates.

A complete Early Triassic succession developed only in the eastern and central Southern Alps. A maximum of nine horizons/members with thicknesses of 10–150 m each occurs in the Werfen Formation (Broglio Loriga *et al.* 1983, 1990): the Tesero Horizon (reworked oolite shoals), and the Mazzin (middle and lower ramp), Andraz (peritidal lagoon with evaporites), Seis (lower to middle ramp, lagoonal deposition at the top), Gastropodenoolith (middle to upper ramp, lagoonal deposition at the top), Campil (upper shoreface to offshore transition), Val Badia (middle to upper ramp), Cencenighe (middle ramp to lagoon with reworked oolite shoals) and San Lucano members (low-energy ramp and lagoon) (Fig. 13.33). Members within the Werfen Formation and their lithostratigraphic equivalents in the Servino Formation have diachronous ages across the Southern Alps.

As a result of subsequent early Anisian uplift, the upper members of the Werfen Formation were either not deposited or were not preserved within the central Southern Alps. On regional structural highs, the late Permian Bellerophon Formation is bounded by an angular/erosional unconformity and directly overlain by late Anisian (early–mid-Illyrian) fluvial to carbonate ramp deposits (Richthofen to Contrin formations; Fig. 13.33). In the western Southern Alps no deposits equivalent to the Tesero Horizon and Andraz Member of the Werfen Formation developed. At the western end of the Southern Alps, the Late Permian to mid-Anisian interval is represented by a depositional and erosional gap (Fig. 13.33).

Accommodation analysis for the Early Triassic indicates that low-amplitude third-order eustatic sea-level changes were superimposed on generally steady total subsidence (eastern Lombardy, western Dolomites). Depocentres in the eastern Dolomites show slightly accelerated subsidence from the late Induan to the late Olenekian (Zühlke 2000) with maximum rates of 260 mm/ka. Southern high areas, buried below the present-day Po Plain and regional structural highs, for example NW of Lake Como (western Southern Alps) and Recoaro (central Southern Alps), constituted the principal source areas for siliciclastic input to the Early Triassic shelf. Uplift of these source areas, and increased clastic input into adjacent basins (e.g. Campil Member, central Southern Alps) was dominant in Olenekian (late Smithian) times. Current sequence stratigraphic models for the Early Triassic basin fill are restricted by the limited biostratigraphic resolution (based on bivalves and ammonoids), uncertainties in the absolute duration of Early Triassic ranges and the lack of large-scale depositional geometries (low angle carbonate–clastic ramps).

*Early Anisian*

Basin development of the Southern Alps in Anisian times shows marked facies differentiation in time and space across the region. The present overview can, therefore, only present a simplified outline of its evolution. The thickness of the early Anisian basin fill ranges from 0 m (west) to 400 m (east) in the western Southern Alps, and from 0–220 m (west) to 600 m (east) in the central Southern Alps (Fig. 13.34).

In the eastern Southern Alps and parts of the central Southern Alps, carbonate-evaporite ramps of the Lower Serla/Sarl and Lusnizza formations conformably overlie the Early Triassic Werfen Formation. Further to the west, the Lower Serla/Sarl Formation was erosionally truncated or did not develop at all (Fig. 13.33). The western and southern Dolomites (central Southern Alps) were the site of several large structural highs with a long-term depositional/erosional gap, which lasted until the early Pelsonian or the early Illyrian (Fig. 13.35). In the western Southern Alps, carbonate–evaporite ramps of the Carniola di Bavegno and Lower Serla/Sarl formations conformably overlie the Servino Formation and are succeeded by alluvial to shoreface clastics (Maniva Horizon) and subtidal to lagoonal deposits (lower/middle Angolo Formation; Fig. 13.33).

In the eastern and central Southern Alps, stacked carbonate ramps of the Lower Serla/Sarl and Olang formations persisted until the Late Bithynian (*Ismidicum* Zone) or the earliest Pelsonian, respectively. An intermittent decrease in accommodation in late Aegean (?) to early Bithynian times resulted in short-lived subaerial exposure and alluvial to nearshore deposition (Piz da Peres and Val Leogra horizons) which was restricted to regional structural highs. In the westernmost Southern Alps, fan delta systems of the Bellano Formation, which were fed by uplifted basement source areas, began to prograde towards the east.

Early Anisian depocentres were located in the Carnian Alps, the eastern Dolomites and the western Lombardian Alps. Maximum total subsidence rates in the eastern Dolomites were up to 350 mm/ka, and resulted in initial and complete drowning of late Bithynian ramps. Uplift rates in the western and southern Dolomites ranged between −10 mm/ka and −100 mm/ka. The very strong differential subsidence/uplift in Bithynian to Pelsonian times (see below) is best explained by strike-slip tectonics which resulted in the small-scale regional arrangement of transtensive/transpressive stress fields, triggering the development of structural lows, with associated drowning of carbonate ramps, and structural highs. This resulted in long-term erosional/depositional gaps.

*Late Anisian*

Around the Bithynian–Pelsonian boundary, the basin architecture in the central Southern Alps changed completely. Partitioning of the basin into structural highs/lows became distinct and depocentres moved 30–40 km to the west. A basal erosional/angular unconformity present on structural highs is overlain by alluvial (Voltago Formation), shoreface (Agordo Formation) and carbonate subtidal (Recoaro Formation) deposits. In the late Pelsonian (*Binodosus* Subzone), homoclinal, and distally steepened, carbonate ramps of the Upper Serla/Sarl Formation (30–160 m thick) developed. Coeval structural lows feature dysaerobic to oxic basinal deposition with interbedded turbidites (Dont Formation) shed from adjacent structural highs. The thickness of the Pelsonian basin fill ranges from 0 to 280 m, depending on the structural setting. Basins remained underfilled in the Pelsonian.

Basin development in the central and eastern Southern Alps is very similar. In the westernmost Southern Alps, deposition of the delta system of the Bellano Formation and its distal equivalent, the Angolo Formation, continued up until the late Pelsonian–Illyrian boundary. The Angolo Formation shows a final regressive trend ('peritidal limestones'). The total thickness is up to 400 m (Bithynian–Pelsonian). In eastern Lombardy, local carbonate buildups of the Dosso dei Morti and Camorelli formations developed in the Late Pelsonian (*Balatonicus* to *Bindosus* Subzones). In the Illyrian, pre-existing depocentres were largely abandoned. All structural highs in the western and central Dolomites (Varese area, western Dolomites) were flooded. Basinal deposition in structural lows largely continued from the Pelsonian to the Illyrian. In the central Southern Alps, late Pelsonian carbonate ramps of the Upper Serla/Sarl Formation are bounded by an erosional unconformity or a disconformity. In the early Illyrian, alluvial to shoreface (Richthofen Formation) and

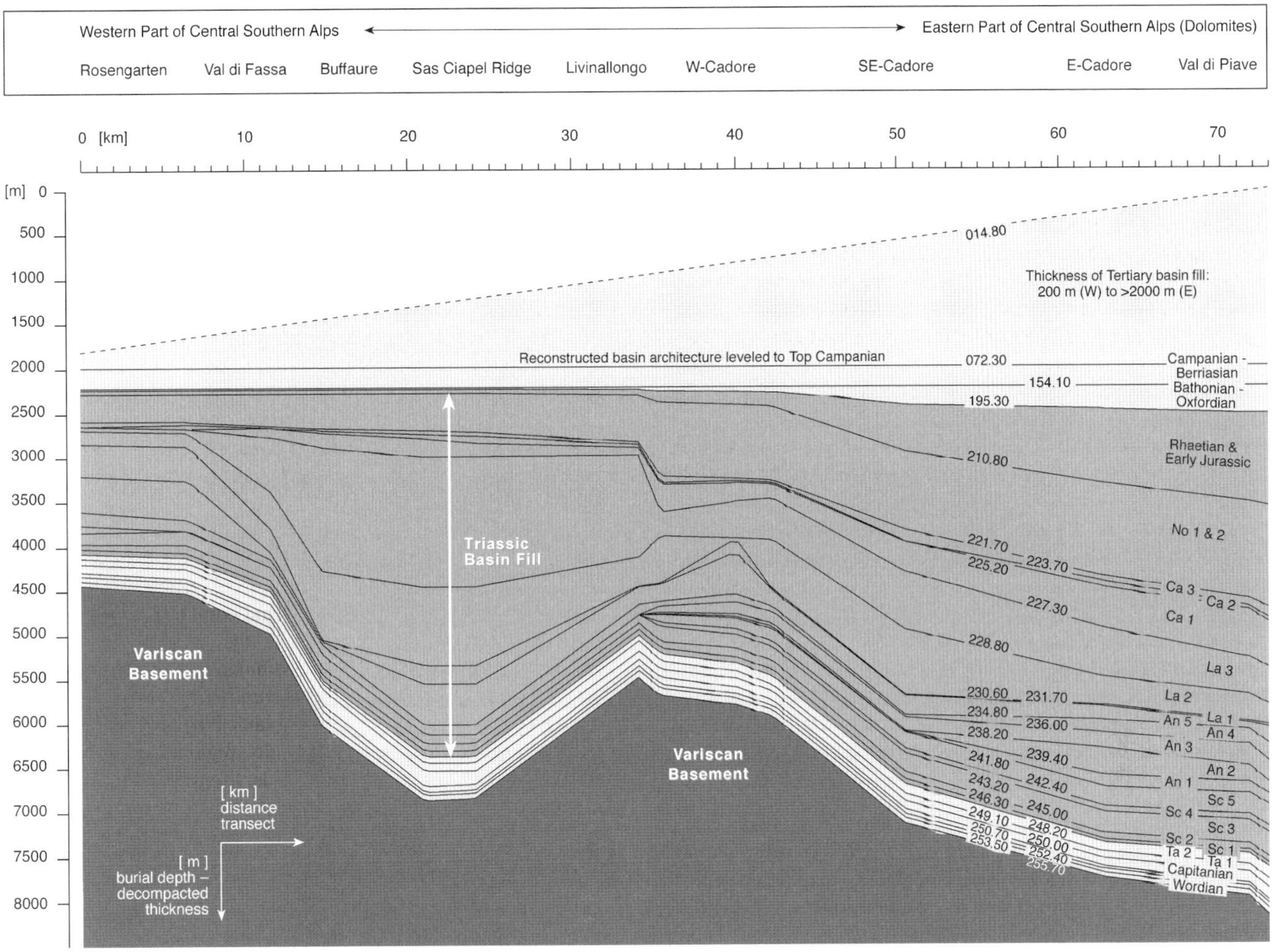


**Fig. 13.34.** Basin geometry and fill of the central Southern Alps along a west–east trending transect levelled to Top Campanian. See Figure 13.32 for the line of transect. Reconstructed basin architecture is shown prior to major Alpine deformation, which was directed SSE–NNW. Data for the Permian, Jurassic and Cretaceous basin fill are partly projected from the other parts of the central Southern Alps, as they have not been preserved along the line of transect. Thickness of the Tertiary basin fill is derived from palaeotemperature indicators. Thickness values range between a minimum of 200 m in the western part (Emmerich *et al.* 2005*a*) of the central Southern Alps and more than 2000 m in the eastern part of the central Southern Alps. Subdivision of the basin fill represents time lines, not lithostratigraphic boundaries. Ages refer to sequence boundaries, abbreviations to sequences (see Fig. 13.33, column A). Legend: dark grey, Variscan basement; middle grey, Triassic basin fill; light grey, Permian, Jurassic, Cretaceous and Tertiary basin fill.

carbonate subtidal (Morbiac Formation) deposition prevailed. In coeval basins, low sedimentation rates and oxic conditions existed (Bivera Formation). The mid-Illyrian (*Reitzi*/Hungarites Zone, *Reitzi* Subzone) shows facies transitions between distally steepened carbonate ramps (Contrin Formation) and narrow marine inlets (Moena Formation) or regional basins (Ambata Formation). In the western Southern Alps, the stratigraphic succession differs between the western and eastern parts of the basin. In the western part, incised valley fills and clastic wedges of the Val Muggiasca Formation are overlain by carbonate ramps of the San Giorgio and Albiga formations. In the eastern part, widespread deposition of the Prezzo Formation persisted during the early to late Illyrian. In the eastern Southern Alps, clastics (Ugovizza, Rio Gelovitz formations) were shed from northern structural highs into adjacent basins (Bivera and Ambata formations).

Differential subsidence decreased during the late Anisian. In the central Dolomites, total uplift/subsidence rates of −10 mm/ka to +140 mm/ka prevailed on former structural highs and rates of 250 mm/ka to >350 mm/ka in depocentres or basins. The key feature of the Pelsonian to Illyrian interval is the development of strongly compartmentalized sub-basins in the eastern, central and westernmost Southern Alps.

A major basin-wide increase in accommodation affected much of the Southern Alps in the mid- to late Illyrian (upper *Reitzi*/*Hungarites* Zone, *Avisianum* Subzone). Subsidence rates for different carbonate ramps vary between 300 and 850 mm/ka (Zühlke 2000; Emmerich *et al.* 2005*a*). Carbonate ramps (Contrin, San Giorgio, Albiga formations) located across the Southern Alps experienced incipient to complete drowning and were covered by basinal anoxic deposits of the lower Livinallongo/Buchenstein Formation (central, eastern Southern Alps, eastern Lombardy) or the 'Grenzbitumenzone' and Varenna Formation (western Lombardy, Ticino). Only local structural highs remained within the photic zone and formed the sites for the initial development of late Illyrian to Ladinian carbonate platforms that the central Southern Alps, in particular, are famous for. Examples of continuous ramp/platform growth between the late Anisian and the Ladinian include the Rosengarten/Catinaccio (Fig. 13.35) and Latemar platforms in the western Dolomites.

**Fig. 13.35.** Early to Late Triassic basin fill of the central Southern Alps (cf. Figs 13.33 & 13.34, Catinaccio/Rosengarten and Val di Fassa). View from the Latemar Range towards the NE to the Catinaccio/Rosengarten and Sella Ranges. The stratigraphic succession is not continuous because the two ranges are separated by the Val di Fassa. Legend: (1–9) Rosengarten/Catinaccio Range, western Dolomites (foreground): (1) Werfen Fm, Seis Member (Mb), Induan/Dienerian, sequence In 2, carbonate-clastic ramp; (2) Werfen Fm, Gastropodenoolith Mb, Olenekian/Smithian, sequence In 3, carbonate-clastic ramp; (3) Werfen Fm, Campil Mb, Olenekian/Smithian, sequence In 3, clastic ramp; (4) Richthofen Fm, Anisian/early Illyrian, sequence An 4, alluvial channel/plain to marginal marine clastic ramp. The basal erosional/angular unconformity includes a hiatus of *c.* 6–7 Ma depending on the timescale applied. In the central Dolomites, the hiatus reaches up to 11–13 Ma (Late Permian to early Illyrian); (5) Morbiac Fm, Anisian/early Illyrian, sequence An 4, subtidal lower carbonate ramp and basin with palaeo-water depths of max. 200 m; (6) Contrin Fm, Anisian/middle Illyrian, sequence An 4, shallow subtidal to peritidal carbonate ramp with incipient to complete drowning at the top; (7) Livinallongo/Buchenstein Fm, Anisian to Ladinian/late Illyrian to middle Longobardian, sequence An 5–La 2, basin margin with palaeo-water depths of max. 800–1000 m; (8) Sciliar/Schlern Fm, Ladinian/early Longobardian (*Gredleri* Zone), sequence La 1, prograding slope of Rosengarten/Catinaccio carbonate platform, subhorizontal facies boudary between basin margin and carbonate platform slope. The middle Illyrian to Fassanian platform interior and slope are located to the left of the image; (9) Sciliar/Schlern Fm, Ladinian/early Longobardian (*Archelaus* Zone), sequence La 2, prograding slope of Catinaccio/Rosengarten carbonate platform, clinoforms with angles of 35–40°. (10–12) Sella Range, central Dolomites (background): (10) Cassian Dolomite II (including platform interior, equivalent to Dürrenstein Fm), Carnian/Julian to early Tuvalian, sequence Ca 1–2, prograding carbonate platform slope and interior; (11) Raibl/Travenazes Fm, Carnian/mid-late Tuvalian, sequence Ca 3, fluvial deposition to marginal marine clastic–evaporite–carbonate ramp; (12) Hauptdolomit/Dolomia Principale, Carnian to Norian/latest Tuvalian to Alaunian, sequence No 1–2, shallow subtidal to peritidal lagoon.

Pre-existing basins (Moena, Ambata, Prezzo formations) persisted into Ladinian times, with continued accumulation of the Livinallongo/Buchenstein Formation. In general, the palaeogeography and the underlying structural setting of the early to mid-Illyrian controlled the subsequent platform–basin distribution until late Ladinian times.

*Latest Anisian to late Ladinian*

The Anisian–Ladinian boundary (Fig. 13.33) has been defined at the base of the *Curionii* Zone (Brack & Rieber 1994; Muttoni *et al.* 2004, Brack *et al.* 2005). Carbonate platforms which developed within the mid- to late Illyrian (*Avisianum* Subzone *sensu* Mietto & Manfrin 1995, upper *Reitzi* Zone *sensu* Brack *et al.* 1996) to mid- to late Longobardian (*Neumayri* Subzone *sensu* Mietto & Manfrin 1995; upper *Archelaus* Zone *sensu* Brack *et al.* 1996) time interval are attributed to the Sciliar/Schlern Formation (eastern, central Southern Alps), and the Esino and San Salvatore formations (western Southern Alps). They do not show a uniform development over the Southern Alps, or even within the three Southern Alps sub-basins. In the central Southern Alps, several platform tops contain internal subaerial exposure surfaces or specific slope geometries, which have been used to define three Sciliar/Schlern platform stages (I–III) and third-order sequences (An 5–La 2; see Fig. 13.33). However, other platforms do not show the same features and cannot be subdivided into the same platform stages or sequences. In general, biostratigraphic ages for carbonate platforms are loosely constrained because they usually depend on geometric projections of ammonoid levels in the basin to platform tops. The few exceptions include platforms in the western Dolomites, where (1) ammonoid levels and biostratigraphic ages are physically traceable from the basin onto the platform slope with sufficient spatial resolution (e.g. Catinaccio/Rosengarten; Maurer 2000); (2) ammonoid levels occur within a non-dolomitized lagoonal succession (e.g. Latemar; Zühlke 2004); or, (3) radio-isotopic ages are available for the platform-top succession (e.g. Latemar; Mundil *et al.* 2003).

Common features of Sciliar/Schlern platforms in the central Southern Alps include: (1) dominant aggradation in the *Reitzi* to *Secedensis* zones, passing to dominant progradation in the *Curionii* to *Archelaus* zones (sensu Brack *et al.* 1996; Maurer 2000); (2) an increase in bathymetric relief between platforms and basins from *c.* 200 m to 800–1000 m; (3) tabular platform geometry with low-angle facies boundaries between lower-slope and basin-margin areas, and offlap at the platform margin (Bosellini 1984; see Fig. 13.35); (4) discontinuous reef belts on the upper foreslope, dominated by biogenic crusts, 'microproblematica', encrusting sponges and subordinate scleractinians (Emmerich *et al.* 2005*b*); (5) the carbonate factory is not restricted to the platform top, but extends into the slope (Keim & Schlager 1999); (6) platforms are usually strongly dolomitized (exceptions include the Latemar, central Southern Alps, and the Esino platform north of Lago d'Iseo, western Southern Alps); and (7) the production potential of Anisian/Ladinian platforms matched the potential of moderately prolific recent platforms (Zühlke *et al.* 2003). A major controversy on orbital and non-orbital controls on carbonate deposition and Mesozoic platform development has developed around the hierarchical cyclicity in the Latemar platform interior (western Dolomites; Goldhammer *et al.* 1993; Preto *et al.* 2001, 2004). The current model (Zühlke 2004) proposes dominant non-orbital, sub-Milankovitch control with subordinate orbital control in the precession, obliquity and short eccentricity bandwidths.

Volcanic ash layers ('Pietra verde') in, for example, the Dont and Livinallongo/Buchenstein formations provide evidence for early volcanic activity in the Southern Alps. They become increasingly common from the Pelsonian into the Fassanian and enable high-resolution U–Pb ages from single zircons to be determined (Mundil *et al.* 2003). Commencing in the early Longobardian *Gredleri* (Sub-)Zone, a volcanic centre with small shallow intrusions was established in the area of Predazzo-Monzoni (central Southern Alps). Shoshonitic basalts indicate a calc-alkaline suite (Castellarin *et al.* 1988). Further volcanic and/or intrusive occurrences exist near Tarvisio (eastern Southern Alps), Recoaro (southern central Southern Alps) and in the subsurface of the present-day Po Plain. Large volumes of volcaniclastics were deposited as ash fall and submarine gravity flows (Zoppe Formation, maximum thickness 420 m; Viel 1979*a*, *b*; Fig. 13.33). Large-scale submarine rockfalls and slumps ('Livello chaotico', 'Agglomerati') on unstable submarine slopes around the volcanic centre of Predazzo/Monzoni were caused by the rise of diapiric anticlines of upper Permian evaporites (Bellerophon Formation). This process was triggered by the differential loading of Ladinian carbonate platforms (Schlern Formation) and coeval basinal deposits (Buchenstein Formation) and by the Longobardian magmatic activity and the related thermal event (Castellarin *et al.* 1998). Schlern platform development close to the volcanic centre was terminated by uplift, suffocation by ash-cloud deposits or submarine collapse ('Conglomerato di Marmolada', maximum thickness 1300 m). Sciliar/Schlern platforms further away from the volcanic centre show continuous growth across the early to mid-Longobardian (Sciliar/Schlern Formation III), albeit with reduced depositional rates. Following the cessation of volcanic activity, subaerial volcanic complexes were rapidly eroded. Turbidites transported large volumes of reworked volcaniclastics to fault-bounded submarine troughs, which cut the early Longobardian palaeogeography. Volcaniclastics continued to be redeposited, in decreasing amounts until the latest Longobardian (Fernazza, Aquatona, Wengen formations, maximum thickness 800–1200 m).

Pre- to synvolcanic platforms of the Sciliar/Schlern Formation in the central Southern Alps show thicknesses of 800–1200 m. Following the subsidence peak in the *Reitzi* Zone, rates gradually decreased to 50–100 mm/ka in the *Gredleri* and *Archelaus* Zones (e.g. western Dolomites; Emmerich *et al.* 2005*a*). Platforms in other parts of the Southern Alps followed the same general trend, but at different rates. The transition from platform aggradation to progradation was primarily controlled by subsidence and not by eustatic sea-level changes (cf. sea-level charts of Haq *et al.* 1988; Hardenbol *et al.* 1998). Early Ladinian platforms could match accommodation rates of up to 460–520 mm/ka without being drowned (Zühlke *et al.* 2003).

During volcanic activity in the central Southern Alps, Esino platform development in the western Southern Alps continued. The cumulative thickness of the Esino platform stages ranges between 500–800 m. Esino platforms were terminated in the late Longobardian (upper *Archelaus* Zone, *Neumayri* Subzone) by a significant decrease in accommodation as indicated by deep karstification (maximum 80 m; Jadoul & Frisia 1988). At the same time calcareous/volcaniclastic turbidites were deposited in the surrounding basins (Wengen Formation, *c.* 400 m thickness; Fig. 13.33).

*Latest Ladinian to early Late Carnian*

Widespread carbonate platform development in the central Southern Alps was re-established in the late Longobardian (*Regoledanus* Zone/Subzone). These platforms belong to the 'Cassian Dolomite', the coeval basins to the San Cassian Formation (Fig. 13.33). Common features of the Cassian platforms include: (1) strong progradation during the early Carnian; (2) a decrease in bathymetric relief between platforms and basins from approximately 500–600 m to less than 100 m; (3) the presence of a thinning- or thickening-outward platform geometry with climbing or descending facies boundaries between lower slope and basin areas, as well as toplap at the platform margin; (4) platform geometry and development was strongly influenced by the inherited volcanic bathymetry (Bosellini 1984); (5) the discontinuous reef belts comprised bindstones and bafflestones with micrite, cements and very subordinate skeletal material; (6) in the early Julian, patch-reefs with frameworks of stromatoporoids, sphinctozoans, inozoans and scleractinians developed, indicating the first reef optimum after the Permian–Triassic faunal crisis (Flügel 2002); and (7) platforms are usually dolomitized (exceptions include the so-called 'Cipit Boulders' which are reef talus blocks which escaped dolomitization). Stacked platforms and basins in the eastern Southern Alps, equivalent to the central Southern Alps, comprise the 'Cassian Dolomite' and the Predil and Rio del Lago formations respectively (Fig. 13.33).

Stratigraphic nomenclature of the Schlern and Cassian platforms in the central Southern Alps is not uniform in the existing literature. Stacked latest Anisian to early Carnian carbonate platforms, distal to the volcanic centres and without intercalated volcaniclastic successions, are referred to as Schlern Platforms. Stacked platforms proximal to the volcanic centres and with intercalated volcaniclastic successions can be subdivided into two groups: (1) pre-volcanic platforms of late Anisian to early Longobardian age, referred to as Sciliar/Schlern platforms; (2) post-volcanic platforms of latest Longobardian to early Carnian age, termed Cassian platforms. Both pre-volcanic Schlern and post-volcanic Cassian platforms may be further subdivided into different platform stages, provided that subaerial unconformities or indicative platform geometries exist (i.e. Schlern Formation I–III, Cassian Dolomite I–II). Indications for this last stratigraphic scheme are, however, not available for all platforms.

A basin-wide decrease in accommodation affected the Cassian platform development in the late Julian (*Austriacum* Zone, *Neoprotrachyceras* Subzone) of the central and eastern Southern Alps. Subtidal to peritidal carbonate or mixed clastic–carbonate successions of the Dürrenstein and Heiligkreuzkofel/Santa Croce formations (central Southern Alps) or Rio Conzen Formation (eastern Southern Alps) either onlap and/or offlap the Cassian platforms (Fig. 13.33). Subsequently, the platforms were subaerially exposed in the early Tuvalian (upper *Dilleri* Zone). Early

Carnian subsidence rates in the central Dolomites range between +20 mm/ka and +220 mm/ka.

The late Longobardian to early Tuvalian succession in the western Southern Alps shows thicknesses of 650 m to >1000 m. Cyclic inter- to supratidal carbonates with intercalated palaeosols ('Calcare Rosso') of latest Ladinian age (lower? *Regoledanus* Zone/Subzone) unconformably overlie the subaerial exposure surface at the top of the Esino platforms and are followed by the 'Calcare Metallifero Bergamasco', which is composed of peritidal carbonates and bounded by another palaeokarst surface (Fig. 13.33). Most of the Julian to early Tuvalian succession shows lateral facies transitions from SW to NE. These comprise: (1) red-beds, conglomerates and delta sandstones of the Val Sabbia Formation prograding from the south (maximum thickness 1000 m); (2) alluvial to sabkha sediments of the lower San Giovanni Bianco Formation; (3) marly lagoonal deposits of the Gorno Formation with interim progradation of oolitic shoals; and (4) cyclic platform carbonates of the Breno Formation (Jadoul & Gnacciolini 1992). Sandstones with volcanic detritus record rapid changes in the composition of volcanics (rhyodacites, latites, olivine basalts, felsics) in source areas to the south of the western Southern Alps during Julian times.

The Dürrenstein and Sante Croce/Heiligkreuzkofel formations of the central Southern Alps and coeval units in the eastern (Rio Conzen Formation) and western Southern Alps (middle Breno, upper Gorno, lower San Giovanni Bianco formations) levelled the previously existing bathymetric relief between the platforms and the basins of the Cassian Dolomite and the San Cassian Formation.

*Late Carnian*

In the early to mid-Tuvalian (upper *Dilleri* to lower *Subbullatus* Zone), accommodation space decreased significantly, following a strong third-order eustatic sea-level fall and low subsidence rates. An erosional unconformity developed across much of the southern Alpine basin. In the central and eastern Southern Alps it is overlain by the fluvial, lagoonal and shoreface sandstones/siltstones, evaporites, shales and dolomites of the Raibl/Travenazes Formation. Thicknesses increase from 30 m in the west to more than 100 m in the east. The Raibl/Travenazes Formation is probably diachronous between the eastern and central Southern Alps. Coastal sabkha, open-marine subtidal and carbonate–evaporitic lagoonal deposits of the middle–upper San Giovanni Bianco Formation (maximum thickness 250 m) prevail in the western Southern Alps. The Raibl/Travenazes Formation in the Southern Alps is not the time-equivalent of the Raibl Formation of the Northern Calcareous Alps (Austria, Germany), where it overlies the late Early Carnian (Julian) to early Norian (Lacian) succession (Fig. 13.31). In the Northern Calcareous Alps, the source areas of the Raibl Formation were the Central European and Fennoscandian ranges. In the Southern Alps, grain size trends indicate a source area in the south, below the present-day Po Plain.

*Latest Carnian to Rhaetian*

In the late Tuvalian (*Anatropites* Zone), clastic input to the southern Alpine basin ended and the carbonate lagoonal deposition of the Hauptdolomit/Dolomia Principale commenced. In the eastern and central Southern Alps the base of the succession is marked by extraformational breccias and conglomerates, while in the western Southern Alps, marginal marine mudstones, intraformational breccias (Castro Formation, 50–250 m thick; Jadoul *et al.* 1992) and subtidal 'Dark dolomites' (50–250 m thick) mark the base. Metre-scale, subtidal–intertidal–supratidal cycles are typical within the Dolomia Principale/Hauptdolomit which covered much of the western Tethyan Shelf. Thicknesses range between 250 m in the western part of the central Southern Alps, to 1500 m in the eastern Southern Alps and up to 2000 m (including the Castro Formation and 'Dark Dolomites') in the western Southern Alps.

Structurally controlled intraplatform basins developed during the deposition of the middle to upper part of the Dolomia Principale/Hauptdolomit, while small, anoxic basins existed in the southern part of the central Southern Alps. The Norian development in the western Southern Alps differs considerably from that in the eastern and central Southern Alps. In the late early Norian, large intraplatform basins developed, which were filled by carbonate turbidites of the Aralalta Formation (200–1000 m thick). Dolomia Principale/Hauptdolomit deposition persisted until the late Lacian (?*Magnus* Zone), when the platform experienced local emergence and clay suffocation. Finally, in the early Alaunian, rapid subsidence and drowning occurred (Jadoul *et al.* 1992). Black shales, marls and subtidal limestones of the Riva Solto Shale Formation and the lower Zu Formation (cumulative thickness 300–1500 m) onlap the top of the Dolomia Principale/Hauptdolomit. In the early Rhaetian, carbonate ramps of the Middle–Upper Zu formations prograded from structural highs (Fig. 13.33).

The Triassic basin fill in the eastern and central Southern Alps is concluded by the Dachstein Formation, the age of which is loosely constrained as latest Norian(?) to Rhaetian or early Hettangian(?). The depositional environment was similar to that of the Dolomia Principale/Hauptdolomit. However, the Dachstein Formation is dolomitized to only a minor extent, or not at all. In the central to eastern Southern Alps, thicknesses increase from 30 m to >1000 m from west to east. In the western Southern Alps, the Upper Zu Formation and the Conchodon Dolomite represent the Rhaetian succession with a combined thickness of 180–220 m. Open-marine carbonate ramps with shoals and coral patchreefs characterize the upper Zu Formation. The Conchodon Dolomite shows subtidal to peritidal mudstones and prograding oolitic bars with partial dolomitization. A depositional gap occurred in the Rhaetian on structural highs in the westernmost Southern Alps.

Subsidence rates during the Norian and Rhaetian were very high. Quantitative models have large error intervals because biostratigraphic resolution is limited and absolute ages vary. Based on the current chronobiostratigraphic framework, Norian subsidence rates in the central Southern Alps range between 320 mm/ka (western Dolomites) and 820 mm/ka (eastern Dolomites). However, in the Rhaetian subsidence decreased significantly to 50 mm/ka and 140 mm/ka in these two areas, respectively. In eastern Lombardy, the Norian–Rhaetian succession is up to 4000 m thick.

## *Western Carpathians (J.M., J.S.)*

The Triassic palaeogeography and structural evolution of the western Tethys has been compiled by many workers, but due to the late Cretaceous–Tertiary accretion, accurate palinspastic reconstruction for the different tectonic units of the Alpine orogen is controversial. This, in turn, makes palaeogeographical reconstructions of the Alpine basins ambiguous (e.g. Zacher & Lupu 1999). Nonetheless it seems probable that the Outer Carpathian unit (which consists of the external nappes of the Carpathian Orogen) belonged to the southern Palaeo-European shelf segment adjacent to the eastern border of the Bohemian Massif and the Małopolska Massif. The Triassic history of this area is unknown since the region underwent diastrophism during the Alpine Orogeny.

In contrast to the Outer Carpathians, the Triassic of the Central Carpathians is well preserved, thus enabling detailed studies of the basin evolution and palaeogeographical reconstructions. In this section the palaeogeographical model of Michalík (1993) is used (Fig. 13.36).

Similarities in facies and biota indicate that during the Early Triassic the Central Carpathian Basin was linked to the Eastern Alpine area. It was situated at the Palaeo-European margin, bordered by the Bohemian and Armorican massifs to the north and the Meliata Ocean to the south (Fig. 13.36). During the Mid-Triassic, the strike-slip zone of the future Penninic oceanic rift began to form and forced the eastward migration of the Carpathian–Alpine blocks. This translatory motion involved fragmentation of the Central Carpathian Basin into several sub-basins (Tatricum, Fatricum, Hronicum), each showing different facies development.

Complex strike-slip tectonics in late Anisian–early Ladinian times were accompanied by the opening of short-lived rifts in which the deeper-water nodular limestones and shales of the Reifling-Partnach facies accumulated. Palynofacies analysis indicates that the topography of the basin was complex and represented a carbonate platform dissected into narrow grabens and broad elevated blocks. The latter were probably partly emergent, as indicated by the presence of much redeposited land plant and vertebrate debris (Ruckwied *et al.* 2004).

Progressive strike-slip movement resulted in closing of the rifts (i.e. 'aborted rifts'; see Bechstädt *et al.* 1978) and replacement of the deep-marine sediments by shallow-marine carbonates of the Wetterstein Complex. In Carnian times, the Central Carpathian basins underwent general uplift and were dominated by either continental (Carpathian Keuper) or shallow-marine (Lunz siliciclastic assemblage) deposition. Clastic sedimentation persisted throughout the Norian, although some transgressive pulses are recorded by dolomitic horizons. Carbonates are dominant in the Hronicum sub-basin where the 200 m thick Hauptdolomit unit was deposited.

The global transgression in Rhaetian times extended into the Central Carpathian basins as indicated by the ubiquitous presence of open-marine, biogenic limestones. The Triassic succession within the basins consists of several sedimentary megacycles (Fig. 13.37), reflecting the changing climatic, eustatic and palaeo-oceanographic conditions in the Western Tethys Ocean. The succession begins with Early Triassic (Induan–Olenekian) clastics accumulated in a huge deltaic fan system (more than 100 000 km$^3$). This material was transported by ephemeral river systems from the area between the Bohemian and the Armorican massifs. The typical product of this system, the Lúžna Formation, is composed of quartz and lithoclastic sandstones, and greywackes with conglomeratic layers, which become finer southwards (Roniewicz 1966; Mišík & Jablonský 1978). In the more distal parts of the fan, up to 1000 m of siltstones, clays and marls were deposited (Fig. 13.37).

In Anisian times a broad carbonate ramp developed under arid climatic conditions on a wide submerged alluvial plain. This large (300 by 1000 km) shallow-marine carbonate ramp comprises the Gutenstein limestone and dolomite facies. Subsidence was controlled by gradual sea-level rise (20–30 mm/ka) and by the compaction of underlying pelitic complexes (another 60–70 mm/ka). The onset of tectonic activity during the late Anisian is recorded by the presence of tsunamites and slump breccias (Michalík 1997). Carbonate platforms evolving in Ladinian times were affected by transtensional stress (Michalík 1993, 1994). Sedimentation rates in intrashelf pull-apart basins were rather low (Reifling Limestone, Partnach Marl, 4–15 mm/ka) compared with the rapidly growing reefal margins that were keeping up with the subsidence rate (up to 400 mm/ka). Differential sedimentation rates accentuated the basinal morphology: the basins attained depths of 1200–1500 m at the end of the Ladinian, when sea level began to fall (Masaryk *et al.* 1993).

Despite intense deformation, the Induan–Ladinian succession of the Tatricum basin has a depositional history similar to that of the Northern Alpine basin. This has been demonstrated by means of sequence stratigraphy (Jaglarz & Szulc 2003).

The Julian was a period characterized by mass transport (about 10 000 km$^3$) of clastics (Lunz/Rheingraben Formation; Fig. 13.37) that completely filled the basins in the Slovako-Carpathian-Austro-Alpine shelf. These rapidly deposited clastic sediments (500–700 mm/ka) were transported from the northern Peri-Tethys area.

An arid climate and relatively stable sea level in Norian times led to the establishment of a carbonate platform system with a continuous reef margin. Extensive backreef flats of the Dachstein Limestone and Hauptdolomit separated the sea from the uplifted blocks where Carpathian Keuper sedimentation was dominant. The sedimentation rate of the Carpathian Keuper was seven times slower than that of the German Keuper because the sediment transport path had to cross the rising Penninic rift valley.

By the end of the Triassic, disintegration of the Tethyan shelves resulted in the megashear model of numerous megablocks separated by strike-slip faults (Michalík 1993, 1994). Lakes and swamps with a rich flora and rare dinosaur fauna (Michalík *et al.* 1976) were established in more distal depressions. Another depression, linked to the Kössen basinal system, was flooded by marine waters and was the site of deposition of a shallow, marginal-marine succession with an abundant neritic fauna (Fatra Formation) (Michalík 1980).

The Triassic–Jurassic boundary is marked by carbon and oxygen isotope excursions and the cessation of carbonate sedimentation, and the related increase in clastic input due to climate change at the beginning of the Hettangian transgression (Michalík 2003).

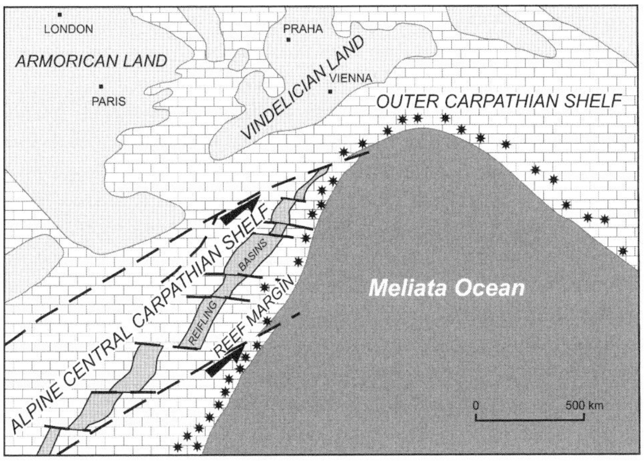


**Fig. 13.36.** Position of the Alpine-Carpathian shelf in relation to the continental Palaeo-Europe and facies distribution of the northern Mediterranean Tethys in the Ladinian. Note formation of tensional intrashelf pull-apart basins under the influence of Middle Triassic rifting. After Michalík (1994).

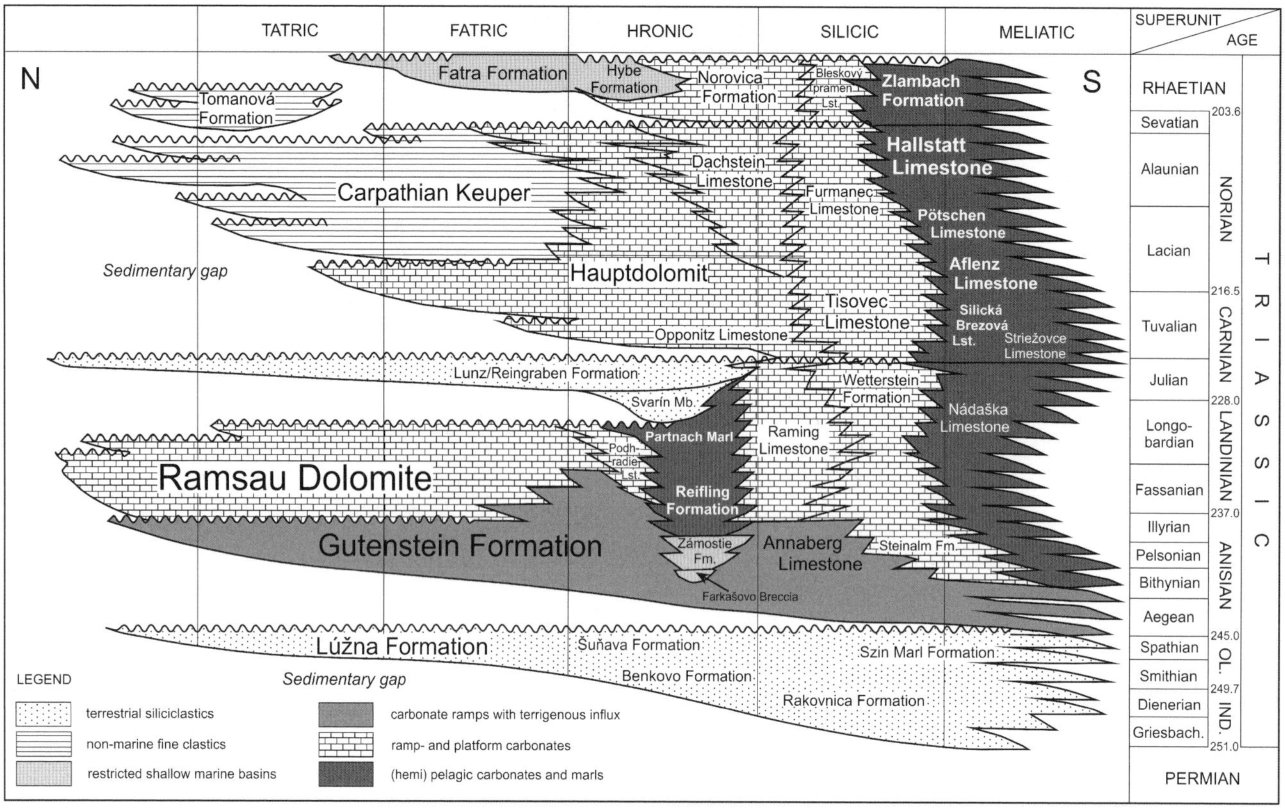


**Fig. 13.37.** Triassic lithostratigraphy of the Western Carpathians. Note transgressive–regressive trends from south to north, and alternation of more humid periods, denoted by terrigenous clastics input, with more arid ones, typically with carbonate sedimentation (modified after Michalík 2003).

## *Hungary (J.H., A.T.)*

In the early phase of the Alpine cycle, the structural units that make up the basement of the Pannonian Basin (Fig. 13.38) were located close to the western termination of the Tethys (Haas *et al.* 1995*a*, 2001, 2004*a*). The present day position of the main structural units, is given in Figure 13.38.

### *Transdanubian Range Unit*

The main part of the Transdanubian Range (Keszthely, Bakony, Vértes, Gerecse and Buda mountains) is made up of formations of Triassic age that show a striking affinity with the corresponding formations in the Southern Alps (Fig. 13.39). The thickness of the Triassic formations may exceed 4000 m. Classic exposures of the Lower and Middle Triassic are found on the Balaton Highland, in the southern part of the Bakony Mountains.

Tectonic factors played a crucial role in the determination of the main trends of basin evolution and facies distribution at this time. However, climatic changes and low- to high-frequency sea-level changes were the important controlling factors. Sea-level rise at the Permian–Triassic boundary resulted in flooding of the Late Permian alluvial plane transforming the area into a homoclinal ramp.

In the northeastern part of the Transdanubian Range, the Triassic succession overlies Late Permian lagoonal dolomites. The lowermost unit comprises shallow subtidal limestones and marls, representing shallow to deeper ramp deposits (Alcsútdoboz Limestone) of Induan age. To the SW, these sediments were replaced by marls of the mud shoal facies (Arács Marl) and dolomites of the restricted lagoon facies (Köveskál Dolomite) (Haas *et al.* 1988*b*; Broglio Loriga *et al.* 1990; Fig. 13.39).

These formations are covered by a siltstone–sandstone unit (Hidegkút Formation) which indicates an increased clastic input at the beginning of Olenekian times (Campil Event in the Southern Alps). Deposition occurred in a subtidal ramp setting. This evolutionary stage was completed by a sea-level fall and a coeval decrease in terrigenous input, resulting in the formation of peritidal-lagoonal dolomites. During the next sea-level rise a marl succession with intercalations of crinoid/bivalve storm coquinas (Csopak Marl) was deposited on the outer ramp below the storm wave base.

During the Anisian the lack of terrigenous input led to deposition of pure carbonates on the ramp (Haas & Budai 1995). In the Early Anisian, dolomite formed in a restricted, periodically hypersaline inner ramp lagoon (Aszófő Dolomite). This is overlain by laminated and thick-bedded, strongly bioturbated limestones (Iszkahegy Limestone). The recurrence of dolostone above (Megyehegy Dolomite) probably reflects the increasing restriction of the inner ramp under drier climatic conditions.

In the Mid-Anisian, extensional tectonic activity commenced, and this was associated with Neo-Tethys rifting (Budai & Vörös 1992). This phase was followed by the onset of volcaniclastic deposition from distant volcanic centres during the Late Anisian.

In the southwestern part of the Transdanubian Range (Balaton Highland), intrashelf basins began to form during Pelsonian times. Peritidal/subtidal carbonates were deposited on the most elevated blocks (Tagyon Formation), whereas in the basinal areas the dolomite passed laterally into the cherty Felsőörs Limestone facies (Vörös *et al.* 2003).

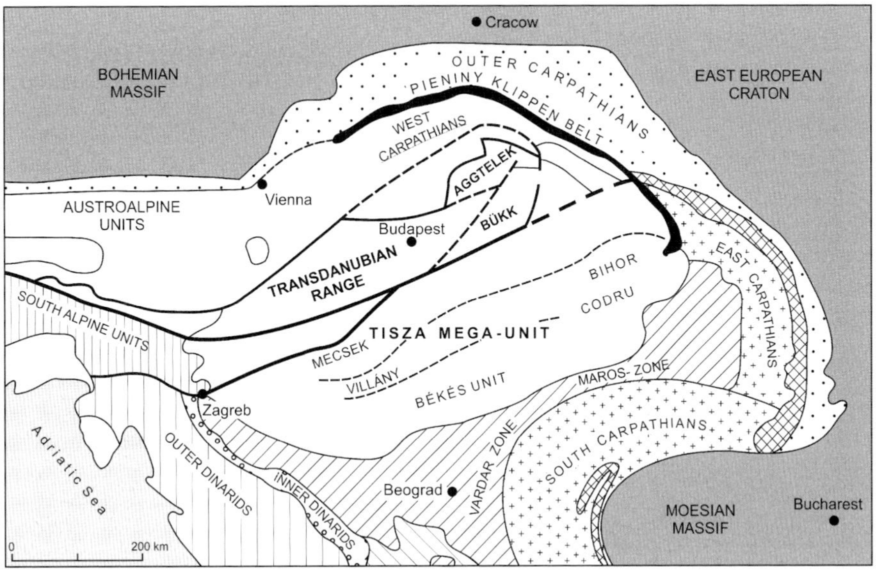


**Fig. 13.38.** The main tectonic units of the pre-Neogene basement of the Pannonian Basin.

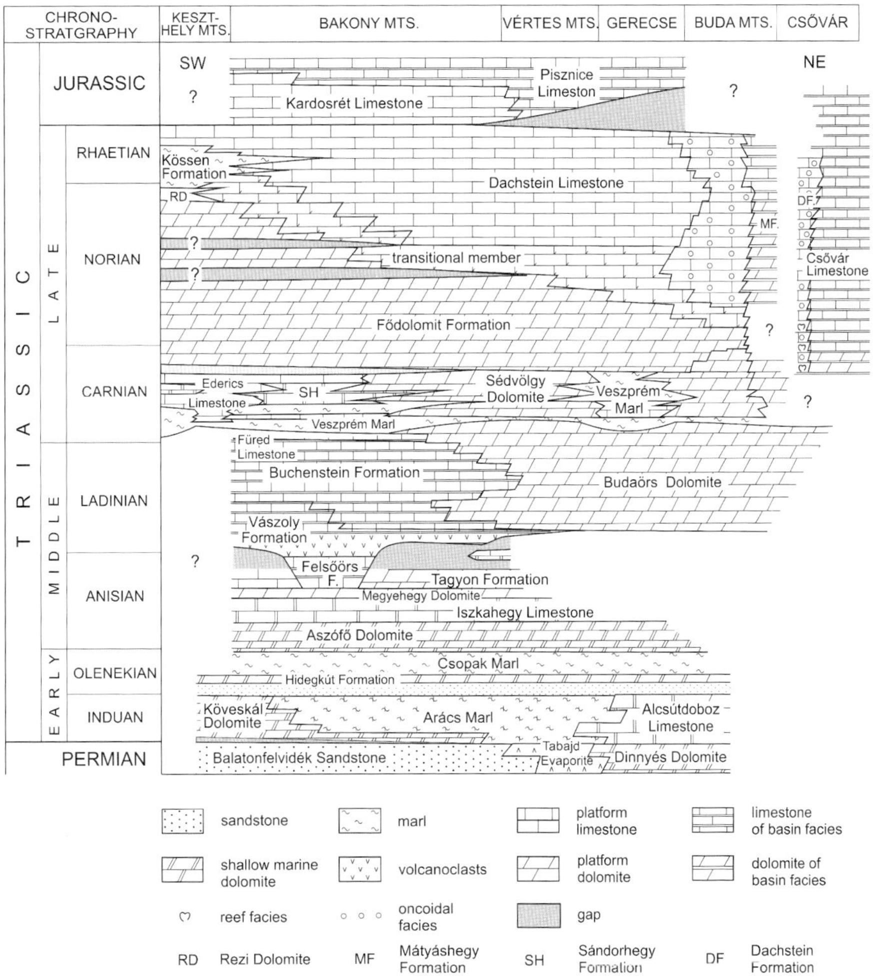


**Fig. 13.39.** Triassic formations and their time and space relation along a SW–NE conceptual cross-section of the Transdanubian Range (after Haas & Budai 1999, modified).

The Anisian–Ladinian boundary interval is characterized by pelagic limestones with volcanic tuff interlayers (Vászoly Formation), which are overlain by red cherty limestones and tuffaceous limestones (Buchenstein Formation). The products of the Mid-Triassic volcanism are mainly rhyodacite/trachyte pyroclastics, predominantly crystal tuffs (Harangi *et al.* 1996). Deposition of pelagic cherty limestones (Füred Limestone) continued until the earliest Carnian in the Balaton Highland area (Fig. 13.39).

In the northeastern part of the Transdanubian Range, Mid-Triassic volcanic activity is indicated only by the presence of very thin tuff horizons. During the Ladinian to earliest Carnian, platform dolomites (Budaörs Dolomite) formed in this area (Fig. 13.39). The inner platform deposits are made up of metre-scale peritidal–subtidal cycles. In the subtidal beds dasycladacean algae may occur in rock-forming quantities.

In the Early Carnian the input of a great amount of clay and silt from distal source areas and carbonate mud from the ambient shallow banks resulted in the deposition of a thick marl succession (Veszprém Marl) (Haas 1994). Rising sea levels in the late Early Carnian led to drowning of significant parts of the platforms. This was followed by a significant phase of platform progradation in the Mid-Carnian. In the Late Carnian the remnant intraplatform basins were filled with carbonates and shales (Sándorhegy Formation).

In the latest Carnian, large carbonate platforms began to form, keeping pace with the rapid sinking (Balog *et al.* 1997). In the early stage of platform evolution, cyclic dolomite (Fődolomit Formation, an equivalent of the Hauptdolomit or Dolomia Principale in the Southern Alps) formed under semiarid conditions.

In small outcrops east of the Danube (Csővár) and in the Buda Mountains in the easternmost Transdanubian Range, the Carnian succession includes, in addition to the platform carbonates, cherty limestones and dolomites of slope and intraplatform basin facies that continued up into the Norian–Rhaetian (Mátyáshegy Formation) and locally even into the Early Jurassic (Csővár Limestone) (Haas *et al.* 1997, 2000).

At the end of the Mid-Norian, as a prelude to the opening of the Ligurian-Penninic Ocean, extensional basins began to form in the southwestern part of the Transdanubian Range, leading to stabilization of the restricted subtidal conditions in this area. Thin-bedded dolomites (Rezi Dolomite) formed in this environment in the area of the Southern Bakony and the Keszthely mountains. In the Late Norian, a significant climatic change led to the enhanced influx of fine terrigenous material and the deposition of organic-rich marl in the restricted basin (Kössen Formation) (Haas 2002).

In the central part of the Transdanubian Range, carbonate platform evolution continued until the end of the Triassic or locally even into the earliest Jurassic (Fig. 13.39). Due to more humid climatic conditions, the pervasive early dolomitization ceased and the Fődolomit Formation was succeeded by the Dachstein Limestone (Haas & Demény 2002).

*Bükk Unit*

The Bükk Mountains are located in northern Hungary, to the south of the Inner West Carpathian units (Fig. 13.38). They comprise Upper Palaeozoic and Triassic–Jurassic formations that were generally affected by Late Jurassic(?)–Cretaceous anchizonal to epizonal metamorphism (Árkai *et al.* 1995). The Bükk Mountains have a parautochthonous core that consists of folded Palaeozoic and Triassic rocks which were overthrust by nappes of accretionary complexes containing blocks of Triassic and Jurassic basalts, radiolarites, and carbonates in Jurassic shales. The Upper Palaeozoic to Mesozoic succession of the Bükk Parautochthonous Unit shows an affinity with the Inner Dinaridic Jadar Block, whereas the accretionary complex may be a dislocated fragment of the Vardar ophiolite mélange (Protić *et al.* 2000).

Upper Permian shallow-marine limestones are overlain by lowermost Triassic stromatolitic and oolitic limestones (Gerennavár Limestone) (Fig. 13.40). The overlying Ablakoskővölgy Formation comprises alternating carbonate and siliciclastic-dominated ramp sediments. The succession shows a deepening-upward trend. A bioturbated limestone unit occurs at the top of the Lower Triassic (Hips & Pelikán 2002).

Platform dolomites, comprising alternating peritidal and subtidal facies, formed in the Anisian (Hámor Dolomite). These are locally overlain by dolomite breccias or conglomerates (Sebesvíz Conglomerate; Fig. 13.40). These conglomerates are similar to those at the same stratigraphic level in the Southern Alps (Richthofen Conglomerate, Ugovitz Breccia) and indicate uplift and subaerial erosion (Velledits 1999). Updoming was probably related to the initiation of rifting and related volcanic activity in connection with the opening of Neo-Tethys.

In Ladinian times, there was intense andesitic/trachytic calc-alkaline volcanic activity resulting in the accumulation of the Szentistvánhegy Meta-andesite, a volcanic complex hundreds of metres thick. This consists of lavas, agglomerates, tuffs, ignimbrites and volcaniclastic sediments (Harangi *et al.* 1996).

Rifting also resulted in facies differentiation, with isolated carbonate platforms and intraplatform basins developing in the area of the Bükk Parautochthonous Unit.

A large part of the central and southern Bükk Mountains (Bükk Highland) is made up of anchimetamorphic platform limestones (Bükkfennsík Limestone) (Fig. 13.40) in which patch-reef facies are recognizable along the southern margin of the plateau. This formation probably began to form in the Ladinian and the upper part is assumed to be of Late Triassic age. In a small area of the southern part of the Bükk Mountains the original depositional texture of the platform limestones was preserved and a cyclic peritidal–lagoonal inner platform and reefal outer platform facies are recognizable (Velledits & Péró 1987; Flügel *et al.* 1992). In a nappe outlier in the northeastern part of the Bükk Mountains, Upper Carnian cyclic peritidal–subtidal limestones, similar to the Dachstein Limestone, are recorded.

In the intraplatform basins the cherty Felsőtárkány Limestone formed coevally with the development of the platforms (Fig. 13.40). Based on radiolarians and conodonts, deposition of the pelagic carbonates began in the Ladinian and continued into the Late Triassic in the southern Bükk Mountains (Velledits 2000).

Volcanic activity continued into the Carnian. Tuffaceous intercalations and basalt lavas (Szinva Metabasalt) occur in both the Felsőtárkány Limestone and the Carnian Vesszős Marl (Szoldán 1990). This occurrence of alkali-tholeiitic volcanism is characteristic of extensional tectonics and therefore assumed to be an indication of intraplate volcanism.

During the Late Triassic the carbonate platforms began to disintegrate and increasingly large parts subsided below the euphotic zone. The hemipelagic Répáshuta Limestone (Fig. 13.40), overlying the platform carbonates, records this process.

*Aggtelek-Rudabánya Unit*

The Aggtelek-Rudabánya Unit is located to the south of the Gemer Palaeozoic, i.e. south of the Rožňava Line in southern Slovakia and northern Hungary (Fig. 13.38) and consists of nappes of different origin. The lower nappe comprises metamor-

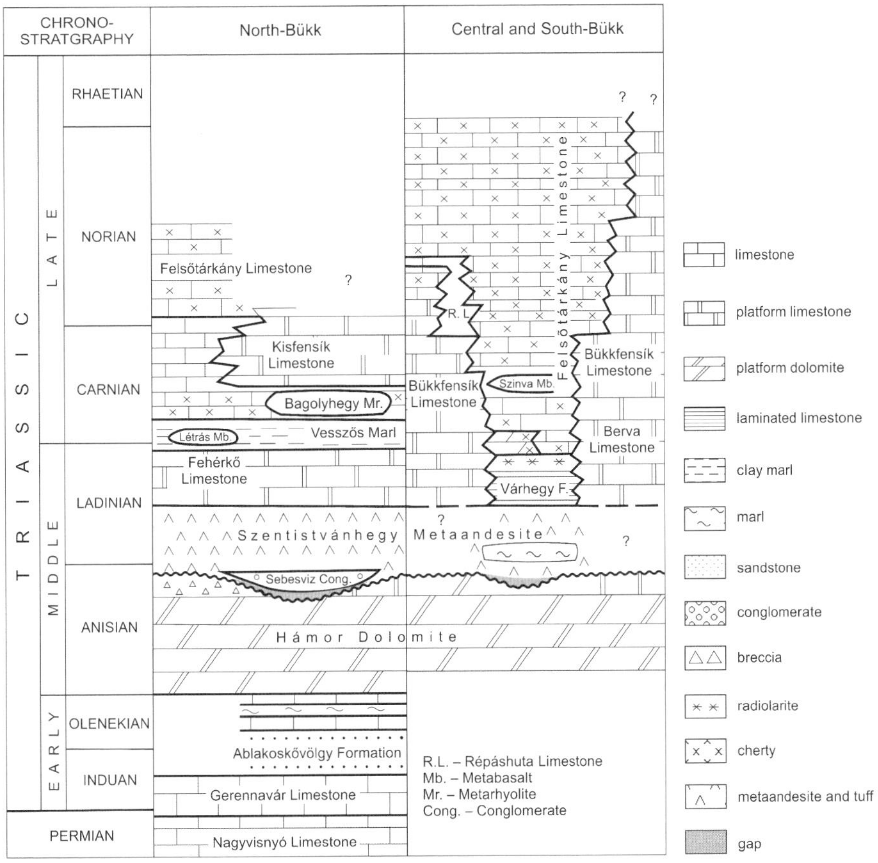


**Fig. 13.40.** Triassic lithostratigraphy of the Bükk Parautochthonous Unit (after Haas *et al.* 2004*a*, modified).

phosed Mesozoic successions. Remnants of oceanic basement are preserved as slivers in the basal evaporitic complex of the non-metamorphosed Aggtelek (Silicic) Unit, which is the uppermost nappe. The Mid–Late Triassic facies succession of the Aggtelek-Rudabánya Unit represents the outer shelf and slope of the northern margin of Neo-Tethys.

In the Late Permian, a wide tidal flat developed along the northern margin of the Tethys Ocean, on which the area of the Aggtelek-Rudabánya Unit was located (Fig. 13.38). Under arid climatic conditions a thick evaporite series (Perkupa Evaporite) accumulated.

Transgression in the Induan led to the development of a microtidal inner ramp–lagoon system in which shales, siltstones and fine-grained sandstones accumulated (Bódvaszilas Sandstone) (Fig. 13.41). Sedimentation was controlled mainly by tidal currents and high-energy storm events (Hips 1998). In the middle part of the Early Triassic the area became part of a well-oxygenated outer-ramp zone characterized by alternating shales and sandstones. Later in the Early Triassic, a significant transgression led to the deposition of argillaceous, silty, sandy carbonates and marls (Szin Marl) in a storm-dominated middle- to outer-ramp setting.

At the end of the Early Triassic the input of fine-grained siliciclastics was markedly reduced and carbonate deposition became dominant on the ramp. The inner ramp gradually became restricted and bioturbated; nodular limestones and marls ('vermicular limestone') formed under dysaerobic conditions (Szinpetri Limestone). Above this, bioturbated and laminated limestones alternate, reflecting the fluctuation between slightly and highly oxygen-depleted conditions. In the Early Anisian the final stage of restriction of the inner ramp was manifested by the formation of dark grey to black limestones and dolomites (Gutenstein Limestone).

The Gutenstein Limestone is overlain by dolomites which show transitional features between the restricted ramp and carbonate platform facies. This is followed by platform sequences made up of alternating thick-bedded dasycladacean and stromatolitic limestones (Steinalm Limestone). The dasycladacean grainstone beds were deposited in the subtidal zone of a well-oxygenated and wave-agitated shallow platform environment (Piros 2002).

Carbonate platform development began in the latter part of the Early Anisian and continued into the Late Anisian on those blocks which remained within the euphotic zone following the Mid-Anisian segmentation of the platforms. On the downfaulted blocks pelagic environments developed above the drowned platforms.

Deposition of platform carbonates (Wetterstein Limestone) continued in the Ladinian to Late Carnian interval across a large part of the Aggtelek (Silica) Nappe. Reef and peritidal–lagoonal facies can be distinguished. The reef facies is mainly made up of reef detritus and cavity-filling cement; however, locally reef-builders (calcareous sponges, corals, hydrozoans) or reef-dwellers (crinoids, brachiopods) are recognizable. Stromatolites are typical in the peritidal beds of the cyclic succession, while the subtidal lagoonal beds consist of calcareous algal grainstones (Piros 2002). The drowning of the platforms occurred in the early Late Carnian (Kovács *et al.* 1989).

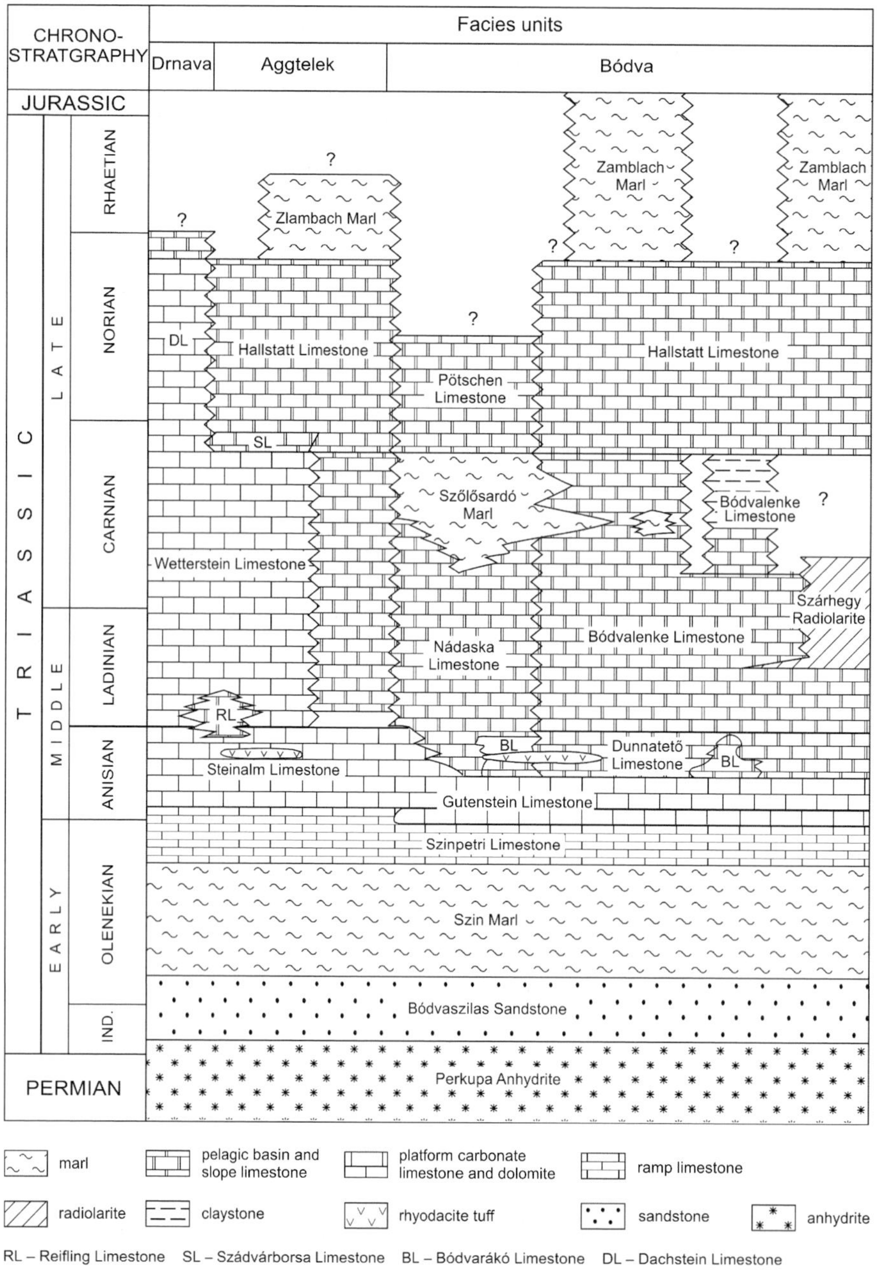


**Fig. 13.41.** Triassic lithostratigraphy of the Aggtelek-Rudabánya Unit (after Haas *et al.* 2004*a*, modified).

In the southern part of the Aggtelek Nappe, slope and periplatform basin facies are characteristic of the Middle Anisian to the Upper Carnian (Nádaska Limestone, Reifling Limestone) (Fig. 13.41). Sedimentation in the periplatform hemipelagic basin changed significantly in the middle part of the Carnian. Marl successions with intercalations of cherty limestones and intrabreccias (Szőlősardó Marl) were deposited (Balogh & Kovács 1981).

In the Bódva Nappe (non-metamorphic succession in the Rudabánya Mountains) the Mid-Anisian to Carnian interval is represented by a deep-marine pelagic facies. The Anisian platform carbonates are overlain by either grey cherty or pinkish limestones. The former indicates an oxygen-depleted depositional environment, whereas the latter formed on a well-oxygenated sea bottom. The Upper Anisian–Upper Carnian succession is made up of alternating red limestones and pelagic bivalve coquinites with thin, red clay and chert intercalations (Bódvalenke Limestone) which were deposited in a well-oxygenated pelagic basin. In the deepest part of the basin radiolarites (Szárhegy Radiolarite) were deposited at the same time (Fig. 13.41).

As a consequence of progressive downfaulting of the platform margins, the area of the Aggtelek Nappe became a deep, pelagic basin by the beginning of the Norian. As in the Northern Calcareous Alps, two characteristic types of basinal facies can be distinguished: the red Hallstatt Limestone and the grey Pötschen Limestone (Fig. 13.41). The Hallstatt Limestone was deposited on well-oxygenated, current-swept slope-terraces above the downfaulted blocks of the platform margin, or in the internal parts of the basin affected by bottom currents. The Pötschen

Limestone formed in the low-angle distal foreslope zones or in protected sub-basins. In several sections the Hallstatt Limestone is overlain by marls of Late Norian age (Zlambach Marl).

*Tisza Mega-unit*
During Triassic times, the Tisza Mega-unit was located on the northern Tethyan shelf margin east of the Bohemian Massif and Vindelician High (Fig. 13.2). The mega-unit is divided into the Mecsek, Villány-Bihor and Papuk-Békés-Lower Codru, North-Backa-Upper Codru (Biharia) zones (Bleahu *et al.* 1994) which comprise the NE–SW striking Alpine nappe systems of present-day central and southern Hungary, northern Serbia and western Romania (Fig. 13.38). The pre-Tertiary basement is covered by thick Tertiary and Quaternary sediments. Triassic outcrops are restricted to the Mecsek and Villány mountains in Hungary, the Papuk and adjacent hills in Croatia, and the Apuseni Mountains in Romania (Bleahu *et al.* 1994). It has long been recognized (Vadász 1935; Nagy 1968) that much of the Triassic of the Tisza Mega-unit shows similarities with the tripartite Germanic epicontinental sequences, although the palaeontological and sedimentological evidence has only recently been published (Kovács & Papsová 1986; Mader 1992; Török 1993*a*, 1997, 1998*a*, 2000; Pálfy & Török 1992; Konrád 1997). The lithostratigraphic subdivision (Fig. 13.42) is based on recent works of Bérczíné Makk (1986, 1993), Wéber (1990), Rálisch-Felgenhauer & Török (1993), Török (1993*a*, 1998*a, b*) and Konrád (1997).

Within the Triassic succession of the Tisza Mega-unit three main phases of palaeoenvironmental evolution are recognized (Török 1997, 1998*a*): (1) Early Triassic and early Mid-Triassic continental and peritidal sediments; (2) Mid-Triassic ramp carbonates; and (3) Late Triassic coastal carbonates and siliciclastic sediments.

Although biostratigraphic data are rare, sporomorphs (Barabás-Stuhl 1981; Bóna 1995; Götz *et al.* 2003), bivalves (Nagy 1968; Szente 1997), brachiopods (Nagy 1968; Török 1993*b*), conodonts (Bóna 1976; Kovács & Papsová 1986), single ammonites (Detre 1973), foraminifers, ostracods (Monostori 1996) and crinoids (Hagdorn *et al.* 1997) have all been used for dating. Most fossils of chronostratigraphic value are found within a very narrow time interval, namely in the Pelsonian–Illyrian.

The Early Triassic succession is a continuation of the Late Permian fluvial sedimentation. The lowermost Triassic siliciclastic sediments (Jakabhegy Sandstone; Fig. 13.42) are divided into three lithologic units (Barabás-Stuhl 1993; Konrád 1997; Barabás & Barabás-Stuhl 2005). The basal unit is a coarse conglomerate ('main conglomerate') containing quartzite, rhyolite, granite and shale pebbles and overlying the Permian Kővágószőlős Sandstone. It is capped by fluvial sand-bar deposits (Barabás-Stuhl 1993), showing fining-upward cycles (Konrád 1997). The second lithologic unit ('pale sandstone') also consists of fining-upward cycles that begin with thin conglomerates and pebbly sandstones and are followed by cross-bedded sandstones and capped by siltstones. The topmost unit of the Jakabhegy Sandstone consists of siltstones and fine-grained sandstones with palaeosol horizons, representing a range of facies, from terrestrial to alluvial and coastal plane environments (Konrád 1997). Intercalations of aeolian dune sands have also been recognized. Based on sporomorphs, the topmost part of the formation is of earliest Anisian age (Barabás-Stuhl 1993). Early Triassic siliciclastic sediments with a maximum thickness of *c.* 470 m have also been encountered in the boreholes in the Great Hungarian Plain (Bérczíné Makk 1998).

Rising sea levels caused the gradual flooding of the area of the Tisza Mega-unit and the development of a mixed siliciclastic–carbonate ramp system (Török 1998*a*). The oldest sediments of the ramp system are greenish-red siltstones (Patacs Siltstone) which are considered to be the lower part of the 'Hungarian Röt' (Török 2000). Pseudomorphs of anhydrite after gypsum, desiccation cracks, bird's eye structures and ripple marks indicate a peritidal origin for the sandstone–siltstone–dolomite cycles that correspond to the lowermost Röt of the Germanic Basin (Török 2000). Phyllopods reflect a hypersaline environment, while lingulid brachiopods are indicators of restricted marine influence. Sporomorphs indicate an Early Anisian age for the Patacs Siltstone (Barabás-Stuhl 1993). The succeeding anhydrite and gypsum layers (Magyarürög Anhydrite) are coastal plain to sabkha deposits (Török 1998*a*) that are overlain by dolomitized peritidal carbonates (Hetvehely Dolomite; Fig. 13.42). The lower part of the 'Hungarian Röt' (Patacs Siltstone) correlates with the lower and middle Röt units of Germany, i.e. Salinar-Röt and Pelit-Röt (Török 2000). In the deepening-upward succession bituminous limestones (Viganvár Limestone) with bivalve coquinas (Szente 1997) are interpreted as storm-influenced, temporarily anaerobic to dysaerobic mid-ramp deposits (Török 1998*a*). The topmost part of the Hungarian Röt (Rókahegy Dolomite) correlates with the Myophoria beds of the Germanic Röt (Török 2000). Dolomitized calcarenites (ooid packstones) may represent small carbonate sand bars rather than thick shoal successions.

Anisian mid- and outer-ramp deposits are characterized by flaser-bedded limestones and marlstones (Lapis Limestone) with numerous tempestites and hummocky cross-laminated calcisiltite beds, indicating permanent storm activity. In the Mecsek and Villány mountains the deepest facies is represented by brachiopod beds (Zuhánya Limestone), representing outer ramp deposits (Török 1993*a*). Open-marine conditions are indicated by the presence of ammonites and conodonts (Kovács & Rálisch-Felgenhauer 2005; Kovács *et al.* 2005) as well as the maximum abundance of marine acritarchs (Götz *et al.* 2003). A Bithynian–Pelsonian age for these beds is based on crinoids (Hagdorn *et al.* 1997) and palynomorphs (Götz *et al.* 2003). The Lapis Limestone corresponds to the lower and middle part of the Polish and German Lower Muschelkalk (lower Jena Formation; Török 2000); the Zuhánya Limestone represents a stratigraphical equivalent of the German and Polish Terebratel Beds (Götz *et al.* 2003).

In the upper Anisian (Illyrian) significant spatial differences occur in the grade of dolomitization and facies development. In the western Mecsek Mountains and the Villány Mountains, carbonates are extensively dolomitized (Csukma Dolomite). These beds formed in a supratidal to peritidal zone of the inner ramp (Fig. 13.42). In the central part of the Mecsek Mountains, limestones with intercalated beds of ooid/crinoid packstones/grainstones prevail (Kozár Limestone). These sediments are considered to be reworked crinoidal bioherms and may mark a relative sea-level fall (Török 1998*a*).

The lower Ladinian is characterized by bituminous oncoidal packstones and bivalve shell beds (*Trigonodus* coquinas). The calcarenites are interpreted as ooid/crinoid shoals which were transported offshore into the laminated to bioturbated mudstone/wackestone mid-ramp facies. The oncoidal packstones are of backshoal origin and considered as landward counterparts of oolite shoals (Török 1993*a*). The oncoidal beds are overlain by laminated organic-carbon-rich calcareous marls, representing the latest carbonate facies of the Ladinian (Kantavár Calcareous Marl; Fig. 13.42). The monotonous succession contains an abundant but low-diversity ostracod and gastropod fauna, as well as charophytes and plant fragments (Monostori 1996), indicating freshwater conditions, probably due to a climate change that is

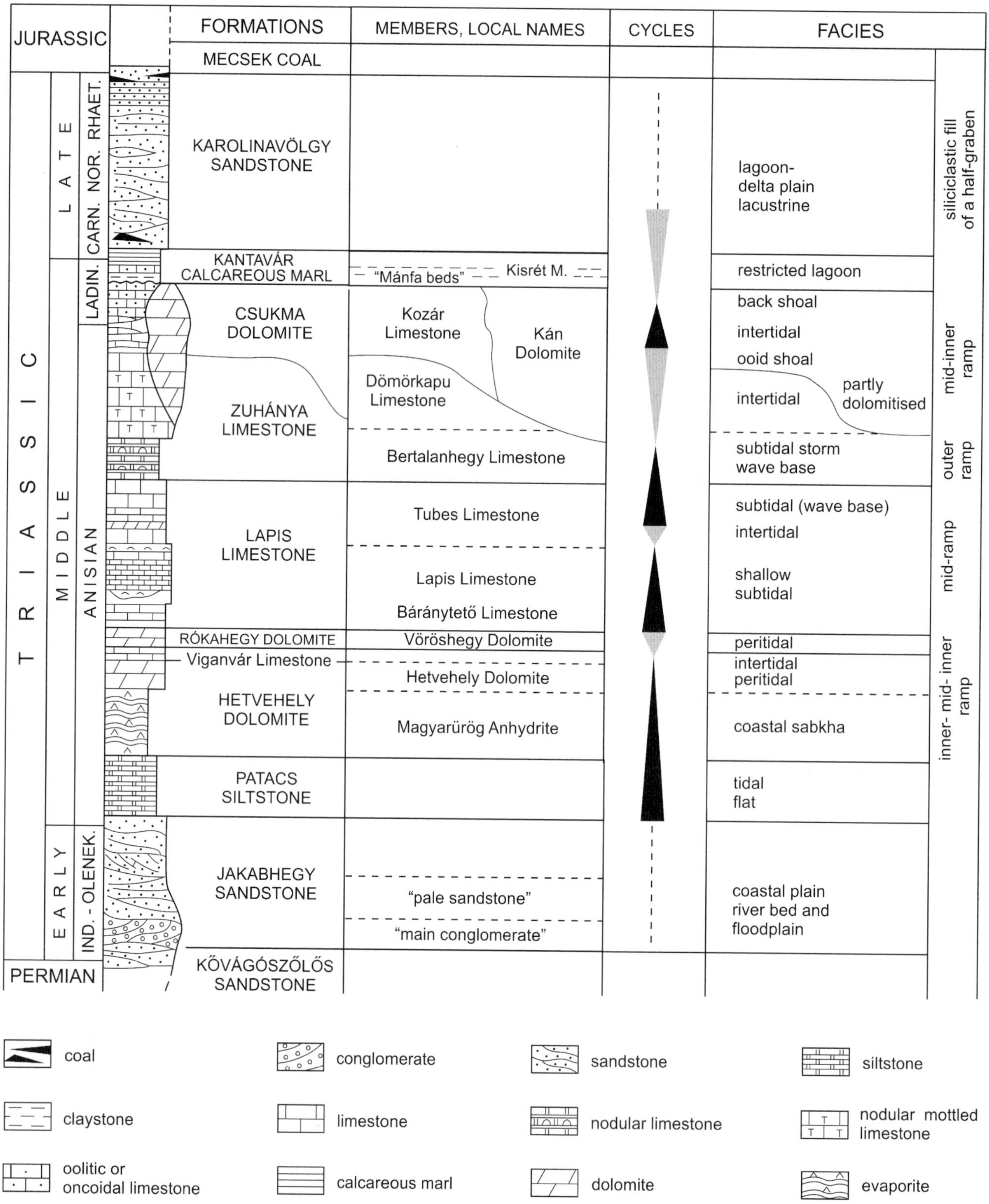


**Fig. 13.42.** Triassic lithostratigraphy and facies interpretation of the Mecsek Mountains (after Török 1998*b*, modified). Third-order cycles after Török (2000) and Götz *et al.* (2003).

also reflected in the gradually enhanced terrestrial input (Haas *et al.* 1995*b*).

An initial sequence stratigraphic interpretation of Middle Triassic ramp deposits of the Mecsek Mountains was published by Török (2000) and refined by Götz *et al.* (2003). Four third-order depositional sequences were recognized (Fig. 13.42) and correlated with third-order sequences of the Germanic Basin (Török 2000; Götz *et al.* 2003, 2005).

The Late Triassic is characterized by the differentiation of facies units within the Tisza Mega-unit into dolomites (western Mecsek Mountains, Villány Mountains, Codru and Papuk Mountains), siliciclastics (eastern Mecsek Mountains) and mixed carbonate–siliciclastic sequences (Bihor Mountains), all of which are similar both to the Germanic and to the Carpathian Keuper. The Late Triassic microflora of the Mecsek Mountains is very similar to that of the Carpathian Keuper. Characteristic index fossils of the Germanic realm, e.g. *Rhaetipollis germanicus,* are absent from both areas (Bóna 1995; Ruckwied *et al.* 2006; Ruckwied 2008). A rapidly subsiding half-graben structure developed in the eastern Mecsek Mountains, resulting in the formation of up to 500 m of arkosic sandstones and siltstones (Karolinavölgy Sandstone). Depositional environments include marginal marine, lagoonal, and deltaic to lacustrine settings (Nagy 1968). Elsewhere in the Tisza Mega-unit the Late Triassic is mainly represented by thinner mixed siliciclastic dolomitic successions (Bleahu *et al.* 1994). The upward transition of these beds into the Jurassic sequence is continuous in the Mecsek Mountains but a significant gap is observed in the Villány Mountains (Nagy & Nagy 1976).

## Palaeontology (S.F.B., A.E.G., J.S.)

The biotic crisis following the Permian–Triassic extinction is visible in the Lower Triassic successions of Central Europe where the lowermost Triassic deposits are extremely poor in faunal remains. The first organisms reappearing, both in the Alpine and the Germanic Lower Triassic, are microgastropods, some bivalves and lingulids which comprise typical assemblages of generalists that survived from the Permian. Other fossils include stromatolites, which are particularly well developed in the Germanic Basin (see below). The stromatolites are composed of interfingering, laminated segments of microbial origin (Paul & Peryt 2000) and small (<0.5 cm) lenticular sponge bodies (most probably dictyid Hexactinellida; Szulc 2003*b*). Sponge/microbial stromatolites also occur at other levels in the Triassic with high-stress environments, for example in the Röt and Middle Muschelkalk (Szulc 1997) and the Lower Keuper (Hagdorn *et al.* 1999; Bachmann 2002) of the Germanic Basin, and in the Reichenhaller and Gutenstein carbonates in the Alpine basins (Spötl 1988; Rychlinski & Szulc 2005).

It would appear that the small-size metazoan–bacterial associations that built the Lower Triassic stromatolites facilitated the survival and recovery of reef-forming organisms after the Permian–Triassic mass extinction. In Middle Triassic (Pelsonian) times, hexactinellid sponges, accompanied by the first scleractinian corals, gave rise to the oldest *in situ* reefs in the western Tethys province. The best developed Pelsonian sponge buildups occur in western Upper Silesia (Bodzioch 1994). The other reef-builders in these reefs include crinoids, brachiopods, encrusting foraminifers, serpulids and several species of scleractinian corals (Morycowa 1988).

The buildups occur in a belt (*c.* 150 km in length and 30 km in width) stretching from western Upper Silesia to the western Holy Cross Mountains (Fig. 13.5B). From the palaeobiogeographical point of view, the coral reefs in Silesia belong to the circum-Tethyan reef belt rather than to the epicontinental Germanic Basin.

Faunal migration and speciation within the Western Tethys domain is a problematical issue because, in contrast to the thoroughly analysed and synthesized data on biota from the Germanic Basin, studies on the Alpine faunal distribution and palaeobiogeography are dispersed and a modern integrated synthesis is lacking. It is, however, generally accepted that faunal migration was from the Tethys Ocean toward the Peri-Tethys Basin although faunal exchange was more complex than this, since some species evolved in the Germanic Basin and thereafter expanded to other regions, including the Tethys Ocean. An evolutionary pattern such as this involves, most particularly, microfaunal organisms. For instance, some species of the late Olenekian–Anisian foraminifer family Involutinidae appeared first in the Germanic Basin and afterwards in the Tethys Ocean (Gazdzicki *et al.* 1975). Similarly, some Middle Triassic conodont species (Narkiewicz & Szulc 2004) and Late Triassic ostracods (Beutler & Szulc 1999) evolved in the Germanic Basin and migrated to the Tethys basins. Comparison of the ratios between Tethyan and local forms, analysed in the Germanic Basin in relation to third-order depositional sequences, indicates that episodes of intensive migration of Tethyan forms coincide with transgressive phases, whereas the stabilized conditions during highstand phases favoured the origin of local species (Szulc 2000; Narkiewicz & Szulc 2004).

Faunal migration from the Tethys changed over time. Between the late Induan and early Anisian (Aegean), some groups (e.g. foraminifers, cephalopods) moved to southern Poland from the Palaeo-Tethys (Asian province) and the eastern Neo-Tethys basins (Parnes 1965; Glazek *et al.* 1973; Gazdzicki *et al.* 1975; Trammer 1975, 1979; Mostler 1993). In Pelsonian times, the eastern Neo-Tethys seaway, along with the mid-Neo-Tethys (Southern Alpine basins), became the most important migration pathways for the Muschelkalk faunal community (Buch 1849; Mojsisovics 1882; Bukowski 1895; Assmann 1937; Mostler 1993; Hagdorn & Gluchowski 1993; Hagdorn 1996*a, b*; Hagdorn *et al.* 1996). A striking affinity between the Muschelkalk in Silesia and in the Southern Alpine province is particularly evident for the fauna of the Pelsonian maximum transgression stage (Terebratula Beds in Upper Silesia and Recoaro Formation in the Southern Alps) (Bechstädt & Brandner 1970; De Zanche *et al.* 1992; Hagdorn & Gluchowski 1993; Hagdorn *et al.* 1996; Brack *et al.* 1999). A similar pattern can be seen in the faunal communities of the Transdanubian Range and the Mecsek Mountains which are very close to the above-mentioned regions (Pálfy & Török 1992; Hagdorn *et al.* 1997; Szente 1997). All of this would suggest that there was free communication between all of the above-mentioned basins.

In conclusion, the most probable communication pathway between the Germanic Basin and the Tethys Ocean for faunal migration in Anisian–Ladinian times was through the spreading belt of the Neo-Tethys rift which divided the Adria Plate and the later Rhodopes and Tisza microplates (Fig. 13.2). This north–south orientated spreading centre continued northward and joined the Silesian area via the reactivated Silesian-Moravian Fault (Fig. 13.3). In Ladinian times a western, poorly developed connection (see discussion in Szulc 2000) opened and Tethyan organisms migrated through the Swabian-Hessian Depression into SE Poland (Hagdorn & Simon 1993). It is also likely, as suggested by Mostler (1993), that the main migration pathway during Ladinian times comprised the western branch of the Neo-Tethys spreading belt, striking from Sicily towards the western part of the Germanic Basin (Fig. 13.2). In Ladinian–Norian times migration progressed through the same pathways, although migration events were short and episodic, due to the significant uplift of the Germanic area. In the Rhaetian this communication system persisted but a new marine seaway opened to the west, i.e. to the Proto-Atlantic Ocean.

The marine vertebrate fauna of the Germanic Basin include fishes and reptiles (Schoch & Wild 1999*a*). The diverse fish fauna comprises actinopterygians, represented by teeth, scales and complete specimens, rare coelacanths, and lungfishes (Schultze & Kriwet 1999). The group of marine reptiles is dominated by placodonts (*Placodus*, *Cyamodus*), sauropterygians (*Nothosaurus*, *Cymatosaurus*, *Simosaurus*) and thalattosaurs (*Blezingeria*); ichthyosaur (*Mixosaurus*) remains are rare. As for the invertebrates, the southern marine gateways of the Germanic Basin served as immigration pathways for these fossil groups. Therefore, the stratigraphic appearance and lateral occurrence of marine vertebrates provide additional information on the connecting seaways between the northwestern Tethys shelf and the Germanic Basin and the eustatic history of both palaeogeographic settings.

Triassic terrestrial vertebrate remains yield important data for the interpretation of the tetrapod evolution. Late Triassic fossils from localities in Germany (Schoch & Wild 1999*b*, *c*) and Poland (Dzik *et al.* 2000) improved our understanding of the diversification of giant stegocephalians (*Mastodonsaurus*), the origin of turtles (*Proterochersis*), early dinosaur phylogeny (*Plateosaurus*), and the evolution of mammals (therapsids). Famous excavation sites for Triassic vertebrates in Central Europe are situated in southern Germany (Trossingen (e.g. Seemann 1933) and Kupferzell (e.g. Schoch & Wild 1999*c*)) and Switzerland (Frick (e.g. Sander 1992) and Monte San Giorgio (e.g. Rieppel 1992)).

## Summary

Triassic facies development in Central Europe is characterized by two different palaeogeographic settings: (1) the NW Tethys shelf area (Tethyan or Alpine realm) and (2) the northern, peripheral, semi-closed Germanic Basin (Germanic realm). The sedimentary successions of both realms reflect the long-term transgressive evolution following a global sea-level lowstand at the end of the Permian, and a recovery of marine and terrestrial ecosystems after the most severe mass extinction in Earth's history.

Deposits of the Alpine realm document a marine development associated with the westward opening of the Tethys Ocean. In contrast, the Germanic Basin was lacking open marine conditions for most of the Triassic period. Marine incursions were controlled by connecting seaways between the Germanic Basin and the NW Tethys shelf. Major flooding occurred in the Pelsonian and at the time around the Fassanian–Longobardian boundary. These flooding phases affected both domains and are clearly documented in the sedimentary record by the presence of open-marine faunal elements. Within the Alpine realm, an increasing differentiation of depositional environments occurred from Ladinian times onwards. This resulted in the development of reef-dominated platforms, intrashelf and open-marine basins. In the Germanic realm, the marine evolution of the basin terminated in the early Carnian. A subsequent major flooding phase commenced during mid-Rhaetian times and gave rise to the transgressive systems of the succeeding Lower Jurassic stage. Facies diachroneity is a common feature in the Germanic Basin and is a result of the Tethyan ingressions. Tectonic movements are documented in both realms during the Triassic. They are represented by major unconformities and the deposition of seismites.

Biostratigraphic correlation of Alpine and Germanic deposits is most successful using palynology, which is applicable in both continental and marine environments. Recent magnetostratigraphic data provide a good basis for stratigraphic refinement. Depositional sequences have been described from Alpine and Germanic sedimentary successions but these require further refinement, in particular with respect to high-resolution sequence stratigraphy and cyclostratigraphy in the Milankovitch frequency band.

A. Wetzel (Basel) is thanked for helpful suggestions and improvements to the section on Switzerland. We thank R. Hoffmann and K. Hlawatsch (Halle) for drafting many of the figures, and T. Bechstädt (Heidelberg) for reviewing this chapter. We are very grateful to an anonymous reviewer who did a very thorough review of the manuscript and made many comments and suggestions that substantially contributed to improving this chapter.

## References

AEPPLER, R. 1974. Der Rhätsandstein von Tübingen – ein kondensiertes Delta. *Neues Jahrbuch für Geologie und Paläontologie, Abhandlungen*, **147**, 113–162.

AIGNER, T. 1985. *Storm Depositional Systems*. Lecture Notes in Earth Sciences, **3**, Springer, Berlin.

AIGNER, T. & BACHMANN, G. H. 1992. Sequence-stratigraphic framework of the German Triassic. *Sedimentary Geology*, **80**, 115–135.

AIGNER, T., SCHAUER, M., JUNGHANS, W.-D. & REINHARDT, L. 1995. Outcrop gamma-ray logging and its applications: examples from the German Triassic. *Sedimentary Geology*, **100**, 47–61.

AIGNER, T., HORNUNG, J., JUNGHANS, W.-D. & PÖPPELREITER, M. 1999. Baselevel cycles in the Triassic of the South-German Basin: a short progress report. *In*: BACHMANN, G. H. & LERCHE, I. (eds), Epicontinental Triassic. *Zentralblatt für Geologie und Paläontologie, Teil I*, **1998**(7–8), 537–544.

ALBERTI, F. A. VON 1834. *Beitrag zu einer Monographie des Bunten Sandsteins, Muschelkalks und Keupers, und die Verbindung dieser Gebilde zu einer Formation*. Cotta, Stuttgart.

AMES, R. & FARFAN, P. F. 1996. The environment of deposition of the Triassic Main Buntsandstein Formation in the P and Q quadrants, offshore the Netherlands. *In*: RONDEEL, H. E., BATJES, D. A. J., & NIEUWENHUIJS, W. H. (eds), *Geology of Gas and Oil under The Netherlands* Kluwer, Dordrecht, 167–178.

AMOROSI, A. 1995. Glaucony and sequence stratigraphy: a conceptual framework of distribution in siliciclastic sequences. *Journal of Sedimentary Research*, **B65**, 419–425.

ÁRKAI, P., BALOGH, K. & DUNKL, I. 1995. Timing of low-temperature metamorphism and cooling of the Paleozoic and Mesozoic formations of the Bükkium, innermost Western Carpathians, Hungary. *Geologische Rundschau*, **84**, 334–344.

ASSERETO, R., BOSELLINI, A., FANTINI SESTINI, N. & SWEET, W. C. 1973. The Permian–Triassic boundary in the Southern Alps (Italy). *In*: LOGAN, A. & HILLS, L. V. (eds) *The Permian and Triassic Systems and their Mutual Boundary.* Canadian Society of Petroleum Geologists, Memoirs, **2**, 176–199.

ASSMANN, P. 1926. Die Tiefbohrung "Oppeln". *Jahrbuch der Preussischen Geologischen Landesanstalt*, **46**, 373–395.

ASSMANN, P. 1937. Revision der Fauna der Wirbellosen der oberschlesischen Trias. *Abhandlungen der Preussischen Geologischen Landesanstalt, Neue Folge,* **170**, 1–134.

ASSMANN, P. 1944. Die Stratigraphie der oberschlesischen Trias. Teil 2: Der Muschelkalk. *Abhandlungen des Reichsamts für Bodenforschung*, **2**.

BACHMANN, G. H. 2002. A lamellibranch-stromatolite bioherm in the Lower Keuper (Ladinian, Middle Triassic), South Germany. *Facies*, **46**, 83–88.

BACHMANN, G. H. & KOZUR, H. W. 2004. The Germanic Triassic: correlations with the international chronostratigraphic scale, numerical ages and Milankovitch cyclicity. *Hallesches Jahrbuch für Geowissenschaften, Reihe B*, **26**, 17–62.

BACHMANN, G. H., BEUTLER, G., HAGDORN, H. & HAUSCHKE, N. 1999. Stratigraphie der Germanischen Trias. *In*: HAUSCHKE, N. & WILDE, V. (eds) *Trias, eine ganz andere Welt: Mitteleuropa im frühen Erdmittelalter.* Verlag Dr. Friedrich Pfeil, München, 81–104.

BALDSCHUHN, R., BINOT, F., FLEIG, S. & KOCKEL, F. 2001. Geotektonischer Atlas von Nordwestdeutschland und dem deutschen Nordsee-Sektor. *Geologisches Jahrbuch, Reihe A*, **153**.

BALOGH, K. & KOVÁCS, S. 1981. The Triassic sequence of the borehole Szőlősardó-1. *Annual Report of the Hungarian Geological Institute,*

**1979**, 39–63 [in Hungarian].

Balog, A., Haas, J., Read, J. F. & Coruh, C. 1997. Shallow marine record of orbitally forced cyclicity in a Late Triassic carbonate platform, Hungary. *Journal of Sedimentary Research*, **67**(4), 661–675.

Barabás, A. & Barabás-Stuhl, Á. 2005. Geology of the Lower Triassic Jakabhegy Sandstone Formation, Hungary, SE Transdanubia. *Acta Geologica Hungarica*, **48**, 1–47.

Barabás-Stuhl, Á. 1981. Microflora of the Permian and Lower Triassic sediments of the Mecsek Mountains (South Hungary). *Acta Geologica Hungarica*, **24**(1), 49–97.

Barabás-Stuhl, Á. 1993. Palynological revaluation of Lower Triassic and Lower Anisian formations of Southeast Transdanubia. *Acta Geologica Hungarica*, **36**(4), 405–458.

Baud, A. & Mégard-Galli, J. 1975. Évolution d'un bassin carbonaté du domaine alpin durant la phase pré-océanique: cycles et séquences dans le Trias de la zone briançonnaise des Alpes Occidentales et des Préalpes. *9th International Congress on Sedimentology*, 6–13 July 1975, Nice, 45–50.

Baud, A., Richoz, S., Cirilli, S. & Marcoux, J. 2003. Low latitude marine Permian-Triassic transition: a microbial world. *15th International Congress on Carboniferous and Permian Stratigraphy*, 10–16 August 2003, Utrecht, Abstracts, 41–42.

Bechstädt, T. & Brandner, R. 1970. Das Anis zwischen St. Vigil und dem Höhlensteintal (Pragser- und Olanger Dolomiten, Südtirol). *Festband des Geologischen Instituts, 300-Jahr-Feier Universität Innsbruck*, 9–103.

Bechstädt, T. & Schweizer, T. 1991. The carbonate-clastic cycles of the East-Alpine Raibl group: results of third-order sea-level fluctuations in the Carnian. *Sedimentary Geology*, **70**, 241–270.

Bechstädt, T., Brandner, R. & Mostler, H. 1976. Das Frühstadium der alpinen Geosynklinalentwicklung im westlichen Drauzug. *Geologische Rundschau*, **65**, 616–648.

Bechstädt, T., Brandner, R., Mostler, H. & Schmidt, K. 1978. Aborted rifting in the Triassic of the Eastern and Southern Alps. *Neues Jahrbuch für Geologie und Paläontologie, Abhandlungen*, **156**, 157–178.

Becker, A. 2000. Der Faltenjura: geologischer Rahmen, Bau und Entwicklung seit dem Miozän. *Jahresbericht und Mitteilungen des Oberrheinischen Geologischen Vereins, Neue Folge*, **82**, 317–336.

Becker, F., Lutz, M., Hoppe, A. & Etzold, A. 1997. Der Untere Muschelkalk am Südostrand des Schwarzwaldes – Lithostratigraphie und Gammastrahl-Log-Korrelation. *Jahresbericht und Mitteilungen des Oberrheinischen Geologischen Vereins, Neue Folge*, **79**, 91–109.

Becker, L., Poreda, R. J., Hunt, A. G., Bunch, T. E. & Rampino, M. 2001. Impact event at the Permian–Triassic boundary: evidence from extraterrestrial noble gases in fullerenes. *Science*, **291**, 1530–1533.

Becker, L., Poreda, R. J., Basu, A. R., Pope, K. O., Harrison, T. M., Nicolson, C. & Iasky, R. 2004. Bedout: a possible end-Permian impact crater offshore of Northwestern Australia. *Science*, **304**, 1469–1476.

Bércziné Makk, A. 1986. Mesozoic formation types of the Great Hungarian Plain. *Acta Geologica Hungarica*, **29**(3–4), 261–282.

Bércziné Makk, A. 1993. Szeged Dolomite Formation, Csanádapáca Dolomite Formation. *In:* Haas, J. (ed.) *Lithostratigraphic Units of Hungary, Triassic*. Magyar Állami Földtani Intézet, MOL Rt. Budapest, 265–269 [in Hungarian].

Bércziné Makk, A. 1998. Triassic and Jurassic formation types of the Great Hungarian Plain and Tokaj Mountains. *In:* Bérczi, I. & Jámbor, Á. (eds) *Magyarország geológiai képződményeinek rétegtana*. MOL Rt., Magyar Állami Földtani Intézet, Budapest, 281–298 [in Hungarian].

Bertelsen, F. 1980. *Lithostratigraphy and Depositional History of the Danish Triassic*. Geological Survey of Denmark, Series B, **4**.

Beutler, G. 1988. Die Bedeutung der Ostrakoden für die Abgrenzung des Räts in der Mitteleuropäischen Senke. *Freiberger Forschungshefte, Reihe C*, **419**, 11–17.

Beutler, G. 1995. *Stratigraphie des Keupers. Quantifizierung der altkimmerischen Bewegungen in Nordwestdeutschland Teil I*. Bundesanstalt für Geowissenschaften und Rohstoffe, Report **113087**.

Beutler, G. 1998. Keuper. *In:* Bachmann, G. H., Beutler, G. & Lerche, I. (eds) Excursions of the International Symposium on the Epicontinental Triassic, Halle (Saale), September 1998. *Hallesches Jahrbuch für Geowissenschaften, Reihe B*, **6**, 45–58.

Beutler, G. & Häusser, I. 1981. Über den Schilfsandstein der DDR. *Zeitschrift für Geologische Wissenschaften*, **10**, 511–525.

Beutler, G. & Schüler, F. 1978. Über altkimmerische Bewegungen im Norden der DDR und ihre regionale Bedeutung (Fortschrittsbericht). *Zeitschrift für Geologische Wissenschaften*, **6**, 403–420.

Beutler, G. & Schüler, F. 1979. Über Vorkommen salinarer Bildungen in der Trias im Norden der DDR. *Zeitschrift für Geologische Wissenschaften*, **7**, 903–912.

Beutler, G. & Schüler, F. 1987. Probleme und Ergebnisse der lithostratigraphischen Korrelation der Trias am Nordrand der Mitteleuropäischen Senke. *Zeitschrift für Geologische Wissenschaften*, **15**, 421–436.

Beutler, G. & Szulc, J. 1999. Die paläogeographische Entwicklung des Germanischen Beckens in der Trias und die Verbindung zur Tethys. *In*: Hauschke, N. & Wilde, V. (eds) *Trias, eine ganz andere Welt: Mitteleuropa im frühen Erdmittelalter*. Verlag Dr. Friedrich Pfeil, München, 71–80.

Beutler, G., Hauschke, N. & Nitsch, E. 1999. Faziesentwicklung des Keupers im Germanischen Becken. *In*: Hauschke, N. & Wilde, V. (eds) *Trias, eine ganz andere Welt: Mitteleuropa im frühen Erdmittelalter*. Verlag Dr. Friedrich Pfeil, München, 129–174.

Bleahu, M., Mantea, Gh., *et al.* 1994. Triassic facies types, evolution and paleogeographic relations of the Tisza Megaunit. *Acta Geologica Hungarica*, **37**, 187–234.

Blendinger, E. 1988. Palynostratigraphy of the Late Ladinian and Carnian in the southeastern Dolomites. *Review of Palaeobotany and Palynology*, **53**, 329–348.

Bloos, G. 1979. Über den Jura am großen Haßberg (Unterfranken, N-Bayern) mit Bemerkungen zum Rät. *Stuttgarter Beiträge zur Naturkunde*, **B 44**, 1–53.

Bodzioch, A. 1994. Paleoecology of hexactinellid sponges from the epicontinental Triassic of Poland. *In*: Van Soest, R., Van Kempen, T. & Braekman, J.-C. (eds) *Sponges in Time and Space*. Balkema, Rotterdam, 35–44.

Boigk, H. & Schöneich, H. 1974. Perm, Trias und älterer Jura im Bereich der Mittelmeer-Mjösen-Zone und des Rheingrabens. *In*: Illies, J. H. & Fuchs, K. (eds) *Approaches to Taphrogenesis*. Inter-Union Commission on Geodynamics, Scientific Reports, **8**, E. Schweizerbart'sche Verlagsbuchhandlung (Nägele u. Obermiller), Stuttgart, 60–71.

Bóna, J. 1976. Triassic conodonts from Villány Mountains. *Geologica Hungarica Series Geologica*, **17**, 229–253 [in Hungarian with German abstract].

Bóna, J. 1995. Palynostratigraphy of the Upper Triassic formations in Mecsek Mts. (Southern Hungary). *Acta Geologica Hungarica*, **17**, 230–253.

Borkhataria, R. 2004. *Integrated exploration- and production-scale reservoir prediction in "grainy" and "muddy" epeiric carbonate ramp deposits: The Muschelkalk (Triassic), The Netherlands*. PhD thesis, University of Tübingen.

Boronin, V. P. & Petrov, P. P. 1986. *Paleomagnetic Directions and Pole Positions: Data for the USSR*, issue 6. Soviet Geophysical Committee. World Data Center-B Catalogue, Moscow.

Bosellini, A. 1984. Progradation geometries of carbonate platforms: examples from the Triassic of the Dolomites, northern Italy. *Sedimentology*, **31**, 1–24.

Bourquin, S. & Guillocheau, F. 1996. Keuper stratigraphic cycles in the Paris Basin and comparison with cycles in other Peritethyan basins (German Basin and Bresse-Jura Basin). *Sedimentary Geology*, **105**, 159–182.

Bourquin, S., Vairon, J. & Le Strat, P. 1997. Three-dimensional evolution of the Keuper of the Paris basin based on detailed isopach maps of the stratigraphic cycles: tectonic influences. *Geologische Rundschau*, **86**, 670–685.

Brack, P. & Rieber, H. 1993. Towards a better definition of the Anisian/Ladinian boundary: new biostratigraphic data and correlations of boundary sections from the Southern Alps. *Eclogae Geologicae Helvetiae*, **86**(2), 415–527.

Brack, P. & Rieber, H. 1994. The Anisian/Ladinian boundary: retrospective and new constraints. *Albertiana*, **13**, 25–36.

Brack, P., Mundil, R., Oberli, F., Meier, M. & Rieber, H. 1996. Biostratigraphic and radiometric age data question the Milankovitch characteristics of the Latemar cycles (Southern Alps, Italy). *Geology*, **24**(4), 371–375.

BRACK, P., RIEBER, H. & URLICHS, M. 1999. Pelagic successions in the Southern Alps and their correlation with the Germanic Middle Triassic. *In*: BACHMANN, G. H. & LERCHE, I. (eds) Epicontinental Triassic. *Zentralblatt für Geologie und Paläontologie, Teil I*, **1998**(7–8), 853–876.

BRACK, P., RIEBER, H., NICORA, A. & MUNDIL, R. 2005. The Global boundary Stratotype Section and Point (GSSP) of the Ladinian Stage (Middle Triassic) at Bagolino (Southern Alps, Northern Italy) and its implications for the Triassic time scale. *Episodes*, **28**(4), 233–244.

BRANDNER, R. 1984. Meeresspiegelschwankungen und Tektonik in der Trias der NW-Tethys. *Jahrbuch der Geologischen Bundesanstalt (Wien)*, **126**, 435–475.

BRANDNER, R. & MOSTLER, H. 1982. Der geologische Aufbau des Schlerngebietes und seiner weiteren Umgebung. *In*: MOSTLER, H. (ed.) *Jahrestagung der Österreichischen Geologischen Gesellschaft. Exkursionführer.* Seis an Schlern, Südtirol, 1–42.

BRENNER, K. & VILLINGER, E. 1981. Stratigraphie und Nomenklatur des südwestdeutschen Sandsteinkeupers. *Jahreshefte des Geologischen Landesamts Baden-Württemberg*, **23**, 45–86.

BRGM 1964. Mouthe. *Carte géologique détaillée de la France 1:50'000*, feuille No 530. Service de la Carte géologique de France, Orléans.

BRGM 1965. Champagnole. *Carte géologique détaillée de la France 1:50'000*, feuille No 582. Service de la Carte géologique de France, Orléans.

BRGM 1975. Quingey. *Carte géologique détaillée de la France 1:50'000*, feuille No 529. Service de la Carte géologique de France, Orléans.

BROGLIO LORIGA, C., MASETTI, C. & NERI, C. 1983. La Formazione di Werfen (Scitico) delle Dolomiti occidentali: sedimentologia e biostratigrafia. *Rivista Italiana di Paleontologia e Stratigrafia*, **88**(4), 501–598.

BROGLIO LORIGA, C., NERI, C., PASINI, M. & POSENATO, R. 1988. Marine fossil assemblages from Upper Permian to lowermost Triassic in the Western Dolomites/Italy. *Memorie della Società Geologica Italiana*, **34**, 5–44.

BROGLIO LORIGA, C., GÓCZÁN, F., *et al.* 1990. The Lower Triassic sequences of the Dolomites (Italy), Transdanubian Mid-Mountains (Hungary), their correlation. *Memorie di Scienze Geologiche, Padova*, **42**, 41–103.

BRUGMAN, W. A. 1986. *A palynological characterization of the Upper Scythian and Anisian of the Transdanubian Central Range (Hungary) and the Vincentinian Alps (Italy)*. PhD Thesis, State University Utrecht.

BUCH, L. VON 1845. Über einige merkwürdige Muschel-Reste des oberen Italiens. *Monatsberichte der Königlich Preussischen Akademie der Wissenschaften Berlin*, **1845**, 25–28.

BUCH, L. VON 1849. Über schlesischen und italienischen Muschelkalk. *Zeitschrift der Deutschen Geologischen Gesellschaft*, **1**, 246–247.

BÜCHI, U. P., LEMCKE, K. WIENER, G. & ZIMDARS, J. 1965. Geologische Ergebnisse der Erdölexploration auf das Mesozoikum im Untergrund des schweizerischen Molassebeckens. *Bulletin der Vereinigung Schweizerischer Petroleum-Geologen und -Ingenieure*, **32**(82), 7–38.

BUDAI, T. & VÖRÖS, A. 1992. Middle Triassic history of the Balaton Highland: extensional tectonics, basin evolution. *Acta Geologica Hungarica*, **35**(3), 237–250.

BUKOWSKI, G. VON 1895. Cephalopodenfunde in dem Muschelkalk von Braic in Süddalmatien. *Verhandlungen der Königlich-Kaiserlichen Geologischen Reichsanstalt*, **12**, 319–323.

BURCHETTE, T. P. & WRIGHT, V. P. 1992. Carbonate ramp depositional systems. *Sedimentary Geology*, **79**, 3–57.

BUSER, S., GRAD, K., OGORELEC, B., RAMOVŠ, A. & ŠRIBAR, L. 1988. Stratigraphical, paleontological and sedimentological characteristics of Upper Permian Beds in Slovenia, NW Yugoslavia. *Memorie della Società Geologica Italiana*, **34**, 195–210.

CAMERON, T. D. J., CROSBY, A., BALSON, P. S., JEFFERY, D. H., LOTT, G. K., BULAT, J. & HARRISON, D. H. 1992. *United Kingdom Offshore Regional Reports: The Geology of the Southern North Sea*. HMSO for British Geological Survey, London.

CAMPBELL, I. H., CZAMANSKE, G. K., FEDORENKO, V. A., HIL, R. I. & STEPANOV, V. 1992. Synchronism of the Siberian Traps and the Permian-Triassic boundary. *Science*, **258**, 1760–1763.

CASTELLARIN, A., LUCCHINI, F., ROSSI, P. L, SELLI, L. & SIMBOLI, G. 1988. The Middle Triassic magmatic-tectonic arc development in the Southern Alps. *Tectonophysics*, **146**, 79–89.

CASTELLARIN, A., SELLI, L., PICOTTI, V. & CANTELLI, L. 1998. Tettonismo e diapirismo medio Triassico delle Dolomiti. *In*: BOSELLINI, A. & STEFANI, C. (eds) *Geologia delle Dolomiti*. Memorie di Società Geologica Italiana, **53**, 145–169.

CHANNELL, J. E. T., KOZUR, H. W., SIEVERS, T., MOCK, R., AUBRECHT, R. & SYKORA, M. 2003. Carnian-Norian biomagnetostratigraphy at Silicka Brezova (Slovakia): correlation to other Tethyan sections and to Newark Basin. *Palaeogeography, Palaeoclimatology, Palaeoecology*, **191**, 65–109.

CLEMENS, S. C., WANG, P. & PRELL, W. L. (eds) 2003. Asian monsoons and global linkages on Milankovitch and sub-Milankovitch time scales. *Marine Geology*, **201**, 1–250.

CROSS, T. A. & LESSENGER, M. A. 1997. Correlation strategies for clastic wedges. *In*: COALSON, E. B., OSMOND, J. C. & WILLIAMS, E. T. (eds) *Innovative Applications of Petroleum Technology in the Rocky Mountain area*. Rocky Mountain Association of Geologists, Denver, 183–203.

CROSS, T. A. & LESSENGER, M. A. 1998. Sediment volume partitioning: rationale for stratigraphic model evaluation and high-resolution stratigraphic correlation. *In*: GRADSTEIN, F. M., SANDVIK, K. O. & MILTON, N. J. (eds) *Sequence Stratigraphy – Concepts and Applications*. Norwegian Petroleum Society, Special Publications, **8**, 171–195.

DADLEZ, R. & KOPIK, J. 1963. Problem of the Rhaetian in western Poland in the light of the profile at Ksiaz Wielkopolski. *Kwartalnik Geologiczny*, **7**, 131–155.

DADLEZ, R., MAREK, S. & POKORSKI, J. (eds) 1998. *Paleogeographical Atlas of the Epicontinental Permian and Mesozoic in Poland (1: 2,500,000)*. Panstwowy Instytut Geologiczny, Warszawa.

DE ZANCHE, V., FRANZIN, A., GIANOLLA, P., MIETTO, P. & SIORPAES, C. 1992. The Piz da Peres section (Valdaora-Olang, Pusteria Valley, Italy). A reappraisal of Anisian stratigraphy in the Dolomites. *Eclogae Geologicae Helvetiae*, **85**, 127–143.

DEBELMAS, J. 1986. L'héritage hercynien à l'origine des grands bassins sédimentaires français. *Bulletin du Centre de Recherches Elf Exploration Production*, **10**, 151–161.

DEBRAND-PASSARD, S., COURBOULIEX, S. & LIENHARDT, M.-J. 1984. *Synthèse géologique du sud-est de la France*. Mémoires du Bureau de Recherches Géologiques et Minières, **125 & 126**.

DECZKOWSKI, Z. 1997. Norian and Rhaetian. Sedimentation, paleogeography and paleotectonics. *In*: MAREK, S. & PAJCHLOWA, M. (eds) The epicontinental Permian and Mesozoic in Poland. *Prace Panstwowego Instytutu Geologicznego*, **153**, 144–150 [in Polish with English abstract].

DECZKOWSKI, Z. & GAJEWSKA, I. 1977. Early Cimmerian and Laramian structural blocks of the Foresudetic monocline. *Kwartalnik Geologiczny*, **21**, 467–479 [in Polish].

DEMONFAUCON, A. 1982. *Le Muschelkalk supérieur de la Vallée de la Moselle, Grand Duché de Luxembourg*. PhD Thesis, University of Dijon.

DERCOURT, J., GAETANI, M., *et al.* 2000. *Atlas Peri-Tethys, Palaeogeographical Maps*. Commission de la Carte Géologique du Monde/ Commission for the Geologic Map of the World, Explanatory Notes, Gauthier-Villars, Paris.

DETRE, C. 1973. The first and best preserved ammonoid fossil from the Triassic of Mecsek. *In*: *Annual Report of the Hungarian Geological Institute, 1971*, Budapest, 277–282 [in Hungarian with German abstract].

DEUTSCHE STRATIGRAPHISCHE KOMMISSION (ed.) 2002. *Stratigraphic Table of Germany 2002*. Geo-Forschungs-Zentrum, Potsdam.

DEUTSCHE STRATIGRAPHISCHE KOMMISSION (ed.) 2005. Stratigraphie von Deutschland IV, Keuper. *Courier Forschungsinstitut Senckenberg*, **253**.

DIEDRICH, C. 2000. Neue Wirbeltierfährten aus dem Unteren Muschelkalk (Mitteltrias) des Osnabrücker Berglandes und Teutoburger Waldes (NW-Deutschland) und ihre stratigraphische und paläogeographische Bedeutung im Germanischen Becken. *Neues Jahrbuch für Geologie und Paläontologie, Abhandlungen*, **217**, 369–395.

DITTRICH, D. 1989. Der Schilfsandstein als synsedimentär-tektonisch geprägtes Sediment – eine Umdeutung bisheriger Befunde. *Zeits-*

*chrift der Deutschen Geologischen Gesellschaft*, **140**, 295–310.

DOLENEC, M. & OGORELEC, B. 2001. Organic carbon isotope variability across the P/Tr boundary in the Idrijca Valley section (Slovenia): A high resolution study. *Geologija*, **44**, 331–340.

DOLENEC, T. & RAMOVŠ, A. 1998. Isotopic changes at the Permian-Triassic boundary in the Idrijca Valley (W. Slovenia). *Rudarsko-metalurski zbornik. Materiali in okolje*, **3–4**, 405–411.

DOLENEC, M., OGORELEC, B. & LOJEN, S. 2003. Upper Carboniferous to Lower Triassic carbon isotopic signature carbonate rocks of the western Tethys (Slovenia). *Geologica Carpathica*, **54**, 217–228.

DRONKERT, H., BLÄSI, H.-R. & MATTER, A. 1990. Facies and origin of Triassic evaporites from the NAGRA boreholes, Northern Switzerland. *Geologischer Bericht (Landeshydrologie und geologie)*, **12**, 1–120.

DUALEH, A. R. A. 1995. Charakteristik, Entstehung und geologische Bedeutung der Querplattung im Wellenkalk von Rüdersdorf. *Berliner Geowissenschaftliche Abhandlungen, Reihe A*, **168**, 249–257.

DUCHROW, H. 1968. Zur Keuper-Stratigraphie in Südostlippe (Trias, Nordwestdeutschland). *Zeitschrift der deutschen Geologischen Gesellschaft*, **117**, 620–662.

DUCHROW, H. 1984. Der Keuper im Osnabrücker Bergland. Mit einer Revision der nordwestdeutschen Keupergliederung. *In:* KLASSEN, H. (ed.) *Geologie des Osnabrücker Berglandes*. Naturwissenschaftliches Museum, Osnabrück, 221–333.

DZIK, J., SULEJ, T., KAIM, A., & NIEDŹWIECKI, R. 2000. A late Triassic tetrapod graveyard in the Opole Silesia (SW Poland). *Przegląd Geologiczny*, **48**, 226–235.

ECKE, H.-H. 1986. *Palynologie des Zechsteins und Unteren Butsandsteins im Germanischen Becken*. PhD Thesis, University of Göttingen.

EDEL, J. B. & DURINGER, P. 1997. The apparent polar wander path of the European plate in Upper Triassic-Lower Jurassic times and the Liassic intraplate fracturing of Pangaea: new palaeomagnetic constraints from NW France and SW Germany. *Geophysical Journal International*, **128**, 331–344.

EMMERICH, A., GLASMACHER, U. A., BAUER, F., BECHSTÄDT, T. & ZÜHLKE, R. 2005*a*. Meso-/Cenozoic basin and carbonate platform development in the SW-Dolomites unraveled by basin modelling and apatite FT analysis: Rosengarten and Latemar (Northern Italy). *Sedimentary Geology*, **175**, 415–438.

EMMERICH, A., ZAMPARELLI, V., BECHSTADT, T. & ZÜHLKE, R. 2005*b*. The reefal margin and slope of a Middle Triassic carbonate platform (Dolomites, Italy). *Facies*, **50**, 573–614.

ERNI, A. 1926. Zur Rhätfrage im Schweizer Juragebirge. *Centralblatt für Mineralogie, Abteilung* B, **7**, 241–253.

ERWIN, D. H. 1993. *The Great Paleozoic Crisis: Life and Death in the Permian*. Columbia University Press, New York.

ERWIN, D. H. 1994. The Permo-Triassic extinction. *Nature*, **367**, 231–236.

ERWIN, D. H., BOWRING, S. A. & YUGAN, J. 2002. End-Permian mass extinctions: A review. *In:* KOEBERL, C. & MACLEOD, K. G. (eds) *Catastrophic Events and Mass Extinctions: Impacts and Beyond*. Geological Society of America, Special Papers, **356**, 363–383.

ETZOLD, A. & SCHWEIZER, V. 2005. Der Keuper in Baden-Württemberg. *In:* Deutsche Stratigraphische Kommision (ed.): Stratigraphie von Deutschland IV, Keuper. *Courier Forschungsinstitut Senckenberg*, **253**, 214–258.

FABRE, A. 1986. *Le temps dans la construction des courbes de dérive apparente du pôle paléomagnetique: Application à l'Europe du Permien au Jurassique*. PhD Thesis, University of Brest.

FAIRBRIDGE, R. W. 1986. Monsoons and paleomonsoons. *Episodes*, **9**, 143–149.

FEIST-BURKHARDT, S., GÖTZ, A. E., RUCKWIED, K. & RUSSELL, J. W. 2008. Palynofacies patterns, acritarch diversity and stable isotope signatures in the Lower Muschelkalk (Middle Triassic) of N Switzerland: Evidence of third-order cyclicity. *Eclogae Geologicae Helvetiae* (in press).

FILIPOVIĆ, I., JOVANOVIĆ, D., SUDAR, M., PELIKÁN, P., KOVÁCS, S., LESS, G. & HIPS, K. 2003. Comparison of the Variscan – Early Alpine evolution of the Jadar Block (NW Serbia) and "Bükkium" (NE Hungary) terranes; some paleogeographic implications. *Slovak Geological Magazine*, **9**, 3–21.

FISCHER, A. G. 1964. The Lofer cyclothems of the alpine Triassic. *Kansas Geological Survey, Bulletin*, **169**, 107–149.

FISCHER, H., HAUBER, L. & WITTMANN, O. 1971. *Geologischer Atlas der Schweiz 1:25'000, Erläuterungen zum Blatt Nr. 59 Basel*. Schweizerische Geologische Kommission, Basel.

FISHER, M. J. 1972. The Triassic palynofloral succession in England. *Geoscience and Man*, **4**, 101–109.

FISHER, M. J. & MUDGE, D. C. 1990. Triassic. *In:* GLENNIE, K. W. (ed.) *Introduction to the Petroleum Geology of the North Sea*, 3rd edn. Blackwell Scientific Publishing, Oxford, 191–214.

FISHER, M. J. & MUDGE, D. C. 1998. Triassic. *In:* GLENNIE, K. W. (ed.) *Petroleum Geology of the North Sea*, 4th edn. Blackwell Scientific Publishing, Oxford, 212–244.

FLÜGEL, E. 2002. Triassic reef patterns. *In*: KIESSLING, W., FLÜGEL, E. & GOLONKA, J. (eds) *Phanerozoic Reef Patterns*. Society for Sedimentary Geology (SEPM), Special Publications, **72**, 391–464.

FLÜGEL, E., VELLEDITS, F., SENOWBARI-DARYAN, B. & RIEDEL, P. 1992. Rifforganismen aus "Wettersteinkalken" (Karn?) des Bükk-Gebirges, Ungarn. *Geologisch-Paläontologische Mitteilungen Innsbruck*, **18**, 35–62.

FONTAINE, J. M., GUASTELLA, G., JOUAULT, P. & DE LA VEGA, P. 1993. F15-A: a Triassic gas field on the eastern limit of the Dutch Central Graben. *In*: PARKER, J. R. (ed.) *Petroleum Geology of Northwest Europe*, Proceedings of the 4th Conference, London, 29 March–1 April 1992. Geological Society, London, 583–593.

FREUDENBERGER, W. 1996. Trias. *Erläuterungen zur geologischen Karte von Bayern 1:500 000*, 4th edn. Bayerisches Geologischeslandesamt, Munich, 65–89.

FRISCH, U. & KOCKEL, F. 1999. Quantification of Early Cimmerian movements in NW-Germany. *In*: BACHMANN, G. H. & LERCHE, I. (eds) Epicontinental Triassic. *Zentralblatt für Geologie und Paläontologie, Teil I*, **1998**(7–8), 571–600.

FRITSCH, D. & HÜSSNER, H. 1996. Sequenz- und Zyclostratigraphie der Kössener Schichten (Ober-Trias, Nördliche Kalkalpen). *Zentralblatt für Geologie und Paläontologie, Teil I*, **1995**, 1–2, 73–86.

FRUTH, I. & SCHERREIKS, R. 1982. Hauptdolomit (Norian) stratigraphy, paleogeography and diagenesis. *Sedimentary Geology*, **32**, 195–231.

FUCHS, A. & ZWENGER, W. H. 1995. Conodonten im unteren Muschelkalk (Trias) von Rüdersdorf. *Berliner Geowissenschaftliche Abhandlungen*, **A 168**, 287–291.

FÜCHSEL, J. C. 1761. Historia terrae et maris ex historia Thuringiae per montium descriptionem eruta. *Acten der Erfurter Academie*, **1761**.

FUGLEWICZ, R. 1980. Stratigraphy and palaeogeography of Lower Triassic in Poland on the basis of megaspores. *Acta Geologica Polonica*, **30**, 417–470.

GAETANI, M. 2000. Early Ladinian (238–235 Ma). *In:* DERCOURT, J., GAETANI, M. *et al.* (eds) *Atlas Peri-Tethys, Palaeogeographical Maps*. Commission de la Carte Géologique du Monde/Commission for the Geologic Map of the World, Gauthier-Villars, Paris, 33–40.

GAETANI, M., GNACCOLINI, M., JADOUL, F. & GARZANTI, E. 1998. Multiorder sequence stratigraphy in the Triassic system of the western Southern Alps. *In*: DE GRACIANSKY, P.-C., HARDENBOL, J., JACQUIN, T. & VAIL, P. R. (eds) *Mesozoic and Cenozoic Sequence Stratigraphy of European Basins*. Society for Sedimentary Geology (SEPM), Special Publications, **60**, 701–717.

GAJEWSKA, I. 1997. Middle Triassic: Muschelkalk-Lower Keuper. Sedimentation, paleogeography and paleotectonics. *In*: MAREK, S. & PAJCHLOWA, M. (eds) The epicontinental Permian and Mesozoic in Poland. *Prace Panstwowego Instytutu Geologicznego*, **153**, 144–150 [in Polish with English abstract].

GALLET, Y., KRYSTYN, L. & BESSE, J. 1998. Upper Anisian and Lower Carnian magnetostratigraphy from the northern Calcareous Alps (Austria). *Journal of Geophysical Research*, **103**, 605–622.

GALTON, P. M. 1986. Prosauropod dinosaur *Plateosaurus* (= *Gresslyosaurus*) (Saurischia; Sauropodomorpha) from the Upper Triassic of Switzerland. *Geologica et Paleontologica*, **20**, 167–183.

GÄRTNER, H. & RÖHLING, H.-G. 1993. Zur lithostratigraphischen Gliederung und Paläogeographie des Mittleren Muschelkalks im Nordwestdeutschen Becken. *In*: HAGDORN, H. & SEILACHER, A. (eds) *Muschelkalk. Schöntaler Symposium 1991*. Goldschneck-Verlag, Werner K. Weidert, Korb, 85–103.

GARZANTI, E. 1985. The sandstone memory of the evolution of a Triassic volcanic arc in the Southern Alps, Italy. *Sedimentology*, **32**, 423–433.

GAUPP, R. 1991. Zur Fazies und Diagenese des Mittelrät-Hauptsandsteins im Gasfeld Thönse. *In:* Das Gasfeld Thönse in Niedersachsen – Ein Unikat. *Veröffentlichungen der Niedersächsischen Akademie der*

*Geowissenschaften*, **6**, 34–55.

Gaupp, R., Voigt, T., Lützner, H., Müller, H. & Föhlisch, K. 1998. Stratigraphy and sedimentological evolution of Lower and Middle Triassic deposits in the SE part of the Germanic Triassic Basin. *In*: Bachmann, G. H., Beutler, G. & Lerche, I. (eds) Excursions of the International Symposium on the Epicontinental Triassic, Halle (Saale), September 1998. *Hallesches Jahrbuch für Geowissenschaften, Reihe B*, **6**, 99–120.

Gawlick, H-J., Krystyn, L., Lein, R. & Mandl, G. W. 1999. Tectonostratigraphic concept for the Juvavic domain. *Tübinger Geowissenschaftliche Arbeiten, Reihe A*, **52**, 95–99.

Gazdzicki, A., Trammer, J. & Zawidzka, K. 1975. Foraminifers from the Muschelkalk of southern Poland. *Acta Geologica Polonica*, **25**, 286–298.

Gehrmann, O. & Aigner, T. 2002. Der Schilfsandstein (Obere Trias) bei Heilbronn (SW-Deutschland): Hinweise auf tidale Einflüsse. *Neues Jahrbuch für Geologie und Paläontologie, Abhandlungen*, **223**(3), 377–403.

Geiger, M. E. & Hopping, C. A. 1968. Triassic stratigraphy of the southern North Sea basin. *Philosophical Transactions of the Royal Society of London*, **B 254**, 1–36.

Geluk, M. C. 1999. Palaeogeographic and structural development of the Triassic in the Netherlands – new insights. *In*: Bachmann, G. H. & Lerche, I. (eds) Epicontinental Triassic. *Zentralblatt für Geologie und Paläontologie, Teil I*, **1998**(7–8), 545–570.

Geluk, M. C. 2005. *Stratigraphy and tectonics of Permo-Triassic basins in the Netherlands and surrounding areas*. PhD Thesis, Utrecht University.

Geluk, M. C. & Röhling, H.-G. 1997. High-resolution sequence stratigraphy of the Lower Triassic "Buntsandstein" in the Netherlands and northwestern Germany. *Geologie en Mijnbouw*, **76**, 227–246.

Geluk, M. C. & Röhling, H.-G. 1999. High-resolution sequence stratigraphy of the Lower Triassic Buntsandstein: a new tool for basin analysis. *In*: Bachmann, G. H. & Lerche, I. (eds) Epicontinental Triassic. *Zentralblatt für Geologie und Paläontologie, Teil I*, **1998**(7–8), 727–746.

Geluk, M. C., Plomp, A. & Van Doorn, T. H. M. 1996. Development of the Permo-Triassic succession in the basin fringe area, southern Netherlands. *In*: Rondeel, H. E., Batjes, D. A. J. & Nieuwenhuijs, W. H. (eds) *Geology of Gas and Oil under The Netherlands*. Kluwer, Dordrecht, 57–78.

Geluk, M. C., Brückner-Röhling, S. & Röhling, H.-G. 2000. Salt occurrences in the Netherlands and Germany: new insights in the formation of salt basins. *In*: Geertman, R. M. (ed.) *Proceedings of the 8th World Salt Symposium*. Elsevier, Amsterdam, 131–136.

Geyer, O. F. & Gwinner, M. P. 1968. *Einführung in die Geologie von Baden-Württemberg*, 2nd edn. E. Schweizerbart'sche Verlagsbuchhandlung (Nägele u. Obermiller), Stuttgart.

Geyer, O. F. & Gwinner, M. P. 1986. *Geologie von Baden-Württemberg*, 3rd edn. E. Schweizerbart'sche Verlagsbuchhandlung (Nägele u. Obermiller), Stuttgart.

Gianolla, P. & Jacquin, T. 1998. Triassic sequence stratigraphy of Western European Basins. *In*: De Graciansky, P.-C., Hardenbol, J., Jacquin, T. & Vail, P. R. (eds) *Mesozoic and Cenozoic Sequence Stratigraphy of European Basins*. Society for Sedimentary Geology (SEPM), Special Publications, **60**, 643–650.

Gianolla, P., de Zanche, V. & Mietto, P. 1998. Triassic sequence stratigraphic in the Southern Alps (northern Italy): definition of sequences and basin evolution. *In*: De Graciansky, P.-C., Hardenbol, J., Jacquin, T. & Vail, P. R. (eds) *Mesozoic and Cenozoic Sequence Stratigraphy of European Basins*. Society for Sedimentary Geology (SEPM), Special Publications, **60**, 719–747.

Glazek, J. & Roniewicz, P. 1976. Clastic dykes of the Buntsandstein in the Holy Cross Mts. *Przeglad Geologiczny*, **24**, 456–458.

Glazek, J., Trammer, J. & Zawidzka, K. 1973. The Alpine microfacies with *Glomospira densa* (Pantic) in the Muschelkalk of Poland and some related paleogeographical and geotectonic problems. *Acta Geologica Polonica*, **23**, 463–482.

Glowacki, E. & Senkowiczowa, H. 1969. Some notes on the Triassic from SE Poland. *Kwartalnik Geologiczny*, **13**, 338–355 [in Polish with English abstract].

Góczán, F., Haas, J. & Oravecz-Scheffer, A. 1987. Permian-Triassic boundary in the Transdanubian Central Range. *Acta Geologica Hungarica*, **30**, 35–58.

Goldhammer, R. K., Dunn, P. A. & Hardie, L. A. 1987. High-frequency glacio-eustatic oscillations with Milankovitch characteristics recorded in northern Italy. *American Journal of Sciences*, **287**, 853–892.

Goldhammer, R. K., Harris, M. T., Dunn, P. A. & Hardie, L. A. 1993. Sequence stratigraphy and system tract development of the Latemar Platform, middle Triassic of the Dolomites (Northern Italy): outcrop calibration keyed by cycle stacking patterns. *In*: Louks, R. G. & Sarg, J. F. (eds) *Carbonate Sequence Stratigraphy: Recent Developments and Applications*. American Association of Petroleum Geologists (AAPG), Memoirs, **57**, 353–388.

Goldsmith, P. J., Hudson, G. & Van Veen, P. 2003. Triassic. *In*: Evans, D., Graham, C., Armour, A. & Bathurst, P. (eds) *The Millennium Atlas: Petroleum Geology of the Central and Northern North Sea*. Geological Society, London, 105–127.

Golebiowski, R. 1989. *Stratigraphie und Biofazies der Kössener Formation (Obertrias, Nördliche Kalkalpen)*. PhD Thesis, University of Vienna.

Götz, A. E. 1995. Neue Conodonten aus dem Unteren Muschelkalk (Trias, Anis) des Germanischen Beckens. *Geologisch-Paläontologische Mitteilungen Innsbruck*, **20**, 51–59.

Götz, A. E. 1996. Fazies und Sequenzanalyse der Oolithbänke (Unterer Muschelkalk, Trias) Mitteldeutschlands und angrenzender Gebiete. *Geologisches Jahrbuch Hessen*, **124**, 67–86.

Götz, A. E. 2004. Zyklen und Sequenzen im Unteren Muschelkalk des Germanischen Beckens. *Hallesches Jahrbuch für Geowissenschaften, Reihe B*, **18**, 91–98.

Götz, A. E. & Feist-Burkhardt, S. 1999. Palynofazies im Unteren Muschelkalk der Sondierbohrung Benken. *Nagra Interner Bericht*, **00–44**, Teil B, 1–10.

Götz, A. E. & Feist-Burkhardt, S. 2000. Palynofacies and sequence analysis of the Lower Muschelkalk (Middle Triassic, German basin). *In*: Bachmann, G. H. & Lerche, I. (eds) Epicontinental Triassic. *Zentralblatt für Geologie und Paläontologie, Teil 1*, **1998**(9–10), 877–891.

Götz, A. E., Török, Á., Feist-Burkhardt, S. & Konrád, Gy. 2003. Palynofacies patterns of Middle Triassic ramp deposits (Mecsek Mts., S Hungary): A powerful tool for high-resolution sequence stratigraphy. *Geoaustria-Mitteilungen der Gesellschaft der Geologie und Bergbaustudenten in Österreich*, **46**, 77–90.

Götz, A. E., Szulc, J. & Feist-Burkhardt, S. 2005. Distribution of sedimentary organic matter in Anisian carbonate series of S Poland: evidence of third-order sea-level fluctuations. *International Journal of Earth Sciences*, **94**, 267–274.

Gradstein, F. M., Agterberg, F. P., Ogg, J. G., Hardenbol, J., van Veen, P., Thierry, J. & Huang, Z. 1995. A Triassic, Jurassic and Cretaceous time scale. *In*: Berggren, W. A., Kent, D. V. & Aubry, M.-P. (eds) *Geochronology, Time Scales and Global Stratigraphic Correlation*. Society for Sedimentary Geology (SEPM), Special Publications, **54**, 95–126.

Gradstein, F. M., Ogg, J. G. & Smith, A. 2004. *A Geologic Time Scale 2004*. Cambridge University Press, Cambridge.

Haas, J. 1994. Carnian basin evolution in the Transdanubian Central Range, Hungary. *Zentralblatt für Geologie und Paläontologie, Teil 1*, **1992**(11–12), 1233–1252.

Haas, J. 2002. Origin and evolution of Late Triassic backplatform and intraplatform basins in the Transdanubian Range, Hungary. *Geologica Carpathica*, **53**(3), 159–178.

Haas, J. & Budai, T. 1995. Upper Permian–Triassic facies zones in the Transdanubian Range. *Rivista Italiana di Paleontologia e Stratigrafia*, **101**(3), 249–266.

Haas, J. & Budai, T. 1999. Triassic sequence stratigraphy of the Transdanubian Range (Hungary). *Geologica Carpathica*, **50**, 459–475.

Haas, J. & Demény, A. 2002. Early dolomitisation of Late Triassic platform carbonates in the Transdanubian Range (Hungary). *Sedimentary Geology*, **150**(3–4), 225–242.

Haas, J., Góczán, F., Oravecz-Scheffer, A., Barabás-Stuhl, Á., Majoros, Gy. & Bérczi-Makk, A. 1988*a*. Permian-Triassic boundary in Hungary. *Memorie della Società Geologica Italiana*, **34**, 221–241.

Haas, J., Tóthné Makk, Á., Góczán, F., Oravecz-Scheffer A., Oravecz, J. & Szabó, I. 1988*b*. Lower Triassic key sections in the

Transdanubian Mid-Mountains. *Annales Instituti Geologici Publici Hungarici*, **65**(2).
Haas, J., Kovács, S., Krystyn, L. & Lein, R. 1995*a*. Significance of Late Permian–Triassic facies zones in terrane reconstructions in the Alpine-North Pannonian domain. *Tectonophysics*, **242**, 19–40.
Haas, J., Kovács, S. & Török, Á. 1995*b*. Early Alpine shelf evolution in the Hungarian segment of the Tethys margin. *Acta Geologica Hungarica*, **38**, 95–110.
Haas, J., Tardiné Filácz, E., Oravecz-Scheffer, A., Góczán, F. & Dosztály, L. 1997. Stratigraphy and sedimentology of an Upper Triassic toe-of-slope and basin succession at Csővár–1, North Hungary. *Acta Geologica Hungarica*, **40**, 111–177.
Haas, J., Korpás, L., *et al.* 2000. Upper Triassic basin and slope facies in the Buda Mts. based on study of core drilling Vérhalom tér, Budapest. *Földtani Közlöny*, **130**(3), 371–421 [in Hungarian].
Haas, J., Haas, J., Hámor, G., Jámbor, Á., Kovács, S., Nagymarosy, A. & Szederkényi, T. 2001. *Geology of Hungary*. Eötvös University Press, Budapest.
Haas, J., Bércziné Makk, A., *et al.* 2004*a*. *Geology of Hungary. Triassic*. Eötvös University Press, Budapest. [in Hungarian].
Haas, J., Hips, K., Pelikán, P., Zajzon, N., Götz, A. E. & Tardi-Filácz, E. 2004*b*. Facies analysis of marine Permian-Triassic boundary sections in Hungary. *Acta Geologica Hungarica*, **47**(4), 297–340.
Haas, J., Demény, A., Hips, K. & Vennemann, T. W. 2006*a*. Carbon isotope excursions and microfacies changes in marine Permian–Triassic boundary sections in Hungary. *Palaeogeography, Palaeoclimatology, Palaeoecology*, **237**, 160–181.
Haas, J., Demény, A., Hips, K., Zajzon, N., Weiszburg, T. G., Sudar, M. & Pálfy J. 2006*b*. Biotic and environmental changes in the Permian–Triassic boundary interval recorded on a western Tethyan ramp in the Bükk Mountains, Hungary. *Global and Planetary Change*, **55**(1–3), 136–154.
Hagdorn, H. 1991*a*. Biostratigraphy. *In:* Hagdorn, H., Simon, T. & Szulc, J. (eds) *Muschelkalk. A Field Guide*. Goldschneck-Verlag, Werner K. Weidert, Korb, 10–13.
Hagdorn, H. 1991*b*. The Muschelkalk in Germany – an introduction. *In*: Hagdorn, H., Simon, T. & Szulc, J. (eds) *Muschelkalk - A Field Guide*. Goldschneck-Verlag, Werner K. Weidert, Korb, 7–21.
Hagdorn, H. 1996*a*. Trias-Seelilien. *Geologisch-Paläontologische Mitteilungen Innsbruck*, **21**, 1–17.
Hagdorn, H. 1996*b*. Palökologie der Trias-Seelilie *Dadocrinus*. *Geologisch-Paläontologische Mitteilungen Innsbruck*, **21**, 19–45.
Hagdorn, H. 2004. *Muschelkalkmuseum Ingelfingen*. Edition Lattner, Heilbronn.
Hagdorn, H. & Gluchowski, E. 1993. Paleobiogeography and stratigraphy of Muschelkalk echinoderms (Crinoidea, Echinoidea) in Upper Silesia. *In*: Hagdorn, H. & Seilacher, A. (eds) *Muschelkalk. Schöntaler Symposium 1991*. Goldschneck-Verlag, Werner K. Weidert, Korb, 165–176.
Hagdorn, H. & Nitsch, E. 1999. Zum Begriff "Trias" – Ein geschichtlicher Abriß. *In*: Hauschke, N. & Wilde, V. (eds) *Trias, eine ganz andere Welt: Mitteleuropa im frühen Erdmittelalter*. Verlag Dr. Friedrich Pfeil, München, 13–21.
Hagdorn, H. & Reif, W. E. 1988. "Die Knochenbreccie von Crailsheim" und weiter Mitteltrias-Bonebeds in Nordost-Württemberg – Alte und neue Deutungen. *In*: Hagdorn, H. (ed.) *Neue Forschungen zur Erdgeschichte von Crailsheim*. Goldschneck-Verlag, Werner K. Weidert, Korb, 116–143.
Hagdorn, H. & Rieppel, O. 1999. Stratigraphy of marine reptiles in the Triassic of Central Europe. *In*: Bachmann, G. H. & Lerche, I. (eds) Epicontinental Triassic. *Zentralblatt für Geologie und Paläontologie, Teil I*, **1998**(7–8), 651–678.
Hagdorn, H. & Simon, T. 1993. Ökostratigraphische Leitbänke im Oberen Muschelkalk. *In*: Hagdorn, H. & Seilacher, A. (eds) *Muschelkalk. Schöntaler Symposium 1991*. Goldschneck-Verlag, Werner K. Weidert, Korb, 193–208.
Hagdorn, H., Gluchowski, E. & Boczarowski, A. 1996. The crinoid fauna of the *Diplopora* Dolomite (Middle Muschelkalk, Upper Anisain) at Piekary Slaskie in Upper Silesia. *Geologisch-Paläontologische Mitteilungen Innsbruck*, **21**, 47–87.
Hagdorn, H., Konrád, Gy. & Török, Á. 1997. Crinoids from the Muschelkalk of Mecsek Mountains and their stratigraphical significance. *Acta Geologica Hungarica*, **40**(4), 391–410.
Hagdorn, H., Szulc, J., Bodzioch, A. & Morycowa, E. 1999. Riffe aus dem Muschelkalk. *In*: Hauschke, N. & Wilde, V. (eds) *Trias, eine ganz andere Welt: Mitteleuropa im frühen Erdmittelalter*. Verlag Dr. Friedrich Pfeil, München, 309–320.
Hambach, U., Reinhardt, L., Wonik, T., Port, G., Krumsiek, K. & Ricken, W. 1999. Orbital forcing in a low-latitude playa system: evidence from evolutionary spectral analyses (ESA) of geophysical and geochemical data from the Steinmergel-Keuper (Late Triassic, S-Germany). *Terra Nostra*, **99**(4), 97–100.
Haq, B. U., Hardenbol, J. & Vail, P. R. 1988. Mesozoic and Cenozoic chronostratigrahy and cycles of sea-level change. *In*: Wilgus, C. K., Hastings, B. S., Kendall, C. G. S. C., Posamentier, H. W., Ross, C. A. & van Wagoner, J. C. (eds) *Sea-level Changes: An Integrated Approach*. Society for Sedimentary Geology (SEPM), Special Publications, **42**, 71–108.
Harangi, Sz., Szabó, Cs., Józsa, S., Szoldán, Zs., Árváné Sós, E., Balla, M. & Kubovics, I. 1996. Mesozoic igneous suites in Hungary: implications for genesis and tectonic setting in the nortwestern part of Tethys. *International Geology Review*, **38**, 336–360.
Hardenbol, J., Thierry, J., Farley, M. B., Jacquin, T., De Graciansky, P.-C. & Vail, P. R. 1998. Mesozoic and Cenozoic sequence chronostratigraphic framework of European basins. *In*: De Graciansky, P.-C., Hardenbol, J., Jaquin, T. & Vail, P. R. (eds) *Mesozoic and Cenozoic Sequence Stratigraphy of European Basins*. Society for Sedimentary Geology (SEPM), Special Publications, **60**, 3–15.
Hauber, L. 1980. The geology of the salt field Rheinfelden – Riburg, Switzerland. *In*: Coogan, A. H. & Hauber, L. (eds) *Proceedings 5th Symposium on Salt*, vol. I. Northern Ohio Geological Society, Cleveland, 83–90.
Haubold, H. 1999. Tracks of the Dinosauromorpha from the Lower Triassic. *In*: Bachmann, G. H. & Lerche, I. (eds) Epicontinental Triassic. *Zentralblatt für Geologie und Paläontologie, Teil I*, **1998**(7–8), 783–795.
Hauer, F. von 1846. *Die Cephalopoden des Salzkammergutes aus der Sammlung seiner Durchlaucht, des Fürsten von Metternich*. Braumüller & Seidel, Wien.
Haunschild, H. 1985. Der Keuper in der Forschungsbohrung Obernsees. *Geologica Bavarica*, **88**, 103–130.
Haunschild, H. & Salger, M. 1978. Der Sandsteinkeuper im fränkisch-württembergischen Grenzgebiet unter besonderer Berücksichtigung neuer Tiefenaufschlüsse. *Geologische Blätter NO-Bayerns*, **28**, 177–202.
Henry, B., Rouvier, H., Le'Goff, M., Leach, D., Macquar, J. C., Thibieroz, J. & Lewchuk, M. T. 2001. Paleomagnetic dating of widespread remagnetization on the southeastern border of the French Massif Central and implications for fluid flow and Mississippi Valley-type mineralization. *Geophysical Journal International*, **145**, 368–380.
Heunisch, C. 1999. Die Bedeutung der Palynologie für Biostratigraphie und Fazies in der Germanischen Trias. *In*: Hauschke, N. & Wilde, V. (eds) *Trias, eine ganz andere Welt: Mitteleuropa im frühen Erdmittelalter*. Verlag Dr. Friedrich Pfeil, München, 207–220.
Hiete, M. 2004. *Umweltveränderungen in der Permo-Trias. Geochemische Charakterisierung – Zeitreihenanalyse – Modellierung*. PhD Thesis, Braunschweig University of Technology.
Hips, K. 1998. Lower Triassic storm-dominated ramp sequence in northern Hungary: an example of evolution from homoclinal through distally steepened ramp to Middle Triassic flat-topped platform. *In*: Wright, V. P. & Burchette, T. P. (eds) *Carbonate Ramps*. Geological Society, London, Special Publications, **149**, 315–338.
Hips, K. & Haas, J. 2006. Calcimicrobial stromatolites at the Permian–Triassic boundary in a Tethyan section, Bükk Mountains, Hungary. *Sedimentary Geology*, **185**(3–4), 239–253.
Hips, K. & Pelikán, P. 2002. Lower Triassic shallow marine succession in the Bükk Mountains, NE Hungary. *Geologica Carpathica*, **53**, 1–17.
Hirsch, F. 1992. Circummediterranean Triassic eustatic cycles. *Israel Journal of Earth Sciences*, **40**, 29–38.
Hirschmann, C. 1959. Über Conodonten aus dem Oberen Muschelkalk des Thüringer Beckens. *Freiberger Forschungshefte, Reihe C*, **76**, 34–86.

HOFMANN, B. 1979. Blei-, Zink-, Kupfer- und Arsenvererzungen im Wellengebirge (Unterer Muschelkalk, Trias) am südlichen und östlichen Schwarzwald. *Mitteilungen der Naturforschenden Gesellschaft Schaffhausen*, **31**, 157–196.

HOFMANN, F. 1981. *Geologischer Atlas der Schweiz 1:25'000, Erläuterungen zum Blatt Nr. 74 Neunkirch*. Schweizerische Geologische Kommission, Basel.

HOLSER, W. T., SCHÖNLAUB, H.-P., *et al.* 1989. A unique geochemical record at the Permian/Triassic boundary. *Nature*, **337**, 39–44.

HOLSTEIN, B. 2004. Palynologische Untersuchungen der Kössener Schichten (Rhät, Alpine Obertrias). *Jahrbuch der Geologischen Bundesanstalt (Wien)*, **144**, 261–365.

HOMEWOOD, P. W., GUILLOCHEAU, F., ESCHARD, R. & CROSS, T. A. 1992. Corrélations haute résolution et stratigraphie génétique: une démarche intégrée. *Bulletin des Centres de Recherches Exploration-Production Elf-Aquitaine*, **16**, 357–381.

HOPF, H. & MARTENS, T. 1992. Erster Nachweis von Dinosaurierresten im Steinmergelkeuper der Drei Gleichen bei Arnstadt – Ein Beitrag zur Fauna des Mittleren Keupers Thüringens. *Zeitschrift für Geologische Wissenschaften*, **20**, 327–335.

HORNUNG, J. 1999. Dynamische Stratigraphie, Reservoir- und Aquifer-Sedimentologie einer alluvialen Ebene: Der Stubensandstein in Baden-Württemberg (Obere Trias, Mittlerer Keuper). *Tübinger Geowissenschaftliche Arbeiten, Reihe A: Geologie, Paläontologie, Stratigraphie*, **56**, 1–156.

HORNUNG, J. & AIGNER, T. 1999. Reservoir and aquifer characterization of fluvial architectural elements: Stubensandstein, Upper Triassic, Southwest Germany. *Sedimentary Geology*, **129**, 215–280.

HORNUNG, J. & AIGNER, T. 2002*a*. Reservoir architecture in a terminal alluvial plain: an outcrop analogue study (Upper Triassic, Southern Germany), Part I: Sedimentology and petrophysics. *Journal of Petroleum Geology*, **25**, 3–30.

HORNUNG, J. & AIGNER, T. 2002*b*. Reservoir architecture in a terminal alluvial plain: an outcrop analogue study (Upper Triassic, Southern Germany). Part II: Cyclicity, controls and models. *Journal of Petroleum Geology*, **25**, 151–178.

HORNUNG, J. & AIGNER, T. 2004. Sedimentary architecture and poroperm-characterisation of fluvial sandstones: A case study of the "Coburger Sandstein" (Franconia, Germany). *Hallesches Jahrbuch für Geowissenschaften, Reihe B*, **18**, 121–138.

HOTH, K., RUSBÜLT, J., ZAGORA, K., BEER, H. & HARTMANN, O. 1993. Die tiefen Bohrungen im Zentralabschnitt der mitteleuropäischen Senke 1962–1990. *Schriftenreihe für Geowissenschaften*, **2**.

HOUNSLOW, M. W. & MCINTOSH, G. 2003. Magnetostratigraphy of the Sherwood Sandstone Group (Lower and Middle Triassic), south Devon, UK: detailed correlation of the marine and non-marine Anisian. *Palaeogeography, Palaeoclimatology, Palaeoecology*, **193**, 325–348.

HOUNSLOW, M. W., POSEN, P. E. & WARRINGTON, G. 2004. Magnetostratigraphy and biostratigraphy of the Upper Triassic and lowermost Jurassic succession, St. Audrie's Bay, UK. *Palaeogeography, Palaeoclimatology, Palaeoecology*, **213**, 331–358.

HUEY, R. B. & WARD, P. D. 2005. Hypoxia, global warming, and terrestrial late Permian extinctions. *Science*, **308**, 398–401.

IRVING, E. 1977. Drift of the major continents since the Devonian. *Nature*, **270**, 304–309.

JACOBSEN, V. W. & VAN VEEN, P. 1984. The Triassic offshore Norway north of 62° N. *In:* SPENCER, A. M. *et al.* (eds) *Petroleum Geology of the North European Margin*. Norwegian Petroleum Society, 317–327.

JADOUL, F. & FRISIA, B. S. 1988. Le evinosponge: ipotesi genetiche di cementi calcitici nella piattaforma ladinica delle Prealpi Lombarde. *Rivista Italiana di Paleontologia e Stratigrafia*, **94**, 81–104.

JADOUL, F. & GNACCIOLINI, M. 1992. Sedimentazione ciclica nel Trias lombardo: osservazioni e prospettive. *Rivista Italiana di Paleontologia e Stratigrafia*, **97**, 307–328.

JADOUL, F., BERRA, F., FRISIA, S., RICCHIUTO, T. & RONCHI, P. 1992. Stratigraphy paleogeography and genetic model of Late Carnian carbonate breccias (Castro Formation, Lombardy, Italy). *Rivista Italiana di Paleontologia e Stratigrafia*, **97**, 355–392.

JAGLARZ, P. & SZULC, J. 2003. Middle Triassic evolution of the Tatricum sedimentary basin: an attempt of sequence stratigraphy to the Wierchowa Unit in the Polish Tatra Mountains. *Annales Societatis Geologorum Poloniae*, **73**, 169–182.

JOHNSON, H., WARRINGTON, G. & STOKER, S. J. 1994. Permian and Triassic of the Southern North Sea. *In*: KNOX, R. W. O'B. & CORDEY, W. G. (eds) *Lithostratigraphic Nomenclature of the UK North Sea*. British Geological Survey, Keyworth, Nottingham, 113–125.

JORDAN, P. 1992. Evidence for large-scale decoupling in the Triassic evaporites of Northern Switzerland: an overview. *Eclogae Geologicae Helvetiae*, **85**, 677–693.

JORDAN, P. 1994. Evaporite als Abscherhorizonte – Eine gefügekundlich-strukturgeologische Untersuchung am Beispiel der Nordschweizer Trias. *Beiträge zur Geologischen Karte der Schweiz, Neue Folge*, **164**, 1–79.

JUBITZ, K. B., ZNOSKO, J. & FRANKE, D. (eds) 1987. *Lithologic Paleogeographic Map of the Buntsandstein (1: 500000)*. International geological correlation programme 86, Southwest border of the East-European Platform. Zentrales Geologisches Institut, Berlin.

JUBITZ, K. B., ZNOSKO, J. & FRANKE, D. (eds) 1988. *Lithologic paleogeographic map of the Muschelkalk (1: 500000)*. International geological correlation programme 86, Southwest border of the East-European Platform. Zentrales Geologisches Institut, Berlin.

KACHROO, R. K. 1989. Uppermost Triassic Conodonts from the Kössen Formation of the Northern Calcareous Alps (Austria). *Jahrbuch der Geologischen Bundesanstalt (Wien)*, **132**, 665–676.

KAIHO, K., KAJIWARA, Y., *et al.* 2001. End-Permian catastrophe by a bolide impact: evidence of a gigantic release of sulfure from the mantle. *Geology*, **29**, 817–818.

KATINAS, V. 1997. Magnetostratigraphy of the lower Triassic sediments from boreholes Kernai-1 and Zvelsenai-1 in West Lithuania. *Litosfera*, **1**, 39–45.

KEDŻIERSKI, J. 2000. *Sequenzstratigraphie des Muschelkalks im östlichen Teil des Germanischen Beckens (Deutschland, Polen)*. PhD Thesis, Martin Luther University Halle-Wittenberg.

KEDŻIERSKI, J. & SZULC, J. 1996. Anisian conodonts of Lower Silesia and their significance for reconstruction of the Muschelkalk transgression in the eastern part of the Germanic Basin. *In*: DZIK, J. (ed.) *Sixth European Conodont Symposium (ECOS VI), Abstracts*, Warsaw, 28.

KEFERSTEIN, C. 1824. Versuch einer vergleichenden Darstellung der geognostischen Verhältnisse in Württemberg und Norddeutschland, besonders in Hinsicht des Steinsalzgebirges. *Correspondenzblatt der Württembergischen Landwirtschaftlichen Vereinigung*, **5**, 331–360.

KEIM, L. & SCHLAGER, W. 1999. Automicrite facies on steep slopes (Triassic, Dolomites, Italy). *Sedimentary Geology*, **139**, 261–283.

KELBER, K.-P. 2005. Makroflora (Die Keuperfloren). *In:* DEUTSCHE STRATIGRAPHISCHE KOMMISSION (eds) Stratigraphie von Deutschland IV – Keuper. *Courier Forschungsinstitut Senckenberg*, **253**, 32–41.

KELBER, K.-P. & HANSCH, W. 1995. Keuperpflanzen. Die Enträtselung einer über 200 Millionen Jahre alten Flora. *Museo*, **11**, 1–157.

KEMPF, O., HINDERER, M. & HORNUNG, J. 2002. Sediment budget of the upper Middle Keuper in SW Germany. *Zentralblatt für Geologie und Paläontologie, Teil I*, **2001**(3–4), 257–270.

KENT, D. & OLSEN, P. E. 1999. Astronomically tuned geomagnetic polarity timescale for the Late Triassic. *Journal of Geophysical Research*, **104**(B6), 12831–12841.

KENT, D. V. & TAUXE, L. 2005. Corrected Late Triassic latitudes for continents adjacent to the North Atlantic. *Science*, **307**, 240–244.

KERSHAW, S., GUO, L., SWIFT, A. & FAN, J. 2002. ?Microbialites in the Permian-Triassic boundary interval in Central China: structure, age and distribution. *Facies*, **47**, 83–90.

KINDLIMANN, R. 1985. Ein bisher unerkannt gebliebener Zahn eines synapsiden Reptils aus dem Rät von Hallau (Kanton Schaffhausen, Schweiz). *Mitteilungen der Naturforschenden Gesellschaft Schaffhausen*, **32**(1981/85), 199–207.

KLAUS, W. 1960. Sporen der karnischen Stufe der ostalpinen Trias. *Jahrbuch der Geologischen Bundesanstalt (Wien)*, Sonderband **5**, 107–183.

KLAUS, W. 1964. Zur sporenstratigraphischen Einstufung von gipsführenden Schichten in Bohrungen. *Erdöl-Zeitschrift*, **4**, 119–132.

KOCKEL, F. (ed.) 1995. Structural and palaeogeographical development of the German North Sea sector. *Beiträge zur regionalen Geologie der Erde*, **26**, 1–96.

KONRÁD, Gy. 1997. *Sedimentary analysis of Lower and Middle Triassic sequences, Southeastern Hungary*. PhD thesis. Hungarian Academy of Sciences, Budapest [in Hungarian with English abstract].

Konrád, Gy. 1998. Synsedimentary tectonic events in Middle Triassic evolution of the SE Transdanubian part of the Tisza Unit. *Acta Geologica Hungarica*, **41**, 327–342.

Köppen, A, 1997. Faziesentwicklung in der frühen Obertrias Mitteleuropas – ein sequenzstratigraphischer Vergleich. *Gaea Heidelbergensis*, **2**, 1–233.

Köppen, A. & Carter, A. 2000. Constraints on provenance of the central European Triassic using detrital zircon fission track data. *Palaeogeography, Palaeoclimatology, Palaeoecology*, **161**, 193–204.

Korte, C. & Kozur, H. W. 2005. Carbon isotope trends in continental lake deposits of the uppermost Permian to Lower Olenekian: Germanic Lower Buntsandstein (Calvörde and Bernburg Formations). *Hallesches Jahrbuch für Geowissenschaften, Reihe B*, **19**, 87–94.

Kotanski, Z. 1994. Middle Triassic Dasycladaceae of the Upper Silesian-Cracow region and their stratigraphical and palaeoecological significance. *3rd International Meeting of Peri-Tethyan Epicratonic Basins. Excursion Guidebook*, Cracow, 59–66.

Kovács, S. & Papsová, J. 1986. Conodonts from the *Paraceratites binodosus* zone (Middle Triassic) from the Mecsek Mts., Southern Hungary and from the Choc Nappe of the Low Tatra Mts., Czechoslovakia. *Geologickij Zbornik Geologica Carpathica*, **37**, 59–74.

Kovács, S. & Rálisch-Felgenhauer, E. 2005. Middle Anisian (Pelsonian) platform conodonts from the Triassic of the Mecsek Mts. (South Hungary) – Their taxonomy and stratigraphic significance. *Acta Geologica Hungarica*, **48**, **1**, 69–105.

Kovács, S., Less, Gy., Piros, O., Réti, Zs. & Róth, L. 1989. Triassic formations of the Aggtelek–Rudabánya Mountains (Northeastern Hungary). *Acta Geologica Hungarica*, **32**(1–2), 31–63.

Kovács, S., Rálisch-Felgenhauer & E., Bóna, J. 2005. Middle Anisian (Pelsonian) platform conodonts from the Triassic of the Villány Hills, South Hungary. *Acta Geologica Hungarica*, **48**(1), 107–115.

Kozur, H. 1968. Conodonten aus dem Muschelkalk des germanischen Binnenbeckens und ihr stratigraphischer Wert. Teil 1: Conodonten vom Plattformtyp und stratigraphische Bedeutung der Conodonten aus dem Oberen Muschelkalk. *Geologie*, **17**, 930–946.

Kozur, H. 1972. Die Conodontengattung *Metapolygnathus* Hayashi 1968 und ihr stratigraphischer Wert. *Geologisch-Paläontologische Mitteilungen Innsbruck*, **2**, 1–37.

Kozur, H. 1973. Faunenprovinzen in der Trias und ihre Bedeutung für die Klärung der Paläogeographie. *Geologisch-Paläontologische Mitteilungen Innsbruck*, **3**, 1–41.

Kozur, H. 1974*a*. Biostratigraphie der germanischen Mitteltrias. *Freiberger Forschungshefte, Reihe C*, **280**, 1–71.

Kozur, H. 1974*b*. Probleme der Triasgliederung und Parallelisierung der germanischen und tethyalen Trias. Teil I. *Freiberger Forschungshefte, Reihe C*, **298**, 139–198.

Kozur, H. 1999. The correlation of the Germanic Buntsandstein and Muschelkalk with the Tethyan scale. *In*: Bachmann, G. H. & Lerche, I. (eds) Epicontinental Triassic. *Zentralblatt für Geologie und Paläontologie, Teil I*, **1998**(7–8), 701–725.

Kozur, H. W. 2003. Integrated ammonoid-, conodont and radiolarian zonation of the Triassic. *Hallesches Jahrbuch für Geowissenschaften, Reihe B*, **25**, 49–79.

Krainer, K. & Lutz, D. 1995. Middle Triassic basin evolution and stratigraphy in the Carnic Alps (Austria). *Facies*, **33**, 167–184.

Krämer, F. & Kunz, H. 1969. Leithorizonte und Schichtausfälle im Buntsandstein Hessens und Thüringens. *Oberrheinische geologische Abhandlungen*, **18**, 67–76.

Kräusel, K. & Leschik, G. 1956. Die Keuperflora von Neuewelt bei Basel. 2. Leschik, G., Die Iso- und Mikrosporen. *Schweizerische Paläontologische Abhandlungen*, **72**, 1–70.

Krimmel, V. 1980. Epirogene Paläotektonik zur Zeit des Keupers (Trias) in Südwest-Deutschland. *Arbeiten aus dem Institut für Geologie und Paläontologie an der Universität Stuttgart, Neue Folge*, **76**, 1–75.

Krull, E. S. & Retallack, G. J. 2000. $\partial^{13}C$ profiles from paleosols across the Permian-Triassic boundary: Evidence for methane release. *Bulletin of the Geological Society of America*, **112**(9), 1459–1472.

Krull, E. S., Lehrmann, D. J., Druke, D., Kessel, B., Yu, Y. Y. & Li, R. 2004. Stable isotope stratigraphy across the Permian-Triassic boundary in shallow marine carbonate platforms, Nanpanjiang Basin, South China. *Palaeogeography, Palaeoclimatology, Palaeoecology*, **204**, 297–315.

Krystyn, L. 1978. Eine neue Zonengliederung im alpin-mediterranen Unterkarn. *Schriftenreihe der erdwissenschaftlichen Kommission der Österreichischen Akademie der Wissenschaften*, **4**, 37–75.

Krystyn, L. 1988. Zur Rhät-Stratigraphie in den Zlambach-Schichten (vorläufiger Bericht). *Sitzungsberichte der Österreichischen Akademie der Wissenschaften (Mathematisch-naturwissenschaftliche Klasse)*, **196**, 21–36.

Krzywiec, P. 2004. Triassic evolution of the Klodawa salt structure: basement-controlled salt tectonics within the Mid-Polish Trough (Central Poland). *Geological Quarterly*, **48**, 123–134.

Kustatscher, E., Manfrin, S., Mietto, P., Posenato, R. & Roghi, G. 2006. New biostratigraphic data on Anisian (Middle Triassic) palynomorphs from the Dolomites, Italy. *Review of Palaeobotany and Palynology*, **140**, 79–90.

Kutzbach, J. E. 1994. Idealized Pangean climates: sensitivity to orbital change. *In*: Klein, G. D. (ed.) *Pangea: Paleoclimate, Tectonics, and Sedimentation During Accretion, Zenith, and Breakup of a Supercontinent*. Geological Society of America, Special Papers, **288**, 41–55.

Kutzbach, J. E. & Gallimore, R. G. 1989. Pangean climates: Megamonsoons of the megacontinent. *Journal of Geophysical Research*, **94**(D3), 3341–3357.

Laemmlen, M. 1996. Die Keuper-Lithostratigraphie bei Fulda mit einem Einblick in den Bau des Fuldaer Grabens. *Geologisches Jahrbuch, Reihe A*, **145**, 3–66.

Landesamt für Geologie, Rohstoffe und Bergbau Baden-Württemberg (LGRB) 2004. *Lithostratigraphic Code*. World Wide Web addresses: http://www.lgrb.uni-freiburg.de/lgrb/download_pool/symbolschl-jan2004-erltext.pdf and http://www.lgrb.uni-freiburg.de/lgrb/download_pool/symbolschl040625.doc

Laubscher, H. 1961. Die Fernschubhypothese der Jurafaltung. *Eclogae Geologicae Helvetiae*, **54**, 221–282.

Laubscher, H. 1975. Viscous components in Jura folding. *Tectonophysics*, **27**, 239–254.

Lehrmann, D. J. 1999. Early Triassic calcimicrobial mounds and biostromes of the Nanpanjiang basin, south China. *Geology*, **27**, 359–362.

Lehrmann, D. J., Ramezani, J., *et al*. 2006. Timing of recovery from the end-Permian extinction: Geochronologic and biostratigraphic constraints from south China. *Geology*, **34**, 1053–1056.

Lepper, J. & Röhling, H.-G. 1998. Buntsandstein. *In:* Bachmann, G. H., Beutler, G. & Lerche, I. (eds) Excursions of the International Symposium on the Epicontinental Triassic, Halle (Saale), September 1998. *Hallesches Jahrbuch für Geowissenschaften, Reihe B*, Beiheft **6**, 27–34.

Lepper, J. & Uchman, A. 1995. Marine Einflüsse im Mittleren Buntsandstein der Hessischen Senke - dargestellt am Bespiel des Weserprallhanges an der Ballertasche bei Hannoverisch Münden. *Zentralblatt für Geologie und Paläontologie*, **1994**(1–2), 175–186.

Loope, D. B., Steiner, M. B., Rowe, C. M. & Lancaster, N. 2004. Tropical westerlies over Pangaean sand seas. *Sedimentology*, **51**, 315–322.

Lucas, S. G. 1999. Tetrapod-based correlation of the nonmarine Triassic. *In*: Bachmann, G. H. & Lerche, I. (eds) Epicontinental Triassic. *Zentralblatt für Geologie und Paläontologie, Teil I*, **1998**(7–8), 497–521.

Lund, J. J. 1977. Rhaetic to Lower Liassic palynology of the onshore south-eastern North Sea basin. *Danmarks geologiske Undersøgelse, 2nd Series*, **109**, 1–129.

Mader, D. 1992. *Evolution of Palaeoecology and Palaeoenvironment of Permian and Triassic Fluvial Basins in Europe*, Vol. 1. *Western and Eastern Europe*. Gustav Fischer Verlag, Stuttgart.

Mädler, K. 1964. Die geologische Verbreitung von Sporen in der deutschen Trias. *Beihefte zum Geologischen Jahrbuch*, **65**, 1–147.

Mandl, G. W. 1984. Zur Trias des Hallstätter Faziesraumes – ein Modell am Beispiel Salzkammergut (Nördliche Kalkalpen). *Mitteilungen der Gesellschaft der Geologie- und Bergbaustudenten*, **30–31**, 133–176.

Marek, S. & Pajchlowa, M. (eds) 1997. The epicontinental Permian and Mesozoic in Poland. *Prace Panstwowego Instytut Geologicznego*, **CLIII** [in Polish with English summary].

Marsaglia, K. M. & Klein, G. 1983. The paleogeography of Paleozoic and Mesozoic storm depositional systems. *Journal of Geology*, **91**, 117–141.

Martini, I. P., Rau, A. & Tongiorgi, M. 1986. Syntectonic sedimentation in a Middle Triassic rift, Northern Apennines, Italy. *Sedimentary Geology*, **47**, 191–219.

Masaryk, P., Lintnerová, O. & Michalík, J. 1993. Sedimentology, lithofacies and diagenesis of the sediments of the Reifling intraplatform basins in the central Western Carpathians. *Geologica Carpathica*, **44**, 233–249.

Massari, F. 1988. Some thoughts on the Permo-Triassic evolution of the South-Alpine area (Italy). *Memorie della Società Geologica Italiana*, **34**, 179–188.

Maurer, F. 2000. Growth mode of Middle Triassic carbonate platforms in the Western Dolomites (Southern Alps, Italy). *Sedimentary Geology*, **134**, 275–286.

Mégard-Galli, J. & Faure, J.-L. 1988. Tectonique distensive et sédimentation au Ladinien supérieur - Carnien dans la zone briançonnaise. *Bulletin de la Societé géologique de France*, 8, **IV**(5), 705–715.

Menning, M. 1995. A numerical time scale for the Permian and Triassic periods: an integrated time analysis. *In*: Scholle, P. A., Peryt, T. M. & Ulmer-Scholle, D. S. (eds) *The Permian of Northern Pangea*. Springer-Verlag, Berlin, 77–97.

Menning, M., Gast, R., Hagdorn, H., Käding, K.-C., Simon, T., Szurlies, M. & Nitsch, E. 2005. Zeitskala für Perm und Trias in der Stratigraphischen Tabelle von Deutschland 2002, zyklostratigraphische Kalibrierung der höheren Dyas und Germanischen Trias und das Alter der Stufen Roadium bis Rhaetium 2005. *Newsletters on Stratigraphy*, **41**, 173–210.

Merki, P. 1961. Der obere Muschelkalk im östlichen Schweizer Jura. *Eclogae Geologicae Helvetiae*, **54**, 127–220.

Michalík, J. 1980. A paleoenvironmental and paleoecological analysis of the northern Tethyan nearshore region in the latest Triassic time. *Rivista Italiana di Paleontologia e Stratigrafia*, **85**, 1047–1067.

Michalík, J. 1993. Mesozoic tensional basins in the Alpine – Carpathian shelf. *Acta Geologica Hungarica*, **36**, 395–403.

Michalík, J. 1994. Notes on the paleogeography and paleotectonics of the Western Carpathian area during the Mesozoic. *Mitteilungen der Österreichischen Geologischen Gesellschaft*, **86**, 101–110.

Michalík, J. 1997. Tsunamites in a storm-dominated Anisian ramp (Vysoka Formation, Male Karpaty Mts., Western Carpathians). *Geologica Carpathica*, **48**, 221–229.

Michalík, J. (ed.) 2003. *IGCP 458: Triassic/Jurassic Boundary Events*. Third Field Workshop, Stará Lesná, Slovakia, Tatra Mountains, 11–15 October 2003, Bratislava.

Michalík, J., Planderová, E. & Sýkora, M. 1976. To the stratigraphic and paleogeographic position of the Tomanová Formation in the uppermost Triassic of the West Carpathians. *Geologica Carpathica*, **27**, 299–318.

Michalík, J., Masaryk, P., Lintnerová, O., Papšová, J., Jendrejáková, O. & Reháková, D. 1992. Sedimentology and facies of a storm-dominated Middle Triassic carbonate ramp (the Vysoká Formation, Malé Karpaty Mts, Western Carpathians). *Geologica Carpathica*, **43**, 213–230.

Michelsen, O. & Clausen, O. R. 2002. Detailed stratigraphic subdivision and regional correlation of the southern Danish Triassic succession. *Marine and Petroleum Geology*, **19**, 563–587.

Mietto, P. & Manfrin, S. 1995. A high-resolution ammonoid standard scale in the Tethys realm. A preliminary report. *Bulletin de la Société géologique de France*, **166**, 539–563.

Mietto, P., Gianolla, P., Manfrin, S. & Preto, N. 2003. Refined ammonoid biochronostratigraphy of the Bagolino section (Lombardian Alps, Italy), GSSP candidate for the base of the Ladinian Stage. *Rivista Italiana di Paleontologia e Stratigrafia*, **109**, 449–462.

Milewska, Z. & Moryc, W. 1981. Triassic microfauna from the Carpathian Foreland. *Materialy V Krajowej Konferencji Paleontologow*, Kielce-Sosnowiec, 1981, 15–24 [in Polish].

Mišík, M. & Jablonský, J. 1978. Lower Triassic quartzites and conglomerates in the Malé Karpaty Mts (pebble analysis, transport direction, genesis). *Acta Geologica et Geographica Universitas Comenianae, Geologica*, **33**, 5–36 [in Slovak].

Mojsisovics, J. A. G. E. 1879. *Die Dolomitriffe von Südtirol und Venetien. Beiträge zur Bildungsgeschichte der Alpen*. Hölder, Wien.

Mojsisovics, J. A. G. E. 1882. Die Cephalopoden der Mediterranen Triasprovinz. *Abhandlungen der Königlich-Kaiserlichen Geologischen Reichsanstalt*, **10**, 1–322.

Monostori, M. 1996. Ostracods and charophytes from the Triassic Kantavár Formation, Mecsek Mts, Hungary. *Acta Geologica Hungarica*, **39**(3), 311–317.

Morbey, S. J. 1975. The palynostratigraphy of the Rhaetian stage, Upper Triassic in the Kendelbachgraben, Austria. *Palaeontographica, Abteilung B*, **152**, 1–75.

Mørk, A., Embry, A. F. & Weitschat, W. 1989. Triassic transgressive-regressive cycles in the Sverdrup Basin, Svalbard and the Barents Shelf. *In*: Collinson, J. D. (ed.) *Correlation of Hydrocarbon Exploration*. Proceedings of the Norwegian Petroleum Society Conference, Graham & Trotman, London, 113–130.

Mørk, A., Vigran, J. O., Korchinskaya, M. V., Pchelina, T. M., Fefilova, L. A., Vavilova, M. N. & Weitschat, W. 1992. Triassic rocks in Svalbard, the Arctic Soviet islands and the Barents Sea. *In*: Vorren, T. O., Bergsager, E., Dahl-Stahmnes, Ø. A., Holter, E., Johansen, B., Lie, E. & Lund, T. B. (eds) *Arctic Geology and Petroleum Potential*. Norwegian Petroleum Society, Special Publication **2**, Elsevier, Amsterdam, 457–479.

Moryc, W. 1971. Triassic of the middle Carpathians Foreland. *Rocznik Polskiego Towarzystwa Geologicznego*, **41**, 419–486 [in Polish with English abstract].

Morycowa, E. 1988. Middle Triassic Scleractinia from the Cracow-Silesia region, Poland. *Acta Palaeontologica Polonica*, **33**, 91–121.

Mostler, H. 1993. Das Germanische Muschelkalkbecken und seine Beziehungen zum tethyalen Muschelkalkmeer. *In:* Hagdorn, H. & Seilacher, A. (eds) *Muschelkalk. Schöntaler Symposium 1991.* Goldschneck-Verlag, Werner K. Weidert, Korb, 11–14.

Mostler, H. & Rossner, R. 1984. Mikrofazies und Palökologie der höheren Werfener Schichten (Untertrias) der Nördlichen Kalkalpen. *Facies*, **10**, 87–144.

Müller, A. H. 1970. Neue Funde seltener Ceratiten aus dem germanischen Muschelkalk und Keuper. *Monatsberichte der deutschen Akademie der Wissenschaften zu Berlin*, **12**, 632–642.

Müller, W. H., Huber, M., Isler, A. & Kleboth, P. 1984. *Erläuterungen zur geologischen Karte der zentralen Nordschweiz 1:100 000.* Geologische Spezialkarte, **21**. Schweizerische Geologische Kommission, Basel.

Mundil, R., Brack, P., Meier, M., Rieber, H. & Oberli, F. 1996. High resolution U-Pb dating of Middle Triassic volcaniclastics: Time-scale calibration and verification of tuning parameters for carbonate sedimentation. *Earth and Planetary Science Letters*, **141**, 137–151.

Mundil, R., Metcalfe, I., Ludwig, K. R., Renne, P. R., Oberli, F. & Nicoll, R. S. 2001. Timing of the Permian-Triassic biotic crisis: implications from new zircon U/Pb age data (and their limitations). *Earth and Planetary Science Letters*, **187**, 131–145.

Mundil, R., Zühlke, R., *et al.* 2003. Cyclicities in Triassic platform carbonates: synchronizing radio-isotopic and orbital clocks. *Terra Nova*, **15**(2), 81–87.

Muttoni, G., Kent, D. V., Brack, P., Nicora, A. & Balini, M. 1997. Middle Triassic magnetostratigraphy and biostratigraphy from the Dolomites and Greece. *Earth and Planetary Science Letters*, **146**, 107–120.

Muttoni, G., Nicora, A., Brack, P. & Kent, D. V. 2004. Integrated Anisian–Ladinian boundary chronology. *Palaeogeography, Palaeoclimatology, Palaeoecology*, **208**, 85–102.

Nagy, E. 1968. *The Triassic of Mecsek Mountains.* Annales Instituti Geologici Publici Hungarici, **51**(1) [in Hungarian with German abstract].

Nagy, E. & Nagy, I. 1976. The Triassic of Villány Mountains. *Geologica Hungarica, Series Geologica*, **17**, 111–227 [in Hungarian with German abstract].

Narkiewicz, K. 1999. Conodont biostratigraphy of the Muschelkalk (Middle Triassic) in the central part of the Polish lowland. *Geological Quarterly*, **43**, 313–328.

Narkiewicz, K. & Szulc, J. 2004. Controls of migration of conodont fauna in peripheral oceanic areas. An example from the Middle Triassic of the Northern Peri-Tethys. *Géobios*, **37**, 425–436.

Nawrocki, J. 1997. Permian to Early Triassic magnetostratigraphy from Central European Basin in Poland: implications on regional and worldwide correlations. *Earth and Planetary Sciences Letters*, **152**,

37–58.

Nawrocki, J. 2004. The Permian–Triassic boundary in the Central European Basin: magnetostratigraphic constraints. *Terra Nova*, **16**, 139–145.

Nawrocki, J. & Becker, A. 2008. Magnetostratigraphy of selected Triassic rocks from the Brześć Kujawski IG-1 and Ksiaz Wielkopolski IG-2 boreholes (Central European Basin, Poland). *Geological Quarterly* (in press).

Nawrocki, J. & Szulc, J. 2000. The Middle Triassic magnetostratigraphy from the Peri-Tethys basin in Poland. *Earth and Planetary Science Letters*, **182**, 77–92.

Nawrocki, J., Kuleta, M. & Zbroja, S. 2003. Buntsandstein magnetostratigraphy from the northern part of the Holy Cross Mountains. *Geological Quarterly*, **47**, 253–260.

Neri, C. & Stefani, M. 1998. Sintesi cronostratigrafica e sequenziale dell' evoluzione permiana superiore e triassica delle Dolomiti. *In*: Bosellini, A. & Stefani, M. (eds) *Geologia delle Dolomiti*. Memorie della Società Geologica Italiana, **53**, 417–463.

NITG 2004. *Geological Atlas of the Netherlands – Onshore (1:1.000.000)*. Netherlands Institute for Applied Geoscience TNO, National Geological Survey, Utrecht.

Nitsch, E. 1996. *Fazies, Diagenese und Stratigraphie der Grabfeld-Gruppe Süddeutschlands (Keuper, Trias)*. PhD Thesis, University of Cologne.

Nitsch, E. 2005. Der Keuper in der Stratigraphischen Tabelle von Deutschland 2002: Formationen und Folgen. *Newsletters on Stratigraphy*, **41**, 159–171.

Nolte, J. 1989. Die Stratigraphie und Palökologie des Unteren Hauptmuschelkalks (mo1, Mittl. Trias) von Unterfranken. *Berliner Geowissenschaftliche Abhandlungen*, **A 106**, 303–341.

Ogg, J. G. 2004. The Triassic Period. *In*: Gradstein, F. M., Ogg, J. G. & Smith, A. G. (eds) *A Geological Time Scale*. Cambridge University Press, Cambridge, 271–306.

Ogg, J. G. & Steiner, M. B. 1991. Early Triassic magnetic polarity time scale – integration of magnetostratigraphy, ammonite zonation and sequence stratigraphy from stratotype section (Canadian Arctic Archipelago). *Earth and Planetary Science Letters*, **107**, 69–89.

Olsen, P. E. & Kent, D. V. 1996. Milankovitch climate forcing in the tropics of Pangaea during the Late Triassic. *Palaeogeography, Palaeoclimatology, Palaeoecology*, **122**, 1–26.

Olsen, P. E., Kent, D. V., Cornet, B., Witte, W. K. & Schlische, R. W. 1996. High-resolution stratigraphy of the Newark rift basin (early Mesozoic, eastern North America). *Bulletin of the Geological Society of America*, **108**, 40–77.

Orłowska-Zwolińska, T. 1977. Palynological correlation of the Bunter and Muschelkalk in selected profils from Western Poland. *Acta Geologica Polonica*, **27**, 417–438.

Orłowska-Zwolińska, T. 1983. Palynostratigraphy of the upper part of Triassic epicontinental sediments in Poland. *Prace Instytutu Geologicznego, Wydawnictwa Geologiczne*, **104**, 1–89 [in Polish with English abstract].

Orłowska-Zwolińska, T. 1985. Palynological zones of the Polish epicontinental Triassic. *Bulletin of the Polish Academy of Sciences, Earth Sciences*, **33**, 107–117.

Ortlam, D. 1974. Inhalt und Bedeutung fossiler Beckenkomplexe in Perm und Trias Mitteleuropas. *Geologische Rundschau*, **63**, 850–884.

Pálfy, J. & Török, Á. 1992. Comparison of Alpine and Germano-type Middle Triassic brachiopod faunas from Hungary, with remarks on *Coenothyris vulgaris* (Schlotheim 1820). *Annales Universitatis Scientiarium Budapestinensis de Rolando Eötvös Nominatae, Sectio Geologica*, **29**, 303–323.

Parnes, A. 1965. Triassic ammonites from Israel. *Geological Survey of Israel, Bulletin*, **33**, 1–78.

Parrish, J. T. 1993. Climate of the supercontinent Pangea. *Journal of Geology*, **101**, 215–233.

Parrish, J. T. 1999. Pangaea und das Klima der Trias. *In*: Hauschke, N. & Wilde, V. (eds) *Trias, eine ganz andere Welt: Mitteleuropa im frühen Erdmittelalter.* Verlag Dr. Friedrich Pfeil, München, 37–42.

Paul, J. 1982. Der Untere Buntsandstein des germanischen Beckens. *Geologische Rundschau*, **71**, 795–811.

Paul, J. 1999. Oolithe und Stromatolithen im Unterem Buntsandstein. *In*: Hauschke, N. & Wilde, V. (eds) *Trias, eine ganz andere Welt: Mitteleuropa im frühen Erdmittelalter.* Verlag Dr. Friedrich Pfeil, München, 263–270.

Paul, J. & Ahrendt, H. 1998. Provenance of clastic Triassic sediments (Germanic Basin, Central Europe). *In:* Bachmann, G. H. & Lerche, I. (eds) International Symposium on the Epicontinental Triassic, Halle (Saale), September 1998, abstracts. *Hallesches Jahrbuch für Geowissenschaften, Reihe B*, Beiheft **5**, 136–137.

Paul, J. & Peryt, T. M. 2000. Kalkowsky's stromatolites revisited (Lower Triassic Buntsandstein, Harz Mountains, Germany). *Palaeogeography, Palaeoclimatology, Palaeoecology*, **161**, 435–458.

Peri, M. C. & Farabegoli, E. 2003. Conodonts across the Permian-Triassic boundary in the Southern Alps. *Courier Forschungsinstitut Senckenberg*, **245**, 281–313.

Peryt, T. 1975. Significance of stromatolites for the environmental interpretation of the Buntsandstein (Lower Triassic) rocks. *Geologische Rundschau*, **64**, 143–157.

Pešić, L., Ramovš, A., Sremac, J., Pantić-Prodanović, S., Filipović, I., Kovács, S. & Pelikán, P. 1988. Upper Permian deposits of the Jadar region and their position within the Western Paleotethys. *Memorie della Società Geologica Italiana*, **34**, 211–219.

Peters, T., Matter, A., Isenschmid, C., Meyer, J. & Ziegler, H. J. 1990. Sondierbohrung Kaisten. *Geologischer Bericht*, **10**, 1–286.

Pia, J. 1930. *Grundbegriffe der Stratigraphie mit ausführlicher Anwendung auf die europäische Mitteltrias*. Deuticke Verlag, Leipzig.

Pienkowski, G. 1991. Facies criteria for delimitating Zechstein/Buntsandstein and Permian/Triassic boundaries in Poland. *Zentralblatt für Geologie und Paläontologie*, **4**, 893–912.

Pieńkowski, G., Schudack, M. E. *et al.* 2008. Jurassic. *In:* McCann, T. (ed.) *The Geology of Central Europe. Volume 2: Mesozoic and Cenozoic*. Geological Society, London, 823–922.

Piros, O. 2002. Anisian to Carnian carbonate platform facies and dasycladacean biostratigraphy of the Aggtelek Mts, Northeastern Hungary. *Acta Geologica Hungarica*, **45**(2), 119–151.

Polack, J. B., Toon, O. B., Sagan, J., Summers, A., Baldwin, B. & Camp, W. V. 1976. Volcanic explosions and climatic change: a theoretical assessment. *Journal of Geophysical Research*, **94**, 1071–1083.

Pöppelreiter, M. 1999. Controls on epeiric successions exemplified with the mixed siliciclastic-carbonate Lower Keuper (Ladinian, Germany). *Tübinger Geowissenschaftliche Arbeiten, Reihe A: Geologie, Paläontologie, Stratigraphie*, **51**, 1–206.

Posenato, R. 2001. The Athyridoids of the transitional beds between the Bellerophon and Werfen Formations (Uppermost Permian, Southern Alps, Italy). *Rivista Italiana di Paleontologia e Stratigrafia*, **107**, 197–226.

Posenato, R., Pelikán P. & Hips, K. 2005. Bivalves and brachiopods near the Permian-Triassic boundary from the Bükk Mts. Bálvány North section, Northern Hungary. *Rivista Italiana di Paleontologia e Stratigrafia*, **111**, 215–234.

Preto, N., De Zanche, V., Hardie, L. A. & Hinnov, L. 2001. Middle Triassic orbital signature recorded in the shallow marine Latemar carbonate buildup (Dolomites, Italy). *Geology*, **29**, 1123–1126.

Preto, N., Hinnov, L., De Zanche, V., Mietto, P. & Hardie, L. A. 2004. The Milankovitch interpretation of the Latemar platform cycles (Dolomites, Italy): implications for geochronology, biostratigraphy and Middle Triassic carbonate accumulation. *In*: D'Argenio, B., Fisher, A., Premoli Silva, I. & Weissert, H. (eds) *Cyclostratigraphy. An Essay of Approaches and Case Histories*. Society for Sedimentary Geology (SEPM), Special Publications, **81**, 167–183.

Protić, L., Filipović, I., *et al.* 2000. Correlation of the Carboniferous, Permian and Triassic sequences of the Jadar Block, Sana-Una and "Bükkium" Terranes. *In*: Karamata, S. & Janković, S. (eds) *Proceedings of the International Symposium on Geology and Metallogeny of the Dinarides and Vardar Zone*. Serbian Academy of Sciences and Arts, Collection and Monographs, **1**; Department of Natural Sciences, Mathemathics and Technical Sciences, **1**, 61–69.

Radies, D., Stollhofen, H., Hollmann, G. & Kukla, P. 2005. Synsedimentary faults and amalgamated unconformities: Insights from 3D-seismic and core analysis of the Lower Triassic Middle Buntsandstein, Ems Trough, north-western Germany. *International Journal of Earth Science*, **94**, 863–875.

Radzinski, K.-H. 1999. Zur lithostratigraphischen Gliederung der Bernburg-Formation (Unterer Buntsandstein) im mittleren und nördlichen Teil von Sachsen-Anhalt. *Mitteilungen zur Geologie von Sachsen-*

*Anhalt*, **3**, 73–93.

RAFEK, M. B. 1977. *Platform conodonts from the Middle Triassic Upper Muschelkalk of West Germany and NE France*. PhD Thesis, University of Bonn.

RÁLISCH-FELGENHAUER, E. & TÖRÖK, Á. 1993. Mecsek és Villányi hegység – Mecsek and Villány Mountains. *In*: HAAS, J. (ed.) *Lithostratigraphic Units of Hungary, Triassic*. Magyar Állami Földtani Intézet MOL Rt, Budapest, 232–260 [in Hungarian].

RAMEIL, N., GÖTZ, A. E. & FEIST-BURKHARDT, S. 2000. High-resolution sequence interpretation of epeiric shelf carbonates by means of palynofacies analysis: an example from the Germanic Triassic (Lower Muschelkalk, Anisian) of East Thuringia, Germany. *Facies*, **43**, 123–144.

RAMOVŠ, A. 1982. The Permian–Triassic boundary in Yugoslavia. *Rudarsko-metalurski zbornik*, **29**, 29–31.

RAMPINO, M. R., SELF, S. & STOTHERS, R. B. 1988. Volcanic winters. *Annual Review, Earth and Planetary Sciences*, **16**, 73–99.

RAMPINO, M. R., PROKOPH, A. & ADLER, A. 2000. Tempo of the end-Permian event: High-resolution cyclostratigraphy at the Permian-Triassic boundary. *Geology*, **208**, 643–646.

RASSMUS, H. 1915. Alpine Cephalopoden im niederschlesischen Muschelkalk. *Jahrbuch der Preussischen Geologischen Landesanstalt*, **34**, 283–306.

RAUP, D. M. 1979. The size of the Permo-Triassic bottleneck and its evolutionary implications. *Science*, **206**, 217–218.

REINHARDT, L. 2000. *Dynamic stratigraphy and geochemistry of the Steinmergel-Keuper playa system: a record of Pangaean megamonsoon cyclicity (Triassic, Middle Keuper, Southern Germany)*. PhD Thesis, University of Cologne.

REINHARDT, L. & RICKEN, W. 2000*a*. The stratigraphic and geochemical record of playa cycles: monitoring a Pangaean monsoon-like system (Triassic, Middle Keuper, S. Germany). *Palaeogeography, Palaeoclimatology, Palaeoecology*, **161**, 205–227.

REINHARDT, L. & RICKEN, W. 2000*b*. Climate cycles documented in a playa system: comparison of geochemical signatures derived from subbasins (Triassic, Middle Keuper, German Basin). *In:* BOCK, H., MULLER, R., SWENNEN, R. & ZIMMERLE, W. (eds) West European case studies in stratigraphy. *Zentralblatt für Geologie und Paläontologie, Teil I*, **1999**(3–4), 315–340.

REITZ, E. 1985. Palynologie der Trias in Nordhessen und Südniedersachsen. *Geologische Abhandlungen Hessen*, **86**, 1–36.

RETTIG, B. 1996. Die Solling-Folge (Mittlerer Buntsandstein) im Grenzgebiet Niedersachsen – Thüringen – Hessen. *Mitteilungen aus dem Geologischen Institut der Universität Hannover*, **35**, 1–105.

RHEINHARDT, H. G. 1993. Structure of NE Germany: regional depth and thickness maps of Permian to Tertiary intervals. *In:* SPENCER, A. M. (ed.) *Generation, Accumulation and Production of Europe's Hydrocarbons*. EAGE, Special Publications, **III**, 155–166.

RICHTER-BERNBURG, G. 1974. Stratigraphische Synopsis des deutschen Buntsandsteins. *Geologisches Jahrbuch, Reihe A*, **25**, 127–132.

RICKEN, W., AIGNER, T. & JACOBSEN, B. 1998. Levee-crevasse deposits from the German Schilfsandstein. *Neues Jahrbuch für Geologie und Paläontologie, Monatshefte*, **1998**, 77–94.

ROBERTS, A. M., YIELDING, G., KUSZNIR, N. J., WALKER, I. M. & DORN-LOPEZ, D. 1995. Quantitative analysis of Triassic extension in the northern Viking Graben. *Journal of the Geological Society of London*, **152**, 15–26.

ROGHI, G. 2004. Palynological investigations in the Carnian of the Cave del Predil area (Julian Alps, NE Italy). *Review of Palaeobotany and Palynology*, **132**, 1–35.

RIEPPEL, O. 1992. A new species of the genus *Saurichthys* (Pisces: Actinopterygii) from the Middle Triassic of Monte San Giorgio (Switzerland), with comments on the phylogenetic interrelationships of the genus. *Palaeontographica*, **A 221**, 63–94.

RÖHLING, H.-G. 1991. A lithostratigraphic subdivision of the Lower Triassic in the Northwest German lowlands and the German sector of the North Sea, based on gamma ray and sonic logs. *Geologisches Jahrbuch, Reihe A*, **119**, 3–24.

RÖHLING, H.-G. & BEUTLER, G. 1993. Tectonic events in the Triassic of the Mid-European Basin. *In*: LUCAS, S. G. & MORALES, M. (eds) *The Nonmarine Triassic*. New Mexico Museum of Natural History & Science Bulletin, **3**, 419–420.

ROMAN, A. 2003. *Sequenzstratigraphie und Fazies des Unteren und Mittleren Buntsandsteins im östlichen Teil des Germanischen Beckens (Deutschland, Polen)*. PhD Thesis, Martin Luther University Halle-Wittenberg.

RONIEWICZ, P. 1966. Lower Werfen (Seis) clastic deposits in the Tatra Mts. *Acta Geologica Polonica*, **16**, 1–90 [in Polish].

ROTHE, M. 1993. Die Wüste im Wasser: Zur Fazies, Geochemie und Diagenese des Mittleren Muschelkalks in N-Bayern. *In*: HAGDORN, H. & SEILACHER, A. (eds) *Muschelkalk. Schöntaler Symposium 1991*. Goldschneck-Verlag, Werner K. Weidert, Korb, 111–115.

RUCKWIED. K. 2008. *Palynology of Triassic/Jurassic boundary key sections of the NW Tethyan Ralm (Hungary and Slovakia)*. PhD Thesis, Darmstadt University of Technology.

RUCKWIED, K., GÖTZ, A. E. & SZULC, J. 2004. Palynofacies patterns of Middle Triassic carbonate series of the Hronicum Basin (Tatra Mts., S. Poland): clue to reconstruction of eustatic history. *In*: KEDŻIERSKI, M., LESZCZYNSKI, S. & UCHMAN, A. (eds) *Geologia Tatr: ponadregionalny kontekst sedymentologiczny*. 8th Meeting of Polish Sedimentologists, Zakopane, 117.

RUCKWIED, K., GÖTZ, A. E., PÁLFY, J. & MICHALÍK, J. 2006. Palynomorph assemblages of Triassic/Jurassic boundary key sections of the NW Tethyan realm: Evidence for climatic change. *Volumina Jurassica*, **IV**, 297.

RÜFFER, T. 1995. Entwicklung einer Karbonat-Plattform: Fazies, Kontrollfaktoren und Sequenzstratigraphie in der Mitteltrias der westlichen Nördlichen Kalkalpen (Tirol, Bayern). *Gaea Heidelbergensis*, **1**, 1–288.

RÜFFER, T. 1996. Seismite im Unteren Muschelkalk westlich von Halle. *Hallesches Jahrbuch für Geowissenschaften, Reihe B*, **18**, 119–130.

RÜFFER, T. 1999. Exkurs: Sedimentation und Faziesräume in der nordalpinen Trias. *In*: HAUSCHKE, N. & WILDE, V. (eds) *Trias, eine ganz andere Welt: Mitteleuropa im frühen Erdmittelalter*. Verlag Dr. Friedrich Pfeil, München, 175–204.

RÜFFER, T. & BECHSTÄDT, T. 1998. Triassic sequence stratigraphy in the western part of the Northern Calcareous Alps. *In*: HARDENBOL, J., DE GRACIANSKY, P.-C., JACQUIN, T., FARLEY, M. & VAIL, P. R. (eds) *Mesozoic and Cenozoic Sequence Stratigraphy of European Basins*. Society for Sedimentary Geology (SEPM), Special Publications, **60**, 755–765.

RÜFFER, T. & ZÜHLKE, R. 1995. Sequence stratigraphy and sea-level changes in the Early to Middle Triassic of the Alps: a global comparison. *In*: HAQ, B. U. (ed.) *Sequence Stratigraphy and Depositional Response to Eustatic, Tectonic and Climatic Forcing*. Kluwer, Dordrecht, 161–207.

RYCHLINSKI, T. & SZULC, J. 2005. Facies and sedimentary environments of the Upper Scythian-Carnian succession from the Belanské Tatra Mts., Slovakia. *Annales Societatis Geologorum Poloniae*, **75**, 155–169.

SANDER, P. M. 1992. The Norian *Plateosaurus* bonebeds of Central Europe and their taphonomy. *Palaeogeography, Palaeoclimatology, Palaeoecology*, **93**, 255–299.

SCHLAGER, W. & SCHÖLLNBERGER, W. 1974. Das Prinzip stratigraphischer Wenden in der Schichtfolge der Nördlichen Kalkalpen. *Mitteilungen der österreichischen Geologischen Gesellschaft*, **66–67**, 165–193.

SCHMASSMANN, H. 1953. Das Keuper-Profil von Neue Welt. *Mitteilungen der Naturforschenden Gesellschaften beider Basel*, **19**, 129–153.

SCHOCH, R. & WILD, R. 1999*a*. Die Wirbeltiere des Muschelkalks unter besonderer Berücksichtigung Süddeutschlands. *In*: HAUSCHKE, N. & WILDE, V. (eds) *Trias, eine ganz andere Welt: Mitteleuropa im frühen Erdmittelalter*. Verlag Dr. Friedrich Pfeil, München, 331–342.

SCHOCH, R. & WILD, R. 1999*b*. Die Wirbeltier-Fauna im Keuper von Süddeutschland. *In*: HAUSCHKE, N. & WILDE, V. (eds) *Trias, eine ganz andere Welt: Mitteleuropa im frühen Erdmittelalter*. Verlag Dr. Friedrich Pfeil, München, 395–408.

SCHOCH, R. & WILD, R. 1999*c*. Die Saurier von Kupferzell – Der gegenwärtige Forschungsstand. *In*: HAUSCHKE, N. & WILDE, V. (eds) *Trias, eine ganz andere Welt: Mitteleuropa im frühen Erdmittelalter*. Verlag Dr. Friedrich Pfeil, München, 409–418.

SCHOLGER, R., MAURITSCH, H. J. & BRADNER, R. 2000. Permian–Triassic boundary magnetostratigraphy from the Southern Alps (Italy). *Earth and Planetary Science Letters*, **176**, 495–508.

SCHRÖDER, B. 1977. Unterer Keuper und Schilfsandstein im germanischen Trias-Randbecken. *Zentralblatt für Geologie und Paläonto-*

*logie*, **1976**(5–6), 1030–1056.

SCHRÖDER, B. 1982. Entwicklung des Sedimentbeckens und Stratigraphie der klassischen Germanischen Trias. *Geologische Rundschau*, **71**, 783–794.

SCHUBERT, J. K. & BOTTJER, D. J. 1992. Early Triassic stromatolites as post-mortem extinction disaster forms. *Geology*, **20**, 883–886.

SCHÜLER, F., BEUTLER, G. & FRANTZKE, H. J. 1989. Über synsedimentäre Bruchtektonik an der Grenze Unterer/Mittlerer Buntsandstein auf der Hermundurischen Scholle. *Hallesches Jahrbuch für Geowissenschaften, Reihe B*, **14**, 49–54.

SCHULTZE, H.-P. & KRIWET, J. 1999. Die Fische der Germanischen Trias. *In:* HAUSCHKE, N. & WILDE, V. (eds) *Trias, eine ganz andere Welt: Mitteleuropa im frühen Erdmittelalter.* Verlag Dr. Friedrich Pfeil, München, 239–250.

SCHULZ, E. 1966. Erläuterungen zur Tabelle der stratigraphischen Verbreitung der Sporen und Pollen vom oberen Perm bis untersten Lias. *Abhandlungen des Zentralen Geologischen Instituts*, **8**, 3–20.

SCHULZ, E. & HEUNISCH, C. 2005. Palynostratigraphische Gliederungsmöglichkeiten des deutschen Keupers. *In*: DEUTSCHE STRATIGRAPHISCHE KOMMISSION (eds). Stratigraphie von Deutschland IV – Keuper. *Courier Forschungsinstitut Senckenberg*, **253**, 43–49.

SCHWARZ, H. U. 1975. Sedimentary structures and facies analysis of shallow marine carbonates (Lower Muschelkalk, Middle Triassic, Southwestern Germany). *Contributions to Sedimentology*, **3**, 1–100.

SEEGIS, D. B. 1997. *Die Lehrbergschichten im Mittleren Keuper von Süddeutschland – Stratigraphie, Petrographie, Paläontologie, Genese*. Geo-Regioforschung, **1**, Verlag Manfred Hennecke, Remshalden.

SEEGIS, D. B. 1999. Die Wirbellosen-Fauna des Keupers: Zusammensetzung und ökologische Aussagemöglichkeiten. *In*: HAUSCHKE, N. & WILDE, V. (eds) *Trias, eine ganz andere Welt: Mitteleuropa im frühen Erdmittelalter.* Verlag Dr. Friedrich Pfeil, München, 395–408.

SEELING, M. & KELLNER, A. 2002. Sequenzstratigraphie des Nor und Rhät im Nordwestdeutschen Becken unter Berücksichtigung Süddeutschlands. *Zeitschrift der Deutschen Geologischen Gesellschaft*, **153**, 93–114.

SEEMANN, R. 1933. Das Saurischierlager in den Keupermergeln bei Trossingen. *Jahreshefte des Vereins für vaterländische Naturkunde in Württemberg*, **89**, 129–160.

SEIDEL, G. 1995. *Geologie von Thüringen*. E. Schweizerbart'sche Verlagsbuchhandlung (Nägele u. Obermiller), Stuttgart.

SEIDEL, G. (ed.) 2003. *Geologie von Thüringen*, 2nd edn. E. Schweizerbart'sche Verlagsbuchhandlung (Nägele u. Obermiller), Stuttgart.

SEIDLER, L., STEEL, R. J., STEMMERIK, L. & SURLYK, F. 2004. North Atlantic marine rifting in the Early Triassic: new evidence from East Greenland. *Journal of the Geological Society of London*, **161**, 583–592.

SENGÖR, A. M. C. 1984. *The Cimmeride Orogenic System and the Tectonics of Eurasia*. Geological Society of America, Special Papers, **195**.

SENKOWICZOWA, H. 1962. Alpine fauna in the Röt and Muschelkalk sediments of Poland. *In*: *Księga Pamiątkowa ku czci Prof. J. Samsonowicza*. Wydawnictwo PAN, Warsaw, 239–252 [in Polish with English summary].

SENKOWICZOWA, H. 1966. Roetian facies and stratigraphy in the Holy Cross Mountains. *Kwartalnik Geologiczny*, **10**, 769–784 [in Polish with English abstract].

SIMMS, M. J. & RUFFELL, A. H. 1990. Climatic and biotic change in the Late Triassic. *Journal of the Geological Society of London*, **147**, 321–327.

SIMON, T. 1988. Geologische und hydrogeologische Ergebnisse der neuen Sohlebohrung Bad Rappenau, Baden-Württemberg. *Jahreshefte des Geologischen Landesamtes Baden-Württemberg*, **30**, 479–510.

SKJOLD, L. J., VAN VEEN, P. M., KRISTENSEN, S-E. & RASMUSSEN, A. R. 1998. Triassic sequence stratigraphy of the southern Barents Sea. *In*: DE GRACIANSKY, P.-C., HARDENBOL, J., JACQUIN, T. & VAIL, P.R. (eds) *Mesozoic and Cenozoic Sequence Stratigraphy of European Basins*. Society for Sedimentary Geology (SEPM), Special Publications, **60**, 651–666.

SMITH, A. G. & LIVERMORE, R. A. 1991. Pangea in Permian to Jurassic times. *Tectonophysics,* **187**, 135–179.

SOMMARUGA, A. 1997. *Geology of the Central Jura and the Molasse Basin: New Insights into an Evaporite-based Foreland Fold and Thrust Belt*. Mémoires de la Société Neuchâteloise des Sciences Naturelles, **12**.

SPÖTL, C. 1988. Evaporitische Fazies der Reichenhaller Formation (Skyth/Anis) im Haller Salzberg (Nördliche Kalkalpen, Tirol). *Jahrbuch der Geologischen Bundesanstalt (Wien)*, **131**, 153–168.

SPÖTL, C. & BURNS, S. J. 1991. Formation of $\delta^{18}O$-depleted dolomite within a marine evaporitic sequence, Triassic Reichenhall Formation, Austria. *Sedimentology*, **38**, 1041–1057.

STINGL, V. 1987. Die fazielle Entwicklung des Alpinen Buntsandsteins (Skyth) im Westabschnitt der Nördlichen Kalkalpen (Tirol/Salzburg, Österreich). *Geologische Rundschau*, **76**, 647–664.

SZENTE, I. 1997. Bivalve assemblages from the Middle Triassic of the Mecsek Mts., Southern Hungary: systematics, palaeoecology and palaeogeographical significance. An overview. *Acta Geologica Hungarica,* **40**(4), 411–424.

SZOLDÁN, Zs. 1990. Middle Triassic magmatic sequences from different tectonic settings in the Bükk Mts (NE Hungary). *Acta Mineralogica, Petrographica*, **31**, 25–42.

SZULC, J. 1993. Early Alpine tectonics and lithofacies succession in the Silesian part of the Muschelkalk basin. A Synopsis. *In:* HAGDORN, H. & SEILACHER, A. (eds) *Muschelkalk. Schöntaler Symposium 1991*. Goldschneck-Verlag, Werner K. Weidert, Korb, 19–28.

SZULC, J. 1997. Middle Triassic (Muschelkalk) sponge-microbial stromatolites, diplopores and *Girvanella*-oncoids from the Silesian Cracow upland. *3rd Regional Symposium of International Fossil Algae Association and 3rd International Meeting of IGCP 380, Guidebook and Abstracts*, Cracow, 10–15.

SZULC, J. 1999. Anisian-Carnian evolution of the Germanic basin and its eustatic, tectonic and climatic controls. *In:* BACHMANN, G. H. & LERCHE, I. (eds) Epicontinental Triassic. *Zentralblatt für Geologie und Paläontologie, Teil I*, **1998**(7–8), 813–852.

SZULC, J. 2000. Middle Triassic evolution of the northern Peri-Tethys area as influenced by early opening of the Tethys Ocean. *Annales Societatis Geologorum Poloniae*, **70**, 1–48.

SZULC, J. 2003*a*. Lofer cyclicity: More tectonics than Milankovitch? *Triassic Geochronology and Cyclostratigraphy, A Field Symposium*. St. Christina/Val Gardena, Italy, 2003, Programme and Abstracts, 26.

SZULC, J. 2003*b*. Sponge-microbial stromatolites and coral-sponge reefs recovery in the Triassic of the Western Tethys and northern Peri-Tethys basin. *Berichte des Institutes für Geologie und Paläontologie der Karl-Franzens-Universität Graz/Austria*, **7**, 108.

SZULC, J. 2005. Sedimentary environments of the vertebrate-bearing Norian deposits from Krasiejow, Upper Silesia (Poland). *Hallesches Jahrbuch für Geowissenschaften, Reihe B*, **19**, 161–170.

SZURLIES, M. 2004. Magnetostratigraphy: the key to a global correlation of the classic Germanic Trias – case study Volpriehausen Formation (Middle Buntsandstein), Central Germany. *Earth and Planetary Science Letters*, **227**, 395–410.

SZURLIES, M., BACHMANN, G. H., MENNING, M., NOWACZYK, N. & KÄDING, K.-C. 2003. Magnetostratigraphy and high-resolution lithostratigraphy of the Permian-Triassic boundary interval in Central Germany. *Earth and Planetary Science Letters*, **212**, 263–278.

SZYPERKO-TELLER, A. 1982. Lithostratigraphy of the Buntsandstein in the western Pomerania. *Kwartalnik Geologiczny*, **26**, 341–368 [in Polish with English abstract].

SZYPERKO-TELLER, A. 1997. Lower Triassic. *In*: MAREK, S. & PAJCHLOWA, M. (eds) The epicontinental Permian and Mesozoic in Poland. *Prace Panstwowego Instytut Geologicznego*, **153**, 82–132 [in Polish].

SZYPERKO-TELLER, A. & MORYC, W. 1988. Evolution of the Buntsandstein basin in Poland. *Geological Quarterly*, **32**, 53–72 [in Polish with English abstract].

TANNER, K. M. 1978. Die Keuper-Lias Fundstelle von Niederschönthal, Kanton Baselland. *Bulletin der Vereinigung Schweizerischer Petroleum-Geologen und -Ingenieure*, **44**(106), 13–23.

TATGE, U. 1956. Conodonten aus dem Germanischen Muschelkalk, Teil I. *Paläontologische Zeitschrift*, **30**, 108–127.

THÉVENIAUT, H., BESSE, J., EDEL, J. B., WESTPHAL, M. & DURINGER, P. 1992. A Middle Triassic paleomagnetic pole for the Eurasian plate from Heming (France). *Geophysical Research Letters*, **19**(8), 777–780.

THIERRY, J. 2000. Late Sinemurian (193–191 Ma). *In:* DERCOURT, J.,

GAETANI, M., *et al.* (eds) *Atlas Peri-Tethys, Palaeogeographical Maps*. Commission de la Carte Géologique du Monde/Commission for the Geologic Map of the World, Explanatory Notes, Gauthier-Villars, Paris, Explanatory Notes, 49–60.

TÖRÖK, Á. 1993*a*. Storm influenced sedimentation in the Hungarian Muschelkalk. *In:* HAGDORN, H. & SEILACHER, A. (eds) *Muschelkalk, Schöntaler Symposium 1991*. Sonderbände der Gesellschaft für Naturkunde in Württemberg, **2**, Goldschneck-Verlag, Werner K. Weidert, Korb, 133–142.

TÖRÖK, Á. 1993*b*. Brachiopod beds as indicators of storm events: an example from the Muschelkalk of southern Hungary. *In:* PÁLFY, J. & VÖRÖS, A. (eds) *Mesozoic Brachiopods of Alpine Europe*. Hungarian Geological Society, Budapest, 161–172.

TÖRÖK, Á. 1997. Triassic ramp evolution in Southern Hungary and its similarities to the Germano-type Triassic. *Acta Geologica Hungarica*, **40**, 367–390.

TÖRÖK, Á. 1998*a*. Controls on development of mid-Triassic ramps: examples from southern Hungary. *In:* WRIGHT, V. P. & BURCHETTE, T. P. (eds) *Carbonate Ramps*. Geological Society, London, Special Publications, **149**, 339–367.

TÖRÖK, Á. 1998*b*. Triassic lithostratigraphy of Mecsek-Villány unit. *In*: BÉRCZI, I. & JÁMBOR, Á. (eds) *Magyarország geológiai képződményeinek rétegtana*. MOL Rt., Magyar Állami Földtani Intézet, Budapest, 253–279 [in Hungarian].

TÖRÖK, Á. 2000. Muschelkalk carbonates in southern Hungary: an overview and comparison to German Muschelkalk. *In*: BACHMANN, G. H. & LERCHE, I. (eds) Epicontinental Triassic. *Zentralblatt für Geologie und Paläontologie, Teil I*, **1998**(9–10), 1085–1103.

TORSVIK, T. H. & SMETHURST, M. A. 1999. Plate tectonic modelling: virtual reality with GMAP. *Computers and Geosciences*, **25**, 395–402.

TRAMMER, J. 1971. Middle Triassic (Muschelkalk) conodonts from the SW margin of the Holy Cross Mts. *Acta Geologica Polonica*, **21**, 379–386.

TRAMMER, J. 1972. Stratigraphical and paleogeographical significance of conodonts from the Muschelkalk of the Holy Cross Mts. *Acta Geologica Polonica*, **22**, 219–232.

TRAMMER, J. 1975. Stratigraphy and facies development of the Muschelkalk in the south-western Holy Cross Mts. *Acta Geologica Polonica*, **25**, 179–216.

TRAMMER, J. 1979. The isochronous synsedimentary movements at the Anisian/Ladinian boundary in the Muschelkalk basin and the Alps. *Rivista Italiana di Paleontologia e Stratigrafia*, **85**, 931–936.

TRÜMPY, R. 1980. *An Outline of the Geology of Switzerland*. Schweizerische Geologische Kommission, Wepf & Co., Basel.

URLICHS, M. 1993. Zur Gliederung des Oberen Muschelkalks in Baden-Württemberg mit Ceratiten. *In*: HAGDORN, H. & SEILACHER, A. (eds) *Muschelkalk. Schöntaler Symposium 1991*. Goldschneck-Verlag, Werner K. Weidert, Korb, 151–156.

URLICHS, M. 1999. Cephalopoden im Muschelkalk und Lettenkeuper des Germanischen Beckens. *In*: HAUSCHKE, N. & WILDE, V. (eds) *Trias, eine ganz andere Welt: Mitteleuropa im frühen Erdmittelalter.* Verlag Dr. Friedrich Pfeil, München, 343–354.

USDOWSKI, H.-E. 1962. Die Entstehung der kalkoolitischen Fazies des norddeutschen Unteren Buntsandsteins. *Beiträge zur Mineralogie und Petrographie, Heidelberg*, **8**, 141–179.

UTTING, J., SPINA, A., JANSONIUS, J., MCGREGOR, D. C. & MARSHALL, J. E. A. 2004. Reworked miospores in the Upper Paleozoic and Lower Triassic of the northern circum-polar area and selected localities. *Palynology*, **28**, 75–119.

VADÁSZ, E. 1935. *A Mecsekhegység*. Das Mecsekgebirge. Magyar tájak földtani leírása, Földtani Intézet, Budapest, [in Hungarian with German summary].

VAN ADRICHEM BOOGAERT, H. A. & KOUWE, W. F. P. 1993. Stratigraphic nomenclature of the Netherlands, revision and update by RGD and NOGEPA, Section E Triassic. *Mededelingen van de Rijks Geologische Dienst*, **50**.

VAN DER EEM, J. G. L. A. 1983. Aspects of Middle and Late Triassic Palynology. 6. Palynological investigations in the Ladinian and Lower Karnian of the Western Dolomites, Italy. *Review of Palaeobotany and Palynology*, **39**, 189–300.

VAN DER VOO, R. & TORSVIK, T. H. 2001. Evidence for late Paleozoic and Mesozoic non-dipole fields provides an explanation for the Pangea reconstruction problems. *Earth and Planetary Science Letters*, **187**, 71–81.

VAN DER VOO, R., MAUK, F. J. & FRENCH, R. B. 1976. Permian-Triassic continental configurations and the origin of the Gulf of Mexico. *Geology*, **4**, 177–180.

VAN DER ZWAN, C. J. & SPAAK, P. 1992. Lower and Middle Triassic sequence stratigraphy and climatology of the Netherlands, a model. *Palaeogeography, Palaeoclimatology, Palaeoecology*, **91**, 277–290.

VEEVERS, J. J. 1989. Middle/Late Triassic (230 ± 5 Ma) singularity in the stratigraphic and magmatic history of the Pangean heat anomaly. *Geology*, **17**, 784–787.

VELLEDITS, F. 1999. Anisian terrestrial deposits in the sequence of the Northern Bükk Mts. *Földtani Közlöny*, **129**(3), 327–361 [in Hungarian].

VELLEDITS, F. 2000. Evolution of the area from the Berva Valley to the Hór Valley in the Middle – Upper Triassic. *Földtani Közlöny*, **130**(1), 47–93 [in Hungarian].

VELLEDITS, F. & PÉRÓ, CS. 1987. The Southern Bükk (northern Hungary) Triassic revisited: The Bervavölgy Limestone. *Annales Universitas Scientiarum Budapestinensis di Ronaldo Eötvös Nominatae, Sectio Geologica*, **27**, 17–64.

VIEL, G. 1979*a*. Litostratigrafia ladinica: una revisione. Riconstruzione paleogeografica e paleostrutturale dell'area dolomitica-cadorina (Alpi Meridionali). I. Parte. *Rivista Italiana di Paleontologia*, **85/1**, 88–125.

VIEL, G. 1979*b*. Litostratigrafia ladinica: una revisione. Riconstruzione paleogeografica e paleostrutturale dell'area dolomitica-cadorina (Alpi Meridionali). II. Parte. *Rivista Italiana di Paleontologia*, **85/2**, 297–352.

VISSCHER, H. & BRUGMAN, W. A. 1981. Ranges of selected palynomorphs in the alpine Triassic of Europe. *Review of Palaeobotany and Palynology*, **34**, 115–128.

VISSCHER, H. & COMMISSARIS, A. L. T. M. 1968. Middle Triassic pollen and spores from the Lower Muschelkalk of Winterswijk (The Netherlands). *Pollen et Spores*, **12**, 161–176.

VOIGT, T. & GAUPP, R. 2000. Die fazielle Entwicklung an der Grenze zwischen Unterem und Mittleren Buntsandstein im Zentrum der Thüringer Senke. *Beiträge zur Geologie von Thüringen*, **7**, 55–71.

VOIGT, T. & LINNEMANN, U. 1996. Resedimentation im Unteren Muschelkalk- das Profil am Jenzig bei Jena. *Beiträge für Geologie von Thüringen, Neue Folge*, **3**, 153–167.

VOLLMER, T. 2005. *Paleoclimatology of Upper Triassic playa cycles: new insights into an orbital controlled monsoon system (Norian, German Basin)*. PhD Thesis, University of Cologne.

VÖRÖS, A., BUDAI, T., *et al.* 2003. The Pelsonian substage on the Balaton Highland (Middle Triassic, Hungary). *Geologica Hungarica. Series palaeontologica*, **55**.

WAGNER, R. *et al.* 2008. *Stratigraphical Table of Extra-alpine Poland.* Wydawnictwo Geologiczne, Warsaw (in press).

WARD, P. D., MONTGOMERY, D. R. & SMITH, R. 2000. Altered river morphology in South Africa related to the Permian-Triassic extinction. *Science*, **289**, 1740–1742.

WARRINGTON, G. & IVIMEY-COOK, H. C. 1992. Triassic. *In*: COPE, J. C. W., INGHAM, J. K. & RAWSON, P. F. (eds) *Atlas of Palaeogeography and Lithofacies*. Geological Society of London, Memoirs, **13**, 97–106.

WÉBER, B. 1990. Ladinian and late Triassic beds in the northern foreland of W-Mecsek. *Földtani Közlöny*, **120**, 153–180 [in Hungarian].

WHEELER, H. E. 1964. Baselevel, lithosphere surface, and time-stratigraphy. *Bulletin of the Geological Society of America*, **75**, 599–610.

WIDMER, T. 1991. Stratigraphie und Sedimentologie der Evaporite des Muschelkalks im Basler Tafeljura. *Beiträge zur Geologie der Schweiz, Geotechnische Serie*, **79**.

WIEDMANN, J. 1974. Zum Problem der Definition und Abgrenzung von Obernor (Sevat) und Rhät. *Schriftenreihe der Erdwissenschaftlichen Kommission der Österreichischen Akademie der Wissenschaften*, **2**, 229–235.

WIERER, J. F. 1997. Vergleichende Untersuchungen an Megasporenvergesellschaftungen der alpinen und germanischen Mittel- und Obertrias. *Münchner Geowissenschaftliche Abhandlungen, Reihe A*, **35**, 1–175.

WIGNALL, P. B. 2001. Large igneous provinces and mass extinctions. *Earth-Science Reviews*, **53**, 1–33.

WIGNALL, P. B. & HALLAM, A. 1992. Anoxia as a cause of the Permian-

Triassic mass extinction – facies evidence from Northern Italy and the Western United States. *Palaeogeography, Palaeoclimatology, Palaeoecology*, **93**, 21–46.

WIGNALL, P. B. & HALLAM, A. 1996. Facies change and the end-Permian mass extinction in S. E. Sichuan, China. *Palaios*, **11**, 587–596.

WIGNALL, P. B., MORANTE, R. & NEWTON, R. 1998. The Permo-Triassic transition in Spitsbergen: $\delta^{13}C_{org}$ chemostratigraphy, Fe and S geochemistry, facies, fauna and trace fossils. *Geological Magazine*, **135**, 47–62.

WOLBURG, J. 1969. Die epirogenetischen Phasen der Muschelkalk- und Keuperentwicklung NW-Deutschlands mit einem Rückblick auf den Buntsandstein. *Geotektonische Forschungen*, **32**, 1–65.

WRIGHT, D. T. 1999. The role of sulphate-reducing bacteria and cyanobacteria in dolomite formation in distal ephemeral lakes of the Coorong region, South Australia. *Sedimentary Geology*, **126**, 147–157.

WURSTER, P. 1964*a*. Geologie des Schilfsandsteins. *Mitteilungen des Geologischen Staatsinstituts Hamburg*, **33**, 1–10.

WURSTER, P. 1964*b*. Delta sedimentation in the German Keuper basin. *Developments in Sedimentology*, **1**, 436–446.

WURSTER, P. 1968. Paläogeographie der deutschen Trias und die paläogeographische Orientierung der Lettenkohle in Südwestdeutschland. *Eclogae Geologicae Helvetiae*, **61**, 157–166.

YANG, Z., MOREAU, M. G., BUCHER, H., DOMMERGUES, J. L. & TROUILLER, A. 1996. Hettangian and Sinemurian magnetostratigraphy from the Paris Basin. *Journal of Geophysical Research*, **101**, 8025–8042.

YIN, H., ZHANG, K., WU, S. & PENG, Y. 1996. Global correlation and definition of the Permian–Triassic boundary. *In*: YIN, H. (ed.) *The Palaeozoic–Mesozoic boundary. Candidates for the Global Stratotype Section and Point of the Permian-Triassic Boundary.* China University of Geosciences Press, Wuhan, 3–28.

YIN, H. F., ZHANG, K., TONG, J., YANG, Z. & WU, S. 2001. The global stratotype section and point (GSSP) of the Permian–Triassic boundary. *Episodes*, **24**(2), 102–114.

ZACHER, W. & LUPU, M. 1999. Pitfalls on the race for an ultimate Tethys model. *International Journal of Earth Sciences*, **88**, 111–115.

ZAWIDZKA, K. 1975. Conodont stratigraphy and sedimentary environment of the Muschelkalk in Upper Silesia. *Acta Geologica Polonica*, **25**, 217–257.

ZIEGLER, P. A. 1988. *Evolution of the Arctic–North-Atlantic and the Western Tethys.* American Association of Petroleum Geologists (AAPG), Memoirs, **43**.

ZIEGLER, P. A. 1990. *Geological Atlas of Western and Central Europe*, 2nd edn. Shell Internationale Petroleum Maatschappij B. V. and Geological Society, London.

ZÜHLKE, R. 2000. Fazies, hochauflösende Sequenzstratigraphie und Beckenentwicklung im Anis (mittlere Trias) der Dolomiten (Südalpin, N-Italien). *Gaea Heidelbergensis*, **6**, 1–368.

ZÜHLKE, R. 2004. Integrated cyclostratigraphy of a model Mesozoic carbonate platform – the Latemar (Middle Triassic, Italy). *In*: D'ARGENIO, B., FISHER, A., PREMOLI SILVA, I. & WEISSERT, H. (eds) *Cyclostratigraphy. An Essay of Approaches and Case Histories.* Society for Sedimentary Geology (SEPM), Special Publications, **81**, 183–212.

ZÜHLKE, R., BECHSTÄDT, T. & MUNDIL, R. 2003. Sub-Milankovitch and Milankovitch forcing on a model Mesozoic carbonate platform – the Latemar (Middle Triassic, Italy). *Terra Nova*, **15**(2), 69–80.

# 14 Jurassic

GRZEGORZ PIEŃKOWSKI & MICHAEL E. SCHUDACK (co-ordinators), PAVEL BOSÁK, RAYMOND ENAY, ANNA FELDMAN-OLSZEWSKA, JAN GOLONKA, JACEK GUTOWSKI, G.F.W. HERNGREEN, PETER JORDAN, MICHAŁ KROBICKI, BERNARD LATHUILIERE, REINHOLD R. LEINFELDER, JOZEF MICHALÍK, ECKHARD MÖNNIG, NANNA NOE-NYGAARD, JÒZSEF PÁLFY, ANNA PINT, MICHAEL W. RASSER, ACHIM G. REISDORF, DIETER U. SCHMID, GÜNTER SCHWEIGERT, FINN SURLYK, ANDREAS WETZEL & THEO E. WONG

The Jurassic System (199.6–145.5 Ma; Gradstein *et al.* 2004), the second of three systems constituting the Mesozoic era, was established in Central Europe about 200 years ago. It takes its name from the Jura Mountains of eastern France and northernmost Switzerland. The term 'Jura Kalkstein' was introduced by Alexander von Humboldt as early as 1799 to describe a series of carbonate shelf deposits exposed in the Jura mountains. Alexander Brongniart (1829) first used the term 'Jurassique', while Leopold von Buch (1839) established a three-fold subdivision for the Jurassic (Lias, Dogger, Malm). This three-fold subdivision (which also uses the terms black Jura, brown Jura, white Jura) remained until recent times as three series (Lower, Middle, Upper Jurassic), although the respective boundaries have been grossly redefined. The immense wealth of fossils, particularly ammonites, in the Jurassic strata of Britain, France, Germany and Switzerland was an inspiration for the development of modern concepts of biostratigraphy, chronostratigraphy, correlation and palaeogeography. In a series of works, Alcide d'Orbigny (1842–51, 1852) distinguished stages of which seven are used today (although none of them has retained its original stratigraphic range). Albert Oppel (1856–1858) developed a sequence of such divisions for the entire Jurassic System, crucially using the units in the sense of time divisions.

During the nineteenth and twentieth centuries many additional stage names were proposed – more than 120 were listed by Arkell (1956). It is due to Arkell's influence that most of these have been abandoned and the table of current stages for the Jurassic (comprising 11 internationally accepted stages, grouped into three series) shows only two changes from that used by Arkell: separation of the Aalenian from the lower Bajocian was accepted by international agreement during the second Luxembourg Jurassic Colloquium in 1967, and the Tithonian was accepted as the Global Standard for the uppermost stage in preference to Portlandian and Volgian by vote of the Jurassic Subcommission (Morton 1974, 2005). As a result, the international hierarchical subdivision of the Jurassic System into series and stages has been stable for many years.

Ammonites have provided a high-resolution correlation and subdivision of Jurassic strata (Arkell 1956; Morton 1974). For most Jurassic stratigraphers, the stages are groups of zones and have traditionally been defined by the zones they contain in Europe. Ammonites are the primary tools for biochronology and the Standard Ammonite Zones are assemblage zones, not biozones of the nominal species. One should also bear in mind that bioprovincialism of ammonites can influence and complicate biostratigraphical correlations. In that respect, Central Europe provides the most valuable ammonite finds, as in some regions they represent both sub-Mediterranean and Boreal bioprovinces.

The primary criteria for the recognition of chronostratigraphic units and correlation is the precise ammonite biostratigraphy, supplemented by other biostratigraphic criteria, chemostratigraphy, magnetostratigraphy and sequence stratigraphy (Morton 2005). At present, only four of the stages have ratified Global Stratotype Section and Point (GSSP), namely, the Sinemurian, Pliensbachian, Aalenian and Bajocian. The last, seventh International Congress on the Jurassic System held in Cracow, Poland, advanced progress with the establishment of the Pliensbachian/Toarcian (Elmi 2006) and Oxfordian/Kimmeridgian (Wierzbowski *et al.* 2006) GSSPs. The most difficult Jurassic boundaries to define are the base of the Jurassic System (and Hettangian Stage) and the top of the Jurassic System (and the base of the Cretaceous System). Concerning the former, progress has been made with four GSSP candidate profiles (Bloos 2006). Nevertheless, despite being well subdivided, the Jurassic System is the only one with neither bottom nor top defined.

Jurassic shelf, lagoonal and lacustrine sediments show strong cyclicity observed as sedimentary microrhythms (typically with an alteration of limestone and marl, carbonate-rich and carbonate-poor mudrocks, or more silty and more clayey/organic-rich laminae). Given that these successions represent continuous sedimentation over long periods, they can be used for astronomically calibrated timescales, since the periodicity of these microrhythms is consistent with orbital forcing due to Milankovitch cyclicity. About 70% of the Jurassic is now covered by floating astronomical timescales based on the recognition of Milankovitch cycles (Gradstein *et al.* 2004; Coe & Weedon 2006).

Jurassic outcrops occur in several countries of Central Europe

(Fig. 14.1), with the largest areas in the eastern Paris Basin, the French Jura Mountains and SE France, southern Germany and southern Poland. In the eastern and western Alps, northern Germany, and in the Czech Republic and Slovakia, outcrops are smaller and more scattered. In the other areas (Denmark, the Netherlands, much of northern Germany and Poland), the Jurassic is covered by younger sediments (up to several kilometres thick), but has been studied in boreholes, partly due to its importance for the oil and gas (and other) industries.

The Jurassic System in Central Europe has been studied for about 200 years, but it is still an inspiring source of new ideas. The Jurassic is an important period in the Earth's history and in the evolution of life, and it encompasses some of the most significant global events in geological history (Triassic–Jurassic boundary mass extinction, climate, sea-level and atmospheric $CO_2$ concentration changes, volcanic activities, carbon isotope perturbations, Toarcian anoxic event, variation of marine and non-marine ecosystems, to name a few). The Jurassic System of Central Europe is very diverse and the following sections will provide a regional overview of the stratigraphy, facies and depositional architecture of both marine and non-marine facies. Possible causal mechanisms for stratigraphic boundaries will be discussed, with explanations involving sea-level changes, climate changes and tectonic events. Significant work on the marine and non-marine Jurassic has been carried out in Central Europe. Sequence stratigraphic correlation between fossiliferous marine and non-marine facies (the latter containing fossils of much lower stratigraphic resolution) is one of most important issues discussed.

The principal palaeogeographic tectonic subdivision (sum-

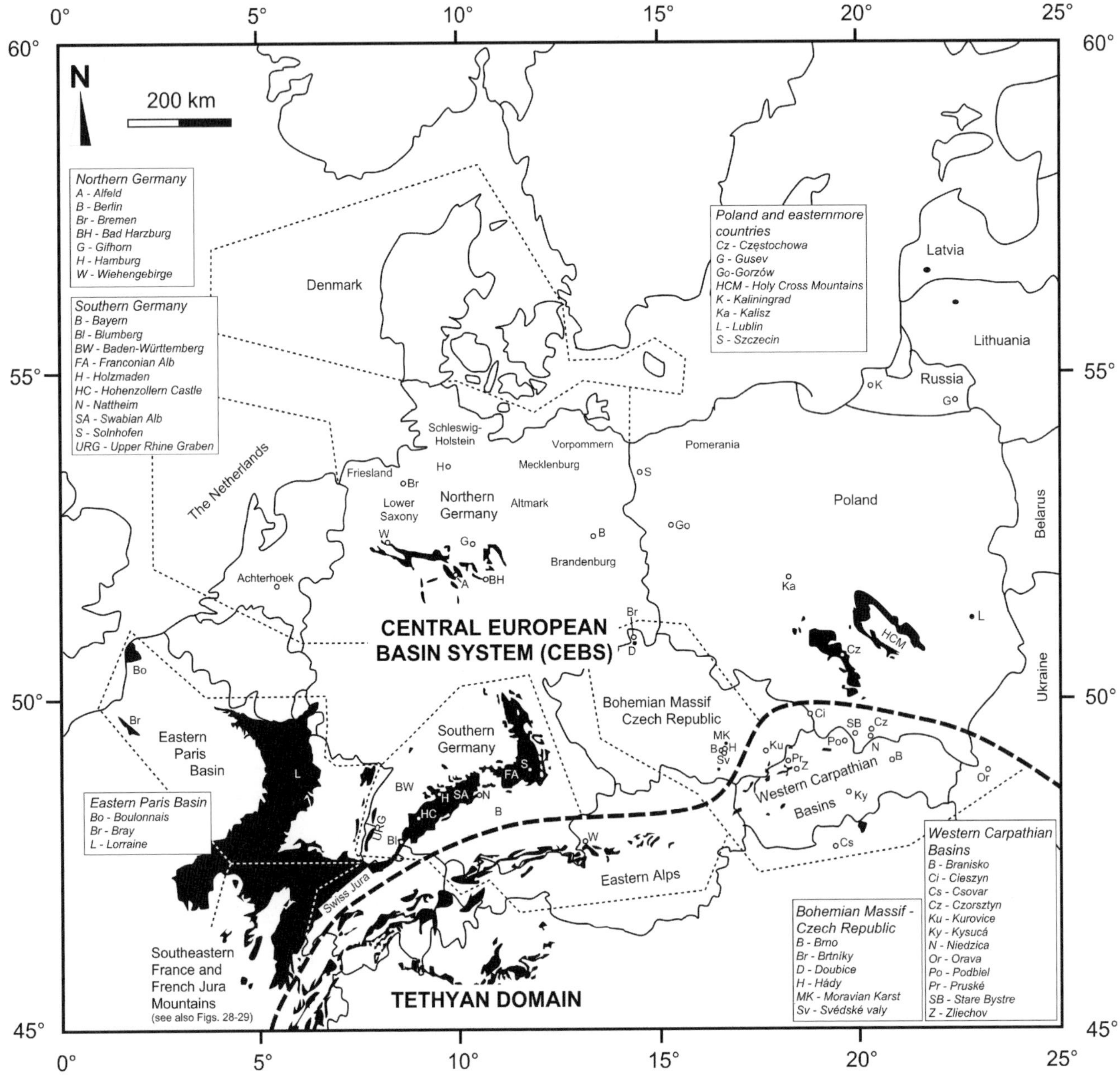


**Fig. 14.1.** Jurassic outcrops in Central Europe (black areas). Very small outcrops are not considered here. The thick dashed line marks the inferred boundary between the Central European Basin System Domain and the Tethyan Domain.

marized in three simplified sketches in Figs 14.2–14.4, which can be used to provide a palaeogeographic overview during study of the detailed sections for each area) follows that in Chapter 16. In that respect, the Jurassic System in Central Europe has developed in two principal geotectonic domains: the Central European Basin System (CEBS, including the southern epi-Variscan basins) and the Tethyan Domain.

In terms of faunal provincialism, the Boreal CEBS Domain generally differs from the Mediterranean Tethyan Domain (Dercourt *et al.* 2000). However, division between particular bioprovinces in the boundary area between these two domains is far from unequivocal; for example, conspicuous Mediterranean (Tethyan) influences can be observed in the CEBS Domain in areas such as south-central Poland, southern Germany, southern France and northwestern Switzerland (often called the peri-Tethyan area). On the other hand, in Early Jurassic times, the Boreal influences extended as far south as Spain (Rosales *et al.* 2004).

In particular, the latest Callovian and Early Oxfordian represent one of the most dynamic intervals in the history of Jurassic Ammonoidea, characterized by one of the highest levels of mixing of Boreal, sub-Mediterranean and even Mediterranean faunas. The massive expansion of Boreal Cardioceratidae from their original 'home' in Arctic areas as far south as SE France brought them into contact with Mediterranean-style faunas rich

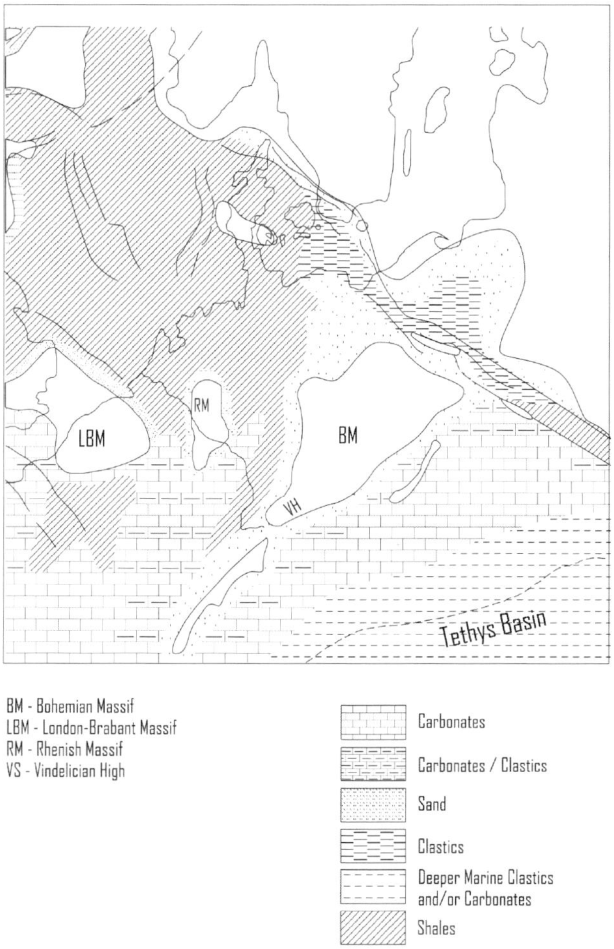


**Fig. 14.2.** Paleogeographic map of Central Europe for the Early Jurassic. Based upon Ziegler (1988), simplified and redrawn.

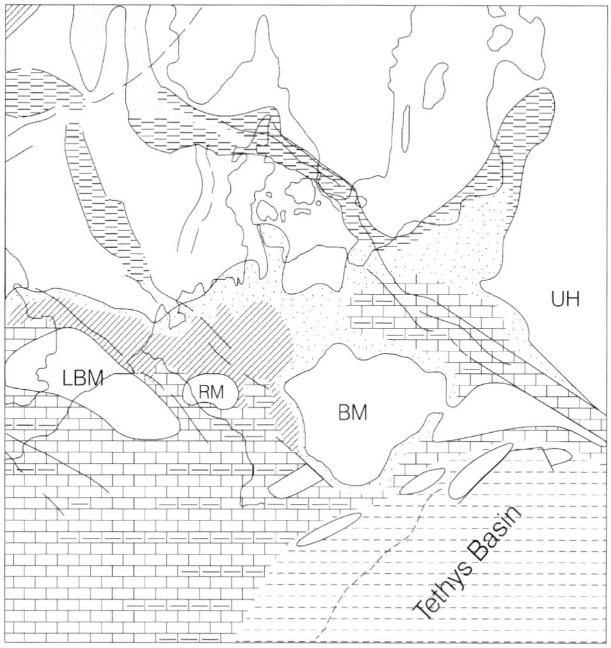


**Fig. 14.3.** Paleogeographic map of Central Europe for the Middle Jurassic. Based upon Ziegler (1988), simplified and redrawn. For legend see Figure 14.2.

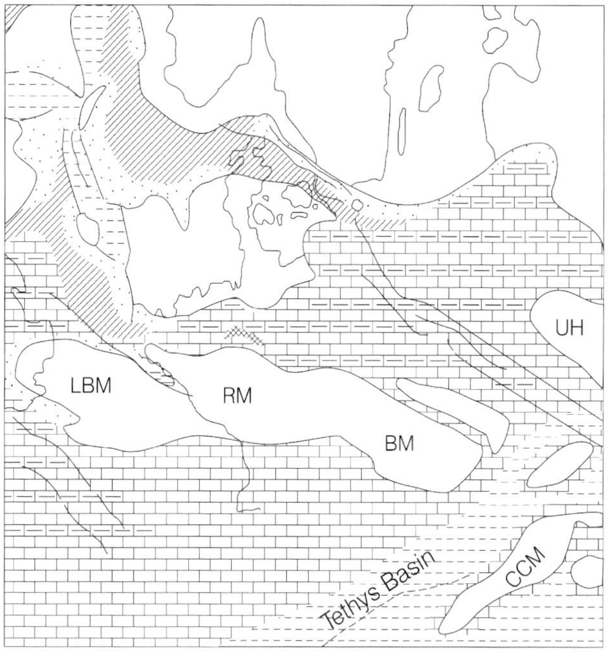


**Fig. 14.4.** Paleogeographic map of Central Europe for the Late Jurassic. Based upon Ziegler (1988), simplified and redrawn. For legend see Figure 14.2.

in Phylloceratidae (Meléndez *et al.* 2006). Similar events provide the framework within which high-resolution inter-bioprovincial correlations are possible, but at the same time makes the delimitation of certain bioprovinces difficult. Generally, the CEBS would largely correspond to the Boreal and sub-Boreal bioprovinces (the southern epi-Variscan basins would represent largely sub-Mediterranean bioprovince with elements of the sub-Boreal bioprovince) and the Tethyan Domain would correspond to the Mediterranean province. Assuming the above, the Jurassic system in the studied area of Central Europe is subdivided into the CEBS Domain (including the southern epi-Variscan basins) and the Tethyan Domain.

## Triassic–Jurassic boundary (J.P.)

The Triassic–Jurassic boundary (TJB) is stratigraphically important but also marks significant global environmental and biotic events. The end of the Triassic is widely regarded as one of the five biggest Phanerozoic mass extinction events (Sepkoski 1996); it coincided with environmental change which included global cooling followed by a warming event (McElwain *et al.* 1999; Guex *et al.* 2004), perturbation of the global carbon cycle (Pálfy *et al.* 2001; Hesselbo *et al.* 2002; Ward *et al.* 2004), and significant sea-level changes (Hallam 1997). Causes of these events are widely debated. Radioisotopic dating suggests that marine extinction was synchronous with the formation of the Central Atlantic Magmatic Province at *c.* 200 Ma (Marzoli *et al.* 1999, 2004; Pálfy *et al.* 2000). At present most evidence suggests a scenario that invokes short-lived but intense volcanism as a trigger. The formation of one of the largest Phanerozoic flood basalt provinces may have induced large-scale environmental changes that ultimately led to the latest-Triassic mass extinction (Hesselbo *et al.* 2002; Pálfy 2003). Alternative hypotheses relate the mass extinction to the effects of a putative bolide impact (Olsen *et al.* 2002) or large and rapid sea-level changes (Hallam & Wignall 1999). Regardless of its cause, the latest-Triassic extinction and contemporaneous environmental events left a distinctive stratigraphic signature that is readily observed in Central European sections.

### *Definition*

The TJB has no accepted GSSP yet. At three of the four proposed candidate sections (St. Audrie's Bay (England), New York Canyon (Nevada, USA) and Utcubamba Valley (Peru), pronounced changes in the ammonoid faunas are used to place the boundary. The first appearance of the smooth, evolute genus *Psiloceras* marks the base of the NW European *Psiloceras planorbis* Zone and the east Pacific *Psiloceras tilmanni* Zone. Ceratitid ammonoids, that dominated the Triassic faunas, did not survive the TJB. The heteromorph *Choristoceras* is regarded as the index fossil of the latest Triassic. In Europe the topmost Rhaetian *Choristoceras marshi* Zone (correlative of the *C. crickmayi* Zone in North America) represents the youngest biochronologic subdivision. At the fourth GSSP candidate, Kunga Island (western Canada), a remarkable turnover in radiolarian faunas offers an alternative biostratigraphic criterion for defining the TJB. Until the GSSP selection is settled, detailed and high-resolution correlation issues will remain hotly debated in the few continuous, fossiliferous marine sections. Generally, however, coarser stratigraphic resolution in most other sections allows unambiguous placement of the TJB as several fossil groups exhibit significant differences between their latest Triassic and earliest Jurassic assemblages.

### *The boundary in Central Europe*

Various tectonostratigraphic units in Central Europe represent a broad spectrum of facies types across the TJB. Epicontinental settings prevailed in the Germanic Basin that contrasts with the shelf environments of western Tethys. Sedimentation was discontinuous in the epicontinental areas of the NW part of Central Europe. The bivalve *Rhaetavicula contorta* is the key biostratigraphic marker of the topmost Rhaetian, developed in a marly facies ('Grès infraliasique') that overlies the marginal marine Keuper. In the eastern part of the Paris Basin and around the Ardennes Massif, the basal Jurassic is represented by *Gryphaea*-bearing limestones of Early Hettangian age as indicated by ammonoids of the genus *Psiloceras*.

In southern Germany marine Hettangian strata transgressively overlie the fluvial or lacustrine topmost Triassic. A preceding regression is marked in northern Bavaria, where the progradation of sandstone over shale is observed. Fluvial sandstone channel fills that cut into Rhaetian lacustrine shale ('Hauptton') (Bloos 1990) is taken as evidence of a significant sea-level fall near the TJB (Hallam 1997, 2001) although its precise timing is not well constrained.

Continuous or near-continuous sedimention across the TJB is better known from different parts of the western Tethyan shelf. In the Southern Alps, the lower members (1–3) of the Zu Limestone consist of Rhaetian carbonates of platform or ramp facies (Jadoul *et al.* 2004). Thin-bedded, micritic limestone of the topmost member (Zu 4) marks a transgression and simultaneous platform drowning. Palynological studies suggest that the TJB is located within the Zu 4 Member (Jadoul *et al.* 2004). A characteristic Triassic foraminiferan assemblage disappears at the top of the Zu 3 Member (Lakew 1990). Also at this level a negative carbon isotope anomaly was observed in several sections in the Monte Albenza area (Galli *et al.* 2005).

The remainder of the Hettangian is represented by the Conchodon Dolomite that was deposited on a prograding Bahamian-type platform. Bivalve faunas occur in the Zu and Conchodon formations and show a significant turnover at the system boundary (Alissanaz 1992; McRoberts 1994; McRoberts *et al.* 1995).

Sections in the Northern Calcareous Alps reveal more facies variability as TJB strata occur from platform through slope to intraplatform basinal settings, although a hiatus of varying duration is widespread at the TJB. Large carbonate platforms and reefs existed in the western Tethyan margin during the Late Triassic. The demise of Dachstein-type reefs and the reefal biota at the close of the Triassic is one of the most dramatic aspects of the TJB events and represents one of the major crises in the history of reef ecosystems (Flügel 2002; Kiessling 2002). The spectacular Steinplatte reef in Tyrol (Piller 1981), although its architecture was recently reinterpreted (Stanton & Flügel 1995), exemplifies the vanishing of carbonate buildups.

One of the first recognized and studied TJB sections occurs in an intraplatform basinal setting at Kendelbachgraben near the Wolfgangsee in Salzkammergut, near Salzburg (see Fig. 14.39) (Suess & Mojsisovics 1868). Here, and in the nearby Tiefengraben section, the TJB is marked by an abrupt lithological change as the latest Rhaetian Kössen Formation is overlain by the 'Grenzmergel' (boundary marl) that grades into alternating marls and limestones (Golebiowski 1990; Golebiowski & Braunstein 1988; Kürschner *et al.* 2007). The lack of ammonites resembles the record in NW Europe, hence correlation with the 'pre-planorbis beds' was suggested (Hallam 1990). The first Jurassic ammonoid, *Psiloceras planorbis*, was found nearby at Breitenberg in the overlying limestone unit. Palynological turnover suggests the placement of the TJB within the Grenzmergel (Morbey 1975; Gerben *et al.* 2004; Kürschner *et al.* 2007). The lithological change manifest in the Grenzmergel could reflect sea-level rise and/or increased terrigenous influx related to sudden climate change. A primary stable isotope signal was not preserved in the carbonate due to diagenetic overprint (Hallam & Goodfellow 1990; Morante & Hallam 1996). However, a negative carbon isotope anomaly at the TJB is documented in the organic matter (Kürschner *et al.* 2007).

Coevally, in an adjacent, relatively deep-water basin, the Zlambach Marl Formation was deposited. Although an offshore facies may be expected to preserve a better ammonoid record, this has been compromised by tectonic deformation and poor outcrops.

Several TJB sections are known from the Western Carpathians, where typically a sharp transition from cyclic, peritidal to shallow subtidal carbonate sedimentation (Fatra Formation) to predominantly terrigenous dark mudstones and shales (Kopienec Formation) occurs in the Fatric Unit (Tomašových & Michalík 2000; Michalík *et al.* 2007). Significant changes across the TJB are documented in the foraminifera (Gaździcki 1983) and bivalve faunas (Kochanová 1967; Michalík 1980).

The Upper Triassic–Lower Jurassic succession of the Transdanubian Range within the Carpathian Basin in Hungary is similar to that in the Northern Calcareous Alps. The TJB transition in carbonate platform facies is well known from the Transdanubian Range in Hungary but the boundary is typically marked by a disconformity. A gap occurs in most sections between the Rhaetian Dachstein Limestone Formation and the overlying Hettangian Kardosrét Formation in the Bakony Mountains, or the Pisznice Formation in the Gerecse Mountains. In a well exposed section at Tata a sharp erosion surface and a slightly angular unconformity suggest that a break in platform evolution was caused by emergence (Haas & Hámor 2001). The Dachstein Formation is rich in megalodontid bivalves (Végh-Neubrandt 1982) that do not occur in Hettangian rocks of similar facies. Although not becoming extinct as a group, megalodontids worldwide show a sharp decline in diversity, abundance and size, possibly an effect of the biocalcification crisis at the TJB (Hautmann 2004). The disappearance of the foraminifera *Triassina hantkeni* is another indicator of the TJB in platform facies.

A small intraplatform basin at Csővár near the northeastern extremity of the Transdanubian Unit preserved a continuous marine TJB transition (Pálfy & Dosztály 2000). Sedimentation occurred in slope, toe-of-slope and basinal settings (Haas & Tardy-Filácz 2004). Interpretation of sea-level history fails to document a significant regression at the TJB; short-term cycles are superimposed on a long-term Rhaetian–Hettangian transgressive trend (Haas & Tardy-Filácz 2004). Ammonoid, conodont and radiolarian biostratigraphy help to constrain the TJB. A stable isotope study of the section yielded evidence of a significant negative carbon isotope excursion at the TJB (Pálfy *et al.* 2001, 2007). Recently recognized at several localities in Europe and North America, this anomaly is interpreted as a geochemical signature of a major carbon cycle perturbation thought to be related to the environmental change and concomitant biotic crisis.

In the Mecsek Mountains of southern Hungary, the TJB occurs within the >1 km thick Mecsek Coal Formation that was deposited in a subsiding half-graben, and records the transition from limnic to paralic coal-bearing facies and deltaic to marginal marine sedimentation between the coal seams. The TJB is identified based on palynologic evidence but requires further studies. The Hettangian strata are of Gresten-type facies that is also known from the Alps (Lachkar *et al.* 1984).

Recently, in the Pomerania region in NW Poland (Kamień Pomorski borehole), Pieńkowski & Waksmundzka (2005) described a succession of Triassic–Jurassic lacustrine/low-energy alluvial deposits preserved in a small tectonic graben. Palynomorph content suggests a position close to the Rhaetian–Hettangian transition. Moreover, just below the sequence boundary identified with the TJB, a characteristic fern peak has been observed that calls for further studies (particularly carbon isotope analyses).

## Climate evolution (G.P., M.E.S.)

Reconstruction of climate change and the related primary causes is exceedingly complex. Numerous factors (e.g. atmosphere composition, ocean circulation, changes in rotational and orbital characteristics of the Earth and the positions of the continents) interact to determine the climate and to make it change in a non-linear way (Page 2004). It is widely accepted that greenhouse effects dominated Jurassic climates worldwide and the Jurassic Period was warm and, for the most part, humid (Chandler *et al.* 1992). However, Kürschner (2001) placed the Jurassic Period in a relatively cooler phase, between Late Permian and mid-Cretaceous warming periods. Yet, the major features of the simulated Jurassic climate include global warming of 5 to 10°C, compared to the present, with temperature increases at high latitudes five times this global average. Tropical regions reached temperatures as high as 40°C during parts of the summer months, while winters were around 0–20°C. Carbon dioxide levels may have been as much as three to five times higher than those of today, as suggested by the stomatal index studies for Aalenian–Bathonian times (Xie *et al.* 2006).

High-latitude oceans during the Jurassic were certainly warmer than they are today and were mostly ice-free. Results from simulations of the Early Jurassic climate show that increased ocean heat transport may have been the primary force generating warmer climates during the Jurassic (Chandler *et al.* 1992), with the Early and Late Jurassic appearing to be the warmest. Extensive evaporates and aeolian sandstones suggest that the Jurassic Period (in the western part of Pangaea) was considerably more arid than the present day (Frakes 1979). Abundance of floral remains and coals suggests that the Central European region was much more humid, at least in Early and Middle Jurassic times. Close to the end of the Jurassic, the presence of evaporates, both in England (Purbeck Group) and Poland/Ukraine, may be related to the spread of an equatorial arid zone across Europe.

The Jurassic climate in Central Europe was controlled by a number of factors, one of them being the palaeogeographic position of this region. The Central European region drifted northward from about 35°N at the beginning of the Jurassic to some 45°N at the end (Smith *et al.* 1994). The most crucial climate change occurred earlier, at the beginning of the Rhaetian, when Norian red-bed sedimentation was replaced by the coal-bearing lacustrine/alluvial facies association with some marine intercalations, suggesting more humid conditions. It seems that the ongoing northward drift of the Central European region was proportionally less significant for the Jurassic climate.

The beginning of the Hettangian was marked by climatic fluctuations indicated by floral changes and isotope compositions. In particular, dramatic changes in pollen floras have long been apparent in Late Rhaetian–earliest Hettangian deposits and suggest pronounced and rather rapid climatic fluctuations in western-central Europe and Greenland (Warrington 1970; Orbell 1973; Hubbard & Boutler 2000). Hubbard & Boutler (2000) proposed a cold episode at the Rhaetian–Hettangian boundary. This view is supported by Guex *et al.* (2004) who postulated sunlight blocking, acid rain and subsequent global cooling triggered by the enormous volcanic activity in the Central Atlantic Magmatic Province. In contrast to this, McElwain *et al.* (1999) suggested a fourfold increase of $CO_2$ at the boundary and a global warming as a consequence. It is possible, however, that the long-term Hettangian warming effect followed a brief cooling event at the Triassic–Jurassic boundary. Some plant fossils from the earliest Jurasic of Poland are xeromorphic (Reymanówna 1991), thus pointing to the existence of a dry season. On the other hand, Arndorff (1993) postulated a humid tropical climate in Early Jurassic times based on the analysis of deltaic palaeosoils. Apparently, local changes of water-table level (e.g. between higher and lower lands) may have been responsible (at least partly) for these conflicting data. To summarize, in terms of temperature and precipitation the earliest Hettangian may have been a time of rapid change.

Formerly, it was considered that the climates of the Jurassic were more equable than today, without polar icecaps and with cold-intolerant organisms extending over a wider range of latitudes (Hallam 1985). More recently, however, this has been questioned (e.g. Crowley & North 1991; Hallam 1994). The 'greenhouse' climate may at times have been punctuated by subfreezing polar conditions and the presence of limited polar ice. Price (1999), summarizing the evidence for Mesozoic glaciations, reports Late Pliensbachian dropstones and glendonite. Interestingly, palaeotemperature variations of Early Jurassic seawater recorded in geochemical trends of belemnites from northern Spain point to sharp recurrent temperature drops during the Late Pliensbachian (Rosales *et al.* 2004). Such rapid drops in temperature could be associated with glaciations and rapid regressions, possibly providing onsets for the subsequent warming phases, transgressions and anoxic events (Morard *et al.* 2003; Rosales *et al.* 2004).

The Toarcian Ocean Anoxic Event is particularly significant. This event was characterized by widespread near-synchronous deposition of organic-rich shales in marine settings, as well as perturbations to several isotopic systems (including a major and sudden perturbation in the global carbon cycle). This event was associated with the massive injection of isotopically light carbon from some 'external' source (such as oceanic gas hydrate or thermally metamorphosed sedimentary organic matter), an increase in atmospheric $CO_2$ content, global warming, a huge increase in continental weathering (estimated at about 400–800%) and the resultant increase in sediment supply (Cohen *et al.* 2004; Hesselbo *et al.* 2007).

Vakhrameev (1991) detected a northward shift of Eurasian latitudinal floral provinces from the mid- to the Late Jurassic. Continuation of this trend would have meant a slight warming through the Late Jurassic. Faunal distributions, as summarized by Hallam (1994), provide a more uniform distribution for many vertebrate groups, whereas others, such as ammonites, belemnites, hermatypic corals and dasycladaceans, show the well-established subdivision into the Boreal and Tethyan realms. Their interpretation in terms of palaeoclimate (i.e. Boreal = cold, Tethyan = warm), however, is under much discussion (Hallam 1984*a* 1994). The southward shift of the boundary between the two realms from the Bathonian to the Tithonian, interpreted as a reaction to climate change, would correlate with a general trend towards cooler water temperatures during the Late Jurassic. A slight cooling would contrast with floristic trends (e.g. Vakhrameev 1991; Krassilov 1997), but the idea is supported by a marked fall of estimated $CO_2$ from around four times the present value at the beginning of the Late Jurassic to about three times that value at the Jurassic–Cretaceous boundary (Berner 1991). The slight reduction of the greenhouse effect caused by lowered concentrations of carbon dioxide in the atmosphere would correlate with the proposed cooling trend. Supplementary palaeotemperature data from the marine realms are provided by the oxygen-isotope ratios in belemnites (Podlaha *et al.* 1998).

Aridity was reported to have increased by Late Jurassic times based on the palaeobotanical and sedimentary record. In Europe, early and mid-Jurassic climates have largely been interpreted as humid (Hallam 1984*b*). The onset of arid conditions, as detected by clay mineralogy, was diachronous, beginning earlier in southern Europe (Oxfordian–Kimmeridgian), and later in NW Europe (Early Tithonian; Wignall & Ruffell 1990; Wignall & Pickering 1993; Ruffell & Rawson 1994), with a maximum in the Early Berriasian (Hallam *et al.* 1991). Hallam (1984*b*, 1994) interpreted the Late Jurassic spread of arid conditions as an orographic effect, caused by the collision of the Cimmeride mountain chain with Eurasia. This would account for the aridity further to the east, but leaves the question open as to why western European landmasses surrounded by the sea should be similarly affected (Hallam 1994). A tentative correlation between the arid phase in the Middle and Late Tithonian and a generally cooler climate, combined with a sea-level lowstand and lower water temperatures, has been demonstrated by Ruffell & Rawson (1994) and Schudack (1999, 2002).

Some more recent summaries of Jurassic temperature trends, mostly based on oxygen isotope data from Central and NW European outcrops and wells (e.g. Jenkyns *et al.* 2002; Buchardt 2003; Van de Schootbrugge *et al.* 2005; Ogg 2004; Wierzbowski 2002, 2004; Wierzbowski & Joachimski 2006; Wierzbowski *et al.* 2006) have been compared in Figure 14.5. These patterns point to: (a) relatively high temperatures during the Hettangian, Sinemurian and Early Pliensbachian, except for the Triassic–Jurassic transition with possibly cooler events; (b) cooler temperatures during the Late Pliensbachian; (c) dramatic warming during the Early Toarcian (probably the highest temperatures for the Jurassic), combined with Oceanic Anoxic Events and black oil shale deposition (e.g. 'Posidonienschiefer') and methane (gas hydrate) releases (Kemp *et al.* 2005; Hesselbo *et al.* 2007); (d) a subsequent cooling trend (variable in details) throughout the Middle Jurassic, with the lowest temperatures for the Jurassic Period around the Callovian–Oxfordian boundary; (e) another warming during the Oxfordian and a warm Kimmeridgian; and

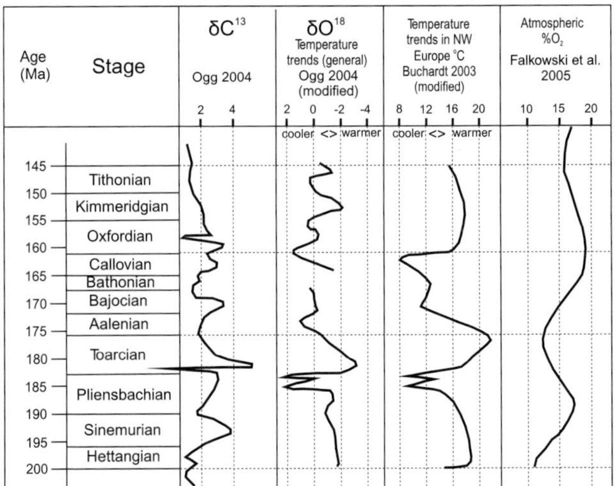


**Fig. 14.5.** Summary of Jurassic climates in Central Europe, combined and slightly amended from various sources (given in the figure).

(f) another drop in temperature just before the end of the Jurassic Period (from the Kimmeridgian into the Tithonian and on into an even colder, if only slightly, Berriasian).

The slight cooling trend near the end of the Jurassic, as confirmed both by oxygen isotope and biogeographical data using marine and non-marine ostracoda (Schudack 1999, 2002), has also been suggested in several more recent papers (e.g. Ogg 2004; Weissert & Erba 2004; Price & Mutterlose 2004). A generally slight increase in temperature throughout the Jurassic, as reported in many textbooks and older literature (e.g. Hallam 1994; Krassilov 1997), has not been confirmed.

The oxygen content of the Jurassic atmosphere may have been considerably lower than suggested so far. According to Falkowski *et al.* (2005), it started at only 10% near the Triassic–Jurassic boundary, rose to about 17–18% near the Sinemurian–Pliensbachian boundary, and decreased again to about 12–13% near the Toarcian–Aalenian boundary. Another rise in oxygen led to a maximum for the Jurassic of about 19% around the Callovian–Oxfordian boundary, with a subsequent decrease (to 15%) near the end of the Jurassic (Fig. 14.5).

## Sequence stratigraphy (G.P., A.P.)

Sequence stratigraphy may be applied in two different ways, either involving detailed sequence analysis based on depositional architecture and cyclicity in the rock record (Posamentier & James 1993; Miall 1997; Surlyk & Ineson 2003), or by the construction of age models based on the correlation with global (Haq *et al.* 1987, 1988; Hallam 1988, 2001; based largely on North Sea and western Europe data) or at least super-regional sea-level charts (Hesselbo & Jenkyns 1998; de Graciansky *et al.* 1998*a*, *b*; Nielsen 2003). The value of Haq's *et al* (1987, 1988) curve and terminology of cycle orders is a much debated issue (Posamentier & James 1993; Miall 1997; Surlyk & Ineson 2003). The terminology should be regarded as only conventional, although fourth and lower-order cycles are often identified with astronomical Milankovitch cycles. Emphasis on the recognition, interpretation and dating of surfaces on the one hand and on the geometry and environmental interpretation of successive systems tracts on the other leads to the integration of both approaches by the determination of correlative significances and ages of key surfaces and derived sea-level curves (Hesselbo & Jenkyns 1998; Pieńkowski 1991*a*, 2004). The high resolution of the Jurassic ammonite biostratigraphy allows good calibration of sequence boundaries, and the Jurassic of Central Europe is regarded as a classic field for sequence stratigraphic correlation. Following the ammonites' bioprovincialism, the cycles were also assigned to the Boreal and Tethyan provinces (Fig. 14.6). Hallam (2001) claimed that the overall pattern appears to be a more or less gradual sea-level rise through the Jurassic interrupted by episodes of comparative stillstands rather than eustatic fall. Several episodes of significant regression (for example those in the Middle–Upper Jurassic of the North Sea) resulted from regional tectonics. Major episodes of sea-level rise took place in the Early Hettangian, Early Sinemurian, Early Pliensbachian, Early Toarcian, Early and Late Bajocian, Middle Callovian and Late Oxfordian to Kimmeridgian (Fig. 14.6). A significant episode of rapid and very extensive regression, possibly global, took place at the end of the Triassic (Hallam 2001). Although there is no unequivocal evidence for glacioeustasy in Jurassic times and most of the sea-level changes can be related to plate tectonics and possibly Milankovitch cycles, some cooling periods and possible glaciations have been suggested, particularly in the Late Pliensbachian times (Price 1999; Morard *et al.* 2003; Rosales *et al.* 2004; Van de Schootbrugge *et al.* 2005).

Major sea-level changes, along with climate changes, might have a significant impact on the migration of biota between the Central European basins and the Tethyan Ocean, the opening Atlantic Ocean and further with the Palaeo-Pacific. Such migrations could facilitate radiation of certain taxa and their spatial distribution (Van de Schootbrugge *et al.* 2005).

In the Jurassic, two first-order subcycles are distinguishable: the Ligurian Cycle, bounded by the early and mid-Cimmerian unconformities, and the North Sea Cycle, bounded by the mid- and upper Cimmerian unconformities. These cycles comprise seven second-order cycles and about 70 third-order cycles (Hardenbol *et al.* 1998).

The Ligurian Cycle commenced in the Late Norian and ended in the Upper Aalenian. The peak transgression occurred in the Early Toarcian. Three second-order cycles are recognized from the Tethyan areas, and four in the Boreal areas. Within these cycles, 27 third-order cycles are identified (de Graciansky *et al.* 1993; Hesselbo & Jenkyns 1998; Jacquin *et al.* 1998; de Graciansky *et al.* 1998*a*, *b*). The cycle is named from the main rift phase that affected the Ligurian part of the Tethys. The North Sea Cycle began in the Upper Aalenian and ended in the Late Berriasian. The peak transgression occurred in the Upper Kimmeridgian (Jacquin *et al.* 1998).

Sequence stratigraphy correlation between marine and non-marine (marginal-marine and continental) facies have been performed in the Early Jurassic of the Polish Basin (Pieńkowski 1991*a*, 2004) and the Danish–Swedish Basin (Pieńkowski 1991*a*, *b*; Surlyk *et al.* 1995; Nielsen 2003) in the Early Jurassic section. Marginal-marine parasequences in the Polish Basin show more complex depositional architecture than a simple flooding–prograding cycle (Pieńkowski 2004).

Parasequences must show correlative significance on a large regional scale. A proper hierarchy of local cycles, parasequences, systems tracts and sequences can only be achieved by careful regional analysis. An excessive number of distinguished parasequences (and consequently sequences) is a major problem in correlating bounding surfaces and sequence stratigraphy units between European basins. Sequence stratigraphic correlation should be aimed at the determination of correlative significances and the ages of key surfaces and derived sea-level curves. The relative sea level is understood as the sum of regional sea-level changes and tectonic subsidence in a given region. It is believed that erosion at sequence boundaries in marginal-marine/non-marine settings was usually coeval with development elsewhere of the lowstand and falling stage systems tract. In contrast, maximum flooding surfaces corresponded with phases of maximum expansion of the basin and basinal facies onto marginal-marine and continental areas. Thus, sequence boundaries play a particularly important correlative role in basinal facies, while maximum flooding surfaces are of particular correlative significance in marginal-marine/continental areas. Stratigraphic significance of the transgressive surfaces is enhanced if they are coupled with their continental correlatives. Particularly important are correlatives of transgressive surfaces, such as documented in the Danish Basin and the Polish Basin (Surlyk *et al.* 1995; Pieńkowski 2004). An abrupt and widespread change from an alluvial to a lacustrine depositional system is usually related to sea-level (= base level) rise and as such can be correlated with a transgressive surface (as a time equivalent). The development of transgression forms a step-wise, retrogradational succession in which, in the landward direction, one can observe the gradual departure of a transgressive surface from its time-correlative

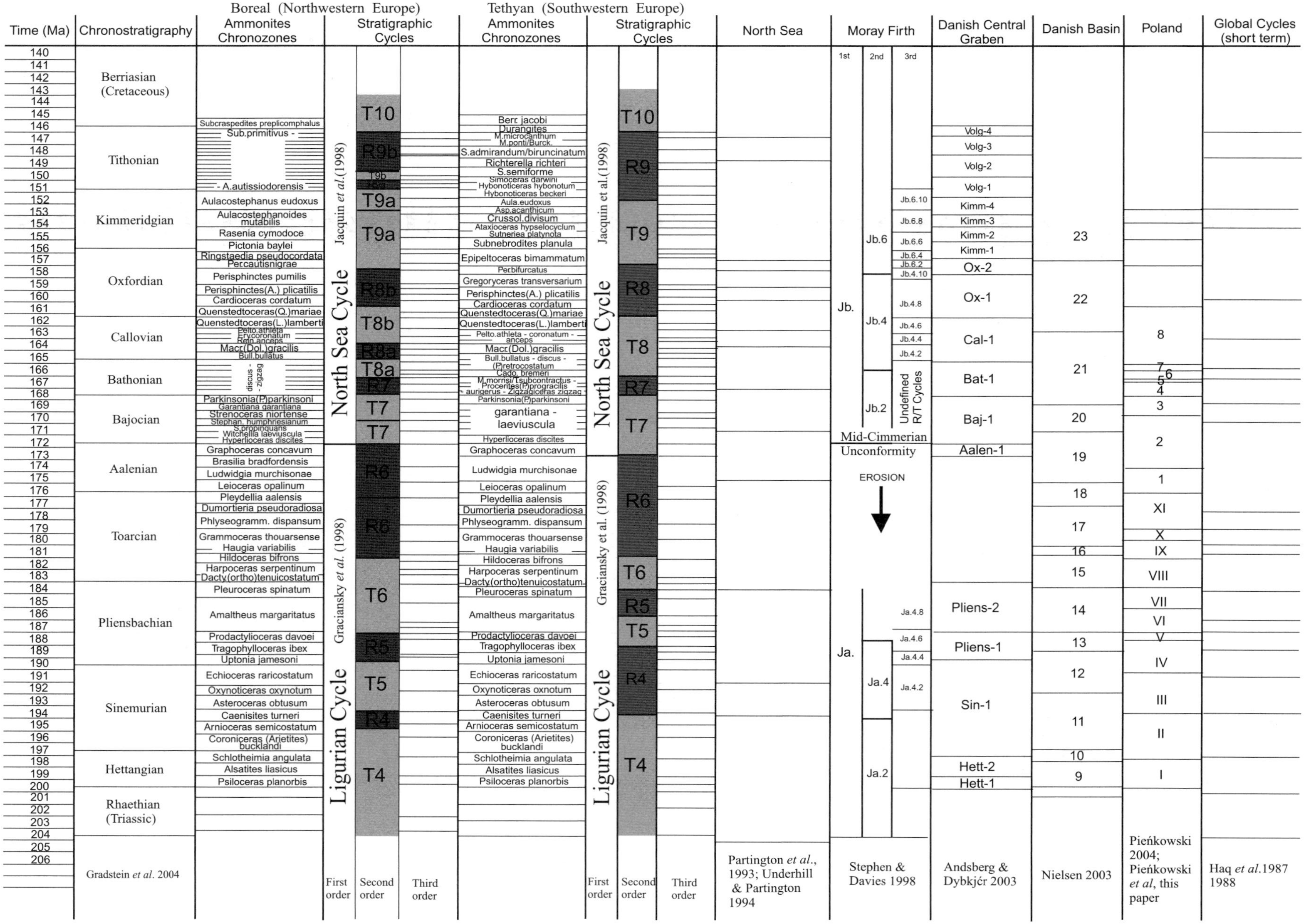


**Fig. 14.6.** Comparison of cycles and sequence stratigraphic key surfaces for the Jurassic in Central Europe. This sequence stratigraphy compilation is based on data from the basins indicated and the Paris Basin, the Eastern Aquitaine and the Subalpine Zone–Tethyan margin (de Graciansky 1993; Hesselbo & Jenkyns 1993; Jacquin *et al.* 1998; de Graciansky *et al.* 1998*a*,*b*).

surface. In consequence, a package of sediments (usually of lacustrine origin) forms above the time-correlative surface of transgression and below the 'real' transgressive surface. This 'pre-transgressive' succession, belonging to a transgressive systems tract is a characteristic feature of transgression development in marginal-marine and continental settings.

A huge increase in sediment supply, associated with carbon cycle perturbations, enhanced continental weathering, and the resulting higher frequency of redeposited sediments in hemipelagic settings may misleadingly simulate the effects of sea-level fall (Hesselbo *et al.* 2007). The effects of such perturbations are much more conspicuous in the marginal-marine settings, where an increase in weathering rates and sediment supply causes rapid progradation of coarser, shallow-water facies and consequently regional regression marked in the relative sea-level curve (Pieńkowski 2004). Such events are valuable for sequence stratigraphic correlation (Pieńkowski 2004), particularly as they reflect short-time and global environmental perturbations (e.g. Early Toarcian carbon cycle perturbation; Hesselbo *et al.* 2007).

### *United Kingdom*

The Moray Firth area comprises a basin which is divided into an inner and outer part and belongs to the North Sea rift triple-junction system that also includes the Viking Graben and the Central Graben. The evolution of the Late Jurassic North Sea rift was initiated after the North Sea thermal doming, which created the Mid-Cimmerian unconformity. The four second-order cycles contain 40 third-order cycles. In the Jurassic System, two first-order subcycles, bounded by the Lower, Mid- and Upper Cimmerian unconformities, five second-order cycles and 14 third-order cycles have been distinguished (Stephen & Davies 1998). However, extensive erosion and non-deposition associated particularly with the Mid-Cimmerian unconformity removed much of the rock record in this area. Better sequence stratigraphy (although only from the Lower Jurassic section) has been obtained from profiles of the Wessex, Bristol Channel and Hebrides basins (Hesselbo & Jenkyns 1998).

### *Denmark*

In the Danish Central Graben, 20 third-order cycles have been identified. They were assigned to several tectonic phases (Andsberg & Dybkjær 2003). After a pre-rift phase (pre-rift megasequence; Surlyk & Ineson 2003), a widespread hiatus with deep erosion occurred. This event was associated with a Toarcian–Aalenian North Sea doming event. Subsequently, during the rift initiation stage, marine sedimentation commenced in the Danish Central Graben (synrift megasequence; Surlyk & Ineson 2003).

Comparing the resultant sea-level curve with global sea-level charts (Haq *et al.* 1987, 1988; Hallam 1988, 2001) one can observe similarities between the Bathonian–Kimmeridgian sections. Due to the formation of the sub-basins, the curves show poor similarities in the younger deposits.

Possible correlations of key correlative surfaces and systems tracts between regions such as southern Sweden and Poland were shown for the Hettangian–Sinemurian section by Pieńkowski (1991*a*, *b*). In contrast, the Middle Jurassic correlations throughout Central Europe show more differences which are related to local tectonics.

### *Poland*

Sequence stratigraphic analysis of this basin is important since it facilitates the correlation between marine and non-marine facies in the Lower Jurassic section (Pieńkowski 1991a, 2004). Siliciclastic, brackish-marine, continental and marine Early Jurassic sedimentation in Poland was particularly sensitive to sea-level changes. Although fossil content provides varied resolution of biostratigraphical subdivisions, the stratigraphical framework based on dinoflagellate cysts, spores and in places ammonites allows stages and sometimes substages to be identified. Sedimentation in the epicontinental basin of Poland was influenced by a number of factors, such as local subsidence and compaction, tectonic activity, and sediment supply. In particular, the latter played an important role in the Early Toarcian, when enhanced continental weathering led to a conspicuous and short-lived progradational–regressive event throughout the Polish Basin. This shallow facies progradation can be linked with a major disturbance in the Earth's environmental systems during the Early Toarcian Oceanic Anoxic Event (Hesselbo *et al.* 2007). Nevertheless, the Early Jurassic sedimentation in the Polish epicontinental basin was chiefly controlled by super-regional sea-level changes. Pronounced and rapid sea-level changes observed in the Late Pliensbachian might have been connected with glaciations (Price 1999). All ten of Exxon's depositional sequences can be distinguished in the Polish Lower Jurassic. On the other hand, regional sea-level changes presented by Hesselbo & Jenkyns (1998) and de Graciansky *et al.* (1998*b*) (Fig. 14.6) give more precise dating of certain events and a much more detailed record of sea-level changes.

Middle and Late Jurassic deposits in Poland are mainly marine and well-dated biostratigraphically. However, due to increasing local tectonic activity, the sequence stratigraphic correlation is less certain and only some of the major correlative surfaces known from western Europe have been distinguished.

### *Summary*

In the Lower Jurassic, the relative sea-level curves of the CEBS show fairly good correlation both with each other and with the global eustatic sea-level curves of Haq *et al.* (1987, 1988) and Hallam (1988, 2001). During this period signals of super-regional ('eustatic') sea-level changes are still prominent due to the relative tectonic quiescence. From Middle Jurassic times the respective curves show more differences. This is evidently related to the tectonic regime: general tectonic quiescence in the Early Jurassic was followed by much more intensive tectonic activity in the Middle–Late Jurassic. This was related to the beginning of the North Sea rifting phase and subsequently the development of the CEBS became more localized, resulting in an increased masking of the eustatic signal from region to region.

In addition, local halokinetic movements of the Zechstein salt had a strong influence on the evolution of some north European basins. Differences between regional sea-level curves may also depend on other factors, e.g. quality and number of data or biostratigraphic resolution. Therefore, comparisons of sea-level curves and cycles need to be treated with due caution. It should be pointed out that the term 'super-regional sea-level changes' would be more proper than 'eustatic', which is used in this chapter rather colloquially. Changes of sea level are registered and dated in north and central European basins (United Kingdom and France – Ligurian Cycle; de Graciansky *et al.* 1998*b*). Most of these changes are believed to be of global (eustatic) character, although the concept of coeval worldwide sea-level changes is a matter of controversy (Cloetingh *et al.* 1985; Ziegler 1988; Cathles & Hallam 1991). One should bear in mind that rift development, including the rate of crustal extension and the rate of subsidence, differed from one structural province to another (Ziegler 1988). This does not impact greatly on the correlations between the north-central European basins in Early Jurassic times (Ligurian Cycle; Jacquin *et al.* 1998; de Graciansky *et al.* 1998*b*; Hesselbo & Jenkyns 1998; Nielsen 2003; Pieńkowski 2004), which show fairly uniform development of transgressive–regressive phases and sequence boundaries. Additionally, it should be noted, that the positions of the Sinemurian and Lower Pliensbachian sequence boundaries in the Danish Basin (Nielsen 2003) differ from most other European regions and the second-order Boreal cyclicity. However, this may be caused by less precise dating or incomplete core material. Comparison of transgressive–regressive facies cycles and depositional sequences for the Early Jurassic Epoch in western Europe shows that the ages of peak transgressions and the main cycle boundaries can still vary regionally according to the pattern of local extension (de Graciansky *et al.* 1998*a*). However, most of the 27 third-order depositional sequences constituting the Ligurian major cycle can be documented from the North Sea to southern Europe. Sea-level changes (both third and second order) in the northern areas of European epicontinental basins (Boreal province) were taken as the basic 'pattern' for the sea level comparison, but in the Middle and Upper Jurassic these differences increased due to differentiated thermal subsidence, increased local faulting, tectonism and halokinesis (Fig. 14.6).

Particularly uniform are the following sequence boundaries (third-order cycles, regressive phases): (1) basal Hettangian–earliest *Planorbis* biochronozone; (2) Upper Hettangian–mid-*Angulata* biochronozone; (3) Mid-Sinemurian–*Turneri/Obtusum* biochronozone boundary (except for the Danish basin); (4) basal Upper Pliensbachian (base of the *Margaritatus* biochronozone), the most uniform Jurassic sequence boundary; (5) uppermost Pliensbachian (latest *Spinatum* biochronozone); (6) Mid-Toarcian (*Variabilis* biochronozone); and (7) Upper Toarcian (mid-*Thouarsense* biochronozone).

From the Middle Jurassic onwards, the sequence boundaries (regressive phases) in Central Europe are less uniform. Even the prominent Mid-Cimmerian unconformity shows differences in dating between the various regions, when it comes to the third-order cycles. Nevertheless, the following sequence boundaries can be indicated as showing more 'uniform' character: (8) Aalenian–Bajocian boundary, approximately; (9) Mid-Bajocian (between Early and Late Bajocian); (10) Upper Callovian (base of *Lamberti* biochronozone); (11) Upper Oxfordian (between *Cautisnigrae* and *Pseudocordata* biochronozones); (12) Mid-Kimmeridgian (base of *Mutabilis* = mid-*Hypselocyclum* biochronozone); (13) Upper Kimmerridgian (late *Mutabilis* = *Acanthicum* biochronozone); (14) Lower Tithonian (base of *Biruncinatum* biochronozone); and (15) Upper Tithonian (base od *Durangites* biochronozone).

## Central European Basin System

Jurassic deposition in the Central European Basin System (including the southernmost epi-Variscan basins representing the northern, passive margin of the Alpine Tethys) underwent a rather uniform evolution during Jurassic times, mainly related to global changes in sea level and regional subsidence caused by extensional faulting. During the Jurassic Period, the CEBS area was represented by a shallow epicontinental sea surrounded by marginal-marine areas and lowlands. River influx resulted in decreased seawater salinity not only in the marginal areas, but also in the Central European sea itself (Röhl *et al.* 2001). The CEBS and the more southern epi-Variscan basins domain comprised several realms distinguished mainly on the basis of faunal provincialism, such as Boreal, sub-Boreal and sub-Mediterranean, the latter developed in the peri-Tethyan area and showing frequent connections with the Tethys Ocean.

### *Denmark (F.S., N.N.-N.)*

The region described in this section covers onshore Denmark, including the island of Bornholm in the Baltic, southernmost Sweden, and the Danish part of the North Sea (Fig. 14.7). The Jurassic of the region has recently been documented in a series of papers in the book *The Jurassic of Denmark and Greenland* (Ineson & Surlyk 2003). An overview and comparison of the Jurassic evolution of Greenland and Denmark was provided by Surlyk & Ineson (2003) and a revision of the lithostratigraphy was presented by Michelsen *et al.* (2003) who also reviewed the Jurassic stratigraphic development.

In the Danish region the Triassic–Jurassic transition is marked by major changes in climate, sea level, depositional settings and facies. Triassic sedimentation in the Danish area was dominated by fluvial sands, lacustrine red-beds, carbonates and evaporites. In the Late Triassic, the northward drift of Pangaea resulted in a major climatic change to more humid conditions which, together with sea-level rise, resulted in a change from continental red-beds to dominantly light grey and drab-coloured shallow-marine and paralic, commonly coal-bearing, deposits in and along the eastern margin of the Danish Basin.

*Structural features, palaeogeography, sea level and climate*

The Danish area was situated at about 37°N at the Triassic–Jurassic transition and drifted slowly northward to reach about 45°N at the end of the Jurassic (Smith *et al.* 1994). The Early Jurassic was a period of tectonic quiescence in the area. The main structural features were already formed in Triassic or earlier times, and include the northern part of the German Basin, the Ringkøbing–Fyn High, the Danish Basin, the Sorgenfrei–Tornquist Zone, the Skagerrak–Kattegat Platform, and the Rønne Graben (Liboriussen *et al.* 1987; EUGENO-S Working Group 1988; Mogensen & Korstgård 2003). In early Mid-Jurassic times large areas in the North Sea, the Norwegian–Danish Basin, the Ringkøbing–Fyn High and the Sorgenfrei–Tornquist Zone were uplifted, heralding the onset of an important phase of late Mid- and Late Jurassic rifting. This uplift event was associated with widespread volcanism in Scania and in the North Sea where the Central Graben, Moray Firth Basin, Viking Graben and Norwegian–Danish Basin coalesce.

Sea-level changes were of major importance controlling Jurassic deposition in the area. At the end of the Triassic a long-term rise commenced, which continued through the Early Jurassic (e.g. Hallam 1988, 2001). The onset of sea-level fall was initiated at the end of the Early Jurassic and the lowest level was reached in Mid-Jurassic times. Sea level began to rise again at the end of the Mid-Jurassic to reach its highest level in the Late Jurassic. The long-term changes were overprinted by many short rises and falls.

Periods with a high sea-level stand were dominated by the deposition of marine clays, whereas a low sea level resulted in coastal and deltaic progradation and the deposition of sand. The long-term fall had an additional important effect as the marine connections between the Tethys Ocean to the south and the Arctic Sea were interrupted. This hindered faunal exchange and

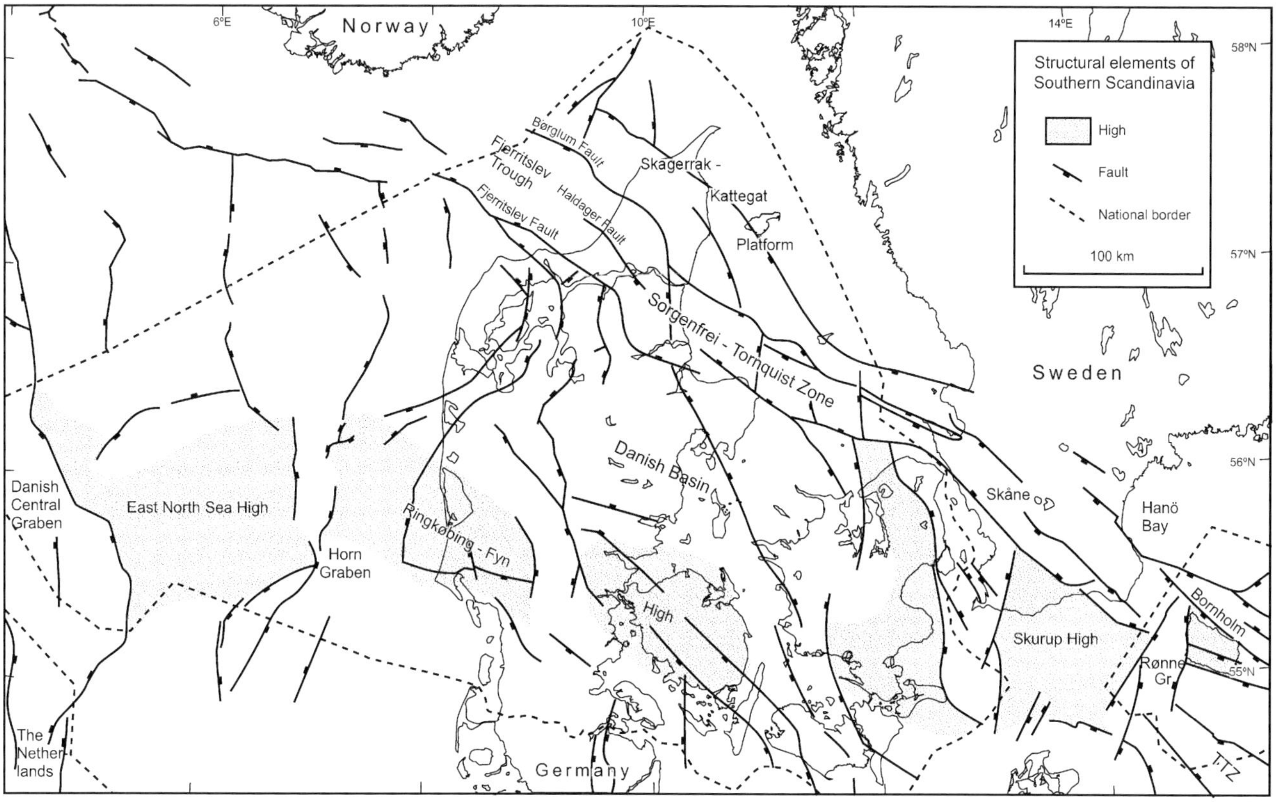


**Fig. 14.7.** Tectonic setting of the Jurassic in southern Scandinavia.

migration, resulting in significant endemism at several time intervals, notably in the Bajocian–Bathonian and the Tithonian. Different faunas thus developed in the north and south, as reflected by the different biostratigraphic schemes for the two regions. These conditions were particularly pronounced in Mid- and latest Jurassic times. Thus, the Jurassic–Cretaceous boundary is not necessarily placed at the same level in the Arctics, and north and south Europe, and different stage names are used for the uppermost Jurassic, i.e. Volgian, Portlandian and Tithonian. The precise correlation between these local stages is not yet fully agreed upon.

The Triassic faunas and floras of the Danish area are very poorly known due to the lack of outcrop and the scarcity of fossils, whereas they are relatively well known for the Jurassic, especially from outcrops on Bornholm and in Scania and from numerous onshore and offshore exploration boreholes. Rich floras are known from the Lower and Middle Jurassic of Bornholm and Scania and marine invertebrate faunas, foraminifers and dinoflagellates are well known from many boreholes and from Bornholm. Late Jurassic faunas and floras are, on the other hand, only known from boreholes.

*The Early Jurassic transgression*

Most of the Danish area became covered by the sea during the Early Jurassic sea-level rise (see Fig. 14.8 for lithostratigraphy). Deltaic, coastal and lacustrine deposition continued along the NE margin of the Danish Basin where the sediments are referred to the Gassum Formation and on Bornholm where they belong to the Rønne Formation (Gravesen *et al.* 1982; Surlyk *et al.* 1995; Michelsen *et al.* 2003). Both formations show a general stepwise backstepping caused by the overall rising sea level.

The Gassum Formation consists mainly of sandstones intercalated with heteroliths, claystones and a few thin coal beds. The sandstones are of both fluvial and shoreface origin and form extensive sheets representing several progradational events (Hamberg & Nielsen 2000; Nielsen 2003). The intercalated claystones are mainly of marine and locally of lacustrine and lagoonal origin. The formation spans the Triassic–Jurassic boundary and is of Late Norian–Rhaetian age, extending into the Hettangian–Early Sinemurian along the NE basin margin.

The Hettangian–lowermost Pliensbachian Rønne Formation is well exposed on the south coast of Bornholm and is up to 500 m thick in the eastern part of the Rønne Graben. The succession passes upwards from the lacustrine and swamp deposits with rootlets and thin coals of the Hettangian Munkerup Member into the progressively more marine-influenced Upper Hettangian–lowermost Pliensbachian Sose Bugt Member (Surlyk *et al.* 1995). The lacustrine clays contain a well preserved flora with ferns, seed ferns, cycads, gingkos and angiosperms representing the widespread *Thaumatopteris* flora, characteristic of the Hettangian and Sinemurian.

Deposition of the Sose Bugt Member was punctuated by the incision of several valleys, which were subsequently filled with fluvial sands and clays, reflecting periods of sea-level fall, which interrupted the longer-term sea-level rise. The lower part of the member consists of alternating thin beds of fine-grained cross-laminated sand and thin beds of clay or heteroliths. Rootlet horizons and thin coals are common. The upper part of the member comprises black non-fossiliferous clay with thin storm silts, and it is topped by open-marine, storm-influenced sands and clays with abundant trace fossils and rare ammonites and

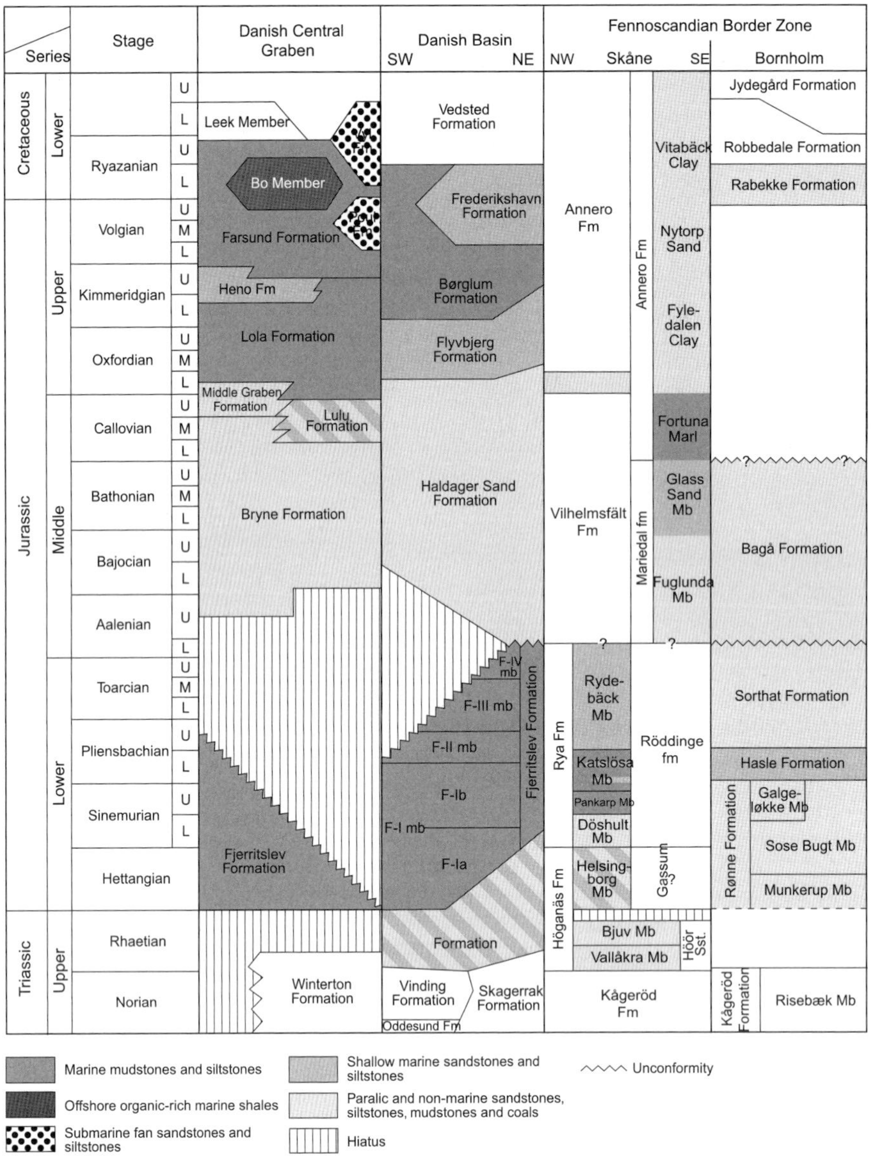


**Fig. 14.8.** Lithostratigraphy of the Jurassic in southern Scandinavia.

bivalves. The Sose Bugt Member is thickly developed in the Rønne Graben.

The partly correlative Upper Sinemurian Galgeløkke Member, which is exposed further to the west along the coast, consists of cross-laminated and large-scale cross-bedded sand alternating with heteroliths and two thin intercalated coal beds. The member shows abundant evidence for strong tidal activity and large, metre-deep cylindrical water escape structures are common, and probably reflect rapid changes in porewater pressure following the tidal rhythms and possibly overprinted by storm surges (Sellwood 1972; Gravesen *et al.* 1982). The member is also present offshore in the Rønne Graben.

The coastal deposits of the Hettangian–Sinemurian Rønne Formation are conformably overlain by a succession up to 140 m thick of mainly fine-grained offshore marine sandstones and coarse siltstones of the Lower Pliensbachian Hasle Formation (Gravesen *et al.* 1982; Surlyk & Noe-Nygaard 1986; Michelsen *et al.* 2003; Nielsen 2003). The position of the coastline was controlled by the major Rønne–Hasle Fault which formed the eastern margin of the deep Rønne Graben along a right-stepping dogleg of the Sorgenfrei–Tornquist Zone connecting the Danish Basin with the Polish Trough. The Hasle Formation shows swaley and hummocky cross-stratification throughout and deposition was influenced by major storms, reflecting that the sea extended uninterrupted from the west-facing coastline to Great Britain. Gravel-lags in the swaley cross-stratified beds contain teeth and bone fragments of fish, plesiosaurs and other reptiles. Rich invertebrate faunas occur at several levels, including diverse ammonite assemblages found in clay-rich intercalations (Malling & Grönwall 1909; Donovan & Surlyk 2003).

The fine-grained, open-marine sediments of the Hasle Formation pass gradually upwards into alternating layers of sand (occasionally pebbly), muddy sand, clays and coals with rootlet beds, forming sharp-based fining-upward units. This succession is referred to the uppermost Pliensbachian–Toarcian, and possibly lowermost Aalenian Sorthat Formation, which is up to 200 m thick (Koppelhus & Nielsen 1994; Michelsen *et al.* 2003). Deposition took place in a wet floodplain environment with rivers, small crevasse deltas, shallow lakes, and swamps (represented by the large number of thin coal seams) (Petersen & Nielsen 1995). Thin marine intercalations with marine trace fossils and dinoflagellates occur in the upper part of the formation which was deposited in lagoons, coastal lakes and distributary channels. The top consists of wave-ripple-laminated and swaley cross-stratified sands with intercalated bioturbated heteroliths deposited in the marine shoreface to offshore transition zone during a period of rising sea level in the Early Toarcian (Koppelhus & Nielsen 1994). An important negative excursion in $\delta^{13}C$ in Toarcian wood has been interpreted as having been caused by voluminous and extremely rapid release of methane from gas hydrates (Hesselbo *et al.* 2000).

In the Danish Basin and the North Sea deposition was dominated by the dark clays forming the Fjerritslev Formation, which overlie the backstepping coarse-grained coastal deposits of the Gassum Formation (Michelsen & Nielsen 1993; Nielsen *et al.* 1989; Nielsen 2003). The sea level rose gradually during the Early Jurassic and the clay-dominated succession shows abundant evidence of storms (Pedersen 1985). The sea was generally well aerated and of normal salinity as reflected by the rich bivalve, gastropod and trace fossil faunas (Michelsen 1975; Pedersen 1985, 1986). Oxygenation at the sea floor decreased with time, and dark, organic-rich clays were widely deposited in the Toarcian, forming the upper part of the Fjerritslev Formation (Michelsen *et al.* 2003).

In the Danish Basin coastal and deltaic areas represented by the uppermost Norian–Lower Sinemurian Gassum Formation were gradually drowned and overlain by clays of the Fjerritslev Formation, which is mainly Early Jurassic in age but locally extends down into the Upper Rhaetian and up into the Lower Aalenian (Michelsen & Nielsen 1991; Nielsen 2003). However, much of the Fjerritslev Formation was eroded during the period of Mid-Jurassic uplift and its former extent is not known in detail. The formation reaches a maximum thickness of more than 1000 m. It consists of relatively uniform dark grey to black claystones with silt and sandstone laminae; deposition took place in deep offshore to lower shoreface environments (Michelsen 1975; Pedersen 1985; Nielsen 2003). A tongue of sediment extends eastwards into Scania where it is placed in the Pankarp Member of the Rya Formation (Sivhed 1984; Frandsen & Surlyk 2003). The formation exhibits a pronounced layer-cake stratigraphy and is subdivided into four informal members, which can be traced over much of the area except where removed by later erosion.

The Early Jurassic transgression continued, punctuated by regressive events, with deposition of sand and erosion of the Skagerrak–Kattegat Platform. Oxygenation at the seafloor decreased drastically at the end of the Pliensbachian and the benthic faunas disappeared. These conditions culminated in the Early Toarcian and came to an end with the onset of regression at the end of the Toarcian.

*Mid-Jurassic uplift*

In Late Aalenian–Early Bajocian times a broad arc, comprising the central North Sea, the Ringkøbing–Fyn High, the Danish Basin and Bornholm, was uplifted and the Fjerritslev Formation was eroded over large areas (Andsbjerg *et al.* 2001). The uplifted area was thus much larger and quite different from the subcircular dome postulated by Underhill & Partington (1994) but conforms well to earlier reconstructions (e.g. Ziegler 1975). On the eastern part of the Ringkøbing–Fyn High erosion cut down into the upper part of the Triassic. The Lower–Middle Jurassic boundary is difficult to identify due to poor biostratigraphic resolution. In the Sorgenfrei–Tornquist Zone it is located in the uppermost part of the Fjerritslev Formation and elsewhere it coincides with a prominent erosion surface, separating the Fjerritslev Formation from the overlying Haldager Sand Formation (Nielsen 2003). Mid-Jurassic subsidence continued in the Sorgenfrei–Tornquist Zone but at a much lower rate. Uplift culminated in early Mid-Jurassic times and was followed by a phase of major volcanism in the North Sea in the triple-junction between the Central Graben, the Moray Firth and the Viking Graben. In Scania there was also widespread volcanism and remnants of more than 70 volcanoes have been found (e.g. Klingspor 1976; Norling *et al.* 1993). The uplifted areas were strongly eroded and began to subside in the late Mid-Jurassic; extensive coarse-grained deltas spread across the eroded surface.

The main period of uplift seems to have taken place in the Early Aalenian and resulted in a complete change in the geography of the region. The marine connection between the Arctic Sea and the Tethys Ocean was interrupted and extensive floodplains and deltas were formed where sand, silt, clay and thin coals were deposited. These layers are referred to the Bryne Formation in the North Sea and to the Haldager Sand Formation in the Danish Basin (Michelsen *et al.* 2003; Nielsen 2003).

On Bornholm the eroded top of the Sorthat Formation is overlain by fluvial and lacustrine gravels, sands, clays with rootlets and carbonaceous clays or coal beds, up to 2.5 m thick, belonging to the Upper Aalenian–Bathonian Bagå Formation which reaches a thickness of more than 190 m (Gry 1969; Michelsen *et al.* 2003). Poorly sorted muddy and pebbly sand beds, locally with boulders of kaolinized granite, occur in the upper part of the Bagå Formation. The boulders were derived from the exposed land surface immediately to the east of the Rønne Fault and were transported out onto the floodplain by debris flows triggered by major earthquakes related to fault movements.

The eroded top of the Bagå Formation forms the present-day land surface and Callovian and Upper Jurassic strata are not known from Bornholm. Elsewhere in the Danish area the Late Jurassic was characterized by a sea-level rise which commenced in late Mid-Jurassic times. The deltas and floodplains were gradually flooded and marine conditions were established almost everywhere. In the Danish Basin the Haldager Sand Formation is poorly dated but the age is probably Aalenian–Callovian. It is more than 150 m thick in the Sorgenfrei–Tornquist Zone and consists of coarse-grained, occasionally pebbly, sandstones interbedded with siltstones and thin coal beds deposited in braided rivers, lakes and swamps in a coastal plain environment.

The Bryne Formation comprises laterally extensive sandstones alternating with thick sandstone and mudstone units deposited in fluvial and lacustrine settings and, in the upper part, in estuarine channels. The formation is not well dated but seems to span the Aalenian–earliest Callovian time interval. The thickness varies greatly from a few metres to a maximum of 289 m, but commonly more than 200 m.

The floodplain deposits of the Bryne Formation are conformably overlain by the 30–60 m thick Callovian Lulu Formation deposited on a coastal plain during sea-level rise. It consists of coarsening-upward units of shallow-marine shoreface sandstones, locally with coaly claystones and coal seams, up to 5 m thick (Andsbjerg 2003; Petersen & Andsbjerg 1996; Michelsen *et al.* 2003). In the southern part of the Central Graben the Bryne Formation is overlain by the 15–56 m thick Upper Callovian–Middle Oxfordian Middle Graben Formation consisting of dark claystones, siltstones, rare sandstones and local coal beds.

*Mid- to Late Jurassic rifting*

The geological evolution of the Central Graben and the Danish Basin was relatively uniform in Early and Mid-Jurassic times, but became markedly different in the Late Jurassic. During the Late Jurassic marine north–south connections were mainly through the Central Graben and periodically through the Sorgenfrei–Tornquist Zone. The Central Graben was characterized by intense rifting and rapid subsidence, whereas the rate of subsidence in the Danish Basin was much less. The Danish Basin was located adjacent to the Baltic Shield and the high sediment influx resulted in a more sand-rich succession and several regressive events.

Mid-Jurassic uplift, erosion and volcanism were succeeded by the onset of rifting in the Danish Basin and especially in the North Sea. The Ringkøbing–Fyn High continued to be a structural feature forming the southern border of the Danish Basin, while the Sorgenfrei–Tornquist Zone was a broad transitional area across which the coastline moved back and forth.

Rifting in the North Sea took place along major faults and the Central Graben developed as a broad asymmetrical half-graben with subsidence mainly along an eastern border fault, the north–south trending Coffee Soil Fault (Japsen *et al.* 2003; Møller & Rasmussen 2003). With increased rifting the graben became progressively fragmented along new faults into narrower grabens.

*Late Jurassic sea-level rise*

In the Danish Basin the floodplain deposits of the Haldager Sand Formation were gradually flooded by the sea and the finer-grained Lower Oxfordian–Upper Kimmeridgian Flyvbjerg Formation was deposited. Locally abundant roots and traces of coal occur at some levels indicating a paralic setting, but most of the formation is of shallow to offshore marine origin. The boundaries of the formation are diachronous, younging towards the NE basin margin and the maximum thickness of 50 m is found in the Sorgenfrei–Tornquist Zone. In the latest Jurassic monotonous grey-green and dark-grey muds of the Børglum Formation, which is up to 300 m thick, were deposited offshore; the deepening lasted from earliest Kimmeridgian to Mid-Volgian (Tithonian) times. A succession of coarsening-upward clay–silt–sandstone units were deposited along the NE margin of the Danish Basin during the Volgian (Tithonian) to Ryazanian (Berriasian) and are referred to the Frederikshavn Formation which is up to 230 m thick. Deposition was mainly in shallow marine to offshore environments. Ammonites and bivalves are common in the lower part, whereas thin coal beds in the Skagerrak–Kattegat Platform area indicate paralic conditions.

In the Central Graben the rising sea level through the Late Jurassic resulted in the flooding of local highs where sand was deposited, while thick successions of offshore clays were deposited in relatively deep waters (Johannessen 2003). These deposits belong to the Upper Callovian–Upper Kimmeridgian Lola Formation, which is up to 1000 m thick. In the southern part of the Central Graben the Middle Graben Formation was succeeded by the shoreface sands of the Kimmeridgian Heno Formation deposited during a short-lived fall in sea level, but otherwise the overall sea-level rise continued. There was thus an increasing marine influence from late Mid-Jurassic through to Late Jurassic times. Regional data indicate that the transgression came from the north and biostratigraphic evidence indicates a southward younging of the transgression. The crests of the fault blocks formed barriers which hindered water exchange and circulation. Water masses became stratified with dysoxic to anoxic conditions at the seafloor reflected by the very high content of organic carbon of algal origin in the clays of the Upper Kimmeridgian–Ryazanian (Berriasian) Farsund Formation. Intercalated gravels and sands of the Volgian (Tithonian) Poul Formation were deposited from sediment gravity flows at the foot of many of the steep fault-controlled slopes.

The Farsund Formation has a maximum thickness of more than 3000 m in the Tail End Graben. It is easy to identify on well logs based on the high gamma-ray log signature. Some of the coarse-grained layers contain large amounts of shell fragments, indicating that the anoxic conditions primarily existed in the deep half-graben basins, whereas oxygenation was good in shallow waters over the submerged highs which served as sediment source areas. The most radioactive part of the Farsund Formation was formerly termed the 'Hot Unit', but is now named the Bo Member (Ineson *et al.* 2003). This member is of Late Volgian (Tithonian) to Late Ryazanian (Berriasian) age and is thus mainly of earliest Cretaceous age since the Tithonian–Berriasian boundary correlates with a level close to the Middle–Upper Volgian boundary. The special depositional conditions of this unit are of great economic significance because the uppermost Jurassic organic-rich layers form the most important source rocks for hydrocarbons in the North Sea.

## *The Netherlands (G.F.W.H., T.E.W.)*

Various publications deal with the regional stratigraphy and geological setting of the Jurassic in the southern North Sea and adjacent areas, and some recent papers with a detailed literature overview include Herngreen *et al.* (2000*a*, 2003), Michelsen *et al.* (2003) and Wong (2007). The present contribution largely follows the Dutch overviews. The lithostratigraphic units are described in detail in Van Adrichem Boogaert & Kouwe (1993–97). Following this classification the Jurassic lithostratigraphic units may include units with latest Triassic and earliest Cretaceous ages. This section concentrates mainly on the most recent work from the Central Graben area.

*Tectonic setting*

During the Triassic and Jurassic the structural outline of the Netherlands progressively changed from one single, extensive basin into a pattern of smaller, fault-bounded basins and highs (Fig. 14.9). According to Ziegler (1990) the change was associated with the disintegration of Pangaea. It occurred in extensional phases of which the Early Cimmerian Phase (ending in the Late Triassic), the Mid-Cimmerian Phase (Aalenian–Callovian) and the Late Cimmerian Phase (Kimmeridgian–Valanginian) (Van Adrichem Boogaert & Kouwe 1993–97; section A) are of relevance for the present compilation. The intervals between these phases were characterized by regional thermal subsidence. The partition between the tectonic elements was accentuated by halokinesis along existing structural trends in the Permian–Triassic strata, while associated salt withdrawal often controlled the distribution of Jurassic depocentres.

During the Jurassic, three major rift systems can be recognized: (1) the north–south orientated Dutch Central Graben–Vlieland Basin system; (2) the east–west orientated Lower Saxony Basin system, extending into Germany; and (3) A NW–SE block-faulted transtensional system comprising the Roer Valley Graben, the Central and West Netherlands basins, and the Broad Fourteens Basin.

Begining in the Rhaetian and continuing into the Early Jurassic the area subsided and a uniform, sheet-like unit of pelitic, open-marine sediments was deposited. Structural complexity gradually increased during Early and Middle Jurassic times, and reached a maximum in the Callovian. This Middle

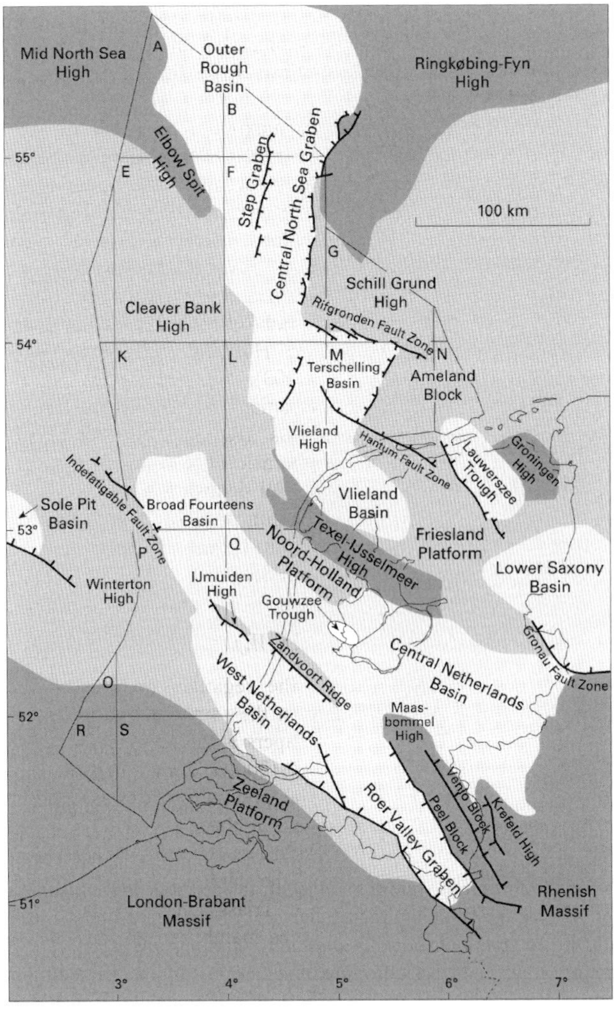


**Fig. 14.9.** Tectonic setting of the Jurassic in the Netherlands and adjacent North Sea area.

Cimmerian Phase in particular affected the northern offshore area of the Netherlands. Due to thermal uplift of the Central North Sea Dome, the centre of which was located further north (mid-way between Scotland and Norway) the truncation of the Aalenian to Bathonian (and older) strata was most rigorous in this area. During the Late Jurassic a mainly extensional tectonic regime, associated with crustal thinning, resulted in the development of the three rift systems each accumulating its own characteristic depositional succession. Rifting resulted in regional differentiation between rapidly subsiding basins and more quiescent platform areas, and this broad pattern persisted into the Early Cretaceous. Outside the major basins, Upper Jurassic sediments are rarely developed and are usually restricted to salt-induced rim synclines or transverse fault zones.

## *Stratigraphy and depositional development*

The siliciclastic Jurassic sediments are subdivided into the Altena, Schieland, Scruff and Niedersachsen groups (Fig 14.10). The three latter groups represent mostly contemporaneous strata that were deposited in different basins. Since the basal unit of the Altena Group is of Rhaetian age, this Triassic stage will be dealt with here. This is also the case for the Ryazanian (Berriasian), the lowermost Cretaceous stage, which includes sediments of the same groups. A brief overview of the various lithostratigrapic units is presented below; for details see Van Adrichem Boogaert & Kouwe (1993–97: sections G & F).

**Altena Group.** The age of the group is Rhaetian to Oxfordian. It consists mainly of argillaceous sediments with some calcareous intercalations in its lower part, and alternating calcareous and clastic deposits in the upper part. Erosion and differential subsidence have resulted in thicknesses varying from a few metres up to 1500 m. The consistent, pelitic and marine lithofacies indicates that the absence of the group on the surrounding highs is mostly due to erosion. However, in places, considerable thinning is apparent, e.g. against the London-Brabant Massif in the south. The most completely developed section is present in the northwestern part of the Roer Valley Graben. Rare exposures can be found in the eastern Netherlands (Achterhoek area). The depth of the base of this group is highly variable, reaching maxima of 3000 m in the West Netherlands Basin and 4000 m in the Central Graben. The group comprises the Sleen, Aalburg, Posidonia Shale, Werkendam and Brabant formations.

Following the last pulse of the Early Cimmerian extensional phase in the earliest Rhaetian, there was a marine transgression across large parts of Europe; in the Netherlands the resulting sediments of the Sleen Formation (20–45 m thick) are predominantly pelitic and contain lacustrine and marine (micro)fossils. During the Hettangian to earliest Toarcian the Aalburg Formation was deposited, consisting of a uniform section of up to 700 m of dark-grey to black claystones. Basin circulation became restricted during the Toarcian, causing dysaerobic bottom conditions. Bituminous shales of the Posidonia Shale Formation, usually 30 m thick, were deposited. Well-oxygenated conditions, alternating with oxygen-poor and reducing periods as demonstrated in the eastern Netherlands Achterhoek area (Herngreen *et al.* 2000*b*), were re-established in the latest Toarcian and Aalenian when deposition of the Lower Werkendam Member commenced. This unit consists of about 200 m of marine silty and oolitic mudstones.

The thermal uplift of the Central North Sea Dome affected the northern parts of the Netherlands and Germany (Pompeckj Block). The doming front gradually shifted southward resulting in a considerable delay between the timing of rifting; e.g. mid-Aalenian in the Central North Sea area and Kimmeridgian in the southern Dutch provinces. The extent of intra-Jurassic truncation and non-deposition decreases away from this dome (Underhill & Partington 1993). Consequently, the corresponding hiatus is most prominent in the Central Graben, where open-marine sedimentation terminated in the Early Bajocian. The Dutch part of the Central Graben remained non-depositional during the Bathonian to Early Callovian. Here, sedimentation resumed in the Middle Callovian in a continental facies (Lower Graben Formation). The uplift event probably also affected the Terschelling, the Dutch part of the Lower Saxony and the Central Netherlands basins. The impact of the Central North Sea uplift is negligible in the southern Broad Fourteens Basin, the West Netherlands Basin and the Roer Valley Graben where Werkendam Formation sedimentation continued. In these southern areas an important Bajocian influx of alternating, marly siltstones and sandstones occurs along the basin margins. These sediments are marine in origin and are assigned to the Middle Werkendam Member. The overlying Upper Werkendam Member comprises again grey claystones. Depositional facies changed to shallow marine, sandy carbonates and marls during the Bathonian (Brabant Formation or 'Cornbrash facies'). At least three carbonate–marl cycles were

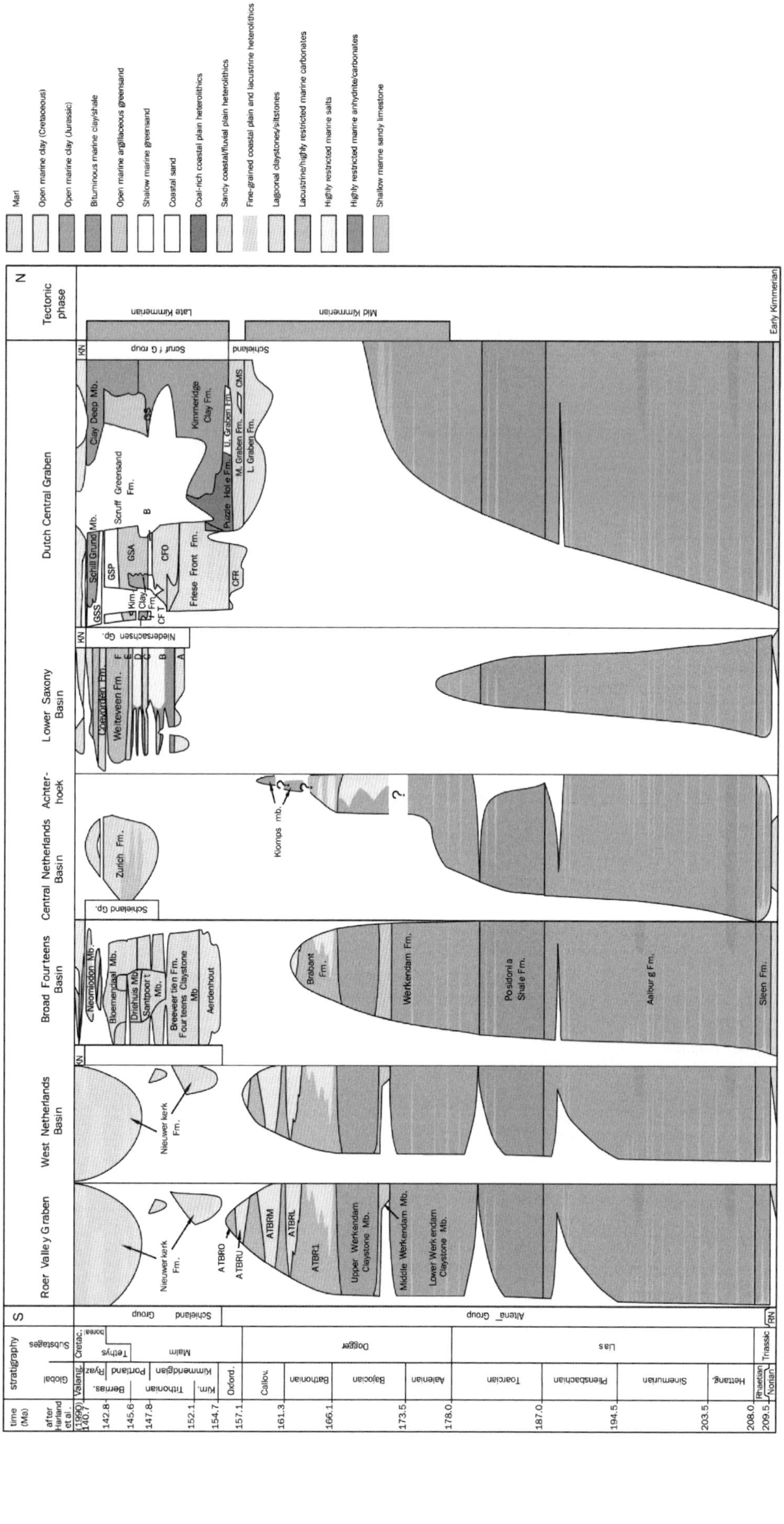


**Fig. 14.10.** Lithostratigraphy of the Jurassic in the Netherlands and adjacent North Sea area.

deposited in the Bathonian to Oxfordian of the southern basins, where a maximum thickness of 350 m can be attained.

The sequence of events in the Achterhoek area differs from the general trend (Herngreen *et al.* 1983, 2000*b*). The sedimentary sequences up to the Middle Bathonian show strong parallels with the successions in the Roer Valley Graben and the German part of the Lower Saxony Basin; the entire area appears to have been a single depositional province. In the Callovian, however, differentiation occurred when an open-marine, calcareous claystone facies was deposited in the Achterhoek (here informally termed the Klomps Member) and adjacent parts of Germany. In contrast, deposition of shallow-marine sandy carbonates and marls in the Roer Valley Graben and West Netherlands Basin persisted into the Oxfordian.

**Schieland Group.** The predominantly continental Schieland Group marks the first phase of deposition following the period of Mid-Cimmerian uplift and erosion. It is subdivided into the Central Graben and Delfland subgroups, a subdivision which is mainly based on the basinal position of the strata. The Central Graben Subgroup comprises the formations confined to the Dutch Central Graben, the Terschelling Basin and the northern Vlieland sub-basin, while the Delfland Subgroup contains those formations which are present in the southern Vlieland sub-basin, the Central Netherlands Basin, the Broad Fourteens Basin, the West Netherlands Basin and the Roer Valley Graben. The age of the group ranges from Callovian to Barremian.

The **Central Graben Subgroup** consists of alternations of sandstones, claystones and coal beds. Deposition marks the coastal-plain to paralic phase in the subsiding Central Graben and Terschelling Basin. It interfingers with marine sediments of the Scruff Group. Due to both onlapping onto syndepositional highs and differential subsidence, the subgroup displays large variations in thickness. The thickest accumulation of approximately 1100 m has been recorded in the fault-bounded, southwestern corner of block F3. The age of the subgroup ranges from Callovian to Early Portlandian (Tithonian) and its base is strongly diachronous (Herngreen & Wong 1989). The subgroup is divided into five formations.

The *Lower Graben Formation* consists predominantly of fluvial and alluvial plain sandstones with intercalations of silty to sandy claystones of Middle to Late Callovian age; near the top a distinct marine influence prevails. This unit displays large thickness variations from a few metres to about 560 m due to onlap onto syndepositional topography and differential subsidence. Sedimentation commenced along the axis of the northern Central Graben.

*Friese Front Formation.* Sedimentation gradually extended into the southern part of the area in the latest Callovian, Oxfordian and Kimmeridgian. The formation comprises regularly alternating clay-, silt- and sandstones with some coal beds and with common dispersed lignitic matter in an upper delta, fluvial plain setting. Marginal marine sediments of the Oyster Ground Claystone Member and the very nearshore Terschelling Sandstone Member, consisting of sandstones in sheets and channels separated by thin, possibly lagoonal, claystones (both members Late Kimmeridgian–early Early Portlandian (Tithonian)), represent the final stages of the formation in the southern Central Graben.

*Middle Graben Formation.* The transition from the characteristic coal seams intercalated with marine beds at the base of this formation to mainly carbonaceous claystones (with a sandstone interval) reflects an abrupt change to finer-grained, lake- and swamp-dominated sedimentation. This shift was accompanied by the first, short-lived marine incursion of the Rifgronden Member (Friese Front Formation) in the southern Central Graben. The formation is up to 420 m thick and of Early to Middle Oxfordian age.

*Upper Graben Formation.* The carbonaceous sandstone bodies separated by a silty claystone section form a stacked prograding coastal-barrier complex, Late Oxfordian in age, and up to 125 m thick in the area of block F3. South of it the Puzzle Hole Formation is found.

The *Puzzle Hole Formation* consists of paralic delta-plain deposits characterized by numerous coal beds. The formation ranges up into the early Late Kimmeridgian; its maximum thickness of about 400 m is attained in subsiding rim synclines around salt diapirs. The thin marine sands that locally occur in the uppermost parts of the formation suggest the presence of a backstepping coastal barrier system. North of the barrier complexes the Kimmeridge Clay Formation represents the open-marine environment. In a southerly direction the Puzzle Hole deposits pass into the fluvial-plain strata of the Friese Front Formation.

The **Delfland Subgroup** consists of alternating fluvial sand- and claystones, channel sands, *in situ* coal beds (Nieuwerkerk and Zurich formations) and palaeosols; dolomites occur in the Zurich Formation. It contains three formations that were deposited in coastal plain environments: the Zurich Formation in the Vlieland and Central Netherlands basins, the Breeveertien Formation in the Broad Fourteens Basin, and the Nieuwerkerk Formation in the West Netherlands Basin and the Roer Valley Graben. The thickness of the subgroup is very variable and depends on the structural setting which differed from basin to basin. The maximum thickness of 1500 m is found in the Broad Fourteens Basin. The age of the subgroup, also differs from basin to basin, and ranges from Oxfordian to Barremian.

In the southern Vlieland sub-basin and the Central Netherlands Basin the Late (latest?) Kimmeridgian to Ryazanian (Berriasian) continental strata are assigned to the Zurich Formation. The lower informal member consists of often variegated fine-grained mudstones with carbonate (mainly dolomite) bands; brackish intercalations may occur. The upper member with frequent coal beds is Ryazanian (Berriasian) in age and represents lacustrine and paralic settings.

In the Broad Fourteens Basin widespread sedimentation began in the Early Kimmeridgian with the sandy fluvial-plain deposits of the Aerdenhout Member. A shift to lacustrine and lagoonal sediments (Fourteens Claystone Member) coincides with the progressive transgression in the Central Graben.

In the rapidly subsiding Roer Valley Graben and the West Netherlands Basin synrift deposition was dominated by braided river-valley fills with great lateral variations in sandbody thickness. The Ardennes and Rhenish massifs were probably the main source area (Den Hartog Jager 1996). The sands alternate with fines deposited in an overbank setting during floods; on the floodplain outside the channels swamps and soils developed. Typical successions are found in the Alblasserdam Member (Nieuwerkerk Formation) which is Kimmeridgian to Barremian in age; however, pre-Portlandian (Tithonian) strata are poorly known.

**Scruff Group.** The largely marine Late Oxfordian to Ryazanian (Berriasian) Scruff Group interfingers with both the mainly continental Schieland Group and the hypersaline lagoonal to lacustrine Niedersachsen Group. The group consists of locally bituminous claystones with thin intercalated carbonate beds assigned to the Kimmeridge Clay Formation, and of glauconitic, sometimes argillaceous, sandstones of the Scruff Greensand Formation. The distribution is limited to the Central Graben which forms the principal depocentre, the Terschelling Basin and the northern part of the Vlieland Basin. The variation in thickness, in particular in quadrant F, is due to strong differential subsidence and to erosion during the Subhercynian and Laramide inversion phases; a maximum thickness of about 800 m is attained in block F3. In the Vlieland Basin a volcanic event, the Zuidwal volcanic dome and associated rocks, separated the northern, marine from the southern, continental sub-basin with the lacustrine Zurich Formation (Herngreen *et al.* 1991).

*Kimmeridge Clay Formation.* From the latest Oxfordian onward sedimentation is distinctly marine with deposition taking place in an outer shelf setting. In the type section F3-3 borehole structureless organic matter, indicative of dysaerobic bottom conditions, is found in the same interval and thin dolomite streaks are common. This interval is dated to the Early Kimmeridgian *Mutabilis* Zone and represents a slight deepening of the Central Graben with decreased clastics input and coeval stagnant water conditions.

The formation includes the Clay Deep Member (Mbr) and its southern extension, the Schill Grund Member. The Clay Deep Mbr consists of rather bituminous claystones, the age varying from late Early Portlandian (Tithonian) to Late Ryazanian (Berriasian); the Upper Portlandian is possibly strongly reduced or even absent. Palynology of the Schill Grund claystones invariably indicates a possibly latest Early to Late Ryazanian (Berriasian) age and offshore open-marine deposition under well-oxygenated bottom conditions.

*Scruff Greensand Formation.* Thick (up to 360 m) sand-dominated sections were deposited probably in topographic depressions on downfaulted graben margins and/or in salt-induced rim synclines. The formation generally has a high glauconite content while the argillaceous matter varies; large amounts of sponge spicules are also present. Deposition took place on a shallow marine shelf where shoaling and continuous reworking (winnowing) resulted in enrichment in coarser-grained sediments. The age of the formation is Early Portlandian (Tithonian) to Late Ryazanian (Berriasian). Four members are differentiated: the Scruff Basal Sandstone (transgressive shoreface setting), the Scruff Argillaceous (deposited at greater water depths), the Scruff Spiculite (open-marine near-coastal with various subenvironments) and Stortemelk members (distinct marine facies with marked influx of near-coastal sporomorphs). Further north, this formation grades into the Kimmeridge Clay Formation.

**Niedersachsen Group.** This group is divided in stratigraphic order into the Weiteveen and Coevorden formations. Its distribution is restricted to the Lower Saxony Basin, where it extends into the Dutch area it has a maximum thickness of just over 500 m.

The *Weiteveen Formation* is of Kimmeridgian and Portlandian (Tithonian) age and consists mainly of anhydritic, marly claystones with limestone intercalations. The basal part is coarse-sandy to conglomeratic (Weiteveen Basal Clastic Mbr). In the basin intercalated halite beds occur (Weiteveen Lower and Upper Evaporite Mbr). The uppermost unit is the Serpulite Member, a limestone-rich claystone characterized by serpulid fragments. The full Weiteveen sequence displays a shoaling trend. Equivalent sediments in the German part of the basin include the Münder Formation.

The *Coevorden Formation* is of Ryazanian (Berriasian) age and consists of lacustrine, marly claystones with occasional limestone beds, notably in the lower part. In Germany the equivalent strata belong to the Bückeberg Formation.

*Upper Jurassic sedimentary history: sequences and comparison*

The Upper Jurassic (to Lower Cretaceous) deposits in NW Europe show a step-by-step southward transgression. The transgressive periods alternated with the partly tectonically controlled phases of short-term progradation of continental siliciclastics. This interaction is reflected in the repeated interdigitation of continental and marine sediments. The largely marine Scruff Group interfingers with the mainly continental Schieland Group and the hypersaline lagoonal to lacustrine Niedersachsen Group. Differential movement of fault blocks was caused by oblique-slip and by halokinesis; together with a high sediment infill, this resulted in repeatedly shifting depocentres. Repetitive intercalation of marine and continental deposits suggests that sedimentation was also influenced by eustatic sea-level changes. Unless otherwise stated, the following overview is based on data from the Central Graben.

After the non-deposition and erosion related to the uplift of the Central North Sea Dome, sedimentation resumed in the Central Graben during the Middle Callovian with the continental Lower Graben Formation. The first marine transgression is found in the top of the Late Callovian Friese Front Formation and further to the south in the basal part of the Rifgronden Member of the same formation. The widespread marine influence continued in the lowermost part of the Middle Graben Formation, specifically between the coal beds and, southward, in the higher parts of the Rifgronden Member. This marine flooding in Late Callovian to earliest Oxfordian times is correlated with cycle LZA-3.2 of Haq *et al.* (1988), more precisely cycle 3.2 of Rioult *et al.* (1991), and corresponds with the J46 maximum flooding surface (MFS) 'Lamberti' in Partington *et al.* (1993). On the basis of dinoflagellate evidence it was concluded that during latest Callovian time a distinct cooling of the sea-surface temperatures (due to climatic control or circulation of colder North Atlantic waters) took place. Taking into consideration detailed sporomorph data (Abbink 1998), the climate reached its coolest and most humid conditions during the Late Callovian to Early (or earliest) Oxfordian.

The major part of the Oxfordian strata are lacustrine to lagoonal. The transition from paralic coal seams intercalated with marine beds to mainly lagoonal carbonaceous claystones (Middle Graben Formation) or alternating clay-, silt- and sandstones (Friese Front Formation) is correlated with ZA.3.2c/3.2d sequence boundary (Rioult *et al.* 1991) and the SB 01 of Coe (1995) which is at the boundary of the *Mariae–Cordatum* Zone. The deposition of the Friese Front, Puzzle Hole and Middle Graben formations is related to a second-order sea-level lowstand (Haq *et al.* 1988; Rioult *et al.* 1991; Norris & Hallam 1995; Sneider *et al.* 1995). This progradation can be correlated with the LZA-4.1 and 4.2 (to 4.3 lowstand) cycles (Haq *et al.* 1988; Rioult *et al.* 1991).

The next distinct marine transgression began at the Late Oxfordian base of the Kimmeridge Clay Formation. This transgression, which equates with cycles ?LZA-4.3 and LZA-4.4 (Haq *et al.* 1988), is thought to incorporate the ?J54a+b and J56 MFS (Partington *et al.* 1993) and represents sequence boundary O6 (Coe 1995). An increasing marine influence, which corresponds with the J62 MFS (Partington *et al.* 1993), is observed in earliest Kimmeridgian sediments assigned to the *Baylei* Zone. A pronounced Early Kimmeridgian sea-level highstand was reached in strata equivalent to the *Mutabilis* Zone. This interval is characterized by structureless organic matter and a cluster of thin dolomite bands thought to represent fourth-order cycles. It is correlated with the sea-level highstand of cycle LZA-4.5 in Haq *et al.* (1988). Kimmeridge Clay sediments with the *Perisseiasphaer-*

*idium pannosum* acme are assigned to the Early Kimmeridgian *Eudoxus-Autissiodorensis* zones. This acme calibrates the tectonically enhanced J63 MFS 'Eudoxus' of Partington *et al.* (1993). The next events in the Kimmeridge Clay are: (1) the *Oligosphaeridium patulum* acme, Late Kimmeridgian *Hudlestoni-Pectinatus* zones, which correlates with the J66a MFS 'Hudlestoni' in Partington *et al.* (1993) and corresponds with the lowstand wedge in transition to the transgressive part of cycle LZB-1.1 in Haq *et al.* (1988); and (2) an interval around the transition *Pallasioides-Rotunda* Zone which may correspond with the J71 MFS (Partington *et al.* 1993) and is correlated with the highstand tract of cycle LZB-1.1 (Haq *et al.* 1988). These two transgressive phases resulted in the second marine interval in the southern Central Graben, the Oyster Ground Member (Friese Front Formation). Simultaneously, the depocentre in the Central Graben shifted from the central/eastern axis to the western margin; this was caused by tectonic tilting and associated halokinesis. During the Late Kimmeridgian the deposition of clastic sediments of the Weiteveen Formation (Fm) in the Lower Saxony Basin was intermittently replaced by the precipitation of evaporites. Possibly these cycles may be correlated with cycles of the Breeveertien Formation in the Broad Fourteens Basin.

A series of Portlandian (Tithonian) dinoflagellate events was observed at the top of the main Kimmeridge Clay member transitional to the basal part of the Clay Deep Member as well as in the Scruff Greensand Formation. The first two events correspond with the J72 MFS 'Okusensis' and J73 MFS 'Anguiformis' of Partington *et al.* (1993) respectively. The third event is latest Early Portlandian (Tithonian), *Oppressus* Zone, and correlates with the LZB-1.4 transgressive systems tract of Haq *et al.* (1988). The Early Portlandian (Tithonian) transgression resulted in the deposition of the Terschelling Member of the Friese Front Formation in coastal settings along the southern margin of the Central Graben. To the north this formation grades into the open-marine Scruff Greensand Formation, and still farther north the latter in turn passes into the Kimmeridge Clay Formation. The depocentre of the Kimmeridge Clay, which was previously situated in the northern part of the Central Graben, now shifted to the southernmost part. In the B quadrant, basin circulation stagnated resulting in the depostion of the bituminous claystones known in the Netherlands as the Clay Deep Member. This member represents the southernmost occurrence of the Kimmeridge 'hot shale' facies in the North Sea area.

Two dinocyst events are recognized in the Ryazanian (Berriasian). The older one is at the transition to the *Kochii-Icenii* Zone, the Early–Late Ryazanian boundary. This is just above the J76 MFS 'Kochi' of Partington *et al.* (1993). The second event is correlated with the *stenomphalus–albidum* boundary which is usually considered to be very late Ryazanian (Berriasian). This event is above the K10 MFS 'Stenomphalus' (Partington *et al.* 1993). Hoedemaeker & Herngreen (2003) indicate a type 1 sequence boundary at the transition of the Clay Deep/Schill Grund Member (Kimmeridge Clay Fm) to the Vlieland Member (Vlieland Sandstone Fm). The succession of strata in the strongly bituminous Clay Deep Member, which loses its bituminous character towards the south, and the well-oxygenated Schill Grund Member most likely belongs to the highstand tract of cycles LZB-1.5 and 1.6 (Haq *et al.* 1988). The last member grades southward into the Stortemelk Member of the Scruff Greensand Formation. Deposition of the Clay Deep and Schill Grund members completely superseded that of the Scruff Greensand Formation by Ryazanian (Berriasian) times.

In continental to marginal marine deposits with marked influx of continent-derived material, the upper Lower to lower Upper Kimmeridgian sporomorphs indicate the onset of a warmer and drier period which culminated in late Late Kimmeridgian and Portlandian (Tithonian) times (e.g. Abbink 1998). In continental strata around the Jurassic–Cretaceous boundary, for example at the transition of the Weiteveen formation to the Coevorden Formation, a remarkable shift from *Classopollis* pollen-dominated sporomorph assemblages to those with common and varied spores has been noted. It is obvious that this change represents a major climatic event. This break is now generally accepted to be indicative of increasing humidity (e.g. Ruffell & Rawson 1994; Abbink 1998).

The Late Cimmerian I pulse, broadly during the Oxfordian, ended the deposition of the marine Altena Group in the Roer Valley Graben, the West Netherlands Basin and the Broad Fourteens Basin, and probably also in the Central Netherlands and Lower Saxony basins. In these basins continental deposits of Late Jurassic (and Early Cretaceous) age strongly predominate. In the Broad Fourteens Basin there is a shift from lacustrine and lagoonal conditions (Fourteens Claystone Member) to fluvial-plain settings (Bloemendaal Member). In the Lower Saxony Basin, this shoaling tendency is demonstrated by the Serpulite Member of the Weiteveen Formation.

The transition of the Weiteveen Upper Marl (the Netherlands) and Katzberg members (Germany) to Serpulite Member coincides with a type 1 sequence boundary (Hoedemaeker & Herngreen 2003). The classic Late Cimmerian Unconformity (also a type 1 sequence boundary) is positioned at the transition of the Lower to Middle Coevorden (the Netherlands) and Wealden 3 lower to upper part (Germany). There is also a type 1 sequence boundary near the top of the Berriasian (Ryazanian) at the transition from the Middle to Upper Coevorden Member (the Netherlands) and Wealden 4 to 5 (including topmost 4, Germany; Hoedemaeker & Herngreen 2003).

*Petroleum geology*

The Posidonia Shale Fm is the main source rock for oil in the Dutch subsurface. Additional source rocks exist in the Coevorden Fm in the Lower Saxony Basin, and generated the oil of the relatively large Schoonebeek field. Coal-bearing strata in the Puzzle Hole, Middle Graben and Friese Front formations may locally have generated gas, however, not in economic quantities. There are no Jurassic reservoir rocks with significant gas accumulations sourced by the widespread Late Carboniferous coals.

Oil and (wet) gas reserves have been discovered in the sandstones of the Lower Graben, Upper Graben and Friese Front formations in the Central Graben. In the Broad Fourteens Basin producible oil has been found in sandstone intervals of the Breeveertien Fm. In the West Netherlands Basin and the Roer Valley Graben various members of the Brabant and Nieuwerkerk formations are locally oil-bearing. The top seals are various Jurassic shaly intervals.

*Magmatic activity*

The information presented in this section is based on the compilation by Sissingh (2004). Intrusions have been found in the Aalburg Formation (Q07–02) and the Lower Werkendam Member (Berkel-1). The (isotopic) ages of the intrusion, however, are much debated and various Early Cretaceous ages are most likely. The intrusive rocks in the Alblasserdam Member (Giessendam-1) and the Rodenrijs Claystone Member (Berkel-2), both in the Nieuwerkerk Formation, are possibly of similar ages. Moreover, in the eastern Netherlands Oldenzaal-2 well, an undated intrusion is found in the Coevorden Member.

An extrusive agglomerate constitutes the Zuidwal Volcanic Formation of the Vlieland Basin. It has been dated at 152 ± 3, 145, and 144 ± 1 Ma; the eruption centre would therefore have been active during Oxfordian–Kimmeridgian or Kimmeridgian–Portlandian (Tithonian) times (Herngreen *et al.* 1991; Sissingh 2004).

## *Northern Germany (E.M.)*

The Jurassic of northern Germany extends over an area of *c.* 100 000 km$^2$, but lies almost entirely in the subsurface. Only 1% crops out, and that is in the southern part of Lower Saxony and in northern parts of Westphalia. The Jurassic of northern Germany also comprises some relicts in Hessen and Saxony (Fig. 14.11). Despite this lack of outcrop, much is known about the underground Jurassic. The main database comprises over 100 000 boreholes (and shafts) from the extensive exploitation for oil, gas, salt, iron ore, caverns/disposal sites, radioactive waste disposal or water. Borehole measurements, cores and drill cuttings provide a huge amount of data and this is supplemented by the *c.* 500 000 km of reflection seismic profiles from across the region.

The Jurassic of northern Germany is situated within the North German Basin which represents the central part of the CEBS. It is an area of long-term subsidence and sediment accumulation. Since the late Palaeozoic a thickness of *c.* 6000 m has accumulated. From Upper Triassic times the basin was subdivided into NW to WSW–ESE striking troughs and highs as a result of halokinetic movement. Where salt accumulated, it pushed upwards as diapirs, leading to widespread erosion in the Middle Jurassic. Thus, the Middle and Upper Jurassic are only incompletely preserved, and the sediments of Bathonian and younger age are extensively eroded and only preserved in restricted sub-basins.

The *Northern German Lias Group* (Norddeutsche Lias Gruppe) is developed primarily in marine shale facies (250 and 1300 m) interfingering to the NE with shallow-marine sands and limnic and terrestrial sediments. The sediments of the Lias Group attain their greatest thickness in NW Lower Saxony and in the Nordoldenburg-Westholstein Trough. This would suggest that this area was an open-marine shale-dominated basin (or part thereof) during the Early Jurassic. This basin extended from the Norwegian–Greenland Sea into the area of the recent North Sea (Hoffmann 1949; Ziegler 1990).

The *Northern German Dogger Group* (Norddeutsche Dogger Gruppe) is less widespread than the Lias and generally absent on the Pompeckj High Block. It consists of shales, and occasional marls or siltstones with intercalated shallow-marine sandstones and iron oolitic units. Sea-bottom relief was variable (and constantly changing) mainly as a result of halokinesis. Sediment supply in the Late Toarcian and Aalenian was from the east, but in the Bajocian, Bathonian and Callovian the source was the Mid-North Sea High and the Ringkøbing–Fyn High, which had been established during the Early Bajocian. The average thickness of the succession is *c.* 400 m, but can increase to 800–1000 m in the Gifhorn Trough.

The *Northern German Malm Group* (Norddeutsche Malm Gruppe) is mainly restricted to the Lower Saxony Basin and the

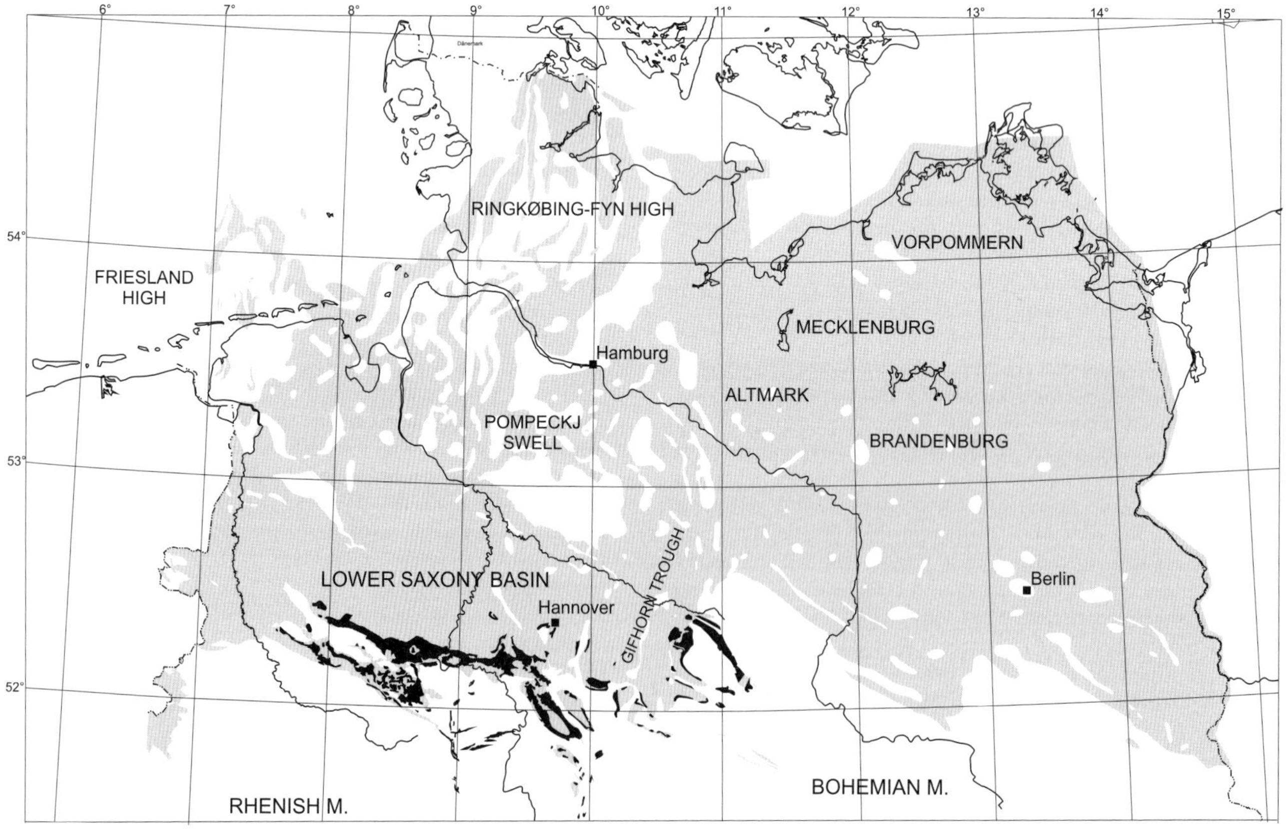


**Fig. 14.11.** Present distribution of Jurassic rocks in north Germany. Black areas represent surface Jurassic; grey areas, subsurface Jurassic. Sources: Baldschuhn *et al.* (2001); BGR 1973–93: Geologische Übersichtskarte Bundesrepublik Deutschland 1:200 000; Geologische Karte der Deutschen Demokratischen Republik ohne känozoische Sedimente, 1:500 000 (1990).

Prignitz-Altmark-Brandenburg Basin. During Late Jurassic times, tectonic activity led to the subdivision of the Lower Saxony Basin. Consequently Oxfordian, Kimmeridgian and Tithonian rocks are more variably developed than those of the Lias and Dogger groups and are generally better exposed. Evaporitic conditions during the Tithonian led to the accumulation of 1000–1500 m of carbonates, anhydrites and halites. In the western part of the Lower Saxony Basin the thickness of the Malm Group can be up to 3000 m, while in the Gifhorn Trough to it is only 700 m.

The *Northern German Jurassic Supergroup* (Norddeutscher Jura) is subdivided into dozens of formations or subformations. Some of the unit names are very old and in need of revision, while others have never been properly described or named. The naming and definition of all of these stratigraphical units will take a long time; a preliminary overview is given in Fig. 14.12. The succession described here as the Northern German Jurassic Supergroup does not exactly correspond to the Jurassic System in that it extends from the Hettangian to the Lower Berriasian of the Cretaceous. This range comprises a time duration of *c.* 60 million years (Mönnig *et al.* 2002).

*Biostratigraphy*

In the Jurassic of northern Germany the most useful fossils are ammonites. The first scientific collections of Jurassic fossils were those of the Roemer brothers in Hildesheim (F.A. Roemer 1836/39; F. Roemer 1857). The majority of the ammonites which now fill the regional museums were collected between 1890 and 1970 when numerous clay pits and small quarries were still in use. Also from this time, there are many important monographs (e.g. J. Roemer 1911; Westermann 1954, 1958). In the museum and geological survey collections there are more than one million Jurassic ammonites, which together represent an excellent database for further investigations.

While the stratigraphy in the outcrops is broadly clear, many problems still exist concerning the subsurface Jurassic. In particular the age of many sandstone bodies is incompletely known. The future subdivision into subzones and faunal horizons will reveal more precise information on the palaeogeography of the region.

Where ammonites are scarce or lacking, correlation has been attempted using microfossils. This became necessary as a result of petroleum prospecting, beginning in 1930, and so most of the micropalaeontological biostratigraphic research has been done for oil companies. In the Jurassic of northern Germany ostracodes are by far the most useful microfossils in terms of stratigraphic correlation, with a very precise resolution. The range of an ostracode biozone is approximately equivalent to an ammonite standard chronozone. Sometimes correlation may be difficult in brackish, limnic or terrestrial deposits with endemic faunas, hence a variety of other microfossils have been used for stratigraphic subdivision. Foraminifera can be good guide fossils but are more valuable for palaeoenvironmental information. In the Upper Jurassic dinoflagellate and charophyte zonations have also been erected (Gramann *et al.* 1997), but these taxa generally have longer stratigraphic ranges than ammonite species.

*Hettangian*

In northern Germany the lithological transition from Rhaetic sandstones to marine Early Jurassic mudstones is gradual, but the system boundary is marked by the sudden appearance of fully marine fossils. The Jurassic transgression began in the NW and extended as far as the Berlin area. East of Berlin limnic terrestrial or brackish sedimentation continued across the Rhaetian–Hettangian boundary and persisted into the Late Sinemurian (Tessin 1995). Generally, the Hettangian (Psilonotenton and Angulatenton formations) consists of 20 m thick shales; only the Bohemian and the Rhenish massifs were fringed by deltaic complexes up to 80 m thick (Psilonoten Sandstone, Liassicus Sandstone). The kerogen-rich shales of the central part of the basin interfinger towards the SW with carbonates of the lower Aalburg Formation of the Netherlands (Herngreen *et al.* 2003). The upper Hettangian is very similar. Of special interest are estuarine red clays in the Altmark (Hoffmann 1949). To the NE, in Mecklenburg, a 2.6 m thick coal has been described (Petzka & Rusbült 2004).

*Sinemurian*

The most interesting Sinemurian deposits comprise a series of thin horizons of sideritic chamosite or limonitic oolites, which have long been exploited as ironstones. Ironstone deposition was associated with the two transgressions. In Friesland and to the SE of the North Sea a shale-filled basin developed and mudstones and bituminous shales (up to 300 m thick) were accumulated. (Hoffmann 1949). Sub-Mediterranean ammonite faunas indicate that there was an opening of the sea towards the south. In Mecklenburg and Brandenburg the Sinemurian comprises marine siltstones with the percentage of sandstones increasing up-section, reflecting the general shallowing of the region. To the NE, in Vorpommern the facies of the Lower Sinemurian is limnic or terrestrial. The subsequent Upper Sinemurian comprises marine siltstones overlain by alternations of red-brown restricted marine mudstones and fine-grained sandstones (40–110 m) corresponding to the Swedish Pankarp Member (Petzka & Rusbült 2004).

*Pliensbachian*

The Lower Pliensbachian is mostly rather thin (5–10 m), comprising mainly marls with intercalated limestone beds showing occasional evidence of reworking. Oolitic iron ores or siderite layers are very common and more widespread than those of the Lower Sinemurian which fringe the northern margins of the Rhenish and Bohemian massifs (Bottke *et al.* 1969). The iron ores were exploited in nine mines until 1962. Following a significant rise in sea level in the middle of the Lower Pliensbachian, the basin was filled almost entirely with grey clays. The Capricornuton Formation (40–180 m, and sometimes including oil shales) was deposited in the NW of Lower Saxony. Across northern Germany the Amaltheenton Formation (Upper Pliensbachian; 70–170 m), comprising marine clays, was deposited. Coarser facies, including siltstones or fine-grained sandstones, occur only to the east of Brandenburg. The Plienbachian ammonite faunas of England and northern Germany are very similar indicating unhindered faunal exchange over open marine stretches.

*Lower Toarcian*

The bituminous, black marls of the Ölschiefer Formation (27–70 m) are the main source rocks for oil fields in the Lower Saxony Basin, as well as the Gifhorn and Holstein troughs. In Mecklenburg and Brandenburg the Lower Toarcian is represented by greenish-grey mudstones with calcareous concretions in the lower part of the succession. Close to the German–Polish border there are intercalations of siltstones and fine-grained sandstones (Petzka & Rusbült 2004).

*Upper Toarcian and Aalenian*

In many regions the top of the Ölschiefer Formation is developed as an event bed which includes numerous fragments of belem-

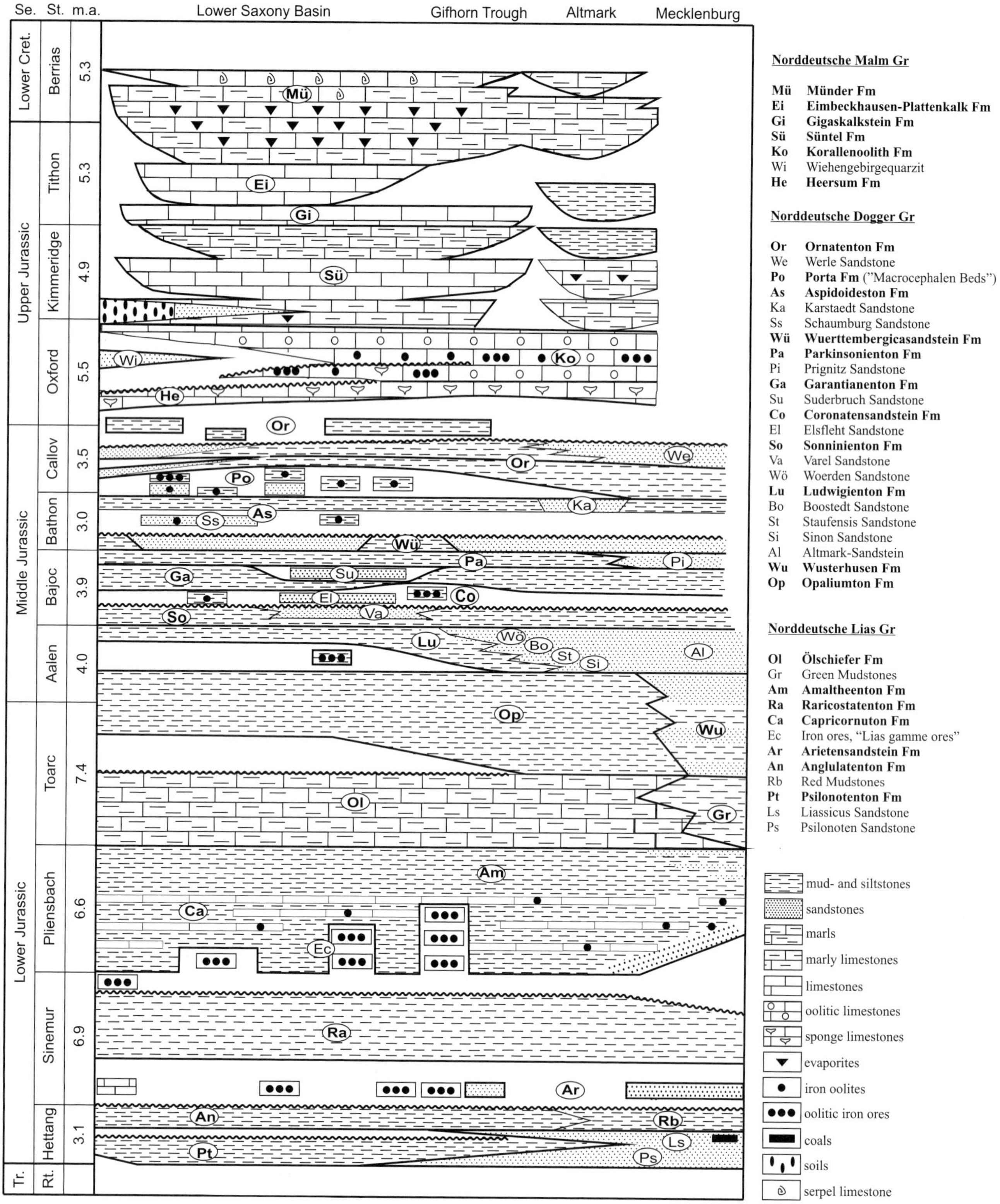


**Fig. 14.12.** Chronostratigraphic diagram of Jurassic stratigraphy and facies variation in north Germany. After Mönnig *et al.* (2002).

nites ('Lias-Zeta-Conglomerate' or 'Dispansum Bench'). According to Vinken *et al.* (1971) this represents a considerable stratigraphic gap. The Upper Toarcian and Lower Aalenium (30–50 m) mainly comprise dark mudstones and shale clays, which are sandy to the SE. In some beds white-shelled ammonites (*Leioceras*) occur. Nodules of pyrite or calcareous concretions are frequent, and thin calcareous units also occur. At the beginning of the Upper Aalenian a distinct shallowing of the basin occurred resulting in a change in depositional conditions which resulted in the formation of oolitic ironstones and sandstones in the inner parts of the basin between the Weser and Ems rivers. A total of seven main iron-ore lenses were deposited, the most important of which is Staffhorst with an extent of 80 $km^2$, a thickness of 2–8 m and an iron content of between 34 and 40%. The Sinon Sandstone (20 m) represents the oldest sandstone of the Middle Jurassic. With a porosity of 20–30% it is an excellent reservoir rock for gas and oil (Brand & Hoffmann 1963).

During the Upper Aalenian a rise in relative sea level resulted in basin deepening. The Ludwigienton Formation comprises oil-bearing sandstones, coal-bearing deposits, mudstones and siltstones with an overall fining to the west. In the Upper Aalenian conglomerates containing Early Jurassic nodules often occur. These were probably derived from the updoming of the Central North Sea High.

The greatest Upper Aalenian thicknesses are limited to the sub-basins in the east, in particular the Gifhorn Trough (800 m) and the Broistedt-Hamburg Trough (>600 m). In this area, the entire succession shows a distinct transgressive tendency with the sandbodies shifting increasingly towards their source area to the NE (Brand & Hoffmann 1963).

*Bajocian*

The Bajocian succession consists mainly of pyrite-rich dark shales subdivided by large sandstone fans and oolitic iron ores. The deeper-marine conditions of the Upper Aalenien with the associated deposition of clays continued into the Lower Bajocian (Disciteston and Sonninienton formations, 100 m). Overlying these mudstones, the Varel Sandstone (7–15 m) extends across NW Germany as a narrow band from Bremen to Poland and has been interpreted as the highstand deposit of the Sonninienton Formation. The Middle Bajocian Elsfleht Sandstone (60–150 m) shows a similar distribution, although its eastern boundary does not extend as far as Hamburg. The maturity of this homogeneous sandstone succession, the frequency of iron ooids and evidence of local erosion suggest that it was deposited in a shallow-marine, high-energy setting.

The Coronaten Bench is a widespread hardground with stromatolites and well-preserved white-shelled Ammonites (*Normannites*, *Stephanoceras, Teloceras*). A stratigraphic gap is very often situated between the Coronaten Beds and the beds of the Upper Bajocian.

The Upper Bajocian comprises dark shales with some sandstone bodies. In the region of Bad Harzburg there is a condensed section with iron oolites (Subfurcaten Oolite). The siltstones of the Garantianenton Formation (50–90 m) were derived from the NW and show evidence of upward coarsening. Their greatest thickness is in the Weser Trough where they continue into the Suderbruch Sandstone (3–22 m), a moderately sorted, medium- to coarse-grained sandstone with porosities between 13 and 18%. It is productive in some oil fields between Bremen and Hamburg. The sediments at the top of the Bajocian indicate deeper marine conditions. The Parkinsoniton Formation (30–50 m) consists of dark grey, micaceous mudstones with many horizons of limonitic concretions. The upper part of this formation shows a high degree of bioturbation caused by suspension feeders. In the north there is evidence of upward coarsening, with the associated influx of limonitic ooids.

*Bathonian*

The Wuerttembergicasandstein Formation (20–150 m) is developed as shoal-like sandbodies or deltaic sands deposited on a stable basin margin. Trace fossil associations and primary sedimentation structures suggest that depositional conditions became increasingly shallow (Bininda 1986). Sheet sands, sometimes with concentrations of *Ostrea knorri.*, dominate the upper parts of the formation. In most areas it is possible to subdivide the Wuerttembergica Sandstone into a lower (4–5 m) and an upper part (15–25 m), separated by a mudstone-dominated unit. In Schleswig-Holstein there are deltaic sands of uncertain age. The Wuerttembergica Sandstone and its equivalent mudstones in the east are capped by a widespread discontinuity.

As in many other regions, the entire Middle Bathonian is absent and occurs only in the region of Gerzen near Alfeld (Brand *et al.* 1990). In comparison with other areas in Europe, the Upper Bathonian is remarkably thick. The Aspidoideston Formation consists of dark mudstones with intercalations of coarse-grained sands. At the base of the Upper Bathonian succession there was a sudden regression which resulted in the development of open-platform conditions. The resultant Schaumburg Sandstone (17–24 m) is a coarse-grained unit deposited in an offshore sand bar facies and occurring only in the western part of the basin (Weser- and Wiehengebirge areas). Tabular cross-bedding indicates that deposition occurred under high-energy conditions. Shell beds including *Meleagrinella echinata* are very frequent. The top of the Schaumburg Sandstone shows an erosion surface which is overlain by an oolitic iron horizon. In the Hildesheim area and further east, the Schaumburg Sandstone is represented by units comprising oolitic concretions. The upper part of the Upper Bathonian begins with the deposition of black shales or dark brown clays with phosphatic concretions and small pyritic ammonites. In some areas the succession shows a coarsening upwards into the Karstädt Sandstone. In Schleswig Holstein and Mecklenburg the entire Bathonian is limnic (Brand & Hoffmann 1963), while in the NE of Mecklenburg sideritic iron ores occur.

*Callovian*

The Lower Callovian is mostly very thin (0.3–2 m) with the thickest units (40–80 m) being deposited in small basins (e.g. rim synclines) associated with salt domes in the area between Hamburg and Berlin. The thin and condensed beds often comprise reworked nodule layers or lumachelles, indicating shallow-water conditions after a major sea-level fall. At that time tectonic movements resulted in the formation of many small local basins and highs with associated shoal areas; these were the primary sites for the accumulation of a variety of oolitic iron ores.

The Ornatenton Formation (15–130 m) has been subdivided into three members (Mönnig 1993). The lower member comprises up to *c.* 90 m of mudstones and siltstones, although muddy sandstones also occur (Werle Sandstone in the NE). The abundant fauna consists mainly of the thin-shelled bivalve *Bositra,* often concentrated in shell beds. Following a minor disconformity the overlying siltstones and fine-grained sandstones include large calcareous concretions and a rich bivalve fauna. The top is marked by a bed of winnowed *Gryphaea* shells. In this bed, bones of large carnivorous dinosaurs have recently been found (Michelis *et al.* 1996; Albat 2000). Overlying this remarkable discontinuity are blue clays of the upper part of the Ornatenton Formation (0–15 m). The reduction in clastic material was a result of the decreased availability of coarse-grained terrigenous material. The presence of boreal faunas is associated with the occurrence of phosphatic nodules and glauconite. All of these changes suggest that there was a major eustatic sea-level rise, with an associated link to colder seas

(Mönnig 1993). The upper part of the Ornatenton Formation is of Late Callovian and Early Oxfordian age.

*Oxfordian*

At the end of the Lower Oxfordian calcareous deposits spread northwards through Europe to cover the entire basin. The strongly bioturbated limestones of the Heersum Formation (10–20 m) are rich in sponge spicules and represent deposition in a moderately deep and tranquil marine environment. In the Hildesheim area, these pass upwards into higher-energy shelly grainstones, reflecting a phase of shallowing. These are unconformably overlain by patch reefs of corals or oolitic limestones (the facies which gave this formation its name – Korallenoolith Formation). The Lower Korallenoolith is a transgressive succession, which passes upwards from monotone oolitic limstones into flat water coralgal facies (Helm *et al.* 2003). At the end of the Middle Oxfordian the western part of the basin was exposed. The Korallenoolith was partly eroded and palaeosoils evolved on a karstic surface of cross-bedded oolites. The regression culminated in the development of fluviodeltaic sandbodies ('Wiehengebirgsquarzite') or a series of shallow-water carbonates and ferruginous sands. In the Wesergebirge and in the Gifhorn Trough the ferruginous deposits are developed as iron ores. The upper part of the Korallenoolith Formation is characterized by the brachiopod *Zeilleria ventroplana* and marks a return to fully marine conditions. In northern Germany the varied Oxfordian succession of carbonate and siliclastics is interrupted by two main disconformities recording periods of maximum regression (Heersum Formation/Korallenoolith and Lower/Middle Korallenoolith). During the Oxfordian the initial salt domes and pillows attained the diapir stage, resulting in the erosion of older sediments across the crests of the salt structures. During the Oxfordian the depositional area was subdivided into two basins, the Lower Saxony Basin in the SW and another in the area of Brandenburg.

*Kimmeridgian*

The Süntel Formation (100 m) contains a wide range of facies, from continental to shallow marine. Typical for the Lower Süntel Formation are the alternations of glauconitic marls, limestones and sandstones. Salinity variations are documented by local occurrences of anhydrite. In the western part of the Lower Saxony Basin terrestrial conditions are reflected by the presence of soils, red-bed clays and dinosaur footprints (Klassen 2003). A return to more stable marine salinities is indicated by the deposition of the marls and limestones of the Middle and Upper Süntel Formation. In some beds brachiopods or the oyster *Exogyra* occur in great abundance.

*Tithonian*

The Gigaskalk Formation (30 m) consists of marine limestones. The closed benches are rich in shell debris and calcareous oolites. Common fossils include bivalves and echinoids. Ammonites (*Gravesia gigas, Gravesia gravesiana*) occur in the Jurassic succession of northern Germany for the last time.

At this time, the Lower Saxony Basin became a shallow isolated gulf. The bituminous limestones and marls of the Eimbeckhausen-Plattenkalk Formation were deposited under brackish to limnic quiescent conditions. The bivalve *Corbula* occurs in some beds in abundance. The Münder Formation also reflects a restricted and evaporitic environment. Red-bed clays and evaporites, including rock salt, are the main lithologies present. In the middle part of the formation, oolites, serpulites or stromatolitic limestones occur. During a sea-level rise at the end of the Jurassic, the sea extended towards the west and some basin highs were flooded. The ostracodes of the Münder Formation suggest that deposition was continuous across the Jurassic–Cretaceous boundary. Thus, the uppermost part of the Northern German Jurassic Group is Berriasian in age (Gramann *et al.* 1997).

## *Poland, Russia (Kaliningrad region), Lithuania, Latvia, Ukraine (G.P., A.F.-O., J.Gu.)*

The Jurassic system of Poland has been described in a number of publications; the most important recent syntheses are, for the Lower Jurassic Pieńkowski (2004), for the Middle Jurassic Dayczak-Calikowska & Moryc (1988), Kopik (1998) and Feldman-Olszewska (1997*b*), and for the Upper Jurassic Kutek (1994), Kutek *et al.* (1984) and Matyja & Wierzbowski (1995, 2000*a*, *b*) and Gutowski *et al.* (2005*a*). Further to the east in Lithuania, Russia (Kaliningrad region) and Latvia, overviews have been published by Gareckij (1985), Feldman-Olszewska *et al.* (1998) and Šimkevičius (1998) with some stratigraphic amendments suggested by Pieńkowski (2004) regarding the Lower Jurassic section. Jurassic sediments in Belarus were described by Mitianina (1978) and Gareckij (1985). Additionally, some correlation with Jurassic sediments in the western Ukraine (Izotova & Popadyuk 1996; Dulub *et al.* 2003; Gutowski *et. al* 2005*a*,*b*) have been made.

The Jurassic system in Poland and adjacent countries is very diverse. Besides the Tethyan Domain (the Jurassic of the Carpathians is described in a separate section of this chapter), the epicontinental deposits of this part of Europe are developed both in siliciclastic facies (Lower Jurassic, most of the Middle Jurassic, i.e. Aalenian, Bajocian & Bathonian deposits, part of the Upper Jurassic deposits) and carbonate facies (Callovian and most of the Upper Jurassic deposits).

*Tectonic development*

The epicontinental Jurassic deposits occurring in the Polish Basin, Lithuania, Latvia, western Belarus and western Ukraine were formed in the eastern epicontinental arm of the CEBS. The zone of maximum thickness runs approximately from west Pomerania (NW) to the Holy Cross Mountains (SE) and, in the Late Jurassic, also to the western Ukraine, and is called the Mid-Polish Trough (Figs. 14.13–14.15). The Mid-Polish Trough, with a length of more than 700 km and a depth of the order of 10 km, was initiated as an elongated sedimentary basin in the latest Permian (Dadlez 1997, 2000, 2001; Dadlez *et al.* 1995). The Mid-Polish Trough generally runs along the Teisseyre-Tornquist Zone (TTZ) and the Trans-European Suture Zone (TESZ) (Guterch *et al.* 1986; Poprawa 1997; Królikowski *et al.* 1999). From the beginning of the Early Jurassic the conspicuous axial zone of the Polish Basin was placed along the Mid-Polish Trough and remained there for 150 million years until its inversion. Therefore, the Early Jurassic deposits initiate a major geological cycle in the epicontinental basin of Poland. According to Poprawa (1997), transtensional reactivation of both the main depocentre along the TTZ (50–90 m/Ma), and the subordinate depocentre located some 80 km to the SW (separated by a local uplift), occurred during the Hettangian–Early Sinemurian. Subsidence varied over time within the Mid-Polish Trough. For example, in Hettangian and Late Sinemurian times the subsidence rate was higher in the Holy Cross area and lower in Pomerania, while the opposite occurred in Early Sinemurian and Early Pliensbachian times (Fig. 14.14). Local displacement of the Late Permian rock salt commenced in the later Early Jurassic

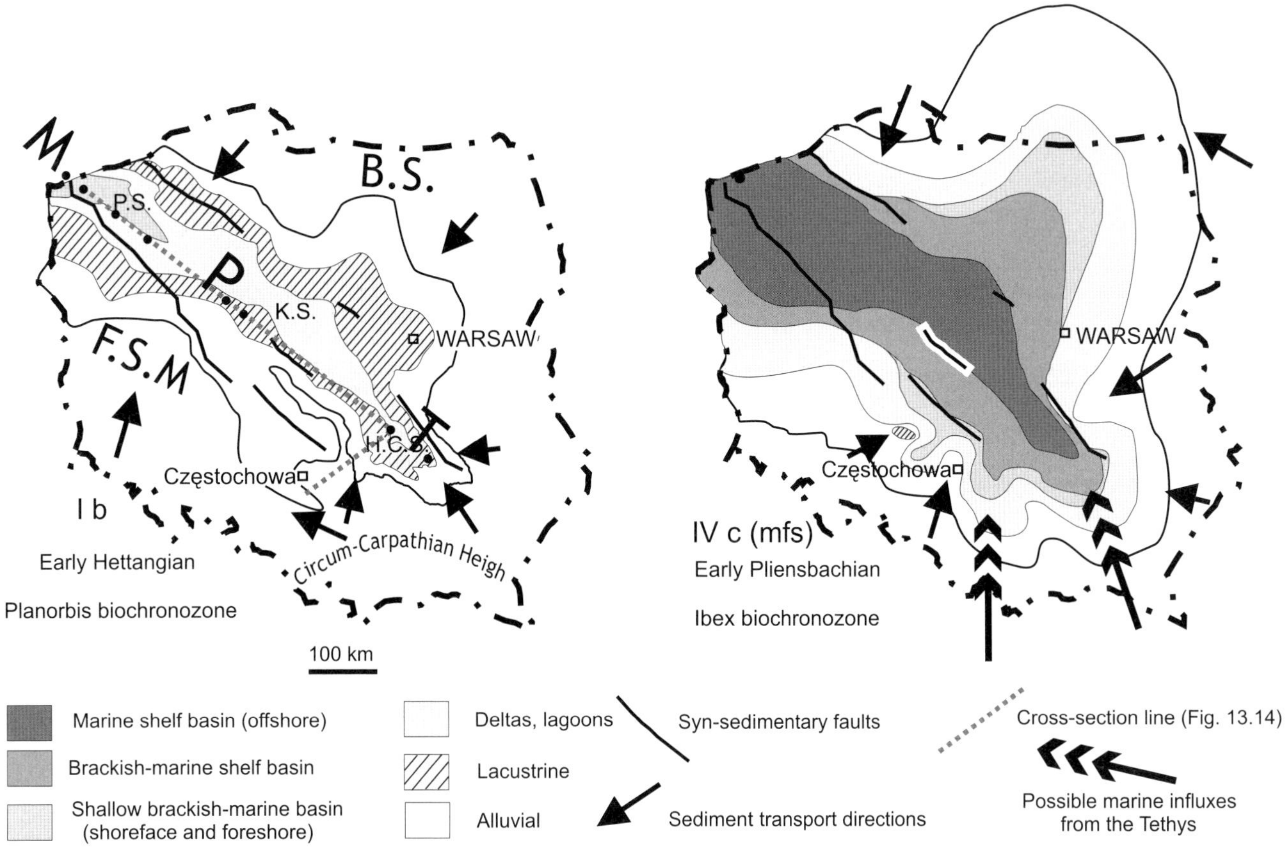


**Fig. 14.13.** Paleogeographic maps showing two stages of Early Jurassic basin development in Poland, Kaliningrad Zone of Russia and Lithuania: in Early Hettangian (late *planorbis* Biochronozone) and Early Pliensbachian (*ibex* Biochronozone). Note the conspicuous alignment of facies along the Mid-Polish Trough and subordinate directions of facies expansion (such as that to the NE). Abbreviations: **B.S.**, Baltic Syneclise (Baltic Basin) area; **F.S.M.**, Fore-Sudetic Monocline; H.C.S., Holy Cross Mountains Section; K.S., Kuiawian Section (including Kutno Depression),; **M.P.T.**, Mid-Polish Trough; P.S., Pomerania Section.

and resulted in the formation of palaeostructures of different order, whose characteristic general arrangement follows a NW–SE orientation (Deczkowski & Franczyk 1988). Despite the existence of some regional fault zones and grabens occurring along the edges of the Mid-Polish Trough, which controlled the sedimentation and led to significant sediment thickness contrasts (e.g. the Nowe Miasto-Iłża Fault, Koszalin-Chojnice Graben, part of Kalisz-Kamieńsk Graben; Dadlez 2001), a gradual decrease in sediment thickness outwards from the axis of the Mid-Polish Trough prevailed in the Jurassic (Dadlez *et al.* 1995; Dadlez 2001). Kutek (2001) proposed a model of asymmetrical, aborted rifting for the Mid-Polish Trough. He postulated 'rifting phases' taking place during the Late Permian–Early Triassic and Late Jurassic, and a 'sag phase' during the Cretaceous. However, Dadlez *et al.* (1995) argued that the term 'rift' was not applicable for the Mid-Polish Trough. It was also suggested that palaeostress patterns were characterized by the alternation of extensional and compressional events driven by distant tectonics related to the geotectonic evolution of the Tethyan and/or Atlantic basins (Dadlez 2001; cf. Lamarche *et al.* 2002). The present authors share this view. The low subsidence rate in areas outside the Mid-Polish Trough resulted in reduced thicknesses of the Jurassic sediments or the absence of some deposits, particularly those of Hettangian (Fig. 14.13), Sinemurian, Aalenian and Bajocian (Fig. 14.15) age. In addition to the slightly subordinate depocentre in the Kalisz area (Poprawa 1997), the extension of the marine or brackish marine facies to the NE, as far as the Kaliningrad region, Lithuania and even Latvia (Baltic Basin Syneclise) (Gareckij 1985; Feldman-Olszewska *et al.* 1998; Šimkevičius 1998; Pieńkowski 2004), is very conspicuous throughout the Jurassic (Fig. 14.13). Persistence of this northern 'Mazurian way', conducive to the expansion of basinal facies, was indicated by Wagner (1998) as 'Peribaltic Bay' (roughly corresponding to the Baltic Basin Syneclise) in the Late Permian, by Pieńkowski (2004) in Early Jurassic times and by Leszczyński (1998) for the Late Valanginian.

In Middle Jurassic times, conspicuous regressions of the sea from many regions of Germany and Scandinavia occurred as a result of significant tectonic events (including tectonic inversions) connected with opening of the Atlantic Ocean. In Aalenian and Bajocian times (Fig. 14.15), the Polish Basin became partly isolated from the basins of western Europe (Dadlez 1998*a*). Simultaneously, the connection with Tethys was opened to the SE through the East Carpathian Gate. The most important palaeotectonic element of the basin was the Mid-Polish Trough, which was characterized by marked subsidence compensated by sedimentation. The main area of subsidence at this time was in the Kutno Depression, located in the central part of the Mid-Polish Trough. In this area the complete lithological profile attains 1000 m in thickness. As in the Early Jurassic times, in the Middle Jurassic the boundaries of the Mid-Polish Trough are hardly controlled by synsedimentary faults. Only in some

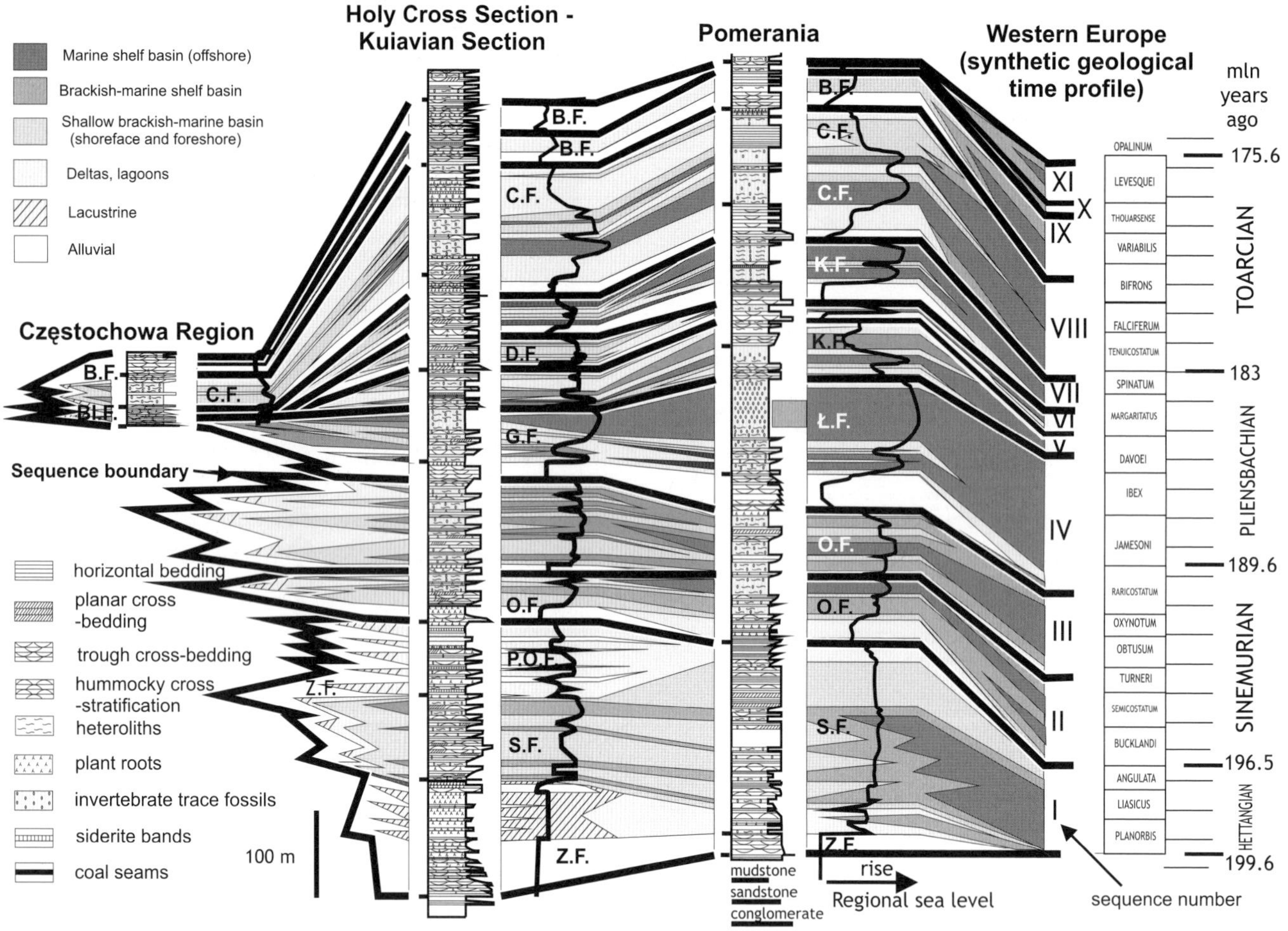


**Fig. 14.14.** Cross-section along and across the Early Jurassic basin in Poland (the cross-section line is shown in the Fig. 14.13). Note fluctuations in subsidence/sedimentation rate along the basin's axis marked by distance between sequence boundaries. Subsidence in the Mid-Polish Trough was highest in the Hettangian, while the maximum expansion of the basin occurred in the Early Pliensbachian and Early Toarcian, which is shown by the sedimentation encroaching on the Częstochowa region.

sections can one observe thickness contrasts showing the presence of tectonically active zones: e.g. the Koszalin–Chojnice Zone (Dadlez 2001) at the NW border of the Mid-Polish Trough, the Nowe Miasto-Iłża Fault (Hakenberg & Świdrowska 1998) in the Holy Cross Mountains segment, and the system of active extensional half-grabens separated the Kutno Depression (the Middle Jurassic depocentre) from the Wielkopolska Ridge in the middle part of the SW border of the Mid-Polish Trough. These zones became inactive at the beginning of the Bathonian times. The remaining sections of the Mid-Polish Trough are defined only by an increase of thickness from the marginal area of the craton towards the axis of the Mid-Polish Trough, with the simultaneous lack of Aalenian–Lower Bathonian sediments on the East European Platform (Fig. 14.15). This type of sedimentation was probably caused by the activity of deep-seated faults. Within the Mid-Polish Trough, the row of elongated salt structures parallel to its axis were activated in the Middle Jurassic (Dadlez 1998*b*). Salt movement is indicated by reduced sediment thicknesses and in places by the erosion of older deposits at the tops of salt-pillows.

In Late Jurassic times, the SE (peri-Carpathian) segment of the Polish Basin was strongly influenced by tectonic processes in the Tethys area (e.g. Ziegler *et al.* 1995; Golonka *et al.* 2000*a*; Kutek 2001; Poprawa *et al.* 2002). Therefore, its tectonic history is relatively complex. Some old crustal fractures (such as the Holy Cross Fault) became more conspicuous during the Late Jurassic. A series of analogue models was used to demonstrate the multistage development of the Mid-Polish Trough which was influenced by such oblique basement strike-slip faults (Gutowski & Koyi 2007). The Małopolska Massif, a generally positive structure, subsided in the Late Jurassic (Kutek 1994, 2001). The depocentre of the Polish Basin remained in the SE (peri-Carpathian) segment of the Mid-Polish Trough, where the Upper Jurassic deposits attain a maximum thickness of >1450 m (Niemczycka & Brochwicz-Lewiński 1988). Recently, evidence has been found of syndepositional activity along the NE margin of the Mid-Polish Trough in the Oxfordian and Kimmeridgian (Gutowski *et al.* 2003*a*,*b*). Analysis of the Late Jurassic palaeothickness patterns and depositional system architecture (Gutowski *et al.* 2005*a*) indicates that during the Oxfordian and Early Kimmeridgian the depocentre was located along the SW margin of the SE segment of the Mid-Polish Trough and propagated to the Lviv region (Western Ukraine) in the Tithonian–Early Berriasian. Simultaneously, the open shelf system (sponge megafacies) was replaced by shallow-marine sediments in central Poland not later than the earliest Kimmeridgian, whereas huge sponge–microbial buildups developed in the Lviv region through to the Early Berriasian. A carbonate ramp system overstepped onto older Jurassic sediments or even directly onto Palaeozoic basement in more proximal parts of the basin in the western Ukraine.

*Stratigraphy, facies, depositional architecture and sequence stratigraphy*

**Lower Jurassic.** Lower Jurassic sediments developed as an epicontinental association of siliciclastic, terrigenous deposits. They comprise sandstones, mudstones and shales/claystones with thin, subordinate intercalations of siderite, lignite and rare dolomites or limestones. The maximum thickness of the Early Jurassic deposits in the Polish Basin is >1300 m in the Kutno sub-basin (depression) of the Mid-Polish Trough (Feldman-Olszewska 1997*a*, 1998*b*) and thins out to 0 m to the NE, SW and SE (Fig. 14.13). These strata represent the Kamienna Group, which is subdivided into 12 formations (Pieńkowski 2004) (Fig. 14.14).

*Lower Hettangian.* The Zagaje Fm comprises conglomerates in its lowermost part and sandstones, mudstones and coals in the upper part. The depositional systems are alluvial and lacustrine (Fig. 14.13). However, outside of the Mid-Polish Trough this formation may also be of Middle–Upper Hettangian, Sinemurian or younger age (Fig. 14.14). In the Mid-Polish Trough the Zagaje Fm also includes some underlying Rhaetian-age sediments.

*Middle Hettangian* (in Pomerania, also upper part of Lower Hettangian and Upper Hettangian). The Skłoby Fm (Mid-Polish Trough, Fore-Sudetic Monocline) consists of heteroliths (understood herein as a mixed mudstone–sandstone lithology with lenticular, wavy and flaser bedding) and sandstones. Depositional environments include brackish-marine, nearshore, deltaic and barrier-lagoon.

*Upper Hettangian.* The Przysucha Ore-Bearing Fm (restricted to the Holy Cross Section area) comprises mudstones with siderites, heteroliths and sandstones. Dominating environments include barrier-lagoon and deltaic.

*Sinemurian.* The Ostrowiec Fm consists of heteroliths and sandstones representing brackish-marine, nearshore, deltaic, fluvial, barrier-lagoon environments; in the Pomeranian section of the Mid-Polish Trough it comprises also some intercalations of marine heteroliths.

*Lower Pliensbachian.* The Łobez Fm is restricted to Pomerania and comprises marine mudstones and heteroliths. The Gielniów Fm is developed in the Mid-Polish Trough except for Pomerania and in the Fore-Sudetic Monocline, and consists of heteroliths, sandstones, mudstones representing brackish-marine to marine, nearshore, deltaic, barrier-lagoon environments. Both the Łobez and Gielniów formations represent the maximum marine influences observed in the Early Jurassic deposits in Poland (Figs. 14.13, 14.14).

*Upper Pliensbachian.* The Komorowo Fm is developed in Pomerania and consists of sandstones, heteroliths and mudstones deposited in deltaic and alluvial environments; in the central part of the Pomeranian section of the Mid-Polish Trough deposition was also in the nearshore–marine environment. The coeval Drzewica Fm is developed in the Mid-Polish Trough, except for Pomerania, and consists of sandstones and heteroliths deposited in brackish-marine, nearshore, deltaic and alluvial environment.

*Pliensbachian* (in general). The Blanowice Fm is distinguished only in the Częstochowa area and consists of sandstones, mudstones and coals deposited in alluvial, lacustrine and deltaic environments. The coeval Olsztyn Fm is distinguished only in the Baltic Basin Syneclise area and is represented by sandstones deposited in a fluvial environment. In the eastern part of Poland (in the area of Lublin) fluvial sandstones, preserved in river palaeovalleys that cut down into Carboniferous strata, contain floral remains suggesting a Pliensbachian–Toarcian age for these sediments (Szydeł & Szydeł 1981).

*Lower Toarcian.* The Ciechocinek Fm, occurring throughout the entire area of the Early Jurassic epicontinental basin of Poland, is composed of characteristic greenish or grey mudstones and heteroliths, subordinately sandstones, deposited in a large brackish-marine embayment or lagoon fringed by a deltaic environment. In the middle part of this formation one can observe sandstones of deltaic, barrier or alluvial origin representing a conspicuous shallowing event observed in the whole basin. This shallowing event was not connected with a sea-level fall, but most probably with the enhanced continental weathering and sediment supply, which can be linked with the Early Toarcian Anoxic Event and associated environmental perturbations (Hesselbo *et al.* 2007). The Early Jurassic basin in Poland and more eastern countries reached its maximum extent in the Early Toarcian, although marine influences were not as strong as in the Early Pliensbachian.

*Upper Toarcian.* The Borucice Fm occurs in the entire epicontinental basin of Poland and is composed of sandstones deposited in a fluvial, subordinately deltaic environment. This formation represents a final infilling stage in the Early Jurassic Polish basin, preceding a long period of erosion/non-depositional between the Early and Mid-Jurassic epochs.

The results of successive studies have allowed the establishment of a stratigraphic framework both between the local regions in the Polish Basin and in geological time. Of particular value were ammonite records, but thus far these have only been reported from the West Pomerania region and only from the Pliensbachian deposits (Kopik 1962, 1964; Dadlez & Kopik 1972; Kopik & Marcinkiewicz 1997). Four standard biochronozones have been distinguished: *jamesoni* (with *Polymorphus*, *Brevispinum* and *Jamesoni* subzones), *Ibex* (with *Valdani* and *Luridum* subzones), *Margaritatus* (no subzones specified) and *Spinatum* (*Apyrenum* Subzone). It is worth mentioning that the *Ibex* biochronozone is the most complete, documented by the most numerous and diversified ammonites and it shows the most extensive spatial range (Dadlez & Kopik 1972).

Additionally, finds of dinoflagellate cysts, such as the *Luehndea spinosa* (Morgenroth) (Barski & Leonowicz 2002) define the stratigraphic position between, inclusively, the *Margaritatus* Zone (Late Pliensbachian) and the *Tenuicostatum* Zone (Early Toarcian). Other dinoflagellate cysts are also reported: *Dapcodinium priscum* was noted in the Hettangian strata and cysts of the *Liasidium*, *Mendicodinium* and *Nannoceratopsis* genera were reported from several horizons of the Early Jurassic deposits in Poland. In continental and marginal-marine deposits the main stratigraphic indices are megaspores (Marcinkiewicz 1971, 1988). Marcinkiewicz (1988) proposed three megaspore assemblages (*Nathorstisporites hopliticus* assemblage, *Horstisporites planatus* assemblage and *Paxillitriletes phyllicus* assemblage), dividing the Early Jurassic into three megaspore zones (Hettangian–Early Sinemurian, Late Sinemurian–Pliensbachian and Toarcian, respectively). These assemblages are characterized by a predominance of one or two species, with the simultaneous presence of other megaspores in smaller numbers.

Miospores (bisaccate pollen and spores) are of regional stratigraphic significance, particularly in the Hettangian–Sinemurian strata (Lund 1977; Dybkjaer 1988, 1991; Waksmundzka 1998; Ziaja 1991, 2001). Occurrences of the pollen species *Pinuspollenites minimus* accompanied by *Concavispor-*

*ites toralis*, *Concavisporites divisitorus*, *Trachysporites asper*, *Dictyophyllidites mortoni* and *Zebrasporites interscriptus* indicate a Hettangian age (Lund 1977; Dybkjaer 1988, 1991; *Pinuspollenites–Trachysporites* Zone). The regular presence of the spore species *Lycopodiumsporites semimuris* suggests an Early Sinemurian age (younger than Hettangian) within the *Nathorstisporites hopliticus* Zone (Lund 1977; Dybkjaer 1988; 1991; Pieńkowski & Waksmundzka 2002; – *Cerebropollenites macroverrucosus* Zone). Another miospore which has a well-established stratigraphic significance is *Aratrisporites minimus* (Schulz 1967; Rogalska 1976; Karaszewski 1974; Ziaja 1991; 2001) which occurs in the Hettangian–Early Sinemurian deposits. Miospores are of less stratigraphic significance in strata younger than the Early Sinemurian.

Bivalve fossils in the epicontinental Lower Jurassic of Poland have been recorded from marine, brackish-marine and continental deposits (Karaszewski & Kopik 1970; Dadlez & Kopik 1972; Kopik & Marcinkiewicz 1997; Kopik 1988, 1998; Pieńkowski 2004). Only a few forms of stratigraphical significance have been reported. The earliest forms, of some disputable stratigraphic value, are represented by *Cardiinidae–Cardinia follini* and *Cardinia ingelensis*, assigned by Troedsson (1951) to Lias alpha 1 and alpha 2 (Hettangian). Another form of possible stratigraphic significance is *Tancredia erdmanni*, an endemic form reported from the Sinemurian deposits of Scania (Kopik 1962), as well as other forms such as *Cardinia phillea* d'Orbigny, *Pleuromya forchhammeri* Lund, *Nuculana (Dactryomya) zieteni*, and *Pronoella* cf. *elongata* (Pliensbachian). Some bivalves may be tentatively used as auxiliary stratigraphic tools, but their greatest significance is in palaeoenvironmental interpretation.

Foraminifera are also generally of poor stratigraphic significance, but they provide valuable palaeoenvironmental information (Kopik 1960, 1964; Jurkiewicz 1967; Karaszewski & Kopik 1970; Dadlez & Kopik 1972). The rich foraminifera assemblage from the marine deposits of Early Pliensbachian age from Pomerania is dominated by Nodosariidae (Kopik 1988). Primitive agglutinating forms are indicative of the penetration of the inland basin by marine transgressions (Kopik 1988).

Finds of well-preserved floristic macrofossils are scattered, except for very common plant roots, providing excellent palaeoenvironmental indicators. Their biostratigraphical significance is of lesser importance. The same applies to the rich and diversified ichnofauna, both invertebrate (Pieńkowski 1985) and dinosaur footprints (Gierliński 1991; Gierliński & Pieńkowski 1999; Gierliński *et al.* 2001, 2004).

Sedimentation in the shallow, epeiric Early Jurassic basin of Poland was particularly sensitive to changes in sea level (Figs. 14.13, 14.14). Analyses of accommodation space variations within regular progradational successions associated with highstand systems tracts, as well as analyses of sedimentary structures, indicate that the Early Jurassic basin in Poland was generally not deeper than some tens of metres (usually 10 to 20 m).

Sedimentation was influenced by a number of factors, including local subsidence and compaction, displacement of rock salt masses, sediment supply (for example the brief and widespread progradation of shallow facies observed in the Lower Toarcian), and tectonic activity. The Early Jurassic in Poland is characterized by generally weak to moderate synsedimentary tectonic activity. However, some local tectonic structures played more important roles (for example faults and grabens active in Pliensbachian times in Pomerania as well as the Nowe Miasto-Iłża Fault Zone in the Holy Cross area). Nevertheless, Early Jurassic sedimentation in the Polish Basin was mainly controlled by regional sea-level changes (Fig. 14.14).

Sequence stratigraphy studies in the Polish Basin (Pieńkowski 1991*a*, 2004) were aimed at both detailed sequence analysis based on depositional architecture and cyclicity in the rock record, and the construction of age models based on the correlation of key surfaces with super-regional sea-level charts (Haq *et al.* 1987, 1988; Hesselbo & Jenkyns 1998; de Graciansky *et al.* 1998*a*,*b*; Nielsen 2003). An internally consistent sequence stratigraphic scheme for Poland (with successions of sequences, systems tracts and parasequences) can be compared with fossiliferous marine sediments of the Ligurian Cycle of the United Kingdom and France (Hesselbo & Jenkyns 1998; de Graciansky *et al.* 1998*a*,*b*) (Fig. 14.14). In the Polish Basin, lowstand (LST) and falling stage systems tracts (FSST) correspond with erosion/non-deposition stages at the sequence boundaries. Transgressive systems tracts (TSTs) prevail in the sedimentary record and are represented either by retrogradational or aggradational facies architecture, and highstand systems tracts (HSTs) are represented by progradational facies architecture. The beginning of each TST is associated with alluvial sediments (in the depocentre of the basin; near the axis of the Mid-Polish Trough alluvial sediments may be replaced with deltaic or marsh sediments). Correlative significance of transgressive surfaces and maximum flooding surfaces is enhanced when they are coupled with their non-marine correlative surfaces. Ten of the Exxon Early Jurassic depositional sequences were identified in the Polish Lower Jurassic and are labelled I–X, although the two uppermost ones from Poland (IX and X – Late Toarcian) are often amalgamated and difficult to differentiate. The regional cross-sections and cross-sections for the entire Polish basin showing dominant depositional systems and sequence stratigraphic correlation, as well as 'time-tuned' palaeogeographical maps of the Polish basin in the Early Jurassic, are presented in Fig. 14.13.

Major sea-level falls in the Polish Basin (shrinking phases of the basin), associated with large-scale (second order) cycles of Haq *et al.* (1987) and Hesselbo & Jenkyns (1998), are identified with the following stages (Pieńkowski 2004): (1) erosional Triassic/Jurassic boundary (base of sequence I); (2) latest Hettangian (latest *Angulata* Zone, base of sequence II); (3) late Sinemurian (latest Turneri–early *Obtusum* Zone, base of sequence III); (4) latest Sinemurian (mid-*Raricostatum* Zone, base of sequence IV); (5) late Early Pliensbachian (earliest *Davoei* Zone, base of sequence V); (6) earliest Late Pliensbachian (transition latest *Davoei* Zone–earliest *Margaritatus* Zone, base of sequence VI); (7) mid-Late Pliensbachian (late *Margaritatus* Zone, base of sequence VII); (8) latest Pliensbachian (late *Spinatum* Zone, base of sequence VIII); (9) mid-Toarcian (late *Bifrons*–early *Variabilis* Zone, base of sequence IX); (10) late Toarcian (mid-*Thouarsense* Zone, base of sequence X); (11) latest Toarcian (late *Levesquei* Zone–erosional Lower–Middle Jurassic boundary).

On the other hand, maximum sea-level stages, associated with expanding phases of the Polish Basin and maximum range of the marine/brackish-marine facies occurred in: (1) Mid-Hettangian (mid-*Liasicus* Zone); (2) Early Sinemurian (mid-*Semicostatum* Zone); (3) mid-Late Sinemurian (early *Oxynotum* Zone); (4) Early Pliensbachian (late *Ibex* Zone) (Fig. 14.13); (5) Late Pliensbachian (early *Spinatum* Zone); (6) Early Toarcian (depending on the region, *Tenuicostatum* or *Falciferum* Zone) with a progradation/shallowing event in the middle, correlated with the Oceanic Anoxic Event; and (7) enhanced continental weathering/sediment supply, not with sea-level fall; (8) Middle Toarcian (disputable, mid-*Variabilis* Zone).

Poland-wide comparison of sequence boundaries shows that the erosional boundaries of depositional sequences I , II, VI and

IX are particularly conspicuous and, additionally, lower boundaries of sequences I and VI are characterized by the deepest erosion. The lower boundary of sequence I also marks a very important Triassic–Jurassic boundary. The initial sedimentation of coarse alluvial sediments of sequence I (except for western Pomerania, where erosion was much less, and finer-grained sediments marked the onset of Jurassic sedimentation) shows a broad lateral extent in Poland, producing a particularly conspicuous super-regional bounding surface. Similar conditions control the lower boundary of sequence VI. Within the continental deposits at the basin margins (usually beyond the Mid-Polish Trough), the lower boundaries of depositional sequences I, II, VII and IX are also associated with conspicuous erosion, which could remove part (or all) of the previously deposited sediments in the marginal parts of the basin. Pronounced and rapid sea-level changes observed in the Upper Pleinsbachian may have been linked with glaciations (Price 1999; Morard *et al.* 2003; Rosales *et al.* 2004). Marine or brackish-marine transgressions invaded the Polish basin from the NW and west (Fig. 14.13). Episodic connections with the Tethys remain hypothetical due to the lack of sediments, although the presence of marine influences in the Holy Cross Section (Hettangian) and in the region of Częstochowa (Lower Pliensbachian and Lower Toarcian) makes such a supposition probable. Episodic connections with the Tethys might have occurred particularly during the periods of maximum sea level (Fig. 14.13). Such connections might have been significant for biota migrations between the Tethys and the CEBS, and for additional migrations (Van de Schootbrugge *et al.* 2005). For example, the Middle Hettangian maximum flooding event might have provided a migration path for the dinoflagellate cyst *Liasidium variabile*, which appeared earlier in the German Basin (Brenner 1986) and in the Polish Basin (Pieńkowski 2004) than in the rest of the Central European Basin (Van de Schootbrugge *et al.* 2005).

Generally, Pliensbachian and Toarcian Lower Jurassic formations in Poland correspond to the (?)continental Jotvingiai Group in the Kaliningrad Region and Lithuania (Gareckij 1985; Feldman-Olszewska *et al.* 1998; Šimkevičius 1998). The occurrence of marginal-marine sediments in the Baltic Basin area (Bartoszyce IG-1 borehole), corresponding to the Early Pliensbachian transgression, as well as the discovery of a crucial erosional sequence boundary in this borehole (the lower boundary of sequence VI, marked also by the different sandstone provenance separating Lower from Upper Pliensbachian; Pieńkowski 2004), allow the existing stratigraphical scheme to be modified.

Consequently, the Olsztyn Fm would represent both the Lower and Middle Pliensbachian. The same would apply to the sandy Neringa Fm of the Kaliningrad region and Lithuania, possibly including the lowermost, sandy part of the superimposed Lava Fm, which shows a similar lithology but different spore/pollen ratio (Šimkevičius 1998). The upper part of the Lava Fm, dominated by argillaceous sediments, would correspond to the Ciechocinek Fm (Lower Toarcian), while Upper Toarcian sediments are probably missing in the Baltic Basin.

Lower Jurassic deposits do not occur in Belarus (Mitianina 1978; Gareckij 1985). The presence of Lower Jurassic deposits in SE Poland and in the Ukraine has been reported from the Carpathian Foredeep (foreland basin). In SE Poland (Księżpol–Lubaczów area), possible Lower Jurassic sandstones, mudstones and conglomerates have been described by Moryc (2004). These sediments may have been deposited in the SE extension of the Mid-Polish Trough. In the Ukrainian part of the Carpathian Foredeep (Drohobycz region), the thickness of the terrigenous Lower Jurassic varies from 200 to *c.* 2000 m (Dulub *et al.* 2003). Such differences in thickness are interpreted in terms of synsedimentary tectonics and possibly extensional basin formation. The local stratigraphy is provisional and partly based on palynomorph finds. The Lower Jurassic succession is divided into four informal lithostratigraphical units (called 'series'), conventionally assigned to: Hettangian (mudstones/siltstones with quartzitic sandstones–Komarnivska series, up to 560 m thick); Sinemurian (dominated by mudstones, locally sandstones–Bortiatinska series, up to 290 m thick); Pliensbachian (mudstones, in lower part sandstones, in upper part intercalations of limestones and anhydrites – Podolecka series, up to 580 m thick); and Toarcian (sandstones, mudstones, in places limestones and coals – Medienicka series, up to 580 m thick). The Medienicka series is erosive at the base and covers a broader area than the underlying Komarnivska, Bortiatinska and Podolecka series. The Medienicka series is also eroded of the top and this is associated with a prominent erosional event at the base of the Middle Jurassic. In the Podolecka and Medienicka series, the presence of the marine bivalves *Nucula amygdaloides*, *'Inoceramus' ambiguus*, *Meleagrinella ptchelincevalle* and *Posidonia dagestanica* is indicative of transgressions (Dulub *et al.* 2003). The Ukrainian Fore-Carpathian Basin was not connected with the Polish Basin but was temporarily connected with Tethys (Dulub *et al.* 2003).

**Middle Jurassic.** Information on the Middle Jurassic of the epicontinental Polish Basin has been derived from a series of several hundred deep boreholes, and exposures existing in the area of the Polish Jura Chain. The most important synthesis works are those by Daniec (1970), Dayczak-Calikowska (1976, 1977*a*,*b*, 1979, 1987), Deczkowski (1977), Kopik (1979, 1998), Maliszewska (1998, 1999), Moryc (2004) and Ryll (1983). The northernmost and southeastern parts of the Polish Basin overlap the areas of Lithuania and the Kaliningrad Region (Russia) (Šimkevičius 1998), Western Belarus (Mitianina 1978), Ukraine (Dulub *et al.* 2003) and Moldova (Gareckij 1985).

Middle Jurassic sediments in the epicontinental basin of Poland, the Kaliningrad region of Russia, Lithuania and west Ukraine were developed mostly as siliciclastic, terrigenous deposits (Aalenian–Bathonian) and to a lesser extent as carbonate/siliciclastic deposits (Middle/Upper Bathonian–Callovian) (Fig. 14.16). The maximum thickness of the Middle Jurassic deposits in the Polish Basin exceeds 1000 m in the depocentre of the Mid-Polish Trough (Kujavian Region; Fig. 14.16) (Dayczak-Calikowska & Moryc 1988; Feldman-Olszewska 1998*b*). In areas outside of the Mid-Polish Trough, sedimentation was disrupted by many non-depositional and/or erosional periods related to sea-level falls. The rise of global sea-level led to transgressions which resulted in the deposition of thin sedimentary covers. The total thickness of the Middle Jurassic deposits in this zone does not exceed 300 m (average *c.* 150 m) (Dayczak-Calikowska & Moryc 1988; Feldman-Olszewska 1998*b*,*c*). In the marginal parts of the basin (Kaliningrad region of Russia and south Lithuania), continental and brackish sediments of Bajocian and Bathonian age occur only in tectonic depressions in the Curonian and North Gusev–Kybartai areas. Only the Callovian deposits covered most of the area (Šimkevičius 1998; Feldman-Olszewska *et al.* 1998). Callovian sedimentation also occurred in the area of western Belarus and in the area of the Pripyat-Dnieper Basin providing a connection with the Polish and Russian basins (Gareckij 1985).

In the Ukraine, Middle Jurassic deposits occur in the Lviv Depression, which constitutes the southeasternmost extension of the Mid-Polish Trough. Here the thickness of the sediments

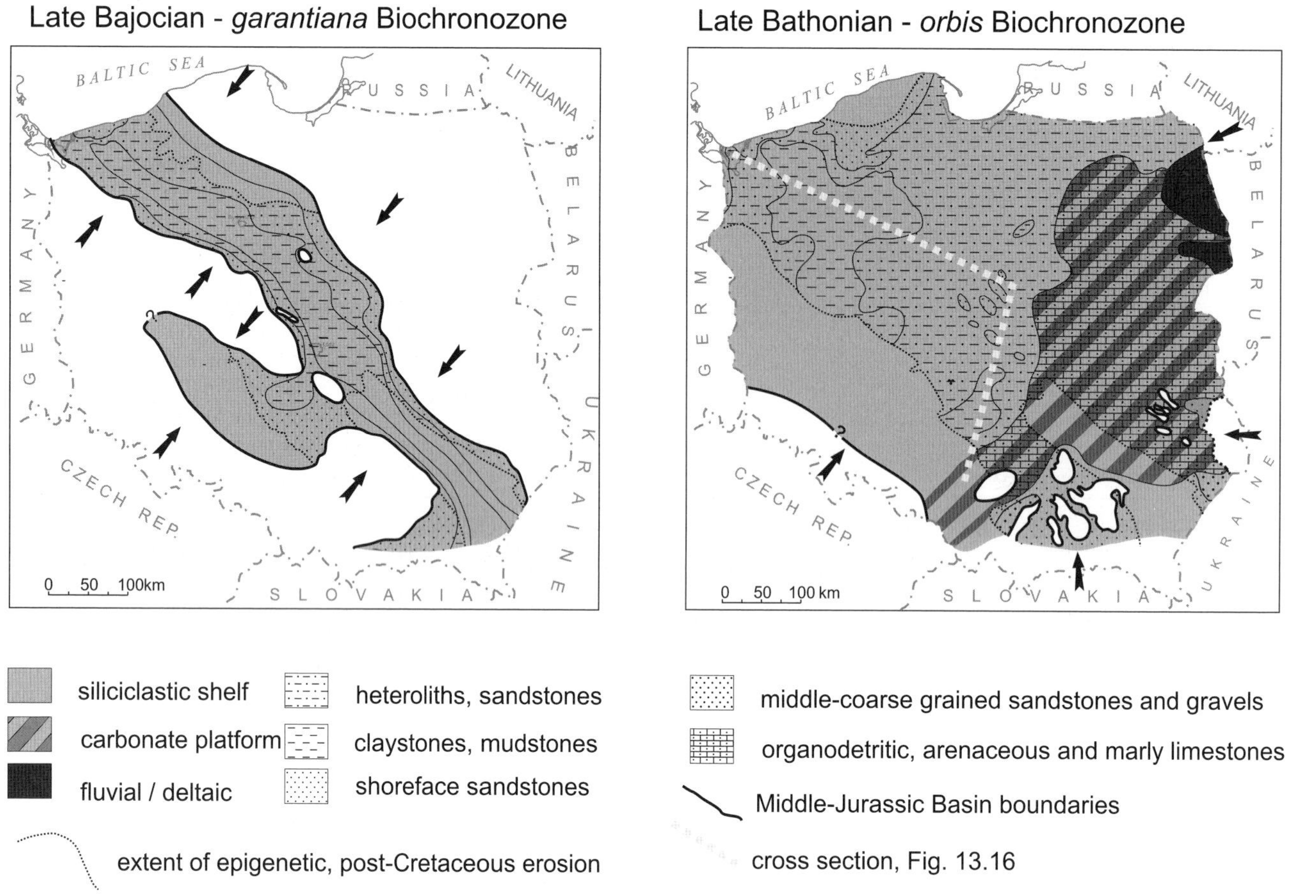


**Fig. 14.15.** Palaeogeographic maps showing two stages of the Middle Jurassic basin development in Poland: expansion phase in Late Bathonian (*orbis* Biochronozone) and shrinking phase in Late Bajocian (*garantiana* Biochronozone).

exceeds 600 m. The Callovian deposits show a retrogradational backstepping to the NE; however Callovian deposits do not cross the edge of the East European Platform (Dulub *et al.* 2003). In Moldova (Dobrudza Foredeep) over 1000 m of Middle Jurassic age sediments have been documented. The lithofacies and tectonic history of the area suggest a relationship between the Ukrainian and Moldovian parts of the basin (Gareckij 1985).

The Middle Jurassic deposits of the Polish Lowland lack formal lithostratigraphical division. Some lithostratigraphic units were informally distinguished in the Polish Jura Chain by Kopik (1998).

The depositional architecture of the Middle Jurassic basin in Poland has been discussed by Feldman-Olszewska (1997*b*, 1998*a*). The most recent study (Feldman-Olszewska 2006) specified, or changed, interpretations of some of the Middle Jurassic successions in the central part of the basin. Middle Jurassic deposits of Lithuania, Belarus, Ukraine and Moldova were studied by Gareckij (1985), Šimkevičius (1998) and Dulub *et al.* (2003).

*Lower Aalenian.* Sandstones with subordinate intercalations of mudstones, and in places carbonaceous detritus, occur. The main depositional systems are estuary/foreshore, and in the NW part of the basin, alluvial. Lower Aalenian deposits are only present in the Mid-Polish Trough. In the western Ukraine they form the lower part of the Kohanivska Formation.

*Upper Aalenian.* Black, organic-rich claystones with pyrite, pyritized flora detritus and marly-sideritic concretions occur; mudstones and sandstones occur in marginal parts of the basin. The basin was restricted and dysoxic/anoxic although, in the NW part of the basin, shoreface to alluvial environments occur. These deposits are found only in the Mid-Polish Trough (including western Ukraine, lower part of the Kohanivska Formation)

*Lower Bajocian.* At this time the basin showed a considerable facies differentiation. In the central and southeastern part of the Mid-Polish Trough (including western Ukraine, lower part of the Kohanivska Formation), claystones, heteroliths and in the upper part sandstones predominated. The main depositional systems are dysoxic shelf to lower/middle shoreface. In Pomerania mudstones, heteroliths, sandstones, sandstones with chamosite occur, and in the northwesternmost parts of the basin, sandstones with carbonaceous detritus and thin coal intercalations occur. The dominant depositional systems are shoreface to alluvial. In the northeastern margin of the Upper Silesian Coal Basin (Kościelisko Beds), fine- to coarse-grained sandstones with kaolinite, carbonaceous detritus, siderite, rare chamosite and intercalations of mudstones occur mainly in shoreface/foreshore depositional systems. In the tectonic depressions of the Kaliningrad region of Russia and Lithuania (lower part of the Įsrutis Formation), coaly sandstones and mudstones occur; depositional systems include swamps, lakes, alluvial.

*Upper Bajocian* (Fig. 14.15). Deposits occur in the lower part of the so-called Ore-Bearing Clay Formation in the Polish Lowland (beyond the East European Platform), in the Polish Jura Chain and the northeastern margin of the Upper Silesian Coal

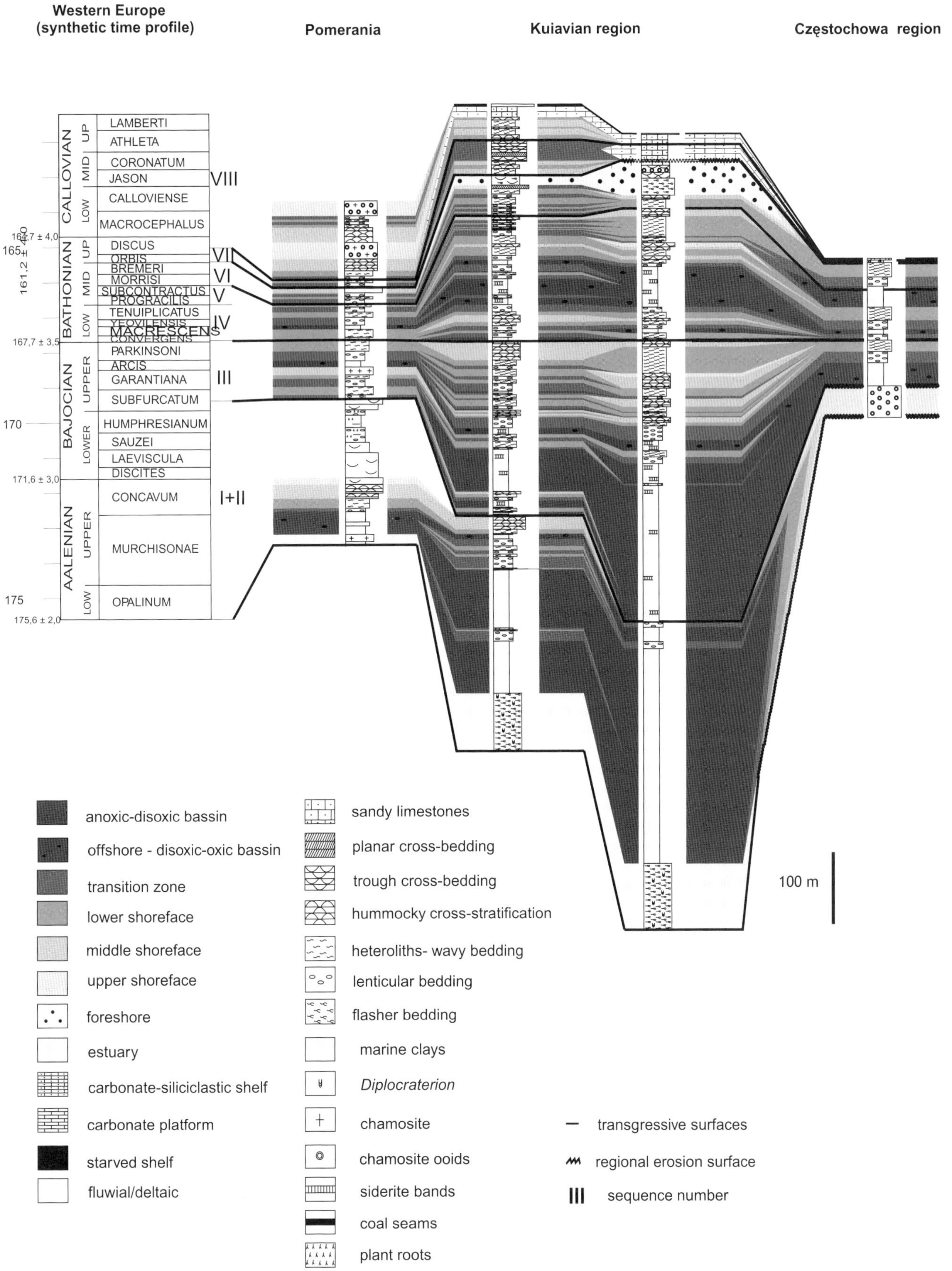


**Fig. 14.16.** Cross-section along and across the Middle Jurassic basin in Poland (the cross-section line is shown in Fig. 14.15).

Basin, as well as part of the Kohanivska Formation in western Ukraine and Moldavia. The predominant lithology is black claystones and mudstones with sideritic concretions and several siderite ore levels. Along the marginal part of the basin (including tectonic depressions in the Kaliningrad region and Lithuania, middle part of the Įsrutis Formation) and in the uppermost part of the Bajocian succession of the Polish Lowland, heteroliths and sandstones (with chamosite in the NE part of the Dobrudza Fordeep in Moldavia) occur. The main depositional systems are offshore to lower/middle shoreface, with subordinate upper shoreface to alluvial settings and in the Kaliningrad Region and Lithuania, swamps and lakes.

*Lower Bathonian.* Black claystones and mudstones with sideritic concretions and several ore levels occur. In the marginal parts of the basin and in the tectonic depressions of the Kaliningrad region and Lithuania (upper part of the Įsrutis Formation) heteroliths, sandstones with carbonaceous detritus and ferruginous oolites are found. The depositional systems include upper offshore, transitional, lower shoreface; in the marginal parts of the basin, shoreface/foreshore; in the Kaliningrad region and Lithuania, alluvial, lake, and swamp. The mian occurrences of lower Bathonian deposits is in the Mid-Polish Trough, the western part of the Polish Lowlands, western Ukraine and Moldova.

*Middle Bathonian.* Sandstones, and rarer heteroliths and mudstones (in Pomerania, with chamosite; in the East-European Platform, with carbonaceous detritus) are the main lithologies present. In the southeastern part of the basin, arenaceous limestones and gaizes (dispersed biogenic silica in a carbonate matrix) with ferruginous oolites occur. The depositional systems are lower-upper shoreface, foreshore and alluvial. In the southwestern part of the Polish Basin (Polish Jura Chain, northeastern part of the Upper Silesian Coal Basin and the Gorzów Block) claystones with coquina beds, sideritic concretions and thin ore levels occur. The depositional systems are upper offshore–transition zone–lower shoreface. Middle Bathonian deposits occur in the entire epicontinental basin of Poland and western Ukraine.

*Upper Bathonian* (Fig. 14.15). Claystones and mudstones (dominating in the western part of the Polish Basin and Polish Jura Chain), sandstones heteroliths (in the central and northern part of the Polish Basin), sandstones with chamosite and ferruginous oolites (western part of the Peribaltic Basin), dolomites, arenaceous limestones, gaizes, crinoidal limestones and mudstones occur. In eastern and southeastern parts of the Polish Basin ferruginous oolites are also present. Depositional systems range from upper offshore in the west to upper shoreface/foreshore/lagoons in the east and north. Upper Bathonian deposits occur in the entire Polish Basin in the Kaliningrad region and in Lithuania (Liepona Formation) and western Ukraine (upper part of the Kohanivska Formation).

*Lower Callovian.* Sandstones, dolomites, limestones, marls and heteroliths occur, and often contain glauconite, chlorite, cherts or ferruginous oolites. The depositional system was the shoreface zone of a carbonate-siliciclastic shelf. Lower Callovian deposits occur in the Mid-Polish Trough, Polish Jura Chain, western Ukraine (Javoriv Formation) and probably in northern Lithuania.

*Middle and Upper Callovian.* In the western part of the Polish Basin claystones and mudstones, with pyrite, pyritized flora detritus and marly-sideritic concretions, associated with chloritic sandstones and ferruginous oolites occur. In the central, southern and northeastern parts of the Polish Basin are condensed marls and nodular limestones with basal conglomerates, a rich fauna, including stromatolites (the so-called 'nodular bed') occur. In the eastern part of the basin conglomerates and crinoidal limestones are present. In the Kaliningrad region, Lithuania and western Belarus calcareous sands, sandstones (often with ferruginous oolites) limestones, marls, siltstones and clays are found. In Ukraine and the Moldovan foredeeps sandstones, heteroliths, dolomites and limestones, in places with ferruginous oolites or chamosite occur. The depositional systems were a deep carbonate-siliciclastic shelf in the western part of the Polish Basin, a starved basin in the central part, and a shallow carbonate-siliciclastic shelf and carbonate ramp in the eastern and southeastern part of the basin (eastern Poland, Lithuania, Belarus, Ukraine). The Middle and Upper Callovian deposits occur across the entire Polish epicontinental basin the Kaliningrad region and Lithuania (Papartine and Skinija formations), the western part of the Pripyat'-Dneper Basin in Belarus, western Ukraine (Javoriv Formation) and Moldova.

Much of the Middle Jurassic in the Polish Basin is well documented in terms of biostratigraphy, since deposits contain rich ammonite and foraminiferal faunas, supplemented by less numerous ostracods and spores (Dayczak-Calikowska 1977*b*; Kopik *et al.* 1997; Feldman-Olszewska 1997*b*; Kopik 1998; Matyja & Wierzbowski 2000*b*; Moryc 2004). Initial studies on dinoflagellate cysts were published by Poulsen (1998) and Barski *et al.* (2004).

Only in the Mid-Polish Trough are all the Middle Jurassic biochronozones stratigraphically documented by ammonites. In Aalenian–Lower Bajocian deposits diagnostic ammonites occur only in the central and southern parts of the basin, whereas the Bathonian and Callovian biochronozones have the most complete stratigraphic evidence in northwestern Poland. Outside of the Mid-Polish Trough one can observe smaller or greater stratigraphical gaps, and ammonite fauna mark the transgressive intervals only.

In Lithuania and the Kaliningrad region of Russia ammonites occur only in the Middle and Upper Callovian sediments (Šimkevičius 1998). In Ukraine and Moldova, Upper Bajocian, Bathonian and Callovian ammonites (Gareckij 1985; Dulub *et al.* 2003) have been found. These ammonites are similar to those occurring in the southeastern part of the Mid-Polish Trough (Moryc 2004). As yet, no standard ammonite zones have been distinguished in Ukraine and Moldova.

Despite the more abundant ammonite fauna and the more precise stratigraphical framework, the Middle Jurassic sequence stratigraphic scheme in Poland is still tentative due to the less precise sedimentological studies. Detailed studies have only been carried out in the central part of the Mid-Polish Trough (Feldman-Olszewska 2006) and a stratigraphic scheme has been proposed. For other areas of Poland some correlative surfaces (maxima of transgressions and regressions) can be distinguished (Fig. 14.16, 14.17) (see also palaeogeographical maps in Feldman-Olszewska 1998*a*).

The first Middle Jurassic transgression entered the area of the Polish Lowland in the Aalenian. In the central and southern parts of the Mid-Polish Trough the Aalenian deposits lie concordantly on Upper Toarcian alluvial sediments. It is not clear whether this transgression occurred in the *Opalinum* Zone, or in the Upper Aalenian. As noted, the lowest part of the Middle Jurassic succession encompasses estuarine/foreshore sediments which contain only Aalenian age foraminifera. The first ammonites indicating the *Murchisonae* Zone appear higher up in the profile. A short-lived and inconspicuous sea-level fall occurred in the *Murchisonae* Zone. This sea-level fall can probably be correlated with a maximum regression marked in this zone by Hallam (1988).

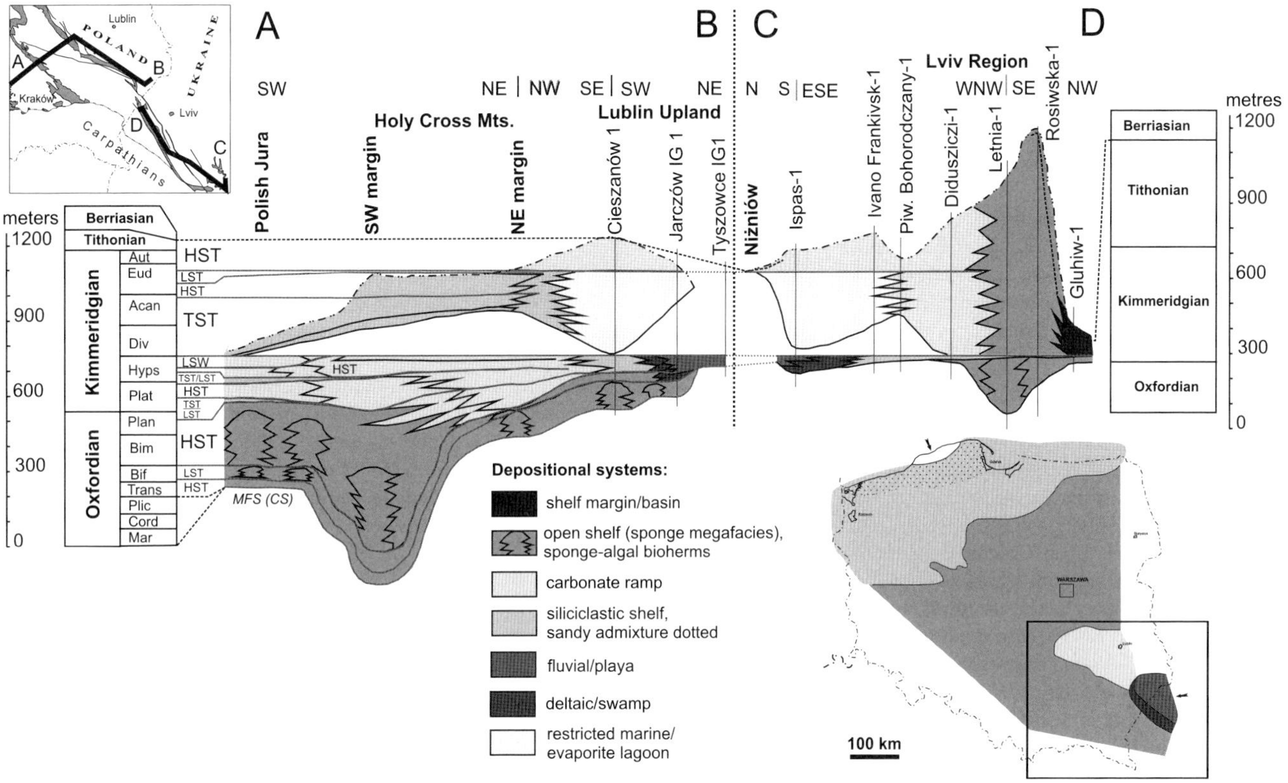


**Fig. 14.17.** Upper Jurassic sedimentation in Poland and western Ukraine: idealized cross-sections through the Late Jurassic epicontinental sedimentary basin of the SE margin of the East European Platform in SE Poland and western Ukraine (after Gutowski *et al.* 2005*a*), along the lines indicated in the sub-Cenozoic geological sketch map (upper left corner); flattened at tops of the sedimentary megasequences discussed in text (*Hypselocyclum* and *Divisum* zones boundary of the Early Kimmeridgian and mid-Eudoxus Zone of the Late Kimmeridgian). Sub-Mediterranean ammonite zones: Mar, *Mariae*; Cord, *Cordatum*; Plic, *Plicatilis*; Trans, *Transversarium*; Bif, *Bifurcatus*; Bim, *Bimammatum*; Plan, *Planula*; Plat, *Platynota*; Hyps, *Hypselocyclum*; Div, *Divisum*; Acan, *Acanthicum*; Eud, *Eudoxus*; Aut, *Autissiodorensis*. System tracts: HST, highstand; LST, lowstand; MFS (CS), maximum flooding surface (condensed section); TST, transgressive. Palaeographic map of Poland (lower right corner) presents approximately the end of the Middle Oxfordian *Transversarium* Chron (in the NW part modified after Gaździcka (1998), depositional systems marked as on the cross-section.

The areal extent of the second Middle Jurassic transgression was also limited to the Mid-Polish Trough area and commenced in Upper Aalenian times (*Murchisonae* or *Concavum* Zone). Maximum flooding probably occurred in the *Sauzei* Zone or the lowest part of the *Humphresianum* Zone (the *Romani* Subzone). At this time the sea covered the area of the Mid-Polish Trough and the western part of the Polish Basin (northeastern margin of Upper Silesia, the Gorzów Block and the Szczecin Trough) while some areas remained exposed (e.g. Wielkopolska Ridge). A stratigraphic gap, encompassing the *Subfurcatum* Zone, has been noted in the NE margin of Upper Silesia (Kopik 1998). Furthermore, lithological changes (from fine to coarse sediment) in the central part of the Polish Basin suggest a sea-level fall at this time. The second Middle Jurassic sedimentary cycle of the Polish Basin cannot be correlated with any of Haq *et al.*'s (1988) cycles but the maximum and minimum sea level can easily be correlated with Hallam's (1988) eustatic curve (Fig. 14.18).

The subsequent transgression began in the *Garantiana* Zone and was of similar magnitude to the previous one. The maximum flooding surface would correspond to the beginning of the *Parkinsoni* Zone. Subsequently, the sea retreated from the Gorzów Block and Szczecin Trough and a coarse (sandstone) facies was deposited in the centre of the Polish Basin, which is connected with a sea-level fall at the end of the *Parkinsoni* Zone (the *Bomfordi* Subzone) and the beginning of the *Convergens* Zone. The stratigraphic range of this third sedimentary cycle does not fit to the curve presented by Haq *et al.* (1987, 1988).

The fourth transgression was of much wider extent than the previous ones. Besides the Mid-Polish Trough, the sea covered the southwestern part of the Polish Basin and for the first time encroached over the edge of the East European Platform. Abundant ammonite fauna indicate that this transgression is of middle-late *Convergens* Zone age. The following maximum flooding surface is dated at the end of the *Macrescens* Zone. The part of the cycle between the transgressive surface and the maximum flooding surface (TST) would correspond to cycle LZA-2.2 of Haq *et al.* (1987, 1988).

The overlying regressive deposits cannot be dated precisely due to the poverty of ammonite fauna. Ammonites occur mainly in the Polish Jura Chain where the Upper Bajocian and almost all Bathonian deposits are developed in the ore-bearing clay facies. Single ammonite finds from the central part of the Polish Basin suggest that shallowing of the sea followed presumably to the end of the *Tenuiplicatus* Zone.

The minor fifth sedimentary cycle follows, with a TST probably embracing the *Progracilis* Zone, while regression would be dated at the *Subcontractus* Zone. The lack of ammonite fauna does not allow precise dating. The age of the sea-level fall would correspond to the shelf margin wedge (SMW) of cycle LZA-2.2 (Haq *et al.* 1987, 1988).

The sixth transgressive phase began in the *Morissi* Zone, while

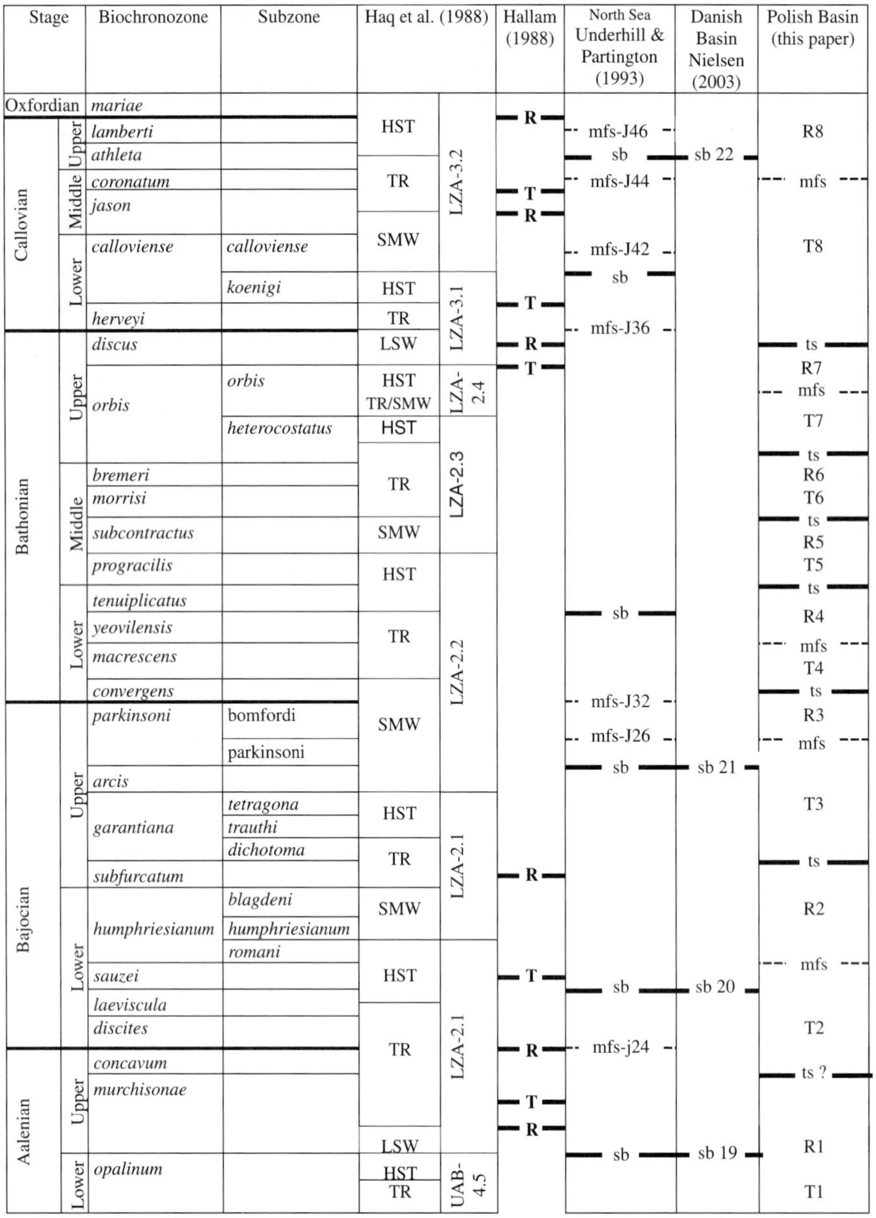


**Fig. 14.18.** Comparison of the Middle Jurassic sequence stratigraphy surfaces from the Polish Basin and other parts of the Fennoscandian Border Zone. Abbreviations: HST, highstand systems tract; LSW, lowstand wedge; SMW, shelf margin wedge; TR, transgressive deposits. **R**, minimum sea level; **T**, maximum sea level; mfs, maximum flooding surface; sb, sequence boundary; R, regression; T, transgression.

the regressive phase was connected with the *Bremeri* Zone or the beginning of the *Orbis* Zone. It is evidenced by the occurrence of one ammonite, *Eohecticoceras discoangulatum* Tsereteli, and dinoflagellate cysts. The regressive phase would correspond to the stratigraphic gap embracing probably the upper part of the *Bremeri* Zone and the *Heterocostatus* Subzone of the *Orbis* Zone, which was confirmed for the Szczecin Trough and the Gorzów Block area. The entire sixth cycle would then correspond to the transgressive deposits (TR) of cycle LZA-2.3 of Haq *et al.* (1987, 1988).

The seventh transgression had a very wide range. During the *Orbis* Zone, the sea covered extensive areas of the Polish part of the East European Platform. The regressive part of this cycle corresponds to the sea-level fall marked on the curve presented by Hallam (1988).

The final Middle Jurassic transgression commenced during the *Discus* Zone; however, the sea did not cover the East-European Platform extensively before the *Calloviense* Zone. In consequence of a considerable rise in sea level, for the first time the Polish and Russian basins were periodically connected through the Pripyat Dneper Basin (Gareckij 1985; Thierry 2000). The similarity of ammonite fauna between Russian and Belarus-Lithuanian basins tends to support a hypothesis of such periodic connections (Gareckij 1985). It is very difficult to indicate the maximum flooding surface, because the Middle and Upper Callovian deposits in most of the Polish Basin are strongly condensed and developed as a nodular bed, several to tens of centimetres thick, which spans four ammonite biochronozones (*Jason–Lamberti* Zone) (Dayczak-Calikowska & Moryc 1988; Feldman-Olszewka 1998*a*). Condensed Middle Callovian deposits extend to westernmost Belarus, where about 2 m of nodular dolomitic limestones occur, which are covered with 2 m of sandy-oolithic marls with foraminiferal fauna of Upper Callovian age (Mitianina 1978). The arrangement of facies in the western part of the Polish Basin (Pomerania), where the profile is more complete (Dayczak-Calikowska 1977*b*), suggests that the maximum deepening of the sea occurred in the *Coronatum* Zone. This cycle continues into Oxfordian times. The last Middle Jurassic cycle of the Polish Basin correlates with cycles LZA-3.1 and LZA-3.2 of Haq *et al.* (1987, 1988) and with two cycles marked by Hallam (1988) approximately at the same time (Fig. 14.18).

**Upper Jurassic.** During the Late Jurassic, the Polish Basin was mainly filled by clastic sediments in the NW segment of the Mid-Polish Trough and in its NE branch ('Mazurian Way', Baltic Basin), as well as in Belarus, Lithuania and Latvia (Pożaryski & Brochwicz-Lewiński 1978; Kutek *et al.* 1984; Dadlez *et al.* 1995; Kutek 2001). In the central and SE (peri-Carpathian) segments, extending from central Poland to western Ukraine, carbonate sedimentation predominated. During the Late Jurassic the SE segment of the Mid-Polish Trough was part of the European shelf adjacent to the south to the Tethys Ocean. Seven Late Jurassic depositional systems have been recognized in the Polish and Ukrainian margin of the East European Platform (Gutowski *et al.* 2005*a*).

(1) A shelf slope/basin depositional system has been identified to date only in the Ukrainian part of the basin. It is represented by the Karolina and Moranci formations (Zhabina & Anikeeva 2002) and consists of dark, often bituminous shales, biomicrites and mudstones which contain abundant planktonic fauna, mainly calpionellids and radiolarians (Linetskaya & Lozyniak 1983; Dulub *et al.* 2003).

(2) An open shelf system (sponge megafacies) is defined, according to Matyja & Pisera (1991) as carbonates and marls, both bedded and biohermal, containing numerous siliceous sponges. The system was characterized by the high relief of the sea bottom, with elevations of about 200 m. This uneven relief was caused by microbial-sponge bioherm buildups (Matyja *et al.* 1992; Matyja & Wierzbowski 1996). The system was extensive along the northern Tethyan shelf in Europe and is commonly interpreted as having been deposited during exceptional sea-level highstands, with water depths of *c.* 400 m on the shelf.

(3) A carbonate ramp system developed in central Poland (Kutek *et al.* 1984) and was formed by prograding shallow-marine carbonates such as oolites, oncolites and various bioclastic and biogenic limestones (Kutek 1969; Gutowski 1998, 2004*a,b*). The carbonate ramp system can be divided into three subsystems: (3.1) An external carbonate ramp characterized mainly by oncomicrites, biomicrites, micritic limestones and marls with abundant benthic fauna, often preserved in life position and/or creating patch reefs or biostromes. The faunal assemblages consist mainly of nerineids, corals, diceratids, rynchonellids, terebratulids, myids and oysters; (3.2) Oolitic barriers composed of large-scale cross-bedded oolitic/bioclastic grainstones; and (3.3) Protected lagoons and tidal flats, with laminites and lithographic-type limestones. Rhizoid, tee-pee and fenestral structures and also aggregations of coalified flora, including large cycadacean tree trunks, indicate an extremely shallow, foreshore or tidal flat environment with subaerial conditions (Gutowski 1998, 2004*b*).

(4) A siliciclastic shelf system is characterized by marls and clays usually intercalated with oyster shellbeds. These deposits contain coquina beds, mainly of storm origin, which are widely distributed in central and NW Poland (Kutek 1994; Kutek *et al.* 1984; Gutowski 1998).

(5) A fluvial/playa system is present in the upper part of the Sokal Formation, western Ukraine (Slavin & Dobrynina 1958; Zhabina & Anikeeva 2002; Dulub *et al.* 2003) and the Tyszowce Formation in the SE Lublin Upland (Niemczycka 1976*b*). This system is characterized by red, brown, yellow, green and grey sandstones, mudstones and conglomerates, usually arranged in fining-upward cycles. The sedimentary environment was continental (Niemczycka 1976*a,b*; Zhabina & Anikeeva 2002). In the upper part of the succession evaporites (e.g. anhydrites and gypsum), probably deposited in alkaline lakes, are intercalated.

(6) A deltaic/swamp system is present in the lower part of the Sokal Formation (Slavin & Dobrynina 1958; Zhabina & Anikeeva 2002; Dulub *et al.* 2003) and the Jarczów Formation (Niemczycka 1976*b*). More distal parts of the Sokal and Tyszowce formations include marine intercalations of dolomitic marls and dolomites (Gutowski *et al.* 2005*a*). The system comprises mudstones with abundant coalified flora and thin coal intercalations. Rhizoidal structures were observed (Niemczycka 1976*b*). The sediments were deposited in swamps and lagoons (Niemczycka 1976*a,b*; Zhabina & Anikeeva 2002). According to Gutowski *et al.* (2005*a*), these sediments may be, at least partly, deltaic in origin due to their palaeogeographic setting in the transitional zone between the fluvial and marine systems. Thus, this system would be coeval with the fluvial/playa system, and represent a more humid environment.

(7) A restricted marine/evaporite lagoon system consists of anhydrites and dolomites of the Rawa Ruska (Dulub *et al.* 2003) and Ruda Lubycka formations (Niemczycka 1976*b*). These sediments were deposited in restricted marine or lagoon conditions (Niemczycka 1976*a,b*).

The area of Central and SE Poland and western Ukraine formed part of the northern Tethyan shelf during the Late Jurassic. Early Oxfordian sedimentation began with carbonates of the open shelf sponge megafacies (Matyja 1977; Matyja & Pisera 1991; Gutowski 1998; Matyja & Wierzbowski 1995; Izotova & Popadyuk 1996). In western Belarus, the Lower Oxfordian is represented by limestones of sublittoral to littoral origin. They show progressively shallowing facies and decreasing thickness eastward (Mitianina 1978). Successively, from Middle Oxfordian times, the more proximal parts of the Polish Basin were divided into two different facies regions with completely different sedimentation histories: the western one in the Holy Cross Mountains and the western Lublin Upland of Poland, dominated by marine carbonates and marls, and the eastern one in the SE Lublin Upland and the Lviv area of Ukraine, where clastic continental/deltaic facies and restricted marine evaporites prevailed. A shallow-marine carbonate ramp prograded from the western Lublin Upland to the NE margin of the Holy Cross area in the latest *transversarium* Chron of the Middle Oxfordian (Gutowski 1998), and then, during the Latest Oxfordian–Early Kimmeridgian onto the SW margin of the Holy Cross area and on to the Nida Depression (Matyja *et al.* 1989). This carbonate ramp was submerged at the turn of *hypselocyclum* and *divisum* chrones of the Early Kimmeridgian (Kutek 1994; Gutowski 1998; Gutowski *et al.* 2005*a*) and was overlain by oyster shellbeds and marls deposited in more open marine conditions. The top of the succession in the Holy Cross Mountains is clearly erosional and the Albian–Cenomanian transgressive sandstones directly overlie even the Lower Kimmeridgian, (*Divisum* Zone strata) in places (Gutowski 1998). Younger Upper Jurassic sediments, including Upper Kimmeridgian and Volgian units (see Zeiss (2003) for details of the correlation of the Volgian and

Tithonian–Berriasian) are preserved in the NW margin of the Holy Cross Mountains and further to the NW (Kutek 1994; Kutek & Zeiss 1994).

The Upper Jurassic succession of the NW part of the Mid-Polish Trough, the Baltic Basin and adjacent areas of the East European Platform in Poland, Lithuania and Latvia is covered by younger sediments, except for some outcrops in Lithuania. However, the Jurassic succession has been recognized in hundreds of boreholes (Dadlez 1976, 1988; Dąbrowska 1970; Dembowska 1973, 1976, 1979*a*,*b*; Dembowska & Marek 1975; Šimkievicius 1985; Niemczycka & Brochwicz-Lewiński 1988). Early Oxfordian sedimentation commenced with carbonates of the sponge megafacies. Subsequently, in Late Oxfordian times, sedimentation changed to marls, mudstones and clays deposited on a siliciclastic-carbonate shallower shelf. Deepening of the basin in the Late Kimmeridgian and Early and Middle Volgian (Tithonian) resulted in deposition of claystones containing a rich ammonite fauna (Pałuki Formation), which represent a deeper shelf setting. Finally, anhydrites, carbonates and other Purbeck-type sediments of the Kcynia Formation were deposited in the narrow and restricted basin of the Late Volgian (Tithonian). The Upper Jurassic sediments have been recognized in the area of SE Poland (SE Lublin Upland) and West Ukraine (Lviv region) in several boreholes (Izotova & Popadyuk 1996) and in a few exposures in the region of Niżniów on the Dnister river, west Ukraine (Alth 1881; Gutowski *et al.* 2005*b*). In the western Ukraine, clastic facies prograded from NE to SW and south over the sponge carbonates and formed a correlative multicoloured horizon (Izotova & Popadyuk 1996). This multicoloured horizon was overlain by a series of dolomites and anhydrites in the proximal, NE part of the basin, whereas the carbonates of the sponge megafacies, including huge bioherm buidups, developed above the horizon in more distal parts of the basin.

A sequence stratigraphic scheme for the Upper Jurassic succession in SE Poland and western Ukraine has recently been proposed by Gutowski *et al.* (2005*a*). Studies of depositional architecture within a biostratigraphical framework have distinguished three megasequences which resulted from relative sea-level changes. Their boundaries (identified with sea-level falls) have been dated biostratigraphically in central Poland as follows: Lower Kimmeridgian *Divisum–Hypselocyclum* zone boundary, uppermost Upper Kimmeridgian and Lower Berriasian. Analysis of thicknesses and depositional system distributions within these sequences indicates that the depocentre was located in the SW margin of the peri-Carpathian segment of the Mid-Polish Trough during the Oxfordian and Early Kimmeridgian, and propagated in Tithonian times to the Lviv region (western Ukraine). The thickness pattern of the sequences, as well as proximity trends of the system tracts within the sequences, clearly coincides with depocentre propagation. These observations suggest that formation of the sequences was strictly associated with relative sea-level changes resulting from super-regional tectonic events, possibly related to oscillation of the Tethyan continental margin due to alternation of interplate stresses according to the model of Cloethingh (1986). Kutek (1994) suggested that this mechanism was the controlling factor of Late Jurassic tectonic events in SE epicontinental Poland. Although the proposed mechanism definitely did not have a global effect, its fairly isochronous results can be observed widely in sedimentary basins of epicontinental Europe adjacent to the Tethyan shelf. For example, the distinct extensional event in the Late Oxfordian *bimammatum* Chron that resulted in transgression and enhanced thickness in the SE segment of the Mid-Polish Trough coincides with similar events in the Swiss Jura Mountains (see Allenbach 2002, fig. 15). This event corresponds strictly with the mixing and sudden invasions of ammonite fauna from different bioprovinces of Europe during the *bimammatum* Chron, which is connected with a major relative sea-level rise (Matyja & Wierzbowski 1995). Another widespread event associated with sea-level fall has been observed at the turn of the Early Kimmeridgian *Hypselocyclum* and *Divisum* Zone (Matyja & Wierzbowski 2000*a*). This can be correlated with the sequence boundary and tectonic event marking the beginning of the depocentre shift towards the Lviv region. Correlation of the recognized depositional sequences with the global standard sea-level curves of Haq *et al.* (1987) and Hallam (1988) would be misleading when done in a simple, direct way because there are several difficulties and misunderstandings in the correlation of the sub-Mediterranean ammonite zonal scheme used as a standard and the sub-Boreal/Boreal zonal schemes used (e.g. Matyja & Wierzbowski 1995; Zeiss 2003). Moreover, a clear tectonic cause of the Late Jurassic sequences and events suggests rejection of a global paradigm as a standard for interpreting the sedimentary cyclicity observed in the SE segment of the Mid-Polish Trough (Gutowski *et al.* 2005*a*).

## *Eastern Paris Basin (B.L.)*

Geological maps and sections were first compiled for the Paris Basin in the eighteenth century (Pomerol 1989). During the second half of the twentieth century, the interest of oil companies led to the gathering of a large amount of well data (Mascle *et al.* 1994). Consequently, publications on the basin are especially numerous, and several useful syntheses were published in the 1980s. Mégnien *et al.* (1980) provided a general overview of the basin (stratigraphy, palaeogeography), whereas Enay & Mangold (1980) produced facies maps at the substage level. In 1987, Cavelier & Lorenz completed these syntheses, and more recently Guillocheau *et al.* (2000) provided a sequence stratigraphic correlation of well logs in a geodynamic perspective.

Jurassic deposits mainly crop out in a large continuous belt extending from southern Belgium to southern Lorraine and connected to Burgundy and the Jura Mountains (Fig. 14.19). Additionally, more isolated outcrops occur on the edges of the Alsace Graben (i.e. Rhine Graben) and in two exhumed anticlinal folds (Bray and Boulonnais) situated at the western limit of the area. All of these separate outcrops have their origin in Cenozoic tectonics, although they originally formed part of the same Jurassic depositional basin. This section focuses mainly on the region of Lorraine.

The Paris Basin is interpreted as an intracratonic basin whose Cadomian–Variscan basement was affected by faults that controlled sedimentation during Jurassic times (Le Roux 1980, 1999, 2000). Major basement faults include: (1) the Vittel Fault separating the Morvan-Vosges Zone to the south from the Saxothuringian Zone to the north; (2) the Metz Fault separating the Saxothuringian Zone from the Rhenohercynian Zone; (3) the Bray-Bouchy Fault separating the Cadomian block from the Rhenohercynian Zone; (4) the Variscan Front, which defines the southern limit of the Anglo-Brabrant Massif; and (5) a series of faults orientated mainly north–south that cut and delimit the Central Armorican Zone, and are termed the Sennely, Loire, St Martin de Bossenay and Vermenton faults (Fig. 14.19).

Accommodation curves (Fig. 14.20) reveal a general subsidence trend varying from regular for the Lias, decreasing into the onset of the Dogger, and increasing up into the Oxfordian, and then decreasing thereafter. These rates correspond to second-order stratigraphic cycles which have been interpreted as being related to geodynamic events which affected the basin, such as

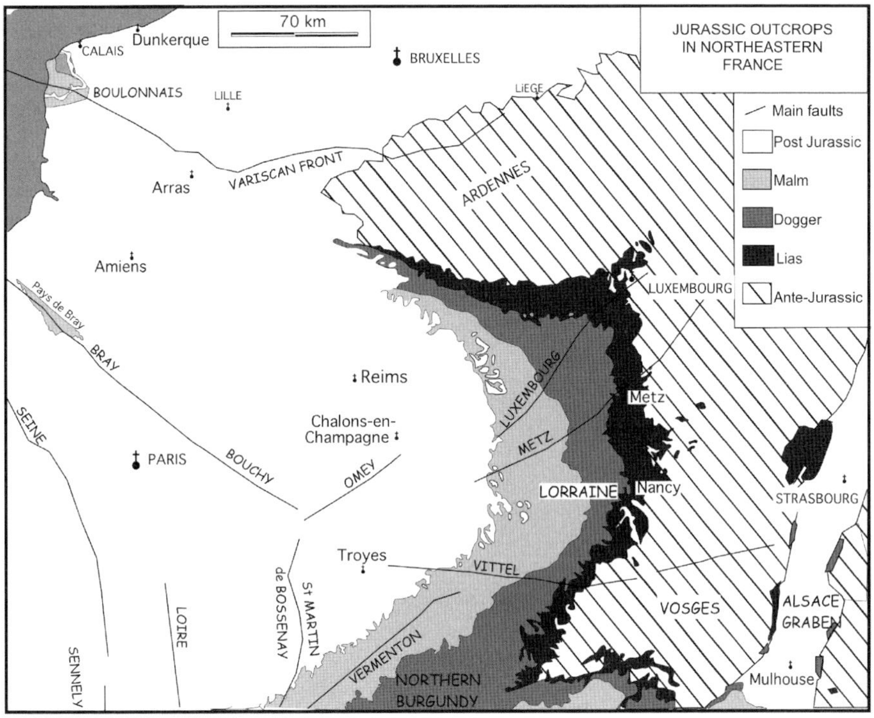


**Fig. 14.19.** The Jurassic of the eastern Paris Basin.

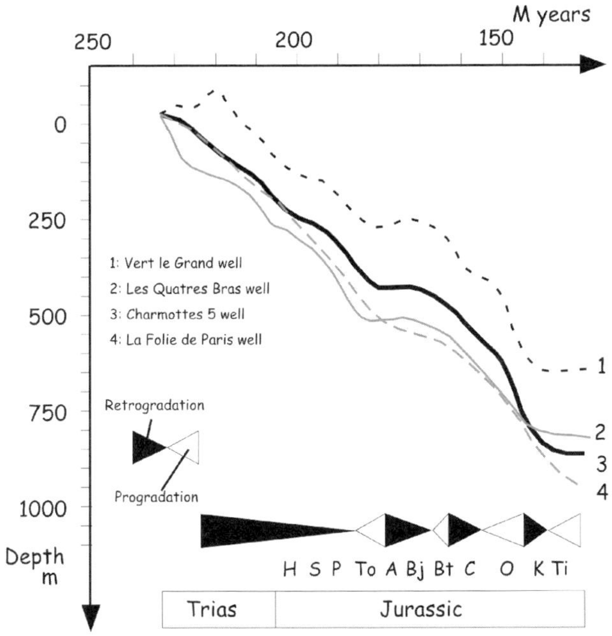


**Fig. 14.20.** Accommodation curves calculated from four wells of the Paris Basin (redrawn from Guillocheau *et al.* 2000).

Tethyan rifting during the Early Jurassic, doming in the North Sea and rifting of the central Atlantic in Middle Jurassic times, and rifting of the North Atlantic in Late Jurassic times. This general trend of subsidence varies according to the local structural situation. For instance, the Middle Oxfordian corresponds to a period of very high creation of accommodation space in Lorraine where it was compensated by the high carbonate production. In contrast, in Burgundy which was consistently a relatively elevated area (Rat 1987), the Middle Oxfordian is not represented by thick deposits. Within the basin local variations in subsidence and palaeobathymetry have been described in detail for Early Jurassic deposits by Robin (1997). Analyis of isopachs (and other) maps reveals the role of major faults in the differential subsidence rates (Fig. 14.21). Synsedimentary deformation has also been directly demonstrated (André 2003). Sections from the Boulonnais area reveal that accommodation space creation was particularly low along the margin of the Ardennes landmass (Thierry *et al.* 1996). This emergent area was a constant feature of the regional palaeogeography as demonstrated by the local recurrence of terrigenous sediments (quartz, clay, organic content) (Fig. 14.22). In contrast, there is no evidence of relief in the region of the Vosges Massif.

A summary of the outcropping lithostratigraphic units is presented in Fig. 14.23, including their probable age assignments relative to the biochronological framework provided by the Groupe Français d'études du Jurassique (Cariou & Hantzpergue 1997). The *Planula* Zone (the last Tethyan zone in the Oxfordian) and the *Hauffianum* Subzone have, however, been removed because of the (controversial) suggestion that they are equivalent to the *Baylei* Zone (the first Kimmeridgian Boreal zone) as indicated by Matyja & Wierzbowski (2003). Corresponding lithostratigraphic units do not contain ammonites. Due to the complexity of the scheme, some parts such as the Minette or Oxfordian have been simplified. The Oxfordian has recently been reviewed and subdivided at the formation and member levels (Carpentier 2004). Details of geometries and ages in sandstones of the Lower Lias around Luxembourg can be found in Müller (1987) together with an important bibliography. Northern and southern extremities of the region are not included because the present state of knowledge (Megnien *et al.* 1980) remains unsatisfactory in several aspects. Figure 14.24 is an illustration of a synthetic section from central Lorraine showing outcropping formations and their thicknesses.

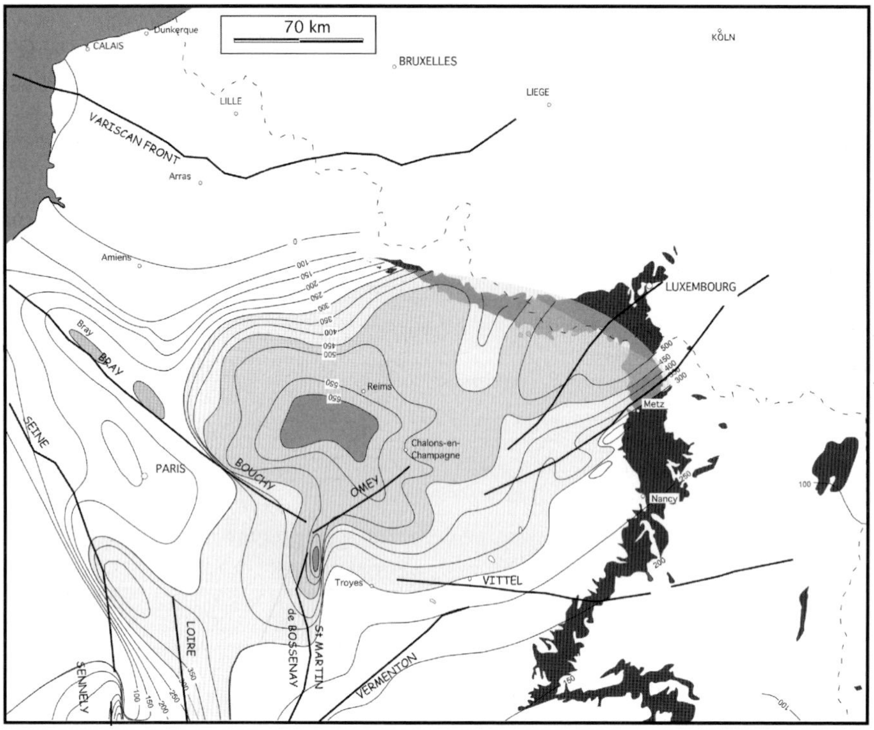


**Fig. 14.21.** Isopach of total Lias and main faults in the eastern Paris Basin (mainly redrawn from Lefavrais-Raymond *in* Megnien *et al.* 1980; Alsace data recalculated from Schmitt 1987).

*Unit boundaries*

In the eastern Paris Basin, the boundary between the Triassic and the Early Jurassic deposits is represented by a grey marly transitional bed (*c.* 30 cm thick) between argillaceous deposits of the Argiles de Levallois Formation and the first calcareous bed of the Calcaire à gryphées Formation, which contains a Hettangian ammonite (*Psiloceras psilonotum*). The Argiles de Levallois Formation is considered to be Triassic on the basis of its very poor fossil content: very rare *Myophoria*, *Euestheria minuta brodiena*, *Astacolus* sp, *Lingulina collenoti* and the ostracod *Hungarella* sp B (Durand *in* Megnien *et al.* 1980, vol. 103, p. 36 with references therein). Palynological studies (Hanzo *et al.* 1991; Rauscher *et al.* 1995) have placed the boundary between the Rhaetian and the Hettangian within the so-called 'zone de transition' or pre-*Planorbis* bed. Ammonites found in the marly transition bed are controversially considered as Schlotheimiids (Guérin-Franiatte & Müller 1978, 1986; Mouterde & Corna in Cariou & Hantzpergue 1997).

In the main outcropping eastern belt, the boundary between the Jurassic and the Cretaceous is an erosional surface. The youngest Jurassic deposits belongs to the Dolomites verdâtres supérieures Formation. The last known ammonites are from the *Gravesiana* Zone. In the centre of the basin the Tithonian is more complete (Ponsot 1994). In the eastern part of the basin, Jurassic strata would have been subjected to erosion throughout much of the Cretaceous (Le Roux & Harmand 2003). In Boulonnais, attributions to ammonite zones continue up to the *Kerberus* Zone (Geyssant *et al.* 1993; Deconinck *et al.* 1996). Marine and continental deposits (Purbeckian/Wealdian facies) terminate the Jurassic record. Rocks overlying the Jurassic–Cretaceous unconformity are dated as Valanginian (Megnien *et al.* 1980). In the Boulonnais, Deconinck *et al.* (2000) and Schnyder (2003) have recently interpreted some Purbeckian deposits as derived from a tsunami triggered by either an earthquake or the impact of a bolide in the Palaeo-Barents Sea.

*Sedimentation and sequence stratigraphic interpretation*

**Lower Jurassic.** Sedimention commenced with the deposition of alternating carbonates and marls in infralittoral to circalittoral conditions in the centre of the basin (Hanzo *et al.* 1994, 2000). Near the Ardennes Massif, sandstones of the Grès d'Hettange or Grès de Luxembourg were deposited in shallower mesotidal environments (Berners 1983; Mertens *et al.* 1983; Müller 1987). The younger part of the Early Jurassic succession is predominantly marly with some occurrences of carbonates and sandstones. It is interpreted as mainly circalittoral with shallower and more detritic environments close to the Ardennes Massif. The end of Early Jurassic sedimentation is marked by the deposition of iron oolitic sediments interpreted as subtidal sandwave complexes (Teyssen 1984; Guillocheau *et al.* 2002).

**Middle Jurassic.** The lowermost sediments comprise sandy marls that pass rapidly into carbonates which include bioclasts, ooids, oncoids and coral reefs. These sediments, and their bounding surfaces, correspond to infralittoral to emergent environments which were organized in several third order sequences. In the northern part of the basin, the production of quartz detritus continued. During Callovian times, marls once more predominate while iron oolitic sediments and condensed zones are also common, especially in the southern part of the basin (Collin *et al.* 2001, 2005; Collin & Courville 2006).

**Upper Jurassic.** Marly sediments are the oldest of the Upper Jurassic sediments. Subsequently a carbonate ramp and then a platform formed with extensive development of reefal and perireefal environments (Carpentier *et al.* 2007). The prograding trend continues on up to the Kimmeridgian when marly sediments with ammonites and oysters are deposited again in Lorraine. Finally, the Tithonian history is marked by the presence

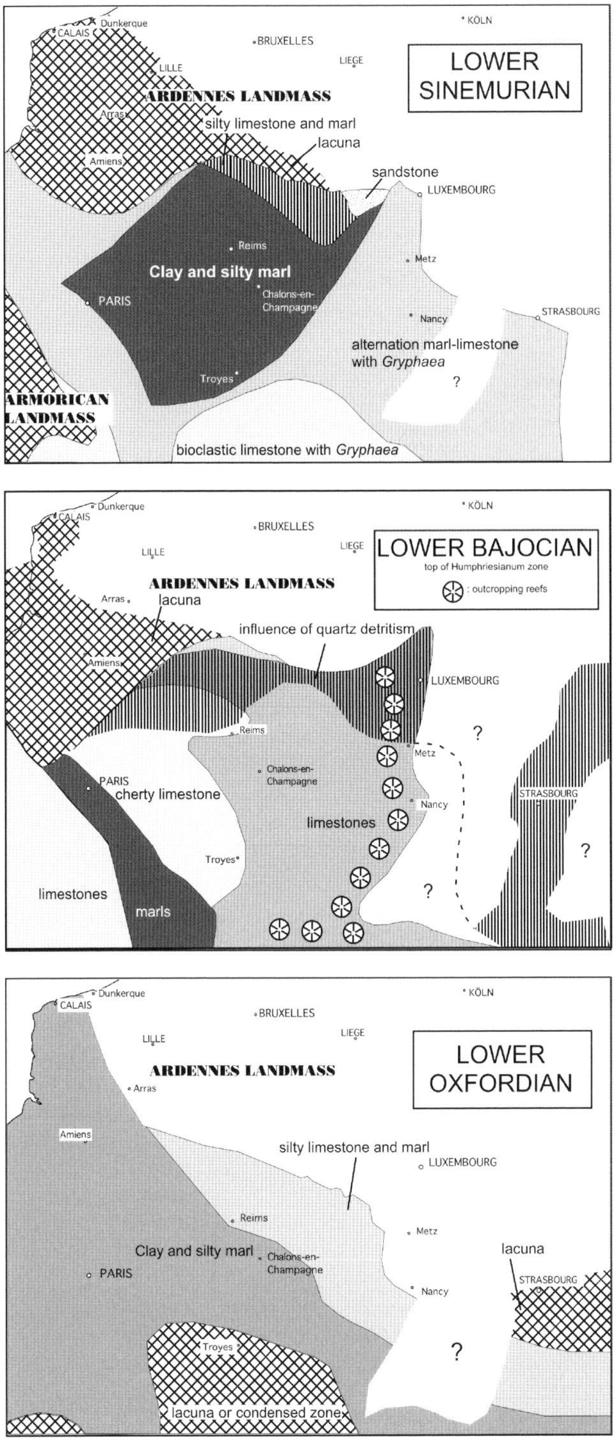


**Fig. 14.22.** Palaeogeography and facies of the eastern Paris Basin at three times during the Jurassic.

of carbonates and dolomites, providing evidence of the very shallow and sheltered environments.

*Sequence stratigraphy*

Sequence stratigraphic interpretations of the Jurassic of the Paris Basin have flourished since the initial paper of Vail *et al.* (1987). Cycles of various orders, of various schools, and based on various databases (outcrops, drilling cores, well logs, seismic profiles) are available: the most comprehensive interpretations are from Vail *et al.* (1987), Ponsot (1994), Jacquin *et al.* (1998), Guillocheau (1991) and Guillocheau *et al.* (2000). Despite the focus on Normandy and Dorset, the study of Rioult *et al.* (1991) is also worth noting. Early Jurassic studies include those of Hanzo *et al.* (1992), Hanzo & Espitalié (1994), Bessereau & Guillocheau (1994), de Graciansky *et al.* (1998*a*,*b*) and Robin (1997). Studies more focused on the Dogger are from Gaumet *et al.* (1996), Garcia *et al.* (1996), Garcia & Dromart (1997), Thiry-Bastien (1998, 2002) and Thierry *et al.* (1996). The Callovo-Oxfordian has also been the subject of some specialized theses (Collin 2000; Vincent 2001; Carpentier 2004) and some articles (Carpentier *et al.* 2007), whereas the Kimmeridgian and Tithonian have been the target of specialized studies mainly in the Boulonnais (Geyssant *et al.* 1993; Deconinck *et al.* 1996; Tribovillard *et al.* 2001).

According to the different interpretations, there is broad consensus with regard to the positions of the main sequence boundaries and the maximum flooding surfaces of second-order sequences (Fig. 14.24). Herein, we include a synthetic section of central Lorraine on which some cycles have been plotted with the help of biostratigraphy (Fig. 14.24). A first maximum flooding surface (MFS) is located in or near the Schistes carton Formation; the following sequence boundary (SB) is located nearby the Minette Formation. A second extensive MFS corresponds to the Oolithe à *Clypeus ploti* Formation (*Acris* Subzone, *Parkinsoni* Zone). The following SB is more controversial, but probably corresponds to the Bajocian–Bathonian boundary. A third MFS occurs at the beginning of the Oxfordian in the Argiles de la Woëvre Formation. The following SB is, however, controversial and most probably occurs close to the Middle–Upper Oxfordian boundary. The last MFS is placed within the organic facies of the Marnes à Exogyres supérieures Formation. Smaller cycles have also been proposed (Fig. 14.24) based on local studies. The correlation of third-order cycles based on biochronological grounds leads to considerable inconsistencies, and these remain a matter for both geological and epistemological discussions (see Miall & Miall 2001) and require additional work to achieve resolution.

*Palaeontology*

Palaeontological databases for the region are extensive, with the work being published in a series of monographs beginning in the nineteenth century. However, many groups are in need of systematic revision and many localities are not well known. Indirectly, the biostratigrahy of the eastern Paris Basin has benefited from the synthesis by Cariou & Hantzpergue (1997) and their numerous parallel scales. Additionally, a palynostratigraphic scale has been compiled for the entire Jurassic of Alsace (Schmitt 1987; Rauscher & Schmitt 1990).

**Lower Jurassic.** The deposits of the Lower Jurassic are generally well dated with ammonites at the subzonal or more precise levels in many cases. The ammonite zonal frame is well established and stable since the original synthesis published by Megnien *et al.* (1980), together with updates from Allouc & Guérin-Franiatte (1981), Colbach *et al.* (2003*a*,*b*), Guérin-Franiatte & Hanzo (1992), Guérin-Franiatte (1988, 1994, 2003), Guérin-Franiatte *et al.* (1983, 1991, 2000), Hanzo & Guérin-Franiatte (1985), and Hanzo *et al.* (1987). Foraminifers have been studied both in isolation (Ruget & Hanzo 1992) and in conjunction with ammonites (Guérin-Franiatte *et al.* 1983). For other organisms, there have been some advances in the study of Early Jurassic belemnites (Weis 1999; Weis & Delsate 2005),

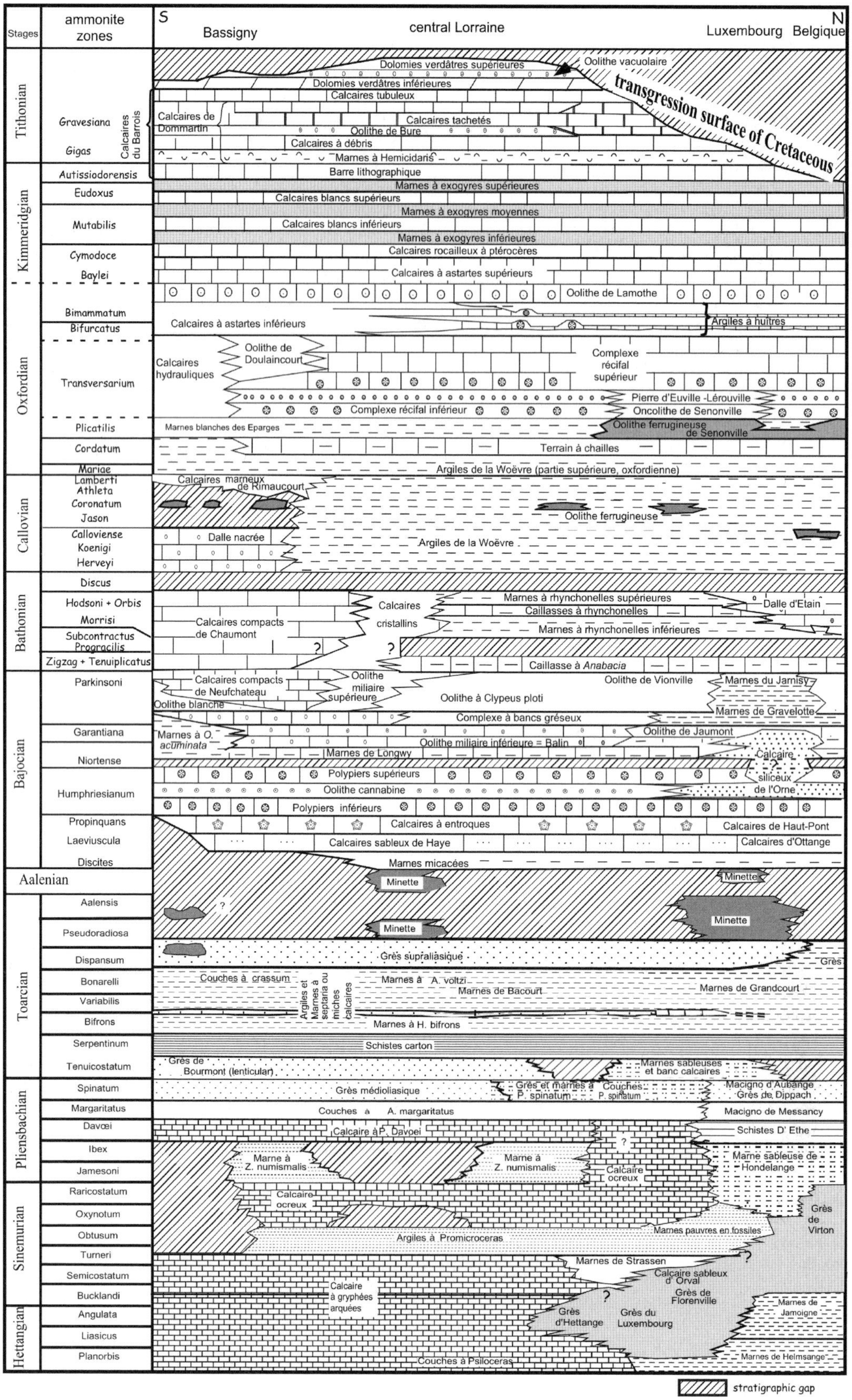


**Fig. 14.23.** Lithostratigraphic chart of the eastern Paris Basin. Because the outcrop belt is not rectilinear, a vertical cannot be precise in this schema.

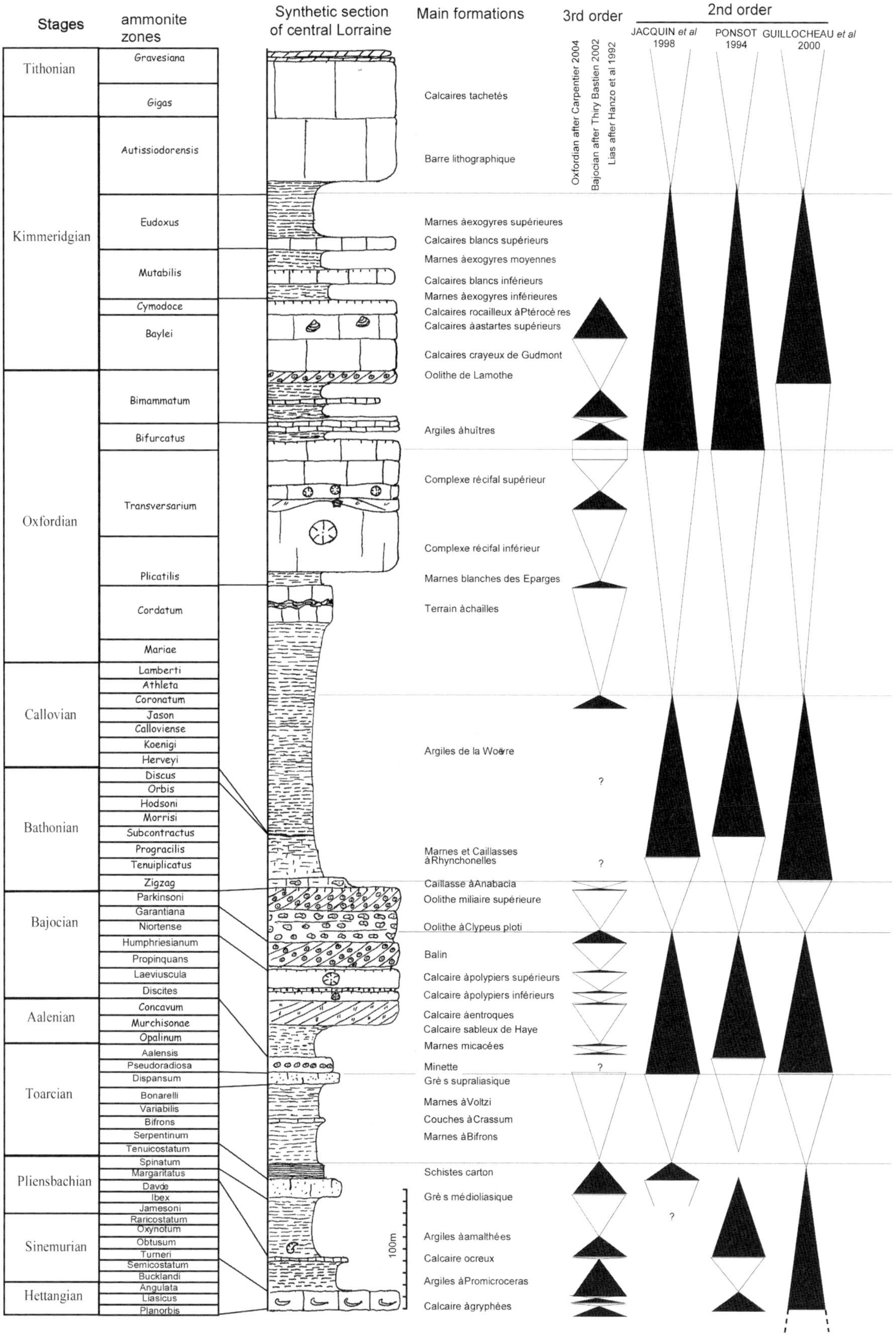


**Fig. 14.24.** Synthetic section of central Lorraine and sequence stratigraphic interpretation. The three second-order interpretations on the right hand are related to the local log by biostratigraphic correlation.

brachiopods (Almeras & Hanzo 1991), *Gryphaea* (Hary 1987; Nori & Lathuilière 2003), gastropods (Meier & Meiers 1988), ophiurids (Thuy 2005) and vertebrates (Delsate's 2007) or communities (Heinze 1991; Guérin-Franiatte *et al.* 1995; Hanzo *et al.* 2000; Faber & Weis 2005; Delsate & Thuy 2005).

**Middle Jurassic.** Deposits of Middle Jurassic age have yielded fewer ammonites due to the development of a shallow carbonate platform; nevertheless, the collection of new specimens has allowed the existing biostratigraphical framework to be modified (e.g. Poirot 1992; Mangold *et al.* 1995; Courville & Bonnot 1998; Courville *et al.* 1998, 2004; Courville & Cronier 2003, 2004*a*, 2005; Courville & Marchand 2003). In terms of carbonates, the taxonomy of the Bajocian corals was recently revised (Lathuilière 2000, and reference herein). A zonation based on dinoflagellate cysts has also been compiled (Huault 1999). More recently, the Boulonnais area has been analysed and the stratigraphy of the region is now better constrained (Vidier *et al.* 1993; Thierry *et al.* 1996; Courville & Cronier 2004*b*). Additional studies have focused on brachiopods (Garcia *et al.* 1996; Garcia & Dromart 1997), fossil wood (Garcia *et al.* 1998), echinoids (Vadet & Slovik 2001; Thuy 2003; Moyne *et al.* 2005), belemnites (Weis 2006), crustaceans (Cronier & Courville 2004) and mixed assemblages (Heinze 1991; Fayard *et al.* 2005).

**Upper Jurassic.** Ammonite occurrences in the Upper Jurassic are variable, given their facies dependence. The schemes proposed by Enay & Boullier (1981) and Marchand (1986) on the basis of ammonites and brachiopods provided a good basis for more recent studies on the Oxfordian (Thierry *et al.* 2006). The sedimentological studies by Carpentier (2004), Carpentier *et al.* (2004, 2005, 2006*a*), Olivier *et al.* (2004) and Lorin *et al.* (2004) applied these studies to constrain depositional ages. The work by Hantzpergue (1989) on European Kimmeridgian ammonites includes work on faunas from the eastern part of the Paris Basin. This work also illuminated the problems of Kimmeridgian sedimentation in this area, which appears rather less continuous than reference sections from the Poitou region would suggest. Recent work has focused on other benthic organisms including echinoids (Vadet *et al.* 2001, 2002), crinoids (David 1998; David & Roux 2000), molluscs (Heinze 1991; Fürsich & Oschmann 1986; Oschmann 1988), crustaceans (Breton *et al.* 2003; Carpentier *et al.* 2006*b*) and mixed communities (Poirot 1987; Collin & Courville 2000; Laternser 2001; Lathuilière *et al.* 2003; Courville & Villier 2003). A study on integrated stratigraphy is currently being carried out and will provide an opportunity to study a 500 m vertical section from the Callovian to the Upper Kimmeridgian (initial results in Lathuilière *et al.* 2002, 2003, 2006*a*,*b*,*c*; Huault *et al.* 2006).

*Geochemistry and mineral stratigraphy*

There is no complete chemostratigraphic record of the Jurassic of the Paris Basin. Partial studies, however, have allowed palaeotemperature estimations based on $\delta^{18}O$ of biological remains to be made (Picard *et al.* 1998; Picard 2001; Collin 2000; Nori & Lathuilière 2003; Lathuilière *et al.* 2002, 2003) and these suggest that in the Callovo-Oxfordian there was a phase of cooling at the very beginning of the Malm. Vincent *et al.* (2004) have used bulk rocks to decipher the role of diagenesis in the isotopic signal. Other partial studies describe rare earth element (REE) composition of teeth (Picard *et al.* 2002) or trace element records (Vincent 2001).

Analysis of the organic geochemistry of Early Jurassic rocks has been undertaken through Rock-eval pyrolysis and suggests that the nature of organic matter results from palaeogeographic features, namely the proximity of terrigenous sources, high subsidence and high sedimentation rates (Hanzo & Espitalié 1994; Disnar *et al.* 1996, with references therein). The highest values correspond to transgressive pulses; the 'Schiste carton', for example, constitutes the best source rock for the basin and provides a good illustration of this rule (Mascle *et al.* 1994). Similar conclusions have been proposed for Kimmeridgian black shales (Geyssant *et al.* 1993; Bialkowski *et al.* 2000; Tribovillard *et al.* 2001). Significant changes in molecular components were described by Landais & Elie (1999) along the Dogger–Malm transition. These were compared to palynological changes recorded from the same interval (Huault *et al.* 2003).

Recent mineralostratigraphic studies have noted that there are important changes in clay mineral assemblages in the Callovo-Oxfordian (*Mariae* Zone, *Scarburgense* Subzone) (Esteban *et al.* 2006). These are attributed to the development of connections between the young Atlantic Ocean and the Paris Basin (Pellenard *et al.* 1999). A bentonite has been described near the *Plicatilis* base (Oxfordian) and this may have been derived from the Zuidwal (NW Netherlands) active volcanic centre (Pellenard *et al.* 2003) (see above). Clay mineral assemblages have facilitated the stratigraphical zonation in the Upper Jurassic of the Boulonnais area (Deconinck 1987; Deconinck *et al.* 1982, 1996) as well as characterizing the dry climatic phase at the end of the Jurassic (Schnyder 2003).

## *Southern Germany (D.U.S., R.R.L., G.S.)*

The Jurassic of southern Germany, comprising the federal states of Baden-Württemberg and Bavaria, is part of the NW Tethyan epicontinental shelf, bordering the Alpine Realm. The succession consists of marine epicontinental sediments. In outcrop, the Jurassic sediments form the Swabian and the Franconian Alb and their forelands. Additionally, there are isolated areas with Jurassic sediments in the Upper Rhine region. The Jurassic extends further towards the SE, subcropping below the northern Alpine Molasse sediments, where it is known from petroleum exploration.

The Jurassic of southern Germany is a classic area of geological and palaeontological research, being linked with the names of Quenstedt (1856–58, 1883–88), Oppel (1856–58; who developed the idea of the chronozone here) and Gümbel (1894), to name but a few. However, this does not mean that the Jurassic of southern Germany has been conclusively studied and interpreted. On the contrary, there exist several questions on fundamental stratigraphical problems and correlations, as well as on sedimentological and palaeogeographical interpretations, that are open to lively discussion, as shown here.

For field guides with outcrop descriptions, refer to Geyer & Gwinner (1984) and Rosendahl *et al.* (2006) for the Swabian Alb, and the 'Wanderungen in die Erdgeschichte' series covering many areas of the Franconian Alb (e.g. Meyer & Schmidt-Kaler 1990*b*; Schmidt-Kaler *et al.* 1992).

*Stratigraphy and general remarks*

Traditional names for the three Jurassic series used in southern Germany refer to the lithology and its appearance in outcrop, namely the 'Schwarzer Jura', 'Brauner Jura' and 'Weißer Jura' or Lias, Dogger and Malm, respectively, all representing informal lithostratigraphic units. These popular names do not fit with international convention and are thus omitted here in favour of international terms (Lower, Middle, Upper or Early, Middle, Late Jurassic, respectively).

The correlation between the federal states of Baden-Württemberg and Bavaria is also complicated by the fact that both areas are investigated separately by the relevant federal institutions. This separation is compounded by the different facies that developed, mainly in the Upper Jurassic, and by the Ries impact crater which formed in the Miocene and now separates Swabia from Franconia.

The traditional subdivision by Quenstedt (1856–58) of each Jurassic series into six subunits (alpha, beta, gamma, delta, epsilon, zeta), was used for a long time, but has led to some confusion. In particular with regard to the correlation between Baden-Württemberg and Bavaria, these originally lithostratigraphic units have often been misunderstood as bio- or chronostratigraphic units, which they are not. Therefore, these formerly popular names are omitted here in favour of the now officially defined formations following international standards (Fig. 14.25) (Villinger & Fleck 1995; Deutsche Stratigraphische Kommission 2002). The new formation names are, however, often based on longstanding traditional terms introduced by Quenstedt (1843, 1856–58, 1883–88), Engel (1908), Roll (1931), Gwinner (1962) and Geyer & Gwinner (1962). Correlation with Quenstedt's now obsolete terms is discussed in Geyer & Gwinner (1984, 1991), Heizmann (1998), and Meyer & Schmidt-Kaler (1996). Thicknesses are compiled after Geyer & Gwinner (1984), Villinger & Fleck (1995) and Meyer & Schmidt-Kaler (1996).

*Lower Jurassic*

In the Early Jurassic, southern Germany was covered by an epicontinental sea, forming part of the northern Tethys shelf. It was bordered by the Bohemian landmass in the east and by the adjacent Vindelician landmass in the SE (Fig. 14.2). Between the Bohemian landmass and the Rhenish Island in the NW, the Hessian Seaway (= 'Hessische Straße') represented the connection with the North Sea Basin. A subtropical climate is indicated by the fossil fauna, and several rivers brought considerable siliciclastic input at times. Initially, the Vindelician landmass, which comprised large parts of present-day southern Bavaria, became increasingly flooded. The overall transgressive character of the Lower Jurassic sediments resulted in a predominance of dark claystones and black shales, condensation and discontinuity surfaces. Today, the Lower Jurassic (up to 150 m) mainly forms the foreland of the Swabian and Franconian Alb (Geyer & Gwinner 1991; Meyer & Schmidt-Kaler 1996; Heizmann 1998).

**Hettangian.** Deposition of the Psilonotenton Formation (up to 15 m) commenced above a hiatus with the 'Psilonotenbank', a characteristic limestone bed with reworked older sediments and bioclasts, thus indicating transgression. The initial transgression, probably coming from the north and SW, is dated by Hettangian-age ammonites of the middle *Planorbis* Zone (Bloos 1976, 2004). Towards NE Swabia, the facies changes to coarse-grained sandstones lacking ammonites. The main part of the formation consists of clays and silty clays with varying sand content and occasional sandstone layers; pyrite and coal lenses occur frequently. In addition to ammonites, small echinoid spines and bivalves also occur (Bloos 1976; Geyer & Gwinner 1984). The base of the overlying Angulatenton Formation (up to 10 m) is defined by a limestone bed ('Oolithenbank') which contains siliciclastic sand and bioclasts in the west, changing to oolitic ironstone in the eastern part and thus indicating its transgressive character. It is overlain by dark silty clays with intercalated sandstone lenses (Bloos 1976; Geyer & Gwinner 1984). In the eastern part of Swabia, the clay facies of the Angulatenton is replaced by the fine-grained sandstones of the Angulatensandstein Formation (up to 20 m) (Geyer & Gwinner 1984). Marine bivalves form several coquinas (Bloos 1976).

Further to the east, in Franconia, two lateral equivalents to these formations exist. The Bamberg Formation (up to 35 m) exhibits fine, planar-bedded marine sands and clays. These sands, with occasional marine bivalves, bioturbation, wave ripples and slumps, were transported from the north by coast-parallel currents. The base is marked by a characteristic bed containing bivalves ('Cardinienbank') (Meyer & Schmidt-Kaler 1996).

Further towards the east, the Bayreuth Formation (up to 20 m) (= 'Gümbelscher Sandstein') was deposited. The cross-bedded deltaic sands with lenses of clays famous for their Early Jurassic flora were derived from the Vindelician landmass in the SE (Meyer & Schmidt-Kaler 1996).

**Sinemurian.** The Hettangian–Sinemurian boundary is marked by a hiatus. The Arietenkalk Formation (up to 25 m) is characterized by fossil-rich limestone beds with intercalated clay layers. The base is defined by the 'Kupferfelsbank', a limestone bed with locally abundant iron ooids and bored pebbles. Gryphaeid oysters, giant ammonites (Arietitidae), brachiopods and echinoderm clasts are the most important fossils in this formation (Geyer & Gwinner 1984).

The Arietenkalk Formation is overlain by the Obtususton Formation (up to 65 m). The dark grey clays and marly clays often exhibit concretions of siderite and phosphorite; quartz sand and mica increase upwards. Several fossil-rich marl layers occur in the upper part of the succession; each marks the onset of a different ammonite fauna. Other common fossils include brachiopods, bivalves, ammonites and crinoids (Geyer & Gwinner 1984).

Towards the east, both formations grade into the coarse siliciclastic sands of the Gryphaeensandstein Formation (up to 8 m). This coarse marine sandstone with reworked basal sandstone clasts, bivalves and ammonites represents the flooding of the underlying deltaic sands described above (Meyer & Schmidt-Kaler 1996).

**Pliensbachian (Carixian–Domerian).** The Sinemurian–Pliensbachian boundary is marked by a hiatus. The Numismalismergel Formation (up to 15 m) is a succession of grey marls with intercalated marly limestone beds, exhibiting numerous pyritic U-shaped burrows and other trace fossils. The greatest thickness of marls occurs in the middle part of the succession. Only in eastern Swabia, near the 'Ries High', and in eastern Bavaria, does the facies change to coarse siliciclastic sandstones. This formation is often rich in fossils, especially belemnites, brachiopods, bivalves, ammonites and crinoids, indicating well-oxygenated conditions (Geyer & Gwinner 1984; Meyer & Schmidt-Kaler 1996). The original type locality of the Pliensbachian Stage is located in the central part of Swabia (Schlatter 1977, 1980). The Numismalismergel Formation reflects a broad deepening trend for the region (Meyer & Schmidt-Kaler 1996).

The Upper Pliensbachian Amaltheenton Formation (up to 40 m) consists of dark grey clays and marly clays with occasional marly limestone beds, the latter often occurring as concretionary layers. Towards the top, the marly limestones increase, forming the Costatenkalk Member. As in the underlying formation, the marly limestone beds often appear mottled due to ichnofabric. The body fossils (ammonites, belemnites, gastropods, bivalves, crinoids) are often preserved in pyrite and are mostly concentrated in certain beds (Urlichs 1977; Geyer & Gwinner 1984).

**Toarcian.** The Lower Toarcian Posidonienschiefer Formation ('Posidonia shale'; up to 35 m) has become world-famous for its

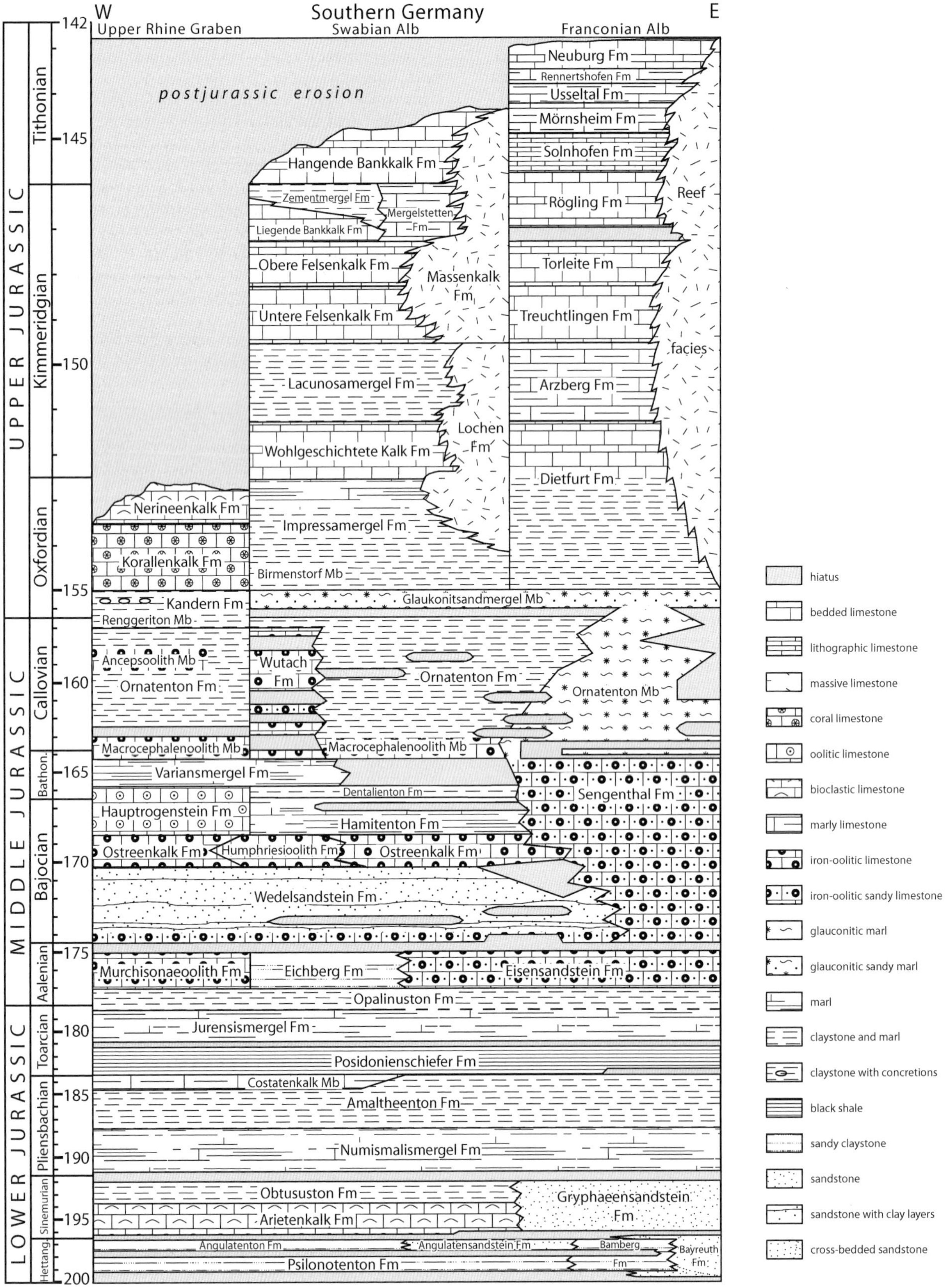


**Fig. 14.25.** Stratigraphy and facies distribution of the Jurassic of southern Germany. Note different time scales for each of the three series, thus taking into account the differences in thickness and complexity. Formations, correlation and timescale modified from Deutsche Stratigraphische Kommission (2002) and Bloos *et al.* (2005). In Franconia, the limit between the Jurensismergel and the Opalinuston Formation is somewhat vague since the latter appears earlier than in Swabia; hence the boundary is indicated by a dashed line.

uniquely preserved fauna (ichthyosaurs and other reptiles, fishes, giant crinoid colonies on driftwood, numerous cephalopods etc.), particularly from the Konservat-Lagerstätte of Holzmaden (Riegraf *et al.* 1984; Urlichs *et al.* 1994; Heizmann 1998). The succession consists of characteristic bituminous black shales, marls and marly limestones (Geyer & Gwinner 1984). Light-coloured shales are mainly formed by coccoliths (Müller & Blaschke 1969), representing one of the first mass bloomings of coccolithophorid algae in Earth history. The bituminous shales also yield a low-diversity microfauna of foraminifera (Riegraf 1985). The excellent preservation of the fossils, sometimes even with soft tissue, is due to anoxic conditions, not only within the sediment but also partly within the bottom water, hampering the decay of organic matter. The extent and the genetic interpretation of these anoxic conditions, however, has been the subject of controversial discussion (e.g. Brenner & Seilacher 1978; Kauffman 1978, 1981). According to the most recent studies (Röhl *et al.* 2001; Schmid-Röhl *et al.* 2002), anoxic conditions unfavourable for benthic fauna, prevailed during a relative sea-level lowstand resulting in an enclosed stagnant basinal environment. As water circulation improved during sea-level highstands, the anoxic conditions were punctuated by short periods (weeks to years) of oxygenated bottom water. Though facies was mainly controlled by sea-level and palaeoclimate, no indications were found for ocean-wide anoxic events (Schmid-Röhl *et al.* 2002). The coastal facies of SE Bavaria consists of a limestone unit containing ammonites and quartz sand (Meyer & Schmidt-Kaler 1996).

In the Late Toarcian, conditions for benthic life had distinctly improved as evidenced by the presence of the Jurensismergel Formation (up to 35 m). This succession of partly calcareous marls yields cephalopods, small ahermatypic corals, brachiopods, bivalves and gastropods. Some condensation horizons occur, and in sections with reduced thickness there is evidence of reworking and lateral transport (Geyer & Gwinner 1984; Bruder 1968).

The Jurensismergel Formation is overlain by the dark, clayey Opalinuston Formation (see below) whose deposition had already commenced in the latest Toarcian according to the most recent stratigraphic revision, including the Torulosum Subzone in the Toarcian. In Franconia, the limit between these two formations is somewhat vague since the Opalinuston Formation appears earlier than in Swabia (Bloos *et al.* 2005).

*Middle Jurassic*

As with the Early Jurassic, the Middle Jurassic of southern Germany is a time of predominantly (fine-)clastic deposition in a tropical climate. The Vindelician landmass, still present at the beginning, was finally eroded and submerged during the Middle Jurassic (Fig. 14.3). Dark clays and oolitic ironstones are the most common sediments from this period. Condensation and discontinuity surfaces occur frequently. The Middle Jurassic sediments (up to 280 m) form the transition between the foreland and the lower part of the slope of the Swabian and Franconian Alb (Geyer & Gwinner 1991; Meyer & Schmidt-Kaler 1996).

**Aalenian.** As noted above, deposition of the Opalinuston Formation (60–170 m) commenced in the latest Toarcian. This thick homogenous succession, which was deposited within a very short time, consists of clays, with some quartz sand and mica towards the top. The shells of ammonites, such as *Leioceras opalinum*, and bivalves are often preserved in aragonite. The mollusc fauna is rich in individuals, but of low taxonomic diversity, and some parts are void of macrofossils, indicating restricted conditions. Towards the eastern coast, a rich gastropod fauna indicates better environmental conditions (Kuhn 1935). Remarkably, a coarse-clastic coastal facies is nowhere developed in southern Germany. Kobler (1972) suggested tropical weathering and low relief in the hinterland. Morphologically, this formation tends to form landslides, while natural outcrops are scarce (Dietl & Etzold 1977; Geyer & Gwinner 1984).

In the Upper Aalenian, the lithologies become more variable, comprising clays, sandstones and oolitic ironstones; three different formations can be distinguished. In middle and eastern Swabia, the Eichberg Formation (15–65 m; Bloos *et al.* 2005) comprises a succession of sandy claystones with intercalated horizons of well-sorted sandstones. Deposition occurred in a relatively shallow shelf-sea with sediment being transported from the north and NE. Bivalves, cephalopods, crinoids and numerous trace fossils occur (Dietl & Etzold 1977; Geyer & Gwinner 1984). Towards the west and east, there is a change to oolitic ironstones, a most typical sediment for the Middle Jurassic, not just in southern Germany. The genetic interpretation of oolitic ironstones is manifold and controversial, due to the fact that different origins are possible. However, a common feature of the Jurassic sedimentary ironstones is their apparent link with discontinuity surfaces, either regressional or transgressional (Burkhalter 1995). A microbial origin for the goethite/chamosite ooids and stromatolitic crusts from the French Middle Jurassic has been suggested by Préat *et al.* (2000). In the Upper Rhine area, the Murchisonaeoolith Formation (10–30 m) represents a mixed facies of iron ooids, quartz sand and limestones (Geyer & Gwinner 1991; Bloos *et al.* 2005). Thus, the lithology resembles the Eisensandstein Formation (25–35 m) of eastern Swabia and Bavaria. It consists mainly of iron-rich sandstones where sandy limestone beds with bivalves as well as claystones are intercalated; oolitic ironstones occur in several layers. In eastern Swabia, the iron ores were exploited up until the middle of the twentieth century; the former Aalen-Wasseralfingen mine can be visited. In the vicinity of the Vindelician-Bohemian landmass, the coastal facies is characterized by massive sandstones and thick oolitic ironstones that were channelized (Meyer & Schmidt-Kaler 1996).

**Bajocian.** Above a hiatus, the Bajocian begins with the so-called Sowerbyioolith, a basinwide condensed layer partly rich in iron ooids (Fig. 14.25). The main part of the Wedelsandstein Formation (up to 50 m), which is named after the trace fossil *Zoophycos*, consists of sandy claystones and marls with common siderite concretions. Several sandstone beds exhibit flaser bedding and laterally pinch out. In general, the quartz sand content within this formation increases upward and from NE to SW. Discontinuity surfaces are indicated by reworking and bored concretions. While bivalves and ammonites are the predominant fossils, hermatypic corals locally occur in eastern Swabia. The section is concluded by fossil-rich limestones with quartz sand (Geyer & Gwinner 1984).

In the Middle Bajocian, iron ooids are distributed basinwide. The Ostreenkalk Formation (up to 30 m; Bloos *et al.* 2005) represents a succession of marly limestones and claystones with numerous oysters. In the western Swabian Alb, oolitic ironstones are predominant in the Humphriesioolith Formation (*c.* 35 m; Bloos *et al.* 2005). At the base of this formation, hermatypic corals occur in the vicinity of the Hohenzollern Castle. Both formations are partly rich in pyrite, bivalves and cephalopods, indicating slightly restricted bottom-water oxygen conditions in the basinal facies (Geyer & Gwinner 1984, 1991).

The Upper Bajocian Hamitenton Formation (up to 40 m; Bloos *et al.* 2005) is lithologically similar to the Middle Bajocian formations described above. Oolitic ironstones occur at the base (Subfurcatenoolith) and top (Parkinsonioolith) of the formation which mainly comprises dark claystones (Dietl 1977; Geyer & Gwinner 1984). In the Upper Rhine area, the Hauptrogenstein Formation (40–85 m) represents higher-energy conditions and deposition on a shallow-water carbonate platform. This is most clearly indicated by thick calcareous oolite beds with cross-bedding, corals, nerineid gastropods, echinoderms and oncolites (Geyer & Gwinner 1991; Geyer *et al.* 2003).

In Bavaria, the Bajocian is represented by the lower part of the Sengenthal Formation (0–12 m), a strongly condensed iron-oolitic succession (Zeiss 1977; Schmidt-Kaler *et al.* 1992; Groiss *et al.* 2000).

**Bathonian.** The Hauptrogenstein Formation continues up into the Lower Bathonian (Zigzag Zone; Ohmert 2004) as does the Sengenthal Formation in Bavaria, while the Swabian facies of the Hamitenton Formation is similarly followed by the dark claystones of the Dentalienton Formation (up to 70 m; Dietl 1977). Numerous bivalves and ammonites occur in this formation which is otherwise marked by condensation, reworking and discontinuity surfaces (Geyer & Gwinner 1984). In the Middle to Upper Bathonian, the clay-dominated facies of the Variansmergel Formation (up to 85 m) extends to the Upper Rhine area. It consists of fossil-rich marls with thin beds of marly limestones and abundant rhynchonellid brachiopods (Geyer & Gwinner 1991). It is more complete than the coeval deposits of Swabia and Franconia, where numerous hiatuses and condensation occur.

**Callovian.** In Swabia, the Bathonian–Callovian boundary is marked by the oolitic ironstones of the Macrocephalenoolith Member of the Ornatenton Formation which began in the uppermost Bathonian (*Orbis* Zone; cf. Dietl *et al.* 1979; Geyer & Gwinner 1984). In Swabia it is overlain by the claystones of the Ornatenton Formation (up to 60 m), which is rich in pyritic ammonites (e.g. *Kosmoceras ornatum*), but rather poor in benthic organisms, thus indicating phases of low oxygenation. The benthic fauna is represented by the bivalve *Bositra*, crustaceans and small ahermatypic corals. Benthic calcareous foraminifera can be used to characterize different facies types (Blank 1990). From the central basinal facies of Swabia, a highly diverse fauna of radiolarians and planktonic foraminifera was described by Riegraf (1986, 1987*a*,*b*), the latter also occurring in eastern Franconia. The radiolarian fauna is mainly Tethyan with only rare Boreal elements.

The Ancepsoolith Member, another oolitic ironstone horizon, is intercalated in the upper part of the Ornatenton Formation in the western Swabian Alb. In the southwestern part of Swabia, the Ornatenton is replaced by the Wutach Formation (*c.* 6.5 m; Bloos *et al.* 2005), a succession of marly to calcareous oolitic ironstones. These iron ores were exploited near Blumberg during World War II. A layer of phosphoritic concretions ('Lamberti-Knollen') marks the top of the Middle Jurassic (Geyer & Gwinner 1984). The formation continues into the Oxfordian with dark, glauconitic claystones (Glaukonitsandmergel Member, see below). In Bavaria, the Ornatenton Member (0–15 m; part of the Sengenthal Formation) consists of glauconitic marls with pyrite (Zeiss 1977; Meyer & Schmidt-Kaler 1996). In the Upper Rhine area, the Callovian ends within the Renggeriton Member of the Kandern Formation (see below).

*Upper Jurassic*

In the Late Jurassic, a carbonate-dominated depositional system was established in southern Germany. The succession of predominantly light-coloured limestones and marls (400–600 m) indicates mainly well-oxygenated water. A reefal facies, established in the Middle Oxfordian, was part of an extensive facies belt characterized by frequent siliceous sponge reefs spanning the northern Tethys shelf (Fig. 14.26). Coral reefs, however, are also present, becoming increasingly important towards the end of the Late Jurassic, and mirroring the overall shallowing sea-level trend. In the latest Jurassic, the Hessian Seaway was closed at times by the continous land barrier of the London-Brabant-Rhenish-Bohemian Land, resulting in a stronger Tethyan influence. Towards the west, the adjacent platform facies of the Paris Basin and the Swiss Jura partly reaches the southern German realm in the Upper Rhine area. In the SW, the shelf facies deepens gradually towards the pelagic facies of the Helvetian Basin (Schilt Formation and Quinten Formation; cf. Schneider 1962; Lupu 1972; Bertleff *et al.* 1988; Meyer & Schmidt-Kaler 1990*a*), while the transition in the SE towards the pelagic facies of the eastern Alpine Hochstegen Marble (Kiessling 1992; Kiessling & Zeiss 1992) is deeply buried beneath the Alpine nappes. The climate remained warm but became increasingly arid. The fine-grained siliciclastics were transported from the north, while the micritic mud was probably derived from the shallow-water carbonate platform of the Swiss Jura (B. Ziegler 1987; Selg & Wagenplast 1990; Geyer & Gwinner 1991; Meyer & Schmidt-Kaler 1989, 1996; Pittet *et al.* 2000; Leinfelder *et al.* 2002).

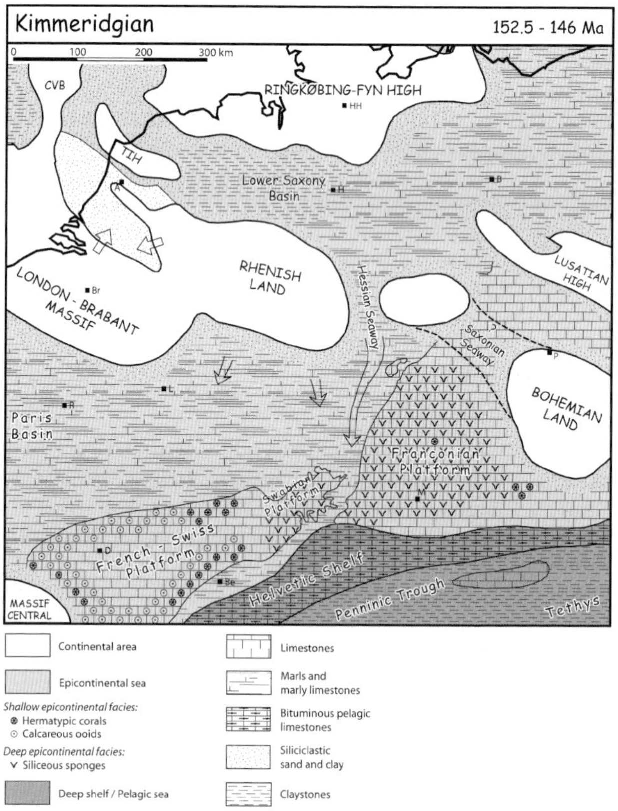


**Fig. 14.26.** Kimmeridgian palaeogeography and general facies distribution of southern Germany and adjacent areas. Abbreviations: CVB, Cleaver Bank High; TIH, Texel-Ijsselmeer High. A, Amsterdam; B, Berlin; Be, Bern; Br, Brussels; D, Dijon; HH, Hamburg; H, Hannover; L, Luxemburg; M, Munich; P, Prague; R, Reims. Combined and modified after Gwinner (1976), Meyer (1981), Meyer & Schmidt-Kaler 1989, Ziegler (1990) and Dercourt *et al.* (2000).

**Lower Oxfordian.** In southern Germany, the base of the Upper Jurassic is formed by the Glaukonitsandmergel Member, a condensed section with a very reduced thickness (0.3–5 m). The glauconitic marls, which contain detrital quartz, represent the uppermost part of the Ornatenton Formation and thus of the 'Braunjura' facies. An early Oxfordian age is indicated by the presence of ammonites of the *Mariae* or *Cordatum* Zones (Zeiss 1955; Munk & Zeiss 1985). Riegraf (1987*a*,*b*) described planktonic foraminifera from this member and from the lowermost part of the Impressamergel Formation (see below).

At the eastern side of the Upper Rhine Graben, positioned in the far SW of Germany, the Upper Jurassic commenced with the Kandern Formation (*c*. 85 m). The basal part is formed by the dark clays of the Renggeriton Member whose lowermost part is Callovian in age. The upper part consists of marly clays with numerous calcareous concretions (Geyer & Gwinner 1991; Geyer *et al.* 2003).

**Middle to Upper Oxfordian of the Upper Rhine Graben area.** In contrast to the facies dominated by siliceous sponges and cephalopods prevailing in the Oxfordian of southern Germany (see below), the Upper Rhine Graben area differs markedly by exhibiting the same shallow-water coral facies as is developed in the adjacent carbonate platforms of the Swiss Jura and NE France (Geyer & Gwinner 1991; Meyer & Schmidt-Kaler 1989, 1990*a*).

The Middle Oxfordian Korallenkalk Formation (*c*. 60 m), which is well exposed near Basel, contains a variety of corals, brachiopods, echinoderms and ooids (Geyer & Gwinner 1991; Geyer *et al.* 2003). The Korallenkalk Formation is overlain by the Upper Oxfordian Nerineenkalk Formation (>16 m) with abundant gastropods in its upper part. Younger Jurassic deposits in this area were eroded in post-Jurassic times (Geyer & Gwinner 1991). These formations, which were deposited in a carbonate ramp setting, show a clear shallowing-upward trend with higher-energy deposits and partially subaerial exposure in the uppermost part (Laternser 2001).

**Late Jurassic reefal facies (massive limestones) (Oxfordian to Tithonian).** Beginning in the early Late Jurassic a reefal facies, dominated by siliceous sponges, was established in the southern German part of the northern Tethys shelf (Leinfelder *et al.* 2002). This facies is generally massive in contrast to the otherwise bedded limestones and marls. Commencing with small and isolated patch-reefs, the reefal facies extended through time to form large and continuous reef complexes in the Middle and Upper Kimmeridgian (Gwinner 1976; Meyer & Schmidt-Kaler 1989, 1990*a*). The main reef-builders were siliceous sponges (both hexactinellids and lithistids), which owed their reef-building capacity to the intergrowth with thrombolitic to stromatolitic microbial crusts (Schrammen 1924; Aldinger 1961; Leinfelder *et al.* 1993, 1994, 1996; Schmid 1996; Krautter 1997; Leinfelder 2001). In general, these reefs can be classified as siliceous sponge-microbialite reef mounds. Hermatypic corals only appear within the reefal facies diachronously from the Late Kimmeridgian onwards, becoming increasingly abundant towards the Tithonian. This trend is interpreted by most authors as mirroring a general shallowing trend on the northern Tethys shelf where the siliceous sponge reefs represent a deeper ramp setting of *c*. 50–150 m water depth (Ziegler 1967; Gygi & Persoz 1987; Selg & Wagenplast 1990; Leinfelder 1993; Leinfelder *et al.* 1994, 1996, 2002; Werner *et al.* 1994; Schmid 1996; Krautter 1997; Pittet & Mattioli 2002; see also discussion in Keupp *et al.* 1990). In contrast to this 'classic' bathymetric model, other authors suggest a shallow-water origin for the siliceous sponge facies (Kott 1989; Koch 2000). Such an interpretation, however, would place siliceous sponge-dominated facies and hermatypic corals in the same bathymetric position, and thus require a controlling factor other than bathymetry to explain the separation of both facies. Although water temperatures and nutrient control might be considered as likely possibilities, it would be difficult to postulate significant temperature or nutrient gradients in such a hypothetically large, relatively flat shallow-water platform. Moreover, the adjacent bedded cephalopod facies, as described here, totally lack any unequivocal shallow-water features such as dasycladacean algae or thick cross-bedded oolithic grainstones, both of which are common in genuine shallow-water facies (e.g. in the neighbouring Swiss Jura and Upper Rhine area or in Iberia; Leinfelder *et al.* 1994, 1996). The optimum habitat for the pervasive ammonites is also generally considered to be in waters deeper than *c*. 50 m (Ziegler 1967; Gygi 1999). In addition, the so-called tuberoids which represent a particular type of intraclast, namely disintegrated pieces of microbial crusts and/or siliceous sponges, are not generated by wave action and reworking, but are formed *in situ*, as noted by Fritz (1958) and Aldinger (1961), as also evidenced by their occurrence close to the reefs.

The interpretation of the Recent hexactinellid sponge reefs on the western Canadian shelf (Krautter *et al.* 2001) and their environment, though different in some respects, generally supports the traditional bathymetric model. Conversely, several features previously thought to indicate shallow-water conditions have proven to be not diagnostic. For example, rare gypsum pseudomorphs (Koch & Schweizer 1986) can be produced by sulphur-oxidizing bacteria (Ehrlich 1990), and the interpretation of *Tubiphytes* as an oncoid type (Kott 1989) has been shown to be erroneous (for discussion see Schmid 1996; Henssel *et al.* 2002). However, the origin of allochem-type particles within the sponge mounds has not yet been proven. We assume that these particles comprise both deeper-water-generated microbial particles and shallow-water-derived sands swept into deeper parts of the shelf where they became incorporated within the mounds (cf. Leinfelder *et al.* 1996).

In the Swabian Alb, the Lochen Formation (up to >200 m) represents the lower reefal facies of the Late Jurassic, extending from the Oxfordian to the Lower Kimmeridgian (Fig. 14.25). Around the reefs a small-sized fauna occurred ('Lochen facies'; Geyer & Gwinner 1984), the main faunal elements of which include siliceous sponges, ammonites, brachiopods and echinoderms. Benthic foraminiferal associations from bedded and massive facies can also be distinguished (Wagenplast 1972; Schmalzriedt 1991). The reefal facies commenced with small and isolated patch-reefs in the Middle Oxfordian, increasing in areal extent over time. Mound development was frequently complex, with small mounds clustering to form larger buildups (Schmid *et al.* 2001). This facies is mostly restricted to the western and middle Swabian Alb, and is separated from the reefal facies of Bavaria in the east by a basinal structure, the 'Swabian Marl Basin' (Meyer & Schmidt-Kaler 1989, 1990*a*).

The Lochen Formation of the Swabian Alb is followed by the similar facies of the Massenkalk Formation (up to >300 m), also representing a massive reefal facies. Unlike the older reefal facies, however, the Massenkalk Formation comprises large reef complexes where either siliceous sponges or corals predominate. In Franconia, no formation name has yet been defined for an equivalent massive reef facies (e.g. Flügel & Steiger 1981; Brachert 1986; Lang 1989). There, deposition began in the Middle Oxfordian when sedimentation switched from glauconitic condensation to the marls of the lower Dietfurt Formation (see below). While the Swabian reef facies was initially more patchy, it formed a more or less continuous reef area in the Upper Kimmeridgian. In contrast, the reef facies of the Franconian Alb appears to have been characterized from the onset by distinct reef-facies tracts, partly prevailing throughout the Late Jurassic (cf. Meyer & Schmidt-Kaler 1989, 1990*a*).

Contrary to what the established term 'reef facies' might suggest, these limestones do not represent massive reefs with metazoan frameworks. The term 'reef facies', as used, comprises all types of reefal sediments including mound-type reefs and peri-reef carbonate sands. This has to be emphasized since there is an ongoing debate as to the nature of this facies, including the question of whether this term should be used at all. According to Koch *et al.* (1994), the majority of these sediments consists of a peloid–lithoclast–ooid sand facies rather than representing true reefs. According to this model, true reefs do occur within this facies, but are only small and of subordinate importance within the sand units. On the other hand, as Meyer (1994) has pointed out, these sediments are often stabilized by stromatolitic or thrombolitic microbial crusts, resulting in synsedimentary hardened reef-like sandbodies which may form steep margins, a feature that cannot be formed by uncemented sandbodies. However, the term 'reef facies' or 'massive limestone' should only be used as a descriptive term for the variety of facies types present. If, and to what degree, these facies types should be considered reefal must be determined in each individual case. A further question is whether the micritic parts of the older mounds represent hard automicrites related to the activity or decay of microbial matter, or to trapped accumulations of soft allochthonous mud. With regard to the southern German Upper Jurassic mounds, both interpretations are possible (Leinfelder & Keupp 1995; Schmid *et al.* 2001), but their mutual proportions and growth/accumulation patterns have not been clarified thus far.

**Middle Oxfordian to Lower Kimmeridgian.** In the Swabian Alb, the Middle to Upper Oxfordian is represented by the Impressamergel Formation (25–125 m), a succession of marls with intercalated limestones where the percentage of limestones increases towards the formation top (Bimammatumbänke Member). Brachiopods, belemnites and ammonites (*Plicatilis* and *Bifurcatus* zones) are widespread. Radiolarian and planktonic foraminiferal faunas, found in the Swabian and Franconian Alb (Riegraf 1987*b*), indicate a pelagic influence and not too shallow water depths. Towards SW Swabia, a special facies with siliceous sponge biostromes is developed in the lowermost part of the formation (Birmenstorf Member). The Impressamergel Formation forms the very base of the steep slope of the Swabian Alb and thus is mostly covered by debris (Geyer & Gwinner 1984). Clays, derived from the Rhenish landmass towards the SE, also reached the western part of Bavaria, and formed the marly lower part of the Dietfurt Formation (35–65 m). In eastern Bavaria, a broad belt rich in siliceous sponge reef facies ('Franconian main reef tract') trending north–south developed and persisted until the Early Tithonian (Meyer & Schmidt-Kaler 1989).

The Impressamergel Formation is overlain by the Wohlgeschichtete Kalk Formation (10–150 m). This represents a homogeneous succession of regularly bedded limestones with a bank thickness of 10–60 cm, separated by thin marl layers or stylolithic joints. Ammonites are the predominant faunal element, representing the *Planula* Zone. Until recently, this formation was regarded as Late Oxfordian in age (e.g. Geyer & Gwinner 1984; Leinfelder *et al.* 1994), but Schweigert & Callomon (1997) suggested that the Oxfordian–Kimmeridgian boundary is at the base of the *Planula* Zone and thus at the base of the Wohlgeschichtete Kalk Formation (Fig. 14.25). Siliceous sponges (see below) may form small biostromes or patch-reefs within the bedded cephalopod facies. This facies continues in Bavaria in the upper part of the Dietfurt Formation (see above), where the Ries-Wiesent reef-facies tract begins to develop, separating the Bavarian from the Swabian realms (Meyer & Schmidt-Kaler 1989). In the upper part of the formation, a mainly Tethyan radiolarian fauna with few Boreal elements was found on the southern Franconian Alb, probably indicating deep neritic (?50 m) conditions (Kiessling 1997).

The Lacunosamergel Formation (10–75 m) is intercalated between two limestone units; good outcrops are scarce. The bedding planes of the grey marls sometimes show glauconitic veneers, indicating frequent condensation in a deep ramp environment. Ammonites of the *Platynota*, *Hypselocyclum* and *Divisum* zones are widespread (Schick 2004*a*,*b*,*c*). Within the bedded facies a particular type of patch-reef (termed 'Lacunosastotzen') occurs. In these reefs, rhynchonellid brachiopods are significantly abundant (Geyer & Gwinner 1984). Siliceous sponges were more common in the adjacent massive reef facies (see above), but these patch-reefs presumably grew in deeper water. This peculiar reef type is coeval with the development of pure microbialites and microbialite-rich reefs in SW Europe, which has been interpreted by Leinfelder (2001) to represent transgressive environmental settings rich in nutrients and with a predisposition for the development of local or widespread dysoxic environments.

Towards the east, beyond the Ries-Wiesent reef-facies tract (see above), the facies changes to more calcareous, but otherwise similar deposits of the Arzberg Formation (25–40 m). This formation contains several lithostratigraphic marker horizons such as the Crussoliensis-Mergel (Meyer & Schmidt-Kaler 1989).

**Upper Kimmeridgian.** The Untere Felsenkalk Formation (20–60 m) forms the steep slope in most parts of the Swabian Alb. Since the massive limestone facies (Massenkalk Formation) predominates in this time period (*Mutabilis-Pseudomutabilis* Zone), bedded limestones, while not common, are nevertheless present. In the upper part of the Untere Felsenkalk Formation, a characteristic glauconitic marker bed ('Glaukonitbank') occurs, indicative of longer periods of non-deposition and probably related to a transgressive phase. There is, however, no indication of biostratigraphic condensation. The Untere Felsenkalk Formation is characterized by well-bedded cephalopod-bearing limestones with rare thin marls. Both the percentage of limestones and bedding thickness increase towards the formation top, with limestone beds up to 150 cm thick present (Geyer & Gwinner 1984). In the Bavarian realm, a large platform consisting of thick-bedded carbonates, the Treuchtlingen Formation (up to 60 m), developed (Fig. 14.27). In contrast to all of the other bedded carbonates described here, this formation is characterized by a succession of thick beds with an average thickness of 1 m (Kott 1989; Meyer & Schmidt-Kaler 1990*b*, 1996). These beds represent a succession of biostromes formed by siliceous sponges and thrombolites, intercalated with micritic units (Henssel *et al.* 2002). Bioherms are only locally developed. This platform can be assigned to an average water depth just below storm wavebase, based on the fauna (predominantly siliceous sponges and cephalopods) and the lack of unequivocal shallow-water elements (Fig. 14.27; Meyer & Schmidt-Kaler 1990*a*; Selg & Wagenplast 1990). This is in contrast with the shallow-water interpretation of Kott (1989) as discussed above. A deeper

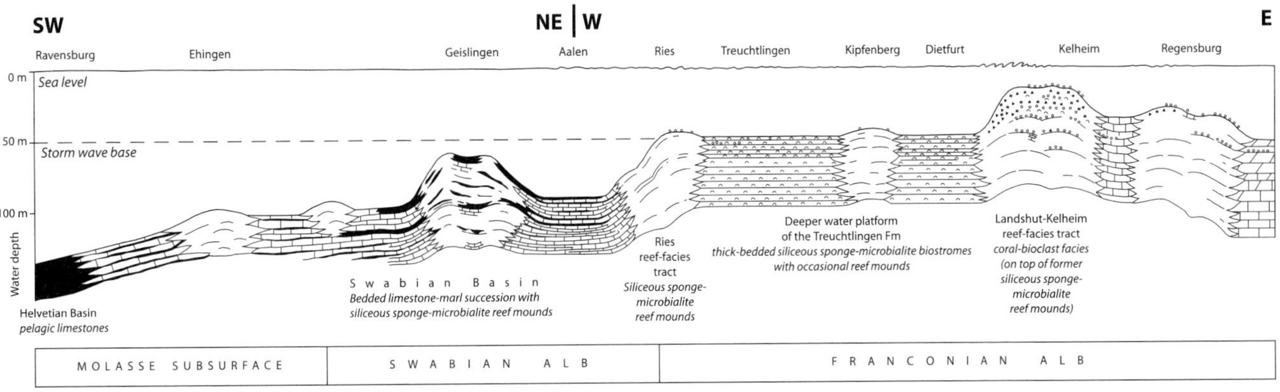


**Fig. 14.27.** Schematic section showing the southern German shelf sea during the middle Kimmeridgian; vertical exaggeration ×2.5 (compiled and modified after Meyer 1981; Selg & Wagenplast 1990).

bathymetric interpretation is corroborated by the presence of the sessile foraminifer *Tubiphytes morronensis* which is found throughout the Upper Jurassic, but whose bright white tests occur in rock-forming abundance here. Since the test thickness of this particular foraminifer depends on light and thus water depth, it can be used as a palaeobathymetric indicator (Schmid 1996). This period also marks the first occurrences of hermatypic corals in the Upper Jurassic of southern Germany (i.e. outside of the Upper Rhine area, see above).

The Swabian Obere Felsenkalk Formation (10–40 m), comprising bedded limestones, is not very widespread, being mostly replaced by massive limestones of the Massenkalk Formation. The pure limestone beds with a mean thickness of 10–40 cm contain abundant chert nodules and ammonites of the early *Beckeri* Zone, belemnites, and bivalves (Geyer & Gwinner 1984). The Bavarian equivalent, the Torleite Formation (20–40 m), marks both a period of distinct shallowing as well as expansion of the coral facies. Though the reefal morphology becomes flatter, several small depressions between the reefal areas were still present within the platform (Meyer & Schmidt-Kaler 1989, 1996).

The Liegende Bankkalk Formation (10–150 m) comprises bedded limestones and marls with a bed thickness of 10–40 cm; chert nodules occur locally. Ammonites indicate the late *Beckeri* Zone (cf. Schweigert *et al.* 1996). In the vicinity of the massive limestone facies, breccias and slumps are common (Geyer & Gwinner 1984). This formation is restricted to the western and middle Swabian Alb. The lower boundary is marked by a discontinuity or even angular disconformity, possibly of tectonic origin (Schweigert 1995; Schweigert & Franz 2004).

Within this formation, there are locally occurring laminated limestones (in particular the Nusplingen Plattenkalk), which resemble the famous Solnhofen Lithographic Limestones of Franconia (see below) (Schweigert 1998; Zügel *et al.* 1998; Dietl & Schweigert 1999, 2004). In the coeval Massenkalk Formation, corals are abundant, as in the Arnegg reef. The formation shallows up from siliceous-sponge to coral facies (Paulsen 1964; Laternser 2001) and contains the famous silicified coral faunas of Nattheim and Gerstetten in east Swabia (Geyer & Gwinner 1984; Reiff 1988).

The Zementmergel Formation (up to 170 m) is a marl-dominated formation, deposited in depressions and sometimes interdigitating with the siliceous sponge or coral reef buildups (Geyer & Gwinner 1984). Lateral transitions, partly comprising coral debris beds, into both reef facies types occur locally, depending on the position on the former palaeorelief. The boundary between the Liegende Bankkalk Formation and the Zementmergel Formation is strongly diachronous (Pawellek 2001; Schweigert & Franz 2004) (Fig. 14.25). The intercalation of limestones within this formation makes the positioning of partial sections rather difficult (Schweigert 1995; Schweigert & Franz 2004). Towards the eastern Swabian Alb, a clear distinction between the Liegende Bankkalk Formation and the Zementmergel Formation is impossible, and sometimes the succession may even begin with marls directly above the Obere Felsenkalk Formation, which in such cases was often misinterpreted as the Liegende Bankkalk Formation. Thus, the Mergelstetten Formation (up to >120 m) has been erected, replacing the Liegende Bankkalk Formation and the Zementmergel Formation in the eastern Swabian Alb (Schweigert & Franz 2004). This consists of bioturbated thin-bedded marly limestones with marl layers poor in macrofossils; breccias and slumps occur mainly in its lower part. Both the base and top of the formation are marked by discontinuity surfaces (Schweigert & Franz 2004).

The Brenztaltrümmerkalk Member, a bioclastic and oolitic limestone with shallow-water components (e.g. dasycladaceans, nerineids, diceratids, corals), is also restricted to the eastern Swabian Alb (not figured in the stratigraphic chart, but positioned between the Mergelstetten Formation and the Massenkalk Formation from which the shallow-water components derived) (Reiff 1958; Geyer & Gwinner 1984; Schweigert & Vallon 2005).

In SE Germany, the Rögling Formation (up to 40 m) represents the bedded facies which was deposited in the depressions between the reefal areas that prevailed in the south (Meyer & Schmidt-Kaler 1989). The lower boundary of the Tithonian has not yet been defined by international ratification, but it is supposed to lie within the Rögling Formation (Groiss *et al.* 2000) (Fig. 14.25).

A 20 cm thick red marl layer at the base of the Rögling Formation marks a distinct hiatus related to a regional tectonic event (Fig. 14.25) (Schweigert 1993; Schweigert & Franz 2004) and explains the thickness differences in the succession (due to more marked subsidence in the Swabian realm).

**Lower Tithonian.** In SW Germany, the Hangende Bankkalk Formation (up to 200 m) begins above a discontinuity (not shown in Fig. 14.25 due to the small scale), and marks the onset of the Tithonian (Roll 1931; Schweigert 1996, 2000). The well-bedded limestone succession with subordinate marls resembles the

Wohlgeschichtete Kalk Formation (see above) in outcrop. Apart from bivalves and brachiopods, fossils are fairly rare. Ammonites of the lower *Hybonotum* Zone are present, proving the Early Tithonian age. There exist lateral transitions to the siliceous sponge reef facies, but coral limestones also occur in more shallow areas in central Swabia. Where deposited in depressions between reefs, sediment thickness is increased due to slumping (Schweigert 1996). Due to post-Jurassic erosion, the original upper boundary of the Hangende Bankkalk Formation is not preserved.

At the same time in Bavaria, the upper part of the Rögling Formation (see above), the Solnhofen and the Mörnsheim formations were deposited, all containing lithographic limestones. In general, the elevations between the depressions were formed by older siliceous sponge-microbial reef mounds, their tops often overgrown by corals (Flügel *et al.* 1993). The characteristic laminated fabric of the lithographic limestones is due to the absence of bioturbation, probably caused by hypersaline and/or oxygen-depleted stagnant bottom waters. Many of the thicker limestone beds ('Flinze') are interpreted as turbidites, occurring in the deeper parts of the depressions such as at Solnhofen. The currents which brought micritic lime mud and caused the mixing of surface and poisonous bottom water were probably caused by monsoonal winds (Viohl 1998). Accordingly, the organisms which come from different habitats were all either carried in from shallow-water and island areas surrounding the depressions or sank through the water column (for further discussion of the depositional models, see Keupp 1977*a*,*b*; Barthel 1978, Barthel *et al.* 1978, Viohl 1998).

The Solnhofen Formation (40–90 m) belongs to the *Hybonotum* Zone (Groiss *et al.* 2000), and is the type locality of the Solnhofen Lithographic Limestones (Solnhofener Plattenkalke). These beds contain the Fossil-Lagerstätten of Solnhofen and Eichstätt, world-famous for the ancestral bird *Archaeopteryx* and numerous other well-preserved fossils (Barthel 1978; Viohl 1998; Wellnhofer 1999). Large slumped intervals ('Krumme Lagen') are intercalated in the succession mainly in the Solnhofen Formation.

The Solnhofen Formation is overlain by the Mörnsheim Formation (30–60 m), the boundary partly marked by a hardground (Wings 2000). The formation consists of bedded limestones and lithographic limestones rich in cephalopods from the late *Hybonotum* Zone, a date which is also corroborated by the radiolarian fauna (Meyer & Schmidt-Kaler 1989; Groiss *et al.* 2000). While the depositional setting was similar to that of the underlying formation, life conditions for benthic organisms had improved due to more open-marine circulation (Meyer & Schmidt-Kaler 1983).

On the large carbonate platform of southern Bavaria, a siliceous sponge facies was still widespread, but corals increasingly flourished along its northern and eastern, probably elevated, margins (Meyer & Schmidt-Kaler 1989, 1990*a*; Meyer 1994). This, together with the extensive reefal debris beds, is indicative of a distinct shallowing trend. However, sea level was still high enough to allow for a mainly Tethyan radiolarian ingression through the southern Bavarian platform (Zügel 1997), corroborating observations on nannoplankton distributions by Keupp (1977*a*). The younger Upper Jurassic formations, starting with the Usseltal Formation (up to 40 m), have been largely subjected to post-Jurassic erosion, which prevents comprehensive palaeogeographic reconstructions. In Swabia, no sediments from this time have been preserved. The Usseltal Formation (*Mucronatum* Zone; Scherzinger & Schweigert 2003) commences with bedded limestones, shifting to marls in the upper part. The sediments, which may contain bivalve debris beds with shallow-water bioclasts, were deposited between reefal buildups (Meyer & Schmidt-Kaler 1983, 1989). The overlying Rennertshofen Formation (*c.* 50 m) comprises bedded limestones, with variable bed thicknesses (Meyer & Schmidt-Kaler 1989), of the *Mucronatum* and *Vimineus* zones (Scherzinger & Schweigert 2003). The limestone beds may contain shallow-water derived reefal debris (Meyer & Schmidt-Kaler 1983). The bedded limestones and marls of the Neuburg Formation (*c.* 50 m) contain ammonites of the *Ciliata* to *Palmatus* zones in the lower part, but the environment becomes increasingly shallow towards the top, with occasional indicators (e.g. bivalves and gastropods) of partially brackish conditions (Barthel 1969). The uppermost part may be lowermost Upper Tithonian in age (for discussion see Schweigert & Scherzinger 2004). In the subsurface of the Cenozoic Molasse Basin, Tithonian beds younger than the Neuburg Formation contain a shallow-marine lagoonal facies with coral reef limestones, grading into the Early Cretaceous mixed carbonate–evaporite Purbeck facies, clearly indicating very shallow conditions and an arid climate (Meyer & Schmidt-Kaler 1989; Meyer 1994; Flügel 2004: 766). The southward transition to the pelagic facies of Tethys is deeply buried beneath the Alpine nappes.

*Tentative sequence stratigraphic interpretation*

Outcrop conditions of the south German Jurassic as well as the dominance of fully marine, often deeper shelf sediments have to date hindered complete and conclusive sequence stratigraphic interpretation of the entire succession. Hence we hope that the following tentative interpretation will stimulate further research on this subject. In particular, we do not attempt to correlate with existing global sea-level curves, nor to streamline interpretation.

As a whole, the Lower Jurassic succession appears to be richer in detrital quartz and poorer in organic matter during lowstand wedge depositions, which often are not well developed. Transgressive intervals are well represented, being characterized by condensation levels, ammonite shell beds, and discontinuity surfaces including hardgrounds and phosphorite deposits. They may be richer in organic matter or in carbonates than the rest of the succession. Highstand deposits contain lower amounts of organic matter but frequently show the abundance of detrital quartz increasing upwards.

Sequence stratigraphic interpretation of the Middle Jurassic is difficult. Oolitic ironstone intervals may be interpreted as small-scale stacked transgressive–regressive cycles with an overall transgressive trend. Highstand intervals are characterized by claystones, in part with increasing contents of quartz sand.

Owing to better outcrop conditions and to the higher heterogeneity of facies development, interpretation of sequence stratigraphy or 'dynamic stratigraphy' of the Upper Jurassic is based on partially differing methods. Brachert (1992) has discussed the importance of marker beds and facies successions within siliceous sponge mounds. Based on the assumption that sponge mound development should be enhanced during times of reduced allochthonous influx, Leinfelder (1993) and Leinfelder *et al.* (1994) have used waxing and waning patterns of reef mound facies as well as glauconitic and other condensation horizons and cross-comparison with other European regions for an initial comprehensive sequence stratigraphic interpretation of the entire Upper Jurassic. Both papers also stated that the distribution of marl versus carbonate intervals is not a sufficient criterion for dynamic interpretation since climatic variations in rainfall patterns must have played an important role. Pittet *et al.* (2000) and Pittet & Mattioli (2002) have focused on high-resolution dynamic stratigraphic interpretation of the bedded facies by using a combination of plankton, sedimentological and sequential data. Pawellek (2001) and Pawellek & Aigner (2003) have compared bedded and massive facies using a variety of proxies, such as planktonic productivity, land plant spore and other organisms, gamma ray logs, architectural styles and other criteria on various parts of the Upper Jurassic. Although the results are not fully identical when considering details, it is interesting that despite the different methods and approaches, many of the overall results are compatible. For instance, Leinfelder (1993) has emphasized major flooding intervals positioned around the *hypselocyclum/divisum* Chron (in part based on the position of the *Lacunosa* patch-reefs) as well as intra-*Acanthicum*, intra-*Eudoxus* and near-base-*Hybonotum* event (as highlighted by expansion episodes of siliceous sponge-mound growth). Focusing on the Upper Kimmeridgian and Tithonian, Pawellek (2001) has also identified the intra-*Acanthicum*, intra-*Eudoxus* and base-*Hybonotum* flooding events, but depicted some additional ones. A comparison of sequence stratigraphic interpretations with other Late Jurassic sedimentary basins in Europe is given by Ruf *et al.* (2005).

## SE France and French Jura mountains (R.E.)

The Mesozoic sedimentary basin of SE France (i.e. SE France Basin) originally extended across the outer zones of the Alps (Subalpine ranges) and the Rhone valley, the SE border of the Massif Central from the Corbières to Ardèche, Provence and Jura. However, Cenozoic Alpine tectonics deformed the region, resulting in scattered outcrops often with incomplete stratigraphical records, and mainly developed on the margins. This has hindered palaeostructural and palaeogeographic reconstructions and the situation only changed with access to borehole data from the oil industry in the central part of the basin. These data revealed that the area formed a large Mesozoic-age area of subsidence (Fig. 14.28).

### *Tectonic setting*

The SE France Basin formed on Variscan basement, the structure of which is hard to reconstruct since it was strongly overprinted by subsequent Alpine tectonics. From the few outcropping Variscan remnants (e.g. Outer Crystalline Massifs, Maures and Corsica, Briançonnais), it would appear that it formed part of the Variscan Internides (see Kroner *et al.* 2008). The Briançonnais coal basin marks the southern boundary with the Variscan Externides. Basin formation was closely related to Tethyan rifting which began close to the Middle–Upper Triassic boundary, but the basic structural pattern was probably inherited from the older Variscan fault network.

As noted above, the present situation is the result of Alpine tectonics with associated NW-directed compression (Debelmas 1986). Deformation resulted in the marked differences between (a) the narrow and SW–NE orientated Northern Subalpine Ranges in Dauphiné and Savoy, in front of the Aiguilles Rouges-Mont Blanc and Belledonne crystalline massifs (Vercors, Chartreuse, Bauges, Bornes and Chablais), and (b) the largely outcropping and west–east folded Southern Subalpine Ranges in Diois and the Alpes de Haute-Provence (Diois-Baronnies, Digne nappe, Castellane and Nice arcs) (Figs. 14.28, 14.29).

### *The Mesozoic basin and Jurassic development*

The Jurassic transgression occurred at the end of a relatively quiescent phase of deposition in late Triassic times. Triassic sediment thicknesses are relatively consistent along the basin margins (100–300 m) but increase towards the centre (up to >1000 m), mainly due to normal thickening of the evaporitic complex. The extent and boundaries of the Triassic depositional area are broadly structural, coinciding with those of the future Jurassic basin. The development of the SE France Basin during the Triassic resulted from new stress conditions related to the Tethyan opening.

### *Structural pattern of the SE France Basin*

The development of the basin can be traced by examining the geometries of the deposits within the basin at various times (Fig. 13.29). A series of SW–NE (or cévenol) and west–east striking faults delimit the main part of the basin. The former were the main structures involved in basin formation. Faults along the Cévennes border and the Durance river were directly related to basin subsidence. Secondary, parallel, faults (e.g. Corconne and Nimes faults, Subdauphiné Fault) controlled important topographic features within the basin, for example forming the boundary with the deep-marine areas and controlling active slopes. The west–east orientated faults (e.g. Ventoux-Lure Fault, North Provence Fault, transverse faults on the Cévennes border and Maures) were more involved in basin partitioning. For example, from the Tithonian onwards the Ventoux-Lure Fault marked the southern boundary of the Cretaceous Vocontian Basin. Similarly, the existence of a high to the south of the basin, and probably bounded by a west–east orientated fault, has been suggested by facies analysis.

Basin highs are indicated on Figures 14.28 and 14.29 in their present locations and orientations (subsequent translation being related to Alpine deformation). The Dauphiné High was a significant, if discontinuous, structure extending from the Belledonne Massif (La Mure dome) to the north, to the Durance and Moyen Verdon highs to the south. Other, albeit less well-defined highs, include the St-Julien High south of the Pelvoux Massif and the Tinée High to the west of the Argentera Massif. Additional highs provided internal basin structure, for example the Cévennes High. To the south, the highs are associated with the northern margin of the Iberia–Corsica–Sardinia Block, which was connected with the Briançonnais High during Mesozoic times. This latter high was a major unit of the French–Italian inner Alps and also forms the eastern boundary of the Mesozoic SE France Basin.

The interaction of fault activity and the locations of the various basin highs led to the partition of the basin into areas with different evolutionary histories. These regions include the Vivarais-Cévennes area close to the SE Massif Central faults, the Languedoc area to the west of the Nime Fault (and extending to the NE along the Dauphiné Basin of the northern Subalpine Ranges), the Vocontian area which was the main depocentre of the Mesozoic basin, the Provence area to the south which continued eastwards into the Provence Platform and the Moyen Verdon High.

### *Jurassic depositional history*

The sedimentary evolution, in Jurassic times, of SE France can be related to the history of Tethys. In particular, there was a major change coincident with the opening of the Ligurian-Piedmontese Ocean, which resulted in changes in both subsidence and depositional patterns. During the Early Jurassic and up to the beginning of the Middle Jurassic (i.e. to Bathonian times), the SE France Basin was defined by extensional activity which resulted in the formation of a series of horsts and grabens with different subsidence histories (e.g. Barféty *et al.* 1986; Dardeau *et al.* 1988, 1990, 1994; Elmi 1990; de Graciansky *et al.* 1993; Grand 1988). From Late Bathonian times onwards, the entire basin began to subside, and this period was coincident

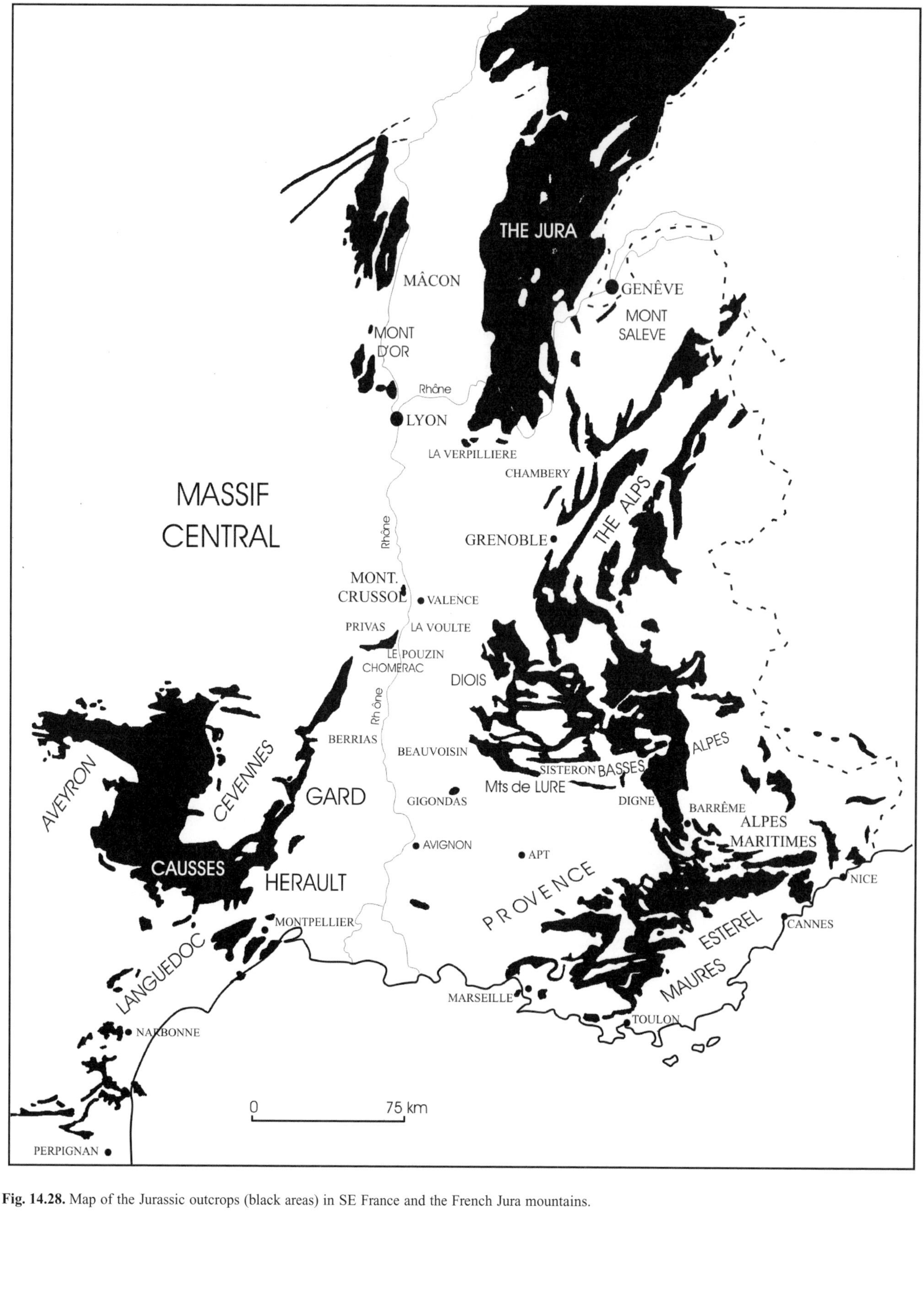


**Fig. 14.28.** Map of the Jurassic outcrops (black areas) in SE France and the French Jura mountains.

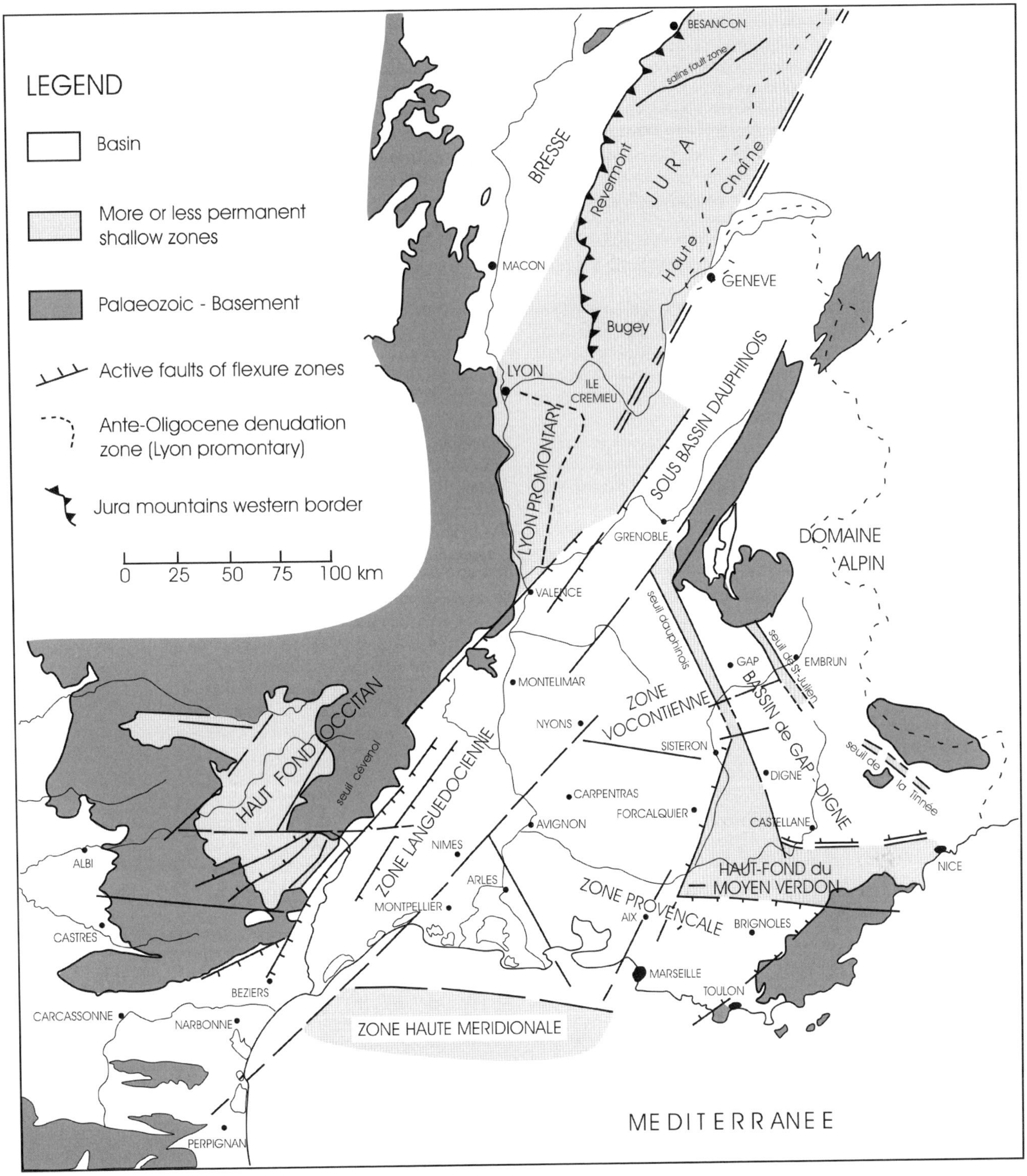


**Fig. 14.29.** Sedimentary structural setting of the Mesozoic SE France Basin and Jura Range. From Baudrimont & Dubois (1977), modified and completed.

with high deposition rates. This phase of marked subsidence is assumed to be related to post-rift thermal activity. Up until Middle Oxfordian times, sedimentation kept pace with the high subsidence rates in the basin centre; along the margins, however, deposition rates were relatively low. From the Late Oxfordian onwards, subsidence became more marked along the basin margins, and in these areas sedimentary thicknesses are greater than in the central parts of the basin.

*Defining the Jurassic in SE France*

Originally, the Rhaetian was included in the Jurassic since it was thought that it heralded the widespread Early Jurassic transgression. The Jurassic proper commences with the basal Hettangian stage, but in the SE France Basin the Triassic–Jurassic boundary is uncertain due to the absence of the index species of the lowermost *Planorbis* Zone and Subzone. The earliest ammonite faunas (Digne-Gap Basin, Ardèche, Mont d'Or Lyonnais) are from the *Psilonotum* horizon. In the major part of the SE France Basin and Jura where they occur, the oldest marine deposits (presumably Hettangian in age) are devoid of ammonites and yield only benthic faunas (bivalves, echinids).

The top of the Jurassic is defined by the lower boundary of the Cretaceous and its lowermost Berriasian stage. For historical reasons, the SE France Basin and the Jura region are fundamental with regard to the Jurassic–Cretaceous boundary. On the one hand, the need for such a boundary was clear, based on the fact that on the platform areas surrounding the basin the Jurassic ends with the deposition of subaerial or/and lacustrine units (the so-called Purbeckian facies). Such units are common in the Jura area, where the Dubisian (pseudo)stage, a synonym for the Purbeckian, was defined. On the other hand, the more complete marine successions in the SE France Basin (with ammonite and calpionellid successions etc.) were expected to provide sedimentary and facies continuity. This, however, was not detailed enough, and so the main boundary is defined internationally (see above).

A further complication is the fact that there are inherent difficulties in correlating between the Tethyan and Boreal strata and faunas. At the present time, in the Tethyan Realm the boundary is placed at the base of the lowest Berriasian zone, i.e. the *Grandis* (or *Euxinus*) Zone. Over much of the SE France Basin, a lithological change is obvious between the Ardèche (Broyon, Le Pouzin) or Vocontian (Le Chouet) 'Calcaires blancs' below and the overlying Berriasian succession of limestones and marls or clayey limestones (often including one or several discontinuities). The boundary at the top of the 'Calcaire blancs', which is coincident with the A and B calpionellid zones at Broyon and Angles, is considered to be a third-order sequence boundary (Be1), but it is not well localized in the Berriasian stratotype and occurs far below the first Berriasian ammonites (Jan du Chêne *et al.* 1993).

Despite these problems, the SE France Basin contains a variety of sections and/or localities which serve as potential global stratotype sections for four of the Jurassic stages: Bathonian (Bas Auran section, south of Digne, Alpes de Haute-Provence); Oxfordian (Thuoux and Savournon sections, near Serres, north of Sisteron, Alpes de Haute-Provence); Kimmeridgian (Mount Crussol, Ardèche (type section of Crussolian, Rollier) and Châteauneuf d'Oze sections, Alpes de Haute-Provence (as secondary GSSP in the sub-Mediterranean Province in addition to the primary GSSP in the sub-Boreal Province); and Tithonian (Mount Crussol and Canjuers sections, Var).

*Stratigraphy and depositional development*

The extent and complexity of the Jurassic in SE France is such that it is impossible to bring everything together in a synthetic stratigraphical chart. Moreover, regional studies often use informal lithological units which do not follow the precise recommendations for the definition of lithostratigraphical formations and subunits. The situation, unfortunately, has not improved with the advent of work on sequence stratigraphy in the region.

This section does not follow the standard threefold division of the Jurassic. The stratigraphical succession will be divided into five sedimentary bodies, each of which can easily be identified both within the basin as well as along the basin margins. The units are bounded by discontinuities, which are particularly obvious on the surrounding platforms. Since the 'Synthèse Géologique du Sud-Est de la France' was published by the French Bureau de Recherches Géologiques et Minières (BRGM; Debrand-Passard *et al.* 1984), several other studies have proposed new interpretations based on sequence stratigraphical concepts (e.g. de Graciansky *et al.* 1998*a*,*b*, 1999; Jacquin *et al.* 1998; Gaillard *et al.* 2004). In terms of biostratigraphy for the region, the main work is that of the Groupe Français d'Etude du Jurassique (Cariou & Hantzpergue 1997).

**Calcareous Lower Jurassic (or Lias) (Hettangian up to Domerian *p.p.*).** In the central part of the SE France Basin (southern Subalpine Ranges) there are no outcrops of Lower Jurassic age (in some areas, part of the Middle Jurassic is also absent). It is only recognized from the deepest boreholes, where precise dates are often inadequate or dubious (e.g. Baudrimont & Dubois 1977). The classic distinction between the 'Lias calcaire' and the 'Lias marneux' is clear, but neither the 'Lias marneux' nor the 'Dogger' can be further subdivided.

The Jurassic transgression commenced during the latest Triassic and Rhaetian stage and forms part of the first (T/R4) of the second-order transgressive–regressive (T/R) cycles identified by de Graciansky *et al.* (1998*a*,*b*) in Tethyan western Europe. During the Hettangian transgression, the sea spread over much of the Alps and the Rhône Valley extending as far as the eastern border of the Massif Central. Initial sedimentation was neritic with the deposition of shallow-marine oolitic or bioclastic units, as seen in the area extending from the inner Alps to the Ardèche (basal carbonate complex) and the Corbières (*Diademopsis* Limestones) areas. These are comparable with the English 'Pre-*Planorbis* beds'. More open-marine environments, characterized by nodular limestones and clays or shales with ammonites, are dated as latest Early Hettangian (*Planorbis* Zone and Subzone, *Psilonotum* horizon) and are found in the northern Subalpine ranges and Mont Joly (Helvetic nappe), the Lyons Promontary, the Ardèche and the Gap-Digne areas. However, the *Planorbis* horizon is not recognized. The maximum flooding surface for the transgression was later in the Alpes Maritimes, or along the northern edge of the Provence Platform where the earliest ammonite faunas are from the upper part of the *Planorbis* Zone (*Johnstoni* Subzone).

The transgression continued, through several third-order depositional sequences, during Middle and Late Hettangian through to Early Sinemurian times. Peak transgression coincided with the *Turneri* Zone. Clayey and thick units of fine-grained limestones in the Subalpine area pass laterally into bioclastic limestones along the margins of the subsiding platforms. The well-known 'Calcaires à gryphées' are the dominant facies of the Sinemurian which locally commenced in Upper Hettangian times (southern Jura), but occurs later on the Cévennes border (Lotharingian) and in Provence (Carixian). The proximal parts of the Provence Platform, as well as the Corbières and Causses areas, also include dolomitic deposits, and these are frequently associated with neritic, oolitic or algal limestones.

The Upper Sinemurian (Lotharingian) and lowermost lower Pliensbachian (Carixian) deposits (up to the *Ibex* Zone) represent an extensive regressive phase, which was interrupted by transgressive events interpreted as resulting from deformation related to Tethyan extension. The most noteworthy of these events is the *Raricostatum* Zone event (Late Sinemurian), which has been identified in Provence, the Subalpine ranges, the Helvetic nappe and the Jura Mountains. The most frequent facies found are crinoidal limestones with phosphatic nodules or/and fossils and ferruginous oolites. The Sinemurian–Pliensbachian boundary is often marked by a discontinuity or condensed deposits and a lithological change, especially on the platform areas (e.g. Causses, Provence, Lyons Promontary and Jura). In the subsiding areas (Subalpine ranges), crinoidal limestones and cherts are found on the raised edges of faulted and/or tilted blocks. Locally

(Digne area) these are cut by an erosional truncation surface and are interpreted as lowstand deposits of the regressive half-cycle of the second-order T/R4 cycle.

As early as the *Ibex* Zone, a broad transgression marked the onset of the T/R5 cycle. This spread out during the Late Carixian and several third-order sequences were deposited. These are characterized by the presence of bioturbated limestones, alternating with clayey limestones and marls. The peak transgression is located in the lowermost Domerian, *Stokesi* Subzone (or Zone) and corresponds to the presence of crinoidal limestones (Subalpine ranges, Cévennes border, Provence Platform) or limestones and marls with ferruginous oolites (Lyons Promontary).

**Marly Lower Jurassic (or Lias) (Domerian *pro parte minima* up to Aalenian *p.p.*).** Lithological changes observed between the 'Lias Calcaire' and the 'Lias marneux' correspond with, or immediately follow, the *Stokesi* Zone (or Subzone) maximum flooding surface. Black homogeneous micaceous shales (Amaltheid or Domerian Marls) are extensive across the subsiding basin and its margins (e.g. Subalpine ranges, Causses). These sediments were deposited during the infilling phase of a regressive cycle (second-order regressive half-cycle R5 of de Graciansky *et al.* 1998*a*,*b*). On the platform areas (e.g. Corbières, Lyons Promontary, Jura) these sediments overlie a hiatus which corresponds (more or less) to the duration of the Carixian–Domerian boundary. The end of the regressive phase, and maximum regression, were marked by the deposition of bioclastic limestones with pectinids (Corbières) or *Harpax* shell beds (e.g. Mont d'Or lyonnais) and crinoidal limestones (e.g. Cévennes border). In contrast, there was no change in sedimentation type in the Causses area where the deposition of homogeneous micaceous black shales with rare calcareous layers or nodules was continuous.

The Pliensbachian–Toarcian boundary is often marked by an unconformity (e.g. Provence, Corbières, Languedoc and Causses, Cévennes border, Lyons Promontary and Jura). This is related to tectonic activity which is well documented in the Subalpine area. In some areas (e.g. Digne area) the uppermost Pliensbachian beds were eroded

The Toarcian marks the onset of a new transgressive–regressive cycle (T/R6) which extends into the Middle Aalenian (*Bradfordense* Zone). This was a time of active subsidence and rapid accumulation of sediment. The earliest deposits, of lowermost Lower Toarcian age (*Semicostatum* Zone), are absent or extremely condensed, except in those parts of the basin which were most rapidly subsiding (e.g. Digne area). The generally low accumulation rate can be interpreted in terms of sediment starvation following the widespread and rapid Toarcian transgression.

The Early and Middle *(pars)* Toarcian transgressive phase reached its maximum during the earliest *Bifrons* Zone (*Bifrons* Subzone). Locally (distal Provence Platform) these deposits both directly and unconformably overlie the uppermost Plienbachian crinoidal limestones. In the subsiding areas (e.g. Digne, Serre-Ponçon) thick sections of alternating marls and clayey limestones were accumulated. Lower Toarcian black carbonaceous organic-rich shales ('Schistes carton') are extensive across the region from Corbières as far as the Jura area, as well as in the Causses-Languedoc and the Cévennes border.

Following the peak transgression, the regressive phase of the second-order transgressive–regressive cycle T/R5 corresponds to the period of maximum accommodation space creation. During the Middle–Late Toarcian infilling phase, marls and/or alternating marls and limestones were deposited (e.g. northern Subalpine ranges, Corbières, Causses and Languedoc), with the exception of the central part of the basin (Digne area) where sediment starvation occurred (this corresponds to a gap in the *Variabilis*, *Thouarsense* and *Insigne* zones). Deposition recommenced during the Late Toarcian–Aalenian and is marked by the accumulation of calcareous silts and silty shales, up to several hundred metres thick. These units overlie the distal part of the adjacent platform. In the Digne area these sediments are truncated by an unconformable erosional surface (lowermost *Aalensis* Zone) which marks the end of the infilling phase. This surface corresponds to the mid-Cimmerian unconformity in NW Europe. On the margins of the basin (e.g. Cévennes, Provence, Lyons Promontary and Jura), marls and crinoidal or bioclastic limestones or mudstones with ferruginous or phosphatic oolites were deposited.

**Calcareous Middle Jurassic (or Dogger) (Aalenian *p.p.* up to Middle Bathonian *p.p.*).** In many areas of the SE France Basin, the change from marly Early Jurassic to Middle Jurassic carbonates is a transitional one. In some areas, however, there are signs of sedimentary instability at this time, although the precise period is variable. This instability was related to the events which occurred at the transition of the Lower to Middle Jurassic, and which were related to the mid-Cimmerian unconformity in NW Europe. This unconformity is related to both eustatic changes as well as local tectonic activity. Thus, the precise age of the unconformity varies across Europe. In the Tethyan areas the maximum regression occurred in the lower *Discites* Zone of the Bajocian, i.e. between the *Walkeri* and *Subtectum* (= *Discites*) subzones (Jacquin *et al.* 1998).

The Aalenian and lowermost Lower Bajocian age successions were deposited in the final stages of a regressive cycle (half-cycle R6 of de Graciansky *et al.* 1998*a*,*b*). On the stable areas, such as the Lyons Promontary (e.g. Mont d'Or Lyonnais, Ile Crémieu, Bas-Bugey) and the Jura Mountains, Toarcian ferruginous oolite facies, often discontinuous, are present, and the deposition of these units was continuous almost up into the Aalenian. They were subsequently succeeded by Middle (e.g. Lyons Promontary, Causses and Languedoc) or upper Aalenian (e.g. Jura Mountains) 'Calcaires à *Zoophycos*' and various platform carbonates, limestones with cherts and oncolites (e.g. Corbières), crinoidal and/or oolitic limestones (e.g. Causses and Languedoc, Mont d'Or Lyonnais) and sandy limestones or sandstones (e.g. northern Subalpine ranges). On the Provence Platform, there are no deposits of Aalenian age (beds of the *Concavum* Zone may be present at the base of the transgressive Bajocian deposits). The subsiding areas of the basin are characterized by thick successions which are generally more calcareous than the underlying Toarcian deposits (e.g. mudstones and marlstones in the Digne area, fucoids marls in the Ardèche).

The onset of the Bajocian transgressive phase (cycle T/R7; de Graciansky *et al.* 1998*a*,*b*; Jacquin *et al.* 1998) often began as early as the latest Aalenian (*Concavum* Zone). The transgression attained its maximum extent in the Early Bathonian (*Zigzag* Zone, *Macrescens* Subzone). In the subsiding Digne and Gap areas alternating calcareous mudstones and marlstones, several hundred metres thick, were accumulated, suggesting that there was active subsidence at this time. Only the uppermost part (Upper Bajocian) of this basinal succession extends across the adjacent Provence carbonate platform, where it directly overlies the Carixian limestones and hardgrounds. The boundary between the two transgressive pulses is presumably related to an extensional event which resulted in block tilting in the subalpine ranges and along the eastern border of the Massif Central. Thus, in the Ardèche region, Bajocian deposits are often missing or discontinuous, except in the north (i.e. La Voulte, Crussol) where crinoidal limestones or phosphatic fossil-bearing beds crop out. Platform carbonates occur in the Causses-Languedoc region (cherts, limestones often dolomitized, white oolitic limestones) and in the Corbières area.

In the Jura Mountains, an extensive carbonate platform (crinoidal limestones with coral bioherms and biostromes at two levels) was deposited during an Early Bajocian transgressive phase. The distal part of this platform extends towards the SE to the margin of the Dauphiné Basin. Overlying the top bored surface, the 'Calcaires à huîtres' and 'Calcaires oolithiques' correspond to a Late Bajocian transgressive phase. In the Haute-Chaîne region these grade laterally to the 'Marnes de la (cascade) de la Queue de Cheval' (Horse's Tail Waterfall). On the Lyons Promontary, discontinuous condensed beds yielding Late Aalenian (*Concavum* Zone) and Early Bajocian faunas are the only evidence of the initial transgressive phase between the Aalenian crinoidal limestones ('Pierre de Couzon') below and the Late Bajocian siliceous limestones ('Ciret') above.

The Early Bathonian represents a major drowning event corresponding to the time of peak transgression (*Zigzag Zone, Macrescens* Subzone) which coincided with the onset of a regressive cycle (half-cycle R7). This drowning event is marked by the deposition of the 'Terres Noires' Formation (de Graciansky *et al.* 1993), a thick section of black silty shales which were developed from Late Bathonian times onwards and extend across the entire SE France Basin with the exception of the margins. Early Bathonian non-depositional areas extend onto the Lyons Promontary (e.g. Ile Crémieu) and the Bresse border of the Jura Mountains (e.g. the Revermont), the proximal Provence Platform and the Cévennes border. The initial onlapping beds are of various ages, ranging from Early Bathonian up to Middle Bathonian (*Bremeri* Zone) or Late Bathonian (*Retrocostatum* Zone) times. Facies transitional to the basinal Terres Noires are developed on the distal platform, the Bugey area ('Calcaires à taches'), in the Haut-Jura area ('Calcaires de la Haute-Chaîne') of the Jura Mountains, as well as to the north of Ardèche and the Aubenas Basin along the SE Massif Central border, and the Provence Platform ('Calcaires à *Zoophycos*').

**Middle–Upper Jurassic 'Terres Noires' (Late Bathonian *p.p.* up to Middle Oxfordian *p.p.*).** On the platform areas the end of the Middle Bathonian is represented by a major unconformity and erosional surface related to the rifting and opening of the Ligurian-Piedmontese Ocean. This was the final extensional event before the onset of post-rift thermal subsidence and subsequent widespread subsidence of the SE France Basin. It also marked the commencement of the T/R8 transgressive/regressive cycle (Jacquin *et al.* 1998) which de Graciansky *et al.* (1999) divide into two cycles (T/R8a and 8b).

The Late Bathonian–Early Callovian transgressive phase is typified in the SE France Basin by the lower member of the 'Terres Noires' Formation (700 up to 1000 m) below the 'Repère médian' (100 m) and dated as the *Bullatus* Zone. The lower member is reduced on the intrabasinal highs (e.g. Dorsale dauphinoise, St-Julien and La Tinée highs) which were completely submerged during the Early Callovian peak transgression (*Gracilis* Zone). On the distal Provence Platform, deposition of the 'Calcaires à *Zoophycos*' continued and the proximal part received bioclastic limestones and overlying dolomites. On the Jura platform, transgression is indicated by the renewal of deposition as early as the latest Middle Bathonian (e.g. Ile Crémieu and Revermont ('Calcaires à silex' and 'Choin')) and this was followed by the Late Bathonian 'Marnes des Monts d'Ain', and subsequent latest Late Bathonian (*Discus* Zone)–Early Callovian bioclastic or oolithic limestones. On the highs along the Ardèche border the transgressive deposits were characterized by marly limestones of Late Bathonian ('Calcaires de la Clapouze, de l'Arénier' etc) and Early Callovian age ('Couches de Gette et de Naves').

During the regressive phase which followed the late Early Callovian peak transgression, the 'Terres Noires' facies once again accumulated in the basin. This unit corresponds to the upper member overlying the 'repère médian' (*c.* 200 m thick) and includes the 'marnes feuilletées and plaquettes' with 'pseudobioherms' of the Laragne-Aurel and Barcillonnette areas. Encroachment of the basinal marly facies onto the margins is much more accentuated at this time. On the Cévennes border, the successions are also more calcareous (e.g. 'Couches des Vans et des Assions') and the top is truncated by a discontinuity within the Middle Callovian *Coronatum* Zone. On the other hand, the proximal platform (e.g. Causses) was not drowned, unlike the Provence Platform. Therefore the 'Calcaires à *Zoophycos*' in the transitional area and the platform carbonates on the proximal Provence Platform were truncated by the same discontinuity. In the Jura Mountains, the hiatus at the top of the 'Alternance calcareo-argileuse' and 'Calcaires d'Arnans' (from *Gracilis* Zone, *Patina* Subzone up to *Coronatum* Zone, *Obductum* Subzone) encompasses the entire *Coronatum* Zone (Ile Crémieu and Bas-Bugey) or only the upper *Grossouvrei* Subzone in Revermont, Haut-Bugey and the Inner (or Helvetic) Jura Mountains.

Following de Graciansky *et al.* (1999), the upper Middle Callovian *Coronatum* Zone unconformity would mark the beginning of the second-order transgressive–regressive cycle T/R8b and define the regression maximum. The rapid subsidence of the SE France Basin is associated with active synsedimentary faulting on the basin margins. Additionally, the contrasting sediment thicknesses between the basin and the surrounding platforms provide evidence of differential subsidence across the region.

In the basin, Late Callovian–Early Oxfordian sediments, corresponding to the upper part of the upper Member of the 'Terres Noires' Formation, form units up to 1000 m (Nyons) or 1500 m (Chorges) thick. At Beauvoisin the last of the 'pseudobioherms' (cf. VI.2) developed within these beds (Gaillard *et al.* 1985, 1992). The units represent the transgressive half-cycle and the lower part of the regressive half-cycle of T/R8 up to the upper boundary of the 'Terres Noires' Formation. This upper boundary is marked by the rapid change alternating mudstones and marlstones (known as the 'alternance argovienne') which were deposited from the uppermost *Antecedens* Subzone or from the boundary of the *Antecedens–Parandieri* subzones upwards. The peak transgression is indicated by a short period of sediment starvation which is marked by the presence of a nodular layer, often with phosphatic ammonites (*Mariae* Zone, *Scarburgense* Subzone).

On the distal platforms, the Late Callovian and Early Oxfordian is generally represented by either a gap in sedimentation or the deposition of condensed sections (e.g. the Ardèche, with the exception of La Voulte-sur-Rhône and the Crussol areas where 'Terres Noires' facies are present), and is marked by the 'Banc bleu' of Early Oxfordian age. On the distal Provence Platform condensed beds of the *Trezeense* and *Lamberti* subzones were deposited; in the Causses region (inner platform) discontinuous beds overlying dolomites with *Athleta, Lamberti* and *Cordatum p.p.* faunas are present. In the Corbières area dolomitization

(Lower Dolomites) prohibits the recognition of beds of this age. In the Jura Mountains, the latest Middle Callovian events correspond to the reappearance of the Haute-Chaîne (or Helvetic) High along the inner margin of the range. Late Callovian–Early Oxfordian non-deposition or/and condensed or reworked discontinuous beds characterize deposition on this high. Towards the NW, on the outer Jura, a unit containing phosphatic fossils dated as the *Mariae* Zone, *Scarburgense* Subzone also yields reworked Late or even Middle Callovian elements. The overlying marls contain pyritized ammonites (*Renggeri* Marls) and calcareous nodules ('Couches à *Sphérites*') and are dated as Early and Middle (*p.p.*) Oxfordian.

**Calcareous Upper Jurassic (or Malm) (Middle Oxfordian *p.p.* up to Tithonian).** The final phase of Jurassic sedimentation in the region was characterized by the increase in the amount of carbonate present. The deposition of sediments typical of open-marine conditions attained their maximum extent at this time mainly as a result of active subsidence (and drowning) of the basin margins. The Upper Jurassic limestones represent the end of the second-order T/R8 regressive half-cycle (Jacquin *et al.* 1998) or the T/R8a (de Graciansky *et al.* 1999) and T/R9 cycles (exept for the upper part of the Berriasian). Latest Middle Oxfordian (*Transversarium* Zone) beds were the first widespread Late Jurassic deposits across the SE France Basin and the lower boundary of this unit is often correlated with the erosional surface which cut various Callovian and even Bathonian beds. This unit represents the so-called 'Argovian transgression and unconformity' of some authors.

In the Subalpine ranges as well as in the La Voulte-sur-Rhône and Crussol areas 'Argovian' alternating marlstones and mudstones (300–400 m thick in the Diois area) include Middle and Upper Oxfordian units (extending up to the 'Bancs Roux' (*Bimammatum* Zone, *Hypselum* Subzone)). In more proximal situations, the same beds are represented by limestones (e.g. Ardèche, distal Provence Platform, Moyen Verdon High). Increasingly, clays become less common and eventually disappear across the region (i.e. *Bimammatum* and *Planula* Zones). In the Subalpine area, the 'Barre (cliff) rauracienne' includes two zones with the same calcareous facies, while in the Ardèche area two formations can be distinguished ('Couches de Joyeuses' Formation below and 'Calcaires du Pouzin' Formation above). Dolomites are also well represented, for example in the Causses and the proximal parts of the Provence Platform (Upper Oxfordian) and the Corbières (Lower Dolomite; Oxfordian).

In the Jura Mountains, the Middle Oxfordian limestones and marls of the Birmensdorf Beds (slope facies) on the Haute-Chaîne High represent the NE continuation of the Ardéchois facies. Sponge and algal bioherms as well as alternating marls and limestones ('Calcaires Hydrauliques') developed in the southern Jura Mountains and typify the distal platform. The proximal platform 'Rauracian' carbonate extends to the NW and beyond the Salins Fault Zone. Following a short hiatus, the deposition of a series of units, including the Effingen and Geissberg Beds (*Bifurcatus* Zone) and the 'Calcaires Lités' Formation (*Bimammatum* Zone) in the SE, and the Besançon Marls ('Marnes à Astartes' of Franche-Comté; type area of the Sequanian Stage) in the NW, mark the recurrence of fine-grained detritic deposition. These clastic sediments subsequently covered the Rauracian carbonate platform. The renewed onset of clastic deposition also coincided with the subsidence of the Haute-Chaîne High. In Late Oxfordian times, carbonates (*Planula* Zone) were once again predominant as marked by the deposition of the 'Calcaires pseudolithographiques'. These pass laterally to the NW into oolitic and bioclastic limestones which contain small coral patches and correspond to the second, so-called Sequanian, carbonate platform. The uppermost part of this platform is probably Early Kimmeridgian in age. To the NW, the lagoonal fine-grained Besançon Limestones (= 'Calcaires à *Astartes*') form part of the Sequanian Stage in the Franche-Comté type area.

Kimmeridgian and Tithonian depositional development across the region was similar to that of the Upper Oxfordian. In the Subalpine region, the Cévennes border and the Languedoc areas, the Lower Kimmeridgian up to the 'Vire à *Crussoliceras*' displays alternating limestones and marlstones (La Louyre Limestones). These are overlain by Upper Kimmeridgian and Tithonian limestones (= 'Barre tithonienne'). Intercalated breccias in the Vocontian Tithonian are interpreted as either being related to slope deposition (redeposition) or to sea-bottom sediment reworking by storm waves generated by tropical hurricanes (Raja-Gabaglia 1995; Séguret *et al.* 2001). In the Ardèche region, Upper Kimmeridgian limestones are subdivided into the La Beaume Limestones (*Acanticum* and Eudoxus *p.p.* Zones) and the Ruin-like Païolive Limestones (= Crussol Castle Limestones) (*Eudoxus p.p.* and *Beckeri* Zones). The Lower Tithonian, which comprises mainly nodular mudstones, is clearly divided from the Late Tithonian 'Calcaires blancs ardéchois', with calpionellids. On the Provence Platform, the Causses and the Corbières, Kimmeridgian and Tithonian bioclastic or gravelly limestones are often dolomitized.

In the Jura Mountains, Sequanian platform carbonates were onlapped during Early Kimmeridgian times. This was approximately coeval with the deposition of the Cephalopod Beds to the SE (from the Alpine sea) and the *Pterocera* Beds in the NW (from the Paris Basin). The maximum extent of the ammonite-bearing beds is dated at the *Divisum* Zone. Flooding, however, was not so extensive, and the carbonate platform continued to flourish.

Indeed, during Kimmeridgian–Tithonian times the platform extended basinwards. The formation of the Jura Mountains coral complex commenced as early as late Early Kimmeridgian times and includes oncolitic or bioclastic limestones with coral patches and lagoonal or inner platform deposits with stromatoporids or/and bioturbation (e.g. 'tubulures'). Progradation of the Tithonian coral complex is illustrated at Salève, near Geneva, and at Bec de l'Echaillon near Grenoble, where the reef complex extends up into the Berriasian (as in Provence). On the proximal platform the establishment of protected muddy environments or/and tidal flats heralded the lagoonal/lacustrine Purbeckian deposits, whose upper part is of Early Cretaceous age.

Towards the SW, in the Bas-Languedoc (e.g. Séranne Mountains) bioclastic sediments with rich coral buildups, deposited as early as latest Kimmeridgian times, form an extensive barrier reef. During the Tithonian the barrier reef was onlapped by gravels (including dasycladals) from the backreef area. On the Provence Platform, the reef complex (Provence White Limestones) is best developed in the Verdon Canyon to the north of Grasse. In this area, reef development commenced above the *Hybonotum* Zone and extends up to the Cretaceous (Berriasian to Valanginian), where it is intercalated with lagoonal/lacustrine Purbeckian deposits. Thus, only the lowermost massive and coral-rich parts of the reef (300 m thick in the Verdon Canyon) would appear to be Tithonian in age. In the Corbières area, predominantly inner-platform infralittoral deposits ('Calcaires massifs à *Anchispirocyclines*') are found, and these pass laterally into evaporitic beds (evolving towards dissolution breccias). This entire succession is overlain by another solution breccia at a time corresponding to the Jurassic–Cretaceous boundary (Brèche-limite).

*Palaeohydrothermal activity*
Carbonate 'pseudobioherms' are recognized from the Early Bathonian to early Middle Oxfordian 'Terres Noires' Formation. Following a recent study on Beauvoisin pseudobioherms (Gaillard *et al.* 1985, 1992) such structures are now interpreted as proof of palaeohydrothermal activity within the area of maximum subsidence in the SE France Basin (Vocontian Trough; see Fig. 14.29) and related to extensional tectonic and active synsedimentary faulting. Stable isotopic studies ($\delta^{13}C$ and $\delta^{18}O$) and evidence from the biological communities (mainly Lucinid bivalves) present within the SE France Basin suggest that the pseudobioherms are similar to those presently observed in cold seeps with dominant $CH_4$. Fluids of cold seeps facilitated chemosynthesis by bacteria, probably symbiotic with Lucinid bivalves, and carbonate precipitation.

*Palaeogeography*
The palaeogeography of the SE France Basin (including the Jura region) has been outlined in a series of recent publications. The *Synthèse paléogéographique du Jurassique Français* presented by the French Research Jurassic Group (Enay & Mangold 1980) and the *Synthèse géologique du Sud-Est de la France* edited by the BRGM (Debrand-Passard *et al.* 1984) provide maps of the region. The BRGM maps are limited to the SE France Basin (including the Jura and Burgundy areas) at a scale of 1:1 500 000 and provide more detail, while the facies and interpretative maps of the French Research Jurassic Group are at a smaller scale but place the SE France Basin in the larger context of France. More recently, the palaeogeographical interpretations of Ziegler (1988) and those of the Tethys (Dercourt *et al.* 1993) and Peri-Tethys (Dercourt *et al.* 2000) programmes deal with areas larger than that of the SE France Basin, i.e. western and central Europe (Ziegler 1988) or the Tethys and adjacent regions (Dercourt *et al.* 1993, 2000), and are largely based on palinspastic reconstructions. The Ziegler (1988) maps show timespans corresponding to several Jurassic stages, while Dercourt *et al.* (1993, 2000) favour shorter timespans selected on the basis of the greater number of constraining geophysical and palaeomagnetic data.

## *Swiss Jura Mountains (P.J., A.W., A.G.R.)*

The geographic term 'Jura' has in German a double meaning: first, stratigraphically it comprises the period of the 'Jurassic', and second, regionally it encompasses the hills build by mainly mid-Mesozoic rocks in Bavaria (Fränkischer Jura), Swabia (Schwäbischer Jura) and Switzerland (Schweizer Jura). For the latter, it comprises the Neogene fold-and-thrust belt (Folded Jura) extending from Lake Annecy in eastern France to the Zurich area in northern Switzerland, as well as the undeformed Mesozoic sedimentary cover (Tabular Jura) extending from the southern end of the Upper Rhine Graben to southern Germany.

*Early Jurassic*
The area of the eastern and central Swiss Jura occupied a position between the Swabian Basin in the NE and the Rhodanian Basin in the SW (Fig. 14.30). The relatively thin Early Jurassic strata suggest a low subsidence rate (e.g. Wildi *et al.* 1989; Wetzel *et al.* 2003). Thickness variations, however, imply differential subsidence. Following some marine ingressions during the Late Triassic (e.g. Etzold & Schweizer 2005), the area was flooded during the Early Hettangian, but remained a submarine high; this continued to be important for sedimentary facies development until the Middle Jurassic. The two basins and

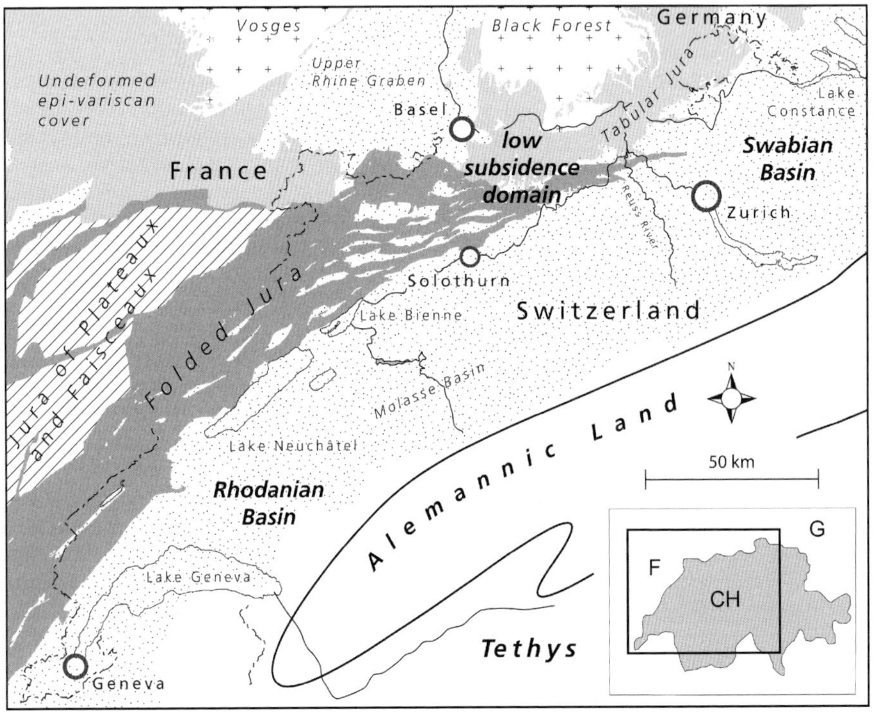


**Fig. 14.30.** Map of Folded and Tabular Jura in NW Switzerland and adjacent France and Germany . The main palaeogeographic entities of the Early Jurassic shown are the Swabian Basin, the Rhodanian Basin, both separated by a low subsidence domain, and the Alemannic Land.

the intervening swell have been separated from the Tethys by the so-called 'Alemannic landmass'. Initially a SW-trending peninsula extending from the Bohemian-Vindelician landmass to the west, the Alemannic landmass became an archipelago during the Early Jurassic, a submarine swell in the Middle Jurassic and vanished completely in the Late Jurassic.

The Early Jurassic strata of the Rhodanian Basin are only poorly exposed in the western Jura and await further investigation (Schegg *et al.* 1997; Sommaruga 1997). The basal Jurassic deposits represent the *Planorbis* Zone (Corna 1985). They are followed by a sequence about 50 m thick of Hettangian to Early Pliensbachian strata showing many similarities to their eastern equivalents discussed below (Bitterli 1972; Meyer *et al.* 2000). In contrast, the *Margaritatus* Zone is represented by 80 to 250 m of argillaceous and marly shales in the Geneva (Meyer *et al.* 2000) and Lake Neuchâtel areas (Bitterli 1972), respectively. In the Geneva area, latest Pliensbachian and Toarcian strata are only reported from a highly tectonized outcrop near Belgarde (France) where they are represented by some 20 m of ferruginous crinoidal limestones and shales interbedded with marly limestones (Meyer 2000). In the Lake Neuchâtel area (Bitterli 1972) and in the northwestern Jura (Fig. 14.31), Early Toarcian bituminous *Posidonia* shale-type sediments comparable to the Rietheim Member of the eastern Jura (see below) are some tens of metres thick. A maximum of 150 to 400 m for the whole Rhodanian Early Jurassic interval has been estimated (Trümpy 1980; Debrand-Passard *et al.* 1984).

In contrast, the continuation of the Swabian Basin into Switzerland is well documented in outcrops as well as from borehole data (e.g. Jordan 1983; Schlatter 1991; Nagra 2001). Because of the low total thickness of the Early Jurassic sediments, (22 m–*c.* 70 m), the entire succession is traditionally considered as one single stratigraphic unit, commonly known as the Lias (or Liassic). However, a formal description according to modern rules of stratigraphic nomenclature has been attempted only recently when Reisdorf *et al.* (2008) introduced the term Staffelegg Formation (previously just 'Lias') (Fig. 14.31). The first Jurassic transgression in the Swiss Jura is documented by the Schambelen Member (previously Insektenmergel, Psilonotenschichten, Psiloceras-Schichten, Planorbisschichten, Infralias; e.g. Schalch 1919; Jordan 1983; Nagra 2001) composed of terrigenous mudstones, the lower part being organic-rich. The lower boundary is synchronous within the *Planorbis* Zone; it is defined by a transgressive surface overlying Norian-age variegated dolomite-bearing shales or Rhaetian sandstones and terrigenous mudstones (e.g. Frey 1969; Tanner 1978; Jordan 1983). The top is within the *Liasicus* Zone (Reisdorf *et al.* 2008). To the east only deposits belonging to the *Planorbis* Zone are preserved (Hallau Bed; previously 'Psilonotenkalk' *sensu* Altmann 1965; e.g. Achilles & Schlatter 1986). To the SW the Schambelen Member wedges out due to subsequent erosion (Reisdorf *et al.* 2008). Early Hettangian to Late Sinemurian strata constitute the Beggingen Member (previously Cardinienschichten, Angulatenschichten, Arietenkalk, Gryphitenkalk, Arcuataschichten; e.g. Delhaes & Gerth 1912; Heim 1919; Schlatter 1976; Jordan 1983). This member consists of calcarenites, tens of centimetres thick, interlayered with some terrigenous mudstones. In the SW, in the Weissenstein area, the deposits of the *Liasicus* Zone are *Plagiostoma*-bearing, phosphoritic calcarenites, with a high quartz content at the base (Reisdorf *et al.* 2008). In northern Switzerland and southern Germany, condensed calcarenites with siderite and iron ooids representing the *Angulata* Zone are found above an erosive base documented by a hiatus covering the *Extranodosa* Subzone, (the base of the interval is the Schleitheim Bed; previously Schweizerische Cardinienbank, Angulatusbank, Angulatenbank, Eisenoolithische Folge; e.g. Bloos 1979; Jordan 1983; Schlatter 1989, 2001; Hofmann *et al.* 2000). Bivalves are abundant, especially *Cardinia* and *Plagiostoma* (Schalch 1919). The deposits of the *Angulatus* Zone wedge out to the SW due to subsequent erosion, but reappear further to the SW (Buxtorf 1907).

Further up in the stratigraphy, an erosive unconformity may cut down some tens of centimetres into the underlying limestones (i.e. Schleitheim Bed, Schambelen Member or Upper Triassic sediments). This unconformity is overlain by Early Sinemurian (*Bucklandi* Zone) calcarenites; in the east, this interval is condensed and consists of wacke- to packstones with iron ooids (the base of this interval is the Gächlingen Bed; previously Kupferfelsbank, Schweizer Cardinienschichten, Eisenoolithische Folge; e.g. Jordan 1983; Hofmann *et al.* 2000). To the west it passes into sparitic calcarenites (the base of this interval is the Courtemautruy Bed; previously Schweizer Cardinienschichten, Cardinienbänke; for details see Reisdorf *et al.* 2008). To the SW the Gächlingen Bed grades into an Fe-rich horizon and finally wedges out.

The overlying interval consists of fossiliferous, coarse calcarenites and intercalated terrigenous mudstones, rich in *Gryphaea*, forming the upper part of the Beggingen Member (*Bucklandi* to *Obtusum* Zone; e.g. Pratje 1922; Bloos 1976). This comprises phosphoritic, sparitic limestones and hardgrounds. To the south and SW, roughly north of Olten, the upper part of the Beggingen Member grades into the basal sandstones of the Weissenstein Member (see below).

Up-section, to the north (Tabular Jura, NE Switzerland) the Frick Member (previously Obtusus-Tone *sensu* Schlatter 1991; Obtusum-Schichten *sensu* Jordan 1983) comprises monotonous, terrigenous mudstones (*Obtusum* to *Raricostatum* Zone) up to 20 m thick (e.g. Schlatter 1999; Beher 2004; Reisdorf *et al.* 2008). Progressively from SW to NE, the Frick Member is overlain by the Fasiswald Member (previously Obliqua-Schichten *sensu* Delhaes & Gerth 1912; *sensu* Heim 1919; *sensu* Jordan 1983; 'Mittlerer Lias' *sensu* Buxtorf 1907; Oberer Arietenkalk after Mühlberg 1908). This consists of alternating quartz-bearing limestones and terrigenous mudstones; at the top phosphoritic deposits and/or hardgrounds may be present. Biostratigraphically, the Fasiswald Member is ascribed to the Early Sinemurian (*Semicostatum* Zone) to Early Pliensbachian (Reisdorf *et al.* 2008). Towards the SW and NE the facies interdigitates with the increasingly thick (6–25 m) quartz sandstones of the Weissenstein Member (*Semicostatum* to *Obtusum* Zone; previously Feinsandkalklage after Jordan 1983; Oberer Arietenkalk, Oberer Gryphitenkalk, Gryphäenkalke, Obtusussandsteine; Buxtorf 1907; Delhaes & Gerth 1912; Heim 1919; Fischer & Luterbacher 1963). To the west and NW marly mudstones with intercalated nodular limestones and layered concretions form the 14–20 m thick Mont Terri Member (previously Obtusustone, Obliqua-Schichten, Mittellias; Buxtorf 1910). In the upper part of this member phosphoritic limestones and belemnite-rich marls occur. The biostratigraphic range of the Mont Terri Member is not yet completely clear (Reisdorf *et al.* 2008).

In the Tabular and the Eastern Folded Jura the Beggingen, Weissenstein, Frick and Fasiswald Members together constitute up to 80% of the thickness of the Early Jurassic Staffelegg Formation. Since the *Angulata* and *Bucklandi* zones comprise only a few tens of centimetres of deposits, sediment accumulation mainly occurred during the *Semicostatum* to *Raricostatum* zones. In the Mont Terri area, however, 70% of the thickness formed during the Pliensbachian and Toarcian (Reisdorf *et al.* 2008).

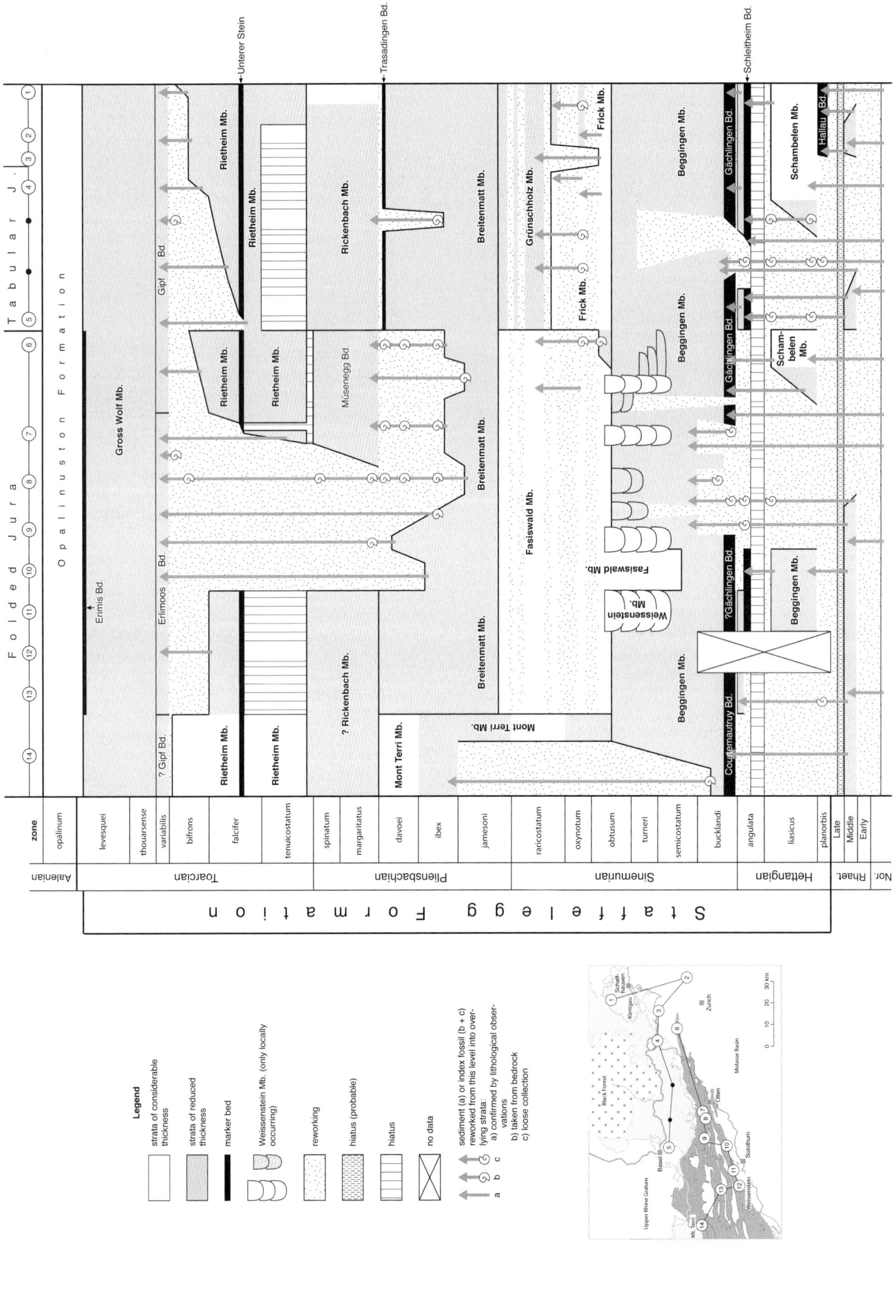


**Fig. 14.31.** Early Jurassic biostratigraphy and lithostratigraphy (after Reisdorf *et al.* 2008).

In the Tabular Jura in NE Switzerland, the Late Sinemurian and Pliensbachian are represented by a succession of marls and biodetritic limestones, some 3 m thick (up to 14 m in the NE); reworking and condensation repeatedly occurred (for details see Buxtorf 1907; Jordan 1983; Schlatter 1982, 1991, 2000; Reisdorf *et al.* 2008). Several members can be distinguished: including the Grünschholz Member (condensed, phosphoritic and glauconitic marls and nodular limestones, *Raricostatum* to *Jamesoni* Zone; previously Obliqua-Schichten *sensu* Schlatter 1991); the Breitenmatt Member (condensed, belemnite-rich, phosphoritic marls and limestones, *Jamesoni* to *Davoei* Zone; previously Numismalis-Schichten, Davoei-Schichten, Uptonienschichten) with the Trasadingen Bed at the top (previously Davoei-Bank; e.g. Schlatter 1991); and the Rickenbach Member (belemnite-rich, condensed, phosphoritic and glauconitic marls and nodular limestones; *Margaritatus* to *Tenuicostatum* Zone; previously Amaltheen-Schichten, Margaritatus-Schichten, Spinatus-Schichten, Mittlerer Lias *sensu* Buxtorf 1907; Blaugraue Mergel, Basisschicht after Kuhn & Etter 1994). Coeval with the latter, the Müsenegg Bed, that only extends as far as the Late Pliensbachian, documents intense reworking further to the SW of fossil-rich, phosphoritic marls and limestones (*Margaritatus* to *Spinatum* Zone; previously Kondensiertes Pliensbachium after Jordan 1983). A vertically embedded ichthyosaur skull within the Müsenegg Bed provided new biostratigraphic insights (Maisch & Reisdorf 2006*a*,*b*; Wetzel & Reisdorf 2008). The major part of the Toarcian is represented by the Rietheim Member (*Tenuicostatum* to *Bifrons* Zone; previously Posidonomyenschiefer, Posidonienschiefer *sensu* Kuhn & Etter 1994; schistes carton; Reisdorf *et al.* 2008) and the Gross Wolf Member (*Variabilis* to *Levesquei* Zone; previously Variabilis Horizont, Jurensis-Mergel, Jurensis-Schichten, Pleydellienbank; e.g. Jordan 1983; Tröster 1987). The distinctive bituminous Rietheim Member is very similar, in terms of the facies present, to its coeval counterparts in SW Germany (Posidonienschiefer-Formation; LGRB 2004) and southern France. The so-called 'Unterer Stein' represents a widely occurring marker bed (*Exaratum* Subzone; Kuhn & Etter 1994). The thickness, however, gradually decreases due to erosion to some tens of centimetres in the central Jura Mountains, but increases to >20 m towards the west (e.g. Hölder 1964). Locally in the Folded Jura (north and west of Olten) the member is missing due to erosion of the earliest Late Toarcian. In the Folded Jura the unconformity below the centimetre-thick Erlimoos Bed (*Variabilis* Zone) cuts down into the underlying strata; locally into the Müsenegg Bed and the Breitenmatt Member (Reisdorf *et al.* 2008). The Erlimoos Bed (previously Kondensiertes Pliensbachium after Jordan 1983) contains phosphorite and glauconite; overgrowth by stromatiform algae is common. To the north, above an erosive base, belemnite-rich marls occur. These grade laterally into a discontinuous, centimetre-thick iron-bearing or iron-oolitic limestone (Gipf Bed, previously Variabilis Horizont *sensu* Jordan 1983; e.g. Tröster 1987). The Gipf and Erlimoos beds are overlain by an alternation of condensed, fossil-rich marls and nodular limestones that constitute the Gross Wolf Member. Further up in the stratigraphy, grey terrigenous mudstones form the transition to the Middle Jurassic (e.g. Etter 1990).

*Middle Jurassic*

During the Middle Jurassic shallow-water deposits, including reef and backreef sediments, dominated to the NW and an open basin, dominated by alternating mudstones and marl limestones formed to the SE. These two main facies realms are know as the Celtic (or Rauracian) and the Argovian realms, respectively. Figure 14.32 provides an overview of the Middle Jurassic bio- and lithostratigraphy. Formations have been introduced only for

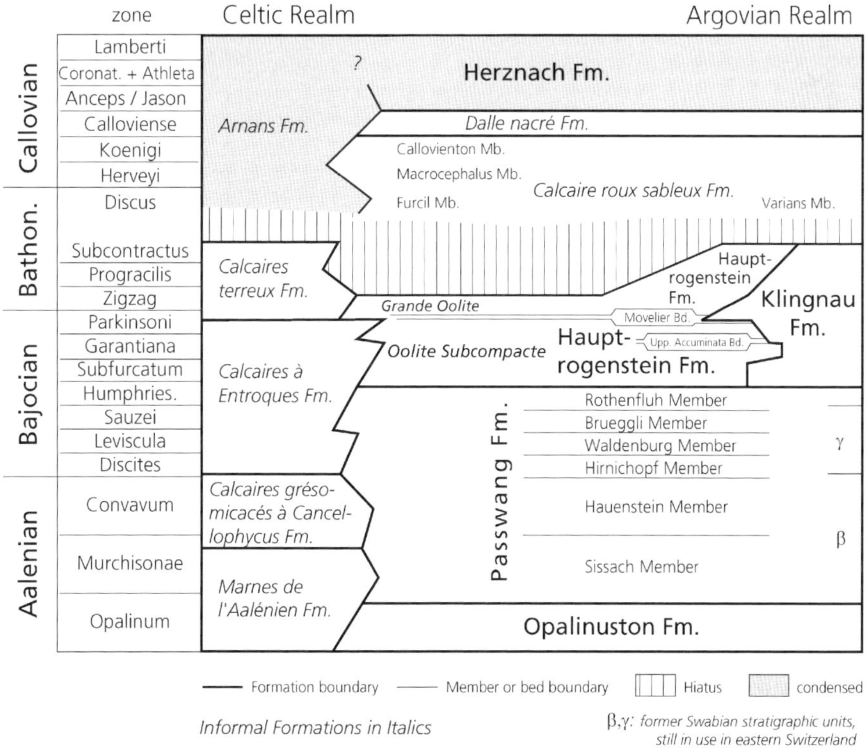


**Fig. 14.32.** Middle Jurassic biostratigraphy and lithostratigraphy (based on Allia 1996; Burkhalter 1996; Charollais & Badoux 1990; Dietl & Gygi 1998; Gonzalez & Wetzel 1996; Gygi 2000*a*).

successions in the eastern Swiss Jura. The classic stratigraphic units of the western Swiss Jura are treated here as informal formations.

**Opalinuston Formation.** The Opalinuston Formation in northern Switzerland is represented by 80–120 m of grey mudstones, and is lithologically similar to the succession in SW Germany. In northern Switzerland the Opalinuston Formation accumulated during the Early Aalenian in a shallow epicontinental shelf sea which was subdivided into small swells and depressions. The relief was formed by synsedimentary differential subsidence (Wetzel & Allia 2003).

Water depth was in the range of storm wavebase and somewhat below (about 20–50 m; Wetzel & Allia 2000, 2003; Wetzel & Meyer 2006). Isopachs and facies indicate some morphological differentiation; sediments on swells were occasionally reworked (Wetzel & Allia 2000) and the palaeoflow of storm-induced currents was directed to the depocentres (Fig. 14.33). Within the mudstones 20 coarsening-upward cycles can be distinguished. With respect to the chronometric timescale used (Gradstein *et al.* 2004), these cycles may represent Milankovitch precession cycles (Wetzel & Allia 2003).

Towards the SW, the mudstones are replaced by sandy marlstones, which are traditionally considered to form the lower part of the (informal) 'Marne de l'Aalenien Formation' (Fig. 14.32).

**Passwang Formation.** The Passwang Formation comprises a number of unconformity-bounded coarsening-upward successions formed within a shallow, mixed siliciclastic and carbonate depositional environment in an epicontinental sea (Burkhalter 1996). These coarsening-upward successions commence with siliciclastic mudstones that grade into micritic to arenitic limestones and end with a top bed consisting of ooidal ironstones. The latter formed during periods of non-deposition ('starvation'). Ooidal ironstones may also occur within the coarsening-upward successions, marking either transgressional or regressional discontinuities. The Passwang Formation can be subdivided into five members.

The lowermost Sissach Member (*Comptum* Subzone to *Murchisonae* Zone) varies in thickness between 2 m in the south Jura and >25 m in the north Jura. Where fully developed (south of Basel), three coarsening-upward successions are present (limestone–iron oolite, mudstone–limestone–iron oolite, limestone–iron oolite); however, these are not fully developed. Towards the south, the thickness decreases as does the mud content. Where the Sissach Member is thin, its upper part is either condensed or missing owing to syngenetic erosion.

The following three members, Hauenstein Member (lower and middle *Concavum* Zone), Hirnichopf Member (late *Concavum* to early *Discites* Zone), and Waldenburg Member (late *Discites* to *Laeviuscula* Zone and possibly early *Sauzei* Zone), occur in a shallow trough which follows the orientation of the Rhenish Lineament and is bounded by north–south trending structures with Basel to the west and Olten to the south (cf. Fig. 14.33; Boigk & Schöneich 1974). The Hauenstein Member is 1–10 m thick and consists of a mudstone–limestone succession, the Hirnichopf Member is 1 to >10 m thick and comprises a mudstone–limestone–iron oolite succession, and the Waldenburg is 1 to >15 m thick and is made up of a mudstone–iron oolite–mudstone succession.

The Brüggli Member consists of a mudstone–limestone–iron oolite succession; its thickness distribution contrasts with that of the members below it in that it is thinnest (<20 m) in the depocentre. To the east the thickness increases to >20 m, and to the west to >40 m.

The Rothenfluh Member (*Blagdeni* Zone; Gonzalez & Wetzel 1996) consists of marly, bioclastic mud- and wackestones interbedded with fine-grained nodular limestones, and occurs throughout the entire Folded Jura. It is up to 25 m thick in the west and 10 m in the east Jura.

Correlations between the Passwang Formation and the coeval (informal) formations of the western Jura, the 'Calcaires grésomicacés á Cancellophycus Formation' and the lower part of the

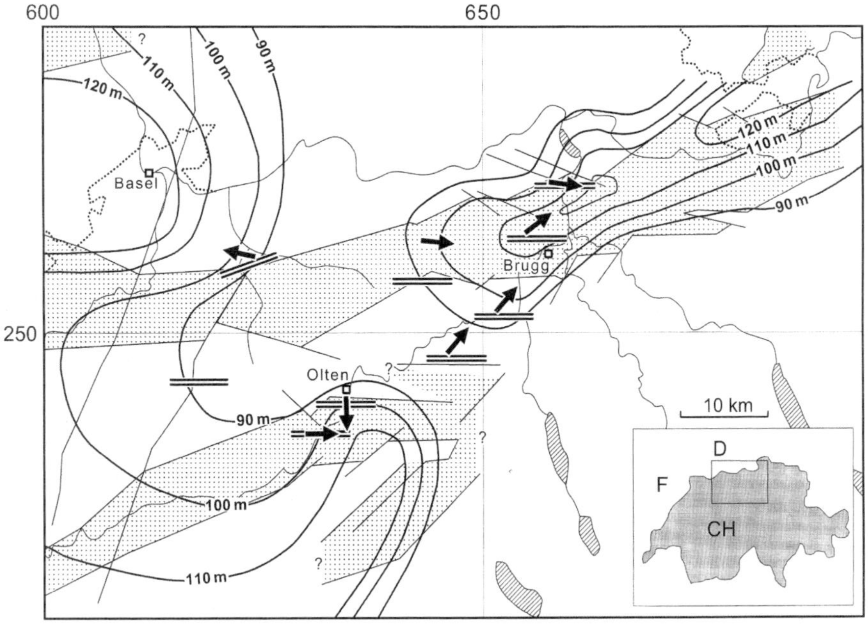


**Fig. 14.33.** Isopachs, palaeoflow directions (arrows) and the orientation of wave-ripple crests (double lines) in the Opalinuston Formation and the location of Late Palaeozoic basins (stippled) within the crystalline basement (after Wetzel & Allia 2003).

'Calcaires á Entroques Formation' (Fig. 14.32) have not yet been studied in detail.

**Hauptrogenstein Formation and coeval formations.** During the Middle Jurassic a shallow-marine carbonate platform, the Burgundy Platform or 'Plate-Forme Septentrionale', developed in Central Europe (Fig. 14.34). During the Middle Bajocian to Middle Bathonian the western parts of this carbonate platform were dominated by bioclastic calcarenites ('Calcaires á entroques' Formation'; Fig. 14.32), whereas in the eastern and central areas a broad oolitic belt developed, extending southward to the marginal basins of the opening Tethys (e.g. Ziegler 1990). The oolitic series is named the Hauptrogenstein Formation in northern Switzerland and southwestern Germany (e.g. Ernst 1989; LGRB 2004). Further to the east the platform facies is replaced by a marl-dominated facies (Klingnau Formation in Switzerland; Fig. 14.32; Hamitenton-Formation (Upper Bajocian), Dentalienton Formation (Lower Bathonian) in SW Germany; LGRB 2004) which probably formed in a somewhat deeper part of the epicontinental sea. It consists mainly of mudstones with intercalated (nodular) limestones, up to some tens of metres thick.

The Hauptrogenstein Formation is composed of three shallowing-upward successions, each capped by a hardground. These successions are informally named the Lower Oolitic, the Upper Oolitic and the Coarse Oncolite/Spatkalk units (Gonzalez & Wetzel 1996). The lower two units comprise the Lower Hauptrogenstein, and the upper one the Upper Hauptrogenstein of previous authors (e.g. Schmassmann 1945). The Lower and Upper Hauptrogenstein correspond to the 'Oolithe subcompacte Formation' and the 'Grand Oolithe Formation' of the French authors (Fig. 14.32).

The first sequence (Lower Oolitic Unit) began to form during the *Blagdeni* Subzone with marly beds and intercalated tempestites which increase in frequency up-section. Within this interval echinoderm lagerstätten occur (e.g. Hess 1975; Meyer 1988). Oolitic sedimentation began in the central Jura in the *Niortense/Subfurcatum* Subzone. The 0.2 to 2 m thick, cross-bedded oolites are interpreted to have been deposited in a tidal, shallow-marine high-energy setting. At the same time, the oolitic beds in the eastern Jura contain up to 35% mud, and a low-energy setting is inferred (Lower Acuminata Beds). During the *Garantiana* Zone oolite belts prograded to the east reaching the Aare River. Up to 70 m of oolites accumulated during a period of moderate sea-level rise and steady subsidence.

Depostion of the second succession began in the early *Parkinsoni* Zone. The production of ooids had ceased during a sea-level highstand and marls and bioclastic limestone accumulated in northern Switzerland (Homomya Marls in the west Jura, Upper Acuminata Beds in the central and east Jura). Subsequently, a drop in relative sea level during the late *Parkinsoni* Zone re-established ooid production (Upper Oolitic Unit).

The third shallowing-upward succession commenced during

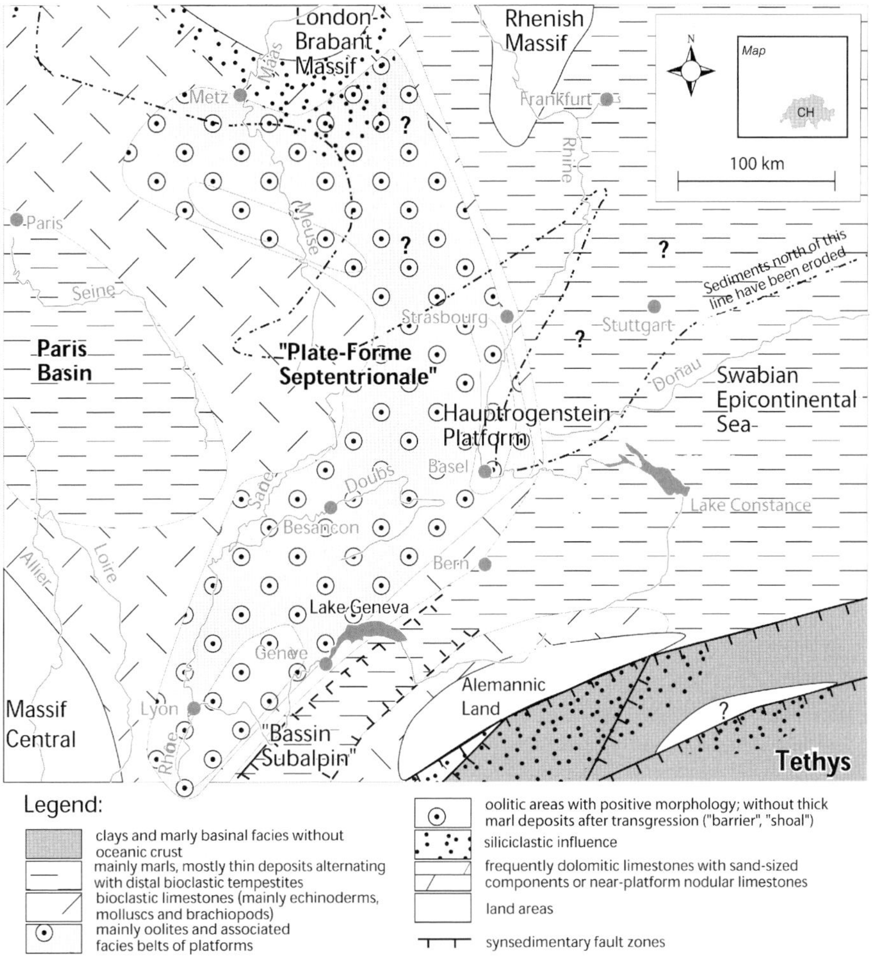


**Fig. 14.34.** Palaeogeographic, palinspastic reconstruction of Central Europe during the late Bajocian based on the compilation by Gonzalez (1993, modified). East and south of the Alpine realm the palaeogeographic/palinspastic reconstruction is uncertain.

the latest Bajocian and earliest Bathonian (*Zigzag* Zone). Marly sediments, rich in coarse bioclasts (Movelier Beds), are again interpreted as have been deposited during a relative sea-level highstand. They are overlain by micritic oncolites in the western Jura. To the east, sparry bioclastic, locally cross-bedded limestones occur (Spatkalk). These were probably deposited by storms and tides. The deposition of the Spatkalk lasted until the middle Lower Bathonian, prograding eastward and covering the top of the marly Klingnau Formation.

The facies belts within the Hauptrogenstein and Klingnau formations suggest that, north–south trending, tidal-influenced oolitic barriers evolved in the Middle Jurassic. Backbarrier facies belts formed to the west and include micrites, pelmicrites, patch-reefs and oncolites. Off-barrier assemblages formed to the east of the barrier. A decrease in the production of sediments, as evidenced by platform-wide facies changes, and in the decrease of the sediment thickness were probably related to changes in water circulation and/or climate. On the other hand, more or less abrupt changes in thickness and facies within the successions suggest differential subsidence.

**Bathonian to Callovian formations.** In the Swiss Jura, as in southern Germany, late Lower Bathonian sediments are absent (Dietl 1994; Dietl & Gygi 1998). The Upper Bathonian–Callovian succession of the central Swiss Jura Mountains is characterized by two shallowing-upward sedimentary cycles (Bitterli 1979), which are here informally denoted as the 'Calcaire roux sableux Formation' (Late Bathonian to Early Callovian) and the 'Dalle nacrée Formation' (Early Callovian; Fig. 14.32). It is herein suggested that the 'Varians Bed' of the eastern Swiss Jura represents a coeval equivalent of the lower 'Calcaire roux Formation'. These cycles resulted from marginal flooding of a low-relief carbonate bank to the west and from basinward progradation of the shallow-water facies. Both cycles typically commence with basinal marls and grade through marly and muddy calcarenites into washed calcarenites which are topped by a submarine hardground. The hardgrounds are interpreted as being formed diachronously (Bitterli 1979) and are comparable with those of the Callovian of the Paris Basin which resulted from the lithification of stable carbonate sands near wavebase. The hardgrounds are generally overlain by iron-oolitic marls. The iron oolites are thought to have formed coevally with the hardgrounds; most of the ooids, however, were dispersed into the slightly more basinal marly sediments. The iron was probably derived from the underlying clayey and marly sediments and was carried up as ferrous iron in pore water expelled by compaction. Near the surface it was oxidized and brought to the surface by burrowing organisms where the iron oolites formed.

In the western Folded Jura most of the Callovian, and possibly the Late Bathonian, is represented by a thin (up to 4 m thick) iron oolitic and glauconitic limestone (informally 'Arnans Formation'; Mangold 1970). The existence of an equivalent to the 'Dalle nacrée Formation' is doubtful (Wernli 1989 in Charollais & Badoux 1990).

The Herznach Formation comprises a thin, but apparently continuous iron-oolitic marl and limestone succession of *Anceps* to *Lamberti* Zone (Gygi 2000*a*). Thickness varies between *c.* 1 m in NW Switzerland and 3.4 m in the Herznach area. At the type locality, where the ore was mined during World War II, ammonites are the dominant element of the macrofauna (Jeannet 1951). This is taken by Gygi (2000*a*) as evidence that the sediments were deposited in relatively deep water.

*Late Jurassic*

The Late Jurassic formations have recently been revised in the central and eastern Folded Jura and adjacent areas of the Tabular Jura (Fig. 14.35). In the western Folded Jura no formations have yet been established. Consequently the classic stratigraphic units are treated here as informal formations.

**Oxfordian formations.** In Late Jurassic times, a wide, carbonate-dominated shelf covered the realm of today's Jura Mountains (Fig. 14.36). This was connected, via the Helvetic Shelf, to the Tethys (e.g. Wildi *et al.* 1989; Ziegler 1990). Subsidence accelerated during the Oxfordian (e.g. Wetzel *et al.* 2003) and facies architecture was affected by synsedimentary differential subsidence along faults inherited from older lineaments (e.g. Allenbach 2001, 2002; Allenbach & Wetzel 2006). None of these, however, cut through the Mesozoic sedimentary cover.

Lithostratigraphy and facies have been studied extensively (P.A. Ziegler 1956; M.A. Ziegler 1962; Gygi 1969, 1992, 2000*a*,*b*; Bolliger & Burri 1970). The biostratigraphy based on ammonites was established mainly by Gygi (1995, 2000*a*, and references therein). The widely used platform-to-basin transition scheme was reconstructed on the basis of bio- and mineralostratigraphic correlations (Gygi & Persoz 1986; Fig. 14.35). A correlation with the Oxfordian deposits of the French Jura has been published by Enay *et al.* (1988). More recently, a sequence stratigraphic interpretation has been proposed by Gygi *et al.* (1998). Selected intervals, calibrated by high-resolution sequence stratigraphy and cyclostratigraphy, have been analysed by Pittet (1996), Plunkett (1997), Dupraz (1999) and Hug (2003). The formation of platform and basin facies in space and time and their relationship to pre-existing structures was analysed in detail by Allenbach (2001, 2002) and Allenbach & Wetzel (2006). The terminology of formations and members and their biostratigraphic attribution follow Gygi (1995, 2000*b*; Fig. 14.31). The major sequence boundaries are labelled according to Hardenbol *et al.* (1998), and the chronometric ages are based on Gradstein *et al.* (2004). To the north, very shallow depositional environments predominated, whereas to the south deeper epicontinental basins developed. Siliciclastic material was derived from the north (Rhenish Massif) during the Early Oxfordian and later from the NE (Bohemian Massif). Carbonate was produced on the platforms, especially during times of rising and high relative sea levels. Subsidence, sea-level changes and sediment input resulted in a slow, step-wise progradation and intermittent retrogradation of the platform to the SE (e.g. Gygi 1969; Fig. 14.37). In a very simplified way, three major lithologies can be recognized in the study area.

(1) A condensed interval, *c.* 0.5–1 m thick, consists of iron oolites, some stromatolites and wacke- to packstones. This formed during the Early to early Middle Oxfordian in NE Switzerland (the so-called Schellenbrücke Bed; Gygi 1981). At the same time, marls of the Bärschwil Formation accumulated farther to the west, (Gygi & Persoz 1986).

(2) Marl–limestone alternations consisting of centimetre- to decimetre-thick beds accumulated during the Middle and early Late Oxfordian (Effingen Formation). The entire series is today up to 240 m thick. The carbonate content varies within a section; this variation is interpreted to reflect climatic and sea-level changes (e.g. Pittet 1996; Pittet & Strasser 1998), some of which are related to Milankovitch cycles. Some of these beds display the characteristics of tempestites, but oscillatory ripples were not found. Consequently, deposition below storm wavebase is inferred.

(3) Shallow-water carbonates formed during the Middle and Late Oxfordian and comprise well-bedded limestones, calcare-

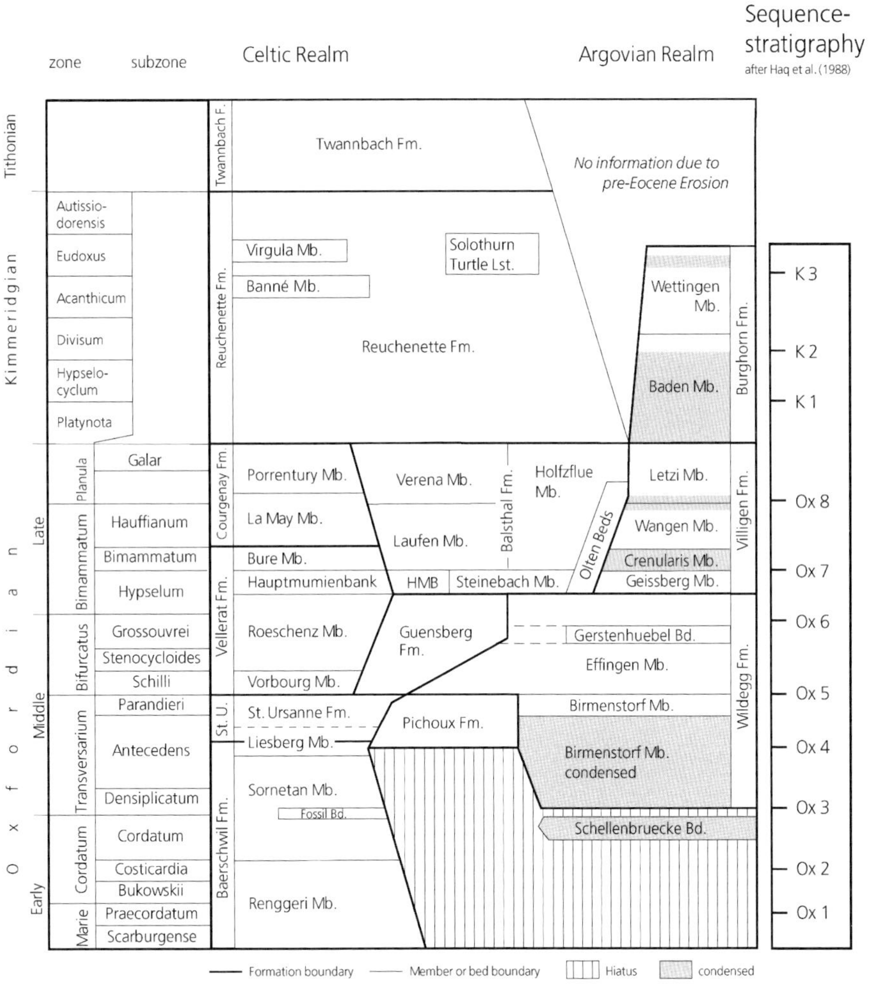


**Fig. 14.35.** Biostratigraphy and lithostratigraphy of the Upper Jurassic based on Gygi (1995, 2000*b*, modified); sequence boundaries after Haq *et al.* (1988).

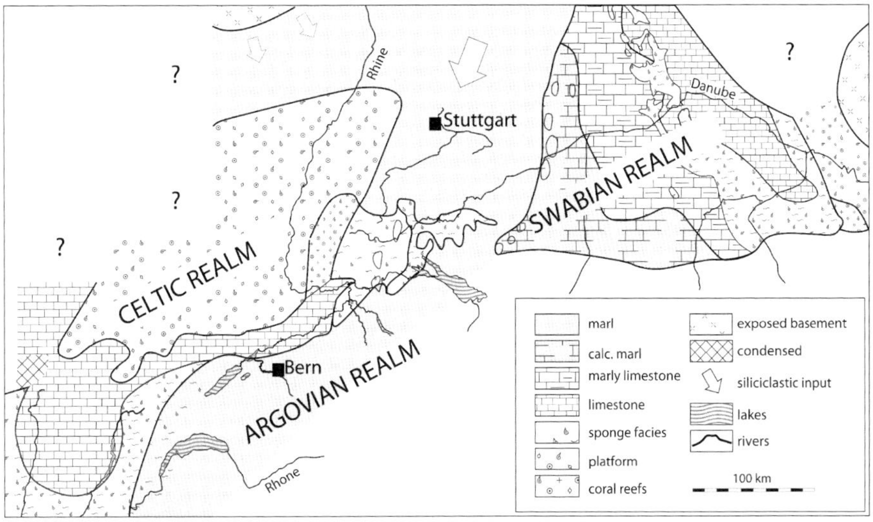


**Fig. 14.36.** Palaeogeographic map of the Swiss Jura Mountains and adjoining areas during the Middle Oxfordian (from Allenbach 2001).

nites including oolites and oncolites and reefal limestones. The well-bedded limestones consist of mud to wackestones containing bioclasts. Oolites, oncolites, and calcarenites formed on the landward side of the patch-reef belt (for details, see Gygi 1969, 1990). The platform margin and fringe is a geometrically and lithologically complex system consisting of a patch-reef belt and inter-reef mud-, wacke- and packstones containing a considerable amount of broken platform organisms (e.g. Gygi 1969, 1990;

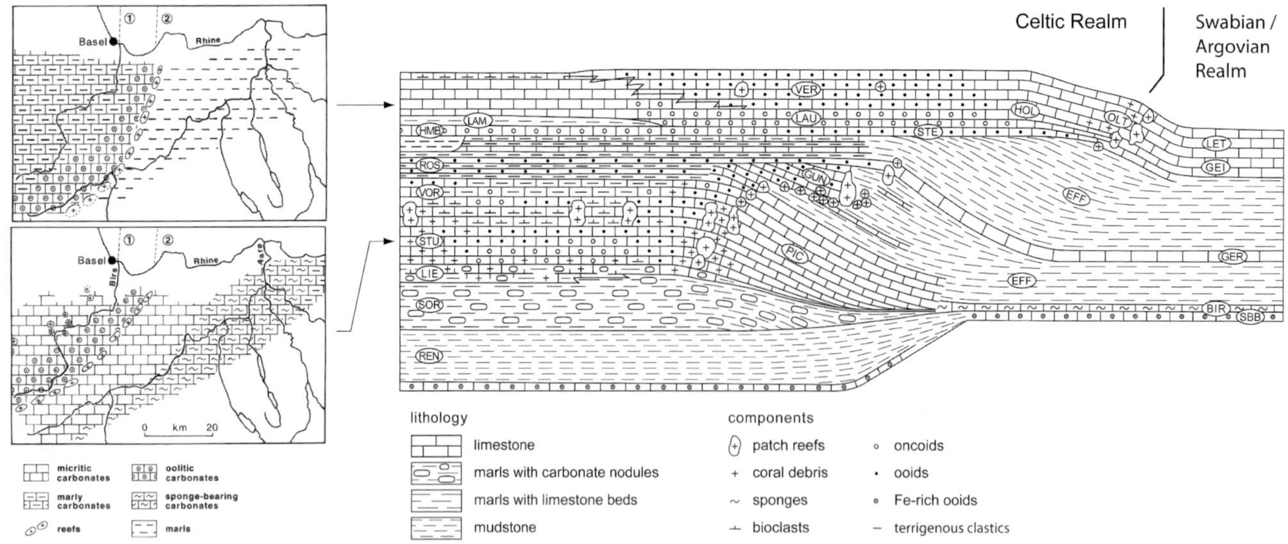


**Fig. 14.37.** (Left) Palaeogeographic maps of the Middle (bottom) and Late Oxfordian (top), based on Gygi (1990), but palinspastically restored (Wetzel *et al.* 2003). Note that facies boundaries were mainly NE–SW during the Middle Oxfordian and north–south during the Late Oxfordian. The facies boundaries are in spatial vicinity to Late Palaeozoic structures or in continuation along-strike of the Rhenish Lineament (1) and associated fault (2). (Right) Geometry and correlation of Oxfordian sediments in northern Switzerland (after Gygi & Persoz 1986; Wetzel & Strasser 2001, modified). Labels refer to stratigraphic units (in alphabetical order): BIR, Birmenstorf Mb; EFF, Effingen Mb; GEI, Geissberg Mb; GER, Gerstenhuebel Beds; GUN, Guensberg Fm; HMB, Hauptmumienbank Mb; HOL, Holzflue Mb; LAM, La May Mb; LAU, Laufen Mb; LET, Letzi Mb; LIE, Liesberg Mb; OLT, Olten Beds; PIC, Pichoux Fm; REN, Renggeri Mb; ROS, Roeschenz Mb; SBB, Schellenbruecke Bed; SOR, Sornetan Mb; STE, Steinebach Mb; STU, St. Ursanne Fm; VER, Verena Mb; VOR, Vorbourg Mb.

Bolliger & Burri 1970). Behind the patch-reef belt, a lagoonal area with small reefs, micrites and oncolites developed.

The facies boundaries of the Lower to Middle Oxfordian deposits coincide fairly well with the NE–SW trending Late Palaeozoic structures in the subsurface.The palaeogeographic maps published by Gygi (1969, 1990) indicate that the facies boundaries shifted with time (Fig. 14.37). During the Early Oxfordian, they were preferentially NE–SW orientated. During the Middle to Late Oxfordian, the platform–basin transition was oriented – as before – NE–SW in the southern part of the area. The eastern boundary of the platform, however, shifted further to the west and was oriented roughly north–south with a spatial relation to the Rhenish Lineament and associated faults (Krohe 1996; Allenbach & Wetzel 2006). On the platform itself, differential subsidence led to small-scale variations in facies and thickness (Bolliger & Burri 1970; Pittet 1996; Allenbach 2001, 2002; Fig. 14.38).

**Kimmeridgian to Tithonian Formations.** In the eastern part of the Folded Jura and the adjacent Tabular Jura, post-Oxfordian sediments have been affected by pre-Eocene erosion (Trümpy 1980). In some areas sediments of Oxfordian and Callovian age have also been eroded. Therefore, in this area the platform to basin transition and the relationships between the facies are difficult to decipher. In the distal part, the typically mudstone-dominated facies was replaced by a carbonate-rich facies that is also encountered in SW Germany. In the Eastern Swiss Tabular Jura, the well-bedded carbonate-dominated Villingen Formation (up to 50 m thick), is overlain by the Burghorn Formation (*Playnota* to *Eudoxus* Zone) consisting of the condensed glauconitic marly limestone of Baden and the oolithic Wettingen members (Gygi 2000*a*). In SW Germany, the sedimentary record continues up to the *Beckeri* Zone (i.e. Schwarzenbach and Felsenkalke formations; Gygi 1969, 2000*a*; Gygi & Persoz 1986).

In the eastern and central Folded Jura and adjacent areas, almost the entire Kimmeridgian (*Playnota* to *Beckeri* Zone) is represented by predominantly calcareous open to restricted platform sediments some 150 to 200 m thick (Reuchenette Formation; Gygi 2000*a*; Hug 2003; Jank *et al.* 2006*a*,*b*). In several places and at different stratigraphic levels, dinosaur bones and track sites, including footprints of *Diplodocus*-type animals and bones of *Stegosaurus*, point to the existence of emergent regions of considerable extent (Meyer 1990, 1993; Meyer & Hunt 1998; Marty *et al.* 2003).

In the Geneva area, the Kimmeridgian is represented by a succession beginning with shallow-marine carbonate-dominated facies and ending with backreef carbonates (the informal 'Calcaires pseudo-lithographiques Formation' (some 150 m, *Planula* Zone) and the 'Calcaire á Cephalopode Formation' (some 50 m, *Platynota* Zone)). The forereef is represented by the bioclastic, sometimes dolomitic 'Tabalcon Formation' (some 15 m, *Eudoxus* Zone). The 'Calcaires Récifaux Formation' consists of some 75 m of bioherms and concomitant sediments pointing to the existence of a distinct barrier reef during the *Beckeri* Zone. The backreef is reached in the 'Landaize Formation' of the late *Beckeri* Zone (some 50 m; Bernier 1984; Charolais & Badoux 1990).

The Tithonian and the transition into the Cretaceous during the *Gravesia* Zone are represented in the Geneva area (Charolais & Badoux 1990) by the thin 'Chailley' (in the north) and 'Etiolets' (in the south) formations, and the younger tidal sediments, up to 90 m thick, of the 'Vouglans Formation', which are overlain by the brackish-water sediments (including gypsum) of the 'Purbeckian', or Goldberg Formation (Haefeli 1966), which is today believed to be completely of Cretaceous age

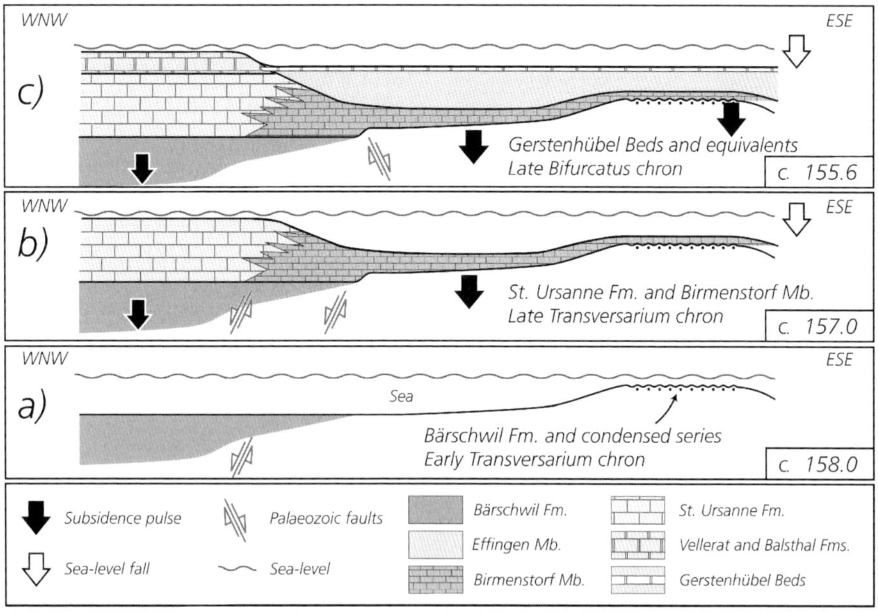


**Fig. 14.38.** Schematic representation showing how differential subsidence affected the facies development in northern Switzerland. (**a**) During the Early Oxfordian, subsidence in the NW provided accommodation space for the Baerschwil Formation whereas non-deposition or condensation occurred on a swell further to the SE. (**b**) As clastic input ceased in the early Middle Oxfordian, platform carbonates prograded south(east)ward. (**c**) During the Late Oxfordian, enhanced subsidence in the SE provided accommodation space for the sediments of the Effingen Member; to the NW platform carbonate accumulation continued. All sketches from Allenbach (2001, 2002).

(Strasser & Davaud 1983; Deconinck & Strasser 1987). To the NE, in the Lake Bienne area, the Tithonian is represented by the partly dolomitic limestone (some 100 to 150 m thick) of the Twannbach Formation (Haefeli 1966; Mojon & Strasser 1987). In most other parts of the Swiss Jura, Tithonian sediments are missing due to non-deposition or later pre-Eocene erosion.

### *Bohemian Massif, Czech Republic (P.B.)*

Jurassic sediments of the Bohemian Massif occur only in small and isolated areas, much of the original cover having been removed by Late Cretaceous–Cenozoic erosion. Remnants of the Jurassic sediments are preserved in regions characterized by stronger subsidence (Dvořák 1956; Bosák 1978) and include north Bohemia (Doubice, Brtníky, Bělá River valley) and central Moravia (in the area of Brno, the Hády hills, Nová hora, Stránská skála, Švédské valy; for detailed review see Eliáš 1981). Pebbles of Jurassic rocks have been found in Late Cretaceous deposits (Soukup 1952), in Neogene Badenian deposits of the Carpathian Foredeep (J. Hladil, pers. comm., 2004; Krystek 1974) and in Neogene and Pleistocene terrace sediments (Zapletal 1925; Krut'a 1953; Dvořák 1956; Losos *et al.* 2000).

The Jurassic sediments of the Czech Republic represent a sedimentary cycle of Callovian to Kimmeridgian age (Eliáš 1981). The Callovian–Oxfordian transgression was followed by a period of continental erosion/non-deposition characterized by a stratigraphical gap and the absence of sediments younger than Middle Triassic and possibly Carnian age. The Jurassic transgression progressed both from the Boreal and Tethyan realms (Uhlig 1882; Oppenheimer 1930; Eliáš 1984) and covered extensive parts of the Bohemian Massif (Koutek 1927, Fabian 1935), as indicated by the distribution of pebbles of Jurassic rocks preserved in younger sediments. In the area of the Moravian Karst, Jurassic sediments filled a shallow north–south trending depression eroded into Devonian carbonates (Panoš 1964). The original thickness of the sedimentary cover was comparatively low (Počta 1890; Fabian 1935) and was further reduced by penecontemporaneous weathering, chemical denudation and erosion.

There are two models to explain the connection between the Boreal and Tethyan realms through the Bohemian Massif: Počta (1890), Oppenheimer (1934), Dvořák (1963, 1966) and Eliáš (1974, 1984) favoured a narrow strait model along the Elbe Zone, between the Bohemian Massif to the south and the Sudetic Block to the north; a broader transgression model was favoured by Fabian (1935). The view of Fabian (1935) is supported by an extensive distribution of pebbles of Jurassic rocks, but recent palaeotectonic reconstructions indicate that the Jurassic transgression spread along the crustally weak Elbe Zone in the Bohemian Massif and that the Sudetic Block was coevally uplifted (e.g. Scheck *et al.* 2002; Ventura and Lisker 2003).

#### *North Bohemia*

The Jurassic deposits of North Bohemia (Bruder 1882, 1887; Dvořák 1966) are subdivided into two major lithostratigraphical units. The lower unit (Brtníky Formation, 12–14 m thick) comprises quartzose sandstones with interbedded conglomerates. These clastics are of Callovian to Early Oxfordian age (documented by finds of *Hecticoceras hecticum*; Bruder 1887). The Brtníky Formation represents a nearshore/foreshore depositional system (beach sands to sand bar deposits).

The overlying Doubice Formation (>100 m thick) is mostly dolomitic. The lower 4–5 m comprises sandy dolosparite with sponge spicules, while the bulk of the formation is mainly dolosparite with rare intradolosparite and peldolosparite interbeds. In places, sedimentary structures indicative of currents occur (Eliáš 1981). The Doubice Formation is mainly Oxfordian in age, as indicated by the rich fauna including the ammonites *Ochetoceras canaliculatum*, *Gregoriceras transversarium* and probably *Epipeltoceras bimammatum*. The uppermost part of the

Doubice Formation comprises *c.* 20 m of dark limestones with Kimmeridgian ammonites *Oppelia tenuilobata* (Bruder 1887). The Doubice dolomites are interpreted as having been deposited in a shallow-water, open-shelf depositional system, with periods of nearshore/foreshore sedimentation. Some parts of the profile (e.g. collapsed breccia deposits) are interpreted as being of supratidal zone origin. The source for the dolomitizing brines is interpreted as being in the intertidal/supratidal zone (Eliáš 1981).

*Moravian Karst area*

Jurassic deposits occurring within the Blansko Graben discordantly overlie Proterozoic granitoids (Brno Massif) and Late Devonian limestones. The Jurassic deposits of the Moravian Karst area can be subdivided into five units. The basal clastic unit (maximum 15 m; stratigraphy after Bosák 1978) comprises sandy biocalcarenites with echinoids and *Nubecullinella bigoti* (Hanzlíková & Bosák 1977), which belong to the *Quenstedticeras lamberti* Zone (Oxfordian, *Cardioceras cordatum* Zone; Uhlig 1880, 1882). This is overlain by 7 m of grey, glauconite-rich sandy pelmicrites and pelbiomicrites ('platy limestones'), containing an *Ammodiscus-Milliolina* biofacies. In places where the basal clastic unit is not developed, the platy limestone unit forms the base of the Jurassic system.

The middle unit consists of siliceous limestones (*c.* 30 m) with irregularly silicified rhax and sponge-rhax biomicrites. Eliáš (1981) characterized this facies as a rhax and sponge-rhax biofacies which passes into spiculites, sometimes with abundant glauconite (in places with marked dolomitization). This unit contains chert lenses and thin siliceous layers and, in the upper part, abundant quartz/chalcedony geodes which represent replaced gypsum/anhydrite nodules (Přichystal *et al.* 1999; Losos *et al.* 2000). The lower third of the section contains silicoflagellates, calcareous nannoflora, *Tolypamina* and diversified *Ophthalmidium* species. These fossils suggest the *Gregoriceras transversarium* Zone (Oxfordian). The middle part of the unit contains algae and sponges with rare *Thuramina*, *Tolypammina* and *Opthalmidium* species, and belongs to the *Epipeltoceras bimammatum* Zone (Oxfordian). The upper third of the unit, containing, in places, cavernous limestones and which is rich in geodes, contains blue algae, *Acicularia* and some *Salpingoporella*.

The siliciclastic limestone is overlain by a dolomitic limestone unit (2 m) composed of micrites to biodolomicrites, sometimes with cherts. It contains numerous foraminifers (*Thurammina*, *Eomarssonella*, Rotaliidae, Lagenidae) and ostracods. The uppermost unit comprises silicified breccias with an allitic/ferrolitic matrix and containing sponge spicules, as well as remnants of echinoids and terebratulid brachiopods. This fauna is probably of Kimmeridgian–Tithonian age (Bosák 1978). These breccias were found only in blocks underlying Cenomanian sands and clays, and thus the thickness cannot be precisely estimated.

The depositional environment of the Jurassic deposits in the Moravian Karst is interpreted as a shelf-lagoon system characterized by marked sea-level variations resulting in periodic emersion (e.g. presence of supratidal zone is evidenced by vadose structures such as silica-replaced sulphate nodules or geodes; Eliáš 1981). Sea-level changes were either eustatic or related to tectonic activity within the Blansko Graben (Hanzlíková & Bosák 1977).

*Brno and its surroundings*

The Jurassic deposits in the area of Brno discordantly overlie granitoids of the Brno Massif or Late Devonian and Early Carboniferous limestones (initial profiles were published by Uhlig (1882), Oppenheimer (1907, 1926, 1934), Koutek (1926) and later by Eliáš (1981)). Transgressive deposits are represented by a 4 m thick biosparite unit with sponge spicules and a rich macrofauna, and are overlain by a strongly dolomitized dolosparite unit with bryozoans, algae and rare corals (Uhlig 1882).

The upper part of the Jurassic succession is represented by four units: (1) the lower limestone (with cherts) unit (27 m thick) is composed of poorly bedded, slightly dolomitized biomicrites to pelmicrites with tiny stromatolitic structures. Abundant echinoderm remnants occur in the lower 3 m of this unit; (2) the overlying, 24 m thick unit is represented by silicified and dolomitized biosparites with intercalations abundant in pellets, ooids and rare small coral patch-reefs. This unit belongs to the *Perisphinctes plicatilis* Zone (Middle Oxfordian; Eliáš 1981); and (3, 4) A thin (3–4 m) unit of crinoidal limestones comprising massive biosparite rudstones (Uhlig 1882) is overlain by the uppermost unit of well-bedded limestone with chert (12 m). This upper unit contains abundant lithoclasts, ooids, coated grains and bioclasts (mostly intrabiosparite), fossils and was assigned to the *Gregoriceras transversarium* and *Epipeltoceras bimmamatum* zones (Upper Oxfordian). However, finds of the Early Kimmeridgian ammonite *Aulacostephanus* sp. have also been reported (J. Hladil, pers. comm., 2004).

In Švédské valy and Slatina (Slatina 1 borehole), a *c.* 130 m thick succession of Jurassic deposits occurs. The strata are tectonically inclined (about 20°). The basal beds comprise very thin sandstones (subgreywackes) which are overlain by dolomitic limestones and dolomites (dolosparites/biodolosparites facies). Clay-rich intercalations occur near the base. The lowermost (*c.* 40 m) of the basal beds are barren in terms of fauna, while up-section there are abundant lithoclasts, sponge spicules, rhaxes, foraminifers, echinoderms and other fossils. The fossil occurrences are coincident with intercalations of greenish marlstones. The uppermost 75 m of the profile contains cherts.

A fairly diverse faunal assemblage with more than 130 species was described by Oppenheimer (1907) from the Švédské šance quarry and this fauna suggests an age corresponding to the *Epipeltoceras bimmamatum* Zone. The depositional environments of the Jurassic sediments from the Brno region can be interpreted as representing a transition from the inner part of the carbonate platform (Slatina and Švédské valy), through the shelf-lagoon (Stránská skála) and into the inner part of the shelf-lagoon system (Nová Skála & Hády).

## Tethyan Domain

The evolution of the Tethyan Domain was governed by seafloor spreading and intensive vertical and strike-strip movements. The western end of the Tethys opened in the Early Jurassic with rifting, which continued (with a particularly intensive phase in the Callovian–Oxfordian) until the end of the Jurassic period, when a major period of plate reorganization (opening of the Central Atlantic–Ligurian–Penninic oceanic system), accompanied in places by magmatic events, occurred in the Tethyan Domain (Lewandowski *et al.* 2005). In the Jurassic, the Tethyan Domain in Switzerland, Austria, Poland and Slovakia represented a mosaic of different terranes detached from the European epi-Variscan platform separated by oceanic lithosphere and transformed by several major tectonic events governed by the ongoing convergence between Africa and Europe. In terms of palaeobiogeographic provinces it represents the Mediterranean bioprovince.

## *Austro-Alpine and Penninic units in the Eastern Alps (M.W.R.)*

The Eastern Alps form a mountain belt in Austria and southern Germany (Fig. 14.39). Towards the west they are separated from the Western Alps by the Rhine Valley; towards the east they continue into the Carpathians, albeit separated by the Vienna Basin. To the south they are separated from the Southern Alps by the Periadriatic Lineament. To the north they are thrust over the Alpine Foreland (Molasse Basin) (e.g. Kurz *et al.* 2001*a*).

Units derived from the stable European continental lithosphere (Helvetic and Penninic continental units), the Penninic oceanic lithosphere, and the Austro-Alpine units are among the main tectonic elements incorporated into the Eastern Alps (for summary see Neubauer *et al.* 2000). Usually, there is an inconsistent use of terminology between the Eastern and Western Alps: the Valais, Brianconnais and Piemontais units are conventionally combined into the Penninic units (North, Middle and South Penninic units; for discussion and summary of Eastern Alpine units see Kurz *et al.* 2001*a*).

In terms of geology, the Eastern Alps are a complex orogen that resulted from the still-active convergence between Africa and Europe. The Cretaceous period represents the period of main orogenic activity (e.g. Faupl & Wagreich 2000) related to the Alps. Therefore, the reconstruction of Jurassic tectonics, nappe configuration and sedimentary geology is important for the interpretation of Alpine deformation (e.g. Gawlick *et al.* 1999; Mandl 2000; Frisch & Gawlick 2003) (see Frotzheim *et al.* 2008; Reicherter *et al.* 2008).

Monographs on the Eastern Alps were published by Tollmann (1977, 1985) and Oberhauser (1980). A lithostratigraphic overview with a detailed analysis of the Jurassic was provided by Tollmann (1976). Special volumes that include Jurassic aspects have been published on the geodynamic evolution of the Eastern Alps (Flügel & Faupl 1987), metamorphosis (Frey *et al.* 1999), and overviews on special topics (Neubauer & Höck 2000). A lithostratigraphic chart of the Eastern Alps was recently published by Piller *et al.* (2004) (compare with Fig. 14.42).

This overview focuses on the Jurassic sedimentary development of the Austro-Alpine and Penninic domains. Orogeny, tectonics and metamorphosis are reviewed in Frotzheim *et al.* 2008 and Scheck-Wenderoth *et al.* 2008 and are therefore not treated in detail here.

*Palaeogeographic and tectonic overview*
During the Late Triassic and the earliest Jurassic, the Austro-Alpine region was part of the European shelf (for summary see Mandl 2000). Opening processes in the Atlantic region affected the opening of the Penninic Ocean as a continuation of the Western Alpine Ligurian-Piemontais Ocean (Alpine Tethys) and the formation of Penninic tectonic units during the Jurassic (Fig. 14.40). This resulted in the breakup of Pangaea (e.g. Tollmann 1987*b*; Ziegler 1990; Stampfli *et al.* 1998; Stampfli & Mosar 1999). During most of the Jurassic, the Austro-Alpine units formed an independent microplate (Channell *et al.* 1992) north of Apulia, and represent the continental crust to the south of the Penninic Ocean. From north to south the Jurassic palaeogeographic configuration was (Fig. 14.40): (1) the North (Valais) and Middle (Brianconnais) Penninic units attached to the European Plate; (2) the South Penninic unit (Piemontais) with oceanic crust; (3) the Lower Austro-Alpine unit forming the northern margin of the Austro-Alpine domain; (4) the Middle Austro-Alpine unit; and (5) the Upper Austro-Alpine unit with

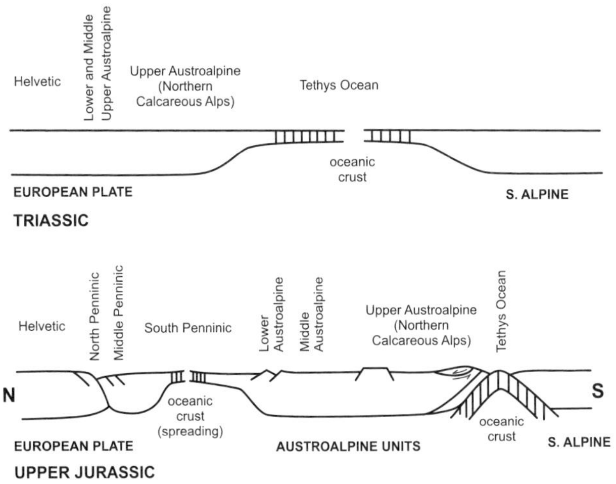


**Fig. 14.40.** Schematic plate tectonic reconstruction of the Penninic, Austro-Alpine, and adjacent domains during the Late Jurassic, modified after Decker *et al.* (1987), Tollmann (1987*b*) and Faupl & Wagreich (2000). Not to scale. For details about the Northern Calcareous Alps domain see Figure 14.41.

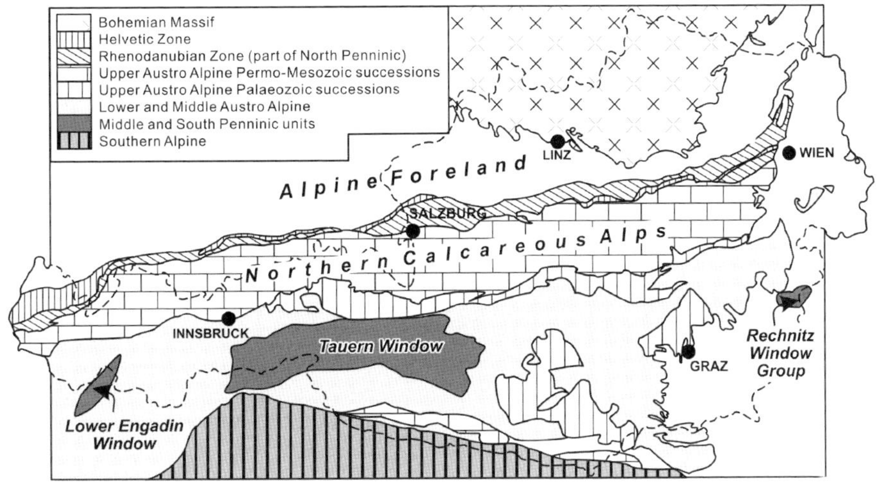


**Fig. 14.39.** Simplified map of tectonic units of the Eastern Alps. After Faupl & Wagreich (2000).

the Northern Calcareous Alps, forming the southern margin of the Austro-Alpine domain (Tollmann 1987*b*; Neubauer *et al.* 2000). These units represent different palaeogeographic and tectonic domains, but their definitions, especially the separation between Lower and Middle Austro-Alpine units, is controversal (e.g. Clar 1973; Frank 1987; Tollmann 1987*b*; Frisch & Gawlick 2003). Nevertheless, this classification is considered useful in most parts of the Austro-Alpine nappe pile (e.g. Hoinkes *et al.* 1999; Neubauer *et al.* 2000) and is therefore used herein.

Prior to the opening of the Penninic Ocean, the Austro-Alpine domain comprised a laterally extensive carbonate shelf (for summary see Mandl 2000; Piller *et al.* 2000). The shelf area was represented by the Northern Calcareous Alps (NCA). According to the shelf configuration, the NCA can be separated into three tectonic subunits representing Triassic facies belts (Fig. 14.41): (1) the palaeogeographically north-northwesternmost unit is the Bajuvaric Realm with the Keuper and dolomitic facies belts; (2) the Tyrolic Realm comprises the reefal and lagoonal facies; and (3) the Juvavic unit comprises the SSE platform ('Dachstein Platform') and the pelagic Hallstatt facies representing the transition towards the Tethys Ocean (Haas *et al.* 1995). Towards the SE, the NCA were bordered by the 'Hallstatt-Meliata-Ocean' (Kozur 1992). The character of this ocean and its palaeogeographic position are, however, controversial (e.g. Tollmann 1981; Haas *et al.* 1995; Kozur & Mostler 1992; Schweigl & Neubauer 1997). Indeed, Gawlick *et al.* (1999) see no argument for its separation at all. A different interpretation, summarized by Neubauer *et al.* (2000) but rejected by Mandl (2000), is the 'dual shelf model'. This suggests that Juvavic units formed an opposite southern shelf and that the 'Hallstatt-Meliata-Ocean' was situated between the 'Austro-Alpine units *sensu stricto*' in the north and an 'Upper Juvavic unit' in the south.

The Triassic shelf configuration of the NCA units is of crucial importance for the palaeogeographic and tectonic development during the Jurassic. Beginning in the Jurassic, rifting and opening of the Penninic Ocean caused initial displacement of the Juvavic nappe complexes (Mandl 2000). Around the Middle–Late Jurassic boundary, the onset of closure of the Tethys Gulf then

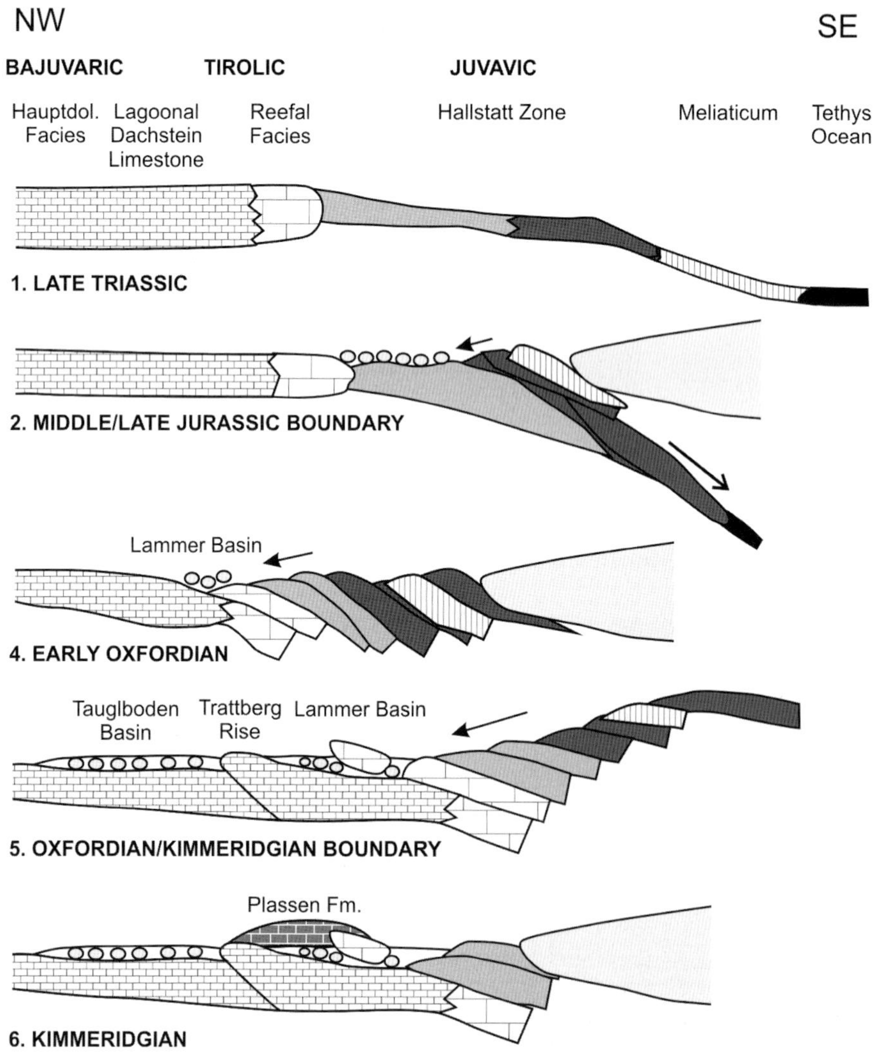


**Fig. 14.41.** Reconstruction of the tectonic development and nappe configurations during the Jurassic in the middle part of the Northern Calcareous Alps shows the influence of the primary Triassic configuration and the formation of the neoautochthonous cover during the Kimmeridgian. After Gawlick *et al.* (1999, 2002). This scheme follows the concept that the 'Hallstatt Meliata Ocean' was situated south of the Juvavic domain (see text). (Compare with Fig. 14.40).

caused nappe stacking in the NCA and the transportation of Juvavic sliding units over the Tyrolic units (Cimmeric Orogeny) (Tollmann 1981, 1987*a*,*b*; Gawlick *et al.* 1999). This nappe configuration was then sealed by Upper Jurassic sedimentation (neo-authochthonous cover; Mandl 1984). These latter sediments are usually interpreted as representing a period of tectonic quiescence (see Frisch & Gawlick 2003 for an alternative view).

Commencing with the Cretaceous orogenic events, the Austro-Alpine unit received its essential internal nappe structure. Faupl & Wagreich (2000) summarized two main lower Cretaceous tectonic processes: the ongoing closure of the Tethys and the initiation of subduction processes within the South Penninic unit. The general nappe transport direction was towards the WNW and north (Ratschbacher 1986; Neubauer *et al.* 2000).

*Penninic tectonic units*

The Penninic tectonic units (e.g. Hoinkes *et al.* 1999) are well known from the Western and Central Alps, and represent the lowermost tectonic unit. In the Eastern Alps they occur in a series of tectonic windows. These are the Lower Engadine Window along the Swiss–Austrian border, the Tauern Window in the central part, and the Rechnitz Window Group in the east of the Eastern Alps. Parts of the rocks forming the Penninic units were subject to Alpine metamorphism and comprise a stratigraphic range from the Late Proterozoic(?) through to the Palaeogene. Metamorphism was caused by the subduction of Penninic units below the Austro-Alpine continental lithosphere to the south (Frisch *et al.* 1987; Hoinkes *et al.* 1999). The non-metamorphic Cretaceous to Palaeogene Rhenodanubian Flysch Zone (e.g. Oberhauser 1995) is also considered to be part of the North Penninic Realm (for discussion see Faupl & Wagreich 2000; Wagreich 2001).

Sediments of Middle Penninic origin (Figs 14.40, 14.42) are known from the western part of the Eastern Alps. Jurassic to Lower Cretaceous deep-water carbonate sediments and Upper Jurassic carbonate breccias occur, the latter being formed on a north-facing slope during a phase of rifting (Gruner 1981; Froitzheim & Rubatto 1998). Palaeogeographically towards the

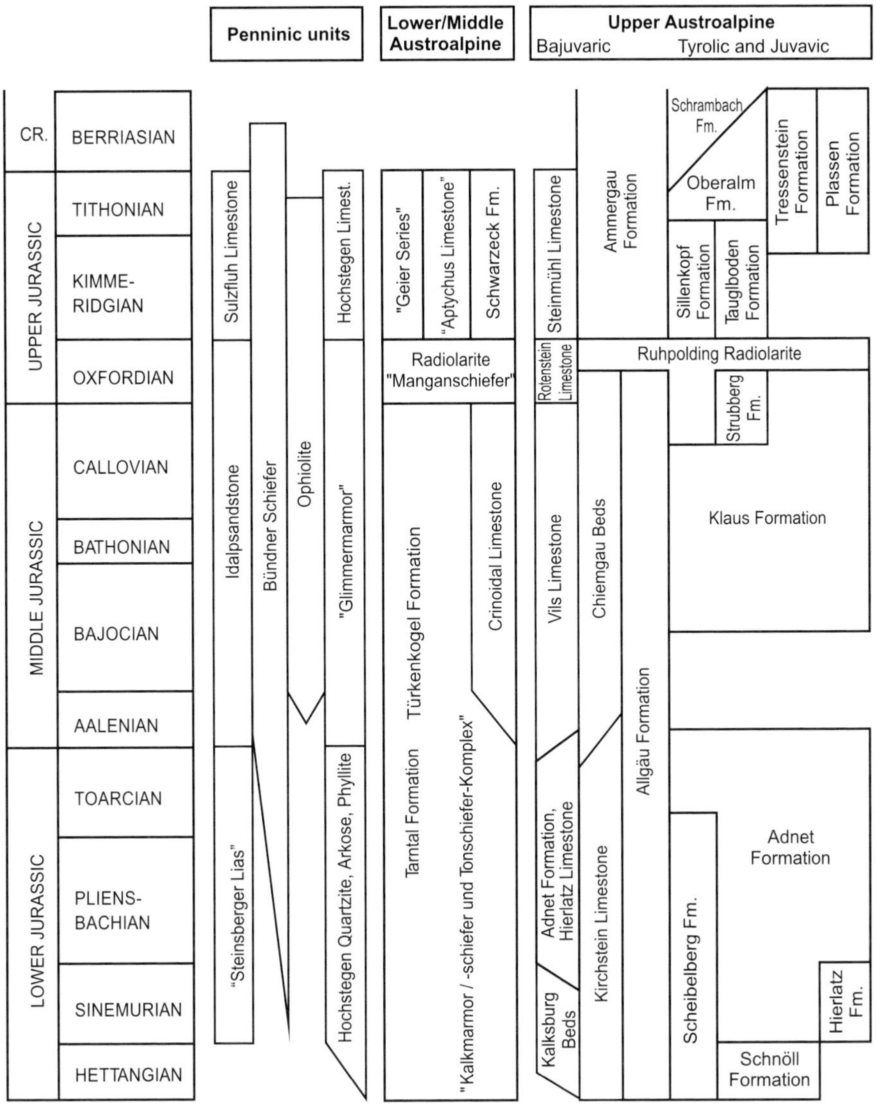


**Fig. 14.42.** Jurassic lithostratigraphy of the Austro-Alpine and Penninic units in the Eastern Alps. Modified and simplified after Piller *et al.* (2004) according to literature data (see text).

south, the Sulzfluh Nappe represents a separate Middle Penninic Unit, probably reflecting an intra-oceanic platform. Upper Jurassic shallow-water sediments of this unit are represented by the Sulzfluh Limestone, which is best developed in Switzerland (Ott 1969; Bertle 1973): The Lower and Middle Jurassic development was strongly influenced by siliciclastic sedimentation. During the late Middle Jurassic, there was a change to carbonate-dominated sedimentation and parts of the Upper Jurassic are represented by a carbonate platform comprising reefal sediments. According to Ott (1969), this sedimentary evolution reflects an important palaeogeographic change in the area and a generally transgressive trend.

The metamorphic South Penninic rocks of the Tauern Window were differentiated into four facies belts (Frasl & Frank 1966; Tollmann 1977) comprising Jurassic rocks. From north to south these are the Hochstegen, Brennkogel, Glockner and Fusch facies. The Hochstegen facies consists of Lower–Middle Jurassic quartzites, arkoses and marbles as well as Upper Jurassic limestones with cephalopods and microfauna (Kiessling 1992; Kiessling & Zeiss 1992). The Brennkogel facies was deposited during the opening stage of the oceanic trough. It contains Jurassic–Cretaceous phyllites and breccias probably derived from a northern 'Hochstegen swell zone' (Tollmann 1977). The Glockner facies comprises the metamorphic Bündner Schiefer, a succession of Jurassic to Lower Cretaceous shales, marls and shaly limestones with local sandstones, breccias and arkoses (e.g. Kleberger *et al.* 1981; Frisch *et al.* 1987; Reitz *et al.* 1990) with intercalations of ophiolites representing oceanic seafloor. In part this represents a metamorphic equivalent of the deep-water carbonate facies (Faupl & Wagreich 2000). A recent overview of the geodynamics of the Tauern Window was provided by Kurz *et al.* (2001*b*).

As summarized by Faupl & Wagreich (2000), the non-metamorphic Upper Jurassic–Lower Cretaceous succession of the Ybbsitz Zone (South Penninic domain in Lower Austria) is similar to the Arosa Zone in eastern Switzerland. The sequence comprises a succession of Upper Jurassic cherts and radiolarites (Rotenberg Fm) overlain by calpionellid limestones (Fasslgraben Fm) grading into Lower Cretaceous turbidites. These latter sediments probably mark the onset of subduction in the Penninic Zone. The Lower/Middle Gresten Fm of this zone formed part of the European Helvetic Shelf at the time of deposition (Decker 1990).

*Lower and Middle Austro-Alpine units*

The Lower Austro-Alpine unit forms the framework of the tectonically deeper Penninic tectonic units to the NW and NE of the Tauern Window as well as in the Rechnitz Window Group (Tollmann 1977). As with the Penninic tectonic units, these were subjected to Alpine metamorphosis (Hoinkes *et al.* 1999). Following the opening of the Penninic Ocean, the Lower Austro-Alpine Unit represented the Jurassic northern passive continental margin of the Austro-Alpine lithosphere, facing the South Penninic Unit with oceanic lithosphere to the north. Contemporaneously with the Upper Jurassic initiation of further rifting, slope breccias were formed along fault transects. Häusler (1987) described fan deposits related to these tectonic events: the Lower/Middle Jurassic Türkenkogel and Tarntal formations are characterized by slates and breccias, partly coarsening upwards. These formations are overlain by early Late Jurassic radiolarites and the metamorphic Schwarzeck Fm comprising green phyllites and olistoliths. The 'Geier Series' is a time equivalent of the Schwarzeck Fm (e.g. Tollmann 1977). The Jurassic/Cretaceous development of the northern Austro-Alpine margin and the Early Cretaceous change from a passive to an active continental margin has been described by Frisch *et al.* (1987).

The Middle Austro-Alpine unit in the Eastern Alps forms a nappe system of crystalline and metamorphic rocks, 530 km long and 60–140 km wide, situated on top of the Penninic–Lower Austro-Alpine windows and tectonically below the Upper Austro-Alpine unit. It contains only a thin, incomplete Permian–Mesozoic sedimentary cover with rare fossils, which is dominated by the Triassic (Tollmann 1977). An example of this is the so-called Stangalm-Mesozoic east of the Tauern Window, with Lower–Middle Jurassic schists, early Late Jurassic red radiolarites, and late Late Jurassic 'Aptychus limestones'. Tollmann (1977) suggested that the thin sediment cover resulted from deposition on a structural high resulting in a condensed section. A different view, including a critical discussion on the definition of a Middle Austro-Alpine unit, was recently published by Frisch & Gawlick (2003).

*Upper Austro-Alpine unit: Northern Calcareous Alps*

The NCA nappe complex forms a thrust belt of sedimentary rocks, 500 km long and 20–50 km wide. Mesozoic carbonates predominate, but clastic sediments are also frequent at several stratigraphic levels. Recently, the Mesozoic sedimentation and tectonics were reviewed by Mandl (2000) and Faupl & Wagreich (2000). A thorough lithostratigraphic overview, partly still in use, was published by Tollmann (1976).

**Platform drowning at the Triassic–Jurassic boundary.** During the Late Triassic, an extensive carbonate platform with prominent reefs (Dachstein Formation and 'Upper Rhaetian Reef Limestones' or Steinplatte Limestone) and adjacent pelagic limestones with rich cephalopod faunas (Hallstatt Zone) were formed along the Tethys shelf (for summary see Piller *et al.* 2000; Mandl 2000). At the beginning of the Jurassic, this Austro-Alpine shelf drowned completely. This was accompanied by coral extinctions and the global disappearance of coral reefs (Leinfelder *et al.* 2002). Gawlick *et al.* (1999) suggested that drowning was most likely caused by reduced sedimentation rates, rather than by increased subsidence rates at the Triassic–Jurassic boundary. Upper Triassic carbonate platform sediments are overlain by Lower Jurassic pelagic sediments, separated by a drowning unconformity (Böhm 1992, 2003). Subsequently, pelagic sediments predominated in the NCA. Previous assumptions that Upper Triassic reef growth continued until the basal Jurassic ('Rhätoliassic reef limestones'; Fabricius 1959) have been rejected by later studies. Triassic–Jurassic boundary transitions from western parts of the NCA were described by Ehes & Leinfelder (1988) and Krainer & Mostler (1997).

**Early Jurassic pelagic carbonate platforms.** The early Early Jurassic depositional patterns were largely controlled by the complex palaeorelief formed by the drowned Rhaetian carbonate platforms (Böhm 1992). This led to the formation of extensive pelagic carbonate platforms. Red crinoidal (Hierlatz Fm) and cephalopod limestones (Adnet Fm) were deposited on the top and slopes of pelagic platforms. Neptunian dykes filled with these sediments cut down into Upper Triassic limestones for more than 100 m. Basinal sediments are represented by the Allgäu Fm (= 'Lias-Fleckenmergel'), which comprise bedded, grey limestones partly rich in organic material (Jacobshagen 1965). This unit, ranging from the Hettangian to the Callovian, overlies Upper Triassic basinal sediments (Kössen Fm).

The Lower Jurassic palaeorelief is best studied in the central part of the NCA, SE Salzburg, at the classic locality of the Adnet

Group (Adnet Limestones; Böhm 2003). In addition to its use as a decorative stone since Medieval times (Kieslinger 1964), the sediments of the Adnet Group provide a textbook example for a Triassic reef community (e.g. Bernecker *et al.* 1999) and a drowned carbonate platform (Garrison & Fischer 1969; Schlager & Schöllnberger 1974; Schlager 1981). Böhm *et al.* (1999) demonstrated how Lower Jurassic sedimentation prograded over the primary relief (summary in Böhm 2003). During the Hettangian, sedimentation occurred on the lower slope of the pelagic platform, with poorly oxygenated water favouring abundant siliceous sponges (Schnöll Fm), as well as in basinal settings with condensed glauconitic limestones (Kendlbach Fm). Repeated submarine erosion and non-sedimentation as well as possible hydrothermal activity led to the development of a laterally continuous, ferromanganese crust, the so-called 'Marmorea Crust'. The mineralogy and geochemistry of Lower Jurassic ferromanganese crusts were studied by Krainer *et al.* (1994) and Böhm *et al.* (1999). During the Sinemurian, the sediments of the pelagic platforms reflect a return to 'normal' water chemistry. The upper slope was characterized by thin-bedded micritic limestones rich in intraclasts with ferromanganese coatings and crinoidal limestones, while red nodular limestones were deposited on the deeper slope (Adnet Fm). Sedimentation changed again during the Pliensbachian. The presence of breccia layers indicate synsedimentary tectonic activity, which led to the formation of mass flows eroding the underlying sediment (Böhm *et al.* 1995). During the Toarcian, another change in depositional conditions is indicated by the dominance of fine-grained turbidites, increased pelagic influence, and reduced carbonate sedimentation (Böhm 1992). In certain tectonic units the Adnet Fm is replaced by the Sinemurian–Pliensbachian crinoidal limestones of the Hierlatz Fm (Vörös 1991).

**Opening of the Penninic Ocean.** While subsidence during the early Early Jurassic showed a continuity with the Upper Triassic patterns, the late Early Jurassic and Middle Jurassic subsidence can be related to rifting activities along the Penninic rift zone (Gawlick *et al.* 1999). During the late Early Jurassic, rifting with subsequent opening of the Penninic Ocean commenced, leading to the separation of the Austro-Alpine units from the stable European continent. Formation of oceanic crust commenced during the Middle Jurassic (e.g. Weissert & Bernoulli 1985). From this time, the Austro-Alpine Unit became an independent microplate located north of Apulia (Channell *et al.* 1992). This was accompanied by subsidence and changes in sedimentary patterns.

*Middle Jurassic subsidence and condensed sedimentation*

Little information is available for the Middle Jurassic successions of the NCA. Ongoing subsidence resulted in condensed sedimentation and Gawlick *et al.* (1999) have suggested that much of the central part of the NCA represented a pelagic plateau unaffected by tectonic activity. Despite the different tectonic patterns, the sediments of the Middle Jurassic are similar to those of the Early Jurassic, although they are generally less abundant. The basinal carbonate sediments are still represented by the Allgäu Fm, but pelagic platform and slope carbonates are represented by the Klaus Fm. This latter formation is comparable to the Adnet Fm and is a nodular cephalopod-rich limestone rich in ferromanganese crusts. It discordantly overlies Upper Triassic and Lower Jurassic sediments (e.g. Krystyn 1971). Middle Jurassic block faulting and its influence on sedimentary patterns have been described from the Bajuvaric units of the western Eastern Alps by Lackschewitz *et al.* (1991).

**Callovian–Oxfordian radiolarite basins.** A fundamental change in tectonic activity and deposition led to the formation of widespread radiolarite-rich basins in the NCA during Callovian–Oxfordian times (e.g. Ruhpolding Radiolarite; Diersche 1980). This change termed the 'Ruhpoldinger Wende' (Schlager & Schöllnberger 1974) is related to the initial pulse of the Alpine Orogeny. This pulse was related to the onset of closure of the Permo–Triassic Tethys Gulf (Figs 14.40, 14.41) accompanied by the detachment of Triassic–Jurassic shelf facies zones from their basement followed by nappe stacking; tectonic sliding units from the Juvavic realm were transported over the Tyrolic nappes (Tollmann 1981, 1987*a*; Gawlick *et al.* 1999). The movement of fault blocks and sliding units resulted in a complex seafloor topography. Palaeo-oceanographic changes related to these topographic changes, rather than great water depths, are suggested as the controls on the widespread radiolarite deposition (Baumgartner 1987).

Various tectonic models exist for the closure of the Tethys Gulf (e.g. Tollmann 1981; Faupl 1997), and these have been summarized by Faupl & Wagreich (2000). Further summaries and discussions on tectonics around the Middle–Late Jurassic boundary were given by Gawlick *et al.* (1999) and Mandl (2000); studies of Tethyan radiolarites were, among others, conducted and summarized by Baumgartner (1987).

The development and controlling factors of radiolarite basin formation are best studied in the central part of the NCA (e.g. Diersche 1980; Gawlick & Suzuki 1999; Gawlick *et al.* 1999; Missoni *et al.* 2001; summary by Gawlick *et al.* 2002). In this area, Gawlick *et al.* (2002) differentiated between three types of radiolarite basins (Fig. 14.41) indicating the migration of tectonic activity through time. The Lammer Basin type is the oldest one, containing the Lower Callovian to Middle–Late Oxfordian Strubberg Fm with mass flows and slides originating from the former Hallstatt Zone. The Tauglboden Basin with the Tauglboden Fm, ranging from the Oxfordian–Kimmeridgian boundary to the Early Tithonian, contains mass flows and slides originating from the Trattberg Rise (Schlager & Schlager 1973; Gawlick *et al.* 1999). The latter was a tectonically elevated area that separated the southern Lammer Basin from the northern Tauglboden Basin. Gawlick *et al.* (2002) interpreted these basins as deep-sea trenches formed in front of advancing nappes as a result of tectonic processes. From Kimmeridgian to Early Tithonian, the Sillenkopf Fm was deposited in the area of the former Lammer Basin, now called the Sillenkopf Basin, which is related to tectonic shortening.

**Kimmeridgian onset of carbonate platforms.** The Kimmeridgian to Tithonian was a period of tectonic quiescence, when sedimentation continued on the palaeorelief created by the emplacement of the Juvavic sliding units and the accompanying block faulting (neoautochthonous cover of Mandl 1984). This structural relief provided a base for the first development of shallow-water carbonate platforms since the beginning of the Jurassic; these developed above Juvavic units (Tollmann 1981, 1987*a*; Gawlick *et al.* 1999). This prominent change of sedimentary patterns is also expressed in the basinal sediments, which show a change from radiolarite to carbonate sedimentation (Oberalm Fm).

Kimmeridgian to Berriasian carbonate platform sediments (Plassen Fm and Lerchkogel Limestone) are up to 1000 m thick (Schlagintweit *et al.* 2003) and mirror the global flourishing of reefs during the Late Jurassic (Kiessling *et al.* 1999; Leinfelder *et al.* 2002). Shallow-water carbonates comprise a rich fauna of stromatoporoids, corals, micro-encrusters and green algae (e.g. Fenninger & Hötzl 1965; Fenninger 1967; Fenninger & Holzer 1972; Steiger & Wurm 1980; Steiger 1981; Dya 1992; Darga & Schlagintweit 1991; Schlagintweit & Ebli 1999; Rasser & Fenninger 2002; Schlagintweit *et al.* 2003). Stable isotope studies were conducted by Rasser & Fenninger (2002). Traditionally, Upper Jurassic platforms of the NCA are interpreted as 'Bahamian-type' carbonate platforms with steep slopes (Fenninger 1967; Steiger & Wurm 1980). Later investigations, however, suggested the existence of ramp structures (Schlagintweit & Ebli 1999; Schlagintweit *et al.* 2003). Platform slope sediments are supposed to be represented by the Tressenstein Fm, a thick sequence of carbonate breccias containing shallow-water detritus (Fenninger & Holzer 1972; Lukeneder *et al.* 2003). The link between shallow-water and basinal sediments is represented by the turbiditic Barmstein Limestone, intercalated within the basinal Oberalm Fm (Flügel & Pölster 1965; Hötzl 1966; Flügel & Fenninger 1966; Fenninger & Holzer 1972; Steiger 1981; Schütz & Hüssner 1997; Boorova *et al.* 1999; Rasser *et al.* 2003). Carbonate platform development most probably terminated during the Berriasian. Fenninger & Holzer (1972) and Schlagintweit *et al.* (2003) describe radiolarian-bearing sediments overlying the Plassen Fm at its type locality. Additional sediments overlying this formation are not known. In contrast, the basinal carbonates of the Oberalm Fm continue to the Lower Cretaceous. The increased terrigenous influx up-section (Schrambach and Rossfeld formations) reflects the onset of Alpine deformation (Faupl & Wagreich 2000).

Sliding units responsible for the development of Upper Jurassic shallow-water carbonates were derived from the Juvavic units transported over Tyrolic nappes, a feature that is best developed in the central part of the NCA (Gawlick *et al.* 1999). Therefore, pelagic sediments prevail in the western part of the NCA, which are dominated by the Bajuvaric nappes. These are dominated by the Ammergau Fm and its equivalents (Quenstedt 1951; Fenninger & Holzer 1972; Tollmann 1976).

### *Western Carpathian Basins (J.G., M.K., J.M.)*

The Western Carpathians are subdivided into an older (Palaeo-Alpine) internal range known as the Central Carpathians and the younger (Neo-Alpine) external one, known as the Outer (or Flysch) Carpathians. The Outer (Flysch) Carpathians are composed of deep-marine successions ranging in age from Jurassic to Early Miocene (Ślączka 1996). These deposits were folded and overthrust during Miocene times (Alpine Orogeny), forming north-verging nappes detached from their original basement (Ślączka 1996) and thrust over Miocene deposits of the Carpathian Foredeep on the border of the European Craton.

*Outer Western Carpathians*

A complicated structure known as the Pieniny Klippen Belt (PKB) (Fig. 14.43) is situated in an accretionary zone which developed during the collision of the Central Carpathians and the Northern European Plate. The PKB is composed of several successions of mainly deep- and shallow-water limestones, covering a timespan from the Early Jurassic to the Late Cretaceous (Birkenmajer 1986; Golonka *et al.* 2000*b*). This strongly tectonized structure is about 600 km long and 1–20 km wide, stretching from Vienna (Austria) in the west, to Poiana Botizii (Romania) in the east. The PKB is separated from the present-

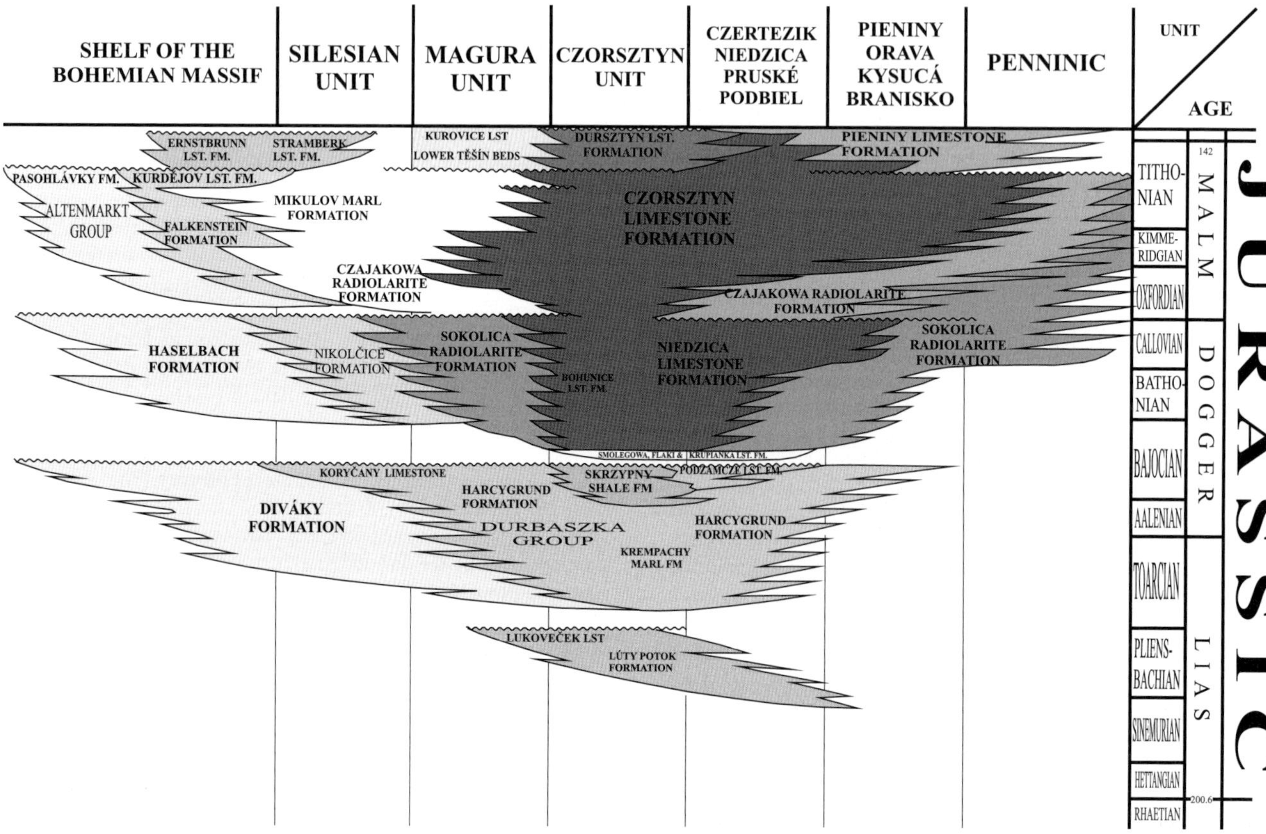


**Fig. 14.43.** Lithostratigraphical scheme of the Pieniny Klippen Belt and surrounding regions.

day Outer Carpathians by a Miocene subvertical strike-slip fault (Birkenmajer 1986). The original domain of the PKB and adjacent units is also called the Oravicum (e.g. Plašienka 1999).

The Jurassic history of the Outer Carpathian basins reflects the evolution of an extension of the central Atlantic rift system continuing eastwards into the Alpine Tethys, which included the Ligurian, Penninic, Pieniny (Vahic) and Magura basins. The central Atlantic and Alpine Tethys began to rift during the Early Jurassic. In the Pieniny and Magura basins the synrift stage lasted from the Middle Jurassic until the Tithonian. Late Jurassic (Oxfordian–Kimmeridgian) history of both basins reflects the strong facies differentiation. However, if the Pieniny Basin was a part of the Neotethys branch, rifting probably started during the Early Jurassic, earlier than in the Magura Basin. Within the deeper basinal zones sedimentation of radiolarites and mixed siliceous/carbonate deposits took place, whereas the shallower zones were completely devoid of siliceous intercalations. Major reorganization of the area was related to crustal stretching beneath the Alpine Tethys and North European Platform. In the southern part of the North European Platform, north of the Pieniny and the Magura basins, rifting commenced during Late Jurassic times when the Silesian Basin in the Outer Western Carpathians, the Sinaia Basin in the Eastern Carpathians, and the Severin Basin in the Southern Carpathian were formed.

*Central Western Carpathians*

The Central Carpathian block during Jurassic times was bordered by the Alpine Tethys to the north and the Meliata Ocean to the south. The area between the two oceans was divided into six palaeogeographic domains, partially reflected by present-day tectonic units. From north to south these were the Tatric, Fatric, Veporic, Gemeric, Hronic and Silicic domains (Andrusov *et al.* 1973) (Fig. 14.44). To the west the Central Carpathian block was connected with the Austro-Alpine plate. The Meliata oceanic crust was subducted at the end of the Jurassic and the southern margin of the Austro-Alpine–Central Carpathian microcontinent collided with various small blocks (Froitzheim & Manatschal 1996). Carbonate platforms on these blocks became emergent and were subsequently karstified. Fragments of these platforms are also included in the Central Carpathians. This collision also caused uplifts and tensional stress within the Central Carpathian sedimentary area. The Tatric and Veporic domains were also uplifted, but remained submerged. In contrast subsidence continued in the Fatric Domain lying between the latter two domains. During the Jurassic and Early Cretaceous, the central, more rapidly subsiding part of this domain (Zliechov Basin) was rimmed by marginal slope areas (with shallower sedimentation). The basinal part of the Fatric Domain is presently exposed within the Krížna Nappe, while the slope areas are exposed within the Vysoká, Beckov, Belá, Ďurčiná, Suchy Wierch, Havran and Humenné partial nappes (Mahel 1986). The position of the Hronic Domain, similar to that of the Alpine Bajuvaric, is uncertain to some extent. Development of the Hronic Domain facies indicates its original position further to the west than the other Central Carpathian units.

The Lower and Middle Jurassic succession in the southernmost

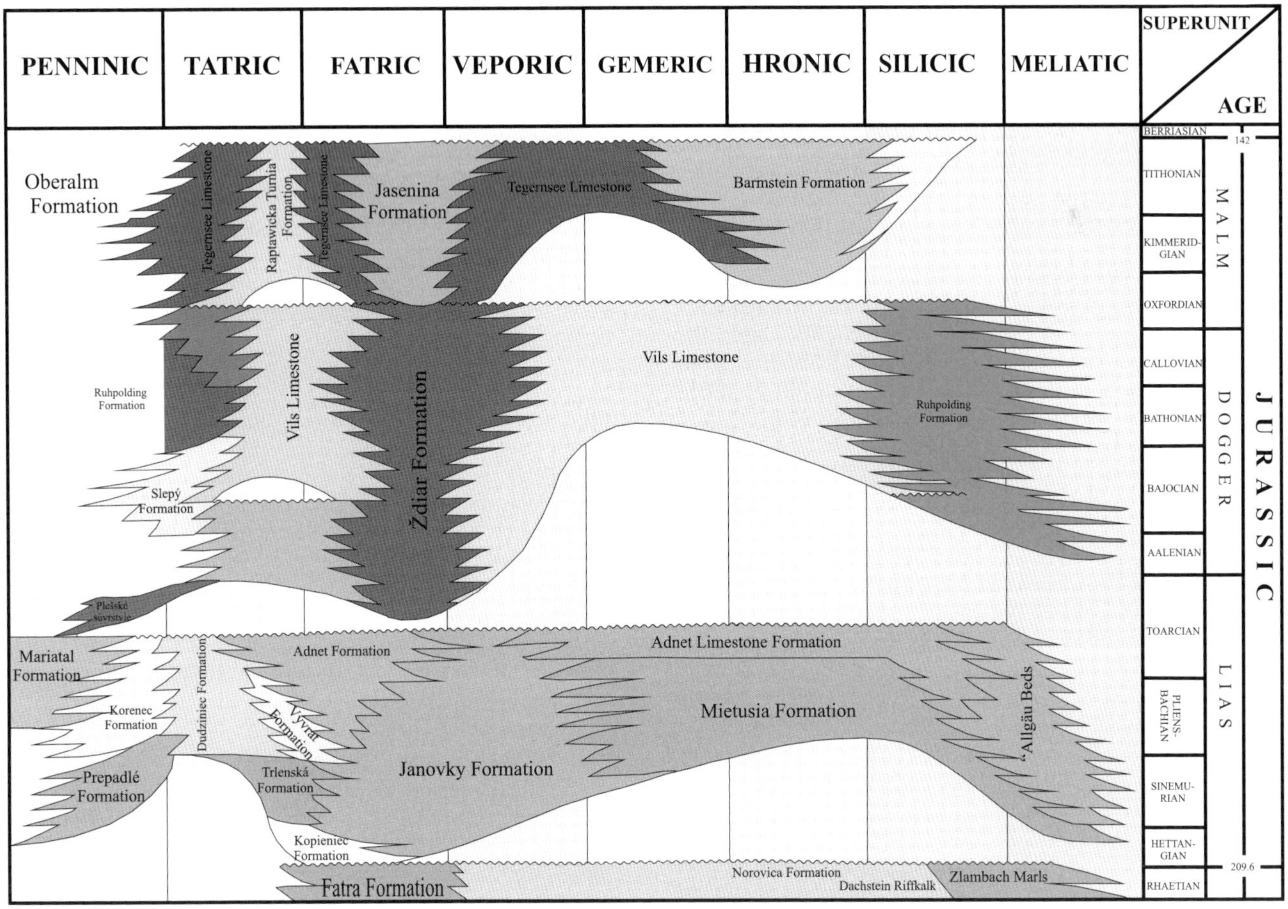


**Fig. 14.44.** Lithostratigraphical scheme of the Central Carpathian units.

part of the Western Carpathian block (called also the Inner, or Cimmerian Carpathians) is represented by pelagic facies similar to those of the Alpine Juvavic (Kaiser-Weidich & Schairer 1990; Lobitzer 1994). Fragments of Upper Jurassic neritic limestone successions have also been described from several locations (Michalik 1993, 1994, and references therein). The sedimentary record of this region was terminated by Late Cimmerian deformation of the area.

*Outer Carpathian basins*

The Jurassic of the Outer Carpathian basins (Fig. 14.43) developed between the Central Carpathian block and the North European Platform (Golonka *et al.* 2005; Ślączka *et al.* 2006). The complex Mesozoic tectonics of the Outer Carpathians also produced a series of ridges separating deep-water basins (Golonka *et al.* 2005). The Pieniny Basin was located between the Central Carpathian block and the Czorsztyn Ridge. The Magura Basin was situated between the Czorsztyn Ridge and the Silesian Ridge. The Pieniny Basin, the Magura Basin and the Czorsztyn Ridge were parts of the Alpine Tethys, which opened during Pliensbachian–Aalenian times. The Alpine Tethys, the Ligurian and Penninic oceans and the Pieniny and Magura basins represent the extension of the Central Atlantic system (Golonka 2000). Basin opening was related to the closure of the Meliata Ocean. The Czorsztyn Ridge became pronounced during the Middle Jurassic. The occurrence of the mafic (basalt) intrusions in the eastern termination of the Czorsztyn Ridge in the Novoselica Klippen (Lashkevitsch *et al.* 1995; Krobicki *et al.* 2005; Golonka *et al.* 2005) would appear to support the thermal origin of the ridge as being related to oceanic spreading. During the Jurassic–Early Cretaceous the Czorsztyn Ridge was submerged and did not supply clastic material to the Pieniny and Magura basins. This observation provides an argument against the origin of the ridge as a rifted fragment of the European Platform. On the other hand, the presence of non-volcanic rock fragments (such as quartz pebbles derived from a sialic substrate) in Jurassic slope sediments (mostly crinoidal limestones) of the Czorsztyn Ridge calls for a more cautious approach concerning the source area dilemma.

The Silesian Basin was located between the Silesian Ridge and the cratonic part of the North European Platform (Golonka *et al.* 2005; Ślączka *et al.* 2006). The Jurassic–Early Cretaceous Silesian Ridge originated as a result of the fragmentation of the European Platform in this area (Golonka *et al.* 2003, 2005). Formation of the extensional Silesian Basin included a strong strike-slip component which resulted in the development of a complex rotated block system. The emerged fragments of these blocks supplied material to the basin.

The deepest part of the Pieniny Basin is documented by the presence of the extremely deep-water Jurassic–Early Cretaceous deposits (pelagic limestones and radiolarites) of the Zlatna Unit (Sikora 1971; Golonka & Sikora 1981; Golonka & Krobicki 2002), later described also as the Ultra-Pieniny Succession (Birkenmajer 1988; Birkenmajer *et al.* 1990) or the Vahicum (e.g. Plašienka 1999). The transitional slope sequences between the deepest basinal units and the ridge units are termed the Pieniny, Branisko (Kysuca), and Czertezik successions (Fig. 14.43). The relatively shallow deposits known as the Czorsztyn Succession occupied the Czorsztyn Ridge. According to Birkenmmajer (1986) the Czorsztyn Succession can be traced from the area of Vienna through western Slovakia, Poland, eastern Slovakia to Transcarpathian Ukraine and perhaps northernmost Romania (Bombiţă *et al.* 1992).

Strongly condensed Jurassic–Early Cretaceous pelagic cherty limestones (of the Maiolica-type facies) and radiolarites were deposited in the Magura Basin. The Grajcarek or Hulina Succession (equivalents of the tectonic Grajcarek Unit, *sensu* Birkenmajer 1970, 1986, 1988) or the Hulina Unit (Golonka & Sikora 1981; Golonka *et al.* 2000*b*; Golonka & Krobicki 2002, 2004; Golonka *et al.* 2003) was deposited in the extremely deep-water basinal zone of the Magura Basin. The palaeogeographic extent of the Magura Basin remains somewhat enigmatic and speculative, as does the supposed existence of oceanic crust below the Magura Basin. The presumable transitional southern slope successions of the Magura Basin are known from some outcrops located north of the Czorsztyn Ridge (such as Zawiasy and Stare Bystre in Poland; Golonka & Krobicki 2002, 2004). The northern slope carbonate deposits are known from the Kurovice area in Moravia (Czech Republic) (Picha *et al.* 2006; Ślączka *et al.* 2006).

The Silesian Ridge succession is known only from exotic pebbles in deep-marine rocks (Książkiewicz 1960; Golonka *et al.* 2000*b*). The origin of the Silesian Ridge was perhaps related to the Jurassic separation of the Bucovinian-Getic microplate from the European plate. However, direct connection between these terranes is obscured due to the occurrence of the remnants of the Transylvanian Ocean in the area of the eastern end of the Pieniny Klippen Basin. These remnants are known from the Iňačovce-Krichevo unit in eastern Slovakia and Ukraine (Soták *et al.* 2000, 2002). The Silesian Basin is represented by shallow-water shelf and slope successions (known from the Baška area in the Czech Republic and from the Andrychów klippes in Poland) as well as by basinal deep-water pelagic and coarser-grained successions known from the vicinity of Cieszyn in the Czech Republic and Poland.

Generally, Lower Jurassic–lower Middle Jurassic dark/black terrigenous deposits of the Outer Carpathian basins were deposited in an oxygen-reduced environment. Middle Jurassic–lowest Cretaceous crinoidal and nodular red limestones (of the Ammonitico Rosso type) of the ridges were deposited in a better oxygenated environment which contrasted with the dysoxic basins with radiolarites or cherty (of the Maiolica–Biancone type) limestones and black shales and turbiditic deposits (Birkenmajer 1986; Mišík 1994; Aubrecht *et al.* 1997; Picha *et al.* 2006; Ślączka *et al.* 2006). Four sedimentary cycles can be recognized in the Jurassic sedimentary record.

**First sedimentary cycle (Sinemurian to Early Bajocian).** The sedimentary history of the future Alpine Tethys in the West Carpathians began during the Early Jurassic in a single basin. During this time, the southern European shelf was gradually inundated by a prograding Tethyan transgression. A thick succession of poorly studied sediments comprising redeposited dark/black sandstones and siltstones of the Gresten type as well as limestones (Diváky Formation) was deposited in a series of local depressions. Mudstones and siltstones of the Durbaška Group were deposited in an extensive submarine delta and more distal submarine fans also formed. The oldest Jurassic (Hettangian–Sinemurian) rocks of the Alpine Tethys units are preserved only in the Slovakian and Ukrainian parts of the region. They are represented by locally developed limestones (Lúty Potok, Lukoveček, Koryčany limestone formations). The presence of younger Toarcian–Lower Bajocian *Bositra* (*Posidonia*) black shales with spherosiderites (Skrzypny Shale Formation), as well as dark marls and limestones of the widespread Tethyan Fleckenkalk/Fleckenmergel facies (of the Krempachy Marl, Harcygrund Shale and Podzamcze Limestone formations; see Birkenmajer 1977) indicate the oxygen-depleted conditions (Birkenmajer 1986; Tyszka 1994, 2001).

**Second sedimentary cycle (Late Bajocian to Callovian).** During the Middle Jurassic, rifting commenced in the central Atlantic (Withjack *et al.* 1998) and the Alpine Tethys. The oldest oceanic crust in the Ligurian-Piemont Ocean in the southern Apennines and in the Western Alps has been dated as late as the Middle Jurassic (see Ricou 1996). Bill *et al.* (2001) date the onset of oceanic spreading of the Alpine Tethys as Bajocian. According to Winkler & Ślączka (1994) the Pieniny data fit well with the supposed opening of the Ligurian-Penninic Ocean. In both the Pieniny and the Magura basins the synrift stage lasted from late Early Jurassic until Tithonian times (Aubrecht *et al.* 1997).

One of the most rapid changes in sedimentation within this basin took place between the Early and Late Bajocian when sedimentation of terrigenous clastics continued along the continent (Haselbach and Nikolčice formations). Well-oxygenated crinoidal limestones (Smolegowa, Krupianka and Flaki Limestone formations) replaced the clastic sedimentation of the Early–early Middle Jurassic period on the shelf. The Bajocian emergence of the Czorsztyn Ridge, which divided the Carpathian part of Alpine Tethys into the Pieniny and Magura basins, was related to the post-rift phase of basin evolution (Golonka *et al.* 2003, 2005). Subsequent deposition (from latest Bajocian times) of the red nodular Ammonitico Rosso-type limestones (the Niedzica and Czorsztyn Limestone formations) was controlled by Meso-Cimmerian extension which produced tectonically differentiated blocks accompanied by formation of neptunian dykes and scarp-breccias on the Czorsztyn Ridge (e.g. Birkenmajer 1986; Michalík 1993, 1994; Mišík 1994; Aubrecht *et al.* 1997; Wierzbowski *et al.* 1999; Aubrecht 2001; Aubrecht & Túnyi 2001). At the same time, the first episode of radiolarite sedimentation (the Sokolica Radiolarite Formation) took place in the Pieniny and Magura basins (Birkenmajer 1977, 1986; Mišík 1999), and this resulted in a marked facies differentiation between the deepest successions and the shallow (ridge) ones. Ammonitico Rosso-type ridge limestones were dominated by bivalve (*Bositra*) filaments (Wierzbowski *et al.* 1999), while in the basinal deposits Bositra was gradually replaced by Radiolaria (Golonka & Sikora 1981).

**Third sedimentary cycle (Oxfordian to Middle Tithonian).** Rifting began in the southern part of the North European Platform, north of the Magura Basin. In the Silesian Basin of the Western Carpathians, black marls (Altenmarkt Group, Falkenstein Formation, Kurdějov Limestone, Mikulov Marls) and locally pelagic limestones of the Maiolica type (Olszewska & Wieczorek 2001) were deposited (Pescatore & Ślączka 1984; Picha *et al.* 2006; Ślączka *et al.* 2006).

The Late Jurassic (Oxfordian–Kimmeridgian) history of the Alpine Tethys reflects the most marked facies differentiation. Mixed siliceous/carbonate sedimentation occurred in the Pieniny and Magura basins. The greatest deepening is indicated by the widespread Oxfordian radiolarites (Czajakowa Radiolarite Formation), which occur in all the basinal successions. The ridge zone (Czorsztyn Succession) is completely devoid of siliceous intercalations at that time. Sedimentation of the Ammonitico Rosso facies, the Czorsztyn Limestone Formation with abundant *Globuligerina* ('*Protoglobigerina*') (Oxfordian) and *Saccocoma* (Kimmeridgian) continued on the Czorsztyn Ridge between the Pieniny and Magura basins. The flourishing of planktonic *Globuligerina* foraminifers in the ridge facies occurred simultaneously with the maximum development of radiolarians within the basinal zones (Wierzbowski *et al.* 1999). A similar basinal–ridge facies relationship is known from several European Alpine regions (e.g. Betic Cordillera, Southern Alps, Karavanke and Ionian Zone).

The Silesian Ridge between the Magura and Silesian basins was also characterized by shallow-water limestone sedimentation (Golonka *et al.* 2005). These limestones are known only from the exotic pebbles redeposited in the Magura and Silesian basins.

**Fourth sedimentary cycle (Middle to Late Tithonian).** During the Late Jurassic, carbonate platforms with reefs (Erstbrunn Limestone, Štramberk Limestone; Olszewska & Wieczorek 2001) developed along the European continental shelf. Deepening of the Silesian Basin in the Outer Carpathians was associated with the sedimentation of pre-turbiditic black, mainly redeposited marls (?Kimmeridgian–Tithonian). The rapid supply of shallow-water clastic material to the basin may have been related to the strong tectonoeustatic sea-level fluctuations known from that time. Marls (Vendryně Formation) pass gradually upwards into calcareous turbidites (Cieszyn Limestone; see Słomka 1986) which created several submarine fans. Black sediments mark the beginning of a new euxinic cycle that lasted until the Early Cretaceous. Subsidence in the Silesian Basin was accompanied by the extrusion of basic lava (teschenites) in the Western Carpathians and diabase-melaphyre within the 'black flysch' of the Eastern Carpathians (Golonka *et al.* 2000*b*; Lucińska-Anczkiewicz *et al.* 2002). The Silesian Basin probably extended southeastwards through the Eastern Carpathian Sinaia Basin as far as to the Southern Carpathian Severin Zone (Săndulescu & Visarion 2000).

Major plate reorganization occurred during the Tithonian. The Central Atlantic began to expand into the area between Iberia and the Newfoundland shelf (Ziegler 1988). The Ligurian-Penninic Ocean reached its maximum width and oceanic spreading stopped. The Tethyan plate reorganization followed the global pattern. This reorganization was expressed by Neo-Cimmerian tectonic movements, which resulted in extensive gravitational faulting (Birkenmajer 1958, 1986; Michalík 1990, 1994; Michalík & Reháková 1995; Krobicki 1996; Krobicki & Słomka 1999; Golonka *et al.* 2003). Several tectonic horsts and grabens were formed, rejuvenating some older, Eo- and Meso-Cimmerian faults which uplifted the shallow intrabasinal Czorsztyn Ridge as documented by facies diversification (Dursztyn Limestone Formation), and the presence of hardgrounds and condensed beds with ferromanganese-rich crusts and/or nodules, sedimentary/stratigraphic hiatuses, sedimentary breccias, neptunian dykes and/or faunal redeposition (e.g. the famous ammonite coquinas of the so-called 'Rogoźnik Beds' *sensu* Arkell 1956; see also Kutek & Wierzbowski 1986). Additionally, these movements subdivided the basin into different zones each with their own water circulation patterns; probably upwelling (Golonka & Krobicki 2001).

*The Central Western Carpathians*

The Central Carpathian block formed part of a microcontinent which comprised the source area of the Austro-Alpine units. In consequence, many palaeogeographical zones in the Carpathians and Alps are similar, or even identical (Tollmann 1976). The Carpathian–Alpine microcontinent was detached by Alpine Tethys rifting from the European shelf at the end of the Triassic (Bertotti *et al.* 1993; Michalík 1993, 1994). From earliest Jurassic times it moved ESE and converged with Apulia (Ratschbacher *et al.* 1989). At the end of the Jurassic, it collided with the Tisa-Pelsonian block of present-day northern Hungary, resulting in the closure of the Meliata Ocean.

**First sedimentary cycle (Hettangian to Middle Toarcian).** At the very beginning of the Jurassic, a large part of the Central Carpathians emerged, and it was only in the Fatric Basin that marine claystones, with occasional sandstones and sandy organodetrital limestones (Kopieniec Formation), were deposited. During the Sinemurian and Lotharingian, the previously elevated Tatric and Veporic domains were submerged. River deltas (Baboš Quartzite) passed distally into sandy limestones (Trlenská Formation). Crinoidal and organodetrital limestones (Dudziniec, Mietusia, Vývrat, Prístodolok formations) were deposited during the Pliensbachian. A deeper hemipelagic setting was characterized by the bioturbated limestones and marls of the Janovky Formation. The red nodular limestones and marls of the Adnet Formation indicate a slow sedimentary rate at the end of the Early Jurassic. In the poorly studied Hronic Basin, the Early Jurassic sedimentary sequence began with the crinoidal limestones of the Mietusia Formation. The cycle was terminated by the condensed red nodular Adnet Limestone. The margins of the spreading Alpine Tethys were affected by tensional stresses forming new grabens (Plašienka 1987; Plašienka *et al.* 1991, 1997). These grabens were filled by extensive breccias, deep-marine clastics and black shales (Prepadlé, Korenec, Mariatal formations).

**Second sedimentary cycle (Late Toarcian to Early Oxfordian).** A new sedimentary cycle characterized by bathymetric diversification of the area commenced in the Late Toarcian and continued through the Middle Jurassic. Tilted blocks along the Tatric northern margin were exposed to erosion and supplied material, ranging from breccias (Pleš Breccia; Michalík 1984) to turbidites (Slepý Formation). In the Fatric Basin, a similar zonation was established. Organodetrital and crinoidal limestones were deposited in the shallower zones. A calciturbidite facies developed on the slopes passing basinward into siliceous limestones, radiolarites and dark marls (the Ždiar Formation). In the Hronic Basin, the Middle Jurassic sedimentary cycle consists of well-sorted crinoidal limestones (Vils Formation).

**Third sedimentary cycle (Late Oxfordian to Middle Tithonian).** The diversification of bathymetry continued during the Late Jurassic enhancing the pattern of elevated and basinal areas within the Central Carpathian block. Small carbonate platforms (Raptawicka Turnia Formation) evolved on elevations marking a new sedimentary cycle, which started during the Oxfordian. The sedimentation of the Ammonitico Rosso limestone developed in the deeper slope zones, while at the same time the bottom of the pull-apart Fatric (Zliechov) Basin was covered by the dark marlstones of the Jasenina Formation. In the Hronic Domain the Ammonitico Rosso facies was dominant in the shallower zones, while pelagic planktonic carbonates of the Oberalm Formation with turbidite members (Barmstein Limestone; Steiger 1981; Boorová *et al.* 1999) characterized the deeper parts of the basin.

The subduction of the Meliata-Halstatt Ocean and the collision of the Tisza-Pelsonian block with the Central Carpathian block were concluded at the end of the Jurassic (Plašienka *et al.* 1997; Golonka *et al.* 2000*b*). This resulted in deformation, shallowing (Schlagintweit & Ebli 1999) and, finally, in complete winnowing of the southern (inner) part of the Western Carpathians and Northern Alps.

## Summary

The Jurassic was an important period in the Earth's history, with massive outpourings of basaltic igneous rocks, mass extinctions, significant variations in climate, sea level and atmospheric $CO_2$ and anoxic events (Hesselbo *et al.* 2002, 2007). The Late Triassic and Jurassic geological history is intricately linked with the progressive breakup of the supercontinent of Pangaea associated with the Tethys–Central Atlantic rift/wrench system which evolved at that time (Ziegler 1990). The Jurassic, however, also coincided with the greatest extent of Pangaea, following the docking of southern China to Laurasia in the Pliensbachian. However, this period of complete continental assembly was ephemeral, and in the Early Jurassic the area of central and western Europe was criss-crossed by a series of shallow seaways. The opening of new ocean basins in the Mediterranean area, the Central Atlantic and the Caribbean led to the ultimate breakup of Pangaea.

Formerly, it was considered that the climates of the Jurassic were more equable than today, although more recent data suggest that the 'greenhouse' climate may have occasionally alternated with subfreezing polar conditions and the presence of limited polar ice (Price 1999). High-latitude oceans during the Jurassic, however, were certainly warmer than they are today and were mostly ice-free.

During the Jurassic Period, the area covered by the Central European Basin System (CEBS) comprised a shallow epicontinental sea surrounded by marginal-marine areas and lowlands. Fluvial influx resulted in decreased seawater salinity not only in the marginal areas, but also in the Central European sea itself (Röhl *et al.* 2001). The CEBS and southernmost epi-Variscan basin domain comprised several realms distinguished mainly on the basis of faunal provincialism, such as Boreal, sub-Boreal and sub-Mediterranean, the latter developed in the peri-Tethyan area and showing frequent connections with the Tethys Ocean.

Stratigraphically, the Jurassic can be subdivided into three main units. The original subdivision used within Central Europe (i.e. 'black Jura', 'brown Jura', 'white Jura') has been replaced by three Series (Lower, Middle, Upper Jurassic), although the series boundaries have been grossly redefined. Stratigraphically, the Jurassic is typified by the abundance of fossil material, particularly ammonites. Indeed, these have facilitated the development of high-resolution correlation and subdivision of the Jurassic strata (Arkell 1956; Morton 1974). While ammonites are still the primary tools for biochronology, the fact that they are provincial complicates biostratigraphical correlations. This, however, is not such a great problem in Central Europe, since the region contains both sub-Mediterranean and Boreal bioprovinces.

The latest Triassic–early Jurassic commenced with a major pulsed transgression, related to continued lithospheric extension and associated rifting, combined with sea-level rise. Recurrent sea-level pulses provided a useful tool for sequence stratigraphy correlation, particularly in the Lower Jurassic marine and non-marine strata across the CEBS (Pieńkowski 1991*a*, 2004; de Graciansky *et al.* 1998*a*, *b*). This resulted in the establishment of a broad, open-marine shelf sea across much of Germany, the Paris Basin, the southern and central North Sea and Denmark, and was coincident with a change from non-marine to marine deposition across much of the region. Indeed, the initial connections between Tethys to the south and the Arctic Sea to the north may well have been established during the Rhaetian. By the end of the Early Jurassic, however, large parts of western and central Europe were occupied by epicontinental seas. Within this marine environment, sediment was predominantly sourced from the east

(East European Platform, Bohemian Massif) reflecting continuing uplift in this region. Indeed, the lack of major source areas at this time is problematic, when constrasted with the volumes of clay-sized sediment which were deposited over much of the region. Other possible sources include the Fennoscandian and Laurentian–Greenland areas (Hesselbo *et al.* 2002, 2007). Also of note at this time are the Hettangian and early Toarcian anoxic events which were related to phases of sea-level rise. At these times, the lack of sediment supply to southern regions resulted in the deposition of highly sediment-starved limestones, whereas expanded 'black shales' accumulated where abundant clay-sized sediment was available. The Toarcian Ocean Anoxic Event is particularly significant, being characterized by the widespread near-synchronous deposition of organic-rich shales in marine settings, as well as perturbations to several isotopic systems (including a major and sudden perturbation in the global carbon cycle). This event was associated with the massive injection of isotopically light carbon from some 'external' source, an increase in atmospheric $CO_2$ content, global warming, a huge increase in continental weathering and a resulting increase in sediment supply (Hesselbo *et al.* 2007).

The coeval change in climate from semiarid to humid occurred as a result of the northward drift of the continents and the increasing maritime influence. As noted above, greenhouse effects dominated Jurassic climates and although the Late Pliensbachian was cooler, by Late Jurassic times aridity had increased (possibly an orographic effect due to the collision of the Cimmeride mountain chain with Europe, but also evident on other continents).

The principal rift systems of the region, which had been initiated during the Early Triassic, remained active during the Early Jurassic (Ziegler 1990). The central and western Mediterranean area continued to be affected by rift and wrench tectonics during the early Jurassic, while in the Alpine domain rifting became increasingly important in the south Alpine and Austro-Alpine realms, as well as in the Penninic, Helvetic and Dauphinois areas (Ziegler 1990). Rift-related volcanism, however, was at a very low level.

In Mid-Jurassic times, the uplift of the North Sea rift dome had a marked influence on the palaeogeography of Europe. Uplift resulted in the separation of the Arctic Sea and Tethys which resulted in the development of carbonate platforms in SW Europe. Additionally, the high acted as a major sediment source shedding material both to the north into the Viking Graben and to the south to the Netherlands and northern Germany. The formation of the North Sea Dome was also accompanied by extensive volcanic activity (mainly late Bajocian–Bathonian), concentrated at the triple-junction with subsidiary centres in the southern Viking Graben, Egersund Basin, coastal Norway and the Central Graben.

Following crustal separation in the Tethys domain, the late Middle and Late Jurassic evolution of western and central Europe was dominated by intensified crustal extension across the Arctic–North Atlantic rift system (Ziegler 1990). This entailed a change in the regional stress regime that particularly affected Central Europe. Regressive sedimentary facies (carbonate ramps, deltas, coastal plains) and widespread erosion of pre-existing strata characterized much of the Mid-Jurassic. At the time of peak regression, marine connections between the Arctic and Tethys were severed, leading to marked faunal provinciality.

During Callovian to Tithonian times, rift/wrench activity resulted in major changes in the palaeogeographic framework. Broad-scale, stress-induced lithospheric deflections, the development of new thermal anomalies and the collapse of the North Sea rift dome resulted in changes in basin outlines and clastic sources. Sedimentation patterns within these basins, particularly in the slowly subsiding platform areas, were largely controlled by eustatic changes (Ziegler 1990). Sediment supply to the more northerly regions of central and western Europe progressively decreased, resulting in sediment condensation in deep-marine environments. In the Kimmeridgian and Tithonian, euxinic sea-bottom conditions developed in the North Sea area. Rifting in the North Sea ended in the latest Jurassic, but continued on the Atlantic margins into the Early Cretaceous.

The Earth in the Late Triassic and Jurassic was subjected to extreme geological events, just as at any other time period, namely massive extraterrestrial impacts and episodic flood basalt volcanism. Several large (>30 km) impact craters of Late Triassic to Jurassic age are now known and these are mostly well dated by radiometric or biostratigraphic means (Hesselbo *et al.* 2002). These include: (1) the Manicouagan Crater (Quebec, Canada, 100 km diameter) dated as 15 Ma before the Triassic–Jurassic boundary (i.e. Rhaetian age). It lies on the same palaeolatitude as other substantial craters, and it is possible that these all form part of a linear crater chain resulting from the pre-impact breakup of a particularly large extraterrestrial body; (2) the Aalenian–Bajocian Puchezh-Katungi Crater in Russia is 80 km in diameter; (3) the Mjolnir Crater, Barents Sea, has a diameter of 40 km and an impact site in a marine basin in the Barents Sea. The impact occurred just above the Jurassic–Cretaceous boundary; and (4) the Morokweng Crater, South Africa, occurs at the Jurassic–Cretaceous boundary, and has a diameter of between 70 and 340 km.

However, it is worth noting that since most Jurassic ocean floor has been subducted, it is likely that other impacts, with a more cryptic geological record, also occurred (Hesselbo *et al.* 2002). Together, the effects of these events are either masked in the geological history of Central Europe or have not yet been recognized, since the epicentres are located some distance from the area. Their effects are likely to have been global. Of particular interest is the relationship between mass extinctions and extraterrestrial impacts.

Three major continental flood basalt provinces have also been recognized as being of Late Triassic–Jurassic age (Hesselbo *et al.* 2002). These appear to pre-date, by a few million years, major phases of continental breakup and seafloor spreading in what was to become the Central Atlantic area and in SW Gondwana. As with the cratering, it is possible to make a case for linkage to mass extinctions since there is remarkable agreement between the ages of large igneous provinces and mass extinctions. The Triassic–Jurassic boundary was the first and greatest of the extinctions at this time. Indeed, it is one of the five largest mass extinctions in the Phanerozoic, affecting organisms in marine (ammonites, bivalves and reef ecosystems) and terrestrial (tetrapods, flora) environments. The evidence suggests that the extinction was catastrophic in that it apparently took place in less than 40 000 years. A second extinction event occurred in the early Toarcian and was coincident with flood basalts and poorly oxygenated bottom waters. The third extinction took place in the Tithonian, affecting primarily European bivalves and some other benthic organisms.

This is a contribution to IGCP project 506 'Marine and Non-marine Jurassic: Global Correlation and Major Geological Events'.

## References

Abbink, O.A. 1998. *Palynological investigations in the Jurassic of the North Sea region.* Laboratory of Palaeobotany and Palynology

Contribution Series, **8**.

Achilles, H. & Schlatter, R. 1986. Palynostratigraphische Untersuchungen im "Rhät-Bonebed" von Hallau (Kt. Schaffhausen) mit einem Beitrag zur Ammonitenfauna im basalen Lias. *Eclogae geologicae Helvetiae*, **79**, 149–179.

Albat, F. 2000. Land- und Schwimmsaurier aus dem Jura des Weser-Wiehengebirges. *In:* Fundort Nordrhein-Westfalen. Millionen Jahre Geschichte. *Schriften zur Bodendenkmalpflege in Nordrhein-Westfalen*, **5**, 217–219.

Aldinger, H. 1961. Die Schwammfazies im Weißen Jura Schwabens. *Jahresberichte und Mitteilungen des oberrheinischen geologischen Vereines, Neue Folge*, **43**, 99–103.

Alissanaz, A. 1992. The late Triassic-Hettangian bivalve turnover in Lombardy (Southern Alps). *Rivista Italiana di Paleontologia e Stratigrafia*, **97**, 431–454.

Allenbach, R.P. 2001. Synsedimentary tectonics in an epicontinental sea: A new interpretation of the Oxfordian basins of northern Switzerland. *Eclogae geologicae Helvetiae*, **94**, 265–287.

Allenbach, R.P. 2002. The ups and downs of "Tectonic Quiescence" – recognizing differential subsidence in the epicontinental sea of the Oxfordian in the Swiss Jura Mountains. *Sedimentary Geology*, **150**, 323–342.

Allenbach, R.P & Wetzel, A. 2006. Spatial patterns of Mesozoic facies relationships and the age of the upper Rhinegraben Lineament. *International Journal of Earth Sciences*, **95**, 803–813.

Allia, V. 1996. *Sedimentologie und Ablagerungsgeschichte des Opalinustons in der Nordschweiz.* PhD thesis, Universität Basel.

Allouc, J. & Guérin-Franiatte, S. 1981. Le Domérien supérieur et le Toarcien inférieur en Lorraine centrale, nouvelles observations lithostratigraphiques et biostratigraphiques à Jouy-Aux-Arches, près Metz (Moselle). *Bulletin d'information des géologues du Bassin de Paris*, **18**(2), 45–50.

Almeras, Y. & Hanzo, M. 1991. Les rhynchonellidés du Calcaire à gryphées d'Hettange (Sinémurien- NE France): étude des peuplements et enregistrement des variations du paléoenvironnement. *Palaeogeography, Palaeoclimatology, Palaeoecology*, **86**, 313–329.

Alth, A. 1881. Wapień niżniowski i jego skamieliny. *Pamiętnik Akademia Umiejętności, Wydział Matematyczno - Przyrodniczy*, **6**, 1–149.

Altmann, H.J. 1965. *Beiträge zur Kenntnis des Rhät-Lias-Grenzbereichs in Südwest-Deutschland.* PhD thesis, Universität Tübingen.

Andre, G. 2003. *Caractérisation de la structuration de l'Est du Bassin de Paris: discrimination des déformations synsédimentaires mésozoïques.* Thesis Université Nancy 1.

Andrusov, D., Bystrický, J. & Fusán, O. 1973. Outline of the structure of the West Carpathians: A guidebook for geological excursion. *Xth Congress of the Carpathian-Balkan Geological Association,* Bratislava 1973, 5–45.

Andsbjerg, J. 2003. Sedimentology and sequence stratigraphy of the Bryne and Lulu Formations, Middle Jurassic, Danish Central Graben. *In*: Ineson, J.R. & Surlyk, F. (eds) *The Jurassic of Denmark and Greenland.* Geological Survey of Denmark and Greenland Bulletin, **1**, 301–347.

Andsbjerg, J. & Dybkjær, K. 2003. Sequence stratigraphy of the Jurassic of the Danish Central Graben. *In*: Ineson, J.R. & Surlyk, F. (eds) *The Jurassic of Denmark and Greenland.* Geological Survey of Denmark and Greenland Bulletin, **1**, 265–346.

Andsbjerg, J., Nielsen, L.H., Johannessen, P.N. & Dybkjær, K. 2001. Divergent development of two neighbouring basins following the Jurassic North Sea doming event: the Danish Central Graben and the Norwegian–Danish Basin. *In:* Martinsen, O.J. & Dreyer, T. (eds) *Sedimentary Environments Offshore Norway – Palaeozoic to Recent.* Norwegian Petroleum Society (NPF), Special Publications, **10**, 175–197.

Arkell, W.J. 1956. *Jurassic Geology of the World.* Oliver and Boyd, Edinburgh.

Arndorff, L. 1993. Lateral relations of deltaic palaeosols from the Lower Jurassic Rønne Formation on the island of Bornholm, Denmark. *Palaeogeography, Palaeoclimatology, Palaeoecology,* **100**, 235–250

Aubrecht, R. 2001. New occurrences of the Krasín Breccia (Pieniny Klippen Belt, West Carpathians): indication of Middle Jurassic synsedimentary tectonics. *Acta Geologica Universitae Comenianae*, **56**, 35–56.

Aubrecht, R. & Túnyi, I. 2001. Original orientation of neptunian dykes in the Pieniny Klippen Belt (Western Carpathians): the first results. *Contributions to Geophysics and Geodesy*, **31**, 557–578.

Aubrecht, R., Mišík, M. & Sýkora, M. 1997. Jurassic synrift sedimentation on the Czorsztyn Swell of the Pieniny Klippen Belt in Western Slovakia. *In:* Plašienka, D., Hók, J., Vozár, J. & Ellecko, M. (eds) *Alpine Evolution of the Western Carpathians and Related Areas*, Dionýz Stur, Bratislava, 53–64.

Baldschuhn, R., Binot, F., Fleig, S. & Kockel, F. 2001. Geotektonischer Atlas von Nordwestdeutschland und dem deutschen Nordsee-Sektor. *Geologisches Jahrbuch, Reihe A,* **153**, 3–95.

Barféty, J.-C., Amaudric du Chaffaut, S., Gidon, M., Pécher, A., Roux, M. & Bourseau, J.-P. 1986. Les terrains sédimentaires du Mont-Pelvoux (zone dauphinoise, Alpes occicdentales françaises): nature, âge et implications paléostructurales. *Comptes rendues de l'Academie des Sciences, Paris, série 2,* **303**(6), 491–494.

Barski, M. & Leonowicz, P. 2002. Dinoflagellates of Lower Juarassic outcrops at Kozłowice and Boroszów (southern Poland). *Przegląd Geologiczny.*, **50**(5), 411–414.

Barski, M., Dembicz, K. & Praszkier, T. 2004. Biostratygrafia i paleośrodowisko środkowej jury z kamieniołomu Ogrodzieniec. *Tomy Jurajskie*, **2**, 61–68.

Barthel, K.W. 1969. Die obertithonische, regressive Flachwasser-Phase der Neuburger Folge in Bayern. *Bayerische Akademie der Wissenschaften, Mathematisch-Naturwissenschaftliche Klasse, Abhandlungen, Neue Folge,* **142**, 1–174.

Barthel, K.W. 1978. *Solnhofen. Ein Blick in die Erdgeschichte.* Ott, Thun.

Barthel, K.W., Swinburne, N.H.M. & Conway Morris, S. 1978. *Solnhofen. A Study in Mesozoic Palaeontology.* Cambridge University Press, Cambridge .

Baudrimont, A.F. & Dubois, P. 1977. Un bassin mésogéen du domaine péri-alpin: le sud-est de la France. *Bulletin du Centres de Recherches Exploration-Production Elf-Aquitaine*, **1**, 261–308.

Baumgartner, P.O. 1987. Age and genesis of Tethyan Jurassic radiolarites. *Eclogae geologicae Helvetiae,* **80**(2), 831–879.

Beher, E. 2004. Ostracodenfauna und Biostratigraphie im Ober-Sinemurium von Süddeutschland und der Nordschweiz. *Stuttgarter Beiträge zur Naturkunde, Serie B,* **349**, 1–171.

Bernecker, M., Weidlich, O. & Flügel, E. 1999. Response of triassic reef coral communities to sea-level fluctuations, storms and sedimentation: evidence from a spectacular outcrop. *Facies*, **40**, 229–280.

Berner, R.A. 1991. A model for atmospheric $CO_2$ over Phanerozoic time. *American Journal of Science*, **291**, 339–376.

Berners, H.P. 1983. A lower Liassic offshore bar environment, contribution to sedimentology of the Luxemburg sandstone. *Annales de la Société géologique de Belgique*, **106**, 87–102.

Bernier, P. 1984. Les formations carbonatées du Kimméridgien et du Portlandien dans le jura méridional. Stratigraphie, micropaléontologie, sédimentologie. *Documents du laboratoire géologiques de Lyon*, **92**, 1–803.

Bertle, H. 1973. Zur Geologie des Fensters von Gargellen (Vorarlberg) und seines kristallinen Rahmens. *Mitteilung der Gesellschaft für Geologie- und Bergbaustudenten*, **22**, 1–60.

Bertleff, B.W., Joachim, H., *et al.* 1988. Ergebnisse der Hydrogeothermiebohrungen in Baden-Württemberg. *Jahreshefte des Geologischen Landesamtes Baden-Württemberg,* **30**, 27–116.

Bertotti, G., Picotti, V., Bernoulli, D. & Castellarin, A. 1993. From rifting to drifting: tectonic evolution of the South-Alpine upper crust from the Triassic to the Early Cretaceous. *Sedimentary Geology,* **86**, 53–67.

Bessereau, G. & Guillocheau, F. 1994. Sequence stratigraphy and organic matter distribution of the Lias of the Paris Basin. *In:* Mascle, A. (ed.) *Hydrocarbon and Petroleum Geology of France.* European Association of Petroleum Geoscientists, Special Publications, **4**, 107–119.

BGR 1973–93. Geologische Übersichtskarte 1:200 000. Bundesanstalt für Geowissenschaften und Rohstoffe.

Bialkowski, A., Tribovillard, N.-P., Verges, E. & Deconinck, J.-F. 2000. Etude haute résolution de la distribution et de la granulométrie des constituants organiques sédimentaires dans le Kimméridgien-Tithonien du Boulonnais (Nord de la France). Application à l'analyse séquentielle. *Comptes rendus de l'Académie des Sciences*

*Paris*, **331**, 451–458.

BILL, M., O'DOGHERTY, L., GUEX, J., BAUMGARTNER, P.O. & MASSON, H. 2001. Radiolarite ages in Alpine-Mediterranean ophiolites: Constraints on the oceanic spreading and the Tethys-Atlantic connection. *Geological Society of America Bulletin*, **113**, 129–143.

BININDA, R. 1986. Cornbrash-Sande im zentralen Teil des Niedersächsischen Beckens. *Osnabrücker Naturwissenschaftliche Mitteilungen*, **12**, 7–45.

BIRKENMAJER, K. 1958. Submarine erosional breaks and Late Jurassic synorogenic movements in the Pieniny Klippen Belt geosyncline. *Bulletin de L'Académie Polonaise des Sciences, Série des Sciences de la Terre*, **8**, 551–558.

BIRKENMAJER, K. 1970. Pre-Eocene fold structures in the Pieniny Klippen Belt (Carpathians of Poland). *Studia Geologica Polonica*, **31**, 1–77 [in Polish with English summary].

BIRKENMAJER, K. 1977. Jurassic and Cretaceous lithostratigraphic units of the Pieniny Klippen Belt, Carpathians, Poland. *Studia Geologica Polonica*, **45**, 1–158.

BIRKENMAJER, K. 1986. Stages of structural evolution of the Pieniny Klippen Belt, Carpathians. *Studia Geologica Polonica*, **88**, 7–32.

BIRKENMAJER, K. 1988. Exotic Andrusov Ridge: its role in plate-tectonic evolution of the West Carpathian Foldbelt. *Studia Geologica Polonica*, **91**, 7–37.

BIRKENMAJER, K., KOZUR H. & MOCK R. 1990. Exotic Triassic pelagic limestone pebbles from the Pieniny Klippen Belt of Poland: a further evidence for Early Mesozoic rifting in West Carpathians. *Annales de la Societe Geologique de Pologne*, **60**, 3–44.

BITTERLI, P. 1972. Erdölgeologische Forschungen im Jura. *Bulletin der Vereinigung schweizerischer Petroleum-Geologen und -Ingenieure*, **39**, 13–22.

BITTERLI, P. 1979. *Cyclic sedimentation in the Upper Bathonian-Callovian of the Swiss Jura mountains. Symposium 'Sédimentation jurassique W européen'*. ASF Publication spéciale, **1** Association Sedimentologistes Français.

BLANK, R. 1990. Die kalkschaligen benthonischen Foraminiferen des Ober-Bajocium bis Unter-Callovium der südwestlichen Schwäbischen Alb, Baden-Württemberg. *Tübinger mikropaläontologische Mitteilungen*, **8**, 1–213.

BLOOS, G. 1976. Untersuchungen über Bau und Entstehung der feinkörnigen Sandsteine des Schwarzen Jura α (Hettangium u. tiefstes Sinemurium) im schwäbischen Sedimentationsbereich. *Arbeiten aus dem Institut für Geologie und Paläontologie der Universität Stuttgart, Neue Folge*, **71**, 1–269.

BLOOS, G. 1979. Über den Jura am Grossen Haßberg (Unterfranken, N-Bayern) mit Bemerkungen zum Rät. *Stuttgarter Beiträge zur Naturkunde, Serie B*, **44**, 1–53.

BLOOS, G. 1990. Eustatic sea-level changes in the Upper Keuper and in the Lower Lias of Central Europe. *Les Cahiers de l'Université Catholique de Lyon, Série Sciences*, **3**, 5–16.

BLOOS, G. 2004. Psiloceratids of the earliest Jurassic in the North-West European and Mediterranean Provinces – Remarks and new observations. *Stuttgarter Beiträge zur Naturkunde, Serie B*, **347**, 1–15.

BLOOS, G. 2006. Towards the definition of the Triassic/Jurassic systems boundary. *Volumina Jurassica*, **IV**, 277.

BLOOS, G., DIETL, G. & SCHWEIGERT, G. 2005. Der Jura Süddeutschlands in der STD 2002. *Newsletters in Stratigraphy*, **41**, 263–277.

BÖHM, F. 1992. Mikrofazies und Ablagerungsmilieu des Lias und Dogger der Nordöstlichen Kalkalpen. *Erlanger geologische Abhandlungen*, **121**, 57–217.

BÖHM, F. 2003. Lithostratigraphy of the Adnet Group (Lower to Middle Jurassic, Salzburg, Austria). *In:* PILLER, W. E. (ed.) *Stratigraphia Austriaca*. Österreichische Akademie der Wissenschaften, Erdwissenschaftliche Kommission, **16**, 217–229.

BÖHM, F., DOMMERGUES, J.-L. & MEISTER, L. 1995. Breccias of the Adnet Formation: indicators of a Mid-Liassic tectonic event in the Northern Calcareous Alps (Salzburg/Austria). *Geologische Rundschau*, **84**, 272–286.

BÖHM, F., EBLI, O., KRYSTYN, L., LOBITZER, H., RAKUS, M. & SIBLIK, M. 1999. Fauna, stratigraphy and depositional environment of the Hettangian-Sinemurian (Early Jurassic) of Adnet (Salzburg, Austria). *Abhandlungen der Geologischen Bundesanstalt*, **56**, 143–271.

BOIGK, H. & SCHÖNEICH, H. 1974. Perm, Trias und älterer Jura im Bereich der Mittelmeer-Mjösen-Zone und des Rheingrabens. *In:* ILLIES, J.H. & FUCHS, K. (eds) *Approaches to Taphrogenesis*. Inter-Union Commission on Geodynamics, Scientific Report, Schweizerbart, Stuttgart, 60–71.

BOLLIGER, W. & BURRI, P. 1970. Sedimentologie von Shelf-Carbonaten und Beckenablagerungen im Oxfordien des zentralen Schweizer Jura. *Beiträge zur geologischen Karte der Schweiz, Neue Folge*, **140**.

BOMBIȚĂ, G., ANTONESCU, E., MALATA, E., MÜLLER, C. & NEAGU, T. 1992. Pieniny-type Mesozoic formations from Maramureş, Romania (Second part). *Acta Geologica Hungarica*, **35**(2), 117–144.

BOOROVÁ, D., LOBITZER, H., SKUPIEN, P. & VASICEK, Z. 1999. Biostratigraphy and facies of Upper Jurassic-Lower Cretaceous pelagic carbonate sediments (Oberalm-, Schrambach- and Roßfeld-Formation) in the Northern Calcareous Alps, South of Salzburg. *Abhandlungen der Geologischen Bundesanstalt*, **56**(2), 273–318.

BOSÁK, P. 1978. Rudice Plateau in the Moravian Karst – Part III. Petrography and diagenesis in carbonate rocks and silicites of the Jurassic relict near Olomučany (in Czech). *Acta Museae Moraviae, Scientia naturalis*, **62**, 7–28.

BOTTKE, H., DENGLER, H., *et al.* 1969. Sammelwerk Deutsche Eisenerzlagerstätten: 2. Eisenerze im Deckgebirge (Postvarizikum). 1. Die marinsedimentären Eisenerze des Jura in NW-Deutschland. *Beihefte zum Geologischen Jahrbuch*, **79**, 1–391.

BRACHERT, T. 1986. Kontinuierliche und diskontinuierliche Sedimentation im süddeutschen Oberjura (unteres Kimmeridge; Ludwag/Oberfranken, Nördliche Frankenalb). *Facies*, **15**, 233–284.

BRACHERT, T. 1992. Sequence stratigraphy and paleo-oceanography of an open-marine mixed carbonate/siliciclastic succession (Late Jurassic, Southern Germany). *Facies*, **27**, 191–216.

BRAND, E. & HOFFMANN, K. 1963. Stratigraphie und Fazies des nordwestdeutschen Jura und Bildungsbedingungen seiner Erdöllagerstätten. *Erdöl und Kohle, Erdgas, Petrochemie*, **16**, 437–450.

BRAND, E., ČEPEC, P., HAHN, W., JORDAN., R., PRAUSS, M. & WESTERMANN G.E.G. 1990. Zum Ober-Bathonium (Mittlerer Jura) im Raum Hildesheim, Nordwestdeutschland. Mega- und Mikropaläontologie, Biostratigraphie. *Geologisches Jahrbuch, Reihe A*, **121**, 1–323.

BRENNER, K. & SEILACHER, A. 1978. New aspects about the origin of the Toarcian Posidonia Shales. *Neues Jahrbuch für Geologie und Paläontologie, Abhandlungen*, **157**, 11–18.

BRENNER, W. 1986. Bemerkungen zur Palynostratigraphie der Rhät-Lias-Grenze in SW-Deutschland. *Neues Jahrbuch für Geologie und Paläontologie, Abhandlungen*, **173**, 131–145.

BRETON, G., CARPENTIER, C., HUAULT, V. & LATHUILIERE, B. 2003. Decapode Crustaceans from the Kimmeridgian of Bure (Meuse, France). Second symposium on Mesozoic and Cenozoic decapod crustaceans, Boxtel-Maastricht Sept. 2003. *Contributions to Zoology*, **72**(2–3), 91–93.

BRONGNIART, A. 1829. *Tableau des Terrains qui Composent L'écorce du Globe on Essai sur la Structure de la patrie Connue de la Terre*. Paris.

BRUDER, G. 1882. Neue Beiträge zur Kenntnis der Juraablagerungen im nördlichen Böhmen I. *Sitzungsberichte der Akademie der Wissenschaften Wien*, **85**, 450–490.

BRUDER, G. 1887. Paläontologische Beiträge zur Kenntnis der nordböhmischen Juragebilde. *Lotos*, **36**, 72–110.

BRUDER, H.J. 1968. Ökologische, geochemische und sedimentologische Untersuchungen im Lias zeta (Oberes Toarcium) Schwabens, mit Berücksichtigung des obersten Lias epsilon. *Arbeiten aus dem Geologisch-Paläontologischen Institut der Universität Stuttgart, Neue Folge*, **56**, 1–165.

BUCH, L. VON, 1839. *Über den Jura in Deutschland*. Königlich Preussische Akademie der Wissenschaften, Berlin.

BUCHARDT, B. 2003. Oxygen isotope palaeotemperatures from the Jurassic in Northwest Europe. *In*: INESON, J.R. & SURLYK, F. (eds) *The Jurassic of Denmark and Greenland*. Geological Survey of Denmark and Greenland Bulletin, **1**, 9–22.

BURKHALTER, R.M. 1995. Ooidal ironstones and ferruginous microbialites: origin and relation to sequence stratigraphy (Aalenian and Bajocian, Swiss Jura mountains). *Sedimentology*, **42**, 57–74.

BURKHALTER, R.M. 1996. Die Passwang-Alloformation (unteres Aalénien bis unteres Bajocien) im zentralen und nördlichen Schweizer Jura. *Eclogae geologicae Helvetiae*, **89**, 875–934.

BUXTORF, A. 1907. Geologische Beschreibung des Weissensteintunnels und seiner Umgebung. *Beiträge zur Geologischen Karte der Schweiz, Neue Folge*, **XXI**.

BUXTORF, A. 1910. Einige Bemerkungen über das Rhät im schweizerischen Juragebirge und den Gebirgsbau der Vorbourg-Kette. *Eclogae geologicae Helvetiae,* **9**(3), 358–365.

CARIOU, E. & HANTZPERGUE, P. 1997. Biostratigraphie du Jurassique ouest européen et méditerranéen. *Bulletin du Centre de Recherche Elf Exploration-Production*, **17**, 422.

CARPENTIER, C. 2004. *Géométries et environnements de dépôt de l'Oxfordien de l'Est du Bassin de Paris*. Thesis, Université Nancy 1.

CARPENTIER, C., LATHUILIERE, B. & FERRY, S. 2004. La plate-forme carbonatée oxfordienne de Lorraine: arguments pour une ouverture vers la Mer germanique/The Oxfordian carbonate platform of Lorraine: evidences for an opening toward the Germanic Sea. *Comptes rendus Geosciences*, **336**, 59–66.

CARPENTIER, C., MARTIN-GARIN, B. LATHUILIÈRE, B. & FERRY S. 2005. L'Oxfordien de l'Est du Bassin de Paris: corrélations des épisodes récifaux entre la Lorraine et la Bourgogne. *Bulletin d'information des géologues du Basin de Paris*, **42**(3), 23–29.

CARPENTIER, C., MARTIN-GARIN, B. LATHUILIÈRE, B. & FERRY, S. 2006*a*. Correlation of reefal Oxfordian episodes and climatic implications in the eastern Paris Basin (France). *Terra Nova*, **18**(3), 191–201.

CARPENTIER, C., BRETON, G., HUAULT, V. & LATHUILIERE, B. 2006*b*. Crustacés Décapodes du Kimméridgien de Bure (Meuse, France). *Geobios,* **39,** 617–629.

CARPENTIER, C., LATHUILIÈRE, B., FERRY, S. & SAUSSE, J. 2007. Sequence stratigraphy and tectonosedimentary history of the Lower and Middle Oxfordian of the eastern Paris Basin (Northeastern France). *Sedimentary Geology*, **197**, 235–266.

CATHLES, L.M. & HALLAM, A. 1991. Stress-induced changes in plate density, Vail sequences, epeirogeny and short-lived global sea-level fluctuations. *Tectonics*, **10**, 659–671.

CAVELIER, G. & LORENZ, J. 1987. Aspect et évolution géologiques du Bassin Parisien. *Bulletin d'information des géologues du Bassin de Paris, mémoirs hors-séries,* **6**, 1–271.

CHANDLER, M.A., RIND, D. & RUEDY, R. 1992. Pangaean climate during the Early Jurassic: GCM simulations and the sedimentary record of paleoclimate. *Geological Society of America Bulletin,* **104**, 543–559.

CHANNELL, J.E.T., BRANDNER, R., SPIELER, A. & STONER, J. S. 1992. Paleomagnetism and paleogeography of the Northern Calcareous Alps (Austria). *Tectonics,* **11**, 792–810.

CHAROLLAIS, J. & BADOUX, H. 1990. *Suisse lémanique, Pays de Genève et Chablais*. Guides écologiques régionaux, Masson, Paris.

CLAR, E. 1973. Review of the structure of the Eastern Alps. *In:* DE JONG, K. A. & SCHOLTEN, K. (eds) *Gravitiy and Tectonics*. Wiley, New York.

CLOETHINGH, S. 1986. Intraplate stresses: a new mechanism for relative fluctuations of sea level. *Geology*, **14**, 617–620.

CLOETHINGH, S., MCQUEEN, H. & LAMBECK, K. 1985. On a tectonic mechanism for regional sea level variations. *Earth and Planetary Science Letters*, **75,** 157–166.

COE, L.A. 1995. A comparison of the Oxfordian successions at Dorset, Oxfordshire, and Yorkshire. *In:* TAYLOR, P.D. (ed.) *Field Geology of the British Jurassic*. Geological Society, London, 151–172.

COE, A.L. & WEEDON, G.P. 2006. Jurassic cyclostratigraphy: recent advances, implications and problems. *Volumina Jurassica,* **IV**, 156–157.

COHEN, A.S., COE, A.L., HARDING, S.M. & SCHWARK, L. 2004. Osmium isotope evidence for the regulation of atmospheric $CO_2$ by continental weathering. *Geology*, **32**, 157–160.

COLBACH, R., GUÉRIN-FRANIATTE, S. & MAQUIL, R. 2003*a*. Un remarquable site fossilifère dans le Sinémurien inférieur de Bertrange (Grand-duché de Luxembourg). *Ferrantia,* **36**, 53–64.

COLBACH, R., GUÉRIN-FRANIATTE, S. & MAQUIL, R. 2003*b*. Nouvelles données paléontologiques dans l'Hettangien du plateau de Burmerange (Grand -Duché de Luxembourg). *Ferrantia,* **36**, 45–52.

COLLIN, P.Y. 2000. *Environnements, géochimie et processus de formation de séries condensées au Callovo-Oxfordien: du Bassin de Paris à des considérations globales*, Thesis, Université de Bourgogne.

COLLIN, P.Y. & COURVILLE, P. 2000. Paléoenvironnements et biostratigraphie d'une série oxfordienne non condensée de référence (Saint-Blin-Sémilly, Haute-Marne). *Géologie de la France*, **1**, 59–63.

COLLIN, P.Y. & COURVILLE, P. 2006. Sedimentation and palaeogeography of the eastern part of the Paris Basin (France) at the Middle-Upper Jurassic boundary. *Comptes rendus Geosciences*, **338**(12–13), 824–833.

COLLIN, P.Y., COURVILLE, P., LOREAU, J.P., THIERRY, J. & PELLENARD P. 2001. Condensed series and crisis of carbonate sedimentation at the Middle-Upper Jurassic limit: consequences of global palaeoenvironmental changes. *Abstracts 21st IAS meeting of sedimentology,* Davos.

COLLIN, P.Y., LOREAU, J.P. & COURVILLE, P. 2005. Depositional environments and iron ooid formation in condensed sections (Callovian Oxfordian, South-eastern part of the Paris basin, France). *Sedimentology*, **52**(5) 969–985.

CORNA, M. 1985. L'Hettangien du Jura méridional. *Les Cahiers de l'Institut Catholique de Lyon,* **14**, 135–143.

COURVILLE, P. & BONNOT, A. 1998. Faunes ammonitiques et biochronologie de la zone à Athleta et de la base de la zone à Lamberti (Callovien supérieur) de la Côte de Meuse (France) Intérêts des faunes nouvelles d'Aspidoceratidae. *Revue de Paléobiologie*, **17**(2), 307–346.

COURVILLE, P. & CRONIER, C. 2003. Les Kosmoceratidae autour de la limite callovien moyen/supérieur: approche biostratigraphique. *In: Colloque «Une paléontologie évolutive: Hommage au Professeur Henri Tintant»*, Séance spécialisée SGF, 21–22 nov. 2003, Dijon, 25.

COURVILLE, P. & CRONIER, C. 2004*a*. Le Callovien et l'Oxfordien à Latrecey-Ormoy-sur-Aube (Haute-Marne). Enregistrements sédimentaire, paléontologique et biostratigraphique. *Bulletin Annuel de l'Association Géologique Auboise*, **24–25**, 31–40.

COURVILLE, P. & CRONIER, C. 2004*b*. Jurassic of the Boulonnais (Northern France). Guidebook. *In: Palaeontological Association Annual Meeting*, 17–20 Déc. 2004, Lille.

COURVILLE, P. & CRONIER, C. 2005. Diversity or disparity in the Jurassic (Upper Callovian) genus Kosmoceras (Ammonitina): a morphometric approach. *Journal of Paleontology*, **79**(5) 944–952.

COURVILLE, P. & MARCHAND, D. 2003. Contrôle des relais et des transgressions fauniques (Ammonites) pendant le callovien-oxfordien dans le bassin parisien: paléoprofondeur ou paléotempérature? *In: Colloque «Une paléontologie évolutive: Hommage au Professeur Henri Tintant»*, Séance spécialisée SGF, 21–22 nov. 2003, Dijon, 5.

COURVILLE, P. & VILLIER, L. 2003. L'Oxfordien moyen et supérieur de l'Est du Bassin Parisien (France). L'exemple de Latrecey (Haute-Marne): aspects fauniques, paléoenvironnementaux et stratigraphiques. *Revue de Paléobiologie*, **22**(1), 175–196.

COURVILLE, P., BONNOT, A., COLLIN, P.-Y., CONTINI, D. & MARCHAND, D. 1998. Coupures morphologiques et biochronologie chez les Kosmoceratinae de l'Est de la France (Callovien inférieur pp. à Callovien supérieur pp.). *Comptes rendus de l'Académie des Sciences Paris,* **327**, 685–691.

COURVILLE, P., BONNOT, A., COLLIN, P.Y., MARCHAND, D. & RAFFRAY, M. 2004. Le Callovien dans l'Est du Bassin Parisien. Exemple de Bologne-Marault (Haute-Marne): Interprétation biostratigraphique. *Bulletin Scientifique de Bourgogne*, **52**(2) 4–16.

CRONIER, C. & COURVILLE, P. 2004. A rich and highly endemic decapod crustacean fauna from the Middle Jurassic of North-East France. *Palaeontology*, **47**(4), 999–1014.

CROWLEY, T.J. & NORTH, G.R. 1991. *Paleoclimatology*. Clarendon Press, Oxford.

DĄBROWSKA, Z. 1970. Jura górna w niecce mogłeńsko-łódzkiej. *Biuletyn Instytut Geologicznego,* **221**, 5–103.

DADLEZ, R. 1976. Zarys geologii podłoża kenozoiku w basenie południowego Bałtyku. *Biuletyn Instytutu Geologicznego*, **285**.

DADLEZ, R. 1988. Epikontynentalne baseny permu i mezozoiku w Polsce. *Geological Quarterly*, **33**(2), 175–198.

DADLEZ, R. 1997. Epicontinental basins in Poland. Devonian to Cretaceous – relationships between the crystalline basement and sedimentary infill. *Geological Quarterly*, **41**, 419–432.

DADLEZ, R. 1998*a*. Explanatory note. *In*: DADLEZ R., MAREK S. & POKORSKI J. (eds) *Palaeogeographical Atlas of the Epicontinental Permian and Mesozoic in Poland, 1:2.500.000.* Polish Geological Institute, Warszawa, 3–6.

DADLEZ, R. 1998*b*. *Mapa tektoniczna cechsztyńsko-mezozoicznego kompleksu strukturalnego na Niżu Polskim. 1:500.000.* Państwowy Instytut Geologiczny, Warszawa.

DADLEZ, R. 2000. Pomeranian Caledonides (NW Poland), fifty years of controversies: a review and new concept. *Geological Quarterly*, **44**, 221–236.

DADLEZ, R. 2001. Explanatory note. *In: Mid-Polish Trough – Geological Cross Sections. 1:200 000*. Warszawa, 19–29.

DADLEZ, R. & KOPIK J. 1972. Selected problems of Liassic stratigraphy and sedimentation in the area between Świnoujście and Gryfice (North-West Poland). *Geological Quarterly*, **16**(2), 620–636 [in Polish with English summary].

DADLEZ, R., NARKIEWICZ, M., STEPHENSON, R.A., VISSER, M.T.M. & VAN WEES, J.-D. 1995. Tectonic evolution of the Mid-Polish Trough: modelling implications and significance for central European geology. *Tectonophysics*, **252**, 179–185.

DANIEC, J. 1970. Middle Jurassic. *In*: *The stratigraphy of the mesozoic in the margin of the Góry Świętokrzyskie*. Prace Instytutu Geologicznego, **56**, 99–133 [in Polish with English summary].

DARDEAU, G., ATROPS, F., FORTWENGLER, D., DE GRACIANSKY, P.-C. & MARCHAND, D. 1988. Jeu de blocs et tectonique distensive au Callovien et à l'Oxfordien dans le bassin du Sud-Est de la France. *Bulletin de la Société géologique de France, (8), IV,* **5**, 771–777.

DARDEAU, G., FORTWENGLER, D., DE GRACIANSKY, P.-C., MARCHAND, D. & MARTINOD, J. 1990. Halocinèse et jeu de blocs dans les Baronnies: diapir de Propiac, Montolieu, Condorcet (Département de la Drôme, France). *Bulletin des Centres de Recherche Exploration-Production Elf-Aquitaine*, **14**(1), 111–159.

DARDEAU, G., MARCHAND, D. & FORTWENGLER, D. 1994. Tectonique synsédimentaire et variations du niveau marin pendant le dépôt de la formation des Terres Noires (Callovien supérieur-Oxfordien moyen; bassin du Sud-Est de la France). *Comptes rendues de l'Académie des Sciences Paris, série 2,* **319**, 559–565.

DARGA, R. & SCHLAGINTWEIT, F. 1991. Mikrofazies, Paläontologie und Stratigraphie der Lerchkogelkalke Tithon-Berrias des Dietrichhorns Salzburger Land Nördliche Kalkalpen. *Jahrbuch der Geologischen Bundesanstalt*, **134**(2), 205–226.

DAVID, J. 1998. *Adaptation morphologique, croissance et production bioclastique chez les crinoïdes pédonculés actuels et fossiles (Pentacrines et Millericrinina) application paléoécologique aux gisements du Jurassique supérieur des Charentes et du Nord-est du bassin de Paris*. Thesis, l'Université de Reims Champagne Ardennes.

DAVID, J. & ROUX, M. 2000. Modèle actuel de production bioclastique par les crinoides pédonculés. Application au calcaire à entroques d'Euville (Oxfordien de la Meuse). *Comptes rendus de l'Académie des Sciences Paris,* **330**, 111–116.

DAYCZAK-CALIKOWSKA, K. 1976. The Aalenian and Lower Bajocian of the southern Kujawy. *Geological Quarterly*, **20**(4), 751–763 [In Polish with English summary].

DAYCZAK-CALIKOWSKA, K. 1977*a*. Stratygrafia i paleogeografia. Jura środkowa. *In*: Budowa geologiczna wschodniej części niecki mogileńsko-łódzkiej (strefa Gopło-Ponętów-Pabianice). *Prace Instytutu Geologicznego,* **80**, 65–75.

DAYCZAK-CALIKOWSKA, K. 1977*b*. The Upper Bathonian and Callowian in northwest Poland. *Prace Instytutu Geologicznego,* **84**, 69 [in Polish with English summary].

DAYCZAK-CALIKOWSKA, K. 1979. Middle Jurassic. *In*: *The Geological Structure of Szczecin Trough and Gorzów Block*. Prace Instytutu Geologicznego, **96**, 57–62 [in Polish with English summary].

DAYCZAK-CALIKOWSKA, K. 1987. Middle Jurassic. *In*: *Geological Structure of Pomeranian Swell and its Basement*. Prace Instytutu Geologicznego, **119**, 116–123 [in Polish with English summary].

DAYCZAK-CALIKOWSKA, K. & MORYC, W. 1988. Evolution of sedimentary basin and paleotectonics of the Middle Jurassic in Poland. *Geological Quarterly,* **32**(1), 117–136 [in Polish with English summary].

DEBELMAS, J. 1986. L'héritage hercynien à l'origine des grands bassins sédimetaires français. *Bulletin des Centres de Recherche Exploration-Production Elf-Aquitaine*, **10**(1), 151–161.

DEBRAND-PASSARD, S., COURBOULEIX, S. & LIÉNHARDT, M.-J. 1984. *Synthèse géologique du Sud-Est de la France*. Mémoires du Bureau de Recherches Géologiques et Miniéres, Stratigraphie et Paléogéographie, **125**.

DECKER, K. 1990. Plate tectonics and pelagic facies: Late Jurassic to Early Cretaceous deep-sea sediments of the Ybbsitz ophiolite unit (Eastern Alps, Austria). *Sedimentary Geology*, **67**, 85–99.

DECKER, K., FAUPL, P. & MÜLLER, A. 1987. Synorogenic sedimentation on the Northern Calcareous Alps during the Early Cretaceous. *In:* FLÜGEL, H.W. & FAUPL, P. (eds) *Geodynamics of the Eastern Alps*. Deuticke, Vienna, 126–141.

DECONINCK, J.-F. 1987. Minéraux argileux des faciès purbeckiens: Jura suisse et Français, Dorset (Angleterre) et Boulonnais (France). *Annales de la Société géologique du Nord,* **106**, 285–297.

DECONINCK, J.F. & STRASSER, A. 1987. Sedimentology, clay mineralogy and depositional environment of Purbeckian green marls (Swiss and French Jura). *Eclogae geologicae Helvetiae,* **80**, 753–772.

DECONINCK, J.-F., CHAMLEY, H., DEBRABANT, P. & COLBEAUX, J.-P. 1982. Le Boulonnais au Jurassique supérieur: données de la minéralogie des argiles et de la géochimie. *Annales de la Société géologique du Nord,* **102**, 145–152.

DECONINCK, J.-F., GEYSSANT, J. R., PROUST, J. N. & VIDIER, J. P. 1996. Sédimentologie et biostratigraphie des dépôts kimméridgiens et tithoniens du Boulonnais. *Annales de la Société géologique du Nord, 2ème série,* **4**, 57–170.

DECONINCK, J.-F., BAUDIN, F. & TRIBOVILLARD, N. 2000. The Purbeckian facies in the Boulonnais: a tsunami deposit hypothesis (Jurassic-Cretaceous boundary, northern France). *Comptes rendus de l'Académie des Sciences Paris,* **330**, 527–532.

DECZKOWSKI, Z. 1977. Geology of the Permo-Mesozoic cover and its basement in the eastern part of the Fore-Sudetic Monocline (Kalisz-Częstochowa area). *Prace Instytutu Geologicznego,* **82**, 63 [in Polish with English summary].

DECZKOWSKI, Z. & FRANCZYK, M. 1988. Palaeothickness, lithofacies and palaeotectonics of epicontinental Lower Jurassic in Poland. *Geological Quarterly*, **32**(1), 105–115 [in Polish with English summary].

DE GRACIANSKY, P.-C., DARDEAU, G., DUMONT, T., JACQUIN, T., MARCHAND, D., MOUTERDE, R. & VAIL, P.R. 1993. Depositional sequence cycles, transgressive-regressive facies cycles, and extensional tectonics: example from the southern Subalpine Jurassic basin, France. *Bulletin de la Société géologique de France*, **164**(5), 709–718.

DE GRACIANSKY, P.-C., DARDEAU, G., *et al.* 1998*a*. Ammonite biostratigraphic correlation and early Jurassic sequence stratigraphy in France: comparisons with some U.K. sections. *In*: DE GRACIANSKY *et al.* (eds) *Mesozoic and Cenozoic Sequence Stratigraphy of European Basins*. Society of Economic Paleontologists and Mineralogists, Special Publications, **60**, 583–622.

DE GRACIANSKY, P.-C., JACQUIN, T. & HESSELBO, S. P. 1998*b*. The Ligurian cycle: an overview of lower Jurassic 2nd-order transgressive/regressive facies cycles in western Europe. *In*: DE GRACIANSKY *et al.* (eds) *Mesozoic and Cenozoic Sequence Stratigraphy of European Basins*. Society of Economic Paleontologists and Mineralogists, Special Publications, **60**, 467–479.

DE GRACIANSKY, P.-C., DARDEAU, G., *et al.* 1999. Les Terres Noires du Sud-Est de la France (Jurassique moyen et supérieur). Interprétation en termes de stratigraphie séquentielle. *Bulletin des Centres de Recherche Exploration-Production Elf-Aquitaine*, **22**(1), 35–69.

DELHAES, W. & GERTH, H. 1912. Geologische Beschreibung des Kettenjura zwischen Reigoldswil (Baselland) und Oensingen (Solothurn). *Geologische und Paläontologische Abhandlungen, Neue Folge,* **11**, 1–97.

DELSATE, D. 2007. World Wide Web address: http://www.mnhn.lu/colsci/dedo/publi.asp

DELSATE, D. & THUY, B. 2005. Biostratigraphie et Paléontologie de l'Hettangien en Belgique et au grand Duché du Luxembourg. *Memoirs of the Geological Survey of Belgium,* **51**, 1–96.

DEMBOWSKA, J. 1973. *Portland na niżu Polski*. Prace Instytutu Geologicznego, **70**.

DEMBOWSKA, J. 1976. Jura górna. *In*: *Perm i mezozoik niecki pomorskiej*. Prace Instytutu Geologicznego, **79**, 78–87.

DEMBOWSKA, J. 1979*a*. Systematyzowanie stratygrafii jury górnej w Polsce północnej i środkowej. *Geological Quarterly,* **23**(3), 617–630.

DEMBOWSKA, J. 1979*b*. Jura górna. *In*: *Budowa geologiczna niecki szczecińskiej i bloku Gorzowa*. Prace Instytutu Geologicznego, **96**, 62–69.

DEMBOWSKA, J. & MAREK, S. 1975. Développment du bassinde sedimentation sur la base plaine de Pologne à la limite du Jurassique et du Crétacé. *Mémoires du Bureau de Recherches Géologiques et Miniéres*, **86**, 110–116.

DEN HARTOG JAGER, D.G. 1996. Fluviomarine sequences in the Lower Cretaceous of the West Netherlands Basin: correlation and seismic expression. *In:* RONDEEL, H.E., BATJES, D.A.J. & NIEUWENHUIJS, W.H. (eds) *Geology of Gas and Oil Under the Netherlands*. Kluwer, Dordrecht, 229–242.

DERCOURT, J., RICOU, L.E. & VRIELYNCK, B. (eds) 1993. *Atlas Tethys Paleoenvironmental maps*. Gauthier-Villars, Paris.

DERCOURT, J., GAETANI, M., *et al.* (eds) 2000. *Atlas Peri-Tethys. Palaeogeographical Maps*. Gauthier-Villars, Paris.

DEUTSCHE STRATIGRAPHISCHE KOMMISSION 2002. *Stratigraphische Tabelle von Deutschland 2002*. Deutsche Stratigraphische Kommission, Potsdam.

DIERSCHE, V. 1980. Die Radiolarite des Oberjura im Mittelabschnitt der Nördlichen Kalkalpen. *Geotektonische Forschung*, **58**, 1–217.

DIETL, G. 1977. The Braunjura (Brown Jurassic) in Southwest Germany. *Stuttgarter Beiträge zur Naturkunde, Serie B*, **25**, 1–41.

DIETL, G. 1994. Der hochstetteri-Horizont – ein Ammonitenfaunen-Horizont (Discus-Zone, Ober-Bathonium, Dogger) aus dem Schwäbischen Jura. *Stuttgarter Beiträge zur Naturkunde, Serie B*, **202**, 1–39.

DIETL, G. & ETZOLD, A. 1977. The Aalenian at the type locality. *Stuttgarter Beiträge zur Naturkunde, Serie B*, **30**, 1–13.

DIETL, G. & GYGI, R. 1998. Die Basis des Callovian (Mittlerer Jura) bei Liesberg BL, Nordschweiz. *Eclogae geologicae Helvetiae*, **91**, 247–260.

DIETL, G. & SCHWEIGERT, G. 1999. Nusplinger Plattenkalk: Eine tropische Lagune der Jura-Zeit. *Stuttgarter Beiträge zur Naturkunde, Serie C*, **45**, 1–62.

DIETL, G. & SCHWEIGERT, G. 2004. The Nusplingen Lithographic Limestone – a "fossil lagerstaette" of Late Kimmeridgian age from the Swabian Alb (Germany). *Rivista Italiana di Paleontologia e Stratigrafia*, **110**, 303–309.

DIETL, G., EBEL, K. & HUGGER, R. 1979. Zur Stratigraphie und Ammonitenfauna der Varians-Schichten (Mittel- und unterstes Ober-Bathonium) von Talheim am Lupfen (südwestl. Schwäbische Alb). *Paläontologische Zeitschrift*, **53**, 182–197.

DISNAR, J. R., LE STRAT, P., FARJANEL, G. & FIKRI, A. 1996. Sédimentation de la matière organique dans le nord est du Bassin de Paris: conséquences sur le dépôt des argilites carbonées du Toarcien inférieur. *Chemical Geology*, **131**, 15–35.

DONOVAN, D.T. & SURLYK, F. 2003. Lower Jurassic (Pliensbachian) ammonites from Bornholm, Baltic Sea, Denmark. *In*: INESON, J.R. & SURLYK, F. (eds) *The Jurassic of Denmark and Greenland*. Geological Survey of Denmark and Greenland Bulletin, **1**, 555–583.

D'ORBIGNY, A. 1842–51. Céphalopodes jurassiques. *In: Paléontologie française*. Paris.

D'ORBIGNY, A. 1852. *Cours élementaire de paléontologie et de géologie stratigraphiques*. Paris.

DULUB, V.G., ZHABINA, N. M., OGORODNIK, M.E. & SMIRNOV, S.E. 2003. *The explanatory note to the stratigraphy of Jurassic deposits of Ukrainian Carpathian foreland; Stryj Jurassic basin*. Ukrainian State Geological Research Institute [in Ukrainian].

DUPRAZ, C. 1999. Paléontologie, paléoecologie et évolution des faciès récifaux de l'Oxfordien Moyen-Supérieur (Jura suisse et français). *GeoFocus*, **2**, 247.

DVOŘÁK, JAR. 1956. To the extent of Jurassic sediments in the Bohemian Massif in the vicinity of Brno city. *Věstnik Ústředniho Ústavu geologickeho*, **31**(6), 284–285 [in Czech].

DVOŘÁK, JOS. 1963. Jurassic. *In:* KALÁŠEK, J. (ed.) *Explanations to General Geological Map of the ČSSR, sheet Brno*. Nakl. ČSAV, 171 [in Czech].

DVOŘÁK, JOS. 1966. Jurassic. *In:* SVOBODA, J. (ed.) *Regional Geology of Czechoslovakia. Part I. The Bohemian Massif.* Nakl. ČSAV, 483–487.

DYA, M. 1992. *Mikropaläontologische und fazielle Untersuchungen im Oberjura zwischen Salzburg und Lofer*. PhD thesis, Technische Universität Berlin.

DYBKJÆR, K. 1988. Palynological zonation and stratigraphy of the Jurassic section in the Gassum No. 1-borehole, Denmark. *Danmarks Geologiske Undersøgelse, Serie A*, **21**, 1–72.

DYBKJÆR, K. 1991. Palynological zonation and palynofacies investigation of the Fjerritslev Formation (Lower Jurassic – basal Middle Jurassic) in the Danish Subbasin. *Danmarks Geologiske Undersøgelse, Serie A*, **30**, 1–150.

EHES, H. H. & LEINFELDER, R. R. 1988. Laterale und vertikale Faziesentwicklung der Rhät/Unterlias-Sedimentation im Wallberg-Blankenstein-Gebiet (Tegernsee, Nördliche Kalkalpen). *Mainzer geowissenschaftliche Mitteilungen*, **17**, 53–94.

EHRLICH, H.L. 1990. *Geomicrobiology*. Marcel Dekker, New York.

ELIÁŠ, M. 1974. Microfacies investigation of carbonates of oil-perspective areas on example of authochthonous Jurassic of southeastern slopes of the Bohemian Massif. *Zemný Plyn Nafta*, **19** (3) 359–374 [in Czech].

ELIÁŠ, M. 1981. Facies and paleogeography of the Jurassic of the Bohemian Massif. *Sbornik geologickych ved. Geologie*, **35**, 75–144.

ELIÁŠ, M. 1984. The Jurassic in the Bohemian Massif. *In:* SUK, M. (ed.) *Geological History of the Territory of the Czech Socialist Republic*. Academia, Praha, 149–153.

ELMI, S. 1990. Stages in the evolution of Late Triassic and Jurassic carbonate platforms: the western margin of the Subalpine Basin (Ardèche, France). *In*: TUCKER, M.E. (ed.) *Carbonate Platforms: Facies, Sequences and Evolution*. International Association of Sedimentologists, Special Publications, **9**, 109–144.

ELMI, S. 2006. Pliensbachian/Toarcian boundary: the proposed GSSP of Peniche (Portugal). *Volumina Jurassica*, **IV**, 5–16.

ENAY, R. & BOULLIER, A. 1981. L'âge du complexe récifal des côtes de Meuse entre Verdun et Commercy et la stratigraphie de l'Oxfordien dans l'Est du bassin de Paris. *Geobios*, **14**(6), 727–771.

ENAY, R. & MANGOLD, C. (eds) 1980. *Synthèse paléogéographique du Jurassique Français*. Documents des Laboratoires de Géologie de Lyon, hors série, **5**.

ENAY, R., CONTINI, D. & BOULLIER, A. 1988. Le Séquanien-type de Franche-Comté (Oxfordien supérieur): datations et corrélations nouvelles, conséquences sur la paléogéographie et l'évolution du Jura des régions voisines. *Eclogae geologicae Helvetiae*, **81**, 295–363.

ENGEL, T. 1908. *Geognostischer Wegweiser durch Württemberg (3rd edn)*. Schweizerbart, Stuttgart.

ERNST, M. 1989. *Das Mesozoikum der Vorbergzone auf Blatt Kandern/ Südbaden (TK 8211): Kartierung, Stratigraphie und Paläogeographie unter besonderer Berücksichtigung der Fazies im Braunjura, speziell des Hauptrogensteins*. PhD thesis, Universität Freiburg.

ESTEBAN, L., BOUCHEZ, J.L. & TROUILLER, A. 2006. The Callovo-Oxfordian argillites from the eastern Paris Basin: Magnetic data and petrofabrics. *Comptes rendus Geosciences*, **338**, 867–881.

ETTER, W. 1990. *Paläontologische Untersuchungen im unteren Opalinuston der Nordschweiz*. PhD thesis, Universität Zürich.

ETZOLD, A. & SCHWEIZER, V. 2005. Der Keuper in Baden-Württemberg. *In:* DEUTSCHE STRATIGRAPHISCHE KOMMISION (ed.) *Stratigraphie von Deutschland IV, Keuper.* Courier Forschungs- Institut Senckenberg, **253**, 214–258.

EUGENO-S WORKING GROUP 1988. Crustal structure and tectonic evolution of the transition between the Baltic Shield and the North German Caledonides (the EUGENO-S Project). *Tectonophysics*, **150**, 253–348.

FABER, A. & WEIS, R. 2005. Le Grès de Luxembourg: intérêt scientifique et patrimonial de ses sites fossilifères. *Ferrantia*, **44**, 161–164.

FABIAN, H.J. 1935. Sedimentpetrographische Bemerkung über Sedimente des oberen Jura von Olomučany bei Brünn. *Firgenwald*, **2**, 84–86.

FABRICIUS, F. H. 1959. Vorschlag zur Umbenennung von "Oberrhätkalk" in "Rhätolias-Riffkalk" (Nördliche Kalkalpen). *Neues Jahrbuch für Geologie und Paläontologie, Monatshefte*, **1959**, 546–549.

FALKOWSKI, P.G., KATZ, M.E., *et al.* 2005. The rise of oxygen over the past 205 Million years and the evolution of large placental mammals. *Science*, **309**, 2202–2204.

FAUPL, P. 1997. Austria. *In:* MOORES, E. M. & FAIRBRIDGE, R. W. (eds) *Encyclopedia of European and Asian Regional Geology*. Chapman & Hall, London, 51–63.

FAUPL, P. & WAGREICH, M. 2000. Late Jurassic to Eocene Palaeogeography and Geodynamic Evolution of the Eastern Alps. *Mitteilungen der Österreichischen Geologischen Gesellschaft*, **92**, 79–94.

FAYARD, J.-P., GROSS, N., LAJOURNADE, J.-B., LATHUILIÈRE, B., VAILLY, G. & WEIS, R. 2005. *Fossiles et minéraux de la carrière d'Ottange-Rumelange*. Geolor & AGMP ed.

FELDMAN-OLSZEWSKA, A. 1997*a*. Depositional systems and cyclicity in the intracratonic Early Jurassic basin in Poland. *Geological Quarterly*, **41**(4), 475–490.

FELDMAN-OLSZEWSKA, A. 1997*b*. Depositional architecture of the Polish epicontinental Middle Jurassic basin. *Geological Quarterly*, **41**(4), 491–508.

FELDMAN-OLSZEWSKA, A. 1998*a*. Early Aalenian – Callovian Palaeogeography. *In*: DADLEZ, R., MAREK, S. & POKORSKI, J. (eds) *Palaeogeographical Atlas of the Epicontinental Permian and Mesozoic in*

*Poland, 1:2.500.000*. Polish Geological Institute, Warszawa, Pl. 37–48.

Feldman-Olszewska, A. 1998*b*. Middle Jurassic thickness. *In*: Dadlez, R., Marek, S. & Pokorski, J. (eds) *Palaeogeographical Atlas of the Epicontinental Permian and Mesozoic in Poland, 1:2.500.000*. Polish Geological Institute, Warszawa, Pl. 49.

Feldman-Olszewska, A. 1998*c*. Lower and Middle Jurassic cross sections. *In*: Dadlez, R., Marek, S. & Pokorski, J. (eds) *Palaeogeographical atlas of the epicontinental Permian and Mesozoic in Poland. 1:2.500.000*. Polish Geological Institute, Warszawa, Pl. 50.

Feldman-Olszewska, A. 2006. Sedimentary environments of the Middle Jurassic epicontinental deposits from the central part of the Polish Basin (Kuiavian Region). *Volumina Jurassica,* **IV**, 86.

Feldman-Olszewska, A., Grigelis, A. & Šimkevičius, P. 1998. Geological-structural evolution of the Permian and Mesozoic basins. Lower and Middle Jurassic. *In*: Marek, S. & Grigelis, A. (eds) *Atlas. Structural evolution of the Permian–Mesozoic complex of northern Poland, Lithuania and adjacent Baltic areas. 1:2.000.000*. Warszawa, 13–16, P. 9–10.

Fenninger, A. 1967. Riffentwicklung im oberostalpinen Malm. *Geologische Rundschau*, **56**, 171–185.

Fenninger, A. & Holzer, H. L. 1972. Fazies und Paläogeographie des oberostalpinen Malm. *Mitteilungen der Geologischen Gesellschaft Wien*, **63**, 52–141.

Fenninger, A. & Hötzl, H. 1965. Die Hydrozoa und Tabulozoa der Tressenstein- und Plassenkalke (Ober-Jura). *Mitteilungen des Museums für Bergbau, Geologie und Technik*, **27**, 1–63.

Fischer, H. & Luterbacher, H. 1963. Das Mesozoikum der Bohrungen Courtion I (Kt. Fribourg) und Altishofen (Kt. Luzern). *Beiträge zur Geologischen Karte der Schweiz, Neue Folge,* **115**, 1–40.

Flügel, E. 2002. Triassic reef patterns. *In:* Kiessling, W., Flügel, E. & Golonka, J. (ed.) *Phanerozoic Reef Patterns*. Society of Economic Paleontologists and Mineralogists, Special Publications, **72**, 391–464.

Flügel, E. 2004. *Microfacies of Carbonate Rocks – Analysis, Interpretation and Application*. Springer, Berlin.

Flügel, E. & Steiger, T. 1981. An Upper Jurassic sponge-algal buildup from the northern Frankenalb, West Germany. *In*: Toomey, D.F. (ed.) *European Fossil Reef Models*. Society of Economic Paleontologists and Mineralogists, Special Publications, **30**, 371–397.

Flügel, E., Alt, T., Joachimski, M.M., Riemann, V. & Scheller, J. 1993. Korallenriff-Kalke im oberen Malm (Unter-Tithon) der Südlichen Frankenalb (Laisacker, Marching): Mikrofazies-Merkmale und Fazies-Interpretation. *Geologische Blätter für Nordost-Bayern,* **43**, 33–56.

Flügel, H. W. & Faupl, P. 1987. *Geodynamics of the Eastern Alps*. Deuticke, Vienna.

Flügel, H. W. & Fenninger, A. 1966. Die Lithogenese der Oberalmer Schichten und der mikritischen Plassenkalke (Tithonium, Nördliche Kalkalpen. *Neues Jahrbuch für Geologie und Paläontologie, Abhandlungen*, **123**, 249–280.

Flügel, H. W. & Pölster, P. 1965. Lithogenetische Analyse der Barmstein-Kalkbank B2 nordwestlich von St. Koloman bei Hallein (Tithonium, Salzburg. *Neues Jahrbuch für Geologie und Paläontologie, Monatshefte*, **123**, 281–310.

Frakes, L.A. 1979. *Climate Throughout Geologic Time*. Elsevier, Amsterdam.

Frandsen, N. & Surlyk, F. 2003. An offshore transgressive–regressive mudstone-dominated succession from the Sinemurian of Skåne, Sweden. *In:* Ineson, J.R. & Surlyk, F. (eds) *The Jurassic of Denmark and Greenland*. Geological Survey of Denmark and Greenland Bulletin, **1**, 543–554.

Frank, W. 1987. Evolution of the Austroalpine elements in the Cretaceous. *In:* Flügel, H.W. & Faupl, P. (eds) *Geodynamics of the Eastern Alps*. Deuticke, Vienna, 379–406.

Frasl, G. & Frank, W. 1966. *Einführung in die Geologie und Petrographie des Penninikums im Tauernfenster mit besonderer Berücksichtigung des Mittelabschnittes im Oberpinzgau*. Der Aufschluss, Salzburg.

Frey, M. 1969. Die Metamorphose des Keupers vom Tafeljura bis zum Lukmaniergebiet. *Beiträge zur geologischen Karte der Schweiz, Neue Folge,* **137**, 1–160.

Frey, M., Desmons, J. & Neubauer, F. (eds) 1999. The new metamorphic map of the Alps. *Schweizer Mineralogische und Petrographische Mitteilungen*, **79**.

Frisch, W. & Gawlick, H.-J. 2003. The nappe structure of the central Northern Calcareous Alps and its disintegration during Miocene tectonic extrusion - a contribution to understanding the orogenic evolution of the Eastern Alps. *International Journal of Earth Sciences*, **92**, 712–727.

Frisch, W., Gommeringer, K., Kelm, U. & Popp, F. 1987. The upper Bündner Schiefer of the Tauern window - a key to understanding Eoalpine orogenic processes in the Eastern Alps. *In:* Flügel, H. W. & Faupl, P. (eds) *Geodynamics of the Eastern Alps*. Deuticke, Vienna, 55–69.

Fritz, G.K. 1958. Schwammstotzen, Tuberolithe und Schuttbreccien im Weißen Jura der Schwäbischen Alb. *Arbeiten aus dem Geologisch-Paläontologischen Institut der Technischen Hochschule Stuttgart, Neue Folge,* **13**, 1–118.

Froitzheim N. & Manatschal G. 1996. Kinematics of Jurassic rifting, mantle exhumation, and passive-margin formation in the Austroalpine and Penninic nappes (eastern Switzerland). *Geological Society of America Bulletin*, **108**, 1120–1133.

Froitzheim, N., Plašienka, D. & Schuster, R. 2008. Alpine tectonics of the Alps and Western Carpathians. *In*: McCann, T. (ed.) *The Geology of Central Europe. Volume 2: Mesozoic and Cenozoic*. Geological Society, London, 1141–1232.

Froitzheim, N. & Rubatto, D. 1998. Continental breakup by detachment faulting: field evidence and geochronological constraints (Tasna nappe, Switzerland). *Terra Nova*, **10**, 171–176.

Fürsich, F.T. & Oschmann, W. 1986. Storm shell beds of *Nanogyra virgula* in the upper Jurassic of France. *Neues Jahrbuch für Geologie und Paläontologie, Abhandlungen,* **172**(2), 141–161.

Gaillard, C., Bourseau, J.-P., Boudeulle, M., Pailleret, P., Rio, M. & Roux, M. 1985. Les pseudobiohermes de Beauvoisin (Drôme): un site hydrothermal sur la marge téthysienne à l'Oxfordien. *Bulletin de la Société géologique de France*, **8**(I/1), 69–78.

Gaillard, C., Rio, M. & Rollin, Y. 1992. Fossil chemosynthetic communities related to vents or seeps in sedimentary basins: the pseudobioherms of Southeastern France compared to other world examples. *Palaios*, **7**, 451–465.

Gaillard, C., Emmanuel, L., *et al.* 2004. Une séquence disséquée du bassin à la plate-forme, l'épisode carbonaté de l'Oxfordien moyen dans le Sud-Est de la France. *Bulletin de la Société géologique de France*, **175**(2), 107–119.

Galli, M.T., Jadoul, F., Bernasconi, S.M. & Weissert, H. 2005. Anomalies in global carbon cycling and extinction at the Triassic/Jurassic boundary: evidence from a marine C-isotope record. *Palaeogeography, Palaeoclimatology, Palaeoecology,* **216**(3–4), 203–214.

Garcia, J.P. & Dromart, G. 1997. The validity of two biostratigraphic approaches in sequence stratigraphic correlations: brachiopod zones and marker-beds in the Jurassic. *Sedimentary Geology,* **114**, 55–79.

Garcia, J.P., Laurin, B. & Sambet, G. 1996. Les associations de brachiopodes du Jurassique moyen du bassin de Paris: une échelle biochronologique ponctuée de niveaux-repères pour la contrainte des corrélations séquentielles à haute résolution. *Bulletin de la Société géologique de France,* **167**, 435–451.

Garcia, J.P., Philippe, M. & Gaumet, F. 1998. Fossil wood in Middle-Upper Jurassic marine sedimentary cycles of France: relations with climate, sea-level dynamics, and carbonate-plateform environments. *Palaeogeography, Palaeoclimatology, Palaeoecology,* **141,** 199–214.

Gareckij, R. G. (ed.) 1985. Osadkonakoplenie i paleogeografija zapada Wostoczno-Ewropejskoj Płatformy w mezozoje. Jurskaja sistema (contribution to the IGCP Project no. 86). *Nauka i Technika,* 10–172.

Garrison, R. E. & Fischer, A. G. 1969. Deep-water limestones and radiolarites of the Alpine Jurassic. *In*: Friedman, G.M. (ed.) *Depositional Environments in Carbonate Rocks*. Society of Economic Paleontologists and Mineralogists, Special Publications, **14**, 20–56.

Gaumet, F., Garcia, J.-P., Dromart, G. & Sambet, G. 1996. Contrôle stratigraphique des faciès, géométries et profils de dépôt de la plateforme carbonatée bourguignonne au Bathonien-Callovien. *Bulletin de la Société géologique de France*, **167**(3), 409–421.

Gawlick, H.-J. & Suzuki, H. 1999. Zur stratigraphischen Stellung der Strubbergschichten in den Nördlichen Kalkalpen (Callovium - Oxfordium). *Neues Jahrbuch für Geologie und Paläontologie,*

*Abhandlungen*, **211**, 233–262.

Gawlick, H.-J., Frisch, W., Vecsei, A., Steiger, T. & Böhm, F. 1999. The change from rifting to thrusting in the Northern Calcareous Alps as recorded in Jurassic sediments. *Geologische Rundschau*, **87**, 644–657.

Gawlick, H.-J., Frisch, W., Missoni, S. & Suzuki, H. 2002. Middle to Late Jurassic radiolarite basins in the central part of the Northern Calcareous Alps as a key for the reconstruction of their early tectonic history - an overview. *Memorie della Societa Geolgogica Italiana*, **57**, 123–132.

Gaździcka, E. 1998. Middle Oxfordian Tenuicostatum Zone Paleogeography. *In*: Dadlez R., Marek S., & Pokorski J. (eds) *Palaeogeographical atlas of the epicontinental Permian and Mesozoic in Poland, 1:2.500.000.* Polish Geological Institute, Warszawa.

Gaździcki, A. 1983. Foraminifers and biostratigraphy of Upper Triassic and Lower Jurassic of the Slovakian and Polish Carpathians. *Acta Palaeontologica Polonica*, **44**, 109–169.

Gerben, B., Kuerschner, W. & Krystyn, L. 2004. Palynology of the Triassic - Jurassic transition in the Northern Calcareous Alps (Austria). *Abstracts 32nd International Geological Congress*, Florence, 1141.

Geyer, O.F. & Gwinner, M.P. 1962. *Der Schwäbische Jura.* Sammlung geologischer Führer, **40**, Borntraeger, Berlin.

Geyer, O.F. & Gwinner, M.P. 1984. *Die Schwäbische Alb und ihr Vorland* (3rd edn). Sammlung geologischer Führer, **67**, Borntraeger, Berlin.

Geyer, O.F. & Gwinner, M.P. 1991. *Geologie von Baden-Württemberg* (4th edn). Schweizerbart, Stuttgart.

Geyer, O.F., Schober, M. & Geyer, M. 2003. *Die Hochrhein-Regionen zwischen Bodensee und Basel.* Sammlung geologischer Führer, **94**, Borntraeger, Berlin.

Geyssant, J. R., Vidier, J.-P., Herbin, J.-P., Proust, J.-N. & Deconinck, J.-F. 1993. Biostratigraphie et paléoenvironnement des couches de passage Kimméridgien/Tithonien du Boulonnais (Pas de Calais): nouvelles données paléontologiques (ammonites), organisation séquentielle et contenu en matière organique. *Géologie de la France*, **4**, 11–24.

Gierliński, G. 1991. New dinosaur ichnotaxa from the Early Jurassic of the Holy Cross Mountains, Poland. *Palaeogeography, Palaeoclimatology, Palaeoecology*, **85**(1–2), 137–148.

Gierliński, G. & Pieńkowski, G. 1999. Dinosaur track assemblages from Hettangian of Poland. *Geological Quarterly*, **43**(3), 329–346.

Gierliński, G., Niedźwiedzki, G. & Pieńkowski, G. 2001. Gigantic footprint of a theropod dinosaur in the Early Jurassic of Poland. *Acta Palaeontologica Polonica*, **46**(3), 441–446.

Gierliński, G., Pieńkowski, G. & Niedźwiedzki, G. 2004. Tetrapod track assemblage in the Hettangian of Sołtyków, Poland, and its paleoenvironmental background. *William A.S. Sarjeant (1935–2002), a celebration of his life and ichnological contribution, Special Issue*, **3**, *Ichnos*, **11** (3–4), 195–213.

Golebiowski, R. 1990. Facial and faunistic changes from Triassic to Jurassic in the Northern Calcareous Alps (Austria). *Les Cahiers de l'Université Catholique de Lyon, Série Sciences*, **3**, 175–184.

Golebiowski, R. & Braunstein, R.E. 1988. A Triassic/Jurassic boundary section in the northern Calcareous Alps (Austria). *Berichte der Geologischen Bundesanstalt*, **15**, 39–46.

Golonka, J. 2000. *Cambrian-Neogene Plate Tectonic Maps.* Wydawnictwa Uniwersytetu Jagiellońskiego, Kraków.

Golonka, J. & Krobicki, M. 2001. Upwelling regime in the Carpathian Tethys: a Jurassic-Cretaceous palaeogeographic and palaeoclimatic perspective. *Geological Quarterly*, **45**, 15–32.

Golonka, J. & Krobicki, M. 2002. Permian-Early Cretaceous opening of the Carpathian Basins. *Geolines*, **14**, 24–25.

Golonka, J. & Krobicki, M. 2004. Jurassic paleogeography of the Pieniny and Outer Carpathian basins. *Rivista Italiana di Paleontologia e Stratigrafia*, **110**(1), 5–14.

Golonka, J. & Sikora, W. 1981. Microfacies of the Jurassic and Lower Cretaceous sedimentarily thinned deposits of the Pieniny Klippen Belt in Poland. *Biuletyn Instytutu Geologicznego*, **31**, 7–37 [in Polish with English summary].

Golonka, J., Oszczypko, N. & Ślączka, A. 2000*a*. Geodynamic evolution and paleogeography of the Carpathian-Panonnian region – a global perspective. *Slovakian Geological Magazine*, **6**, 139–142.

Golonka, J., Oszczypko, N. & Ślączka, A. 2000*b*. Late Carboniferous – Neogene geodynamic evolution and paleogeography of the circum-Carpathian region and adjacent areas. *Annales de la Societe Geologique de Pologne*, **70**, 107–136.

Golonka, J., Krobicki, M., Oszczypko, N., Ślączka, A. & Słomka, T. 2003. Geodynamic evolution and palaeogeography of the Polish Carpathians and adjacent areas during Neo-Cimmerian and preceding events (latest Triassic–earliest Cretaceous). *In:* McCann, T. & Saintot, A. (eds) *Tracing Tectonic Deformation Using the Sedimentary Record.* Geological Society, London, Special Publications, **208**, 138–158.

Golonka, J., Gahagan, L., Krobicki, M., Marko, F., Oszczypko, N. & Ślączka, A. 2005. Plate tectonic evolution and paleogeography of the Circum-Carpathian Region. *In:* Picha, F. & Golonka, J. (eds) *The Carpathians and their Foreland. Geology and Hydrocarbon Resources.* American Association of Petroleum Geologists, Memoirs, **84**, 1–60.

Gonzalez, R. 1993. *Die Hauptrogenstein-Formation der Nordwestschweiz (mittleres Bajocien bis unteres Bathonien).* PhD thesis, Universität Basel.

Gonzalez, R. 1996. Response of shallow-marine carbonate facies to third-order and high-frequency sea-level fluctuations: Hauptrogenstein Formation, Northern Switzerland. *Sedimentary Geology*, **102**, 111–130.

Gonzalez, R. & Wetzel, A. 1996. Stratigraphy, and paleogeography of the Hauptrogenstein and Klingnau Formations (middle Bajocian to late Bathonian), northern Switzerland. *Eclogae geologicae Helvetiae*, **89**, 695–720.

Gradstein F., Ogg J.G. & Smith A. 2004. *A Geologic Time Scale.* Cambridge University Press, Cambridge.

Gramann, F., Heunisch, C., *et al.* 1997. Das Niedersächsische Oberjura-Becken – Ergebnisse interdisziplinärer Zusammenarbeit. *Zeitschrift der Deutschen Geologischen Gesellschaft*, **148**(2), 165–236.

Grand, T. 1988. Mesozoic extensional inherited structures on the European margin of the Ligurian Tethys. The example of the Bourg-d'Oisans half-graben, western Alps. *Bulletin de la Société géologique de France*, **8** (IV,4), 613–621.

Gravesen, P., Rolle, F. & Surlyk, F. 1982. Lithostratigraphy and sedimentary evolution of the Triassic, Jurassic and Lower Cretaceous of Bornholm, Denmark. *Danmarks Geologiske Undersøgelse, Serie B*, **7**, 1–51.

Groiss, J.Th., Haunschild, H. & Zeiss, A. 2000. *Das Ries und sein Vorland.* Sammlung geologischer Führer, **92**, Borntraeger, Berlin.

Gruner, U. 1981. Die jurassischen Breccien der Falknis-Decke und altersäquivalente Einheiten in Graubünden. *Beiträge zur Geologischen Karte der Schweiz*, **154**.

Gry, H. 1969. Megaspores from the Jurassic of the island of Bornholm, Denmark. *Meddelelser fra Dansk Geologisk Forening*, **19**, 69–89.

Guérin-Franiatte, S. 1988. Corrélations biostratigraphiques dans le Lias inférieur du Bassin parisien. Rapports avec l'ensemble du NW européen. *Abstracts 2nd international Symposium on Jurassic Stratigraphy, Lisboa*, 85–100.

Guérin-Franiatte, S. 1994. Biostratigraphie et paléobiogéographie des ammonites. Une synthèse pour le Lias inférieur de France. *Geobios*, **17**, 265–273.

Guérin-Franiatte, S. 2003. Biostratigraphie dans le Lias du Grand Duché de Luxembourg: le sondage de Capellen. *Ferrantia*, **36**, 65–77.

Guérin-Franiatte, S. & Hanzo, M. 1992. La base du Sinémurien dans la région d'Hettange, N-E France: biozonation. *Bulletin d'information des géologues du Bassin de Paris*, **29**(2), 15–20.

Guérin-Franiatte, S. & Müller, A. 1978. Découverte au Luxembourg belge de Schlotheimidae primitives (Ammonites dans les préplanorbis beds (Hettangien inférieur) *Annales de la Société géologique de Belgique*, **101**, 399–403.

Guérin-Franiatte, S. & Müller, A. 1986. L'Hettangien dans le Nord Est du Bassin de Paris: biostratigraphie et évolution sédimentaire. *Annales de la Société géologique de Belgique*, **109**, 415–429.

Guérin-Franiatte, S., Hanzo, M. & Ruget, C. 1983. L'Hettangien en Lorraine centrale : nouvelles observations lithologiques et biostratigraphiques dans la région de Nancy. *Bulletin de la Société géologique de France, Série 7*, **25**(6), 943–952.

Guérin-Franiatte, S., Hary, A. & Müller, A. 1991. La formation des Grès de Luxembourg, au Lias inférieur: reconstitution dynamique du paléoenvironnement. *Bulletin de la Société géologique de*

*France*, **162**(4), 763–773.

Guérin-Franiatte, S., Hary, A. & Müller, A. 1995. Paléoenvironnements et facteur temps: observations dans le Lias inférieur du Nord-est du Bassin parisien. *Geobios*, **18**, 207–219.

Guérin-Franiatte, S., Knapp, G. & Müller, A. 2000. L'Hettangien en bordure nord du Massif de l'Eifel (Allemagne occidentale). Relations avec le bassin parisien. *Zentralblatt für Geologie und Paläontologie*, **3–4**, 357–370.

Guex, J., Bartolini, A., Atudorei, V. & Taylor, D. 2004. High-resolution ammonite and carbon isotope stratigraphy across the Triassic-Jurassic boundary at New York canyon (Nevada). *Earth and Planetary Science Letters*, **225**, 29–41.

Guillocheau, F. 1991. Mise en évidence de grands cycles transgression-régression d'origine tectonique dans les sédiments mésozoïques du Bassin de Paris. *Comptes rendus de l'Académie des Sciences Paris, série 2*, **312**, 1587–1593.

Guillocheau, F., Robin, C., *et al.* 2000. Meso-Cenozoic geodynamic evolution of the Paris basin: 3D stratigraphic constraints; *Geodinamica Acta*, **13**, 189–246.

Guillocheau, F., Robin, C., Mettraux, M., Dagallier, G., Robin, F.X. & Le Solleuz, A. 2002. Le Jurassique de l'Est du bassin de Paris. *Bulletin d'Information des Géologues du Bassin de Paris*, **39**, 23–47.

Gümbel, C.W. 1894. *Geologie von Bayern, II. Band. Geologische Beschreibung von Bayern*. Th. Fischer, Kassel.

Guterch, A., Grad, M., Materzok, R. & Perchuć, E. 1986. Deep structure of the Earth's crust in the contact zone of the Palaeozoic and Precambrian platforms in Poland (Tornquist-Teissere Zone). *Tectonophysics*, **128**(2) 251–279.

Gutowski, J. 1998. Oxfordian and Kimmeridgian of the northeastern margin of the Holy Cross Mountains, Central Poland. *Geological Quarterly*, **42**(1), 59–72.

Gutowski, J. 2004*a*. Early Kimmeridgian oolitic sedimentary cycle in the Wierzbica quarry, Poland. *Tomy Jurajskie*, **2**, 37–48 [in Polish with English summary].

Gutowski, J. 2004*b*. Middle Oxfordian coral facies of the Bałtów region, NE margin of the Holy Cross Mts., Poland. *Tomy Jurajskie*, **2**, 17–27.

Gutowski, J. & Koyi, H.A. 2007. Influence of oblique basement strike-slip faults on the Mesozoic evolution of the south-eastern segment of the Mid-Polish Trough. *Basin Research*, **19**, 67–86.

Gutowski, J., Krzywiec, P. & Pożaryski, W. 2003*a*. From extension to inversion – sedimentary record of Mesozoic tectonic evolution within the marginal fault zone, SE Mid-Polish Trough. *Geolines*, **16**, 38–39.

Gutowski, J., Krzywiec, P., Walaszczyk, I. & Pożaryski, W. 2003*b*. Od ekstensji do inwersji – zapis aktywności NE brzeżnej strefy uskokowej świętokrzyskiego segmentu bruzdy śródpolskiej w osadach jury górnej i kredy na podstawie interpretacji danych sejsmiki refleksyjnej. *Tomy Jurajskie*, **1**, 124–125.

Gutowski, J., Popadyuk, I.V. & Olszewska, B. 2005*a*. Upper Jurassic – Lowermost Cretaceous in the epicontintinental sedimentary basin of SE Poland and W Ukraine. *Geological Quarterly*, **49**, 31–44.

Gutowski, J., Popadyuk, I.V. & Olszewska, B. 2005*b*. Niżniów limestone (Western Ukraine) – stratigraphy, facies development and regional implications. *Geological Quarterly*, **49**, 45–52.

Gwinner, M.P. 1962. Geologie des Weißen Jura der Albhochfläche (Württemberg). *Neues Jahrbuch für Geologie und Paläontologie, Abhandlungen*, **115**, 137–221.

Gwinner, M.P. 1976. Origin of the Upper Jurassic limestones of the Swabian Alb (Southwest Germany). *Contributions to Sedimentology*, **5**, 1–75.

Gygi, R.A. 1969. Zur Stratigraphie der Oxford-Stufe (oberes Jura-System) der Nordschweiz und des süddeutschen Grenzgebietes. *Beiträge zur Geologischen Karte der Schweiz, Neue Folge*, **136**.

Gygi, R.A. 1981. Oolithic iron formations: marine or not marine? *Eclogae geologicae Helvetiae*, **74**, 233–254.

Gygi, R.A. 1990. Die Paläogeographie im Oxfordium und frühesten Kimmeridgium in der Nordschweiz. *Jahreshefte des Geologischen Landesamtes Baden-Württemberg*, **32**, 207–222.

Gygi, R.A. 1992. Structure, pattern of distribution and paleobathymetry of Late Jurassic microbialites (stromatolites and oncoids) in northern Switzerland. *Eclogae geologicae Helvetiae*, **85**, 799–824.

Gygi, R.A. 1995. Datierung von Seichtwassersedimenten des Späten Jura in der Nordwestschweiz mit Ammoniten. *Eclogae geologicae Helvetiae*, **88**, 1–58.

Gygi, R.A. 1999. Ammonite ecology in Late Jurassic time in northern Switzerland. *Eclogae geologicae Helvetiae*, **92**, 129–137.

Gygi, R.A. 2000*a*. Integrated stratigraphy of the Oxfordian and Kimmeridgian (Late Jurassic) in northern Switzerland and adjacent southern Germany. *Denkschriften der Schweizerischen Akademie der Naturwissenschaften*, **104**.

Gygi, R.A. 2000*b*. Annotated index of lithostratigraphic units currently used in the Upper Jurassic of northern Switzerland. *Eclogae geologicae Helvetiae*, **93**, 125–146.

Gygi, R.A. & Persoz, F. 1986. Mineralostratigraphy, litho- and biostratigraphy combined in correlation of the Oxfordian (Late Jurassic) formations of the Swiss Jura range. *Eclogae geologicae Helvetiae*, **79**, 385–454.

Gygi, R.A. & Persoz, F. 1987. The epicontinental sea of Swabia (southern Germany) in the Late Jurassic - factors controlling sedimentation. *Neues Jahrbuch für Geologie und Paläontologie, Abhandlungen*, **176**, 49–65.

Gygi, R.A., Coe, A.L. & Vail, P.R. 1998. Sequence stratigraphy of the Oxfordian and Kimmeridgian stages (Late Jurassic) in northern Switzerland. *In*: de Graciansky, P.-C., Hardenbol, J., Jacquin, T. & Vail, P. (eds) *Mesozoic and Cenozoic Sequence Stratigraphy of European Basins*. Society of Economic Paleontologists and Mineralogists, Special Publications, **60**, 527–544.

Haas, J. & Hámor, G. 2001. Geological garden in the neighborhood of Budapest, Hungary. *Episodes*, **24**, 257–261.

Haas, J. & Tardy-Filácz, E. 2004. Facies changes in the Triassic-Jurassic boundary interval in an intraplatform basin succession at Csővár (Transdanubian Range, Hungary). *Sedimentary Geology*, **168**, 19–48.

Haas, J., Kovacs, S., Krystyn, L. & Lein, R. 1995. Significance of Late Permian-Triassic facies zones in terrane reconstruction in the Alpine-North Pannonian domain. *Tectonophysics*, **242**, 19–40.

Haefeli, Ch. 1966. *Die Jura/Kreide-Grenzschichten im Bielerseegebiet (Kt. Bern)*. PhD thesis, Universität Bern.

Hakenberg, M. & Świdrowska, J. 1998. Rozwój południowo-wschodniego segmentu bruzdy polskiej i jego związek ze strefami uskoków ograniczających (od permu do późnej jury). *Przegląd Geologiczny*, **46**(6), 503–508.

Hallam, A. 1984*a*. Distribution of fossil marine invertebrates in relation to climate. *In*: Brenchley, P.J. (ed.) *Fossils and Climate*. Wiley, London, 107–125.

Hallam, A. 1984*b*. Continental humid and arid zones during the Jurassic and Cretaceous. *Palaeogeography, Palaeoclimatology, Palaeoecology*, **47**, 195–223.

Hallam, A. 1985. A review of Mesozoic climates. *Journal of the Geological Society of London*, **142**, 433–445.

Hallam, A. 1988. A revaluation of Jurassic eustasy in the light of new data and the revised Exxon curve. *In*: Wilgus, C., Hastings, B., Ross, C., Posamentier, H., van Wagoner, J. & Kendall, L.G.St.C. (eds) *Sea-level Changes: An Integrated Approach*. Society of Economic Paleontologists and Mineralogists, Special Publications, **42**, 261–273.

Hallam, A. 1990. Correlation of the Triassic-Jurassic boundary in England and Austria. *Journal of the Geological Society of London*, **147**, 421–424.

Hallam, A. 1994. Jurassic climates as inferred from the sedimentary and fossil record. *In*: Allen, J.R.L., Hoskins, B.J., Sellwood, B.W., Spicer, R.A. and Valdes, P.J. (eds) *Palaeoclimates and their modelling*. Chapman and Hall, London, 79–88.

Hallam, A. 1997. Estimates of the amount and rate of sea-level change across the Rhaetian–Hettangian and Pliensbachian–Toarcian boundaries (latest Triassic to early Jurassic). *Journal of the Geological Society of London*, **154**, 773–779.

Hallam, A. 2001. A review of the broad pattern of Jurassic sea-level changes and their possible causes in light of current knowledge. *Palaeogeography Palaeoclimatology Palaeoecology*, **167**, 23–37.

Hallam, A. & Goodfellow, W.D. 1990. Facies and geochemical evidence bearing on the end-Triassic disappearance of the Alpine reef ecosystem. *Historical Biology*, **4**, 131–138.

Hallam, A. & Wignall, P.B. 1999. Mass extinctions and sea-level changes. *Earth-Science Reviews*, **48**, 217–250.

Hallam, A., Grose, J.A. & Ruffell, A.H. 1991. Palaeoclimatic significance of changes in clay mineralogy across the Jurassic - Cretaceous in England and France. *Palaeogeography, Palaeoclimatology, Palaeoecology*, **81**, 173–187.

Hamberg, L. & Nielsen, L.H. 2000. Singled, sharp-based shoreface sandstones and the importance of stepwise forced regression in a shallow basin, Upper Triassic Gassum Formation, Denmark. *In:* Hunt, D. & Gawthorpe, R.L. (eds) *Sedimentary Responses to Forced Regressions*. Geological Society, London, Special Publications, **172**, 69–89.

Hantzpergue, P. 1989. Les ammonites kimméridgiennes du haut-fond d'Europe occidentale. (Perisphinctidae, Aulacostephanidae et Aspidoceratidae). Biochronologie, systématique, évolution, paléobiogéographie. *Cahiers de paléontologie*, **428**.

Hanzlíková, E. & Bosák, P. 1977. Microfossils and microfacies of the Jurassic relict near Olomučany (Blansko district). *Věstnik Ústředniho Ústavu Geologického*, **52**, 73–79.

Hanzo, M. & Espitalie, J. 1994. Relationship between organic matter and sedimentation in the Lias of Lorraine (France). *In :* Mascle, A. (ed.) *Hydrocarbon and Petroleum Geology of France*. European Association of Petroleum Geoscientists, Special Publications, **4**, 121–136.

Hanzo, M. & Guérin-Franiatte, S. 1985. Une coupe continue dans le Lias inférieur et moyen de Lorraine septentrionale. *Cahiers de l'Institut Catholique de Lyon*, **14**, 175–188.

Hanzo, M., Hilly, J., Guérin-Franiatte, S. & Mangold, C. 1987. Durée des discontinuités et des séquences : exemple du passage Hettangien - Sinémurien dans la region. *Bulletin de la Société géologique de France*, **3**(6), 1107–1112.

Hanzo, M., Peniguel, G., Doubinger, J. & Adloff, M.-C. 1991. Zonation palynologique et analyse géochimique organique, pour préciser les paléomilieux lors de la transgression liasique à Cattenom (Moselle, France). *Cahiers de Micropaléontologie, Nouvelle Série*, **5**, 55–74.

Hanzo, M., Guérin-Franiatte, S., Espitalie, J. & de Graciansky, P. Ch. 1992. Source-rocks and Liassic Sequence Stratigraphy in Lorraine (Eastern Paris Basin, France). *International Symposium on Mesozoic and Cenozoic Sequence Stratigraphy of European Basins*, 344–345.

Hanzo, M., Lathuilière, B. & Péniguel, G. 1994. L'alternance calcaire-marne d'origine climatique établie pour la formation du Calcaire à gryphées (Lorraine, France). *Comptes rendus de l'Académie des Sciences Paris*, **319**, 915–920.

Hanzo, M., Lathuilière, B., *et al.* 2000. Paléoenvironnements dans le Calcaire à gryphées du Lias de Lorraine, de la carrière de Xeuilley au Bassin parisien. *Eclogae geologicae Helvetiae*, **93**, 183–206.

Haq, B.U., Hardenbol, J. & Vail, P.R. 1987. Chronology of fluctuating sea levels since the Triassic. *Science*, **235**, 1156–1167.

Haq, B.U., Hardenbol, J. & Vail, P.R. 1988. Mesozoic and Cenozoic chronostratigraphy and cycles of sea-level change. *In*: Wilgus, C., Hastings, B., Ross, C., Posamentier, H., van Wagoner, J. & Kendall, L.G.St.C. (eds) *Sea-level Changes: An Integrated Approach*. Society of Economic Paleontologists and Mineralogists, Special Publications, **42**, 71–108.

Hardenbol, J., Thierry, J., Farley, M.B., Jacquin, T., de Graciansky, P.-C. & Vail, P. 1998. Mesozoic and Cenozoic sequence chronostratigraphic framework of European basins. *In:* de Graciansky, P.-C., Hardenbol, J., Jacquin, T. & Vail, P. (eds) *Mesozoic and Cenozoic Sequence Stratigraphy of European Basins*. Society of Economic Paleontologists and Mineralogists, Special Publications, **60**, 3–13.

Hary, A. 1987. Epifaune et endofaune de *Liogryphaea arcuata* (Lamarck). *Travaux scientifiques du Museum d' Histoire naturelle du Luxembourg*, **10**, 77.

Häusler, H. 1987. The northern Austroalpine margin during the Jurassic: Breccias from the Radstädter Tauern and Tarntaler Berge. *In:* Flügel, H. W. & Faupl, P. (eds) *Geodynamics of the Eastern Alps*. Deuticke, Vienna, 103–111.

Hautmann, M. 2004. Effect of end-Triassic $CO_2$ maximum on carbonate sedimentation and marine mass extinction. *Facies*, **50**, 257–261.

Heim, A. 1919. *Geologie der Schweiz. Bd. 1: Molasseland und Juragebirge*. Leipzig (Tauchnitz).

Heinze, M. 1991. Evolution bentonischer Faunengemeinschaften im subborealen Jura des Pariser Beckens und in der äthiopischen Faunenprovinz des Beckens von Kachchh (Indien)- ein Vergleich. *Beringeria, Würzburger geowissenschaftliche Mitteilungen*, **4**, 3–126.

Heizmann, E.P.J. (ed.) 1998. *Vom Schwarzwald zum Ries. Erdgeschichte mitteleuropäischer Regionen*, **2**, Pfeil, München.

Helm, C., Reuter, M. & Schülke, I. 2003. Die Korallenfauna des Korallenooliths (Oxfordium, Oberjura, NW-Deutschland): Zusammensetzung, Stratigraphie und regionale Verbreitung. *Paläontologische Zeitschrift*, **77**(1), 77–94.

Henssel, K., Schmid, D.U. & Leinfelder, R.R. 2002. Computergestützte 3D-Rekonstruktionen in der Paläontologie anhand von Serienschnitten. *Mathematische Geologie*, **6**, 131–142.

Herngreen, G.F.W. & Wong, Th.E. 1989. Revision of the "Late Jurassic" stratigraphy of the Dutch Central North Sea Graben. *Geologie en Mijnbouw*, **68**(1), 73–105.

Herngreen, G.F.W., de Boer, K.F., Romein, B.J., Lissenberg, Th. & Wijker, N.C. 1983. Middle Callovian beds in the Achterhoek, eastern Netherlands. *Mededelingen Rijks Geologische Dienst*, **37**(3), 95–123.

Herngreen, G.F.W., Smit, R. & Wong, Th.E. 1991. Stratigraphy and tectonics of the Vlieland Basin, the Netherlands. *In:* Spencer, A.M. (ed.) *Generation, Accumulation and Production of Europe's hydrocarbons*. European Association of Petroleum Geoscientists, Special Publication **1**, 175–192.

Herngreen, G.F.W., Kerstholt, S.J. & Munsterman, D.K. 2000*a*. Callovian-Ryazanian ('Upper Jurassic') palynostratigraphy of the Central North Sea and Vlieland Basin, the Netherlands. *Mededelingen Nederlands Instituut voor Toegepaste Geowetenschappen TNO*, **63**, 3–99.

Herngreen, G.F.W., van den Bosch, M. & Lissenberg, Th. 2000*b*. Nieuwe inzichten in de stratigrafische ontwikkeling van Jura, Krijt en Onder-Tertiair in de Achterhoek. *Grondboor & Hamer*, **54**(4), 71–92.

Herngreen, G.F.W., Kouwe, W.F.P. & Wong, Th.E. 2003. The Jurassic of the Netherlands. *In*: Ineson, J.R. & Surlyk, F. (eds) *The Jurassic of Denmark and Greenland*. Geological Survey of Denmark and Greenland Bulletin, **1**, 217–229.

Hess, H. 1975. Die fossilen Echinodermen des Schweizer Juras. *Veröffentlichungen des Naturhistorischen Museums Basel*, **8**.

Hesselbo, S.P. & Jenkyns, H.C. 1998. British Lower Jurassic sequence stratigraphy. *In:* de Graciansky, P.-C., Hardenbol, J., Jacquin, T. & Vail, P. (eds) *Mesozoic and Cenozoic Sequence Stratigraphy of European Basins*. Society of Economic Paleontologists and Mineralogists, Special Publications, **60**, 561–581.

Hesselbo, S.P., Gröcke, D.R., Jenkyns, H.C., Bjerrum, C.J., Farrimond, P., Bell, H.S.M. & Green, O.R. 2000. Massive dissociation of gas hydrate during a Jurassic oceanic anoxic event. *Nature*, **406**, 392–395.

Hesselbo, S.P., Robinson, S.A., Surlyk, F. & Piasecki, S. 2002. Terrestrial and marine mass extinction at the Triassic–Jurassic boundary synchronized with major carbon-cycle perturbation: A link to initiation of massive volcanism? *Geology*, **30**, 251–254.

Hesselbo, S.P., Jenkyns, H.C., Duarte, L.V. & Oliveira, L.C.V. 2007. Carbon-isotope record of the Early Jurassic (Toarcian) Oceanic Anoxic Event from fossil wood and marine carbonate (Lusitanian Basin, Portugal). *Earth and Planetary Science Letters*, **253**, 455–470.

Hoedemaeker, Ph.J. & Herngreen, G.F.W. 2003. Correlation of Tethyan and Boreal Berriasian – Barremian strata with emphasis on strata in the subsurface of the Netherlands. *Cretaceous Research*, **24**, 253–275.

Hölder, H. 1964. *Jura. Handbuch der stratigraphischen Geologie IV.* Enke, Stuttgart.

Hoffmann, K. 1949. Zur Paläogeographie des nordwestdeutschen Lias und Dogger. *In:* Bentz, A. (ed.) *Erdöl und Tektonik in Nordwestdeutschland*. Amt für Bodenforschung, Hannover, 113–129.

Hofmann, F., Schlatter, R. & Weh, M. 2000. *Erläuterungen zum Blatt 1011 Beggingen (Südhälfte) mit SW-Anteil von Blatt 1012 Singen.* Geologischer Atlas der Schweiz 1:25.000, Schweizerische geologische Kommission.

Hoinkes, G., Koller, F., Rantitsch, G., Dachs, E., Höck, V., Neubauer, F. & Schuster, R. 1999. Alpine metamorphism of the Eastern Alps. *Schweizer Mineralogische und Petrographische Mitteilungen*, **79**, 155–182.

Hötzl, H. 1966. Zur Kenntnis der Tressenstein-Kalke (Ober-Jura, Nördliche Kalkalpen. *Neues Jahrbuch für Geologie und Paläontolo-*

*gie, Abhandlungen,* **123**(3), 281–310.

Huault, V. 1999. Zones de kystes de dinoflagellés de l'intervalle Aalénien-Oxfordien sur la bordure méridionale du bassin de Paris. *Review of Palaeobotany and Palynology,* **107**, 145–190.

Huault, V., Elie, M. & Ruck-Mosser, R. 2003. Variabilité spatiale du signal palynologique dans le bassin de Paris à la limite Dogger-Malm. *Comptes rendus Geosciences,* **335**, 401–409.

Huault, V., Lathuilière, B. & Carpentier, C. 2006. Les assemblages palynologiques du Jurassique supérieur du site de Bure (sondage Est 205). *7ème Colloque du GdR FORPRO,* La Grande Motte, 2–4 may 2006, 187.

Hubbard, R.N.B.L. & Boutler, M.C. 2000. Phytogeography and palaeoecology in Western Europe and Eastern Greenland near the Triassic-Jurassic boundary. *Palaios,* **15**, 120–131.

Hug, W.A. 2003. Sequenzielle Faziesentwicklung der Karbonatplattform im Oberen Oxford des Schweizer Jura. *GeoFocus,* **7**, 1–156.

Ineson, J.R. & Surlyk, F. (eds) 2003. *The Jurassic of Denmark and Greenland.* Geological Survey of Denmark and Greenland Bulletin, **1**.

Ineson, J.R., Bojesen-Koefoed, J.A., Dybkjær, K. & Nielsen, L.H. 2003. Volgian–Ryazanian 'hot shales' of the Bo Member (Farsund Formation) in the Danish Central Graben, North Sea: stratigraphy, facies, and geochemistry. *In:* Ineson, J.R. & Surlyk, F. (eds) *The Jurassic of Denmark and Greenland.* Geological Survey of Denmark and Greenland Bulletin, **1**, 403–436.

Izotova, T.S. & Popadyuk, I.V. 1996. Oil and gas accumulations in the Late Jurassic reefal complex of the West Ukrainian Carpathian foredeep. *In:* Ziegler P.A. & Horvath F. (eds) *Peri Tethys Memoir 2: Structure and Prospects of Alpine Basins and Forelands.* Memoir Museum National Histoire Naturelle, **170**, 375–390.

Jacobshagen, V. 1965. Die Allgäu-Schichten (Jura-Fleckenmergel) zwischen Wettersteingebirge und Rhein. *Jahrbuch der Geologischen Bundesanstalt,* **108**, 1–114.

Jacquin, T., Dardeau, G., Durlet, C., de Graciansky, P.-C. & Hantzpergue, P. 1998. The North Sea cycle: an overview of 2nd-order transgressive/regressive facies cycles in western Europe. *In* de Graciansky *et al.* (eds) *Mesozoic and Cenozoic Sequence Stratigraphy of European Basins.* Society of Economic Paleontologists and Mineralogists, Special Publications, **60**, 445–466.

Jadoul, F., Galli, M.T., Berra, F., Cirilli, S., Ronchi, P. & Paganoni, A. 2004. The Late Triassic–Early Jurassic of the Lombardy Basin: Stratigraphy, palaeogeography and palaeontology. *Guide to Post-congress Field Trip P68, 32nd International Geological Congress.*

Jan du Chêne, R., Busnardo, R., *et al.* 1993. Sequence-stratigraphic interpretation of Upper Tithonian-Berriasian reference sections in South-East France: a multidisciplinary approach. *Bulletin des Centres de Recherche Exploration-Production Elf-Aquitaine,* **17**(1), 151–181.

Jank, M., Meyer, C. A. & Wetzel, A. 2006*a*. Late Oxfordian to Late Kimmeridgian carbonate deposits of NW Switzerland (Swiss Jura): stratigraphical and palaeogeographical implications in the transition area between the Paris Basin and the Tethys. *Sedimentary Geology,* **186**, 237–263.

Jank, M., Wetzel, A., & Meyer, C. A. 2006*b*. Late Jurassic sea-level fluctuations in NW Switzerland (Late Oxfordian to Late Kimmeridgian): closing the gap between the Boreal and Tethyan realm in Western Europe. *Facies,* **52**, 487–519.

Japsen, P., Britze, P. & Andersen, C. 2003. Upper Jurassic – Lower Cretaceous of the Danish Central Graben: structural framework and nomenclature. *In:* Ineson, J.R. & Surlyk, F. (eds) *The Jurassic of Denmark and Greenland.* Geological Survey of Denmark and Greenland Bulletin, **1**, 233–246.

Jeannet, A. 1951. Stratigraphie und Paläontologie des oolithischen Eisenerzlagers von Herznach und seiner Umgebung. *Beiträge zur Geologie der Schweiz, geotechnische Serie,* **5**, 1–240.

Jenkyns, H.C., Jones, C., Gröcke, D.R., Hesselbo, S.P. & Parkinson, D.N. 2002. Chemostratigraphy of the Jurassic System: applications, limitations and implications for palaeoceanography. *Journal of the Geological Society of London,* **159**, 351–378.

Johannessen, P.N. 2003. Sedimentology and sequence stratigraphy of paralic and shallow marine Upper Jurassic sandstones in the northern Danish Central Graben. *In:* Ineson, J.R. & Surlyk, F. (eds) *The Jurassic of Denmark and Greenland.* Geological Survey of Denmark and Greenland Bulletin, **1**, 367–402.

Jordan, P. 1983. Zur Stratigraphie des Lias zwischen Unterem Hauenstein und Schinznach (Solothurner und Aargauer Faltenjura). *Eclogae geologicae Helvetiae,* **76**, 355–379.

Jurkiewicz, I. 1967. The Lias of the western part of the Mesozoic zone surrounding the Świętokrzyskie (Holy Cross) Mountains and its correlation with the Lias of the Cracow-Wieluń Range. *Biuletyn Instytutu Geologicnego,* **200**(2), 5–111.

Kaiser-Weidich, B. & Schairer, G. 1990. Stratigraphische Korrelation von Ammoniten, Calpionellen und Nannoconiden aus Oberjura und Unterkreide der Nördlichen Kalkalpen. *Eclogae geologicae Helvetiae,* **83**(2), 353–387.

Karaszewski, W. 1974. On the Hettangian-Sinemurian Boundary in the Extra-Carpathian Poland. *Bulletin de l'Academie Polonaise des Sciences, Série Sciences de la Terre,* **22**(1), 33–36.

Karaszewski, W. & Kopik, J. 1970. Lower Jurassic. *In: The Stratigraphy of the Mesozoic in the Margin of the Góry Świętokrzyskie.* Prace Instytutu Geologicznego, **56**, 65–98 [in Polish with English summary].

Kauffman, E.G. 1978. Benthic environments and paleoecology of the Posidonienschiefer (Toarcian). *Neues Jahrbuch für Geologie und Paläontologie, Abhandlungen,* **157**, 18–36.

Kauffman, E.G. 1981. Ecological reappraisal of the German Posidonienschiefer (Toarcian) and the stagnant basin model. *In:* Gray, J., Boucot, A.J. & Berry, W.B.N. (eds) *Communities of the Past.* Hutchinson Ross, Stroudsburg/Pennsylvania, 311–381.

Kemp, D.B., Coe, A.L., Cohen, A.S. & Schwark, L. 2005. Astronomical pacing of methane release in the Early Jurassic period. *Nature,* **437**, 396–399.

Keupp, H. 1977*a*. Ultrafazies und Genese der Solnhofener Plattenkalke (Oberer Malm, Südliche Frankenalb). *Abhandlungen der Naturhistorischen Gesellschaft Nürnberg,* **37**, 1–128.

Keupp, H. 1977*b*. Der Solnhofener Plattenkalk - ein Blaugrünalgen-Laminit. *Paläontologische Zeitschrift,* **51**, 102–116.

Keupp, H., Koch, R. & Leinfelder, R. 1990. Steuerungsprozesse der Entwicklung von Oberjura-Spongiolithen Süddeutschlands: Kenntnisstand, Probleme und Perspektiven. *Facies,* **23**, 141–174.

Kieslinger, A. 1964. *Die nutzbaren Gesteine Salzburgs.* Berglandbuch, Salzburg.

Kiessling, W. 1992. Paleontological and facial features of the Upper Jurassic Hochstegen Marble (Tauern Window, Eastern Alps). *Terra Nova,* **4**, 184–197.

Kiessling, W. 1997. Radiolarien im nordbayerischen Oberjura. *Geologische Blätter für Nordost-Bayern,* **47**, 25–51.

Kiessling, W. 2002. Secular variations in the Phanerozoic reef ecosystem. *In:* Kiessling, W., Flügel, E. & Golonka, J. (eds) *Phanerozoic Reef Patterns.* Society of Economic Paleontologists and Mineralogists, Special Publications, **72**, 625–690.

Kiessling, W. & Zeiss, A. 1992. New palaeontological data from the Hochstegen Marble (Tauern Window, Eastern Alps). *Geologisch-Paläontologische Mitteilungen Innsbruck,* **18**, 187–202.

Kiessling, W., Flügel, E. & Golonka, J. 1999. Fluctuations in the carbonate production of Phanerozoic reefs. *In:* Insalaco, E., Skelton, P. W., Palmer, T. J. (eds) *Carbonate Platform Systems: Components and Interactions.* Geological Society, London, Special Publications, **178**, 191–216.

Klassen, H. 2003. Zur Entwicklungsgeschichte des nördlichen Osnabrücker Berglandes. *Osnabrücker Naturwissenschaftliche Mitteilungen,* **29**, 13–44.

Kleberger, J., Sägmüller, J. J. & Tichy, G. 1981. Neue Fossilfunde aus der mesozoischen Schieferfülle der Hohen Tauern zwischen Fuschertal und Wolfbachtal (Unterpinzgau/Salzburg). *Geologisch-Paläontologische Mitteilungen Innsbruck,* **10** (9), 275–288.

Klingspor, I. 1976. Radiometric age-determinations of basalts, dolerites and related syenite in Skåne, southern Sweden. *Geologiska Föreningens i Stockholm Förhandlingar,* **98**, 195–216.

Kobler, H.-U. 1972. Geochemische, sedimentologische und ökologische Untersuchungen im Braunen Jura alpha (Opalinuston) der Schwäbischen Alb. *Arbeiten aus dem Geologisch-Paläontologischen Institut der Universität Stuttgart, Neue Folge,* **66**, 1–134.

Koch, R. 2000. Die neue Interpretation der Massenkalke des Süddeutschen Malm und ihr Einfluß auf die Qualität von Kalksteinen für technische Anwendungen (Beispiele aus der Fränkischen Alb). *Archaeopteryx,* **18**, 43–65.

KOCH, R. & SCHWEIZER, V. 1986. Erster Nachweis von Evaporiten im Weißen Jura der Schwäbischen Alb. *Naturwissenschaften,* **73**, 325.

KOCH, R., SENOWBARI-DARYAN, B. & STRAUSS, H. 1994. The Late Jurassic "Massenkalk Fazies" of Southern Germany: calcareous sand piles rather than organic reefs. *Facies,* **31**, 179–208.

KOCHANOVÁ, M. 1967. Zur Rhaet-Hettang Grenze in den Westkarpaten. *Západné Karpaty séria paleontológia*, **7**, 7–102.

KOPIK, J. 1960. Mikropaleontologiczna charakterystyka liasu i dolnego doggeru Polski. *Geological Quarterly,* **4**(4), 921–936 [in Polish with English summary].

KOPIK, J. 1962. Faunistic criteria of stratigraphical subdivision of the Lias in North-Western and Central Poland. *In: Księga Pamiątkowa ku czci prof. J. Samsonowicza*. Polska Academia Nauk, 271–312.

KOPIK, J. 1964. Stratigraphy of the Lower Jurassic based on the fauna of the Mechowo IG-1 borehole. *Biuletyn Instytutu Geologicznego*, **189**, 43–55 [in Polish with English summary].

KOPIK, J. 1979. Callovian of the Częstochowa Jura (South-Western Poland). *Prace Instytutu Geologicznego,* **93.**

KOPIK, J. 1988. Lower Jurassic – invertebrates. *In:* MALINOWSKA, L. (ed.) *Geology of Poland, Atlas of Guide and Characteristic Fossils, 3 ( 2b).* Wydawnictwa Geologiczne, Warszawa, 21–42.

KOPIK, J. 1998. Lower and Middle Jurassic of the north-eastern margin of the Upper Silesian coal basin. *Biuletyn Państwowego Instytutu Geologicznego,* **378**, 67–120.

KOPIK, J. & MARCINKIEWICZ, T. 1997. Jura dolna - biostratygrafia. *In:* MAREK, S. & PAJCHLOWA. M. (eds) *The Epicontinental Permian and Mesozoic in Poland.* Prace Państwowego Instytutu Geologicznego, **153**, 196–204.

KOPIK, J., MARCINKIEWICZ, T. & DAYCZAK-CALIKOWSKA, K. 1997. Middle Jurassic. Biostratigraphy. *In*: MAREK, S. & PAJCHLOWA, J. (eds) *The Epicontinental Permian and Mesozoic in Poland.* Prace Państwowego Instytutu Geologicznego, **153**, 236–263 [in Polish with English summary].

KOPPELHUS, E.B. & NIELSEN, L.H. 1994. Palynostratigraphy and palaeoenvironments of the Lower to Middle Jurassic Bagå Formation of Bornholm, Denmark. Palynology, **18**, 139–194.

KOTT, R. 1989. Fazies und Geochemie des Treuchtlinger Marmors (Unter- und Mittel-Kimmeridge, Südliche Frankenalb). *Berliner geowissenschaftliche Abhandlungen, Reihe A,* **111**, 1–115.

KOUTEK, J. 1926. Contribution to knowledge of chert-bearing Jurassic limestones on Stránská skála near Brno. *Věstnik Státskoho geologického Ústředniho*, **2**, 172–182.

KOUTEK, J. 1927. To the question of the depth of Jurassic sea at Brno. *Časopsis Vlasteneckého spolku muzejniho v Olomouci*, **38**, 1–5 [in Czech].

KOZUR, H. 1992. The evolution of the Meliata-Hallstatt ocean and its significance for the early evolution of the Eastern Alps and Western Carpathians. *Palaeogeography Palaeoclimatology Palaeoecology,* **87**, 109–135.

KOZUR, H. & MOSTLER, H. 1992. Erster paläontologischer Nachweis von Meliaticum und Süd-Rubabanyaicum in den Nördlichen Kalkalpen (Österreich) und ihre Beziehung zu den Abfolgen der Westkarpaten. *Geologisch-Paläontologische Mitteilungen Innsbruck*, **18**, 87–129.

KRAINER, K. & MOSTLER, H. 1997. Die Lias-Beckenentwicklung der Unkener Synklinale (Nördliche Kalkalpen, Salzburg) unter besonderer Berücksichtigung der Scheibelberg Formation. *Geologisch-Paläontologische Mitteilungen Innsbruck*, **22**, 1–41.

KRAINER, K., MOSTLER, H. & HADITSCH, J. G. 1994. Jurassische Beckenbildung in den Nördlichen Kalkalpen bei Lofer (Salzburg) unter besonderer Berücksichtigung der Manganerz-Genese. *Abhandlungen der Geologischen Bundesanstalt*, **50**, 257–293.

KRASSILOV, V.A. 1997. Long time scale Phanerozoic temperature curve inferred from the shifts of phytogeographical boundaries. *Mededelingen Nederlands Instituut voor Toegepaste Geowetenschappen*, **58**, 35–42.

KRAUTTER, M. 1997. Aspekte zur Paläökologie postpaläozoischer Kieselschwämme. *Profil,* **11**, 199–324.

KRAUTTER, M., CONWAY, K.W., BARRIE, J.V. & NEUWEILER, M. 2001. Discovery of a "living dinosaur": globally unique modern hexactinellid sponge reefs off British Columbia, Canada. *Facies,* **44**, 265–282.

KROBICKI, M. 1996. Neo-Cimmerian uplift of intraoceanic Czorsztyn pelagic swell (Pieniny Klippen Belt, Polish Carpathians) indicated by the change of brachiopod assemblages. *In:* RICCARDI, A.C. (ed.) *Advances in Jurassic Research.* Geo Research Forum, **1–2**, 255–264.

KROBICKI, M. & SŁOMKA, T. 1999. Berriasian submarine mass movements as results of tectonic activity in the Carpathian Basin. *Geologica Carpathica*, **50**, 42–44.

KROBICKI, M., BUDZYŃ, B., *et al.* 2005. Petrography and mineralogy of the Late Jurassic – Early Cretaceous volcanic rocks in the Ukrainian part of the Carpathians. 6th meeting of the Mineralogical Society of Poland, Special Papers, **25**, 323–328.

KROHE, A. 1996. Variscan tectonics of central Europe: postaccretionary intraplate deformation of weak continental lithosphere. *Tectonics*, **15**, 1364–1388.

KRÓLIKOWSKI, C., PETECKI, Z. & ŻÓŁTOWSKI, Z. 1999. Main structural units in the Polish part of the East-European Platform in the light of gravimetric data. *Biuletyn Państwowego Instytutu Geologicznego*, **386**, 5–58 [in Polish, with English summary].

KRONER, U., MANSY, J.-L. *et al.* 2008. Variscan tectonics. *In*: MCCANN, T. (ed.) *The Geology of Central Europe. Volume 1: Precambrian and Palaeozoic.* Geological Society, London, 599–664.

KRUT'A, T. 1953. New finds of geodes and minerals in gravel terraces and riverbeds on southern Moravia. *Acta Museae Moraviae, Scientia naturalis*, **38**, 101–111 [in Czech].

KRYSTEK, I. 1974. Results of sedimentological research of Lower Badenian sediments in the Carpathian Foredeep (Moravia). *Folia Scientia Rerum Naturalis J.E. Purkyně Universitae Geologorum*, **15**, 8 [in Czech].

KRYSTYN, L. 1971. Stratigraphie, Fauna und Fazies der Klaus-Schichten (Aalenium-Oxford) in den östlichen Nordalpen. *Verhandlungen der Geologischen Bundesanstalt*, **1971**(3), 486–509.

KSIĄŻKIEWICZ, M. 1960. Outline of the paleogeography in the Polish Carpathians. *Prace Instytutu Geologicznego*, **30**, 209–231.

KUHN, O. 1935. Revision der Opalinuston-(Dogger Alpha)-Fauna in Franken, mit Ausschluß der Cephalopoden. *Paläontologische Zeitschrift,* **17**, 109–158.

KUHN, O. & ETTER, W. 1994. Der Posidonienschiefer der Nordschweiz: Lithostratigraphie, Biostratigraphie, Fazies. *Eclogae geologicae Helvetiae,* **87,** 113–138.

KÜRSCHNER, W. 2001. Leaf sensor for $CO_2$ in deep time. *Nature*, **411**, 247–248.

KÜRSCHNER, W., BONIS, N. R. & KRYSTYN, L. 2007. Carbon-isotope stratigraphy and palynostratigraphy of the Triassic-Jurassic transition in the Tiefengraben section — Northern Calcareous Alps (Austria). *Palaeogeography, Palaeoclimatology, Palaeoecology,* **244**, 257–280.

KURZ, W., NEUBAUER, F., GENSER, J., UNZOG, W. & DACHS, E. 2001*a*. Tectonic evolution of Penninic Units in the Tauern Window during the Paleogene: constraints from structural and metamorphic geology. *In:* PILLER, W. E. & RASSER, M. W. (eds) *Paleogene of the Eastern Alps*. Österreichische Akademie der Wissenschaften, Vienna, 347–376.

KURZ, W., NEUBAUER, F., FRITZ, H., PILLER, W. E., & GENSER, J. 2001*b*. Overview of the Paleogene of the Eastern Alps. *In:* PILLER, W. E. & RASSER, M. W. (eds) *Paleogene of the Eastern Alps*. Österreichische Akademie der Wissenschaften, Vienna, 11–56.

KUTEK, J. 1969. Kimeryd i najwyższy oksford południowo-zachodniego obrzeżenia mezozoicznego Gór Świętokrzyskich. Cz. 2: Paleogeografia. *Acta Geologica Polonica*, **19**, 221–231.

KUTEK, J. 1994. Jurassic tectonic events in south-eastern cratonic Poland. *Acta Geologica Polonica*, **44**(3–4), 167–221.

KUTEK, J. 2001. The Polish Permo-Mesozoic Rift Basin. *In:* ZIEGLER, P.A., CAVAZZA, W., ROBERTSON, A.H.F. & CRASQUIN-SOLEAU, S. (eds) *Peri-Tethys Memoir 6: Peri-Tethyan Rift/Wrench Basins and Passive Margins*. Mémoires du Musée Histoire Naturelle, **186**, 213–236.

KUTEK, J. & WIERZBOWSKI, A. 1986. A new account on the Upper Jurassic stratigraphy and ammonites of the Czorsztyn succession, Pieniny Klippen Belt, Poland. *Acta Geologica Polonica*, **36**, 289–316.

KUTEK, J. & ZEISS, A. 1994. Biostratigraphy of the highest Kimmeridgian and Lower Volgian in Poland. *Geobios*, **17**.

KUTEK, J., MATYJA, B.A. & WIERZBOWSKI, A. 1984. Late Jurassic biogeography in Poland and its stratigraphical implications. *In:* MICHELSEN. O. & ZEISS, A. (eds) *International Symposium on Jurassic Stratigraphy,* Erlangen 1984. Geological Survey of Denmark, Symposium, **3**.

LACHKAR, G., BÓNA, J. & PAVILLON, M.J. 1984. The Liassic Gresten facies: palynological data and paleogeographical significance. *Acta Geologica Hungarica*, **27**(3–4), 409–416.

Lackschewitz, K. S., Grützmacher, U. & Henrich, R. 1991. Paleoceanography and rotational block faulting in the Jurassic Carbonate Series of the Chiemgau Alps (Bavaria). *Facies*, **24**, 1–24.

Lakew, T. 1990. Microfacies and cyclic sedimentation of the Upper Triassic (Rhaetian) Zu Limestone (Southern Alps). *Facies*, **22**, 187–232.

Lamarche, J., Bergerat, F., Lewandowski, M., Mansy, J.L., Świdrowska, J. & Wieczorek, J. 2002. Variscan to Alpine heterogenous palaeo-stress above a major Paleozoic suture in the Carpathian foreland (southeastern Poland). *Tectonophysics*, **357**, 55–80

Landais, P. & Elie, M. 1999. Utilisation de la géochimie organique pour la détermination du paléoenvironnement et de la paléothermicité dans le Callovo-Oxfordien du site de l'Est de la France. *Actes des journées scientifiques CNRS/ANDRA Bar le Duc 1997, Editions EDP Sciences*, 35–61.

Lang, B. 1989. Die Schwamm-Biohermfazies der Nördlichen Frankenalb (Urspring; Oxford, Malm): Mikrofazies, Palökologie, Paläontologie. *Facies*, **20**, 199–274.

Lashkevitsch, Z. M., Medvedev, A. P. & Krupskiy, Y. Z. 1995. *Tectonomagmatic Evolution of Carpathians*. Naukova Dumka, Kiev [in Russian].

Laternser, R. 2001. *Oberjurassische Korallenriffe von Nordostfrankreich (Lothringen) und Südwestdeutschland*. PhD thesis, Universität Stuttgart.

Lathuiliere, B. 2000. Les coraux constructeurs du Bajocien inférieur de France. *Geobios*, **33**, 51–72, 153–181 (2 parts).

Lathuiliere, B., Bartier, D., *et al.* 2002. Climats kimméridgiens du site de Bure (Nord Est de la France). *Documents des Laboratoires de Géologie de Lyon*, **156**, 142–143.

Lathuiliere, B., Gauthier-Lafaye, F., *et al.* 2003. Paléoenvironnements du Kimméridgien de Bure. *Colloque FORPRO, La Grande Motte*, 4.

Lathuilière, B., Carpentier, C., Huault, V. & Martin-Garin, B. 2006*a*. Les assemblages coralliens du Jurassique supérieur du site de Bure. *7ème Colloque du GdR FORPRO, La Grande Motte 2006*, 188.

Lathuilière, B., Boullier, A., Carpentier, C., Huault, V. 2006*b*. Les brachiopodes oxfordiens et kimméridgiens du site de Bure. *7ème Colloque du GdR FORPRO, La Grande Motte 2006*, 186.

Lathuilière, B., Carpentier, C., Huault, V. & Martin-Garin, B. 2006*c*. Biological zonation of Oxfordian reefs. *Volumina Jurassica*, **IV**, 120.

Leinfelder, R.R. 1993. Upper Jurassic reef types and controlling factors – a preliminary report. *Profil*, **5**, 1–45.

Leinfelder, R.R. 2001. Jurassic reef ecosystems. *In*: Stanley, G.D., Jr. (ed.) *The History and Sedimentology of Ancient Reef Systems*, Kluwer/Plenum, New York, 251–309.

Leinfelder, R.R. & Keupp, H. 1995. Upper Jurassic mud mounds: allochthonous sedimentation versus autochthonous carbonate production. *In*: Reitner, J. & Neuweiler, F. (coord.) Mud mounds: a polygenetic spectrum of fine-grained carbonate buildups. *Facies*, **32**, 17–26.

Leinfelder, R.R., Nose, M., Schmid, D.U. & Werner, W. 1993. Microbial crusts of the Late Jurassic: composition, palaeoecological significance and importance in reef construction. *Facies*, **29**, 195–230.

Leinfelder, R.R., Krautter, M., *et al.* 1994. The origin of Jurassic reefs: current research developments and results. *Facies*, **31**, 1–56.

Leinfelder, R.R., Werner, W., *et al.*. 1996. Paleoecology, growth parameters and dynamics of coral, sponge and microbolite reefs from the Late Jurassic. *In*: Reitner, J., Neuweiler, F. & Gunkel, F. (eds): *Global and Regional Controls on Biogenic Sedimentation. I. Reef Evolution. Research Reports*. Göttinger Arbeiten zur Geologie und Paläontologie, **Sb2**, 227–248.

Leinfelder, R.R., Schmid, D.U., Nose, M. & Werner, W. 2002. Jurassic reef patterns – the expression of a changing globe. *In*: Kiessling, W., Flügel, E. & Golonka, J. (eds) *Phanerozoic Reef Patterns*. Society of Economic Paleontologists and Mineralogists, Special Publications, **72**, 465–520.

Le Roux, J. 1980. La tectonique de l'auréole orientale du bassin de Paris. *Bulletin de la Société géologique de France*, **22**(4), 655–662.

Le Roux, J. 1999. Le contexte structural de l'est du bassin parisien et les relations avec la sedimentation. *Bulletin d'Information des Géologues du Bassin de Paris*, **36**(1), 7–13.

Le Roux, J. 2000. Structuration du nord-est du Bassin de Paris. *Bulletin d'Information des Géologues du Bassin de Paris*, **37**, 13–34.

Le Roux, J. & Harmand, D. 2003. Origin of the hydrographic network in the Eastern Paris basin and its border massifs. Hypothesis, structural, morphologic and structural consequences. *Géologie de la France*, **1**, 105–110.

Leszczyński, K. 1998. Late Valanginian palaeogeography. *In:* Dadlez, R., Marek, S. & Pokorski, J. (eds) *Palaeogeographical atlas of the Epicontinental Permian and Mesozoic in Poland, 1:2.500.000*. Polish Geological Institute, Warszawa, Pl. 60.

Lewandowski, M., Krobicki, M., Matyja, B.A. & Wierzbowski, A. 2005. Palaeogeographic evolution of the Pieniny Klippen Basin using stratigraphic and palaeomagnetic data from the Veliky Kamenets section (Carpathians, Ukraine). *Palaeogeography, Palaeoclimatology, Palaeoecology*, **216**, 53–72.

LGRB 2004. *Geologische Schichtenfolge von Baden-Württemberg*. Landesamt für Geologie, Rohstoffe und Bergbau Baden-Württemberg. World Wide Web address: http://www.lgrb.uni-freiburg.de/lgrb/download_pool/schicht_1.pdf

Liboriussen, J., Ashton, P. & Tygesen, T. 1987. The tectonic evolution of the Fennoscandian Border Zone. *In:* Ziegler, P.A. (ed.) Compressional intra-plate deformations in the Alpine Foreland. *Tectonophysics*, **137**, 21–29.

Linetskaya, L.V. & Lozyniak, P.Y. 1983. Tintinidae and Radiolaria of the Upper Jurassic reefal complex; Forecarpathian deep. *Palaeontological Studies*, **20**, 24–28 [in Russian].

Lobitzer, H., Filácz, E. *et al.* 1994. Mesozoic of Northern Calcareous Alps of Salzburg and Salzkammergut area, Austria. *In: Shallow Tethys 4 - Pre-Symposium Excursion*, 1, 1–44.

Lorin, S., Courville, P., Collin, P.-Y., Thierry, J. & Tort, A. 2004. Modalités de réinstallation d'une plate-forme carbonatée après une crise sédimentaire : exemple de la limite Oxfordien moyen-Oxfordien supérieur dans le Sud-Est du Bassin de Paris. *Bulletin de la Société géologique de France*, **175**(3), 289–302.

Losos, Z., Přichystal, A. & Richterová, D. 2000. Anhydrite and barite inclusions in Jurassic geodes from Moravia and their genetic significance. *Geologické výzkumy na Moravě a ve Slesku v roce 1999*, 66–68 [in Czech].

Lucińska-Anczkiewicz, A., Villa, I.M., Anczkiewicz, R. & Ślączka, A. 2002. $^{40}Ar/^{39}Ar$ dating of alkaline lamprophyres from the Polish Western Carpathians. *Geologica Carpathica*, **53**, 45–52.

Lukeneder, A., Krystyn, L., Rasser, M.W. & Märzendorfer, G. 2003. Ammonite biostratigraphy of the Upper Jurassic Loser section (Northern Calcareous Alps, Salzkammergut). *In:* Piller, W.E. (ed.) *Stratigrafia Austriaca*. Österreichische Akademie der Wissenschaften, Erdwissenschaftliche Kommission, **16**, 217–229.

Lund, J.J. 1977. Rhaetic to Lower Liassic palynology of the onshore south-eastern North Sea Basin. *Danmarks Geologiske Undersøgelse, Serie 2*, **109**, 1–129.

Lupu, M. 1972. Mikrofazielle Untersuchung eines Quintnerkalk-Profils der Mittagsfluh in Vorarlberg. *Verhandlungen der Geologischen Bundesanstalt*, **1972**, 281–287.

McElwain, J.C., Beerling, D.J. & Woodward, F.I. 1999. Fossil plants and global warming at the Triassic–Jurassic boundary. *Science*, **285**, 1386–1390.

McRoberts, C.A. 1994. The Triassic–Jurassic ecostratigraphic transition in the Lombardian Alps, Italy. *Palaeogeography, Palaeoclimatology, Palaeoecology*, **110**, 145–166.

McRoberts, C.A., Newton, C.R. & Alissanaz, A. 1995. End-Triassic bivalve extinction: Lombardian Alps, Italy. *Historical Biology*, **9**, 297–317.

Mahel, M. 1986. *Geological Structure of the Czechoslovak Carpathians: The Paleoalpine Units 1*. Veda Editorial House, Bratislava [in Slovak].

Maisch, M.W. & Reisdorf, A.G. 2006*a*. Evidence for the longest stratigraphic range of a post-Triassic Ichthyosaur: a *Leptonectes tenuirostris* from the Pliensbachian (Lower Jurassic) of Switzerland. *Geobios*, **39**, 491–505.

Maisch, M.W. & Reisdorf, A.G. 2006*b*. Erratum to the article "Evidence for the longest stratigraphic range of a post-Triassic Ichthyosaur: a *Leptonectes tenuirostris* from the Pliensbachian (Lower Jurassic) of Switzerland". *Geobios*, **39**, 491–505. *Geobios*, **39**, 743–746.

MALISZEWSKA, A. 1998. New petrological data on carbonate mineralogy in the Middle Jurassic siliciclastic deposits of the Kujawy region (Polish Lowlands). *Geological Quarterly,* **42**(4), 401–420.

MALISZEWSKA, A. 1999. Middle Jurassic. *In: Diagenesis of the Upper Permian and Mesozoic Deposits of the Kujawy Region (Central Poland).* Prace Państwowego Instytutu Geologicznego, **162**, 78–93 [in Polish with English summary].

MALLING, C. & GRÖNWALL, K.A. 1909. En Fauna i Bornholms Lias. *Meddelelser fra Dansk Geologisk Forening*, **3**, 271–316.

MANDL, G. 1984. Zur Tektonik der westlichen Dachsteindecke und ihres Hallstätter Rahmens (Nördliche Kalkalpen, Österreich. *Mitteilungen der Österreichischen Geologischen Gesellschaft*, **77**, 1–31.

MANDL, G. 2000. The Alpine sector of the Tethys shelf – Examples of Triassic to Jurassic sedimentation and deformation from the Northern Calcareous Alps. *Mitteilungen der Österreichischen Geologischen Gesellschaft*, **92**, 61–78.

MANGOLD, C. 1970. Stratigraphie des étages Bathonien et Callovien du Jura méridional. *Documents du Laboratoire de Géologie, Faculté des Sciences, Lyon,* **40**.

MANGOLD, C., POIROT, E., LATHUILIERE, B. & LE ROUX, J. 1995. Biochronologie du Bajocien supérieur et du Bathonien de Lorraine. *Geobios*, **17**, 343–349.

MARCHAND, D. 1986. *L'évolution des Cardioceratinae d'Europe occidentale dans leur contexte paléogéographique.* PhD thesis, Université de Bourgogne.

MARCINKIEWICZ, T. 1971. The stratigraphy of the Rhaetian and Lias in Poland based on megaspore investigations. *Prace Instytutu Geologicznego*, **65**, 1–58 [in Polish with English summary].

MARCINKIEWICZ, T. 1988. Lower Jurassic – megaspores. *In:* MALINOWSKA, L. (ed.) *Geology of Poland, Atlas of Guide and Characteristic Fossils, 3 (2b).* Wydawnictwa Geologiczne, Warszawa, 64–70.

MARTY, D., HUG, W. A., IBERG, A. H., CAVIN, L., MEYER, Ch. A. & LOCKLEY, M. G. 2003. Preliminary report on the Courtedoux dinosaur tracksite from the Kimmeridgian of Switzerland. *Ichnos Special Issue*, **11**, 209–219.

MARZOLI, A., RENNE, P.R., PICCIRILLO, E.M., ERNESTO, M., BELLIENI, G. & DE MIN, A. 1999. Extensive 200-million-year-old continental flood basalts of the Central Atlantic Magmatic Province. *Science*, **284**, 616–618.

MARZOLI, A., BERTRAND, H., *et al.* 2004. Synchrony of the Central Atlantic magmatic province and the Triassic-Jurassic boundary climatic and biotic crisis. *Geology*, **32**, 973–976.

MASCLE, A., BERTRAND, G. & LAMIRAUX, C. 1994. Exploration for and production of oil and gas in France: a review of the habitat, present activity, and expected developments). *In:* MASCLE, A. (ed.) *Hydrocarbon and Petroleum Geology of France.* European Association of Petroleum Geoscientists, Special Publications, **4**, 3–27.

MATYJA, B.A. 1977. The Oxfordian in the south-western margin of the Holy Cross Mts. *Acta Geologica Polonica*, **1**, 41–64.

MATYJA, B.A. & PISERA, A. 1991. Late Jurassic European sponge megafacies: general perspective. *3rd International Symposium Jurassic Stratigraphy, Poitiers, Abstracts*, 81.

MATYJA, B.A. & WIERZBOWSKI, A. 1995. Biogeographic differentiation of the Oxfordian and Early Kimmeridgian ammonite faunas of Europe, and its stratigraphic consequences. *Acta Geologica Polonica*, **45**, 1–8

MATYJA, B.A. & WIERZBOWSKI, A. 1996. Sea bottom relief and bathymetry of late Jurassic sponge megafacies in Poland. *Georesearch Forum*, **1–2**, 333–340.

MATYJA, B.A. & WIERZBOWSKI, A. 2000*a*. Biostratigraphical correlations between the Subboreal Mutabilis Zone and the Submediterranean Upper Hypselocyclum – Divisum Zones of the Kimmeridgian: new data from Northern Poland. *Georesearch Forum*, **6**, 129–136.

MATYJA, B.A. & WIERZBOWSKI, A. 2000*b*. Ammonites and stratigraphy of uppermost Bajocian and Lower Bathonian between Częstochowa and Wieluń, Central Poland. *Acta Geologica Polonica,* **50**(2), 191–209

MATYJA, B.A. & WIERZBOWSKI, A. 2003. Correlation chart of standard chronostratigraphic ammonite zonations at the Oxfordian/Kimmeridgian boundary. *International Subcommission on Jurassic Stratigraphy Newsletter,* **30**, 25–27.

MATYJA, B.A., GUTOWSKI, J. & WIERZBOWSKI, A. 1989. The open shelf-carbonate platform succession at the Oxfordian/Kimmeridgian boundary in the SW margin of the Holy Cross Mts: stratigraphy, facies and ecological implications. *Acta Geologica Polonica*, **39**(1–4), 29–48.

MATYJA, B. A., WIERZBOWSKI, A. & RADWAŃSKI, A. (eds) 1992. Guide Book and Abstracts. Oxfordian and Kimmeridgian Joint Working Groups Meeting, Warszawa and Central Polish Uplands.

MEGNIEN, C. *et al.* 1980. Synthèse géologique du bassin de Paris. *Mémoires du Bureau de Recherches Géologiques et Miniéres,* **101–103.**

MEIER, H. & MEIERS, K. 1988. Die Gastropodenfauna der *"Angulata-*zone" des Steinbruchs "Reckingerwald" bei Brouch. *Travaux scientifiques du Museum d' Histoire naturelle du Luxembourg*, **13**.

MELÉNDEZ, G., PAGE, K.N., WRIGHT, J.K., & ATROPS, F. 2006. The ammonite faunas of the Callovian/Oxfordian boundary interval in Europe and their relevance to the establishment of an Oxfordian GSSP. *Volumina Jurassica,* **IV**, 185.

MERTENS, G., SPIES, E.D. & TEYSSEN, T. 1983. The Luxemburg sandstone Formation (Lias), a tide controlled deltaic deposit. *Annales de la Société géologique de Belgique,* **106**, 103–109.

MEYER, C.A. 1988. Paläoökologie, Biofazies und Sedimentologie von Seeliliengemeinschaften aus dem Unteren Hauptrogenstein des Nordwestschweizer Jura. *Revue de Paléobiologie,* **7**, 359–433.

MEYER, C.A. 1990. Sauropod tracks from the Upper Jurassic Reuchenette Formation (Kimmeridgian, Lommiswil, Kt.Solothurn) of Northern Switzerland. *Eclogae geologicae Helvetiae*, **83** (2), 389–397.

MEYER, C.A. 1993. A sauropod megatracksite from the Late Jurassic of Northern Switzerland. *Ichnos*, **2**, 1–10.

MEYER, C.A. & HUNT, A.P. 1998. The first stegosaurian dinosaur (Ornitischia: Thyreophora) form the Late Jurassic of Switzerland. *Neues Jahrbuch der Geologie und Paläontologie, Monatshefte*, **1998**, 141–145.

MEYER, M. 2000. Structure du "diapir" de Champfromier (Jura, Ain, France). *Eclogae geologicae Helvetiae*, **93**, 221–229.

MEYER, M., MEISTER, C. & WERNLI, R. 2000. Stratigraphie du Lias de Champfromier (Ain). *Géologie de la France,* **1**, 47–57.

MEYER, R.K.F. 1981. Malm (Weißer oder Oberer Jura). *In*: HAUNSCHILD, H. & JERZ, H. (eds) *Erläuterungen zur Geologischen Karte von Bayern 1:500 000 (3rd edn).* Bayerisches Geologisches Landesamt, München, 62–68.

MEYER, R.K.F. 1994. "Moosburg 4", die erste Kernbohrung durch den Malm unter der bayerischen Molasse. *Erlanger geologische Abhandlungen,* **123**, 51–81.

MEYER, R.K.F. & SCHMIDT-KALER, H. 1983. *Erdgeschichte sichtbar gemacht: Ein geologischer Führer durch die Altmühlalb.* Bayerisches Geologisches Landesamt, München.

MEYER, R.K.F. & SCHMIDT-KALER, H. 1989. Paläogeographischer Atlas des süddeutschen Oberjura (Malm). *Geologisches Jahrbuch,* **A115**.

MEYER, R.K.F. & SCHMIDT-KALER, H. 1990*a*. Paläogeographie und Schwammriffentwicklung des süddeutschen Malm – ein Überblick. *Facies,* **23**, 175–184.

MEYER, R.K.F. & SCHMIDT-KALER, H. 1990*b*. Treuchtlingen, Solnhofen, Mörnsheim, Dollnstein. *Wanderungen in die Erdgeschichte,* **1**, Pfeil, München.

MEYER, R.K.F. & SCHMIDT-KALER, H. 1996. Jura. *In*: FREUDENBERGER, W. & SCHWERD, K. (eds) *Erläuterungen zur Geologischen Karte von Bayern 1:500.000 (4th edn).* Bayerisches Geologisches Landesamt, München, 90–111.

MIALL, A.D. 1997. *The Geology of Stratigraphic Sequences*. Springer, Berlin.

MIALL, A.D. & MIALL, C.E. 2001. Sequence stratigraphy as a scientific enterprise: the evolution and persistence of conflicting paradigms. *Earth-Science Review,* **54**, 321–348.

MICHALÍK, J. 1980. A paleoenvironmental and paleoecological analysis of the West Carpathian part of the northern Tethyan nearshore region in the latest Triassic time. *Rivista Italiana di Paleontologia e Stratigrafia*, **85**, 1047–1064.

MICHALÍK, J. 1984. Some remarks and interpretation of geological development and structure of the NW part of the Malé Karpaty Mts (Western Carpathians). *Geologicny Zborník, Geologica Carpathica,* **35**(4), 489–504.

MICHALÍK, J. 1990. Paleogeographic changes in the West Carpathian region during Kimmerian tectonic movements. *Acta Geologica et Geographica Universitatis Comeniana, Geologica,* **45**, 43–54.

MICHALÍK, J. 1993. Mesozoic tensional basins in the Alpine-Carpathian shelf. *Acta geologica Hungarica,* **36**(4), 395–403.

MICHALÍK, J. 1994. Notes on the paleogeography and paleotectonics of the Western Carpathian area during the Mesozoic. *Mitteilungen der Österreichischen Geologischen Gesellschaft*, **86**, 101–110.

MICHALÍK, J. & REHÁKOVÁ, D. 1995. Sedimentary records of Early Cretaceous tectonic activity in the Alpine-Carpathian region. *Slovak Geological Magazine*, **2**, 159–164.

MICHALIK, J., LINTNEROVA, O., GAZDZICKI, A. & SOTAK, J. 2007. Record of environmental changes in the Triassic-Jurassic boundary interval in the Zliechov Basin, Western Carpathians. *Palaeogeography, Palaeoclimatology, Palaeoecology*, **244**, 71–88.

MICHELIS, I., SANDER, M., METZDORF, R. & BREITKREUZ, H. 1996. Die Vertebratenfauna des Calloviums (Mittlerer Jura) aus dem Steinbruch Störmer (Wallücke, Wiehengebirge). *Geologie und Paläontologie in Westfalen*, **44**, 1–66.

MICHELSEN, O. 1975. Lower Jurassic biostratigraphy and ostracods of the Danish Embayment. *Danmarks Geologiske Undersøgelse II. Række*, **104**.

MICHELSEN, O. & NIELSEN, L.H. 1991. Well records on the Phanerozoic stratigraphy in the Fennoscandian Border Zone, Denmark. Hans-1, Sæby-1, and Terne-1 wells. *Danmarks Geologiske Undersøgelse, Serie A*, **29**.

MICHELSEN, O. & NIELSEN, L.H. 1993. Structural development of the Fennoscandian Border Zone, offshore Denmark. *Marine and Petroleum Geology*, **10**, 124–134.

MICHELSEN, O., NIELSEN, L.H., JOHANNESSEN, P.N., ANDSBJERG, J. & SURLYK, F. 2003. Jurassic lithostratigraphy and stratigraphic development onshore and offshore Denmark. *In:* INESON, J.R. & SURLYK, F. (eds) *The Jurassic of Denmark and Greenland*. Geological Survey of Denmark and Greenland Bulletin, **1**, 147–216.

MIŠIK, M. 1994. The Czorsztyn submarine ridge (Jurassic-Lower Cretaceous, Pieniny Klippen Belt): an example of a pelagic swell. *Mitteilungen der Österreichischen Geologischen Gesellschaft*, **86**, 133–140.

MIŠIK, M. 1999. Contribution to the lithology and paleogeography of radiolarites in the Western Carpathians. *Mineralogia Slovakiae*, **31**, 491–506.

MISSONI, S., SCHLAGINTWEIT, F., SUZUKI, H. & GAWLICK, H.-J. 2001. Die oberjurassische Karbonatplatformentwicklung im Bereich der Berchtesgadener Kalkalpen (Deutschland) - eine Rekonstruktion auf der Basis von Untersuchungen polymikter Brekzienkörper in pelagischen Kieselsedimenten (Sillenkopf-Formation). *Zentralblatt für Geologie und Paläontologie*, **2000**(1–2), 117–143.

MITIANINA, I.W. 1978. Jurassic system. *In:* GOLUBCOV, W.K. (ed.) *Stratigraphical and Palaeontological Studies in Belarus*. Belarussian Scientific-Geological Institute. Minsk, 142–145 [in Russian].

MOGENSEN, T.E. & KORSTGÅRD, J.A. 2003. Triassic and Jurassic transtension along part of the Sorgenfrei–Tornquist Zone in the Danish Kattegat. *In:* INESON, J.R. & SURLYK, F. (eds) *The Jurassic of Denmark and Greenland*. Geological Survey of Denmark and Greenland Bulletin, **1**, 439–458.

MOJON, P.O. & STRASSER, A. 1987. Microfaciès, sédimentologie et micropaéontologie du Purbeckien de Bienne (Jura suisse occidental). *Eclogae geologicae Helvetiae*, **80**(1), 37–58.

MØLLER, J.J. & RASMUSSEN, E.S. 2003. Middle Jurassic – Early Cretaceous rifting of the Danish Central Graben. *In:* INESON, J.R. & SURLYK, F. (eds) The *Jurassic of Denmark and Greenland*. Geological Survey of Denmark and Greenland Bulletin, **1**, 247–264.

MÖNNIG, E. 1993. Die Ornatenton-Formation in NW-Deutschland. *Newsletters on Stratigraphy*, **28**(2/3), 131–150.

MÖNNIG, E. *et al.* 2002. Jura. *In:* DEUTSCHE STRATIGRAPHISCHE KOMMISSION (ed.) *Stratigraphische Tabelle von Deutschland 2002*. Deutsche Stratigraphische Kommission, Potsdam.

MORANTE, R. & HALLAM, A. 1996. Organic carbon isotopic record across the Triassic-Jurassic boundary in Austria and its bearing on the cause of the mass extinction. *Geology*, **24**, 391–394.

MORARD, A., GUEX, J., BARTOLINI, A., MORETTINI, E. & WEVER, P. 2003. A new scenario for the Domerian-Toarcian transition. *Bulletin de la Société géologique de France*, **174**, 351–356

MORBEY, S.J. 1975. The palynostratigraphy of the Rhaetian stage, Upper Triassic, in the Kendelbachgraben, Austria. *Palaeontographica, Abteilung B*, **152**, 1–75.

MORTON, N. 1974. The definition of standard Jurassic Stages [Paper prepared by "Jurassic Working Group" of Mesozoic Era Subcommittee of the Geological Society of London, Colloque du Jurassique à Luxembourg 1967]. *Mémoires du Bureau de Recherches Géologiques et Miniéres*, **75**, 83–93.

MORTON, N. 2005. Chronostratigraphic units in the Jurassic and their boundaries: definition, recognition and correlation, causal mechanisms. *In:* JINGENG SHA & YONGDONG WANG (eds) *International Symposium on the Jurassic Boundary Events – the First Symposium of the International Geoscience Program IGCP 506, Nanjing 2005, Abstracts*, 60–62.

MORYC, W. 2004. Middle and ?Lower Jurassic deposits in the Księżpol-Lubaczów area (SE Poland). *Biuletyn Państwowego Instytutu Geologicznego*, **408**, 5–72 [in Polish with English summary].

MOYNE, S., THIERRY, J., MARCHAND, D., NICOLLEAU, P., PINEAU, J.P., COURVILLE, P. & SAUCÈDE, T. 2005. Le genre *Nucleolites* (Echinoidea, Cassiduloidea) du Bajocien à l'Oxfordien dans le Bassin de Paris: apport des données architecturales à la systématique et à la phylogénie. *Geobios*, **38**(4), 519–532.

MÜHLBERG, F. 1908. *Erläuterungen zur geologischen Karte der Umgebung von Aargau, 1:25000 (Spez.-Karte 45)*. Sauerländer & Co.

MÜLLER, A. 1987. Structures géologiques et répartition des faciès dans les couches méso- et cénozoïques des confins nord-est du Bassin Parisien. *Bulletin d'Information des Géologues du Bassin de Paris*, mémoirs hors-série, **6**, 87–103.

MÜLLER, G. & BLASCHKE, R. 1969. Zur Entstehung des Posidonienschiefers (Lias). *Naturwissenschaften*, **56**, 635.

MUNK, C. & ZEISS, A. 1985. Neue Untersuchungen zur Stratigraphie des Callovien und Oxfordien in Bayern. *Geologische Blätter für Nordost-Bayern*, **34/35**, 407–447.

NAGRA 2001. Sondierbohrung Benken, Untersuchungsbericht. *Nagra Technische Berichte*. **1(2)**.

NEUBAUER, F. & HÖCK, V. (eds) 2000. *Aspects of Geology in Austria*. Mitteilungen der Österreichischen Geologischen Gesellschaft, **92**.

NEUBAUER, F., GENSER, J. & HANDLER, R. 2000. The Eastern Alps: result of a two-stage collision process. *In:* NEUBAUER, F. & HÖCK, V. (eds) *Aspects of Geology in Austria*. Mitteilungen der Österreichischen Geologischen Gesellschaft, **92**, 117–134.

NIELSEN, L.H. 2003. Late Triassic – Jurassic development of the Danish Basin and the Fennoscandian Border Zone, southern Scandinavia. *In:* INESON, J.R. & SURLYK, F. (eds) *The Jurassic of Denmark and Greenland*. Geological Survey of Denmark and Grenland Bulletin, **1**, 459–526.

NIELSEN, L.H., LARSEN, F. & FRANDSEN, N. 1989. Upper Triassic – Lower Jurassic tidal deposits of the Gassum Formation on Sjælland, Denmark. *Danmarks Geologiske Undersøgelse*, *Serie A*, **23**, 30.

NIEMCZYCKA, T. 1976*a*. Jura górna na obszarze wschodniej Polski (między Wisłą a Bugiem). *Prace Instytutu Geologicznego*, **77**, 1–87.

NIEMCZYCKA, T. 1976*b*. Litostratygrafia osadów jury górnej na obszarze lubelskim. *Acta Geologica Polonica.*, **26**(4), 569–601.

NIEMCZYCKA, T. & BROCHWICZ-LEWIŃSKI, W. 1988. Rozwój górnojurajskiego basenu sedymentacyjnego na niżu Polskim. *Geological Quarterly*, **32**(1), 137–156

NORI, L. & LATHUILIÈRE, B. 2003. Form and environment of *Gryphaea arcuata*. *Lethaia*, **36**, 83–96.

NORLING, E., AHLBERG, A., ERLSTRÖM, M. & SIVHED, U. 1993. Guide to the Upper Triassic and Jurassic geology of Sweden. *Research Papers. SGU Series*, Ca 82, **71**.

NORRIS, M.S. & HALLAM, A. 1995. Facies variations across the Middle-Upper Jurassic boundary in Western Europe and the relationship to sea-level changes. *Palaeogeography, Palaeoclimatology, Palaeoecology*, **116**, 189–245.

OBERHAUSER, R. 1980. *Der Geologische Aufbau Österreichs*. Springer, Vienna.

OBERHAUSER, R. 1995. Zur Kenntnis der Tektonik und der Paleogeographie des Ostalpenraumes zur Kreide-, Paläozän- und Eozänzeit. *Jahrbuch der Geologischen Bundesanstalt*, **138**, 369–432.

OGG, J.G. 2004. The Jurassic Period. *In:* GRADSTEIN F., OGG J.G. & SMITH A. (eds) *A Geologic Time Scale*. Cambridge University Press, Cambridge, 307–343.

OHMERT, W. 2004. Neue Ammonitenfunde aus der Hauptrogenstein-Formation (Mitteljura) des Breisgaus (Oberrhein). *Jahresberichte und Mitteilungen des oberrheinischen geologischen Vereins, Neue Folge*, **86**, 337–350.

OLIVIER, N., CARPENTIER, C., *et al.* 2004. Coral-microbialite reefs in pure carbonate versus mixed carbonate-siliciclastic depositional environments: the example of the Pagny-sur-Meuse section (Upper Jurassic, Northeastern France). *Facies,* **50**, 229–255.

OLSEN, P.E., KENT, D.V., *et al.* 2002. Ascent of dinosaurs linked to an iridium anomaly at the Triassic-Jurassic boundary. *Science*, **296,** 1305–1307.

OLSZEWSKA, B. & WIECZOREK, J. 2001. Jurassic sediments and microfossils of the Andrychów Klippes (Outer Western Carpathians). *Geologica Carpathica*, **52**, 217–228.

OPPEL, A. 1856–58. *Die Juraformation Englands, Frankreichs und des südwestlichen Deutschlands.* Ebner & Seubert, Stuttgart.

OPPENHEIMER, J. 1907. Der Malm der Schwedenschanze bei Brünn. *Beiträge zur Paläontologie und Geologie des Österreichisch-Ungarischen Orients*, **20**, 221–271.

OPPENHEIMER, J. 1926. Der Malm der Stránská skála bei Brünn. *Acta Museae Moraviae, Scientia naturalis*, **24**, 1–31.

OPPENHEIMER, J. 1930. Analogien der oberdevonische und oberjurasische Transgresionen am Ostrande der böhmischen Masse. *Verhandlungen des Naturforschenden Vereines Brünn*, **62**, 1–3.

OPPENHEIMER, J. 1934. Beiträge zur Paläographie Mährens. *Verhandlungen des Naturforschenden Vereines Brünn*, **64**(1932), 1–14.

ORBELL, G. 1973. Palynology of the British Rhaeto-Liassic. *Bulletin of the Geological Survey of Great Britain*, **44**, 1–44.

OSCHMANN, W. 1988. Upper Kimmeridgian and Portlandian marine macrobenthic associations from Southern England and Northern France. *Facies,* **8**, 49–82.

OTT, W. F. 1969. *Zur Geologie des Sulzfluhkalkes (Malm) in Graubünden und Vorarlberg*. PhD thesis, Technische Hochschule Darmstadt.

PAGE, K.N. 2004. Jurassic. *In:* SELLEY, R.C., COCKS, L.R.M. & PLIMER, J.R. (eds) *Encyclopedia of Geology,* ***3***. Elsevier, Amsterdam, 352–360.

PÁLFY, J. 2003. Volcanism of the Central Atlantic Magmatic Province as a potential driving force in the end-Triassic mass extinction. *In:* HAMES, W.E., MCHONE, J.G., RENNE, P.R. & RUPPEL, C. (eds) *The Central Atlantic Magmatic Province: Insights from Fragments of Pangea.* American Geophysical Union, Geophysical Monograph Series, **136**, 255–267.

PÁLFY, J. & DOSZTÁLY, L. 2000. A new marine Triassic-Jurassic boundary section in Hungary: preliminary results. *In:* HALL, R.L. & SMITH, P.L. (eds) *Advances in Jurassic Research 2000.* Geo Research Forum, **6**, 173–179.

PÁLFY, J., MORTENSEN, J.K., CARTER, E.S., SMITH, P.L., FRIEDMAN, R.M. & TIPPER, H.W. 2000. Timing the end-Triassic mass extinction: First on land, then in the sea? *Geology*, **28**, 39–42.

PÁLFY, J., DEMÉNY, A., HAAS, J., HETÉNYI, M., ORCHARD, M. & VETÖ, I. 2001. Carbon isotope anomaly and other geochemical changes at the Triassic–Jurassic boundary from a marine section in Hungary. *Geology*, **29**, 1047–1050.

PÁLFY, J., DEMÉNY, A., *et al.* 2007. Triassic-Jurassic boundary events inferred from integrated stratigraphy of the Csővar section, Hungary. *Palaeogeography, Palaeoclimatology, Palaeoecology,* **244**, 11–33.

PANOŠ, V. 1964. Der Urkarst im Ostflügel der Böhmischen Masse. *Zeitschrift für Geomorphologie., Neue Folge*, **8**(2), 105–162.

PARTINGTON, M.A., COPESTAKE, P., MITCHENER, B.C. & UNDERHILL, J.R. 1993. Biostratigraphic calibration of generic stratigraphic sequences in the Jurassic-lowermost Cretaceous (Hettangian to Ryazanian) of the North Sea and adjacent areas. *In:* PARKER, J.R. (ed.) *Petroleum Geology of Northwest Europe*. Graham & Trotman, London, 371–386.

PAULSEN, S. 1964. Aufbau und Petrographie des Riffkomplexes von Arnegg im höheren Weißen Jura der Schwäbischen Alb (Württemberg). *Arbeiten aus dem Geologisch-Paläontologischen Institut der Technischen Hochschule Stuttgart, Neue Folge,* **42**, 1–98.

PAWELLEK, T. 2001. Fazies-, Sequenz-, und Gamma-Ray-Analyse im höheren Malm der Schwäbischen Alb (SW-Deutschland) mit Bemerkungen zur Rohstoffgeologie (Hochreine Kalke). *Tübinger geowissenschaftliche Arbeiten, Reihe A,* **61**.

PAWELLEK, T. & AIGNER, T. 2003. Stratigraphic architecture and gamma ray logs of deeper ramp carbonates (Upper Jurassic, SW Germany). *Sedimentary Geology,* **159**, 203–240.

PEDERSEN, G.K. 1985. Thin, fine-grained storm layers in a muddy shelf sequence: an example from the Lower Jurassic in the Stenlille 1 well, Denmark. *Journal of the Geological Society of London,* **142**, 357–374.

PEDERSEN, G.K. 1986. Changes in the bivalve assemblage of an Early Jurassic mudstone sequence (the Fjerritslev Formation in the Gassum 1 well, Denmark). *Palaeogeography, Palaeoclimatology, Palaeoecology,* **53**, 139–168.

PELLENARD, P., DECONINCK, J.F., MARCHAND, D., THIERRY, J., FORTWENGLER, D. & VIGNERON, G. 1999. Contrôle géodynamique de la sédimentation argileuse du Callovien - Oxfordien moyen dans l'Est du Bassin de Paris : influence eustatique et volcanique. *Comptes rendus de l'Académie des Sciences Paris,* **328**, 807–813.

PELLENARD, P., DECONINCK, J.-F., HUFF, W. D., THIERRY, J., MARCHAND, D., FORTWENGLER, D. & TROUILLER, A. 2003. Characterization and correlation of Upper Jurassic (Oxfordian) bentonite deposits in the Paris Basin and the subalpine basin, France. *Sedimentology,* **50**, 1035–1060.

PESCATORE, T. & ŚLĄCZKA, A. 1984. Evolution models of two flysch basins: the Northern Carpathians and the Southern Appenines. *Tectonophysics*, **106**, 49–70.

PETERSEN, H.I. & ANDSBJERG, J. 1996. Organic facies development within Middle Jurassic coal seams, Danish Central Graben, and evidence for relative sea-level control on peat accumulation in a coastal plain environment. *Sedimentary Geology,* **106**, 259–277.

PETERSEN, H.I. & NIELSEN, L.H. 1995. Controls on peat accumulation and depositional environments of a coal-bearing coastal plain succession of a pull-apart basin; a petrographic, geochemical and sedimentological study, Lower Jurassic, Denmark. *International Journal of Coal Geology,* **27**, 99–129.

PETZKA, M. & RUSBÜLT, J. 2004. Jura. *In:* KATZUNG, G. (ed.) *Geologie von Mecklenburg-Vorpommern.* Schweizerbart, Stuttgart.

PICARD, S. 2001. *Evolution des eaux ouest téthysiennes (température, bathymétrie) au cours du Jurassique moyen à supérieur à partir des enregistrements géochimiques (delta18O, delta13C, Terres rares) de faunes marines*. PhD thesis, Université Lyon 1.

PICARD, S. GARCIA, J.P., LECUYER, C., SHEPPARD, S.M.F., CAPPETTA, H. & EMIG, C. 1998. Delta18O values of coexisting brachiopods and fish: temperature differences and estimates of paleo-water depths. *Geology,* **26**(11), 975–978.

PICARD, S., LECUYER, C., BARRAT, J.-A., GARCIA, J. P., DROMART, G. & SHEPPARD, S.M.F. 2002. Rare earth element contents of Jurassic fish and reptile teeth and their potential relation to seawater composition (Anglo-Paris Basin, France and England). *Chemical Geology,* **186**, 1–16.

PICHA, F., STRÁNIK, Z. & KREJČI, O. 2006. Geology and hydrocarbon resources of the Outer Western Carpathians and their foreland, Czech Republic. *In:* GOLONKA, J. & PICHA, F. (eds) *The Carpathians and their Foreland: Geology and Hydrocarbon Resources.* American Association of Petroleum Geologists, Memoirs, **84,** 49–173.

PIEŃKOWSKI, G. 1985. Early Liassic trace fossil assemblages from the Holy Cross Mountains, Poland: their distribution in continental and marginal marine environments. *In:* ALLEN CURRAN. H. (ed.) *Biogenic Structures: Their Use in Interpreting Depositional Environments.* Society of Economic Paleontologists and Mineralogists, Special Publications, **35**, 37–51.

PIEŃKOWSKI, G. 1991*a*. Eustatically-controlled sedimentation in the Hettangian-Sinemurian (Early Jurassic) of Poland and Sweden. *Sedimentology*, **38**, 503–518.

PIEŃKOWSKI, G. 1991*b*. Liassic Sedimentation in Scania, Southern Sweden: Hettangian-Sinemurian of the Helsingborg Area. *Facies*, **24**, 39–86.

PIEŃKOWSKI, G. 2004. *The epicontinental Lower Jurassic of Poland.* Polish Geological Institute, Special Papers, **12**.

PIEŃKOWSKI, G. & WAKSMUNDZKA, M. 2002. *Spektra palinologiczne środowisk sedymentacyjnych dolnej jury w Polsce*. Polish Geological Institute.

PIEŃKOWSKI, G. & WAKSMUNDZKA, M. 2005. Rhaetian/Hettangian boundary in Pomerania, Poland. *In:* JINGENG SHA & YONGDONG WANG (eds) *International Symposium on the Jurassic Boundary Events – the First Symposium of the International Geoscience Program IGCP 506, Nanjing 2005, Abstracts*, 72.

PILLER, W.E. 1981. The Steinplatte Reef complex, part of an Upper Triassic carbonate platform near Salzburg, Austria. *In:* TOOMEY, D.F. (ed.) *European Fossil Reef Models.* Society of Economic Paleontologists and Mineralogists, Special Publications, **30**, 261–290.

PILLER, W.E., DAXNER-HÖCK, G., *et al.* 2000. Palaeontological highlights in Austria. *Mitteilungen der Österreichischen Geologischen Gesellschaft*, **92**, 195–234.

PILLER, W.E., EGGER, H., *et al.* 2004. *Die Stratigraphische Tabelle von Österreich 2004 (sedimentäre Schichtfolgen).* Österreichische stratigraphische Kommission und Kommission für die paläontologische und stratigraphische Erforschung Österreichs. Österreichische Akademie der Wissenschaften.

PITTET, B. 1996. *Contrôles climatiques, eustatiques et tectoniques sur des systèmes mixtes carbonates-siliciclastiques de plate-forme: exemples de l'Oxfordien (Jura suisse, Normandie, Espagne).* PhD thesis, Université de Fribourg.

PITTET, B. & MATTIOLI, E. 2002. The carbonate signal and calcareous nannofossil distribution in an Upper Jurassic section (Balingen-Tieringen, Late Oxfordian, southern Germany). *Palaeogeography, Palaeoclimatology, Palaeoecology,* **179**, 71–96.

PITTET, B. & STRASSER, A. 1998. Depositional sequences in deep-shelf environments formed through carbonate-mud export from the shallow platform (Late Oxfordian, German Swabian Alb and eastern Swiss Jura. *Eclogae geologicae Helvetiae,* **91**, 149–169.

PITTET, B., STRASSER, A. & MATTIOLI, E. 2000. Depositional sequences in deep-shelf environments: a response to sea-level changes and shallow-platform carbonate productivity (Oxfordian, Germany and Spain). *Journal of Sedimentary Research,* **70**, 392–407.

PLAŠIENKA, D. 1987. Lithologic, sedimentologic and paleotectonic character of the Borinka Unit in the Malé Karpaty Mts. *Mineralia Slovakia*, **19**(3), 217–230 [in Slovak].

PLAŠIENKA, D. 1999. *Tektonochronológia a paleotektonický model jursko-kriedového vývoja centralnych Západných Karpat.* Veda, Bratislava.

PLAŠIENKA, D., MICHALÍK, J., KOVÁČ, M., GROSS, P. & PUTIŠ, M. 1991. Paleotectonic evolution of the Malé Karpaty Mts: an overview. *Geologica Carpathica*, **42**(4), 195–208.

PLAŠIENKA, D., GRECULA, P., PUTIŠ, M., HOVORKA, D. & KOVÁČ, M. 1997. Evolution and structure of the Western Carpathians: an overview. *In:* GRECULA, P., HOVORKA, D. & PUTIŠ, M. (eds) *Geological Evolution of the Western Carpathians.* Geocomplex Bratislava, 1–24.

PLUNKETT, J.M. 1997. *Early diagenesis of shallow platform carbonates in the Oxfordian of the Swiss Jura Mountains.* PhD thesis, Université de Fribourg.

POČTA, PH. 1890. Über den Inhalt eines Quareqno ollens von Ruditz. *Věstník Královské České Společnosti nauk Tř. math.-přírodověd,* **1.**

PODLAHA, O.G., MUTTERLOSE, J., & VEIZER, J. 1998. Preservation of $\delta^{18}O$ and $\delta^{13}C$ in belemnite rostra from the Jurassic/early Cretaceous successions. *American Journal of Science*, **298**, 324–347.

POIROT, E. 1987. *Le Terrain à chailles (Oxfordien inférieur et moyen) du Toulois (Lorraine).* Diplôme d' études supérieures, Université de Nancy.

POIROT, E. 1992. *Le Bajocien (pars) et le Bathonien de Lorraine centrale Biostratigraphie, Paléontologie.* Diplome de recherches doctorales, Université de Nancy.

POMEROL, C. 1989. Naissance et développement de la géologie du bassin parisien au cours des XVIIIe et XIX siècles. *Bulletin d'Information des Géologues du Bassin de Paris*, **26**(2), 9–20.

PONSOT, C. 1994. Sequence stratigraphy of the Jurassic series of the Paris-London Basin. *In:* MASCLE, A. (ed.) *Hydrocarbon and Petroleum Geology of France.* European Association of Petroleum Geoscientists, Special Publications, **4**, 77–105.

POPRAWA, P. 1997. Late Permian to Tertiary dynamics of the Polish Trough. Trans-European Suture Zone, Europrobe TESZ-Meeting, *Terra Nostra*, **97**(11), 104–109.

POPRAWA, P., MALATA, T. & OSZCZYPKO, N. 2002. Ewolucja tektoniczna basenów sedymentacyjnych polskiej części Karpat zewnętrznych w świetle analizy subsydencji. *Przegląd Geologiczny*, **50**, 1092–1108.

POSAMENTIER, H.W. & JAMES, D.P. 1993. An overview of sequence-stratigraphic concepts: uses and abuses. *In:* POSAMENTIER, H.W. *et al.* (eds) *Sequence Stratigraphy and Facies Associations.* International Association of Sedimentologists, Special Publications, **18**, 3–18.

POULSEN, N.E. 1998. Bajocian to Callovian (Jurassic) dinoflagellate cysts from central Poland. *Acta Geologica Polonica,* **48**, 237–245.

POŻARYSKI, W. & BROCHWICZ-LEWIŃSKI, W. 1978. On the Polish Trough. *Geologie en Mijnbouw,* **57**(4), 545–557.

PRATJE, O. 1922. Lias und Rhät im Breisgau (Erster Teil). *Mitteilungen der Großherzoglichen Badischen Geologischen Landesanstalt*, **9**, 277–352.

PRÉAT, A., MAMET, B., DE RIDDER, C., BOULVAIN, F. & GILLAN, D. 2000. Iron bacterial and fungal mats, Bajocian stratotype (Mid-Jurassic, northern Normandy, France). *Sedimentary Geology,* **137**, 107–126.

PRICE, G.D. 1999. The evidence and implications of polar ice during the Mesozoic. *Earth-Science Reviews*, **48**, 183–210.

PRICE, G.D. & MUTTERLOSE, J. 2004. Isotopic signals from late Jurassic–early Cretaceous (Volgian–Valanginian) sub-Arctic belemnites, Yatria River, Western Siberia. *Journal of the Geological Society of London,* **161**, 959–968.

PŘICHYSTAL, A., LOSOS, Z. & RICHTEROVÁ, D. 1999. Genesis of Jurassic silica geodes in Moravia. *Berichte der Deutschen Mineralogischen Gesellschaft, Beiheifte European Journal of Mineralogy,* **11**, 183.

QUENSTEDT, F.A. 1843. *Das Flözgebirge Württembergs. Mit besonderer Rücksicht auf den Jura.* Laupp, Tübingen.

QUENSTEDT, F.A. 1856–1858. *Der Jura.* Laupp, Tübingen.

QUENSTEDT, F.A. 1883–88. *Die Ammoniten des Schwäbischen Jura. Bd. I-III.* Schweizerbart, Stuttgart.

QUENSTEDT, W. 1951. Geologische Exkursion in das Achental-Gebiet (Tirol). *Geologica Bavarica*, **6**, 55–64.

RAJA-GABAGLIA, A. 1995. *Stratigraphie et faciès de tempête de la rampe carbonatée du Jurassique supérieur du bassin du Sud-Est (France): calcarénites, brèches, corps glissés.* PhD Thesis, Université Montpellier II.

RASSER, M. W. & FENNINGER, A. 2002. Biostratigraphy of Dasycladales in the Northern Calcareous Alps: a critical review and comparisons with other occurrences using similarity indices. *In:* BUCUR, I.I. & FILIPESCU, S. (eds) *Research Advances in Calcareous Algae and Microbial Carbonates.* Cluj University Press, Cluj-Napoca, 167–190.

RASSER, M.W., VASICEK, Z., SKUPIEN, P., LOBITZER, H. & BOOROVA, D. 2003. Die Schrambach-Formation an ihrer Typuslokalität (Unter-Kreide, Nördliche Kalkalpen, Salzburg): Lithostratigraphische Formalisierung und "historische" Irrtümer. *In:* PILLER, W. E. (ed.) *Stratigrafia Austriaca.* Österreichische Akademie der Wissenschaften Erdwissenschaftliche Kommission, **16**, 193–216.

RAT, P. 1987. La Bourgogne, structure positive post-hercynienne. *Bulletin d'Information des Géologues du Bassin de Paris, mémoirs hors-série,* **6**, 143–165.

RATSCHBACHER, L. 1986. Kinematics of Austro-Alpine cover nappes: changing translation path due to transpression. *Tectonophysics*, **125**, 335–356.

RATSCHBACHER, L., FRISCH, W., NEUBAUER, F., SCHMID, S.M. & NEUGEBAUER, J. 1989. Extension in compressional orogenic belts: the eastern Alps. *Geology,* **17**, 404–407.

RAUSCHER, R. & SCHMITT, J.-P. 1990. Recherches palynologiques dans le Jurassique d'Alsace (France). *Review of Palaeobotany and Palynology,* **62**, 107–156.

RAUSCHER, R., HILLY, J., HANZO, M. & MARCHAL, C. 1995. Palynologie des couches de passage du Trias supérieur au Lias dans l'Est du bassin parisien. Problèmes de datation du « Rhétien » de Lorraine. *Sciences géologiques Bulletin,* **48**(1–3), 159–185.

REICHERTER, K., FROITZHEIM, N., *et al.* 2008. Alpine tectonics north of the Alps. *In*: MCCANN, T. (ed.) *The Geology of Central Europe.* Geological Society, London, 000–000.

REIFF, W. 1958. Beiträge zur Geologie des Albuchs und der Heidenheimer Alb. *Arbeiten aus dem Geologisch-Paläontologischen Institut der Technischen Hochschule Stuttgart, Neue Folge*, **17**, 1–142.

REIFF, W. 1988. Die Korallenvorkommen von Gerstetten. Fazielle und stratigraphische Zuordnung im Oberen Weißen Jura der östlichen Schwäbischen Alb. *Jahreshefte des Geologischen Landesamtes Baden-Württemberg,* **30**, 357–371.

REISDORF, A.G., MAISCH, M.W., SCHLATTER, R. & WETZEL, A. 2008. A huge Sinemurian *Ichthyosaurus* skull and its lithostratigraphic framework in northern Switzerland. *Eclogae geologicae Helvetiae (in press.)*

REITZ, E., HÖLL, R., HUPAK, W. & MEHLTRETTER, C. 1990. Palynologischer Nachweis von Unterkreide in der Jüngeren (Oberen) Schieferhülle des Tauernfensters (Ostalpen). *Jahrbuch der Geologischen Bundesanstalt*, **133**(4), 611–618.

REYMANÓWNA, M. 1991. Two conifers from the Liassic of Odrowąż in Poland. *In:* KOVAR-EDER, J. (ed.) *Palaeoenvironmental Development in Europe and Regions Relevant to its Palaeofloristic Evolution*. Proceedings Pan-European Palaeobotanical Conference, Vienna, Naturhistorisches Museum Wien, 307–310.

RICOU, L.-E. 1996. The plate tectonic history of the past Tethys Ocean. *In:* NAIRN, A.E.M., RICOU, L.-E., VRIELYNCK, B. & DERCOURT, J. (eds) *The Ocean Basins and Margin, 8, The Tethys Ocean*. Plenum Press, New York/London, 3–70.

RIEGRAF, W. 1985. *Mikrofauna, Biostratigraphie und Fazies im Unteren Toarcium Südwestdeutschlands und Vergleiche mit benachbarten Gebieten*. Tübinger Mikropaläontologische Mitteilungen, **3**.

RIEGRAF, W. 1986. Callovian (Middle Jurassic) radiolaria and sponge spicules from Southwest Germany. *Stuttgarter Beiträge zur Naturkunde, Serie B*, **123**, 1–31.

RIEGRAF, W. 1987*a*. Planktonic foraminifera (Globuligerinidae) from the Callovian (Middle Jurassic) of Southwest Germany. *Journal of Foraminiferal Research*, **17**, 190–211.

RIEGRAF, W. 1987*b*. Planktonische Foraminiferen und Radiolarien im Callovium und Oxfordium (Jura) Süddeutschlands. *Neues Jahrbuch für Geologie und Paläontologie, Abhandlungen*, **176**, 91–103.

RIEGRAF, W., WERNER, G. & LÖRCHER, F. 1984. *Der Posidonienschiefer. Biostratigraphie, Fauna und Fazies des südwestdeutschen Untertoarciums (Lias epsilon)*. Enke, Stuttgart.

RIOULT, M., DUGUE, O., JAN DU CHENE, R., PONSOT, C., FILY, G., MORON, J.-M. & VAIL, P.R. 1991. Outcrop sequence stratigraphy of the anglo-Paris basin, Middle to Upper Jurassic (Normandy, Maine, Dorset). *Bulletin des Centres de Recherche Exploration-Production Elf Aquitaine*, **15**(1), 101–194.

ROBIN, C. 1997. *Mesure stratigraphique de la déformation. Application à l'évolution jurassique du bassin de Paris*. Mémoires Géosciences Rennes, **77**.

ROEMER, C.F. 1857. Die Jurassische Weserkette. *Zeitschrift der Deutschen Geologischen Gesellschaft*, **9**, 581–728.

ROEMER, F.A. 1836/39. *Die Versteinerungen des norddeutschen Oolithengebirges*. Hannover.

ROEMER, J. 1911. *Die Fauna der Aspidoides-Schichten von Lechstedt bei Hildesheim*. PhD thesis, Universität Göttingen.

ROGALSKA, M. 1976. *Stratygrafia jury dolnej i środkowej na obszarze Niżu Polskiego na podstawie badań sporowo-pyłkowych*. Prace Instytutu Geologicznego, **78.**

RÖHL, H.-J., SCHMID-RÖHL, A., OSCHMANN, W., FRIMMEL, A. & SCHWARK, L. 2001. The Posidonia Shale (Lower Toarcian) of SW-Germany: an oxygen-depleted ecosystem controlled by sea level and palaeoclimate. *Palaeogeography, Palaeoclimatology, Palaeoecology*, **165**, 27–52.

ROLL, A. 1931. Die Stratigraphie des Oberen Malm im Lauchertgebiet (Schwäbische Alb) als Unterlage für tektonische Untersuchungen. *Abhandlungen der Preußischen geologischen Landesanstalt, Neue Folge*, **135**, 1–164.

ROSALES, I., QUESADA S. & ROBLES S. 2004. Paleotemperature variations of Early Jurassic seawater recorded in geochemical trends of belemnites from the Basque-Cantabrian basin, northern Spain. *Palaeogeography, Palaeoclimatology, Palaeoecology*, **203**, 253–275.

ROSENDAHL, W., JUNKER, B., MEGERLE, A. & VOGT, J. 2006. *Schwäbische Alb*. Wanderungen in die Erdgeschichte, **18**, Pfeil, Müchen.

RUF, M., LINK, E., PROSS, J. & AIGNER, T. 2005. A multi-proxy study of deeper-water carbonates (Upper Jurassic, southern Germany): combining sedimentology, chemostratigraphy and palynofacies. *Facies*, **51**, 326–349.

RUFFELL, A.H. & RAWSON, P.F. 1994. Palaeoclimate control on sequence stratigraphic patterns in the late Jurassic to mid-Cretaceous, with a case study from Eastern England. *Palaeogeography, Palaeoclimatology, Palaeoecology*, **110**, 43–54.

RUGET, C. & HANZO, M. 1992. Les foraminifères et la sédimentation du Lias inférieur et moyen des forages de Cattenom (Lorraine, France): première approche. *Cahiers Université catholique Lyon, série des Sciences* , **5**, 81–91.

RYLL, A. 1983. Stratygrafia i paleogeografia. Jura środkowa. *In: Budowa geologiczna niecki warszawskiej (płockiej) i jej podłoża*. Prace Instytutu Geologicznego, **103**, 138–148 [in Polish].

SĂNDULESCU, M. & VISARION M. 2000. Crustal structure and evolution of the Carpathian-Western Black Sea area. *Romanian Geophysics*, **7**, 228–231.

SCHALCH, F. 1919. A. Geologisch-stratigraphischer Teil. *In:* SCHALCH, F. & PEYER, B. Über ein neues Rhätvorkommen im Keuper des Donau-Rheinzuges. *Mitteilungen der Badischen geologischen Landesanstalt*, **8**, 263–298.

SCHECK, M., BAYER, U., OTTO, V., LAMARCHE, J., BANKA, D. & PHARAOH, T. 2002. The Elbe Fault System in North Central Europe – a basement controlled zone of crustal weakness. *Tectonophysics*, **360**, 281–290.

SCHECK-WENDEROTH, M., KRZYWIEC, P., ZÜHLKE, R., MAYSTRENKO, Y. & FROITZHEIM, N. 2008. Permian to Cretaceous tectonics. *In*: MCCANN, T. (ed.) *The Geology of Central Europe*. Geological Society, London, 000–000.

SCHEGG, R., LEU, W., CORNFORD, C. & ALLEN, P. 1997. New coalification profiles in the molasse basin of western Switzerland: implication for the thermal ans geodynamic ecolution of the Alpine foreland. *Eclogae geologicae Helvetiae*, **90**, 79–96.

SCHERZINGER, A. & SCHWEIGERT, G. 2003. Ein Profil in der Usseltal- und Rennertshofen-Formation der südlichen Frankenalb (Unter-Tithonium). *Zitteliana, Reihe A*, **43**, 3–16.

SCHICK, H. 2004*a*. Gliederung und Typusprofil der Lacunosamergel-Formation (Ober-Jura, Schwäbische Alb). *Stuttgarter Beiträge zur Naturkunde, Serie B*, **346**, 1–25.

SCHICK, H. 2004*b*. Bio- and lithostratigraphic studies on the Lower Kimmeridgian of the Swabian and Franconian Alb. *Rivista Italiana di Paleontologia e Stratigrafia*, **110**, 279–288.

SCHICK, H. 2004*c*. The stratigraphical significance of *Cymaceras guembeli* for the boundary between Platynota Zone and Hypselocyclum Zone, and the correlation between Swabian and Franconian Alb. *Zitteliana, Reihe B*, **44**, 51–59.

SCHLAGER, W. 1981. The paradox of drowned reefs and carbonate platforms. *Geological Society of America Bulletin*, **92**, 197–211.

SCHLAGER, W. & SCHLAGER, M. 1973. Clastic sediments associated with radiolarites (Tauglbodenschichten, Upper Jurassic, Eastern Alps). *Sedimentology*, **20**, 65–89.

SCHLAGER, W. & SCHÖLLNBERGER, W. 1974. Das Prinzip der stratigraphischen Wenden in der Schichtfolge der Nördlichen Kalkalpen. *Mitteilungen der Geologischen Gesellschaft Wien*, **66/67**, 165–194.

SCHLAGINTWEIT, F. & EBLI, O. 1999. New Results on microfacies, biostratigraphy and sedimentology of Late Jurassic – Early Cretaceous platform carbonates of the Northern Calcareous Alps. *Abhandlungen der Geologischen Bundesanstalt*, **56**(2), 379–418.

SCHLAGINTWEIT, F., GAWLICK, H.-J. & LEIN, R. 2003. Die Plassen-Formation der Typlokalität (Salzkammergut, Österreich) - neue Daten zu Fazies, Sedimentologie und Stratigraphie. *Mitteilungen der Gesellschaft für Geologie- und Bergbaustudenten*, **46**, 1–34.

SCHLATTER, R. 1976. Die Stufe des Lotharingium im unteren Lias des Klettgau (Kanton Schaffhausen, Schweiz). *Stuttgarter Beiträge zur Naturkunde, Serie B*, **121**, 1–21.

SCHLATTER, R. 1977. The biostratigraphy of the Lower Pliensbachian at the type locality (Pliensbach, Württemberg, SW-Germany). *Stuttgarter Beiträge zur Naturkunde, Serie B*, **27**, 1–29.

SCHLATTER, R. 1980. Biostratigraphie und Ammonitenfauna des Unter-Pliensbachium im Typusgebiet (Pliensbach, Holzmaden und Nürtingen; Württemberg, SW-Deutschland). *Stuttgarter Beiträge zur Naturkunde, Serie B*, **65**, 1–261.

SCHLATTER, R. 1982. Zur Grenze Pliensbachian-Toarcian im Klettgau (Kanton Schaffhausen, Schweiz). *Eclogae geologicae Helvetiae*, **75**, 759–771.

SCHLATTER, R. 1989. Ein geologischer Querschnitt durch den Randen von Schleitheim, nach Schaffhausen bis Thayngen (Exkursion H am 30. März 1989). *Jahresberichte und Mitteilungen des oberrheinischen geologischen Vereins, Neue Folge*, **71**, 149–165.

SCHLATTER, R. 1991. Biostratigraphie und Ammonitenfauna des Ober-Lotharingium und Unter-Pliensbachium im Klettgau (Kanton Schaffhausen, Schweiz) und angrenzender Gebiete. *Schweizerische Paläontologische Abhandlungen*, **113,** 1–133.

SCHLATTER, R. 1999. Erstnachweis der *denotatus*-Subzone (Unter-Lotharingium) im Klettgau (Kanton Schaffhausen, Schweiz). *Profil*, **16,** 121–124.

SCHLATTER, R. 2000. Erstnachweis der *taylori*-Subzone (Lias, Unter-Pliensbachium) im Wutachgebiet (Baden-Württemberg). *Jahrbuch der Gesellschaft für Naturkunde Württemberg*, **156**, 67–72.

SCHLATTER, R. 2001. Erstnachweis der Unterfamilie Arietitinae HYATT (Ammonoidea) aus der "Oolithenbank" (Hettangium, Angulata-Zone) Südwestdeutschlands. *Stuttgarter Beiträge zur Naturkunde, Serie B*, **303**, 1–5.

SCHMALZRIEDT, A. 1991. Die Mikrofauna in Schwämmen, Schwammriff- und "Normal"-Fazies des unteren und mittleren Malm (Oxfordium und Kimmeridgium, Ober-Jura) der westlichen und mittleren Schwäbischen Alb (Württemberg). *Tübinger mikropaläontologische Mitteilungen*, **10**, 1–120.

SCHMASSMANN, H. 1945. *Stratigraphie des mittleren Doggers der Nordwestschweiz*. PhD thesis, Universität Basel.

SCHMID, D.U. 1996. Marine Mikrobolithe und Mikroinkrustierer aus dem Oberjura. *Profil*, **9**, 101–251.

SCHMID, D.U., LEINFELDER, R.R. & NOSE, M. 2001. Growth dynamics and ecology of Upper Jurassic mounds, with comparisons to Mid-Palaeozoic mounds. *In*: HAYWICK, D.W. & KOPASKA-MERKEL, D.C. (eds) Carbonate mounds: sedimentation, organismal response, and diagenesis. *Sedimentary Geology*, **145**, 343–376.

SCHMID-RÖHL, A., RÖHL, H.-J., OSCHMANN, W., FRIMMEL, A. & SCHWARK, L. 2002. Palaeoenvironmental reconstruction of Lower Toarcian epicontinental black shales (Posidonia Shale, SW Germany): global versus regional control. *Geobios*, **35**, 13–20.

SCHMIDT-KALER, H., TISCHLINGER, H. & WERNER, W. 1992. *Sulzkirchen und Sengenthal - zwei berühmte Fossilfundstellen am Rande der Frankenalb*. Wanderungen in die Erdgeschichte, **4**, Pfeil, München.

SCHMITT, J.-P. 1987. *Les microflores du Jurassique intérets stratigraphiques, paléogéographiques et paléoclimatiques. Etude palynologique du Jurassique en Alsace*. Thesis, University of Strasbourg.

SCHNEIDER, J. 1962. *Der Jura in Erdölbohrungen des westlichen Molassetroges*. Hermann-Aldinger-Festschrift, Schweizerbart, Stuttgart.

SCHNYDER, J. 2003. *Le passage Jurassique-Crétacé: événements instantanés, variations climatiques enregistrées dans les faciès purbeckiens français (Boulonnais, Charentes) et anglais (Dorset). Comparaison avec le domaine téthysien*. PhD thesis, Université Lille.

SCHRAMMEN, A. 1924. Zur Revision der Jura-Spongien von Süddeutschland. *Jahresberichte und Mitteilungen des oberrheinischen geologischen Vereines, Neue Folge*, **13**, 125–154.

SCHUDACK, M. 1999. Ostracoda (marine/nonmarine) and paleoclimate history in the late Jurassic of Central Europe and North America. *Marine Micropaleontology*, **37**, 273–288.

SCHUDACK, M. 2002. Late Jurassic ostracod biogeography, shell chemistry, and palaeoclimate in Europe and North America. *Abstracts 6th International Symposium on the Jurassic System, Palermo*.

SCHULZ, E. 1967. Sporenpaläontologische Untersuchungen Rhätoliassichen Schichten im Zentralteil des Germanischen Beckens. *Paläontologische Abhandlungen, Abteilung B*, **2**, 427–633.

SCHÜTZ, S. & HÜSSNER, H. 1997. Sedimentäre Rhythmen im Oberjura der Nördlichen Kalkalpen. *Geologische Blätter für Nordost-Bayern und angrenzende Gebiete*, **47**, 273–288.

SCHWEIGERT, G. 1993. Die Ammonitengattungen *Gravesia* Salfeld und *Tolvericeras* Hantzpergue und ihre Bedeutung für den Grenzbereich Oberkimmeridgium/Untertithonium im Schwäbischen Jura. *Geologische Blätter für Nordost-Bayern*, **43**, 167–186.

SCHWEIGERT, G. 1995. Neues zur Stratigraphie des schwäbischen Oberjura. *Laichinger Höhlenfreund*, **30**, 49–60.

SCHWEIGERT, G. 1996. Die Hangende Bankkalk-Formation im schwäbischen Oberjura. *Jahresberichte und Mitteilungen des oberrheinischen geologischen Vereines, Neue Folge*, **78**, 281–308.

SCHWEIGERT, G. 1998. Die Ammonitenfauna des Nusplinger Plattenkalks (Ober-Kimmeridgium, Beckeri-Zone, Ulmense-Subzone, Baden-Württemberg). *Stuttgarter Beiträge zur Naturkunde, Serie B*, **267**, 1–61.

SCHWEIGERT, G. 2000. New biostratigraphic data from the Kimmeridgian/Tithonian boundary beds of SW Germany. *GeoResearch Forum*, **6**, 195–202.

SCHWEIGERT, G. & CALLOMON, J.H. 1997. Der *bauhini*-Faunenhorizont und seine Bedeutung für die Korrelation zwischen tethyalem und subborealem Oberjura. *Stuttgarter Beiträge zur Naturkunde, Serie B*, **247**, 1–69.

SCHWEIGERT, G. & FRANZ, M. 2004. Die Mergelstetten-Formation, eine neue Gesteinseinheit im Oberjura der östlichen bis mittleren Schwäbischen Alb. *Jahresberichte und Mitteilungen des oberrheinischen geologischen Vereines, Neue Folge*, **86**, 325–335.

SCHWEIGERT, G. & SCHERZINGER, A. 2004. New efforts for a revision and correlation of the ammonite fauna of the Neuburg Formation (Tithonian, SW Germany). *Rivista Italiana di Paleontologia e Stratigrafia*, **110**, 311–320.

SCHWEIGERT, G. & VALLON, L. H. 2005. First record and correlation value of *Aulacostephanus* cf. *subundorae* (PAVLOW) (Ammonoidea, Upper Jurassic) from SW Germany. *Neues Jahrbuch für Geologie und Paläontologie, Monatshefte*, **2005**, 65–82.

SCHWEIGERT, G., KRISHNA, J., PANDEY, B. & PATHAK, D.B. 1996. A new approach to the correlation of the Upper Kimmeridgian Beckeri Zone across the Tethyan Sea. *Neues Jahrbuch für Geologie und Paläontologie, Abhandlungen*, **202**, 345–373.

SCHWEIGL, J. & NEUBAUER, F. 1997. Structural evolution of the central Northern Calcareous Alps: Significance for the Jurassic to Tertiary geodynamics in the alps. *Eclogae geologicae Helvetiae*, **90**, 303–323.

SÉGURET, M., MOUSSINE-POUCHKINE, A., RAJA-GABAGLIA, G. & BOUCHETTE, F. 2001. Storms deposits and storm-generated coarse carbonate breccias on a pelagic outer shelf (South-East Basin, France). *Sedimentology*, **48**, 231–254.

SELG, M. & WAGENPLAST, P. 1990. Beckenarchitektur im süddeutschen Weißen Jura und die Bildung der Schwammriffe. *Jahreshefte des Geologischen Landesamtes Baden-Württemberg*, **32**, 171–206.

SELLWOOD, B.W. 1972. Tidal flat sedimentation in the Lower Jurassic of Bornholm, Denmark. *Palaeogeography, Palaeoclimatology, Palaeoecology*, **11**, 93–106.

SEPKOSKI, J.J., JR. 1996. Patterns of Phanerozoic extinction: a perspective from global data bases. *In:* WALLISER, O.H. (ed.) *Global Events and Event Stratigraphy in the Phanerozoic*. Springer, Berlin, 35–51.

SIKORA W. 1971. Outline of the tectonogenesis of the Pieniny Klippen Zone in Poland in the light of the new geological data. *Annales Societatis Geologorum Poloniae*, **61**, 221–238 [in Russian].

ŠIMKIEVIČIUS, P. 1985. Jurassic system: Polish Lithuanian Depression. *In:* GARETSKI, R.G. (ed.) *Sedimentation and Paleogeography of the Western Part of the East European Platform in Mesozoic Time.* Nauka i Technika, Minsk, 34–42 [in Russian].

ŠIMKIEVIČIUS, P. 1998. Jurassic of the south-eastern Baltic. *Lithology and Clay Minerals*, Geologijos Institutas, Vilnius, **170**.

SISSINGH, W. 2004. Palaeozoic and Mesozoic igneous activity in the Netherlands: a tectonomagmatic review. *Netherlands Journal of Geosciences/Geologie en Mijnbouw*, **83**(2), 113–134.

SIVHED, U. 1984. Litho- and biostratigraphy of the Upper Triassic – Middle Jurassic in Scania, southern Sweden. *Sveriges Geologiska Undersökning, Serie C*, **806**, 31.

ŚLĄCZKA, A. 1996. Oil and gas in the northern Carpathians. *In*: WESSELY, G. & LIEBL, W. (eds) *Oil and Gas in Alpidic Thrustbelts and Basins of Central and Eastern Europe*. European Association of Geoscience Engineering, Special Publications, **5**, 187–195.

ŚLĄCZKA, A., KRUGLOW, S., GOLONKA, J., OSZCZYPKO, N. & POPADYUK, I. 2006. The general geology of the Outer Carpathians, Poland, Slovakia, and Ukraine. *In:* PICHA, F. & GOLONKA, J. (eds) *The Carpathians and their Foreland. Geology and Hydrocarbon Resources.* American Association of Petroleum Geologists, Memoirs, **84**, 1–70.

SLAVIN, V.I. & DOBRYNINA, V.Y. 1958. Stratigraphy of the Precarpathian deep. *Bulletin of the Moscowian Natural Society*, **33**(2), 43–54 [in Russian].

SŁOMKA, T. 1986. Statistical approach to study of flysch sedimentation – Kimmeridgian-Hauterivian Cieszyn Beds, Polish Outer Carpathians. *Annales de la Societe Geologique de Pologne*, **56**, 227–336 [in Polish with English summary].

SMITH, A.G., SMITH, D.G. & FUNNELL, B.M. 1994. *Atlas of Mesozoic and Cenozoic Coastlines*. Cambridge University Press, Cambridge.

SNEIDER, J.S., DE CLARENS, P. & VAIL, P.R. 1995. Sequence stratigraphy of the Middle to Upper Jurassic, Viking Graben, North Sea. *In:* STEEL, R.J. (ed.) *Sequence Stratigraphy on the Northwest European Margin.* NPF Special Publications, **5**, 167–197.

SOMMARUGA, A. 1997. Geology of the central Jura and the Molasse Basin: New insights into an evaporate-based foreland fold and thrust belt. *Mémoires de la Société Neuchâteloise des Science naturelles*, **12**(1), 176.

SOTÁK, J., BIROŇ A., PROKEŠOVA R. & SPIŠIAK J. 2000. Detachment control of core complex exhumation and back-arc extension in the East Slovakian Basin. *Slovak Geological Magazine*, **6**, 130–132.

SOTÁK, J., VOZÁROVÁ, A. & VOZÁR, J. 2002. The East Slovak triple junction area: collisional puzzle of the West Carpathian-Pannonian-East Carpathian units. *Geologica Carpathica*, **53**, 123–125.

SOUKUP, J. 1952. Cretaceous in area of Svitavy and its youngest strata. *Věstnik Ústředniho Ústavu geologického.*, **27**, 75–87 [in Czech].

Stampfli, G.M. & Mosar, J. 1999. The making and becoming of Apulia. *Memorie della Societa Geolgogica Italiana*, **51**, 141–154.

Stampfli, G.M., Mosar, J., Marquer, D., Marchant, R., Baudin, T. & Borel, G. 1998. Subduction and obduction processes in the Swiss Alps. *Tectonophysics*, **296**, 159–204.

Stanton, R.D., Jr. & Flügel, E. 1995. An accretionary distally steepened ramp at an intraplatform basin margin: an alternative explanation for the Upper Triassic Steinplatte 'reef' (Northern Calcareous Alps, Austria). *Sedimentary Geology*, **95**, 269–286.

Steiger, T. 1981. Kalkturbidite im Oberjura der Nördlichen Kalkalpen (Barmstein-Kalke; Salzburg, Österreich). *Facies*, **4**, 215–348.

Steiger, T. & Wurm, D. 1980. Faziesmuster oberjurassischer Plattform-Karbonate (Plassen-Kalke, Nördliche kalkalpen Steirisches Salzkammergut Österreich. *Facies*, **2**, 241–284.

Stephen, K.J. & Davies, R.J. 1998. Documentation of Jurassic sedimentary cycles from the Moray Firth Basin, United Kingdom North Sea. *In:* de Graciansky, P.-C., Hardenbol, J., Jacquin, T. & Vail, P. (eds) *Mesozoic and Cenozoic Sequence Stratigraphy of European Basins*. Society of Economic Paleontologists and Mineralogists, Special Publications, **60**, 481–506.

Strasser, A. & Davaud, E. 1983. Black pebbles of the Purbeckian (Swiss and French Jura): lithology, geochemistry and origin. *Eclogae geologicae Helvetiae*, **76**, 551–580.

Suess, E. & Mojsisovics, E. 1868. Studien über die Trias- und Jurabildungen in den östlichen Alpen. Die Gebirgsgruppe des Osterhornes. *Jahrbuch der kaiserlich-königlichen geologischen Reichsanstalt*, **18**, 168–200.

Surlyk, F. & Ineson, J.R. 2003. The Jurassic of Denmark and Greenland: key elements in the reconstruction of the North Atlantic Jurassic rift system. *In:* Ineson, J. R. & Surlyk, F. (eds) *The Jurassic of Denmark and Greenland*. Geological Survey of Denmark and Grenland Bulletin, **1**, 9–22.

Surlyk, F. & Noe-Nygaard, N. 1986. Hummocky cross-stratification from the Lower Jurassic Hasle Formation of Bornholm, Denmark. *Sedimentary Geology*, **46**, 259–273.

Surlyk, F., Arndorff, L., *et al.* 1995. High-resolution sequence stratigraphy of a Hettangian–Sinemurian paralic succession, Bornholm, Denmark. *Sedimentology*, **42**, 323–354.

Szydeł, Z. & Szydeł R. 1981. Profil utworów liasu na obszarze Lubelskiego Zagłębia Węglowego. *Przegląd Geologiczny*, **11**, 568–571.

Tanner, K.M. 1978. Die Keuper-Lias Fundstelle von Niederschönthal, Kanton Baselland. *Bulletin der Vereinigung schweizer Petroleum-Geologen und -Ingenieure*, **44**(106), 13–23.

Tessin, R. 1995. Zur Entwicklung des Raums Rüdersdorf (Ostbrandenburg) im Jura. *Berliner geowissenschaftliche Abhandlungen, Reihe A*, **168**, 43–53.

Teyssen, T. 1984. Sedimentology of the Minette oolitic ironstones of Luxembourg and Lorraine: a Jurassic subtidal sandwave complex. *Sedimentology*, **31**, 195–211.

Thierry, J. 2000. Middle Callovian. *In:* Dercourt, J., Gaetani, M., *et al.* (eds) *Atlas Peri-Tethys. Palaeogeographical Maps*. Gauthier-Villars, Paris, 71–83.

Thierry, J., Vidier, J.-P., Garcia, J.-P. & Marchand, D. 1996. Le Dogger du Boulonnais: lithostratigraphie, biostratigraphie et stratigraphie séquentielle des séries à l'affleurement. *Annales de la Société géologique du Nord* (2ème série), **4**(4), 127–155.

Thierry, J., Marchand, D., Fortwengler, D., Bonnot, A. & Jardat, R. 2006. Les ammonites du Callovien-Oxfordien des sondages Andra dans l'Est du bassin de Paris: synthèse biochronostratigraphique, intérêts paléoécologique et paléobiogéographique. *Comptes rendus Geosciences*, **338**, 834.

Thiry-Bastien, P. 1998. *Séquences de dépôt et paléoenvironnements sur la bordure S.W. du Massif Ardennais: comblement et ennoyage d'une plate-forme carbonatée au Bathonien supérieur-Callovien inférieur*. DEA Pal & Sed, Université de Bourgogne.

Thiry-Bastien, P. 2002. *Stratigraphie séquentielle des calcaires bajociens de l'Est de la France (Jura-Bassin de Paris)*. Thesis, Université Lyon 1.

Thuy, B. 2003. Les échinides du Bajocien de Rumelange (Grand-Duché de Luxembourg). *Ferrantia*, **36**, 79–123.

Thuy, B. 2005. Les ophiures de l'Hettangien inférieur de Vance (B), Bereldange/Bridel et Bourglinster (L). *Memoirs of the geological Survey of Belgium*, **51**, 33–57.

Tollmann, A. 1976. *Analyse des klassischen nordalpinen Mesozoikums*. Deuticke, Vienna.

Tollmann, A. 1977. *Geologie von Österreich, Band 1*. Deuticke, Vienna.

Tollmann, A. 1981. Oberjurassische Gleittektonik als Hauptformungsprozeß der Hallstätter Region und neue Daten zur Gesamttektonik der Nördlichen Kalkalpen in den Ostalpen. *Mitteilungen der Österreichischen Geologischen Gesellschaft*, **74/75**, 167–195.

Tollmann, A. 1985. *Geologie von Österreich, Band 2*. Deuticke, Vienna.

Tollmann, A. 1987*a*. Late Jurassic/Neocomian gravitational tectonics in the Northern Calcareous Alps in Austria. *In:* Flügel, H. W. & Faupl, P. (eds) *Geodynamics of the Eastern Alps*. Deuticke, Vienna, 112–125.

Tollmann, A. 1987*b*. The alpidic evolution of the Eastern Alps. *In:* Flügel, H. W. & Faupl, P. (eds) *Geodynamics of the Eastern Alps*. Deuticke, Vienna, 361–378.

Tomašových, A. & Michalík, J. 2000. Rhaetian/Hettangian passage beds in the carbonate development in the Krizna Nappe (central Western Carpathians, Slovakia). *Slovak Geological Magazine*, **6**, 241–249.

Tribovillard, N., Bialkowski, A., Tyson, R.V., Lallier-Verges & Deconinck, J.-F. 2001. Organic facies variation in the Late Kimmeridgian of the Boulonnais area (Northernmost France). *Marine and Petroleum Geology*, **18**, 371–389.

Troedsson, G. 1951. On the Höganäs series of Sweden. *Lunds Universitets Arsskrift, N.F. Adv. 2*, **47**(1), 1–269.

Tröster, J. 1987. Biostratigraphie des Obertoarcium und der Toarcium/Aalenium Grenze der Bohrungen Weiach, Beznau, Riniken und Schafisheim (Nordschweiz). *Eclogae geologicae Helvetiae*, **80**, 431–447.

Trümpy, R. 1980. *Geology of Switzerland. Part A: An Outline of the Geology of Switzerland*. Wepf & Co, Basel/New York.

Tyszka, J. 1994. Response of Middle Jurassic benthic foraminiferal morphogroups to disoxic/oxic conditions in the Pieniny Klippen Basin, Polish Carpathians. *Palaeogeography, Palaeoclimatology, Palaeoecology*, **110**, 55–81.

Tyszka, J. 2001. Microfossil assemblages as bathymetric indicators of the Toarcian/Aalenian "Fleckenmergel"-facies in the Carpathian Pieniny Klippen Belt. *Geologica Carpathica*, **52**, 147–158.

Uhlig, V. 1880. Über die Juraablagerungen in der Umgebung von Brünn. *Verhandlungen der kaiserlich-königlichen geologischen Reichsanstalt Wien*, **14**, 67–79.

Uhlig, V. 1882. Die Jurabildungen in der Umgebung von Brünn. *Beiträge zur Paläontologie des Österreichisch-Ungarischen Orients*, **1**, 111–182.

Underhill, J.R. & Partington, M.A. 1993. Jurassic thermal doming and deflation in the North Sea: implications for sequence stratigraphic evidence. *In:* Parker, J.R. (ed.) *Petroleum Geology of Northwest Europe*. Graham & Trotman, London, 697–706.

Underhill, J.R. & Partington, M.A. 1994. Use of genetic sequence stratigraphy in defining and determining a regional tectonic control on the 'Mid-Cimmerian Unconformity' – implications for North Sea basin development and the global sea-level chart. *In:* Weimer, P. & Posamentier, H.W. (eds) *Siliciclastic Sequence Stratigraphy: Recent Developments and Applications*. American Association of Petroleum Geologists, Memoirs, **58**, 449–484.

Urlichs, M. 1977. Stratigraphy, ammonite fauna and some ostracods of the Upper Pliensbach at the type locality (Lias, SW-Germany). *Stuttgarter Beiträge zur Naturkunde, Serie B*, **28**, 1–13.

Urlichs, M., Wild, R. & Ziegler, B. 1994. Der Posidonien-Schiefer des unteren Juras und seine Fossilien. *Stuttgarter Beiträge zur Naturkunde, Serie C*, **36**, 1–95.

Vadet, A. & Slovik, D. 2001. Les oursins du Bajocien de Liocourt. *Société d'Histoire Naturelle du Boulonnais*, **22**(1), 1–48.

Vadet, A., Remy, N. & Wille, E. 2001. Echinides du Corallien des Ardennes. *Société d'Histoire Naturelle du Boulonnais*, **21**, 1–63.

Vadet, A., Pannier, P. & Marignac, C. 2002. Les oursins de l'Oxfordien de Foug. *Société d'Histoire Naturelle du Boulonnais*, **22**(2), 1– 44.

Vail, P.R., Colin, J.-P., Jan-du-Chene, R., Kuchly, J., Mediavilla, F. & Trifilieff, V. 1987. La stratigraphie séquentielle et son application aux corrélations chronostratigraphiques dans le Jurassique du Bassin de Paris. *Bulletin de la Société géologique de France*, **7**, 1301–1321.

VAKHRAMEEV, V.A. 1991. *Jurassic and Cretaceous Floras and Climates of the Earth*. Cambridge University Press, Cambridge.

VAN ADRICHEM BOOGAERT, H.A. & KOUWE, W.F.P. 1993–97. Stratigraphic nomenclature of the Netherlands, revision and update by RGD and NOGEPA. *Mededelingen Rijks Geologische Dienst*, **50**.

VAN DE SCHOOTBRUGGE, B., BAILEY, T.R., ROSENTHAL, Y., KATZ, M.E., WRIGHT, J.D. & MILLER, K.G. 2005. Early Jurassic climate change and the radiation of organic-walled phytoplankton in the Tethys Ocean. *Paleobiology*, **31**(1), 73–97.

VÉGH-NEUBRANDT, E. 1982. Triassische Megalodontaceae. *Entwicklung, Stratigraphie und Paläontologie*. Akadémiai Kiadó, Budapest.

VENTURA, B. & LISKER, F. 2003. Long-term landscape evolution of the northeastern margin of the Bohemian Massif: apatite fission-track data from Erzgebirge (Germany). *International Journal of Earth Sciences (Geologische Rundschau)*, **92**, 691–700.

VIDIER, J.P., MARCHAND, D., BONNOT, A. & FORTWENGLER, D. 1993. The Callovian and Oxfordian of the Boulonnais area in northern France: new biostratigraphic data. *Acta geologica Polonica*, **43**(3–4), 169–182.

VILLINGER, E. & FLECK, W. 1995. Symbolschlüssel Geologie (Teil I) und Bodenkunde Baden-Württemberg. *Informationen Geologisches Landesamt Baden-Württemberg*, **5**, 1–69.

VINCENT, B. 2001. *Sédimentologie et géochimie de la diagenèse des carbonates. Application au Malm de la bordure Est du Bassin de Paris*. PhD thesis, Université de Bourgogne/ANDRA.

VINCENT, B., EMMANUEL, L. & LOREAU, J.-P. 2004. Signification du signal isotopique (delta$^{18}$O, delta$^{13}$C) des carbonates néritiques: composante diagénétique et composante originelle (Jurassique supérieur de l'Est du bassin de Paris, France). *Comptes rendus Geosciences*, **336**, 29–39.

VINKEN, R. *et al.* 1971. *Geologische Karte von Niedersachsen 1 :25000. Erläuterungen zu Blatt Dingelbe 3826*. Niedersächsisches Landesamt für Bodenforschung, Hannover.

VIOHL, G. 1998. Die Solnhofener Plattenkalke - Entstehung und Lebensräume. *Archaeopteryx*, **16**, 37–68.

VÖRÖS, A. 1991. Hierlatzkalk - a peculiar Austro-Hungarian Jurassic facies. *Jubiläumsschrift 20 Jahre Geologische Zusammenarbeit Österreich-Ungarn*, **1**, 145–154.

VON HUMBOLDT, F.W.H.A. 1799. *Über die unterirdischen Gasarten und die Mittel ihren Nachtheil zu vermindern. Wiewag: Ein Beitrag zur Physik der Praktischen Bergbaukunde*. Braunschweig.

WAGENPLAST, P. 1972. Ökologische Untersuchung der Fauna aus Bank- und Schwammfazies des Weißen Jura der Schwäbischen Alb. *Arbeiten aus dem Institut für Geologie und Paläontologie der Universität Stuttgart, Neue Folge*, **67**, 1–99.

WAGNER, R. 1998. Zechstein – Thickness. *In:* DADLEZ, R., MAREK, S. & POKORSKI, P. (eds) *Palaeogeographical Atlas of the Epicontinental Permian and Mesozoic in Poland, 1:2.500.000*. Polish Geological Institute, Warszawa, Pl. 9.

WAGREICH, M. 2001. Paleocene - Eocene paleogeography of the Northern Calcareous Alps (Gosau Group, Austria). *In:* PILLER, W. E. & RASSER, M. W. (eds) *Paleogene of the Eastern Alps*. Österreichische Akademie der Wissenschaften, Vienna, 57–76.

WAKSMUNDZKA, M. 1998. *Opracowanie palinologiczne próbek z wiercenia Pągów – 1*. Polish Geological Institute.

WARD, P.D., GARRISON, G.H., HAGGART, J.W., KRING, D.A. & BEATTIE, M.J. 2004. Isotopic evidence bearing on Late Triassic extinction events, Queen Charlotte Islands, British Columbia, and implications for the duration and cause of the Triassic/Jurassic mass extinction. *Earth and Planetary Science Letters*, **224,** 589–600.

WARRINGTON, G. 1970. The stratigraphy and palaeontology of the "Keuper" Series in the central Midlands of England. *Quarterly Journal of the Geological Society*, **126**, 183–223.

WEIS, R. 1999. Die Belemniten der Minette Formation (ob. Toarcium-ob.Aalenium) Luxemburgs. *Travaux scientifiques du Musée national d'Histoire naturelle de Luxembourg*, **32**, 207–246.

WEIS, R. 2006, Bélemnites (Cephalopoda, Coleoidea) du Bajocien de Rumelange (Luxembourg). *Bulletin de la Société des naturalistes luxembourgeois*, **106**, 151–165.

WEIS, R. & DELSATE, D. 2005. Présence de bélemnites précoces dans l'Hettangien de Belgique. *Memoirs of the geological Survey of Belgium*, **51**, 27–31.

WEISSERT, H. & BERNOULLI, D. 1985. A transform margin in the Mesozoic Tethys: evidence from the Swiss Alps. *Geologische Rundschau*, **74**, 665–679.

WEISSERT, H. & ERBA, E. 2004. Volcanism, CO2 and palaeoclimate: a Late Jurassic–Early Cretaceous carbon and oxygen isotope record. *Journal of the Geological Society of London*, **161**, 695–702.

WELLNHOFER, P. 1999. Der bayerische Urvogel, *Archaeopteryx bavarica*, aus den Solnhofener Schichten. *Kulturstiftung der Länder – Patrimonia*, **177**, 1–24.

WERNER, W., LEINFELDER, R.R., FÜRSICH, F.T. & KRAUTTER, M. 1994. Comparative palaeoecology of marly coralline sponge-bearing reefal associations from the Kimmeridgian (Upper Jurassic) of Portugal and Southwestern Germany. *Courier Forschungsinstitut Senckenberg*, **172**, 381–397.

WESTERMANN, G.E.G. 1954. Monographie der Otoitidae (Ammonoidea). *Beihefte zum Geologischen Jahrbuch*, **15**, 1–364.

WESTERMANN, G.E.G. 1958. Ammoniten-Fauna und Stratigraphie des Bathonien NW-Deutschlands. *Beihefte zum Geologische Jahrbuch*, **32**, 1–103.

WETZEL, A. & ALLIA, V. 2000. The significance of hiatus beds in shallow-water mudstones: an example from the Middle Jurassic of Switzerland. *Journal of Sedimentary Research*, **70**, 170–180.

WETZEL, A. & ALLIA, V. 2003. Der Opalinuston in der Nordschweiz: Lithologie und Ablagerungsgeschichte. *Eclogae geologicae Helvetiae*, **96**, 451–469.

WETZEL, A. & MEYER, C. A. 2006. The dangers of high-rise living on a muddy seafloor: an example of crinoids from shallow-water mudstones (Aalenian, northern Switzerland). *Palaios*, **21**, 155–167.

WETZEL, A. & REISDORF, A.G. 2008. Ichnofabrics elucidate entombing and burial history of a vertically embedded ichthyosaur skull. *In:* BUATOIS, L., MÁNGANO, G., BROMLEY, R., GENISE, J. & MELCHOR, R. (eds) *Ichnology at the Crossroads*. Society of Economic Paleontologists and Mineralogists, Special Publications, **88**.

WETZEL, A. & STRASSER, A. 2001. Sedimentology, palaeoecology, and high-resolution sequence stratigraphy of a carbonate-siliciclastic shelf (Oxfordian, Swiss Jura Mountains). *In:* FUNK, H. & WORTMANN, U. (eds) *21st IAS Meeting of Sedimentology (Davos, Switzerland), Excursion Guides*. International Association of Sedimentologists, 33–51.

WETZEL, A., ALLENBACH, R. & ALLIA, V. 2003. Reactivated basement structures affecting the sedimentary facies in a tectonically "quiescent" epicontinental basin: an example from NW Switzerland. *Sedimentary Geology*, **157**, 153–172.

WIERZBOWSKI, A., JAWORSKA, M. & KROBICKI, M. 1999. Jurassic (Upper Bajocian–lowest Oxfordian) ammonitico rosso facies in the Pieniny Klippen Belt, Carpathians, Poland: its fauna, age, microfacies and sedimentary environment. *Studia Geologica Polonica*, **115**, 7–74.

WIERZBOWSKI, A., COE, A., *et al.* 2006. A potential stratotype for the Oxfordian /Kimmeridgian boundary: Staffin Bay, Isle of Skye, UK. *Volumina Jurassica*, **IV**, 17–34.

WIERZBOWSKI, H. 2002. Detailed oxygen and carbon isotope stratigraphy of the Oxfordian in Central Poland. *International Journal of Earth Sciences (Geologische Rundschau)*, **91**, 304–314.

WIERZBOWSKI, H. 2004. Carbon and oxygen isotope composition of Oxfordian –Early Kimmeridgian belemnite rostra: palaeoenvironmental implications for Late Jurassic seas. *Plalaeogeography, Palaeoclimatology, Palaeoecology* **203**, 153–168.

WIERZBOWSKI, H. & JOACHIMSKI, M. 2006. The carbon and oxygen isotope records of Upper Bajocian-Bathonian calcareous fossils from the Polish Jura Chain. *Volumina Jurassica*, **IV**, 220–222.

WIGNALL, P.B. & PICKERING, K.T. 1993. A palaeoecological and sedimentological analysis of fault-controlled deposition in the Kimmeridgian (Late Jurassic) of N.E. Scotland. *Journal of the Geological Society of London*, **150**, 323–340.

WIGNALL, P.B. & RUFFELL, A.H. 1990. The influence of a sudden climatic change on marine deposition in the Kimmeridgian of northwest Europe. *Journal of the Geological Society of London*, **147,** 365–371.

WILDI, W., FUNK, H., LOUP, B., EDGARDO, A. & HUGGENBERGER, P. 1989. Mesozoic subsidence history of the European marginal shelves of the alpine Tethys (Helvetic realm, Swiss Plateau and Jura). *Eclogae geologicae Helvetiae*, **82,** 817–840.

WINGS, O. 2000. Ein Hartgrund als neuer Aspekt bei der Interpretation der untertithonischen Solnhofener Plattenkalke. *Archaeopteryx*, **18**, 75–92.

WINKLER, W. & ŚLĄCZKA, A. 1994. A Late Cretaceous to Paleogene geodynamic model for the Western Carpathians in Poland. *Geologica Carpathica*, **45**, 71–82.

Withjack, M.O., Schlische, R.W. & Olsen, P.O. 1998. Diachronous rifting, drifting, and inversion on the passive margin of central eastern North America: an analog for other passive margins. *American Association of Petroleum Geologists, Bulletin* **82,** 817–835.

Wong, Th.E. 2007. Jurassic. *In:* Wong, Th.E., Batjes, D.A.J. & De Jager, J. (eds) *Geology of the Netherlands.* Royal Netherlands Academy of Arts and Sciences, Amsterdam, 107–126.

Xie, S., Sun, B., Yan, D., Xiao, L. & Wei, L. 2006. Leaf cuticular characters of *Ginkgo* and implications for paleoatmospheric CO2 in the Jurassic. *Progress in Natural Science,* **16**, 258–263.

Zapletal, K. 1925. About the morphology of Moravia. *Acta Museae Moraviae, Scientia naturalis*, **22–23**, 179–191 [in Czech].

Zeiss, A. 1955. Zur Stratigraphie des Callovien und Unter-Oxfordien bei Blumberg (Südbaden). *Jahreshefte des Geologischen Landesamtes Baden-Württemberg,* **1**, 239–266.

Zeiss, A. 1977. Jurassic stratigraphy of Franconia. *Stuttgarter Beiträge zur Naturkunde, Serie B,* **31**, 1–32.

Zeiss, A. 2003. The Upper Jurassic of Europe: its subdivision and correlation. *In*: Ineson, J.R. & Surlyk, F. (eds) *The Jurassic of Denmark and Greenland.* Geological Survey of Denmark and Greenland Bulletin, **1**, 75–114.

Zhabina, N.M. & Anikeeva, O.V. 2002. Stratigraphy and facies of the Upper Jurassic deposits of the Ukrainian Carpathian foreland. *In:* Popadyuk, I.V. (ed.) *Regional Geology Studies: Stratigraphy, Basin Analysis, Tectonics; Western and Southern Ukraine Petroleum Provinces.* Ukrainian State Geological Research Institute, Report 0100u002630, 61–122 [in Ukrainian].

Ziaja, J. 1991. The Lower Liassic microflora from Odrowąż in Poland. *In:* Kovar-Eder, J. (ed.) *Palaeoenvironmental Development in Europe and Regions Relevant to its Palaeofloristic Evolution.* Proceedings Pan-European Palaeobotanical Conference, Vienna, Naturhistorisches Museum Wien, 337–339.

Ziaja, J. 2001. Ocena wieku odkrywki w Odrowążu (Sołtykowie) na podstawie badań sporowo-pyłkowych. *In:* Pieńkowski, G. & Grabowski, J. (eds) *2nd Symposium on Jurassic System, Starachowice.* Polish Geological Society Warszawa, Proceedings, **36**.

Ziegler, B. 1967. Ammoniten-Ökologie am Beispiel des Oberjura. *Geologische Rundschau,* **56**, 439–464.

Ziegler, B. 1987. Der Weiße Jura der Schwäbischen Alb. *Stuttgarter Beiträge zur Naturkunde, Serie C,* **23**, 1–71.

Ziegler, M.A. 1962. *Beiträge zur Kenntnis des unteren Malm im zentralen Schweizer Jura.* PhD thesis, Universität Zürich.

Ziegler, P.A. 1956. Geologische Beschreibung des Blattes Courtelay (Berner Jura), und zur Stratigraphie des Sequanien im zentralen Schweizer Jura. *Beiträge zur geologischen Karte Schweiz, Neue Folge,* **102**.

Ziegler, P.A. 1975. Geologic evolution of the North Sea and its tectonic framework. *American Association of Petroleum Geologists, Bulletin,* **59**, 1073–1097.

Ziegler, P.A. 1988. *Evolution of the Arctic-North Atlantic and the Western Tethys.* American Association of Petroleum Geologists, Memoirs, **43**.

Ziegler, P.A. 1990. *Geological Atlas of Western and Central Europe.* Shell Internationale Petroleum Maatschappij B.V.

Ziegler, P.A., Cloethingh, S. & Van Wees, J.-D. 1995. Dynamics of intra-plate compressional deformation: the Alpine foreland and other examples. *Tectonophysics*, **252**, 7–59.

Zügel, P. 1997. Discovery of a radiolarian fauna from the Tithonian of the Solnhofen area (southern Franconian Alb, southern Germany). *Paläontologische Zeitschrift,* **71**, 197–209.

Zügel, P., Riegraf, W., Schweigert, G. & Dietl, G. 1998. Radiolaria from the Nusplingen Lithographic Limestone (Late Kimmeridgian, SW Germany). *Stuttgarter Beiträge zur Naturkunde, Serie B,* **268**, 1–43.

# 15 Cretaceous

SILKE VOIGT & MICHAEL WAGREICH (co-ordinators), FINN SURLYK, IRENEUSZ WALASZCZYK, DAVID ULIČNÝ, STANISLAV ČECH, THOMAS VOIGT, FRANK WIESE, MARKUS WILMSEN, BIRGIT NIEBUHR, MIKE REICH, HANSPETER FUNK, JOSEF MICHALÍK, JOHN W. M. JAGT, PETER J. FELDER & ANNE S. SCHULP

During the Cretaceous (145.5–65.5 Ma; Gradstein *et al.* 2004), Central Europe was part of the European continental plate, which was bordered by the North Atlantic ocean and the Arctic Sea to the NW and north, the Bay of Biscay to the SW, the northern branch of the Tethys Ocean to the south, and by the East European Platform to the east (Fig. 15.1). The evolution of sedimentary basins was influenced by the interplay of two main global processes: plate tectonics and eustatic sea-level change. Plate tectonic reconfigurations resulted in the widening of the Central Atlantic, and the opening of the Bay of Biscay. The South Atlantic opening caused a counter-clockwise rotation of Africa, which was coeval with the closure of the Tethys Ocean. Both motions terminated the Permian–Early Cretaceous North Sea rifting and placed Europe in a transtensional stress field. The long-term eustatic sea-level rise resulted in the highest sea level during Phanerozoic times (Haq *et al.* 1988; Hardenbol *et al.* 1998). Large epicontinental shelf areas were flooded as a consequence of elevated spreading rates of mid-ocean ridges and intra-oceanic plateau volcanism, causing the development of extended epicontinental shelf seas and shelf-sea basins (Hays & Pitman 1973; Larson 1991).

A new and unique lithofacies type, the pelagic chalk, was deposited in distal parts of the individual basins. Chalk deposition commenced during middle Cenomanian–early Turonian times. Chalk consists almost exclusively of the remains of planktonic coccolithophorid algae and other pelagic organisms, and its great thickness reflects a high rate of production of the algal tests. The bulk of the grains are composed of low-magnesium calcite, representing coccolith debris with a subordinate amount of foraminifers, calcispheres, small invertebrates and shell fragments of larger invertebrates (Håkansson *et al.* 1974; Surlyk & Birkelund 1977; Nygaard *et al.* 1983; Hancock 1975, 1993).

## The Jurassic–Cretaceous boundary

The base of the Cretaceous System is not yet defined by the International Commission on Stratigraphy. A major fall in sea level led to an interval of high faunal and floral endemism and extreme facies differentiation in Tethyan and Boreal regions. This means that pan-European correlations of Jurassic–Cretaceous boundary beds based on macrofossils are problematical. A proposed biostratigraphic index taxon is the first occurrence of the Tethyan ammonite *Berriasella jacobi* at the base of the Berriasian within Magnetochron M19n (Zakharov *et al.* 1996; Gradstein *et al.* 2004). Stratigraphically well-defined boundary sections are not sufficiently documented in Central Europe.

## Palaeoclimate and sea-level changes

The Cretaceous period witnessed the climax of the Mesozoic–Cenozoic greenhouse climate when climate belts expanded towards the high latitudes and polar ice caps were absent for most of the time. During Early Cretaceous (Berriasian–Barremian) times, palaeoclimate conditions were still relatively cool, but entered full-greenhouse conditions in the Aptian with the onset of maximum rates of oceanic crust formation and related tectonic $CO_2$ production (Larson 1991; Wilson *et al.* 2002). The Cretaceous thermal maximum was reached in the early to mid-Turonian, with unusually warm sea-surface temperatures (33–34 °C) reported for the tropical oceans (Norris *et al.* 2002; Wilson *et al.* 2002; Schouten *et al.* 2003). The later Cretaceous was a period of long-term climate cooling (Kolodny & Raab 1988; Jenkyns *et al.* 1994). Central Europe was located in a central position between two important climate belts and biogeographic realms: the mid-latitude Boreal Realm to the north, and the subtropical Tethyan Realm to the south, and was repeatedly affected by immigration of marine cool- and warm-water faunas.

### *Palaeoclimate and palaeoceanography*

Palaeobotanical studies of well-preserved floras in Bohemia show that the climate of the Central European island during the Cenomanian was subtropical humid but seasonally dry, with favourable conditions for abundant fires during the dry season (Velenovský & Viniklář 1926–31; Knobloch 1999; Falcon-Lang *et al.* 2001). Leaf physiognomy of these floras shows mean annual temperatures of 17–20°C (Herman *et al.* 2002). A seasonally humid warm-temperate to subtropical climate is also indicated by Santonian fossil wood occurrences in the Liège-Limburg Basin (Meijer 2000). Middle and late Cenomanian coastal marine fauna document warm–temperate water conditions and communication between both the Boreal and the Tethyan realms. Stable oxygen isotopic composition of Cenomanian–Turonian marine invertebrates from the Anglo-Paris and the North German basins indicates temperatures of 15–20°C in the upper water column (S. Voigt *et al.* 2004), and the occurrence of scleractinian corals in the latest Maastrichtian Liège-Limburg Basin implies temperatures of 20–25°C in shallow waters (Liebau 1978).

The Cretaceous period was also a time of major palaeoceanographic change, marked by the deposition of black shales during times of oceanic anoxia (Schlanger & Jenkyns 1976). Global oceanic anoxic events (OAEs) in the early Aptian and latest Cenomanian caused widespread occurrence of anoxic conditions

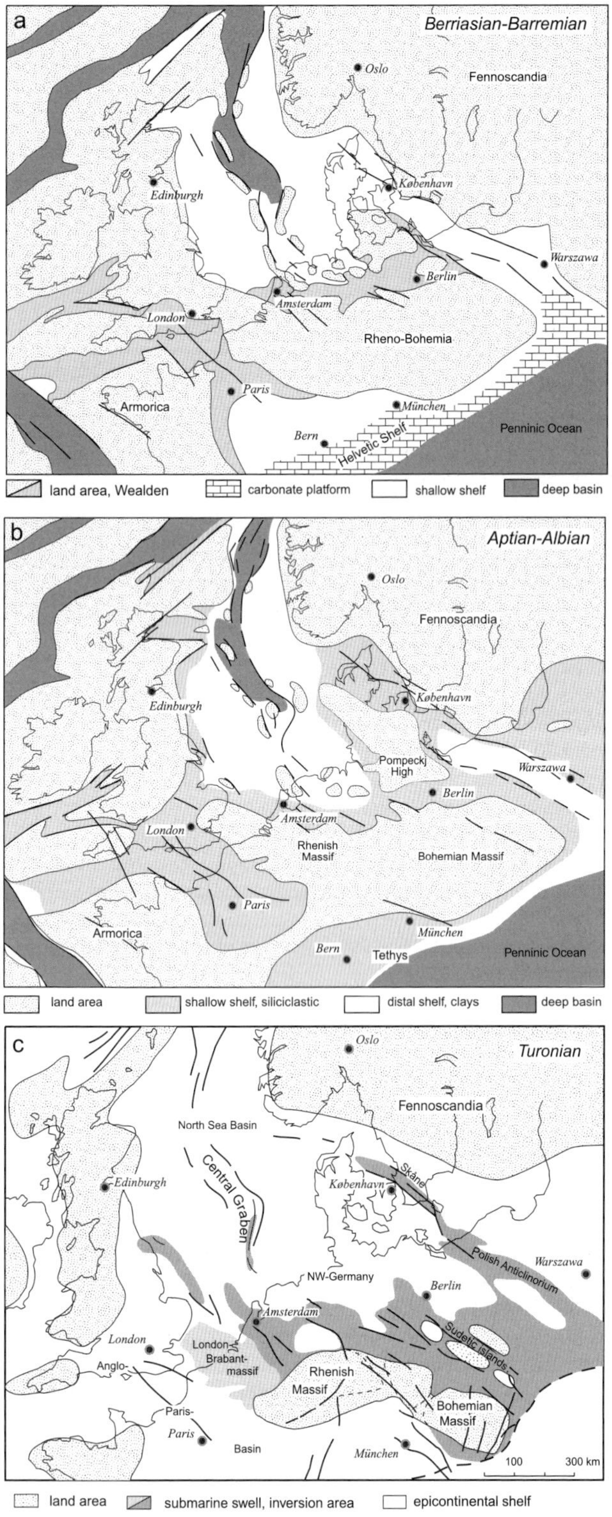


**Fig. 15.1.** Central Europe palaeogeography during three Cretaceous time intervals. (a) Berriasian to Barremian; (b) Aptian to Albian (both modified after Ziegler 1990; Mutterlose & Böckel 1998); (c) Late Cretaceous (Turonian; modified after Ziegler 1990; S. Voigt *et al.* 2003).

across the shelf basins of Central Europe. The early Aptian OAE 1a is represented by black shales in the Western Carpathians (Veřovice and Koňhora formations), in the Lower Saxony Basin and the Polish Trough (Fischschiefer). The deposition of platform limestones ceased in the Helvetics (Schrattenkalk Formation). The latest Cenomanian OAE 2 is represented by the occurrence of black shales in the North Sea (Black Band Bed), the North German Basin (Hesseltal Formation) and numerous Alpine basins of the Eastern Alps and Western Carpathians, as well as by widespread hardground formation and condensation in marginal areas (e.g. Bornholm, Bohemian Cretaceous Basin).

### *Sea-level change*

The tectonically induced long-term eustatic Cretaceous sea-level rise was superimposed by high-order mostly eustatic sea-level changes, which were responsible for repeated transgressions and regressions in the Central European basins exerting control on the development of sedimentary successions. Whereas most Central European basins were influenced by terrestrial and brackish-lacustrine sedimentation during the Berriasian, the Valanginian and Hauterivian periods are characterized by significant transgressions, which favoured the spread of marine calcareous mud and clay-dominated facies (Fig. 15.1). Overall regressive conditions in the Barremian resulted in restricted oceanographic conditions in marginal epeiric seas and the isolation of individual basins. Several transgressions and regressions during Aptian–early Albian times favoured coastal onlap, the enlargement of marine depositional areas, and faunal connections between Boreal and Tethyan realms. The middle Albian transgression flooded large areas of former land, created linkages between isolated basins and favoured the expansion of a uniform facies distribution. During the Cenomanian sea-level rise, Central Europe was almost completely flooded and basinal siliciclastic sedimentation was substituted by the deposition of chalk (Fig. 15.1). The position of the coastlines is known only for a few locations (e.g. in the Bohemian Cretaceous Basin) due to the scarcity of preserved shoreline and marginal deposits. The pattern of repeated transgressions and regressions continued in Coniacian–mid-Campanian times, but without further significant coastal onlap causing progradation of terrigenous sedimentation. The late Campanian–Maastrichtian period was characterized by a eustatic sea-level fall, which caused the retreat of the sea from the central parts of Central Europe.

## Stratigraphy

### *Biostratigraphy*

The classic biostratigraphic subdivision of the Cretaceous System is based on ammonites, which provide a framework of high temporal resolution. Provincialism and the sporadic occurrence of ammonites in a variety of sedimentary successions resulted in the establishment of additional biozonations based on macrofauna (belemnites, inoceramids, echinoids and brachiopods), microfauna (planktonic and benthic foraminifers, ostracods) and microflora (coccoliths and dinoflagellates). The Coniacian–Maastrichtian boreal macrofossil zonation is based mainly on lineages of belemnites, such as the *Gonioteuthis* lineage (late Coniacian–early Campanian), the *Belemnitella* lineage (early–late Campanian and late Maastrichtian) and the *Belemnella* lineage (latest Campanian–early Maastrichtian). A high-resolution zonation based on micromorphic brachiopods is established for the upper Campanian–Maastrichtian chalk of northern Germany, Denmark and England (Steinich 1965; Surlyk 1970, 1984; Johansen & Surlyk 1990).

Central Europe has one potential Global Boundary Stratotype Section and Point (GSSP) that defines the base of the Coniacian stage. The Turonian–Coniacian boundary lies in the upper part (FO of the inoceramid *Cremnoceramus deformis erectus*; Walaszczyk & Wood 1999) of the Salzgitter-Salder section (Lower Saxony Basin). A boundary stratotype is a section that contains a designated point in a stratigraphic sequence of essentially continuous deposition chosen for its correlation potential.

Macrofaunal zonations are widely established in the epicontinental basins of Central Europe as a result of more than a century of fossil collection. For example, the biozonation in the North German Basin is based on ammonites (Hiss 1982*a*, 1983; Kaplan *et al.* 1984, 1996, 1998; Kaplan & Kennedy 1996; Schmid & Ernst 1975; Lommerzheim 1995; Kennedy & Kaplan 1997; Niebuhr *et al.* 1997; Niebuhr 2003, 2004), inoceramid bivalves (Tröger 1989; Wiedmann *et al.* 1989; Walaszczyk 1997; Walaszczyk & Wood 1999), echinoids (Ernst 1968; 1970, 1972; Schulz 1985) and belemnites (Ernst 1964, 1968; Schulz 1979; Christensen 2000), and is integrated with an event stratigraphic concept that comprises bio- and tephro-events (Ernst *et al.* 1983, 1996; Wood *et al.* 1984; Ernst & Wood 1995; Wray *et al.* 1996; Wiese 2000; Wilmsen & Niebuhr 2002). Similar macrofossil zonations are also established for the Cretaceous succession in the Mid-Polish Trough and the basins in the surroundings of the Bohemian Massif (inoceramids (Walaszczyk 1988, 1992, 2004; Walaszczyk & Wood 1998), belemnites (Kongiel 1962) and ammonites (Cieśliński 1959; Błaszkiewicz 1980; Marcinowski 1980)), the Danish Basin (belemnites (Christensen 1975, 1986, 1993, 1996; Christensen & Schulz 1997), ammonites (Kennedy *et al.* 1980; Kennedy & Christensen 1991; Birkelund 1993)) and the Liège-Limburg Basin (Christensen & Schmid 1987; Jagt 1989, 1999; Jagt *et al.* 1987; Kennedy & Jagt 1995; Keutgen 1996, 1997).

High-resolution microfossil zonations have been established for borehole successions and many hydrocarbon fields based on first and last occurrences and abundance peaks. Several microfossil zonations have been established for the chalk based on foraminifers, dinoflagellate cysts, ostracods and coccoliths (Carter & Hart 1977; Perch-Nielsen 1985; Burnett *et al.* 1998; Varol 1998). Microbiostratigraphic subdivisions with foraminifers and ostracods are also applied in the North German Basin (Keller 1982; Weiss 1982; Koch 1977; Schönfeld 1990; Reich 2000; Diener *et al.* 2004*a*), and the Mid-Polish Trough (Pożaryska 1957; Herrig 1966; Pożaryska & Peryt 1979; Peryt 1980, 1983; Frenzel 2000), and are supplemented by divisions with calcareous nannofloras (Kemper *et al.* 1978; Mutterlose 1992; Jagt *et al.* 1995*a*, *b*) and dinoflagellates (Schiøler *et al.* 1997)

Stratigraphic divisions of Berriasian brackish–alluvial Wealden deposits are based on ostracods (Wolburg 1949, 1959; Kemper 1973; Elstner & Mutterlose 1996) and palynomorphs (Döring 1965). Biostratigraphic ages of the fluvial deposits are based on spores, pollen and dinoflagellate assemblages (Batten *et al.* 1987, 1988; Streel *et al.* 1994; Svobodová 1999). In addition, regional zonations are developed for some Central European basins. For example, the Liège-Limburg Basin is subdivided by ecozonation-based bioclast assemblages, which are calibrated against zonations of benthic forams and ostracods (Bless *et al.* 1987; Felder & Bless 1989).

### *Independent stratigraphic tools*

Cretaceous biostratigraphy is combined with independent stratigraphic tools, such as isotope ($\delta^{13}C$, $^{87}Sr/^{86}Sr$) and magnetic stratigraphy, which facilitate interbasinal long-range correlation. Variations in the carbon isotope signal of marine sediments are a measure of changes in the global carbon cycle and are used in Central Europe to correlate the distinct signals of oceanic anoxic events (e.g. Lintnerova *et al.* 2000; Wissler *et al.* 2003) and to correlate Boreal and Tethyan biozonations (S. Voigt & Hilbrecht 1997; Wiese 1999; Jarvis *et al.* 2006; S. Voigt *et al.* 2007). Carbon isotope stratigraphy of longer time intervals can provide temporal resolutions of up to 100 ka. Strontium isotope stratigraphy is based on the long residence time of strontium in seawater, where the $^{86}Sr/^{87}Sr$ ratio of seawater is constant over a particular period of time (McArthur *et al.* 2001). The application of strontium isotope stratigraphy in Central Europe involves the dating of chalk successions and platform carbonates (McArthur *et al.* 1992; Vonhof & Smit 1996; Steuber 2001). The Cretaceous period witnessed a long period of normal polarity in the Earth's magnetic field during Aptian–Santonian time. Repeated reversals of polarity occurred only during Early Cretaceous (Berriasian–early Aptian) and latest Cretaceous (Santonian–Maastrichtian) times, and are then used for magnetostratigraphy (Channell *et al.* 1992, 1993; Hambach & Krumsiek 1991).

### *Cycle and sequence stratigraphy*

The rhythmic bedding of clays and chalk at some levels in the Cretaceous succession is interpreted as reflecting climatic changes within the Milankovitch frequency band (e.g. Gale *et al.* 1999). The bedding commonly shows a pronounced cyclicity on a decimetre scale in the form of clay–marl, marl–chalk, chalk–flint, or laminated–bioturbated cycles related to the 20 ka precession cycle (e.g. Gale 1995; Zijlstra 1994; Scholle *et al.* 1998; Stage 1999; Damholt & Surlyk 2004). The presence of cyclicity may reflect changes in plankton productivity, possibly coupled with changes in humidity and associated freshwater runoff from land and the influx of clay. Superimposed bedding cycles also resolve the signals of short (100 ka) and long (405 ka) eccentricity. Bedding cycles are increasingly being used for correlation purposes, e.g. in chalk hydrocarbon reservoirs of the Danish North Sea sector (Scholle *et al.* 1998; Stage 1999), and in Hauterivian (Mutterlose & Ruffell 1999), Cenomanian (Gale 1995; Wilmsen 2003), Campanian (Niebuhr 2004, 2005) and Maastrichtian (Zijlstra 1994) successions of the North German and the Liège-Limburg basins.

The application of sequence stratigraphic techniques to Cretaceous basins in Central Europe is well developed in basins which are dominated by siliciclastic sedimentation (Wonham *et al.* 1997; Voigt & Tröger 1996; Uličný 2001) or carbonate platform development (Föllmi *et al.* 1994). Sequence stratigraphy in chalk-dominated successions is at an early stage and is not straightforward. A well-executed sequence stratigraphic model has, however, been developed for the Cenomanian of the North German Basin (Wilmsen 2003). Other models exist for Turonian and Maastrichtian chalk deposits (Wiese *et al.* 2004*a*; Schiøler *et al.* 1997).

## Tectonic setting

The Early Cretaceous evolution of sedimentary basins in Central Europe followed structures that had developed in the Jurassic. The rapidly subsiding graben system of the North Sea and the Lower Saxony Basin as its southern extension were filled with several thousand metres of sediments (Ziegler 1990; Kockel 1991; Senglaub *et al.* 2005). The WNW–ESE striking Central Netherlands Basin, the Lower Saxony Basin, the Altmark-Fläming Basin and the Prignitz Basin were arranged in an *en echelon* structural pattern (Nöldecke & Schwab 1977) reflecting a transtensional stress regime (Ziegler 1990), and were filled with up to 4000 m of Lower Cretaceous deposits (Senglaub *et al.* 2005). These basins were linked by north–south striking narrow basin structures (e.g. Gifhorn Trough) containing more than 1000 m of Lower Cretaceous deposits. All of these basins as well as the Danish Basin and the Mid-Polish Trough were subject to continuous sediment accumulation during the Early Cretaceous, although the primary thickness of Upper Jurassic and Lower Cretaceous deposits is difficult to assess due to Late Cretaceous inversion of most of these basin structures. During transgressions, the area of sedimentation spread over major parts of the slowly subsiding Central European Basin.

Late Cretaceous global plate tectonic changes caused modification of the tectonic stress field in Europe. The commencement of subduction at the northern Tethys margin and the opening of the Bay of Biscay resulted in a major reconfiguration of sedimentary basins. The concomitant interplay of extensional and compressional tectonics placed the European continental plate in a stress field which was dominated by NW–SE striking thrust faults. These caused the development of new, rapidly subsiding basins, halokinetic structures, and the inversion of former depocentres. Along zones of structural weakness, such as the Sorgenfrei-Tornquist Zone, the Elbe Fault System, the Roer Valley Graben, the Osning Thrust or the Mid-Polish Trough, inversion tectonics caused the formation of thrust faults, marginal basins with differential rates of subsidence, and block-fault bounded structural highs. The latter served as local source areas for sediment supply (Figs 15.1, 15.2).

The southern mobile margin of Central Europe comprising the Alps and the Western Carpathians forms part of the northwestern Tethyan palaeogeographic belt, which was repeatedly influenced by convergence between the European and the African plates. More or less continuous Cretaceous sedimentation occurred at the southern edge of the European plate, which was part of the northern Alpine Tethys during the Cretaceous, and forms part of the Alpine Helvetic nappes today. In the Eastern Alps and the Western Carpathians, Cretaceous geodynamics are controversial because of younger polyphase deformations overprinting Mesozoic structures. A variety of models have been proposed for the

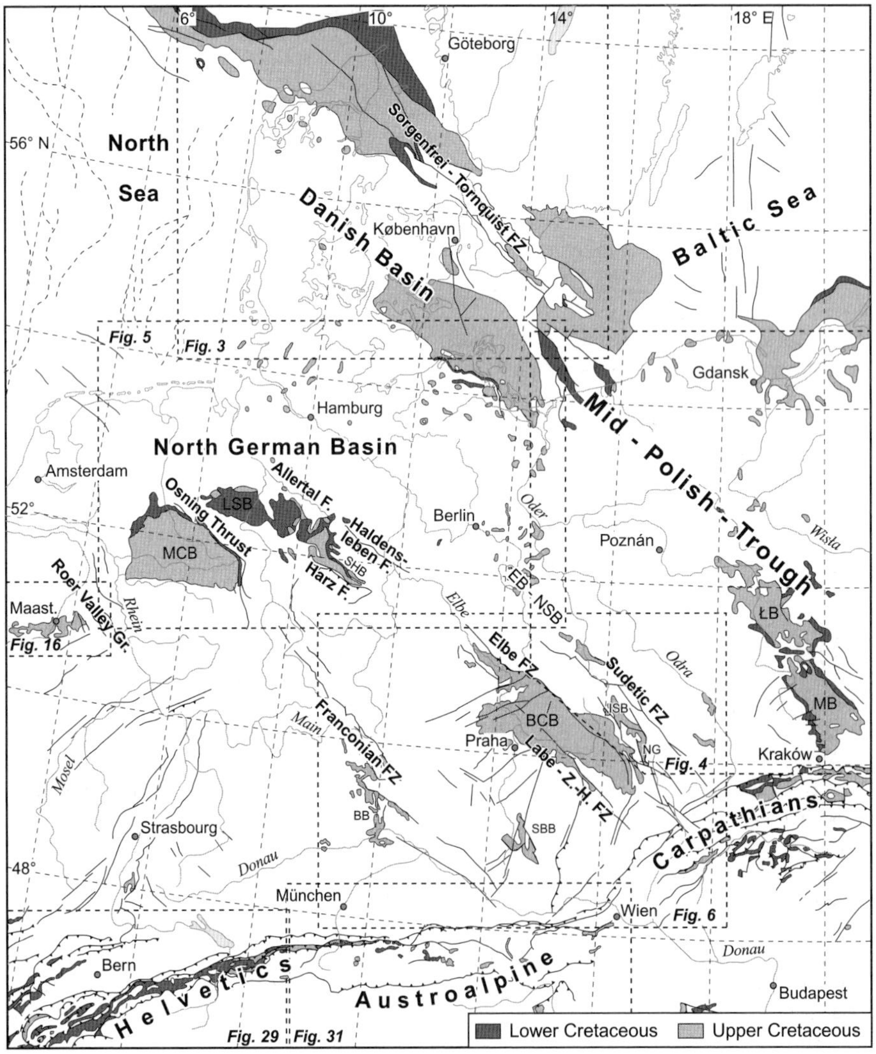


**Fig. 15.2.** Geological map of Central Europe showing the present-day distribution of Lower and Upper Cretaceous strata when the Quaternary sediment cover is removed (Asch 2004). Abbreviations: BB, Braunau Basin; BCB, Bohemian Cretaceous Basin; EB – NSB, East Brandenburg – North Sudetic Basin; ISB, Intrasudetic basins; Labe – Z. H. FZ, Labe – Železné Hory Fault Zone; ŁB, Łodz Basin; LSB, Lower Saxony Basin; MB, Miéchow Basin; MCB, Münsterland Cretaceous Basin: NG, Nysa Graben; SBB, South Bohemian Basins; SHB, Subhercynian Cretaceous Basin.

evolution of the Alps during the Cretaceous, differing especially in the inferred positions and timing of subduction zones and collisions, and thus also in the positions of major sedimentary basins along these active continental margins (e.g. Trümpy 1988; Channell *et al.* 1992; Stampfli & Borel 2002) (see also Frotzheim *et al.* 2008; Reicherter *et al.* 2008).

### *Mid-Polish Trough*

The formation and sedimentary infill of Cretaceous Central European basins is ultimately linked to the reconfiguration of the tectonic stress field in Europe. The Mid-Polish Trough was a NW–SE-orientated elongate basin, with higher rates of subsidence in the Late Jurassic to Early Cretaceous that evolved to a positive anticline in the Late Cretaceous as a consequence of inversion tectonics (Fig. 15.2, 15.3). It was bordered by Fennoscandia and the Ringkøbing-Fyn High to the north and NE, passed into the North German Basin in the west, was bordered by the Central European Island to the SW, and passed into the East European Platform in the NE.

### *Mid-Polish Anticlinorium*

During the Cretaceous, as during most of the Mesozoic, the NW-SE trending broad Mid-Polish Trough was a rift or aulacogen structure that became inverted during latest Cretaceous–Palaeogene times (Pożaryski 1977; Kutek & Głazek 1972; Kutek 2001). The inverted axial part of the Mid-Polish Trough is represented by the Mid-Polish Anticlinorium (Fig. 15.3). Inversion of the Mid-Polish Trough is considered to have been controlled mainly by compressional intraplate stress that built up in the Carpathian foreland during collision of the Inner Carpathian orogenic wedge with the European passive margin (Marcinowski & Radwański 1983; Kutek 2001). Many authors suggest that the onset of inversion was in the Santonian (Stephenson *et al.* 1993; Dadlez *et al.* 1995; Jaskowiak-Schoeneich & Krassowska 1988; Marek 1997), but new seismic data show that inversion movements had already commenced during the late Turonian and intermittently persisted into the Maastrichtian and Palaeocene (Krzywiec 2006). Earliest inversion movements were focused on the margins of the Mid-Polish Trough. Whereas the NE margin of the Mid-Polish Trough is devoid of compressionally-reactivated salt structures, its SW margin is characterized by strong inversion-related salt tectonics. Progressive inversion of the axial parts of the Mid-Polish Trough was accompanied by the uplift of its pre-Zechstein floor and by deep truncation of the Mesozoic. Inversion movements ceased towards the end of the Palaeocene, as evidenced by the burial of the Mid-Polish Swell beneath essentially flat-lying Eocene and younger series.

The Mid-Polish Anticlinorium is paralleled by two zones of synclines: the Pomeranian–Warsaw–Lublin–Lviv synclines to the NE, and the Usedom–Szczecin–Łódź–Miechów synclines to the SW. Due to subsequent erosion most of the anticline is devoid of Cretaceous sediments. Although the uplift of the Mid-Polish Trough was most probably fairly uniform along its strike, the Mesozoic cover thins towards the southeastern part as a result of erosion, which cut down into much older deposits of Jurassic and Triassic age, and in the most uplifted axial zone into

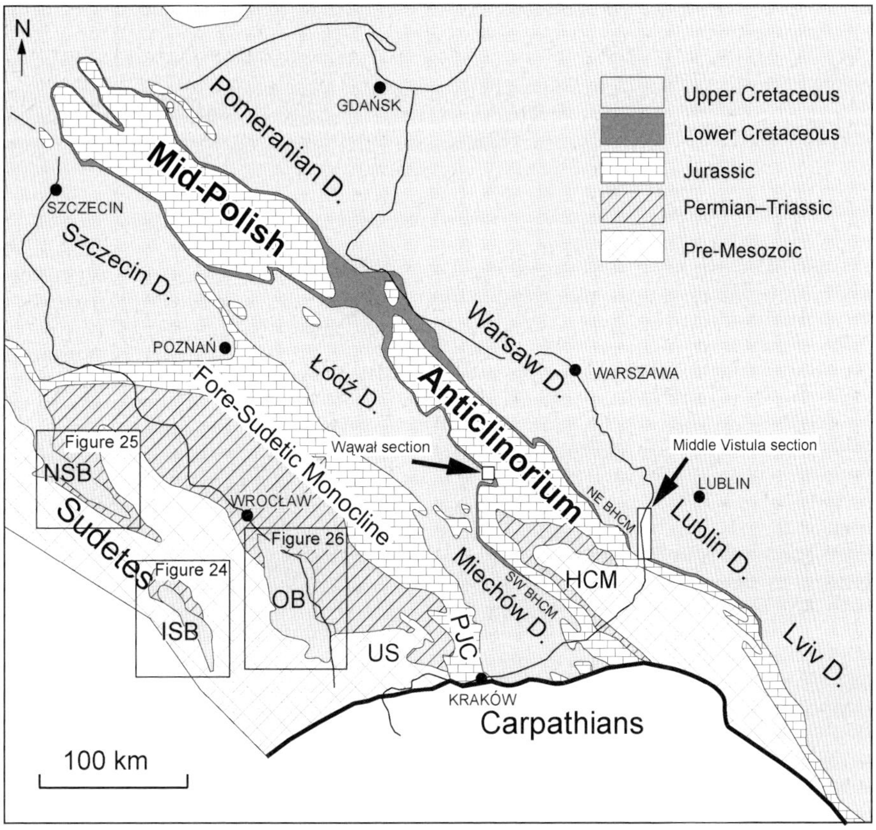


**Fig. 15.3.** Geological pre-Cenozoic sketch-map of Poland with adjacent territories (simplified after Pożaryski *et al.* 1979) Abbreviations: HCM, Holy Cross Mountains; ISB, Intrasudetic Basin and Upper Nysa Trough; NEB HCM, NE border of the Holy Cross Mountains; OB, Opole Basin; NSB, North Sudetic Basin; PJC, Polish Jura Chain; SW BHCM, SW border of the Holy Cross Mountains; US, Upper Silesia.

Palaeozoic and Precambrian rocks (Holy Cross Mountains). The Szczecin–Łódź–Miechów synclines pass into the Fore-Sudetic Monocline in the SE which is composed of Triassic and Jurassic sediments. Cretaceous deposits are only preserved as erosional relicts in isolated fault-bounded depressions (e.g. Opole Basin; Fig. 15.3). Further surface outcrops of Cretaceous deposits occur in the southeastern Miechów Depression close to the boundary with the Polish Jura Chain (Fig. 15.3, Smoleński 1906; Sujkowski 1934; Różycki 1937; Kowalski 1948; Rutkowski 1965; Marcinowski 1974; Walaszczyk 1992). More complete Cretaceous successions are preserved in the NE synclines. Surface outcrops occur in the Lublin and Lviv synclines in the Southern Polish Uplands, especially in the transition zone between the Mid-Polish Anticlinorium and the synclines around the Holy Cross Mountains (Fig. 15.3; e.g. Cieśliński & Pożaryski 1970). The well known Middle Vistula River section is located at the NE border of the Holy Cross Mountains, exposing a succession of Albian–Upper Cretaceous–Danian sediments (Pożaryski 1938, 1948; Błaszkiewicz 1980; Marcinowski & Radwański 1983; Walaszczyk 2004).

### *Danish Basin*

The Danish Basin is bordered to the NE by the Sorgenfrei-Tornquist Zone and to the SW by the Ringkøbing-Fyn High (EUGENO-S Working Group 1988). Towards the NW it passes into the Norwegian–Danish Basin and further into the greater North Sea Basin, including the Central Graben (Fig. 15.4). The Sorgenfrei-Tornquist Zone is a fundamental zone of crustal weakness, marking the boundary between the old and stable Baltic Shield to the NE and the deep sedimentary basins to the SW. The zone has experienced a long and complex history of normal and strike-slip faulting and was involved in Cretaceous and Cenozoic inversion tectonics (e.g. Liboriussen *et al.* 1987; Hansen *et al.* 2000; Vejbæk & Andersen 2002; Mogensen & Korstgård 2003; Ziegler 1990). The Ringkøbing-Fyn High is dissected by a number of north–south trending grabens, the most important of which is the Central Graben in the North Sea which contains prolific oil and gas reserves.

The Danish Basin is part of the Northern Permian Basin that was formed by rifting in Late Carboniferous–earliest Permian times, and was filled with more than 10000 m of sediments. Late Cretaceous subsidence was by thermal contraction overprinted by the effects of several inversion phases, causing uplift and the reversal of old normal faults. A system of straits and gulfs bordered by basement ridges was formed by transpressive inversion NE of the Sorgenfrei-Tornquist Zone in Skåne (SW Sweden) (e.g. Surlyk & Christensen 1974; Norling & Bergström 1987; Erlström & Gabrielson 1992; Erlström & Sivhed 2001). This region was characterized by the deposition of shallow-marine carbonates, and in some areas by mixed siliciclastics and carbonates.

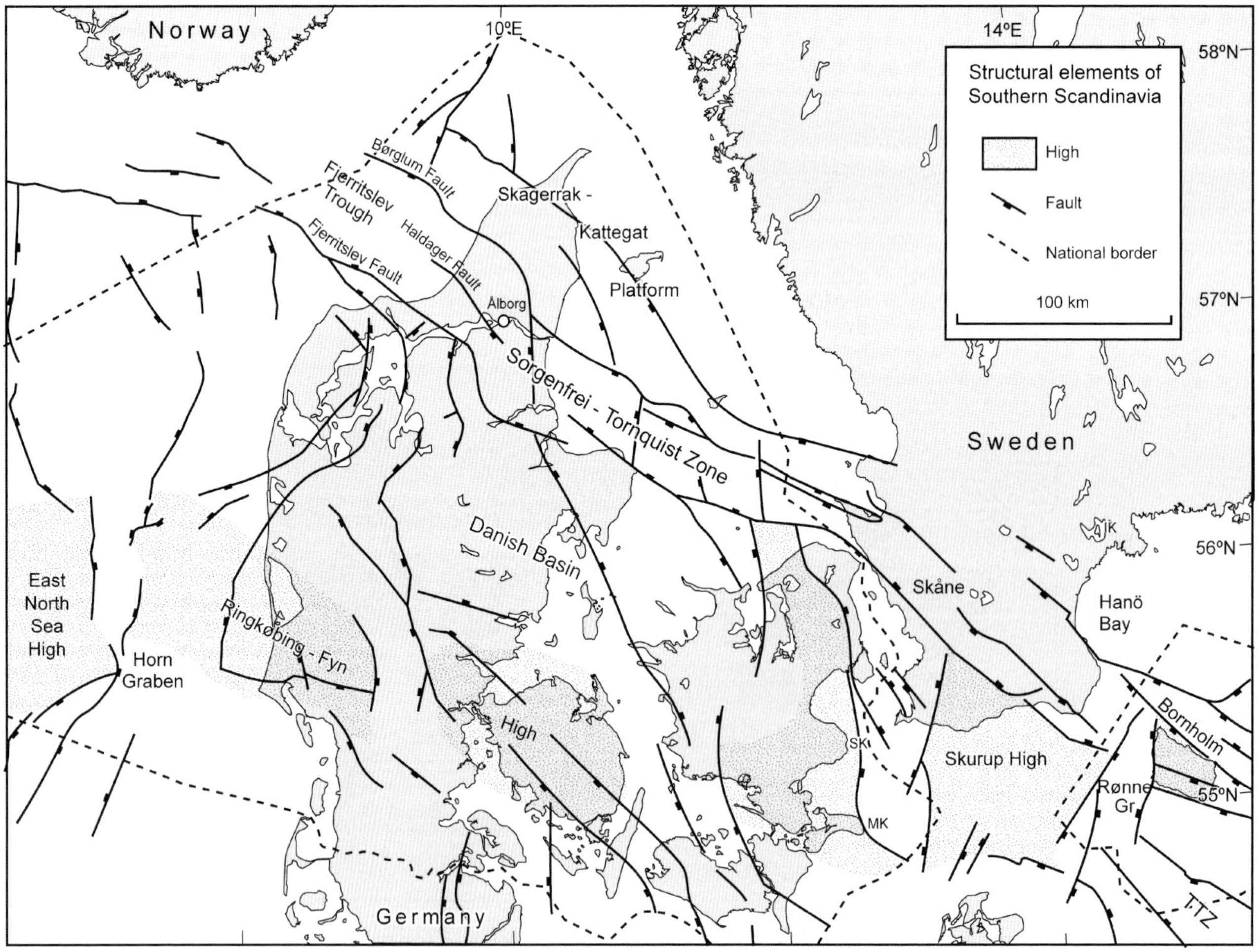


**Fig. 15.4.** Map showing the tectonic structures of the Danish Basin. Abbreviations: IK, Ivö Klack; MK, Møns Klint; SK, Stevns Kint.

### *North German Basin*

The North German Basin is linked to the North Sea Basin and is situated north of the massifs of Rheno-Bohemia, which formed the dissected Central European Island during Cretaceous times. The basin is bordered towards the east by the structure of the Mid-Polish Trough and towards the west by the Texel-IJsselmeer High. Cretaceous sedimentation in the North German Basin was controlled by the evolution of various sub-basins with high subsidence rates in Late Jurassic and Early Cretaceous times, and by the areal extension of marine deposition towards a broad epicontinental shelf in the early Late Cretaceous. During latest Cretaceous time, compression led to inversion of Jurassic to Cretaceous basins and to the formation of individual thrust-related basins mainly filled by siliciclastic deposits.

The *Lower Saxony Basin* is 200–250 km long and 70 km wide, and is orientated WNW–ESE. It is bordered to the north by the Pompeckj High (Pompeckj Block) that extends eastwards into the North Mecklenburg High (Fig. 15.5). During Late Jurassic–Early Cretaceous times, the basin experienced a period of extension related to contemporaneous rifting in the Central North Sea Graben (Ziegler 1990; Baldschuhn *et al.* 1991). The high rate of basin subsidence began in the Late Jurassic Kimmeridgian and continued into the late Aptian (Scheck *et al.* 2003). After a period of tectonic quiescence (Albian–late Turonian), the Lower Saxony Basin was subjected to crustal shortening and salt movements from the Late Cretaceous to the Palaeocene as a result of inversion tectonics (Betz *et al.* 1987; Baldschuhn *et al.* 1991; T. Voigt & von Eynatten 2004; Senglaub *et al.* 2005; T. Voigt *et al.* 2006).

The *Münsterland Cretaceous Basin* forms a broad syncline of Upper Cretaceous deposits on Variscan basement at the northern margin of the Rhenish Massif. The basin is bordered to the north by the NW–SE striking Osning Thrust, where the Lower Saxony Basin was thrust over the Münsterland Cretaceous Basin during Late Cretaceous inversion (Fig. 15.5). To the west, near the border with the inverted Central Netherlands Basin, sedimentary NW–SE orientated folds are developed. Faults with the same orientation predominate in the central and eastern basin and point to SW–NE orientated compression (Hiss & Seibertz 2000). The depocentre of the Münsterland Cretaceous Basin comprises up to 2500 m of Upper Cretaceous sediments and is situated close to the northwestern basin margin (Vorosning Trough) in front of the Ibbenbüren High, where the highest rates of inversion (*c.* 7000 m) had occurred (Betz *et al.* 1987; Senglaub *et al.* 2005). Towards the south, the basin is bordered by proximal Upper Cretaceous clastic sediments which overlie the folded Upper Carboniferous. During Cenomanian–Turonian

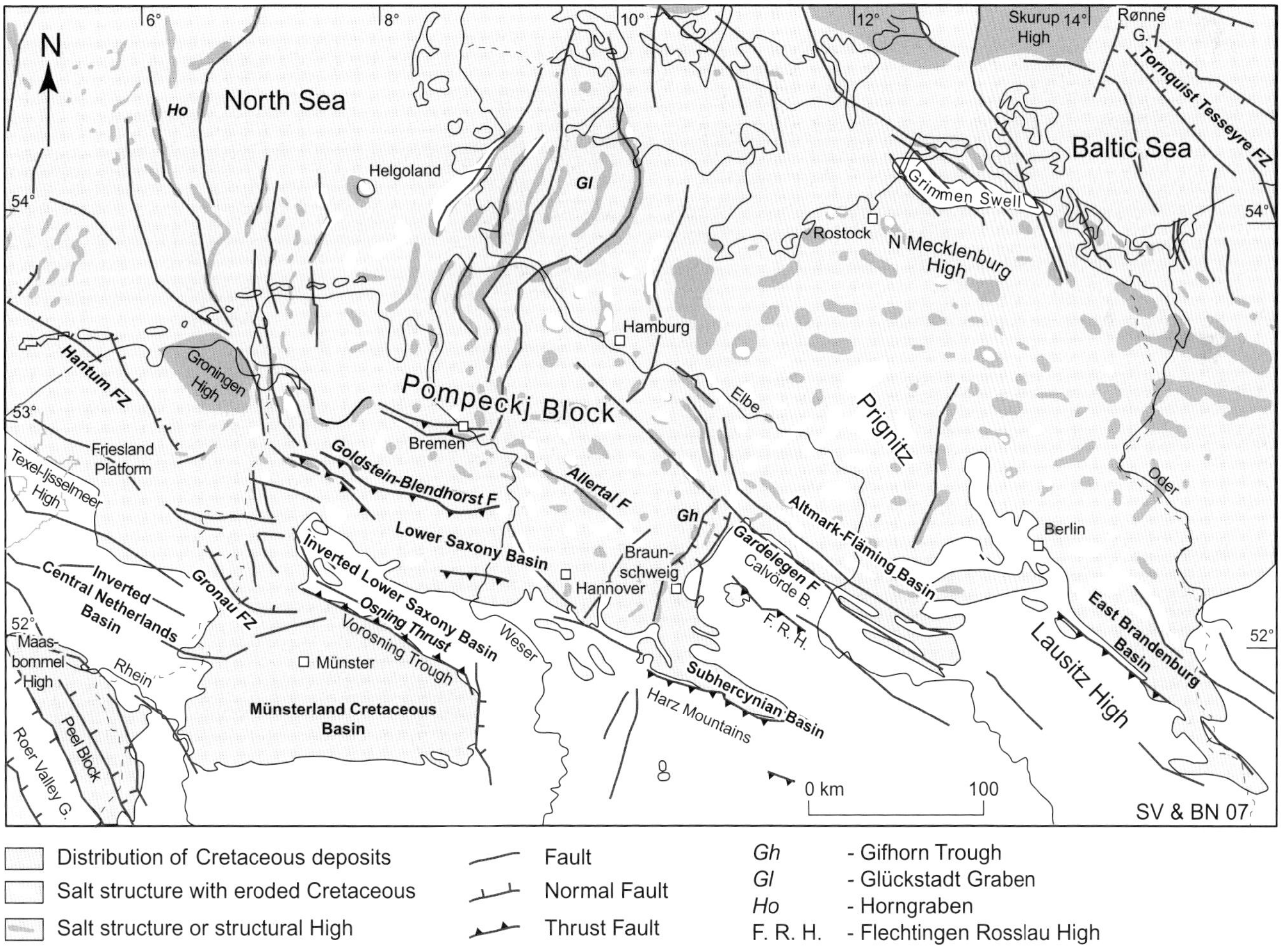


**Fig. 15.5.** Map showing the tectonic structures and salt domes of the North German Basin during Late Cretaceous inversion tectonics and the recent surface and subsurface distribution of Cretaceous rocks. Data are compiled from Diener (1968), Stratigraphische Kommission Deutschlands (2000), Baldschuhn *et al.* (2001), Mazur *et al.* (2005) and Worum *et al.* (2005).

times, the Münsterland Cretaceous Basin was part of the North German Basin. It became separated later as a result of the early Coniacian to Campanian inversion (Baldschuhn & Kockel 1997*a*, *b*).

The *Subhercynian Cretaceous Basin* is an elongated basin, 90 km long and only 15 km wide, located to the north of the uplifted basement block of the Harz Mountains (Fig. 15.5). The basin fill forms a deep asymmetric syncline with an overturned southern limb. The thickness of Upper Cretaceous deposits exceeds 2500 m in the depocentre near the southern basin margin. No separate basin development can be detected from Permian to Early Cretaceous times. The entire region formed part of the Central European Basin from late Permian through to Early Cretaceous times and part of the extended Central European carbonate shelf during Cenomanian–Turonian times. Formation of the Subhercynian Cretaceous Basin began in the late Turonian and continued through to the Campanian. The clastic-dominated basin fill was derived from inverted intrabasinal highs during Coniacian–Campanian times. From Santonian times, the northwestward thrusted Harz area became the main source areas for the clastic sediments. Erosion of the 2000–3000 m thick Mesozoic cover occurred in a timespan of <5 Ma (Kockel 1991; T. Voigt & Eynatten 2004). Exhumation of the Harz basement commenced in the early Campanian.

The Late Cretaceous *Altmark-Fläming Basin* north of the Gardelegen Fault is 150 km long and 60 km wide (Fig. 15.5). The basin is covered by thick Cenozoic deposits. The maximum thicknesses of the entire Upper Cretaceous succession are in the order of 1300 m according to seismic data. The southern boundary is formed by uplifted basement structures including the Flechtingen-Roßlau High and the Calvörde Block which became partly thrust onto the deeply subsided depocentre of the basin (Bülstringen Syncline) at the southern basin margin, but form, in general, large basement flexures with a throw of 1500 m and 3500 m respectively (Schulze 1964). The northeastern basin margin is formed by the broad anticline of the inverted Prignitz-Lausitz High. The basin is subdivided by a couple of equidistant NW–SE striking faults and narrow salt-injected anticlines. In the northern part of the basin rare diapirs cut through the Upper Cretaceous successions. The base of the Altmark-Fläming Basin fill comprises Upper Triassic to Lower Cretaceous strata. Basin formation and deformation ceased in the Campanian, as constrained by transgressive Masstrichtian deposits unconformably covering the deformational structures (Diener 1967).

The Cretaceous sedimentary infill of the North German Basin can be subdivided into three major sedimentary sequences, the development of which was mainly triggered by tectonically controlled basin evolution and global eustasy (Hiss *et al.* 2005). The first sequence (Berriasian to early Albian) is characterized and dominated by strong subsidence in the Lower Saxony and the Altmark-Fläming basins. The second sequence (middle Albian to early Coniacian) reflects sedimentation on a tectonically inactive (until late Turonian) or rather active shelf (late Turonian to early Coniacian) during a long-term cycle of sea-level change. The sedimentary stacking patterns were mainly controlled by eustatic sea-level fluctuations of higher frequency. The third sequence (middle Coniacian to Maastrichtian) was controlled by compressive tectonics and accelerated halokinetic movements of salt domes and pillows along major fault zones, as well as the next long-term cycle of sea-level change. A multitude of integrated stratigraphic data provide a framework that enables excellent time control with high-resolution correlation potential both in an intra- and interbasinal context, as well as into areas outside of Central Europe.

### *Liège-Limburg Basin*

Late Cretaceous rejuvenation of graben-bounding faults resulted in inversion and truncation of the Roer Valley Graben and the formation of the Liège-Limburg Basin at the north flank of the Anglo-Brabant Massif in the southern Netherlands (Fig. 15.2) (Gras 1995). A pulse of clastic influx in the late Santonian to early Campanian marks the commencement of the Roer Valley Graben uplift. The infill of the Liège-Limburg Basin was governed by this inversion and differential block faulting as well as by a long-term relative sea-level rise that led to a change from siliciclastic to carbonate sedimentation (Rossa 1987; Bless & Fernandez Narvaiza 1993, 1996). Inversion ceased in the middle late Maastrichtian, when large portions of the graben were flooded and a condensed sequence of marine carbonates was deposited.

### *Basins around the Bohemian Massif*

Reactivation of inherited crustal-scale shear zones in the basement of the Bohemian Massif during the mid-Cretaceous led to the formation of a number of intracontinental basins on the Bohemian Massif and at its periphery. The largest of these is the Bohemian Cretaceous Basin (Fig. 15.2). This basin comprises a number of structural sub-basins filled with deposits of Cenomanian through to Santonian age that span the present-day territories of Germany, the Czech Republic and Poland. The Bohemian Cretaceous Basin also includes the Cretaceous successor of the Intrasudetic Basin, and the Nysa Graben (Fig. 15.2; e.g. Jerzykiewicz & Wojewoda 1986; Valečka 1984; Valečka & Skoček 1991; Uličný 2001). The major structural feature that governed the basin's evolution is the Elbe Fault Zone, an array of NW–SE orientated faults reflecting a large-scale zone of crustal weakness (Fig. 15.2; see Scheck-Wenderoth *et al.* 2008). Reactivation of these Variscan shear zones caused the formation of the Cretaceous basins on and around the Bohemian Massif, such as the North Sudetic Basin in the north and the Braunau-Regensburg and Wasserburg basins in the south (Fig. 15.6). The South Bohemian basins formed at the intersection of the NW-trending Jáchymov Fault Zone and the NNE-trending Blanice-Rodl Fault Zone. The NNE-trending fault zones are part of a conjugate set along with the NW-trending Franconian, Jáchymov and Elbe Fault zones (cf. Brandmayr *et al.* 1995). Apart from these basins, autochthonous Cretaceous deposits occur on the SE slope of the Bohemian Massif, beneath the foreland basin deposits and flysch nappes of the West Carpathians (the Waschberg-Ždánice Zone) (Fig. 15.6).

## Palaeogeography

The Cretaceous palaeogeography of Central Europe is difficult to reconstruct, since large areas were affected by Late Cretaceous inversion that led to the erosion of Lower Cretaceous deposits. Later Cenozoic uplift and tilting of Central Europe resulted in widespread erosion of deposits of Late Cretaceous age. During Early Cretaceous times terrigenous deposits prevail and are limited to actively subsiding basin structures. The distribution of Lower Cretaceous continental and marginal marine sandstones, basement cooling ages, and the presence of pebbles derived from Lower Cretaceous deposits in younger sediments reflect the existence of several islands which had evolved from a larger landmass consisting of the Pompeckj High, the Anglo-Brabant Massif, the Rhenish Massif and the Bohemian Massif (Fig. 15.1). Whereas basins north of the Rhenish and Bohemian massifs

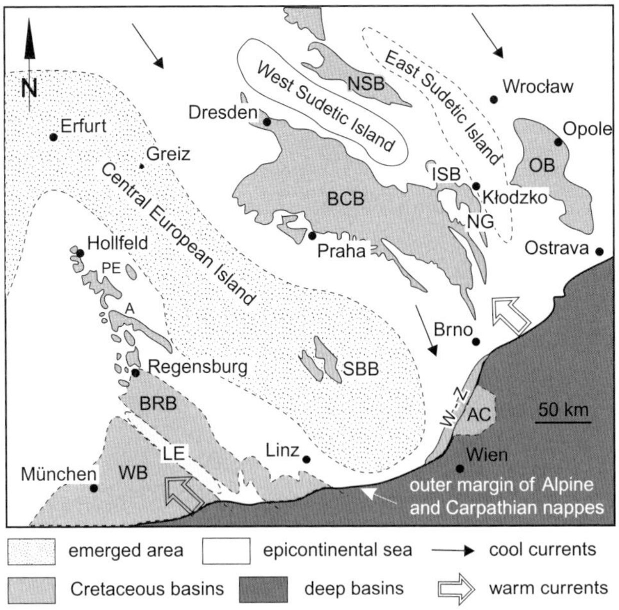


**Fig. 15.6.** Simplified Late Cretaceous (Turonian) palaeogeography of the Bohemian Cretaceous Basin and adjacent areas. Abbreviations: A, Amberg area; AC, Autochthonous Cretaceous of the SE slope of the Bohemian Massif; BCB, Bohemian Cretaceous Basin; BRB, Braunau-Regensburg Basin; ISB, Intrasudetic Basin; NG, Nysa Graben; NSB, North Sudetic Basin; OB, Opole Basin; PE, Parkstein-Erbendorf area; SBB, South Bohemian Basins; WB, Wasserburg Basin; W-Z, Waschberg-Ždánice Zone; (adapted from Fuchs *et al.* 1984; Valečka & Skoček 1991).

experienced continental to marine sedimentation from the Berriasian into the Maastrichtian, the history of basins around the Bohemian Massif is restricted to the global sea-level high in Cenomanian–Santonian times, and was subject to fluvial and marginal-marine sedimentation. In the context of the Cenomanian–Turonian transgression, the stepwise onlap onto older Mesozoic successions and Variscan basement resulted in the development of marine straits between the Sudetics, Bohemia and the Rhenish Massif, forming marine connections between basins of the Alpine domain at the northern Tethys and the Boreal basins of NW Europe (Fig. 15.1c). Cretaceous basins of the Alpine domain are dominantly influenced by syn- and post-depositional Alpine tectonics, and are part of the Helvetic, Penninic, Austro-Alpine and Carpathian nappe piles today (see Reicherter *et al.* 2008).

The following description of Cretaceous basins in Central Europe are arranged with respect to their age and position within the two main palaeogeographic domains, the Epicontinental Basins and the Alpine Basins. The first group is divided into: (1) Early Cretaceous epicontinental basins; (2) Late Cretaceous epicontinental basins; and (3) basins on and around the Bohemian Massif.

## Early Cretaceous epicontinental basins

### *Mid-Polish Trough (I.W.)*

Early Cretaceous sedimentation in the Mid-Polish Trough was strongly associated with the location of subsiding areas within the basin, and extended only slightly towards the SW and NE (Fig. 15.7). The Mid-Polish Trough is subdivided into three sedimentary basins, characterized by different tectonic subsidence and sedimentary records. These are the Pomeranian (in the NW), the Kujavian (in the central area) and the Małopolski (in the SE) basins (Figs 15.3, 15.7, 15.8). Maximum subsidence was associated with the axial zone of the Mid-Polish Trough (i.e. the Kujavian part of the trough, where the succession reaches the maximum thickness of 650 m) decreasing considerably towards the NE and SW (Marek 1989). The Lower Cretaceous succession is dominated by deposits of a siliciclastic shelf system, with subordinate occurrences of deltaic, fluvial, swamp-lacustrine, lagoonal and marine calcareous deposits (Raczyńska 1979; Marek 1989, 1997; Leszczyński 1997*a*). The carbonates are limited to the SE part of the basin (Marek 1989).

The Early Cretaceous evolution of the basin was controlled by eustasy and regional extensional tectonics (Fig. 15.7), shown by the concentration of subsidence in the Mid-Polish Trough as well as syndepositional faulting (Pożaryski 1970; Marek 1983; Kutek & Marcinowski 1996). The Berriasian–early middle Albian evolution of the Polish Lowland basin can be divided into three stages: (1) early Berriasian; (2) late Berriasian–Barremian; and (3) Aptian–early middle Albian. The early Berriasian is the latest part of a Late Jurassic sedimentary cycle. The late Berriasian–Barremian marks the period of the main Early Cretaceous transgression, while the Aptian–early middle Albian is marked by an initial transgression, followed by strong uplift in the Carpathian domain and a dominantly regressive phase (Figs 15.7 & 15.8).

*Early Berriasian*

A middle Volgian–early Berriasian regression was a regional phenomenon resulting, in part, from the global sea-level lowstand around the Jurassic–Cretaceous boundary, and partly from intraplate tectonic activity in Europe (Haq *et al.* 1988; Jacquin & de Graciansky 1998). This time interval was characterized by brackish, hypersaline to freshwater deposits (Purbeck facies) lithostratigraphically referred to as the Kcynia Formation. The lower Berriasian part of the formation is characterized by marly clays deposited in brackish environments (Marek 1989). The interval is well represented only in the Kujavian sub-basin of the Mid-Polish Trough and thins towards the marginal areas. Here middle Tithonian sediments are directly overlain by basal marine deposits of the late Berriasian transgression (Marek 1989, 1997; Leszczyński 1997*a*).

*Late Berriasian–Barremian*

The late Berriasian to Barremian interval marks the main transgressive period in the Early Cretaceous evolution of the Mid-Polish Trough. It is represented by marine sandstones and shales, with some carbonates in the SE. Ammonites of Tethyan origin testify to a marine connection along the Polish Rift with the Carpathian domain (Kutek *et al.* 1989). The stratigraphic gap associated with the basal unconformity (= Late Cimmerian unconformity of Stille 1924; see also Jacquin & de Granciansky 1998) may extend from the middle Tithonian to early Berriasian (Kutek *et al.* 1989). Erosion on structural highs and basin margins generated longer hiatuses.

Three transgressive–regressive cycles can be distinguished within this stage: (1) late Berriasian–early early Valanginian, with the regression in the late early Valanginian; (2) late Valanginian, with the regression at the end of the stage; and (3) Hauterivian–Barremian, with the regression in the Barremian (Fig. 15.8 and below). The classic Valanginian Wąwał section is the only surface exposure of the Neocomian strata in extra-Carpathian Poland (Kutek et al. 1989). It is represented by an

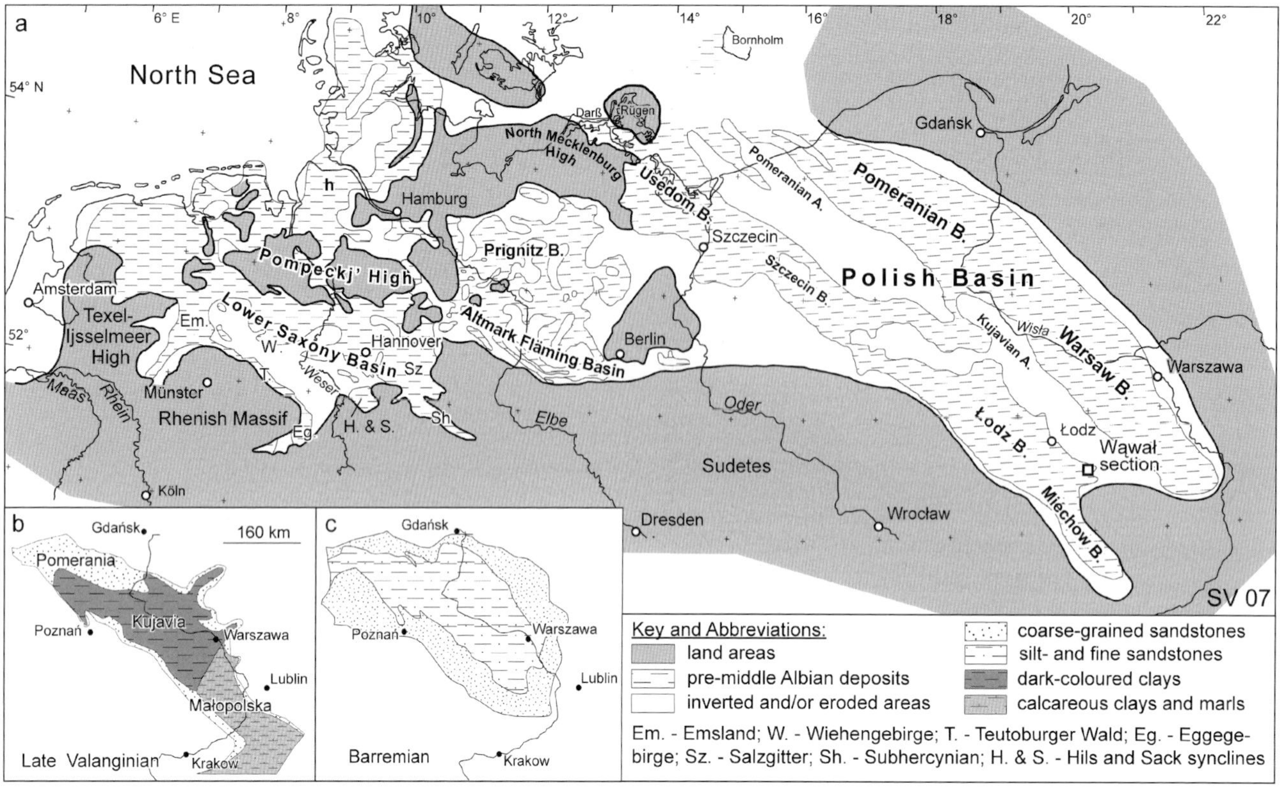


**Fig. 15.7.** Early Cretaceous palaeogeography of northern Central Europe (North German Basin and Mid-Polish Trough) during the early Aptian transgression showing the main depositional basins, the distribution of pre-middle Albian age deposits, and the assumed position of coastlines (**a**). Insets: facies distribution in the Mid-Polish Trough during the late Valanginian transgression (**b**) and the Barremian regression (**c**). Data are compiled from Schott *et al.* (1967–69), Diener (1967) and Marek (1997).

outcrop near the village of Wąwał, located to the south of the axis of the Mid-Polish Anticlinorium (Fig. 15.3).

1. Berriasian–early Valanginian: the first Early Cretaceous transgression came from the area of the Tethys Ocean. In the late Berriasian and early Valanginian (*Platylenticeras* zone), an epicontinental sea existed in the area of the Mid-Polish Trough, with both Tethyan and Boreal influences. This is indicated by the co-occurrence of ammonites from both of these regions, including *Riasanites*, *Surites*, *Tollia*, *Peregrinoceras*, *Malbosiceras*, *Euthymiceras*, *Neocosmoceras*, *Pseudosubplanites*, *Berriasella*, *Himalayites* (all Tethyan), and *Platylenticeras* (Boreal). The calcareous facies at the base of the transgression passes into dark-coloured siliciclastic sediments. The sea was limited to the Mid-Polish Trough, with only a slight extension to the east in the central (Kujavian) part. The maximum thickness of this part of the Cretaceous is between 80 and 160 m. Almost no influence is noted from salt tectonics. The rate of transgression decreased in the early Valanginian *Polyptychites* zone, causing the shallowing of the sea and relatively pronounced freshwater influxes in some areas. Northern ammonites are recorded only in the central Kujavian sub-basin, which shows more Boreal influences. Here, the lower Valanginian succession (*Polyptychites* zone) is up to 160 m thick.

2. Late Valanginian: subsequent transgression led to a marked extension of the sea to the NE and SW. Siliciclastic sediments dominate in the central and NW parts of the basin and grade into more calcareous facies towards the SE. The maximum thickness of upper Valanginian deposits is 50 m in the NW, and 70 m in the calcareous facies to the SE. An intense faunal exchange with the Tethys Ocean is indicated in the late Valanginian by the occurrence of the ammonite genera *Bochianites*, *Saynoceras*, *Astieria*, *Leopoldia*, *Necomites*, and *Valanginites*, but also towards the Boreal Atlantic by the presence of *Neocraspedites*, *Dichotomites* and *Polyptychites*.

3. Hauterivian–Barremian: following a short period of regression at the end of the Valanginian, the Hauterivian period was transgressive, as documented by the greater extent of marine sediments within the basin. The central and NW parts of the basin continue to be dominated by dark-coloured siliciclastic facies that grade into carbonates towards the SE. The subsequent regression occurred in the early Barremian. Maximum thicknesses are typically 120 m, but locally in tectonically controlled depressions can extend up to 217 m. Parts of the Hauterivian succession were eroded very early in early Barremian, Aptian and early Albian times. Ammonites of the genera *Endemoceras* and *Simbirskites* indicate ongoing connection with the Boreal Atlantic area.

### *Aptian–Albian*

The Aptian to early middle Albian interval is represented by sandstones and shales, which are partly non-marine. The basin was open towards the NW and closed towards the SE by a land area that formed part of the Carpathian domain. A short-lived marine ingression is noted in the Aptian. Corresponding sediments are dominated by sandstones (Mogilno Formation), and can be subdivided further into three members (Pagórki, Gopło

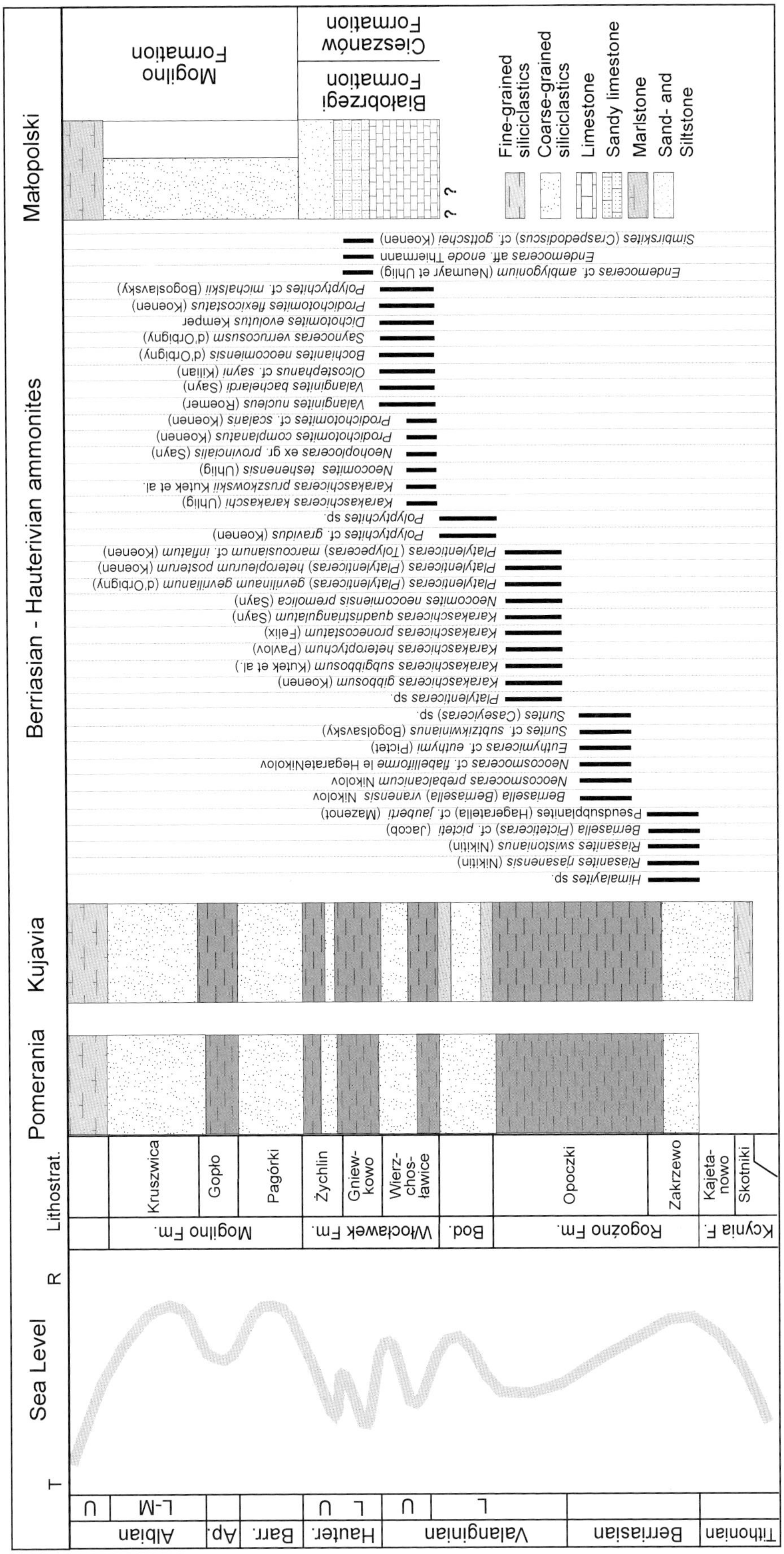


**Fig. 15.8.** Lower Cretaceous successions of the Mid-Polish Trough along a NW-SE transect from Pomerania to Małopolski showing their litho- and biostratigraphical subdivision in relation to relative sea-level change (R, Regression; T, Transgression) and ammonite occurrences; compiled after Marek (1989, 1997), Leszczyński (1997*b*).

and Kruszwica members). The maximum thickness of the formation is *c.* 200 m. The commencement of intense salt tectonics is documented from this time. The occurrence of additional minor marine ingressions in the Aptian is indicated by the presence of glauconitic deposits. The major Cretaceous transgression began early in the middle Albian. Basal transgressive sediments are light-coloured sands. The middle–upper Albian sequences are composed of terrigenous siliciclastics rich in glauconite and phosphatic concretions. Silicious siliciclastics and spongiolites are common in the upper Albian succession. Albian deposits are overlain by up to 2.5 km of Upper Cretaceous sediments. These consist mainly of carbonates.

### *Lower Saxony Basin (S.V.)*

The Lower Saxony Basin can be divided into a series of sub-basins. The Emsland and the northern Wiehengebirge area are depocentres in the west and the Hannover–Braunschweig area forms a sub-basin in the east (Fig. 15.7). Towards the southern basin margin, proximal sediments are preserved in the Teutoburger Wald, the Eggegebirge, the Salzgitter area and the Subhercynian Cretaceous Basin (Fig. 15.9).

In the Emsland area, outcrops with Berriasian to Barremian sediments are bounded by east–west striking salt anticlines. The northern Wiehengebirge area exposes Berriasian to earliest late Hauterivian sediments, which crop out along east–west striking anticlines and synclines, created by salt movements (Baldschuhn & Kockel 1996). Sediments younger than late Hauterivian were eroded during Late Cretaceous basin inversion. The most distal sediments were deposited in the Hannover–Braunschweig area. A complete Lower Cretaceous (Berriasian–Albian) succession comprises up to 1300 m of sediments. Outcrops occur along NNE–SSW striking synsedimentary active salt anticlines (Bettenstedt & Dietz 1957).

The southern marginal facies of the Lower Saxony Basin crops out in the Teutoburger Wald and Eggegebirge areas over a distance of 150 km (Fig. 15.7a). Marine sandstones (Osning Sandstone) mark a coastline which was active during Early Cretaceous (early Valanginian to early Albian) times. Thicknesses range from 800 m in the NW Teutoburger Wald to 10–40 m in the Eggegebirge area. A Valanginian–Aptian coastal environment along the southern basin margin is exposed in the Salzgitter area, which is famous for its economically important iron ores. Ore accumulation was controlled by high rates of tectonic subsidence of a SW–NE striking graben and half-graben system related to the Salzgitter anticline (Kolbe 1962, 1970). Additional Berriasian to Albian sediments were accumulated in the Hils and Sack synclines. The deposits are partly of marginal

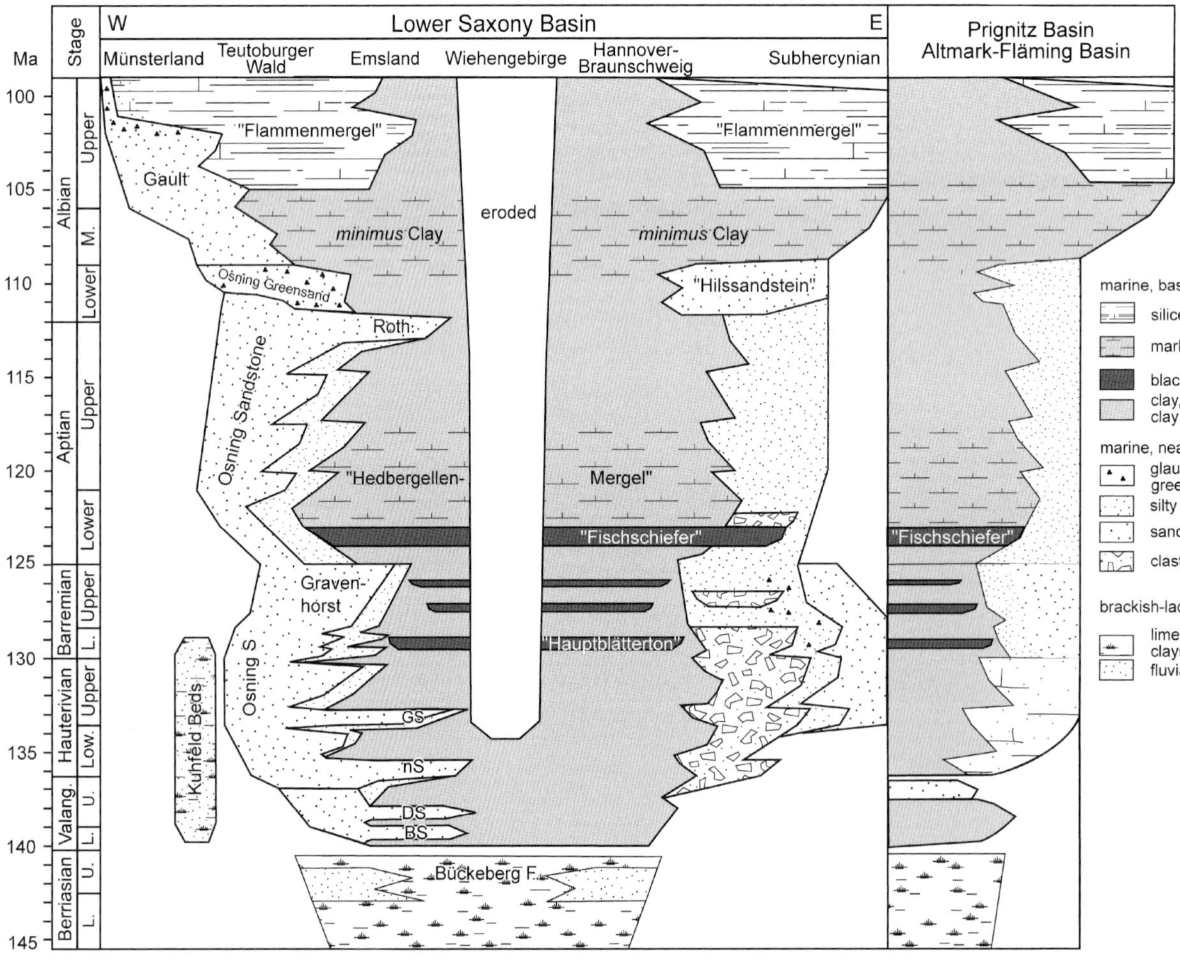


**Fig. 15.9.** Chronostratigraphic diagram of Lower Cretaceous lithofacies in the Lower Saxony Basin, the Altmark-Fläming Basin and the Prignitz Basin. For the position of localities see Figure 15.7. Timescale is after Gradstein *et al.* (2004). Abbreviations: BS, Bentheim Sandstone; DS, *Dichotomites* Sandstone; GS, Gildehaus Sandstone; nS, *noricum* Sandstone; Roth., Rothenberg Sandstone.

marine and non-marine origin. The Subhercynian Cretaceous Basin also exposes a southern marginal facies, with outcrops of Hauterivian–Berriasian nearshore to coastal and non-marine deposits.

The main temporal and spatial pattern of Early Cretaceous sedimentary basin fill was controlled by third- and second-order sea-level changes allowing a division into four intervals: (1) Berriasian, (2) Valanginian–Hauterivian, (3) Barremian–earliest Aptian, and (4) early Aptian–early Albian (Fig. 15.9). Sedimentary thicknesses were clearly controlled by differential subsidence in relation to tectonic movements along NW–SE trending faults. Summaries of the faunal and sedimentary evolution in the Early Cretaceous Lower Saxony Basin are provided by Mutterlose & Bornemann (2000), Michael (1974, 1979), and Kemper (1979). Schott *et al.* (1967–69) and Baldschuhn & Kockel (1996) have published detailed palaeogeographic and palaeotectonic maps.

*Berriasian*

The Berriasian was a period of widespread regression, causing the isolation of sedimentary basins in northern Europe. The Lower Saxony Basin, in common with other basins in southern England and northern France, can be characterized by a succession of non-marine sediments (the so-called 'Wealden') deposited under brackish-lacustrine conditions (Fig. 15.9). The sediments consist of non-marine brackish-lacustrine clays, siltstones, sandstones and rare coal seams (Wicher 1940). The biostratigraphic division is based on ostracods (Wolburg 1949, 1959; Kemper 1973; modified by Elstner & Mutterlose 1996) and palynomorphs (Döring 1965). Marine floras and faunas are rare in the upper Berriasian and represent several short-lived marine incursions from the west, documented by palynomorphs and foraminifera (Strauss *et al.* 1993). In particular, the short-lived marine transgression in the mid-Berriasian can be recognized in all of the sub-basins (Diener 1974; Döring 1965). The Wealden facies onlaps older Mesozoic successions, thus documenting a brief extensional phase within the basin.

In the western Emsland area, Wealden deposits are widespread and comprise up to 400 m of dark carbonate-poor mudstones with several thin limestone beds. Sandstones are rare. Successions of non-marine fluviolacustrine sediments up to 700 m thick occur in the central part (Wiehengebirge to Hannover). Along the Weser river, fluviodeltaic sands of the Bückeberg Formation interdigitate with sandstones, siltstones, silty clays, *Neomiodon* limestones and coal seams (Mutterlose 1992; Wilde & Schultka 1996). The coarser clastics were derived from the Rhenish Massif. In the Hannover area, a large fan is interpreted as a transgressive barrier sand deposited parallel to the coast (Pelzer 1988). The sandstone fan contains turtle and dinosaur remains (Obernkirchen area) and dinosaur footprints (near Münchehagen). Further eastwards, the sandy sediments of the Bückeberg Formation interfinger with clays in the Peine area.

*Valanginian–Hauterivian*

During Valanginian–Hauterivian times, a long-term eustatic sea-level rise led to flooding of the Lower Saxony Basin and the establishment of full marine conditions. The initial transgressions in the early Valanginian (FO of *Platylenticeras*) and earliest late Valanginian came from the southern North Sea via the East Netherlands High and reached the eastern parts of the Altmark-Fläming Basin (Fig. 15.5 & 15.7). The early Valanginian transgression also opened marine passages towards the Tethys due to the opening of the Carpathian seaway. Three transgressions in the earliest Hauterivian (*Endemoceras amblygonium* ammonite Zone), the early late Hauterivian (*Aegocrioceras* Beds), and the latest Hauterivian (*Simbirskites discofalcatus* Zone) led to an increase in the areal extent of marine sedimentation (Fig. 15.9). The second transgression, in particular, resulted in a widening of the Lower Saxony Basin towards the north and NE, and towards the south by flooding of the Eggegebirge area.

Basinal Valanginian marine sediments consist of up to 350 m of dark-grey silty clays, with low carbonate contents and sideritic nodules. The main area of marine offshore sedimentation was situated in the western Emsland area (Fig. 15.7 & 15.9) (Hinze 1988). Benthic associations are impoverished due to oxygen-depleted bottom-water conditions (Kemper 1978; Kemper *et al.* 1978; Mutterlose 1992). Two bodies of sandstone prograde into the basin, and are part of a retrogradational facies deposited during the Valanginian transgressions. The Bentheim and the *Dichtomites* sandstones intercalate with claystones of the *Polyptychites* and *Dichtomites* beds, respectively, and reflect a nearshore environment east of the Texel-IJsselmeer High (Fig. 15.7 & 15.9; Füchtbauer 1955). The sedimentary thickness of basinal Valanginian successions decreases towards the east, with up to 300 m in the northern Wiehengebirge and 100 m in the Hannover–Braunschweig area.

Basinal Hauterivian deposits of the Lower Saxony Basin occur in the areas between the northern Wiehengebirge and Hannover–Braunschweig, where 300–400 m of dark-grey, carbonate-poor silty clays occur (Fig. 15.9). Locally, the lowermost Hauterivian is represented by shallow-marine carbonates (Michael & Pape 1971). In part, the Hauterivian claystones are rhythmically bedded because of orbitally forced variability in carbonate production (Mutterlose & Ruffell 1999). Towards the west (Emsland), two distinct (up to 500 m) sandstone horizons (*noricum* sandstone and Gildehaus Sandstone) prograde into the basin and represent highstand deposits of lower and lower upper Hauterivian sequences (Fig. 15.9).

Proximal Valanginian–Hauterivian sediments are exposed along the southern margin in the Teutoburger Wald and the Eggegebirge, and in the Salzgitter and Subhercynian areas. The Valanginian transgressions led to flooding of parts of the Rhenish Massif. Here, marine sandstones form the basal beds of the Valanginian–Aptian Osning Sandstone. The homogenous composition of the Osning Sandstone indicates a uniform source area. The grain size increases from the NW Teutoburger Wald to the Eggegebirge, where conglomerates contain well-rounded clasts of quartz, chert, coal, siderite, limestone and clay. A marine fauna (molluscs, brachiopods and echinoderms) indicates deposition in a shallow-marine setting. In the Subhercynian and Salzgitter areas, marine oolithic ironstones are intercalated with shallow limestones (Fig. 15.9) (Knappe & Tröger 1988; Rödiger 1933). Valanginian to lower Barremian estuarine deposits (Kuhfeld Beds) are known from the northern margin of the Rhenish Massif, in the western Münsterland area (Fig. 15.9). The Kuhfeld Beds comprise up to 200 m of sand, gravel and clays with isolated coal deposits, and interdigitate with marine deposits towards the north (Herngreen *et al.* 1994).

*Barremian–earliest Aptian*

The transition from the Hauterivian into the Barremian was marked by a significant change in the depositional style of marine sedimentation as a consequence of overall regressive conditions. The Lower Saxony Basin formed a semi-enclosed epicontinental sea bordered towards the north by the Pompeckj High, which restricted the exchange of water masses. Barremian-age basinal sediments were dominated by dark-grey to black carbonate-poor clays associated with abundant finely laminated clays, known as 'Blätterton' horizons (Fig. 15.9). The Blätterton horizons are enriched in organic matter (total organic carbon (TOC) = 4–8%) and were deposited under anoxic conditions indicating sustained water column stratification. Restricted conditions and reduced bottom-water oxygenation favoured the evolution of endemic marine biota (calcareous nannofossils, foraminifera, belemnites and ammonites). The onset of Blätterton deposition was diachronous across of the basin, occurring earlier in basinal (Upper Hauterivian, *Simbirskites discofalcatus* Zone) than in marginal settings (late early Barremian, *Aulacoteuthis belemnite* Zone). The period of restricted conditions continued until the eustatic sea-level rise in the early Aptian (*Deshayesites deshayesi* ammonite Zone). The Barremian sequence of dark clays and Blätterton horizons has an average thickness of *c.* 200 m in the Hannover–Braunschweig area, increasing to 400 m in the Emsland where the clays grade into sands in the late Barremian.

In marginal areas, the Barremian regression resulted in both erosion and non-deposition as well as the massive progradation of marine sandstones into the basin. In the NW Teutoburger Wald, the sedimentary stacking pattern evolved from silty clays (Schierloh Beds) in the lower Barremian to sandstones (Gravenhorst Sandstone) in the upper Barremian. The age of the Gravenhorst Sandstone is dated by the index belemnites *Oxyteuthis germanica* and *Oxyteuthis depressa*. In the Salzgitter area, the Barremian was the main phase of conglomeratic clastic iron ore deposition (Fe contents up to 40%). The ore deposits occur in lenticular bodies 1–2 km in length and are up to 100 m thick. High rates of chemical weathering led to the transport and mineralization of Fe-rich solutions into a nearshore environment, where reworked limonitic fragments accumulated. A nearshore to dune coastal environment with a thickness of 180 m is exposed in the Subhercynian Cretaceous Basin (Nöldecke 1963).

*Early Aptian–early Albian*

A eustatic sea-level rise in the early Aptian *Deshayesites deshayesi* Zone terminated the period of restricted palaeoceanographic conditions in the Lower Saxony Basin (Fig. 15.9). New marine gateways between the Tethys and the Boreal oceans opened via northern France and southern England, and allowed the exchange of water masses and marine faunas (Fig. 15.1b). Endemic Barremian faunas were replaced by cosmopolitan surface-water communities and later by benthic associations (Mutterlose & Böckel 1998). A horizon of finely laminated black shales (Fischschiefer) is a marker bed for this significant oceanographic turnover (Fig. 15.9). Its high organic carbon content (TOC = 3.6–7%) is mostly of marine origin, and surface-water floras and faunas indicate open pelagic conditions (Littke *et al.*, 1998; Bischoff & Mutterlose 1998). The Fischschiefer is distributed basin-wide from southern coastal settings to the southern North Sea Basin in the north. In basinal settings, the Fischschiefer is overlain by the grey and multicoloured *Hedbergella* Marls, which indicate the complete ventilation of the water column. Subsequent late Aptian to early Albian basinal sedimentation is dominated by carbonate-poor grey clays, which may be rich in glauconite. Mean Aptian succession thicknesses range from 200 to 250 m in the Emsland and the Hannover–Braunschweig area to 25 m in the Hils and Sack synclines.

In the marginal area of the Teutoburger Wald, transgressive early Aptian-age sandy-silty sediments extend towards the SE, shifting the coastal sandstone facies (Osning Sandstone) towards the Eggegebirge. In the latest Aptian and early Albian the progradation of sandstones into the basin is documented by the Rothenberg Sandstone (Emsland), the Dörenthe Sandstone (Teutoburger Wald), and the Hils Sandstone (Hannover–Braunschweig area).

## Prignitz Basin, Altmark-Fläming Basin (S.V.)

The Prignitz and the Altmark-Fläming basins are bordered by the Flechtingen High in the south, the East Brandenburg High in the east, and the Pompeckj High in the north (Fig. 15.7). The sedimentary fill of these basins is similar to that of the Lower Saxony Basin, but rates of basin subsidence were distinctly lower. The Prignitz and Altmark-Fläming basins are recorded only from boreholes. The most complete successions of Berriasian–Albian sediments occur in synsedimentary rim synclines of salt anticlines with thicknesses of up to 1000 m. On local highs and towards marginal areas (North Mecklenburg High, East Brandenburg High), the thickness of the sedimentary sequence decreases to less than 100 m and is associated with various hiatuses (Diener *et al.* 2004*b*).

Berriasian Wealden sediments consist of coal seams, clays and silts, rich in plant debris and represent floodplain deposits of a fluvio-lacustrine system (Fig. 15.9). The occurrence of agglutinated foraminifera suggests brief marine incursions. Thicknesses are variable, from up to 500 m along salt structures to a few metres on local highs. Valanginian deposits comprise up to 80 m of marine siltstones and clays locally preserved in the rim synclines of salt diapirs. Hauterivian-age sediments transgressively overlie Wealden deposits, and proximal deposits along the southern and northern basin (towards the Pompeckj High) margins comprise several metres of sands and silts. Basinal Hauterivian sediments consist of 30 m of basal glauconite and up to 600 m of marls and marly limestones. Barremian thicknesses are between 20 and 100 m in the basin, thinning to a few metres of marginal sandstones along the North Mecklenburg High. The thickness of Aptian clays and claystones is *c.* 100 m.

## Bornholm

Rifting processes resulted in differential subsidence of the Rønne Graben which, in combination with eustatic sea-level changes, controlled deposition at Bornholm (Fig. 15.7). Early Cretaceous deposition commenced with the fluvial sand and gravel of the lower Berriasian Rabekke Formation, and was overlain by clay containing coal and wood deposited in near-coast swamps (Gravesen *et al.* 1982). In the late Berriasian, sedimentation continued with fine-grained and medium- to coarse-grained coastal quartz sand of the Robbedale Formation. The upper Berriasian–Valanginian Jydegård Formation was deposited in a large lagoon-lake complex, dominated by clayey sediments, which were bordered towards the south by sandy and clayey backbarrier sediments, washover sands, small meandering channels and tidal channels (Noe-Nygaard & Surlyk 1988). Deposition of the Robbedale and the Jydegåred formations was strongly influenced by tectonic activity. Above the Jydegård Formation is a hiatus that accounts for the Hauterivian, Barremian and Aptian stages. In the Albian, fully marine deposition returned to the area as a result of several transgressions. Most of the Albian deposits were removed by erosion. However, Albian clasts occur within the basal conglomerate of the middle Cenomanian of the Arnager Greensand Formation.

## Late Cretaceous epicontinental basins

Major eustatic sea-level changes resulted in two distinct transgressive–regressive cycles separating the Late Cretaceous shelf sea of northern Central Europe. They comprise a late Albian–early Coniacian and a late Coniacian–Maastrichtian succession. Each of these is characterized by a distinct distribution of facies. Late Cretaceous inversion tectonics commenced in the late Turonian but the main phases occurred in Santonian–Campanian and early Palaeocene times.

### *Danish Basin (F.S.)*

Late Cretaceous deposition in the North Sea–Danish region was preceded by an important and protracted mid- to Late Jurassic rifting event, followed by local oblique-slip movements during the Early Cretaceous. The Late Cretaceous was a time of relative tectonic quiescence, but important pulses of compression and inversion exerted a profound influence on chalk deposition, since reversals of fault movement and uplift of local blocks commonly triggered extensive mass movements of chalk that was subsequently redeposited in slope and basinal settings.

The Danish Basin and the surrounding region was throughout Late Cretaceous times dominated by the deposition of pure chalk, following an initial Cenomanian phase with quartzose sand in some areas; a few marly intervals occur in the younger parts of the succession. The main depocentres were located over the deep Jurassic basins. The chalk reaches a maximum thickness of more than 1500 m in the Central Graben, and exceeds 2000 m in the northern North Sea and along the Sorgenfrei-Tornquist Zone (Stenestad 1972; Liboriussen *et al.* 1987; Surlyk *et al.* 2003; Ineson *et al.* 2005). Chalk deposition took place below the photic zone, and water depths varied from tens to many hundreds of metres over the deepest parts of the Central Graben and the Danish Basin. The deposition of chalk came to an end at the Danian–Palaeocene boundary when siliciclastic sediments were introduced into the basins, resulting from the uplift of landmasses adjacent to the North Sea, in particular the Scottish Highlands and the Norwegian landmass (e.g. Ziegler 1990).

The classic paradigm of chalk deposition comprises quiet pelagic deposition in relatively deep water of carbonate debris from minute pelagic coccolithophorid algae which lived in the photic zone in the upper water masses. This was punctuated by local redeposition. Recent interpretations of conventional and 3D seismic data show, however, that the chalk sea was a highly dynamic depositional setting governed by strong, long-living bottom current systems which created a dramatic seafloor relief with amplitudes of several hundred metres (Lykke-Andersen & Surlyk 2004; Surlyk & Lykke-Andersen 2007). The chalk was thus commonly developed as major contourite systems, comprising valley and ridge systems, moats, channels and drifts. Evidence for such systems has been recorded from the Baltic, Øresund, Kattegat, onshore Denmark, and the North Sea, including the Danish, Norwegian, German and Dutch sectors, as well as from the Paris Basin. In addition to local fault-controlled subsidence or inversion chalk deposition was also greatly influenced by halokinesis in many areas. Halokinetic movements commenced during the Triassic and continued throughout the Late Cretaceous, resulting in the formation of salt pillows, domes, ridges and diapirs. Some of the resulting structures had seafloor expression during chalk deposition indicated by the presence of hardgrounds and thinned, condensed and winnowed chalk successions across the structures.

*Stratigraphic succession*

The chalk succession is placed in the poorly named Chalk Group, which to the north in the North Sea gives way to the siliciclastic, clay-dominated Shetland Group. A detailed and coherent lithostratigraphic scheme is difficult to establish for the Chalk Group due to its monotonous nature, and because it is mainly known from wells drilled on structural highs where the successions are commonly condensed and developed differently from those in basinal areas. The first formal lithostratigraphic subdivision of the Chalk Group in the North Sea region (Deegan & Scull 1977) still forms the basis of the current scheme (Fig. 15.10). The Chalk Group in the Danish sector has been subdivided into informal units 1–6 (Lieberkind *et al.* 1982), and correlations with the other North Sea regions are summarized by Surlyk *et al.* (2003). Recently, a new stratigraphic scheme has been proposed for the uppermost Maastrichtian–lower Danian succession in eastern Denmark (Surlyk *et al.* 2006).

The chalk and skeletal sands exposed in mainland Denmark, Skåne and on Bornholm are mainly dated by belemnites (Christensen 1975, 1986, 1993, 1996; Christensen & Schulz 1997) and ammonites (Kennedy *et al.* 1980; Kennedy & Christensen 1991; Birkelund 1993), but the most detailed zonation of the onshore chalk is based on micromorphic brachiopods (Surlyk 1984). Application of sequence stratigraphic techniques to chalk and related deposits of the Danish area is at an early stage and not straightforward. In the deeply buried North Sea succession, wells are positioned on structural highs where omission surfaces, winnowed horizons and hardgrounds may be due to local fault-controlled or halokinetic growth of seafloor relief (Farmer & Barkved 1999). Several of the main lithostratigraphic boundaries are commonly developed as extensive unconformities and may reflect eustatic sea-level changes (Bramwell *et al.* 1999). Important sequence-bounding unconformities are widely identified at top-lower, middle and upper Hod, top Tor, and top-lower Ekofisk formation levels and, in the Danish sector, additionally at the top of the Ekofisk Formation (Bramwell *et al.* 1999). Major sea-level falls, such as those in the latest Maastrichtian and earliest Danian, resulted in hardground formation and in some areas in an increased influx of clay (Surlyk 1997).

*North Sea region*

The Chalk Group is distributed widely over the central and southern North Sea and extends into the South Viking Graben and onto the East Shetland Platform. It is of Cenomanian–Danian age and is commonly 1–2 km thick in the graben areas. The group consists of pure chalk and limestone, marly chalk, marl and calcareous shale. Flint nodules occur at many levels. Towards the north (*c.* 60°N) it is interdigitated with the siliciclastic mudstone-dominated Shetland Group.

The Cenomanian Hidra Formation consists of fine-grained, white to pale grey, occasionally pink, strongly bioturbated chalky limestones with interbedded dark grey to reddish brown mudstones. Clay-rich chalk and fine-grained siliciclastic deposits are common in the lower part of the formation as well as fringing palaeoshorelines and salt structures. Cleaner chalk dominates in the basin centre together with calcarenitic and siliciclastic turbidites (Kennedy 1987). It is considered to be equivalent to Unit 1 of the Chalk Group in the Danish sector (Figs 15.10 & 15.11). The Hidra Formation is typically 30–70 m thick (up to *c.* 170 m thick in the Central Graben) and is absent or condensed over some contemporaneous structural highs.

The Blodøks Formation is of latest Cenomanian–early Turonian age and consists of black mudstones overlain by weakly to

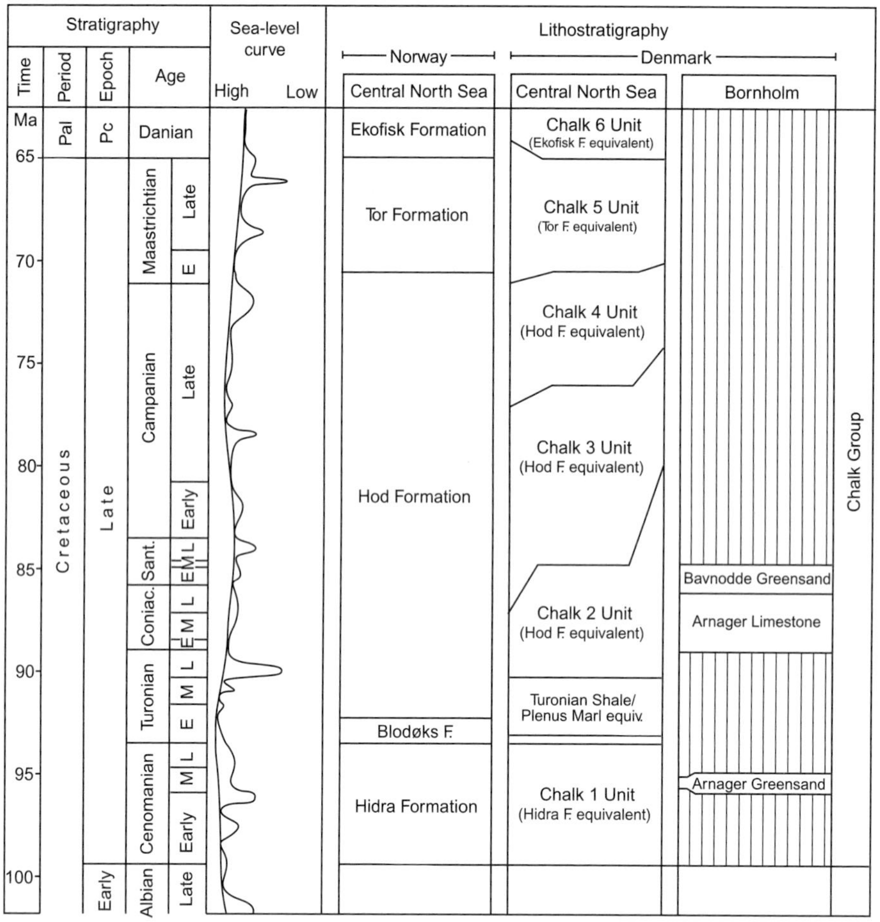


**Fig. 15.10.** Chronostratigraphy of the Danish Basin showing the lithostratigraphical units by Deegen & Scull (1977) and Lieberkind *et al.* (1982) in comparison to the global sea-level curve by Haq *et al.* (1988) scaled against the GTS 2004 (Gradstein *et al.* 2004).

moderately calcareous, red, green and grey mudstones and argillaceous limestones. It is up to 120 m thick in the Norwegian sector. Deegan & Scull (1977) referred to this unit as the 'Plenus Marl Formation', and it is widespread in the UK sector where it attains a maximum thickness of 28 m. The well-known Plenus Marl of onshore southern England is older than the North Sea Plenus Marl Formation, which appears to be a correlative of the younger Black Band of Yorkshire (Johnson & Lott 1993). The Plenus Marl Formation of the North Sea was, therefore, renamed the Black Band Bed by Johnson & Lott (1993), and included in the Blodøks Formation by Isaksen & Tonstad (1989). The Black Band Bed was deposited during a phase of stagnant, poorly oxygenated bottom waters.

The Hod Formation is of mid-Turonian–Campanian age and consists predominantly of white to pale grey, occasionally pink or red, fine-grained, argillaceous, chalky limestone. It is mainly 200–700 m thick and is present over much of the central North Sea where it onlaps and covers intrabasinal ridges. The formation has a relatively high content of clay but there are intervals of pure chalk, particularly in its lower part. The clean chalks constitute important hydrocarbon reservoirs in the Hod and Valhall fields. In the Danish and Norwegian sectors the formation is commonly subdivided into three units. The lower unit is of Turonian age and constitutes the main part of the formation. It consists mainly of laminated, burrowed chalk with a low clay content, and common laminated grainstone turbidites. Bioturbation increases towards the top of the lower unit where marl–limestone cycles become common. The middle unit is of Turonian–Santonian age, generally has a higher clay content, and is cyclically bedded. The upper unit, which is of Santonian–early Campanian age, is cyclically bedded but has a lower clay content and contains allochthonous intercalations. A major unconformity separates the lower and middle parts of the formation, and may justify the definition of a new formation for the lower unit. The middle and upper Hod Formation are also separated by an unconformity.

The Tor Formation is of Maastrichtian age but may locally extend down into the upper Campanian. It consists of white or pale grey chalk, and is the most widespread of the Chalk Group formations, occurring throughout the North Sea. It is more than 250 m thick in the depocentres within the Central Graben, but it is generally less than 150 m thick where it overlies Lower Cretaceous or older sediments on intrabasinal highs and graben-marginal ridges. The Tor Formation contains the most important hydrocarbon reservoir intervals in the Chalk Group. The lower part of the formation consists of bioturbated pelagic chalk showing an upward transition into laminated–bioturbated cycles (Scholle *et al.* 1998; Damholt & Surlyk 2004). In the southern part of the Danish sector, the upper Tor Formation is typically developed as cyclically alternating laminated high-porosity, and bioturbated low-porosity chalk. The individual cycles and their stacking patterns can be traced over long distances (Scholle *et al.*

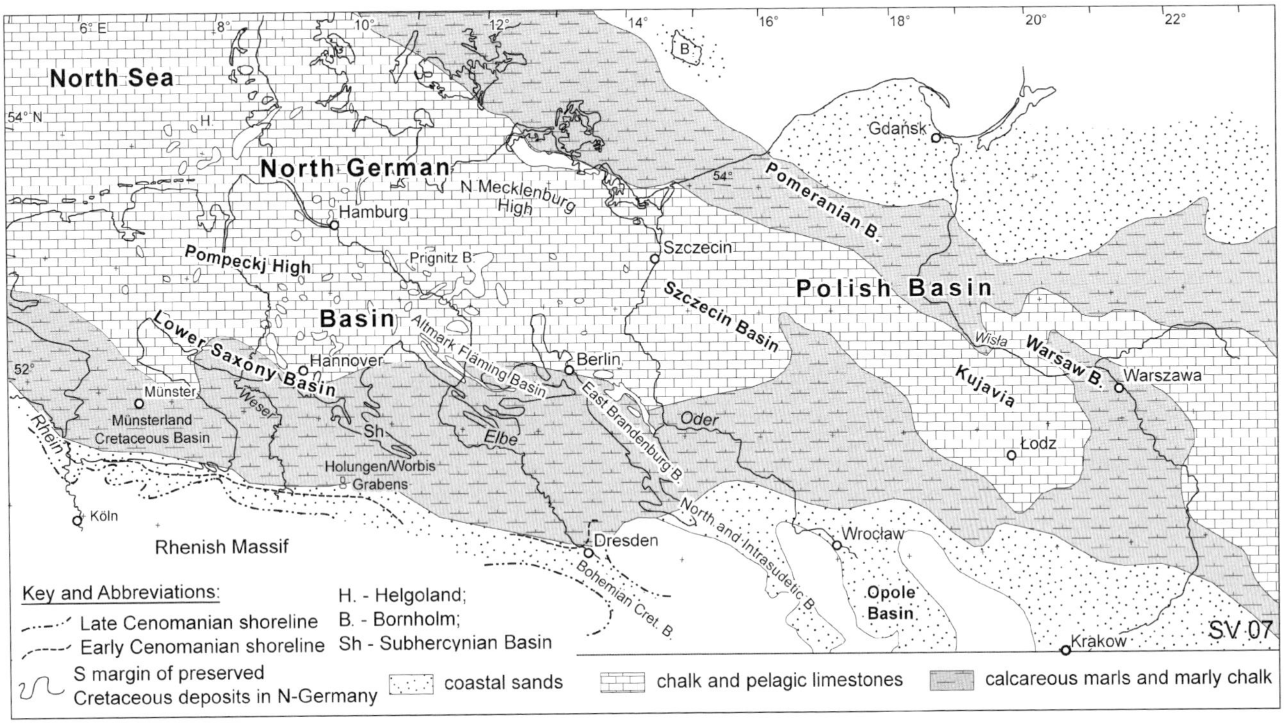


**Fig. 15.11.** Palaeogeographic map of northern Central Europe showing the distribution of Middle Cenomanian facies as a result of the major sea-level rise. Data compilation from Tröger (1964), Musstopf (1966), Diener (1967), Jaskowiak-Schoeneich & Krassowska (1998), Marek (1997), Kennedy *et al.* (1980) and Wilmsen *et al.* (2005).

1998). They have recently been interpreted to reflect variations in oxygenation at the seafloor probably on the 22 ka precession scale (Damholt & Surlyk 2004). The top of the formation, coinciding with the Cretaceous–Tertiary boundary, is developed as a hardground that represents a regional unconformity.

*Danish Basin and adjacent areas*

All of the Upper Cretaceous stages are represented in the Danish Basin and adjacent areas, but exposed strata are all of Maastrichtian age except on Bornholm where small outcrops of older units occur (Fig. 15.4). Proximal, relatively coarse-grained, shallow-marine carbonates mainly known from onshore exposures, notably in southern Sweden and Denmark, pass basinwards into pelagic chalk, commonly reworked into large contourite drifts and locally redeposited down submarine slopes (Surlyk 1997; Surlyk *et al.* 2003; Lykke-Andersen & Surlyk 2004; Surlyk & Lykke-Andersen 2007). Basinal chalk is well exposed in a number of mainly very large quarries in northern Jylland and in coastal cliffs and quarries on Sjælland and Møn. The most impressive locality is the coastal cliff Møns Klint (klint = cliff) where sheets of chalk have been thrust up in a nappe-like thrust belt by glaciers advancing from the south and east during the latest Pleistocene. The locality is situated over the eastern end of the Ringkøbing-Fyn High and the chalk in the thrust sheets is of relatively shallow-water nature compared to the chalk exposed in northern Jylland and elsewhere. This is indicated by the presence of omission surfaces, one or two thin hardgrounds, abundant flint bands, and the very high content of small benthic fossils, dominated by bryozoans, serpulids, brachiopods, and other small suspension feeders. Larger fossils include bivalves, notably large thick-shelled *Pycnodonte*, echinoids, crinoids, asteroids, belemnites and rare ammonites and nautiloids; other aragonite-shelled fossils are generally rare to absent (Surlyk 1972; Surlyk & Birkelund 1977). The combined evidence from fossils and flint bands allows the precise correlation of the individual thrust sheets (Surlyk 1984). The chalk of the thrust sheets in the southern part of the cliff belongs to one *c.* 65 m thick unit of lower Maastrichtian chalk, whereas that in the northern part represents the higher parts of the lower Maastrichtian, possibly extending into the lowermost upper Maastrichtian. The chalk in northern Jylland around the town of Ålborg is of deeper-water origin and is relatively poor in macrofossils compared to the chalk of Møns Klint, but large ammonites, especially *Baculites*, are quite common. Flint is sparse, probably reflecting a paucity of siliceous sponges in the deeper-water basinal areas.

New seismic data from Øresund, Kattegat and the Baltic Sea show that the chalk seafloor was extremely irregular in many areas, with large valleys and ridges, channels, moats and drifts. In Kattegat a major moat and drift system with abundant smaller channels, scours and mounds was developed adjacent to the southwestward-dipping slope of the inverted Sorgenfrei-Tornquist Zone (Surlyk & Lykke-Andersen 2007). The marked relief of the chalk seafloor was formed by bottom currents mainly flowing towards the NW parallel to bathymetric contours and to the axis of the Danish Basin. The morphology of the chalk depositional system is similar to modern contourite systems which are common along the lower slopes of the continental margins (Lykke-Andersen & Surlyk 2004).

The coastal cliff of Stevns Klint shows excellent exposures over a length of 15 km through the upper Maastrichtian, across the Cretaceous–Tertiary boundary and into the lower Danian (Fig. 15.4; Surlyk *et al.* 2006). The lowermost part of the succession consists of white upper Maastrichtian chalk, showing wavy bedding outlined by scattered bands of flint nodules belonging to the Sigerslev Member of the Tor Formation. The undulating bedding corresponds to the smallest-scale mound-like structures seen on seismic profiles recorded immediately offshore (Anderskouv *et al.* 2007). The bedding was probably caused by the combined effect of bottom currents and benthic growth, notably of bryozoans. The wavy-bedded chalk passes upwards into almost horizontally bedded chalk with a very low content of benthic fossils and characterized by the ichnofossil *Zoophycos* forming the upper part of the Sigerslev Member. This is topped by a double incipient hardground showing nodular hardening and erosion. A prominent nodular flint band occurs *c.* 30 cm below the upper hardground and forms a marker bed that can be traced along the length of the cliff. The upper hardground is overlain by chalk rich in bryozoans and deposited in low, asymmetrical mounds which migrated towards the south (Surlyk 1997; Larsen & Håkansson 2000). The mounds started as small and rather flat structures which did not show any organized growth pattern. During growth a regular asymmetric mound shape developed and the crests of the mounds shifted towards the south, probably governed by northward-flowing nutrient-rich non-erosional bottom currents, following the model proposed for the larger Danian bryozoan mounds (Thomsen 1976, 1983). The hardgrounds and the associated seaward shift in facies are interpreted as representing an important sequence boundary formed during a major fall in sea level (Surlyk 1997).

The uppermost Maastrichtian is also represented by localities in northern Jylland but here deposition took place in somewhat deeper water than at Stevns Klint and the chalk is less fossiliferous, rather monotonous, and does not show pronounced facies changes or hardgrounds. A few marl layers, however, occur and they contain Tethyan pelagic foraminifers.

*Bornholm*

On the south coast of Bornholm, lowermost Cretaceous sands and clays of the Jydegård Formation are unconformably overlain by the middle Cenomanian Arnager Greensand Formation (Figs 15.10 & 15.11). This formation commences with a 40 cm thick basal conglomerate containing complex phosphorite nodules, with primary nodules forming parts of secondary nodules, and all within a greensand matrix. The primary nodules contain ammonites from two lower Albian zones whereas the matrix of the secondary nodules contains ammonites from the lower Cenomanian (Ravn 1925; Kennedy *et al.* 1980), indicating a history of repeated phases of sedimentation, non-sedimentation, mineralization and erosion at the Early–Late Cretaceous transition. This has traditionally been interpreted as reflecting repeated transgression and regression, but the area is situated in an important inversion zone and was periodically isolated from an influx of terrigenous sediments, causing significant condensation at certain levels. The Arnager Greensand Formation is *c.* 85 m thick and consists of grey-green, glauconitic, argillaceous quartz sandstone. The sediment is completely bioturbated and contains ammonites, belemnites, bivalves, gastropods, brachiopods and foraminifers. The top of the formation is penetrated by a dense network of *Thalassinoides* burrows.

The Arnager Greensand is overlain by the Coniacian Arnager Limestone Formation. The boundary between the two formations is complex and marked by a phosphorite conglomerate, again with several generations of phosphorite nodules. The conglomerate yields specimens of the belemnite *Praeactinocamax plenus* providing a late Cenomanian age for the multiple phases of sedimentation, non-sedimentation, mineralization and erosion. The Arnager Limestone Formation is 12–20 m thick, greyish-white and shows a wavy, mound-like bedding structure, which may have been caused by the baffling of ooze by a dense thicket of sponges, which are extremely common (Noe-Nygaard & Surlyk 1985). The chalky limestone has a high silica content, occurring as minute cristobalite lepispheres. The chalk was never deeply buried and, thus, the silica has generally not been transformed into flint nodules. Macrofossils are relatively rare except for sponges and large inoceramid bivalves. Macrofossil density and diversity, however, both increase markedly in the upper, more clay-rich, part of the formation.

The Arnager Limestone Formation is erosionally overlain by the Santonian Bavnodde Greensand which is *c.* 70 m thick and consists of glauconitic, argillaceous quartz sandstones which are strongly burrowed and contains abundant bivalves, gastropods, brachiopods, belemnites and ammonites. Some of the sandstone layers show structures indicating the occurrence of storms.

*Skåne*

The Sorgenfrei-Tornquist Zone passes through southern Sweden in Skåne, and separates the chalk-dominated Danish Basin to the SW from an area towards the NE dominated by shallow-marine skeletal carbonate sands (Fig. 15.4). The Sorgenfrei-Tornquist Zone underwent several phases of inversion and uplift during Late Cretaceous times and was represented by a series of elongate basement islands and peninsulas. Conglomerates with boulders of basement rocks were deposited along the ridges and their deposition probably resulted from tsunamis, and thus allows tentative dating of the main tectonic events. The Upper Cretaceous carbonates of Skåne are mainly dated by belemnites, which are extremely common at some localities (Christensen 1975, 1986). Towards the NE the carbonates onlap weathered and kaolinized basement hills. An extremely fossiliferous exhumed rocky shore is exposed at Ivö Klack (Fig. 15.3; Surlyk & Christensen 1974). The large gneiss and granite boulders are encrusted by an epifauna which shows a clear zonation. The overhanging part of the boulders is encrusted mainly by large serpulid worm tubes, and the vertical sides are encrusted by the large inarticulate brachiopod *Ancistrocrania stobaei* and oysters. In contrast, the top surfaces are covered by spondylid bivalves. Highly diverse faunas of brachiopods, gastropods, bryozoans and bivalves, including the northernmost rudists, occur beneath and between the boulders. The remains of large marine and terrestrial reptiles are common but not well preserved. Most of the outcropping carbonates in Skåne are of late early Campanian age, belonging to the zone of *Belemnellocamax mammilatus*, but localities with lower Maastrichtian carbonates also occur, belonging to the zone of *Belemnella lanceolata* (Christensen 1975, 1996). Upper lower Campanian greensand is exposed at the remarkable locality of Åsen. This deposit contains abundant oysters which had clearly been attached to thin mangrove-like stems or branches, and remains of early flowering plants (Friis & Skarby 1981).

## *Mid-Polish Trough (I.W.)*

During Late Cretaceous times the evolution of the Polish lowland was strongly influenced by eustatic changes and the inversion of the Mid-Polish Trough. The area of marine sedimentation extended markedly beyond the area of the Mid-Polish Trough over the course of the Cenomanian sea-level rise (Fig. 15.11). Inversion of the Mid-Polish Trough commenced in the axial zone and influenced the palaeogeographic evolution during late Turonian–Maastrichtian times. Uplift of the Pomeranian-Kujavian Anticline exerted control on subsidence and thickness relationships within the basin, and resulted in the post-depositional erosion of Cretaceous strata from the axial zone (Fig. 15.12). Investigation of the inversion history is, therefore, limited to data derived from the bordering synclines. Various studies suggest that tectonic inversion commenced either very early (e.g. Jaskowiak-Schoeneich & Krassowska 1988; Krassowska 1997) or very late in the Late Cretaceous (e.g. Kutek & Głazek 1972; Hakenberg & Świdrowska 1998; Świdrowska & Hakenberg 1999). Recent geophysical investigations indicate that uplift along the axis of the Mid-Polish Trough began in the late Turonian (Dadlez *et al.* 1995; Gutowski *et al.* 2003; Krzywiec 2006).

Across much of the Polish lowland Upper Cretaceous sediments are preserved in the subsurface in the marginal synclines and over vast areas of NE Poland. Surface exposures occur in the area of the Southern Polish Uplands north of the Carpathian arc. The best exposures are located along the NE and SW borders of the Holy Cross Mountains (Cieśliński & Pożaryski 1970), and in the Polish Jura Chain (Rutkowski 1965; Marcinowski 1970, 1974; Marcinowski & Radwański 1983; Walaszczyk 1992). The most complete record of Upper Cretaceous strata is exposed in the so-called Middle Vistula section, which is located to the east of the northeastern margin of the Holy Cross Mountains (Fig. 15.3), and represents a standard succession for extra-Carpathian Upper Cretaceous deposits in Poland (Pożaryski 1938, 1948; Pożaryska 1952; Cieśliński 1959; Gaździcka 1978; Błaszkiewicz 1980; Peryt 1980; Marcinowski & Radwański 1983; Machalski & Walaszczyk 1987; Walaszczyk 1987, 1992, 2004).

*Stratigraphic succession*

In the course of the major late Albian and Cenomanian sea-level rise, much of the Polish lowlands evolved into a broad and shallow epicontinental shelf (Marcinowski 1980; Marcinowski & Radwański 1983; Marcinowski & Wiedmann 1985, 1990). The marine ingression approached the area from the NW and rapidly connected the Polish lowland with the Tethys Ocean in the south (Marcinowski & Wiedmann 1985, 1990). In the Cenomanian, the geography and structure of the lowland basin was, as in late Albian times, controlled by the evolution of the Mid-Polish Trough, which formed a distinct morphological depression. As a consequence of the rapid sea-level rise, areas of marginal siliciclastic deposition were shifted away from the axial zone of the Mid-Polish Trough towards northeastern Poland and the area of the present Miechów Depression (Figs 15.11 & 15.12). In Middle Cenomanian times, the sea also encroached far to the SW, covering the area of Opole and the Sudetes. Marginal siliciclastic sediments were also deposited in the area of the present Fore-Sudetic Monocline, but have been subsequently

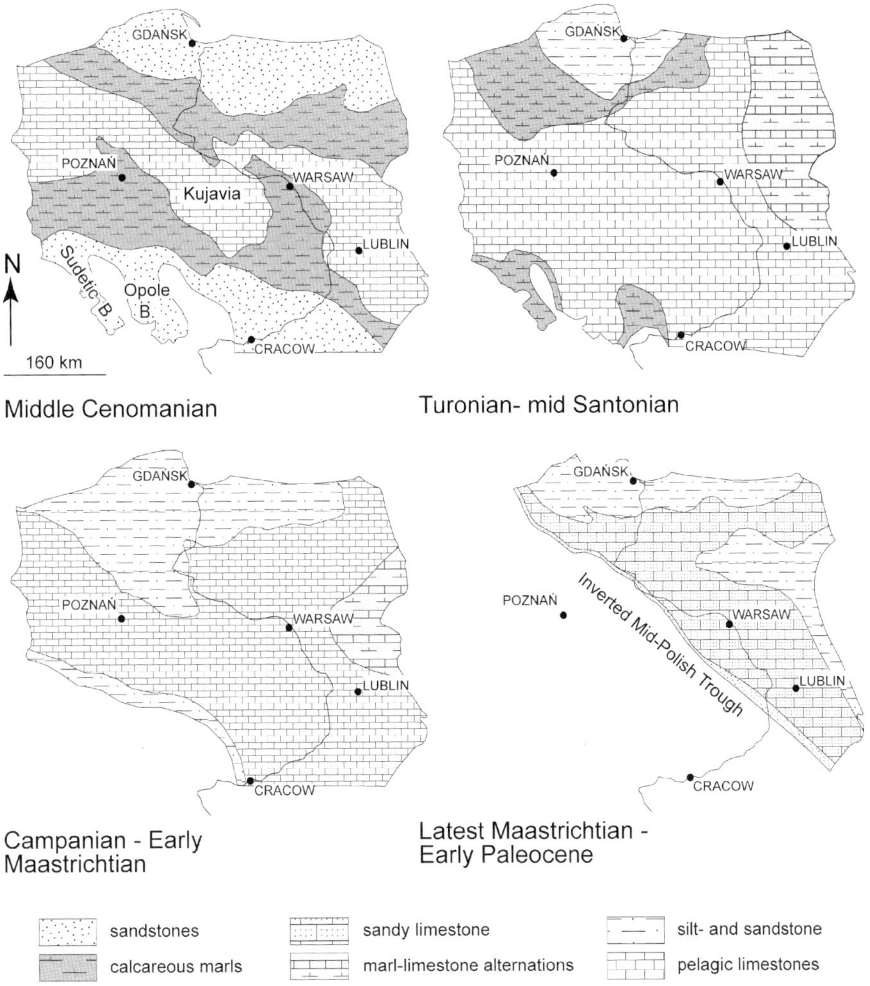


**Fig. 15.12.** Palaeogeographic sketch maps showing the Late Cretaceous facies distribution in the area of Poland; compiled and modified after Marek (1997) and Krassowska (1997).

eroded. These sediments are mainly glauconitic sands, frequently grading upwards into marly sands, with phosphatic nodules. The central part of the basin, along the axis of the Mid-Polish Trough, is characterized by chalk facies represented, at this stage, by various limestone microfacies, marls and siliceous marls. The main depocentres are located along the Mid-Polish Trough. In the strongly subsiding Kujavian segment of the Mid-Polish Trough, the Cenomanian succession reaches 150 m. The thickness of Cenomanian-age deposits decreases markedly towards the NE and SW of the Mid-Polish Trough. Local depocentres are also developed in the axial part of the Miechów Depression in marginal siliciclastic facies, where great thicknesses are noted (200 m). Outside of the Mid-Polish Trough and the Miechów Depression, Cenomanian successions are markedly thinner. In the southern part of the basin, close to the present Carpathians, the succession is strongly reduced, mostly due to condensation and stratigraphic gaps, which are related to discontinuities such as hardgrounds, erosional and omission surfaces (e.g. Cieśliński 1959, 1976; Marcinowski 1980; Marcinowski & Walaszczyk 1985; Walaszczyk 1987).

Commencing with the Turonian (and ending in the late Maastrichtian) the Polish lowland was almost entirely characterized by various chalk facies. Areas of siliciclastic sedimentation are found in the north, close to the land area of Fennoscandia (Fig. 15.12). Beginning in the middle Turonian, the axis of the Meta-Carpathian arc shifted markedly toward the south. Whereas sedimentation in Albian–early Turonian times was characterized by condensation, non-deposition and omissions, thick carbonate successions accumulated in the northern part of the depositional area. The area of reduced sedimentation shifted further to the south, close to the northern boundary of the Carpathian domain.

Further palaeogeographic change occurred during Coniacian–Santonian times, when the sea retreated from the Opole, Intrasudetic and North Sudetic basins. The area of maximum subsidence and corresponding thickness of Upper Cretaceous deposits is inferred to be along the axis of the Mid-Polish Trough, particularly in the Kujavian segment. In Santonian to Maastrichtian times, during the main phase of basin inversion, the depocentres moved toward the NE and SW into the marginal synclines. As a result of asymmetric inversion, regression occurred in the southwestern Szczecin–Łódź–Miechów synclines during mid-Maastrichtian times, whereas in the northeastern Pomeranian–Warsaw–Lublin synclines, marine sedimentation continued until the early Palaeocene (Fig. 15.12).

## North German intrashelf basins (middle Albian to early Coniacian) (M.W., F.W.)

The evolution of the North German Basin as a part of the Late Cretaceous epicontinental shelf commenced with the major middle Albian transgression in the context of the global late Cretaceous eustatic rise (Kemper 1978; Hancock & Kauffman 1979; Hardenbol *et al.* 1998). As a result, wide parts of previously emergent areas drowned, the Late Jurassic to Early Cretaceous sub-basins ceased to exist, and one large epicontinental shelf area developed, bordered to the south by Rheno-Bohemia (Fig. 15.11).

The lithologies from the middle Albian to the upper Cenomanian document a facies turnover from the predominantly Early Cretaceous siliciclastic system to the Late Cretaceous mainly calcareous biosedimentary system. Basin evolution was mainly controlled by thermal subsidence and sea-level change. Accordingly, the early Late Cretaceous facies areas of the North German Basin can be subdivided into three approximately east–west trending zones.

(1) Distal zone: in the north the Pompeckj High and its eastward extensions, the North Mecklenburg and East Brandenburg highs, form a distal and tectonically stable high, pierced by a variety of salt diapirs. To the NE of this structure was the subsiding Danish Basin (Figs 15.5 & 15.11).

(2) Medial zone: south of the Pompeckj Block was a subsiding area with higher accumulation rates. This area was broadly coincident with the Early Cretaceous Lower Saxony and Altmark-Fläming basins. Individual subsidence centres (intrashelf basins) are often referred to as independent basins (e.g. Münsterland Cretaceous Basin, Lower Saxony Basin, Subhercynian Cretaceous Basin, Altmark-Fläming Basin, East Brandenburg Basin).

(3) Proximal zone: to the south, close to Rheno-Bohemia, a proximal facies belt characterized by marginal deposits and strongly reduced thicknesses or depositional gaps occurred. Successions were best developed to the north of the Rhenish Massif, and during middle Albian–early Cenomanian times in the Subhercynian Cretaceous and the East Brandenburg basins.

Middle Albian to early Coniacian sedimentation in the North German Basin was controlled by the asymmetric transgressive (middle Albian–late Turonian)–regressive (late Turonian–early Coniacian) second-order sea-level cycle, punctuated by numerous third-order depositional sequences (Fig. 15.13; Wiese *et al.* 2000, 2004*a*; Wilmsen 2003; Wilmsen & Wiese 2004). During the transgressive hemicycle, several pronounced transgressions occurred in the early middle Albian (onset of coastal onlap onto the Palaeozoic massifs), the late Albian, the early Cenomanian, the middle Cenomanian, and the late Cenomanian. Continuous transgressive development ceased with the Cenomanian–Turonian boundary interval, but slow progressive Turonian sea-level rise culminated in the late Turonian. The early Coniacian is characterized by a relative sea-level fall.

*Distal zone (Pompeckj High/Block)*

The sedimentary thickness of the Pompeckj High is strongly reduced in comparison to the central zone of the North German Basin. It was a fully pelagic zone from the Albian–Cenomanian to the end of the Cretaceous with little terrigenous input. Outcrops are rare (Helgoland, Lüneburg and Staffhorst) and most data derive from oil wells (e.g. Best *et al.* 1989; Niebuhr *et al.* 1999).

The early middle Albian increase in carbonate content indicates the onset of pelagic sedimentation and more uniform facies, and is an excellent feature for geophysical log correlation across the Pompeckj High (Best *et al.* 1989). At Helgoland, pelagic sedimentation begins with middle–upper Albian grey, belemnite-bearing marls ('Graue *minimus*-Kreide') onlapping onto the Aptian marls (Best *et al.* 1989). The unit is strongly condensed (<2 m) and rests on a basal transgressive conglomerate. At the southern margin of the Pompeckj High (Staffhorst shaft), *c.* 75 m of middle–upper Albian grey marlstones overlie Jurassic (Dogger) sediments (Frieg *et al.* 1989*a*), and grade into more carbonate-rich, plankton-dominated sediments towards the east (Schleswig-Holstein), which rest on Triassic (Keuper) strata (Heinz 1926; Elstner & Kemper 1989; Best *et al.* 1989). In the region of the North Mecklenburg High, *c.* 20–35 m (minimum 2 m) of upper Albian sediments unconformably overlie pre-Cretaceous to pre-Albian rocks and comprise a 1 m thick pebble- and phosphorite-bearing, sandy-glauconitic transgression horizon and fossiliferous marlstones with *Aucellina gryphaeoides* and

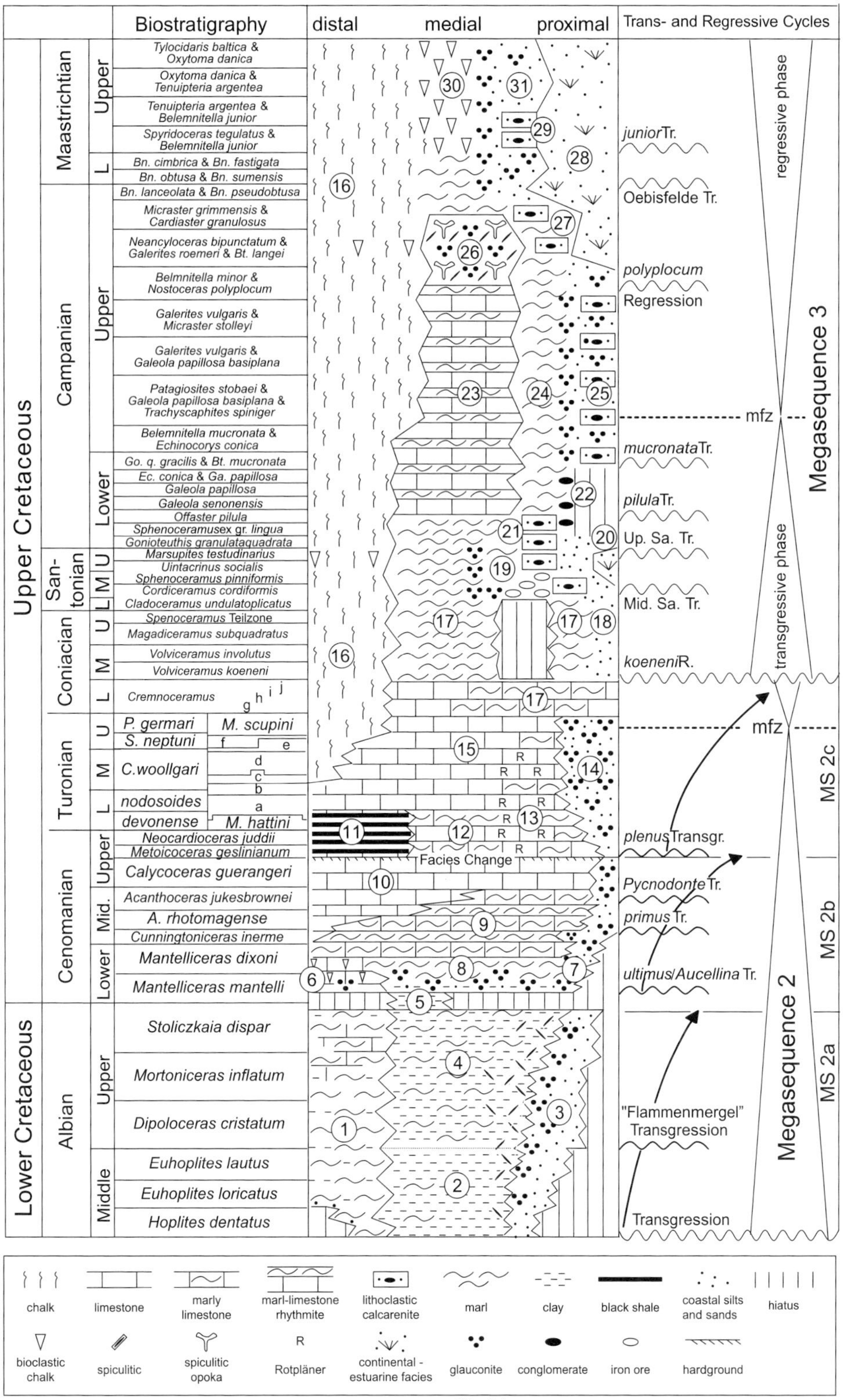


a. *Mytiloides mytiloides/ My. labiatus* Zone
b. *Mytiloides hercynicus/ subhercynicus* Zone
c. *Inoceramus cuvieri/ apicalis* Zone
d. *Inoceramus lamarcki/cuvieri/apicalis* Assemblage Zone
e. *I. perplexus/cuvieri/stuemckei/inaequvalvis* Assemblage Zone
f. *I. perplexus/My. labiatoidiformis/striatoconcentricus* Assemblage Zone
g. *Cremnoceramus deformis erectus* Zone
h. *Cremnoceramus waltersdorfensis hannovrensis* Zone
i. *Cremnoceramus crassus inconstans* Zone
j. *Cremnoceramus crassus crassus/ Cr. deformis deformis* Zone

Abbreviations:
*C.* = *Collignoniceras*
*My.* = *Mytiloides*
*M.* = *Mammites*
*W.* = *Watinoceras*
*P.* = *Prionocyclus*
*S.* = *Subprionocyclus*

**Fig. 15.13.** Integrated chronostratigraphic scheme for the middle Albian to Maastrichtian period showing the proximal to distal facies in the North German Basin in relation to sea-level change (Stratigraphische Kommission Deutschlands 2000) and the development of sedimentary megasequences *sensu* Hiss *et al*. (2005). Circled numbers in the lithofacies column refer to lithological units discussed in the text and shown in Figure 15.14.

*Neohibolites minimus* (Diener 2000*a*, *b*; Diener *et al.* 2004*b*) (Unit 3 in Fig. 15.13).

In Helgoland, the Cenomanian–Turonian deposits are *c.* 30 m thick. The succession commences with red marly limestones (Rote Cenoman-Kreide, equivalent to the *ultimus/Aucellina* transgression) of early Cenomanian age, bioclastic calcarenites (Helgoland Fm; Unit 6 in Fig. 15.13) and several metres of late Cenomanian fine-grained pelagic limestones (equivalent to the Brochterbeck Fm) (Best *et al.* 1989; Wood & Schmid 1991; Niebuhr *et al.* 2007; Unit 10 in Fig. 15.13). White limestone deposits (Feste Schreibkreide) with some intervals of red-coloured chalk and a calcarenite dominate the succession in late Cenomanian–Turonian times. Pelagic carbonate production was interrupted in the earliest Turonian (*Mytiloides*) by the deposition of black shales, as a response to the global oceanic anoxic event (OAE II) (Unit 11 in Fig. 15.13). Middle and late Turonian deposits comprise chalk with red flints, and are overlain by sediments of middle Coniacian age indicating a sedimentary hiatus (Schmid & Spaeth 1991; Wood & Schmid 1991). Late Turonian chalk sedimentation is also recorded to the north of the Pompeckj High at Lägerdorf (Ernst & Schulz 1974).

At Lüneburg (eastern part of the Pompeckj High), the Cenomanian succession differs from other successions in the area in terms of its greater thickness (70 m) and its marlier facies which is typical of the medial zone (see below). Higher rates of sediment accumulation are related to the prolongation of the north–south trending Braunschweig-Gifhorn Fault Zone (see Baldschuhn *et al.* 2001). The Turonian commences with alternating red (Rotpläner) and white (Weißpläner) limestones, grey marls and thin black shales (Söhlde Fm, Unit 13 in Fig. 15.13). Some beds contain abundant accumulations of inoceramid bivalves. Lower Turonian Rotpläner are also recorded from the northern part of the Pompeckj High (Schwedeneck borehole; Schönfeld *et al.* 2000). The upper Turonian succession is dominated by white limestones with intercalated marl seams (Unit 15 in Fig. 15.13). Lithologically, this facies succession is comparable with that developed in the medial zone (see below). During middle late Turonian times, the deposition of flint-bearing chalks which grade into calcareous marls (Emscher Facies) indicates a significant facies change (Unit 17 in Fig. 15.13).

In the easternmost part of the Pompeckj High (Mecklenburg), the Cenomanian succession consists of *c.* 30–40 m of marly limestones and limestones. Turonian sediments have an average thickness of 150–170 m. In some salt-related rim synclines, for example in the NW part of the Prignitz-Lausitz High, thicknesses can be much higher (e.g. 400 m near Kraak and Wesenberg; Diener *et al.* 2004*a*). In the lower Turonian, pelagic limestones (Rotpläner) are developed only in north and NW Brandenburg as well as in SW Mecklenburg (Reich 2000; Diener *et al.* 2004*a*). In other areas of Mecklenburg, lower and middle Turonian strata consist of marls, marlstones and marly limestones. Upper middle to upper Turonian deposits comprise marly limestones and chalks with flint layers, as well as siliceous chalk in the uppermost Turonian (Petzka & Reich 2000; Diener *et al.* 2004*a*).

*Medial zone*

In the medial zone (the former Lower Saxony Basin *sensu stricto*), the sediments became increasingly marly following the middle Albian transgression (Unit 1 in Fig. 15.13; Mutterlose 2000). As a consequence, basinal marls ('*minimus*-Schichten') and their proximal equivalents spread beyond the former basin margins. Over the course of the late Albian transgression, deposition changed to the typical spiculitic, partly radiolarian-bearing marls and clayey marls (Flammenmergel; Unit 4 in Fig. 15.13), which is found from the Münsterland in the west to the western Subhercynian area in the east (Frieg *et al.* 1989*a*, 1990). The thickness of the middle and upper Albian in the 'basinal' Hannover area may exceed 300 m (Kirchrode boreholes; Fenner 2001).

The lithology of the Cenomanian succession of the medial zone is similar all across northern Germany (Hiss 1982*a*, 1983; Kaplan *et al.* 1984, 1998; Ernst & Rehfeld 1997; Lehmann 1999; Niebuhr *et al.* 2001, 2007; Wilmsen 2003, 2004). Commonly, Cenomanian marls overlie the Albian Flammenmergel with a stratigraphic gap due to a pronounced sea-level lowstand across the Albian–Cenomanian boundary. In the distal part of the central zone (northern Münsterland, Hannover area, Staffhorst), a clay-rich horizon (Bemeroder member; Kemper 1984; Unit 5 in Fig. 15.13) documents the lowstand sediments (Niebuhr *et al.* 1999; Wilmsen 2003). This was subsequently overlain by a thin glauconitic unit that represents the early Cenomanian *ultimus/Aucellina* transgression (Ernst *et al.* 1983; Unit 7 in Fig. 15.13).

The overlying unit comprises bioturbated, greenish silty marls, 5–40 m thick, with thin nodular bioclastic marly limestones (Herbram Fm, Unit 8 in Fig. 15.13). The moderately fossiliferous marls are of earliest Cenomanian age (*Mantelliceras mantelli* Zone) and represent an inner shelf facies (Hiss 1985; Wilmsen 2003). During the late early Cenomanian and early middle Cenomanian transgressions, a distinct facies change occurred towards rhythmically bedded marl–limestone (Baddeckenstedt Fm, up to 60 m thick) representing a mid-shelf environment (Unit 9 in Fig. 15.13). The asymmetric decimetre- to metre-thick bedding cycles can be correlated across NW Europe, and are orbitally forced by the 20 ka precession cycle (Gale 1995; Gale *et al.* 1999; Wilmsen & Niebuhr 2002). The marl–limestone couplets are bioturbated and rich in macrofossils (ammonites, inoceramids and other bivalves, sponges, brachiopods, gastropods, irregular echinoids, serpulids, scaphopods; Wilmsen 2003). Marl beds become thinner towards the top of the unit, and macrofauna increasingly sparse (Wilmsen 2003).

The overlying middle to lower upper Cenomanian limestones are pure, pelagic coccolith limestones with carbonate contents up to 95% and rare macrofossil occurrences (Brochterbeck Fm; Unit 10 in Fig. 15.13). This facies represents the Cenomanian outer shelf setting in northern Germany (Wilmsen 2003). Its deposition commenced with the maximum flooding interval following the *primus* transgression (Wilmsen 2003; Wilmsen & Wood 2004), above the Mid-Cenomanian Event (Ernst *et al.* 1983). At the basin margins, the deposition of pelagic limestones commenced later (late middle Cenomanian *Pycnodonte* transgression). Here, they cover older strata like a pelagic drape with an almost constant thickness of 14–16 m in northern Germany, and document a third-order sea-level highstand (Wilmsen 2003).

The coastal onlap of the Cenomanian sea-level rises resulted in the development of a pronounced wedge-shaped stratigraphic architecture with thicknesses ranging from a few metres in proximal settings or swell areas (see below) to as much as 120–150 m in the central zone (e.g. Wunstorf near Hannover; T. Meyer 1990; Wilmsen 2003). Although the thicknesses vary, Cenomanian sedimentation became increasingly influenced by oceanic conditions, as is evident from the reduced terrigenous input and increased carbonate content, the shift in the main planktonic carbonate producers from calcispheres to coccolithophorids, the disappearance of rich and diverse benthic and nektobenthic invertebrate communities, and the uniform facies and homogenized accumulation (Gale *et al.* 2000; Wilmsen *et al.* 2005). The collapse of pelagic carbonate production at the boundary of the *Calycoceras guerangeri* and *Metoicoceras geslinianum* zones led to a prominent facies change (Fig. 15.13) that marked a change in the tectonosedimentary regime. Subsequent regression and differential basin subsidence resulted in variations in the early and middle Turonian facies of the Münsterland Cretaceous Basin and eastern Lower Saxony/ Saxony-Anhalt intrashelf basins.

In the basinal parts of the intrashelf basins (Münsterland, Lower Saxony/Saxony-Anhalt), upper Cenomanian–lower Turonian deposits (up to 30 m thick) comprise black shales or alternations of black shales and grey limestone beds (Hesseltal Formation, Unit 11 of Fig. 15.13, e.g. Wunstorf, Halle, Lengerich) (Hilbrecht & Dahmer 1994; Lehmann 1999; S. Voigt *et al.* 2007). Basinal black shales interdigitate with condensed successions of reddish bioclastic limestones (Rotpläner, up to 10 m) in Lower Saxony and Saxony-Anhalt, and with an alternation of greenish marls and limestones (maximum 20 m, Unit 12 in Fig. 15.13) in the Münsterland (Frieg *et al.* 1989*b*). These are overlain by middle Turonian grey to white massive limestones in deeper shelf areas and by reddish nodular limestones on swells (Söhlde Fm, units 13 and 15 in Fig. 15.13) (Niebuhr *et al.* 2000; Wiese *et al.* 2004*a*). In the Münsterland Cretaceous Basin, a thin basal glauconitic bed (Bochum Greensand) occurs. Some intervals are characterized by acme occurrences of inoceramids (early and middle Turonian *Mytiloides* and *lamarcki* events; Ernst *et al.* 1983). Lower to middle Turonian thicknesses are highly variable and range from 25 to 50 m.

Late Turonian sedimentation is characterized by a facies change towards the shelf-wide uniform deposition of pure massive limestone with variable thicknesses of up to 120 m in basins and up to 4 m on highs in Lower Saxony and Saxony-Anhalt (Wiese *et al.* 2004*a*; Wood *et al.* 1984) (Salder Fm, Unit 15 in Fig. 15.13). The condensed facies comprise nodular limestones and specific faunal assemblage, in particular during sea-level lows (*Conulus* Facies; Wiese & Kröger 1998). A distinct late Turonian faunal event (*Hyphantoceras* Event, *neptuni* Zone) occurs in all areas and marks an abundance peak of a diverse macroinvertebrate assemblage (ammonites, inoceramids, echinoids) within the otherwise poorly fossiliferous limestones (Metzdorf 1992; Wood & Ernst 1998). A unique facies development occurs in the Lengerich area of the Münsterland, where more than 400 m of poorly differentiated marl–limestone alternations accumulated in a local subsidence centre (Lengerich Fm, Kaplan 1992; Wiese & Kaplan 2001; Niebuhr *et al.* 2007).

Another facies change towards alternating marls and limestones occurred in the latest Turonian (*Mytiloides scupini* Zone, Erwitte Fm) in each of the intrashelf basins in the Münsterland, Lower Saxony and Saxony-Anhalt areas (Unit 17 in Fig. 15.13). The 45 m thick succession represents the highest sea level of the middle Albian–early Coniacian sea-level cycle. An early Coniacian sea-level fall resulted in the deposition of thick, marly and silty limestones (Upper Limestone member) with abundant inoceramids, which grade into calcareous marls (Emscher Fm; Frieg *et al.* 1989*b*). Tectonic activity in the latest early Coniacian resulted in unconformities between the Emscher Fm and upper Turonian sediments on basement highs (e.g. Saxony-Anhalt). The associated erosion partly cut down to the Triassic (Buntsandstein), as is evident from lithoclasts in lower Coniacian tempestites (Ernst *et al.* 1997).

*Proximal zone (north of Rheno-Bohemia)*

The proximal facies of the middle Albian–early Coniacian sea-level cycle is best exposed along the northern margin of the Rhenish Massif, which formed the southern margin of the Münsterland Cretaceous Basin (see Frieg *et al.* 1990). It is, furthermore, well documented from boreholes in the East Brandenburg Basin (Musstopf 1966) (Fig. 15.11). At the SW margin of the Münsterland Cretaceous Basin, conglomeratic and sandy-spiculitic strata (Keddinghausen Beds) and greensands (Wünnenberg and Rüthen beds) of middle–late Albian age unconformably overlie Palaeozoic basement (Unit 3 in Fig. 15.13; Hiss & Speetzen 1986). These transgressive sediments represent nearshore deposits and are lateral equivalents of the basinal spiculitic marls (Flammenmergel). The Cretaceous transgression had, thus, reached the southern margin of the Münsterland Cretaceous Basin during middle–late Albian times (Hiss & Speetzen 1986). The Wünnenberg and Rüthen beds are overlain by lower Cenomanian sediments.

During the Cenomanian, a significant southward retreat of the coastline onto the Rhenish and Bohemian massifs occurred (see coastlines in Fig. 15.11; Musstopf 1966; Hiss 1982*b*; Frieg *et al.* 1990). The proximal facies comprise a diachronous complex of sandstones, glauconitic sandstones, glauconitic marls and marly limestones (e.g. Essen Greensand Fm), often associated with a basal clay/ironstone conglomerate (Hiss 1982*a*; Unit 7 in Fig. 15.13). Its base is mainly lower lower Cenomanian, while its top may range from lower Cenomanian to upper Cenomanian (e.g. SW Münsterland Cretaceous Basin, Frieg *et al.* 1990; East Brandenburg Basin, Musstopf 1966). Extreme condensed successions occur in relation to palaeocliffs (Bochum or Frömern (Hiss 1982*c*), Kassenberg quarries and surroundings (Wiedmann & Schneider 1979)), where the succession extends as high as the upper Turonian (Lommerzheim 1976). Here, reddish, fossiliferous limestones and condensed glauconitic calcarenitic marls accumulated in isolated pockets within the Palaeozoic basement.

The uppermost Cenomanian proximal deposits north of the Rhenish Massif comprise the so-called ‘Kalkknollenbank’, a strongly bioturbated, mineralized, partly lithified and reworked bed (some decimetres thick). This unit is indicative of sediment starvation and erosion (Hiss 1982*a*), and corresponds at the base with the collapse in carbonate production of the basinal areas (Facies Change; Hiss 1983; Kaplan *et al.* 1998).

Turonian-age proximal sediments consist of glauconitic marls and limestones in the Dortmund area and of glauconitic fossiliferous sandstones and limestones towards the north and NE (middle Turonian Bochum Greensand, upper Turonian Soest Greensand) (Unit 14 in Fig. 15.13). The glauconitic beds prograded basinwards as a result of third-order regressions and were intercalated with basinal limestones (Frieg *et al.* 1989*b*). In the latest Turonian, no proximal facies is preserved because of the maximum flooding of the middle Albian–early Coniacian sea-level cycle. Local uplift in the NE part of the Münsterland Cretaceous Basin (Teutoburger Wald) and erosion down to the Jurassic are represented by the greensands of the Timmeregge and Borgholzhausen areas (upper Turonian *scupini* Zone; Elbert 1901; Kaplan & Best 1984; Kaplan 1994) and by late Turonian–early Coniacian submarine slides (Voigt 1962; Skupin 1990).

Further proximal sediments occur in the Subhercynian Cretaceous Basin, north of the Harz Mountains, in the Holunger Graben in Thuringia, and at Meissen in Saxony. In the Subhercynian area, reduced middle–upper Albian siliceous sands replace the basinal siliceous marls (Flammenmergel, e.g. at Weddebach, see Ernst & Wood 2004), although these disappear further towards the east. Proximal early Cenomanian-age sediments are represented by thin glauconitic sandstones and marls grading into marl–limestone alternations. On local highs, polymict lithoclastic conglomerates and greensands of early to early middle Cenomanian age onlap Early Cretaceous ‘Neocomian’ sandstones or

Triassic strata (e.g. at Langenstein: Horna 1997; Wilmsen 2003). With the early middle Cenomanian *primus* transgression, the area of proximal sedimention shifted southward and the Subhercynian area became part of the medial shelf.

In the central Thuringian Basin, local exposures of Cretaceous rocks (marine lower and middle Cenomanian; maximum 55 m) are preserved in two small, NNE-SSW striking graben systems (Worbis and Holunger grabens; Fig. 15.11; Seebach 1868; Diener 1966; Tröger 1969; Tröger & Schubert 1993; see also Tröger 2000*a*). Lithologically, the succession can be subdivided into three units, each commencing with a (conglomeratic) base and glauconitic siltstone and sandstones, grading transgressively into calcareous siltstones in the lower parts and marl–limestone in the upper parts, indicative of progressive deepening. Although high-resolution stratigraphy and correlation with other areas is difficult due to the scarcity of index fossils, the entire succession follows the observed transgressive trend for the Cenomanian in northern Germany (Wilmsen 2003). The development of the sedimentary succession demonstrates that the area of the Holungen and Worbis grabens was already completely flooded in the late early Cenomanian, and sediments are preserved as erosional relicts. Wagenbreth (1961) suggested that the flooding of Thuringia extended as far as the area of the present Thuringian Slate Mountains (see also Meyer 2000), and this has been supported by recent fission track dates from the Ruhla Crystalline Complex, which indicate that uplift of this area did not commence prior to Santonian–Campanian times (Thomson & Zeh 2000).

### *North German Basin related to inversion (Coniacian–Maastrichtian) (T.V., B.N., M.R.)*

The Coniacian–Maastrichtian time interval was characterized by inversion tectonics. Tectonic activity commenced in the late Turonian and extended towards the margins during the Santonian leading to complete inversion of the former Lower Saxony Basin, the Prignitz-Lausitz High and the Grimmen High, and uplift of the Harz Mountains (Baldschuhn *et al.* 1985, 1991; Kockel 1991; Baldschuhn in Niebuhr *et al.* 1999; Diener *et al.* 2004*a*; Figs 15.5 & 15.14). Rapidly subsiding marginal troughs were formed in relation to inversion structures in the Münsterland, the Subhercynian and the Altmark-Fläming basins. In addition, the intrusion of Zechstein salt resulted in the formation of rim synclines, which may contain several hundred metres of sediments of middle Santonian and Campanian age (Niebuhr 1995). Tectonic uplift of these structures gradually ceased during Campanian–Maastrichtian times, and was accompanied by the formation of peneplains and subsequent covering by shallow clastic sediments.

The middle Coniacian–Maastrichtian time interval represents a long-term sea-level cycle that reached its maximum flooding in the early Middle Campanian (*Patagiosites stobaei*/*Galeola papillosa basiplana*/*Trachyscaphites spiniger* Zone). Superimposed transgressions in the middle and late Santonian, mid-early Campanian (*Offaster pilula* Zone), latest early Campanian (*Belemnitella mucronata*), early and early late Maastrichtian (*Belem-*

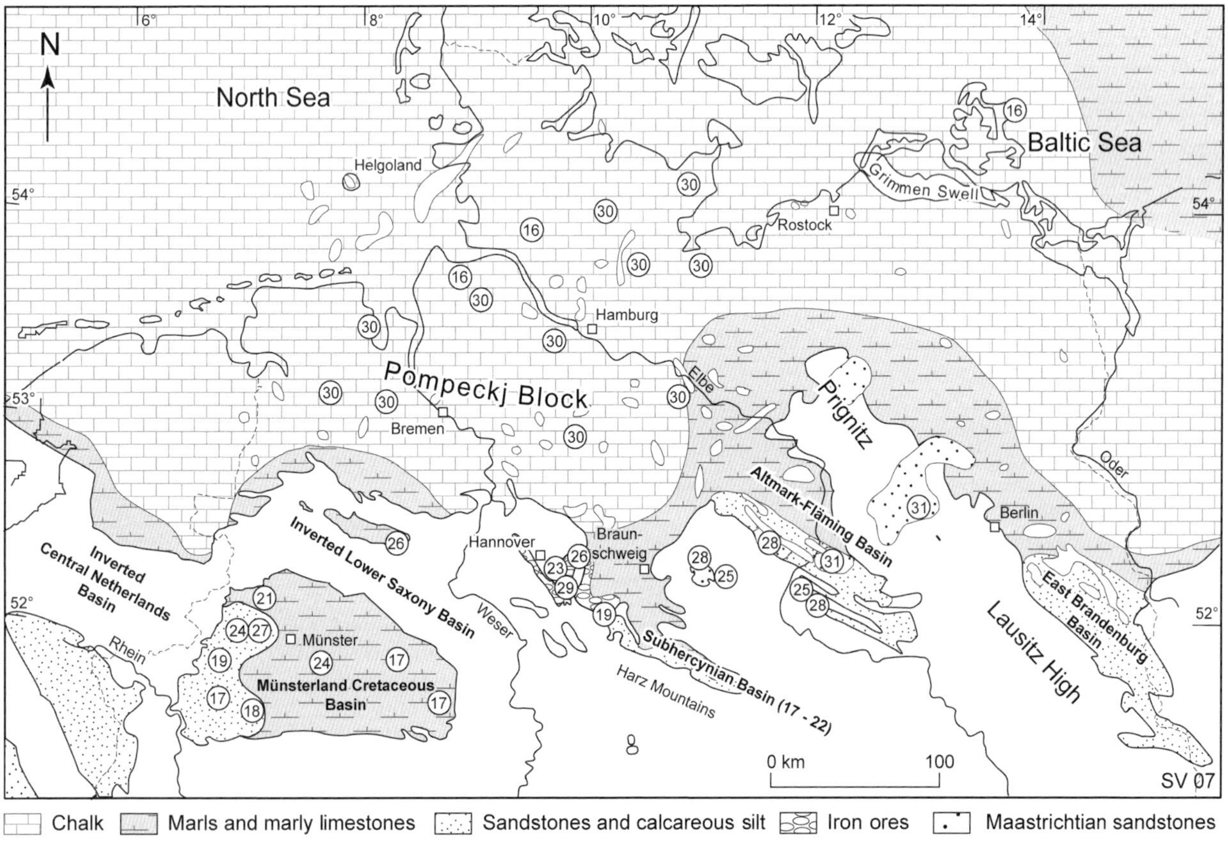


**Fig. 15.14.** Palaeogeographic map showing the Santonian–Early Campanian facies distribution in the North German Basin. Note the distribution of Maastrichtian alluvial and coastal sandstones. Data are compiled from Diener (1968), W. M. Felder (1975, 1976), Marek (1997), Jaskowiak-Schoeneich & Krassowska (1998), Stratigraphische Kommission Deutschlands (2000). Circled numbers refer to lithological units of Figure 15.13 (see text for discussion).

*nitella junior*) and two major regressions in the middle Coniacian (*Volviceramus koeneni*) and early late Campanian (*Nostoceras polyplocum*) correspond to third-order sea-level changes (Ernst 1968; Ulbrich 1974; Niebuhr & Ernst 1991; Niebuhr 1995, 2005). Apart from local continental sands and clays, the Coniacian–Maastrichtian succession was deposited in inner and outer shelf environments. In the distal zone, pelagic chalk sedimentation continued from the Turonian (Niebuhr *et al.* 1999; Diener *et al.* 2004*a*; Niebuhr *et al.* 2007). In areas proximal to inverted structures, the base of the Coniacian–Maastrichtian sequence can be recognized by a facies change from pelagic carbonates to a dominance of siliciclastics expressed by the occurrence of dark-coloured marls (Emscher Marls, carbonate content 10–50%). These marls grade northwards into basinal chalks (Figs 15.13 & 15.14; e.g. Niebuhr *et al.* 1999).

The distribution of distal facies is mainly related to the structure of the Pompeckj High (northern Lower Saxony, Schleswig-Holstein and Mecklenburg-Vorpommern) and is dominated by pelagic chalk sedimentation at estimated water depths of 150 to 200 m during periods of maximal flooding in mid-Campanian times (e.g. Lägerdorf, Kronsmoor, Hemmoor sections; Unit 16 in Fig. 15.13; Schönfeld *et al.* 2000). Maximum chalk thicknesses can reach 1000 m in rim synclines in northern Lower Saxony, Schleswig-Holstein, and SW Mecklenburg (Baldschuhn & Jaritz 1977; Diener *et al.* 2004*a*). Depositional changes are indicated by episodically occurring flint maxima (lower Campanian, upper Maastrichtian) or the presence of coarse-grained bioclastic chalk ('Grobkreide') rich in inoceramid and oyster debris (Santonian–Campanian boundary, upper Campanian). The late Maastrichtian relative sea-level fall is indicated by glauconitic, bioclastic limestones (Reitbrook Fm; Unit 30 in Figs 15.13 & 15.14), which are well developed in a *c.* 100 km long belt between Bremen, Hamburg and western Mecklenburg representing a transitional facies between chalk and proximal glauconitic marls and greensands (Fahrion 1984; Schönfeld *et al.* 2000; Petzka & Reich 2000; Diener *et al.* 2004*a*). In the vicinity of inversion structures, Emscher marl sedimentation (Unit 17 in Figs 15.13 & 15.14) continued until early Campanian times. Areas affected by structural uplift are stratigraphically less complete from the middle Coniacian to the lower Santonian (Niebuhr 1995; Niebuhr *et al.* 2000). In proximal settings, transgressive Santonian iron ores unconformably overlie older strata due to the reworking of iron-rich Jurassic sediments (Braunschweig–Peine area, Altmark-Fläming Basin; Unit 19 in Figs 15.13 & 15.14) (E. Voigt 1929; Ernst 1975; Niebuhr 1995). Littoral sediments of Coniacian and Santonian age are recorded from the Subhercynian Cretaceous Basin and from several boreholes in the Altmark-Fläming Basin (Reich 2000, and references therein).

The mid-early Campanian (*pilula* Zone) transgression is associated with glauconitic and bioclastic sediments in proximal settings close to inversion structures. In the rim synclines of salt diapirs (e.g. Hannover–Braunschweig area), sedimentation changed from the siliciclastic Emscher Fm to well bedded marly limestones and marl–limestone rhythmites (Misburg Formation; Unit 23 in Figs 15.13 & 15.14), which persisted for more than 7 Ma (Niebuhr 1995). The latest early Campanian (*mucronata* Zone) transgression led to the maximum flooding period of the Coniacian–Maastrichtian sea-level cycle during early mid-Campanian times, and resulted in the southward extension of the chalk facies into the Hannover–Braunschweig area (Meerdorfer Schreibkreide; Ernst 1968; Niebuhr 1995). This transgression is associated with conglomerates, glauconitic sandstones, marlstones and limestones, and Salzgitter-type iron ores in proximal settings (Beienrode Formation; Unit 25 in Figs 15.13 & 15.14), which unconformably overlie pre-Cretaceous strata at the flanks of inverted structures (e.g. west of Hannover, near Magdeburg, Grimmen High; Kaplan & Röper 1998; Niebuhr & Ernst 1991; Niebuhr 1995). In all hemipelagic areas of the North German Basin, sedimentation changed significantly with the early late Campanian (*polyplocum* zone) regression. Bioclastic, spiculitic carbonates with abundant hexactinellid sponges yield a rich shallow-water invertebrate assemblage (Stemwede and Althen formations; Unit 26 in Figs 15.13 & 15.14) (Niebuhr 1995; Niebuhr *et al.* 1997; Kaplan & Röper 1998). In marginal settings, Maastrichtian strata are developed as coastal quartz sands and lacustrine clays with a diverse pollen and spore assemblage (Walbeck Formation; Unit 28 in Figs 15.13 & 15.14) (Krutzsch & Mibus 1973; Niebuhr & Ernst 1991; Krutzsch & Prokoph 1992; Schulz & Niebuhr 2000). Coeval, marine greensands (up to 300 m thick) are known from boreholes in Lower Saxony and the Altmark-Fläming Basin and mark the approximate position of the Maastrichtian shoreline (Unit 31 in Figs 15.13 & 15.14; Niebuhr *et al.* 2007). Bioturbated horizons with ooidal ironstones are tentatively interpreted to be related to the early late Maastrichtian (*junior* Zone) transgression. Near Hannover, coarse-grained conglomerates and shallow-marine bryozoan calcarenites transgressively cover inversion structures, resting unconformably on Triassic Buntsandstein sediments (Unit 29 in Figs 15.13 & 15.14) (E. Voigt 1951; Niebuhr 1995).

*Münsterland Cretaceous Basin*

From middle Coniacian times onwards, Cenomanian to early Coniacian hemipelagic limestones became progressively replaced by clastic deposits. The Vorosning Trough SW of the Osning Thrust was filled with 1500–2000 m of monotonous Coniacian–lower Campanian marly Emscher Fm (Unit 17 in Figs 15.13 & 15.14), which derived from eroded Lower Cretaceous and Jurassic deposits of the uplifting Lower Saxony Basin. Occasionally, slumps (middle and upper Coniacian) and distal turbidites and debrites (lower–middle Campanian Stromberg, Beckum and Vorhelm members; Hiss & Seibertz 2000; Niebuhr *et al.* 2007) are intercalated. Towards the central and southern Münsterland Cretaceous Basin, subsidence rates were lower and sedimentary thicknesses of the Emscher marls are reduced.

Strongly uplifted source areas in the west (South Netherland High) and in the NW (Gronau and Ochtrup anticlines, Ibbenbüren High) provided coarser clastics from eroded Triassic and probably even Carboniferous rocks. In the western Münsterland Cretaceous Basin, the Coniacian marls progressively grade into foreshore greensands (Emscher Greensands; Unit 19 in Figs 15.13 & 15.14) and Santonian proximal marine sandstones (Recklinghausen and Haltern formations; Unit 18 in Figs 15.13 & 15.14) (Arnold 1964). Locally, upper Santonian and lower Campanian litho- and bioclastic calcarenites (Burgsteinfurt Fm; Unit 21 in Figs 15.13 & 15.14) (Hiss 1995) occur in the central Münsterland Cretaceous Basin. Lower and middle Campanian sediments comprise sandy marlstones (Holtwick and Coesfeld formations; Unit 24 in Figs 15.13 & 15.14) (Hauschke *et al.* 1999), and are overlain by shallow-marine, partly glauconitic calcarenites and turbidites of late Campanian age (Baumberge Fm; Unit 27 in Figs 15.13 & 15.14).

*Subhercynian Cretaceous Basin*

As in the Münsterland Cretaceous Basin, rates of subsidence (which commenced in the Turonian) were not evenly distributed across the Subhercynian Cretaceous Basin. Sedimentation of hemipelagic limestones continued until early Coniacian times and changed progressively to clastic deposition during Coniacian and Santonian times. Coniacian–early Campanian proximal strata comprise conglomerates, sandstones and calcareous siltstones. The source areas for clastic marine deposits were situated in the east although activity along the Harznordrand Thrust dates back to the Coniacian. A significant change in the sediment source area occurred during the middle Santonian when the rapidly uplifted Harz area was eroded, and sediments were subsequently transported into the basin (T. Voigt *et al.* 2006). The vertical uplift of the Harz Block relative to the subsiding Subhercynian Cretaceous Basin was of the order of 7000 m. The southern basin margin, which included Upper Cretaceous deposits, was progressively upturned by the active thrust and at least five syntectonic unconformities (progressive unconformities) formed at the margin of the growth structure (Unit 19 in Figs 15.13 & 15.14) (Cloos 1917; Mortimore *et al.* 1998; Niebuhr *et al.* 2000; T. Voigt *et al.* 2004).

The middle Coniacian Halberstadt Formation (up to 150 m thick) was deposited in a high-energy nearshore environment (*involutus* sandstone). Late Coniacian and early Santonian sediments are limited to the narrow basin axis immediately in front of the uplifting Harz due to a regression. Consequently, a widespread unconformity was developed at the margins of the basin, being particularly marked at the active southern basin margin. Here, middle Santonian deposits rest on an angular unconformity over older units (Upper Triassic to Coniacian). In the western part of the basin, deposition of the conglomeratic sandstones of the Sudmerberg Formation (>180 m thick) continued from the middle through the upper Santonian. This transgression led to the deposition of fossil-rich middle Santonian foreshore sands (Salzberg Formation, 250 m) in the eastern part of the basin, which was gradually replaced by a coastal succession in the late Santonian Heidelberg Formation (450 m; Patzelt 2000). Here, coastal plain deposits with coals and palaeosoils interdigitate with nearshore and tidal sediments (T. Voigt *et al.* 2006). This proximal facies at the eastern basin margin pass into a 10 km broad facies belt of cross-bedded coastal sandstones. The pure quartz sands of Coniacian and Santonian age grade into the monotonous Emscher Marls (2000 m) which accumulated in the basin axis immediately in front of the active Harznordrand Thrust (Unit 17 in Figs 15.13, 15.14 & 15.15) (Roll 1953). Marl sedimentation continued into the early Campanian (Unit 22 in Figs 15.13 & 15.14) (Ulbrich 1971, 1974). Further uplift of the Harz Block resulted in continued tilting and erosion. Deposition of marly, partly conglomeratic sands of the Heimburg and the Blankenburg formations (latest Santonian, earliest Campanian; Unit 21 in Figs 15.13 & 15.14) was restricted to a narrow area immediately in front of the central part of the Harznordrand Thrust. Both formations rest unconformably on steeply inclined Permian to upper Santonian strata at the NE margin of the Harz area (Tröger 2000*b*; T. Voigt *et al.* 2004). In early Campanian times, the Harz was unroofed from its Mesozoic cover. In consequence, Devonian slates and Carboniferous greywackes were eroded and redeposited. The fine-grained conglomerates and calcareous, often bioclastic sandstones pass basinward to spongiolithic marls with a thickness of at least 400 m (Tröger 2000*b*; T. Voigt *et al.* 2006).

*Altmark-Fläming Basin*

The evolution of the Altmark-Fläming Basin is very similar to that of the Subhercynian Cretaceous Basin. Cenomanian (30–60 m) to Turonian (40–270 m) hemipelagic limestones dominate across the entire basin (Schulze 1964). Sediment thicknesses decrease from NW to SE. These deposits are overlain by a thick succession of silty marls (foreshore deposits) of Coniacian and Santonian age (at least 600 m). In the lower Coniacian, and again in the middle to upper Santonian, marine sandstone beds 2–15 m thick are intercalated (Schulze 1964). A more proximal facies of marine sands occurs in the central Altmark-Fläming Basin immediately adjacent to the strongly uplifted northern margin of the Calvörde Block. The Coniacian to Santonian succession comprises predominantly shoreface sandstones and nearshore conglomerates derived from older sediments (Buntsandstein to Lower Cretaceous) and, additionally, thick horizons of clastic ironstones, probably reworked from Jurassic sideritic claystones (Nöldecke 1967). All of these Upper Cretaceous deposits in the Altmark-Fläming Basin were tilted along the southern basin margin and folded to form two narrow synclines during inversion. Lower Campanian deposits are not preserved in the Altmark-Fläming Basin except at the northernmost transition to the Pompeckj High, where chalk was cored, suggesting that initially there was a wider distribution of Campanian sediments. Upper Campanian and Maastrichtian deposits are composed of marine to deltaic glauconitic sands of considerable thickness (250–600 m) (units 29 and 31 in Figs 15.13 & 15.14; Nennhausen Formation, Ahrens *et al.* 1965; Niebuhr *et al.* 2007). The distribution of these units reflects the end of inversion tectonics since they show no relation to the former boundaries of the Altmark-Fläming Basin. The only slightly deformed Maastrichtian transgressive surface covers both tilted Cretaceous sediments in the basin and inverted areas and diapirs (Diener 1967).

*Western Pomerania (Rügen-Usedom)*

In the course of the late Albian and Cenomanian transgressions, the Rügen-Usedom area was widely flooded and became a basinal part of the extended Northern European epicontinental chalk sea (Figs 15.5 & 15.11). Upper Albian marine sediments are widely distributed and cover local highs and lows as well (Brückner & Petzka 1967). The base of the upper Albian strata is formed by a 1–10 m thick bed of glauconitic sandstones with pebbles and phosphorites, and is overlain by 2–30 m of green-greyish to reddish-brown clay-rich marls and marls with fossils such as oysters and belemnites (*Aucellina, Neohibolites*). The difference in thickness between structural high and lows indicates active deformation during Early Cretaceous times (Diener *et al.* 2004*b*).

A complete Upper Cretaceous succession is present in Western Pomerania, but exposed outcrops are restricted to isolated ice-rafted deposits and the chalk deposits on the Jasmund peninsula on the island of Rügen. The sedimentation area is bounded by the Grimmen High to the SW and the inverted Pomeranian-Kujavian Anticline to the NE (Brückner & Petzka 1967). Sedimentary hiatuses within the Santonian–Campanian and Maastrichtian are found along the margins of these highs (Figs 15.5 & 15.14). Cenomanian and lower Turonian deposits are represented in the Rügen-Usedom area by marly limestones and limestones, which were overlain by a succession of Coniacian to Maastrichtian chalks (Unit 16 in Figs 15.13 & 15.14). During the late Campanian, a transgression led to the onlap of marine sediments on older Upper Cretaceous (Turonian–Coniacian) strata along the flanks of the Grimmen High and the Pomeranian-Kujavian Anticline. In the Rügen area, Upper Cretaceous deposits attain a maximum thickness of >600 m, while 30 km to the north of the island, the thickness exceeds 1130 m (G 14–1 borehole; Petzka & Reich 2000; Diener *et al.* 2004*a*).

Basinal chalks of early Maastrichtian age (*Belemnella obtusa, B. sumensis*, *B. cimbrica* and *B. fastigata* zones) are well exposed in a number of quarries and in coastal cliff exposures at Rügen (Rügen Member Herrig *et al.* 1996; Reich & Frenzel 2002;

Niebuhr *et al.* 2007). The most impressive outcrop is the coastal cliff between Sassnitz and Lohme, where sheets of chalk are thrust in a nappe-like belt by glaciers advancing from the north and east during the late Pleistocene. The chalk consists of a highly diverse, boreal micro- and macrofaunal assemblage (Reich & Frenzel 2002), and represents an outer shelf to upper bathyal facies with estimated water depths of 150–300 m (Nestler 1965; Frenzel 2000). The facies of the Rügen chalk is rather monotonous, and hardgrounds, similar to those of the English and Danish chalk, are absent. Chalk sedimentation in the Rügen area was influenced by the southern part of the Skurup High (Figs 15.3 & 15.5). This high is bordered by the Sorgenfrei-Tornquist Zone and bounded on all sides by faults. These structures had a conspicuous influence on the local seafloor relief as well as sedimentation during Late Cretaceous inversion movements. During the early Maastrichtian, the uplift of the Grimmen High and the Møn Block led to the influx of nutrient-rich and oxygen-rich cooler waters from the North Sea. These tectonic movements resulted in the deposition of thick successions of seismites and up to 6–7 m thick slumped units in the higher parts of the Rügen chalk (Steinich 1972). It is believed that tectonic activity was linked to the reactivation of a NW–SE orientated fault system along the southern margin of the Skurup High (Fig. 15.5).

## *Liège-Limburg Basin (J.W.M.J., P.J.F., A.S.S.)*

The Santonian–Maastrichtian succession of the Liège-Limburg Basin has a detailed lithostratigraphy (Fig. 15.15). Biostratigraphic ages are based on spores, pollen and dinoflagellate assemblages for the basal fluvial deposits (Batten *et al.* 1987, 1988; Streel *et al.* 1994), and on ammonoid and belemnitellid cephalopods, inoceramid bivalves, benthic foraminifers, and dinoflagellates for the marine succession (Christensen & Schmid 1987; Jagt 1989, 1999; Jagt *et al.* 1987, 1995*a, b*; Kennedy & Jagt 1995, 1998; Keutgen 1996; 1997; Schiøler *et al.* 1997). Additionally, a regional ecozonation has been developed on the basis of bioclast assemblages, which are calibrated against benthic foraminifera and ostracods (Bless *et al.* 1987; P.J. Felder & Bless 1989). Upper Cretaceous litho- and biostratigraphy, in combination with ecozonation, enables the reconstruction of the complex relation of facies and local tectonics. Preliminary data on sequence stratigraphy (Schiøler *et al.* 1997), strontium isotope stratigraphy (Vonhof & Smit 1996) and cyclostratigraphy (Zijlstra 1994) are available for the upper Maastrichtian in the type area of Maastricht. In the Liège-Limburg Basin there are no deposits of Early Cretaceous age. To the north of the Roer Valley Graben on the adjoining Peel Block, strata of Hauterivian–Albian age have been cored in boreholes (Fig. 15.5) (Burgers & Mulder 1991; Gras & Geluk 1999; Mulder *et al.* 2003).

*Middle Santonian–earliest Campanian*

During the mid-Santonian, inversion of the Roer Valley Graben led to the reactivation of older faults, and created tension between the Anglo-Brabant Massif and the Roer Valley Graben (Fig. 15.16). The area SW of the graben subsided and formed a flat river valley which was filled by alluvial deposits comprising sands, silty clays and lignite (Hergenrath Member) (Fig. 15.17). Towards the west (along the Stavelot and the Anglo-Brabant massifs) the unit rests on eroded Palaeozoic rocks. Fossil wood occurrences indicate that the flora consisted of gymnosperms with subordinate angiosperms and suggest a seasonal humid warm-temperate to subtropical climate (Meijer 2000). In the Aachen area, the alluvial deposits have a thickness of *c.* 60–70 m, in contrast to other areas where thicknesses are lower (10–30 m). In the mid- to late Santonian, the inverted Roer Valley Graben formed a structural high that was eroded and acted as a source area for siliciclastics. In the type area south of Aachen, up to 60 m of cross-bedded delta and shoreface sands were accumulated along or close to the coast (Aken Member). Lateral equivalents in the Campine area yield ammonoid and belemnitellid cephalopods and inoceramid bivalves (Jagt *et al.* 1995*a*).

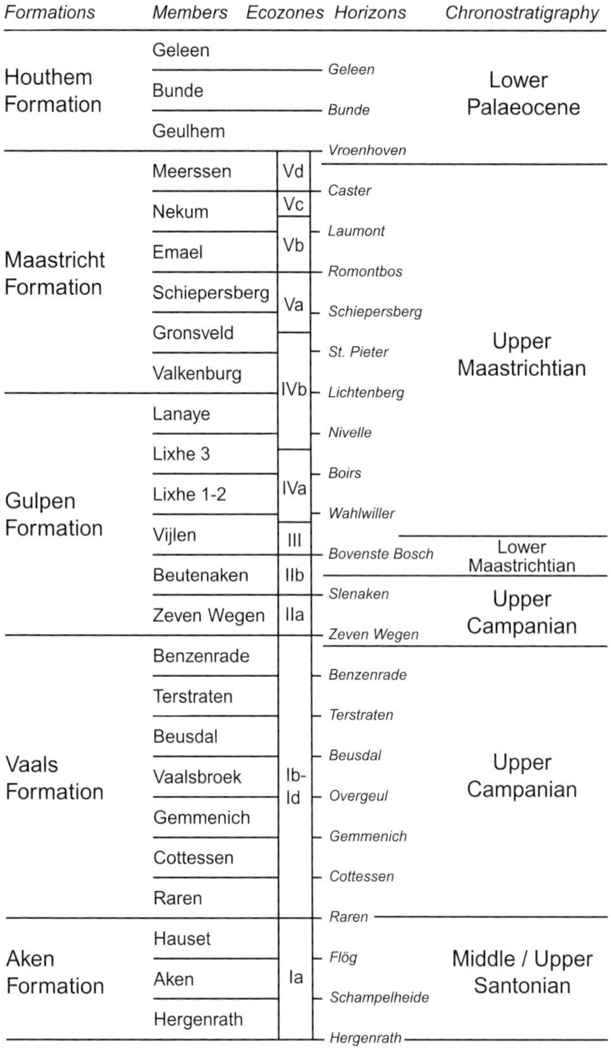


**Fig. 15.15.** Lithostratigraphy of Upper Cretaceous and Palaeogene strata in the extended type area of the Maastrichtian Stage (after W.M. Felder 1975, 1996; W.M. Felder & Bosch 2001) and its relation to ecozonation (after P.J. Felder 2003) and chronostratigraphy. Note that stage and substage boundaries are subject to change, and occasionally lack the precision suggested here.

*Early Campanian to early late Campanian*

The continuing uplift of the Roer Valley Graben resulted in the supply and progradation of coarse siliciclastics towards the south (southern Limburg). The Stavelot and Brabant massifs did not serve as sediment source areas at this time. Reactivation of older faults, as well as the initiation of new ones, led to the uplift of local highs, such as the Hulsberg High (Fig. 15.16). Shoreface

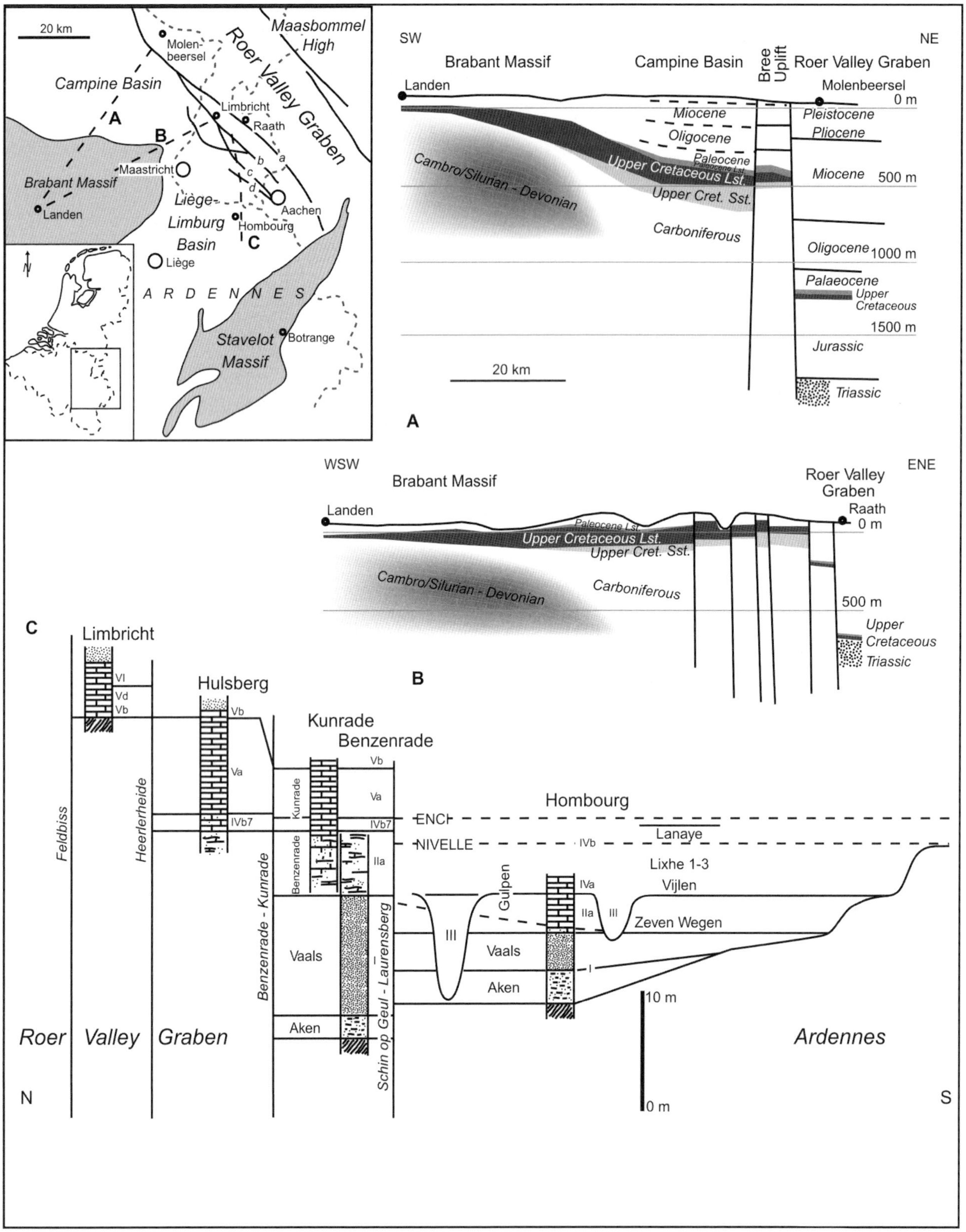


**Fig. 15.16.** Structural map (inset) and cross-sections (**A**, **B**, **C**) of the Liège-Limburg Basin. The Roer Valley Graben became inverted during middle Santonian–early Maastrichtian times. The Brabant and Stavelot Massifs formed structural highs. For more detailed information see Bless & Felder (1989), Bless *et al.* (1991*a*,*b*), and P.J. Felder (2003), as well as P.J. Felder (1995, 1996, 2001), P.J. Felder *et al.* (1985), De Batist & Versteeg (1999), Dusar & Lagrou (2004) and Vandenberghe *et al.* (2004) for the Campine area, and Geluk (1990), Geluk *et al.* (1994), Gras (1995), and Gras & Geluk (1999) for the Roer Valley Graben. Latin numbers in cross-section (C) indicate ecozones by Bless *et al.* (1987). Abbreviations: a, Feldbiss Fault; b, Heerlerite Fault; c, Benzenrade Kunrade Fault; d, Schin op Geul–Laurensberg Fault.

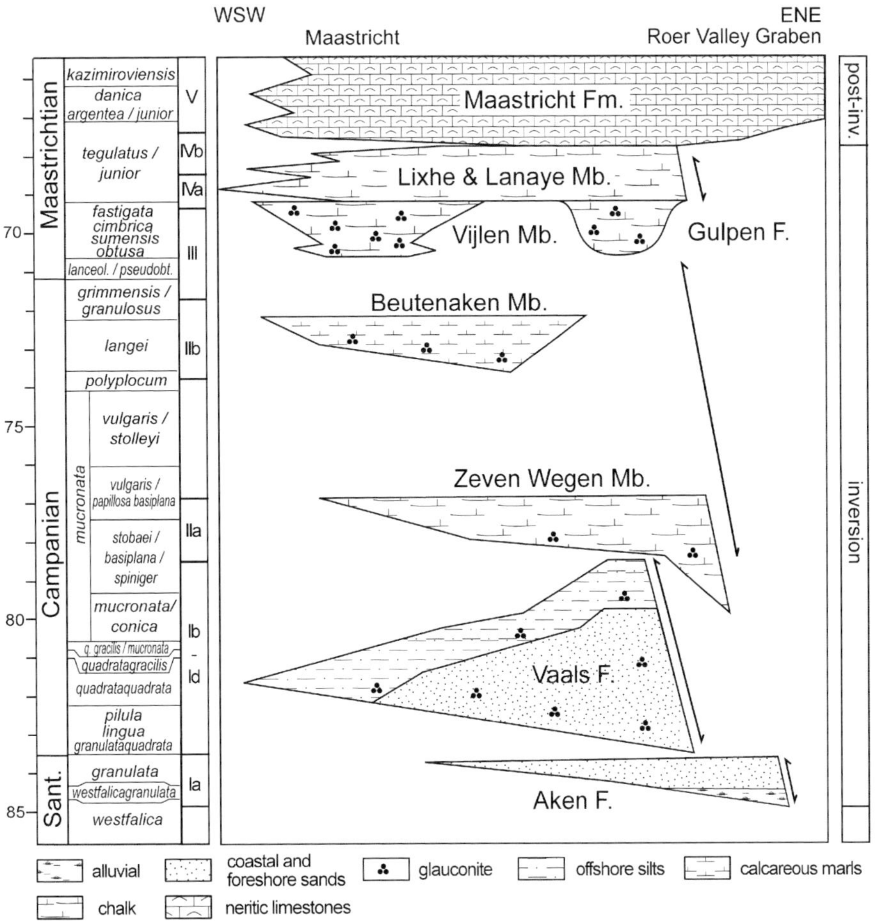


**Fig. 15.17.** Chronostratigraphic diagram of the sedimentary infill in the Liège-Limburg Basin in relation to boreal macrofossil zonation and inversion tectonics. The timescale is after Gradstein *et al.* (2004). Latin numbers indicate regional ecozonation (Bless *et al.* 1987).

and upper foreshore sediments comprise alternations of fine-grained, glauconitic sands and bioturbated silty sands, which were deposited in numerous channels and grade into finer clastics towards the west (Vaals Formation) (Fig. 15.17). Locally, fossiliferous sandstones also occur. The Vaals Formation is separated from the underlying unit by a conglomerate (Raren Horizon), which represents erosion as a result of regression. On the Hulsberg High, no or very little sediment was deposited (Fig. 15.16C). The grain size decreases towards the upper part of the succession, where glauconitic calcareous silts with several hardgrounds also occur (Benzenrade Member). The succession is 60–100 m thick, and can be up to *c.* 150 m in the type area (Albers 1976; Albers & Felder 1979). Its early early Campanian to early late Campanian age (*granulataquadrata*, *lingua/quadrata* and *stobaei/basiplana* zones) is based mainly on the presence of cephalopods.

*Late Campanian to early late Maastrichtian*

In the late Campanian the influx of siliciclastic material decreased, and inner- and middle neritic carbonates predominated. The limestones consist of fine- to coarse-grained bioclastic grainstones, reaching a total thickness of *c.* 175 m (Gulpen Formation). This formation is confined to the area south of the Benzenrade and Schin op Geul faults, and is well developed in the Liège area (Fig. 15.16).

The lowermost units comprise chalks with basal glauconite and occasional flints towards the west (Zeven Wegen Member; up to 30 m) and glauconitic calcareous clays and marls (Beutenaken Member; up to 10 m) (Figs 15.15 & 15.17). The Zeven Wegen Member has erosional unconformities at its base and top, which are related to regressions. In the Campine area, only remnants of the originally thicker sediments remain preserved on the Anglo-Brabant Massif. South of Limburg, remnants of the Zeven Wegen and Beutenaken members have been encountered, and the varying thicknesses indicate synsedimentary active faulting and erosion. On the Hulsberg High, no sediments were deposited. A considerable mid to late Campanian sea-level fall in combination with further uplift and block tilting of the Roer Valley Graben resulted in erosion in the middle part of the Gulpen Formation (Figs 15.16C & 15.17). Gulleys up to 70 m deep were washed out near Vijlen, cutting into the underlying sediments. As a result of progressive erosion, older Cretaceous strata were locally completely removed. During the subsequent transgression the gulley was filled stepwise with glauconitic chalks. All of these strata in the gulley are referred to as the Vijlen Member, which is of early to early late Maastrichtian age (ecozone III, *obtusa* to *fastigata* zones) and has a thickness of 15–25 m (up to 100 m in the gully) (Keutgen 1996, 1997; P.J. Felder & Bless 1994).

The overlying sediments comprise up to 25 m of white chalks

with irregular flint nodules (Lixhe Member), and *c.* 20 m of coarser-grained biocalcarenites (Lanaye Member), which represent a sea-level highstand and increased shallowing from a low- to a high-energy environment (Figs 15.17 & 15.18). Rhythmic concentrations of flint nodules are related to orbitally forced (precession) changes in both climate and palaeoceanography (Zijlstra 1994). Flint nodules are concentrated into particular units suggesting that this sequence was controlled by long and short eccentricities. The mean cycle thickness increases from decimetres to a metre, and reflects an increase in mean deposition rate from 2 to 5 cm/ka. Characteristic faunal changes (substitution of the echinoid genus *Echinocorys* by *Hemipneustes*) in the upper Lixhe Member (Lixhe 3) document a rise in sea-water temperatures. In addition, the results of quantitative palynology demonstrate a link between pollen constituents and superimposed short-term cooling trends (P.J. Felder *et al.* 2003). Upper Lixhe Member (Lixhe 3) strata have been recognized in all wells of the region, with the exception of the Hulsberg borehole. This would suggest that tilting and subsidence during the deposition of this interval also occurred on the Anglo-Brabant Massif. The presence of calcareous nannofossils and planktonic foraminifera indicates oceanic conditions and water depths of the order of 80–150 m for the upper parts of the Gulpen Formation (Villain 1977; Zijlstra 1994).

*Late Maastrichtian to Palaeocene*

During the middle late Maastrichtian (ecozone IVb, *tegulatus/junior* Zone), inversion of the Hulsberg High and the Roer Valley Graben ceased, and the former began to subside. The higher positioned blocks to the east underwent erosion which led to the influx and deposition of coarse-grained phosphatic/glauconitic and pyritic bioclastic sands, which form the base of the Maastricht Formation (Lichtenberg Horizon; original definition of the 'système maestrichtien' by Dumont 1849). On the Hulsberg High and to the north of it, the Lichtenberg Horizon is a distinct erosive contact. Towards the SE, increasingly older strata are covered by deposits of the Lichtenberg Horizon. During this phase, the motion along the Schin op Geul and

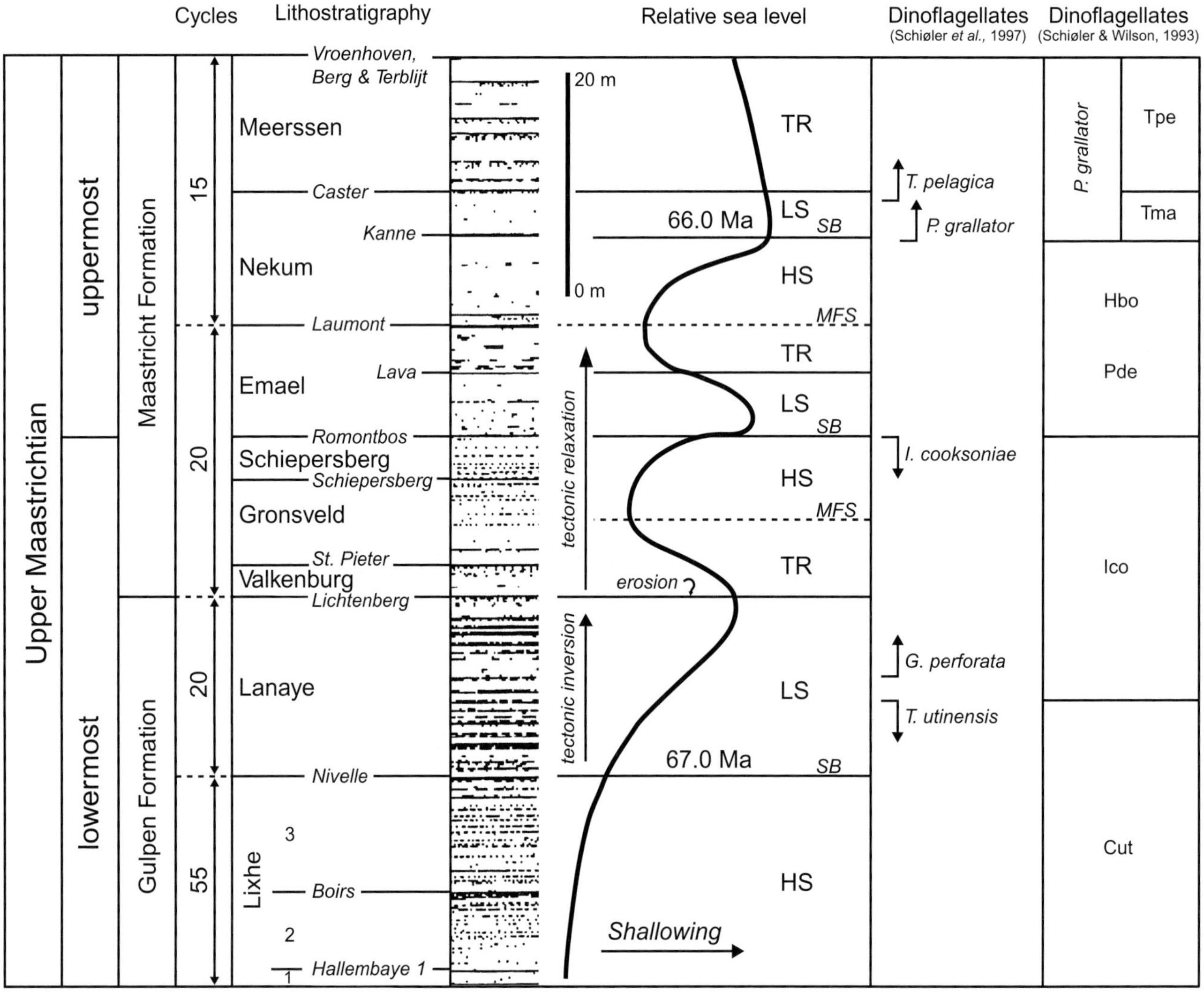


**Fig. 15.18.** Stratigraphic scheme showing late Maastrichtian number of 20 ka precession cycles (Zijlstra 1994), lithostratigraphy (members and horizons), relative sea-level fluctuations, dinoflagellate first appearance datums (FADs) and last appearance datums (LADs), and dinoflagellate biozonation (modified from Schiøler *et al.* 1997) of the ENCI quarry at Maastricht. Abbreviations: HS, highstand; LS, lowstand; *MFS*, maximum flooding surface; *SB*, sequence boundary; TR, transgression.

Kunrade faults reversed for the first time, while the Roer Valley Graben subsided and became an area of marine sedimentation. Sediments at Molenbeersel belong to ecozone IVb (Fig. 15.15; Bless *et al.* 1993). Subsequently, during ecozone Va, ongoing block tilting and subsidence of the Roer Valley Graben along the Schin op Geul Fault shifted the depocentre towards the NE, as indicated by the increase in sediment thickness from the Lanaye (5.5 m) to Hulsberg (70 m thick) areas.

The Maastricht Formation comprises weakly indurated, fine- to coarse-grained bioclastic limestones, which contain abundant reworked chalk clasts and low concentrations of quartz and heavy minerals (Fig. 15.18). To the east, the sequence grades into an alternation of more indurated bioclastic limestones (so-called 'Kunrade limestone'). The common occurrence of sea grass indicates shallow depositional depths (20–40 m). Microfossil evidence suggests a middle sublittoral environment with subtropical temperatures (Liebau 1978). Scleractinian corals indicate palaeotemperatures of 20–25°C. The unit occurs throughout southern Limburg and contiguous areas of Belgium and has a thickness of 45–90 m. The formation is absent due to erosion in the area south of the St Geertruid-Gulpen-Vaals area and north of the Heerlerheide Fault. The occurrence of karst horizons and palaeosols in the upper Maastrichtian–Palaeocene succession suggests shallow depositional depths and a balance between tectonic subsidence/uplift, sedimentation and sea-level rise (Campine area; see Bless *et al.* 1993). Grain sizes increase in the upper Maastricht Formation, where coarse- to very coarse-grained bioclastic limestones with hardgrounds, fossil debris and omission surfaces also occur. These reflect a shallow high-energy setting (2–15 m), which subsequently led to the establishment of a broad carbonate platform (Liebau 1978).

## Basins around the Bohemian Massif (D.U., S.Č., I.W., F.W.)

### *Bohemian Cretaceous Basin (D.U., S.Č.)*

The term 'Bohemian Cretaceous Basin' is used here for the main part of the Bohemian Cretaceous Basin system that extends between Saxony, Bohemia and Moravia, and is largely governed by the Lausitz and Labe-Železné Hory fault zones as two overlapping strands of the Elbe Fault Zone. The Cretaceous deposits of the Intrasudetic Basin and the Nysa Graben were originally connected to the Bohemian Cretaceous Basin, but became isolated due to subsequent Late Cretaceous–Cenozoic uplift and the erosion of Cretaceous strata (Fig. 15.19) (see below).

The Bohemian Cretaceous Basin existed from the early Cenomanian to the early Santonian (11–12 Ma; Fig. 15.20); the maximum preserved thickness of Cretaceous strata is *c.* 1000 m while the lithofacies show pronounced local variations (Fig. 15.21). The tectonosedimentary evolution of the basin can be divided into three stages: early to middle Cenomanian (Phase I), latest Cenomanian to late Turonian (Phase II), and Coniacian to early Santonian (Phase III; Uličný *et al.* 2003*a*). During Phase II, two large sub-basins evolved: the Lužice (Lausitz)-Jizera sub-basin and the Orlice-Žďár sub-basin (Fig. 15.22). Major, long-term trends in relative sea-level change within the Bohemian Cretaceous Basin, such as the late Cenomanian rise, the early Turonian peak and the mid-Turonian low, have clear counterparts in many other European basins and have been correlated as eustatic events (e.g. Valečka & Skoček 1991; Uličný *et al.* 1993, 1997*a*, *b*; Voigt & Tröger 1996; Laurin & Uličný 2004; S. Voigt *et al.* 2006). In addition, recent research demonstrates that

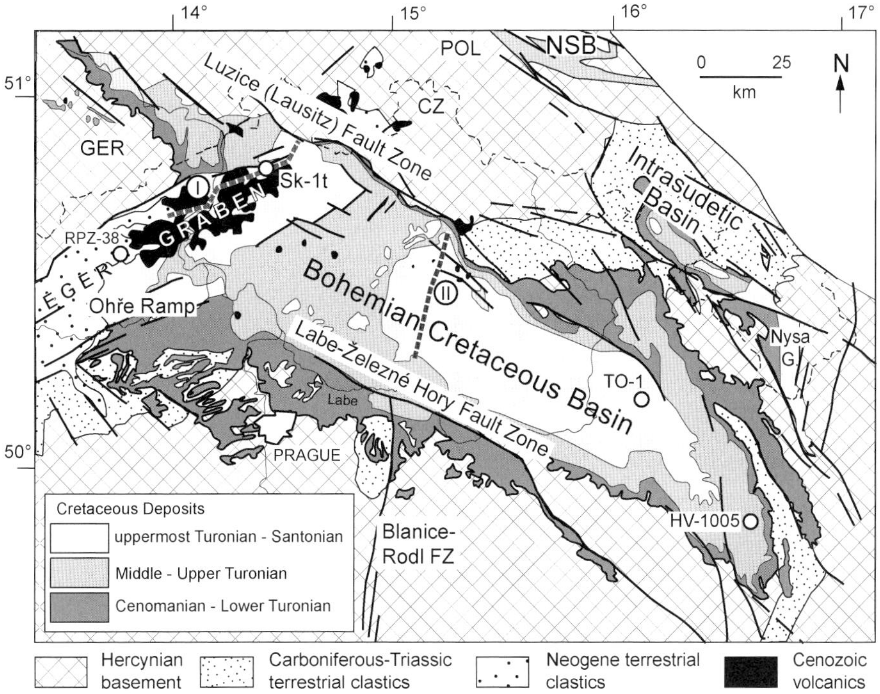


**Fig. 15.19.** Schematic geological map of the Bohemian Cretaceous Basin and its surroundings showing the relationship to major tectonostratigraphic units of the Bohemian Massif. Stippled lines labelled I and II are locations of cross-sections in Figure 15.23. HV-1005, RPZ-38, Sk-1t, TO-1 are boreholes shown in Figure 15.21.

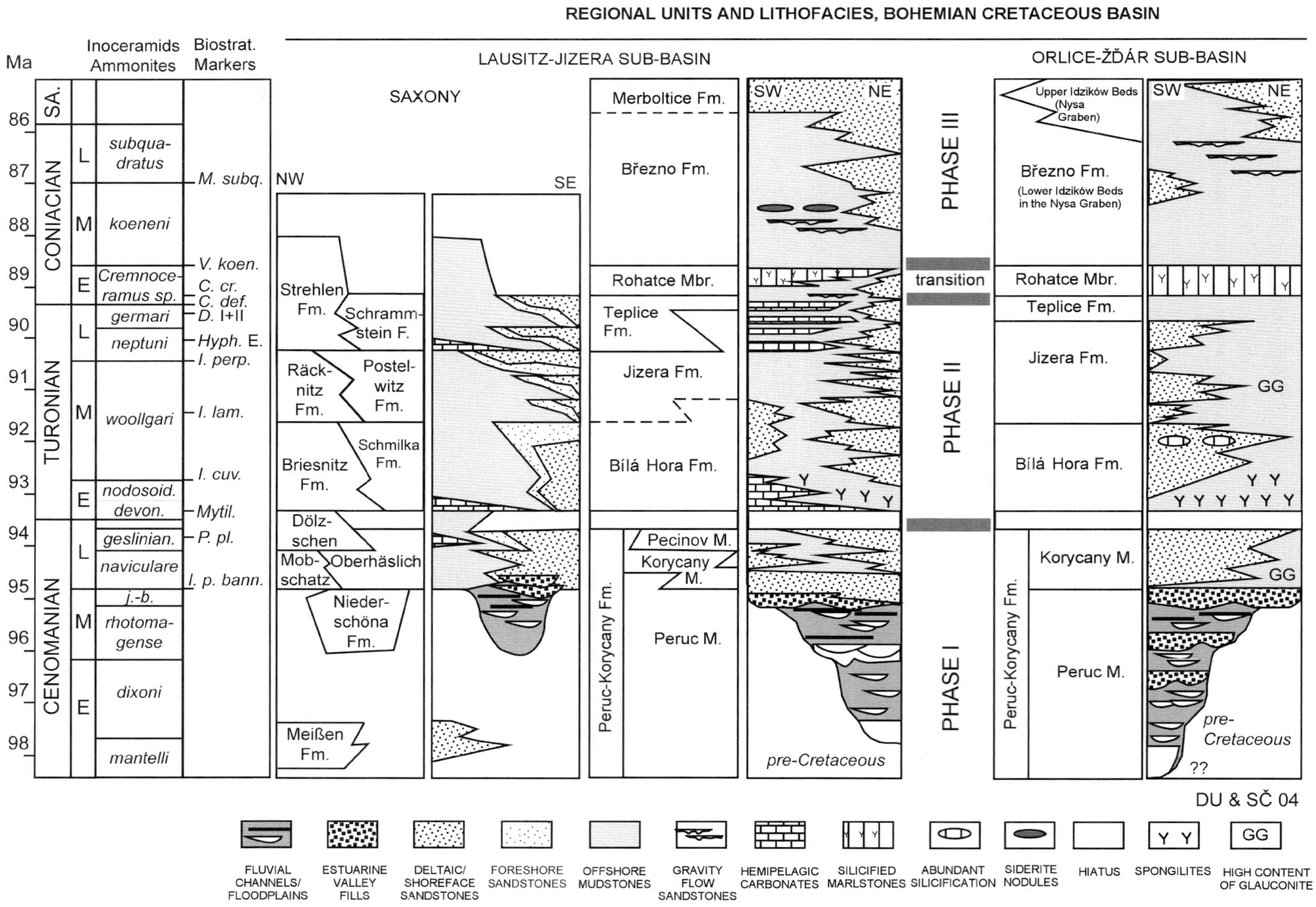


**Fig. 15.20.** Chronostratigraphic diagram showing lithofacies and main regional units in the Lausitz-Jizera and the Orlice-Žd'ár sub-basins of the Bohemian Cretaceous Basin. Ammonite and inoceramid zonations are after Hardenbol *et al.* (1998) plotted against the timescale of Gradstein *et al.* (2004). Biostratigraphic markers significant for the Bohemian Cretaceous: *I. p. bann.*, first occurrence (FO) of *Inoceramus (pictus) bannewitzensis*; *P. pl.*, FO of *Praeactinocamax plenus*; *Mytil.*, FO of *Mytiloides* bivalves; *I. cuv.*, FO of *Inoceramus cuvieri*; *I. lam.*, FO of *Inoceramus lamarcki*; *I. perp.*, FO of *Inoceramus perplexus*; *Hyph*. E., *Hyphantoceras* event *sensu* Ernst *et al.* (1983); DI+II, *Didymotis* Events I and II *sensu* Čech (1989); *C. def.*, FO of *Cremnoceramus deformis erectus*; *C. cr.*, FO of *Cremnoceramus crassus crassus*; *V. koen.*, FO of *Volviceramus koeneni*, *M. subq.*, FO of *Magadiceramus subquadratus*. Regional lithostratigraphic units are after Čech *et al.* (1980) and Prescher (1981). Rocky shore facies and local intrabasinal hiatuses are not shown. Phases I–III are tectonostratigraphic phases of basin evolution, explained in text.

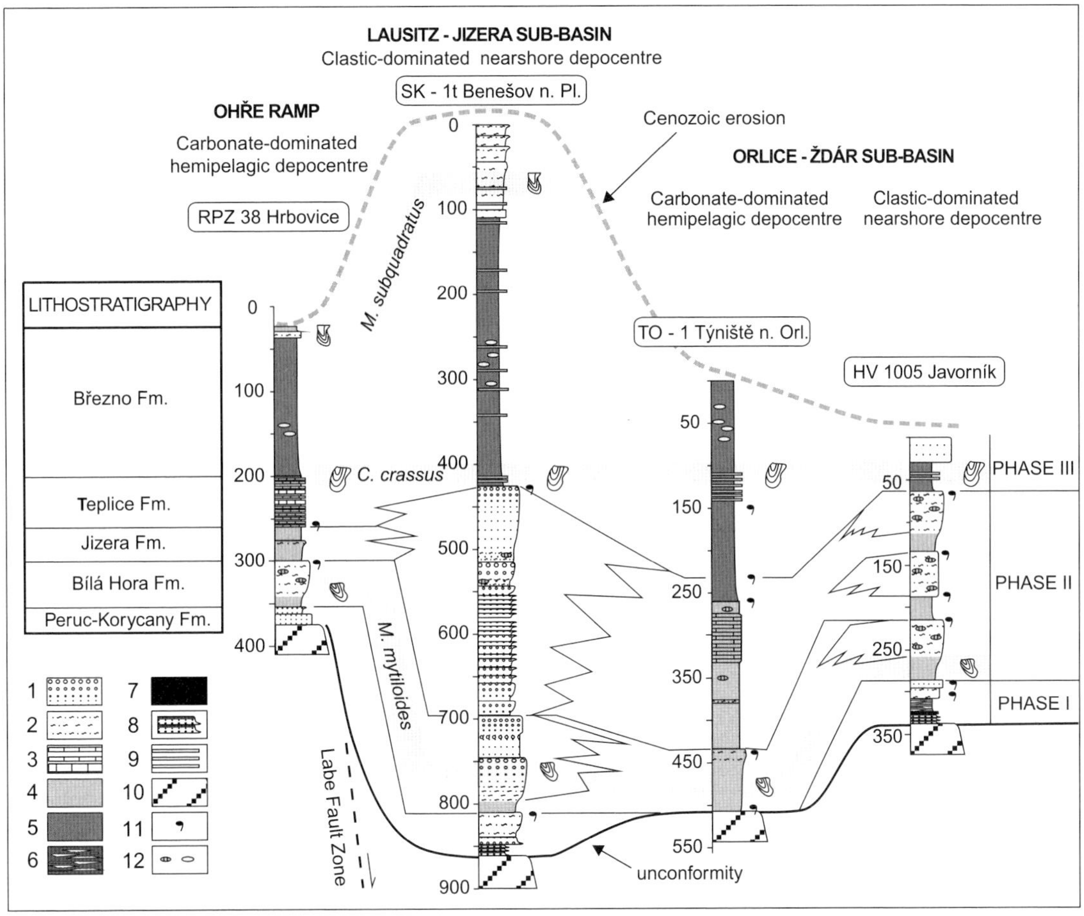


**Fig. 15.21.** Lithostratigraphy and biostratigraphic correlation across the sub-basins of the Bohemian Cretaceous Basin. Locations of boreholes are shown in Figure 15.19. Lithostratigraphy is of Čech *et al.* (1980). Key: 1, fine- to coarse-grained quartzose sandstones (Quadersandstein); 2, calcareous spiculitic sandstones; 3, hemipelagic limestones; 4, marlstones; 5, claystones; 6, estuarine sand and mud; 7, coal; 8, fluvial sediments; 9, silicified calcareous claystones (Rohatce Member); 10, pre-Cretaceous rocks; 11, glauconite; 12, limestone and clay ironstone concretions.

stratigraphic architecture was significantly controlled by both tectonic activity and the spatially variable sediment supply (Laurin & Uličný 2004; Uličný *et al.* 2003*a*).

The following sections summarize the main stages in the evolution of the basin palaeogeography and sedimentary infill. More detailed information about regional aspects and lithostratigraphy is provided in Herčík *et al.* (2003).

*Cenomanian*

Cretaceous sedimentation in the Bohemian Cretaceous Basin commenced in the Cenomanian and is characterized by a deepening-upward facies succession (Fig. 15.20). The facies are represented by a diverse range of fluvial, estuarine, shoreface, offshore and rocky-shore sediments, which were deposited in response to the interplay of moderate subsidence, basement-controlled topography, and sea-level changes. The Cenomanian long-term relative sea-level rise and the superimposed high-order transgressions exerted a predominant control on sediment accumulation.

The earliest deposits of the Bohemian Cretaceous Basin are of early Cenomanian age and are limited to the Meissen area in Saxony (Prescher & Tröger 1989; Tröger 2003) and the Blansko Graben in Moravia (Čech *et al.* 1996*a*; Svobodová 1999). While the marine conglomerates at Meissen represent the most proximal facies of the North German Basin, the sediments of the Blansko Graben are of fluvial and estuarine origin and belong to the Peruc Member. However, the more extensive fluvial and estuarine successions of the Peruc Member and the Niederschöna Formation are of middle Cenomanian age (Fig. 15.20; Čech *et al.* 1980; Pacltová 1981; Uličný *et al.* 1997*b*; T. Voigt 1998; Tröger 1996, 2003).

The basement structures inherited from the Variscan Orogeny and the early post-orogenic evolution of the Bohemian Massif dominated the palaeogeography in the middle Cenomanian (Fig. 15.22A). A prominent valley, filled by fluvial and, later, estuarine deposits, existed to the north of the Blanice-Rodl Fault Zone. Many tributaries of this valley, together with other parts of the Cenomanian drainage system, followed the WNW-orientated structural trend of the Elbe Fault Zone system (T. Voigt 1998; Uličný *et al.* 2003*b*). Another early and middle Cenomanian fluvial-estuarine valley system existed in eastern Bohemia and western Moravia, and drained towards the Tethys Ocean in the SE (Fig. 15.22A). The origin of the fluvial to estuarine filling of the palaeovalleys is considered to be a consequence of a long-term base-level rise punctuated by several shorter cycles of relative sea-level rise and fall during the early and middle

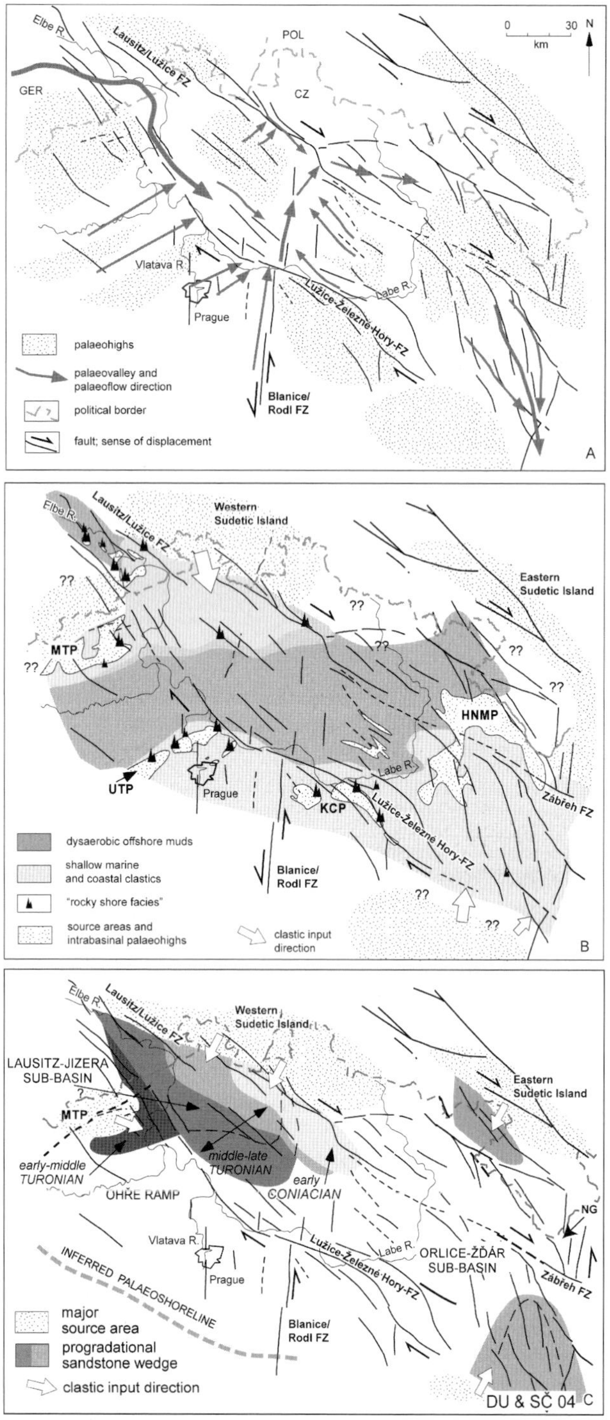


**Fig. 15.22.** Schematic maps showing the tectonic structures and palaeogeography of the Bohemian Cretaceous Basin between the middle Cenomanian and early Coniacian. (**A**) Middle Cenomanian palaeodrainage systems, prior to establishment of main sub-basins and source areas. (**B**) Late Cenomanian palaeogeography after the *Metoicoceras geslinianum* Zone transgression. (**C**) Turonian–early Coniacian sandy deltaic systems and their relationships to sub-basins and source areas. The overall shape of the sandstone bodies is highly simplified: each lobe represents an area of numerous subordinate prograding wedges. Jizera and Bílá Hora Formation clastics are not separated in the Orlice-Žd'ár sub-basin. Abbreviations: HNMP, Holice-Nové Město Palaeohigh; KCP, Kolín-Čáslav Palaeohigh; MTP, Most-Teplice Palaeohigh; NG, Nysa Graben; UTP, Unhošt'-Tursko Palaeohigh.

Cenomanian (e.g. Čech *et al.* 1996*a*; Uličný & Špičáková 1996; Voigt & Tröger 1996; Tröger 2003). Towards the end of the middle Cenomanian, estuarine conditions were established over a large part of the Bohemian Cretaceous Basin. The coasts of Cenomanian estuaries as well as river floodplains and the uplands beyond the depositional areas were covered by abundant vegetation, as documented by many studies of well-preserved floras in Bohemia (Peruc Member; Velenovský & Viniklář 1926–31; Knobloch 1999). The occurrence of abundant halophytic vegetation types in Cenomanian nearshore floras illustrates the importance of tidal processes (e.g. Uličný *et al.* 1997*b*; Nguyen-Tu *et al.* 2002).

The transgression in the early late Cenomanian (*C. naviculare* Zone) led to backfilling of the remaining relief with fluvial and tidal-influenced estuarine deposits, as exemplified by the Pecínov reference section (Špičáková & Uličný 1996; Uličný *et al.* 1997*b*). While tide-influenced conditions prevailed during most phases of the long-term relative sea-level rise, storm-dominated coasts are indicated by the presence of hummocky cross-stratified sandstones of the Korycany Member in parts of central Bohemia (Špičáková & Uličný 1996). In the course of the *C. naviculare* Zone, fully marine conditions were established in the central and northern parts of the Bohemian Cretaceous Basin (Fig. 15.20). Wedges of quartz sandstone began to prograde southwards and northwards from the newly-established source areas in the north (Lausitz Block or West Sudetic Island, north of the Lausitz Fault Zone and Erzgebirge Block) and the SE part (Moldanubian and Moravian blocks) (Figs 15.19 & 15.22B). In Saxony, basinal glauconitic calcareous mud- and siltstones (Mobschatz Formation) interfinger with proximal massive quartzose sandstones (Oberhäslich Formation; Tröger 2003).

A major relative sea-level rise in the early *M. geslinianum* Zone, partly caused by a eustatic rise, led to the flooding of many small palaeohighs and the establishment of fully marine conditions over much of the basin (Fig. 15.22B). Siltstones, mudstones and marly siltstones were deposited offshore below the storm wavebase over much of the central and western parts of the basin (upper part of the informal Pecínov Member in Central Bohemia (Uličný *et al.* 1997*b*) and Dölzschen Formation in Saxony (Tröger 1996)). Proximal equivalents of this facies include sandstones of the uppermost Korycany Member and the Dölzschen Formation ('Pennrich Sandstone'; Geinitz 1871–75), which formed several clastic wedges prograding from the source areas of the Lausitz and Erzgebirge blocks (Fig. 15.22B). Benthic fauna associated with this facies is known as the 'Pennrich fauna' (Häntzschel 1933). Coeval prograding glauconitic sandstones in the southeastern Orlice-Žd'ár sub-basin were sourced by the Moravian and Moldanubian basement blocks and thin away towards the north.

In many places, conglomeratic and bioclastic facies, associated with rocky shores, were deposited in the vicinity of small islands of Variscan basement, mostly along active faults (Fig. 15.22B). This cliff and swell facies occurs at several isolated localities, and along island chains in the Saxonian part of the Elbe Fault Zone (Seifert 1955; T. Voigt *et al.* 1994; Tröger 2003; S. Voigt *et al.* 2006) and in the Labe-Železné Hory Fault Zone in central Bohemia (Žítt *et al.* 1997, 1998; Klein *et al.* 1979). In contrast to the coeval offshore and nearshore facies, the limestones and the carbonate-rich matrix of conglomerates in the cliff facies are characterized by rich and diverse warm-water faunal assemblages (Tröger 1956; 2003).

The latest Cenomanian *N. juddii* Zone is documented from the offshore and cliff facies in Saxony (Lausitz-Jizera sub-basin), where the positive $\delta^{13}C$ anomaly of the Cenomanian Turonian

Boundary Event is recorded in a complete succession (S. Voigt *et al.* 2006). In Bohemia, a condensed glauconitic/phosphatic lag deposit at the base of the Bílá Hora Formation yields calcareous nannoplankton, which indicates a condensed record of the *N. juddii* Zone (Čech *et al.* 2005). However, most of the sections across the Cenomanian–Turonian boundary in the Bohemian Cretaceous Basin are characterized by glauconitic/phosphatic deposits, which contain a mixture of redeposited late Cenomanian and early Turonian fossils, and indicate condensation and winnowing of the latest Cenomanian strata (Uličný *et al.* 1993, 1997*a*; Košťák *et al.* 2004).

While global sea-level trends played a significant role in the Cenomanian relative sea-level changes, the establishment of new subsiding depocentres along the two main fault zones marked the onset of the subsequent phase of the tectonosedimentary evolution of the Bohemian Cretaceous Basin. The uplift of adjoining clastic source areas commenced in the late Cenomanian (Fig. 15.22B, C).

*Turonian*

During the latest Cenomanian–late Turonian phase of basin evolution (Phase II), two main depocentres were situated along the Lužice (Lausitz) Fault Zone, and the southeastern part of the Labe-Železné Hory Fault Zone (Fig. 15.22B). Late Cenomanian to late Turonian subsidence was characterized by moderate movement along these fault zones (*c.* 70–100 m/Ma).

The largest depocentre during this stage of basin evolution was the Lausitz-Jizera sub-basin located to the south of the West Sudetic Island (Figs 15.22C & 15.23A). The Turonian to early Coniacian sandstones, up to *c.* 750 m thick, form the scenic rock cliffs of North Bohemia and Saxony, and represent a prograding deltaic and shoreface depositional system (Uličný 2001; Laurin & Uličný 2004). The siliciclastic source was the uplifted block of the West Sudetic Island (Scupin 1936). The distal regions were characterized by the deposition of offshore clays and marls, and hemipelagic marl–limestone alternations (Čech *et al.* 1996*b*; Laurin & Uličný 2004; Seifert 1955; Prescher 1981). The high

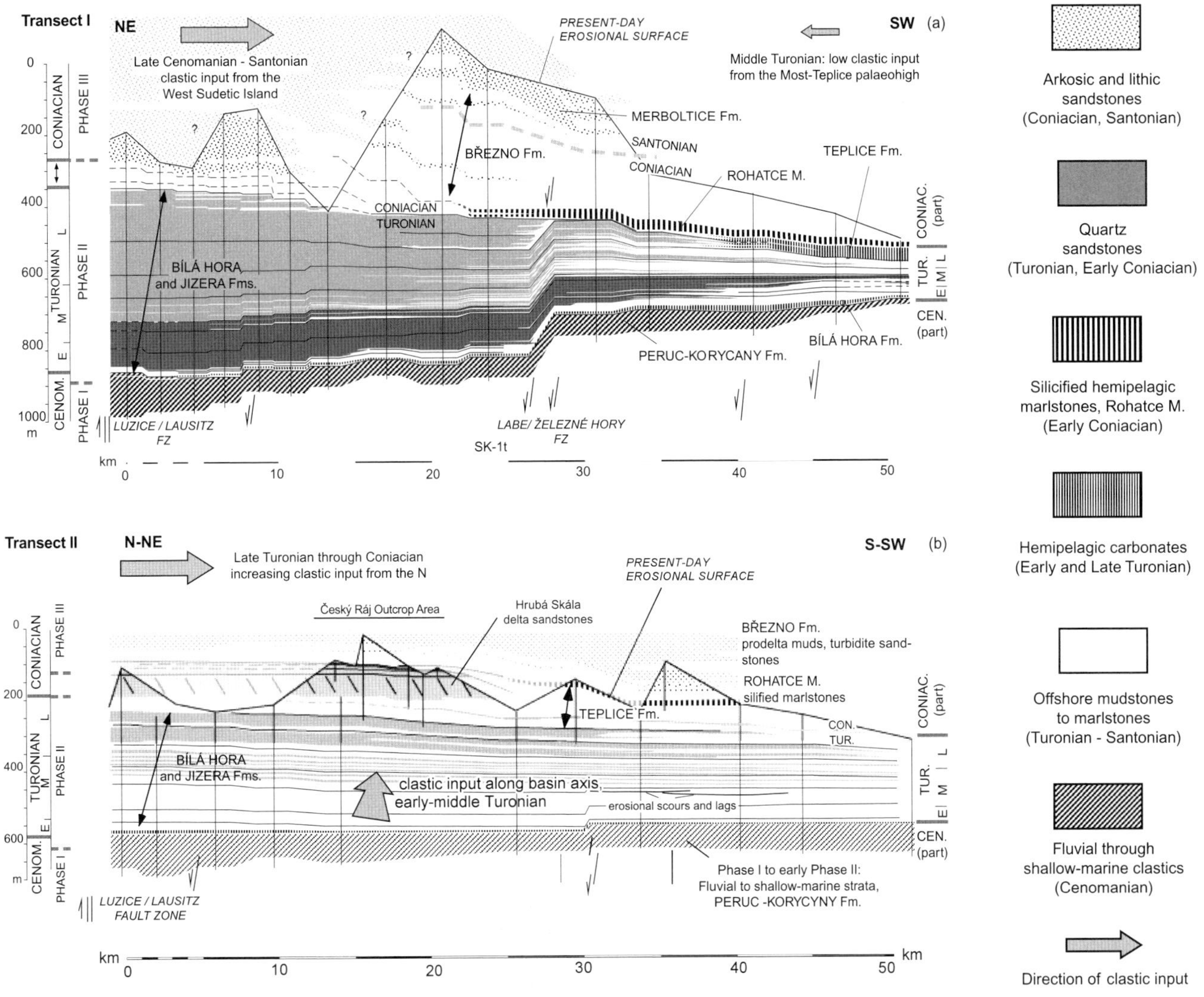


**Fig. 15.23.** Regional stratigraphic cross-sections of the Lausitz-Jizera sub-basin (I and II; 25 times vertical exaggeration). Correlation panels are based on well-log, core and outcrop data. Correlation lines are flooding surfaces. (**A**) Cross-section I intersects the Lausitz-Jizera sub-basin and the Ohře Ramp. Note maximum progradation of sandstone bodies during middle Turonian and the effect of syndepositional faulting on geometry of the depocentre during the late Turonian. (**B**) Cross-section II: early and middle Turonian clastic wedges from the west did not reach into this area. Maximum clastic deposition occurred in the early Coniacian.

early Turonian sea level led to widespread clastic starvation and the deposition of hemipelagic carbonates over significant parts of the basin (e.g. Valečka & Skoček 1991). Dysaerobic bottom conditions that had existed in parts of the basin in the late Cenomanian were replaced by well-oxygenated conditions resulting from more intense, basin-wide water-mass circulation (Uličný *et al.* 1997*a*).

The depocentre of the Orlice-Žd'ár sub-basin received clastics from uplifted parts of the Moldanubian and Moravian blocks located to the south of the Železné Hory Fault Zone. The proximal parts of this depocentre were subsequently uplifted and eroded, so that its original extent remains speculative. The present-day Orlice-Žd'ár sub-basin preserves only the distal parts of progradational clastic wedges as erosional relicts, probably analogous to those of the Lausitz-Jizera sub-basin (Fig. 15.22C). The sediments consist of spicule-rich, silica-cemented sandstones (Bílá Hora Formation), and several glauconite-rich sandstones (Jizera Formation) including varying degrees of bioclastic material.

The spatial facies architecture was controlled by the interplay between relative sea-level change and sediment supply, which differed considerably across the basin and resulted in variable stacking patterns (Uličný 2001). After the early Turonian relative sea-level high of the *M. mytiloides* Zone, a relative sea-level low was reached in early middle Turonian times. Subsequently, relative sea level rose slowly in the late Turonian to early Coniacian, superimposed by a number of higher-frequency sea-level stillstands and falls. Increased differential subsidence and intrabasinal uplift during the late Turonian resulted in pronounced tectonic differentiation of the sub-basins. In the western part of the Lausitz-Jizera sub-basin, the Ohře ramp was formed because of a rise of basin-floor topography, and this supported the spatial separation of the clastic-dominated nearshore and carbonate-dominated hemipelagic depocentres (Fig. 15.22C) (Laurin & Uličný 2004).

The Bohemian Cretaceous Basin formed a seaway between the Boreal and Tethyan realms, and basin-wide water-mass circulation influenced the Turonian depositional system. Mostly unidirectional, axial basinal currents led to sand redistribution along the coarse-grained delta fronts and shorefaces, and the formation of winnowed lags as well as the deposition of glauconite and phosphate-rich horizons in the fine-grained hemipelagic offshore facies (Uličný 2001; Laurin & Uličný 2004). The currents are interpreted as being tidal in origin, which is also supported by the occurrence of bidirectional cross-bedding in sandstones of early middle Turonian age in the western part of the sub-basin (Fig. 15.22C) (Valečka 1979; T. Voigt 1996*a*). In the Saxonian part of the Lausitz-Jizera sub-basin, a storm-dominated shoreface regime is interpreted in the middle Turonian (T. Voigt 1994, 1996*b*), whereas the occurrence of storm wave-built structures is very limited elsewhere in the basin (Uličný 2001).

The hemipelagic offshore sedimentation was characterized in the late Turonian by a change towards increased carbonate production (Teplice and Strehlen formations), coeval with the influx of boreal faunal assemblages (Čech *et al.* 1996*b*; Wiese *et al.* 2004*b*). This transition is considered to have been caused by multiple processes, such as the improved water circulation due to tectonic activity along the Elbe Fault System and the trapping of coarse-grained clastics in depocentres between the Lausitz and Labe-Železné Hory fault zones (Laurin & Uličný 2004), as well as higher carbonate productivity in relation to the influx of Boreal water masses during the eustatic sea-level rise (Wiese *et al.* 2004*b*). Spectral analysis of the hemipelagic strata suggests that fluctuations in carbonate content were primarily driven by the long eccentricity cycle, mediated by changes in siliciclastic flux due to movements of the shoreline (Laurin & Uličný 2004).

*Coniacian–Santonian*

Most of the Coniacian–Santonian stratigraphic record represents the third phase of basin evolution. This was characterized by the deposition of thick clastic wedges with a higher percentage of marine mud and less mature sandstones, and by significant changes in the basin geometry (Fig. 15.21). Although subsidence rates had begun to increase and local intrabasinal uplifts had already formed in the late Turonian (Laurin & Uličný 2004), early Coniacian deposition was still characterized by the prevalence of quartz sands in the nearshore clastics, and the marked influence of marine currents. Therefore, the early Coniacian period is considered as a transition between phases II and III in the evolution of the Bohemian Cretaceous Basin.

The earliest Coniacian deposition is characterized by thick deltaic sandstones exposed in the Český Ráj region of the Lužice-Jizera sub-basin (Fig. 15.23B). The accommodation at the basin margin that allowed development of the 60–80 m thick sandstone bodies was probably generated due to accelerated tectonic subsidence (Uličný *et al.* 2002). The deposition of this delta complex was terminated by flooding during the *C. crassus* Zone (Čech in Uličný *et al.* 2003*a*). Over much of the basin, this time interval is characterized by the occurrence of silicified marlstones to claystones (Rohatce Member). Subsequently, the basin fill was characterized by thick, mud-dominated offshore deposits (Březno Formation), which grade laterally and vertically into nearshore sandstones with significant arkosic and lithic components (Valečka & Rejchrt 1973; Čech *et al.* 1980; Herčík *et al.* 2003).

A detailed reconstruction of the basin shape and infill style of Phase III is difficult because of the incomplete preservation of middle Coniacian through Santonian strata. However, it is clear that *c.* 450 m of clastics sourced from the West Sudetic Island accumulated in the Lausitz-Jizera sub-basin. The common occurrence of sandy turbidites during the *V. koeneni–M. subquadratus* inoceramid zones and the increased feldspar content in the Březno Formation mudstones, were interpreted by earlier authors as a sign of increased tectonic activity (Klein *et al.* 1979). More recently, the turbidites have been reinterpreted as distal storm deposits (Valečka 1984; Wojewoda 1997), although Uličný *et al.* (2003*a*) interpret them as gravity flow deposits related to deltaic systems. The Merboltice Formation (early Santonian) probably represents shallow-water deltaic deposits that may be analogous to the nearshore sandstones of the Březno Formation.

In the Orlice-Žd'ár sub-basin, a major change in basin geometry occurred during the Coniacian. The depocentre shifted from the southern edge of the sub-basin to the NE and extended into the present-day Nysa Graben (Fig. 15.23B). The Snieżnik Massif became the main source of clastics for the Nysa Graben as well as for much of the Orlice-Žd'ár sub-basin from the *V. koeneni* inoceramid Zone onwards. The southern part of the Orlice-Žd'ár sub-basin contains only tens of metres of clastics of the *P. tridorsatum* Zone, dominated by shallow-water arkosic sandstones and sourced from the SSE (Klein *et al.* 1979).

The timing of tectonic events that controlled the changes in basin geometry and infill style between the late Turonian and middle Coniacian, separating phases II and III of basin evolution, fits within the timespan of the classic 'Ilsede Phase' of deformation of the Alpine foreland, as originally defined by Stille (1924). Although the precise changes in kinematic behaviour of individual structures are difficult to assess, due to incomplete preservation of Coniacian strata, it is clear that the late Turonian–Coniacian was a time of significant change both in terms of deformation rates and possibly in the palaeostress field. These changes may have been related to the emplacement of the first Inner Carpathian nappes (cf. Mortimore *et al.* 1998), and were coeval with the opening of the Gosau and the South Bohemian basins (see below). Sediments younger than early Santonian were eroded during the subsequent uplift that occurred in relation to Late Cretaceous inversion of the Bohemian Cretaceous Basin and the Palaeogene compression of the Alpine foreland (Ziegler 1990; Coubal 1990).

### *South Bohemian Basins (S.Č., F.W.)*

The South Bohemian Basins (Figs 15.2 & 15.6) consist of two grabens, the Budějovice and Třeboň basins, separated by a basement horst and developed along two major shear zones: the NW–SE directed Jáchymov Fault Zone, and the NNE-trending Blanice-Rodl Fault Zone (Vrána & Šrámek 1999; cf. Brandmayr *et al.* 1995). The grabens probably formed as pull-apart structures, and are developed on metamorphic basement of the Moldanubian Terrane and granites of the Moldanubian and Central Bohemian plutons. The maximum thickness of Cretaceous sediments is 320–340 m.

The grabens are filled with alluvial fan, floodplain and lacustrine sediments characterized by poorly sorted sandstones, grey and red silts and clays arranged in several fining-upward cycles (Slánská, 1976), and assigned to the Klikov Formation (Malecha 1966). According to macroflora (Němejc 1958), palaeocarpology (Knobloch 1985, 1991) and microflora (Pacltová 1961, 1990), the age of the Klikov Formation is assumed to be late Turonian–Santonian. A probable Turonian age is estimated for the clastic succession with coal clasts (Budějovice Formation) just beneath the Klikov Formation (Slánská 1974). The presence of marine microplankton in the lower part of some cycles indicates shallow-marine influence, while the upper parts of the cycles are interpreted as being of fluviolacustrine origin (cf. Pacltová 1990; Čtyřoký 1965). The fluvial system of the South Bohemian basins drained southwards into the Tethys Ocean.

Similar graben structures preserve Cretaceous deposits further towards the NW in the Thuringian-Franconian Slate Mountains. At Ida-Waldhaus near Greiz (Fig. 15.6), in a small graben structure within the Palaeozoic of the Thuringian-Franconian Slate Mountains, erosional relicts of Lower Triassic carbonates (Muschelkalk) have karstified surfaces, which yield clays with pollen of Coniacian–Campanian age (Krutzsch & Schulz 1966; Diener 1968; Klaua 1974).

### *Intrasudetic Basin and Nysa Graben (I.W.)*

The inner-Sudetic Cretaceous is represented by the Cretaceous deposits of the Intrasudetic Basin and the Nysa Graben (Fig. 15.24), which form separate tectonic units in the NE part of the Bohemian Cretaceous Basin. The Intrasudetic Basin is located at the northern periphery of the Bohemian Massif, and was an independent structural and depositional unit from early Carboniferous times onward. It is interpreted as a pull-apart basin related to the activity of the Elbe Fault and the Intrasudetic Fault Zone. The Intrasudetic Basin comprises three synclines which are the result of post-Cretaceous deformation: the Krzeszów Syncline in the NW, the Batorów Syncline in the SE, and the central Police Syncline (Fig. 15.24).

The Nysa Graben is a much younger tectonic structure, which formed as a separate sedimentary basin at the Turonian–Coniacian transition. The Nysa Graben is a strongly asymmetric graben (Fig. 15.24), which is interpreted as a rollover-related structure caused by deep listric downfaulting on a fault which now separates the Nysa Graben from the Snieżnik Massif (Wojewoda 1997). The Nysa Graben is still tectonically active. The Intrasudetic marine Cretaceous succession ranges in thickness from 350 m in the Batorów Syncline (Góry Stołowe – Table Mountains) to over 1200 m in the Nysa Graben, and is dated as Cenomanian to Santonian in age.

In the NW Krzeszów Syncline the marine deposits are underlain by freshwater sediments (Radwanski 1975). The lowermost part of the Police and Batorow syncline successions is represented by glauconitic sandstones of late Cenomanian age, which rest on the Variscan crystalline basement in the SW, or on non-marine Permian clastics in the NE (Figs 15.4 & 15.11). An Upper Cenomanian spongiolite-bearing mudstone overlies the sandstone and passes gradually into the middle Turonian Radków Bluff Sandstone which is up to 80 m thick and forms the most scenic part of the Table Mountains. Fine-grained sediments of late middle and early late Turonian age overlie the Radków Bluff Sandstone, and grade upwards into the Skalniak-Szczeliniec Sandstone, which is up to 70 m thick. The latter is of late Turonian–Coniacian age and forms the highest parts of the Table Mountains. The sandstones are characterized by transitional lower and sharp upper boundaries.

The Turonian–Coniacian sandstones (Radków Bluff and Skalniak-Szczeliniec sandstones) represent progradational units on the inner shelf (Fig. 15.24). Because of the high rates of tectonic subsidence, progradation of the sandy units resulted in the development of characteristic sets of giant-scale cross-bedded sandstones (up to 18 m thick; Wojewoda 1986, 1997; Jerzykiewicz & Wojewoda 1986). Bed inclination within the sets indicates a SW-orientated progradation, whereas the inclination of the large-scale sets themselves indicates NW (Radków Bluff Sandstone) and SE (Skalniak-Szczeliniec Sandstone) orientated coastal longshore transport. Large-scale trough cross-bedding occurs in the upper part of the sandstone units and proximal tempestites and shore deposits occur on the top. Thicknesses and grain sizes of the sandstone units decrease towards the SW.

The upper Cenomanian–Turonian succession of the Nysa Graben consists mainly of fine-grained siliciclastics. Thick sandstone units, such as those present in the Intrasudetic Basin, are absent and the marked sedimentary thickness indicates significantly higher rates of basin subsidence. Fan-deltas, associated with the fault scarps of the Nysa Graben, were the sources of gravity flows. The Nysa Graben coarsening-upward succession consists of turbidites to nearshore clastics (Idzików beds; Fig. 15.24) (Jerzykiewicz 1971). The highest part of the succession is represented by sandstones and conglomerates of the Upper Idzików Member, which entirely wedges out towards the east.

### *North Sudetic Basin (Outer Sudetic Cretaceous) (I.W.)*

The North Sudetic Basin is located in Lower Silesia, north of the Sudetes Mountains in southwestern Poland, and forms the southeastern prolongation of the East Brandenburg Basin (Figs 15.2 15.4, 15.6 & 15.25). The basin is a syncline that was formed as a result of Santonian–early Campanian and late Maastrichtian–Palaeocene movements. The syncline is subdivided by older Mesozoic faults, which were reactivated during the Late Cretaceous (Bałazińska & Bossowski 1979; Bossowski & Bałazińska 1982). The Cretaceous succession represents the youngest part of the sedimentary infill, an evolution that commenced during

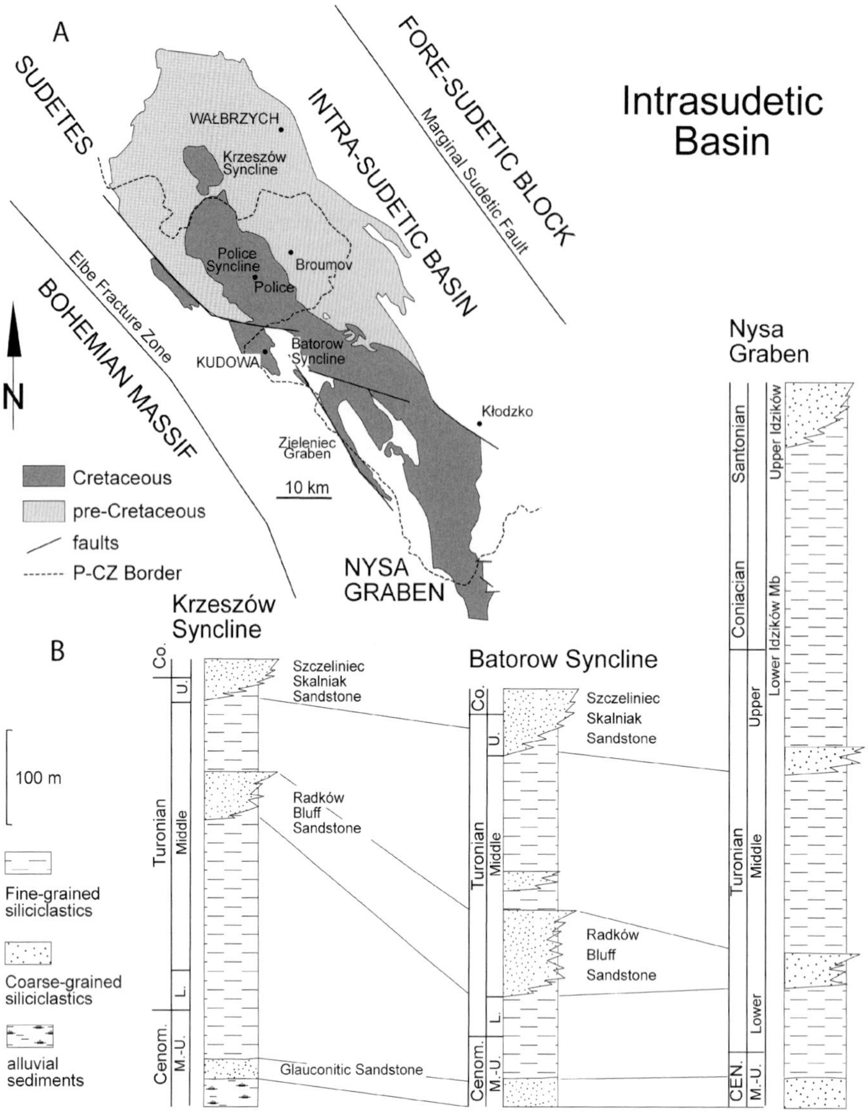


**Fig. 15.24.** (**A**) Map showing the distribution of Cretaceous deposits in the Intrasudetic Basin and the Nysa Graben. (**B**) Sketched lithological logs for the Intrasudetic Basin (Krzeszów and Batorow Synclines) and the Nysa Graben; compiled and modified after Wojewoda (1997). Map compiled and simplified after Cymerman (2004).

Carboniferous times. Cretaceous strata rest more or less undisturbed on units of Triassic, Permian and Late Palaeozoic age.

The Cretaceous succession is best exposed in the eastern and less so in the central parts of the basin. With thicknesses of up to 1300 m, the succession ranges from the middle (possibly lower) Cenomanian to the middle Santonian. Tectonic uplift in the mid-late Santonian led to regression and terminated marine sedimentation in the North Sudetic Basin. Cenomanian to Coniacian deposits are entirely of marine origin; the lower-middle Santonian deposits in the southeastern part of the basin consist of brackish and lacustrine sediments (Fig. 15.25).

The Cretaceous of the North Sudetic Basin represents a single sedimentary cycle, which contains two or three poorly documented transgressive–regressive subsidiary cycles (Fig. 15.25). The main part of the succession is composed of a marl–limestone unit (Cenomanian to Coniacian age) which occurs in the central and northwestern part of the basin and is underlain by Cenomanian sands and conglomerates. Towards the SE, the sediments are increasingly clastic. Coniacian marlstones are overlain by marine mudstones in the western part of the basin (Węgliniec Formation of Milewicz 1985), and by marine and brackish sandstones with clay and coal intercalations (Czerna Formation of Milewicz 1985) in the east (= the Ober- and Überquader of Scupin 1912–13). The biostratigraphy of the succession is based primarily on inoceramids. The ammonite record is rather poorly known.

## *Opole Basin (I.W.)*

The Opole Basin covers an area of 260 km$^2$ (Kotański & Radwański 1977). The Cretaceous succession of the basin comprises an interval from the middle Cenomanian to the middle Coniacian, but it possibly extended earlier into the Santonian. Cretaceous deposits of the Opole Basin represent an erosional relict of an originally extensive area of sedimentation that covered the areas of the Cracow-Silesian and the Fore-Sudetic

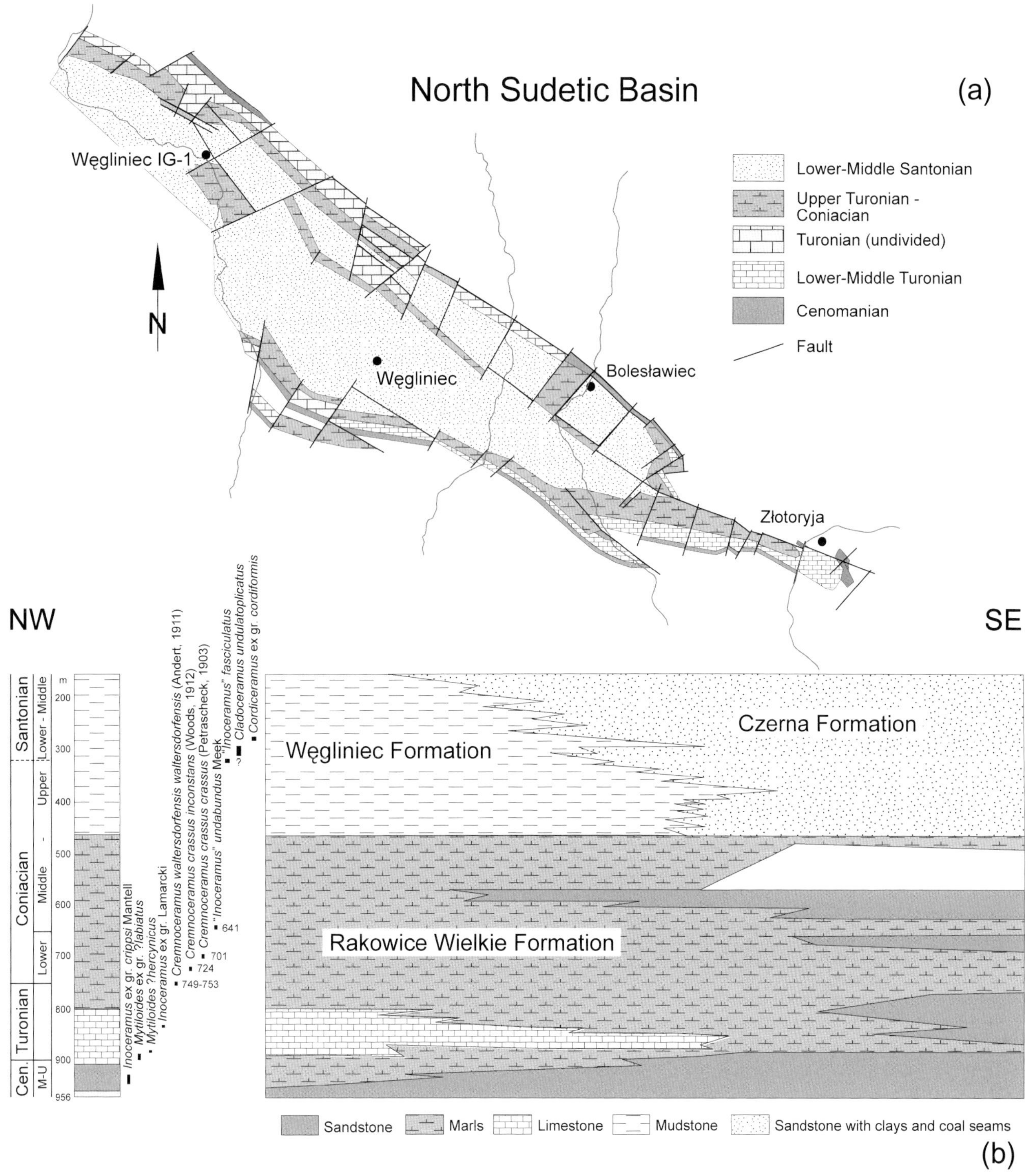


**Fig. 15.25.** (**A**) Geological sketch-map showing the distribution of Upper Cretaceous rocks in the North Sudetic Basin. (**B**) Chronostratigraphy, inoceramid ranges and lithostratigraphy of the Cretaceous succession in the North Sudetic Basin. Data compiled after Milewicz (1988, 1997). Inoceramid ranges are reinterpreted from Milewicz' (1988).

Monocline, and was connected with the Cretaceous shelf of the Polish lowlands further to the north and NE (Figs 15.4, 15.6 & 15.26). A significant increase in the rate of subsidence occurred in the Opole Basin during the mid-Turonian. Due to Palaeogene faulting, the Opole Basin is subdivided into a number of variously dipping tectonic blocks that were subject to erosion (Kotański & Radwański 1977; Fig. 15.26).

Cretaceous deposits of the Opole Basin are mostly subsurface successions, overlain by moderately thick Neogene sediments (60–70 m on average), comprising marine and continental

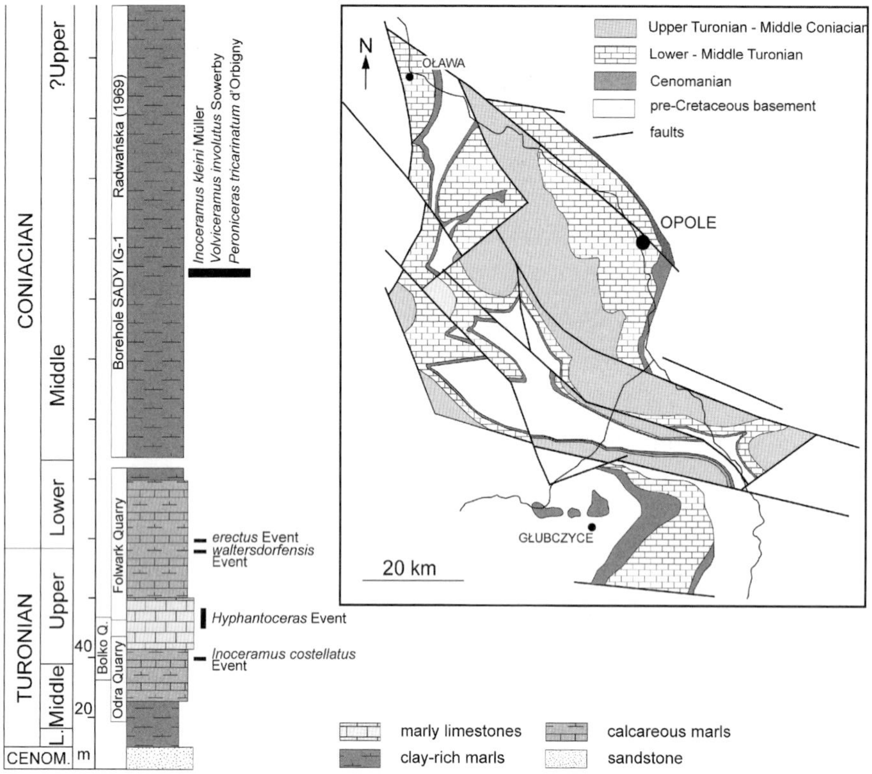


**Fig. 15.26.** Geological sketch-map and stratigraphic succession of the Opole Cretaceous Basin. The map is after Kotański & Radwański (1977); the geological log is after Walaszczyk (1992), Olszewska-Nejbert (2005) and Radwańska (1969).

Miocene, Pliocene and Pleistocene deposits. The best exposures of Cretaceous strata are concentrated in the eastern basin, close to the town of Opole from where a detailed stratigraphic succession is known, and supplemented by borehole data (Biernat 1960; Alexandrowicz 1974*a*, *b*; Tarkowski 1991). Additional surface occurrences are known from the town of Brzeg to the north and near the town of Głubczyce to the south of the Opole Basin (Fig. 15.26).

The Cretaceous succession transgressively overlies rocks of Triassic and Carboniferous age, as well as the crystalline basement of the Eastern Sudetes. The sub-Cenomanian relief was a complicated network of valleys that caused marked thickness differences at this stage, varying from some metres up to 50 m (Kotański & Radwański 1977). The relief could partly have been related to karst processes. The succession commences with greyish-green glauconitic sandstone that yields sponges, bivalves, brachiopods, ammonites and belemnites. *Acanthoceras rhotomagense* (Defrance), *Turrilites costatus* Lamarck and *Praeactinocamax plenus* indicate the presence of the middle and upper Cenomanian substages. Cenomanian deposits vary from quartz sands to marly sands. The local occurrence of conglomerates is limited to areas of higher relief. The quartz material was derived from the Sudetic islands in the west and the Cracow-Silesian area to the south (Kotański & Radwański 1977).

In the early Turonian, sedimentation was dominated by clayey marls, clays and glauconitic clays. Whereas marly sedimentation occurred mostly along the valley structures, the plains between the valleys were dominated by carbonate sedimentation. An increased input in clastic material can be observed towards the western basin margin. Reduced thicknesses of Cenomanian and lower Turonian, sediments indicate low rates of basin subsidence. However, locally, greater thicknesses are noted in the valleys of the pre-Cenomanian relief. In the middle Turonian, the sedimentary thickness increases significantly towards the NE indicating enhanced rates of tectonic subsidence (Kotański & Radwański 1977). This pattern was maintained during late Turonian and Coniacian times.

The Cretaceous succession in the Opole Basin represents a symmetric cycle with respect to the carbonate content (Fig. 15.26). Carbonate values increase gradually from the Cenomanian up to the lower upper Turonian, from marly sands through to marly clays up into the marly limestone. In the late late Turonian, the carbonate content decreases gradually from marls and clayey marls to marly clays, and these dominate the upper lower and middle Coniacian (e.g. Alexandrowicz 1974*a*, *b*; Alexandrowicz & Radwan 1973). Because of the simple symmetric pattern, the Cretaceous succession in the Opole Basin was originally interpreted as a single transgressive–regressive cycle, with the transgressive maximum in the middle late Turonian (Alexandrowicz 1974*b*; Tarkowski 1991). An alternative explanation, however, interprets the marly limestones as shallow-water deposits and the underying and overlying marls representing the deeper-water environments (Kędzierski & Uchman 2001). Analysis of the fish faunas led to similar conclusions (Niedźwiedzki & Kalina 2003). The final regression from the area post-dates the youngest recognized sediments (i.e. the middle Coniacian), and could be as late as Santonian times, as suggested by a Santonian belemnite found in karst deposits of the Bolko Quarry near the town of Opole (Wegner 1913; Walaszczyk 1992).

### *Braunau-Regensburg and Wasserburg basins (F.W.)*

The Cretaceous succession of the Braunau-Regensburg and Wasserburg basins unconformably overlies Jurassic sediments and Variscan-age rocks of the Bohemian Massif (Figs 15.2 & 15.6) (Schröder *et al.* 1997). Synsedimentary differential subsidence resulted in significant thickness variations (500–1000 m) of the Albian to Campanian successions (Schröder 1987; Meyer 1989). Surface outcrops of Cretaceous deposits occur only in the area of Regensburg (Braunau-Regensburg Basin). The deposits comprise fluvial, nearshore and shallow-marine Albian to Campanian sediments (*c.* 500 m) (Fig. 15.27). Towards the Alpine foreland in the south, boreholes penetrated offshore sediments of the Braunau-Regensburg and the Wasserburg basins beneath Neogene continental deposits ('Molasse'; Fig. 15.27) (Wicher & Bettenstaedt 1957). The formerly uniform sedimentation area was later separated by uplift and erosion along Variscan-age structures. Stratigraphic subdivision is based mainly on ammonites, inoceramids and foraminifera (Egger 1907; Dacqué 1939; Ziegler 1957; Wiedmann 1979; Förster *et al.* 1983, 1984; Ernst *et al.* 1984; Hilbrecht 1986*a*, *b*; Weiss 1982; Weidich 1987; Korsitztke 1995). In addition, stable isotope analyses in the Cenomanian–Turonian boundary interval (Hilbrecht 1986*a*; Hilbrecht *et al.* 1996) enable precise correlations to be established with other areas. Further details on the lithostratigraphy and sedimentology of the area are provided by Tillmann (1964), Meyer (1981*a*, 1996, 2000) and Fay (1983).

Due to its emergent position, the Lower Cretaceous record in the region is limited. In the Wasserburg Basin, sandstones, marly clays and limestones of Berriasian–Barremian age are noted from boreholes, recording the initial sedimentation of the northern Tethyan margin onto the Bohemian Massif (Fig. 15.6). In the late Albian, the area of sedimentation extended towards the north over the course of the eustatic sea-level rise, and conglomerates and glauconitic sandstones (Gault) transgressively overlie the older basement.

In the marginal area (Regensburg-Amberg), alluvial to coastal coarse-grained sands and iron ores are interbedded with kaolinitic and organic carbon-rich clays (Schutzfels Schichten) of Albian to early Cenomanian age (Figs 15.6 & 15.27) (Pfeuffer 1983; Gudden 1984). These beds seal the karstified pre-Cretaceous surface (e.g. Gall *et al.* 1973; Meyer 1981*b*; Tillmann 1986). Towards the SE of the Braunau-Regensburg Basin, coastal sediments grade into mid- to late Cenomanian-age shallow-marine greensands (Regensburger Grünsand), which yield a diverse marine fauna and reflect the progressive flooding of the Regensburg embayment in the context of the Cenomanian sea-level rise (Trusheim 1936; Meyer 1981*b*; Förster *et al.* 1983; Kauffmann *et al.* 2000). Flooding resulted in the differentiation of marginal and distal facies, which continued from Turonian through to Santonian times.

The most proximal strata in the region occur in the Parkstein-Erbendorf area (Fig. 15.27), where fluvial to nearshore coarse-grained and micaeous sandstones, some kaolinitic, and interbedded coal-bearing clays were deposited (Meyer 1981*a*). The youngest unit is a plant-yielding clay (?Santonian–Campanian), which represents a facies influenced by terrigenous input from the Bohemian Massif to the NE (Gothan 1941; Knobloch 1973).

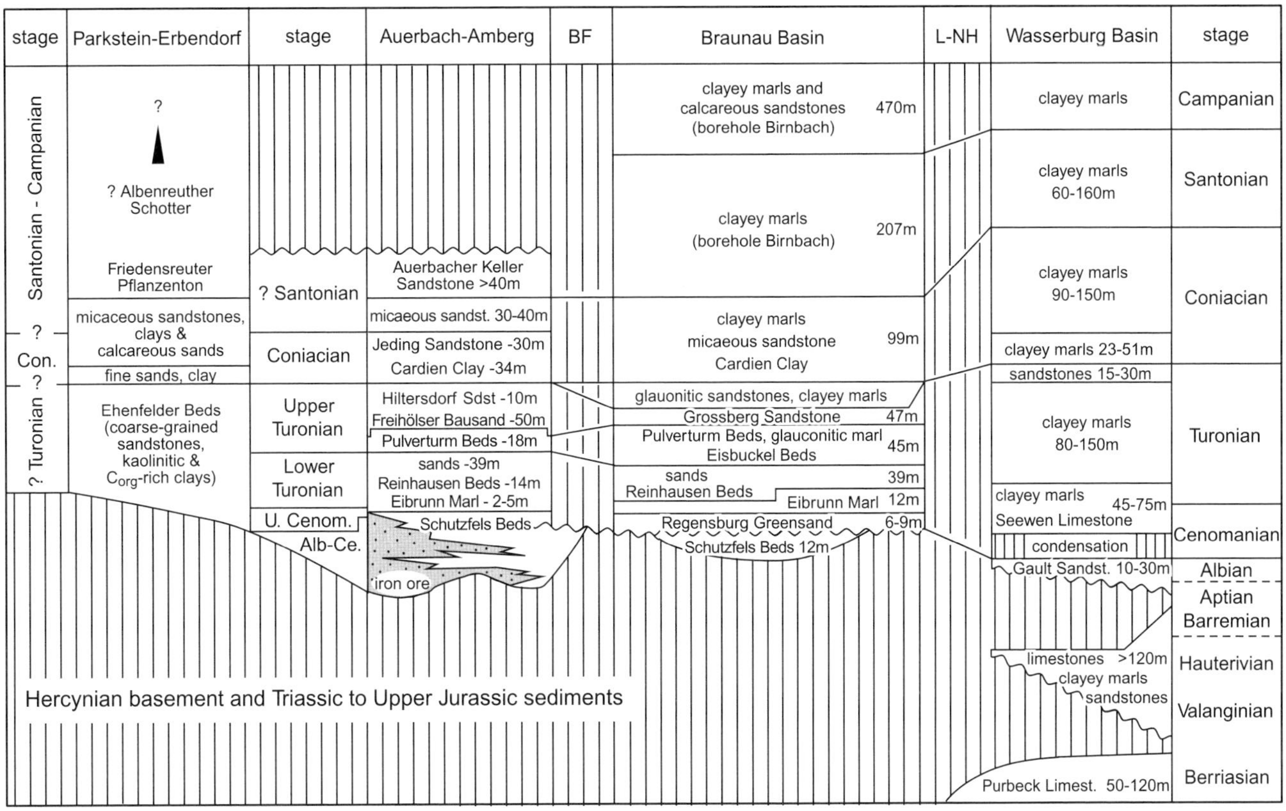


**Fig. 15.27.** Generalized lithostratigraphic framework of the Braunau-Regensburg and Wasserburg basins with special emphasis on the proximal facies of the Regensburg area (Parkstein-Erbendorf, Auerbach-Amberg). No data are available for the Bavarian Forest (BF) and the Landshut-Neuöttingen High (L-NH) because of later uplift and erosion. Data are compiled after Lang (1981) and Meyer (2000).

The deposition of cobbles up to 70 cm in diameter reflects the terminal regression and the proximity of the shoreline.

The shallow-marine succession in the Auerbach-Amberg area is stratigraphically more complete. The Regensburg Greensand is overlain by 2–12 m of grey, glauconitic marls (Eibrunner Mergel) reflecting continuous deepening. Ammonites (*Metoicoceras geslinianum*) date the lower part of the Eibrunner Mergel as late Cenomanian. The upper part is of early Turonian age (*I. labiatus*; see Hilbrecht 1986*b*). The overlying lower Turonian succession consists of glauconitic and siliceous limestones (Reinhausener Schichten, 20 m) and poorly sorted sandstones with chert nodules (Knollensand, 20–25 m), which reflect the southward progradation of siliciclastic deposits into the Regensburg embayment. Renewed transgression in the late Turonian is indicated by the deposition of coarse-grained calcareous sandstones, glauconitic marls and glauconitic marly limestones (Pulverturm Kalke; 20–25 m). During the latest Turonian, either a sea-level fall or tectonic acticity resulted in the deposition of marginal coarse-grained, glauconitic and calcareous sandstones (Grossberger Sandstein), and brackish-limnic plant-bearing sandstones and clays (Meyer 1981*a*). A third marine ingression is indicated in the Coniacian by fossiliferous clays (Cardienton), which are associated with the maximum coastal onlap (Ziegler 1957). In the most proximal Parkstein-Erbendorf area, coeval strata include fine-grained sands and clays intercalated with coarse-grained fluvial sandstones, documenting the magnitude of the transgressive pulse. The progradation of Coniacian marine sandstones (Jeding Sandstone, Glimmersandstein) and Santonian fluviolimnic sediments (Auerbacher Keller Sandstein) indicate a renewed regression.

Owing to its distal position, only the Cenomanian–Turonian parts of the succession in the Braunau-Regensburg and Wasserburg basins can be correlated with the Auerbach-Amberg area (Meyer 2000). Increased subsidence during the late Coniacian was associated with the deposition of more than 750 m of undifferentiated clayey marls with intercalated (calcareous) sandstones. In the Wasserburg Basin, sedimentation commenced with the deposition of the pelagic Seewen Limestone in the uppermost Cenomanian following a period of condensation. This suggests a short-lived facies link to the Helvetian Shelf. The subsequent Turonian to Campanian succession is represented by clayey and silty marls (260–600 m).

### *Waschberg-Ždánice Zone and autochthonous equivalents (F.W., S.Č.)*

In Lower Austria, allochthonous Mesozoic (Jurassic to Miocene) strata are exposed within the Molasse in the Klippen Belt of the Waschberg Zone and in its northeastward prolongation, the Ždánice Zone of Moravia (Czech Republic) (Fig. 15.6). In the literature this area is often referred to as the Waschberg-Ždánice Zone. Coarse glauconitic shelf sandstones and clayey siltstones of mid-Turonian to early Coniacian age are locally exposed (Klementer Schichten of Glaessner 1931; Kollmann *et al.* 1977; Stránik *et al.* 1996; Summesberger *et al.* 1999*a*). These are overlain by greywackes and silty calcareous slope claystones (Pálava Formation: Coniacian to upper Campanian, Stránik *et al.* 1996). In Moravia, both formations have an approximate thickness of 135 m.

At the SE margin of the Bohemian Massif (Lower Austria), autochthonous equivalents of the Waschberg-Ždánice are known from several boreholes (Fig. 15.6) (Fuchs *et al.* 1984). Cenomanian–Turonian sediments are dominated by greensands, which are overlain by Turonian–Santonian marls and subsequently by prograding sandstones. The overlying unit of Santonian–Campanian glauconitic marls and calcareous sandstones is possibly equivalent to the Pálava Formation (Summesberger *et al.* 1999*a*).

At the SW margin of the Bohemian Massif (upper Austria, south of Linz; Fig. 15.6), Cenomanian to Turonian autochthonous deposits are dominated by sandstones, and overlain by a transgressive unit of a fining-upward succession of silts and clays. Stratigraphically, this interval may be coeval to the transgressive Coniacian Cardienton in the Regensburg area. In the overlying unit, renewed regression is indicated by the progradation of shoreface and nearshore sandstones (Harmannsdorfer and Thanner Sandstein). These sandstones were overlain by fluviolimnic feldspar-bearing wackes and arkoses (Teufelsgraben Formation). The precise age of this unit is unclear although it is assumed to be Late Cretaceous–Palaeogene (Fuchs *et al.* 1984).

## Alpine Cretaceous (M.Wa., H.F., J.M.)

The Alps and the Carpathians constitute the classic segment of the Alpine fold-and-thrust belt situated in the Central European region. Cretaceous rocks were identified for the first time in the late eighteenth century. In the early nineteenth century detailed investigations and correlations by geologists and palaeontologists, such as Sedgwick & Murchison (1832), were undertaken, followed by monographs on various aspects of Cretaceous rocks and fossils of the Alps and the Carpathians, for example Escher von der Linth (1853), Reuss (1854), Štur (1860), Gümbel (1861) and Redtenbacher (1873). Special emphasis is given in this section to units that comprise classic areas of geological and palaeontological investigations, for example the Swiss Helvetics and the Austrian Gosau Group.

The Alps can be divided into the Western Alps, the Central (Swiss) Alps, between the Rhône Valley in France and the Rhine Valley at the Swiss–Austrian Border, and the Eastern Alps between the Rhine Valley to the west and the Neogene Vienna Basin at the border of Austria with the Czech and the Slovak republics toward the east (Fig. 15.28). To the east of the Vienna Basin, the Western Carpathians begin at the Malé Karpaty Mountains and continue across the territory of eastern Moravia (Czech Republic), southernmost Poland and Slovakia. The Cenozoic Eastern Slovakian Basin separates the Western Carpathians from the Eastern Carpathians.

The Alps and the Western Carpathians constitute a classic thrust orogen. It originated within the NW Tethys palaeogeographic belt due to repeated convergence between the European and the African plates. Several orogenic phases can be distinguished. The Jurassic–Cretaceous 'Eo-Alpine' orogeny was followed by Meso- and Neo-Alpine deformational events (e.g. Faupl & Wagreich 2000; see also Froitzheim *et al.* 2008; Reicherter *et al.* 2008).

The evolution of the orogen, especially the Cretaceous geodynamics in the Eastern Alps and the Western Carpathians, are discussed in detail in the literature because of the polyphase young deformation overprinting the Mesozoic structures, the incompleteness of the sedimentary record and the weakly constrained palaeogeographic and palaeotectonic positions of some tectonic units. A variety of proposed models for the evolution of the Alps during the Cretaceous have been proposed, differing especially in the inferred positions and timing of subduction zones and collisions, and thus also in the positions of major sedimentary basins along these active continental margins (e.g. Trümpy 1988; Channell *et al.* 1992; Faupl & Wagreich 1992*a*, 2000; Eynatten & Gaupp 1999; Wagreich & Faupl 1994;

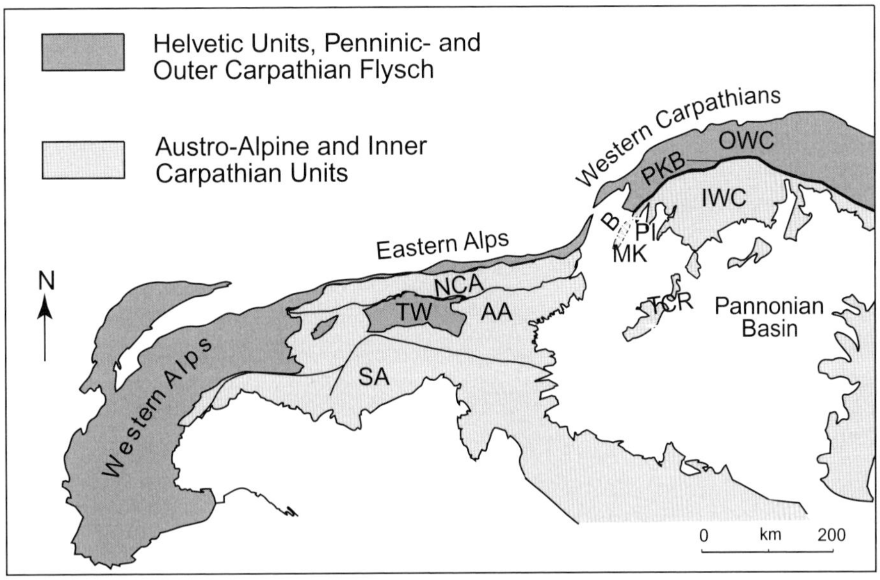


**Fig. 15.28.** Overview map of the Alps and the Carpathians, including several of the units discussed in the text. Abbreviations: AA, Austroalpine units; MK, Malé Karpaty Mountains; NCA, Northern Calcareous Alps; Pie, Pieniny Klippen Belt; PI, Považsky Inovec Mountains; SA, Southern Alps; TCR, Transdanubian Central Range; TW, Tauern Window; VB, Vienna Basin.

Winkler 1988, 1996; Wortmann *et al.* 2001; Stampfli & Borel 2002).

Three major tectonic units with different types of sedimentary basins and basement units can be distinguished within the Cretaceous Alps and their continuation into the Western Carpathians (Fig. 15.28): (1) The Helvetic, Outer Carpathians and other comparable European shelf units, platforms and basins on continental crust (including Subpenninic units *sensu* Schmid *et al.* 2004) today form the northernmost thrust complexes of the orogen, and are partly continuous into autochthonous successions of the Alpine foreland; (2) The Penninic units and comparable units of the Liguria-Piemont-Penninic ocean system and units derived from thinned continental crust are partly overthrust onto Helvetic units *sensu lato*, and exposed as large tectonic windows below overthrusting units of more internal derivation; and (3) The Austro-Alpine (including Fatric and Tatric Inner West Carpathian units) and the Southern Alpine units originated from the northern margin of the Adriatic plate. The Austro-Alpine domain is subdivided into several nappe complexes, including large metamorphic basement complexes with little Mesozoic sedimentary cover. Within the Upper Austro-Alpine unit, the Northern Calcareous Alps represent a complicated pile of cover nappes including significant Cretaceous to Palaeogene strata.

In the segments of the Eastern Alps and the Western Carpathians, Alpine Orogeny commenced with the closure of a Triassic Tethys Gulf (Hallstatt-Meliata Ocean; e.g. Channel & Kozur 1997) within the Austro-Alpine domain during the Jurassic to Early Cretaceous. Contemporaneously, the Penninic Ocean (part of the Liguria-Piemont Oceanic domain; Alpine Tethys of Stampfli 2000) opened by oblique rifting and spreading between the European shelf and the Austro-Alpine microplate, and this was related to the opening of the Atlantic Ocean (Frisch 1979; Stampfli *et al.* 2002). The Penninic-Austro-Alpine plate boundary and its continuation into the Western Carpathians changed from transtensional to transpressional during the mid-Cretaceous (Wagreich 2003). From Early Cretaceous times onwards, the sedimentary cover of the Northern Calcareous Alps was sheared off from its basement and stacked into a complex nappe pile. Deposition of synorogenic to post-orogenic strata followed until renewed orogenesis during the Eocene to Oligocene.

## *Definition of the major basins and palaeogeographic domains*

*Helvetic/Ultrahelvetic and Outer West Carpathian units*

Helvetic is a term used in two ways. Originally it was (and still is) used to describe a set of nappes on the northern border of the Alps in Switzerland. From the first quarter of the twentieth century the same term has also been used as a palaeogeographic name representing the depositional area on the southern border of the European continent during Mesozoic times in the Swiss transect.

The Helvetic nappes extend from the western part of the eastern Alps (Austria and Germany), where they disappear below the Austro-Alpine nappe system (Adria), through all of Switzerland and into eastern France, where they are replaced by the nappes of the Dauphinois in Savoie (Fig. 15.29). For historical reasons some of these units have different names in different parts of Switzerland. The Swiss Committee of Stratigraphy is currently trying to unify the lithostratigraphic nomenclature.

The Helvetic domain comprises sedimentary strata deposited on the shelf and upper continental slope of the European continent in a passive-margin setting during the Cretaceous (Fig. 15.30). The Early Cretaceous comprises a southward-prograding carbonate platform inlcuding times of condensation and/or non-sedimentation (phases of drowning) as well as intervals of increased detrital input from the north and NE. Following the Cenomanian transgression, basinal hemipelagic to pelagic sediments dominate until Maastrichtian times. Towards the south the transition to the palaeogeographic area of the Valais (North Penninic) Trough (which opened in Late Jurassic–Early Cretaceous times; see Steinmann 1994) is marked by the presence of hemipelagic to pelagic deeper-water sediments throughout the

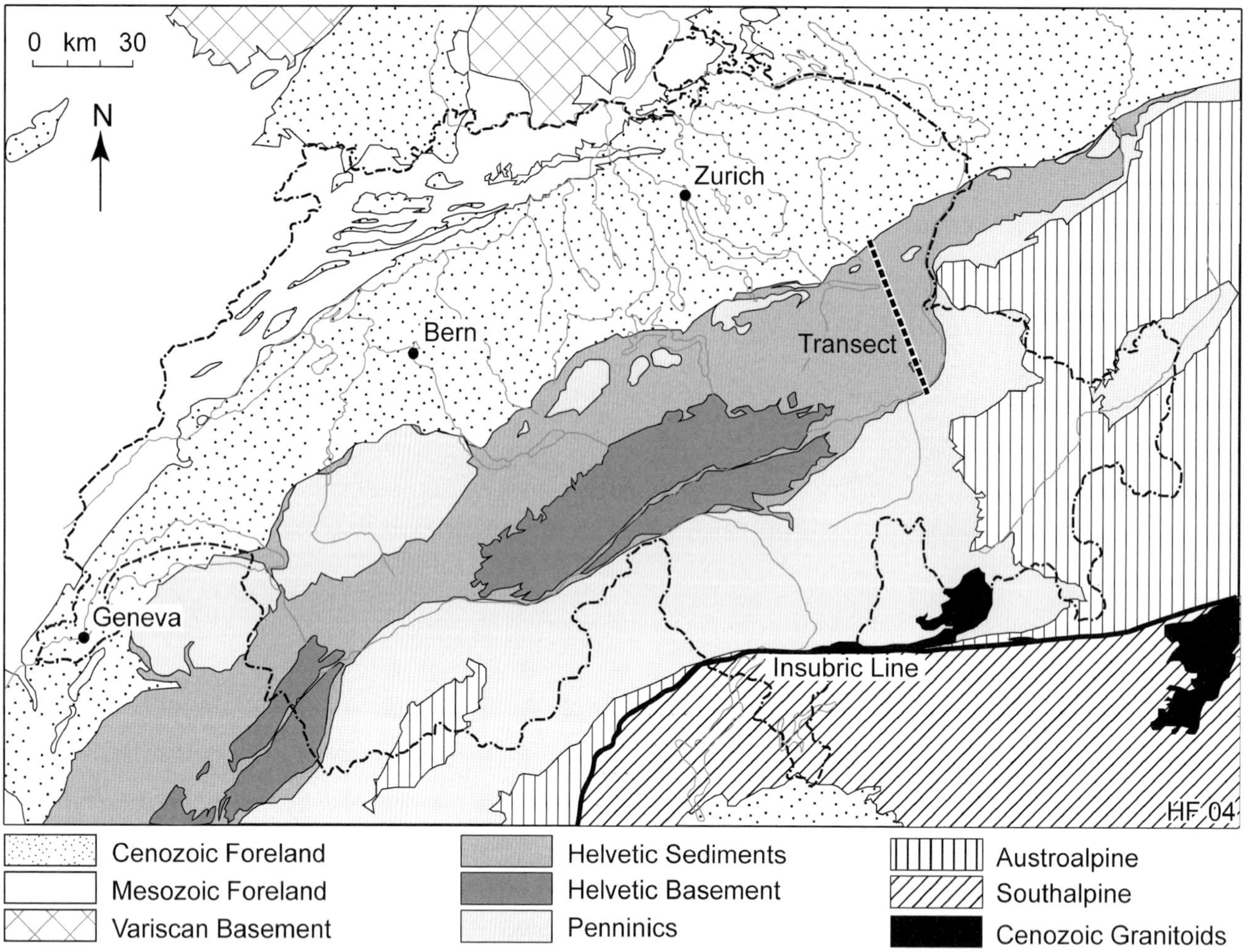


**Fig. 15.29.** Tectonic map of Switzerland (redrawn by H. Funk after Trümpy 1980) showing the Helvetic nappes. Black dashed line is the transect along which Cretaceous sedimentation is discussed in the text and shown in Figure 15.37.

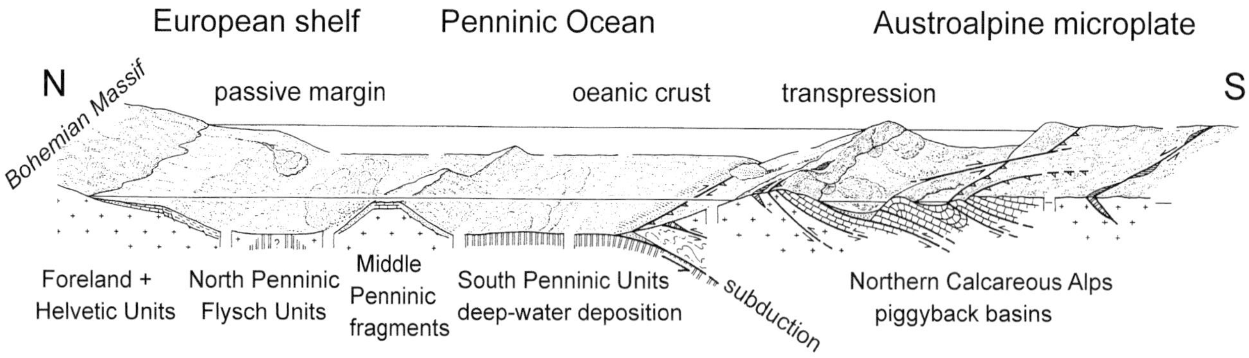


**Fig. 15.30.** Palaeogeographic cross-section from the European shelf into the Eastern Alps showing the main tectonosedimentary units and the formation of piggyback basins on the Austro-Alpine plate.

Cretaceous (Ultrahelvetic Zone and its equivalents in the Gresten Klippen Zone in eastern Austria, Fig. 15.30).

The Outer West Carpathians comprise several basins formed by extension of the eastern part of European shelf between the Bohemian and Ukrainian massifs. Outer basins (Godula, Magura) were separated by the elevated Czorsztyn Ridge from inner basins (Pieniny, Kysuca) situated at the margin of the Penninic Ocean. The position of this area enabled temporary connections with Boreal basins via the Mid-Polish Trough (Michalík 2002).

*Penninic basins*

The Penninic units comprise different parts of the Ligurian-Piemontais-Penninic-Valais oceanic systems, and include remnants of marginal continental fragments. The opening of these partly oceanic basins was linked to the Jurassic opening of the North Atlantic (Frisch 1979). These units can be subdivided into the North (Valais), Middle (Briançonnais) and South Penninic (Piemontais) (Fig. 15.30), which developed due to extension and spreading between the European foreland/Helvetic zones and the Austro-Alpine microplate during Middle Jurassic (Piemontais/South Penninic) and Early Cretaceous (Valais/North Penninic) times (e.g. Stampfli & Borel 2002). In the Western Carpathians, units such as the Vahic Ocean and parts of the Pieniny Klippen Belt may be correlated to the Penninic realm (e.g. Faupl & Wagreich 1992*a*). Mesozoic to Palaeogene parts of the Penninic units are preserved as non-metamorphic cover nappes, comprising mainly deep-marine (flysch) units in France, Switzerland and Austria, while other parts occur in various stages of metamorphism within tectonic windows below the overriding Austro-Alpine units (e.g. the Bündnerschiefer of the Engadin and the Tauern Window).

Sedimentation within the (North) Penninic Rhenodanubian Flysch Zone began during Early Cretaceous times. The successions are characterized by a variety of carbonate-dominated and siliciclastic deep-marine deposits (e.g. Hesse & Butt 1976; Schnabel 1992; Mattern 1999; Egger *et al.* 2002). In Switzerland there is evidence for oceanic crust forming the basement of parts of the North Penninic deep-marine succession. A continuation of parts of the Rhenodanubiuan Flysch into the Magura Flysch in the east was suggested by Schnabel (1992).

Typical North Penninic deep-marine basin fills are present in eastern Switzerland in the Prätigau area (Prätigau Flysch). The opening of the North Penninic Trough and the onset of turbiditic sedimentation appears to correlate roughly with the beginning of subduction in the South Penninic Ocean. In the Helvetic domain, the subsidence and separation of the Ultrahelvetic Zone is interpreted as a result of extension within the North Penninic Trough.

The Middle Penninic Units mainly comprise parts of the Briançonnais microcontinent (Stampfli 1993) and its northern and southern slopes. Its inferred continuation into the Eastern Alps (i.e. the position of the Zentralgneiss block of the Tauern Window) is still strongly debated (e.g. Frisch 1979; Faupl & Wagreich 1992*a*, 2000; Oberhauser 1995; Schmid *et al.* 2004).

In the South Penninic domain, deep-water clastics and pelagic successions of Cretaceous age are ubiquitous (e.g. Weissert & Bernoulli 1985; Winkler *et al.* 1985). Penninic nappes in eastern Switzerland, e.g. the Arosa Zone and the Platta Nappe, form a complex of imbricated slices containing Lower Cretaceous pelagic limestones and black marl–limestone rhythmites (Calpionella Limestone, Palombini Shales), overlain by Cenomanian–Turonian flysch (Verspala Flysch). Non-metamorphosed deep-water strata of the melange units of the Arosa and Ybbsitz zones (e.g. Decker 1990) overlie Jurassic ophiolites and record pelagic drape during the Early Cretaceous and mid-Cretaceous orogeny. Metamorphic South Penninic successions are known from tectonic windows in the Eastern Alps, such as the Tauern Window (Fig. 15.31), including ophiolitic complexes and metamorphosed Jurassic–Cretaceous shales (Bündnerschiefer).

Flysch units of the Préalpes Romande (Upper Prealpine nappes: Gets, Simme, Dranse, Sarine nappes) in Switzerland represent a complex evolution of deep-water basins along the accretionary wedge of the South Penninic–Adriatic margin (Gasinski *et al.* 1997). The South Penninic Gurnigel Formation and the Schlieren Formation represent the filling of a trench in front of the accretionary wedge. Forearc and backarc basins filled by deep-water turbidites are inferred, e.g. the Hundsrück and Mocausa formations.

In the Western Carpathians, units of inferred Penninic position were mostly subducted below the internal nappes. Remnants of supposed peri-Penninic units, such as the Belice Unit in the Považsky Inovec Mountains (Plašienka & Ožvoldová 1996), contain Cretaceous radiolarites and red shales.

*Austro-Alpine and Southern Alpine basins*

The Austro-Alpine units ('Ostalpin' in the German–Austrian literature) and its correlated units of the Central Western Carpathians (Fatric and Tatric units) are a conspicuous feature of the Alps east of Graubünden. Based on palaeomagnetic data the Austro-Alpine domain is considered to be a partly independent microplate situated along the northern margin of the Adriatic (Apulian) plate, and representing the northern tip of continental fragments of African affinity during the Cretaceous (e.g. Chan-

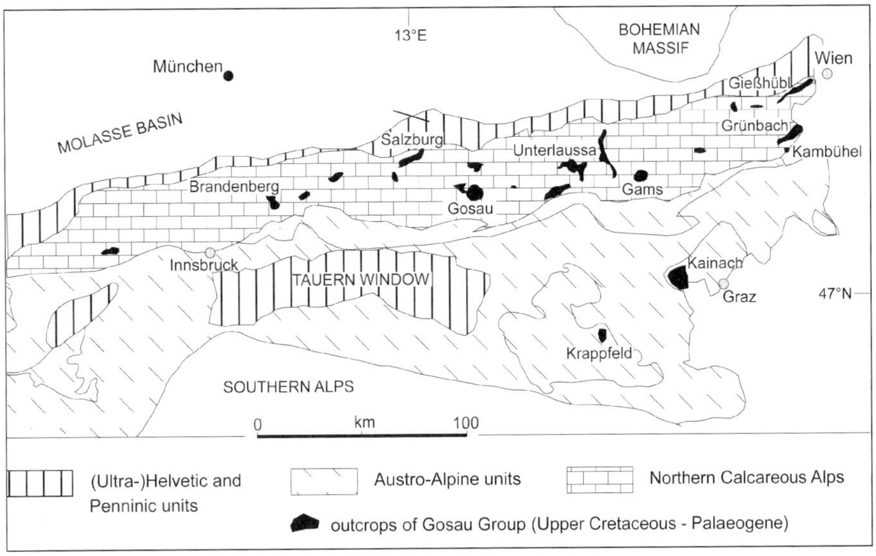


**Fig. 15.31.** Tectonic sketch-map of the Eastern Alps indicating major tectonic units and occurrences of basins yielding sediments of the Upper Cretaceous Gosau Group (Wagreich & Faupl 1994).

nell *et al.* 1992; Haubold *et al.* 1999; see also Stampfli & Borel 2002). Eo-Alpine deformation strongly influenced Cretaceous sedimentation and the formation of sedimentary basins within the Austro-Alpine domain. Thus, a complex history of synorogenic basins with strongly varying geometries and short-lived subsidence and uplift events characterizes the Austro-Alpine realm, especially during mid- and Late Cretaceous times (Fig. 15.30).

The best documented Cretaceous successions of the Austro-Alpine domain are preserved within the Northern Calcareous Alps (Fig. 15.31). Cretaceous deformation resulted in thrusting and faulting within the Northern Calcareous Alps. Based upon a restoration of younger faulting (Frisch *et al.* 1998), the Eastern Alps had about half the length of the present-day mountain chain during the Late Cretaceous.

Cretaceous deep-water successions including turbidites are also known from the Upper Austro-Alpine Ortler Zone and the Lower Austro-Alpine Samaden/Bernina nappe in Switzerland (Finger 1978; Caron *et al.* 1982; Bernoulli & Winkler, 1990). These are intercalated with hemipelagic marlstones.

The evolution of the Cretaceous of the Southern Alps can be partly linked to Austro-Alpine geodynamics (e.g. Lombardian Flysch; Bernoulli & Winkler 1990; Bersezio & Fornaciari 1994). Cretaceous deformation, metamorphism and thrusting in the Southern Alps is minor in comparison to the Austro-Alpine realm, enabling large-scale restoration of basins of the Mesozoic passive margin of the Adriatic plate (e.g. Doglioni & Bosellini 1987; Bertotti *et al.* 1993). Pelagic limestones, turbiditic successions and shallow-water platforms are the main facies.

## *Early Cretaceous Helvetic/Ultrahelvetic basins (Berriasian–Aptian)*

Only a small part of the Helvetic area can be studied in outcrops. This area represents a portion of the former northern shelf of the Tethys (see Fig. 15.1). In Figure 15.32a the remnants of this shelf are shown in a palinspastic view demonstrating the north–south orientated distribution of proximal, intermediate and distal facies of the Tethyan northern shelf. Nappe formation and piling as well as erosion have removed most of the sediments and the reconstruction is problematic (Heim 1916; Trümpy 1969; Ferrazzini & Schuler 1979).

Most of the major lithostratigraphic units of the Cretaceous can be recognized throughout all of the Helvetic tectonic units in Switzerland from west to east. While they change in thickness due to synsedimentary tectonics (Strasser 1979; Funk 1985), changes related to sea level and differential compaction are only minor. The main facies changes take place in a NNW (landward, proximal) to SSE (seaward, distal) direction. The history of Cretaceous sedimentation in the Helvetic unit will therefore be shown along a cross-section in eastern Switzerland as a representative example (Figs 15.29 & 15.32).

### *Stratigraphic succession*

During Late Jurassic times, a carbonate platform prograded from the region of the present-day Jura Mountains in NE Switzerland towards the SE and reached the northernmost part of the Helvetic area by late Tithonian times (Gygi & Persoz 1986; Funk 1990; Mohr & Funk 1995). This latest Jurassic–earliest Cretaceous carbonate platform is documented by the presence of intertidal as well as reefal limestones (Tros Member; Mohr 1992) in the northern tectonic units of the Helvetics (Faschas section in Fig. 15.32). Its time-equivalent basinal facies is the uppermost part of the Quinten Limestone with hemipelagic to pelagic micritic sediments. The succession represents sequence S0 (Funk *et al.* 1993; Föllmi *et al.* (1994) and is dated in the distal part on the basis of calpionellids (Mohr 1992; Mohr & Funk 1995).

The lower Berriasian is mainly represented by basinal sediments that comprise up to 200 m of marls and marly limestones (sequence S1; Zementstein Formation) (Heim 1916; Diegel 1973). The formation name is derived from the combination of clay and limestone; the relative proportion of these lithologies present is the ideal mixture to produce concrete. Redistributed sediments (e.g. calciturbidites, debris flows and mudflows) from the platform are intercalated and extend far into the basin (Gassen Beds) (Mohr 1992). The platform itself is documented only by very thin layers of marly sediments with miliolids and algae as well as lagoonal or supratidal clays with charophytes in a few very proximal outcrops.

The upper Berriasian–lower Valanginian sequences S2 and S3 consist of platform limestones (Oehrli Formation; Grasmück-Pfluger 1962; Burger 1986) and marls and clays (Palfris Formation; Burger 1986; Burger & Strasser 1981), which form locally downlapping foresets (Mohr 1992). The separation of sequences S2 and S3 by a marly layer is visible only in the shallow-water facies. Within the Palfris Formation, which represents the environment beyond the platform and can reach several hundreds of metres in thickness, no sequence boundary between S2 and S3 can be determined. In the platform region the top of the sequence is often represented by a hardground with borings and karstification in the platform limestones, documenting a phase of non-sedimentation and erosion (Burger 1986). The age of the end of sequence S3 can be dated as early Valanginian (Burger 1986; Mohr 1992).

The lower to upper Valanginian sequence S4 commences with fossiliferous marls and marly limestones (Vitznau Formation; Burger & Strasser 1981). Towards the south, the formation grades into a succession of alternating marls and marly limestones with a higher siliciclastic content. Towards the top of the succession the marls are replaced by prograding platform limestones of the Betlis Formation (Strasser 1982). The platform limestones lack hermatypic organisms and are dominated by echinoderms and bryozoan debris. Locally, lenses of coarse quartz sand occur in calarenites (Funk 1971). Chert nodules are also common. The higher input of terrestrial siliciclastics and nutrient-rich waters is possibly related to climate-induced intensified erosion on the European continent, thus causing the observed change in carbonate facies.

This climate change may have caused the subsequent crisis in carbonate platform development (D1). While thin, highly condensed phosphatic, glauconitic and quartz-rich sediments (Gemsmättli Bed) occur in the north, the southern part comprises micritic limestones (Diphyoides Formation) with sponge spicules, radiolarian and calcispheres (Burger & Strasser 1981; Strasser 1982; for $\delta^{13}C$ analysis see Lini *et al.* 1992; Föllmi *et al.* 1994). The Gemsmättli Bed is diachronous from distal (middle early Valanginian) to proximal areas (earliest Hauterivian; Baumberger & Heim 1907; Funk 1971; Haldimann 1977). A time transgressive onlap onto sequence S4 for this drowning unconformity can be reconstructed, while deepening is also well documented by the ammonite and belemnite faunas.

The Hauterivian sequences S5 and S6 are represented by siliceous limestones (Kieselkalk Formation). Two coarsening- and shallowing-upward sequences are topped by a condensed, glauconite-rich, partly phosphatic layer. In the proximal areas both sequences are dominated by crinoidal packstones with up to 10% of detrital quartz. Cross-bedding and channelled structures are common. The distal part is a finer-grained siliceous limestone

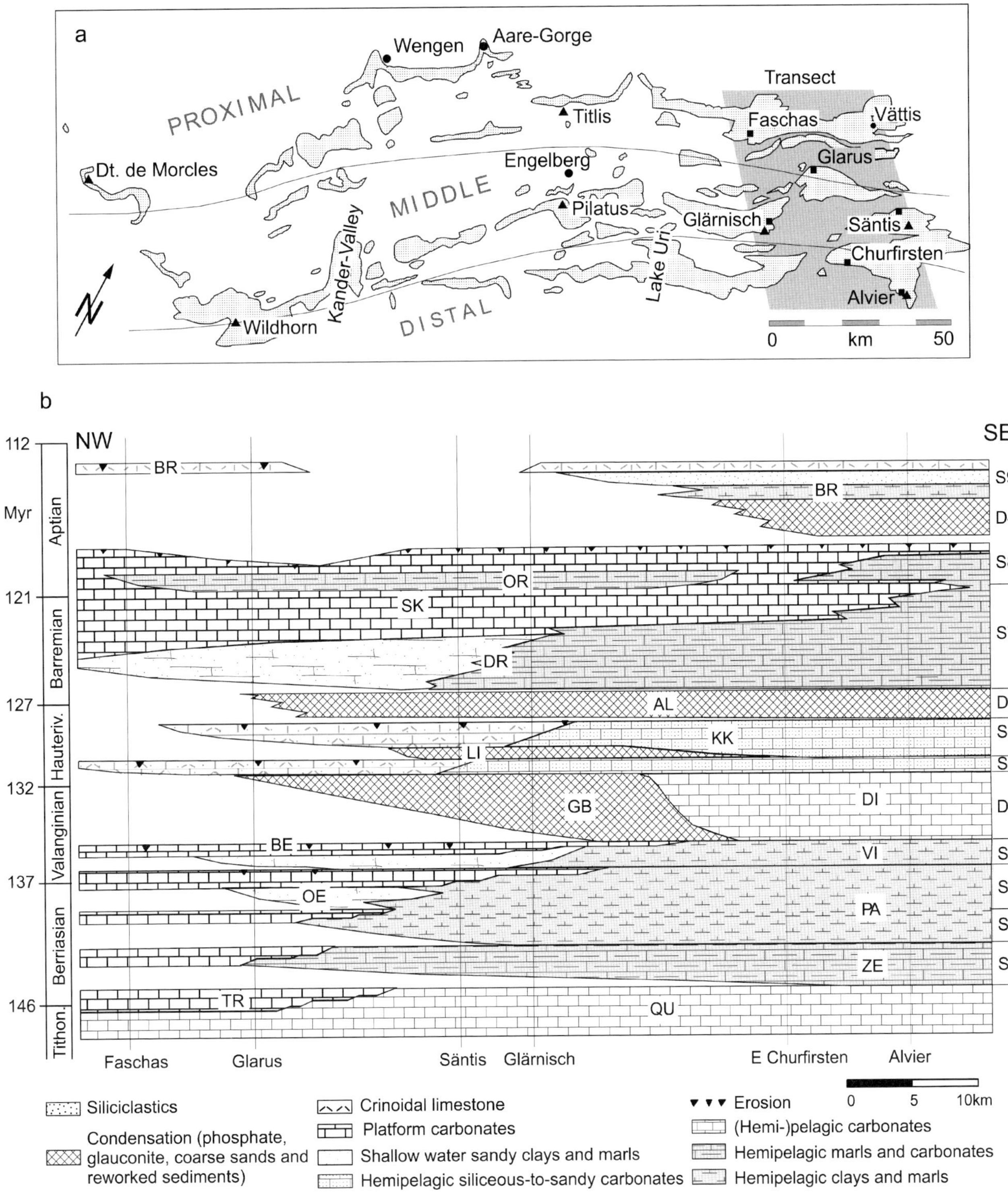


**Fig. 15.32.** Palinspastic reconstruction (**a**) and chronostratigraphic diagram (**b**) of Early Cretaceous lithostratigraphic units in the Helvetics. Dotted fields in the map represent outcrops of sediments of Barremian age (after Herb 1988). The space between the fields represents eroded material and is the minimal possible space (for discussion see Trümpy 1969; Ferrazzini & Schuler 1979). The two lines are arbitrary and help in discussion of prograding and retrograding platform environments. Quadrangles represent sections, triangles are Mountains peaks, and circles are localities. The time–space diagram is redrawn after Funk *et al.* (1993) and Föllmi *et al.* (1994). Timescale is after Gradstein *et al.* (2004). S1–S9 and D1–D5 are sedimentary sequences and drowning unconformities, respectively. Abbreviations: QU, Quinten-Formation; TR, Tros-Member; ZE Zementstein Formation; PA, Palfris Formation; OE, Oehrli Formation; VI, Vitznau Formation; BE, Betlis-Formation; GB, Gemsmättli Bed; DI, Diphyoides Formation; KK, Helvetic Kieselkalk; LI, Lidernen Bed; AL, Altmann Member; DR, Drusberg Formation; SK, Schrattenkalk-Formation; OR, Orbitolina Bed; BR, Brisi Member.

characterized by higher iron contents (Funk 1969, 1971, 1975). A phase of platform drowning is regionally represented by a condensed bed (Lidernen Bed; D2 in Föllmi *et al.* 1994). The sedimentation of the siliceous limestones commenced in the early Hauterivian and ended in the latest Hauterivian. Locally, a hardground with silicified fossils on top of this sequence represents another phase of drowning (D3).

The Barremian to lower Aptian sequences S7 and S8 are formed by a prograding carbonate platform. Shallow-water marls (Drusberg Marls) are replaced by the shallow-water limestones of the Schrattenkalk Formation, which contains both rudists and corals (Wissler 2001). The base of the Schrattenkalk Formation becomes younger in age towards the south and SE. A well documented marly event marks the base of sequence S8 (*Orbitolina* Bed). During the early Aptian (S8) the platform margin reaches its most distal SE position. Tectonic movements must have taken place at that time, as indicated by the presence of a fault system at the top of the Schrattenkalk filled with sandy glauconite (Greber & Ouwehand 1988). The top of the sequence S8 is represented by drowning phase D4 (Gebhard 1985; Ouwehand 1987; Föllmi & Ouwehand 1987).

The lower part of the Aptian sequence S9 (Brisi Member of the Garschella Formation; Föllmi & Ouwehand 1987) begins with fine-grained, partly glauconitic sandstones and is followed by coarser-grained sandstones and crinoidal, often cross-bedded limestones. The crinoidal limestone is the youngest shallow-water carbonate-in the Cretaceous of this area. The increased influence of nutrients together with increased carbon dioxide concentrations and rising sea levels were stress factors for the carbonate-building organisms on the Helvetic platform (Wissler *et al.* 2003). A final drowning event (D5) is represented by phosphorite nodules (Twäriberg Bed). This final drowning terminates the shallow-water evolution of the early Cretaceous Helvetic platform in the late Aptian.

The overlying Albian strata consist mainly of pelagic and hemipelagic sediments (Fig. 15.33) (Selun Member of the Garschella Formation, Twäriberg Bed). Albian deposits comprise a complex facies with several horizons of condensation (Niederi bed, Durschlägi Bed, Plattenwald Bed, Kamm Bed), and glauconitic silty to sandy limestones and sandstones (Sellamatt Bed, Aubrig Bed) (Föllmi 1986; Föllmi & Ouwehand 1987; Ouwehand 1987). Regionally a unit of deep-water stromatolites forms the top of the Albian.

### *Outer Western Carpathians (Early Cretaceous)*

In the Pieniny Klippen Zone of the Outer Western Carpathians, Berriasian–Barremian age biodetrital limestones of small shallow-water carbonate platforms (Fig. 15.34) were deposited along the margins of the Czorsztyn High (Birkenmajer 1977). Large parts of this high were emergent at the time. The southern slope of the high was covered by pelagic limestones (Maiolica-type Pieniny Limestone Formation). In the intrashelf depression, dark dysoxic shaly sediments (Těšín and Tlumačov formations) with only subordinate limestones (Těšín and Kurovice formations) were deposited (Vašíček *et al.* 1994). Nearshore environments on buried Jurassic reefs were characterized by limestones (Olivetská Hora, Kopřivnice Limestone). During late Valanginian and Barremian times, fluvial influx from the continent became more pronounced and clastic influx increased (Plaňava and Hradiště formations).

During Aptian to early Campanian times, sedimentation was strongly controlled both by rising sea levels and by the greenhouse climate (Michalík & Vašíček 1989). The global oceanic anoxic event OAE 1 is manifested by lower Aptian black shale deposition (Veřovice, Koňhora formations). The black shales are overlain by a late Aptian–Albian clastic wedge (Chlebovice Conglomerate and the turbiditic Lhotka Formation), which passed into shaly basinal deposits (Hluk and Wronine formations). On the periphery of the Penninic Basin, deposition of pelagic limestones (Brodno Formation) continued, passing (both laterally and vertically) into red nodular limestones and siliciclastics (Podmiedznik, Chmielowa formations) and red marls (Rudina Formation) on deeper slopes of the Czorsztyn Ridge.

### *Penninic basins (Early Cretaceous)*

In the Eastern Alps, the Upper Jurassic–Cretaceous succession of the South Penninic Ybbsitz Zone, including the Kahlenberg Nappe near Vienna (Decker 1990; Homayoun & Faupl 1992), comprises calpionellid limestones with thin turbidites (Fasselgraben Formation) passing into carbonate-dominated turbidites (Glosbach Formation, Haselgraben Formation, Barremian–Aptian) and a thick siliciclastic-rich sandy turbidite interval (Ybbsitz Formation, Albian–Cenomanian). Turbidite deposits of the Ybbsitz Zone, as well as the mid-Cretaceous of the Kahlenberg Nappe, commonly contain chrome spinel in the heavy mineral assemblages, a significant feature of Lower to mid-Cretaceous turbiditic sediments of the South Penninic domain (e.g. Wildi 1985; Pober & Faupl 1988; Faupl *et al.* 1997).

Metamorphic Penninic (mainly South Penninic) Cretaceous strata are present in the Tauern Window and other Penninic windows in the Eastern Alps (Fig. 15.35, column 8). These classic Bündnerschiefer successions comprise thick phyllite complexes including metamorphic turbidite successions.

Lower Cretaceous non-metamorphic flysches of the Rhenodanubian Flysch Zone display a pattern of alternating carbonate-dominated and siliciclastic intervals (e.g. Plöchinger & Prey 1993; Mattern 1999). The succession (Fig. 15.35, column 4) commences with the carbonate-dominated Neocomian (mainly Barremian–Aptian; equivalent to the Tristel Formation in Switzerland and Vorarlberg; Piller *et al.* 2004). The overlying Albian-age siliciclastic flysch (Gault-Flysch and Rehbreingraben Formation; Wortmann *et al.* 2004) is characterized by glauconite-rich sandstone turbidites. A conspicuous interval of red shales is present in Austria and southern Bavaria, marking a time of reduced turbidite input into the deep-water basin during Albian to early Cenomanian times (Wagreich *et al.* 2006).

### *Northern Calcareous Alps (Early Cretaceous)*

Successions of deep-water carbonate and marls predominate in the Northern Calcareous Alps (NCA) (Fig. 15.35, columns 9–13). Synorogenic clastic successions and marl facies of the Lower Cretaceous comprise pelagic limestones at their base grading up into a cyclic shale–limestone facies. Resedimented clasts of shallow-water carbonates (e.g. Schlagintweit 1991) provide evidence that small carbonate platforms were present in the northern parts of the NCA during the Early Cretaceous, but were later completely eroded. The deposits are interpreted as pelagic sediments of the deep-water shelf to slope of the passive margin of the Austro-Alpine microplate. The presence of siliciclastic synorogenic strata marked the change to a tectonically active margin due to compression in the Austro-Alpine–Penninic boundary (Winkler 1996; Eynatten & Gaupp 1999; Wagreich 2003).

Kimmeridgian–early Berriasian pelagic deep-water limestones (Oberalm Formation) comprise cherty, bedded micrites and

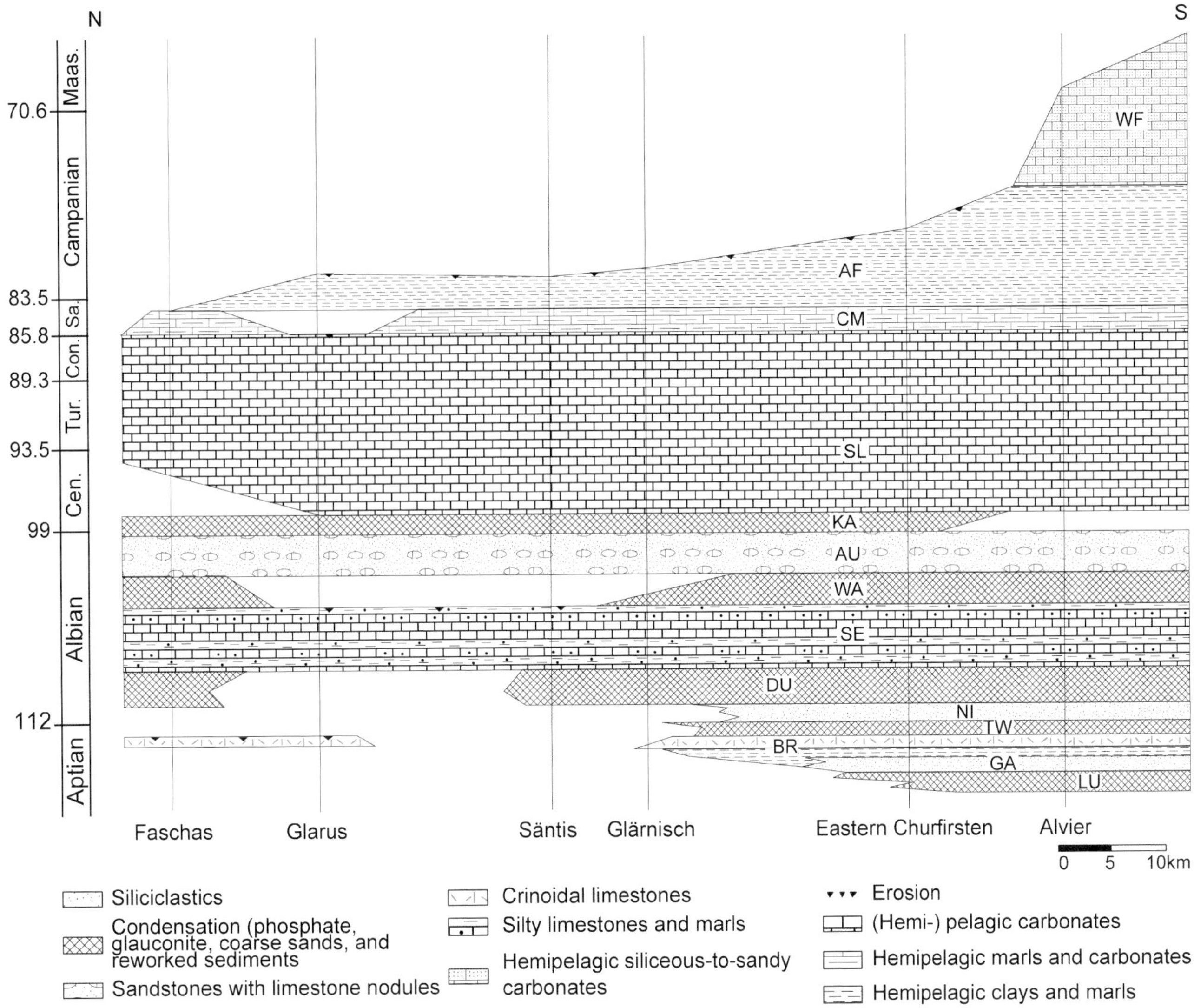


**Fig. 15.33.** Chronostratigraphic diagram of Late Cretaceous lithostratigraphic units in the Helvetics of eastern Switzerland. Timescale is after Gradstein *et al.* (2004). For palaeogeographic position of the sections see Figure 15.37. Units from bottom to top: LU, Luitere Bed; GA, Garschella Fm; BR, Brisi Member; TW, Twäriberg Bed; NI, Niederi Bed; DU, Durschlägi Bed; SE, Sellamatt Bed; WA, Wannenalp Bed; AU, Aubrig Bed; KA, Kamm-Bed; SL, Seewen Formation; CM, Choltal Member; AF, Amden Formation; WF, Wang Formation.

include prominent carbonate turbidites. The microfauna is dominated by radiolarians, calpionellids and foraminifera (e.g., Weidich 1990; Reháková *et al.* 1996; Boorová *et al.* 1999). Turbiditic beds within the Oberalm Formation contain a diverse resedimented shallow-water fauna of calcareous algae and foraminifera indicating an early Berriasian age. The Upper Jurassic to Berriasian carbonate platforms (Plassen Formation; Schlagintweit & Ebli 1999; Schlagintweit 2004) can be regarded as the source for the shallow-water detritus. These pelagic limestones grade into Berriasian-age grey marly limestones and limestone–marl rhythmites (Schrambach Formation; Tollmann 1976; Vašíček & Faupl 1999; Rasser *et al.* 2003). Sandy turbidites are largely absent in the Schrambach Formation, while the amount of marl intercalations increases upwards.

In some nappe complexes of the NCA (Tirolic units west and south of Salzburg; Reichraming and Lunz nappes further to the east), deep-water limestones grade diachronously into synorogenic terrigenous clastics (Rossfeld Formation) during Valanginian to Aptian time (Fig. 15.35) (Faupl & Tollmann 1979; Decker *et al.* 1987; Vašíček & Faupl 1998). This Rossfeld Basin is interpreted as a deep-water foreland to piggyback basin located at the front of the overthrusting NCA nappes (Faupl & Tollmann 1979; Schweigl & Neubauer 1997). The Rossfeld Basin fill comprises a coarsening-upward succession of marls and sandstones, grading into deep-water conglomerates/breccias as well as slump sediments deposited on an active north-facing slope. The sandstones contain considerable amounts of siliciclastic and ophiolitic detritus from southern source terrains, including chrome spinels from ophiolites of the Tethys-Vardar-Hallstatt suture (Pober & Faupl 1988; Eynatten & Gaupp 1999). Similar deposits are present in the Thiersee Syncline of the Western NCA (?Berriasian–Barremian/Aptian; Darga & Weidich 1986) and in the Tatric units of the Western Carpathians.

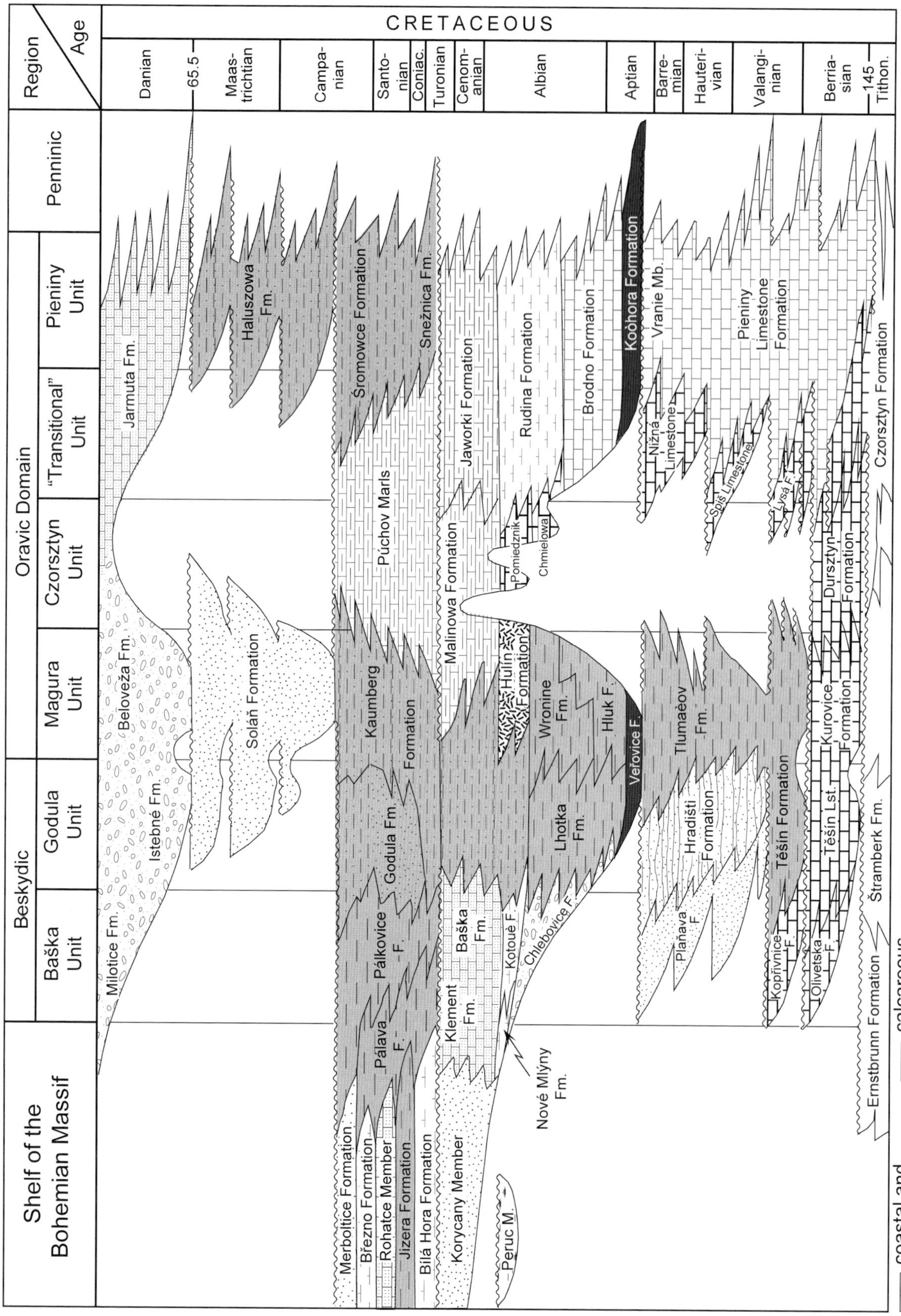

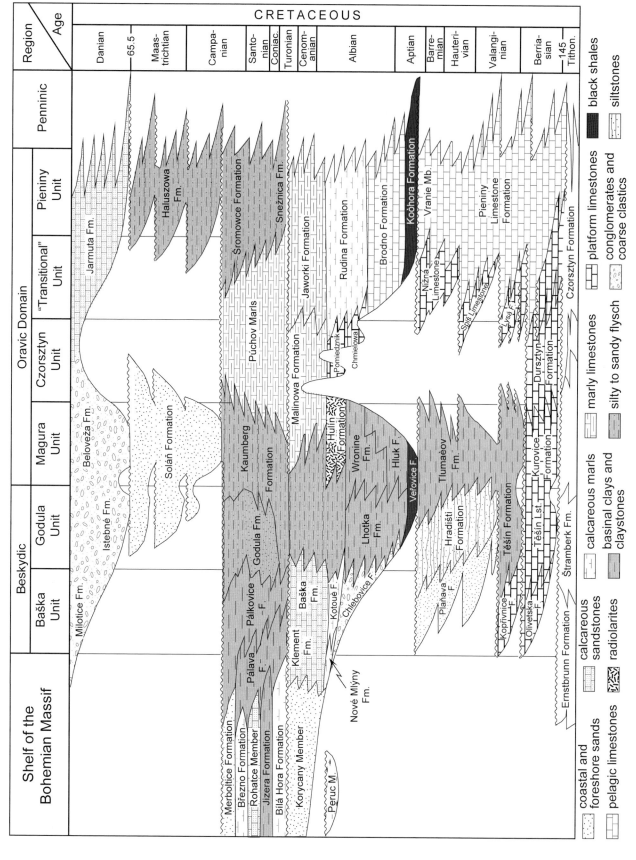

**Fig. 15.34.** Chronostratigraphic diagram showing lithostratigraphic Cretaceous units of the outer Western Carpathians.

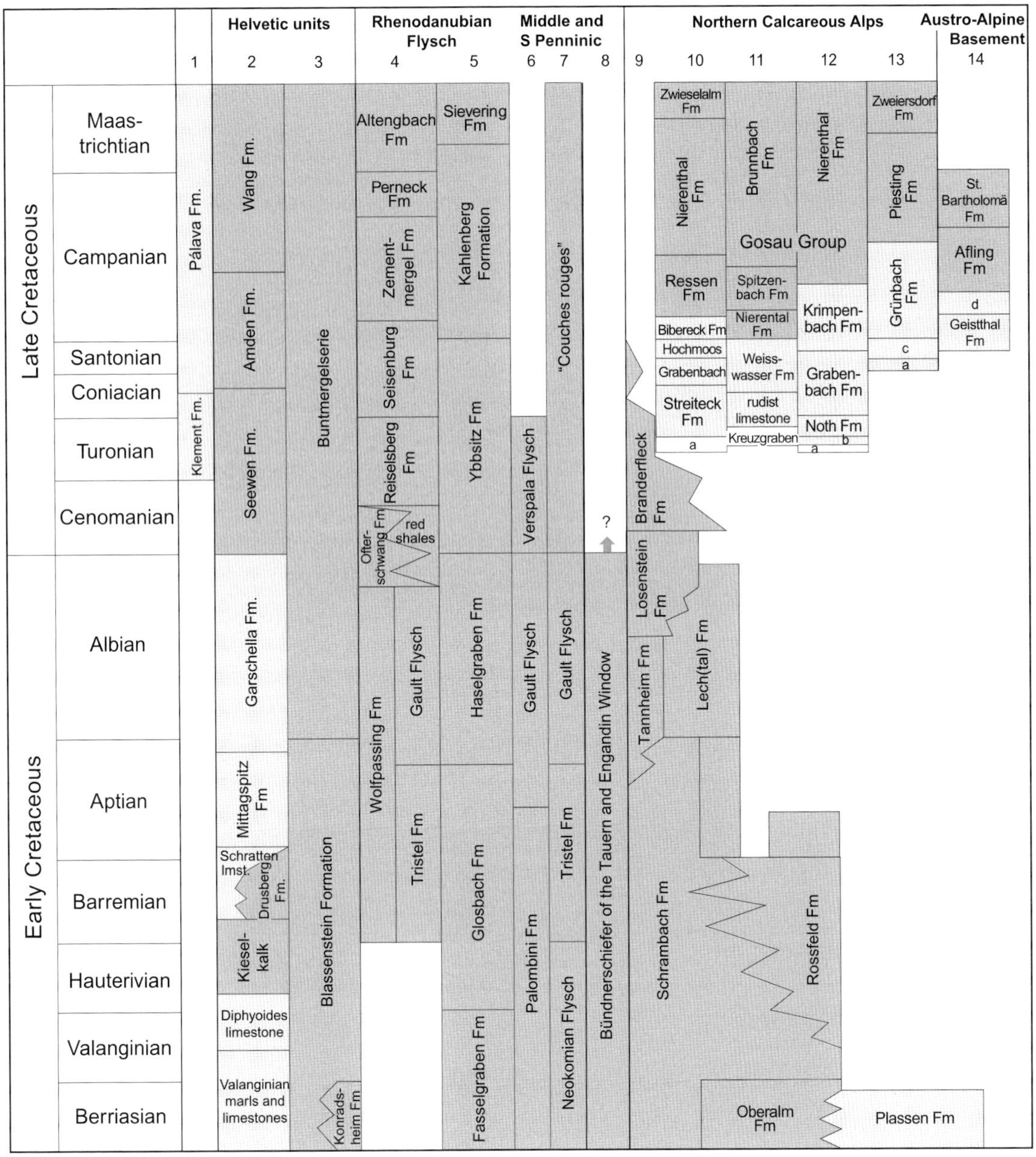


**Fig. 15.35.** Overview of the major lithostratigraphic Cretaceous units of the Eastern Alps along a north–south transect. Tectonic units: 1, Waschberg Zone; 2, Helvetic units; 3, Ultrahelvetic Gresten Klippen Zone; 4, Rhenodanubian Flysch Zone, Greifenstein Nappe and main nappe; 5, Ybbsitz Zone and Kahlenberg Nappe; 6, Arosa Zone; 7, Middle Penninic Tasna and Sulzfluh nappes; 8, metamorphic Penninic Bündnerschiefer of the Tauern Window; 9, lowermost thrust units of the Northern Calcareous Alps (NCA) (Allgäu–Ternberg–Frankenfels Nappe System); 10, higher thrust units of the NCA, Gosau Group of the type Gosau area; 11, Gosau Group of Unterlaussa; 12, Gosau Group of Gams; 13, Gosau Group of Grünbach; 14, Gosau Group of Kainach on top of Austro-Alpine metamorphic complexes south of the NCA. Facies key: white = terrestrial; medium grey = shallow-marine; dark grey = deep-marine. Abbreviations: a, Kreuzgraben Formation; b, Schönleiten Formation; c, Maiersdorf Formation; d, St. Pankrazen Formation.

### *Central Western Carpathians and Hungary (Early Cretaceous)*

Lower Cretaceous successions in the Central Western Carpathians, including equivalents of the Austro-Alpine units, were mainly deposited in hemipelagic basinal environments; olistolites, slope debris, slumped bodies, and slope fan deposits become increasingly important in younger formations. Shallow-marine deposits occur mainly reworked as pebbles within younger conglomerates. Upper Hauterivian to lower Albian carbonate platforms developed on elevated blocks of the Tatric High. These were mostly destroyed by subsequent erosion following tectonic uplift.

In the Tatric High, Upper Jurassic to Lower Cretaceous limestone successions overlie Kimmeridgian and Tithonian condensed 'Ammonitico Rosso' red nodular limestones. Neocomian platform limestones are present in the Kadlubek Unit (Michalík *et al.* 1994; Lefeld *et al.* 1985), and consist of microsparitic peletal wackestones with rare oncolites. In the Kuchyňa Unit, a proximal facies with calciturbidite beds is developed (Staré

Hlavy Formation; Michalík *et al.* 1993). This formation consists of thick-bedded organodetritic wackestone to packstone with Berriasian to Valanginian calpionellids, aptychi, belemnite rostra, brachiopods, bivalves and cyrtocrinoids. Calciturbidites form intercalations in more basinal Tithonian–Berriasian-age micritic wackestones (similar to the Oberalm Formation of the NCA). Major basins were filled by schistose marly limestones or by Valanginian–Hauterivian well-bedded cherty limestones (Lučivná Formation).

The Fatric Zone was occupied by the pull-apart Zliechov Basin, typified by Upper Jurassic and Lower Cretaceous pelagic limestones (Borza *et al.* 1980; Michalik 2007), e.g. pale wackestone to packstones of both *Globochaete* and *Calpionella* microfacies with large chert nodules. Breccias (Nozdrovice Breccia Member) were present along the slope of the basin and are composed of intraclasts of Kimmeridgian, lower and upper Tithonian, and lower Berriasian packstones. This unit was deposited during the late Berriasian relative sea-level fall due to synsedimentary faulting. In the Manín Unit, a southern part of the Fatric Zone, Berriasian and lower Valanginian strata are missing and pelagic limestones (Ladce Formation) rest disconformably on the Jurassic substrate. Hemipelagic bioturbated limestones (Mráznica Formation) are of late Valanginian age in the Manín Unit, and of Valanginian to Aptian age in the more distal parts of the Zliechov Basin. Dark marly Valanginian–lower Barremian biomicrites (Hlboč and Kościeliska formations) represent less aerated parts of the basin. Turbidites (Kryta Turbidite Member) provide evidence of a significant Late Cimmerian tectonic event (the Oravice Event; Michalík & Reháková 1997), accompanied by compression in southern units and by input of siliciclastic debris with abundant chrome spinel grains into the basin. Cherty limestones (Kališčo Formation; Michalík *et al.* 1987) in the Manín Unit record moderate shallowing which peaked during the sedimentation of thick-bedded limestones (Lúčkovská Formation).

Upper Hauterivian–lower Albian shallow-water carbonates ('Urgonian-type') commenced with the deposition of slope- and submarine delta fans derived from carbonate platforms prograding basinwards (Muráň Formation (Michalík & Soták 1990) Bohatá Formation, Podhorie Formation, etc.). Many of the carbonate platforms were subsequently eroded. Aptian warming caused decreasing oxygenation and an increase in the carbon content of the basinal sediments (Muránska Lúka, Párnica, Osobitá formations).

Shallow-water Urgonian limestones are widespread in Alpine units of Hungary (e.g. Császár 2002). They also occur as reworked clasts within deep-water limestones and clastic fan deposits similar to synorogenic formations of the NCA (e.g. Rossfeld Formation; Császár & Árgyelán 1994). A complex palaeogeographic setting between the Austro-Alpine and the Southern Alps has been inferred for these platforms and basins (Császár & Árgyelán 1994; Faupl *et al.* 1997).

## *Synorogenic mid-Cretaceous of the Northern Calcareous Alps and the Carpathians*

After the termination of sedimentation within the Rossfeld Basin in the Barremian–early Aptian, synorogenic basin subsidence shifted to tectonically lower (northern) zones of the NCA. Piggyback basins evolved in front of north to NW-propagating thrusts, such as the Tannheim-Losenstein Basin (late Aptian to early Cenomanian; Wagreich 2003), and the Kreideschiefer Basin in the westernmost NCA (Leiss 1992; May & Eisbacher 1999; Eynatten & Gaupp 1999). Deposits of the Tannheim-Losenstein Basin (Fig. 15.30) form the core of faulted and partly overturned, narrow synclines. Within these units pelagic limestones are overlain by a few tens of metres of marlstones and calcareous shales followed by a 100–350 m thick coarsening-upward clastic cycle (Losenstein Formation; Fig. 15.35, column 9; Wagreich 2003).

The late Aptian to middle/late Albian calcareous shales and marlstones (Tannheim Formation; Zacher 1966) can be classified as hemipelagites, and comprise a mixture of an autochthonous biogenic carbonate fraction (mainly planktonic foraminifera and calcareous nannoplankton) and a terrigenous siliciclastic fine silt and clay fraction, together with varying amounts of organic carbon. A bathyal depositional depth of at least a few hundred metres has been estimated based on the high content of planktonic foraminifera and the lack of shallow-water foraminifera (Weidich 1990). Black shales with up to 2% of organic carbon are present in the lower Albian, including oceanic anoxic event OAE1b with ammonites such as *Leymeriella tardefurcata* (Kennedy & Kollmann 1979; Wagreich & Sachsenhofer 1999; Kennedy *et al.* 2000). These shales and marlstones are overlain by a 100 to 350 m thick coarsening-upward cycle (Losenstein Formation; middle Albian–lowermost Cenomanian; Kollmann 1968; Weidich 1990), comprising turbidites, deep-water conglomerates and slump horizons. In the lower part of this succession, thin sandy turbidites and laminated siltstone-shale intervals prevail. Sandstone beds are up to 30 cm thick and show grading and both complete and partial Bouma cycles. Conglomerates increase up section. Both normal- and inversely graded clast-supported conglomerates and matrix-supported pebbly mudstones and pebbly sandstones are found. Overall, the thickness of the pebbly mudstones and slumped intervals increases in the upper part of the succession. Slump intervals comprise folded beds of laminated siltstone–shale intervals with only rare sandstone intercalations. The uppermost preserved facies include thick slumped intervals and boulder conglomerates. This facies association was interpreted as a coarse-grained deep-water slope apron deposited along the active northern margin of the Austro-Alpine microplate (Wagreich 2001, 2003).

Synorogenic breccias, sandstones and marls (Branderfleck Formation; Cenomanian–Turonian; up to early Campanian in the western NCA; Gaupp 1982; Weidich 1984; Faupl & Wagreich 1992*b*) partly conformably overlie older formations, but also unconfomably overlie faulted and folded Triassic to Jurassic strata and thus indicate early Cenomanian folding and erosion in the NCA. Basal breccias and shallow-water sandstones containing orbitolinids pass into tens of metres of deep-water hemipelagic and turbiditic deposits, including a series of large limestone olistoliths (up to 8 m in diameter).

In the central Western Carpathians similar synorogenic mid-Cretaceous formations are present. During middle Albian times, former carbonate platforms were submerged and covered by marls (Zabijak and Butkov formations). The basins in the central Carpathians were mostly filled by thick (300–600 m), frequently bioturbated marls with siltstone and sandstone intercalations, and rare olistoliths (Poruba Formation; Wagreich 2001), which grade into fine-grained Cenomanian sandstones and shales (Belušské Slatiny Formation). During Turonian and early Coniacian times, the sedimentation in the central Carpathian basins was mostly terminated by the prograding front of superficial nappes.

## *Late Cretaceous Helvetic/Ultrahelvetic basins*

During the Late Cretaceous pronounced subsidence of the Helvetic and Ultrahelvetic units occurred, and this was associated with a facies change from shallow-water carbonates to pelagic and hemipelagic marls and limestones (Föllmi 1989). No sequence stratigraphic work has been done for the Upper Cretaceous succession of the Helvetics.

From Cenomanian times onwards pelagic limestones and marls were deposited but these were locally removed by pre-Cenozoic erosion (Fig. 15.33) (Herb 1988). Pelagic micritic limestones up to 200 m thick, partly rich in planktonic foraminifera (Seewen Limestone), are dated with the planktonic foraminifera as early Cenomanian to Coniacian (Bolli 1945). Inoceramids are the only frequent macrofossils. A reddish unit (up to several metres thick) of these limestones represents the latest Cenomanian to earliest Turonian oceanic anoxic event OAE 2. In Santonian times increased detrital input led to the deposition of marl up to 20 m thick in water depths of several hundred metres (Choltal Member of the Seewen Formation; Oberhänsli-Langenegger 1978).

The overlying laminated marly claystones are 220 m thick and of late Santonian to late Campanian age (Amden Formation; Oberhänsli-Langenegger 1978). They differ from the underlying marls in their darker colour. The depositional depth on the outer shelf has been estimated to extend from *c.* 200 m to more than 500 m (Oberhänsli-Langenegger 1978). The youngest Cretaceous formation is of late Campanian to late Maastrichtian age and occurs only in the highest nappes. It consists of fine-grained and partly siliceous limestones and silty marls (Wang Formation; Stacher 1980). In central Switzerland, the most distal successions begin with debris flow breccias (some decimetres up to 30 m), which comprise components of older Cretaceous units. In eastern Switzerland, there is a conformable succession of upper Santonian to Maastrichtian sediments, but towards the SW the Maastrichtian limestones overlie successively older units, reaching the Malm in a section in Canton Bern (Regenboldshorn; Stacher 1980). Tectonic movements along local faults were responsible for the generation of the debris flows (Günzler-Seiffert 1952). While in the south sedimentation continues into the early Palaeocene, subaerial erosion becomes important in the northern region due to the formation of a foreland bulge in connection with the Alpine Orogeny (Herb 1988; Allen *et al.* 1991).

The Ultrahelvetic units in the Eastern Alps, e.g. the Gresten Klippen Zone deposited south of the Helvetic shelf, are represented by a variegated succession of pelagic and hemipelagic marls and shales (Buntmergelserie). Black shales and limestones predominate from Aptian to Cenomanian times up to a distinct black shale interval at the Cenomanian–Turonian boundary. The Turonian to upper Campanian is characterized by red marls and limestones (e.g. Kollmann & Summesberger 1982; Hu *et al.* 2005). Campanian to Maastrichtian marls display increasing amounts of clay and silt. Late Campanian ammonites are reported from this interval in Upper Austria (Kennedy & Summesberger 1984, 1999).

### *Late Cretaceous Penninic basins*

Various models for flysch basin palaeogeography and subsidence, especially during the Late Cretaceous, have been discussed. Hesse (1982) suggested a dormant deep-sea trench while Trümpy (1988) favoured a transform setting. The onset of thick siliciclastic flysches during the mid- to Late Cretaceous has been interpreted as a consequence of the onset of compression or subduction in the Liguria-Piemont-Penninic ocean system (Mattern 1999).

In the Rhenodanubian Flysch Zone the Cenomanian to Turonian is characterized by a thick siliciclastic, sandstone-rich succession of turbidites (Reiselsberg Formation; Mattern 1999). Several intervals of mainly red shales (lower Cenomanian, Coniacian to Santonian, upper Campanian) indicate times of low siliciclastic input into the basin. Carbonate-dominated flysch is present in the Campanian (Zementmergel Formation, Piesenkopf Formation), including prominent carbonate mud turbidites. A succession >1000 m thick of siliciclastic flysches with subordinate hemipelagic shales and some bentonites follows (Altlengbach Formation; Maastrichtian–lower Eocene; e.g. Egger *et al.* 2002). The Laab Nappe in the Vienna Woods area near Vienna displays Coniacian to Campanian basin plain to outer fan deposits (Kaumberg Formation), which continue into the Western Carpathian flysches.

### *Late Cretaceous Austro-Alpine Gosau basins*

Upper Cretaceous deposits of the Eastern Alps show continuous deposition only in the Helvetic and Penninic realms, whereas the Austro-Alpine realm was characterized by the development of more complex and shorter-lived basins along the Penninic–Austro-Alpine active margin.

In the Turonian, as a consequence of the Eo-Alpine Orogeny, most of the deformed Austro-Alpine domain was elevated above sea level. In front of the Austro-Alpine microplate, an accretionary wedge existed as a result of subduction of the Penninic Ocean under a dextral transpressional regime (Fig. 15.30). This wedge comprised tectonic slices of Austro-Alpine units and obducted ophiolite remnants. The NCA, which had probably already been sheared off from their metamorphic basement, were situated during this time at this tectonically active continental margin.

In late Turonian times, a new sedimentary cycle began with the deposition of the Gosau Group, which rests unconfomably upon the Eo-Alpine-deformed pre-Gosau strata of the NCA and also on metamorphic Austro-Alpine basement south of the NCA (Fig. 15.35, columns 10–14). As unconformable Upper Cretaceous strata are widespread in the Alpine–Carpathian mountain chain, the term Gosau has been used from the NCA to Slovakia, Hungary and Romania for such deposits (e.g. Willingshofer *et al.* 1999). Basin formation is considered to be the result of the complex interplay of sedimentation and tectonism during the Late Cretaceous history of the entire Austro-Alpine block, and several models have been proposed, inlcuding compressional piggyback and synthrust basins (Eisbacher & Brandner 1995; Ortner 2001) or extensional and pull-apart basins (Wagreich 1995; Neubauer *et al.* 1995; Schweigl & Neubauer 1997; Willingshofer *et al.* 1999; Wagreich & Decker 2001).

The Gosau Group of the NCA can be divided into two subgroups as a consequence of the different basin geometries and subsidence histories (Wagreich 1993, 1995; Wagreich & Faupl 1994). The lower Gosau Subgroup (upper Turonian–Campanian; Maastrichtian-Palaeogene only in the southeastern NCA) consists of diachronous terrestrial deposits at the base and passes gradationally into shallow-marine successions (Fig. 15.36). At the base, karst bauxites of probable Turonian age are present (Mindszenty & D'Argenio 1987), providing evidence of pronounced subaerial exposure of at least parts of the NCA at this time. Sandstones and sandy limestones together with rudist-bearing limestones of nearshore facies, storm-influenced inner- and outer-shelf sandstone–marl facies and shelf/slope fine-grained transitional facies are present in the lower Gosau Subgroup (Wagreich & Faupl 1994; Sanders *et al.* 1997; Sanders 1998; Summesberger *et al.* 1999*b*; Sanders & Höfling 2000; Wagreich 2003). Locally, high contents of ophiolitic detritus are

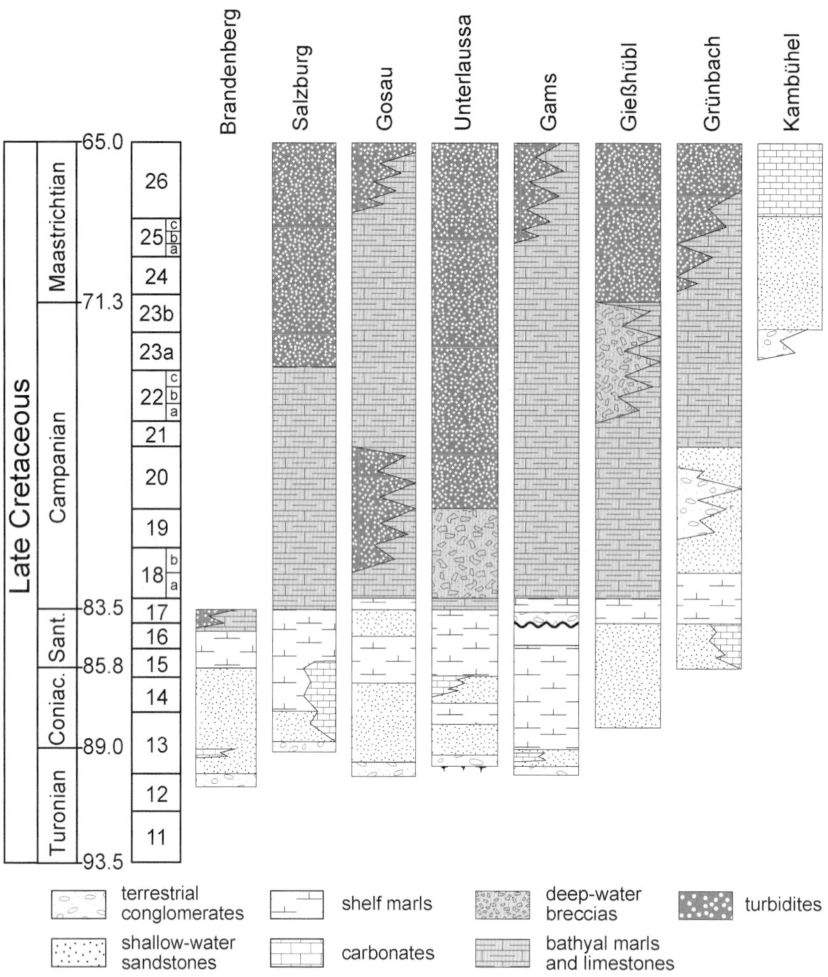


**Fig. 15.36.** Chronostratigraphy, nannoplankton zonation and facies of the Gosau Group of the Northern Calcareous Alps (Wagreich & Faupl 1994; Faupl & Wagreich 2000).

a conspicuous feature of the sandstones of this subgroup. The lower Gosau Subgroup was mainly deposited in small strike-slip basins (Fig. 15.37; Wagreich & Decker 2001) which originated due to extension or transtension following mid-Cretaceous thrusting and transpression along the Penninic–Austro-Alpine boundary (Wagreich & Faupl 1994).

The upper Gosau Subgroup comprises deep-water deposits (Fig. 15.36), such as hemipelagic and pelagic slope marls (Nierental Formation; Butt 1981; Wagreich & Krenmayr 2005) and a broad variety of deep-water clastics, deposited above and below the calcite compensation level (Fig. 15.38). Facies distribution and palaeocurrent data indicate a pronounced fault-controlled relief of a generally north-facing palaeoslope (Wagreich & Faupl 1994). A conspicuous angular unconformity separates the lower and the upper subgroup (Faupl 1983), and parts of the lower Gosau Subgroup have been eroded along this unconformity. In contrast to the lower subgroup, the terrigenous material of the deep-water successions comprises predominantly metamorphic detritus. Shallow-water components, such as corallinacea, orbitoid foraminifera and bryozoa, suggest that there was a carbonate platform to the south of the NCA (Wagreich & Faupl 1994).

The subsidence event leading to the deposition of the upper Gosau Subgroup shifted diachronously from the Santonian–Campanian from the NW towards the SE of the NCA, with the easternmost parts of the NCA subsiding as late as the Maastrichtian. This strong subsidence pulse has been related to subcrustal tectonic erosion, eliminating parts of the accretionary wedge along the northern margin of the Austro-Alpine plate (Wagreich 1993, 1995).

The Gosau Group overlying metamorphic Austro-Alpine units south of the NCA (Gosau Group of Kainach and Krappfeld), displays a different sedimentary and tectonic evolution (Neubauer *et al.* 1995; Willingshofer *et al.* 1999; Wagreich & Siegl-Farkas 1999) to that of the NCA. Sedimentation began as late as Santonian–early Campanian times with terrestrial conglomerates and lacustrine marls (Ebner & Rantitsch 2000). A rapid subsidence event led to basin deepening and the deposition of Campanian deep-water marls and turbidites (Willingshofer *et al.* 1999). Sedimentation ended in the latest Campanian to early Maastrichtian.

Transgressive Upper Cretaceous deposits of the Transdanubian Central Range (Bakony Mountains) in Hungary have been interpreted as an extensional collapse basin and display a similar

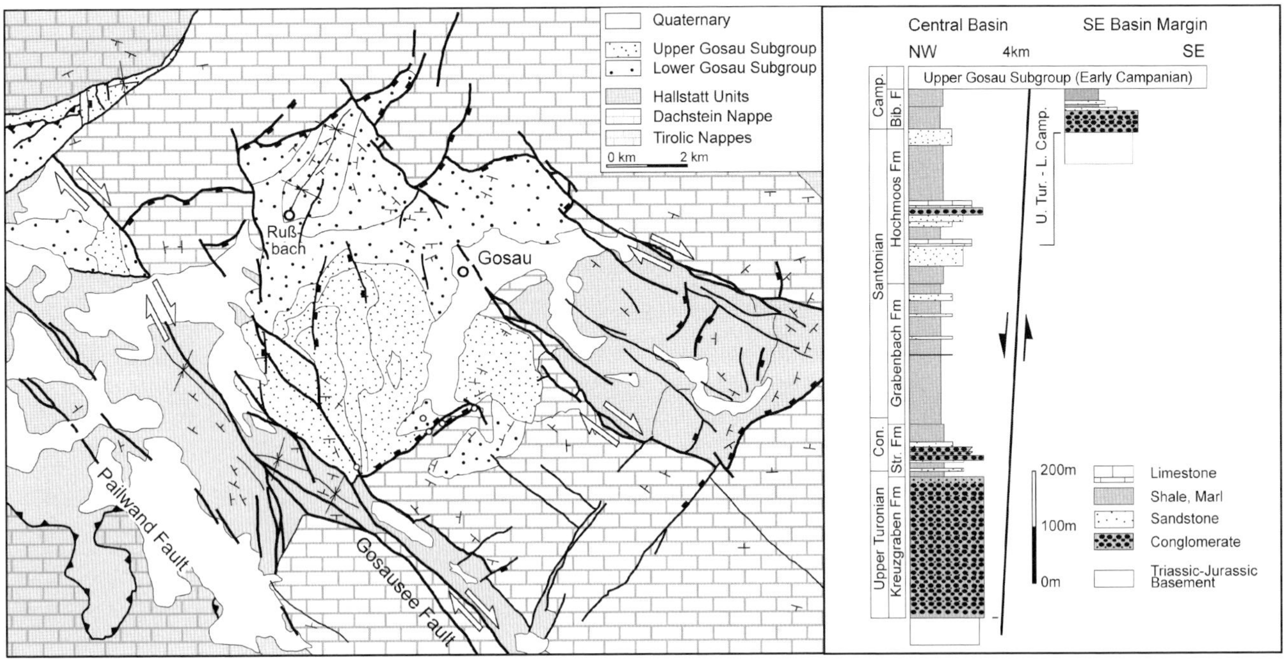


**Fig. 15.37.** Geological sketch-map of the Gosau type area and stratigraphy of the lower Gosau Subgroup. Note dextral strike-slip faults and linked normal faults which define a late Turonian to Santonian pull-apart basin (Wagreich & Decker 2001) and the strong thickness changes along basin-margin normal faults.

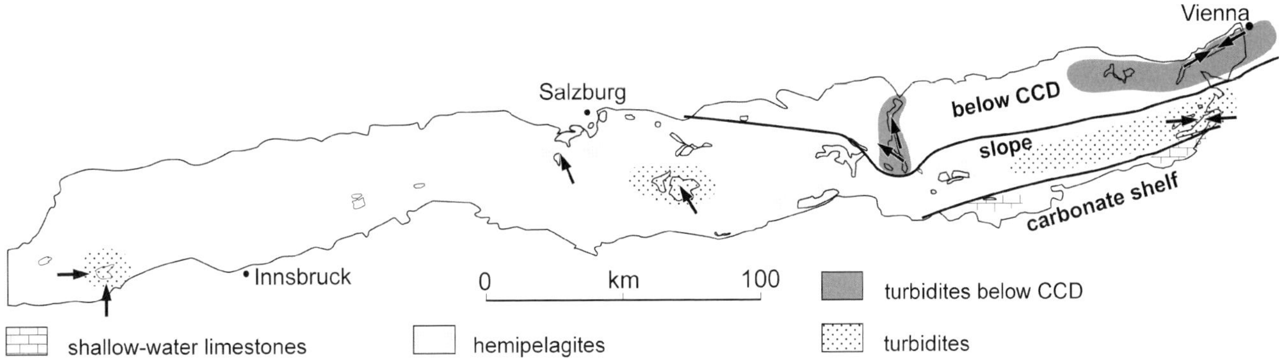


**Fig. 15.38.** Palaeogeography of the Northern Calcareous Alps in the late Maastrichtian. A northward deepening from a carbonate shelf in the SE to turbidite fans below the calcite compensation depth (CCD) has been recognized (modified from Wagreich & Faupl 1994).

evolution to the Gosau Group of Kainach and Krappfeld in Austria (Haas 1999; Wagreich & Siegl-Farkas 1999). Terrestrial to lacustrine strata overlie prominent karst bauxite horizons of Turonian age (e.g. Mindszenty & D'Argenio 1987) and grade up into a marine deepening succession comprising marls and limestones of late Santonian to Campanian age (Polany Marl Formation; Lantos *et al.* 1997; Siegl-Farkas & Wagreich 1997; Bodrogi *et al.* 1998). Campanian carbonate platforms (Ugod Formation) include steep erosional slopes characterized by the deposition of megabreccias into the deeper water basin (Haas 1999).

*Stratigraphic succession*

Upper Cretaceous deposits of the Gosau (Upper Austria) and Rußbach (Salzburg) areas in the NCA comprise the type locality of the Gosau Group. Historical descriptions include Lilienbach (1830) and Sedgwick & Murchison (1832). Several classic monographs on Cretaceous palaeontology of the nineteenth century rely largely on material from the fossiliferous lower part of the Gosau type area, for example Reuss (1854), Zittel (1866) and Redtenbacher (1873). The basin fill comprises *c.* 1000 m of upper Turonian to lowermost Campanian terrestrial and shallow-water sediments of the lower Gosau Subgroup, which are unconformably overlain by more than 1200 m of deep-water deposits of the upper Gosau Subgroup (Fig. 15.35 & 15.36). The upper Gosau Subgroup seals the upper Turonian–Santonian basin-bounding faults, as these deep-water deposits onlap the Triassic substrata (Wagreich 1988). Reconstruction of the basin geometry of the lower Gosau Subgroup suggests that the original structure was a 6–8 km wide and 10–12 km long pull-apart basin (Wagreich & Decker 2001).

The biostratigraphy, lithostratigraphy and sedimentology of the basin fill have been recently discussed in detail by Kollmann & Summesberger (1982), Höfling (1985), Tröger & Summesberger (1994), Summesberger & Kennedy (1996), Wagreich (1992, 1998), Sanders *et al.* (1997), Sanders & Pons (1999) and Steuber (2001). Lithostratigraphy is based on Weigel (1937) and Kollmann (1982) (Figs 15.35 & 15.36). The base comprises an interval up to 350 m of alluvial fan conglomerates (Kreuzgraben Formation) of probable late Turonian age, which is overlain by a transgressive succession of upper Turonian to Coniacian shallow-marine marls and backstepping coarsening-upward fan delta paracycles (Wagreich 1988, 1998). Foraminiferal assemblages suggest water depths of *c.* 150 to 300 m at maximum flooding in early Santonian times. The lower Santonian comprises storm-influenced shelf and nearshore sediments up to 250 m thick, grading into upper Santonian fossiliferous nearshore/shoreface sandstones and marls, including prominent rudist bioherms (Höfling 1985; Sanders & Pons 1999; Steuber 2001). The top of the Santonian is formed by a 20 m thick bedded sandstone interval which yielded an abundant mollusc fauna, with 23 gastropod taxa (Kollmann 1980), 50 bivalve taxa (Dhondt 1984) and 22 ammonite taxa (Summesberger 1979, 1980, 1985).

In the nearby Bad Ischl area (Wagreich 1998) the most spectacular Upper Cretaceous coral reef in the Eastern Alps was described by Sanders *et al.* (1999). In its lower part, the reef consists of poorly exposed shaly limestones rich in rudists and relatively small-sized scleractinians, overlain by boundstones of lamellar-encrusting corals up to more than a metre in size, and subordinate hemispherical and columnar corals.

The boundary between the lower Gosau Subgroup and the upper Gosau Subgroup in the type area is characterized by a short period of uplift and erosion, followed by rapid subsidence into bathyal depths. Based on the increasing amounts of planktonic foraminifera in the overlying marls, rapid deepening occurred in early Campanian times. The overlying, up to 350 m thick, sandstone-rich turbidite fan deposits (lower Campanian) display a pronounced proximal–distal trend from the Gosau area to the NW (Wagreich & Krenmayr 2005). Upper Campanian–Maastrichtian marly (hemi-)pelagic limestones (Wagreich & Krenmayr 1993) grade into a limestone-turbidite interval (Butt 1981; Krenmayr 1996). Sedimentation rates are *c.* 25 mm/ka. During the late Maastrichtian, the percentages of turbidites increased and turbidite sedimentation continued up to early Eocene times (Fig. 15.35).

*Cretaceous–Palaeogene boundary in the Gosau Group*

Several sites with a fairly complete record of the Cretaceous–Palaeogene boundary were found within the Gosau Group of the NCA at Gosau (Elendgraben section), at Gams (Knappengraben section; Egger *et al.* 2004) and near Berchtesgaden/Lattengebirge (Herm *et al.* 1981; Preisinger *et al.* 1986; Lahodynsky 1988; Peryt *et al.* 1993). A detailed biostratigraphy and magnetostratigraphy was established for these sites, and several impact-related features were reported from the deep-water boundary clays of the Gosau Group, such as iridium enrichment and shocked quartz (Preisinger *et al.* 1986).

## *Late Cretaceous Western Carpathians*

In the Outer Western Carpathians, the Cenomanian transgression extends far into the Bohemian Massif (Fig. 15.34). Marly sediments (Nové Mlýny, Kotúč formations), deep-marine units (Godula, Baška, Kaumberg formations) and radiolarites (Hulín Formation) were deposited. The Czorsztyn Ridge was submerged, covered by pelagic red marls (Púchov Marl, Malinowa and Jaworki formations). The marginal zone was more dynamic and is characterized by turbidites of Turonian to early Campanian age (Snežnica Formation, Śromowce Formation).

During the late Campanian to Maastrichtian, extension continued, resulting in basin subsidence. Turbidite sedimentation (Soláň Formation, Haluszowa Formation) predominated in the basins, while the intervening ridges were tilted and eroded (Birkenmajer 1977). Upper Cretaceous to Oligocene redeposition of older deposits affected large parts of Outer Carpathian units, which causes many problems with their stratigraphic correlation. Upper Cretaceous deep-marine red beds (Coniacian–lower Campanian) are characteristic for this part of the Pieniny Klippen Belt successions.

*Upper Cretaceous Gosau successions of the Western Carpathians*

A complex system of thrust units comprising the pre-Alpine basement and various parts of its Mesozoic cover originated during the Turonian in the Central Carpathians, followed by extensional basin formation (Plašienka *et al.* 1997). Upper Cretaceous shallow-marine and freshwater clastics occur at different positions in several tectonic units of the central Western Carpathinas (Michalík & Činčura 1992). They form intercalations in early deep-marine deposits of the palaeo-Alpine accretionary belt and form the basal unit of post-orogenic Gosau sediments in the central Western Carpathian nappe units. Breccias derived from local material (Bartalová, Kržl'a Breccia) filled small karstic cavities on the surface of the carbonates (Malé Karpaty Mountains; Michalík 1984, 2000). The Brezová succession (Fig. 15.39; similar to the Gosau basins of the NCA; Wagreich & Marschalko 1995) commences with freshwater upper Turonian–lower Coniacian biomicritic limestones containing ostracods, gastropods and freshwater algae. Braided river and delta facies (Ostriež Formation) are heterochronous. An early Coniacian age is indicated by foraminifers in the Brezová area, but intercalations with Campanian microfaunas have been reported by Borza (1962). The conglomerates are overlain by 50–150 m of sandstones which passes laterally into sandy limestones with gastropods and marls. Late Coniacian calcareous nannofossils and foraminifera are reported; planktonic foraminifers prevail over benthic forms (Salaj & Gašparíková 1983).

The overlying Santonian–early Campanian succession, 500–600 m thick, comprises alternating graded calcareous sandstones, sandy marls and sandy limestones. The lower and the upper part of the succession correspond to outer platform environments while agglutinated foraminifers and thin coal seams in the middle part of the sequence indicate coastal conditions. Thick (50 m) marls in the upper part of the unit contain a rich foraminiferal microfauna dominated by planktonic forms (Salaj & Gašparíková 1983) and a nannoplankton assemblage indicating an early Campanian age (Bystrická *et al.* 1983). The overlying upper Campanian and Maastrichtian formations comprise a thick succession of greenish-grey marls intercalated with calcarenite sandstones, sandy *Orbitoides* limestones and conglomerates.

## Summary

The Cretaceous evolution of sedimentary basins in Central Europe was influenced by the interplay of two main processes: plate tectonics and eustatic sea-level change. Global plate-tectonic reconfiguration resulted in the widening of the Central

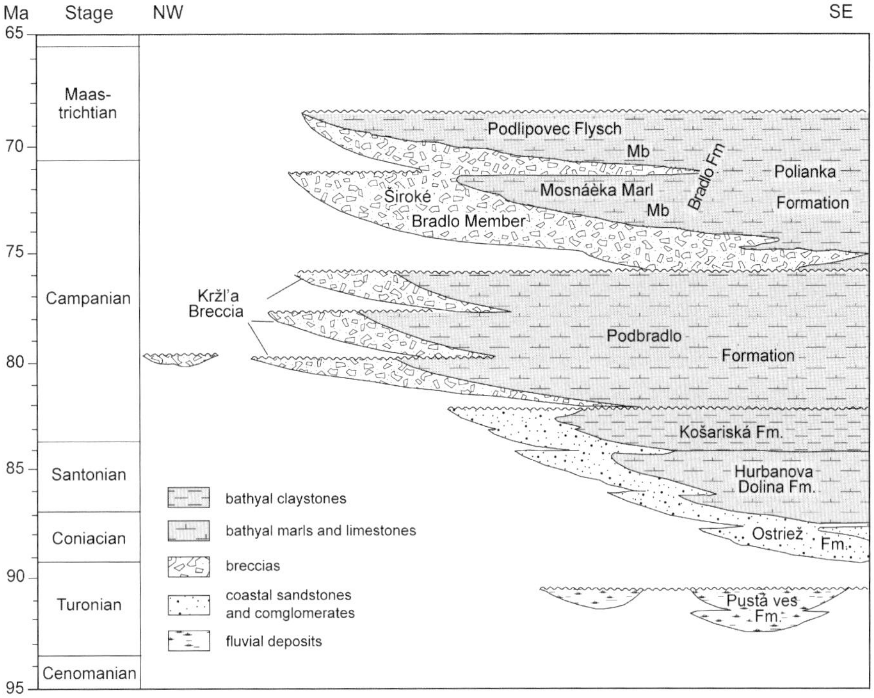


**Fig. 15.39.** Chronostratigraphic diagram of the Upper Cretaceous Gosau succession at the margin of the Western Carpathians (Brezová Basin).

Atlantic, the opening of the Bay of Biscay, and the opening of the South Atlantic Ocean causing a counter-clockwise rotation of Africa coeval with the closure of the Tethys Ocean. Convergence between the European and African plates led to the formation of the Alps and the Western Carpathians as a classic thrust orogen. Several orogenic phases can be distinguished. The Jurassic–Cretaceous, Eo-Alpine orogeny was followed by Meso- and Neo-Alpine deformational events (e.g. Faupl & Wagreich 2000; see also Froitzheim *et al.* 2008; Reicherter *et al.* 2008).

During the Early Cretaceous, ongoing rifting of the North Sea Graben system and the resulting stress pattern produced a variety of smaller, partly isolated basins in Central Europe. The late Palaeozoic–early Mesozoic rifting in the North Sea ceased in late Early Cretaceous times and thermal subsidence prevailed in western and central Europe from the Albian to the Turonian. Elevated spreading rates along mid-ocean ridges and increased rates of intra-oceanic plateau volcanism resulted in the highest global sea level during Phanerozoic times (Haq *et al.* 1988; Hardenbol *et al.* 1998). The former margins of Early Cretaceous basins were flooded worldwide, and several new seaways connected the cold Boreal areas of the Arctic and western Siberia with the warm subtropical Tethys Ocean. Central Europe evolved into an extended epicontinental shelf sea with a variety of intra-shelf basins.

The palaeogeography of southern Central Europe is determined by the convergence of Europe and Africa and can be divided into: (1) a southern European passive margin, which comprising the Helvetic, the Outer Carpathians and other comparable European shelf units on continental crust (including Subpenninic units *sensu* Schmid *et al.* 2004); (2) the units of the Liguria-Piemont-Penninic ocean system; and (3) the northern margin of the Adriatic plate comprising the Austro-Alpine, the Inner Western Carpathians (Fatric, Tatric), and the Southern Alpine units.

## *Early Cretaceous*

The Early Cretaceous evolution of sedimentary basins in the epicontinental domain of Central Europe followed structures that had developed in the Jurassic. The rapidly subsiding graben systems of the North Sea (Central Graben, Danish Basin, Mid-Polish Trough) as well as the basins at its southern extension were filled with several thousand metres of sediments (Ziegler 1990; Kockel 1991: Senglaub *et al.* 2005). The WNW–ESE striking Central Netherlands Basin, the Lower Saxony Basin, the Altmark-Fläming Basin and the Prignitz Basin were arranged in an *en echelon* structural pattern reflecting a transtensional stress regime. These basins were linked by north–south striking narrow basin structures (e.g. Gifhorn Trough). Early Cretaceous sedimentation was dominated by coarse- to fine-grained siliciclastics. While in the Berriasian fluvial and freshwater lacustrine deposits were deposited (Wealden), marine clays and marls have been deposited in northern Central Europe since the Valanginian. The occurrence of sandstones indicates an east–west striking belt of coastal deposits at the northern margin of the Rhenish and Bohemian massifs. Sedimentary thicknesses varied from tens of metres close to rising salt structures, to several thousands of metres in subsiding areas.

In the segments of the Eastern Alps and the Western Carpathians, the Alpine Orogeny commenced with the closure of a Triassic Tethys Gulf (Hallstatt-Meliata Ocean) within the Austro-Alpine domain during the Jurassic to Early Cretaceous (Channel & Kozur 1997). Contemporaneously, the Liguria-Piemont-Penninic Ocean opened by oblique rifting and spreading between the European shelf and the Austro-Alpine microplate, and this was related to the opening of the Atlantic Ocean (Frisch 1979; Stampfli *et al.* 2002). Tectonic stress along the Penninic–Austro-Alpine plate boundary and its continuation into the Western Carpathians changed from transtensional to transpressional during the mid-Cretaceous

(Wagreich 2003). From Early Cretaceous times onwards, the sedimentary cover of the Northern Calcareous Alps was sheared off from its basement and stacked into a complex nappe pile. Deposition of synorogenic to post-orogenic strata followed until renewed orogenesis during the Eocene to Oligocene.

Along the passive margin of southern Central Europe (Helvetic domain), Early Cretaceous strata comprise a southward-prograding carbonate platform including periods of condensation and/or non-sedimentation (phases of drowning) as well as intervals of increased detrital input from the north and NE. Towards the transition to the palaeogeographic area of the Valais (North Penninic) Trough, sedimentary facies are marked by the presence of hemipelagic to pelagic deeper-water sediments (Ultrahelvetic Zone; Fig. 15.29). The Outer West Carpathians comprise several basins formed by extension of the eastern part of the European shelf between the Bohemian and Ukrainian massifs. Outer basins (Godula, Magura) were filled with hemipelagic to pelagic siliciclastic sediments. Inner basins (Pieniny, Kysuca) were separated from clastic source areas by the elevated Czorsztyn Ridge, and were filled with pelagic carbonates similar to those in the southern Alpine domain.

Early Cretaceous sedimentation within the newly opened Valais (North Penninic) Trough was characterized by a variety of carbonate-dominated and siliciclastic deep-marine deposits. The opening of the North Penninic Trough and the onset of turbiditic sedimentation appears to correlate roughly with the beginning of subduction in the South Penninic Ocean. In the South Penninic domain, deep-water clastics and pelagic successions of Cretaceous age are ubiquitous (e.g. Weissert & Bernoulli 1985; Winkler *et al.* 1985).

The Austro-Alpine and the Inner Western Carpathian units were situated along the northern margin of the Adriatic (Apulian) plate (e.g. Stampfli & Borel 2002). Eo-Alpine deformation strongly influenced Cretaceous sedimentation and resulted in the formation of synorogenic basins whose complex histories show strongly varying geometries and short-lived subsidence and uplift events. Faulted and partly overturned successions of deep-water carbonates and marls predominate in the Northern Calcareous Alps. Pelagic sediments are overlain by a thick coarsening-upward clastic succession with abundant slumped intervals and boulder conglomerates. This facies association has been interpreted as a coarse-grained deep-water slope apron deposited along the active northern margin of the Austro-Alpine microplate (Wagreich 2001, 2003).

The evolution of the Cretaceous of the Southern Alps can be partly linked to Austro-Alpine geodynamics. Cretaceous deformation, metamorphism and thrusting in the Southern Alps was minor in comparison to the Austro-Alpine realm, enabling large-scale restoration of basins of the Mesozoic passive margin of the Adriatic plate (e.g. Doglioni & Bosellini 1987; Bertotti *et al.* 1993). Pelagic limestones, turbiditic successions and shallow-water platforms are the main facies.

### *Late Cretaceous*

In the course of the Cretaceous global sea-level rise, large areas of Central Europe were flooded and formed a broad epicontinental shelf with various intrashelf basins. The eustatic long-term sea-level rise commenced in the middle Albian, achieved its maximum rate during the Cenomanian, and was superimposed by several short-term transgressions. The coastlines were shifted far inland and siliciclastic basinal sedimentation was replaced by the deposition of pelagic chalk. Chalk is a marine sediment that consists almost exclusively of the remains of planktonic coccolithophorid algae and other pelagic organisms.

Coeval reactivation of old fault zones (e.g. Elbe Fault Zone, Franconian Fault Zone) led to the formation of new basins on the Variscan basement of the Rhenish and Bohemian massifs (e.g. Münsterland Cretaceous Basin, Bohemian Cretaceous Basin, North and Intrasudetic basins, Opole Basin, Braunau-Regensburg and Wasserburg basins). Here, marine sedimentation occurred in Cenomanian–Santonian (in part Campanian) times and is dominated by coarse- and fine-grained siliciclastic sediments as well as hemipelagic to pelagic limestones in the basinal parts. Coeval fluvio-lacustrine sedimentation occurred in the South Bohemian Basin.

The Late Cretaceous modification of the stress field in Europe resulted in the commencement of inversion tectonics during late Turonian times, when a series of NW–SE striking thrust faults formed along zones of structural weakness (e.g. Sorgenfrei–Tornquist Zone, Elbe Fault Zone, Roer Valley Graben, Osning Thrust, Lausitz Fault). Inversion tectonics led to the uplift of former depocentres, the formation of block-fault-bounded structural highs and of new rapidly subsiding marginal basins. The main phase of inversion occurred in middle Santonian to early Campanian times, when thick successions of siliciclastics (fluvial to coastal and nearshore sandstones) were deposited in the vicinity of inverted structures (e.g. Roer Valley Graben, inverted Central Netherlands Flechtingen-Rosslau and Calvörde blocks and Lower Saxony basins, Harz area, Prignitz-Lausitz High and inverted Mid-Polish Trough). Coarse siliciclastics grade into marly limestones and chalk towards the distal shelf areas in the north (Pompeckj High, Danish Basin). There, a profound palaeorelief consisting of structural grabens and highs led to large-scale mass transport and resedimentation of chalks by low-angle suspension flows resulting in variable chalk thicknesses.

Along the southern continental margin of Europe (Helvetic), the Early Cretaceous shallow carbonate platform evolution was substituted by the deposition of Cenomanian–Santonian-age pelagic carbonates due to deepening of the basin. The accumulation of basinal hemipelagic to pelagic sediments continued until Maastrichtian times. The Alpine domains of the Outer Western Carpathians were involved in compressional tectonics, nappe piling and flysch sedimentation. The onset of thick siliciclastic flysches during mid- to Late Cretaceous has been interpreted as a consequence of the onset of compression or subduction in the Liguria-Piemont-Penninic ocean system (Mattern 1999). In the Turonian, as a consequence of the Eo-Alpine Orogeny, most of the deformed Austro-Alpine domain was elevated above sea level. In front of the Austro-Alpine microplate, an accretionary wedge existed as a result of subduction of the Penninic Ocean under a dextral transpressional regime. Within the Austro-Alpine domain and in the Western Carpathians, complex and short-lived Late Cretaceous basins were developed on top of the nappe pile (Gosau basins). The sedimentary infill of these Turonian–Campanian Gosau basins evolved from terrestrial to shallow-marine successions to a broad variety of deep-water deposits, such as hemipelagic and pelagic slope marls, as well as coarser deep-water clastics deposited above and below the carbonate compensation depth. The strong pulse of increased subsidence has been related to subcrustal tectonic erosion, eliminating parts of the accretionary wedge along the northern margin of the Austro-Alpine plate (Wagreich 1993, 1995).

## References

Ahrens, H., Lotsch, D. & Musstopf, R. 1965. Zur Geologie der Grenzschichten Kreide/Tertiär im Gebiet der Bohrung Nennhausen 2/63. *Abhandlungen des Zentralen Geologischen Instituts*, **1**, 127–

136.

ALBERS, H.J. 1976. Feinstratigraphie, Faziesanalyse und Zyklen des Untercampans (Vaalser Grünsand = Hervien) von Aachen und dem niederländisch-belgischen Limburg. *Geologisches Jahrbuch,* **A34**, 3–68.

ALBERS, H.J. & FELDER, W.M. 1979. Litho-, Biostratigraphie und Palökologie der Oberkreide und des Alttertiärs (Präobersanton-Dan/Paläozän) von Aachen-Südlimburg (Niederlande, Deutschland, Belgien). *In*: WIEDMANN, J. (ed.) *Aspekte der Kreide Europas*. International Union of Geological Sciences, **A6**, 47–84.

ALEXANDROWICZ, S.W. 1974*a*. Opole Cretaceous. *In*: Guide to 46th Annual Meeting of the Geological Society of Poland, 29–38 [in Polish].

ALEXANDROWICZ, S.W. 1974*b*. Lithostratigraphical division of the Upper Cretaceous deposits of the Opole Basin. *Bulletin of the Polish Academy of Sciences, Series of the Geological and Geographical Sciences*, **21**(3/4), 187–198.

ALEXANDROWICZ, S.W. & RADWAN, D. 1973. Kreda opolska–problematyka stratygraficzna i złożowa. *Przegląd Geologiczny*, **4**, 183–188.

ALLEN, P.A., CRAMPTON, S.L. & SINCLAIR H.D. 1991. The inception and early evolution of the North Alpine Foreland Basin. *Basin Research*, **3**, 143–163.

ANDERSKOUV, K., DAMHOLT, T. & SURLYK, F. 2007. Late Maastrichtian chalk mounds, Stevns Klint, Denmark–combined physical and biogenic structures. *Sedimentary Geology*, **200**, 57–72.

ARNOLD, H. 1964. *Die Kreide Westfalens*. Fortschritte in der Geologie von Rheinland und Westfalen, **7**.

ARTHAUD, F. & MATTE, P. 1977. Late Paleozoic strike-slip faulting in southern Europe and northern Africa: Result of a right-lateral shear zone between the Appalachians and the Urals. *Geological Society of America Bulletin*, **88**, 1305–1320.

ASCH, K. 2004. *International Geological Map of Europe and Adjacent Areas*, scale 1: 5 000 000 (Andruck). Bundesanstalt für Geowissenschaften und Rohstoffe (Hrsg.), Hannover.

BAŁAZIŃSKA, J. & BOSSOWSKI, A. 1979. Deep geological structure of central and western parts of the North Sudetic Synclinorium; some new data. *Kwartalnik Geologiczny*, **23**(2), 309–335 [in Polish with Russian and English summary].

BALDSCHUHN, R. & JARITZ, W. 1977. Stratigraphie der Oberkreide in Nordwestdeutschland (Pompeckjsche Scholle). Korrelation der Bohrlochdiagramme und des Kernmaterials. *Geologisches Jahrbuch*, **A38**, 7–9.

BALDSCHUHN, R. & KOCKEL, F. 1996. *Geotektonischer Atlas von NW-Deutschland*. Bundesanstalt für Geowissenschaften und Rohstoffe 1–4, scale 1:300 000.

BALDSCHUHN, R. & KOCKEL, F. 1997*a*. *Geotektonischer Atlas von NW-Deutschland 1:100 000, Blatt Bielefeld C 3914*. Bundesanstalt für Geowissenschaften und Rohstoffe. Report **112 932**.

BALDSCHUHN, R. & KOCKEL, F. 1997*b*. Geotektonischer Atlas von NW-Deutschland 1:100 000, Blatt Rheine C 3910. *Bundesanstalt für Geowissenschaften und Rohstoffe, unpubl. report*, **112 932**.

BALDSCHUHN, R., FRISCH, U. & KOCKEL, F. 1985. Inversionsstrukturen in NW-Deutschland und ihre Genese. *Zeitschrift der Deutschen Geologischen Gesellschaft*, **136**, 129–139.

BALDSCHUHN, R., BEST, G. & KOCKEL, F. 1991. Inversion tectonics in the north-west German Basin. *In:* SPENCER, A.M. (ed.) *Generation, Accumulation and Production of Europe's Hydrocarbonates*. European Association of Petroleum Geoscientists **1**, University Press, Oxford, 149–159.

BALDSCHUHN, R., BINOT, F., FLEIG, S. & KOCKEL, F. 2001. Geotektonischer Atlas von Nordwest-Deutschland und dem deutschen Nordsee-Sektor. *Geologisches Jahrbuch*, **A153**, 1–88.

BATTEN, D.J., STREEL, M., DUSAR, M. & BLESS, M.J.M. 1987. Late Cretaceous palynomorphs from the boreholes Thermae 2002 (Valkenburg a/d Geul, The Netherlands) and 'sGravenvoeren (Belgium). *In*: BLESS, M.J.M., BOUCKAERT, J., LANGGUTH, H.R. & STREEL, M. (eds) Upper Cretaceous and Dinantian geology and hydrogeology of the Thermae boreholes of Valkenburg aan de Geul (South-Limburg, The Netherlands). *Annales de la Société géologique de Belgique*, **110**, 47–51.

BATTEN, D.J., DUPAGNE-KIEVITS, J. & LISTER, J.K. 1988. Palynology of the Upper Cretaceous Aachen Formation of northeast Belgium. *In*: STREEL, M. & BLESS, M.J.M. (eds) *The Chalk District of the Euregio Meuse-Rhine. Selected Papers on Upper Cretaceous Deposits*. Maastricht/Liège Natuurhistorisch Museum Maastricht/Université d'État, Liège, 95–103.

BAUMBERGER, E. & HEIM, A. 1907. Paläontologisch-stratigraphische Untersuchung zweier Fossilhorizonte an der Valangien-Hauterivien-Grenze im Churfirsten-Mattstockgebiet. *Abhandlungen schweizerische paläontologische Gesellschaft*, **34**, 6–33.

BERNOULLI, D. & WINKLER, W. 1990. Heavy mineral assemblages from Upper Cretaceous South- and Austroalpine flysch sequences (Northern Italy and Southern Switzerland): source terranes and palaeotectonic implications. *Eclogae Geologicae Helvetiae*, **83**, 287–310.

BERSEZIO, R. & FORNACIARI, M. 1994. Syntectonic Upper Cretaceous deep-water sequences of the Lombardy Basin (Southern Alps, Northern Italy). *Eclogae Geologciae Helvetiae*, **87**, 833–862.

BERTOTTI, G., PICOTTI, V., BERNOULLI, D. & CASTELLARIN, A. 1993. From rifting to drifting: tectonic evolution of the South-Alpine upper crust from the Triassic to the Early Cretaceous. *Sedimentary Geology*, **86**, 53–67.

BEST, G., ELSTNER, F. & KEMPER, E. 1989. Jüngere Unterkreide in der südlichen Nordsee und in Schleswig-Holstein. *Geologisches Jahrbuch*, **A113**, 317–336.

BETTENSTEDT, F. & DIETZ, C. 1957. Tektonische und erdölgeologische Untersuchungen im Raum Lehrte östlich Hannover. *Geologisches Jahrbuch*, **74**, 463–522.

BETZ, D., FÜHRER, F., GREINER, G. & PLEIN, E. 1987. Evolution of the Lower Saxony Basin. *Tectonophysics*, **13**, 127–170.

BIERNAT, S. 1960. Geological structure of the Opole Cretaceous (Upper Silesia). *Biuletyn Instytutu Geologicznego*, **152**, 172–241.

BIRKELUND, T. 1993. Ammonites from the Maastrichtian White Chalk of Denmark. *Bulletin of the Geological Society of Denmark*, **40**, 33–81.

BIRKENMAJER K. 1977. Jurassic and Cretaceous lithostratigraphic units of the Pieniny Klippen Belt, Carpathians, Poland. *Studia Geologica Polonica*, **45**, 159.

BISCHOFF, G. & MUTTERLOSE, J. 1998. Calcareous nannofossils of the Barremian/Aptian boundary interval in NW-Europe: biostratigraphic and palaeoecologic implications of a high resolution study. *Cretaceous Research*, **19,** 635–661.

BŁASZKIEWICZ, A. 1980. Campanian and Maastrichtian ammonites of the Middle Vistula River valley, Poland: a stratigraphic–paleontological study. *Prace Państwowego Instytutu Geologicznego*, **92**, 1–63.

BLESS, M.J.M. & FELDER, P.J. 1989. Note on the Late Cretaceous of Hockai (Hautes Fagnes, NE Belgium). *Annales de la Société géologique de Belgique*, **112**, 47–56.

BLESS, M.J.M. & FERNÁNDEZ NARVAIZA, M.C. 1993. Onder de Euregio–de verbinding tussen landschap en geologie in de Euregio Maas-Rijn. *Mémoires pour servir à l'explication des Cartes géologiques et minières de la Belgique,* **34**, 1–181.

BLESS, M.J.M. & FERNÁNDEZ NARVAIZA, M.C. 1996. Het veranderend landschap in de Euregio Maas-Rijn. *Annales de la Société géologique de Belgique,* **118**, 1–93.

BLESS, M.J.M., FELDER, P.J. & MEESSEN, J.P.M.T. 1987. Late Cretaceous sea level rise and inversion: their influence on the depositional environment between Aachen and Antwerp. *In*: BLESS, M.J.M., DUSAR, M. & STREEL, M. (eds) Some aspects of the Late Cretaceous in NW Europe. *Annales de la Société géologique de Belgique*, **109**, 333–355.

BLESS, M.J.M., FELDER, P.J. & JAGT, J.W.M. 1991*a*. Repeated Tethyan influences in the early Campanian to middle late Maastrichtian successions of Folx-les-Caves and Orp-le-Petit (eastern Brabant Massif, Belgium). *Annales de la Société géologique de Belgique,* **113**, 179–197.

BLESS, M.J.M., FELDER, P.J., JAGT, J.W.M. & REYNDERS, J.P.H. 1991*b*. The Hautes Fagnes area (NE Belgium) as a monadnock during the Late Cretaceous. *Annales de la Société géologique de Belgique,* **113,** 5–101.

BLESS, M.J.M., DUSAR, M., FELDER, P.J. & SWENNEN, R. 1993. Lithology and biostratigraphy of Upper Cretaceous-Paleocene carbonates in the Molenbeersel borehole (NE Belgium). *Geologie en Mijnbouw,* **71**, 239–257.

BODROGI, I., FOGARASI, A., YAZYKOVA, E.A., SZTANÓ, O. & BÁLDI-BEKE, M. 1998. Upper Cretaceous of the Bakony Mts. (Hungary), sedimentology, biostratigraphy, correlation. *Zentralblatt für Geologie und Paläontologie,* Teil **I**, 1179–1194.

BOLLI, H. 1945. Zur Stratigraphie der Oberen Kreide in den höheren helvetischen Decken. *Eclogae Geologicae Helvetiae,* **32**, 218–328.

Boorová, D., Lobitzer, H., Skupien, P. & Vašíček, Z. 1999. Biostratigraphy and facies of Upper Jurassic-Lower Cretaceous pelagic carbonate sediments (Oberalm-, Schrambach- and Roßfeld-Formation) in the Northern Calcareous Alps, south of Salzburg. *Abhandlungen der Geologischen Bundesanstalt*, **56**, 273–318.

Borza K. 1962. Petrographic investigation of pebbles of sedimentary rocks of Cretaceous and Paleogene conglomerates in the Brezová Mts and the Myjava Highlands. *Geologický Sborník SAV,* **13**, 241–256.

Borza K., Gašparíková V., Michalík J. & Vašíček Z. 1980. An Upper Jurassic – Lower Cretaceous sequence of the Krížna Nappe (Fatric), Strážovské Vrchy Mts. *Geologický zborník Geologica Carpathica.* **31**, 541–562.

Bossowski, A. & Bałazińska, J. 1982. Tectonic-structural evolution of the North-Sudetic Synclinorium. *Biuletyn Instytutu Geologicznego,* **341**, 163–167 [in Polish with Russian and English summary].

Bramwell, N.P., Caillet, G., Meciani, L., Judge, N., Green, M. & Adam, P. 1999. Chalk exploration, the search for a subtle trap. *In*: Fleet A.J. & Boldy S.A.R. (eds) *Petroleum Geology of Northwest Europe: Proceedings of the 5th Conference*. Geological Society, London, 911–937.

Brandmayr, M., Dallmeyer, R. D., Handler, R. & Wallbrecher, E. 1995. Conjugate shear zones in the Southern Bohemian Massif (Austria): implications for Variscan and Alpine tectonothermal activity. *Tectonophysics*, **248**, 97–116.

Brückner, W. & Petzka, M. 1967. Paläogeographie und Lagerungsverhältnisse von Alb und Oberkreide in Nordostmecklenburg (Raum Rügen-Usedom). *Berichte der Deutschen Gesellschaft für geologische Wissenschaften, A, Geologie Paläontologie*, **12**(5), 521–533.

Burger, H. 1986. Fazielle Entwicklung und paläogeographische Rekonstruktion des helvetischen Schelfs während der untersten Kreide in der Zentral- und Ostschweiz. *Eclogae Geologicae Helvetiae,* **79**, 561–615.

Burger, H. & Strasser, A. 1981. Lithostratigraphische Einheiten der untersten Helvetischen Kreide in der Zentral- und Ostschweiz. *Eclogae Geologicae Helvetiae,* **74**, 529–560.

Burgers, W.F.J. & Mulder, G.G. 1991. Aspects of the Late Jurassic and Cretaceous history of The Netherlands. *Geologie en Mijnbouw,* **70**, 347–354.

Burnett, J.A., Gallager, L.T. & Hampton, M.J. 1998. Upper Cretaceous. *In*: Bown, P.R. (ed.) *Calcareous Nannofossil Biostratigraphy.* Chapman and Hall, London, 132–199.

Butt, A. 1981. *Depositional environments of the Upper Cretaceous rocks in the Northern part of the Eastern Alps.* Cushman Foundation for Foraminiferal Research Special Publication, **20**.

Bystrická, H., Gašparíková, V., Köhler, E., Kysela, J., & Salaj, J. 1983. *Excursion Guide to the XVIII European Colloquium of Micropaleontology.* Konferencie, Symposia, Semin. Bratislava, 61–70.

Caron, M., Dösegger, R., Steiger, R. & Trümpy, R. 1982. Das Alter der jüngsten Sedimente der Ortler-Decke (Oberostalpin) in der Val Trupchun (Schweizer Nationalpark, Graubünden). *Eclogae Geologicae Helvetiae*, **75**, 159–169.

Carter, D.J. & Hart, M.B. 1977. Aspects of mid-Cretaceous stratigraphical micropaleontology. *Bulletin of the British Museum (Natural History)*, **29**, 1–135.

Čech, S. 1989. Upper Cretaceous Didymotis Events from Bohemia. *In:* Wiedmann, J. (ed.) *Cretaceous of the Western Tethys*. Proceedings of the 3rd International Cretaceous Symposium, Tübingen 1987. E. Schweizerbart, Stuttgart, 657–676.

Čech, S., Klein, V., Kříž, J. & Valečka, J. 1980. Revision of the Upper Cretaceous stratigraphy of the Bohemian Cretaceous Basin. *Věstník Ústředního Ústavu geologického*, **55**, 277–296.

Čech, S., Svobodová, M. & Bubík, M. 1996*a*. Transgressive mid-Cretaceous sediments of Eastern Bohemia (the Blansko Graben). *Abstract Volume.* 5th International Cretaceous Symposium, Freiberg, 15.

Čech, S., Hradecká, L., Laurin, J., Štaffen, Z., Švábenická, L. & Uličný, D. 1996*b*. Úpohlavy quarry: record of late Turonian sea-level oscillations and synsedimentary tectonic activity. *Stratigraphy and Facies of the Bohemian-Saxonian Cretaceous Basin.* Field Trip Guide, 5th International Cretaceous Symposium, Freiberg, 32–42.

Čech, S., Hradecká, L., Svobodová, M. & Švábenická, L. 2005. Cenomanian-Turonian boundary in the southern part of the Bohemian-Cretaceous Basin, Czech Republic. *Bulletin of Geosciences*, **80**, 321–354.

Channell, J. E. T, & Kozur, H. W. 1997. How many oceans? Meliata, Vardar, and Pindos oceans in the Mesozoic Alpine palaeogeography. *Geology,* **25**, 183–186.

Channell, J. E. T., Brandner, R., Spieler, A. & Stoner, J. 1992. Paleomagnetism and paleogeography of the Northern Calcareous Alps (Austria). *Tectonics*, **11**, 792–810.

Channell, J. E. T., Erba, E. & Lini, A. 1993. Magnetostratigraphic calibration of the Late Valanginian carbon isotope event in pelagic limestones from Northern Italy and Switzerland. *Earth and Planetary Science Letters*, **118,** 145–166.

Christensen, W.K. 1975. Upper Cretaceous belemnites from the Kristianstad area in Scania. *Fossils and Strata, 7*.

Christensen, W.K. 1986. *Upper Cretaceous belemnites from the Vomb Trough in Scania, Sweden.* Sveriges Geologiska Undersökning, Research Papers, **Ca 57**.

Christensen, W.K. 1993. Upper Cretaceous belemnitellids from the Båstad Basin, southern Sweden. *Geologiska Föreningens i Stockholm Förhandlingar*, **115**, 39–57.

Christensen, W.K. 1996. A review of the Upper Campanian and Maastrichtian belemnite stratigraphy of Europe. *Cretaceous Research,* **17**, 751–766.

Christensen, W.K. 2000. Gradualistic evolution in *Belemnitella* from the middle Campanian of Lower Saxony, NW Germany. *Bulletin of the Geological Society of Denmark*, **47**, 135–163.

Christensen, W.K. & Schmid, F. 1987. The belemnites of the Vaals Formation from the C.P.L. quarry at Hallembaye in Belgium–taxonomy, biometry and biostratigraphy. *Geologisches Jahrbuch,* A, **94**, 3–37.

Christensen, W.K. & Schulz, M.-G. 1997. Coniacian and Santonian belemnite faunas from Bornholm, Denmark. *Fossils and Strata*, **44**, 1–73.

Cieśliński, S. 1959. The Albian and Cenomanian in the northern periphery of the Holy Cross Mountains. *Prace Instytutu Geologicznego*, **28**, 71–95.

Cieśliński, S. 1976. Development of the Danish-Polish Trough in the Holy Cross region in the Albian, Cenomanian and Lower Turonian. *Biuletyn Instytutu Geologicznego*, **295**, 249–271.

Cieśliński, S. & Pożaryski, W. 1970. Cretaceous. The stratigraphy of the Mesozoic in the margin of the Holy Cross Mts. *Prace Instytutu Geologicznego*, **56**, 185–229.

Cloos, H. 1917. Tektonische Probleme am Nordrand des Harzes. *Geologische Rundschau*, **7**, 314–451.

Coubal, M. 1990. Compression along faults: example from the Bohemian Cretaceous Basin. *Mineralia Slovaca*, **22**, 139–144.

Császár, G. 2002. *Urgon formations in Hungary.* Geologica Hungarica, Series Geologica, **25**.

Császár, G. & Árgyelán, B.G. 1994. Stratigraphic and micromineralogic investigations on Cretaceous formations of the Gerecse Mountains, Hungary, and their palaeogeographic implications. *Cretaceous Research*, **15**, 417–434.

Čtyřoký, P. 1965. Margaritifera (Pseudounio) ? modelli n. sp., eine neue Najade aus der Oberkreide Südböhmens. *Archiv für Molluskenkunde*, **94**, 115–119.

Cymerman, Z. 2004. *Tectonic map of the Sudetes and the Fore-Sudetic Block, 1 : 200 000.* Państwowy Instytut Geologiczny, Warszawa.

Dacqué, E. 1939. Die Fauna der Regensburger-Keltheimer Oberkreide (mit Ausschluß der Spongien und Bryozoen). *Abhandlungen der Bayrischen Akademie der Wissenschaften, Neue Serie*, **45**, 1–218.

Dadlez, R., Narkiewicz, M., Stephenson, R.A., Visser, M.T.M. & van Wees, J.-D. 1995. Tectonic evolution of the Mid-Polish Trough: modelling implications and significance for central European geology. *Tectonophysics*, 252, 179–195.

Damholt, T. & Surlyk, F. 2004. Laminated-bioturbated cycles in Maastrichtian chalk of the North Sea: oxygenation fluctuations within the Milankovitch frequency band. *Sedimentology,* **51**, 1323–1342.

Darga, R. & Weidich, K.F. 1986. Die Lackbach-Schichten, eine klastische Unterkreide-Serie in der Unkener Mulde (Nördliche Kalkalpen, Tirolikum). *Mitteilungen der Bayerischen Staatssammlung für Paläontologie und historische Geologie*, **26**, 93–112.

De Batist, M. & Versteeg, W.H. 1999. Seismic stratigraphy of the

Mesozoic and Cenozoic in northern Belgium: main results of a high-resolution reflection seismic survey along rivers and canals. *Geologie en Mijnbouw,* **77**, 17–37.

Decker, K. 1990. Plate tectonics and pelagic facies: Late Jurassic to Early Cretaceous deep-sea sediments of the Ybbsitz ophiolite unit (Eastern Alps, Austria). *Sedimentary Geology*, **67**, 85–99.

Decker, K., Faupl, P. & Müller, A. 1987. Synorogenic sedimentation on the Northern Calcareous Alps during the Early Cretaceous. *In*: Flügel, H.W. & Faupl, P. (eds) *Geodynamics of the Eastern Alps*. Deuticke, Vienna, 126–141.

Deegan, C.E. & Scull, B.J. 1977. *A proposed standard lithostratigraphic nomenclature for the Central and Northern North Sea*. Report of the Institute of Geological Sciences, No. 77/25, Bulletin of the Norwegian Petroleum Directorate, No. 1.

Dhondt, A. 1984. Bivalves from the Hochmoos Formation (Gosau-Group), Oberösterreich, Austria. *Annalen des Naturhistorischen Museum Wien*, A, **88**, 41–102.

Diegel, F. 1973. *Zur Korrelation der helvetischen Zementsteinschichten zwischen Glärnisch und Alvier.* Mitteilungen aus dem Geologischen Institut, Swiss Federal Institute of Technology, University of Zürich, NF **166**.

Diener, I. 1966. *Stratigraphisches Korrelationsschema für die Kreide der Deutschen Demokratischen Republik. Abhandlungen des Zentralen Geologischen Instituts*, **5**.

Diener, I. 1967. Die Paläogeographie der Kreide im Nordteil der DDR in Beziehung zu den Nachbargebieten. *Berichte der deutschen Gesellschaft für Geowissenschaften (A: Geologie Paläontologie)*, **12**(3/4), 289–313.

Diener, I. 1968. Kreide. In: Z. G. Institut (ed) Grundriß der Geologie der Deutschen Demokratischen Republik. Band 1. Geologische Entwicklung des Gesamtgebietes, 320–342.

Diener, I. 1974. *Stratigraphie, Lithologie und Paläogeographie der Unterkreide in der DDR*. PhD dissertation, Ernst Moritz Arndt Universität Greifswald.

Diener, I. 2000*a*. 4.2 Mecklenburg-Vorpommern. 4.2.1 Unterkreide. *In:* Stratigraphische Kommission Deutschlands (ed.) *Stratigraphie von Deutschland III. Die Kreide der Bundesrepublik Deutschland.* Courier Forschungsinstitut Senckenberg, **226**, 69–73.

Diener, I. 2000*b*. 4.4 Altmark und Brandenburg. 4.4.1 Unterkreide. *In:* Stratigraphische Kommission Deutschlands (ed.) *Stratigraphie von Deutschland III. Die Kreide der Bundesrepublik Deutschland.* Courier Forschungsinstitut Senckenberg, **226**, 117–120.

Diener, I., Petzka, M., Reich, M., Rusbült, J. & Zagora, I. 2004*a*. 3.8.2 Oberkreide. *In:* Katzung, G. (ed.) *Geologie von Mecklenburg-Vorpommern*. E. Schweizerbart'sche Verlagsbuchhandlung, Stuttgart, 173–186.

Diener, I., Rusbült, J. & Reich, M. 2004*b*. 3.8.1 Unterkreide. *In:* Katzung, G. (ed.) *Geologie von Mecklenburg-Vorpommern*. E. Schweizerbart'sche Verlagsbuchhandlung, Stuttgart, 164–173.

Doglioni, C. & Bosellini, A. 1987. Eoalpine and mesoalpine tectonics in the Southern Alps. *Geologische Rundschau*, **76**, 735–754.

Döring, H. 1965. Die sporenpaläontologische Gliederung des Wealdens in Westmecklenburg (Struktur Werle). *Geologie*, Beihefte, **47,** 1–118.

Dumont, A.H. 1849. Rapport sur la carte géologique du royaume. *Bulletin de l'Académie royale des Sciences, des Lettres et des Beaux-Arts,* **16**, 351–373.

Dusar, M. & Lagrou, D. 2004. Lithostratigraphic reconstruction of the Cretaceous in the subsurface of northern Belgium. *In*: Jagt, J.W.M. & Schulp, A.S. (eds) *Meuse-Rhine Euregio Geologists Meeting, Natuurhistorisch Museum Maastricht, Maastricht (the Netherlands), 28–29 May 2004, Abstracts and programme*. Maastricht (Natuurhistorisch Museum Maastricht), 6–7.

Ebner, F. & Rantitsch, G. 2000. Das Gosaubecken von Kainach–ein Überblick. *Mitteilungen der Gesellschaft der Geologie- und Bergbaustudenten Österreichs*, **44**, 157–172.

Egger, H., Homayoun, M. & Schnabel, W. 2002. Tectonic and climatic control of Paleogene sedimentation in the Rhenodanubian Flysch Basin (Eastern Alps, Austria). *Sedimentary Geology,* **152**, 147–162.

Egger, H., Rögl, F. & Wagreich, M., 2004. Biostratigraphy and facies of Paleogene deep-water deposits at Gams (Gosau Group, Austria). *Annalen des Naturhistorischen Museum Wien*, **106A**, 281–307.

Egger, J. G. 1907. Mikrofauna der Kreideschichten des westlichen bayerischen Waldes und des Gebites um Regensburg. *Bericht des naturwissenschaftlichen Vereines in Passau*, **20**, 1–75.

Eisbacher, G. & Brandner, R. 1995. Role of high-angle faults during heteroaxial contraction, Inntal Thrust Sheet, Northern Calcareous Alps, western Austria. *Geologisch-Paläontologische Mitteilungen Innsbruck*, **20**, 389–406.

Elbert, J. 1901. Das untere Angoumien in den Osningbergketten des Teutoburger Waldes. Verhandlungen des naturhistorischen Vereins der preußischen Rheinlande, Westfalens und des Regierungsbezirks Osnabrück, **58**, 77–167.

Elstner, F. & Kemper, E. 1989. Die Gliederung der Schichtenfolge Ober-Apt /Unter-Cenoman in Bohrungen des Emslandes. *Geologisches Jahrbuch*, A, **113**, 51–71.

Elstner, F. & Mutterlose, J. 1996. The Lower Cretaceous (Berriasian and Valanginian) in NW Germany. *Cretaceous Research*, **17,** 119–133.

Erlström, M. & Gabrielson, J. 1992. *Petrology, fossil composition and depositional history of the Ignaberga limestone, Kristianstad Basin, Scania.* Sveriges Geologiska Undersökning, Research Papers, **Ca 80**.

Erlström, M. & Sivhed, U. 2001. *Intra-cratonic dextral transtension and inversion of the southern Kattegat on the southwest margin of Baltica–seismostratigraphy and structural development.* Sveriges Geologiska Undersökning, Research Papers, **C 832**.

Ernst, G. 1964. Ontogenie, Phylogenie und Stratigraphie der Belemnitengattung *Gonioteuthis* Bayle aus dem nordwestdeutschen Santon/Campan. *Fortschritte in der Geologie von Rheinland und Westfalen*, **7**, 113–174.

Ernst, G. 1968. Die Oberkreide-Aufschlüsse im Raume Braunschweig–Hannover und ihre stratigraphische Gliederung mit Echinodermaten und Belemniten, 1. Teil = Die jüngere Oberkreide (Santon–Maastricht). *Berichte der Naturhistorischen Gesellschaft Hannover, Beiheft*, **5**, 235–284.

Ernst, G. 1970. Faziesgebundenheit und Ökomorphologie bei irregulären Echiniden der nordwestdeutschen Oberkreide. *Paläontologische Zeitschrift*, **44**, 41–62.

Ernst, G. 1972. Grundfragen der Stammesgeschichte bei den irregulären Echiniden der nordwesteuropäischen Oberkreide. *Geologisches Jahrbuch*, A, **4**, 63–175.

Ernst, G. 1975. Die Santon-Transgrssion im Raume Misburg bei Hannover (Stratigraphie, Fauna und Sedimentologie). *Berichte der Naturhistorischen Gesellschaft Hannover*, **119**, 361–377.

Ernst, G. & Rehfeld, U. 1997. Transgressive development in the Early Cenomanian of the Salzgitter area (northern Germany) recorded by sea level controlled eco- and litho-events. *Freiberger Forschungshefte*, C, **468**, 79–107.

Ernst, G. & Schulz, M.-G. 1974. Stratigraphie und Fauna des Coniac und Santon im Schreibkreide-Richtprofil von Lägerdorf (Holstein). *Mitteilungen aus dem Geologisch-Paläontologischen Institut der Universität Hamburg*, **43**, 5–60.

Ernst, G. & Wood, C.J. 1995. Die tiefere Oberkreide des subherzynen Niedersachsens. Terra Nostra. Schriften der Alfred-Wegener-Stiftung, **5/95**, 41–84.

Ernst, G. & Wood, C.J. 2004. Alb /Cenoman vom Weddebach. *In:* Mutterlose, J. & Steffahn, J. (eds.) *Die Kreide des Subherzynen und östlichen Niedersächsischen Beckens*. Bochumer Geowissenschaftliche Arbeiten, **4**, 57–84.

Ernst, G., Schmid, F. & Seibertz, E. 1983. Event-Stratigraphie im Cenoman und Turon von NW-Deutschland. *Zitteliana*, **10**, 531–554.

Ernst, G., Wood, C. J. & Hilbrecht, H. 1984. The Cenomanian-Turonian boundary problem in NW-Germany with comments on the north-south correlation to the Regensburg Area. *Bulletin of the Geological Society of Denmark*, **33**, 103–113.

Ernst, G., Niebuhr, B., Wiese, F. & Wilmsen, M. 1996. Facies development, basin dynamics, event correlation and sedimentary cycles in the Upper Cretaceous of selected areas of Germany and Spain. *In:* Reitner, J., Neuweiler, F. & Gunkel, F. (eds.) *Global and Regional Controls on Biogenic Sedimentation. II. Cretaceous Sedimentation.* Research Reports, Göttinger Arbeiten zur Geologie und Paläontologie, **Sb3**, 87–100.

Ernst, G., Rehfeld, U. & Wood, C.J. 1997. Road cuttings near Vienenburg. *In:* Mutterlose, J., Wippich, M.G.E. & Geisen, M. (eds.) *Cretaceous Depositional Environments of NW Germany.* Bochumer Geologische und Geotechnische Arbeiten, **46**, 29–34.

ESCHER, V.D. LINTH, A. 1853. *Geologische Bemerkungen über das nördliche Vorarlberg und einige angrenzende Gegenden Neue Denkschriften der allgemeinen schweizerischen Gesellschaft für die gesamten Naturwissenschaften*, **13**, 1–136.

EUGENO-S Working Group. 1988. Crustal structure and tectonic evolution of the transition between the Baltic Shield and the North German Caledonides (the EUGENO-S Project). *Tectonophysics*, **150**, 253–348.

EYNATTEN, H. VON & GAUPP, R. 1999. Provenance of Cretaceous synorogenic sandstones in the Eastern Alps: constraints from framework petrography, heavy mineral analysis and mineral chemistry. *Sedimentary Geology*, **124**, 81–111.

FAHRION, H. 1984. Zur Verbreitung und Fazies des Maastricht in Nordwestdeutschland. *Zeitschrift der Deutschen Geologischen Gesellschaft*, **135**, 573–583.

FALCON-LANG, H.J., KVAČEK, J. & ULIČNÝ, D. 2001. Fire-prone plant communities and palaeoclimate of a Late Cretaceous fluvial to estuarine environment, Pecínov quarry, Czech Republic. *Geological Magazine*, **138**, 563–576.

FARMER, C.L. & BARKVED, O.I. 1999. Influence of syndepositional faulting on thickness variations in chalk reservoirs–Valhall and Hod fields. In: FLEET A.J. & BOLDY S.A.R. (eds) *Petroleum Geology of Northwest Europe: Proceedings of the 5th Conference*. Geological Society, London, 949–957.

FAUPL, P. 1983. Die Flyschfazies in der Gosau der Weyerer Bögen (Oberkreide, Nördliche Kalkalpen, Osterreich). *Jahrbuch der Geologischen Bundesanstalt*, **126**, 219–244.

FAUPL, P. & TOLLMANN, A. 1979. Die Roßfeldschichten: Ein Beispiel für Sedimentation im Bereich einer tektonisch aktiven Tiefseerinne aus der kalkalpinen Unterkreide. *Geologische Rundschau*, **68**, 93–120.

FAUPL, P. & WAGREICH, M. 1992*a*. Cretaceous flysch and pelagic sequences of the Eastern Alps: Correlations, heavy minerals, and palaeogeographic implications. *Cretaceous Research*, **13**, 387–403.

FAUPL, P. & WAGREICH, M. 1992*b*. Transgressive Gosau (Coniac) auf Branderfleckschichten (Turon) in den Weyerer Bögen (Nördliche Kalkalpen, Oberösterreich). *Jahrbuch der Geologischen Bundesanstalt*, **135**, 481–491.

FAUPL, P. & WAGREICH, M. 2000. Late Jurassic to Eocene palaeogeography and geodynamic evolution of the Eastern Alps. *Mitteilungen der Österreichischen. Geologischen Gesellschaft*, **92**, 79–94.

FAUPL, P., CSÁSZÁR, G. & MIŠÍK, M. 1997. Cretaceous and Palaeogene sedimentary evolution in the Eastern Alps, Western Carapathians and the North Pannonian region: An overview. *Acta Geologica Hungarica*, **40**, 273–305.

FAY, M. 1983. Sedimentologie und Paläogeographie der tieferen Oberkreide in Ostbayern. *Berliner Geowissenschaftliche Abhandlungen*, A, **49**, 1–57.

FELDER, P.J. 1995. *Bioklasten-onderzoek van Boven-Krijt en Dano-Montiaan afzettingen uit boringen in de Belgische Kempen*. Belgische Geologische Dienst, Professional Paper, **8**.

FELDER, P.J. 1996. Late Cretaceous (Santonian-Maastrichtian) sedimentation rates in the Maastricht (NL), Liège/Campine (B) and Aachen (D) area. *Annales de la Société géologique de Belgique*, **117**, 311–319.

FELDER, P.J. 2001. Bioklasten-stratigrafie of ecozonatie voor het krijt [*sic*] (Santoniaan-Campaniaan-Maastrichtiaan) van Zuid-Limburg en oostelijk België. *Memoirs of the Geological Survey of Belgium*, **47**, 1–141.

FELDER, P.J. 2003. Tektonische bewegingen in Limburg tijdens en na het Krijt–Deel 1. *Sprekende Bodem (Mededelingen van de Afdeling Limburg der Nederlandse Geologische Vereniging)*, **47**, 87–99.

FELDER, P.J. & BLESS, M.J.M. 1989. Biostratigraphy and ecostratigraphy of Late Cretaceous deposits in the Kunrade area (South-Limburg, SE Netherlands). *Annales de la Société géologique de Belgique*, **112**, 31–45.

FELDER, P.J. & BLESS, M.J.M. 1994. The Vijlen Chalk (early Early to early Late Maastrichtian) in its type area around Vijlen and Mamelis (southern Limburg, The Netherlands). *Annales de la Société géologique de Belgique*, **116**, 61–85.

FELDER, P.J., BLESS, M.J.M., DEMYTTENAERE, R., DUSAR, M., MEESSEN, J.P.M.T. & ROBASZYNSKI, F. 1985. *Upper Cretaceous to early Tertiary deposits (Santonian-Paleocene) in northeastern Belgium and South Limburg (The Netherlands) with reference to the Campanian-Maastrichtian*. Belgische Geologische Dienst, Professional Paper, **1**.

FELDER, P.J., KEPPENS, E., DECLERCQ, B., NORMAND, S. & STREEL, M. 2003. Faunal/floral and isotope responses to Milankovitch precession cycles and environmental changes in the upper Gulpen Formation (Upper Maastrichtian) at the CBR-Lixhe and ENCI-Maastricht bv quarries. *Netherlands Journal of Geosciences*, **82**, 275–281.

FELDER, W.M. 1975. Lithostratigrafie van het Boven-Krijt en het Dano-Montien in Zuid-Limburg en het aangrenzende gebied. *In*: ZAGWIJN, W.H. & VAN STAALDUINEN, C.J. (eds) *Toelichting bij geologische overzichtskaarten van Nederland*. Rijks Geologische Dienst, Haarlem, 63–72.

FELDER, W.M. 1996. Historical overview of lithostratigraphic research on the Upper Cretaceous of southern Limburg, the Netherlands. *Geologie en Mijnbouw*, **74**, 287–300.

FELDER, W.M. & BOSCH, P.W. 2001. *Geologie van Nederland, deel 5. Krijt van Zuid-Limburg*. NITG TNO, Delft/Utrecht.

FENNER, J. 2001. The Kirchrode I and II boreholes: technical details and evidence on tectonics, and the palaeogeographic development during the Albian. *Palaeogeography, Palaeoclimatology, Palaeoecology*, **174**, 33–65.

FERRAZZINI, B. & SCHULER, P. 1979. Eine Abwicklungskarte des Helvetikum zwischen Rhone und Reuss. *Eclogae Geologicae Helvetiae*, **72**, 439–454.

FINGER, W. 1978. *Die Zone von Samaden (Unterostalpine Decken, Graubünden) und ihre jurassischen Brekzien*. Mitteilungen des geologischen Instituts ETH Zürich, Neue Folge **224**.

FÖLLMI, K.B. 1986. *Die Garschella- und Seewerkalk-Formation (Aptian-Santonian) im Vorarlberger Helvetikum und Ultrahelvetikum*. PhD thesis, Swiss Federal Institute of Technology, Zürich, No. **8100**.

FÖLLMI, K.B. 1989. Evolution of the mid-Cretaceous triad: platform carbonates, phosphatic sediments and pelagic carbonates along the Northern Tethyan margin. *Lecture Notes in Earth Sciences*, **23**, 1–157.

FÖLLMI, K.B. & OUWEHAND, P. 1987. Garschella-Formation und Götzis-Schichten (Aptian-Coniacian)–Neue stratigraphische Daten aus dem Helvetikum der Ostschweiz und des Vorarlbergs. *Eclogae Geologicae Helvetiae*, **80**, 141–191.

FÖLLMI, K.B., WEISSERT, H., BISPING, M. & FUNK, H. 1994. Phosphogenesis, carbon-isotope stratigraphy, and carbonate-platform evolution along the Lower Cretaceous northern Tethyan margin. *Geological Society of America Bulletin*, **106**, 729–746.

FÖRSTER, R., MEYER, R. K. F. & RISCH, H. 1983. Ammoniten und planktonische Foraminiferen aus den Eibrunner Mergeln (Regensburger Kreide, Nordostbayern). *Zitteliana*, **10**, 123–141.

FÖRSTER, R., MEYER, R. K. F. & RISCH, H. 1984. Das Alter der Eibrunner Mergel im Autobahneinschnitt am Benberg nördlich Regensburg, NE Bayern. *Schriftreihe der Erdwissenschaftlichen Kommissionen*, **7**, 263–270.

FRENZEL, P. 2000. Die benthischen Foraminiferen der Rügener Schreibkreide (Unter-Maastricht, NE-Deutschland). *Neue Paläontologische Abhandlungen* **3**, 1–361.

FRIEG, C., KEMPER, E. & BALDSCHUHN, R. 1989*a*. Mikropaläontologische Gliederung und Abgrenzung von Ober-Alb und Unter-Cenoman in Nordwestdeutschland. *Geologisches Jahrbuch*, A, **113**, 73–193.

FRIEG, C., HISS, M. & MÜLLER, W. 1989*b*. Stratigraphie im Turon und Unterconiac des südlichen und zentralen Münsterlandes. *Münstersche Forschung zur Geologie und Paläontologie*, **69**, 161–186.

FRIEG, C., HISS, M. & KAEVER, M. 1990. Alb und Cenoman im zentralen und südlichen Münsterland (NW-Deutschland) Stratigraphie, Fazies, Paläogeographie. *Neues Jahrbuch für Geologie und Paläontologie, Abhandlungen*, **181**, 325–363.

FRIIS, E.M. & SKARBY, A. 1981. Structurally preserved angiosperm flowers from the Upper Cretaceous of southern Sweden. *Nature*, **291**, 484–486.

FRISCH, W. 1979. Tectonic progradation and plate tectonic evolution of the Alps. *Tectonophysics*, **60**, 121–139.

FRISCH, W., KUHLEMANN, J., DUNKL, I. & BRÜGEL, A. 1998. Palinspastic reconstruction and topographic evolution of the Eastern Alps during late Tertiary tectonic extrusion. *Tectonophysics*, **297**, 1–15.

FROITZHEIM, N., PLAŠIENKA, D. SCHUSTER, R. 2008. Alpine tectonics of the Alps and Western Carpathians. *In*: MCCANN, T. (ed.) *The*

*Geology of Central Europe. Volume 2: Mesozoic and Cenozoic.* Geological Society, London. 1141–1232.

Fuchs, R., Wessely, G. & Schreiber, O. S. 1984. Die Mittel- und Oberkreide des Molasseuntergrundes am Südsporn der Böhmischen Masse. *Schriftreihe der Erdwissenschaftlichen Kommissionen*, **7**, 193–220.

Füchtbauer, H. 1955. Zur Petrographie des Bentheimer Sandsteins im Emsland. *Erdöl und Kohle*, **8,** 616–617.

Funk, H. 1969. Typusprofile der helvetischen Kieselkalk Formation und der Altmann-Schichten. *Eclogae Geologicae Helvetiae,* **62**, 191–203.

Funk, H. 1971. Zur Stratigraphie und Lithologie des Helvetischen Kieselkalkes und der Altmannschichten in der Säntis-Churfirsten-Gruppe (Nordostschweiz). *Eclogae Geologicae Helvetiae,* **64**, 345–433.

Funk, H. 1975. The origin of authigenic quartz in the Helvetic Siliceous Limestone (Helvetischer Kieselkalk), Switzerland. *Sedimentology,* **22**, 299–306.

Funk, H. 1985. Mesozoische Subsidenzgeschichte im Helvetischen Schelf der Ostschweiz. *Eclogae Geologicae Helvetiae,* **78**, 249–272.

Funk, H. 1990. The „Urgonian" platform in the northwestern Tethys. *In:* Rakus, M., Dercourt, J. & Nairn A.E.M. (eds) *Evolution of the Northern Tethys Margin – The Results of IGCP Project 198*, Mémoire Societé Géologique de. France, N.S. **154**, 159–168.

Funk, H., Föllmi, K.B. & Mohr, H. 1993. Evolution of the Tithonian-Aptian Carbonate Platform Along the Northern Tethyan Margin, Eastern Helvetic Alps. *In:* Simo, T., Scott, R.W. & Masse, J.P. (eds) *Cretaceous Carbonate Platforms.* American Association of Petroleum Geologists Memoir, **56**, 387–407.

Gale, A.S. 1995. Cyclostratigraphy and correlation of the Cenomanian stage in Western Europe. *In:* House, M.R. & Gale, A.S. (eds) *Orbital Forcing Timescales and Cyclostratigraphy.* Geological Society, London, Special Publications, **85**, 177–197.

Gale, A.S., Young, J.A., Shackleton, N.J., Crowhurst, S.J. & Wray, D.S. 1999. Orbital tuning of Cenomanian marly chalk successions: towards a Milankovitch time-scale for the Late Cretaceous. *Philosophical Transactions of the Royal Society London*, Series A, **357**, 1815–1829.

Gale, A.S., Smith, A.B., Monks, N.E.A., Young, J.A., Howard, A., Wray, D.S. & Huggett, J.M. 2000. Marine biodiversity through the Late Cenomanian–Early Turonian: Palaeoceanographic controls and sequence stratigraphic biases. *Journal of the Geological Society,* **157**, 745–757.

Gall, H., Müller, D. & Yamani, A. 1973. Zur Stratigraphie und Paläogeographie der Cenoman-Ablagerungen auf der südwestlichen Frankenalb (Bayern). *Neues Jahrbuch für Geologie und Paläontologie, Abhandlungen*, **143**, 1–22.

Gasinski, A., Slaczka, A. & Winkler, W. 1997. Tectono-sedimentary evolution of the Upper Prealpine nappe (Switzerland and France): nappe formation by Late Cretaceous-Paleogene accretion. *Geodinamica Acta*, **10**, 137–157.

Gaupp, R. 1982. Sedimentationsgeschichte und Paläotektonik der kalkalpinen Mittelkreide (Allgäu, Tirol, Vorarlberg). *Zitteliana*, **8**, 33–72.

Gaździcka, E. 1978. Calcareous nannoplankton from the uppermost Cretaceous and Paleogene deposits of the Lublin Upland. *Acta Geologica Polonica*, **28**, 335–275.

Gebhard, G. 1985. Kondensiertes Apt und Alb im Helvetikum (Allgäu und Vorarlberg)–Biostratigraphie und Fauneninhalt. *In:* Kollmann, H. (ed.) *Beiträge zur Stratigraphie und Paläogeographie der mittleren Kreide Zentraleuropas.* Österreichische Akademie der Wissenschaften, Schriftenreihe Erdwissenschaftliche Publikationen, **7**, 94–114.

Geinitz, H.-B. 1871–75. Das Elbthalgebirge in Sachsen. *Paläontographica*, **20,** 1–319.

Geluk, M. 1990. The Cenozoic Roer Valley Graben, southern Netherlands. *Mededelingen van de Rijks Geologische Dienst,* **44**, 65–72.

Geluk, M., Duin, E.J.T., Dusar, M., Rijkers, R.H.B., van den Berg, M.W. & van Rooijen, P. 1994. Stratigraphy and tectonics of the Roer Valley Graben. *In:* van Eck, T. & Davenport, C.A. (eds) Seismotectonics and seismic hazard in the Roer Valley Graben; with emphasis on the Roermond earthquake of April 13, 1992. *Geologie en Mijnbouw,* **73**, 129–141.

Glaessner, M. F. 1931. Geologische Studien in der äußeren Klippenzone. *Jahrbuch der Geologischen Bundes-Anstalt*, **81**, 1–23.

Gothan, W. 1941. Über eine kleine Oberkreide-Flora von Friedensreuth bei Neusadt a.d. Waldnaab (Oberpf.). *Jahresberichte der Preußischen Geologischen Landes-Anstalt*, **60**, 240–247.

Gradstein, F., Ogg, J. & Smith, A. 2004. *A Geologic Time Scale.* Cambridge University Press, Cambridge.

Gras, R. 1995. Late Cretaceous sedimentation and tectonic inversion, southern Netherlands. *Geologie en Mijnbouw,* **74**, 117–127.

Gras, R. & Geluk, M. 1999. Late Cretaceous–Early Tertiary sedimentation and tectonic inversion in the southern Netherlands. *Geologie en Mijnbouw,* **78**, 1–19.

Grasmück-Pfluger, M. 1962. Mikrofazielle Beobachtungen an den Öhrlischichten (Berriasian) der Typlokalität. *Eclogae Geologicae Helvetiae,* **55**, 417–442.

Gravesen, P., Rolle, F. & Surlyk, F. 1982. Lithostratigraphy and Sedimentary evolution of the Triassic, Jurassic and Lower Cretaceous of Bornholm, Denmark. *Geological Survey of Denmark Series B*, **7**, 1–51.

Greber, E.A. & Ouwehand, P.J. 1988. Spaltenfüllungen im Dach der Schrattenkalk-Formation. *Eclogae Geologicae Helvetiae,* **81**, 373–385.

Gudden, H. 1984. Zur Entstehung der nordostbayrischen Kreide-Eisenerzlagerstätten. *Geologisches Jahrbuch, D*, **66**, 3–49.

Gümbel, C. W. 1861. *Geognostische Beschreibung des bayerischen Alpengebirges und seines Vorlandes.* Gotha (Justus Perthes).

Günzler-Seiffert, H. 1952. Alte Brüche im Kreide-Tertiär-Anteil der Wildhorndecke zwischen Rhone und Rhein. *Geologische Rundschau,* **40**, 211–239.

Gutowski, J., Krzywiec, P., Walaszczyk, I. & Pożaryski, W. 2003. Od ekstensji do inwersji–zapis aktywności północno-wschodniej brzeżnej strefy uskokowej świętokrzyskiego segmentu bruzdy duńsko-polskiej w osadach jury górnej i kredy na podstawie interpretacji danych sejsmiki refleksyjnej. *Tomy Jurajskie*, **1**, 124–125.

Gygi, R.A. & Persoz, F. 1986. Mineralostratigraphy, litho- and biostratigraphy combined in correlation of the Oxfordian (Late Jurassic) formations of the Swiss Jura range. *Eclogae Geologicae Helvetiae,* **79**, 385–454.

Haas, J. 1999. Genesis of Late Cretaceous toe-of-slope breccias in the Bakony Mts, Hungary. *Sedimentary Geology,* **128**, 51–66.

Håkansson, E., Bromley, E.G. & Perch-Nielsen, K. 1974. Maastrichtian chalk from North West Europe–a pelagic shelf sediment. *In*: Hsü, K. & Jenkyns, H.C. (eds.) *Pelagic Sediments on Land and Under The Sea.* International Association of Sedimentologists, Special Publications, **1**, 211–233.

Hakenberg, M. & Świdrowska, J. 1998. Evolution of the Holy Cross segment of the Mid-Polish Trough during the Cretaceous. *Geological Quarterly,* **42**(3), 239–262.

Haldimann, P. 1977. *Sedimentologische Entwicklung der Schichten an einer Zyklengrenze der Helvetischen Unterkreide: Pygurus-Schichten und Gemsmättli-Schicht (Valanginian/Hauterivian) zwischen Thunersee und St. Galler Rheintal.* Mitteilungen aus dem Geologischen Institut, Swiss Federal Institute of Technology, University of Zürich, NF **219**.

Hambach, U. & Krumsiek, K. 1991. Magnetostratigraphie im Santon und Campan des Münsterländer Kreidebeckens (NW-Deutschland). *Facies*, **24**, 113–124.

Häntzschel, W. 1933. Das Cenoman und die Plenus-Zone der sudetischen Kreide. *Abhandlungen der Preußischen Geologischen Landesanstalt, Neue Folge*, **150**, 1–161.

Hancock, J. M. 1975. The petrology of the Chalk. *Proceedings of the Geologists' Association*, **86**, 499–535.

Hancock, J.M. 1993. The formation and diagenesis of chalk. *In*: Downing, R.A., Price, M. & Jones, G.P. (eds) *The Hydrogeology of the Chalk of North-west Europe*. Oxford University Press, Oxford, 14–34.

Hancock, J.M. & Kauffman, E.G. 1979. The great transgressions of the Late Cretaceous. *Journal of the Geological Society of London*, **136**, 175–186.

Hansen, D.L., Nielsen, S.B. & Lykke-Andersen, H. 2000. The post-Triassic evolution of the Sorgenfrei-Tornquist Zone–results from thermo-mechanical modelling. *Tectonophysics*, **328**, 245–267.

Haq, B. U., Hardenbol, J. & Vail, P. R. 1988. Mesozoic and Cenozoic chronostratigraphy and cycles of sea-level change. *In:* Wilgus, C. K., Hastings, B. S., Kendall, C. S., Posamentier, H. W., Ross,

C. A. & Van Wagoner, J. C. (eds) *Sea-Level Changes: An Integrated Approach.* SEPM, Tulsa, Special Publications, **42**, 71–108.

Hardenbol, J., Thierry, J., Farley, M.B., Jacquin, T., De Graciansky, P.-C. & Vail, P.R. 1998. Mesozoic and Cenozoic sequence chronostratigraphic framework of European basins. *In:* De Graciansky, P.-C., Hardenbol, J., Jacquin, T. & Vail, P.R. (eds) *Mesozoic and Cenozoic Sequence Stratigraphy of European Basins.* SEPM, Special Publications, **60**, chart 5.

Haubold, H., Scholger, R., Frisch, W., Summesberger, H. & Mauritsch, H.J. 1999. Reconstruction of the geodynamic evolution of the Northern Calcareous Alps by means of paleomagnetism. *Physics and Chemistry of the Earth,* A, **24**, 697–703.

Hauschke, N., Hiss, M. & Wippich, M.G.E. 1999. Untercampan und tiefes Obercampan im Westteil der Baumberge (Münsterland, Nordwestdeutschland). *Scriptum*, **4**, 35–69.

Hays, J. D. & Pitman, W. C. 1973. Lithospheric plate motion, sea level changes and climatic and ecological consequences. *Nature*, **246,** 18–22.

Heim, A. 1916. *Monographie der Churfirsten-Mattstockgruppe*. Beiträge zur geologischen Karte der Schweiz, [NF] **20**.

Heinz, R. 1926. Beitrag zur Kenntnis der Stratigraphie und Tektonik der oberen Kreide Lüneburgs. *Mitteilungen aus dem Mineralogisch-Geologischen Staatsinstitut in Hamburg*, **8**, 1–109.

Herb, R. 1988. Eocaene Paläogeographie und Paläotektonik des Helvetikums. *Eclogae Geologicae Helvetiae,* **81**, 611–657.

Herčík, F., Herrmann, Z. & Valečka, J. 2003. *Hydrogeology of the Bohemian Cretaceous Basin*. Czech Geological Survey.

Herm, D., von Hillebrandt, A. & Perch-Nielsen, K. 1981. Die Kreide/Tertiärgrenze im Lattengebirge (Nördliche Kalkalpen) in mikropaläontologischer Sicht. *Geologica Bavarica*, **82**, 319–344.

Herman, A. B., Spicer, R. A. & Kvacek, J. 2002. Late Cretaceous climate of Eurasia and Alaska: A quantitative approach. *In*: Wagreich, M. (ed.) *Aspects of Cretaceous Stratigraphy and Palaeobiogeography.* Schriftenreihe der Erdwissenschaftlichen Kommission, **15**, 93–108.

Herngreen, G. F. W., Hartkopf-Fröder, C. & Ruegg, G. A. J. 1994. Age and depositional environment of the Kuhfeld Beds (Lower Cretaceous) in the Alstätte Embayment (W-Germany, E-Netherlands). *Geologie en Mijnbouw,* **72,** 375–391.

Herrig, E. 1966. Ostracoden aus der Weißen Schreibkreide (Unter-Maastricht) der Insel Rügen. *Paläontologische Abhandlungen (A: Paläozoologie)*, **2**(4), 693–1024.

Herrig, E., Nestler, H., Frenzel, P., Reich, M. 1996. Discontinuity surfaces in the high Upper Cretaceous of northeastern Germany and their reflection by fossil associations. *In:* Reitner, J., Neuweiler, F. & Gunkel, F. (eds) *Global and Regional Controls on Biogenic Sedimentation. II. Cretaceous Sedimentation.* Göttinger Arbeiten zur Geologie und Paläontologie, Research Reports, **Sb3**, 107–111.

Hesse, R. 1982. Cretaceous-Paleogene flysch zone of the East Alps and Carpathinas: Identification and plate tectonic significance of "dormant" and "active" deep-sea trenches in the Alpine-Carpathian arc. *In*: Legget, J.K. (ed) *Trench-Forearc Geology.* Geological Society, London, Special Publications, 471–494.

Hesse, R. & Butt, A. 1976. Paleobathymetry of Cretaceous turbidite basins of the East Alps relative to the calcite compensation level. *Journal of Geology,* **84**, 505–533.

Hilbrecht, H. 1986*a*. *Der Cenoman/Turon-Grenzbereich bei Hannover, in NW-Westfalen und im Regensburger Raum. – Stratigraphie, Sedimentologie, Geochemie*. Diplom-Arbeit thesis, Freie Universität Berlin.

Hilbrecht, H. 1986*b*. Die Turon-Basis im Regensburger Raum: Inoceramen, Foraminiferen und 'events' der Eibrunner Mergel bei bei Bad Abbach. *Neues Jahrbuch für Geologie und Paläontologie, Abhandlungen*, **172**, 71–82.

Hilbrecht, H. & Dahmer, D.-D. 1994. Sediment dynamics during the Cenomanian-Turonian (Cretaceous) Oceanic Anoxic Event in northwestern Germany. *Facies*, **30**, 63–84.

Hilbrecht, H., Frieg, C., Tröger, K.-A., Voigt, S. & Voigt, T. 1996. Shallow water facies during the Cenomanian-Turonian anoxic event: bio-events, isotopes, and sea level in southern Germany. *Cretaceous Research*, **17**, 229–253.

Hinze, C. 1988. *Erläuterungen zum Blatt 3608 (Bad Bentheim).* Niedersächsisches Landesamt für Bodenforschung Hannover Geologische Karte von Niedersachsen, Map 3608, scale 1:25000.

Hiss, M. 1982*a*. Ammoniten des Cenomans vom Südrand der westfälischen Kreide zwischen Unna und Möhnsee. *Paläontologische Zeitschrift*, **56**(3/4), 177–208.

Hiss, M. 1982*b*. Lithostratigraphie der Kreide-Basisschichten (Cenoman-Unterturon) am Haarstrang zwischen Unna und Möhnsee (südöstliches Münsterland). *Münstersche Forschungen zur Geologie und Paläontologie*, **57**, 59–135.

Hiss, M. 1982*c*. Neue Ergebnisse zur Paläogeographie des Cenomans in Westfalen. *Neues Jahrbuch für Geologie und Paläontologie, Monatshefte*, **9**, 533–546.

Hiss, M. 1983. Biostratigraphie der Kreide-Basisschichten am Haarstrang (SE-Westfalen) zwischen Unna und Möhnsee. *Zitteliana*, **10**, 43–54.

Hiss, M. 1985. Faziesanalyse der Cenoman-Sedimente am Haarstrang zwischen Unna und Möhnsee. *Münstersche Forschungen zur Geologie und Paläontologie*, **63**, 109–170.

Hiss, M. 1995. Erläuterungen zu Blatt 3808 Heek. *Geologische Karte von Nordrhein-Westfalen 1:25 000.*

Hiss, M. & Seibertz, E. 2000. 4.7 Westfalen, Münsterland. *In:* Stratigraphische Kommission Deutschlands (ed.) *Stratigraphie von Deutschland III. Die Kreide der Bundesrepublik Deutschland.* Courier Forschungsinstitut Senckenberg **226**, 132–138.

Hiss, M. & Speetzen, E. 1986. Transgressionssedimente des Mittel- bis Oberalb am SE-Rand der Westfälischen Kreidemulde (NW-Deutschland). *Neues Jahrbuch für Geologie und Paläontologie, Monatshefte*, **11**, 648–670.

Hiss, M., Mutterlose, J., Niebuhr, B. &. Schwerd, K. 2005. Die Kreide in der Stratigraphischen Tabelle von Deutschland 2002. *Newsletters on Stratigraphy,* **41**(1/3), 287–306.

Höfling, R. 1985. Faziesverteilung und Fossilvergesellschaftungen im karbonatischen Flachwasser-Milieu der alpinen Oberkreide (Gosau-Formation). *Münchner Geowissenschaftliche Abhandlungen*, A, **3**, 1–206.

Homayoun, M. & Faupl, P. 1992. Unter- und Mittelkreideflysch der Ybbsitzer Klippenzone (Niederösterreich). *Mitteilungen der Gesellschaft der Geologie- und Bergbaustudenten Österreichs*, **38**, 1–20.

Horna, F. 1997. Die Cenomantransgression von Langenstein: Alter und eventstratigraphische Position. *Neues Jahrbuch für Geologie und Paläontologie, Abhandlungen*, **203** (1), 47–56.

Hu, X., Jansa, L., Wang, C., Sarti, M., Bak, K., Wagreich, M., Michalik, J. & Soták, J., 2005. Upper Cretaceous oceanic red beds (CORBs) in the Tethys: occurrences, lithofacies, age, and environments. *Cretaceous Research*, **26**, 3–20.

Ineson, J.R., Surlyk, F. & Stemmerik, L. 2005. Chalk. *In*: Selley, R.C., Cocks L. R. M. & Plimer, I. R. (eds.) *Encyclopedia of Geology.* Elsevier, Oxford, Vol. 5, 42–50.

Isaksen, D. & Tonstad, K. 1989. *A revised Cretaceous and Tertiary lithostratigraphic nomenclature for the Norwegian North Sea.* Bulletin of the Norwegian Petroleum Directorate, No. **5**.

Jacquin, T., & de Graciansky, P.-C. 1998. Major transgressive/regressive cycles: the stratigraphic signature of European basin development. *In*: de Graciansky, P.-C., Hardenbol, J., Jacquin, T. & Vail, P. R. (eds) Mesozoic and Cenozoic Sequence Stratigraphy of European Basins. SEPM, Special Publications, **60**, 15–29.

Jagt, J.W.M. 1989. Ammonites from the early Campanian Vaals Formation at the CPL quarry (Haccourt, Liège, Belgium) and their stratigraphic implications. *Mededelingen van de Rijks Geologische Dienst,* **43**, 1–33.

Jagt, J.W.M. 1999. Late Cretaceous-Early Palaeogene echinoderms and the K/T boundary in the southeast Netherlands and northeast Belgium–Part 1: Introduction and stratigraphy. *Scripta Geologica,* **116**, 1–57.

Jagt, J.W.M., Felder, P.J. & Meessen, J.P.M.T. 1987. Het Boven-Campanien in Zuid-Limburg (Nederland) en Noordoost-België. *Natuurhistorisch Maandblad,* **76**, 94–110.

Jagt, J.W.M., Burnett, J. & Kennedy, W.J. 1995*a*. Campanian ammonites and nannofossils from southern Limburg, the Netherlands. *Mededelingen van de Rijks Geologische Dienst,* **53**, 49–63.

Jagt, J.W.M., Kennedy, W.J., Burnett, J.A., Christensen, W.K. & Dhondt, A.V. 1995*b*. Santonian macrofauna and nannofossils from northeast Belgium. *Bulletin de l'Institut royal des Sciences naturelles de Belgique, Sciences de la Terre,* **65**, 127–137.

Jarvis, I., Gale, A. S., Jenkyns, H. C. & Pearce, M. 2006. Secular variation in Late Cretaceous carbon isotopes; a new $\delta^{13}C$ carbonate reference curve for the Cenomanian–Campanian (99.6–70.6 Ma). *Geological Magazine*, **143**, 561–608.

Jaskowiak-Schoeneich, M. & Krassowska, A. 1988. Palaeothickness, lithofacies and palaeotectonics of the epicontinental Upper Cretaceous in Poland. *Kwartalnik Geologiczny*, **32**(1), 177–198.

Jenkyns, H. C., Gale, A. S. & Corfield, R. M. 1994. Carbon- and Oxygen isotope stratigraphy of the English chalk and Italian Scaglia and its paleoclimatic significance. *Geological Magazine*, **131**, 1–34.

Jerzykiewicz, T. 1971. A flysch/littoral succession in the Sudetic Upper Cretaceous. *Acta geologica Polonica*, **21**, 165–199.

Jerzykiewicz, T. & Wojewoda, J. 1986. The Radków and Szczeilniec Sandstones: an example of giant foresets on a tectonically controlled shelf of the Bogemian Cretaceous Basin (Central Europe). *In*: Knight, R.J. & McLearn, J. (eds) *Shelf Sands and Sandstones*. Canadian Society of Petroleum Geologists, Memoire **II**, 1–15.

Johansen, M. B. & Surlyk, F. 1990. Brachiopods and the stratigraphy of the Upper Campanian and Lower Maastrichtian chalk of Norfolk, England. *Palaeontology*, **33**, 823–873.

Johnson, H. & Lott, G.K. 1993. Cretaceous of the Central and Northern North Sea. *In*: Knox, R.W. O'B. & Cordey, W.G. (eds) *Lithostratigraphic Nomenclature of the UK North Sea*, Vol. 2. British Geological Survey, Nottingham.

Kaplan, U. 1992. Die Oberkreide-Aufschlüsse im Raum Lengerich/ Westfalen. *Geologie und Paläontologie in Westfalen*, **21**, 7–37.

Kaplan, U. 1994, Zur Stratigraphie und Korrelation des Soester Grünsands, Ober-Turon, Westfalen. *Berichte des Naturwissenschaftlichen Vereins Bielefeld und Umgegend*, **35**, 59–78.

Kaplan, U. & Best, M. 1984. Neue Ergebnisse zur stratigraphischen Stellung und geographischen Verbreitung der 'Rothenfelder Grünsande' (Turbidite) und der submarinen Großgleitung von Halle/ Westfalen. *Osnabrücker naturwissenschaftliche Mitteilungen*, **11**, 17–26.

Kaplan, U. & Kennedy, W.J. 1996. Upper Turonian and Coniacian ammonite stratigraphy of Westphalia, NW-Germany. *Acta Geologica Polonica*, **46**, 305–352.

Kaplan, U. & Röper, M. 1998. Das Campan der Dammer Oberkreide-Mulde unter besonderer Berücksichtigung des Stemweder Berges, NW-Deutschland. *Geologie und Paläontologie in Westfalen*, **50**, 7–30.

Kaplan, U., Keller, S. & Wiedmann, J. 1984. Ammoniten- und Inoceramen-Gliederung des norddeutschen Cenoman. *Schriftenreihe der Erdwissenschaftlichen Kommission*, **7**, 307–347.

Kaplan, U., Kennedy, W.J. & Ernst, G. 1996. Stratigraphie und Ammonitenfaunen des Campan im südlichen Münsterland. *Geologie und Paläontologie in Westfalen*, **43**, 1–133.

Kaplan, U., Kennedy, W.J., Lehmann, J. & Marcinowski, R. 1998. Stratigraphie und Ammonitenfaunen des westfälischen Cenoman. *Geologie und Paläontologie in Westfalen*, **51**, 1–236.

Kauffman, E.G., Herm, D., Johnson, C. C., Harries, P. J. & Höfling, R. 2000. The ecology of Cenomanian lithistid sponge frameworks, Regensburg area, Germany. *Lethaia*, **33**, 214–235.

Kędzierski, M. & Uchman, A. 2001. Ichnofabrics of the Upper Cretaceous marlstones in the Opole region, southern Poland. *Acta Geologica Polonica*, **51**(1), 81–91.

Keller, S. 1982. Die Oberkreide der Sack-Mulde bei Alfeld (Cenoman–Unter-Coniac); Lithologie, Biostratigraphie und Inoceramen. *Geologisches Jahrbuch, A*, **64**, 2–171.

Kemper, E. 1973. Das Berrias (tiefe Unterkreide) in NW-Deutschland. *Geologisches Jahrbuch, Reihe A*, **9**, 47–67.

Kemper, E. 1978. Die Transgressionen der jüngeren Unterkreide am Westrand des Niedersächsischen Beckens. *Geologisches Jahrbuch, A*, **65**, 145–161.

Kemper, E 1979. Die Unterkreide Nordwestdeutschlands. Ein Überblick. *In:* Wiedmann, J. (ed.) *Aspekte der Kreide Europas*. Schweizerbart, Stuttgart, 1–9.

Kemper, E. 1984. Ober-Alb und Unter-Cenoman in Nordwestdeutschland. *Geologisches Jahrbuch, A*, **75**, 465–487.

Kemper, E., Ernst, G. & Thiermann, A. 1978. Die Unterkreide im Wiehengebirgsvorland bei Lübbecke und im Osning zwischen Bielefeld und Bevergern. *In: Symposium deutsche Kreide, Exkursion A1*. Münster, 1–65.

Kennedy, W.J. 1987. Sedimentology of Late Cretaceous–Palaeocene Chalk reservoirs, North Sea Central Graben. *In*: Brooks, J. & Glennie, K. (eds) *Petroleum Geology of North West Europe*. Graham and Trotman, London, 469–481.

Kennedy, W.J. & Christensen, W.K. 1991. Coniacian and Santonian ammmonites from Bornholm, Denmark. *Bulletin of the Geological Society of Denmark*, **38**, 203–226.

Kennedy, W.J. & Jagt, J.W.M. 1995. Lower Campanian heteromorph ammonites from the Vaals Formation around Aachen, Germany, and adjacent parts of Belgium and The Netherlands. *Neues Jahrbuch für Geologie und Paläontologie*, Abhandlungen, **197**, 275–294.

Kennedy, W.J. & Jagt, J.W.M. 1998. Additional Late Cretaceous ammonite records from the Maastrichtian type area. *Bulletin de l'Institut royal des Sciences naturelles de Belgique, Sciences de la Terre*, **68**, 155–174.

Kennedy, W.J. & Kaplan, U. 1997. Ammoniten aus dem Campan des Stemweder Berges, Dammer Oberkreidemulde, NW-Deutschland. *Geologie und Paläontologie in Westfalen*, **50**, 31–245.

Kennedy, W. J. & Kollmann, H. A. 1979. Lower Albian ammonites from the Tannheim Formation near Losenstein, Upper Austria. *Beiträge zur Paläontologie Österreichs*, **6**, 1–25.

Kennedy, W. J. & Summesberger, H. 1984. Upper Campanian ammonites from the Gschliefgraben (Ultrahelvetic, Upper Austria). *Beiträge zur Paläontologie Österreichs*, **11**, 149–206.

Kennedy, W. J. & Summesberger, H. 1999. New Upper Campanian Ammonites from the Gschliefgraben near Gmunden (Ultrahelvetic, Austria). *Beiträge zur Paläontologie Österreichs*, **24**, 23–39.

Kennedy, W.J., Hancock, J.M. & Christensen, W.K. 1980. Albian and Cenomanian ammonites from the island of Bornholm. *Bulletin of the Geological Society of Denmark*, **29**, 203–244.

Kennedy, W.J., Gale, A.S., Bown, P.R., Caron, M., Davey, R.J., Gröcke, D. & Wray, D.S. 2000. Integrated stratigraphy across the Aptian-Albian boundary in the Marnes Bleues, at the Col de Pré-Guittard, Arnayon (Drôme), and at Tartonne (Alpes-de-Haute-Provence), France: a candidate Global Boundary Stratotype Section and Boundary Point for the base of the Albian Stage. *Cretaceous Research*, **21**, 591–720.

Keutgen, N. 1996. Biostratigraphie, Paläoökologie und Invertebratenfauna des Untermaastricht von Aachen (Westdeutschland) und angrenzenden Gebieten (Südostniederlande, Nordostbelgien), Shaker Verlag, Aachen.

Keutgen, N. 1997. *Belemnella (Belemnella)* cf. *praearkhangelskii* Naidin, 1964 from the Vijlen Member at Altembroeck (NE Belgium, Early Maastrichtian). *Geologie en Mijnbouw*, **75**, 341–347.

Klaua, D. 1974. 4.5.3. Kreide. *In:* Hoppe, A. & Seidel G. (eds) *Geologie von Thüringen*, Haack, Gotha, Leipzig 692–698.

Klein, V., Müller, V. & Valečka, J. 1979. Lithofazielle und paläogeographische Entwicklung des Böhmischen Kreidebeckens. *Aspekte der Kreide Europas*. IUGS Series A, **6**, 435–446.

Knappe, H. & Tröger, K.-A. 1988. Die Geschichte von den neuen Meeren. Ursprung des nördlichen Harzvorlandes. Harzmuseum, Wernigerode.

Knobloch, E. 1973. *Debeya insignis* Knobloch aus dem Senon von Friedensreuth. *Geologica Bavarica*, **67**, 172–176.

Knobloch, E. 1985. Paläobotanisch-biostratigraphische Charakteristik der Klikov-Schichtenfolge (Oberturon-Santon) in Südböhmen. *Sborník geologických věd*, **G 40**, 101–145.

Knobloch, E. 1991. Evolution of Middle and Upper Cretaceous floras in Central and Western Europe. *Jahrbuch der geologischen Bundesanstalt*, **134**(2), 257–270.

Knobloch, E. 1999. Neue oder wenig bekannte Pflanzenarten aus den Perucer Schichten (Cenoman) der Böhmischen Masse. *Acta Musei Nationalis Pragae, Series B, Historia Naturalis*, **55**(1-2), 25–60.

Koch, W. 1977. Stratigraphie der Oberkreide in Nordwestdeutschland (Pompeckjsche Scholle). Biostratigraphie in der Oberkreide und Taxonomie von Foraminiferen. *Geologisches Jahrbuch, A*, **38**, 11–123.

Kockel, F. 1991. Die Strukturen im Untergrund des Braunschweiger Landes. – *Geologisches Jahrbuch, A*, **127**, 391–404.

Kolbe, H. 1962. Die Eisenerzkolke im Neokomeisenerzgebiet Salzgitter. *Mitteilungen aus dem Geologischen Staatsinstitut in Hamburg*, **31**, 276–308.

Kolbe, H. 1970. Zur Enstehung und Charakteristik mesozoischer marinsedimentärer Eisenerze im östlichen Niedersachsen. *Clausthaler*

*Hefte zur Lagerstättemkunde und Geochemie der Mineralischen Rohstoffe*, **9**, 161–184.

Kollmann, H. A. 1968. Zur Gliederung der Kreideablagerungen der Weyerer Bögen (O.-Ö.). *Verhandlungen der Geologischen Bundesanstalt*, **1968**, 126–137.

Kollmann, H.A. 1980. Gastropoden aus der Sandkalkbank (Hochmoosschichten, Obersanton) des Beckens von Gosau, (OÖ) *Annalen des Naturhistorischen Museum Wien*, **83**, 197–213.

Kollmann, H. A. 1982. Gosauablagerungen im Becken von Gosau. *In*: Plöchinger, B. (ed.) *Erläuterungen zu Blatt 95 St. Wolfgang im Salzkammergut*. Geologische Bundesanstalt, 30–34.

Kollmann, H.A. & Summesberger, H. 1982. Excursions to Coniacian–Maastrichtian in the Austrian Alps. Working Group on the Coniacian-Maastrichtian Stages, *4th Meeting Gosau Basins in Austria*.

Kollmann, H. A., Bachmayer, F., *et al.* 1977. Beiträge zur Stratigraphie und Sedimentation der Oberkreide des Festlandsockels im nördlichen Niederöstrerreich. *Jahrbuch der Geologischen Bundes-Anstalt*, **120**, 401–447.

Kolodny, Y. & Raab, M. 1988. Oxygen isotopes in phosphatic fish remains from Israel: Paleothermometry of tropical Cretaceous and Tertiary shelf waters. *Palaeogeography, Palaeoclimatology, Palaeoecology*, **64**, 59–67.

Kongiel, R. 1962. On belemnites from the Maastrichtian, Campanian and Santonian sediments in the Middle Vistula Valley (Central Poland). *Prace Muzeum Ziemi*, **5**, 1–148.

Korsitzke, H. D. 1995. Planktonische Foraminiferen der Oberkreide (Cenoman–Campan) am Nördlichen Tethysrand (Süddeutsche Molasse–Untergrund, Regensburger Kreide) Systematik, Stratigraphie sowie Palökologie der Foraminiferengesamtfauna. *Documenta naturae*, **92**, 1–274.

Košťák, M., Čech, S., Ekrt, B., Mazuch, M., Wiese, F., Voigt, S. & Wood, C. J. 2004. Belemnites of the Bohemian Cretaceous Basin in a global context. *Acta Geologica Polonica*, **54**, 511–533.

Kotański, Z. & Radwański, S. 1977. Subsurface geology of the Opole region. Biuletyn Instytutu Geologicznego, **303**, 91–172 [in Polish with Russian and English summary].

Kowalski, W.C. 1948. Geological outline of Cretaceous deposits in the environs of Solca. *Biuletyn Instytutu Geologicznego*, **51**, 5–52.

Krassowska, A. 1997. The epicontinental Permian and Mesozoic in Poland. Upper Cretaceous. *Prace Państwowego Instytutu Geologicznego*, **153**, 367–402 [in Polish].

Krenmayr, H.G. 1996. Hemipelagic and turbiditic mudstone facies associations in the Upper Cretaceous Gosau Group of the Northern Calcareous Alps (Austria). *Sedimentary Geology*, **101**, 149–172.

Krutzsch, W. & Mibus, I. 1973. Sporenpaläontologischer nachweis von kontinentalem Maastricht in Walbeck (Bezirk Brandenburg, DDR). *Abhandlungen des Zentralen Geologischen Instituts*, **18**, 99–108.

Krutzsch, W. & Prokoph, A. 1992. Ablagerungen der oberkretazischen Walbeck-Formation im oberen Allertalgraben (Stratigraphie, Sedimentologie, Palynologie). *Berichte der Naturhistorischen Gesellschaft Hannover*, **134**, 117–133.

Krutzsch, W. & Schulz, E. 1966. Unveröffentlichter Bericht Nr. 47/66 über die sporenpaläontologische Untersuchung von Proben aus der Bohrung Ida-Waldhaus. *Archiv des Zentralen Geologischen Institut*.

Krzywiec, P. 2006. Structural inversion of the Pomeranian and Kuiavian segments of the Mid-Polish Trough—lateral variations in timing and structural style. *Geological Quarterly*, **50**, 151–168.

Kutek, J. 2001. The Polish Permo-Mesozoic Rift Basin. *In*: Ziegler, P.A., Cavazza, W., Robertson, A.H.F. & Crasquin-Soleau, S. (eds) *Peri-Tethys Memoir 6: Peri-Tethyan Rift/Wrench Basins and Passive Margins*. Mémoir Museum Nationale Histoire Naturelle, **186**, 213–236.

Kutek, J. & Głazek, J. 1972. The Holy Cross area, Central Poland, in the Alpine cycle. *Acta Geologica Polonica*, **22**(4), 603–653.

Kutek, J. & Marcinowski, R. 1996. Faunal changes in the Valanginian of Poland: tectonic or eustatic control? *Miteilungen aus dem Geologisch-Paläontologischen Institute der Universität Hamburg*, **77**, 83–88.

Kutek, J., Marcinowski, R. & Wiedmann, J. 1989. The Wąwał Section, Central Poland–an important link between Boreal and Tethyan Valanginian. *In*: Wiedmann, J. (ed.) *Cretaceous of the Western Tethys*. Proceedings 3rd International Cretaceous Symposium, Tübingen 1987. E. Schweizerbart'sche Verlagsbuchhandlung, Stuttgart, 717–754.

Lahodynsky, R. 1988. Lithostratigraphy and sedimentology across the Cretaceous/Tertiary boundary in the Flyschgosau (Eastern Alps, Austria). *Revista Espanola Paleontologia Extraord.*, **1988**, 73–82.

Lang, H. 1981. 5.3. Die Kreide im Untergrund des Molassebeckens (Purbeck-Campan). *In: Erläuterungen zur Geologischen Karte von Bayern 1:500 000. 3. neubearbeitete Auflage.* Bayerisches Geologisches Landesamt, Munich, 71–78.

Lantos, M., Wagreich, M., Siegl-Farkas, A., Bodnár, E. & Császár, G. 1997. Integrated stratigraphic correlation of the Upper Cretaceous sequence in the borehole Bakonyjákó 528. *Advances in Austrian-Hungarian Geological Research*, **1996**, 97–117.

Larsen, N. & Håkansson, E. 2000. Microfacies mosaics across latest Maastrichtian bryozoan mounds in Denmark. *In*: Herrera, C. A. & Jackson, J. B. C. (eds) *Proceedings of the 11th International Bryozoology Association Conference*, 8–12 June 1982, Gosau, 272–281.

Larson, R. L. 1991. Geological consequences of superplumes. *Geology*, **19**, 963–966.

Laurin, J. & Uličný, D. 2004. Controls on a a shallow-water hemipelagic carbonate system adjacent to a siliciclastic margin: example from Late Turonian of Central Europe. *Journal of Sedimentary Research*, **74**, 697–717.

Lefeld, J., Gaśdzicki, A., Iwanow, A. & Krajewski, K. 1985. Jurassic and Cretaceous lithostratigraphic units of the Tatra Mts. *Studia Geologica Polonica*, **84**, 1–86.

Lehmann, J. 1999. Integrated stratigraphy and palaeoenvironment of the Cenomanian-Lower Turonian (Upper Cretaceous) of northern Westphalia, north Germany. *Facies*, **40,** 25–70.

Leiss, O. 1992. Orogenically controlled sedimentation in the Lechtaler Kreideschiefer (Lechtal shale; Cretaceous) and geodynamics of the inner western NCA (Northern Calcareous Alps; Lechtal Alps). *Geologische Rundschau*, **81**, 603–634.

Leszczyński, K. 1997*a*. The Lower Cretaceous depositional architecture and sedimentary cyclicity in the Mid-Polish Trough. *Geological Quarterly*, **41**(4), 509–520.

Leszczyński, K. 1997*b*. The Upper Cretaceous carbonate-dominated sequence of the Polish Lowlands. *Geological Quarterly*, **41**(4), 521–532.

Liboriussen, J., Ashton, P. & Tygesen, T. 1987. The tectonic evolution of the Fennoscandian Border Zone. *Tectonophysics*, **137**, 21–29.

Liebau, A. 1978. Paläobathymetrische und paläoklimatische Veränderungen im Mikrofaunenbild der Maastrichter Tuffkreide. *Neues Jahrbuch für Geologie und Paläontologie, Abhandlungen* **157**, 233–237.

Lieberkind, K., Bang, I., Mikkelsen, N. & Nygaard, E. 1982. Cretaceous and Danian limestone. *In*: Michelsen, O. (ed.) *Geology of the Danish Central Graben*. Geological Survey of Denmark, Series B, No. **8**.

Lilienbach, L. 1830. *Ein Durchschnitt aus den Alpen mit Hindeutungen auf die Karpathen*. Leonhard und Bronns Jb., Heidelberg, 153–220.

Lini, A., Weissert, H. & Erba, E. 1992. The Valanginian carbon isotope event–a first episode of greenhouse climate conditions during the Cretaceous. *Terra Nova,* **4**, 374–384.

Lintnerova, O., Michalík, J., Wissler, L., Biron, A. & Kotulova, J. 2000. Geochemical methods in high resolution stratigraphy of the early Aptian Konhora Formation. *In:* Kovac, M., Vozar, J., Vozarova, A., Michalík, J. & Plasienka, D. (eds) Environmental, structural and stratigraphical evolution of the Western Carpathians. *Slovak Geological Magazine*, **6**(2–3), 231–233.

Littke, R., Jendrzejewski, L., Lokay, P., Shuangqing, W. & Rullkötter, J. 1998. Organic geochemistry and depositional history of the Barremian-Aptian boundary interval in the Lower Saxony Basin, northern Germany. *Cretaceous Research*, **19,** 581–614.

Lommerzheim, A. 1976. Zur Paläontologie, Fazies, Paläogeographie und Stratigraphie der turonen Grünsande (Oberkreide) im Raum Mühlheim/Broich/Speldorf mit einer Beschreibung der Cephalopodenfauna. *Decheniana*, **129**, 197–244.

Lommerzheim, A. 1995. Stratigraphie und Ammonitenfaunen des Santon und Campan im Münsterländer Becken (NW-Deutschland). *Geologie und Paläontologie in Westfalen*, **40**, 1–97.

Lykke-Andersen, H. & Surlyk, F. 2004. The Cretaceous–Palaeogene boundary at Stevns Klint, Denmark: Inversion tectonics or sea-floor topography? *Journal of the Geological Society*, **161**, 343–352.

McArthur, J. M., Kennedy, W. J., Gale, A. S., Thirlwall, M. F., Chen, M., Burnett, J. & Hancock, J. M. 1992. Strontium isotope stratigraphy in the Late Cretaceous: intercontinental correlation of the Campanian/Maastrichtian boundary. *Terra Nova*, **4**, 385–393.

McArthur, J. M., Howarth, R. J. & Bailey, T. R. 2001. Strontium isotope stratigraphy: LOWESS Version 3. Best-fit line to the marine Sr-isotope curve for 0 to 509 Ma and accompanying look-up table for deriving numerical age. *Journal of Geology*, **109**, 155–169.

Machalski, M. & Walaszczyk, I. 1987. Faunal condensation and mixing in the uppermost Maastrichtian/Danian Greensand (Middle Vistula, Central Poland). *Acta Geologica Polonica*, **37**(1–2), 75–92.

Malecha, A. 1966. South Bohemian basins. *In*: Svoboda *et al.* (eds) *Regional Geology of Czechoslovakia. I. Bohemian Massif.* Geological Survey of Czechoslovakia, 408–428.

Marcinowski, R. 1970. The Cretaceous transgressive deposits east of Częstochowa (Polish Jura Chain). *Acta Geologica Polonica*, **20**(3), 413–449.

Marcinowski, R. 1974. The transgressive Cretaceous (Upper Albian through Turonian) deposits of the Polish Jura Chain. *Acta Geologica Polonica*, **24**(1), 117–217.

Marcinowski, R. 1980. Cenomanian ammonites from German Democratic Republic, Poland, and the Soviet Union. *Acta Geologica Polonica*, **30**(3), 215–325.

Marcinowski, R. & Radwański, A. 1983. The mid-Cretaceous transgression onto the Central Polish Uplands (marginal part ofthe Central European Basin). *Zittelina*, **10**, 65–95.

Marcinowski, R. & Walaszczyk, I. 1985. Mid-Cretaceous deposits and biostratigraphy of the Annopol section, central Polish Uplands. *österreichchische Akademie der Wissenschaft Schriftenreihe der Erdwissenschaftlischen Komissionen*, **7**, 27–41.

Marcinowski, R. & Wiedmann, I. 1985. The Albian ammonite fauna of Poland and its palaeogeographical significance. *Acta Geologica Polonica*, **35**, 199–219.

Marcinowski, R. & Wiedmann, I. 1990. The Albian ammonites of Poland. *Palaeontologica Polonica*, **50**, 1–94.

Marek, S. (ed.) 1983. *The geological structure of the Warsaw (Płock) Trough and its basement*. Prace Instytutu Geologicznego, **103**.

Marek, S. 1989. Sedimentäre und paläotektonische Entwicklung der epikontinentalen Unterkreide Polens. *In*: Wiedmann , J. (ed) *Cretaceous of the Western Tethys*. Proceedings 3rd International Cretaceous Symposium, Tübingen 1987. E. Schweizerbart'sche Verlagsbuchhandlung, Stuttgart, 755–770.

Marek, S. 1997. *The epicontinental Permian and Mesozoic in Poland*. Prace Instytutu Geologicznego, **153**.

Mattern, F. 1999. Mid-Cretaceous basin development, paleogeography, and paleogeodynamics of the western Rhenodanubian Flysch (Alps). *Zeitschrift der Deutschen Geologischen Gesellschaft*, **150**, 89–132.

May, T. & Eisbacher, G.H. 1999. Tectonics of the synorogenic 'Kreideschiefer basin', northwestern Calcareous Alps, Austria. *Eclogae Geologica Helvetiae*, **92**, 307–320.

Mazur, S., Scheck-Wenderoth, M. & Krzywiec, P. 2005. Different modes of the Late Cretaceous–Early Tertiary inversion in the North German and Polish basins. *International Journal of Earth Sciences (Geologische Rundschau)*, **94**, 782–798.

Meijer, J. J. F. 2000. Fossil woods from the Late Cretaceous Aachen Formation. *Review of Pylaeobotany and Palynology*, **112**, 297–336.

Metzdorf, R. 1992. Zur Fauna des Hyphantoceras-Event (Oberes Turonium) von Halle und Bielefeld (Westfalen, NW-Deutschland). *Berichte des Naturwissenschaftlichen Vereins Bielefeld und Umgebung*, **33,** 271–331.

Meyer, R. K. F. 1981*a*. 5. Kreide nördlich der Alpen. *In*: Erläuterungen zur Geologischen Karte von Bayern 1:500 000. 3. neubearbeitete Auflage. Bayerisches Geologisches Landesamt, Munich, 68–70.

Meyer, R. K. F. 1981*b*. Die Küste des Obercenoman-Meeres (Oberkreide) westllich von Amberg. *Geologische Blätter für NO-Bayern*, **31**, 306–321.

Meyer, R. K. F. 1989. Die Entwicklung der Kreide-Sedimente im Westteil der Bodenwöhrer Senke. *Erlanger Geologische Abhandlungen*, **117**, 53–96.

Meyer, R. K. F. 1996. 3.4 Kreide. In: Erläuterungen zur Geologischen Karte von Bayern. 4te neubearbeitete Auflage. Bayerisches Geologisches Landesamt, Munich, 112–128.

Meyer, R. K. F. 2000. 4.9 Außeralpine Kreide in Süddeutschland (Regensburger Kreide). *In:* Stratigraphische Kommission Deutschlands (ed.) *Stratigraphie von Deutschland III. Die Kreide der Bundesrepublik Deutschland.* Courier Forschungsinstitut Senckenberg, **226**, 141–147.

Meyer, T. 1990. Biostratigraphische und sedimentologische Untersuchungen in der Plänerfazies des Cenoman von Nordwestdeutschland. *Mitteilungen aus dem Geologischen Institut der Universität Hannover*, **30**, 1–114.

Michael, E. 1974. Zur Palökologie und Faunenführung des norddeutschen Unterkreide-Meeres. *Geologisches Jahrbuch*, **A19,** 1–68.

Michael, E. 1979. Mediterrane Fauneneinflüsse in den borealen Unterkreide-Becken Europas, besonders Nordwestdeutschlands. *In:* Wiedmann, J. (ed) *Aspekte der Kreide Europas.* Schweizerbart, Stuttgart, 305–321.

Michael, E. & Pape, H.-G. 1971. Eine bemerkenswerte Bio- und Lithofazies an der Basis des Unter-Hauterivium Norddwestdeutschlands. *Mitteilungen aus dem Geologischen Institut der Technischen Universität Hannover*, **10,** 43–108.

Michalík, J. 1984. Some remarks and interpretation of geological development and structure of the NW part of the Malé Karpaty Mts (Western Carpathians). *Geologica Carpathica*, **35**, 489–504.

Michalík J. 2000. Excursion into the westernmost Central Carpathians (Slovakia). *6th International Cretaceous Symposium*, August 27 to September 4, 2000, Vienna, Austria.

Michalík, J. 2002. *Tethyan-Boreal Cretaceous Correlation. Mediterranean and Boreal Cretaceous paleobiogeographic areas in Central and Eastern Europe*. VEDA, Bratislava.

Michalík, J. 2007. Sedimentary rock record and microfacies indicators of the latest Triassic to mid-Cretaceous tensional development of the Zliechov Basin (Central Western Carpathians). *Geologica Carpathica* **58**, 443–453.

Michalík, J. & Činčura, J. 1992. Cretaceous shallow marine clastics and continental/freshwater deposits in the Western Carpathians, Czechoslovakia. *Cretaceous Research*, **13**, 157–166.

Michalík, J. & Reháková, D. 1997. West Carpathian records of Upper Jurassic and Lower Cretaceous pelagic sedimentation along northern margin of the Mediterranean Tethys. *In*: Plašienka, D., Hók, J., Vozár, J. & Elečko, M. (eds). *Alpine evolution of the Western Carpathians and related areas.* Bratislava, Geological Survey of Slovak Republic, 65–70.

Michalík, J. & Soták, J., 1990. Lower Cretaceous shallow marine buildups in the Western Carpathians and their relationship to pelagic facies. *Cretaceous Research*, **11**, 211–227.

Michalík, J. & Vašíček, Z. 1989. Lower Cretaceous stratigraphy and paleogeography of the Czechoslovakian Western Carpathians. *In:* Wiedmann J. (ed.) *Cretaceous of the Western Tethys*. Schweizerbart, Stuttgart, 505–523.

Michalík, J., Borza, K., Snopkova, P., Svobodova, M. & Vasicek, Z. 1987. Sucasne trendy v stratigrafii spodnokriedovych utvarov a ich aplikacia na Zapadne Karpaty (Stratigraphy of Upper Cretaceous formations, especially in the Western Carpathians). *Geologicke Prace, Zpravy*, **86**, 179–195.

Michalík, J., Reháková, D. & Žítt, J. 1993. Upper Jurassic and Lower Cretaceous facies, microplankton and crinoids in the Kuchyňa Unit, Malé Karpaty Mts. *Geologica Carpathica*, **44**, 161–176.

Michalík, J., Reháková, D. & Soták, J. 1994. Environments and setting of the Jurassic /Lower Cretaceous succession in the Tatric Area, Malé Karpaty Mts. *Geologica Carpathica*, **45**, 45–56.

Milewicz, J. 1985. Extent of the Rotliegendes in southwestern Poland. *Kwartalnik Geologiczny*, **29**, 679–690 [in Polish].

Milewicz, J. 1988. Cretaceous macrofauna in Węgliniec IG 1 borehole. *Kwartalnik Geologiczny*, **32**(2), 389–403 [in Polish with Russian and English summary].

Milewicz, J. 1997. Upper Cretaceous of the North-Sudetic depression (litho- and biostratigraphy, paleogreography, tectonics and remarks on raw material). *Acta Universitatis Wratislaviensis, Seria Prace Geolgiczno-Mineralogiczne*, **61**, 5–58 [in Polish with English summary].

Mindszenty, A. & D'Argenio, B. 1987. Bauxites of the Northern Calcareous Alps and the Transdanubian Central Range: A comparative estimate. *Rendiconti della Società Geologica Italiana*, **9**, 269–276.

Mogensen, T.E. & Korstgård, J.A. 2003. Triassic and Jurassic transtension along part of the Sorgenfrei-Tornquist Zone in the

Danish Kattegat. *In*: Ineson, J.R. & Surlyk, F. (eds) *The Jurassic of Denmark and Greenland*.Geological Survey of Denmark and Greenland Bulletin, **1**, 439–458.

Mohr, H. 1992. *Der helvetische Shelf der Ostschweiz am Übergang vom späten Jura zur frühen Kreide*. PhD Thesis, Swiss Federal Institute of Technology, Zürich, No. **9805**.

Mohr, H. & Funk, H. 1995. Die Entwicklung der helvetischen Karbonatplattform in der Ostschweiz (Tithonian–Berriasian): Eine sequenzstratigraphische Annäherung. *Eclogae Geologicae Helvetiae*, **88**, 281–320.

Mortimore, R., Wood, C., Pomerol, B. & Ernst, G. 1998. Dating the phases of the Subhercynian epoch: Late Cretaceous tectonics and eustatics in the Cretaceous basins of northern Germany compared with the Anglo-Paris Basin. *Zentralblatt für Geologie und Paläontologie Teil I*, **11/12**, 1349–1401.

Mulder, F.J. de, Geluk, M.C., Ritsema, I., Westerhoff, W.E. & Wong, T.E. 2003. *Geologie van Nederland, deel 7. De ondergrond van Nederland*. Nederlands Instituut voor Toegepaste Geowetenschappen TNO, Utrecht.

Musstopf, R. 1966. Zur Paläogeographie der Oberkreide und des Albs in Ostbrandenburg und in der östlichen Niederlausitz. *Geologie*, **15**(6), 732–736.

Mutterlose, J. 1992. Die Unterkreide-Aufschlüsse (Berrias-Hauterive) im nördlichen Wiehengebirgsvorland (N-Deutschland). *Geologie und Paläontologie in Westfalen*, **21**, 39–113.

Mutterlose, J. 2000. 4.3.1 Unterkreide im Niedersächsischen Becken. *In:* Stratigraphische Kommission Deutschlands (ed.) *Stratigraphie von Deutschland III. Die Kreide der Bundesrepublik Deutschland*. Courier Forschungsinstitut Senckenberg, **226**, 78–101.

Mutterlose, J. & Böckel, B. 1998. The Barremian–Aptian interval in NW Germany: a review. *Cretaceous Research*, **19**, 539–568.

Mutterlose, J. & Bornemann, A. 2000. Distribution and facies patterns of Lower Cretaceous sediments in northern Germany: a review. *Cretaceous Research*, **21,** 733–759.

Mutterlose, J. & Ruffell, A. 1999. Milankovitch-scale palaeoclimate changes in pale-dark bedding rhythms from the early Cretaceous (Hauterivian & Barremian) of eastern England and northern Germany. *Palaeogeography, Palaeoclimatology, Palaeoecology*, **154,** 133–160.

Němejc, F. 1958. Contribution to the stratigraphy of the Třeboň part of the South Bohemian Basins. *Věstník Ústředního ústavu geologického*, **33**, 317–330.

Nestler, H. 1965. Die Rekonstruktion des Lebensraumes der Rügener Schreibkreide-Fauna (Unter-Maastricht) mit Hilfe der Paläoökologie und Paläobiologie. *Geologie* **14**, (Beiheft 19), 1–147.

Neubauer, F., Dallmeyer, R.D., Dunkl, I. & Schirnik, D. 1995. Late Cretaceous exhumation of the Gleinalm dome, Eastern Alps: kinematics, cooling history, and sedimentary response in a sinistral wrench corridor. *Tectonophysics*, **242**, 79–98.

Niebuhr, B. 1995. Fazies-Differenzierungen und ihre Steuerungsfaktoren in der höheren Oberkreide von S-Niedersachsen /Sachsen-Anhalt (N-Deutschland). *Berliner geowissenschaftliche Abhandlungen, A*, **174**, 1–131.

Niebuhr, B. 2003. Late Campanian to Early Maastrichtian ammonites from the white chalk of Kronsmoor (northern Germany)–taxonomy and stratigraphy. *Acta Geologica Polonica*, **53**(4), 257–281.

Niebuhr, B. 2004. Late Campanian nostoceratid ammonites from the Lehrte West Syncline near Hannover, northern Germany. *Acta Geologica Polonica*, **54**(4), 473–487.

Niebuhr, B. 2005. Geochemistry and time-series analyses of orbitally forced Upper Cretaceous marl-limestone rhythmites (Lehrte West Syncline, northern Germany). *Geological Magazine*, **142**(1), 1–25.

Niebuhr, B. & Ernst, G. 1991. Faziesgeschichte und Beckendynamik von Campan, Maastricht und Eozän im Beienroder Becken (E-Niedersachsen). *Zeitschrift der Deutschen Geologischen Gesellschaft*, **142**, 251–283.

Niebuhr, B., Volkmann, R. & Schönfeld, J. 1997. Das obercampane *polyplocum*-Event der Lehrter Westmulde (Oberkreide, N-Deutschland): Bio-/Litho-/Sequenzstratigraphie, Fazies-Entwicklung und Korrelation. *Freiberger Forschungshefte, C*, **468**, 211–244.

Niebuhr, B., Baldschuhn, R., Ernst, G., Walaszczyk, I., Weiss, W. & Wood, C.J. 1999. The Upper Cretaceous succession (Cenomanian–Santonian) of the Staffhorst Shaft, Lower Saxony, northern Germany: integrated biostratigraphic, lithostratigraphic and downhole geophysical log data. *Acta Geologica Polonica*, **49**(3), 175–213.

Niebuhr, B., Wood, C.J. & Ernst, G. 2000. 4.3 Niedersachsen und angrenzende Gebiete. 4.3.2 Isolierte Oberkreide-Vorkommen zwischen Wiehengebirge und Harz. *In:* Stratigraphische Kommission Deutschlands (ed.) *Stratigraphie von Deutschland III. Die Kreide der Bundesrepublik Deutschland*. Courier Forschungsinstitut Senckenberg, **226**, 101–109.

Niebuhr, B., Wiese, F. & Wilmsen, M. 2001. The cored Konrad 101 borehole (Cenomanian–Lower Coniacian, Lower Saxony): calibration of surface and subsurface log data for the lower Upper Cretaceous of northern Germany. *Cretaceous Research*, **22**, 643–674.

Niebuhr, B., Hiss, M., Kaplan, U., Tröger, K.-A., Voigt, S., Voigt, T., Wiese, F. & Wilmsen, M. 2007. Lithostratigraphie der norddeutschen Oberkreide. *Schriftenreihe der Deutschen Gesellschaft für Geowissenschaften*, **55**, 1–136

Niedźwiedzki, R. & Kalina, M. 2003. Late Cretaceous sharks in the Opole Silesia region (SW Poland). *Geologia Sudetica*, **35**, 13–24.

Nguyen Tu, T.T., Kvaček, J., Uličný, D., Bocherens, H., Mariotti, A. & Broutin, J. 2002. Isotopic reconstruction of plant palaeoecology: Case study of Cenomanian floras from Bohemia. *Palaeogeography, Palaeoclimatology, Palaeoecology*, **183**, 43–70.

Noe-Nygaard, N. & Surlyk, F. 1985. Mound bedding in a sponge-rich Coniacian chalk, Bornholm, Denmark. *Bulletin of the Geological Society of Denmark*, **34**, 237–249.

Noe-Nygaard, N. & Surlyk, F. 1988. Wash-over fans and brackish bay sedimentation in the Berriasian-Valanginian of Bornholm, Denmark. *Sedimentology*, **35**, 197–217.

Nöldecke, W. 1963. Lithologische Ausbildung von Unter- und Oberkreide im Bereich des Quedlinburger Sattels, der Halberstädter und Blankenburger Mulde. Exkursionsführer zur 10. *Jahrestagung der Geologischen Gesellschaft in der DDR*, 47–62.

Nöldecke, W. 1967. Überblick über die Eisenerzführung in Jura und Kreide des Nordteils der DDR (Vergleich mit angrenzenden Gebieten). *Berichte der Deutschen Gesellschaft für geologische Wissenschaften, A, Geologie Paläontologie*, **12**(3/4), 315–327.

Nöldecke, W. & Schwab, G 1977. Zur tektonischen Entwicklung des Tafeldeckgebirges der Norddeutsch-Polnischen Senke unter besonderer Berücksichtigung des Nordteils der DDR. *Zeitschrift für angewandte Geologie*, **23**, 369–379.

Norling, E. & Bergström, J. 1987. Mesozoic and Cenozoic tectonic evolution of Scania, southern Sweden. *Tectonophysics*, **137**, 7–19.

Norris, R. D., Bice, K. L., Magno, E. A. & Wilson, P. A. 2002. Jiggling the tropical thermostat in the Cretaceous hothouse. *Geology*, **30**, 299–302.

Nygaard, E., Lieberkind, K. & Frykman, P. 1983. Sedimentology and reservoir parameters of the Chalk Group in the Danish Central Graben. *Geologie en Mijnbouw*, **62**, 177–190.

Oberhänsli-Langenegger, H. 1978. *Mikropaläontologische und sedimentologische Untersuchungen in der Amdener Formation*. Beiträge zur geologischen Karte der Schweiz, [NF] **150.**

Oberhauser, R. 1995. Zur Kenntnis der Tektonik und der Paläogeographie des Ostalpenraumes zur Kreide-, Paleozän- und Eozänzeit. *Jahrbuch der Geologischen Bundesanstalt*, **138**, 369–432.

Olszewska-Nejbert, D. 2005. Development of the Turonian *Conulus* Lagerstätte in the Wielkanoc quarry, Miechów Upland (South Poland). *Annales Societatis Geologorum Poloniae*, **75**, 199–210.

Ortner, H. 2001. Growing folds and sedimentation of the Gosau group, Muttekopf, Northern Calcareous Alps, Austria. *International Journal of Earth Sciences*, **90**, 727–739.

Ouwehand, P.J. 1987. *Die Garschella-Frormation („Helvetischer Gault', Aptian–Cenomanian) der Churfirsten-Alvier Region (Ostschweiz); Sedimentologie, Phosphoritgenese, Stratigraphie*. PhD Thesis, Swiss Federal Institute of Technology, Zürich, No. **8409**.

Pacltová, B. 1961. On some plant microfossils from fresh-water sediments of the Upper Cretaceous (Senonian) in the South-Bohemian Basin. Part 1. *Sborník Ústředního ústavu geologického*, **P 26**, 47–102 [in Czech with English summary].

Pacltová, B. 1981. The evolution and distribution of Normapolles pollen during the Cenophytic. *Review of Palaeobotany and Palynology*, **35**(2–4), 175–208.

Pacltová, B. 1990. Marginal facies of the Bohemian Upper Cretaceous (Palynological study). *In:* Knobloch, E. & Kvaček, Z. (eds)

*Proceedings of the Symposium, Paleofloristic and Paleoclimatic Changes in the Cretaceous and Tertiary, IGCP Project No. 216.* Czech Geological Survey, Prague, 47–53.

PATZELT, H.G. 2000. Probleme der Fazies, Milieuinterpretation und Paläotektonik des höheren Santons im Subherzyn. *Zeitschrift für geologische Wissenschaften*, **28**(3/4), 425–439.

PELZER, G. 1988. *Sedimentologie und Palynologie der Wealden-Fazies im Hannoverschen Bergland.* PhD dissertation, Georg-August-Universität Göttingen.

PERCH-NIELSEN, K. 1985. Mesozoic calcareous nannofossils. *In*: BOLLI, H.M., SAUNDERS, J.B. & PERCH-NIELSEN, K. (eds) *Plankton Stratigraphy.* Cambridge University Press, Cambridge, 329–426.

PERYT, D. 1980. Planktic foraminifera zonation of the Upper Cretaceous in the Middle Vistula Valley, Poland. *Palaeontologia Polonica*, **41**, 3–101.

PERYT, D. 1983. Planktonic foraminiferal zonation of Mid-Cretaceous of the Annopol Anticline (central Poland). *Zitteliana*, **10**, 575–583.

PERYT, D., LAHODYNSKY, R., ROCCHIA, R. & BOCLET, D. 1993. The Cretaceous/Paleogene boundary and planktonic foraminifera in the Flyschgosau (Eastern Alps, Austria). *Palaeogeography, Palaeoclimatology, Palaeoecology*, **104**, 239–252.

PETZKA, M. & REICH, M. 2000. 4.2 Mecklenburg-Vorpommern. 4.2.2 Oberkreide. *In:* STRATIGRAPHISCHE KOMMISSION DEUTSCHLANDS (ed.) *Stratigraphie von Deutschland III. Die Kreide der Bundesrepublik Deutschland.* Courier Forschungsinstitut Senckenberg, **226**, 73–79.

PFEUFFER, J. 1983. Zur Genese der Eisenerzlagerstätten von Auerbach-Sulzbach-Rosenberg-Amberg(Oberpfalz). *Geologisches Jahrbuch, D*, **64**, 3–69.

PILLER, W.E., EGGER, H., *et al.* 2004. *Die stratigraphische Tabelle von Österreich 2004 (sedimentäre Schichtfolgen)* Österreichische Stratigraphische Kommission, Wien.

PLAŠIENKA, D. & OŽVOLDOVÁ, L. 1996. New data about the age of radiolarites from the Belice Unit (Považský Inovec Mts.), Central Western Carpathians. *Slovak Geological Magazine*, **1**, 21–26.

PLAŠIENKA, D., GRECULA, P., PUTIŠ, M., HOVORKA, D., & KOVÁČ, M. 1997. Evolution and structure of the Western Carpathians: an overview. *In*: GRECULA, P., HOVORKA, D. & PUTIŠ, M. (eds) *Geological Evolution of the Western Carpathians.* Geocomplex, Bratislava, 1–24.

PLÖCHINGER, B. & PREY, S. 1993. Der Wienerwald. *Sammlung geologischer Führer*, **59**, 168.

POBER, E. & FAUPL, P. 1988. The chemistry of detrital chromian spinels and its implications for the geodynamic evolution of the Eastern Alps. *Geologische Rundschau*, **77**, 641–670.

POŻARYSKA, K. 1952. The sedimentological problems of Upper Maestrichtian and Danian of the Puławy environment, Middle Vistula. *Biuletyn Państwowego Instytutu Geologicznego*, **81**, 1–104.

POŻARYSKA, K. 1957. Lagenidae du Crétacé supérieur de Pologne. *Palaeontologia Polonica*, **8**, 1–190.

POŻARYSKA, K. & PERYT, D. 1979. The Late Cretaceous and early Paleocene foraminiferal "transitional province" in Poland. *In*: WIEDMANN J. (ed.) *Aspekte der Kreide Europas.* Schweitzerbart, Stuttgart, 293–303.

POŻARYSKI, W. 1938. Senonstratigraphie im Durchbruch der Weichsel zwischen Rachów und Puławy in Mittelpolen. *Biuletyn Państwowego Instytutu Geologicznego*, **6**, 1–94.

POŻARYSKI, W. 1948. Jurassic and Cretaceous between Radom, Zawichost and Kraśnik (Central Poland). *Biuletyn Państwowego Instytutu Geologicznego*, **46**, 1–141.

POŻARYSKI, W. 1970. *The stratigraphy of the Mesozoic at the edge of the Holy Cross Mountains.* Prace Instytutu Geologicznego, **5** [in Polish].

POŻARYSKI, W. 1977. The early Alpine (Laramide Epoch in the Platform development east of the Fore Sudetic and Silesian-Cracovian monoclines. *In*: *Geology of Poland*, vol. 4 *(Tectonics).* Wydawnictwa Geologiczne; Warszawa, 351–416.

PREISINGER, A., ZOBETZ, E., *et al.* 1986. The Cretaceous/Tertiary boundary in the Gosau Basin, Austria. *Nature,* **322,** 797–799.

PRESCHER, H. 1981. Probleme der Korrelation des Cenomans und Turons in der Sächsischen und Böhmischen Kreide. *Zeitschrift für geologische Wissenschaften*, **9**, 367–373.

PRESCHER, H. & TRÖGER, K.-A. 1989. Die Meißner Schichten der Sächsischen Kreide. *Abhandlungen des Staatlichen Museums für Mineralogie und Geologie in Dresden*, **36,** 155–167.

RACZYŃSKA, A. 1979. *The stratigraphy and lithofacies development of the younger Lower Cretaceous in the Polish Lowlands.* Prace Instytutu Geologicznego, **89.**

RADWAŃSKA. Z. 1969. Kreda w otworze Sady IG-1. *Kwartalnik Geologiczny*, **13**(3), 709–710.

RADWAŃSKI, S. 1975. Upper Cretaceous of the Central part of the Sudetes in the light of new borehole materials. *Biuletyn Instytutu Geologicznego*, **278**, 5–59 [in Polish with Russian and English summary].

RASSER, M.W., VAŠÍČEK, Z., SKUPIEN, P., LOBITZER, H. & BOOROVÁ, D. 2003. Die Schrambach-Formation an ihrer Typuslokalität (Unter-Kreide, Nördliche Kalkalpen, Salzburg): Lithostratigraphische Formalisierung und „historische' Irrtümer. *In*: PILLER, W.E. (ed) *Stratigraphia Austriaca.* Österreichische Akademie der Wissenschaften, Schriftenreihe der Erdwissenschaftlichen Kommissionen, **16**, 193–216.

RAVN, J.P.J. 1925. Det cenomane basalkonglomerat på Bornholm. *Danmarks geologiske Undersøgelse*, **42**(2), 1–64.

REDTENBACHER, A. 1873. Die Cephalopodenfauna der Gosauschichten in den nordöstlichen Alpen. *Abhandlungen der Geologischen Reichsanstalt*, **5**, 91–140.

REHÁKOVÁ, D. 2000. Calcareous dinoflagellate and calpionellid bioevents versus sea-level fluctuations recorded in the west Carpathian (Late Jurassic/Early Cretaceous) pelagic environments. *Geologica Carpathica*, **51**, 229–243

REHÁKOVÁ, D., MICHALIK, J. & OŽVOLDOVÁ, L. 1996. New microbiostratigraphical data from several Lower Cretaceous pelagic sequences of the Northern Calcareous Alps, Austria (preliminary results). *Geologisch-Paläontologische Mitteilungen Innsbruck*, Special Volume, **4**, 57–71.

REICH, M. 2000. 4.4 Altmark und Brandenburg. 4.4.2 Oberkreide. *In:* STRATIGRAPHISCHE KOMMISSION DEUTSCHLANDS (ed.) *Stratigraphie von Deutschland III. Die Kreide der Bundesrepublik Deutschland.* Courier Forschungsinstitut Senckenberg, **226**, 120–123.

REICH, M. & FRENZEL, P. 2002. Die Fauna und Flora der Rügener Schreibkreide (Maastrichtium/Ostsee). *Archiv für Geschiebekunde,* **3**(2/4), 73–284.

REICHERTER, K., FROITZHEIM, N., *et al.* 2008. Alpine tectonics north of the Alps. *In*: MCCANN, T. (ed.) *The Geology of Central Europe. Volume 2: Mesozoic and Cenozoic.* Geological Society, London, 1233–1285.

REUSS, A.E. 1854. Beiträge zur Charakterisitk der Kreideschichten der Ostalpen, besonders im Gosauthale und am Wolfgangsee. *Denkschriften der Österreichischen Akademie der Wissenschaften, mathematisch-naturwissenschfatliche Klasse*, **7**.

RÖDIGER, K. 1933. Stratigraphie und Paläogeographie der Unteren Kreide im Gebiet der Eisenerzlager des Salzgitterer Höhenzuges. *Jahrbuch des Halleschen Verbandes für die Erforschung der Mitteldeutschen Bodenschätze und ihre Verwertung*, Neue Folge, **12,** 267–324.

ROLL, A. 1953. Der Harzrand bei Bad Harzburg. *Neues Jahrbuch für Geologie und Paläontologie*, **97**, 90–98.

ROSSA, H.G. 1987. Upper Cretaceous and Tertiary inversion tectonics in the western part of the Rhenish-Westphalian coal district (FRG) and in the Campine area (N Belgium). *In*: BLESS, M.J.M., DUSAR, M. & STREEL, M. (eds) *Some Aspects of the Late Cretaceous in NW Europe.* Annales de la Société géologique de Belgique, **109**, 367–410.

RÓŻYCKI, S.Z. 1937. Alb Cenoman und Turon in der Umgebung der Eisebahnstation Złoty Potok (bei Koniecpol, öslich von Częstochowa). *Sprawozdania Państwowego Instytutu Geologicznego*, **9**(1), 19–68.

RUTKOWSKI , J. 1965. Senonian in the area of Miechów. *Rocznik Polskiego Towarzystwa Geologicznego*, **35**(1), 2–52.

SALAJ, J. & GAŠPARÍKOVÁ, V. 1983. Turonian and Coniacian microbiostratigraphy of the Tethys region on the basis of Foraminifera and nannofossils. *Zitteliana*, **10**, 595–607.

SANDERS, D. 1998. Tectonically controlled Late Cretaceous terrestrial to neritic deposition (Northern Calcareous Alps, Tyrol, Austria). *Facies*, **39**, 139–178.

SANDERS, D. & HÖFLING, R. 2000. Carbonate deposition in mixed siliciclastic-carbonate environments on top of an orogenic wedge (Late Cretaceous, Northern Calcareous Alps, Austria). *Sedimentary Geology*, **137**, 127–146.

SANDERS, D. & PONS, J.M. 1999. Rudist formations in mixed siliciclastic-carbonate depositional environments, Upper Cretaceous, Austria: stratigraphy, sedimentology, and models of development. *Paleogeography, Paleoclimatology, Paleoecology*, **148**, 249–284.

Sanders, D., Kollmann, H. & Wagreich, M. 1997. Sequence development and biotic assemblages on an active continental margin: the Turonian-Campanian of the northern Calcareous Alps, Austria. *Bulletin Societe géologique de France*, **168**, 351–372.

Sanders, D., Baron-Szabo, R. C. & Pons, J. M. 1999. Short description of the largest Upper Cretaceous coral reef of the Eastern Alps (Theresienstein Formation *nom. nov.*), and a newly recognized coral-rudist buildup (Billroth Formation *nom. nov.*), Salzburg, Austria. *Geologisch-Paläontologische Mitteilungen Innsbruck*, **24**, 1–16.

Scheck, M., Bayer, U. & Lewerenz, B. 2003. Salt movements in the Northeast German Basin and its relation to major post-Permian tectonic phases – results from 3D structural modelling, backstripping and reflection seismic data. *Tectonophysics*, **361**, 277–299.

Scheck-Wenderoth, M., Krzywiec, P., Zühlke, R., Maystrenko, Y. & Froitzheim, N. 2008. Permian to Cretaceous tectonics. *In*: McCann, T. (ed.) *The Geology of Central Europe. Volume 2: Mesozoic and Cenozoic*. Geological Society, London, 999–1030.

Schiøler, P., Brinkhuis, H., Roncaglia, L. & Wilson, G.J. 1997. Dinoflagellate biostratigraphy and sequence stratigraphy of the Type Maastrichtian (Upper Cretaceous), ENCI quarry, The Netherlands. *Marine Micropaleontology*, **31**, 65–95.

Schlagintweit, F. 1991. Allochthone Urgonkalke in mittleren Abschnitt der Nördlichen Kalkalpen: Fazies, Paläontologie und Paläogeographie. *Münchner geowissenschaftliche Abhandlungen, A*, **20**.

Schlagintweit, F. 2004. *Murania reitneri* n. sp., a new sclerosponge from the Upper Jurassic of the Northern Calcareous Alps (Plassen Formation, Austria and Germany). *Austrian Journal of Earth Sciences*, **95/96**, 37–45.

Schlagintweit, F. & Ebli, O. 1999. New Results on Microfacies, Biostratigraphy and Sedimentology of Late Jurassic–Early Cretaceous platform carbonates of the Northern Calcareous Alps. Part fi; Tressenstein Limestone, Plassen Formation. *Abhandlungen der Geologischen Bundesanstalt*, **56**(2), 379–418.

Schlanger, S. O. & Jenkyns, H. C. 1976. Cretaceous oceanic anoxic events: Causes and consequences. *Geologie en Mijnbouw*, **55**, 179–184.

Schmid, F. & Ernst, G. 1975. Ammoniten aus dem Campan der Lehrter Westmulde und ihre stratigraphische Bedeutung. 1. Teil: *Scaphites, Bostrychoceras* und *Hoploplacenticeras*. *Berichte der Naturhistorischen Gesellschaft Hannover*, **119**, 315–359.

Schmid, F. & Spaeth, C. 1991. Der braunrote Feuerstein aus dem Turon von Helgoland. *Geologisches Jahrbuch, A*, **120**, 97–104.

Schmid, S.M., Fügenschuh, B., Kissling, E. & Schuster, R., 2004. Tectonic map of the Alps and overall architecture of the Alpine orogen. *Eclogae Geologicae Helvetiae*, **97**, 93–117.

Schnabel, W. 1992. New data on the Flysch Zone of the Eastern Alps in the Austrian sector and new aspects concerning the transition to the Flysch Zone of the Carpathians. *Cretaceous Research*, **13**, 405–419.

Scholle, P.A., Albrechtsen, T. & Tirsgaard, H. 1998. Formation and diagenesis of bedding cycles in uppermost Cretaceous chalks of the Dan Field, Danish North Sea. *Sedimentology*, **45**, 223–243.

Schönfeld, J. 1990. Zur Stratigraphie und Ökologie benthischer Foraminiferen im Schreibkreide-Richtprofil von Lägerdorf/Holstein. *Geologisches Jahrbuch, A*, **117**, 3–151.

Schönfeld, J., Schulz, M.-G. & Spaeth, C. 2000. 4.1 Schleswig-Holstein und nördliches Niedersachsen. *In:* Stratigraphische Kommission Deutschlands (ed.) *Stratigraphie von Deutschland III. Die Kreide der Bundesrepublik Deutschland.* Courier Forschungsinstitut Senckenberg, **226**, 65–69.

Schott, W., Jaritz, W., Kockel, F., Sames, C.-W., Stackelberg, U., Stets, J. & Stoppel, D. 1967–69. *Paläogeographischen Atlas der Unterkreide von Nordwestdeutschland mit einer Übersichtsdarstellung des nördlichen Mitteleuropa. Erläuterungen zum Paläogeographischen Atlas der Unterkreide von Nordwestdeutschland.* Bundesanstalt für Bodenforschung, Hannover.

Schouten, S., Hopmans, E. C., Forster, A., van Breugel, Y., Kuypers, M. M. M. & Sinninghe Damsté, J. S. 2003. Extremely high sea-surface temperatures at low latitudes during the middle Cretaceous as revealed by archael membrane lipids. *Geology*, **31**, 1069–1072.

Schröder, B. 1987. Inversion tectonics along the western margin of the Bohemian massif. *Tectonophysics*, **137**, 93–100.

Schröder, B., Ahrendt, H., Peterek, A. & Wemmer, K. 1997. Post-Variscan sedimentary record of the SW margin of the Bohemian massif: a review. *Geologische Rundschau*, **86**, 178–184.

Schulz, M.-G. 1979. Morphometrisch-variationsstatistische Untersuchungen zur Phylogenie der Belemniten-Gattung *Belemnella* im Untermaastricht NW-Europas. *Geologisches Jahrbuch, A*, **47**, 3–157.

Schulz, M.-G. 1985. Die Evolution der Echiniden-Gattung *Galerites* im Campan und Maastricht Norddeutschlands. *Geologisches Jahrbuch, A*, **80**, 3–93.

Schulz, M.-G. & Niebuhr, B. 2000. 3.2 Stufengliederung der Kreide. 3.2.12 Maastricht. *In:* Stratigraphische Kommission Deutschlands (ed.) *Stratigraphie von Deutschland III. Die Kreide der Bundesrepublik Deutschland.* Courier Forschungsinstitut Senckenberg, **226**, 45–51.

Schulze, G. 1964. Erste Ergebnisse geologischer Untersuchungsarbeiten im Gebiet der Scholle von Calvörde. *Zeitschrift für angewandte Geologie*, **10**, 338–348.

Schweigl, J. & Neubauer, F. 1997. New structural, sedimentological and geochemical data on the Cretaceous geodynamics of the central Northern Calcareous Alps (Eastern Alps). *Zentralblatt für Geologie und Paläontologie*, Teil I, **1996**, 329–343.

Scupin, H. 1936. Zur Paläogeographie des sudetischen Kreidemeeres. *Zeitschrift der Deutschen Geologischen Gesellschaft*, **88**, 213–256.

Sedgwick, A. & Murchison, R. 1832. A sketch of the structure of the Eastern Alps. *Geological Society of London, Transactions*, **23**(2), 301–420.

Seebach, K. 1868. Über die Entwicklung der Kreideformation im Ohmgebirge. Nachrichten von der Königl.Gesellschaft der Wissenschaften und der Georg-Augusts-Universität zu Göttingen, **1886**, 128–138.

Seifert, A. 1955. Stratigraphie und Paläogeographie des Cenomans und Turons im sächsischen Elbtalgebiet. *Freiberger Forschungshefte, C*, **14**, 1–218.

Senglaub, Y., Brix, M. R., Adriasola A. C. & Littke, R. 2005. New information on the thermal history of the southwestern Lower Saxony Basin, northern Germany, based on fission track analysis. *International Journal of Earth Sciences (Geologische Rundschau)*, **94**, 876–896

Siegl-Farkas, Á & Wagreich, M. 1997. Correlation of palyno- (spores, pollen, dinoflagellates) and calcareous nannofossil zones in the Late Cretaceous of the Northern Calcareous Alps (Austria) and the Transdanubian Central Range (Hungary). *Advances in Austrian-Hungarian Geological Research*, **1996**, 127–135.

Skupin, K. 1990. Gesteinsausbildung und Stratigraphie eines Kreide-Vorkommens nordöstlich von Augustdorf/Senne (Nordrhein-Westfalen). *Neues Jahrbuch für Geologie und Paläontologie, Abhandlungen*, **181**, 287–301.

Slánská, J. 1974. Continental Cretaceous and Tertiary Sedimentation in the South Bohemian Basins. *Neues Jahrbuch für Geologie und Paläontologie*, Abhandlungen, **146**, 385–406.

Slánská, J. 1976. A red-bed formation in the south Bohemian Basins, Czechoslovakia. *Sedimentary Geology*, **15**, 135–164.

Smoleński, G. 1906. Das Untersenon von Bonarka. I. Cephalopoden und Inoceramen. Bulletin de l'Académie des Sciences de Cracovie, Classe des Sciences Mathématiques et Naturelles, **8**, 717–729.

Špičáková, L. 1999. Fluvial deposits of the southwestern margin of the Bohemian Cretaceous Basin (Cenomanian, Czech Republic): their spatial and temporal evolution. PhD Thesis, Charles University, Prague [in Czech, with English summary].

Špičáková, L. & Uličný, D. 1996. Eustatic and tectonic controls on fluvial sedimentation, Cenomanian of central Bohemia. *Abstracts, 5th International Cretaceous Symposium and 2nd Workshop on Inoceramids*, Freiberg, 16–24 September 1996.

Stacher, P. 1980. *Stratigraphie, Mikrofazies und Mikropaläontologie der Wang-Formation*. Beiträge zur geologischen Karte der Schweiz, [NF] **152**.

Stage, M. 1999. Signal analysis of cyclicity in Maastrichtian pelagic chalks from the Danish North Sea. *Earth and Planetary Science Letters*, **171**, 75–90.

Stampfli, G.M. 1993. Le Brianconnais, terrain exotique dans les Alpes? *Eclogae Geologicae Helvetiae*, **86**, 1–45.

STAMPFLI, G.M. 2000. Tethyan oceans. *In:* BOZKURT, E., WINCHESTER, J.A. & PIPER, J.D.A. (eds) *Tectonics and Magmatism in Turkey and the Surrounding Area*. Geological Society, London, Special Publications, **173**, 1–23.

STAMPFLI, G.M. & BOREL, G.D. 2002. A plate tectonic model for the Paleozoic and Mesozoic constrained by dynamic plate boundaries and restored synthetic oceanic isochrons. *Earth and Planetary Science Letters*, **196**, 17–33.

STAMPFLI, G.M., BOREL, G., MARCHANT, R. & MOSAR, J. 2002. Western Alps geological constraints on western Tethyan reconstructions. *Journal Virtual Explorer*, **8**, 77–106.

STEINICH, G. 1965. Die artikulaten Brachiopoden der Rügener Schreibkreide. *Paläontologische Abhandlungen (A: Paläozoologie)*, **2**(1), 1–220.

STEINICH, G. 1972. Endogene Tektonik in den Unter-Maastricht-Vorkommen auf Jasmund (Rügen). *Geologie* **20**, (Beiheft) **71/72**, 1–207.

STEINMANN, M. 1994. *Die nordpenninischen Bündnerschiefer der Zentralalpen Graubündens: Tektonik, Stratigraphie und Beckenentwicklung*. PhD thesis, Swiss Federal Institute of Technology, Zürich, No. **10668.**

STENESTAD, E. 1972. Træk af det danske bassins udvikling i Øvre Kridt. *Dansk Geologisk Forenings Årsskrift* (for 1971), 63–69.

STEPHENSON, R.A. & the EUROPROBE WORKING GROUP 1993. Continental rift development in Precambrian and Phanerozoic Europe: Europrobe and the Dniepr-Donets and Polish Trough basins. *Sedimentary Geology*, **86**, 159–175.

STEUBER, T. 2001. Strontium isotope stratigraphy of Turonian-Campanian Gosau-type rudist formations in the Northern Calcareous and Central Alps (Austria and Germany). *Cretaceous Research*, **22**, 429–441.

STILLE, H. 1924. *Grundfragen der vergleichenden Tektonik*. Borntraeger, Berlin.

STRÁNÍK, Z., BUBÍK, M., ČECH, S. & ŠVÁBENICKÁ, L. 1996. The Upper Cretaceous in South Moravia. *Věstník Českého geologického ústavu*, **71**, 1–30.

STRASSER, A. 1979. *The Betlis and Diphyoides limestones of the Lower Cretaceous in central and eastern Switzerland; stratigraphy, microfacies, and sedimentary development*. Mitteilungen aus dem Geologischen Institut der Eidgenössischen Technischen Hochschule und der Universität Zürich, Neue Folge, **225**.

STRASSER, A. 1982. Fazielle und sedimentologische Entwicklung des Betlis-Kalkes (Valanginian) im Helvetikum der Zentral- und Ostschweiz. *Eclogae Geologicae Helvetiae*, **75**, 1–21.

STRATIGRAPHISCHE KOMMISSION DEUTSCHLANDS 2000. *Stratigraphie von Deutschland III. Die Kreide der Bundesrepublik Deutschland*. Courier Forschungsinstitut Senckenberg, **226**.

STRAUSS, C., ELSTNER, F., JAN DU CHENE, R., MUTTERLOSE, J., REISER, H. & BRANDT, K.-H. 1993. New micropaleontological and palynological evidence on the stratigraphic position of the 'German Wealden' in NW-Germany. *Zitteliana*, **20,** 389–401.

STREEL, M., FELDER, P.J. & BLESS, M.J.M. 1994. Excursion 2: Upper Cretaceous, Thursday, 22 September 1994. *Fourth European Palaeobotanical Palynological Conference*, Heerlen/Kerkrade.

ŠTUR, D. 1860. Bericht über die geologische Übersichts–Aufnahme d. Wassergebietes der Waag und Neutra. *Jahrbuch der Geologischen Reichsanstalt*, **11**, 17–149.

SUJKOWSKI, Z. 1934. Roches crétacées entre les villes Pilica et Szczekociny. *Sprawozdania Polskiego Instytutu Geologicznego*, **8**(1), 39–75.

SUMMESBERGER, H. 1979. Eine obersantone Ammonitenfauna aus dem Becken von Gosau (Oberösterreich). *Annalen des Naturhistorischen Museums Wien*, **82**, 109–176.

SUMMESBERGER, H. 1980. Neue Ammoniten aus der Sandkalkbank der Hochmoosschichten (Obersanton; Gosau, Österreich) *Annalen des Naturhistorischen Museums Wien*, **83**, 275–283.

SUMMESBERGER, H. 1985. Ammonite zonation of the Gosau Group (Upper Cretaceous, Austria). *Annalen des Naturhistorischen Museums Wien*, **87**, 145–166.

SUMMESBERGER, H. & KENNEDY, W.J. 1996. Turonian Ammonites from the Gosau Group (Upper Cretaceous; Northern Calcareous Alps; Austria) with a revision of *Barroisiceras haberfellneri* (HAUER 1866). *Beiträge zur Paläontologie Österreichs*, **21**, 1–75.

SUMMESBERGER, H., ŠVÁBENICKÁ, L., HRADECKÁ, L., ČECH, S. & HOFMANN, T. 1999*a*. New palaeontological data on the Klement and Pálava Formations (Upper Cretaceous) in Austria (Waschberg-Zdánice Unit). *Annalen des Naturhistorischen Museums Wien*, **A100**, 39–79.

SUMMESBERGER, H., WAGREICH, M., TRÖGER, K.-A. & JAGT, J.W.M. 1999*b*. Integrated biostratigraphy of the Santonian/Campanian Gosau Group of the Gams Area (Late Cretaceous; Styria, Austria). *Beiträge zur Paläontologie Österreichs*, **24**, 155–205.

SURLYK, F. 1970. Die Stratigraphie des Maastricht von Dänemark und Norddeutschland aufgrund von Brachiopoden. *Newsletters on Stratigraphy*, **1/2**, 7–16.

SURLYK, F. 1972. Morphological adaptations and population structures of the Danish chalk brachiopods (Maastrichtian, Upper Cretaceous). *Det Kongelige Danske Videnskabernes Selskab Biologiske Skrifter*, **19**(2), 1–57.

SURLYK, F. 1984. The Maastrichtian Stage in NW Europe, and its brachiopod zonation. *Bulletin of the Geological Society of Denmark*, **33**, 217–223.

SURLYK, F. 1997. A cool-water carbonate ramp with bryozoan mounds: Late Cretaceous-Danian of the Danish Basin. *In*: JAMES, N. P. & CLARKE, J. D. A. (eds) *Cool-water Carbonates*. SEPM, Special Publications, **56**, 293–307.

SURLYK, F. & BIRKELUND, T. 1977. An integrated stratigraphical study of fossil assemblages from the Maastrichtian white chalk of northwestern Europe. *In*: KAUFMAN, E.G. & HAZEL, J. E. (eds) *Concepts and Methods of Biostratigraphy*. Hutchinson & Ross, Stroudsburg, Penn., 257–281.

SURLYK, F. & CHRISTENSEN, W. K. 1974. Epifaunal zonation on an Upper Cretaceous rocky coast. *Geology*, **2**, 529–534.

SURLYK, F. & LYKKE-ANDERSEN, H. 2007. Contourite drifts, moats and channels in the Upper Cretaceous chalk of the Danish basin. *Sedimentology* **54**, 405–422.

SURLYK, F., DONS, T., CLAUSEN, C. K., & HIGHAM, J. 2003. Upper Cretaceous. *In*: EVANS, D., GRAHAM, C., ARMOUR, A., & BATHURST, P. (eds) *The Millennium Atlas: Petroleum Geology of the Central and Northern North Sea*. Geological Society, London, 213–233.

SURLYK, F., DAMHOLT, T. & BJERAGER, M. 2006. Stevns Klint, Denmark: Uppermost Maastrichtian chalk, Cretaceous–Tertiary boundary, and lower Danian bryozoan mound complex. *Bulletin of the Geological Society of Denmark*, **54**, 1–45.

SVOBODOVÁ, M. 1999. Mid-Cretaceous palynomorphs from the Blansko Graben (Czech Republic): affinities to both Tethyan and Boreal bioprovinces. *Mededelingen Nederlands Instituut voor Toegepaste Geowetenschappen TNO*, **58**, 149–156.

ŚWIDROWSKA, J. & HAKENBERG, M. 1999. Subsidence and the problem of incipient inversion in the Mid-Polish Trough based on thickness maps and Cretaceous lithofacies analyses. *Przeglad Geologiczny*, **47**(1), 61–68 [in Polish].

TARKOWSKI, R. 1991. Stratigraphy, macrofossils and palaeogeography of the Upper Cretaceous from the Opole Trough. *Scientific Bulletins of Stanisław Staszic Academy Mining and Metallurgy*, **1404**, 5–156.

THOMSEN, E., 1976. Depositional environments and development of Danian bryozoan biomicrite mounds (Karlby Klint, Denmark). *Sedimentology*, **23**, 485–509.

THOMSEN, E. 1983. Relations between currents and the growth of Paleocene reef-mounds. *Lethaia*, **16**, 165–184.

THOMSON, S. N. & ZEH, A. 2000. Fission-track thermochronology of the Ruhla Crystalline Complex: New constraints on the post-Variscan thermal evolution of the NW Saxo-Bohemian Massif. *Tectonophysics*, **324**, 17–35.

TILLMANN, H. 1964. IV. Kreide. In: Erläuterungen zur Geologischen Karte von Bayern 1:500 000. Bayerisches Geologisches Landesamt, Munich, 141–161.

TILLMANN, H. 1986. Neue Erkenntnisse zur Landschaftsgeschichte des Cenomans in Ostbayern und zur Frage der altcenomanen Meeresingressionen. *Erlanger Geologische Abhandlungen*, **113**, 137–152.

TOLLMANN, A. 1976. *Analyse des klassischen nordalpinen Mesozoikums. Stratigraphie, Fauna und Fazies der Nördlichen Kalkalpen*. Deuticke, Wien.

TRÖGER, K.-A. 1956. Über Kreideablagerungen des Plauenschen Grundes. *Jahrbuch des Staatlichen Museums für Mineralogie und Geologie Dresden*, **2,** 22–124.

TRÖGER, K.-A. 1964. Die Ausbildung der Kreide (Cenoman bis Coniac) in der Umrandung des Lausitzer Massivs. *Geologie*, **6/7**, 717–730.

TRÖGER, K.-A. 1969. Zur Paläontologie, Biostratigraphie und faziellen Ausbildung der unteren Oberkreide (Cenoman bis Turon), Teil 2 Stratigraphie und fazielle Ausbildung des Cenomans und Turons in Sachsen, dem nördlichen Harzvorland (subherzyne Kreide) und dem Ohm-Gebirge. *Abhandlungen des Staatlichen Museums für Mineralogie und Geologie*, **13**, 1–70.

TRÖGER, K.-A. 1989. Problems of Upper Cretaceous inoceramid biostratigraphy and palaeobiogeography in Europe and western Asia. *In:* WIEDMANN, J. (ed.) *Cretaceous of the Western Tethys. Proceedings of the third International Cretaceous Symposium, Tübingen 1987*. Schweizerbart, Stuttgart, 911–930.

TRÖGER, K.-A. 1996. The Upper Cretaceous of Saxony in the framework of the European Cretaceous development. *Mitteilungen des Geologisch-Paläontologischen Institutes der Universität Hamburg*, **77**, 95–104.

TRÖGER, K. A. 2000*a*. 4.6 Thüringen (Eichsfeld). *In:* STRATIGRAPHISCHE KOMMISION DEUTSCHLANDS (ed.) *Stratigraphie von Deutschland III. Die Kreide der Bundesrepublik Deutschland*, Courier Forschungsinstitut Senckenberg, **226**, 131.

TRÖGER, K.-A. 2000*b*. 4.3 Niedersachsen und angrenzende Gebiete. 4.3.3 Sachsen-Anhalt, östliche Subherzyne Kreide. *In:* STRATIGRAPHISCHE KOMMISSION DEUTSCHLANDS (ed.) *Stratigraphie von Deutschland III. Die Kreide der Bundesrepublik Deutschland*. Courier Forschungsinstitut Senckenberg **226**, 109–117.

TRÖGER, K.-A. 2003. The Cretaceous of the Elbe Valley in Saxony (Germany)–a review. *Carnets de Géologie*, Article 2003/03 (CG2003_A03_KAT) 1–14.

TRÖGER, K. A. & SCHUBERT, J. 1993. Bemerkungen zur Ausbildung und Biostratigraphie des Oberkreide-Profiles im nördlichen Teil des Holunger Grabens (Thüringer Becken). *Zeitschrift für Geologische Wissenschaften*, **21**, 403–415.

TRÖGER, K.-A. & SUMMESBERGER, H. 1994. Coniacian and Santonian inoceramid bivalves from the Gosau-Group (Cretaceous, Austria) and their biostratigraphic and paleobiogeographic significance. *Annalen des Naturhistorischen Museums Wien, A*, **96**, 161–197.

TRÜMPY, R. 1969. Die helvetischen Decken der Ostschweiz–Versuch einer palinspastischen Korrelation und Ansätze zu einer kinematischen Analyse. *Eclogae Geologicae Helvetiae*, **62**, 105–142.

TRÜMPY, R. 1980. *Geology of Switzerland, A Guide Book*. Wepf & Co, Basel.

TRÜMPY, R. 1988. A possible Jurassic-Cretaceous transform system in the Alps and the Carpathians. *In*: CLARK, S. P., JR, BURCHFIEL, B. C. & SUPPE, J. (eds) *Processes in Continental Lithospheric Deformation*. Geological Society of America, Special Papers, **218**, 93–109.

TRUSHEIM, F. 1936. Die geologische Geschichte Süddeutschlands während der Unterkreide und des Cenomans. *Neues Jahrbuch für Geologie und Paläontologie, Abhandlungen, Abt. B*, **75**, 1–108.

ULBRICH, H. 1971. Mitteilungen zur Biostratigraphie des Santon und Campan des mittleren Teils der Subherzynen Kreidemulde. *Freiberger Forschungshefte, C*, **267**, 47–71.

ULBRICH, H. 1974. Die Spongien der Ilsenburg-Entwicklung (oberes Unter-Campan) der Subherzynen Kreidemulde. *Freiberger Forschungshefte, C*, **291**, 1–121.

ULIČNÝ , D. 2001. Depositional systems and sequence stratigraphy of coarse-grained deltas in a shallow-marine, strike-slip setting: the Bohemian Cretaceous Basin, Czech Republic. *Sedimentology*, **48**, 599–628.

ULIČNÝ, D. & ŠPIČÁKOVÁ, L. 1996. Response to high frequency sea-level change in a fluvial to estuarine succession: Cenomanian paleovalley fill, Bohemian Cretaceous Basin. *In:* HOWELL, J.A. & AITKEN, J.F. (eds) *High Resolution Sequence Stratigraphy: Innovations and Applications*. Geological Society, London, Special Publications, **104**, 247–268.

ULIČNÝ, D., HLADÍKOVÁ, J. & HRADECKÁ, L. 1993. Record of sea-level changes, oxygen depletion and the $\delta^{13}C$ anomaly across the Cenomanian-Turonian boundary, Bohemian Cretaceous Basin. *Cretaceous Research*, **14**, 211–234.

ULIČNÝ, D., HLADÍKOVÁ, J., ATTREP, M., ČECH, S., HRADECKÁ, L. & SVOBODOVÁ, M. 1997*a*. Sea-level changes and geochemical anomalies across the Cenomanian-Turonian boundary: Pecínov quarry, Bohemia. *Palaeogeography, Palaeoclimatology, Palaeoecology*, **132**, 265–285.

ULIČNÝ, D., KVAČEK, J., SVOBODOVÁ, M. & ŠPIČÁKOVÁ, L. 1997*b*. High-frequency sea-level fluctuations and plant habitats in Cenomanian fluvial to estuarine succession: Pecínov quarry, Bohemia: *Palaeogeography, Palaeoclimatology, Palaeoecology*, **136**, 165–197.

ULIČNÝ, D. , NICHOLS, G. & WALTHAM, D. 2002. Role of initial depth at basin margins in sequence architecture: field examples and computer models. *Basin Research*, **14**, 347–360.

ULIČNÝ, D., ČECH, S. & GRYGAR, R., 2003*a*. Tectonics and depositional systems of a shallow-marine, intra-continental strike-slip basin: exposures of the Český Ráj region, Bohemian Cretaceous Basin. Excursion Guide, 1st Meeting of the Central European Tectonics Group and 8th meeting of the Czech Tectonic Studies Group. *Geolines*, **16**, 133–148.

ULIČNÝ, D., ŠPIČÁKOVÁ, L., ČECH, S. & LAURIN, J. 2003*b*. Response of depositional style of an intra-continental strike-slip basin to changes in relative activity of basement fault zones: Cenomanian of the Bohemian Cretaceous Basin, Czech Republic. *Abstract Book, 22nd IAS Meeting of Sedimentology*, Opatija, Croatia 2003, 213.

VALEČKA, J. 1979. Paleogeography and lithofacies development in the north-western part of the Bohemian Cretaceous Basin. *Sbornik Geologickych Ved*, **33**, 47–81 [in Czech].

VALEČKA, J. 1984. Storm surge versus turbidite origin of the Coniacian to Santonian sediments in the eastern part of the Bohemian Cretaceous Basin. *Geologische Rundschau*, **73**, 651–682.

VALEČKA, J., & REJCHRT, M. 1973. Litologie a geneze tzv. flyšoidní facie coniaku ve v. části Českého středohoří. *Časopis pro mineralogii a geologii*, **18**, 379–391.

VALEČKA, J. & SKOČEK, V. 1991. Late Cretaceous lithoevents in the Bohemian Cretaceous Basin. *Cretaceous Research*, **12**, 561–577.

VANDENBERGHE, N., VAN SIMAEYS, S., STEURBAUT, E., JAGT, J.W.M. & FELDER, P.J. 2004. Stratigraphic architecture of the Upper Cretaceous and Cenozoic along the southern border of the North Sea Basin in Belgium. *Netherlands Journal of Geosciences (Geologie en Mijnbouw)*, **83**, 155–171.

VAROL, O. 1998. Paleogene. In: BOWN, P.R. (ed.) *Calcareous Nannofossil Biostratigraphy*. Chapman and Hall, London.

VAŠÍČEK, Z. & FAUPL, P. 1998. Late Valanginian cephalopods in relation to the palaeogeographic position of the Rossfeld and Schrambach Formation of the Reichraming Nappe (Northern Calcareous Alps, Upper Austria). *Zentralblatt für Geologie und Paläontologie*, Teil I, **1996**, 1421–1432.

VAŠÍČEK, Z. & FAUPL, P. 1999. Zur Biostratigraphie der Schrambachschichten in der Reichraminger Decke (Unterkreide, oberösterreichische Kalkalpen). *Abhandlungen der Geologischen Bundesanstalt*, **56**(2), 593–624.

VAŠÍČEK, Z., MICHALÍK J. & REHÁKOVÁ D. 1994. Early Cretaceous stratigraphy, paleogeography and life in Western Carpathians. *Beringeria*, **10**, 1–170.

VEJBÆK, O.V. & ANDERSEN, C. 2002. Post mid-Cretaceous inversion tectonics in the Danish Central Graben–regionally synchronous tectonic events? *Bulletin of the Geological Society of Denmark*, **49**, 129–144.

VELENOVSKÝ, J. & VINIKLÁŘ, L. 1926–31. Flora Cretacea Bohemiae. Nové dodatky k české křídové květeně. Díl. I-IV. *Rozpravy Státního geologického ústavu* [German summary].

VILLAIN, J.-M. 1977. Le Maastrichtien dans sa région type (Limbourg, Pays-Bas). Étude stratigraphique et micropaléontologique. *Palaeontographica, A*, **157**, 1–87.

VOIGT, E. 1929. Die Lithogenese der Flach- und Tiefwassersedimente des jüngeren Oberkreidemeeres (eine Parallelisierung orogenetisch bedingter Ablagerungsverhältnisse am Harzrand, in Südschweden und im preußisch-holländischem Grenzgebiet). *Jahrbuch des Halleschen Verbandes für die Erforschung der Mitteldeutschen Bodenschätze und Ihrer Verwertung, N.F.*, **8**, 1–136.

VOIGT, E. 1951. Das Maastricht-Vorkommen von Ilten bei Hannover und seine Fauna mit besonderer Berücksichtigung der Großforaminiferen und Bryozoen. *Mitteilungen aus dem Geologischen Staatsinstitut in Hamburg*, **20**, 15–109.

VOIGT, E. 1962. Frühdiagenetische Deformation der turonen Plänerkalke bei Halle/Westfalen. *Mitteilungen aus dem Geologischen Staatsinstitut in Hamburg*, **31**, 146–275.

VOIGT, S. & HILBRECHT, H 1997. Late Cretaceous carbon isotope stratigraphy in Europe: Correlation and relations with sea level and sediment stability. *Palaeogeography, Palaeoclimatology, Palaeoecology*, **134**, 39–60.

Voigt, S., Wilmsen, M., Mortimore, R. N. & Voigt, T. 2003. Cenomanian palaeotemperatures derived from the oxygen isotopic composition of brachiopods and belemnites: evaluation of Cretaceous palaeotemperature proxies. *International Journal of Earth Sciences (Geologische Rundschau)*, **92,** 285–299.

Voigt, S., Flögel, S. & Gale, A.S. 2004. Midlatitude shelf seas in the Cenomanian-Turonian greenhouse world: temperature evolution and North Atlantic circulation. *Paleoceanography*, **19**, doi: 10.1029/2004PA001015.

Voigt, S., Gale, A. S. & Voigt, T. 2006. Sea level change, carbon cycling and palaeoclimate during the Late Cenomanian of northwest Europe; an integrated palaeoenvironmental analysis. *Cretaceous Research*, **27**, 836–858.

Voigt, S., Aurag, A., Leis, F. & Kaplan, U. 2007. Late Cenomanian to Middle Turonian high-resolution carbon isotope stratigraphy: new data from the Münsterland Cretaceous basin, Germany. *Earth and Planetary Science Letters*, **253**, 196–210.

Voigt, T. 1994. *Faziesentwicklungen und Ablagerungssequenzen am Rand eines Epikontinentalmeeres–Die Sedimentazionsgeschichte der Sächsischen Kreide*. PhD Thesis, Bergakademie Freiberg.

Voigt, T. 1996*a*. Sandstone rocks in the upper Biela Valley. *In*: Voigt, T. *et al.* (eds) *Field Trip B1, 5th International Cretaceous Symposium*, Sept 1996, Freiberg, 52–55.

Voigt, T. 1996*b*. Sea-level changes during Late Cenomanian and Early Turonian in the Saxonian Cretaceous Basin. *Mitteilungen den Geologisch-Paläontologisches Institut, Universität Hamburg*, **77**, 275–290.

Voigt, T. 1998. Entwicklung und Architektur einer fluviatilen Talfüllung–die Niederschöna Formation im Sächsischen Kreidebecken. *Abhandlungen des Staatlichen Museums für Mineralogie und Geologie in Dresden*, **43/44,** 121–139.

Voigt, T. & Eynatten, H. von 2004. Das Subherzyne Becken. *In:* Mutterlose, J. & Steffahn, J. (eds.) *Exkursionsführer: Die Kreide des Subherzynen und östlichen Niedersächsischen Beckens*. Bochumer Geowissenschaftliche Arbeiten, **4**, 1–12.

Voigt, T. & Tröger, K.-A. 1996. Sea-level changes during Late Cenomanian and Early Turonian in the Saxonian Cretaceous Basin. *Mitteilungen den Geologisch-Paläontologisches Institut, Universität Hamburg*, **77**, 275–290.

Voigt, T., Voigt, S. & Tröger, K.-A. 1994. Fazies-Entwicklung einer ertrunkenen Felsküste–die obercenomane Monzonitklippe westlich von Dresden. *Freiberger Forschungshefte, C*, **452,** 23–34.

Voigt, T., Eynatten, H. von & Franzke, H.-J. 2004. Late Cretaceous unconformities in the Subhercynian Cretaceous Basin (Germany). *Acta Geologica Polonica*, **54**(4), 673–694.

Voigt, T., Wiese, F., Eynatten, H., Franzke, H.-J., Gaupp, R. 2006. Facies evolution of syntectonic Upper Cretaceous Deposits in the Subhercynian Cretaceous Basin and adjoining areas (Germany). *Zeitschrift der deutschen Gesellschaft für Geowissenschaften*, **157**, 203–244.

Vonhof, H.B. & Smit, J. 1996. Strontium-isotope stratigraphy of the type Maastrichtian and the Cretaceous/Tertiary boundary in the Maastricht area (SE Netherlands). *Geologie en Mijnbouw*, **75**, 275–282.

Vrána, S. & Šrámek, J. 1999. Geological interpretation of detailed gravity survey of the granulite complex in southern Bohemia and its structure. *Bulletin of the Czech Geological Survey*, **74**, 261–277.

Wagenbreth, O. 1961. Thüringer Jura und Subherzyne Kreide (Versuch eines paläogeographisch-tektonischen Vergleiches). *Geologie*, **10**, 3–8.

Wagreich, M. 1988. Sedimentologie und Beckenentwicklung des tieferen Abschnittes (Santon-Untercampan) der Gosauschichtgruppe von Gosau und Rußbach (Oberösterreich-Salzburg). *Jahrbuch der geologischen Bundesanstalt*, **131**, 663–685.

Wagreich, M. 1992. Correlation of Late Cretaceous calcareous nannofossil zones with ammonite zones and planktonic foraminifera: the Austrian Gosau sections. *Cretaceous Research*, **13**, 505–516.

Wagreich, M. 1993. Subcrustal tectonic erosion in orogenic belts – A model for the Late Cretaceous subsidence of the Northern Calcareous Alps (Austria). *Geology*, **21**, 941–944.

Wagreich, M. 1995. Subduction tectonic erosion and Late Cretaceous subsidence along the northern Austroalpine margin (Eastern Alps, Austria). *Tectonophysics*, **242**, 63–78.

Wagreich, M. 1998. Lithostratigraphie, Fazies und Sequenzstratigraphie der Gosau Gruppe von Bad Ischl und Strobl am Wolfgangsee (Oberturon-Maastricht, Noerdliche Kalkalpen, Oesterreich). *Jahrbuch der Geologischen Bundesanstalt Wien*, **141**, 209–234.

Wagreich, M. 2001. A 400-km-long piggyback basin (Upper Aptian-Lower Cenomanian) in the Eastern Alps. *Terra Nova*, **13**, 401–406.

Wagreich, M. 2003. A slope-apron succession filling a piggyback basin: the Tannheim and Losenstein Formations (Aptian–Cenomanian) of the eastern part of the Northern Calcareous Alps (Austria). *Mitteilungen der Österreichischen Geologischen Gesellschaft*, **93**, 31–54.

Wagreich, M. & Decker, K. 2001. Sedimentary tectonics and subsidence modelling of the type Upper Cretaceous Gosau basin (Northern Calcareous Alps, Austria). *International Journal of Earth Sciences*, **90**, 714–726.

Wagreich, M. & Faupl, P. 1994. Palaeogeography and geodynamic evolution of the Gosau Group of the Northern Calcareous Alps (Late Cretaceous, Eastern Alps, Austria). *Paleogeography, Paleoclimatology, Paleoecology*, **110**, 235–254.

Wagreich, M. & Krenmayr, H.-G. 1993. Nannofossil biostratigraphy of the Late Cretaceous Nierental Formation, Northern Calcareous Alps (Bavaria, Austria). *Zitteliana*, **20**, 67–77.

Wagreich, M. & Krenmayr, H.-G. 2005. Upper Cretaceous oceanic red beds (CORB) in the Northern Calcareous Alps (Nierental Formation, Austria); slope topography and clastic input as primary controlling factors. *Cretaceous Research*, **26**, 57–64.

Wagreich, M. & Marschalko, R. 1995. Late Cretaceous to Early Tertiary palaeogeography of the Western Carpathians (Slovakia) and the Eastern Alps (Austria): implications from heavy mineral data. *Geologische Rundschau*, **84**, 187–199.

Wagreich, M. & Sachsenhofer, R. F. 1999. Organic carbon-rich calcareous shales in the Lower Albian of the Northern Calcareous Alps (Austria). *Zentralblatt für Geologie und Paläontologie,* Teil I, **1997**, 951–962.

Wagreich, M. & Siegl-Farkas, A. 1999. Subsidence analysis of Upper Cretaceous deposits of the Transdanubian Central Range (Hungary). *Abhandlungen der Geologischen Bundesanstalt*, **56**(2), 435–438.

Wagreich, M., Pavlishina, P. & Malata, E. 2006. Biostratigraphy of the lower red shale interval in the Rhenodanubian Flysch Zone of Austria. *Cretaceous Research*, **27**, 743–753.

Walaszczyk, I. 1987. Mid-Cretaceous events at the marginal part of the Central European Basin (Annopol-on-Vistula section, central Poland). *Acta Geologica Polonica*, **37**(1–2), 61–74.

Walaszczyk, I. 1988. Inoceramid stratigraphy of the Turonian and Coniacian strata in the environs of Opole (southern Poland). *Acta Geologica Polonica*, **38**(1/4), 51–61.

Walaszczyk, I. 1992. Turonian through Santonian deposits of the Central Polish Uplands; their facies development, inoceramid paleontology and stratigraphy. *Acta Geologica Polonica*, **42**(1–2), 1–122.

Walaszczyk, I. 1997. Biostratigraphie und Inoceramen des oberen Unter-Campan und unteres Ober-Campan Norddeutschlands. *Geologie und Paläontologie in Westfalen*, **49**, 1–111.

Walaszczyk, I. 2004. Inoceramids and inoceramid biostratigraphy of the Upper Campanian to basal Maastrichtian of the Middle Vistula River section, central Poland. *Acta Geologica Polonica*, **54**(1), 95–168.

Walaszczyk, I. & Wood, C.J. 1999. Inoceramids and biostratigraphy at the Turonian/Coniacian boundary; based on the Salzgitter-Salder Quarry, Lower Saxony, Germany, and the Słupia Nadbrzeżna section, Central Poland. *Acta Geologica Polonica*, **48**(4), 395–434.

Wegner, N.R. 1913. Tertiär und umgelagerte Kreide bei Oppeln (Oberschlesien). *Palaeontographica*, **60**, 175–274.

Weidich, K.F. 1984. Über die Beziehungen des 'Cenoman' zur Gosau in den Nördlichen Kalkalpen und ihre Auswirkungen auf die paläogeographischen und tektonischen Vorstellungen. *Geologische Rundschau*, **73**, 517–566.

Weidich, K. F. 1987. Neue stratigraphische Ergebnisse aus der süddeutschen Kreide, 2: Die Weillohe-Mergel (Coniac) im Golf von Regensburg. *Neues Jahrbuch für Geologie und Paläontologie, Monatshefte*, **7**, 440–448.

Weidich, K. F. 1990. Die kalkalpine Unterkreide und ihre Foraminiferenfauna. *Zitteliana*, **17**, 1–187.

Weigel, O. 1937. Stratigraphie und Tektonik des Beckens von Gosau. *Jahrbuch der Geologischen Bundesanstalt*, **87**, 11–40.

Weiss, W. 1982. Planktonische Foraminiferen aus dem Cenoman und Turon von Nordwest- und Süddeutschland. *Palaeontographica, A*, **178**, 49–108.

Weissert, H.J. & Bernoulli, D. 1985. A transform margin in the Mesozoic Tethys: evidence from the Swiss Alps. *Geologische Rundschau*, **74**, 665–679.

Wicher, C. A. 1940. Zur Stratigraphie der Grenzschichten Jura-Kreide Nordwestdeutschlands. *Öl und Kohle*, **36**, 263–269.

Wicher, C. A. & Bettenstaedt, F. 1957. Zur Oberkreide-Gliederung der bayerischen Innviertel-Bohrungen. *Geologica Bavarica*, **30**, 3–54.

Wiedmann, J. 1979. Die Ammoniten der NW-deutschen, Regensburger und Ostalpinen Oberkeride im Vergleich mit den Oberkreidefaunen des westlichen Mediterrangebietes. *In* Wiedemann J. (ed.) *Aspekte der Kreide Europas*. International Union of Geological Sciences, **A6**, 335–350.

Wiedmann, J & Schneider, H.L. 1979. Cephalopoden und Alter der Cenoman-Transgression von Mühlheim-Broich, SW-Westfalen. *In:* Wiedmann, J. (ed.) *Aspekte der Kreide Europas*. International Union of Geological Sciences, **A6**, 645–680.

Wiedmann, J., Kaplan, U., Lehmann, J. & Marcinowski, R. 1989. Biostratigraphy of the Cenomanian of NW Germany. *In:* Wiedmann, J. (ed.) *Cretaceous of the Western Tethys. Proceedings of the Third International Cretaceous Symposium, Tübingen 1987*. Schweizerbart, Stuttgart, 931–948.

Wiese, F. 1999. Stable isotope data ($\delta^{13}$C, $\delta^{18}$O) from the Middle and Upper Turonian (Upper Cretaceous) of Liencres (Cantabria, northern Spain) with a comparison to northern Germany (Söhlde & Salzgitter–Salder). *Newsletters on Stratigraphy*, **37**, 37–62.

Wiese, F. 2000. On some Late Turonian and Early Coniacian (Upper Cretaceous) heteromorph ammonites from Germany. *Acta Geologica Polonica*, **50**(4), 407–419.

Wiese, F. & Kaplan, U. 2001. The potential of the Lengerich section (Münster Basin, northern Germany) as a possible candidate Global boundary Stratotype Section and Point (GSSP) for the Middle/Upper Turonian boundary. *Cretaceous Research*, **22**, 549–563.

Wiese, F. & Kröger, B. 1998. Evidence for a shallowing event in the Upper Turonian (Cretaceous) *Mytiloides scupini* Zone of northern Germany. *Acta Geologica Polonica*, **48**, 265–284.

Wiese, F., Hilbrecht, H. & Wood, C.J. 2000. 3.2.8 Turon. *In:* Stratigraphische Kommission Deutschlands (ed.) *Stratigraphie von Deutschland III. Die Kreide der Bundesrepublik Deutschland*. Courier Forschungsinstitut Senckenberg, **226**, 27–31.

Wiese, F., Wood, C.J. & Kaplan, U. 2004*a*. 20 years of event stratigraphy in NW Germany; advances and open questions. *Acta Geologica Polonica*, **54**, 639–656.

Wiese, F., Čech ,S., Ekrt, B., Košt'ák, M., Mazuch, M. & Voigt, S. 2004*b*. The Upper Turonian of the Bohemian Cretaceous Basin (Czech Republic) exemplified by the Úpohlavy working quarry: integrated stratigraphy and palaeoceanography of a gateway to the Tethys. *Cretaceous Research*, **25**, 329–352.

Wilde, V. & Schultka, S. 1996. Die sandige Wealden-Fazies (Bückeberg Formation, Berrias, Unterkreide) am Westrand eines Schüttungskörpers bei Osnabrück. *Neues Jahrbuch für Geologie und Paläontologie, Abhandlungen*, **199**, 249–268.

Wildi, W. 1985. Heavy mineral distribution and dispersal pattern in penninic and ligurian flysch basins (Alps, northern Apennines). *Giornale di Geologia*, **47**, 77–99.

Willingshofer, E., Neubauer, F. & Cloetingh, S. 1999. The significance of Gosau-type basins for the Late Cretaceous tectonic history of the Alpine-Carpathian belt. *Physical Chemical Earth, A*, **24**, 687–695.

Wilmsen, M. 2003. Sequence stratigraphy and palaeoceanography of the Cenomanian stage in Northern Germany. *Cretaceous Research*, **24**, 525–568.

Wilmsen, M. 2004. Teil B: Das Cenoman im östlichen Niedersächsischen Becken. *In:* Mutterlose, J. & Steffahn, J. (eds) *Die Kreide des Subherzynen und östlichen Niedersächsischen Beckens*. Bochumer Geowissenschaftliche Arbeiten, **4**, 57–84.

Wilmsen, M. & Niebuhr, B. 2002. Stratigraphic revision of the upper Lower and Middle Cenomanian in the Lower Saxony Basin (northern Germany) with special reference to the Salzgitter area. *Cretaceous Research*, **23**, 445–460.

Wilmsen, M. & Wiese, F. 2004. Exkursion 4: Biosedimentologie des Cenoman und Turon im Nidersächsischen Becken. *In:* Reitner, J., Reich, M. & Schmidt, G. (eds) *Geobiologie 2*. Universitätsdrucke Göttingen. Universitätsverlag, Göttingen, 73–112.

Wilmsen, M. & Wood, C.J. 2004. The Cenomanian of Hoppenstedt, northern Germany: a Subhercynian key section revisited. *Newletters on Stratigraphy*, **40**(3), 209–230.

Wilmsen, M., Niebuhr, B. & Hiss, M. 2005. The Cenomanian of northern Germany: facies analysis of a transgressive biosedimentary system. *Facies*, **51**, 242–263.

Wilson, P. A., Norris, R. D. & Cooper, M. J. 2002. Testing the Cretaceous greenhouse hypothesis using glassy foraminiferal calcite from the core of the Turonian tropics on Demerara Rise. *Geology*, **30**, 607–610.

Winkler, W. 1988. Mid- to early Late Cretaceous flysch and melange formations in the western part of the Eastern Alps. Paleotectonic implications. *Jahrbuch der geologischen Bundesanstalt*, **131**, 341–389.

Winkler, W. 1996. The tectono-metamorphic evolution of the Cretaceous northern Adriatic margin as recorded by sedimentary series (western part of the Eastern Alps). *Eclogae Geologicae Helvetiae*, **89**, 527–551.

Winkler, W. Wildi, W., Stuijvenberg, J. & Caron, C. 1985. Wägital-Flysch et autres flyschs penniques en Suisse Centrale. *Eclogae Geologicae Helvetiae*, **78**, 1–22.

Wissler, L. 2001. *Response of Early Cretaceous sedimentary systems to perturbations in global carbonate cycling: Insights from stratigraphy, sedimentology and geochemical modeling*. PhD thesis Swiss Federal Institute of Technology, Zürich, No. **14380**.

Wissler, L., Funk, H. & Weissert, H. 2003. Response of Early Cretaceous carbonate platforms to changes in atmospheric carbon dioxide levels. *Palaeogeography, Palaeoclimatology, Palaeoecology*, **200**, 187–205.

Wojewoda, J. 1986. Fault-scarp induced shelf sand bodies: Turonian of the Intrasudetic Basin. *In*: Teisseyre, K.A. (ed.) *5th IAS Regional Meeting Excursion Guidebook*, **A-1**, 31–52.

Wojewoda, J. 1997. Upper Cretaceous littoral-to-shelf succession in the Intrasudetic Basin and Nysa Trough, Sudety Mts. *In:* Wojewoda, J. (ed.) *Obszary Zrodlowe: Zapis w Osadach*. VI Spotkanie Sedymentologów, **1**, 81–96.

Wolburg, J. 1949. Ergebnisse der Biostratigraphie nach Ostracoden im nordwestdeutschen Wealden. *In: Erdöl und Tektonik in Nordwestdeutschland.* Amt für Bodenforschung, Hannover, 349–360.

Wolburg, J. 1959. Die Cyprideen des NW-deutschen Wealden. *Senckenbergiana lethaea*, **40**, 223–315.

Wonham, J. P., Johnson, H. D., Mutterlose, J., Stadtler, A. & Ruffell, A. 1997. Characterization of a shallow marine sandstone reservoir in a syn-rift setting: the Bentheim Sandstone Formation (Valanginian) of the Rühlermoor field, Lower Saxony Basin, NWGermany. *In:* Shanley, K.W. & Perkins, B.F. (eds) *Shallow Marine and Nonmarine Reservoirs: Sequence Stratigraphy, Reservoir Architecture and Production Characteristics.* 18th Annual Research Conference. Gulf Coast Section, SEPM (Society for Sedimentary Geology), Tulsa, 427–448.

Wood, C.J. & Ernst, G. 1998. C 2.9 Turonian-Coniacian of Salzgitter-Salder. *In:* Mutterlose, J., Bornemann, A., Rauer, S., Spaeth, C. & Wood, C.J. (eds) *Key Localities of the Northwest European Cretaceous.* Bochumer Geologische und Geotechnische Arbeiten, **48**, 94–102.

Wood, C.J. & Schmid, F. 1991. Upper Cretaceous of Helgoland (NW Germany): Lithology, palaeontology and biostratigraphy. *Geologisches Jahrbuch*, A, **120**, 37–61.

Wood, C.J., Ernst, G. & Rasemann, G. 1984. The Turonian/Coniacian stage boundary in Lower Saxony (Germany) and adjacent areas: the Salzgitter-Salder Quarry as a proposed international standard section. *Bulletin of the Geological Society of Denmark*, **33**, 225–238.

Wortmann, U.G., Weissert, H., Funk, H. & Hauck, J. 2001. Alpine plate kinematics revisited: The Adria problem. *Tectonics*, **20**, 134–147.

Wortmann, U.G., Herrle, J.O. & Weissert, H. 2004. Altered carbon cycling and coupled changes in Early Cretaceous weathering patterns: Evidence from integrated carbon isotope and sandstone records of the western Tethys. *Earth and Planetary Science Letters*, **220**, 69–82.

WORUM, G., MICHON, L., VAN BALENC, R. T., VAN WEESD, J.-D., CLOETHING, S. & PAGNIER, H. 2005. Pre-Neogene controls on present-day fault activity in the West Netherlands Basin and Roer Valley Rift System (southern Netherlands): role of variations in fault orientation in a uniform low-stress regime. *Quaternary Science Reviews*, **24**, 475–490

WRAY, D.S., WOOD, C.J., ERNST, G. & KAPLAN, U. 1996. Geochemical subdivision and correlation of clay-rich beds in Turonian sediments of northern Germany. *Terra Nova*, **8**, 603–610.

ZACHER, W. 1966. Die kalkalpinen Kreideablagerungen in der Umgebung des Tannheimer Tales (Nordtirol). *Mitteilungen der Bayerischen Staatssammlung für Paläontologie und historische Geologie*, **6**, 213–228.

ZAKHAROV, V. A., BOWN, P. & RAWSON, P. F. 1996. The Berriasian Stage and the Jurassic-Cretaceous boundary. *Bulletin de l'Institut Royal des Sciences Naturelles de Belgique, Sciences de la Terre*, **66** (supplement) 7–10.

ZIEGLER, J. H. 1957. Die Fauna des Cardientones der Oberpfalz und die Bedeutung der Foraminiferen für seine Altersbestimmung. *Geologica Bavarica*, **30**, 55–86.

ZIEGLER, P.A. 1990. *Geological Atlas of Western and Central Europe*. Shell Internationale Petroleum Maatschappij BV, The Hague.

ZIJLSTRA, J.J.P. 1994. Sedimentology of the Late Cretaceous and Early Tertiary (tuffaceous) chalk of northwest Europe. *Geologica Ultraiectina*, **119**, 1–192.

ŽÍTT, J., NEKVASILOVÁ, O., *et al.* 1997. Rocky coast facies of the Cenomanian-Turonian boundary interval at Velim (Bohemian Cretaceous basin, Czech Republic); Parts 1–2. *Bulletin of the Czech Geological Survey*, **72**, 83–156.

ŽÍTT, J., NEKVASILOVÁ, O., HRADECKÁ, L., SVOBODOVÁ, M. & ZÁRUBA, B. 1998. Rocky coast facies of the Unhošt'-Tursko High (Late Cenomanian-early Turonian, Bohemian Cretaceous Basin). *Acta Musei Nationalis Pragae, Series B, Historia Naturalis*, **54**, 79–116.

ZITTEL, K.A. 1866. Die Bivalven der Gosaugebilde. *Denkschrift der Österreichischen Akademie der Wissenschaften*, **25**, 73–198.

# 16 Permian to Cretaceous tectonics

MAGDALENA SCHECK-WENDEROTH, PIOTR KRZYWIEC, RAINER ZÜHLKE, Y. MAYSTRENKO & N. FROITZHEIM

Subsequent to the Variscan Orogeny, the lithosphere of Central Europe was subjected to a series of tectonic events in the Latest Palaeozoic and Mesozoic which were related to the ongoing breakup of Pangaea. The Early Mesozoic tectonic evolution of Central Europe was determined by its position between the stable Precambrian Baltic-East European Craton in the north and NW and two competing megarift systems in the NW, west and south. In the NW and west, the Arctic–North Atlantic rift systems heralded the later crustal separation of Laurasia while in the south, the opening of both the Tethyan oceans and the central Atlantic Ocean led to stress changes in the Central European lithosphere. During the late Mesozoic and early Cenozoic, ongoing rifting resulted in crustal separation in the North Atlantic, whereas the successive closure of the Tethyan oceanic basins and continental collision between Africa and Eurasia caused compression in Central Europe. This superposition of plate-boundary-induced stresses led to the development of a complex structural pattern with subsidence and subsequent inversion of numerous sub-basins and uplift of structural highs. These sub-basins are the sites where the preserved geological record can be used to reconstruct the Mesozoic tectonic history.

The aim of this chapter is to provide a brief overview of the tectonic evolution of Central Europe in the period following the Variscan Orogeny, as well as to discuss the tectonic implications for the region resulting from the various plate movements involved. Detailed accounts of the palaeogeography and geology for the region are contained within the relevant Mesozoic chapters. Additionally, excellent palaeogeographic compilations are available for the Tethyan and peri-Tethyan domain (e.g. Decourt *et al.* 1992, 2000; Golonka 2004; Stampfli and Borel 2004), for the North Sea (e.g. Coward *et al.* 2003; Evans *et al.* 2003; Mosar *et al.* 2002*a*, *b*) and for the Norwegian–Greenland Sea (e.g. Brekke 2000; Mosar *et al.* 2002*a*, *b*; Torsvik *et al.* 2002). Our palaeotectonic maps are based on the works of Baldschuhn *et al.* (1996), Coward *et al.* (2003), Dadlez (1997, 2003), Dadlez *et al.* (1998, 2000); Decourt *et al.* (1992, 2000), Doré *et al.* (1999), Evans *et al.* (2003), Golonka (2004), Kockel (1995), Kockel *et al.* (1996), Lokhorst (1998), Mosar *et al.* (2002*b*), Stampfli & Borel (2002) and Ziegler (1990, 1999). These works are supplemented for some of the presented time slices with regional information detailed in the respective chapters.

## Structural overview

The main Mesozoic tectonic elements of Central Europe north of the Alpine Chain can be roughly divided into two domains (Fig. 16.1a): (1) the Permo-Mesozoic Central European Basin System (CEBS) north of the Variscan orogen; and (2) South Central Europe, an area enclosing the relicts of the Variscan Orogen and the Permo-Mesozoic basins which were superimposed upon it. (See Table 16.1 for abbreviations used in figures.)

### *The Central European Basin System (CEBS)*

The CEBS (Fig. 16.1*b*) covers an area extending from the southern North Sea across Denmark, the Netherlands and northern Germany into Poland, and contains the thickest Permian–Cenozoic succession (>10 km) in Central Europe (Scheck-Wenderoth & Lamarche 2005). It has been the site of extensive industrial and academic exploration over the past decades. Representative seismic sections from different parts of the CEBS illustrate the main tectonostratigraphic features related to its tectonic evolution.

An important feature of the CEBS is the presence of a thick layer of Upper Permian Zechstein salt. The presence of this salt layer strongly influenced the Mesozoic structural evolution of the basin in terms of the mechanical decoupling of its basement from its cover. Thin-skinned deformation is predominant in those areas where the original salt layer was at its thickest, whereas at the margins of the basin thick-skinned deformation occurred. The present-day distribution of mobilized Zechstein salt (Fig. 16.2) is controlled by the orientations of two groups of structures (i.e. NW–SE and north–south; see below) as well as being the result of several tectonic phases during Mesozoic and Cenozoic times, each of which triggered pulses of salt movements (Jaritz 1987; Kockel *et al.* 1996; Krzywiec 2002*a*, *b*, 2004*b*, *c*; Scheck *et al.* 2003*a*, *b*).

The CEBS is composed of several sub-basins which were initiated within the continental crust to the north of the Variscan Orogen and SSW of the Precambrian Baltic Shield, beginning in late Carboniferous times. Repeated strain localization within the CEBS from Permian times onward was controlled, to a large degree, by two major groups of structures orientated NW–SE and north–south. All of the large NW–SE trending fault systems coincide with geophysical discontinuities in the deeper crust or even in the upper mantle (Abramovitz & Thybo 2000; Grad *et al.* 1999, 2002; 2003; Gregersen & Voss 2002; Scheck *et al.* 2002*a*; Thybo 2000, 2001; Thybo *et al.* 1998). The fault systems also correlate spatially with old suture zones (Abramovitz & Thybo 2000) and, therefore, may represent domains of reduced strength inherited from Caledonian and Variscan collision processes (Scheck-Wenderoth & Lamarche 2005). The NW–SE trend predominates in three large basins: (1) the Polish Basin; (2), the Norwegian-Danish Basin; and (3) the North German Basin extending westward into the southern North Sea and including the Anglo-Dutch Basin.

The Polish Basin developed above the Teisseyre-Tornquist

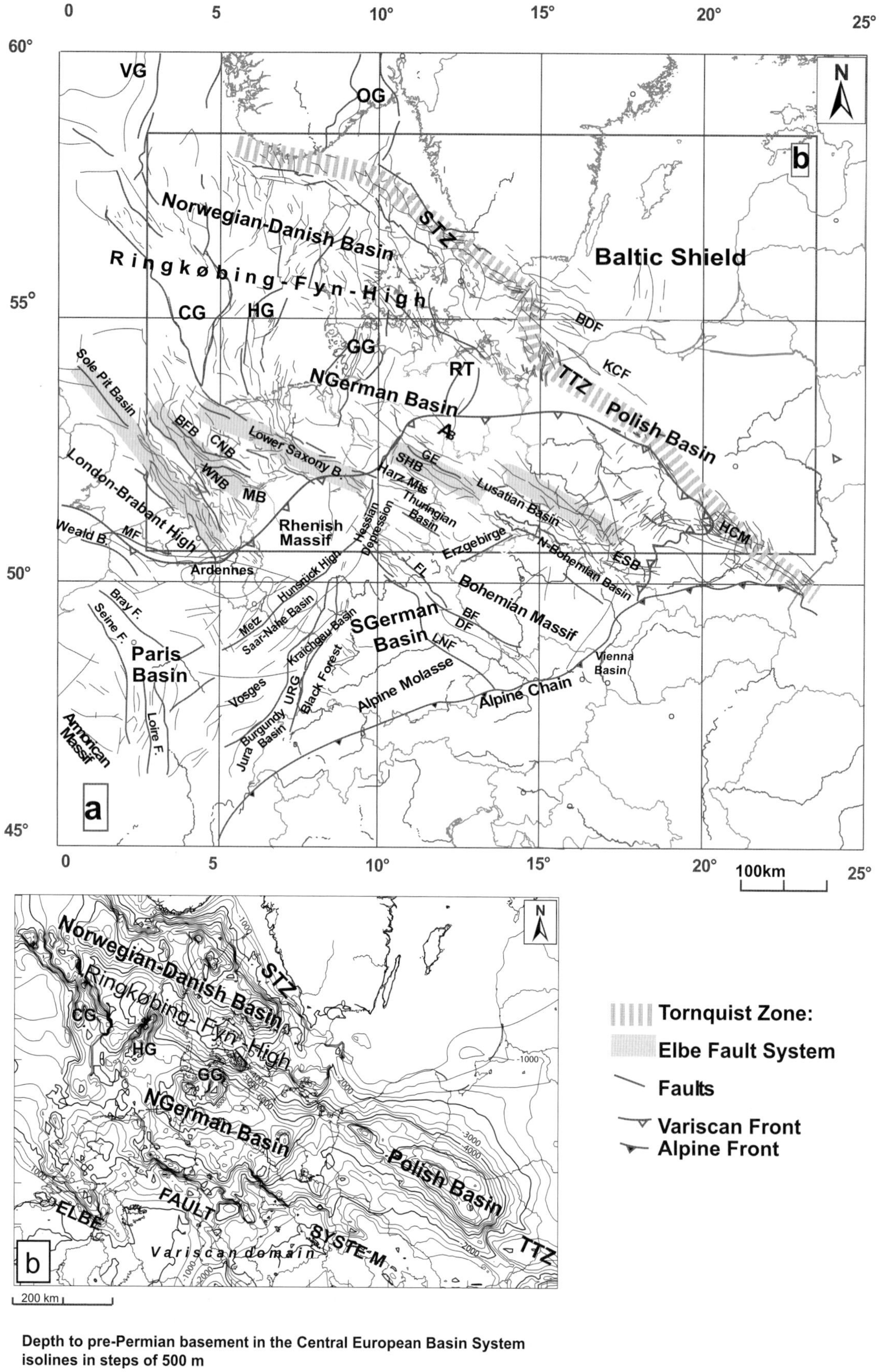


**Fig. 16.1.** (**a**) Overview map of the main Mesozoic structural elements (fault systems and basins) in Central Europe (compiled after Baldschuhn *et al.* 1996; Dadlez *et al.* 1998, 2000; Evans et al. 2003; Freudenberger 1996*b*; Guillocheau *et al.* 2000; Lokhorst 1998; Vejbaek 1997; Ziegler 1999). See Table 16.1 for abbreviations. Large rectangle indicates the area shown in (b). (**b**) Central European Basin System: depth to the top of the pre-Permian, iso lines in 500 m intervals (modified after Scheck-Wenderoth & Lamarche 2005).

**Table 1.** *Abbreviations used in the figures*

| Abbreviation | Name of structural feature |
|---|---|
| AB | Altmark Basin |
| AS | Altmark Swell |
| B | Boulonnais |
| BB | Burgundy Basin |
| BDF | Bornholm-Darlowo Fault Zone |
| BF | Black Forest |
| BFB | Broad Fourteens Basin |
| BF | Bavarian Fault (Bayrischer Pfahl) |
| BrF | Bray Fault |
| C | Copenhagen |
| CG | Central Graben |
| CNB | Central Netherlands Basin |
| DF | Donau Fault |
| EFS | Elke Fault System |
| EHT | East-Holstein Trough |
| FL | Franconian Line |
| FSM | Fore-Sudetic Monocline |
| GE | Gardelegen Escarpment |
| GG | Glückstadt Graben |
| H | Hamburg |
| HCM | Holy Cross Mountains |
| HD | Hessian Depression |
| HG | Horn Graben |
| HH | Hunsrück High |
| ISB | Intra-Sudetic Basin |
| JB | Jura Basin |
| KB | Kraichgau Basin |
| KCF | Koszalin-Chojnice Fault Zone |
| KS | Kuiavian Segment of Mid-Polish Trough |
| LB | Lusatian Basin |
| LBM | London Brabant Massif |
| LNF | Landshut-Neuoetting Fault |
| LSB | Lower Saxony Basin |
| MB | Münsterland Basin |
| MD | Midi Fault |
| MFB | Moray Firth Basin |
| MPS | Mid-Polish Swell |
| NBB | North Bohemian Basin |
| NT | Nida Trough |
| OG | Oslo Graben |
| PB | Pompeckj Block |
| PS | Pomeranian segment of Mid-Polish Trough |
| RFH | Ringkøbing-Fyn High |
| RM | Rhenish Massif |
| RT | Rheinsberg Trough |
| SHB | Subhercynian Basin |
| SNB | Saar-Nahe Basin |
| SPB | Sole Pit Basin |
| STZ | Sorgenfrei-Tornquist Zone |
| TB | Thuringian Basin |
| TTZ | Teisseyre-Tornquist Zone |
| URG | Upper Rhine Graben |
| VB | Valais Basin |
| VG | Viking Graben |
| V-K B | Vosges-Kraichgau Basin |
| W | Warsaw |
| WB | Weald Basin |
| WHT | West-Holstein Trough |
| WNB | West Netherlands Basin |

Zone (Dadlez 2001; Dadlez *et al.* 1995; Kutek 2001; Kutek & Glazek 1972; Pozaryski & Brochwicz-Lewinski 1978; Pozaryski & Zytko 1981; Stephenson *et al.* 2003; Grad & Guterch 2006) which marks the boundary between the Precambrian crust of the Baltic Shield in the NE and the Phanerozoic crust to the SW (Berthelsen 1998; Erlström *et al.* 1997; Grabowska & Bojdys 2001; Grad *et al.* 1999, 2002, 2003; Królikowski & Petecki 2002). The area above this zone was characterized by marked subsidence in Mesozoic times, and is coincident with the axial part of the Polish Basin (i.e. Mid-Polish Trough) (Dadlez *et al.* 1998). The presence of thick Zechstein evaporites within the NW and central segments of the Mid-Polish Trough resulted in partly or fully decoupled evolution of the sedimentary infill (Krzywiec 2002*a*, *b*, 2004*b*, *c*, 2006*a*, *b*). Representative seismic sections across the Polish Basin illustrate the geometry of this basin and its main structural features (Fig. 16.3). In the Polish Basin, the axes of major salt structures (Fig. 16.2) are generally orientated NW–SE. Salt movement probably commenced in the Triassic (Dadlez & Marek 1974; Krzywiec 2002*b*, 2004*a*; Sokolowski 1966). In late Triassic times, intense basement faulting and lateral salt withdrawal resulted in the extrusion of salt onto the basin floor within the central segment of the Mid-Polish Trough (Krzywiec 2004*b*, *c*). Salt movement continued through Jurassic times (Sokolowski 1966), and the salt structures were subsequently reactivated in the late Cretaceous due to regional compression and basin inversion (Krzywiec 2002*a*, *b*, 2004*b*, *c*).

The Sorgenfrei-Tornquist Zone, geographically the NW prolongation of the Teisseyre-Tornquist Zone, is considered to be an intracontinental fault zone within Baltica separating the stable part of the Baltic Shield from its weaker SW margin (Berthelsen 1998; Erlström *et al.* 1997; see also Krawczyk *et al.* 2008). The area to the SE of the Sorgenfrei-Tornquist Zone/Teisseyre-Tornquist Zone was affected by Permian–Cenozoic subsidence, whereas the area to the NE of the structure represents the stable Baltic Shield/East European Platform. Along the Sorgenfrei-Tornquist/Teisseyre-Tornquist Zone, the structural pattern shows a bifurcation from the linear and continuous fault zone of the Teisseyre-Tornquist Zone beneath the Polish Basin to two individual fault zones framing the Norwegian–Danish Basin: the Sorgenfrei-Tornquist Zone in the north and the northern border of the Mid-North Sea–Ringkøbing-Fyn High (Vejbaek 1997) in the south. The Mid-North Sea–Ringkøbing-Fyn High represents a chain of basement highs distributed along a WNW–ESE trending axis from the central North Sea across Denmark to the southern Baltic Sea. This chain separates the Norwegian–Danish and the North German basins (Cartwright 1987).

The North German Basin developed to the south of the Mid-North Sea–Ringkøbing-Fyn High and is bounded to the south by the Elbe Fault System (Scheck *et al.* 2002*b*) (Figs 16.4 & 16.5). The latter comprises a series of NW–SE to WNW–ESE striking en echelon faults which formed at the transition between the North German Basin and the Variscan domain, cropping out at present in the south. These faults were mainly initiated during the Variscan Orogeny as illustrated, for example, by the Late Carboniferous dextral shear which has been recorded from the Elbe Zone near Dresden (Mattern 1996). Most of these faults experienced repeated reactivation during the Mesozoic (Franke & Hoffmann 1999; Franzke *et al.* 2004; Scheck *et al.* 2002*a*; Stackebrandt 1997).

A second group of structures, trending roughly north–south, is also present within the CEBS. The largest of these include the southern segment of the Central Graben, the Horn Graben, the Glückstadt Graben and the Rheinsberg Trough (Fig. 16.1). These north–south elements resulted from Mid-Triassic (Keuper) to Early Jurassic differentiation of the largely WNW–ESE-orientated Permian basins into a series of sub-basins, although some of these grabens may have had an older Palaeozoic history (Heeremans *et al.* 2004; Lie & Andersson 1998). The accelerated Mid-Triassic (Keuper) to Early Jurassic subsidence in north–south grabens was accompanied by salt mobilization. Accordingly, most of the north–south striking salt walls in the northern

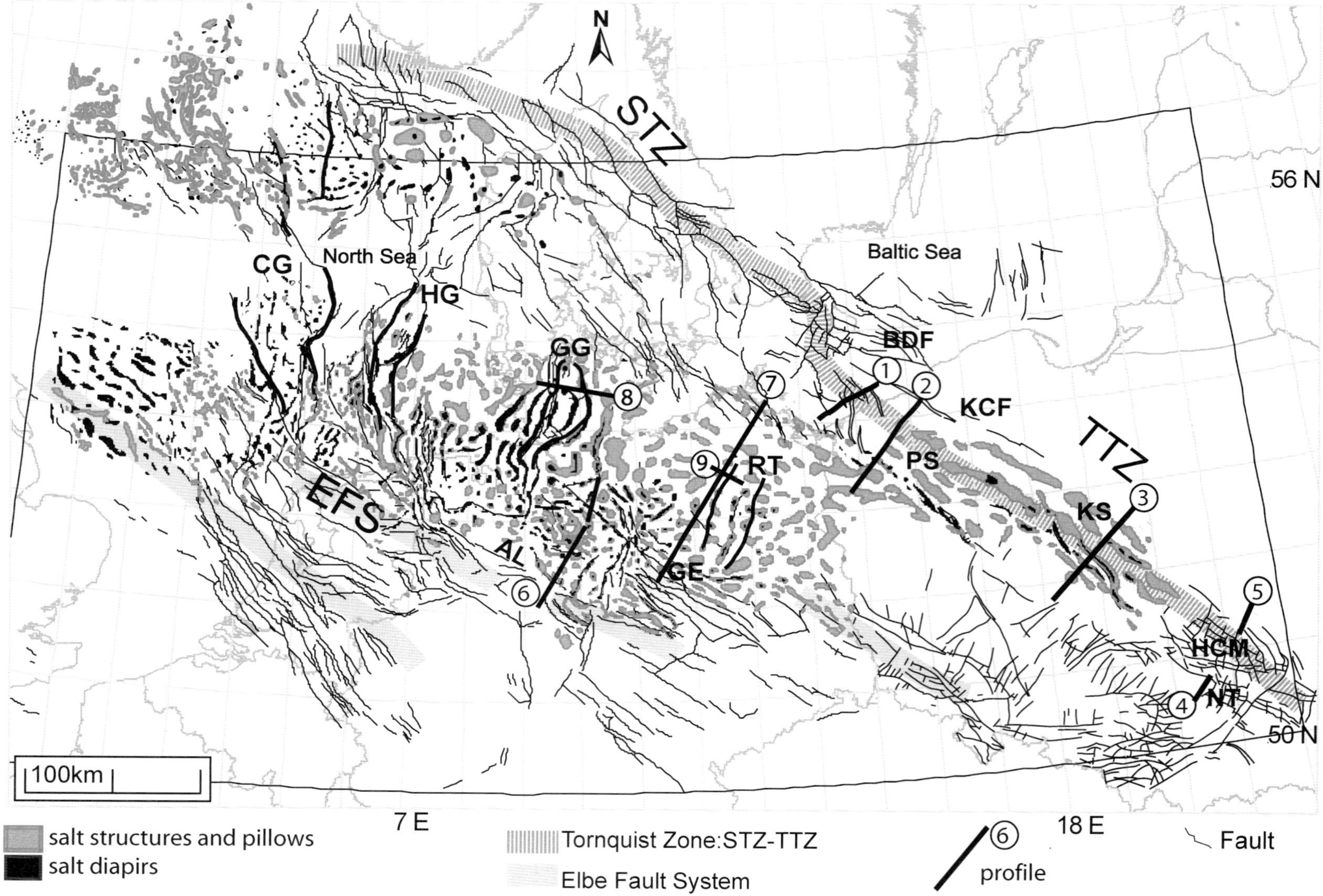


**Fig. 16.2.** Present distribution of salt structures in the Central European Basin System (CEBS) and superimposed main faults (Baldschuhn *et al.* 1996; Dadlez *et al.* 1998; Evans *et al.* 2003; Jaritz 1987; Lokhorst 1998; Nalpas & Brun 1993; Remmelts 1995; Scheck *et al.* 2003*b*). The Zechstein salt influenced the Mesozoic structural evolution by mechanical decoupling of its basement from its cover. This resulted in two types of structures: (1) a province of NNW–SSE to NNE–SSW striking salt walls in the northern half of the southern North Sea and the North German Basin initiated in Mid- to Late Triassic during the accelerated subsidence in the large north–south trending grabens; and (2) a province of NW–SE striking salt structures in the southern half of the southern North Sea and the North German Basin developed in Cretaceous times, coeval with the formation and inversion of NW–SE striking sub-basins. In the Polish basin the salt axes follow the NW–SE direction of the Teisseyre-Tornquist Zone and show pulses of enhanced salt mobilization for the Mid- to Late Triassic, the Jurassic and the Cretaceous. See Table 16.1 for abbreviations. Profiles illustrating the internal structural setting of the CEBS are shown in Figure 16.3 (profiles 1–5), Figure 16.4 (profile 6) Figure 16.5 (profile 7) and Figure 16.6 (profiles 8 and 9).

half of the southern North Sea and the North German Basin (Fig. 16.2) were initiated in Mid- to Late Triassic times. In the Glückstadt Graben, for example, local stratigraphic thickening in the Keuper and Jurassic interval is visible in seismic profiles across the graben (Fig. 16.6a) and some of these profiles also show evidence of syntectonic salt movement (Maystrenko *et al.* 2005). A further example of combined extension and salt deformation during the Late Triassic to Jurassic is present in the Rheinsberg Trough in eastern Germany (Fig. 16.6b). Salt diapirism also accompanied the accelerated subsidence in the Horn and Central grabens (Clausen & Pedersen 1999). Towards the margins of the grabens the north–south trending salt structures become increasingly younger and distinct pulses of salt diapirism are observed in the Jurassic and the Neogene (Jaritz 1987; Maystrenko *et al.* 2005, 2006).

Further differentiation of the CEBS in the Late Jurassic to Early Cretaceous resulted in localized subsidence at the margins of the basin system along the Sorgenfrei-Tornquist Zone and the Elbe Fault System, whereas the central part was uplifted. This uplift is documented by a regional, mostly erosional, unconformity (the so-called Base Cretaceous Unconformity, BCU) in the North German Basin and in the North Sea as well as in the Norwegian–Danish Basin. Locally accelerated subsidence along the margins of the CEBS led to the development of NW–SE orientated sub-basins. Along the southern margin, these sub-basins are superimposed on old Variscan structures along the Elbe Fault System (Sole Pit Basin, Broad Fourteens Basin, Münsterland Basin, Weald Basin, Channel Basin, the West and Central Netherlands Basins, Lower Saxony Basin, Altmark Basin, Subhercynian Basin and North Bohemian Basin). This is indicated by local stratigraphic thickening of the corresponding reflection packages in seismic sections as illustrated, for example, in the Lower Saxony Basin (Fig. 16.4). Subsequently, these sub-basins were the sites of localized uplift during the latest Cretaceous, as also illustrated by a parallel section across the NE German Basin (Fig. 16.5). Coeval with the formation and inversion of the NW–SE striking sub-basins along the Elbe Fault System, a new phase of salt movement is observed which resulted in the production of a series of NW–SE striking salt structures present in the southern part of the southern North Sea and the North German Basin (Fig. 16.2). A similar evolution, with localized Late Jurassic–Early Cretaceous subsidence followed by Late Cretaceous inversion, has also been observed at the northern margin of the CEBS along the Sorgenfrei-Tornquist Zone (Vejbaek 1997).

### *The basins of south Central Europe*

The southern part of Central Europe comprises the area formerly composing the Variscan chain. This domain was successively rifted from late Carboniferous through to Early Permian times (see McCann *et al.* 2008*a*, *b*) and numerous sub-basins developed between the persistent highs of the Anglo-Brabant–Ardennes–Rhenish–Bohemian massifs. The deposition of Early Permian continental clastics was restricted to small, isolated intra-Variscan basins (e.g. Hessian Basin, Thuringian Basin, Saar-Nahe-Basin, Vosges and Kraichgau basins, Intra-Sudetic Basin, Burgundy Basin) but extended southwards during the late Permian and into the Mesozoic, where the South German and the Paris basins developed to the south of the chain of highs. During the Mesozoic, the southern domain became an epicontinental sea at the northern (passive) margin of the Alpine Tethys. To the west, the Armorican Massif separated the intracontinental basins from the shelf of the northern Tethyan margin, but open connections probably existed to the Tethyan shelf in the south. Furthermore, open connections were repeatedly established to the Arctic–North Atlantic domain via the CEBS. From Triassic times, the Mid-Polish Trough was occasionally connected with the Tethys Ocean (Szulc 2000). In the Jurassic the southern basin segment represented a transitional area between the peri-Tethyan and the Tethyan domains (Gutowski *et al.* 2005; Hakenberg & Swidrowska 1997; Kutek 1994, 2001; Pozaryski & Zytko 1981).

The various sub-basins of south Central Europe experienced a rather uniform evolution throughout much of the Mesozoic, and this was mainly determined by eustatic sea-level changes and regional subsidence. Since there is no Zechstein salt present in this region (located to the south of the Zechstein Basin, see McCann *et al.* 2008*b*), the Mesozoic brittle deformation pattern, comprising Mesozoic extensional faulting as well as Cretaceous–Early Tertiary compression, is consistently thick-skinned and mostly restricted to block-wise vertical movements or translations. The area to the south of the Anglo–Brabant–Rhenish–Bohemian chain of highs shows little lateral variation in terms of structural evolution from the Triassic to Late Jurassic. However, in latest Jurassic–early Cretaceous times, an uplift event in Central Europe (i.e. Central European Island) has been reported from an area extending from the Paris Basin in the west to the Bohemian Massif in the east.

The present structural appearance of south Central Europe was mostly determined in Tertiary times, when compressive stresses induced by Alpine collision led to uplift and inversion of east–west to NW–SE striking blocks and downwarping of the southern part of the South German Basin beneath the Alpine foreland. Similarly, the SE part of the inverted Polish Basin was overthrust by the Outer Carpathian orogenic wedge in Tertiary times (Oszczypko 2004, Oszczypko *et al.* 2006), and this resulted in the development of the Carpathian Foreland Basin (Krzywiec 2001; Oszczypko *et al.* 2006).

## Main tectonic phases: plate-tectonic framework and structural evolution of post-Variscan Central Europe

Various attempts have been made to establish a structural scheme for the major tectonic phases in the individual sub-basins of Mesozoic Central Europe, including correlation of the sedimentary successions. This, however, is complicated by the fact that the geodynamic processes involved varied both in time and space across the region. Current plate reconstructions focus either on the reconstruction of the Tethyan (e.g. Decourt *et al.* 1992, 2000; Golonka 2004; Stampfli & Borel 2002; 2004) or the North Atlantic (e.g. Mosar *et al.* 2002*a*, *b*; Torsvik *et al.* 2002) domains, although there have been attempts to combine both (e.g. Evans *et al.* 2003; Ziegler 1999). Here, an attempt has been made to combine these various sources and to complement them with recent research findings. The results are presented below in a series of tectonic phases rather than discrete time slices. Since the Mesozoic history of Central Europe was strongly determined by the regional configuration inherited from the Variscan Orogeny, this overview will commence with an analysis of this important phase.

### *Latest Carboniferous–Early Permian*

During the Carboniferous–Permian transition, much of Central Europe was occupied by the collapsing Variscan mountain chain with its former foreland to the north. Igneous activity was marked across the region, both within the decaying Variscan orogen and in its foreland (Fig. 16.7), and ranged from alkaline

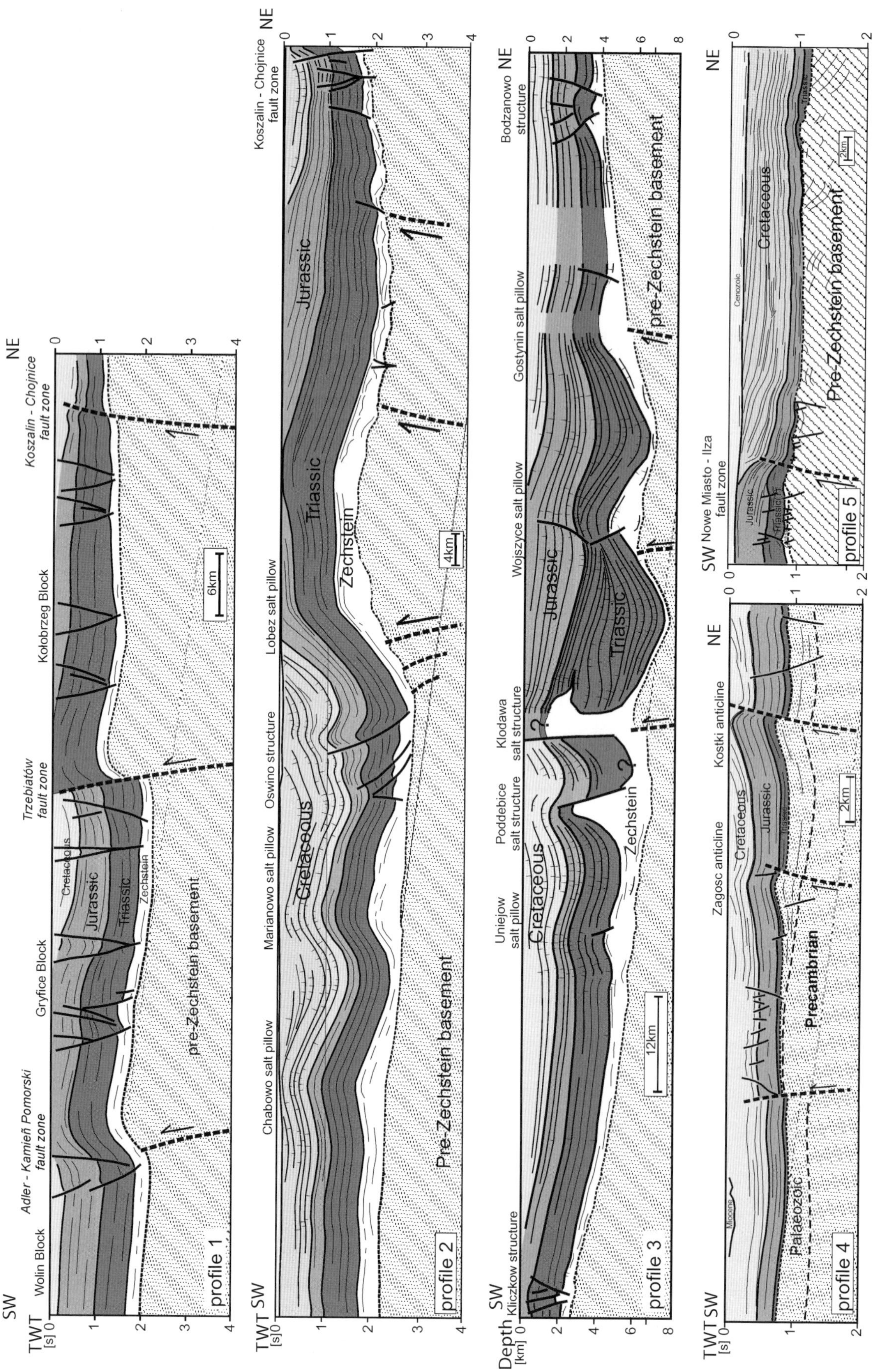
profile 1
SW
NE
TWT [s]
Wolin Block
Adler - Kamień Pomorski fault zone
Gryfice Block
Trzebiatów fault zone
Kołobrzeg Block
Koszalin - Chojnice fault zone
Cretaceous
Jurassic
Triassic
Zechstein
pre-Zechstein basement
6km
profile 2
Chabowo salt pillow
Marianowo salt pillow
Oswino structure
Lobez salt pillow
Koszalin - Chojnice fault zone
Cretaceous
Jurassic
Triassic
Zechstein
Pre-Zechstein basement
4km
profile 3
Depth [km]
Kliczkow structure
Uniejow salt pillow
Poddebice salt structure
Klodawa salt structure
Wojszyce salt pillow
Gostynin salt pillow
Bodzanowo structure
Cretaceous
Jurassic
Triassic
Zechstein
pre-Zechstein basement
12km
profile 4
Miocene
Zagosc anticline
Kostki anticline
Cretaceous
Jurassic
Triassic
Palaeozoic
Precambrian
2km
profile 5
Nowe Miasto - Ilza fault zone
Jurassic
Triassic
Cenozoic
Cretaceous
Pre-Zechstein basement
1km

**Fig. 16.3.** Interpreted line drawings of seismic profiles across the Polish Basin (see Fig. 16.2 for location). Profile 3, vertical scale kilometres; all other profiles, vertical scale seconds, two-way travel time (TWT). Profile 1, from the SW Baltic Sea (NW Mid-Polish Trough), shows some main inversion-related reverse fault zones. Despite later erosion it is still possible to observe an overall divergent seismic pattern and thickness increase towards the main basement fault zones, suggesting their extensional activity prior to inversion during the Triassic and Jurassic. Profile 2, from the NW (Pomeranian) segment of the Mid-Polish Trough, shows regional inversion-related structures: basement blocks uplifted along reverse faults and associated cover deformations developed within the Mesozoic complex (after Krzywiec 2002*a*). Note the overall thickness increase towards the basin centre, and some local thickness variations related to the growth of peripheral structures (e.g. Oświno or Koszalin–Chojnice structures). On a regional scale, the Mesozoic cover was decoupled from the pre-Zechstein basement. Profile 3 is from the central (Kuiavian) segment of the Mid-Polish Trough (after Krzywiec 2004*b*,*c*). A significant thickness increase towards the NE of the Kłodawa salt structure located in the middle of the profile suggests strongly asymmetric subsidence and later inversion controlled by sub-Zechstein basement faults. Profile 4 is from the Nida Trough (after Krzywiec 2002*a*, 2004*c*). The uppermost Cretaceous deposits (Maastrichtian) are characterized by a thickness increase towards the axial parts of the inversion anticlines suggesting that these areas were still sites of subsidence in the Late Cretaceous, and that inversion took place later, most probably in the Palaeogene. Miocene sediments that partly cover the Mesozoic succession belong to the infill of the Carpathian foredeep basin. Within the Nida Trough, a progressive thickness increase of the Jurassic succession is observed towards the NE. Profile 5 is from the SE segment of the Mid-Polish Trough (after Krzywiec 2002*a*). Note thickness changes, local angular unconformities and progradational pattern within the Upper Turonian(?)–Maastrichtian deposits that point towards their relationship with the inversion and indicate uplift of the axial part of the Mid-Polish Trough. Interpreted tops of the Triassic and Zechstein within the hanging-wall are based on long-range correlations across major fault zones due to lack of deep wells and should be regarded as approximate.

intracontinental, rift-related, mantle-derived magmatism in the Oslo Graben (Neumann *et al.* 2002) to dominantly intermediate and felsic, calc-alkaline magmatism with a strong anatectic component in the NE German Basin (Benek *et al.* 1996; Breitkreuz & Kennedy 1999), the Saar-Nahe Basin and the Intra-Sudetic Basin (Romer *et al.* 2001) as well as in the NE–SW striking intramontane basins of the Vosges and Black Forest areas (Freudenberger 1996*b*).

In the CEBS, magmatic activity was extensive, resulting in a thick cover of volcanic products across much of the region (Wilson *et al.* 2004; Ziegler 1990). Thickness variations within the volcanic succession of the CEBS (Fig. 16.7b) suggest that there were focused thermal disturbances along the Sorgenfrei Tornquist Zone in northern Denmark (up to 1500 m drilled) as well as along the NNE–SSW striking Rheinsberg Lineament in NE Germany and NW Poland (up to 2500 m of volcanics drilled; Benek *et al.* 1996; Scheck-Wenderoth & Lamarche 2005).

Traditionally, the tectonic concept of Arthaud & Matte (1977) has been used to explain the structural setting observed in Central Europe for the late Carboniferous–early Permian time interval. This concept assumes the existence of a dextral megashear system between the ongoing subduction in the Urals and the onset of orogenic collapse in the Appalachians and in the European Variscides. The existence of this Late Carboniferous dextral wrench regime is, in essense, largely based on outcrop information derived from locations in Spain, France and Belgium (Arthaud & Matte 1977). Local structural analysis of fault slip data sets in Variscan outcrops of England, Belgium and NE France (Vandycke 1997), eastern Germany (Mattern 1996) and Poland (Lamarche *et al.* 1999, 2002) would appear to confirm this concept and suggest that the Late Carboniferous palaeostress pattern was characterized by north–south to NNE–SSW orientated compression and east–west to WNW–ESE orientated extension. This resulted in the activation of NW–SE striking dextral strike-slip faults and subordinate NNE–SSW striking sinistral faults.

Recently published palaeoplate-tectonic models (e.g. Golonka 2004; Stampfli & Borel 2002; Ziegler 1999) suggest that the initial phases of post-Variscan plate reorganization were related to late Permian–early Triassic backarc extension. This was a consequence of continued subduction of Palaeotethys (Fig. 16.7). Although Gondwana collided with Laurussia in the late Carboniferous, the final closure of Palaeotethys took place during the Cimmerian (Triassic to Jurassic) orogenic cycle. It has been suggested that the continued northward subduction of Palaeotethys was not only responsible for the widespread late Carboniferous calc-alkaline intrusions and volcanism found in the Variscan Alpine–Mediterranean domain, but also that slab roll-back resulted in a general collapse of the Variscan cordillera and large-scale lateral displacement of the terranes (Stampfli & Borel 2002). Such a scenario is supported by thermomechanical finite element models evaluating late-orogenic extension and destruction of the Variscides (Henk 1997). These models indicate that gravitational collapse alone cannot reproduce the observed timing and amount of Permo-Carboniferous crustal thinning, but additional tensile plate boundary forces are required.

In summary, a superposition of backarc extension, transtension and regional thermal destabilization governed the evolution of post-Variscan Central Europe in the late Carboniferous–early Permian prior to Permian subsidence.

### *Early Permian (Rotliegend)*

The Early Permian was characterized by moderate rifting in Central Europe with predominantly NNE–SSW trending normal

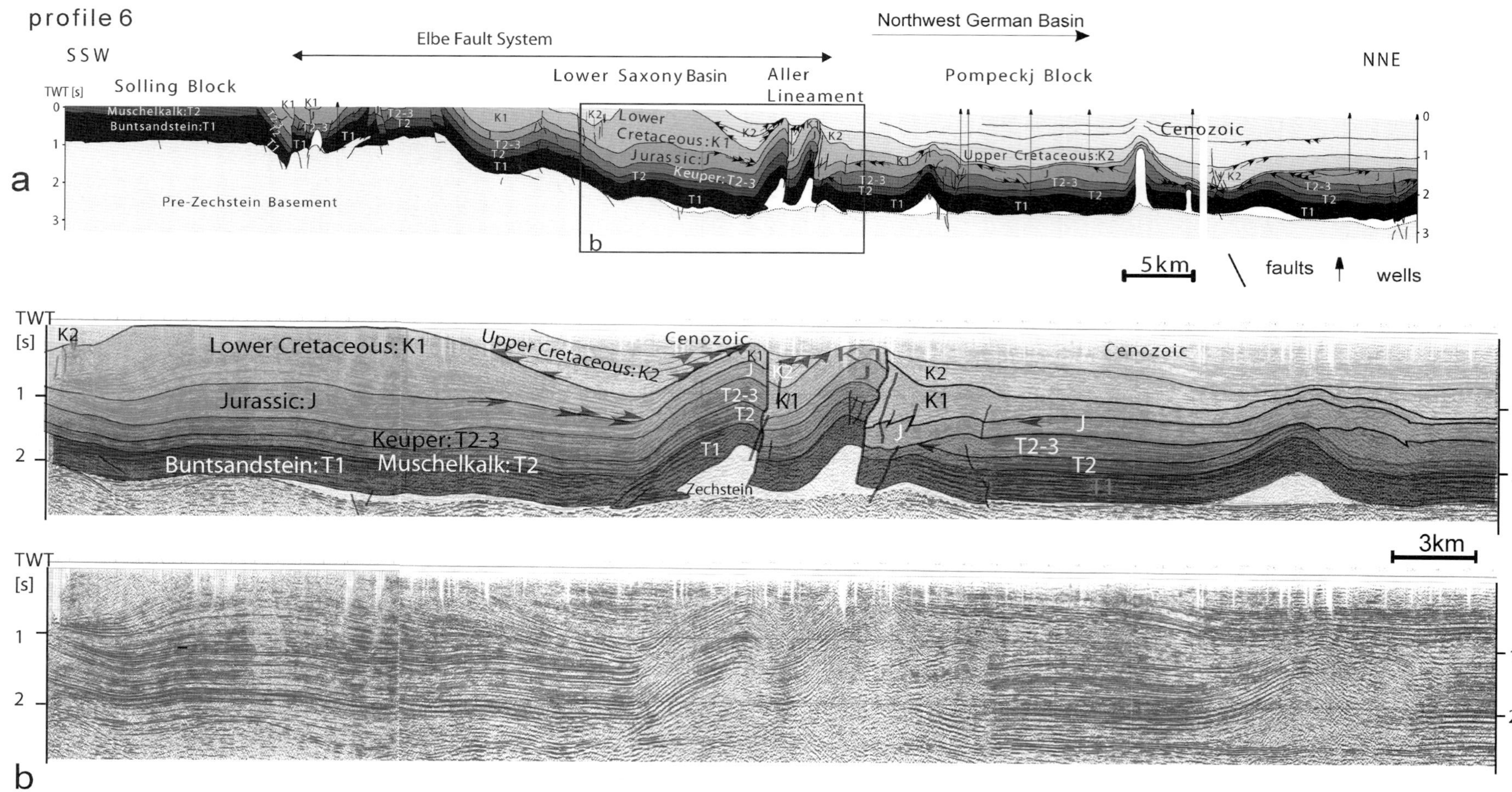


**Fig. 16.4.** Interpreted seismic section (**a**) (vertical scale two-fold exaggerated) and, detail of migrated and coherency-filtered seismic line (**b**) (normal vertical scale) running from the central North German Basin to the southern margin across the inverted Lower Saxony Basin (see Fig. 16.2 for location of profile 6). This line illustrates continuous subsidence in the Early to Mid-Triassic (Buntsandstein and Muschelkalk) represented by parallel, continuous reflections. The overlying reflections, interpreted as Upper Jurassic–Lower Cretaceous, show local stratigraphic thickening and indicate accelerated subsidence in the Lower Saxony Basin at the southern margin of the Central European Basin System compared to the Pompeckj Block further north. Late Cretaceous inversion resulted in basement-involving uplift at the Lower Saxony Basin and folding of the salt cover in the NW German Basin. The tectonic decoupling by the Zechstein salt across large parts of the basin is obvious as well as localized, basement-involving deformation restricted to the Lower Saxony Basin, where salt is thin or absent (modified after Mazur & Scheck-Wenderoth 2005).

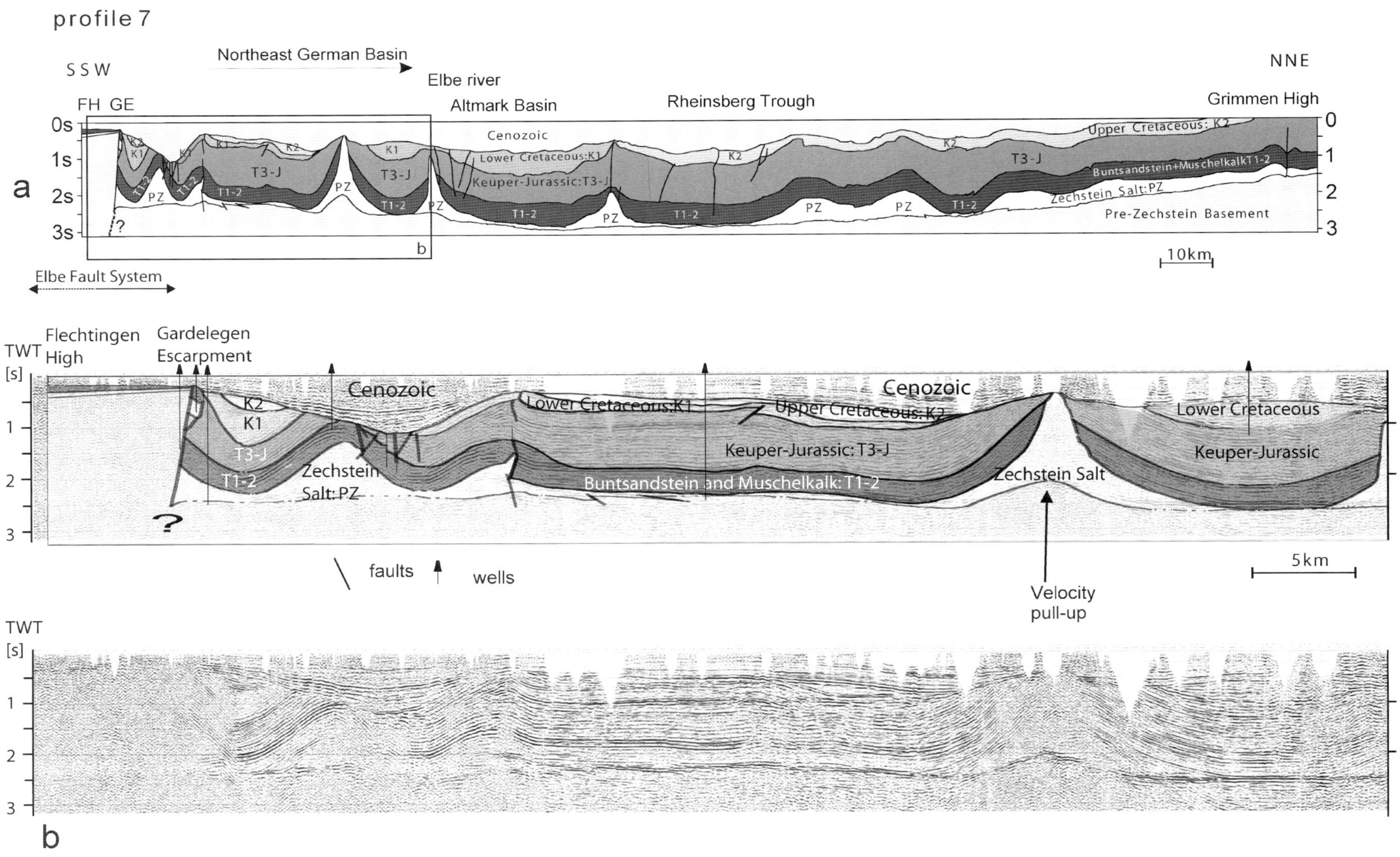


**Fig. 16.5.** Interpreted seismic section DEKORP BASIN9601 (**a**) (vertical scale two-fold exaggerated) and detail of migrated seismic line (**b**) (normal vertical scale) crossing the NE German Basin from south of Rügen to the southern basin margin (see Fig. 16.2 for location of profile 7). The line is perpendicular to the Permo-Triassic basin axis as well as to the WNW–ESE striking inversion structures, but parallel to the NNE–SSW striking Rheinsberg Trough. This line indicates continuous subsidence during the Triassic and Jurassic. At the southern margin localized subsidence is indicated for the Early Cretaceous and inversion for the Late Cretaceous. Deformation is tectonically decoupled by the Zechstein salt below the basin whereas basement deformation is localized and most intense at the Elbe Fault System. There the base of the Zechstein is displaced by 2-second two-way traveltime (TWT) along the Gardelegen Fault. Some smaller basement faults are visible about 50 km north of the Gardelegen Fault and at the northern margin. Further north the base of the Zechstein appears as a strong, continuous signal below salt-depleted areas as well as below salt pillows and diapirs, but the amount of deformation present in the salt basement is negligibly small compared to the amount of deformation present in the cover or at the basin margins.

faults (Fig. 16.8a, b). Early Permian rifting is also recorded along the margins of the future North Atlantic in East Greenland (Coward *et al.* 2003) and along the Norwegian Shelf (Brekke 2000), where Early Permian normal faulting in NNE–SSW striking graben structures is reported. Likewise, NE–SW trending Permian basins developed in NW Britain (Coward *et al.* 2003), and NW–SE directed extension is inferred from Permian normal faulting in southern Britain (Chadwick & Evans 1995).

In north Central Europe, the Early Permian saw the establishment of the Northern and Southern Permian basins, considered to be the oldest basins of the CEBS (Ziegler 1990). These basins contain a thick succession of clastics, the Rotliegend, which is overlain by the Upper Permian Zechstein evaporites. The geometry and mechanisms of basin initiation are still debated since structural resolution of seismic data is poor below the Upper Permian Zechstein salt. Subsidence analysis across the Southern Permian Basin (van Wees *et al.* 2000) suggests late Carboniferous–early Permian crustal extension followed by delayed infilling and thermal subsidence in late Permian to Triassic times as a plausible mechanism for the observed subsidence history. The observation that earliest Rotliegend sediments were deposited in small pull-apart basins between the Mid-North Sea–Ringkøbing-Fyn High as well as the Teisseyre-Tornquist Zone in the north and the Elbe Fault System in the south (Bachmann & Hoffmann 1997; Gast 1988; Scheck & Bayer 1999) indicates that continued dextral shearing along the margins of the basin system (Sorgenfrei Tornquist/Teisseyre-Tornquist Zone and Elbe Fault System) may still have influenced the subsidence pattern during the period of basin initiation. However, the Early Permian Oslo Graben in southern Norway and the earliest Permian extensional structures in northern Germany (Gast 1988; Plein 1995) have NNE–SSW striking axes and thus suggest that there was a component of WNW–ESE directed extension.

Following the initial period of Early Permian rifting, much of northern Central Europe was affected by a phase of thermal subsidence in the Late Rotliegend. The initial, graben-like depocentres of north Central Europe were joined to form the large Northern and Southern Permian basins along NW–SE to WNW–ESE trending axes. These basins were separated by the parallel Mid-North Sea–Ringkøbing-Fyn chain of highs. In the Northern Permian Basin (also termed the Norwegian–Danish Basin; Fig. 16.8c), the thickness of the Rotliegend sedimentary succession rarely exceeds 300 m (Evans *et al.* 2003; Lokhorst 1998). In contrast, the Southern Permian Basin comprising the Southern North Sea, the North German Basin and the Polish Basin, accumulated the thickest Rotliegend sequence in Central Europe with a maximum thickness of 2300 m along the axis of the North German Basin (Bachmann & Hoffmann 1997; McCann 1999; Plein 1995; Scheck & Bayer 1999) and *c.* 1600 m in the Polish Basin (Dadlez *et al.* 1995, 1998; Kiersnowski *et al.* 1995; Lokhorst 1998; Scheck-Wenderoth & Lamarche 2005).

As noted earlier, the rather linear structure of the NW–SE striking Polish Rotliegend Basin is superimposed on the Teisseyre-Tornquist Zone. In contrast, the adjacent North German–Southern North Sea Rotliegend basin has a broader, sag-like structure, slightly elongated in a WNW–ESE direction. The thickness distribution of the Rotliegend sediments (Fig. 16.8c) suggests that post-rift thermal subsidence commenced earlier in the Southern Permian Basin than in the Northern Permian Basin, where the Rotliegend is thinner and considerable post-rift subsidence is observed in Zechstein times (Vejbaek 1997). Alternatively, this observation could suggest that rifting was more extensive in the Southern Permian Basin than in the Northern Permian Basin. According to seismic data, the Rotliegend is absent on the Mid-North Sea–Ringkøbing-Fyn High (Abramovitz & Thybo 2000; Clausen & Pedersen 1999; Scheck *et al.* 2002*c*), suggesting that it represented a structural high during the Early Permian and that its crust was not affected by thermal destabilization.

In south Central Europe, within the area of the collapsing Variscan Orogen, the axes of former Variscan thrusts and folds provided the structural template for intramontane basins developing in the Late Carboniferous–Early Permian. The developing basins formed above former synclines whereas horsts were superimposed on former anticlines (Walter 1992). In southern and southwestern Germany, prominent NNE–SSW orientated Permian basins of this kind preserved several hundred metres of Rotliegend-age sediments between parallel highs forming, from north to south: the Hessian Basin, the Saar-Nahe Basin, the Vosges-Kraichgau Basin and the Burgundy Basin (Freudenberger 1996*a*; Ziegler 1999). Similar structures developed within the Intrasudetic area (Dadlez *et al.* 1998). The majority of these intramontane basins were initiated in Late Carboniferous times, but show continued subsidence with active faulting into the Early Permian. For example the Saar-Nahe Basin (Kukulus & Henk 1999; Schäfer & Korsch 1998; Stollhofen & Stanistreet 1994),

**Fig. 16.6.** Seismic examples across the north–south striking structural elements active as Triassic–Jurassic extensional structures, affected by regional uplift in Mid- to Late Jurassic to Early Cretaceous, by tectonic quiescence in the Late Cretaceous and by renewed subsidence in the Cenozoic. (**a**) Migrated seismic section (below) and interpretation (above) across the central Glückstadt Graben (profile 8 in Fig. 16.2) showing that the deepest part of the graben is still a subject of debate. Different interpretations can be made concerning the thickness of the Lower Triassic Buntsandstein and the location of the base of the Triassic, of which a 'minimum' version is shown here. Major salt movements occurred at the beginning of the Keuper, when the Glueckstadt Graben was affected by extension. The internal seismic pattern of the Keuper, lithostratigraphic data, and palynological investigations (Trusheim 1960) indicate that Permian salt extruded onto the palaeosurface and was dissolved and redeposited within the Keuper strata. Early Jurassic extension and related normal faulting documented in the Lower Saxony Basin and within the Pompeckj Block (Kockel 2002) may also have affected the Glueckstadt Graben, but thick Jurassic sediments are only observed around salt structures. Parts of the Jurassic were eroded in Late Jurassic–Early Cretaceous times as indicated by the respective unconformity. The Upper Cretaceous strata have an almost constant thickness and their parallel reflection pattern indicates a quiet tectonic setting with very minor salt movements in the Late Cretaceous. Salt movements resumed only in the Cenozoic. (**b**) Migrated seismic section (below) and interpretation (above) across the western shoulder of the Rheinsberg Trough ending to the east in the trough centre (profile 9 in Fig. 16.2). The onset of salt mobilization is observed synchronous with the development of the NNE–SSW striking Rheinsberg Trough in the Late Triassic Keuper. This is inferred from stratigraphic thickening in the reflections interpreted as Late Triassic (Keuper)–Jurassic towards the trough centre and showing indications for synsedimentary salt movements in the reflective pattern. The salt is almost completely removed below the trough. While normal faults are present in the Mesozoic cover, the base of the Zechstein appears as a strong, continuous signal below the trough. The Lower Cretaceous rests unconformably on older units of conformal geometry and is truncated upward by an erosional unconformity. The latter separates Cenozoic from older units and indicates severe pre-Cenozoic uplift of the area.

which contains a Namurian to Rotliegend sedimentary succession of up to 7.5 km, formed as a result of sinistral, oblique normal faulting related to extensional, east–west orientated reactivation of the listric Hunsrück Boundary Fault (see McCann *et al.* 2008*b*). In eastern Germany, and southern Poland the Permian evolution of the Thuringian and of the Intrasudetic basins is likewise controlled by Variscan structures but there, active normal faulting took place along NW–SE striking faults.

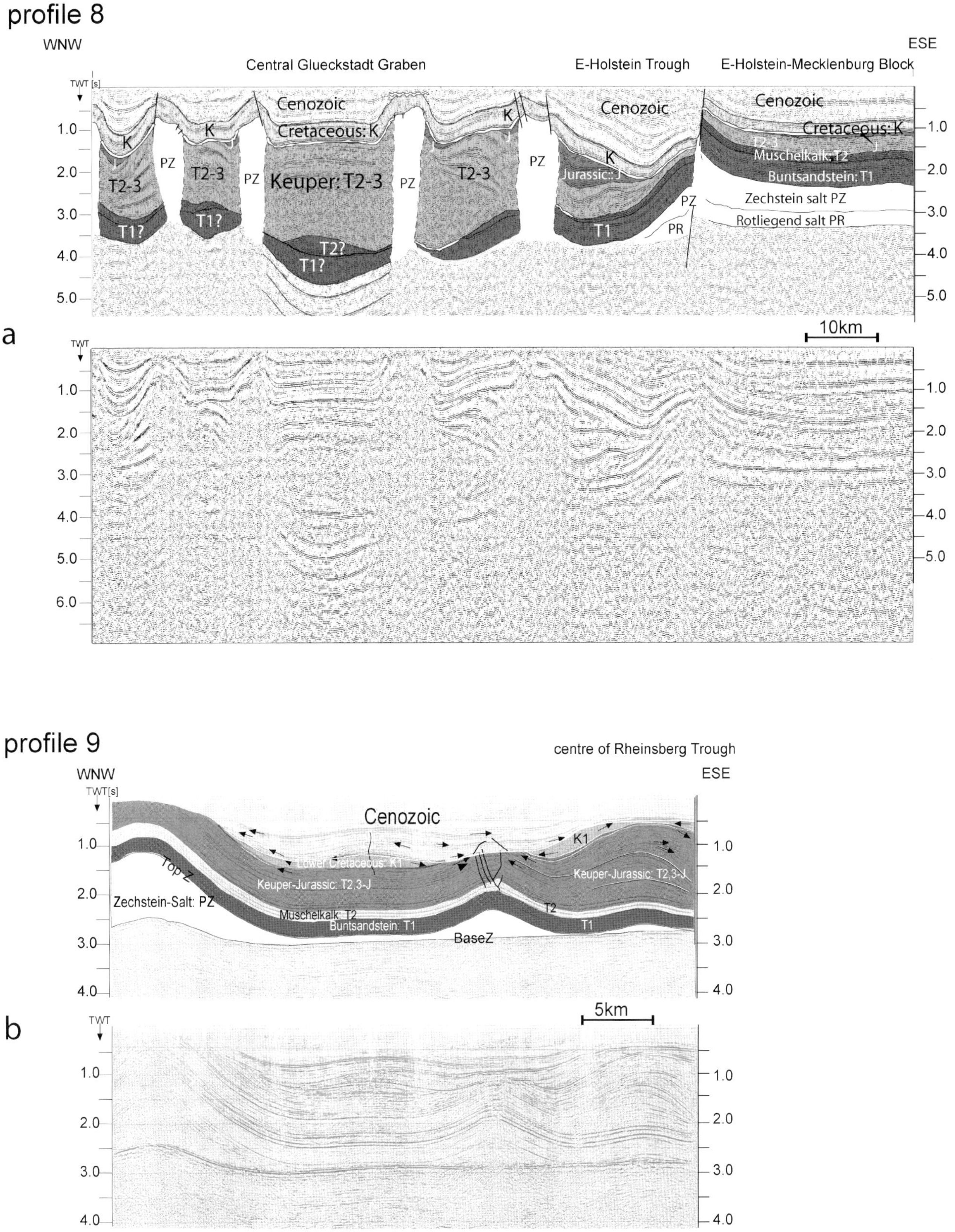

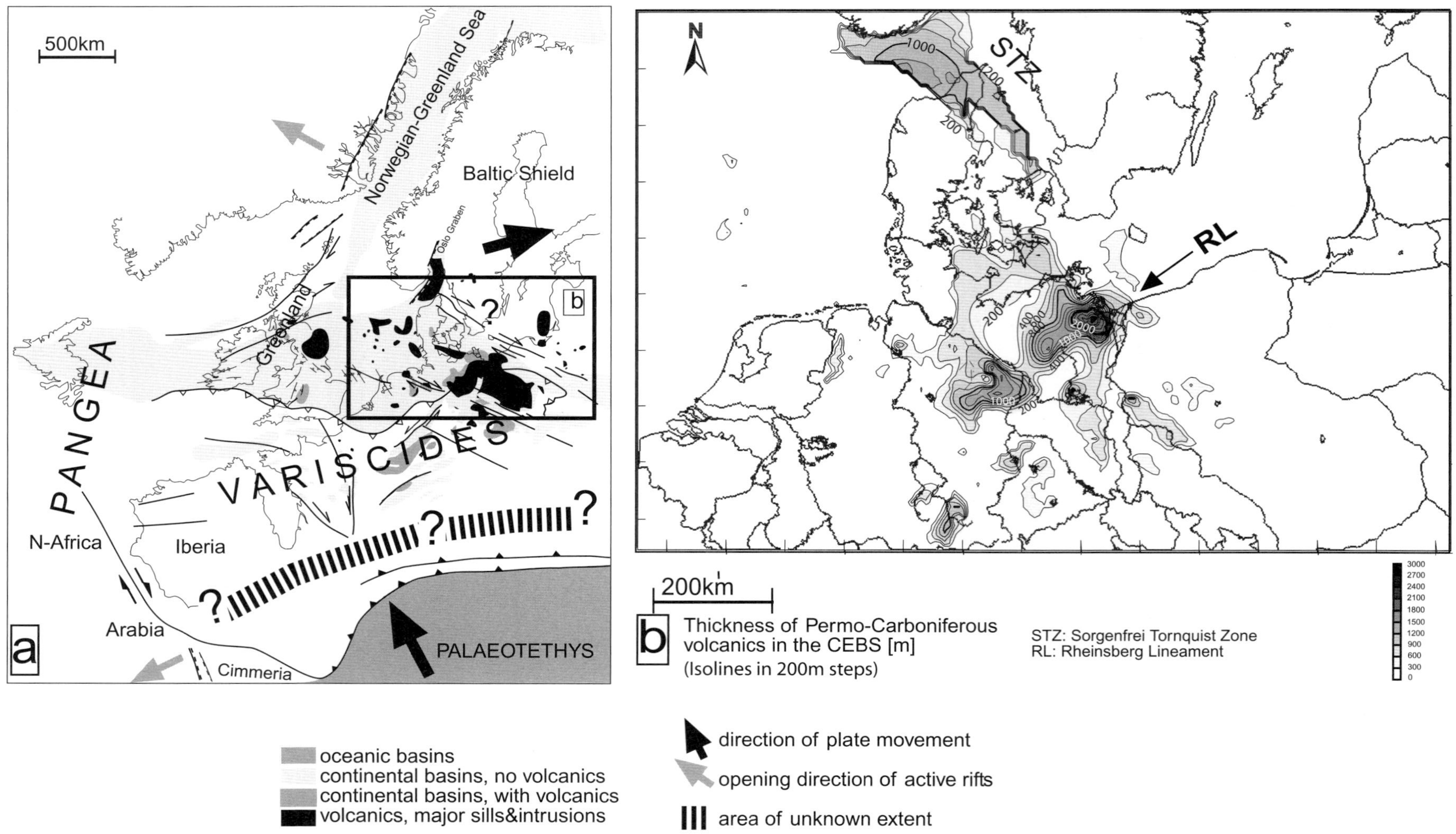


**Fig. 16.7.** (**a**) Palaeotectonic setting in the Late Carboniferous–earliest Permian (*c.* 290 Ma). Widespread documented magmatic activity indicates a heated lithosphere. The collapse of the Variscan orogen took place in a transtensional setting and was enhanced by slab-rollback of the Palaeo Tethys subduction. (**b**) Thickness distribution of Permo-Carboniferous volcanics in the Central European Basin System (CEBS) (modified after Scheck-Wenderoth & Lamarche 2005) showing focused magmatic activity. The axis of the volcanic thickness maximum (direction of arrow) corresponds to the so-called Rheinsberg Lineament (RL).

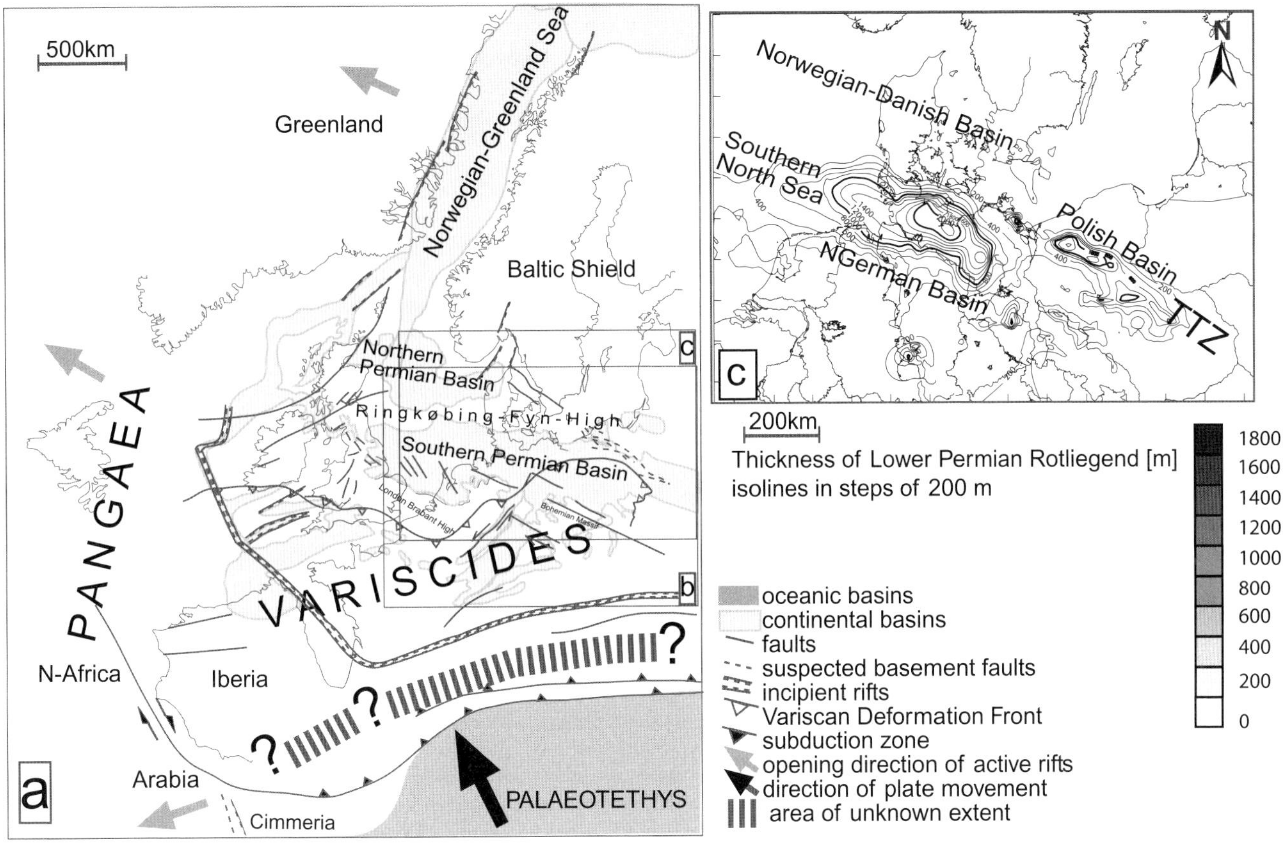


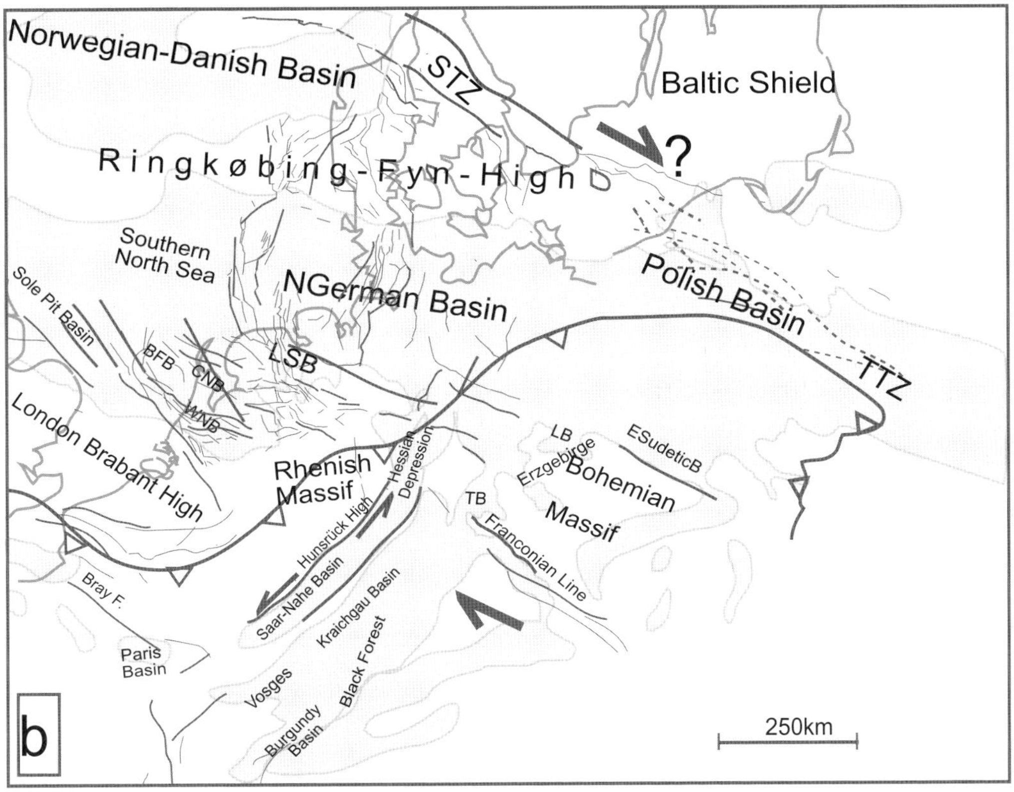


**Fig. 16.8.** (**a**) Palaeotectonic setting in the Early Permian (Rotliegend, *c.* 265 Ma). Continental clastics were deposited in the Northern and Southern Permian basins as well as in intramontane toughs of the Variscan orogen. (**b**) Close-up with outlines of major basins in Central Europe. See Table 16.1 for abbreviations. (**c**) Thickness distribution of Lower Permian Rotliegend clastics in the CEBS indicating earlier subsidence in the Southern Permian Basin (modified after Scheck-Wenderoth & Lamarche 2005).

### *Late Permian to Mid-Triassic*

From the Late Permian to Mid-Triassic, the large-scale plate-tectonic framework of Central Europe (Fig. 16.9) was characterized by continued subduction of the Palaeotethys, by northward propagation of rifting in the future Central Atlantic domain (Steiner *et al.* 1998; Zühlke *et al.* 2004), by opening of the Neotethys Ocean (Ziegler 1988; Ziegler *et al.* 2001; Decourt *et al.* 2000; Gaetani 2000*a*, *b*, *c*; Stampfli *et al.* 2001*a*, *b*; Stampfli & Borel 2002, 2004) as well as by ongoing rifting in the Norwegian–Greenland Sea and the southward propagation of this rift system (Torsvik *et al.* 2002; Boillot 1989). The continued northward subduction of the Palaeotethys under the southern margin of the Eurasian platform (Gaetani 2000*a*; Stampfli *et al.* 2001*a*, *b*) triggered a northward drift and anticlockwise rotation of the Cimmerian terranes, which separated the Palaeotethys to the north and the Neotethys to the south. The western Neotethys was still in an early drifting stage with seafloor spreading having been initiated only in the Early–Middle Permian. Cimmerian terranes featured passive continental margins towards both the Palaeo- and Neotethys. The opening of the Neotethys Ocean and the detachment of the Cimmerian terranes in Permian times away from Fennoscandia promoted the final closure of the Palaeotethys due to progressive subduction in Middle Triassic times (Cimmerian Orogeny; Golonka 2004; Stampfli & Borel 2002). The present post-Alpine suture line runs north of Iran, between the Cimmerian terranes and Europe. Backarc extension and seafloor spreading behind the Palaeotethys subduction zone resulted in a series of small oceanic basins. In the Anisian seafloor spreading started and initiated the Meliata/Hallstatt and Küre backarc oceans (Stampfli & Borel 2004). Westward propagation of rifting and seafloor spreading in the Neotethys continued and further dissected the Hercynian domains of southwestern Europe. A dextral transcurrent regime prevailed at the North African Line between former Laurussia and Gondwana, the influence of which decreased from the Early to the Middle Triassic (Gaetani 2000*b*).

In Central Europe, these plate-boundary processes probably induced minor normal faulting along predominantly north–south directed faults. However, the dominant tectonic regime in Central Europe in Late Permian to Mid-Triassic times was thermal relaxation of the previously heated lithosphere. Accordingly, post-rift thermal subsidence governed the dynamics of the Polish, North German and Norwegian–Danish basins from Permian to Middle Triassic times. Furthermore, the area of Central Europe

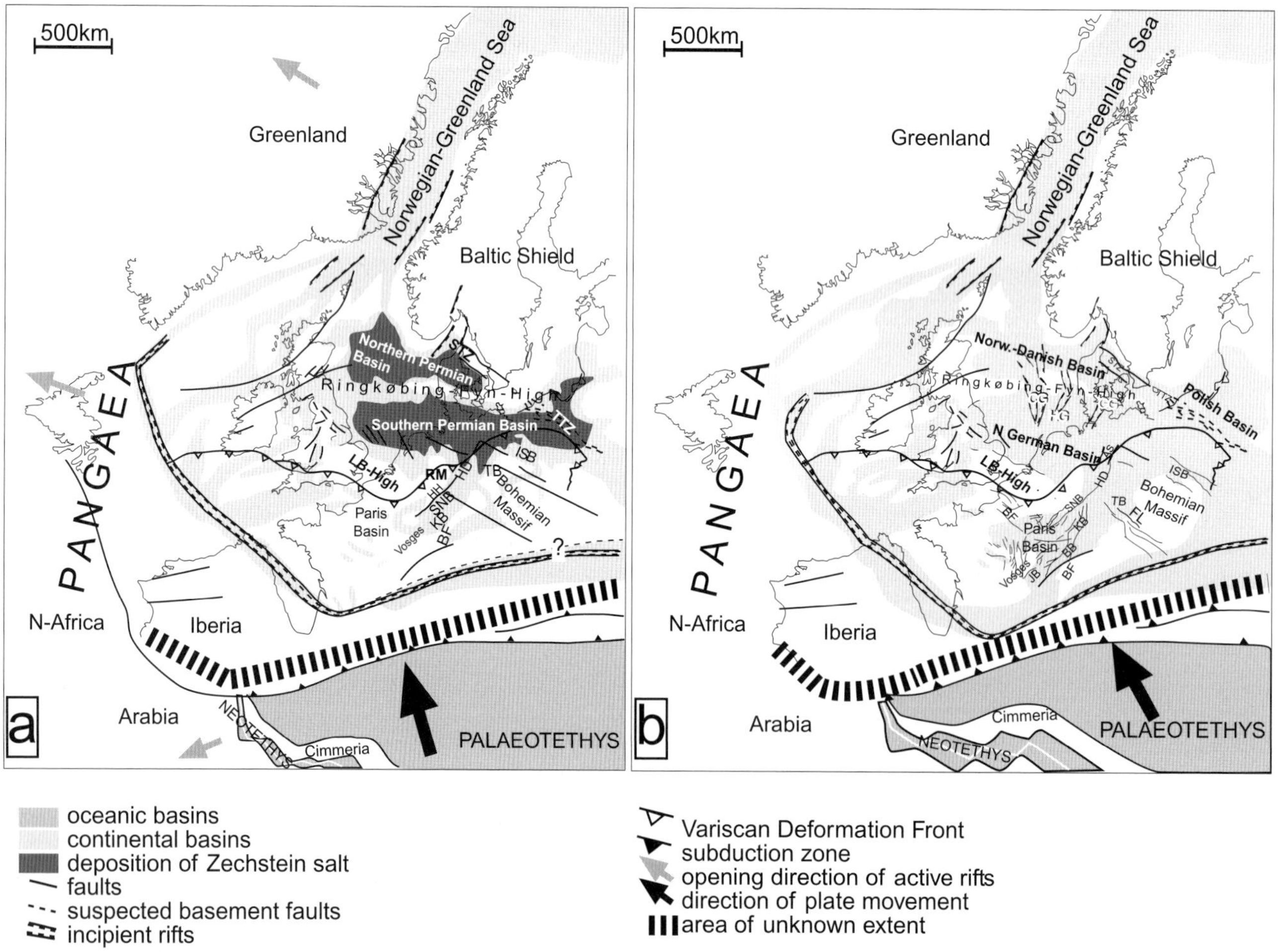


**Fig. 16.9.** (**a**) Palaeotectonic setting in the Late Permian (Zechstein, *c.* 255 Ma). The depositional area widened with respect to the Rotliegend and evaporites were deposited in the Northern and Southern Permian basins. (**b**) Palaeotectonic setting in the Early Triassic (Buntsandstein, 245 Ma). Further widening of the depositional area took place and the South German basins were joined with the Paris Basin. Hatched lines along the Teisseyre-Tornquist Zone indicate area of decoupled deformation between sub- and supra-salt layers. See Table 16.1 for abbreviations. Note the continued widening of the depositional area southward.

was limited by major zones of lithospheric weakness from the areas of active rifting or even plate separation. In the north, the Sorgenfrei-Tornquist Zone/Teisseyre-Tornquist Zone shielded Central Europe against both the stable Baltic Shield and the Proto-North Atlantic rift. To the NW, the initial North Atlantic rift system (Rockall-Faroe Trough, East Greenland rift) bounded western Central Europe. To the south to SW the North African line separated former Laurussia from Gondwana. The Iberian microplate acted as a separate block, being separated from Africa and western Central Europe by transcurrent fault systems (Olivet 1996).

### *Late Permian (Zechstein)*

In the Late Permian, a global glacio-eustatic sea-level rise and ongoing rifting in the Greenland–Norwegian Sea established a seaway from the southern North Sea to the Arctic Ocean (Coward *et al.* 2003; Ziegler 1990, 1999). The resulting marine transgression from the north led to the development of the Zechstein Sea across much of northern Central Europe (Fig. 16.9a) with a widening of the depositional area and sedimentation of evaporites in the central parts of the Northern and Southern Permian basins. The evaporite cycles deposited during this time interval played a crucial role during the later Mesozoic structural evolution when the ductile salt layer moved in response to changing stress fields. Minor faulting, related to east–west orientated extension, has been reported from the southern margin of the Zechstein Basin in the Netherlands (Geluk & Röhling 1997). Over much of the Zechstein Basin it is difficult to detect synsedimentary faults within the Zechstein deposits due to post-depositional salt mobilization. Furthermore, subsequent extensional events, causing post-depositional offsets of the pre-Zechstein basement, complicate this problem. Some tectonic activity is indicated from backstripping analyis in the Polish Basin (Dadlez *et al.* 1995). Reconstructions of the initial salt thickness distribution for the eastern part of the North German Basin suggest that thermal subsidence was the main controlling factor for basin evolution during the Zechstein (Maystrenko 2005; Scheck *et al.* 2003*b*).

Significant areas of the Mid-North Sea–Ringkøbing-Fyn High remained structural highs during the Late Permian (Zechstein) and the Mesozoic. This is documented by a thinned Zechstein and Mesozoic succession on the Mid-North Sea–Ringkøbing-Fyn High when compared to the Danish and North German basins (Clausen & Pedersen 1999; Vejbaek 1997).

In south Central Europe, the Late Carboniferous–Early Permian magmatic event did not result in a level of subsidence comparable to that of the Southern and Northern Permian basins. For example, thermal models of the Paris Basin (Le Solleuz *et al.* 2004) assume a 1500–3500 m high mountain belt at around 300 Ma and indicate that the area subsided to below sea level only 40 Ma later. The individual intra-Variscan basins in the southern domain were not joined together during the later Permian, and the Zechstein transgression in the region was limited by the Anglo-Brabant, Rhenish and Bohemian massifs. This indicates that the area still had considerable topography and that only the deepest intra-Variscan troughs were flooded. Thus, the Zechstein Sea reached the Thuringian Basin, the Saar-Nahe Basin and the Kraichgau Basin via the Hessian Basin between the Rhenish and the Bohemian massifs, but no full evaporitic cycles were deposited (Freudenberger 1996*a*; Ziegler 1990). Similarly, Zechstein sedimentation within the southernmost part of the Polish Basin was restricted, with marginal evaporitic/clastic facies and only partly developed cyclothems (Dadlez *et al.* 1998). This would suggest that the lithosphere underlying the Permian Basins of north Central Europe differs from that which underlies the Variscan chain in the south. It is possible that a thinner lithosphere in the north facilitated more widespread subsidence in comparison with the thickened lithosphere in the core area of the Variscan Orogen to the south.

### *Early to Mid-Triassic: Buntsandstein and Muschelkalk*

During Early to Mid-Triassic times, central and western Europe were characterized by a widening of the depositional areas. The Early Triassic basins extended to the west as far as the British Isles, where rift grabens trended NE–SW and aligned the North Atlantic rift system. The onlap of Early Triassic Buntsandstein continental clastics along the southern margins of the Zechstein basin indicates an expansion of the depositional area to the south (Fig. 16.9b). The Buntsandstein was deposited both in the CEBS of North Central Europe as well as in South Central Europe and the two areas were connected via the north-trending Hessian Basin. The individual troughs of the former Saar-Nahe, Kraichgau and Burgundy basins were connected, forming the larger South German Basin, with its deepest part in the Burgundy sub-basin. The NNE–SSW trending Early Triassic depocentre of the Paris Basin was also joined with the sedimentary system of southern Germany via an east–west orientated connection (Guillocheau *et al.* 2000). In some of the intra-Variscan basins, subsidence slowed down, for example in the Thuringian Basin (Walter 1992) where Buntsandstein deposition was restricted to the axial part of the Zechstein depression, or in the Saar-Nahe Basin where no Triassic is preserved (Kukulus & Henk 1999).

In north Central Europe, continuous subsidence during the Early Triassic is deduced from seismic data over large parts of the North German Basin (Hoffmann & Stiewe 1994; Kockel *et al.* 1996; Kossow & Krawczyk 2002; Maystrenko 2005; Maystrenko *et al.* 2006; Scheck *et al.* 2003*a*). The seismic reflectors correlated with Buntsandstein and Muschelkalk are continuous, parallel and generally not affected by syndepositional faulting (Figs 16.4, 16.5 & 16.6). The average thickness of the Buntsandstein succession in the North German Basin attains a few thousand metres in the central part of the basin (Baldschuhn *et al.* 1996; Maystrenko 2005). Continuous deposition resulted in the accumulation of several hundred metres of Buntsandstein clastics in the Norwegian–Danish Basin (Clausen & Korstgard 1996; Clausen & Pedersen 1999; Vejbaek 1997) and in the Polish Basin (Fig. 16.3) (Dadlez *et al.* 1998; Krzywiec 2002*a*). There, coeval tectonic activity was also minor and, if detected, confined to NW–SE structures, paralleling the main basement fault systems and the Permian basin axis. A small acceleration of the subsidence rate can be observed in the Polish Basin during Zechstein–Scythian times (Dadlez *et al.* 1995, 1998; van Wees *et al.* 2000).

Within the Buntsandstein along the margins of the North German Basin a widespread and marked unconformity, the so-called Hardegsen unconformity, has been mapped. This unconformity has often been interpreted as resulting from tectonic activity (e.g. Beutler & Schüler 1987; Ziegler 1990) but, as noted above, fault activity at the time was limited, and subsidence was relatively uniform and continuous across the North German Basin. Yet, Early Triassic east–west directed extension can be inferred from seismic data in the north-trending Glueckstadt Graben, where the Buntsandstein reaches up to 5000 m in thickness (Fig. 16.6; Maystrenko 2005), and also in the Horn Graben and the graben system of the central North Sea. Furthermore, the development of north–south orientated structures at this time is also evidenced by the formation of the Altmark High in eastern Germany. However, evidence of Buntsandstein-age extensional faulting is rare and, where present, localized along north-striking faults. The relatively few faults together with their localized nature, therefore, cannot explain the general and continuous broadening of the depositional area. Thus, a lowering of the erosional level due to ongoing thermal subsidence and a eustatic rise in sea level superposed by the commencement of east–west orientated extension is proposed as a possible mechanism for the observed subsidence pattern of the shallow Buntsandstein basin of Central Europe.

In the Mid-Polish Trough tectonic activity also appears to have been minor during Early to Mid-Triassic times. Accordingly, the Pomeranian segment of the Mid-Polish Trough is characterized by a rather gentle increase in thickness towards the basin centre (Dadlez 2003). On the other hand, there is some debate as to whether the depositional pattern of the Triassic is masked by a basin-scale mechanical decoupling between the subevaporitic basement and the supra-evaporitic sedimentary infill (Krzywiec 2002*a*, *b*; 2004*c*, 2006*a*; profile 2 in Fig. 16.3). Some suggestions of tectonic activity are found locally, for example the stratigraphic thickening of the Triassic succession towards a basement fault zone in the NW (offshore) part of the Polish Basin (profile 1 in Fig. 16.3). Also within the central (Kuiavian) part of the Mid-Polish Trough, in the vicinity of the Kłodawa salt structure, Early Triassic basement faulting appears to have triggered initial salt movements causing localized lateral thickness variations of the Buntsandstein (Krzywiec 2004*b*, *c*; profile 3 in Fig. 16.3). Furthermore, basement faulting along the Nowe Miasto-Iłża Fault Zone resulted in localized Triassic sedimentation within the axial, SE segment of the Mid-Polish Trough (i.e. Holy Cross Mountains) (Krzywiec 2002*a*; Hakenberg & Świdrowska 1997; profile 5 in Fig. 16.3).

Marine seaways of the Central European basins to the Palaeotethys included the East Carpathian and Moravian gates, which separated the East European Platform and the joint Bohemian and Vindelician massifs (Szulc 2000). Marine connections to the Arctic Sea, which were inherited from the late Permian (Zechstein) configuration, became inactive during the Early Triassic (Gaetani 2000*b*).

The very high accommodation rates recorded in Buntsandstein sediments diminish progressively until they become very uniform in Muschelkalk times (Goggin *et al.* 1997). Two long-term eustatic sea-level rises of *c.* 100–120 m in total took place during the Induan to early Anisian and the late Ladinian to Carnian (Rüffer & Zühlke 1995). The associated reduction in siliciclastic sediment supply in favour of carbonate deposition during the Muschelkalk transgression is interpreted as a response to lithosphere relaxation (Goggin *et al.* 1997). During the Muschelkalk sea-level highstand (Aigner & Bachmann 1993), much of Central Europe around the persistent highs of the Mid-North Sea–Ringkøbing-Fyn High, and the Anglo-Brabant, Rhenish and Bohemian massifs was a marine depositional environment and the basin boundaries expanded beyond those of the underlying Buntsandstein. This is observed in the CEBS but also in the basins of south Central Europe, where Muschelkalk sediments were deposited in the Paris Basin as far south as the Jura Basin. Also, the south German Basin widens to the SE where Muschelkalk sediments onlap the Bohemian Massif and the deepest depocentre was in the area of the Burgundy sub-basin (Freudenberger 1996*a*). In contrast, the Vosges and the Black Forest were structural highs during the deposition of the Muschelkalk. The Moravian seaway became inactive by the late Middle Triassic because of increased sediment input and the gradual change to a compressive stress field at the eastern part of the southern Eurasian margin (Cimmerian precollision condition). Similarily, water circulation by the East Carpathian seaway became more restricted. During the Middle Triassic, the Burgundy seaway, situated between the Bohemian Massif and the Central Massif, evolved as the principal marine seaway between the basins of South Central Europe and the westernmost Neotethys (Gaetani 2000*b*; Schwerd 1996; Trümpi 1988).

Apart from the formation of north-trending basins and highs, the thickness distribution of Muschelkalk (hundreds of metres) is rather uniform across Central Europe, indicating that sea-level rise was eustatic and that it was a period of reduced tectonic activity. However, the presence of synsedimentary faulting in the large north–south orientated grabens as well as the north–south alignment of the connecting troughs between the depositional areas of northern and southern Central Europe suggests the onset of a new tectonic regime, which would govern the structural evolution of the region from Mid-Triassic to Early Jurassic times.

### *Mid- to Late Triassic–Jurassic*

The Triassic–Early Jurassic tectonic events were causally related to ongoing rifting processes in the Tethyan domains of south Central Europe as well as in the Arctic–North Atlantic area in the NW (Fig. 16.10). In the south, plate-tectonic models suggest that north-directed subduction of the Palaeotethys triggered early to late Triassic magmatic/volcanic activity which extends from Turkey to northern Italy; this activity was completed in the Mid-Triassic, and the Cimmerian terranes collided with the southern Eurasian margin. This gave rise to the Cimmerian orogenic cycle extending from Mid-Triassic to Mid-Jurassic times during which the Central and East Iranian and the Cimmerian terranes were accreted to the southern margin of Eurasia (Stampfli & Borel 2002). With the accretion of the Cimmerian terranes to the East European Platform, Pangaea reached its most complete configuration (Norian to Rhaetian). As a result of the Cimmerian collision, all eastern seaways between the Neotethys and the basins of Central Europe were closed and the Burgundy Gate represented the principal open seaway in the Carnian and Norian. The Cimmerian collision affected the Central European basins by far-field intraplate stresses and associated reduced subsidence and inversion continued into the Sinemurian in the basins of south-eastern Central Europe. The Polish Trough, for instance, experienced reduced subsidence or moderate inversion, expressed as depositional gaps or erosional unconformities. Sediment input from the Baltic Shield and intrabasinal highs (Massif Central, Armorican High) was increased and triggered a regressive trend, which is documented across the Central European basins. Clastic input from the north partly bypassed the basins of south Central Europe and the Bohemian Massif and reached the continental shelf of the Neotethys and adjacent backarc basins from the west. Far-field compressive intraplate forces triggered by the Cimmerian collision also affected the Southern Alps, where carbonate platform development was temporarily interrupted during the late Carnian.

Seafloor spreading shifted southward and generated a series of backarc oceanic basins, the Maliac Ocean after the Ladinian, and the Pindos Ocean from the Carnian to Norian. The seafloor spreading axes of the Maliac/Pindos backarc basins and the Neotethys were offset by a major fault which separated the western segment of the southern Eurasian margin with a backarc extensive regime, and the eastern segment with a collisional

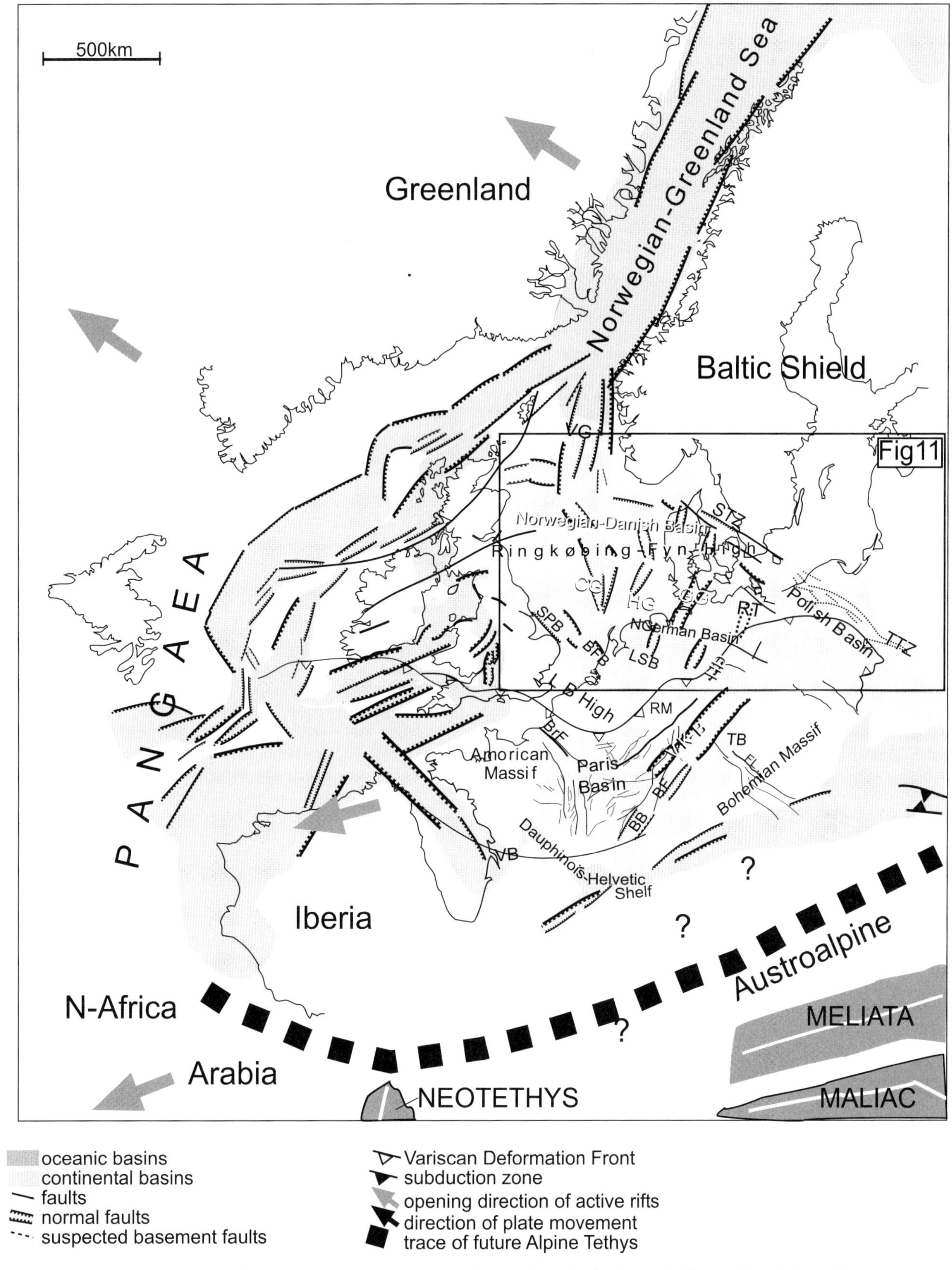


**Fig. 16.10.** Palaeotectonic setting in Mid to Late Triassic (Keuper, *c.* 230–205 Ma) times showing the predominance of northerly trending structures indicating roughly east–west orientated extension. The Central European Basin System in the north and the basins of south Central Europe are connected via the Hessian Basin. The Polish Basin stays as a NW–SE trending depocentre. Hatched lines in the Polish Basin and the Rheinsberg Trough enclose areas of decoupled deformation between sub- and supra-salt layers. See Table 16.1 for abbreviations. Rectangle delineates the area covered by the Triassic isopach map in Figure 16.11.

compressive regime (Stampfli *et al.* 2001*b*). In contrast to the Meliata and Küre oceans, which featured only narrow seaways to the Neotethys, the Pindos and Maliac oceans were open towards the east.

Furthermore, Triassic and Early Jurassic westward propagation of the Neotethys seafloor spreading axis and accelerated crustal extension in the central Atlantic culminated in the Mid-Jurassic separation of Gondwana and Laurussia (Stampfli & Borel 2002) and the marine basins in the future central Atlantic and the Tethys domain joined for the first time to form an east–west trending seaway (Thierry 2000; Stampfli *et al.* 2001*b*). A conspicuously low level of magmatic/volcanic activity in epicontinental Central Europe and the western Neotethys is in clear contrast to the intensive magmatic/volcanic activity of Latest Triassic to earliest Jurassic age in the Central North Atlantic and Bay of Biscay wrench and rift system (Deckart *et al.* 1997; Olsen 1997). The central Atlantic flood basalts form one of the largest magmatic provinces in Phanerozoic history. This accelerated rifting in the central Atlantic resulted in a change from dextral to sinistral transcurrent movement at the North African line (Gaetani 2000*c*). The spreading ridge in the central Atlantic failed to propagate northwards in Jurassic times (Coward *et al.* 2003). Instead stretching was transferred eastward to open the Alpine Tethys during Jurassic times (Coward *et al.* 2003; Stampfli & Borel 2002). Rifting and thermal subsidence, however, have been reported as preceding breakup in the area that would later become the Helvetic Shelf developing at the southern margin of the South German Basin.

The above scenario resulted in a northward drift of Europe, with Central Europe moving to between 30° and 40°N compared to its position in the Permian, when Central Europe was situated between 20° and 30°N (Torsvik *et al.* 2002). Accordingly, there was climatic change from the arid conditions that had predominated in the Permian, to the increasingly humid conditions of the Jurassic (Coward *et al.* 2003). Following regional regression in Central Europe in the Late Triassic, continental deposition was re-established across the region. These sediments were subsequently overlain by the Lower Jurassic marine shales which were deposited following a regional transgression.

In the future NE Atlantic (Norwegian Sea) NW–SE orientated extension (similar to the Early Triassic pattern for this area) occurred along the East Greenland and Norwegian margins (Brekke 2000). This ceased towards the end of the Triassic and the system switched to a regime of passive thermal subsidence. In the Late Triassic, evidence of accelerated subsidence is observed with a north-trending graben system in the central and northern North Sea, and Middle–Late Triassic, rift-related volcanism is observed in the Central Graben (North Denmark; Ziegler 1988). This can also be interpreted in terms of east–west directed extension (Coward *et al.* 2003).

In the CEBS, roughly east–west orientated Mid- to Late Triassic extension is indicated by the formation of north-trending basins, which led to a progressive dissection of the Mid-North Sea–Ringkøbing-Fyn High (Scheck-Wenderoth & Lamarche 2005). Though variations in the structural setting along the Mid-North Sea–Ringkøbing-Fyn High indicate a differentiation into individual blocks beginning in Late Permian (Zechstein) times (Abramovitz & Thybo 1999; Glennie 1997), this process was most effective during the Triassic–Jurassic extension. Rifting resulted in locally increased thicknesses of Triassic deposits in the north–south trending grabens of the CEBS (Fig. 16.11). Within most of these basins, seismic data indicate syndepositional normal faulting and salt mobilization in Triassic to Jurassic times, for example in the Central Graben (Michelsen *et al.* 1987; Sundsbo & Megson 1993) and in the Horn Graben (Best & Kockel 1983; Clausen & Korstgard 1996; Clausen & Pedersen 1999). Maximum extension occurred in Mid–Late Triassic (Keuper) times as recorded by the fill of the NNE–SSW striking Glueckstadt Graben, with a marked thickening of the Keuper deposits (up to 5800 m) in the central part of the basin. The evolving depocentre was flanked by diapiric salt walls which were initiated above normal faults in the sub-salt basement (Fig. 16.6a; Maystrenko *et al.* 2005). Salt rise led to the initiation of long salt walls (several kilometres high, up to 200 km long and several kilometres wide) parallel to the graben axis. The rising salt partially reached the palaeosurface and was subjected to leaching and redeposition. Salt withdrawal was a major factor for the creation of accommodation space not only in the Glueckstadt Graben but also in most other north–south trending basins of the period (Baldschuhn *et al.* 1996; Best & Kockel 1983; Kockel *et al.* 1996). A further example of salt tectonics can be found in the Rheinsberg Trough in eastern Germany, which contains up to 1500 m of Keuper deposits. This basin formed as a major salt rim syncline, 180 km long (in a NNE–SSW direction) and 70 km wide (Scheck *et al.* 2003*a*). Salt withdrawal almost completely balanced extension in the salt cover as indicated by seismic data (Fig. 16.6b) and subsidence restoration (Scheck *et al.* 2003*b*).

From the above examples, it is clear that the tectonic situation changed in Triassic–Jurassic times. A new regime of broadly east–west orientated extension replaced the thermal subsidence phase which had characterized the evolution of the Permian basins. However, an exception to this pattern is the Mid-Polish Trough, where the NW–SE orientated axis of maximum subsidence and sedimentation remained more or less unchanged. The reason for this is that the tectonic evolution of the basin was governed by the crustal-scale Teisseyre-Tornquist Zone (Dadlez *et al.* 1998; Krzywiec 2006*a*). Yet, intense Late Triassic salt movements are also observed within the Mid-Polish Trough. In the Pomeranian segment, this is documented by localized unconformities developed within the Upper Triassic (profile 2 in Fig. 16.3). Basement faulting was most intense in the central (Kuiavian) segment of the basin and eventually led to the development of the Kłodawa salt diapir. This salt structure extruded in Late Triassic times onto the basin floor and is preserved today as a large salt overhang onlapped by the uppermost Triassic deposits (Krzywiec 2004*b*).

In south Central Europe the influence of increased rifting between the Eurasian and African plates also resulted in an overall extensional regime (Ziegler 1990). As in the CEBS, the depositional system changed from a marine to a continental setting during the Late Triassic with occasional marine incursions from the Tethyan shelf areas.

As in the North Sea and the North German Basin, the depositional geometries of the late Triassic Paris Basin indicate a deepening controlled by east–west extension. This is consistent with sinistral movements along the Bray Fault inferred from detailed sequence-stratigraphic studies for mid-late Carnian times (Goggin *et al.* 1997). Additionally, a Late Triassic thermal event coeval with volcanic activity in the Alpine–Pyrenean domain has been reported (Guillocheau *et al.* 2000).

The depositional area of the south German basins widened and subsidence in the region appears to have been largely thermally controlled, although some zonation following the Variscan structural grain (NNE–SSW) is observed in the Vosges-Kraichgau and the Burgundy sub-basins (Freudenberger 1996*b*; Walter 1992). Former intramontane basins of the central Variscan chain, for example, the NW–SE trending Thuringian Basin, became

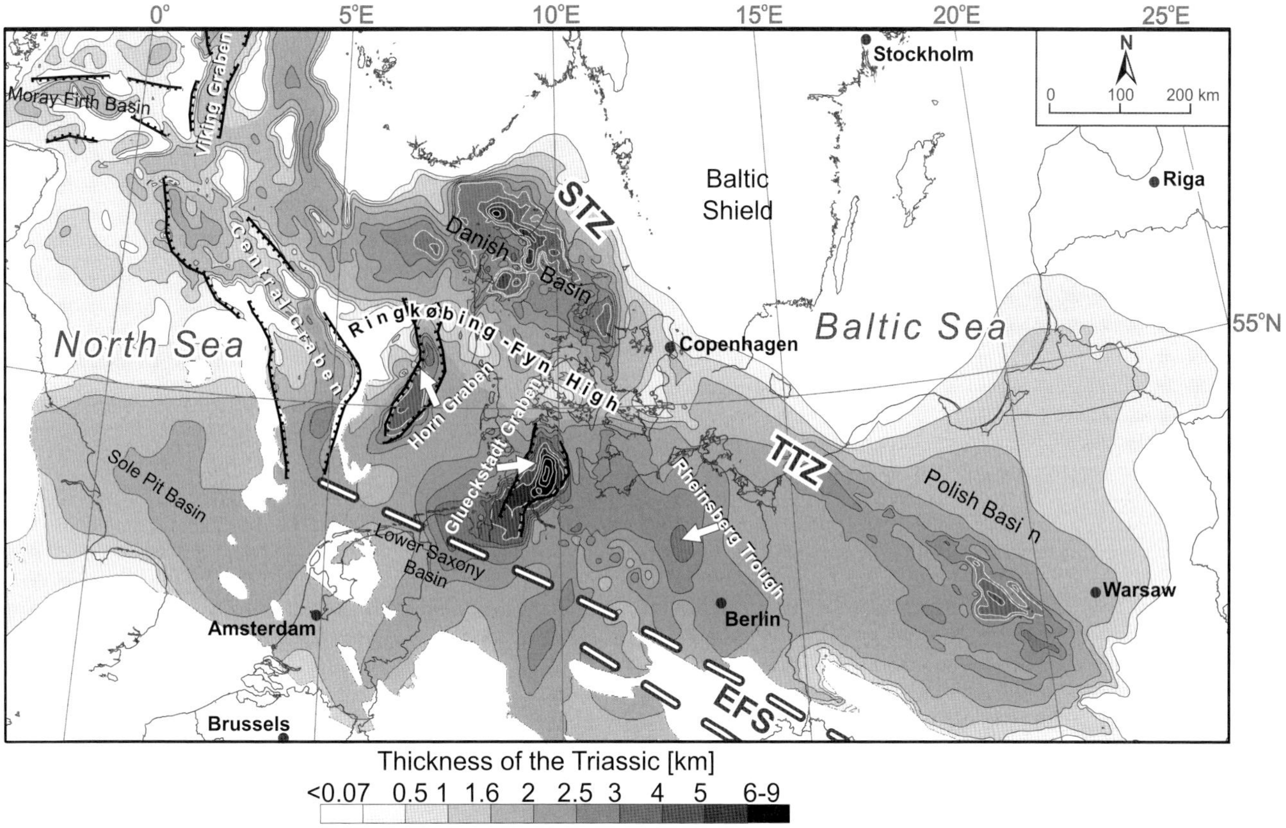


**Fig. 16.11.** Thickness distribution of preserved Triassic deposits in the Central European Basin System (compiled after Ziegler 1990; Vejbaek 1997; Baldschuhn *et al.* 1996, 2001; Scheck *et al.* 2003*b*; Bayer *et al.* 2002). Note the locally increased thickness in north–south orientated grabens and troughs. The NW–SE trend persisted only in the Polish Basin. See Table 16.1 for abbreviations.

less important as depositional areas. Late Triassic sediments are here restricted to the central axis of the basin, and represent its final preserved unit (Walter 1992).

The depositional pattern in the Early Jurassic is controlled by a regional transgression recorded across Central Europe and only minor coeval tectonic activity. In the central North Sea, Mid–Late Jurassic uplift removed much of the initial Early Jurassic succession. Therefore, no conclusions can be drawn on the structural evolution at this time. An exception is the area of the Paris Basin, where east–west orientated extension in the Late Triassic decreased into the Early Jurassic and was superceded by north–south orientated extension which led to the opening of a connection to the Channel Basin (Guillocheau *et al.* 2000). Furthermore, a Liassic thermal event suggests that tectonic activity occurred in the Paris Basin. East–west to NW–SE directed extension is inferred both from microtectonic data as well as synsedimentary north–south faults sealed by Toarcian black shales (Guillocheau *et al.* 2000). Goggin *et al.* (1997) have suggested that the depocentres of the Paris Basin area were controlled by the interplay between NW–SE striking wrench faults and north–south striking normal faults with a prevailing NW–SE extension. During the Rhaetian–Hettangian, deepening, and coeval westward-directed widening of the basin, with onlaps onto the Armorican Massif and in the Boulonnais area, can be observed (Guillocheau *et al.* 2000). A possible north–south connection extended from the Paris Basin across the Massif Central to the rifting in the Alpine Tethys. Connections to the Tethyan realm are also discussed for the southern South German Basin (Aigner & Bachmann 1993) which was at its greatest areal extent in the Early Jurassic (Aigner & Bachmann 1993; Meyer & Schmidt-Kaler 1996).

### *Mid-Jurassic Uplift*

The Mid-Jurassic was the time when the Alpine Tethys developed as an oceanic basin and oceanic spreading commenced in the central Atlantic (Stampfli & Borel 2002) (Fig. 16.12). At the same time, the central North Sea rift system developed. A deep-seated thermal anomaly beneath the Mid-North Sea High is believed to have caused thermal doming in the central North Sea (Underhill & Partington 1993) resulting in regional uplift of mid-Central Europe in the Mid-Jurassic (i.e. Mid-Jurassic or Mid-Cimmerian unconformity). According to this hypothesis, doming-induced uplift led to short-term interruptions in communication between the Norwegian Sea and the Tethyan–Central Atlantic basins. The uplifted area in the North Sea was centred at the triple-junction between the Viking Graben, the Moray Firth Basin and the Central Graben, and basaltic lavas were extruded at the intersection of these three rift basins (Coward *et al.* 2003). North of the central North Sea thermal dome, crustal extension led to initiation of the Viking Graben along north–south to NNE–SSW trending normal faults in the Bathonian. By late Mid-Jurassic times the central North Sea dome collapsed and subsided again, resulting in the re-

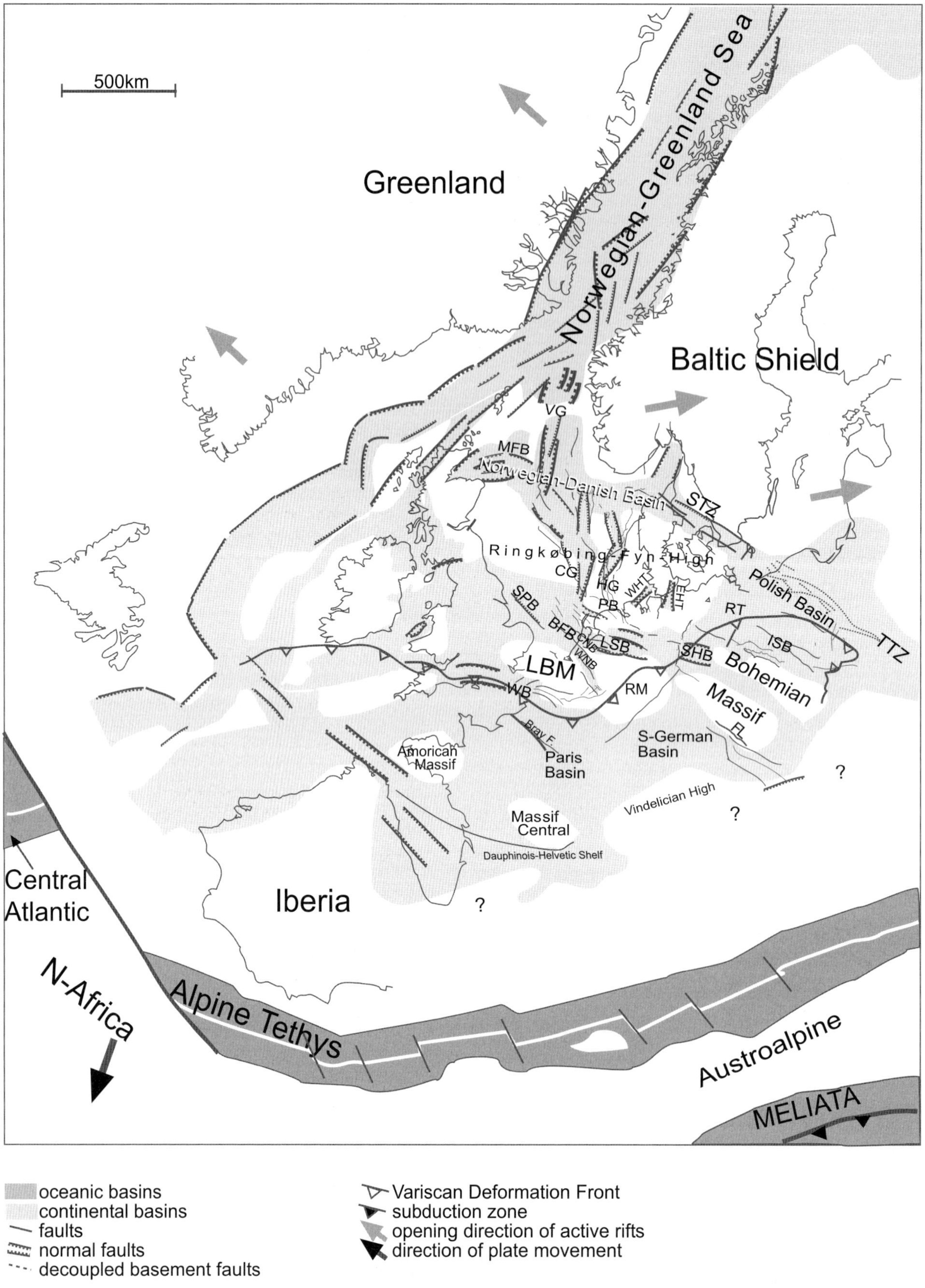


**Fig. 16.12.** Palaeotectonic setting in Mid-Jurassic times (*c.* 160 Ma) when spreading from the Central Atlantic was transferred eastward to open the Alpine Tethys and intense rifting affected the Norwegian–Greenland Sea. The basin system of south Central Europe (Paris Basin, South German Basin) experienced its maximum extent, while large parts of the Central European Basin System represented structural highs. See Table 16.1 for abbreviations.

establishment of open-marine conditions from the North Sea to the Norwegian Sea.

An interesting observation is that Jurassic uplift occurred not only in the North Sea area but also across much of north Central Europe, although it does appear to be diachronous. The area affected by mid-Late Jurassic uplift (possibly continuing into the Early Cretaceous) extended from south of the Sorgenfrei-Tornquist Zone across Denmark to northern Germany, including the Mid-North Sea–Ringkøbing-Fyn High and the southern part of the Danish Basin (Vejbaek 1997) as well as the northern half of the North German Basin (Pompeckji Block; Jaritz 1987). While uplift in the central North Sea and Denmark occurred in the Mid-Jurassic (i.e. Mid-Aalenian, Mid-Cimmerian unconformity; Surlyk & Ineson 2003; Underhill & Partington 1993), it affected the northern half of the North German Basin (e.g. Pompeckji Block) at the end of the Middle Jurassic (Baldschuhn *et al.* 1996; Jaritz 1987). In this area, Jurassic strata are only locally preserved in small salt-rim synclines (Fig. 16.6a; Maystrenko *et al.* 2005, 2006). In the NE German Basin uplift would appear to be of Late Jurassic age, possibly extending into the Early Cretaceous (Kossow & Krawczyk 2002). However, it remains a matter of debate as to which processes caused this large-scale uplift in north Central Europe. The sheer scale of the area affected necessitates an explanation which looks beyond simply lithospheric-scale causes (see below).

In contrast to the elevated northern domain, the basins of south Central Europe experienced their maximum extent during the Jurassic. The Paris Basin (Guillocheau *et al.* 2000) and the South German Basin (Meyer & Schmidt-Kaler 1996) formed a large depositional domain. To the south, the Paris Basin was connected to the Sub-Alpine basins (via the Jura Basin). In the Paris Basin, widespread subsidence is observed to follow a thermal event at the boundary between mid- to late Jurassic. During the Kimmeridgian, accommodation space was at a maximum within the Paris Basin. This was coeval with thermal subsidence and the deposition of marine carbonates (Guillocheau *et al.* 2000). In the Aalenian to Mid-Callovian, depocentre axes were mainly orientated NW–SE (subordinate NE–SW) and these orientations were possibly related to the reactivation of the Variscan-age Bray Fault (Guillocheau *et al.* 2000).

The NW parts of the South German Basin also experienced Mid- to Late Jurassic uplift (i.e. 'Young Cimmerian event'; Meyer & Schmidt-Kaler 1996). The last of the former intra-Variscan basins, the Hessian Basin, similarly underwent uplift and erosion with reactivation of NW–SE and NNE–SSW striking faults and a NNE–SSW orientated central axis of uplift (Meyer & Schmidt-Kaler 1996).

As noted above, it is difficult to explain the observed pattern of uplift across north Central Europe at this time. In contrast, south Central Europe was subsiding. These phenomena were most probably related not only to thermal doming in the central North Sea: the extent of the area where regional uplift is observed is far too large to be explained by a local thermal dome in the central North Sea alone. Additional effective plate-boundary processes (rifting and breakup of the Alpine Tethys, the closure of the SE Neotethys, subduction of the backarc oceanic domains) may have caused regional thermal disequilibrium of the lithosphere in Central Europe, resulting in diachronous uplift across the region.

### *Late Jurassic–Early Cretaceous*

In the Late Jurassic, stepwise northward propagation of the central Atlantic spreading centre exerted a major influence on the ongoing tectonic evolution of Central Europe. Spreading progressed into the Labrador Sea between North America and Greenland and into the Bay of Biscay in Early Cretaceous times (Stampfli & Borel 2002). The opening of the Bay of Biscay (Fig. 16.13) led to an anticlockwise rotation of Iberia (Stampfli & Borel 2002). Early collision took place in the Austro-Carpathian and Balkan areas, related to the beginning of closure of the Maliac–Meliata–Vardar backarc oceanic basins. The latter processes may have induced far-field compression in south Central Europe causing the enigmatic Early Cretaceous uplift in southern Germany in Late Jurassic–Early Cretaceous times (Schwerd 1996).

In the Norwegian Sea (Pascal *et al.* 2002; Torsvik *et al.* 2002) as well as in the northern and the central North Sea (Pascal *et al.* 2002), the Late Jurassic–Early Cretaceous interval was a time of extensive rifting with predominantly east–west directed extension. The relative plate motions resulted in transtensional activity in northern Central Europe with subsidence of narrow NW–SE orientated basins separated by broad continental areas (Fig. 16.13). The basins of south Central Europe were fully connected with the northern shelf of the Alpine Tethys from Late Jurassic times onward (Aigner & Bachmann 1993).

From Early Cretaceous times onward, intense post-rift thermal subsidence governed basin evolution from the Norwegian Sea to the central North Sea (Coward *et al.* 2003). In contrast, the Early Cretaceous was a period of restricted deposition in Central Europe. There, the earliest-Cretaceous unconformity is mostly erosional and the Lower Cretaceous is missing over large parts of the North German Basin (Baldschuhn *et al.* 1996) and the southern North Sea (Evans *et al.* 2003).

In the CEBS, Late Jurassic to Early Cretaceous subsidence was restricted to NW–SE orientated depocentres along the margins of the basin system. An elongated, NW–SE trending depocentre subsided parallel to the Sorgenfrei-Tornquist Zone at the northern margin of the Norwegian–Danish Basin (Surlyk 2003). Analogously, accelerated subsidence in the Polish Basin is reported for the Oxfordian–Kimmeridgian along the Teisseyre-Tornquist Zone where the Mid-Polish Trough represented the area of maximum subsidence (Dadlez *et al.* 1995, 1998). This subsidence was at least partly related to basement faulting, though again, the Zechstein salt filtered this faulting and only a gradual stratigraphic thickening towards the basin centre is observed in seismic sections (Fig. 16.3) (Krzywiec 2002*a*, 2004*c*, 2006*b*). The SE part of the Mid-Polish Trough underwent a period of complex Late Jurassic–Early Cretaceous subsidence as a result of its location in the transitional area between the peri-Tethyan and Tethyan domains (Gutowski *et al.* 2005; Hakenberg & Swidrowska 1997; Kutek 1994, 2001; Pozaryski & Zytko 1981). Seismic data from this area clearly show a Jurassic cover, preserved within the presently inverted axial part of the basin, which is several times thicker than in the adjacent areas (profiles 4 and 5 in Fig. 16.3; Krzywiec 2002*a*). This confirms that the regional basin centre was located within the present-day Holy Cross Mountains during the Jurassic (Kutek & Głazek 1972).

Along the southern margin of the CEBS localized subsidence is also observed in numerous NW–SE trending basins in the latest Jurassic–Early Cretaceous, including the Sole Pit Basin, the Channel Basin, the Broad Fourteens Basin and the Lower Saxony Basin. This was accompanied by a new phase of salt mobilization and formation of respective Early Cretaceous rim synclines (Betz *et al.* 1987; Jaritz 1980, 1987; Nalpas *et al.* 1995; Scheck *et al.* 2002*a*). In addition, new basins with NW–SW trending axes formed above older Variscan basement faults in the area to the south of the CEBS during Jurassic–Lower

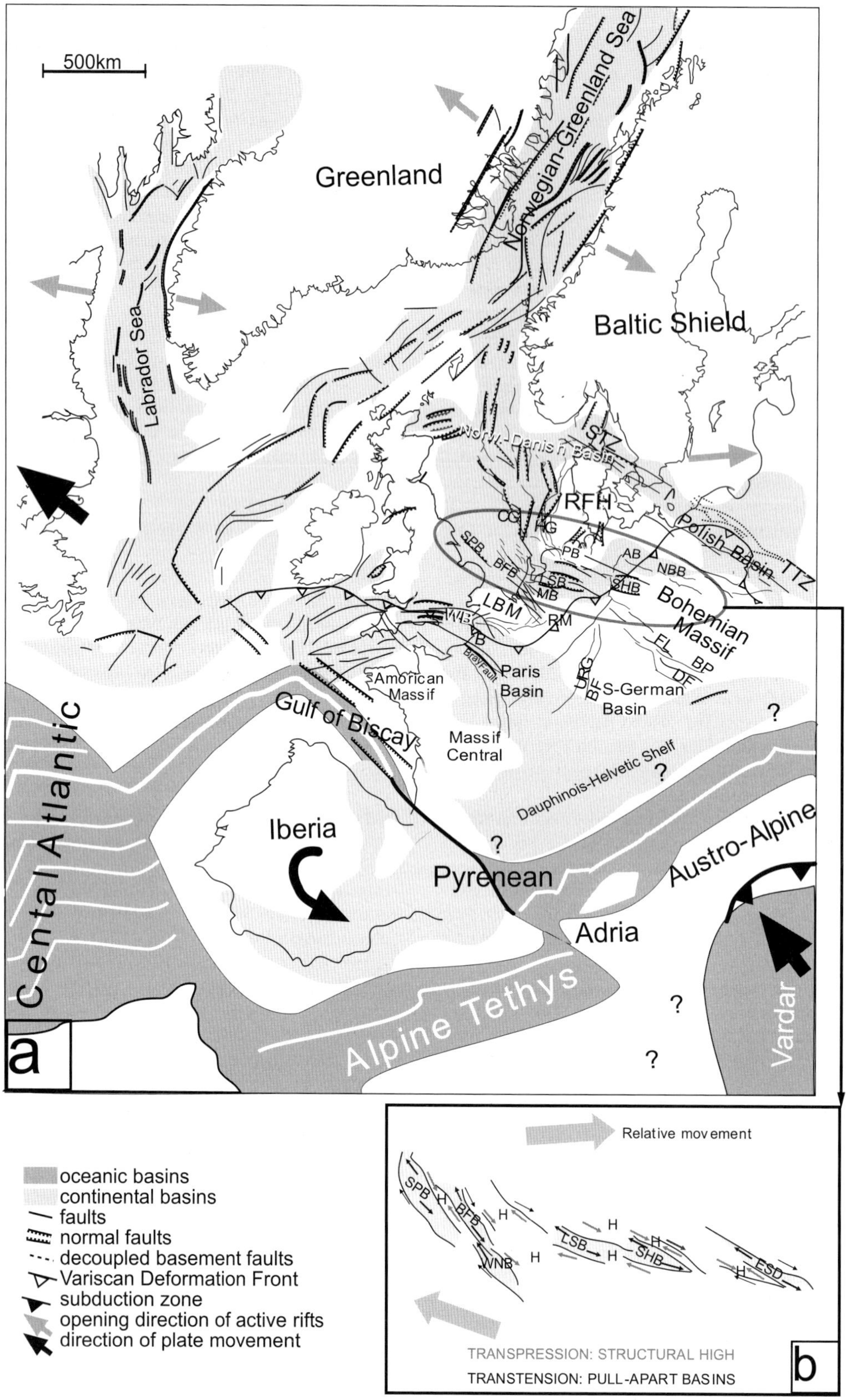


**Fig. 16.13.** (**a**) Palaeotectonic setting in Early Cretaceous times (*c.* 120 Ma) when oceanic spreading took place in the central Atlantic, in the Alpine Tethys and in the Bay of Biscay. Large parts of Central Europe were above the depositional level and subsidence was restricted to NW–SE trending depocentres as the Polish Basin, the northern Norwegian–Danish basin, along the southern margin of the North German Basin and within the Paris Basin. See Table 16.1 for abbreviations. (**b**) Tectonic model for the en-echelon basins at the southern margin of the Central European Basin system. A regional dextral transtensional regime would cause local transtension at the right-stepping dextral faults (NW–SE orientated sub-basins) and local transpression at the left-stepping dextral faults (structural highs between the sub-basins).

Cretaceous times. For example, the Weald Basin (Hansen *et al.* 2002), the Cretaceous Münsterland Basin (Baldschuhn *et al.* 1996) and the North Bohemian Basin (Ulicny *et al.* 2002) are superimposed on Variscan structures.

The Late Jurassic–Early Cretaceous subsidence in Denmark and Poland resulted in linear, NW–SE trending depocentres at the northern margin of the CEBS controlled by the Sorgenfrei-Tornquist and Teisseyre-Tornquist zones, respectively (Vejbaek 1997). In contrast, the various NW–SE orientated basins along the Elbe Fault System at the southern margin of the CEBS show an en echelon distribution. Structural analysis of these sub-basins indicates that latest Jurassic–earliest Cretaceous dextral transtension was a controlling mechanism on their formation (Betz *et al.* 1987; Jaritz 1980, 1987; Nalpas *et al.* 1995; Scheck *et al.* 2002*a*). Indeed, the distribution of basins and highs corresponds to the structural pattern one would expect with a system of stepping dextral strike-slip faults with areas of local transtension and transpression (Fig. 16.13b). As with the subsiding Weald, Münsterland and North Bohemian basins, these basins were underlain by NW–SE orientated Variscan faults, which may have been reactivated, leading to combined strike-slip and normal displacements in the sub-basins along the SW margin of the CEBS.

In south Central Europe, subsidence slowed down or even ceased in the Late Jurassic to Early Cretaceous. Only the southernmost part of Central Europe, forming part of the Dauphinois-Helvetic shelf at the northern margin of the Alpine Tethys, was an area of continuous deposition (Ziegler 1990). In the Paris Basin, a reduced subsidence rate in the Early Cretaceous is reported and the depositional system became increasingly siliciclastic (Guillocheau *et al.* 2000). As in the CEBS, the orientation of the main depocentre (located in the Boulonnais) is NW–SE orientated and probably continues westwards into the Weald Basin. Two unconformities in the Paris Basin are interpreted to be the result of compression (i.e. 'Late Cimmerian') with associated inversion along the Bray Fault and the Armorica margin. This would support the concept proposed by Ziegler (1990) that the plate-boundary processes in the Atlantic and the Bay of Biscay induced east–west to NE–SW orientated compression in western Central Europe.

Across large parts of the South German Basin, deposition ceased at the end of the Jurassic and the basin was subsequently subjected to erosion and karstification. Only some tens of metres of Lower Cretaceous sediments are preserved either in the southern part of the basin (Franconian Platform) or where the strata are partly downwarped below the Tertiary Molasse Basin in the Alpine foreland (Meyer 1996). The former connection between the North and South German basins, the Hessian Basin, also experienced uplift and erosion during Late Jurassic–Early Cretaceous times. Deformation of the South German Basin was associated with the reactivation of NW–SE and NNE–SSW striking faults (Schwerd 1996; Walter 1992). Early Cretaceous uplift was limited to the east by NW–SE striking faults (e.g. Bavarian Fault, Franconian Line, Donau Fault; Meyer 1996). Uplift of the northern part of the South German Basin was accomplished by the formation of a large dome structure to the west of the NW–SE striking main faults (Meyer 1996).

There are arguments for the assumption that the present-day and Early Cretaceous topography of the South German Basin area were broadly similar (Meyer 1996). The area, however, was subsequently deformed by Alpine orogenesis as well as by the evolution of the Upper Rhine Graben. Today, the Triassic–Jurassic succession east of the Upper Rhine Graben is tilted as a result of basin formation and is preserved, with a moderate dip to the east, between the Black Forest and the Bohemian Massif. To the west of the Upper Rhine Graben, the succession dips to the west for the same reason.

In summary, the Late Jurassic–Early Cretaceous was a period of restricted deposition in mainly NW–SE trending depocentres along the margins of the CEBS, and of uplift of large areas in the central part of the CEBS as well as in the area to the south. However, the Early Cretaceous was also a time of very low eustatic sea level, which contributed to the relative elevation of the 'uplifted' areas above the depositional level.

### *Late Cretaceous*

The Late Cretaceous was a period of elevated sea level resulting from the high global rates of seafloor spreading. A sea level 100–200 m higher than today resulted in the development of a series of shallow seaways covering most of the continental landmasses (Torsvik *et al.* 2002). Oceanic spreading in the central Atlantic propagated northward into the Labrador Sea between North America and Greenland (Fig. 16.14) whereas the spreading centre in the Bay of Biscay was abandoned (Stampfli & Borel 2002; Torsvik *et al.* 2002). These divergent plate movements may have induced minor extensional stresses in Central Europe during early Late Cretaceous times. Together with the high global sea level this resulted initially in flooding of much of Central Europe during the Late Cretaceous. In north Central Europe sediments were predominantly carbonates, with clastics being deposited along the southern margin of the CEBS. Sedimentation occurred at a time of tectonic quiescence which appears to correlate with a pause in Alpine orogenic activity (Schwerd 1996). Much of the area of south Central Europe was a region of non-deposition.

Iberia became part of the African plate in late Early Cretaceous and drifted eastward, where its eastern promontory became implicated in Alpine orogenesis. In the other parts of the Tethyan domain, the remaining oceanic backarc basins began to close successively during the latest Cretaceous. Accordingly, orogenic activity moved from the Austro-Carpathian area in the east to the Alpine Tethys area, and extended westwards into the western Alps in the Late Cretaceous (Stampfli & Borel 2002). This convergence induced compressive stresses to the lithosphere of Central Europe, and consequently, early Late Cretaceous subsidence was followed by a phase of inversion, when large parts of Central Europe were affected by uplift.

In the Norwegian Sea, ongoing east–west extension is indicated by minor normal faulting in the early Late Cretaceous, but passive thermal subsidence was the main controlling factor for the depositional system there. In the latest Cretaceous, variations in the dynamics of Atlantic rifting provoked a change in the direction of extension along the Norwegian margin from east–west to WNW–ESE. This is evidenced by minor normal faulting along the NNE–SSW trending fault systems. Towards the end of the Late Cretaceous, uplift and erosion of NNE–SSW striking highs and partial basin inversion is documented, especially close to the area of the future (Eocene) North Atlantic breakup (e.g. Brekke 2000; Doré *et al.* 1999; Gernigon *et al.* 2006; Scheck-Wenderoth *et al.* 2007). Furthermore, the uplift of Norway and Scotland commenced in the Late Cretaceous (Blystad *et al.* 1995). Though the origin of these observed uplift processes is still discussed, they most probably were related to the incipient breakup of the North Atlantic Ocean in concert with early activity related to the impingement of the Iceland plume.

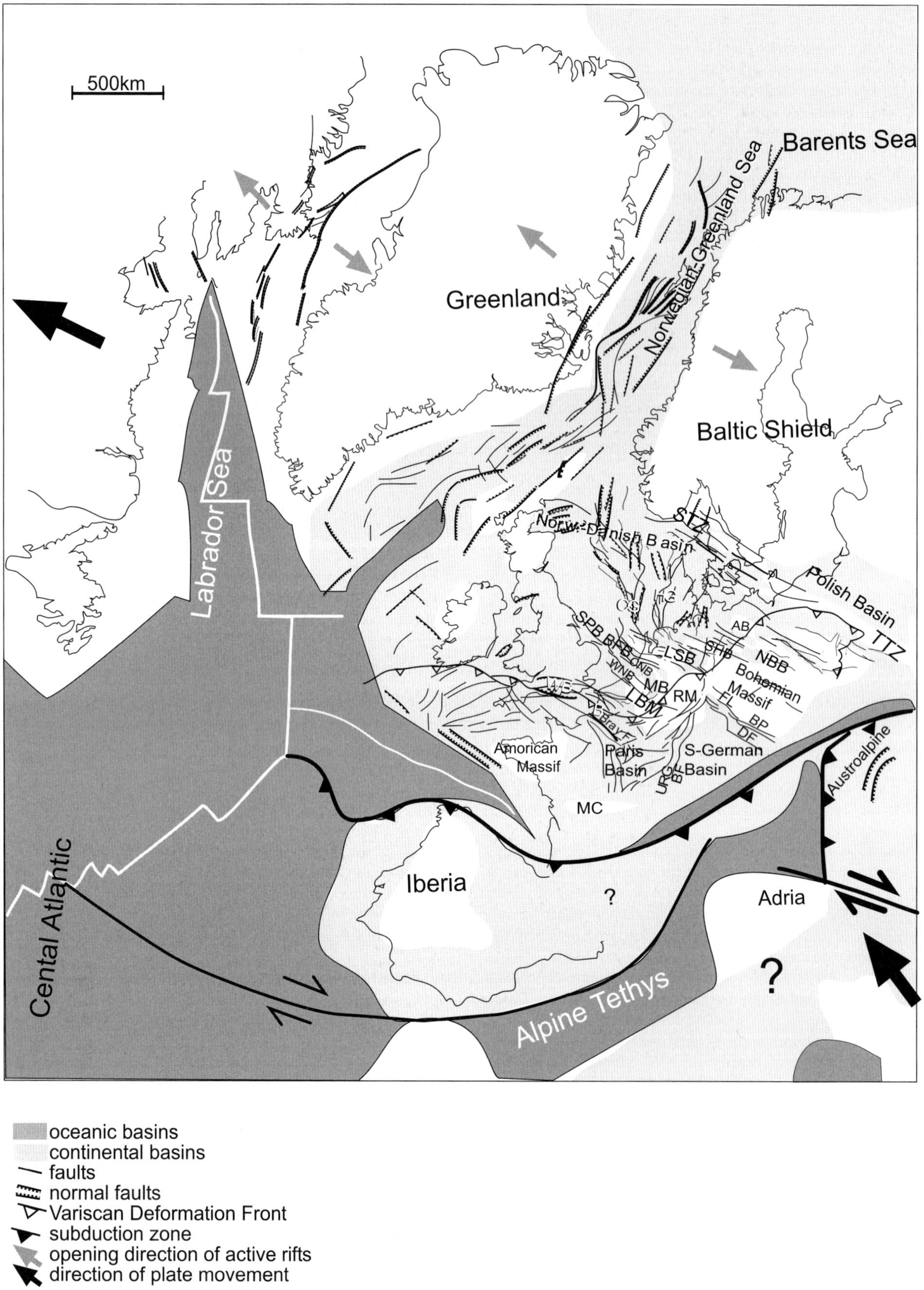


**Fig. 16.14.** Palaeotectonic setting in Late Cretaceous times (*c.* 70 Ma). After flooding of north Central Europe in consequence of a high global sea level, early phases of convergence in the Alpine System in the south induced compression. See Table 16.1 for abbreviations.

### *Late Cretaceous tectonics in the CEBS*

Generally, the thickness distribution of the preserved Upper Cretaceous chalk in the CEBS indicates a clear dominance of NW–SE structural elements (Fig. 16.15). However, it also reflects the localized uplift not only along the Sorgenfrei-Tornquist Zone and the Teisseyre-Tornquist Zone but also along the Elbe Fault System at the southern margin of the North German Basin. The areas affected by Late Cretaceous–Early Cenozoic uplift coincide with depocentres in the preceding Late Jurassic–Early Cretaceous period. Seismic data perpendicular to the Elbe Fault System indicate that many of the reverse or transpressive faults accommodating uplift show normal or transtensional activity during the deposition of the underlying Late Jurassic–Early Cretaceous sediments. Seismic profiles across the Elbe Fault System show this relationship for the Lower Saxony and Altmark basins (Figures 16.4 & 16.5), where the area with stratigraphic thickening of the Lower Cretaceous coincides with the area of maximum uplift during the Late Cretaceous. In addition, Early Cretaceous normal faults show reverse reactivation in the Late Cretaceous. Similar phenomena were also reported from the Sole Pit Basin (Badley *et al.* 1993; Buchanan *et al.* 1996; Nalpas *et al.* 1995) the Weald Basin (Hansen *et al.* 2002), the Broad Fourteens Basin (De Lugt *et al.* 2003; Nalpas *et al.* 1995) and the Subhercynian Basin (Franzke *et al.* 2004; Kossow *et al.* 2001; Otto 2003; Voigt *et al.* 2004). Inversion of the sub-basins along the Elbe Fault System (e.g. Sole Pit, Broad Fourteens, Lower Saxony and Subhercynian basins) was accompanied by a new phase of salt movement during which salt diapirs with NW–SE trending structural axes formed parallel to the uplifted blocks. Thus, basement-involving uplift and uplift of the salt cover were decoupled by salt. The sections shown in Figures 16.4 and 16.5 illustrate the degree of this tectonic decoupling. Basement-involving compressive deformation is localized along the southern margin of the North German Basin where Zechstein salt is thin or missing. Along the Gardelegen Fault, for example, the pre-Zechstein basement south of the fault is uplifted about 5 km with respect to the basin (Fig. 16.5). In contrast, compressive deformation in the central part of the North German Basin is mostly concentrated above the Zechstein salt. This deformation is expressed in the folding of the salt cover with salt-cored anticlines and synclines from where the salt has been withdrawn. The intensity of basement-involving deformation decreases rapidly with increasing distance from the fault system at the southern margin, and the base of the Zechstein is almost continuous below the basin area.

Other NW–SE orientated basins located immediately south of the CEBS were flooded in the Cenomanian and experienced minor extensional faulting followed by Late Cretaceous–Early Tertiary inversion. Prominent examples are the Weald, Münster-

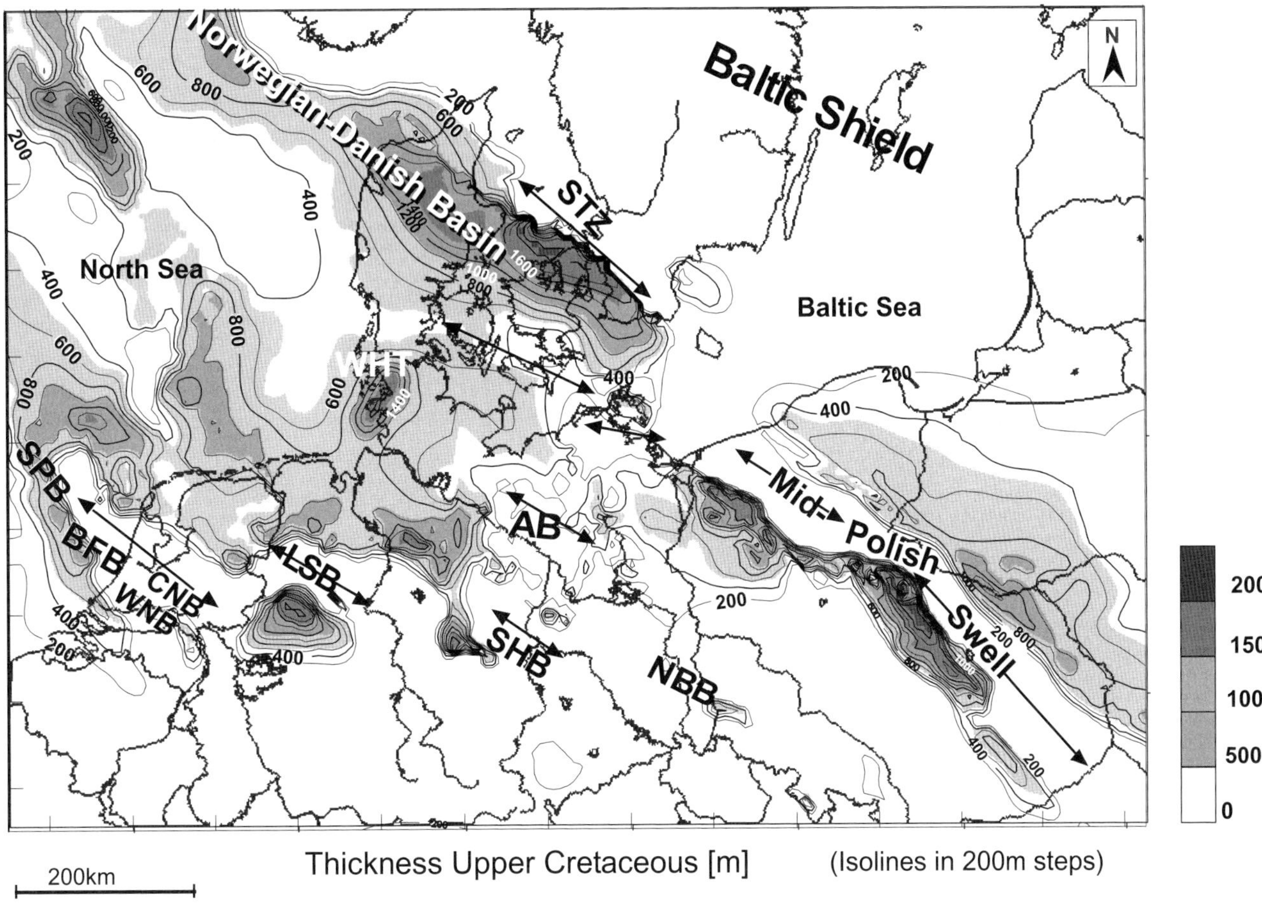


**Fig. 16.15.** The present-day thickness distribution of the Upper Cretaceous in the Central European Basin System (CEBS) reveals a dominance of NW–SE striking, inversion-related structural elements. Uplifted highs at the northern and southern margins of the CEBS as well as in the Polish Basin are bordered by parallel troughs. The present distribution of the Upper Cretaceous is the combined geometrical result of inversion, erosion and sedimentation.

land and North Bohemian basins, all of which were initiated in the Late Jurassic–Early Cretaceous above Variscan basement faults. In the Weald Basin, to the south of the Anglo-Brabant Massif, localized inversion resulted in uplift of the basin centre into a broad dome while the marginal areas to the north and south subsided (Hansen *et al.* 2002). In the Münsterland Basin, WNW–ESE striking folding was accompanied by parallel thrusts to the north. As in other areas, the inverted faults were reactivated Variscan-age structures. In the North Bohemian Basin, thrusting and reverse faulting took place along the WNW–ESE striking Lausitz Fault, which is also of Variscan origin (Franzke *et al.* 2004; Voigt *et al.* 2004). Even some basins in which subsidence had ceased in the earlier Mesozoic (e.g. Thuringian Basin, Intra-Sudetic Basin; Walter 1992) were flooded again in the Late Cretaceous and underwent Late Cretaceous and Palaeocene compressive deformation along NW–SE striking reactivated Variscan basement faults.

In the North Sea, thermal subsidence in the early Late Cretaceous was followed by inversion, which was most intense along the NW–SE striking branch of the Central Graben. Structural analysis of the Upper Cretaceous to Palaeogene succession in the Danish Central Graben (Cartwright 1993; Vejbaek & Andersen 2002) suggests that there was continuous inversion from the Late Hauterivian into Palaeogene times, with three phases of increased intensity in the Late Cretaceous (latest Santonian, Mid-Campanian, late Maastrichtian) and two later phases in the Early Tertiary.

Inversion phases in the Danish Central Graben would appear to be synchronous with inversion phases along the Sorgenfrei-Tornquist Zone at the northern margin of the Norwegian–Danish Basin (Vejbaek & Andersen 2002). In both areas, the location of inversion is spatially linked to Upper Jurassic–Lower Cretaceous, NW–SE trending depocentres (Vejbaek 1997). Furthermore, Late Cretaceous reactivation of older, basement-cutting normal faults has been observed further to the east along the Teisseyre-Tornquist Zone in the axial part of the Polish Basin (Fig. 16.3; Erlström *et al.* 1997; Krzywiec 2002*a*; Krzywiec *et al.* 2003). There, compressional reactivation was accompanied by strike-slip movements, orientated perpendicular (along the Grójec Fault Zone) and parallel (within the Bornholm–Darłowo Fault Zone) to the basin (Dadlez *et al.* 1998; Krzywiec 2002*a*; Krzywiec *et al.* 2003). Due to significant uplift of the axial part of the Mid-Polish Trough and subsequent deep erosion it is difficult, if not impossible, to determine the precise timing of the onset and end of inversion activity. However, evidence from the basin margins suggests that it may have commenced as early as the Late Turonian and ended in the Early Tertiary. In certain parts of the Polish Basin (e.g. Nida Trough) basement fault zones were still extensional during the Maastrichtian, and were first inverted in Early Tertiary times (profile 4 in Fig. 16.3).

As in the North German Basin, a remarkable structural difference can also be observed within the Mid-Polish Trough between the pre-salt basement and the salt cover. There, the pre-Zechstein basement forms a deep regional syncline (>8 km) in the central (Kuiavian) segment of the basin, whereas the salt cover follows the shape of a wide-spanned anticline (profile 3 in Fig. 16.3). In contrast, the pre-Zechstein basement rises (3–4 km) parallel with the Mesozoic in a NW direction (cf. profiles 1 and 2 in Fig. 16.3) and also in the SE part of the basin where the pre-Zechstein basement is uplifted and exposed (Holy Cross Mountains). Similarly to the subsidence phases, inversion of the Mid-Polish Trough was significantly influenced by mechanical decoupling between the sub-salt basement and its cover (Krzywiec 2006*a*, *b*) in the central (Kuiavian) and NW (Pomeranian) segments. As a result, the Mesozoic cover was mostly deformed by fault-propagation folding (profiles 2 and 3 in Fig. 16.3). This folding was locally accompanied by reverse reactivation of peripheral structures developed along the flanks of the Mid-Polish Trough and detached within the Zechstein evaporites. Basement extensional fault zones that were responsible for basin subsidence were reactivated as reverse fault zones and caused uplift of particular basement blocks. Within the areas characterized by either thin or no evaporites, inversion-related reverse basement faulting propagated into the Mesozoic cover (profiles 1, 4 and 5 in Fig. 16.3).

Most of the NW–SE striking inverted blocks in the CEBS are bordered by marginal basins which are truncated by the base-Cenozoic unconformity, an indication that uplift occurred prior to Cenozoic deposition. However, Late Cretaceous sedimentation was partially coeval with inversion in the marginal areas of the Danish Basin along the Sorgenfrei-Tornquist Zone (Nielsen *et al.* 2005; Vejbaek 1997), on both sides of the rising Mid-Polish Swell and along the Elbe Fault System (Figs 16.4 & 16.5). Thus, a temporal change in structural style from early inversion, confined to narrow zones and associated with reverse faulting along pre-existing normal faults, to late inversion which was dominated by gentle basin-wide flexure, is obvious. Nielsen *et al.* (2005) explain this phenomenon with a simple flexural model suggesting that domal, secondary inversion inevitably follows on from primary, convergence-related inversion subsequent to relaxation of the in-plane tectonic stress.

### *Late Cretaceous tectonics in south Central Europe*

In the Paris Basin, as in the CEBS, carbonate sedimentation was re-established in Late Cretaceous times and was concentrated in the NW–SE trending Boulonnais–Weald area. Late Cenomanian east–west orientated extension was followed by a minor phase of NNE–SSW to north–south orientated compression and related inversion (Guillocheau *et al.* 2000). However, inversion in the Paris Basin was less intense than that observed at the margins of the CEBS.

Furthermore, flooding from the Alpine Tethys in the south reached the South German Basin between the Black Forest and the Bohemian Massif and, as in the rest of Central Europe, this was followed by inversion. Long-wavelength, low-amplitude, thick-skinned folding has been described for large parts of the South German Basin resulting in the presently observed wide-spanned undulations of the Mesozoic succession. In addition, Late Cenomanian and Latest Cretaceous compressive deformation is documented from NW–SE striking faults (e.g. Bavarian Fault, Franconian Line) with up to 1500 m of pre-Cenomanian uplift recorded from the Bohemian Massif to the east (Meyer 1996). Similarly, the late Variscan–Early Permian SW–NE trending listric normal faults of the Saar-Nahe Basin were reactivated during Late Cretaceous–Early Tertiary inversion (Kukulus & Henk 1999).

### *Processes during Late Cretaceous compressional deformation*

A striking phenomenon across Central Europe is that basement-involving inversion took place in a very localized manner, with strain localization along restricted zones leaving large undeformed areas between. The orientation and geometry of both inversion structures and transpressively reactivated faults (NW–SE) suggests that Late Cretaceous compression was orientated north–south to NE–SW. Palaeostress directions deduced from a wide variety of areas, including the southern North Sea (Nalpas *et al.* 1995), the North German Basin (Franzke *et al.* 2004; Kossow *et al.* 2001; Otto 2003; Voigt *et al.* 2004; Mazur & Scheck-Wenderoth 2005) and from seismic sections across the Weald Basin (Hansen *et al.* 2002), have been remarkably consistent. Palaeostress analysis of the Polish Basin suggests that NE–SW orientated compression occurred at the Maastrichtian–Palaeocene transition (Holy Cross and Sudety mountains; Lamarche *et al.* 2002; Lamarche *et al.* 1999). Additionally, palaeostress analysis in the chalk formations of the Isle of Wight, Sussex, Kent, Boulonnais, the Mons Basin and NE Belgium (Vandycke & Bergerat 2001) indicate that the area bordering the CEBS to the SW also underwent north–south to NE–SW compression during the Late Cretaceous.

In contrast to the NW–SE striking structures noted above, older north–south striking depocentres have generally not experienced inversion, for example in the Danish Basin (Vejbaek & Andersen 2002) and the North German Basin (Maystrenko *et al.* 2005). A seismic profile across the central Glückstadt Graben (Fig 16.6a) images the more or less constant thickness of the Upper Cretaceous across the graben and shows no signs of Late Cretaceous structural differentiation or inversion. This would also be consistent with a north–south to NE–SW direction of maximum horizontal compression as roughly north–south trending grabens would be subparallel with maximum compression and thus much less prone to inversion than the NW–SE trending structural elements (which are perpendicular to maximum compression).

The origin of the compressional stress field for Late Cretaceous inversion has traditionally been assigned to stresses transmitted from the Alpine orogenic belt into the foreland (Ziegler *et al.* 1995). Early compressive phases are reported from the Pyrenean area, where the onset of continental subduction and backarc basin inversion can be observed from Late Santonian times onward (Sibuet *et al.* 2004). The detailed compressive history of the Alpine Orogeny is still much discussed and different models for the convergent setting have been published (see Reicherter *et al.* 2008). One significant problem is that orogenic activity in Late Cretaceous–Early Tertiary times is confined to the Eastern Alps and Northern Carpathians (Stampfli & Borel 2002) and is thus rather distant from Central Europe. Furthermore, it is not always easy to correlate Late Cretaceous–Early Tertiary orogenic activity in the Eastern Alps and Northern Carpathians with the direction of compression derived from observations in the foreland.

Orogeny in the Eastern Alps and Northern Carpathians most likely produced a NW–SE orientated compression, which is in contrast to the north–south to NE-SW orientated compression indicated by structural investigations from Denmark to southern Germany. A more or less continuous east–west trending subduction zone, extending from the Pyrenees to the eastern Mediterranean and running north of Apulia, has been proposed for the Late Maastrichtian (Schettino & Scotese 2002). The stresses generated from such a suduction zone could result in north–south to NE–SW directed compression in Central Europe. In addition, compressive stresses generated from subduction would already have been effective before the onset of the main deformation phase in the Helvetian domain. Furthermore, ridge-push forces transmitted from seafloor spreading in the incipient North Atlantic Ocean as well as the uplift of the North Atlantic lithosphere due to the Iceland plume may also be considered as acting in conjunction with Alpine orogenic stresses and subduction to cause the Late Cretaceous compressive stress field (Nielsen *et al.* 2005; Ziegler *et al.* 1995).

The inversion of the Mid-Polish Trough may have been triggered by Late Cretaceous and younger collisional events in the Carpathians. These events were relatively complex, and included Middle Albian–Late Turonian thrusting of the Fatric Basin, Late Turonian emplacement of the Fatric-Hronic nappe system, Late Turonian–Early Campanian uplift of the Veporic core and late thrusting of the Fatric-Hronic nappe system, Middle Campanian–Early Maastrichtian thrusting along the outer Tatric edge, and Middle Maastrichtian–Danian closure of the Penninic-Vahic ocean basin (Plasienka 1997). The Pieniny Klippen Belt underwent Aptian–Turonian or Senonian compression, followed by subduction and compression in Campanian, Maastrichtian and Palaeocene times (Birkenmajer 1986). Outer Carpathian compression reflects the collision between the European continent and a series of intra-oceanic arcs, and included the Turonian-age inversion of the Silesian, Sub-Silesian and Skole basins, Campanian and younger inversion of the Magura Basin, Late Eocene–Early Miocene closure of the Outer Carpathian basins, and Miocene folding and thrusting accompanied by formation of the Carpathian Foredeep Basin (Oszczypko 2004).

In summary, a large part of Central Europe was flooded in the Late Cretaceous and was later subjected to compressive deformation. This deformation was localized predominantly along NW–SE striking fault zones of inherited crustal weakness, while older north–south striking depocentres experienced very little inversion. The Cretaceous–Tertiary transition is expressed as an erosional unconformity over the largest part of Central Europe (Figs 16.3–16.6) heralding a new chapter in its tectonic history.

## Summary

The Permian–Cretaceous tectonic evolution of Central Europe can be briefly summarized as the transition from a period of thermally related subsidence to one of active rifting followed by compression. In detail, however, the picture is more complex. As outlined above, Central Europe does not form a single tectonic unit, but rather is subdivided into two domains. The northern domain, the Central European Basin System, was essentially the northern Variscan foreland, while the southern domain was located in the area of the former Variscan Orogen. The relative positions of the two domains, together with the nature of the underlying basement, determined their respective evolutions from Permian–Cretaceous times.

A superposition of backarc extension, transtension and regional thermal destabilization initiated the basins of post-Variscan Central Europe in the late Carboniferous–early Permian prior to Permian subsidence. Following initial rifting in the Early Permian, much of northern Central Europe was affected by a phase of thermal subsidence in the Late Rotliegend that declined in Mid-Late Triassic times. The initial, graben-like depocentres of north Central Europe were joined to form the large Northern and Southern Permian basins along NW–SE to WNW–ESE trending axes. These basins contain a thick succession of clastics, the Rotliegend, which is overlain by evaporite deposits of the Upper Permian Zechstein. During Early to Mid-Triassic times, central and western Europe were characterized by a widening of the depositional areas, and Lower Triassic clastics of the Buntsandstein overstepped the margins of the Zechstein basin. In south Central Europe, within the area of the collapsing Variscan Orogen, the axes of former Variscan thrusts and folds provided the structural template for intramontane basins developing in the Late Carboniferous–Early Permian, but subsidence was less efficient during Permian times than in the CEBS as deposition in the shallow Buntsandstein basin of Central Europe resumed only in the Triassic. During the Muschelkalk sea-level highstand (Aigner & Bachmann 1993), much of Central Europe around the persistent highs of the Mid-North Sea–Ringkøbing-Fyn High, as well as the Anglo-Brabant, Rhenish and Bohemian massifs was a marine depositional environment and the basin boundaries expanded beyond those of the underlying Buntsandstein. North–south alignment of the connecting troughs between the basins of northern and southern Central Europe suggests the onset of a new tectonic regime from Mid-Triassic to Early Jurassic times, which culminated in roughly east–west orientated Mid- to Late Triassic extension preserved in the fill of north-trending grabens and troughs. Only in the Polish Basin does the dominant structural direction, controlled by the Teisseyre-Tornquist Zone, persist throughout the entire basin history.

Regional uplift of mid-Central Europe in the Mid-Jurassic led to short-term interruptions in communication between the Norwegian Sea and the Tethyan–Central Atlantic basins. By late Mid-Jurassic times the central North Sea dome collapsed and subsided again, resulting in the re-establishment of open-marine conditions from the North Sea to the Norwegian Sea. In contrast to the elevated northern domain, the basins of south Central Europe experienced their maximum extent during the Jurassic. The Late Jurassic–Early Cretaceous was a period of very low eustatic sea level and of restricted deposition in mainly NW–SE trending depocentres along the margins of the CEBS, and of the uplift of large areas in the central part of the CEBS as well as in the area to the south. A large part of Central Europe was again flooded in the Late Cretaceous and later subjected to compressive deformation. This deformation was localized predominantly along NW–SE striking fault zones of inherited crustal weakness, while older north–south striking depocentres experienced very little inversion. The Cretaceous–Tertiary transition is expressed as an erosional unconformity over the largest part of Central Europe (Figs 16.3–16.6) heralding a new chapter in its tectonic history.

We would like to thank C. Pascal and R. Stephenson for their very helpful and constructive reviews. The work of M. Scheck-Wenderoth formed part of the DFG-SPP 1135 'Sedimentary Basin dynamics' which was provided with industrial data thanks to the DGMK and the WEG. The Polish Oil & Gas Company, Petrobaltic and the Ministry of the Environment are thanked for providing access to seismic data from the Polish Basin. P. Krzywiec was supported by the Polish State Committee for Scientific Research (KBN)/Polish Geological Institute grant no. 6.89.0012.00.2.

## References


ABRAMOVITZ, T. & THYBO, H. 1999. Pre-Zechstein structures around the MONA LISA deep seismic lines in the southern Horn Graben area. *Bulletin of the Geological Society of Denmark*, **45**, 99–116.

ABRAMOVITZ, T. & THYBO, H. 2000. Seismic images of Caledonian, lithosphere-scale collision structures in the southeastern North Sea along MONA LISA profile 2. *Tectonophysics*, **317**, 27–54.

AIGNER, T. & BACHMANN, G. H. 1993. Sequence stratigraphy of the classic Germanic Triassic. *In:* LUCAS, S. G. & MORALES, M. (eds) *The Nonmarine Triassic*. New Mexico Museum of Natural History & Science, Bulletin **3**.

ARTHAUD, F. & MATTE, P. 1977. Late Paleozoic strike-slip faulting in southern Europe and northern Africa: Result of a right-lateral shear zone between the Appalachians and the Urals. *Geological Society of America Bulletin*, **88**, 1305–1320.

BACHMANN, G. H. & HOFFMANN, N. 1997. Development of the Rotliegend Basin in Northern Germany. *Geologische Jahrbuch*, **D103**, 9–31.

BADLEY, M. E., PRICE, J. D. & BACKSHALL, L. C. 1993. Inversion, reactivated faults and related structures: seismic examples from the southern North Sea. *In:* COOPER, M. A. & WILLIAMS, G. D. (eds) *Inversion Tectonics*. Geological Society, London, Special Publications, **150**, 201–217.

BALDSCHUHN, R., FRISCH, U. & KOCKEL, F. 1996. *Tectonic Atlas of NW-Germany.* Federal Institute for Geosciences and Natural Resources, Hannover.

BALDSCHUHN, R., BINOT, F., FLEIG, S. & KOCKEL, F. 2001. Geotektonischer Atlas von Nordwestdeutschland und dem deutschen Nordsee-Sektor. *Geologisches Jahrbuch Reihe A*, **A,** 153.

BAYER, U. & GRAD, M. *et al.* 2002. The southern margin of the East European Craton: new results from seismic sounding and potential fields between the North Sea and Poland. *Tectonophysics*, **360**, 1–4, 301–314.

BENEK, R., KRAMER, W., *et al.* 1996. Permo-Carboniferous magmatism of the Northeast German Basin. *Tectonophysics*, **266**, 379–404.

BERTHELSEN, A. 1998. The Tornquist Zone northwest of the Carpathians: an intraplate pseudosuture. *Geologiska Föreningen I Stockholm Förhandlingar*, **120**, 223–230.

BEST, G. & KOCKEL, F. 1983. Geological history of the southern Horn Graben. *Geologie en Mijnbouw,* **62**, 25–33.

BETZ, D., FÜHRER, F., GREINER, G. & PLEIN, E. 1987. Evolution of the Lower Saxony Basin. *Tectonophysics*, **137**, 127–170.

BEUTLER, G. & SCHÜLER, F. 1987. Probleme und Ergebnisse der lithostratigraphischen Korrelation der Trias am Nordrand der Mitteleuropäischen Senke. *Zeitschrift für geologische Wissenschaften*, **15**(4), 421–436.

BIRKENMAJER, K. 1986. Stages of structural evolution of the Pieniny Klippen Belt, Carpathians. *Studia Geologica Polonica*, **88**, 7–32.

BLYSTAD, P., BREKKE, H., FAERSETH, R. B., LARSEN, R. B., SKOGSEID, J. & TORUDBAKKEN, B. 1995. *Structural elements of the Norwegian Continental Shelf. Part 2: The Norwegian Sea Region.* NPD Bulletin, Stavanger, Norway, **8**.

BOILLOT, G., MOUGENOT, D., GIRARDEAU, J. & WINTERER, E. L. 1989. Rifting processes on west Galicia margin. *In*: TANKARD, A. J. & BALKWILL, H. R. (eds) *Extensional tectonics and stratigraphy of the North Atlantic margins*. American Association of Petrololeum Geologists, **46**, 363–378.

BREITKREUZ, C. & KENNEDY, A. 1999. Magmatic flare-up at the Carboniferous/Permian boundary in the NE German Basin revealed by SHRIMP zircon ages. *Tectonophysics*, **302**, 307–326.

BREKKE, H. 2000. The tectonic evolution of the Norwegian Sea Continental Margin with emphasis on the voring and More Basins. *In:* NØTTWEDT, A. (ed.) *Dynamics of the Norwegian Margin.* Geological Society, London, Special Publications, **167**, 327–378.

BUCHANAN, P. G., BISHOP, D. J. & HOOD, D. N. 1996. Development of salt related structures in the Central North Sea: results from section balancing. *In:* ALSOP, G. I. & DAVISON, I. (eds) *Salt Tectonics.* Geological Society London, Special Publications, **100**, 111–128.

CARTWRIGHT, J. A. 1987. Transverse structural zones in continental rifts – an example from the Danish Sector of the North Sea. *In:* BROOKS, J. G. K. (ed.). *Petroleum Geology of North West Europe.* Graham & Trotman, London, 441–452.

CARTWRIGHT, J. A. 1993. The kinematics of inversion in the Danish Central Graben. *In:* WILLIAMS, G. D. (ed.) *Inversion Tectonics.* Geological Society, London, Special Publications, **150**, 153–175.

CHADWICK, R. A. & EVANS, D. J. 1995. The timing and direction of Permo-Triassic extension in southern Britain. *In:* BOLDY, S. A. R. (ed.) *Permian and Triassic Rifting in Northwest Europe.* Geological Society, London, Special Publications, **91**, 161–192.

CLAUSEN, O. R. & KORSTGARD, J. A. 1996. Planar detaching faults in the southern Horn Graben, Danish North Sea. *Marine and Petroleum Geology,* **13**, 537–548.

CLAUSEN, O. R. & PEDERSEN, P. K. 1999. Late Triassic structural evolution of the southern margin of the Ringkoebing-Fyn High, Denmark. *Marine and Petroleum Geology,* **16**, 653–665.

COWARD, M. P., DEWEY, J., HEMPTON, M. & HOLROYD, J. 2003. Tectonic evolution. *In:* EVANS, D., GRAHAM, C., ARMOUR, A. & BRATHUST, P. (eds) *The Millenium Atlas: Petroleum Geology of the Central and Northern North Sea.* Geological Society, London, 2.1–2.17.

DADLEZ, R. 1997. Epicontinental basins in Poland: Devonian to Cretaceous – relationship between the crystalline basement and sedimentary infill. *Geological Quarterly,* **41**(4), 419–432.

Dadlez, R. 2001. Holy Cross Mts. area – Crustal structure, geophysical data and general geology. *Kwartalnik Geologiczny*, **45**(2), 99–106.

Dadlez, R. 2003. Mesozoic thickness pattern in the Mid-Polish Trough. *Geological Quarterly*, **47**, 223–240.

Dadlez, R. & Marek, S. 1974. General outline of the Tectonics of the Zechstein – Mesozoic Complex in Central and Northwest Poland. *Biuletyn Instytutu Geologicznego*, **274**, 11–140.

Dadlez, R., Narkiewicz, M., Stephenson, R. A., Visser, M. T. M. & van Wees, J.-D. 1995. Tectonic evolution of the Mid-Polish Trough: modelling implications and significance for central European geology. *Tectonophysics*, **252**, 179–195.

Dadlez, R., Marek, S. & Pokorski, J. 1998. *Palaeogeographic Atlas of Epicontinental Permian and Mesozoic in Poland (1:2 500 000)*. Polish Geological Institute, Warszawa.

Dadlez, R., Marek, S. & Pokorski, J. 2000. *Geological Map of Poland without Cainozoic deposits (1: 1 000 000)*. Polish Geological Institute, Warszawa.

De Lugt, I. R., van Wees, J. D. & Wong, T. E. 2003. The tectonic evolution of the southern Dutch North Sea during the Palaeogene: basin inversion in distinct pulses. *Tectononphysics*, **373**(1–4), 141–159.

Deckart, K., Féraud, G. & Bertrand, H. 1997. Age of Jurassic continental tholeiites of French Guyana, Surinam and Guinea: implications for the initial opening of the Central Atlantic Ocean. *Earth and Planetary Science Letters*, **150**, 205–220.

Decourt, J., Ricou, J. & Vrielynck, B. 1992. *Atlas of Tethys Paleoenvironmental Maps*. Commission de la Carte Géologique du Monde, Paris.

Decourt, J., Gaetani, M., *et al.* 2000. *Atlas Peri-Tethys*. Commission de la Carte Géologique du Monde, Paris.

Doré, A. G., Lundin, E. R., Jensen, L. N., Birkeland, O., Eliassen, P. E. & Filcher, C. 1999. Principal tectonic events in the evolution of the northwest European Atlantic margin. *In:* Fleet, A. J. & Boldy, S. A. (eds) *Petroleum Geology of Northwest Europe: Proceedings of the 5th Conference*. Geological Society, London, 41–61.

Erlström, M., Thomas, S. A., Deeks, N. & Sivhed, U. 1997. Structure and tectonic evolution of the Tornquist Zone and adjacent sedimentary basins in Scania and the southern Baltic Sea area. *Tectonophysics*, **271**, 191–215.

Evans, D. J., Graham, C., Armour, A. & Bathurst, P. 2003. *The Millennium Atlas: Petroleum Geology of the Central and Northern North Sea*. Geological Society, London.

Franke, D. & Hoffmann, N. 1999. Das Elbe-Lineament – bedeutende Geofraktur oder Phantomgebilde? - Teil 2: Regionale Zusammenhänge. *Zeitschrift für geologische Wissenschaften*, **27**(3/4), 319–350.

Franzke, J., Voigt, T., Eynatten, H., Brix, M. R. & Burmeister, G. 2004. Geometrie und Kinematik der Harznordrandstörung, erläutert an Profilen aus dem Gebiet von Blankenburg. *Geowissenschaftliche Mitteilungen Thüringen*, **11**, 39–62.

Freudenberger, W. 1996*a*. Gesteinsabfolge des Deckgebirges nördlich der Donau und im Molasseuntergrund: Perm. *In:* Freudenberger, W. & Schwerd, K. (eds) *Erläterungen zur Geologischen Karte von Bayern 1:500000*. Bayrisches Geologisches Landesamt, München, 55–64.

Freudenberger, W. 1996*b*. Gesteinsabfolge des Deckgebirges nördlich der Donau und im Molasseuntergrund: Trias. *In:* Freudenberger, W. & Schwerd, K. (eds) *Erläterungen zur Geologischen Karte von Bayern 1:500000*. Bayrisches Geologisches Landesamt, München, 65–90.

Gaetani, M. 2000*a*. Olenekian (245–243 Ma). *In*: Dercourt, J., Gaetani, M., Vrielynck, E., Barrier, B., Biju-Duval, B., Brunet, M. F., Cadet, J. P., Crasquin, S. & Sandulescu, M. (eds) *Atlas Peri-Tethys, paleogeographical maps*. Commission de la Carte Géologique du Monde/Commission for the Geologic Map of the World, Paris, Explanatory Notes, 27–32.

Gaetani, M. 2000*b*. Early Ladinian (238–235 Ma). *In:* Dercourt, J., Gaetani, M., *et al.* (eds), *Atlas Peri-Tethys, Palaeogeographical Maps*. Commission de la Carte Géologique du Monde Paris, Explanatory Notes, 33–40.

Gaetani, M. 2000*c*. Late Norian (215–212 Ma). *In*: Dercourt, J., Gaetani, M., Vrielynck, E., Barrier, B., Biju-Duval, B., Brunet, M. F. Cadet, J. P., Crasquin, S. & Sandulescu, M. (eds) *Atlas Peri-Tethys, paleogeographical maps*. Commission de la Carte Géologique du Monde/Commission for the Geologic Map of the World, Paris, Explanatory Notes, 41–48.

Gast, R. E. 1988. Rifting im Rotliegenden Niedersachsens. *Die Geowissenschaften*, **4**, 115–122.

Geluk, M. C. & Röhling, H.-G. 1997. High-resolution sequence stratigraphy of the Lower Triassic "Buntsandstein" in the Netherlands and northwestern Germany. *Geologie en Mijnbouw*, **76**, 227–246.

Gernigon, L., Lucazeau, F., Brigaud, F., Ringenbachd, J.-C., Planke, S. & Le Gall, B. 2006. A moderate melting model for the Vøring margin (Norway) based on structural observations and a thermo-kinematical modelling: Implication for the meaning of the lower crustal bodies. *Tectonophysics*, **412**(3–4), 255–278.

Glennie, K. W. 1997. Recent advances in understanding the southern North Sea Basin: a summary. In: Ziegler, K., Turner, P. & Daines, S. R. (eds) *Petroleum Geology of the Southern North Sea: Future Potential*. Geological Society, London, Special Publications, **123**, 17–29.

Goggin, V., Jaquin, T. & Gaulier, J. M. 1997. Three-dimensional accommodation analysis of the Triassic in the Paris Basin: a new approach in unravelling the basin evolution with time. *Tectonophysics*, **282**, 205–222.

Golonka, J. 2004. Plate tectonic evolution of the southern margin of Eurasia in the Mesozoic and Cenozoic. *Tectonophysics*, **381**, 235–273.

Grabowska, T. & Bojdys, G. 2001. The border of the East-European Craton in south-easterrn Poland based on on gravity and magnetic data. *Terra Nova*, **13**, 92–98.

Grad, M. & Guterch, A. 2006. Lithospheric structure of the TESZ in Poland based on modern seismic experiments. *Geological Quarterly*, **L.**

Grad, M., Janki, T., *et al.* 1999. Crustal structure of the Mid-Polish Trough beneath the Teisseyre-Tornquist Zone seismic profile. *Tectonophysics*, **314,** 145–160.

Grad, M., Guterch, A. & Mazur, S. 2002. Seismic refraction evidence for crustal structure in the central part of the Trans - European Suture Zone in Poland. *In:* Winchester, J. A., Pharaoh, T. C. & Verniers, J. (eds) *Paleozoic Amalgamation of Central Europe*. Geological Society, London, Special Publications, **201**, 295–309.

Grad, M., Jensen, S. L., *et al.* 2003. Crustal structure of the Trans-European suture zone region along POLONAISE'97 seismic profile P4. *Journal Of Geophysical Research,* **108**(B11). DOI: 10.1029/2003JB002426.

Gregersen, S. & Voss, P. 2002. Summary of project TOR: delineation of a stepwise, sharp, deep lithosphere transition across Germany–Denmark–Sweden. *Tectonophysics*, **360**(1–4), 61–73.

Guillocheau, F., Robin, C., *et* al. 2000. Meso-Cenozoic geodynamic evolution of the Paris Basin: 3D stratigraphic constraints. *Geodinamica Acta*, **13**, 189–246.

Gutowski, J., Popadyuk, I. & Olszewska, B. 2005. Late Jurassic – Earliest Cretaceous evolution of the epicontinental sedimentary basin of South-Eastern Poland and Western Ukraine. *Geological Quarterly*, **49**, 31–44.

Hakenberg, M. & Świdrowska, J. 1997. Propagation of the south-eastern segment of the Polish Trough connected with bounding fault zones (from the Permian to the Late Jurassic). *Comptes Rendues Academie de Science de Paris*, **324**(2a), 793–803.

Hansen, D. L., Blundell, D. J. & Nielsen, S. B. 2002. A Model for the evolution of the Weald Basin. *Bulletin of the Geological Society of Denmark*, **49**, 109–118.

Heeremans, M., Timmerman, M.-J., Kirstein, L.-A. & Faleide, J.-I. 2004. New constraints on the timing of Late Carboniferous–Early Permian volcanism in the central North Sea. *In:* Wilson, M., Neumann, E.-R., Davies, G.-R., Timmerman, M.-J., Heeremans, M. & Larsen, B.-T. (eds) *Permo-Carboniferous Magmatism and Rifting in Europe* **223**. Geological Society, London, Special Publications, 177–193.

Henk, A. 1997. Gravitational orogenic collapse vs plate-boundary stresses: a numerical modelling approach to the Permo-Carboniferous evolution of Central Europe. *Geologische Rundschau*, **86**(1), 39–55.

Hoffmann, N. & Stiewe, H. 1994. Neuerkenntnisse zur geologisch-geophysikalischen Modellierung der Pritzwalker Anomalie im Bereich des Ostelbischen Massivs. *Zeitschrift für geologische Wissenschaften*, **22**(1/2), 161–171.

Jaritz, W. 1980. Einige Aspekte der Entwicklungsgeschichte der nordwestdeutschen Salzstöcke. *Zeitschrift der deutschen geologischen Gesellschaft.* **131**, 387–408.

Jaritz, W. 1987. The origin and development of salt structures in Northwest Germany. In: Lerche, I. & O'Brian, J. (eds) *Dynamical Geology of Salt and Related Structures*, Academic Press, Orlando, FL, 479–493.

Kiersnowski, H., Paul, J., Peryt, T. M. & Smith, D. B. 1995. Facies, paleogeography, and sedimentary history of the southern Permian Basin in Europe. *In:* Scholle, P., Peryt, T. M. & Ulmer-Scholle, D. S. (eds) *The Permian of Northern Pangea.* Springer, Berlin 119–136.

Kockel, F. 1995. Structural and paleogeographical developement of the German north sea sector. *In: Beiträge zur Regionalen Geologie der Erde* **26**. Gebrüder Bornträger, Stuttgart.

Kockel, F. 2002. Rifting processes in NW-Germany and the German North Sea Sector. *Geologie en Mijnbouw*, **81**(2), 149–158.

Kockel, F., Best, G., *et al.* 1996. *Tectonic Atlas of NW-Germany 1:300 000.* Bundesanstalt fuer Geowissenschaften und Rohstoffe, Hannover.

Kossow, D. & Krawczyk, C. M. 2002. Structure and quantification of processes controlling the evolution of the inverted NE-German Basin. *Marine and Petroleum Geology*, **19**, 601–618.

Kossow, D., Krawczyk, C., McCann, T., Negendank, J. & Strecker, M. 2001. Structural development of the inverted Northeast German Basin. *In: EUG XI,* 8–12 April 2001, Strasbourg, France, *Journal of Conference Abstracts,* **6**, LS05:SUpo05:PO.

Krawczyk, C. M., McCann, T., Cocks, L. R. M., England, R., McBride, J. & Wybraniec, S. 2008. Caledonian tectonics. *In*: McCann, T. (ed.) *The Geology of Central Europe. Volume 1: Precambrian and Palaeozoic.* Geological Society, London, 303–381.

Królikowski, C. & Petecki, Z. 2002. Lithospheric structure across the Trans-European Suture Zone in NW Poland based on gravity data interpretation. *Geological Quarterly*, **46**(3), 235–245.

Krzywiec, P. 2001. Contrasting tectonic and sedimentary history of the central and eastern parts of the Polish Carpathian Foredeep Basin – results of seismic data interpretation. *Marine & Petroleum Geology*, **18**(1), 13–38.

Krzywiec, P. 2002*a*. Mid-Polish Trough inversion – seismic examples, main mechanisms, and its relationship to the Alpine-Carpathian collision. *EGU Stephan Mueller Special Publication Series*, **1**, 151–165.

Krzywiec, P. 2002*b*. The Oświno structure (NW Mid-Polish Trough) – salt diapir or inversion-related compressional structure? *Geological Quarterly*, **46**(3), 337–346.

Krzywiec, P. 2004*a*. Basin-scale basement control of the evolution of the Mid-Polish Trough. *In: American Association of Petroleum Geologists European Region Conference*, 10–13 October 2004, Prague, 87.

Krzywiec, P. 2004*b*. Triassic evolution of the Klodawa salt structure: basement-controlled salt tectonics within the Mid-Polish Trough (central Poland). *Geological Quarterly*, **48**(2), 123–134.

Krzywiec, P. 2004*c*. Basement vs. salt tectonics and salt-sediment interaction – case study of the Mesozoic evolution of the intracontinental Mid-Polish Trough. *In: 24th Annual GCSSEPM Foundation Bob F. Perkins Research Conference*, Houston, Texas, 343–370.

Krzywiec, P. 2006*a*. Triassic–Jurassic evolution of the Pomeranian segment of the Mid-Polish Trough – basement tectonics and sedimentary patterns. *Geological Quarterly*, **51**, 139–150.

Krzywiec, P. 2006*b*. Structural inversion of the Pomeranian and Kujavian segments of the Mid-Polish Trough – lateral variations in timing and structural style. *Geological Quarterly*, **51**, 151–168.

Krzywiec, P., Kramarska, R. & Zientara, P. 2003. Strike-slip tectonics within the SW Baltic Sea and its relationship to the inversion of the Mid-Polish Trough—evidence from high-resolution seismic data. *Tectonophysics*, **373**(1–4), 93–105.

Kukulus, M. & Henk, A. 1999. Tektonik und Sedimentation im nordwestlichen Saar-Nahe-Becken. *Terra Nostra*, **99**(4), 154–156.

Kutek, J. 1994. Jurassic tectonic events in south-eastern cratonic Poland. *Acta Geologica Polonica*, **44**(3–4), 167–221.

Kutek, J. 2001. The Polish - Mesozoic Rift Basin. *In:* Ziegler, P. A., Cavazza, W., Robertson, A.H.F., & Crasquin-Soleau, S. (eds) *Peri-Tethys Memoir 6: Peri-Tethyan Rift/Wrench Basins and Passive Margins*, Mémoires du Muséum National d'Histoire Naturelle, **186**, 213–236.

Kutek, J. & Głazek, J. 1972. The Holy Cross Area, Central Poland, in the Alpine Cycle. *Acta Geologica Polonica*, **22**(4), 603–653.

Lamarche, J., Mansy, J. L., *et al.* 1999. Variscan tectonics in the Holy Cross Mountains (Poland) and role of the structural inheritance during the Alpine tectonics. *Tectonophysics*, **313**, 171–186.

Lamarche, J., Bergerat, F., Lewandowski, M., Mansy, J. L., Swidrowska, J., Wieczorek, J. 2002. Variscan to Alpine heterogeneous palaeo-stress field above a major Palaeozoic suture in the Carpathian foreland (southeastern Poland). *Tectonophysics*, **357**, 55–80.

Le Solleuz, A., Doin, M.-P., Robin, C. & Guillocheau, F. 2004. From a mountain belt collapse to a sedimentary basin development: 2-D thermal model based on inversion of stratigraphic data in the Paris Basin. *Tectonophysics*, **386**(1–2), 1–27.

Lie, J. E. & Andersson, M. 1998. The deep-seismic image of the crustal structure of the Tornquist Zone beneath the Skagerrak Sea, northwesrn Europe. *Tectonophysics*, **287**, 139–155.

Lokhorst, A. 1998. *NW European Gas Atlas – Composition and Isotope Ratios of Natural Gases.* British Geological Survey, Bundesanstalt für Geowissenschaften und Rohstoffe, Danmarks og Gronlands Geologiske Undersogelse, Nederlands Instituut voor Toegepaste Geowetenschappen, Panstwowy Instytut Geologiczny, European Union.

McCann, T. 1999. The tectono-sedimentary evolution of the Carboniferous foreland basin of NE Germany. *Tectonophysics*, **313**, 119–144.

McCann, T., Skompski, S., *et al.* 2008*a*. Carboniferous. *In:* McCann, T. (ed.) *The Geology of Central Europe. Volume 1: Precambrian and Palaeozoic*. Geological Society, London, 411–529.

McCann, T., Kiersnowski, H., *et al.* 2008*b*. Permian. *In:* McCann, T. (ed.) *The Geology of Central Europe. Volume 1: Precambrian and Palaeozoic*. Geological Society, London, 531–597.

Mattern, F. 1996. The Elbe zone at Dresden – a Late Paleozoic pull-apart intruded shear zone. *Zeitschift der deutschen geologischen Gesellschaft.* **147**(1), 57–80.

Maystrenko, Y. 2005. *Evolution and structure of the Glueckstadt Graben by use of borehole data, seismic lines and 3D structural modelling, NW Germany.* Dissertation, Freie Universität Berlin, GeoForschungsZentrum Potsdam.

Maystrenko, Y., Bayer, U. & Scheck-Wenderoth, M. 2005. The Glueckstadt Graben, a sedimentary record between the North and Baltic Sea in north Central Europe. *Tectonophysics*, **397**, 113–126.

Maystrenko, Y., Bayer, U., Scheck-Wenderoth, M. 2006. 3D reconstruction of salt movements within the deepest post-Permian structure of the Central European Basin System – the Glueckstadt Graben. *Geologie en Mijnbouw*, **85**, 181–196.

Mazur, S. & Scheck-Wenderoth, M. 2005. Constraints on the tectonic evolution of the Central European Basin System revealed by seismic reflection profiles from Northern Germany. *Netherlands Journal of Geosciences*, **84**, 389–401.

Meyer, R. K. 1996. Gesteinsabfolge des Deckgebirges nördlich der Donau und im Molasseuntergrund: Kreide. *In:* Freudenberger, W. & Schwerd, K. (eds) *Erläterungen zur Geologischen Karte von Bayern 1:500000.* Bayrisches Geologisches Landesamt, München, 112–128.

Meyer, R. K. & Schmidt-Kaler, H. 1996. Gesteinsabfolge des Deckgebirges nördlich der Donau und im Molasseuntergrund: Jura. *In:* Freudenberger, W. & Schwerd, K. (eds) *Erläterungen zur Geologischen Karte von Bayern 1:500000.* Bayrisches Geologisches Landesamt, München, 90–111.

Michelsen, O., Frandsen, N., Holm, I., Jensen, T. F., Moller, J. J. & Velbaek, O. V. 1987. Jurassic–Lower Cretaceous of the Danish Central Trough – depositional environments, tectonism, and resevoirs. *Danmarks Geologiske Undersogese*, **A16**, 44.

Mosar, J., Eide, E. A., Osmundsen, P. T., Sommarung, A. & Torsvik, T. H. 2002*a*. Greenland–Norway separation: A geodynamic model for the North Atlantic. *Norwegian Journal of Geology*, **82**(4), 281–298.

Mosar, J., Torsvik, T. H. *et al.* 2002*b*. Opening the Norwegian and Greenland Seas: Plate tectonics in Mid Norway since the Late Permian. *In:* Eide, E. A. (ed.) *Batlas- Mid Norway Plate Reconstruction Atlas with Global and Atlantic Perspectives.* Geological Survey of Norway, Trondheim, 48–59.

NALPAS, T. & BRUN, J.-P. 1993. Salt flow and diapirism related to extension at crustal scale. *Tectonophysics*, **228**, 349–362.

NALPAS, T., LE DOUARAN, S., BRUN, J.-P., UNTERNEHR, P. & RICHERT, J.-P. 1995. Inversion of the Broad Fourteens Basin. (Netherlands offshore), a small-scale model investigation. *Sedimentary Geology*, **95**, 237–250.

NEUMANN, E. R., DUNWORTH, E. A., SUNDVOLL, B. A. & TOLLEFSUND, J. I. 2002. B1 basaltic lavas in CVestfjord-Jeloya area, central Oslo rift: derivation from initial melts formed by progressive partial melting of an enriched mantle source. *Lithos*, **61**(1–2), 21–53.

NIELSEN, S. B., THOMSEN, E., HANSEN, D. L. & CLAUSEN, O. R. 2005. Plate-wide stress relaxation explains European Palaeocene basin inversions. *Nature*, **435**(12 May), 195–198.

OLIVET, J.-L. 1996. La cinématique de la plaque Ibérique. *Bulletin des Centres de Recherches Exploration-Production Elf Aquitaine,* **20**(1), 131–195.

OLSEN, P.E. 1997. Stratigraphic record of the Early Mesozoic breakup of Pangea in the Laurasia-Gondwana rift system. *Annual Review of Earth and Planetary Sciences,* **25**, 337–401.

OSZCZYPKO, N. 2004. The structural position and tectonosedimentary evolution of the Polish Outer Carpathians. *Przeglad Geologiczny*, **52**(8/2), 780–791.

OSZCZYPKO, N., KRZYWIEC, P., POPADYUK, I. & PERYT, T. 2006. Carpathian Foredeep Basin (Poland and Ukraine) – its sedimentary, structural and geodynamic evolution. *In:* PICHA, F., & GOLONKA, J. (eds) *The Carpathians and Their Foreland: Geology and Hydrocarbon Resources*. American Association of Petroleum Geologists, Memoirs, **84**, 293–350.

OTTO, V. 2003. Inversion-related features along the southeastern margin of the North German Basin (Elbe Fault System). *Tectonophysics*, **373**(1–4), 107–123.

PASCAL, C., ANGELIER, J., SELAND, R. T. & LEPVRIER, C. 2002. A simplified model of stress-slip relationships: application to the Frøy field, northern North Sea. *Tectonophysics*, **357**(1–4), 103–118.

PLASIENKA, D. 1997. Cretaceous tectonochronology of the Central Western Carpathians, Slovakia. *Geologica Carpathica*, **48**(2), 99–111.

PLEIN, E. 1995. Norddeutsches Rotliegendbecken, Rotliegend-Monographie Teil II. *In:* DEUTSCHLANDS, S. K. (ed.) *Stratigraphie von Deutschland I.* Courier Forschungsinstitut Senckenberg, Frankfurt (Main), **183**, 193.

POZARYSKI, W. & BROCHWICZ-LEWINSKI, W. 1978. On the Polish Trough. *Geologie en Mijnbow*, **57**(4), 545–557.

POŻARYSKI, W. & ZYTKO, K. 1981. On the Mid-Polish Aulacogen and the Carpathian Geosyncline. *Bulletin l'Academie Polonaise des Sciences, Serie des Sciences de la Terre* **28**(4), 303–316.

REICHERTER, K., FROITZHEIM, N., *et al.* 2008. Alpine tectonics north of the Alps. *In:* MCCANN, T. (ed.) *The Geology of Central Europe. Volume 2: Mesozoic and Cenozoic*. Geological Society, London, 1233–1285.

REMMELTS, G. 1995. Fault related salt tectonics in the North Sea, The Netherlands. *In:* JACKSON, M. P. A., ROBERTS, D. G. & SNELSON, S. (eds) *Salt Tectonics: A Global Perspective*. AAPG, Memoirs, **65**, 261–272.

ROMER, R. L., FÖRSTER, H.-J. & BREITKREUZ, C. 2001. Intracontinental extensional magmatism with a subduction fingerprint: The late Carboniferous Halle Volcanic Complex (Germany). *Contributions to Mineralogy Petrology* **141**(2), 201–221.

RÜFFER, T. & ZÜHLKE, R. 1995. Sequence stratigraphy and sea-level changes in the Early to Middle Triassic of the Alps: a global comparison. *In*: HAQ, B.U. (ed.) *Sequence Stratigraphy and Depositional Response to Eustatic, Tectonic and Climatic Forcing*. Kluwer, Amsterdam, 161–207.

SCHÄFER, A. & KORSCH, R. J. 1998. Formation and fill of the Saar-Nahe Basin (Permo-Carboniferous, Germany). *Zeitschrift der deutschen geologischen Gesellschaft.* **149**(2), 233–269.

SCHECK, M. & BAYER, U. 1999. Evolution of the Northeast German Basin – inferences from a 3D structural model and subsidence analysis. *Tectonophysics*, **313**, 145–169.

SCHECK, M., BAYER, U., OTTO, V., LAMARCHE, J., BANKA, D. & PHARAOH, T. 2002*a*. The Elbe Fault System in North Central Europe – a basement controlled zone of crustal weakness. *Tectonophysics*, **360**, 281–299.

SCHECK, M., LAMARCHE, J., BAYER, U., OTTO, V., MAROTTA, A. M., THYBO, H. & PHARAOH, T. 2002*b*. The role of the Elbe Fault System in north central Europe and parallels with the Tornquist Zone. *In: EGS XXVII*, 21–26 April 2002, Nice, France, *Geophysics Research Abstracts*, EGS02-A-05446; SE4.04-1WE5P-062.

SCHECK, M., THYBO, H., LASSEN, A., ABRAMOVITZ, T. & LAIGLE, M. 2002*c*. Basement structure in the southern North Sea, offshore Denmark, based on seismic interpretation. *In:* WINCHESTER, J. A., PHARAOH, T. C. & VERNIERS, J. (eds) *Paleozoic Amalgamation of Central Europe*. Geological Society, London, Special Publications, **201,** 311–326.

SCHECK, M., BAYER, U. & LEWERENZ, B. 2003*a*. Salt movements in the Northeast German Basin and its relation to major post-Permian tectonic phases - results from 3D structural modelling, backstripping and reflection seismic data. *Tectonophysics*, **361**, 277–299.

SCHECK, M., BAYER, U. & LEWERENZ, B. 2003*b*. Salt redistribution during extension and inversion inferred from 3D backstripping. *Tectonophysics*, **373**(1–4), 55–73.

SCHECK-WENDEROTH, M. & LAMARCHE, J. 2005. Crustal memory and basin evolution in the Central European Basin System - new insights from a 3D structural model. *Tectonophysics*, **397**, 132–165.

SCHECK-WENDEROTH, M., RAUM, T., FALEIDE, J. I., MJELDE, R. & HORSFIELD, B. 2007. The transition from the continent to the ocean – a deeper view on the Norwegian Margin. *Journal of the Geological Society*, **164**, 855–868.

SCHETTINO, A. & SCOTESE, C. R. 2002. Global kinematic constraints to the tectonic history of the Mediterranean region and surrounding areas during the Jurassic and Cretaceous. *In:* ROSENBAUM, G. & LISTER, G. S. (eds) *Reconstruction of the Evolution of the Alpine-Himalayan Orogeny. Journal of the Virtual Explorer* (online), **8**, 149–168.

SCHWERD, K. 1996. Gesteinsabfolge der Alpen. *In:* FREUDENBERGER, W. & SCHWERD, K. (eds) *Erläterungen zur Geologischen Karte von Bayern 1:500000.* Bayrisches Geologisches Landesamt, München, 188–236.

SIBUET, J.-C., SRIVASTAVA, S. P. & SPAKMAN, W. 2004. Pyrenean orogeny and plate kinematics. *Journal of Geophysical Research*, **109**(B08104). DOI: 10.1029/2003JB002514.

SOKOLOWSKI, J. 1966. *The role of halokinesis in the development of Mesozoic and Cainozoic deposits of the Mogilno structure and of the Mogilno - Lódz Synclinorium.* Prace Instytutu Geologicznego, L. [in Polish with English summary].

STACKEBRANDT, W. 1997. Zur Strukturgeologie am Südrand der Nord(ost)deutschen Senke. *Zeitschrift für geologische Wissenschaften.* **25**(1/2), 239–243.

STAMPFLI, G. M. & BOREL, G. D. 2002. A plate tectonic model for the Paleozoic and Mesozoic constrained by dynamic palte boundaries and restored synthetic oceanic isochrons. *Earth and Planetary Science Letters*, **196**, 17–33.

STAMPFLI, G. M. & BOREL, G. D. 2004. The TRANSMED transects in space and time: constraints on the paleotectonic evolution of the Mediterranean domain. *In:* CAVAZZA, W., ROURE, F. M., SPAKMAN, W., STAMPFLI, G. M. & ZIEGLER, P. A. (eds), *The TRANSMED Atlas. The Mediterranean Region from Crust to Mantle.* Springer, Heidelberg, 53–80.

STAMPFLI, G. M., BOREL, G. D., CAVAZZA, W., MOSAR, J. & ZIEGLER, P. A. 2001*a*. *The Paleotectonic Atlas of the Peri-Tethyan Domain.* European Geophysical Society (On CD-ROM).

STAMPFLI, G. M., MOSAR, J., FAVRE, P., PILLEVUIT, A. & VANNAY, J.-C. 2001*b*. Permo-Mesozoic evolution of the western Tethys realm: the Neo-Tethys east Mediterranean basin connection. *In:* ZIEGLER, P. A., CAVAZZA, W., ROBERTSON, A. H. F. & CRASQUIN-SOLEAU, S. (eds), *Peri-Tethys Memoir 6: Peri-Tethyan Rift/Wrench Basins and Passive Margins.* Mémoires du Muséum National d'Histoire Naturelle, **186**, 51–108.

STEINER, C., HOBSON, A., FAVRE, P., STAMPFLI, G. M. & HERNANDEZ, J. 1998. Mesozoic seqeunce of Fuerteventura (Canary Islands): witness of Early Jurassic sea-floor spreading in the Central Atlantic. *Geological Society of America, Bulletin*, **110**/10, 1304–1317.

STEPHENSON R. A., DADLEZ R., VAN WEES J-D., ANDRIESSEN P. 2003. Tectonic subsidence modelling of the Polish Basin in the light of new data on crustal structure and magnitude of inversion. *Sedimentary Geology*, **156**, 59–70.

STOLLHOFEN, H. & STANISTREET, I. G. 1994. Interaction between bimodal volcanism, fluvial sedimentation and basin developement in the Permo-Carboniferous Saar-Nahe-Basin (south-west Germany). *Basin Research*, **6**, 245–267.

SUNDSBO G. O. & MEGSON, J. B. 1993. Structural styles in the Danish Central Graben. *In:* PARKER, J. R. (ed.) *The Petroleum Geology of NW Europe. Proceedings of the 4th Conference*. Geological Society, London, **2**, 1255–1268.

SURLYK, F. 2003. The Jurassic of East Greenland: a sedimentary record of thermal subsidence, onset and culmination of rifting. *In:* INESON, J. R. & SURLYK, F. (eds) *The Jurassic of Denmark and Greenland*. Geological Survey of Denmark and Greenland Ministry of the Environment, Copenhagen, **1**, 659–722.

SURLYK, F. & INESON, J. R. 2003. The Jurassic of Denmark and Greenland: key elements in the reconstruction of the North Atlantic Jurassic rift system. *In:* INESON, J. R. & SURLYK, F. (eds) *The Jurassic of Denmark and Greenland*. Geological Survey of Denmark and Greenland Ministry of the Environment, Copenhagen, **1,** 9–20.

SZULC, J. 2000. Middle Triassic evolution of the Northern Peri-Tethys Area as influenced by early opening of the Tethys Ocean. *Annales Societatis Poloniae*, **70**, 1–48.

THIERRY, J. 2000. Late Sinemurian (193–191 Ma). *In:* DERCOURT, J., GAETANI, M., *et al.* (eds), *Atlas Peri-Tethys, Palaeogeographical Maps*. Commission de la Carte Géologique du Monde, Paris, Explanatory Notes, 49–60.

THYBO, H. 2000. Crustal structure and tectonic evolution of the Tornquist Fan region as revealed by geophysical methods. *Bulletin of the Geological Society of Denmark*, **46**, 145–160.

THYBO, H. 2001. Crustal structure along EGT profile across the Tornquist Fan interpreted from seismic, gravity and magnetic data. *Tectonophysics*, **334**, 155–190.

THYBO, H., PERCHUC, E. & GREGERSEN, S. 1998. Interpretation in statu nascendi of seismic wide-angle reflections based on EUGENO-S data. *Tectonophysics*, **289**, 281–294.

TORSVIK, T. H., CARLOS, D., MOSAR, J., COCKS, L. R. M. & MALME, T. N. M. 2002. Global reconstructions and North Atlantic paleogeography 440 Ma to recent. *In:* EIDE, E. A. (ed.) *Batlas- Mid Norway Plate Reconstruction Atlas with Global and Atlantic Perspectives*. Geological Survey of Norway, Trondheim, 18–39.

TRÜMPI, R. 1988. A possible Jurassic-Cretaceous transform system in the Alps and the Carpathians. *In:* CLARK, S. P. JR, BURCHFIEL, B. C. & SUPPE, J. (eds) *Processes in Continental Lithospheric Deformation. Geological Society of America, Special Papers*, **218**, 93–109.

TRUSHEIM, F. 1960. Mechanism of salt migration in northern Germany. *AAPG Bulletin*, **44**(9), 1519–1540.

ULICNY, D., NICHOLS, G. & WALTHAM, D. 2002. Role of initial depth at basin margins in sequence architecture: field examples and computer models. *Basin Research*, **14**, 347–360.

UNDERHILL, J. R. & PARTINGTON, M. A. 1993. Jurassic thermal doming and deflation in the North Sea: implications of the sequence stratigraphic evidence. *In:* PARKER, J. R. (ed.) *Petroleum Geology of Northwest Europe: Proceedings of the 4th Conference*. Geological Society, London, **1**, 337–345.

VAN WEES, J.-D., STEPHENSON, R. A., *et al.* 2000. On the origin of the Southern Permian Basin, Central Europe. *Marine and Petroleum Geology*, **17**, 43–59.

VANDYCKE, S. 1997. Post- Hercynian britlle tectonics and paleostress analysis in Carboniferous limestones. *Aardkundige- Mededelingen*, **8**, 193–196.

VANDYCKE, S. & BERGERAT, F. 2001. Brittle tectonic structures and palaeostress analysis in the Isle of Wight, Wessex basin, southern U.K. *Journal of Structural Geology*, **23**(2–3), 393–406.

VEJBAEK, O. V. 1997. Dybe strukturer i danske sedimentaere bassiner. *Geologisk Tidsskrift*, **4**, 1–31.

VEJBAEK, O. V. & ANDERSEN, C. 2002. Post-mid-Cretaceous inversion tectonics in the Danish Central Graben – regionally synchronous tectonic events? *Bulletin of the Society of Denmark*, **49**, 139–144.

VOIGT, T., EYNATTEN, H. & FRANZKE, H.-J. 2004. Late Cretaceous unconformities in the Subhercynian Cretaceous Basin (Germany). *Acta Geologica Polonica*, **54**(4), 675–696.

WALTER, R. 1992. *Geologie von Mitteleuropa*. E. Schweizerbart'sche Verlagsbuchhandlung, Stuttgart.

WILSON, M., NEUMANN, E.-R., DAVIES, G.-R., TIMMERMAN, M.-J., HEEREMANS, M. & LARSEN, B.-T. 2004. *Permo-Carboniferous Magmatism and Rifting in Europe*. Geological Society, London, Special Publications, **223**.

ZIEGLER, P. A. 1988. *Evolution of the Arctic–North Atlantic and the western Tethys*. American Association of Petroleum Geologists, Memoirs, **43**.

ZIEGLER, P. A. 1990. *Geological Atlas of Western and Central Europe*. Shell Internationale Petroleum Mij. B.V., The Hague.

ZIEGLER, P. A. 1988. *Evolution of the Arctic-North Atlantic and the Western Tethys*. AAPG Memoirs, **43**.

ZIEGLER, P. A., CLOETINGH, S. & VAN WEES, J.-D. 1995. Dynamics of intra-plate compressional deformation: the Alpine foreland and other examples. *Tectonophysics*, **252**, 7–59.

ZIEGLER, P. A., CLOETINGH, S., GUIRAUD, R., & STAMPFLI, G. M. 2001. Peri-Tethyan platforms; constraints on dynamics of rifting and basin inversion. *Memoires du Museum National d'Histoire Naturelle*, **186**, 9–49.

ZÜHLKE, R., BOUAOUDA, M.-S., OUAJHAIN, B., BECHSTÄDT, T. & LEINFELDER, R. 2004. Quantitative Meso/Cenozoic development of the Central Atlantic continental shelf, western High Atlas, Morocco. *Marine and Petroleum Geology*, **21**, 225–276.

# 17 Palaeogene and Neogene

MICHAEL W. RASSER, MATHIAS HARZHAUSER (co-ordinators), OLGA Y. ANISTRATENKO, VITALIY V. ANISTRATENKO, DAVIDE BASSI, MIRKO BELAK, JEAN-PIERRE BERGER, GIANLUCA BIANCHINI, SAFET ČIČIĆ, VLASTA ĆOSOVIĆ, NELA DOLÁKOVÁ, KATICA DROBNE, SORIN FILIPESCU, KARL GÜRS, ŠÁRKA HLADILOVÁ, HAZIM HRVATOVIĆ, BOGOMIR JELEN, JACEK ROBERT KASIŃSKI, MICHAL KOVÁČ, POLONA KRALJ, TIHOMIR MARJANAC, EMŐ MÁRTON, PAOLO MIETTO, ALAN MORO, ANDRÁS NAGYMAROSY, JAMES H. NEBELSICK, SLAVOMÍR NEHYBA, BOJAN OGORELEC, NESTOR OSZCZYPKO, DAVOR PAVELIĆ, RAJKO PAVLOVEC, JERNEJ PAVŠIČ, PAVLA PETROVÁ, MARCIN PIWOCKI, MARIJAN POLJAK, NEVIO PUGLIESE, REJHANA REDŽEPOVIĆ, HELENA RIFELJ, REINHARD ROETZEL, DRAGOMIR SKABERNE, L'UBOMÍR SLIVA, GERDA STANDKE, GIORGIO TUNIS, DIONÝZ VASS, MICHAEL WAGREICH & FRANK WESSELINGH

Over the last 65 Ma, our world assumed its modern shape. This timespan is divided into the Palaeogene Period, lasting from 65 to 23 Ma and the Neogene, which extends up to the present day (see Gradstein & Ogg (2004) and Gregory *et al.* (2005) for discussion about the Quaternary).

Throughout the Cenozoic Era, Africa was moving towards Eurasia in a northward direction and with a counterclockwise rotation. Numerous microplates in the Mediterranean area were compressed, gradually fusing, and Eurasia underwent a shift from a marine archipelago to continental environments, related to the rising Alpine mountain chains (Figs 17.1 & 17.2). Around the Eocene–Oligocene boundary, Africa's movement and subduction beneath the European plate led to the final disintegration of the ancient Tethys Ocean. The Indo-Pacific Ocean came into existence in the east while various relict marine basins remained in the west. In addition to the emerging early Mediterranean Sea, another relict of the closure of the Tethys was the vast Eurasian Paratethys Sea.

The Oligocene and Miocene deposits of Central Europe are largely related to the North Sea in the north, the Mediterranean Sea in the south and the intermediate Paratethys Sea and its late Miocene to Pliocene successor Lake Pannon. At its maximum extent, the Paratethys extended from the Rhône Basin in France towards Inner Asia. Subsequently, it was partitioned into a smaller western part consisting of the Western and the Central Paratethys and the larger Eastern Paratethys. The Western Paratethys comprises the Rhône Basin and the Alpine Foreland Basin of Switzerland, Bavaria and Austria. The Central Paratethys extends from the Vienna Basin in the west to the Carpathian Foreland in the east where it abuts the area of the Eastern Paratethys. Eurasian ecosystems and landscapes were impacted by a complex pattern of changing seaways and land bridges between the Paratethys, the North Sea and the Mediterranean as well as the western Indo-Pacific (e.g. Rögl 1998; Popov *et al.* 2004). This geodynamically controlled biogeographic differentiation necessitates the establishment of different chronostratigraphic/geochronologic scales.

The geodynamic changes in landscapes and environments were further amplified by drastic climate changes during the Cenozoic. The warm Cretaceous climate continued into the early Palaeogene with a distinct optimum near the Palaeocene–Eocene boundary (Palaeocene–Eocene Thermal Maximum) and the

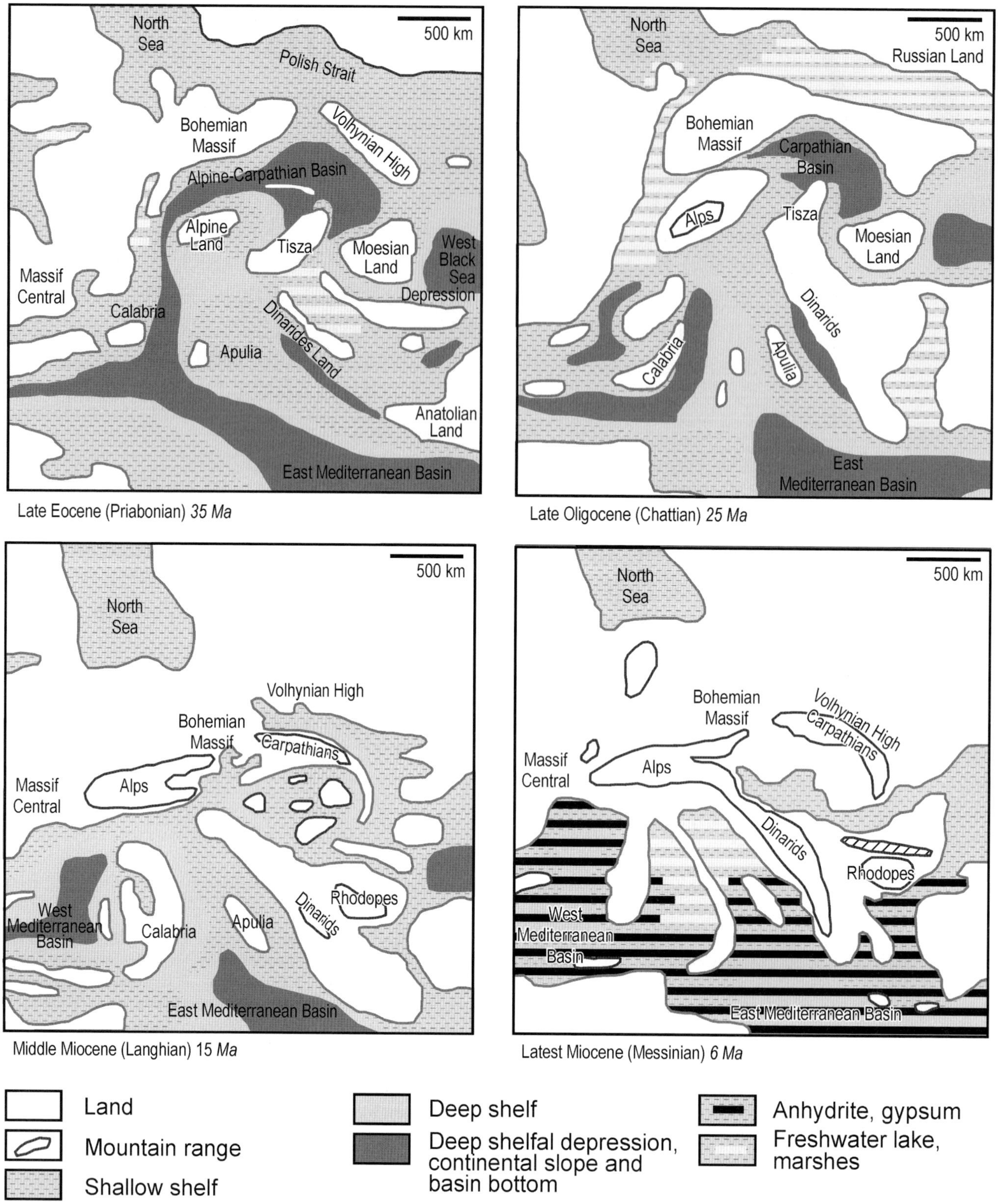


**Fig. 17.1.** Palaeogene–Neogene palaeogeography of Central Europe (after Popov *et al.* 2004).

Early Eocene (Early Eocene Climate Optimum). A gradual decrease in temperature during the later Eocene culminated in the formation of the first icesheets in Antarctica around the Eocene–Oligocene boundary (Zachos *et al.* 2001; Prothero *et al.* 2003). A renewed warming trend that began during the Late Oligocene continued into the Middle Miocene with a climax at the Mid-Miocene Climatic Optimum. The turning point at around 14.2 Ma led to the onset of the Middle Miocene Climate

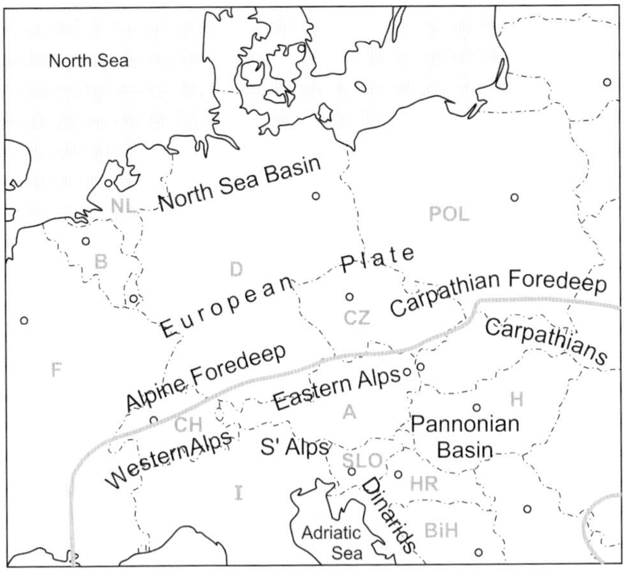


**Fig. 17.2.** Main physiographic and geological units of Central Europe. Grey line marks the border between the European Plate and the Alpine–Carpathian orogenic system. Abbreviations correspond to official country code plates.

Transition indicated by the cooling of surface waters and the expansion of the East Antarctic icesheet (Shevenell *et al.* 2004). A final trend reversal during the Early Pliocene is reflected by a gentle warming until 3.2 Ma (Zachos *et al.* 2001) when the onset of permanent Arctic glaciation heralded the Pleistocene ice ages (see Litt *et al.* 2008).

The Cenozoic history of Central Europe is chronicled in a dense pattern of Palaeogene and Neogene basins. In addition to the more stable North Sea Basin, the majority of these basins were strongly influenced by the Alpine compressive tectonics which caused a general uplift of Europe during the Cenozoic (see Froitzheim *et al.* 2008; Reicherter *et al.* 2008). The marginal position of the seas covering the area and the considerable synsedimentary geodynamic control resulted in incomplete stratigraphic sequences with frequent unconformities, erosional surfaces and depositional gaps.

This chapter deals with the Paleogene and Neogene ("Tertiary") geological development of Central Europe and its adjacent areas. It is structured according to the main geological regions relevant for the Cenozoic: (1) The European Plate; (2) the Alps and Alpine Foredeep; (3) the Carpathians, their foredeep and the Pannonian Basins System; and (4) the Southern Alps and Dinarides. Each subchapter is arranged from west to east, and north to south.

## Palaeomagnetism and palaeogeography (E.M.)

Central Europe is composed of two tectonically contrasting regions: a northern Variscian region and a southern Alpine region (Figs 17.2 & 17.3). The former is called stable Europe in the palaeomagnetic literature, since the generally accepted view is that Europe, north of the Alpine front, behaved as a rigid plate during the Cenozoic Era. However, the number of palaeomagnetic results supporting this view is surprisingly few and most of them were acquired before 1980. The scarcity of good data is especially notable for stable Central Europe. The situation is best characterized by data sets used for calculating stable European Cenozoic palaeomagnetic poles by Van der Voo (1993) who included a single result from stable Central Europe, or more recently by Besse & Courtillot (2002, 2003) who used five (all representing the 16.5–34 Ma time interval). Thus, the Cenozoic apparent polar wander curve (APWC), which serves to represent the displacements of stable Europe with respect to the present-day north and its shift in latitude, is a synthetic one computed by using palaeomagnetic data from all continents and transferred to stable Europe through a plate tectonic reconstruction model (e.g. Besse & Courtillot 2002).

Palaeomagnetic directions computed from the synthetic APWC suggest that stable Europe travelled a few hundred kilometres northward during the Cenozoic, but did not change its orientation (within the limit of the resolution of palaeomagnetic observations, which in this case is *c.* $\pm5°$). This implies that the expected stable European declinations are more or less aligned with the present meridians. The actually measured declinations at several points in stable Europe (e.g. France, Germany, Poland, Czech Republic; Global Palaeomagnetic Database 2005) deviate more from the present meridian than the coeval declination computed from the synthetic APWC. Nonetheless, these deviations cannot be interpreted in terms of tectonics, since the studied rocks, without exception, are igneous rocks, where secular variation of the Earth's magnetic field and poor control on local tectonics can cause bias from the direction of the geomagnetic field.

The stable European pattern of Cenozoic declinations breaks down as soon as we enter the North Alpine Foreland Basin at the southern margin of stable Europe and south of this. The pattern here suggests large-scale movements during the Cenozoic Era, accompanied by counterclockwise (CCW) rotations of variable angles and timings; observations for dominant clockwise rotations are known only from the Apuseni Mountains (Romania) and from the area between the Periadriatic and Sava faults.

Sediments lying directly on the stable European margin exhibit moderate CCW rotation (Scholger & Stingl 2004; Márton *et al.* 2003*a*). The mean angle of rotation is the same in every segment (Fig. 17.3), which is remarkable, since the age of the studied sediments varies between 20 and 7 Ma. The termination of the rotations is not constrained in any of the segments. Therefore, there are alternative solutions to explain these observations. One is that the rotations were simultaneous between longitudes of 12°E and 23°E. In this case, the Bohemian Massif (which is considered to be part of stable Europe) must have been involved in rotation. The other possibility is that the rotations are not coeval and the sediments were detached from the stable European basement. In either case, the observations would require dramatic modification of existing tectonic models.

As we move into the mobile part of Europe, the palaeomagnetic picture becomes fairly complicated. During the Palaeogene, there is no palaeomagnetic evidence for mobility, apart from a general northward travel for all tectonic units (Márton 2001). Rotations begin in the Miocene. Some of these can be related to tectonic escape from the East Alpine realm, others to subduction pull in the Carpathians and the rest to the motion of the Adriatic microplate (Adria).

Notable cases with rotations related to escape tectonics are known from the Eastern Alps and from the Periadriatic-Sava fault system (Fig. 17.3B, areas 10 and 11). In the first case, *c.* 30° of the CCW rotation observed in the sediments of the Miocene intramontane basins (Fig. 17.3B, area 10) are related to lateral extrusion (Márton *et al.* 2000a); in the second (Fig. 17.3B, area 11), the non-uniform, but dominantly clockwise rotations are attributed to right-lateral strike-slip movements (Fodor *et al.* 1998).

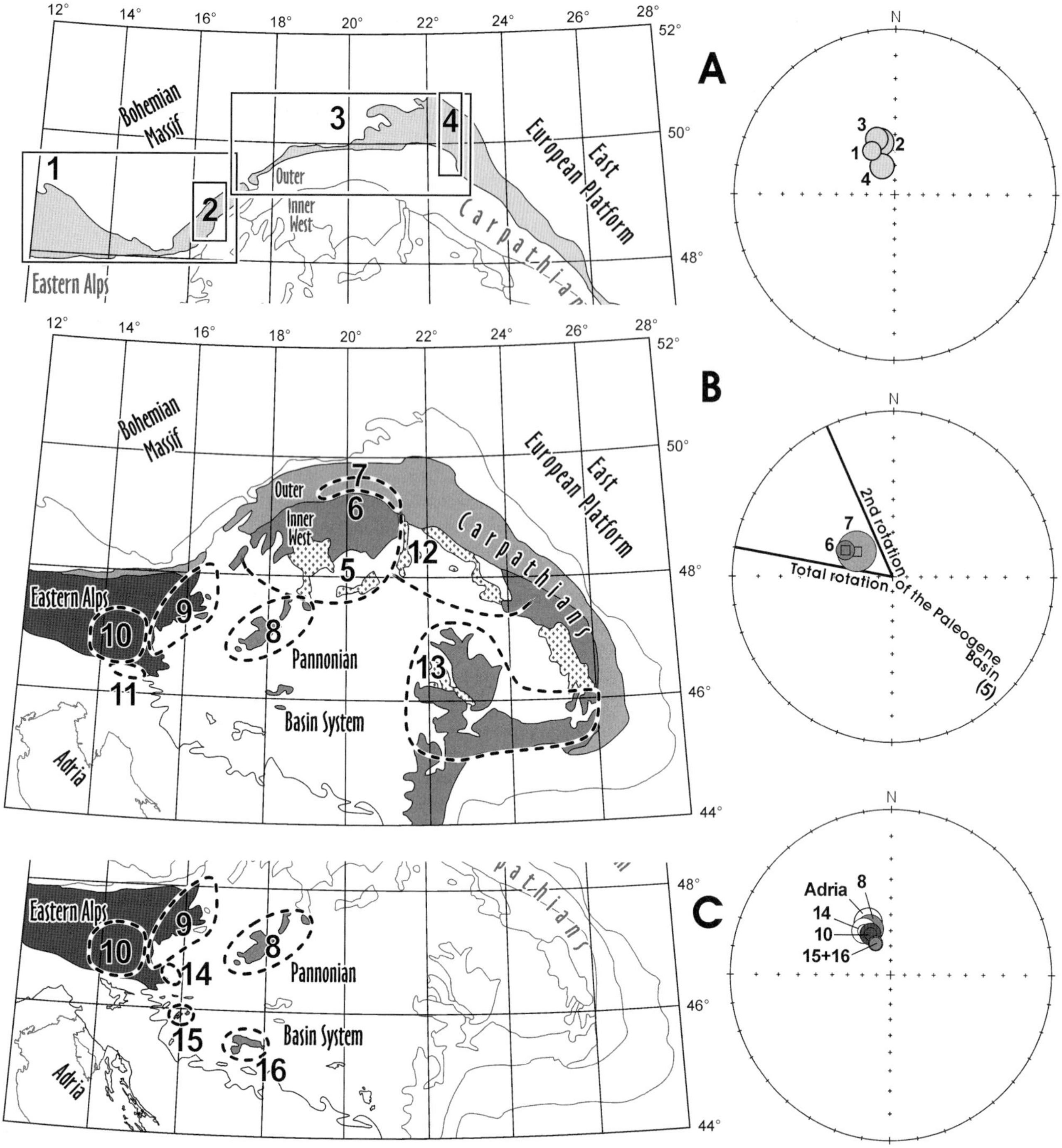


**Fig. 17.3.** Palaeomagnetics. **(A)** Alpine and Carpathian Foredeep. Age of sediments of the four numbered segments from west to east are: 27.5–17.2 Ma, 17.2-16.4 Ma, 16.4-13.0 Ma, 13.0-10.0 Ma (for Paratethyan geological stages refer to Rögl 1996). The stereonet (right side) shows the mean palaeomagnetic directions (declination and inclination) for the segments. The size of the dots corresponds to the size of the confidence circle for each palaeomagnetic direction. **(B)** Eastern Alps - Carpathians - Pannonian Basin. Numbered tectonic units are characterized by regionally coherent rotations, which are due to tectonic escape or subduction pull. Rotations connected to tectonic escape are the first-phase Miocene rotations in area 10 (intramontane basins of the Eastern Alps) and the rotations in area 11 (Periadriatic-Sava fault system). Rotations connected to subduction pull are those observed for areas 5 (North Hungarian-South Slovakian Paleogene basin), 6 (Central West Carpathian Paleogene Basin), 7 (Magura unit of the Outer Western Carpathians), 8 (Transdanubian Range), 12 (East Slovak basin), 13 (Apuseni Mountains). The stereonet shows the angle of the total rotation and that of the younger rotation for area 5, and the palaeomagnetic direction (declination and inclination) for areas 6 and 7. **(C)** Eastern Alps, Western Pannonian Basin. Rotations triggered by rotating Adria are observed for areas 8, 9 (border zone of the Eastern Alps and the Pannonian Basin), 10, 14 (Mura-Zala depression), 15 (Medvednica-Hrvatsko Zagorje), 16 (Slavonian inselbergs). The stereonet on the right side compares the palaeomagnetic direction characterizing the post-Eocene rotation of Adria with those reflecting the youngest rotation of the above listed areas.

Subduction (slab) pull accounts for most of the rotations observed for the Carpathians and for the Pannonian Basin. These rotations occurred during 18.5–17.5 Ma and 16–14.5 Ma (Magura unit of the Outer Western Carpathians (Márton *et al.* 2000*c*); Central West Carpathian Flysch basins (Márton *et al.* 1999*a*); North Hungarian–South Slovakian Palaeogene basin (Márton & Márton 1996; Márton *et al.* 1996; Márton & Pécskay 1998); Transdanubian Range (Márton & Fodor 2003)), close to the Palaeogene–Neogene boundary (e.g. Apuseni Mountains; Panaiotu 1998) and at 14–12 Ma (e.g. East Slovak Basin (Márton *et al.* 2000*b*) and Apuseni Mountains; (Panaiotu 1998)). The resulting rotations are CCW, except in the Apuseni Mountains.

As soon as subduction terminated in the Western Carpathians, at *c.* 14 Ma, a push from Adria and, subsequently, rotation of Adria with respect to Africa (Márton *et al.* 2003*b*) became the dominant driving force for displacements in the Alpine realm. A series of palaeomagnetic observations from the intramontane basins of the Eastern Alps (Márton *et al.* 2000*a*), from the Mura depression (Márton *et al.* 2002*a*) and from Northern Croatia (Márton *et al.* 2002*b*) indicate that *c.* 25° of CCW rotation occurred in the circum-Adriatic region, close to the Miocene–Pliocene boundary (Márton 2005). Moderate CCW rotations observed at the eastern margin of the Eastern Alps and in the bordering basins (Styrian and Vienna basins; Scholger & Stingl 2003, 2004; Scholger *et al.* 2003) and the youngest rotation of the Transdanubian Range (Márton & Fodor 2003) were probably also induced by the rotation of Adria.

Rotations affecting the same tectonic unit are of a cumulative nature. Repeated rotations in the same sense can cause large declination deviation from the present north. The largest declination deviations in the subject area were measured on Lower Miocene and Palaeogene rocks in the North Hungarian–South Slovakian Palaeogene basin (Fig. 17.3B, area 5), in the Transdanubian Range (Fig. 17.3B, area 8) and in the Apuseni Mountains (Fig. 17.3B, area 13), up to 90° in the counterclockwise and in the clockwise sense, respectively. Middle and Late Miocene rocks from the same areas are characterized by moderate rotations (*c.* 25–40°).

Age control on the termination of the youngest rotations is lacking, except for the North Hungarian–South Slovakian Palaeogene basin (14.5 Ma) and for the Apuseni Mountains (12 Ma). Thus, the possibility of large-scale neotectonic movements remains to be explored, especially in the southernmost part of Europe.

## The European Plate: overview (M.W.R.)

The European Plate represented the so-called stable European continent during the Cenozoic northward drift of Africa. It comprises a large epicontinental sedimentation area extending from NW Europe towards Ukraine (Fig. 17.4). During most of the Cenozoic it was separated from the Alpine-Carpathian chain by the Alpine-Carpathian Foreland Basin – often referred to as the Molasse Zone or Molasse Basin – and its precursors as a part of the Palaeogene Tethys, or Oligocene–Miocene Paratethys.

The North Sea Basin (NSB) is a main element of the European Plate. It comprises a belt of Cenozoic deposits in the northern part of Central Europe, extending from England to northern Poland. The Polish Lowlands form its eastward continuation and served as an occasional connection between the NSB and the Eastern Paratethys. Further eastward lies the Volhyno-Podolian Plate forming the SW margin of the East European (= Russian) Platform. Towards the south, the NSB is bordered by the Belgian and German low mountain ranges as well as by the Bohemian Massif.

The Upper Rhine Graben represents an approximately 1100 km long structural element between the shores of the North Sea and the western Mediterranean. It formed a complex

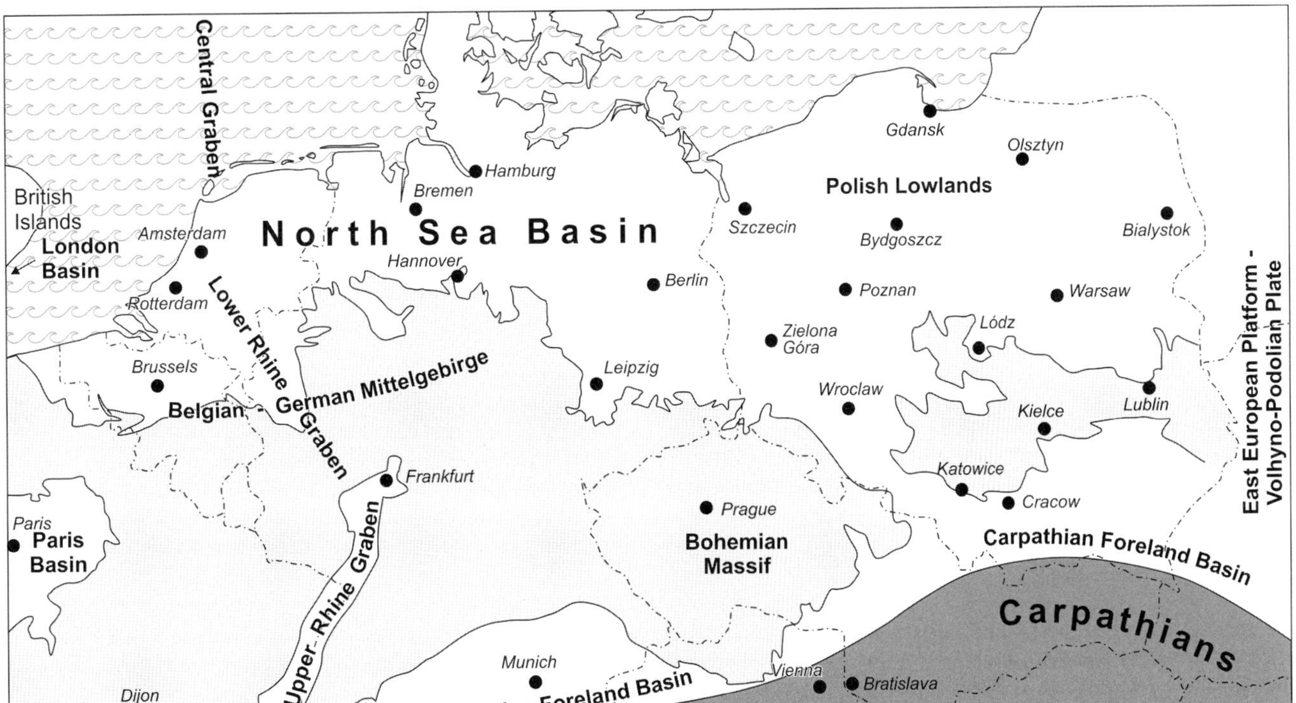


**Fig. 17.4.** Main Palaeogene–Neogene sedimentary basins of the European Plate.

Cenozoic rift system with sedimentation commencing during the Middle Eocene.

During the Paleocene and Eocene, the Helvetic units formed the southern margin of the European Plate, i.e. the northern margin of the Tethys Sea. Towards the south, the Helvetic units pass into the Ultrahelvetic Unit and the Rhenodanubian (Penninic) Flysch Zone. In late Palaeogene times, however, the Helvetic units are also considered by several authors to have constituted a transition to Ultrahelvetic and Penninic deep-marine clastic sedimentation as well as to the Northern Alpine Foreland Basin. Therefore, the Ultrahelvetic Unit is considered in both this and the following section on the Alps and Alpine Foredeep.

## *North Sea Basin: Palaeogene (K.G., F.W., G.S.)*

The Cenozoic North Sea Basin (NSB) was at its most extensive in the Early Eocene, where it comprised the present-day North Sea as well as southern and eastern England, eastern Scotland, Belgium, the Netherlands, northern and eastern Germany, southern Sweden, Denmark, and northern Poland, and the Samland coast of Russia (Fig. 17.4). During the Palaeogene the NSB was a mainly marine semi-enclosed basin (Fig. 17.1) with paralic margins in the SE. It was separated from the Atlantic Ocean by the Thule landbridge at least until the Late Oligocene (Wold 1995). This volcanic barrier resulted from a magma chamber forming at 70 Ma showing at least four magmatic pulses until late Middle Eocene (O'Connor *et al.* 2000).

The NSB was the successor of the German Zechstein Basin, which developed as a result of Permian rifting (see McCann *et al.* 2008). It is bordered by the Belgian and German Uplands (= Mittelgebirge) to the south, by the Fennoscandian Shield to the north and Great Britain to the west. To the east, the NSB was episodically connected to the Eastern Paratethys via the Polish Lowlands. The palaeogeographical limitation to the north is unclear since the Fennoscandian Shield underwent significant uplift (up to 3000 m) from Oligocene times onward. The sediment cover of the shield was subsequently eroded, providing the main source of the NSB sediments younger than Oligocene (Overeem 2002).

*Tectonic setting*

The NSB is subdivided by a series of fault zones that originated in the Mesozoic rift phase (see Michelsen & Nielsen 1993; Kockel 1995; Kockel *et al.* 1996; Mulder *et al.* 2003). The most active of these is the Central Graben which trends in a north–south direction, curving to a SE direction in the offshore Netherlands area where it connects with the Lower Rhine Valley. It is connected to the Upper Rhine Graben via faults through the Rhenish Massif. Additional north–south trending fault zones, such as the Horn Graben and the Brande Trough within the Ringkøbing-Fyn High, the Sieverstedt Fault Zone, the Glückstadt Graben and the Hessian Depression, also terminate in the Upper Rhine Graben. Large areas of the basin are underlain by thick Zechstein salt deposits which influenced the sedimentation history of the basin (Weber 1977).

*Sedimentary and stratigraphic development*

The Palaeogene development of the NSB can be divided into five phases (Figs 17.5, 17.6 & 17.7): the Early–Middle Palaeocene was a continuation of the tropical settings of the Cretaceous, as witnessed by widespread carbonate platform deposits in the entire NSB. It was also a major regressive phase. During the Early–Middle Palaeocene, carbonates were partly deposited in very shallow water as the Houthem, Ciply and Mons formations of Belgium. The Hückelhoven Formation of the Lower Rhine area, the Gödringen sands south of Hannover, and the Wülpen and Wasmansdorf formations of Brandenburg (Eastern Germany) represent clastic sedimentation generally with a high carbonate content (Lotsch *et al.* 1969). In the central part of the basin deep-water carbonates with *Lophelia* reefs (Bernecker & Weidlich 1990) or bryozoan limestones developed. During the Middle Palaeocene a dramatic sea-level fall led to paralic sedimentation spreading into the basin centre.

The Late Palaeocene to Early Eocene was a time of dramatic change. With the Thanetian transgression, the NSB sedimentation regime changed from predominantly calcareous to clastic. Clays and silts, partly with a carbonaceous microfauna (including agglutinated foraminifera and other non-carbonate microfossils) indicate a deep-water environment (e.g. Ølst Formation, Basbek Formation, Helle Formation). The macrofauna from the shallow-water deposits of the Thanet sands of Kent (UK) and Copenhagen (Denmark) indicates a colder climate. The Late Palaeocene Thermal Maximum is not reflected in the fauna of the NSB. Paralic or continental sedimentation is very rare at the southern margin of the basin apart from the estuarine Helmstadt-Halle embayment in Sachsen-Anhalt (Blumenstengel & Krutzsch 2008). The Thanetian transgression is also expressed in Belgium (e.g. Gelinden Formation). The overlying Landen Group begins with shallow-marine sands which were deeply eroded by the following continental Landen deposits. These are terrestrial in the south and lagoonal-brackish in the north (Tienen Formation). The regressive succession appears to be related to the uplift of the Artois axis rather than a sea-level fall within the basin (Dupuis *et al.* 1984). The Landen Group is covered by the partly deeper marine Ieper Group of Early Eocene age.

The marine diatomites of the uppermost Palaeocene to lowermost Eocene Fur Formation of northern Denmark (Homann 1991) are rich in vertebrate remains. They contain numerous (>200) ash layers and probably represent outer neritic depositional settings indicating upwelling on the shelf edge (Bonde 1979). The fish fauna suggests subtropical conditions.

The Eocene commenced with a major transgression that submerged large parts of the NSB. Depositional environments became dominated by dark clays of outer neritic to bathyal waters with ash layers from the Thule volcanism. These clays are rich in macro- and microfauna in the London and Hampshire basins and Belgium, but further to the east are almost unfossiliferous with rare agglutinating foraminifera and pyritized diatoms (*Coscinodiscus*) ('Untereozän 1 and 2', Røsnaes Formation, Zerben Formation). For these clays the term London Clay was originally used across the basin but has now been replaced by

**Fig. 17.5.** Chronostratigraphy and biostratigraphy of the North Sea Basin. The *Bolboforma rotunda*–Lower *Bolboforma reticulata* Zone boundary was lowered according to the match of the NN4–NN5 boundary with the *Uvigerina tenuipustulata*–*Uvigerina acuminata* Zone boundary (C. Müller, pers. comm.). The DN7–DN8 boundary and the NPF14–NPF15 boundary were lowered according to recalibration of ODP drillings in the North Atlantic by Müller & Spiegler (1993) and according to Gürs & Spiegler (2000). The NSB14 lower boundary is lowered due to the intra- Late Miocene age of the top of NSB13 (= upper boundary of the Gramian; pers. obs.). NPM18 is subdivided into a and b in contrast to Gürs & Janssen (2002), who named the upper part of NPM18 as NPM18a. The Nassariid zonation of Gürs (2002) is extended by the Late Oligocene *Nassarius pygmaeus* Zone as well as the Pliocene *N. consociatus* and *N. propinquus* zones.

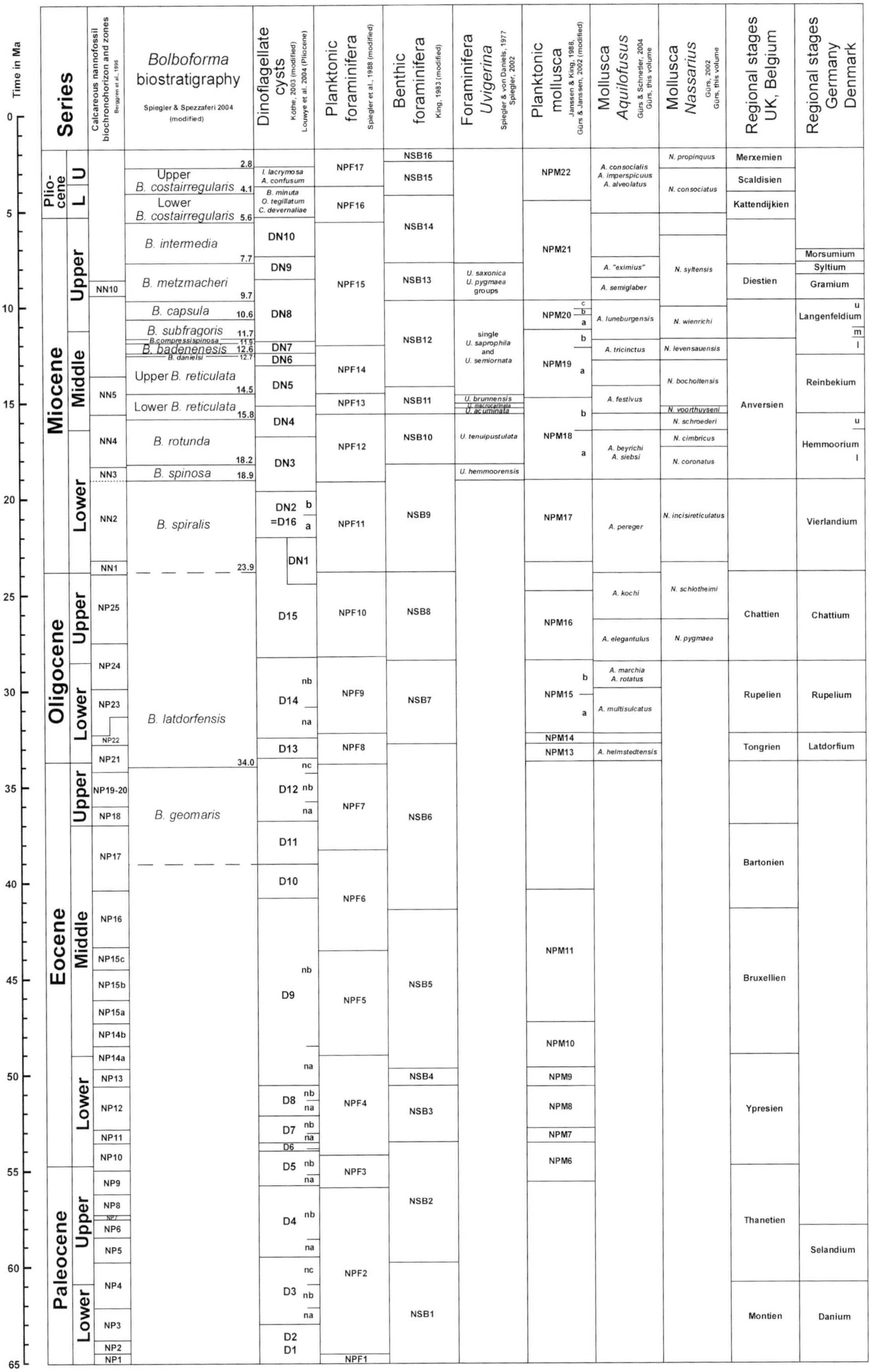
Time in Ma
Series
Calcareous nannofossil biochronohorizon and zones
Berggren et al. 1995
Bolboforma biostratigraphy
Spiegler & Spezzaferi 2004 (modified)
Dinoflagellate cysts
Köthe, 2003 (modified) Louwye et al. 2004 (Pliocene)
Planktonic foraminifera
Spiegler et al., 1988 (modified)
Benthic foraminifera
King, 1983 (modified)
Foraminifera Uvigerina
Spiegler & von Daniels, 1977 Spiegler, 2002
Planktonic mollusca
Janssen & King, 1988, Gürs & Janssen, 2002 (modified)
Mollusca Aquilofusus
Gürs & Schnetler, 2004 Gürs, this volume
Mollusca Nassarius
Gürs, 2002 Gürs, this volume
Regional stages UK, Belgium
Regional stages Germany Denmark
0
5
10
15
20
25
30
35
40
45
50
55
60
65
Plio-cene
L
U
Miocene
Upper
Middle
Lower
Oligocene
Upper
Lower
Eocene
Upper
Middle
Lower
Paleocene
Upper
Lower
NN10
NN5
NN4
NN3
NN2
NN1
NP25
NP24
NP23
NP22
NP21
NP19-20
NP18
NP17
NP16
NP15c
NP15b
NP15a
NP14b
NP14a
NP13
NP12
NP11
NP10
NP9
NP8
NP7
NP6
NP5
NP4
NP3
NP2
NP1
Upper B. costairregularis
Lower B. costairregularis
B. intermedia
B. metzmacheri
B. capsula
B. subfragoris
B. compressispinosa
B. badenenesis
B. danielsi
Upper B. reticulata
Lower B. reticulata
B. rotunda
B. spinosa
B. spiralis
B. latdorfensis
B. geomaris
2.8
4.1
5.6
7.7
9.7
10.6
11.7
11.9
12.6
12.7
14.5
15.8
18.2
18.9
23.9
34.0
I. lacrymosa
A. confusum
B. minuta
O. tegillatum
C. devernaliae
DN10
DN9
DN8
DN7
DN6
DN5
DN4
DN3
DN2 =D16
b
a
DN1
D15
D14
nb
na
D13
nc
D12
nb
na
D11
D10
D9
nb
na
D8
nb
na
D7
nb
na
D6
D5
nb
na
D4
nb
na
D3
nc
nb
na
D2
D1
NPF17
NPF16
NPF15
NPF14
NPF13
NPF12
NPF11
NPF10
NPF9
NPF8
NPF7
NPF6
NPF5
NPF4
NPF3
NPF2
NPF1
NSB16
NSB15
NSB14
NSB13
NSB12
NSB11
NSB10
NSB9
NSB8
NSB7
NSB6
NSB5
NSB4
NSB3
NSB2
NSB1
U. saxonica
U. pygmaea groups
single U. saprophila and U. semiornata
U. brunnensis
U. macrocarinata
U. acuminata
U. tenuipustulata
U. hemmoorensis
NPM22
NPM21
NPM20
c
b
a
NPM19
b
a
NPM18
b
a
NPM17
NPM16
NPM15
b
a
NPM14
NPM13
NPM11
NPM10
NPM9
NPM8
NPM7
NPM6
A. consocialis
A. imperspicuus
A. alveolatus
A. "eximius"
A. semiglaber
A. luneburgensis
A. tricinctus
A. festivus
A. beyrichi
A. siebsi
A. pereger
A. kochi
A. elegantulus
A. marchia
A. rotatus
A. multisulcatus
A. helmstedtensis
N. propinquus
N. consociatus
N. syltensis
N. wienrichi
N. levensauensis
N. bocholtensis
N. voorthuyseni
N. schroederi
N. cimbricus
N. coronatus
N. incisireticulatus
N. schlotheimi
N. pygmaea
Merxemien
Scaldisien
Kattendijkien
Diestien
Anversien
Chattien
Rupelien
Tongrien
Bartonien
Bruxellien
Ypresien
Thanetien
Montien
Morsumium
Syltium
Gramium
u
Langenfeldium
m
l
Reinbekium
u
Hemmoorium
l
Vierlandium
Chattium
Rupelium
Latdorfium
Selandium
Danium

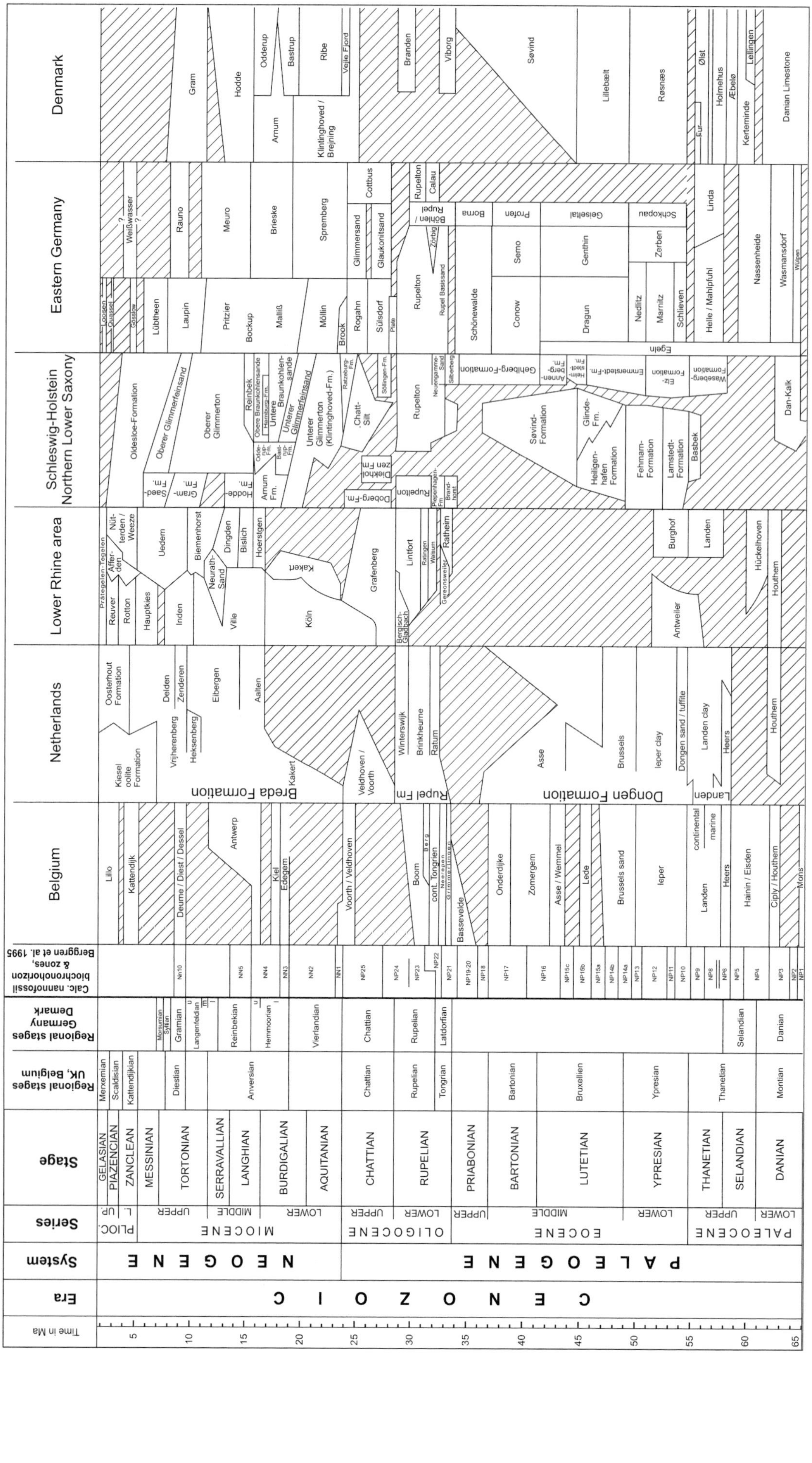


Fig. 17.6. Palaeogene–Neogene lithostratigraphic units of northern and eastern Germany.

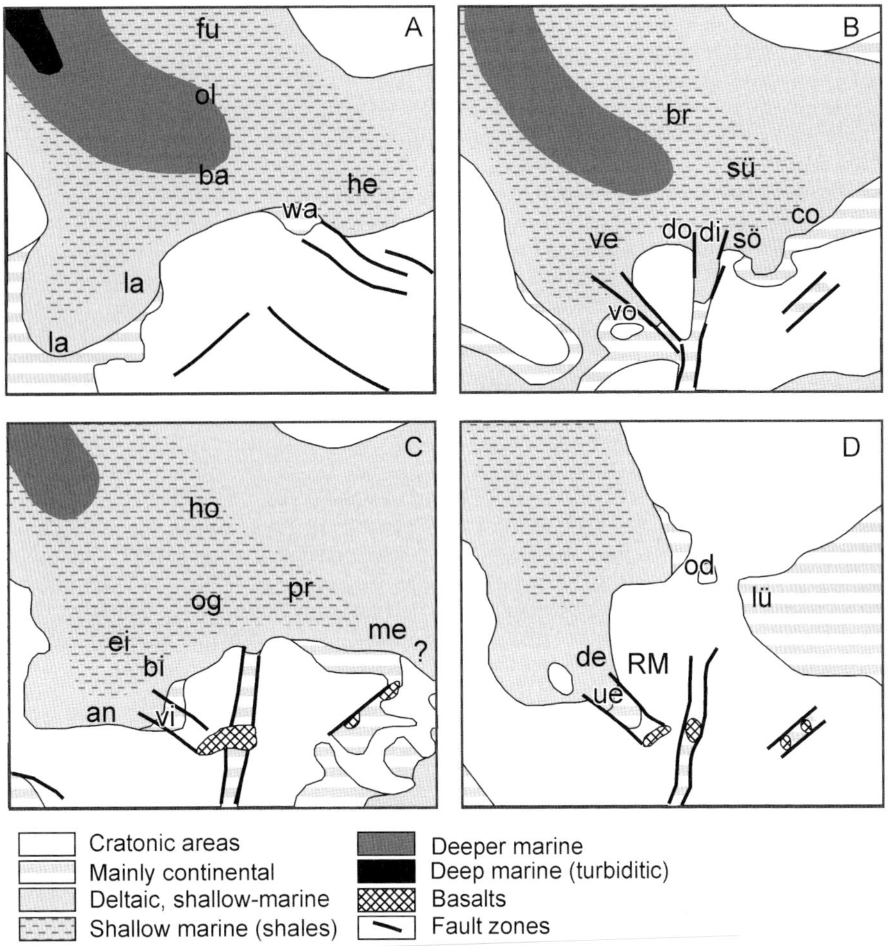


**Fig. 17.7.** Palaeogeography of the North Sea Basin: (**A**) Late Palaeocene; (**B**) Early Chattian; (**C**) Late Middle Miocene–Early Late Serravallian; (**D**) Early Messinian. Abbreviations: an, Antwerp Member (Mbr); ba, Basbek Formation (Fm); bi, Biemenhorst Fm; br, Brejning Fm; co, Cottbus Fm; de, Delden Mbr; di, Diekholzen Fm; do, Doberg Fm; ei, Eibergen Mbr; fu, Fur Fm; he, Helle Fm; ho, Hodde Fm; la, Landen Fm; lü, Lübtheen Fm; me, Meuro Fm; ne, Neureith Fm; od, Oldesloe Fm; og, Oberer Glimmerton; ol, Olst Fm; pr, Pritzier Fm; sö, Söllingen Fm; sü, Sülsdorf Fm; ue, Uedem Fm; ve, Veldhoven Fm; vi, Ville Fm; vo, Voorth Fm; wa, Waseberg Fm. Redrawn from the palaeogeographic Ziegler maps, modified according to new data of K. Gürs.

many regional formation names. In Germany and Denmark the overlying Early Eocene clays (Røsnaes Formation upper part, Fehmarn Formation) are intercalated by brown to reddish clays with a rich microfauna (Fehmarn and Lillebaelt formations). Water stratification, with reduced salinity in the surface layers, is inferred for the dark grey clay intervals deposited in Denmark (Schmitz *et al.* 1996). During deposition of reddish clays, water circulation was restored and a connection to the Atlantic, via the south of the UK, has been proposed by Bonde (1979).

Water depths during the Early Eocene were bathyal in the basin centre and outer neritic towards the south. Dill *et al.* (1996) demonstrated shallower environments in the area of Lower Saxony (Germany). However, their interpretation of the Late Palaeocene to Early Eocene sandy to clayey deposits, as tidal flats and marshes deposited in an estuary (Dill *et al.* 1996), is not followed here.

The Ypresian development of Belgium is one of the classic models of sequence stratigraphy (Vandenberghe *et al.* 1998). The Ieper Clay Formation reveals the strong cyclicity of outer neritic sedimentation, while in Late Ypresian time middle to inner neritic sands and clays indicate shallowing of the sedimentation area (e.g. Egemcappel clay, Egem sands, Merelbeke and Pittem clay).

During the Early Eocene, paralic conditions prevailed along the SE and southern basin margins (e.g. Saxony, Sachsen-Anhalt and Hannover area). In this environment, lignite seams interfinger with marine clays. Clays from the Hannover area have been radiometrically dated by Ahrendt *et al.* (1995) and range from 52.8 Ma to 46.0 Ma. Dinoflagellate cysts indicate zones D5b, D6b, D7a, D8nb and D9na, thus comprising nannoplankton zones NP10 to NP13/early NP14. The youngest unit (Emmerstedt Greensand) represents a substantial marine transgression dividing the lower and the upper seam complexes of this lignite district. In the Lower Rhine area, marine conditions predominated during the Early Eocene. However, the Antweiler Formation indicates paralic environments in the south of the region.

The climate of the Early Eocene in the NSB was subtropical to tropical (Krutzsch *et al.* 1992). Palm trees and mangroves bordered the sea which was inhabited by tropical faunas. Hooyberghs *et al.* (2002) postulated a climate optimum at the end of the Ypresian linked to the invasion of a southern fauna into the basin.

The Middle to Late Eocene witnessed a major sea-level fall and strong sea-level oscillations. A subtropical climate with rainforest vegetation (Mai 1995) and carbonate sedimentation in the shallower marine basin parts has been deduced from fossils.

Lignite formation in the south of the basin (Leipzig–Bitterfeld–Halle district) led to the development of economically important lagerstätten.

In the NE of the German part of the basin, a shelf edge developed at the Early–Middle Eocene transition (Heiligenhafen Formation, dated NP14; Martini 1991). The marked fossil contents (radiolaria and sponge spicules) of the slope clays and silts indicate upwelling ('Unter-Eozän 4'). The outer neritic sediments are replaced to the south and east by inner neritic, partly calcareous, glauconite sands and silts (Glinde Formation, upper part of Nedlitz Formation, Emmerstedt Formation).

During the successive Middle Eocene transgressions the bathyal Søvind marls were deposited over a much broader area than the Lillebaelt clays and neritic sedimentation shifted to the east, where carbonate or non-carbonate silts to fine sandstones of the Conow, Serno and Annenberg formations mark the shelf edge. These formations typically have an age of late NP15 to NP16 (Köthe 1988). Deposition of the Søvind marls continued with decreasing carbonate content until the Late Eocene (NP19/20). A decrease in carbonate content, as well as a coarsening-upward trend, can also be detected in the Upper Serno, Gehlberg and Lower Schönewalde formations. Thus, a more or less continuous shallowing- upward trend can be seen from Middle to Late Eocene times. During the Late Eocene, submarine erosion took place across vast areas of the eastern NSB. Only in the Kysing 1 borehole (Denmark) is a more or less continuous section across the Eocene–Oligocene boundary known (Heilmann-Clausen *et al.* 2001).

The Early Lutetian Brussel Sands of Brabant (Belgium) are marine incised valley fills showing a major hiatus with the underlying Ypresian clays (Vandenberghe *et al.* 1998). Many sand units disconformably overlie one another as a result of the strongly oscillating sea levels. The cyclic sedimentation patterns are also well preserved in the northern Belgian Kallo Complex where alternating glauconitic fine sands and clays can be traced over a vast area. The Late Eocene succession ends with the Bassevelde Sands dated to zone NP19/20 (Vandenberghe *et al.* 2003).

Middle Eocene paralic facies cover the famous Lutetian Geiseltal Lignite District (Germany), the Bartonian Leipzig–Bitterfeld–Halle Lignite District (Eissmann 1970; Eissmann & Litt 1994; Blumstengel *et al.* 1999; Rascher *et al.* 2005) and the Lutetian Helmstedt Formation. Late Eocene paralic areas include the Leipzig Lignite District (Standke 2002). The Helmstedt Formation is covered by the marine Middle Eocene Gehlberg Formation. The marine extension of the basin goes far to the NE where vast amounts of Baltic amber are now found in the marine clays, termed 'Blue Earths' of the Kalingrad area (Standke 1998).

The Oligocene began with a major transgression during NP21 which flooded the Egeln–Halle Lignite District, the Leipzig District (Standke 1997), and large parts of the German Mittelgebirge (Ritzkowski 1999*b*). After a short regressive phase (Vandenberghe *et al.* 2002) a minor transgression was observed in the NSB in zone NP22 (Gürs 2005), which flooded the Upper Rhine Valley via the Hessian Depression (Martini 1973). The most striking transgression took place in the early NP23 when the sea spread over vast areas of the low mountain ranges (Ritzkowski 1987) flooding the Leipzig Bay (Müller 1983; Eissmann & Litt 1994), the Upper Rhine Valley, the Lower Rhine Embayment and northern Belgium (Vandenberghe *et al.* 2002).

Neogene development of the NSB is already evident in the Late Oligocene following a severe regressive phase when the basin was clearly delimited to the east and river systems brought in vast amounts of sediment from the NE and east. Greater parts of the Fennoscandinavian Shield were lowlands and low mountains.

During the Chattian transgression, marine conditions were restored in large parts of the NSB. The NE part of Denmark and the Lower Rhine District were slowly covered by river systems and the coastline retreated inwards (Dybkjaer 2004*a*). Northern parts of eastern Germany were marine influenced throughout the entire Late Oligocene (Lotsch 1981; Standke 2001, 2008*a*). In the SW a semicontinuous connection to the Atlantic developed as shown by faunal evidence (R. Janssen 1979). Other pathways, such as the northern one around Scotland, have been discussed as the only connection (Gripp 1958) but single tropical molluscs such as *Morum*, *Perrona* and *Mitrolumna raulini septentrionalis* Janssen 1979 require a southern connection, the latter showing an affinity to the Chattian of the Aquitaine Basin. A warm climate led to the invasion of a nearly subtropical marine fauna. It is preserved in the Voort Sands of northern Belgium, the Grafenberg Sands of the Lower Rhine Embayment, the Kassel Sands (showing a strong ingression into the Hessian Depression in the early Late Oligocene) and the famous Sternberg erratic boulders of Mecklenburg (Bülow & Müller 2004) and Glaukonitsand in the Lusatia area (Standke 2006). Late Oligocene sediments in northern Belgium are restricted to the Roermond Graben and a small portion of the Central Graben area.

Deep water conditions prevailed in the basin centre. In the Late Chattian a coast with lagoons and barrier islands developed in middle Jutland and this was related to the Ringkøbing-Fyn High (Dybkjaer 2004*a*, *b*).

*Significant stratigraphic boundaries*

The famous Stevns Klint site in the eastern part of Denmark is situated where a continuous section across the Cretaceous–Palaeogene (K/Pg) boundary is developed (Birklund & Bromley 1979).

*Volcanism*

The Late Palaeocene and Early Eocene were times of significant volcanic activity at the Thule ridge. This volcanism provided the NSB with enormous amounts of volcanic ash. Ash layers can be traced as far south as northern Germany. Volcanism commenced in this region in the Late Cretaceous and ended in the late Middle Eocene (O'Connor *et al.* 2000). In the Middle Eocene volcanism began in the Eifel region (western Germany). On the SE margin of the NSB in the Erzgebirge and in the Lusatia (eastern Germany) areas, volcanism started in the lowermost part of the Oligocene (Standke & Suhr 1998).

## North Sea Basin: Neogene (K.G., F.W., G.S.)

*Tectonic setting and development*

The Neogene was the time of infilling of the NSB. Tectonic development was controlled by intraplate stress regimes resulting from variable spreading rates along the Mid-Atlantic rift and Alpine compression. As a result, the NSB underwent basin subsidence, some inversion and salt tectonism (Clausen *et al.* 1999). Strong subsidence was restricted to the Central Graben, the Lower Rhine area, the Elbe Basin and rim sinks of younger salt structures. Salt tectonism was especially common in northern Germany (Weber 1977; Lange *et al.* 1990). Glacioeustacy-controlled tectonism occurred from 12.6 Ma onwards in the northern NSB and became widespread after the Piacenzian–Gelasian boundary (*c.* 2.5 Ma) (Overeem 2002).

The Thule landbridge drowned during the Late Oligocene and a permanent connection to the North Atlantic was established (Wold 1995). There is strong faunal evidence for a direct connection to the Atlantic in the SW for the entire Early Miocene to early Middle Miocene (Figs 17.1 & 17.7) (Janssen 2001; Janssen & Gürs 2002) and for the late Late Pliocene (Marquet 2004). The Dover Strait opened at 4 Ma (Van Vliet-Lanoë *et al.* 2002). A marine connection to the northern Paratethys cannot be entirely excluded for the late Middle Miocene as there are strong similarities in plankton successions (pteropods and bolboforms) with those of the Carpathian fore-deep of the Central Paratethys (Gürs & Janssen 2002; Janssen & Zorn 1993). Fennoscandinavian uplift in the Oligocene narrowed the basin from the north. The centre of the shield experienced some 3000 m of uplift (Overeem 2002) and became a major sediment source for the NSB. Uplift of the Erzgebirge and the Lusatia Block (Brause 1990), as well as enlargement of catchment areas following the retreat of Paratethys in Central Europe, led to a more marked fluvial influence from the SE from Late Miocene times. Another main sediment source was the enlarged Rhine catchment in the south (Zagwijn & Hager 1987; Schäfer *et al.* 2004). Uplift of the Rhenish Massif accelerated in the Pliocene.

The bathyal water depths in the basin centre prevailed until the Early Pliocene. Subsequently the basin was mainly filled with eroded clastics from the uplifting hinterland.

*Palaeomagnetism*

Palaeomagnetic results from the area have been presented by Kuhlmann (2004) for the Pliocene of the central North Sea.

*Sedimentary and stratigraphic development*

The depositional system of the NSB during the Neogene was dominated by the westward progradation of at least three river systems from the Baltic Shield. These rivers were integrated in the Eridanos river system (Overeem 2002) which is a complex of rivers, whose number, source areas and courses varied considerably over time. Neogene development can be subdivided into four phases (Figs 17.5, 17.6 & 17.7).

During the Early to early Middle Miocene, major progradation of the Scandinavian and Baltic rivers took place. During the earliest Miocene a transgression led to the deposition of the lagoonal Vejle-Fjord clays and sands of Denmark (Dybkjaer 2004*a*, *b*; Rasmussen 2004). This lagoon was soon infilled by the fluvial Ribe sands. Marine conditions prevailed in southern Denmark and Schleswig (Klintinghoved Formation). In south-eastern Holstein and Lower Saxony (northern Germany) the middle neritic Lower Mica Clay (Aquitanian to Burdigalian) overlies the Ratzeburg Formation of latest Chattian age (Hinsch 1986*a*, 1994). During the Aquitanian peat formation took place in the Lusatian Lignite District (Standke 2008*b*). Rich macrofloras from these lignites indicate warm climate conditions (Mai 1999, 2000). In the Lower Rhine Embayment the sediment load of the river system balanced subsidence.

A short interruption or slowing down of fluvial input occurred in the NE and eastern parts of the NSB, after which rapid infilling continued (e.g. Bastrup and Odderup sands; Rasmussen 2004). The Miocene transgression in northern Belgium commenced with the deposition of the Edegem sands in the Antwerp region in the Mid- to Late Burdigalian (Janssen 2001; Steurbaut & Verbeek 1988). A second transgression in the Antwerp area is represented by the Kiel Sands with a stratigraphic position between the Edegem Sands and the Antwerp Sands. At the end of the Early Miocene, sediment input from the east ceased and, at a time of low sea level around the Early–Middle Miocene boundary, a large brackish lake developed in the northern German Hamburg Trough (Hinsch 1988) represented by about 100 m of the Hamburg Clay.

This lake was replaced by the sea at the beginning of the Middle Miocene. Shortly afterwards an easterly derived fluvial system was once more established (Upper Lignite Sands). Coevally, the Moorken Seam developed in the Lower Rhine Embayment (Zagwijn & Hager 1987). In the Lusatian Lignite District the paralic and shallow-marine Brieske Formation was deposited (Standke *et al.* 2005; Standke 2006). This transgression is known as the 'Hemmoor transgression' (Anderson 1964) since the Hoerstgen Beds of northern Westphalia (upper Hemmoorian age) disconformably overlie Oligocene strata. The Miste Beds and the Breda Formation in the Peel region (the Netherlands) show the same transgressive history. In northern Belgium the Antwerp and Zondershot sands disconformably rest on older strata. The first could be dated as NN4 (Steurbaut & Verbeek 1988) and DN4 (Louwye *et al.* 2000*a*). The geometry of the prograding lower to middle Miocene sediment bodies indicates water depths of more than 400 m in the central North Sea.

During the early Middle to middle Late Miocene a major transgression restored marine conditions in the NSB. This major Miocene transgression (Reinbek transgression; Anderson 1964) began at the NN4–NN5 boundary (Spiegler 2002). In Denmark the deeper marine Hodde Clay (Rasmussen 1966) overlies the fluviatile Odderup Formation and extends to the NE beyond the Ringkøbing-Fyn High. To the east the predominantly marine Meuro Formation was deposited in Lusatia (Standke *et al.* 2005). To the south the transgression extended into the northern German low mountain range (Hinsch *et al.* 1978). The maximum flooding of this transgression occurred during the late Middle Miocene, when the marine Neurath sands were deposited in the Lower Rhine Embayment. At the same time the Eibergen and Biemenhorst beds, the anoxic Tostedt clays of northern Lower Saxony and southern Schleswig-Holstein, the glauconite bed between the Hodde and Gram formations in Denmark, and the 'Heller Horizont' (Bülow 2000) in Mecklenburg (11.8 Ma: Gürs & Spiegler 2000) were deposited. Deposits from this maximum flooding event have only recently been documented from the Antwerp sands (Louwye *et al.* 2000*a*). Despite the widespread flooding, basin inversion in the Channel region resulted in the simultaneous closure of the southwestern connection with the Atlantic Ocean. The exact timing of the maximum flooding is placed between 12.3 Ma (van Leeuwen 2001) and 11.8 Ma (Gürs & Spiegler 2000).

In Late Miocene times, a continuous sea-level fall (Michelsen *et al.* 1998) and lower subsidence rates in eastern Germany led to the emergence of vast areas. Sedimentation was limited to areas of increased subsidence. While in the early Late Miocene (Tortonian) large parts of Mecklenburg, Schleswig-Holstein, Lower Saxony and Denmark were covered by the sea, during the late Late Miocene (Messinian) the rivers bypassed these regions and sedimentation was displaced towards the delta fronts to the west. Burger (2001) distinguished three heavy mineral facies in the Nieder-Ochtenhausen borehole (Lower Saxony, Germany) belonging to different river systems with different source areas, of which only Norway with the Oslo fan can be specified. Uplift and deep erosion, with the formation of valleys of up to 100 m depth, has been described from northern Belgium (Vandenberghe *et al.* 1998). These structures are filled with the marine Diest and Dessel sands of early Late Miocene age. In the Antwerp area, the coeval Deurne Sands disconformably overlie the older strata.

In Early Pliocene times peat formation took place in the

central part of the Danish North Sea Sector (Rasmussen 2004). Sediment infill in the Lower Rhine Embayment increased (Schäfer *et al.* 2004) and shallow-marine clastic environments prevailed across much of the Netherlands (e.g. Breda Formation; Sliggers & van Leeuwen 1987). However, in the northern part of the Netherlands the *Astarte trigonata* assemblages demonstrate a deeper environment, probably continuing until late Early Pliocene times. Early Pliocene sea-level highstands are represented by the Kattendijk Formation (northern Belgium), the uppermost Breda and basal Oosterhout formations (the Netherlands), and the Coralline Crag Formation (UK). Late Pliocene transgressions are manifested in the Lillo Formation (northern Belgium), the upper Oosterhout and the Maassluis formations (the Netherlands) and in the Red Crag Formation (UK). During the latest Pliocene the sea retreated from most of the basin and did not return to the southern and eastern margins of the NSB until the late Middle Pleistocene.

Evidence of glacial conditions, including the presence of deep permafrost and icebergs in the southern North Sea off the Dutch coast, have been recorded at marine isotope stages (MIS) 100–96 (Kuhlman 2004). These initial glacial intervals produced widespread deposition of fine-grained clastics, derived from enhanced erosion of the deep regolith that formed over the NW European continent in the warm-temperate climates of the earlier Neogene. In the latest Pliocene the rates of progradation and infill increased dramatically as a result of the increasing input of erosion products during glacial intervals. Three glacial and three interglacial periods are detected in northern Germany at this time (Litt *et al.* 2002).

Several biozonation schemes have been elaborated for the Neogene NSB. For open-marine settings, biozonations based on planktonic organisms (e.g. bolboforms: (Spiegler 1999), dinoflagellates (Louwye *et al.* 2000*a*, *b*; Köthe 2003) and pteropods (Gürs & Janssen 2002; Janssen & King 1988)) allow a fine-scaled subdivision of the strata. In nearshore marine settings, biozonation schemes are mainly based on benthic molluscs (Hinsch 1986*b*; Gürs & Weinbrecht 2001; Gürs 2002; Gürs & Schnetler 2004), benthic foraminifera (King 1982; Gramann & von Daniels 1988), bolboforms and dinoflagellates. For terrestrial and paralic deposits, pollen zonations (Krutzsch 2000*a*, *b*; Schäfer *et al.* 2004, and references therein) are available.

*Volcanism*

Some Neogene volcanism developed in the Lusatia and Erzgebirge regions from Early to later Miocene times (Suhr 2003). Early Miocene volcanism is known from the Hessian Depression (Kassel and Vogelsberg) and the Siebengebirge in Nordrhein-Westfalia. In Pliocene times the Eifel volcanism recommenced.

## *Polish Lowlands (M.Pi., J.R.K.)*

The Polish Lowlands Basin (PLB) forms the eastward continuation of the North Sea Basin (Fig. 17.4). Towards the north it was bordered by the Fennoscandinavian Shield while to the south it was bordered by the Bohemian Massif including the Sudetes Mountains, and by the South Polish Uplands including the Holy Cross Mountains (Meta-Carpathians Rampart). Towards the east it was connected to the Ukrainian Massif.

*Palaeogeography and tectonic setting*

The Polish Lowlands are framed by two structural units separated by the Teisseyre-Tonquist lineament. The NE part of the Polish Lowlands belongs to the Precambrian European platform and the SW part to the Variscan Palaeozoic platform. Palaeogene and Neogene sediments developed on the Precambrian platform are rather thin, whereas slow continuous subsidence of the Palaeozoic platform led to the formation of a much thicker sedimentary unit during Palaeogene and Neogene times. In addition, some basins developed along major active structural lineaments and were later filled by thick continental deposits (up to 500 m).

During the Early Palaeocene, the PLB showed a marine connection with the Denmark Basin, the East European Basin, and with western Europe across northern Germany (Fig. 17.1). After a regressive phase, a Middle/Late Eocene transgression from the NW created a connection with cold oceanic waters across the Denmark area. At the same time, a connection with the Tethys was established. During the Oligocene, this connection ceased. Central and eastern parts of the PLB were connected with the Atlantic Ocean. The PLB was separated from the Ukrainian and Belorussian basins by an area of shallow shoals and islands. By the end of the Oligocene, brackish environments became widespread. The Neogene is characterized by increasing continental development with the establishment of large floodplains and lakes. Minor marine ingressions continued in the Pliocene.

*Sedimentary and stratigraphic development*

Neogene deposits are mainly continental, whereas the Palaeogene is mainly marine (Fig. 17.8). The onset of Palaeogene sedimentation, however, is not synchronous in the Polish Lowlands. In the eastern part it began during the Palaeocene, while in the west it commenced during the Middle Eocene or Late Eocene/Early Oligocene (Rupelian). The thickness of the Palaeogene deposits is *c.* 50–100 m but can be up to 300 m in basinal areas.

During the Palaeocene, marine deposition occurred across the entire NE part of the PLB and, locally (Szczecin Depression), in the NW. The Palaeocene PLB is littoral and shallow ($<100$ m), warm-temperate (17–20°C on average) with normal salinity. Palaeocene sediments mostly overlie Upper Cretaceous rocks (Maastrichtian, Campanian), separated by an erosional unconformity. Their mean thickness is 35 m, but areas with increased subsidence (Baltic Basin and Mazury High) can have successions of up to 100 m. The Danian Puławy Formation comprises marine sediments, including marls and limestones with intercalations of glauconite and phosphorite. Absolute dating gave an age of $60.2 \pm 0.9$ Ma (Pożaryska & Kreutzer 1978). Upper Palaeocene (Selandian, Thanetian) sediments include marls, sands and siltstones (Słodkowska 2000). The Thanetian Odra Formation contains brackish/continental lignitic sands, siltstones and clays. Authigenic deposits are weathered crust with residual clays. Kaolinite covers of plutonic and metamorphic rocks can be up to 74 m thick. These sediments are mostly abundant during the Palaeogene and rare during the Neogene.

The PLB Palaeocene can be correlated with the planktonic foraminifera zone NPF1, the benthonic foraminifera zone B1 and the nannoplankton zones NP1 and NP3 (Pożaryska & Szczechura 1968; Piwocki *et al.* 1996). Deposits from the Danian–Thanetian boundary and the Thanetian were dated using phytoplankton assemblage of the D3 and D4 zones (Słodkowska 2000), which are correlated with the NP4 and NP8 nannoplankton zones (Costa & Manum 1988).

Following a regression, marked by an erosional unconformity between the Palaeocene and the Eocene, the palaeogeography of the Polish Lowlands did not change substantially during Early Eocene times. A local transgression from the NW is restricted to the Szczecin Depression. A new transgressive influx from the Ukraine and subsequently from the NW created a connection with cold oceanic waters across the Denmark area. Another

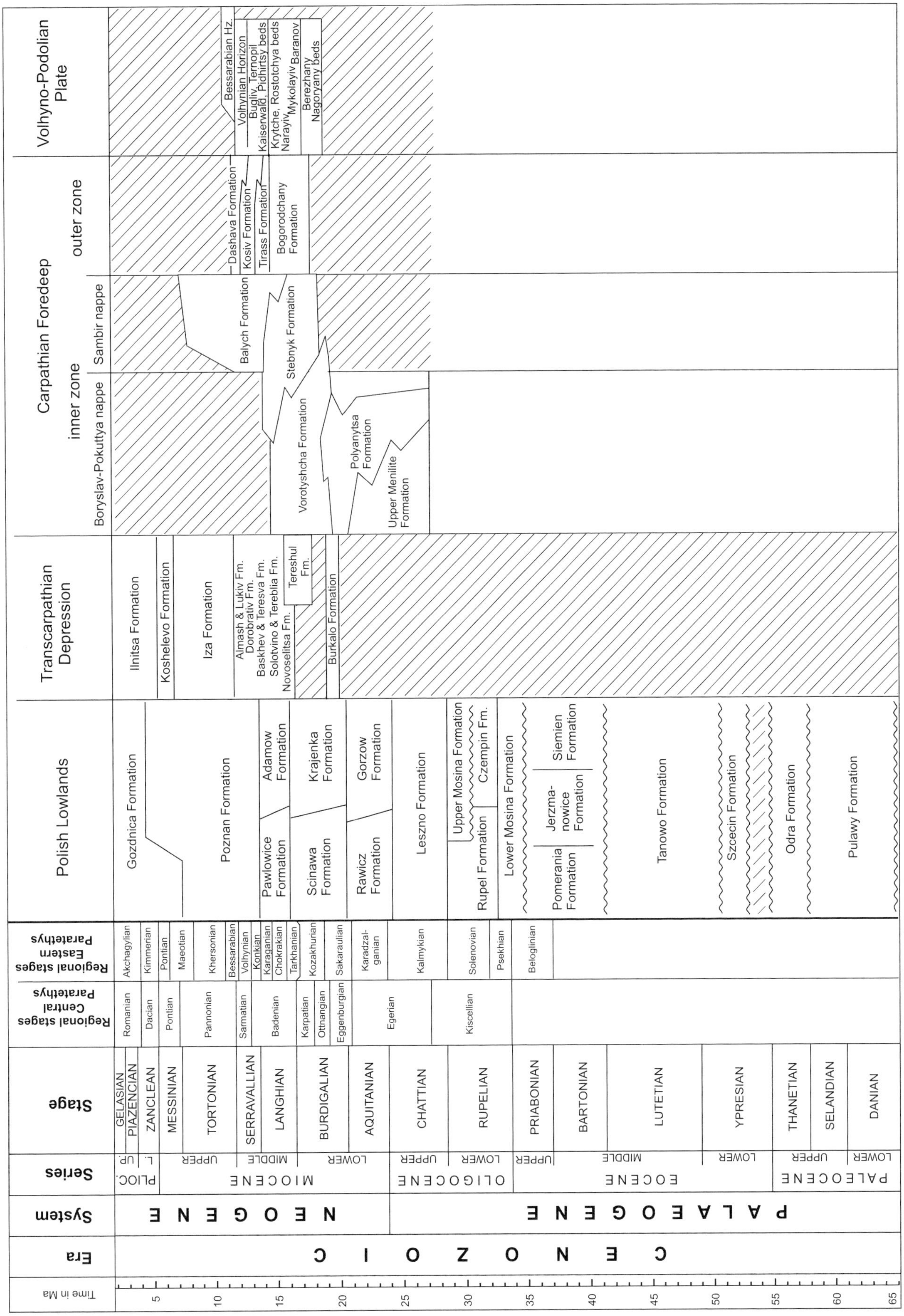


**Fig. 17.8.** Palaeogene–Neogene lithostratigraphic units of NE Europe.

transgression from the Tethys reached the Polish Lowlands from the west, and probably also from the south, during Middle/Late Eocene times. The pelagic Eocene basin was *c*. 100–150 m deep with cold-temperate and normal-salinity water. Average annual temperatures ranged between 16 and 20°C and salinity was not lower than 31–36‰. Around the Eocene–Oligocene boundary, amber-bearing deltas developed along the coasts (Piwocki & Olkowicz-Paprocka 1987; Kasiński & Tołkanowicz 1999).

The oldest Eocene deposits (Lower Eocene), belonging to the Szczecin Formation, include quartz-glauconite sands with gravel and clay intercalations (Ciuk 1973, 1974, 1975). The Middle Eocene is represented by the Tanowo Formation, consisting of lignitic clays, siltstones, and sands with thick lignite seams (Ciuk 1974, 1975). Sediments of the Pomerania Formation (in the north of the PLB) (Ciuk 1974) as well as its lateral equivalents, the Jerzmanowice Formation (west and central part) and the Siemień Formation (in the east) have a Middle/Late Eocene age. The 20-m-thick Pomerania Formation consists of quartz-glauconite sands in the lower part and calcareous sands, siltstones and claystones in the upper part. The deposits of the Jerzmanowice Formation consist of calcareous quartz-glauconite sands with gravel and phosphorite grains, and limestone intercalations within the uppermost part including molluscs, corals and bryozoans. The deposits of the Siemień Formation comprise calcareous quartz-glauconite sands and sandstones with phosphorites and calcareous siltstones, partly with a rich fauna of molluscs and corals as well as amber.

Planktonic foraminifera assemblages of zones NPF6 and NPF7 and the nannoplankton zones NP16–20 are documented (Piwocki *et al.* 1996). The benthic molluscan assemblages of the Pomerania and Siemień formations are located within the BM11A and BM13A zones (Piwocki 2002), which are characteristic for the Upper Eocene of NW Europe, and also for the Latdorfian facies (Hinsch *et al.* 1988).

Around the Eocene–Oligocene transition, a marine transgression encroached from the NW European Basin (Kockel 1988; Gramann & Kockel 1988) towards the Polish Lowlands (Piwocki & Kasiński 1995; Ciuk & Pożaryska 1982). The connection with the Tethys was severed during this time. A shallow epicontinental sea connected with the Atlantic Ocean covered the central and eastern parts of the Polish Lowlands. The seawater was relatively cold (10–20°C) with normal salinity, but slightly oxidizing conditions (Buchardt 1978; Odrzywolska-Bieńkowa *et al.* 1978). The Oligocene Polish Lowland sea was separated from the Ukrainian and Belorussian basins by an area of shoals and islands. The presence of quartz-glauconite sands records a regression at the end of the Early Oligocene. A subsequent short transgression extended as far as the west of the PLB. By the end of the Oligocene, the marine development ceased. The last regression was connected to the uplift of the Sudetes Mountains.

Oligocene deposits are common on the Polish Lowlands with thicknesses ranging from several metres up to >100 m. They commence with the Lower Mosina Formation comprising green quartz-glauconite sands, gravels, phosphorites, siderite concretions and rare amber grains (Ciuk 1970, 1974). The Eocene–Oligocene boundary is difficult to determine but may be placed within the lower Mosina Formation (Odrzywolska-Bieńkowa *et al.* 1981; Piwocki *et al.* 1985, 1996). The marine Rupelian (100 m) crops out in the western part of the Polish Lowlands. It consists of siltstones and claystones with sphaerosiderites and mollusc remains. Similar deposits are common in Germany and are named the Septaria Clays. These deposits interfinger with the brackish/continental Czempin Formation and the marine upper Mosina Formation towards the SE. The Czempin Formation (*c*. 25 m) comprises siltstones and silty sands with lignites. The deposits of the Upper Mosina Formation (*c*. 25 m) include quartz-glauconite sands with silt and clay intercalations. These deposits are overlain by the Leszno Formation in the west, which consists of silty sands.

Dating of the deposits is based on the occurrence of planktonic foraminifers of the Rupelian NPF8 zone and of the benthic B6 zone spanning the Early–Late Oligocene boundary. Nannoplankton assemblages of zones NP21–22 and NP24 have been documented.

Following the regression at the end of the Oligocene, continental and brackish sediments were deposited across the entire basin. This led to the development of widespread coastal plains related to the North Sea Basin (Standke *et al.* 1993). The continental deposits developed mostly as floodplains, meandering river systems (Osijuk 1979; Kasiński 1989) and in residual lakes with extensive lignite deposits.

Miocene lithostratigraphic units include the Lower Miocene Rawicz/Gorzów and Ścinawa/Krajenka, the Middle Miocene Adamów/Pawłowice, and the Upper Miocene/Lower Pliocene Poznań formations. These are continental lignite-bearing sediments of fluviatile and limnic facies. Most of the fluvial deposits were related to the southern tributaries of the Baltic fluvial system. Units of shallow marine and brackish deposits with glauconite and marine microfauna and phytoplankton occur in the western part of the PLB. Lower and Middle Miocene deposits comprise rather monotonous sandy/silty sediments with clay and lignite, while the Upper Miocene is represented by clays with silty/sandy intercalations. Some upper Middle Miocene deposits in SW Poland originated from a brackish marine embayment connected with the Paratethys (Łuczkowska & Dyjor 1971).

Pliocene deposits are represented by the upper part of the Poznań and the Gozdnica formations together with their lithostratigraphic equivalents (e.g the Ziębice Group; Dyjor 1966; Czerwonka & Krzyszkowski 2001). The Poznań Formation comprises clays and silts with sandy intercalations and thin lignites deposited mainly in fluvial (floodplain), lacustrine and limnic settings. Continental sedimentation was interrupted by marine ingressions, which periodically transformed nearshore lakes into brackish lagoons (Kasiński *et al.* 2002). The Pliocene deposits of the Poznań Formation were deposited under temperate and periodically cold-temperate and humid conditions (Stuchlik 1987). During sedimentation, the climate became increasingly arid. The Gozdnica Formation comprises sandy/gravelly clastic deposits with fine silt and clay intercalations developed under conditions comparable to the Poznań Formation.

*Volcanism*

The Lower Silesian volcanics comprise basic volcanic and pyroclastic rocks (up to 200 m) which belong to the eastern part of the Mid-European Volcanic Province. This extends over 700 km in front of the Alpine-Carpathian system. Most of the localities are situated on the Fore-Sudetic Block along the margin of the Sudetes Mountains. Volcanic rocks include basalts, trachytes, tephrites, basanites, phonolite basanites, quartz latites, phoideferous basalts, nephelinites, dolerites, basanitoides, limburgites, ankarites, trachyandesites and trachyphonolites (Wierzchołowski 1993).

## *Volhyno-Podolian Plate (O.Y.A., V.V.A.)*

The Volhyno-Podolian Plate (VPP) (Fig. 17.4) represents the SW margin of the East European (= Russian) Platform. The most significant structures there are the Volhynian and Podolian highs which are oriented in a NW–SE direction between the upper parts of the Western Bug and the valley of the Southern Bug river. In the north a terrace zone of 30–50 m separates the Volhynian High from the Polessye Lowland.

*Tectonic setting*
The basement of the East European Platform in the western Ukraine consists of deformed Archean to Lower Proterozoic rocks. To the west the crystalline basement is covered with a thick platform nappe, comprising up to 2700 m of Mesozoic–Cenozoic sediments. From latest Early Miocene to latest Middle Miocene times, the Podolian-Subdniester Block subsided resulting in the formation of accommodation space. With the beginning of the late Middle Miocene the western part was uplifted (up to 450 m) resulting in the erosion of Middle Miocene deposits (Palienko 1990).

*Sedimentary and stratigraphic development*
Sedimentation of the VPP commenced during the late Early Miocene (Fig. 17.8). The basal Nagoryany beds (2 m) consist of quartz-glauconitic sand and sandstones, with a diverse marine mollusc fauna. They discordantly overlie Upper Cretaceous limestones. The Nagoryany beds are presumably of Karpatian age (= late Burdigalian). The discordantly overlying Berezhany beds (4.5 m) are freshwater limestones and marls, containing ostracods, characean algae and numerous freshwater gastropods.

The Middle Miocene (Badenian regional stage) begins with the Baranov Formation (1 m) comprising glauconitic sands and sandstones with a rich molluscan fauna as well as coralline algae. The Mykolayiv Formation (14.5 m) consists of quartz-glauconitic sandstones rich in bryozoans and serpulids, foraminifers, bivalves, brachiopods and rare echinoderms (Vialov 1986). The Narayiv Formation (25 m) represents the most continuous horizon. Dense corallinacean limestones with huge rodoliths, pectinids, oysters and an impoverished foraminifer fauna are typical (Vialov 1986). The Rostotchya Formation consists of quartz sands and sandstones with molluscs comparable to the Baranov Formation (Vialov 1986; Kulchytsky 1989). A thin layer (10–15 cm) of limestones or calcareous sandstones constitutes the Kryvtche Formation and represents an important marker horizon.

The upper Badenian Pidhirtsy Formation is restricted to the east of the VPP. It comprises sandstones with molluscs, foraminifers and bryozoans (Pishvanova *et al.* 1970; Vialov 1986). The upper Badenian Ternopil beds (6 m) consist of corallinaceans (mainly rhodoliths), grading into clayey glauconitic sand and limestone. The general character of the fauna is the same as in the underlying units, but additionally a biohermal limestone (Podolian Toltry or Miodobory), dominated by coralline algae and vermetids, is found (Vialov 1986).

The uppermost Badenian is represented by the Bugliv Formation (Grischkevich 1970) representing an offshore facies. It includes an impoverished marine fauna with the endemic bivalve *Parvivenus konkensis media* (Sokolow) and can be correlated with the Konkian regional stage in the eastern Paratethys (Vialov 1986).

The late Middle Miocene sediments of the Sarmatian regional stage are transgressive attaining a thickness of 25–100 m (Vialov 1986). In the NE of the VPP the Sarmatian can be clearly correlated with the Volhynian and Bessarabian regional substages of the eastern Paratethys (Grischkevich 1970; Pishvanova *et al.* 1970). The lower part of the the Sarmatian deposits consists of sand (1.2 m) and oolitic sandstone containing a rich endemic mollusc fauna. Up-section, a coarse-grained sand with a huge number of molluscs and foraminifers occurs (Pishvanova *et al.* 1970). In the east of the VPP, biohermal and oolitic limestones developed. The Early Sarmatian bryozoan bioherms cover the tops of the Badenian 'Toltry' limestone.

Upper Middle Miocene and lower Upper Miocene sediments (= Bessarbian regional substage) are restricted to the east of the VPP. Oolitic limestones, nubeculariid-foraminifera limestones and bryozoan bioherms formed parallel to the Badenian 'Toltry' ridge (Vialov 1986; Paramonova 1994; Anistratenko 2000; Anistratenko & Anistratenko 2005). The intensive uplift of the Carpathian Mountains during the latest Middle and early Late Miocene and tectonic reduction of the Subcarpathian Basin cut off the marine connections to the VPP.

## *Upper Rhine Graben (J.P.B.)*

The Upper Rhine Graben (URG) is part of the complex Cenozoic rift system of western and Central Europe that extended from the shores of the North Sea over a distance of some 1100 km into the western Mediterranean (Fig. 17.4). The stratigraphic development of the URG varies in its southern and its northern part (Figs 17.9 & 17.10). Berger *et al.* (2005*a*) subdivided the southern URG into three different units: (1) Southern URG (Basel Horst, Dannemarie Basin, Mulhouse Horst, Mulhouse Basin potassique, Sierentz-Wollschwiller Basin, Rauracian Depression); (2) Southern-Middle URG (Colmar, Sélestat, Erstein, Zorn or Strasbourg Basin, Saverne Fault Zone, Ribeauvillé & Guebwiller); and (3) Northern-Middle URG (Haguenau, Pechelbronn, Rastatt, Karlsruhe, Landau, Bruchsal-Wiesloch Fault Zone). The North Upper Rhine Graben includes the Mainz and Hanau basins.

A general synthesis on the Upper Rhine Graben was recently published in the frame of the EUCOR-URGENT project ('Upper Rhine Graben Evolution and NeoTectonics', Behrmann *et al.* 2000). The stratigraphy and palaeogeography, together with a detailed reference list, were published by Berger *et al.* (2005*a*, *b*). This section presents an overview of these articles. Another study on the Rhine Graben examines the correlation of eustatic sea-level changes, rifting phases, palaeogeography and sedimentary evolution (Sissingh 2003).

*Palaeogeography and tectonic setting*
Palaeogeographic reconstructions of the URG were published by Kuhlemann & Kempf (2002), Sissingh (1998, 2003), Becker & Berger (2004) and Berger *et al.* (2005*b*). Following an initial fluviolacustrine phase of sedimentation (Middle Eocene), the URG was affected by an initial rifting phase that was responsible for the development of large conglomeratic fans along the eastern, western and southern graben margins. The axis of the evolving URG was occupied by salt basins in its southern areas with brackish (with local salt) to lacustrine facies developing in its central parts, and fluviatile to lacustrine facies in its northern part and in the Mainz Basin.

During the Early Rupelian, a general transgression came from the North Sea; following a regressive phase marked by lacustrine (north) and salt (south) deposition during the middle Rupelian, the sea again invaded the entire basin during the Late Rupelian, resulting in a possible connection with the Paratethys Sea via the North Alpine Foreland Basin. During the Late Oligocene, fluviolacustrine sedimentation prevailed, with localized marine ingression in the northern part of the URG.

During the Early Miocene, the southern URG was affected by uplift and erosion. In the northern URG, brackish (rarely marine) sedimentation prevailed. In the Late Burdigalian, the basin was

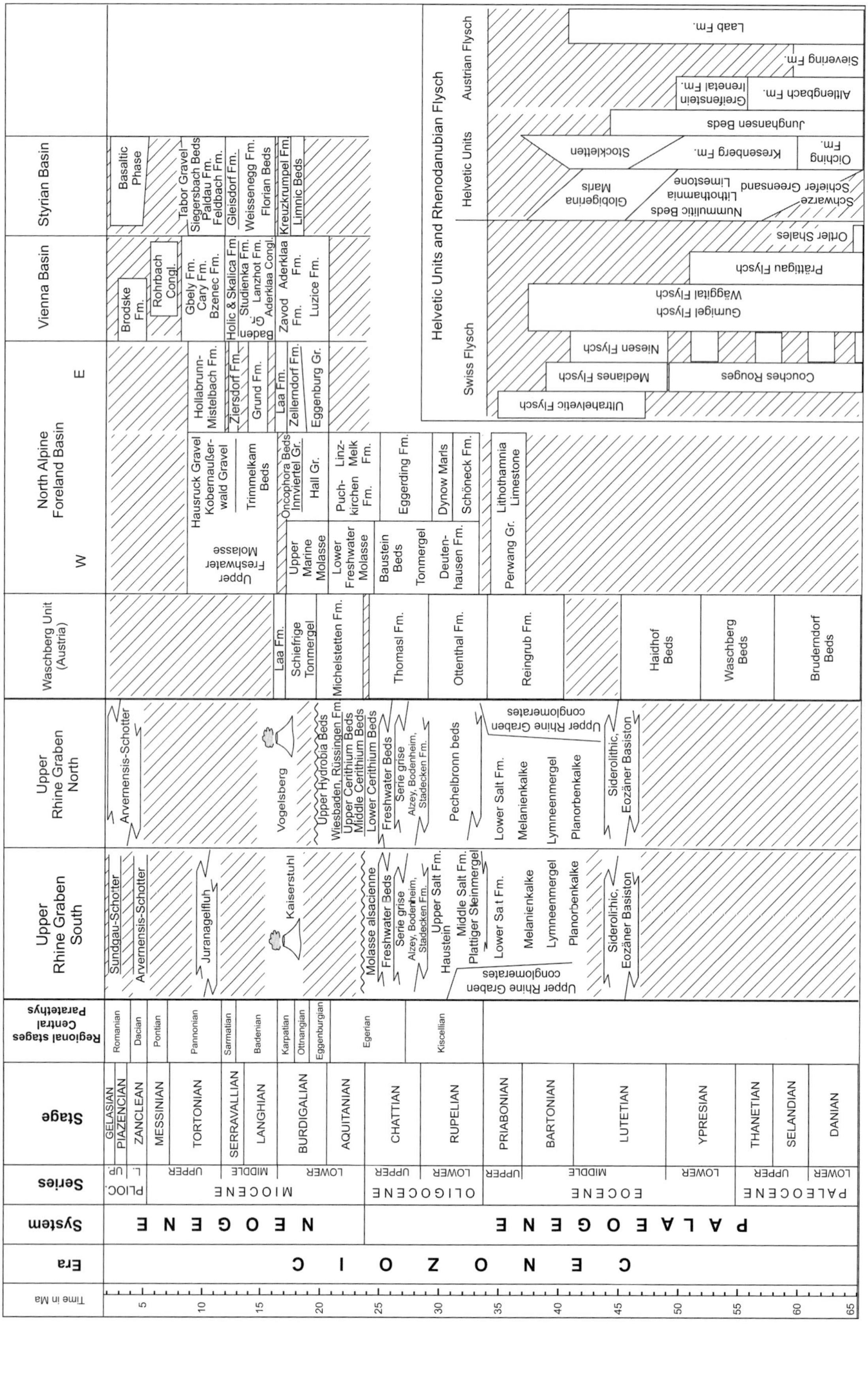


**Fig. 17.9.** Palaeogene–Neogene lithostratigraphic units of the southern part of the European Plate and the North Alpine Foreland Basin.

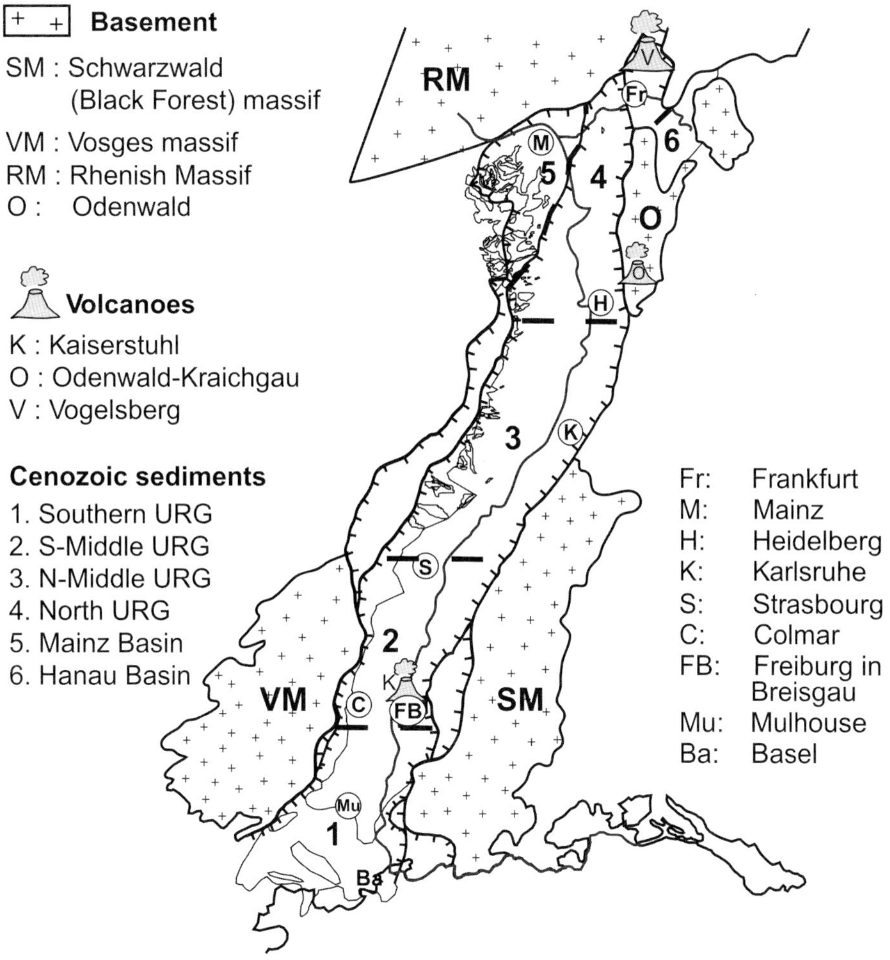


**Fig. 17.10.** Geology of the Upper Rhine Graben.

affected by two important volcanic events (Kaiserstuhl and Vogelsberg events).

Reflection seismic data, calibrated by wells, indicate that south of the city of Speyer a regional erosional unconformity of mid-Burdigalian age cuts progressively deeper southwards into Burdigalian and Oligocene sediments. This unconformity is related to the uplift of the Vosges–Black Forest arch, including the southern part of the URG (Roll 1979; Dèzes *et al.* 2004). During the Late Miocene, the sedimentation was essentially continental, brackish and lacustrine. In the Mainz Basin Langhian-age sediments are absent. In conjunction with progressive uplift of the Vosges–Black Forest arch, the central and southern parts of the URG were subjected to erosion.

*Sedimentary and stratigraphic development*

Eocene sedimentation in the southern Upper Rhine Graben generally commences with Middle to Late Eocene siderolithic deposits (MP19). These are overlain by various sedimentary facies whose deposition was influenced by tectonic processes in the URG. Accumulation of brackish sediments (Lymnaeenmergel) and salt (Lower Salt Formation) took place. Their ages probably range from the Lutetian to the Priabonian (NP12 to NP17). However, it is not clear if sedimentation was continuous or if a gap occurred during the Bartonian (Sissingh 1998). In the west, some undated conglomerates are tentatively assigned to the Lutetian and the Priabonian (Duringer 1988).

On the Mulhouse Horst, brackish marls and lacustrine limestones, probably ranging from Lutetian to Priabonian in age, are present. The Melanien Limestones are of Priabonian age (MP18) at Brunstatt (Schwarz 1997; Tobien 1987). In the eastern part of the basin, some conglomerates (locally dated by mammals (MP18; Tobien 1987)) probably accumulated during the Priabonian.

In the Colmar-Haguenau area a similar development occurs, and includes lacustrine limestones, Lymnaea Marls and salt formation. A brackish complex (Zone Dolomitique) generally overlies these deposits, but it has not been dated. Conglomeratic facies are present at both basin margins (particulary from the Priabonian onwards). Towards the north, the Lower Pechelbronn Beds are partly dated by mammals as Priabonian (MP20; Tobien 1987).

Early Rupelian sedimentation is represented by: (1) the Middle and Upper Salt Formation (Dannemarie Basin); (2) the Middle and Upper Pechelbronn beds (Colmar-Haguenau area) (NP22; Griessemer 2002); (3) the Zone fossilifère and the Streifige Mergel (= Marnes en plaquettes) as well as the Haustein – the latter is dated as NP21–22 (Schuler 1990) and MP21 (Altkirch (see Storni 2002; Hinsken 2003), Mulhouse Horst); and (4) the conglomeratic facies at both basin margins.

The Zone fossilifère and the Middle Pechelbronn Beds represent the first Rupelian transgression from the North Sea (partly corresponding with the global sea-level rise following the Ru1 sequence at 33 Ma; see Hardenbol *et al* 1998). In the Middle Rupelian, the most important marine transgression (second marine Rupelian transgression from the North Sea, corresponding with the global sea-level rise between sequences Ru2 and Ru3; see Hardenbol *et al.* 1998) flooded the entire URG. The sediments associated with this transgression constitute the classical succession from the Foraminiferenmergel to the Fischschiefer and partly to the Meletta-Schichten. These sediments range from NP23 to NP24 (Grimm 2002). They are combined with the Late Rupelian brackish-marine Cyrenenmergel into the so-called Graue Serie (= Série grise), representing an important seismic marker. During the Early Chattian, the fluviatile sediments of the 'Molasse alsacienne' interfingered to the north (Tüllinger Berg) with lacustrine or brackish marls and with the fluviolacustrine Niederroedener Beds. During the Middle and Late Chattian, the lacustrine limestones of the 'Calcaires delémontiens' and the Tüllinger Kalk were deposited. The 'Calcaires delémontiens' are well dated as MP29 to MN1 in the Jura Molasse (Becker 2003; Picot 2002), and the Tüllinger Kalk can be correlated by charophytes with the Middle Chattian *Stephanochara ungeri* Zone. These deposits are overlain by the brackish-lacustrine *Cerithium* Beds.

From the Aquitanian onwards, the southern and middle parts of the URG were subject to erosion. Sediments may have been deposited up to the onset of the uplift of the Vosges and the Black Forest (Burdigalian), or the non-deposition may already have commenced during Middle and Late Aquitanian times, as proposed for the Jura Molasse (see Picot 2002; Becker 2003). Sedimentation locally resumed during the Early Tortonian, with the deposition of the *Dinotherium* and *Hipparion* sands (dated by mammals as MN9). No Messinian sediments are known. In the northern part of the URG, sedimentation continues during the Aquitanian with the deposition of the brackish Upper *Cerithium* Beds, which are overlain by the Rüssingen Formation (formerly *Inflata* Beds), and are followed by the Wiesbaden Formation (formerly Lower *Hydrobia* Beds). According to its correlation with the Mainz Basin (MN1 and MN2; see Reichenbacher 2000), this succession appears to be Aquitanian in age. The Upper *Hydrobia* Beds are still present and may be attributed to the Early Burdigalian (MN3). During the Late Burdigalian an important volcanic event took place at Kaiserstuhl. Following a significant gap (Burdigalian to Messinian), sedimentation was resumed during the Pliocene.

An important sedimentary event is represented by the Sundgau Gravel, which may be Middle Pliocene (MN15–16) in age, based on comparison with the Bresse Graben mammal localities (Petit *et al.* 1996). Locally, the Arvernensis Gravel is present (MN14–MN16; Tobien 1988). Pliocene deposits (dated by spores and pollens) are also known from the vicinity of Colmar and Strasbourg. Following a gap (Burdigalian to Messinian), sedimentation in the northern part resumed in Pliocene times (e.g. Haguenau area).

During the Eocene and Early Oligocene, the northern Upper Rhine Graben was not yet developed and the main structures were influenced by pre-Palaeogene tectonics. From north to south, pre-rift structures include the Rüsselsheim Basin, the Palatinate-Stockstadt Ridge, and Marnheim Bay (Grimm & Grimm 2003). In the Rüsselsheim Basin, Marnheim Bay and the southerly connected northern URG, sedimentation commenced with the terrestrial 'Eozäner Basiston' and 'Basissand'. On the Palatinate-Stockstadt Ridge (particulary on its eastern part, i.e. the Sprendlingen Horst), the famous Messel Formation accumulated in a maar lake (Harms 2001). These sediments are dated by mammals as MP11 (Tobien 1988). The Priabonian Lower Pechelbronn Beds (Rüsselsheim Basin) and 'Green marls-Rote Leitschicht' (Marnheim Bay) overlie the Eocene basal sediments. The 'Green marls-Rote Leitschicht' correlate with the Lutetian *Embergeri* Zone and the Priabonian *Vectensis* Zone (Schwarz 1997). Along the margins of these basins, terrestrial alluvial-fan deposits accumulated during the Lutetian to Early Rupelian (Grimm & Grimm 2003). Eocene sediments are absent in the Hanau Basin.

During the Rupelian, the sedimentary history was similar to that of the Southern URG, with the deposition of the Middle Pechelbronn Beds (first marine Rupelian transgression), the Upper Pechelbronn Beds, the Alzey, Bodenheim, Stadecken and Sulzheim formations (second and third marine Rupelian transgression, corresponding with the 'Serie grise' in the Southern URG), the Niederroedener Beds and the brackish *Cerithium* beds (Grimm *et al.* 2000; Reichenbacher 2000; Grimm & Grimm 2003).

The Upper *Cerithium* Beds cross the Chattian–Aquitanian boundary. The brackish-lagoonal sediments of the Oberrad Formation (= upper part of the Upper *Cerithium* Beds; see Schäfer & Kadolsky 2002) are of Aquitanian age (MN1, MN2; Engesser *et al.* 1993; Försterling & Reichenbacher 2002). The overlying brackish-lacustrine marls and limestones of the Rüssingen Formation (= *Inflata* Beds) still belong to the Aquitanian (MN2a; Engesser *et al.* 1993). In the uppermost part of the Rüssingen Formation, biota indicate a further brackish-marine ingression from the south (Reichenbacher 2000), which was again followed by an ingression from the North Sea (Martini 1981). This ingression characterizes the base of the Wiesbaden Formation (= Lower *Hydrobia* Beds; see Reichenbacher & Keller 2002), which mainly consists of bituminous marls and limestones and is of Aquitanian age, except perhaps in its uppermost part.

During the Burdigalian, brackish sedimentation was progressively reduced and replaced by lacustrine and fluviatile deposits. During the Langhian and the Early Serravallian, sedimentation was essentially continental, brackish or lacustrine in the Northern URG and the Hanau Basin (e.g. Staden Formation, Bockenheim Formation; see Grimm & Hottenrott 2002). A plateau-basalt layer ('Maintrapp'), with a radiometric age of 16.3 Ma, is found between the Staden and Bockenheim formations (Fuhrmann & Lippolt 1987). In the Mainz Basin, no Upper Burdigalian to Upper Serravallian sediments are known. The presence of limnofluviatile Tortonian deposits is represented by the Lautersheim Formation, the *Dinotherium* sands and the Dorn Dürkheim Formation, which are dated at several localities within the Mainz Basin (MN9 and MN11). The presence of several unconformities (Lower Serravallian–Tortonian, Tortonian–Lower Messinian as well as below the Piacenzian Arvernensis Gravels) is still controversial; field and borehole observations indicate three breaks in sedimentation, whereas seismic lines do not show any unconformity during the Mio-Pliocene in the northern part of the URG (Dèzes *et al.* 2004).

Uppermost Miocene to Pliocene sediments are known from some areas of the Mainz Basin and the western part of the Northern URG. They are represented by the 'White Mio-Pliocene' and Bohnerz clays (Rothausen & Sonne 1984; Grimm & Grimm 2003). Piacenzian-age fluviatile sediments are represented by the Arvernensis Gravels and the Weisenau Sands of the northernmost URG and the Mainz Basin and dated by magnetostratigraphy and heavy mineral associations (Fromm

1986; Semmel 1983). Late Pliocene sediments probably exist in the Heidelberg and Frankfurt areas (Hottenrott *et al.* 1995).

## *Helvetic units: western part (J.P.B.)*

Prior to their tectonic incorporation into the Alpine orogenic system during the Eocene, the Helvetic units were part of the stable European continent and formed its southern margin. Towards the south, the Helvetic units pass into the Ultrahelvetic Unit and the Penninic Flysch Zone (see below) (Figs. 17.11 & 17.12). Due to the Alpine Orogeny causing overthrusting and increased subsidence of the Helvetic units, deeper marine *Globigerina*-rich marls and shales were deposited during the Late Eocene. This is, herein, considered to be a transition to the foreland sedimentation of the North Alpine Foreland Basin (see below).

*Sedimentary and stratigraphic development*

The sedimentary history of the Helvetic units can be summarized in a number of stages (Fig. 17.9): (1) continental residual fissure-filling (= siderolithic) and freshwater limestones of Middle Eocene age; and (2) shallow-marine sediments (i.e. nummulitic limestones) indicating the beginning of subsidence during the Early Eocene (perhaps Palaeocene) in eastern Switzerland and during the Middle Eocene in the west; subsidence was accompanied by prominent normal faulting creating different structural blocks. The timing of this faulting, associated with eustatic sea-level changes, was responsible for the sedimentation in the Helvetic domain, as demonstrated by Menkfeld-Gfeller (1995).

From the Lutetian to the Priabonian, these shallow-marine units were covered by micaceous *Globigerina* marls and shales (Stad Schiefer) with an anoxic facies occurring in the NW (*Meletta* Shales). Lutetian to Priabonian deep-marine sediments are present in the Helvetic nappes (Einsiedeln Formation, Steinbach-Gallensis Formation, Bürgen Formation, Globigerinen-mergel, Flysch sudhelvétique, Marnes à Foraminifères, Hohgant Formation). In addition, coastal facies (Klimsenhorn Formation, Wildstrubel Formation) and brackish environments (Couches à Cerithes, Couches des Diablerets, Sanetsch Formation) of the same age are also recognized (see Herb *et al.* 1984; Herb 1988; Menkfeld-Gfeller 1994, 1995, 1997; Weidmann *et al.* 1991).

The western part of the Palaeogene Ultrahelvetic domain is characterized by deep marine sedimentation. This is described and discussed below.

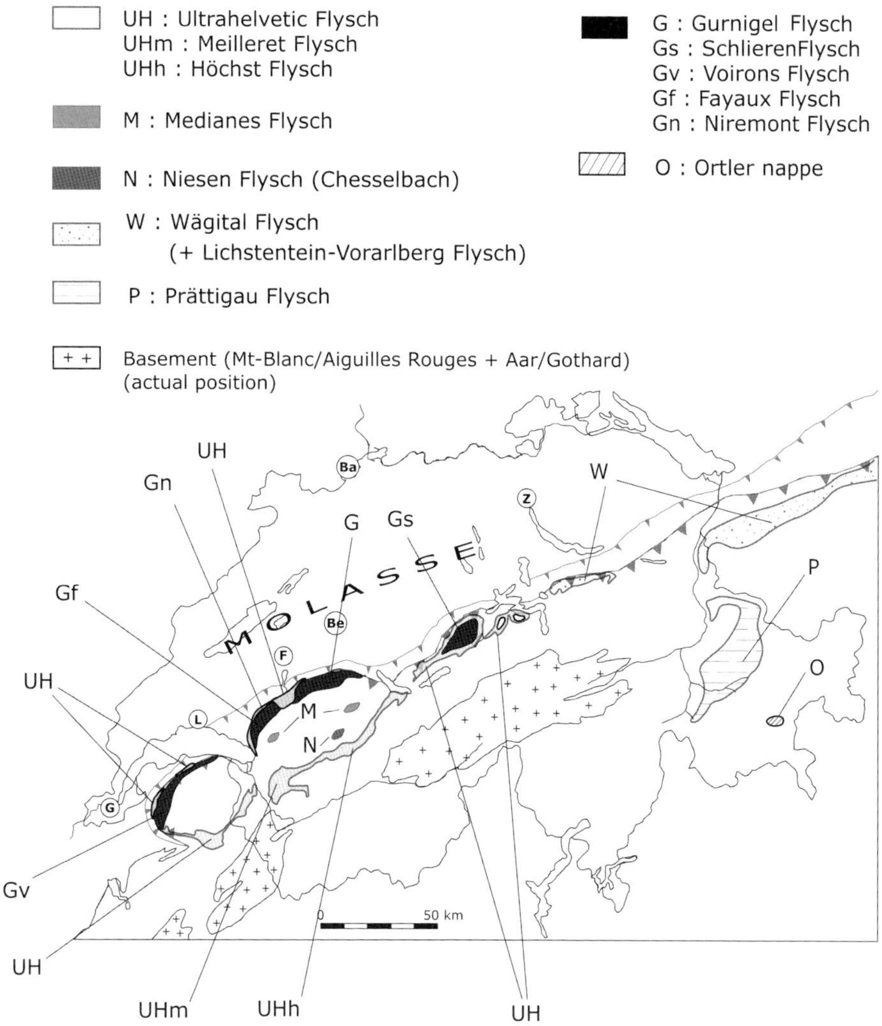


**Fig. 17.11.** Flysch deposits in Switzerland.

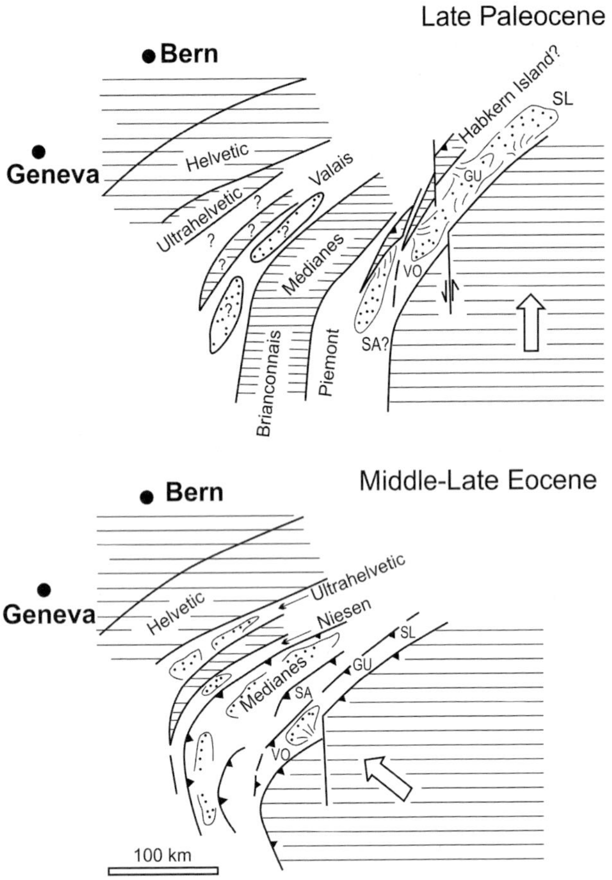


**Fig. 17.12.** Palaeogeography of the Swiss Flysch after Caron *et al.* (1989). Abbreviations: GL, gurnigel; SA, Sarine Slices; SL, Schlieren; VO, Voirons.

### *Helvetic units: eastern part (M.W.R.)*

The Helvetic units in Austria and Bavaria are part of the Eastern Alpine Foreland, and form a narrow, east–west trending belt north of the Alpine orogenic wedge. Sedimentary successions in the Vorarlberg area (westernmost Austria) are comparable to those of Switzerland (see above). Therefore, this section focuses on the occurrences in Bavaria, Salzburg and Upper Austria.

Overviews have previously been published by Richter (1978), Prey (1980), Tollmann (1985), Oberhauser (1991, 1995), Kurz *et al.* (2001) and Rasser & Piller (2001). Most occurrences of the Helvetic Zone in western Austria are tectonically isolated; all of them are considered to be part of the southern Helvetic facies. Classic studies based on the Bavarian occurrences, such as the Kressenberg (Gümbel 1861; Schlosser 1925; Hagn 1967, 1981; Hagn & Wellnhofer 1973; Ziegler 1975, 1983; Rasser & Piller 2001), have been published. However, only rare publications deal with other Bavarian localities, such as Grünten (Reis 1926; Ziegler 1983) and Neubeuern am Inn (Hagn & Darga 1989). Occurrences in Salzburg and Oberösterreich (Austria) are dominated by sediments attributed mostly to the Southern Helvetic facies. They are best developed in the Haunsberg area, north of Salzburg (Traub 1953, 1990; Gohrbandt 1963; Vogeltanz 1970; Prey 1980, 1984; Kuhn & Weidich 1987; Kuhn 1992; Schultz 1998; Rasser & Piller 1999*a*, *b*, 2001).

*Palaeogeography*

From north to south, the central and eastern part of the Helvetic Unit (HU) passes into the Ultrahelvetic Unit (UU), the Rhenodanubian (= Penninic) Flysch Unit (RFU), and the Austro-Alpine units including the Gosau Basin.

Most authors suggest that the Palaeogene depositional environement of the HU as well as the adjacent UU and RFU was morphologically determined by the presence of several submarine highs and island chains. The northernmost high is the Intrahelvetic High (Hagn 1954, 1981; Vogeltanz 1970), which separates a northern (Adelholzen facies) and a southern (Kressenberg facies) Helvetic facies unit. Emersion of this high from latest Maastrichtian to Middle Eocene times, resulted in the development of a sedimentary gap in the northern HU, while sedimentation continued in the southern HU (Hagn 1981). The Pre-Vindelician island chain (Traub 1953) marks the transition from the HU to the UU. The UU can be subdivided into a northern Ultrahelvetic facies, characterized by marls, and a southern Ultrahelvetic facies, characterized by carbonate-free clays (Hagn 1981). The southern Ultrahelvetic facies was separated from the adjacent turbiditic RFU by the Cetic Island Ridge (Hagn 1960, 1981).

The UU represents a depositional realm to the south of the HU. It is characterized by the Cretaceous to Eocene 'Buntmergelserie', comprising marls which contain olistoliths and turbidites probably derived from the Cetic Island Ridge (Faupl 1977).

*Tectonic setting*

The Palaeogene development of the Helvetic shelf was influenced by the Alpine Orogeny. Collisional processes led to the subduction of the European Plate below the African-Adriatic Plate within the Penninic Realm. Subduction resulted in the formation of the Alpine Foreland Basin with a more or less east–west striking basin axis and a corresponding east–west striking shoreline (Prey 1980; Wagner 1998). Sedimentation in the HU ceased in the Late Eocene, when it was completely overthrusted by the northward-moving Alpine nappe system (Hagn 1981).

*Sedimentary and stratigraphic development*

Sediments in Austria and Bavaria show a more or less continuous development from the Jurassic to the Late Eocene (Fig. 17.9). A generalized section of the Palaeogene Helvetic Unit comprises Danian to Upper Thanetian siliciclastic pelagic sediments, followed by uppermost Thanetian algal limestones. These are overlain by Ypresian to Lutetian ferruginous larger foraminiferal limestones and siliciclastic sediments. Deep-marine conditions occurred from the Bartonian to the Priabonian; they are characterized by the marly 'Stockletten". Sedimentation ceased at the Eocene–Oligocene boundary.

The Palaeogene succession begins with Palaeocene marls and marly sands of the Olching Formation. They developed directly above Upper Cretaceous sediments (Traub 1953, 1990). The Danian–Thanetian Olching Formation (P1a–P5; Kuhn & Weidich 1987; Kuhn 1992) represents one of the most fossiliferous Palaeocene units with respect to macrofossils (e.g. Schultz 1998). Its depositional depth was *c.* 50–150 m (Kuhn 1992). The abundance of sands and sand beds intercalated with the marls increases upward. The Olching Formation is overlain by the Thanetian Kroisbach Member, which represents the basal part of the Kressenberg Formation. This member is characterized by quartz sandstones rich in iron concretions, iron ooids, small brachiopods and pycnodont bivalves, as well as coarse-grained sands particularly rich in pycnodont bivalves (formerly known as

'Gryphaeenbank'). Glauconite is generally abundant and increases up-section. The coarsening-upward trend and the termination by ooid-bearing sandstones suggest a shallowing of the depositional system from the Danian to Thanetian. This relative sea-level fall corresponds to a long-term eustatic sea-level fall, which indicates that subsidence during the Palaeocene was low.

The glauconitic sands of the Kroisbach Member pass upwards into red-algae-dominated limestones (compare Kuhn (1992) and modifications by Rasser & Piller (2001)) of the Thanetian Fackelgraben Member. This member is characterized by bedded rhodolith and red algal detritic limestones with thin marly intercalations. It develops gradually from the pycnodont sands below and still contains detritic glauconite.

Near the Palaeocene–Eocene boundary a deepening of the environment is indicated in western Austria by the shift from the red-algae-dominated limestones towards a globigerinid facies (NP9, after Oberhauser 1991). Due to an angular unconformity, these deeper-water sediments are absent in Salzburg. This would suggest that tilting and erosion took place close to the Palaeocene–Eocene boundary. Rasser & Piller (2001) argued that the angular unconformity was related to a tectonic pulse within the Alpine system to the south ('Laramide 3' of Tollmann 1964) which corresponds to a rapid westward shift of the Alpine Nappes (Oberhauser 1995). Consequently, the Alpine Orogeny began to affect the sedimentation in the HU close to the Palaeocene–Eocene boundary.

The Thanetian to Lutetian Kressenberg Formation is characteristic for the earlier Eocene of the HU. The Ypresian commences with the mainly ferrugenic Frauengrube Member (= 'Roterzschichten'). This is characterized by massive, iron-ooid bearing, nummulite limestones and coarse-grained sandstones to fine-grained conglomerates. Quartz grains are frequently coated by iron, while most bioclasts are completely ferruginized. Flat and unfragmented larger foraminifera indicate very low energy conditions. However, the occurrence of high-energy iron ooids and ferruginized allochems in the same sediments suggest the opposite. Consequently, this facies has been interpreted by Rasser & Piller (2001) as representing a mixture of two different environments (e.g. input of iron ooids from ooid bars into the relatively deeper water where the larger foraminifera lived). The Ypresian-age ferrugenic sedimentation ceased with the formation of sand bodies of the Sankt Pankraz Member. In the Haunsberg area, it is characterized by up to 32 m of matrix-free, fine-grained sandstones without fossils. Its development in Bavaria is characterized by a coarse-grained sandstone to fine-grained conglomerate, rich in larger foraminifera. In the Haunsberg area, these sands represent subtidal sandbodies which show a marked fluvial influence, as well as a high degree of reworking (Vogeltanz 1970). The facies succession indicates a shallowing-upward from ooid bars (Frauengrube Member), surrounded by deeper foraminifera-rich sediments, up to the sandbodies of the Sankt Pankraz Member. The Middle Ypresian age of these ferruginous foraminiferal limestones (P7?, after Kuhn 1992) coincides with a long-term eustatic sea-level fall beginning during the Middle Ypresian. The rates of siliciclastic input can be correlated with a short-term eustatic sea-level fall during the latest Ypresian. The accommodation space necessary for the deposition of the ferruginized limestones and the 32-m-thick sandstones requires an increased subsidence rate at that time, suggesting that the subsidence rate was much higher than during the Palaeocene and the Early Ypresian.

Lutetian limestones are represented by the Kressenberg Member and the Weitwies Member (Rasser & Piller 2001). The Kressenberg Member (= 'Schwarzerz Schichten') is characterized by coarse-grained, poorly sorted, limestones containing iron ooids and larger foraminifera. In Bavaria, this member had been mined for its iron (Gümbel 1861; Hagn & Wellnhofer 1973). The Weitwies Member (= 'Fossilschicht') comprises glauconitic bioclastic limestones rich in larger foraminifera. Towards the top these grade into glauconitic marls with nummulitids and molluscs. In the Haunsberg area it also contains phosphate nodules (Traub 1953).

The entire Lutetian succession represents a period of eustatic sea-level fall. Since the described facies pattern indicates a relative sea-level rise, Rasser & Piller (2001) have suggested that the increased subsidence rate continued during the Lutetian. This coincided with the flooding of the northern Helvetic Unit, which represents a backstepping typical for transgressions on carbonate ramps (cf. Dorobek 1995). This feature is typical for foreland basins and was related to the ongoing subduction of the European Plate below the African-Adriatic Plate.

Lutetian shallow-water carbonate deposition was terminated by Bartonian to Priabonian deep-water conditions, and the so-called 'Stockletten' (globigerinid marls, >100 m thick) overlay the Kressenberg Formation. This succession represents an ongoing backstepping of facies belts of the ramp towards the north. The autochthonous subsurface of the later North Alpine Foreland Basin was covered by Bartonian–Priabonian shallow-water carbonates, which were reworked as olistoliths into the 'Stockletten' (Buchholz 1989; Darga 1992; Rasser 2000). Further Eocene–Oligocene shallow-water carbonates of the circum-Alpine area, include occurrences of the HU, were summarized by Nebelsick *et al.* (2003, 2005). The long-term eustatic sea-level fall continued until the Early Priabonian and was followed by a continuous rise up to the Eocene–Oligocene boundary.

## Alps and Alpine Foredeep: overview (M.W.R.)

The Alps are a mountain chain formed during the multiphase Alpine Orogeny (see also Froitzheim *et al.* 2008; Reicherter *et al.* 2008). They are separated into the Western Alps situated west of the Rhine Valley, and the Eastern Alps between the Rhine Valley and the Vienna Basin (Fig. 17.13). The Carpathians represent their eastward continuation. During the Palaeocene and Eocene, the Alpine system formed an archipelago including the Gosau basins. The Penninic tectonic units together with the Rhenodanubian Flysch Unit, formed the northern continuation of the Gosau basins and represent the main element of the Alpine Foredeep. The Helvetic Unit (see above) formed the northern continuation of the Penninic units. Towards the east, the Flysch Zone continues into the Carpathian Foredeep. During the Eocene, the Alpine Orogeny led to subduction of the Penninic oceanic crust and related units beneath the Alps. Together with the Helvetic Unit these were incorporated into the Alpine orogenic wedge, resulting in the termination of sedimentation in the Penninic and Helvetic units, and the Gosau basins during the Eocene. Sedimentary environments and processes changed remarkably during Oligocene and Miocene times.

### *Penninic units: flysch zones in Switzerland (J.P.B.)*

Caron *et al.* (1989) presented a detailed overview of the palaeogeographic development from the Turonian to the Late Eocene subdividing the sucession into three areas (Figs. 17.11 & 17.12): (1) Ultrahelvetic Unit and Niesen- and Medianes Flysch with a north-Tethyan character; (2) the Gurnigel Flysch of Central Tethyan origin; and (3) the south Tethyan Flysch, restricted to the Cretaceous. During the Late Eocene, the

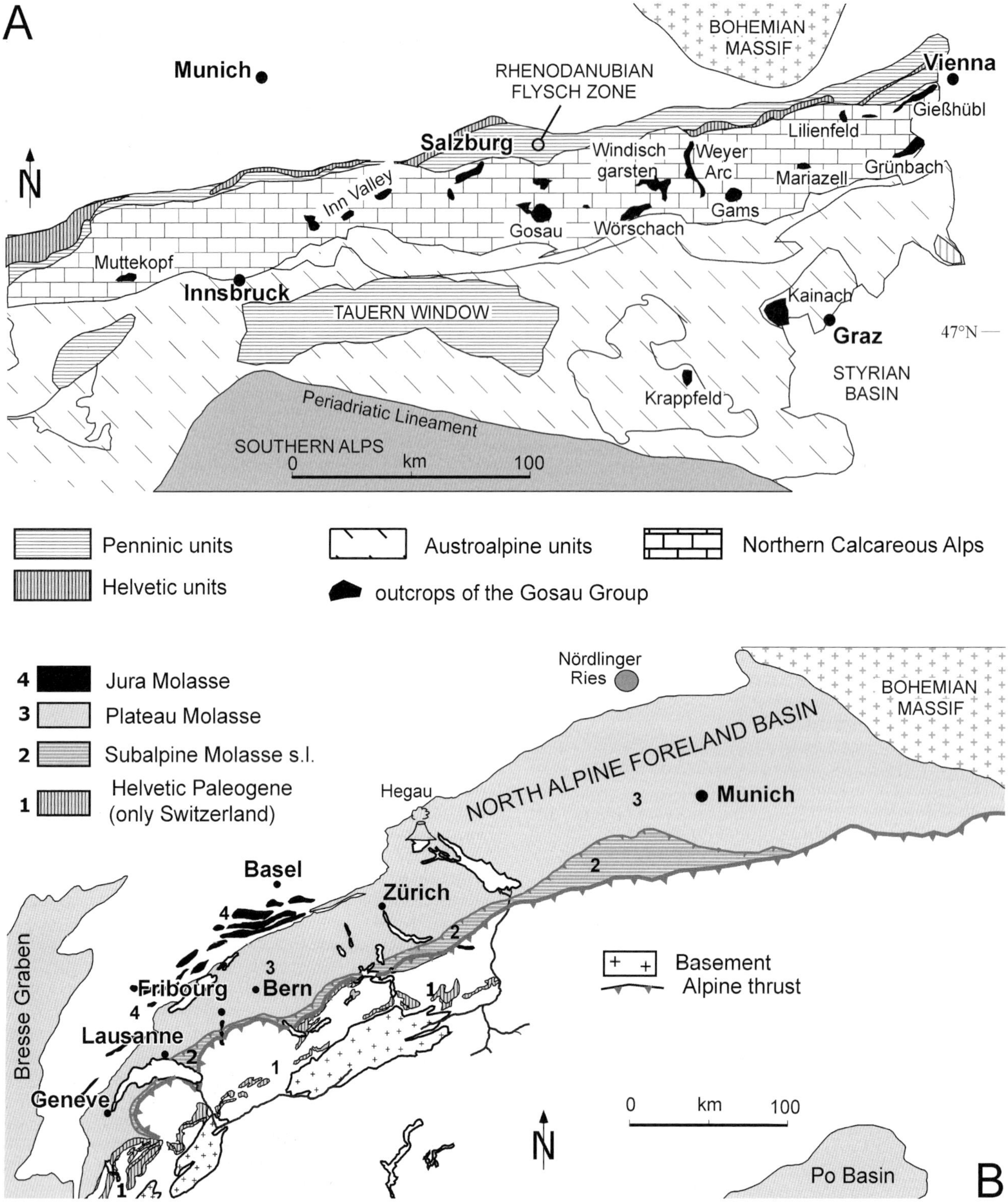


**Fig. 17.13.** Geology of (**A**) the Eastern Alps and adjacent areas and (**B**) the western part of the North Alpine Foreland Basin and the Swiss part of the Western Alps.

thrusting of the Penninic nappes onto the European Foreland marked the end of the deep-marine clastic sedimentation and the creation of the North Alpine Foreland Basin. Increased subsidence rates are reflected by the presence of globigerinid marls in the Helvetic Unit.

The term 'flysch' was defined in Switzerland as a rock stratigraphic unit in the Alpine front ranges (Studer 1827). From a geodynamic point of view, the formation of 'flysch' sediments requires subaerial exposure and high erosion rates in the source areas, short transport distances, and sufficient relief and slope for gravity flow processes to occur. Petrographical and structural analyses clearly demonstrate the role of compressive tectonics on the 'flysch' sedimentation (Caron *et al.* 1989). However, as postulated by Stuijvenberg (1979), eustasy was also responsible for the accumulation of the Gurnigel Flysch.

*Sedimentary and stratigraphic development*

The various structural units which make up the Pre-Alps (from the Arve River in France to Lake Thun) may be situated palaeogeographically in a series of basins extending from the European margin of the Tethys across an oceanic area and onto the southern margin (Adria); from NW to SE these are (Figs. 17.9, 17.11 & 17.13): (1) the distal Helvetic shelf with the Ultrahelvetic Unit; (2) the Valais Trough as an oceanic basin including the Niesen Nappe and North Penninic Mélange; (3) the Briançonnais Microcontinent containing the Pre-Alpes Medianes and Breche Nappes; (4) the Piedmont-Ligurian Ocean including the Gurnigel Flysch and Dranses Nappes; and (5) the South Alpine margin with the Simme Nappe. The orogenic facies of the Pre-Alps (i.e. flysch) were first deposited during the Cretaceous, extending to Middle–Late Eocene times. Olistostromes and mélange formations, which are related to tectonic phases, constitute chaotic units which have been termed 'wildflysch'. Some of these important nappe systems are presented below.

The **Ultrahelvetic nappes** (Lutetian–Bartonian) occur in tectonically complex units, together with Triassic to Late Eocene formations. These units occur on and between the Helvetic nappes, between the Niesen and Wildhorn nappes, and between the Gurnigel Nappe and the sub-Alpine Molasse. The Meilleret Flysch (Homewood 1974) is composed of pelitic and arenitic turbidites, which are cut by coarse clastics. The successions terminate with microbreccias and conglomerates containing abundant shallow-marine fauna (algae, foraminifera, bryozoans and corals). The Höchst Flysch (Ferazzini 1981) contains thick-bedded coarse arenites and conglomerates. According to benthic and planktonic foraminifera as well as nannofossils, the age of these deposits is Middle to Late Eocene. The conglomerates are composed of clasts derived from the Variscan basement and the Triassic–Cretaceous cover. The heavy mineral association comprises zircon, tourmaline, barite and $TiO_2$. The depositional environment was a moderately deep-water environnement, with a tectonically active source in the south, and a short transport distance.

The **Niesen Nappe** is essentially of Maastrichtian age, with a Lutetian upper part (Chesselbach Flysch; Ackermann 1986). This unit is thrust directly over the Ultrahelvetic Unit and is overlain by a mélange (zone submediane; Weidmann *et al.* 1976). The Chesselbach Flysch is composed of arenitic turbidites and shales, with north–south palaeocurrents. Its maximum thickness reaches 200 m. The top of this unit is dated as Middle Eocene by benthic foraminifera. Deposited in a deep-marine environment, this flysch contains a heavy mineral association composed of tourmaline, zircon, $TiO_2$ and apatite.

The **Medianes nappes** are of ?Early to Middle or Late Eocene age (NP15 is recorded), probably even younger (Caron *et al* 1980). This flysch is in stratigraphic continuity with the hemipelagic marls of the Couches Rouges Group (Palaeocene–Middle Eocene; Guillaume 1986). It is highly deformed and commonly associated with (and covered by) chaotic wildflysch deposits (flysch à lentilles de Couches rouges). The heavy minerals are dominated by garnet, zircon, tourmaline and $TiO_2$.

The **Gurnigel Nappe**, known from Bonneville (France) to central Switzerland (Caron 1976; Stuijvenberg 1979), is Maastrichtian to Eocene (Bartonian) in age. Its basal thrust is thought to override the Ultrahelvetic units and Pre-Alpes Medianes, but later reverse faulting has emplaced the front of the Pre-Alpes Medianes over the rear of the Gurnigel Nappe (Caron *et al.* 1980). Several local names have been proposed within this unit, such as the Voirons Flysch (Stuijvenberg 1980), the Fayaux Flysch (Stuijvenberg *et al.* 1976), the Niremont Flysch (Morel 1980) and the Schlieren Flysch (Winkler 1983).

This flysch is mainly composed of turbiditic shales and thin sandstones with fine-grained carbonate turbidites, hemipelagic shales with bentonite layers as well as rare thick-bedded sandstone channels and conglomerates. The thickness ranges from 1.5 km (Gurnigel-Schlieren area) to 2.5 km (Voirons). The original substratum is unknown. The upper limit corresponds to an erosional surface. This flysch comprises classical Bouma-type turbidites and bears the entire facies spectrum of Mutti & Rici Lucchi (1972). The depositional environment was an abyssal, deep-sea fan. The dominant palaeocurrent trend is from west to east (Wildi 1985). The conglomerate clasts are composed of 20% metamorphic, 50% magmatic and 30% sedimentary rocks with two dominant populations: (1) tonalite, quartzite, and dolomicrites (Triassic) with various other Mesozoic and basement rocks; (2) granite, granodiorites and cherts, together with other sedimentary, metamorphic and crystalline rocks. The basement is of South Alpine origin, the Mesozoic clasts were derived from platforms to deep basins situated in the South- and Austro-Alpine units. The heavy mineral association comprises garnet, apatites and staurolite (Wildi 1985). Several bentonite layers (Winkler *et al.* 1985) have their acme in the Late Maastrichtian and the Early Eocene.

The **Wägital Flysch** is recognized in central and eastern Switzerland. It is very similar to the Gurnigel Flysch, and probably represented the geographic transition from the Gurnigel-Schlieren area to the Rhenodanubian Flysch Unit (Trümpy 1980).

*From flysch to wildflysch and to foreland basin sedimentation*

Until the 1980s, many geologists equated the terms 'flysch' and 'turbidites'. Therefore, 'flysch' was used for each turbiditic unit found in the peri-Alpine realm. Thus, several sedimentary units studied in the Helvetic nappes and the sub-Alpine area have been named according to this philosophy, as for example the 'North Helvetic Flysch' (with the well known locality of Engi, rich in fish remains) or the 'Subalpine Flysch'. Incorporating the geodynamic control between the earlier and later stages of the Alpine Orogeny, Homewood & Lateltin (1988) published an exhaustive review of these units and placed them into a molasse (foreland-basin style sedimentation) geodynamic context, with the erection of the Taveyannaz and Val d'Illiez formations replacing the North Helvetic Flysch and the Subalpine Flysch, respectively. The Val d'Illiez Formation passes upward to the littoral facies of the Lower Marine Molasse. Thus, the original conception of the Lower Marine Molasse extended to the Val d'Illiez and Taveyannaz formations.

### *Rhenodanubian Flysch Unit (M.W.R.)*

The Rhenodanubian Flysch Unit (RFU) is part of the Alpine-Carpathian Foreland and received its name from the equivalent occurrences in the Swiss Western Alps. The RFU forms a narrow zone along the northern front of the Eastern Alps (Fig. 17.13). With a length of 520 km it strikes in a west–east direction from the Rhine Valley towards the east and dips below the Neogene of the Vienna Basin and continues into the Carpathians (e.g, Magura Nappe).

*Palaeogeography*
During the Palaeogene, the Northern Calcareous Alps (NCA) were part of the Austro-Alpine Microplate (for summary Faupl & Wagreich 2000; Wagreich 2001; see also Froitzheim *et al.* 2008) situated between the European Plate to the north and the Adriatic Plate to the south (Channel *et al.* 1992). The RFU was part of the Alpine Foredeep to the north of the NCA. Slope deposits of the NCA Gosau Group formed the southern margin of the RFU (Wagreich 2001; Trautwein *et al.* 2001). To the north, it was bordered by the Ultrahelvetic Unit. The RFU was part of the Northern Alpine Foredeep and was formed from eroded material of the rising Alpine mountain chain. In this respect, it was functionally replaced by the North Alpine Foreland Basin during the Oligocene and Neogene. The palaeogeographic origin of the RFU as part of the Valais palaeogeographic domain is a matter of discussion (e.g. Kurz *et al.* 2001, and references therein). Wagreich (2001) assumed that the depositional area of the RFU was situated within the (northern) Penninic domain (compare Faupl & Wagreich 2000).

*Tectonic setting*
The Alpine Orogeny and the development of the Gosau basins were controlled by ongoing convergence between Africa and Europe in late Mesozoic and Cenozoic times. The northward drift of the African-Adriatic Plate led to subduction of the European Plate within the Penninic realm and subsequent uplift of the Austro-Alpine nappe stack. Northward tilting and basin subsidence of the NCA occurred during the latest Cretaceous to Palaeocene. This was caused by tectonic erosion of parts of an accretionary wedge to the north of the NCA (Wagreich 1993, 1995).

*Sedimentary and stratigraphic development*
Sedimentation of the RFU (Fig. 17.9) commenced during the Early Cretaceous with carbonate-dominated deep-marine deposits passing into siliciclastic sediments. Upper Cretaceous turbidites are intercalated with pelitic intervals related to sea-level changes. Palaeogene deposits are characterized by stable heavy minerals (e.g. Wagreich & Marschalko 1995; Trautwein *et al.* 2001). Sedimentation ceased during the Eocene, when the RFU was subducted below the Alpine nappe stack. Cretaceous deep-marine sediments are known from western Austria (Egger 1990, 1995). Palaeogene deep-marine sediments are best developed in SE Bavaria (Freimoser 1972), Salzburg and Lower Austria (Egger 1995). Overviews on the tectonics, stratigraphy and palaeogeography have been published by Egger (1992, 1995), Oberhauser (1995), Wagreich & Marschalko (1995), Adamova & Schnabl (1999) and Faupl & Wagreich (2000). According to these papers, the stratigraphic and sedimentary development of the area can be subdivided into various stages (see below).

The Maastrichtian (CC25) to Palaeocene (NP9) Altlengbach Formation is known from both the central (Salzburg) and the western (Wienerwald, Lower Austria) parts of the RFU (Egger 1995). It extends from the Campanian–Maastrichtian boundary through to the uppermost Palaeocene. The Palaeocene parts of the Altlengbach Formation are restricted to the Acharting Member, the deposition of which began during the Maastrichtian. The Acharting Member is characterized by rhythmic alternations of fine-grained sandstones to siltstones and turbiditic mudstones. The sand- and siltstones have a high carbonate content and include foraminifers and coralline algal fragments. As revealed from heavy minerals (Egger 1990), palaeocurrents from the east prevailed up to the early Palaeocene, changing to a westerly direction during the later Palaeocene.

In Salzburg, the Palaeocene–Eocene boundary interval is present within the Anthering Formation (NP9/P6 to NP11; Egger 1995). Egger *et al.* (1997) subdivided the Anthering Formation into mud turbidites, hemipelagites and bentonites. The mud turbidites are dominated by silty marls and marls, while sandstones and siltstones typical of the Altlengbach Formation are subordinate. Turbidite beds are up to 2 m thick. Hemipelagic claystones are usually bioturbated, contain abundant agglutinated foraminifera, and have relatively high organic carbon content. In contrast to the turbidites, the hemipelagic claystones generally lack planktonic organisms, benthic foraminifera and bioturbation. These are, therefore, interpreted as having formed in an oxygen-deficient environment. Several bentonite layers were found in the type area of the Anthering Formation and were interpreted as volcanic ashes. Egger *et al.* (1997) suggested a short period of marked explosive volcanic activity. The reduced abundance of siliciclastics in the Anthering Formation, when compared to the Altlengbach Formation, is interpreted to be related to a eustatic sea-level rise rather than to tectonic subsidence (Egger *et al.* 1997). The high abundance of bentonites in the pelitic rocks suggests that increased volcanic activity accompanied this transgression.

During the Early Eocene, sedimentation ceased in the Salzburg part of the RFU. In the east Austrian Wienerwald (Vienna Woods) area, the eastern equivalent of the Anthering Formation is represented by the Greifenstein Formation, whose deposition commenced during the Late Palaeocene (NP8; Egger 1995). While the earlier Palaeocene development is comparable between Salzburg and the Wienerwald area (Acharting Member), different sediment types were deposited from the latest Palaeocene onwards. The Greifenstein Beds (e.g. Hösch 1985, cited in Egger 1990) are characterized by thick-bedded, coarse-grained sandstones. In part they are rich in glauconite and nummulites (e.g. Oberhauser 1980). Another Late Palaeocene–Eocene equivalent, but located on a different nappe, are the Laab Beds. Based on fision track data, Trautwein *et al.* (2001) suggested the existence of two basins in the eastern part of the RFU: a main basin close to the NCA nappe stack, and a Laab Basin towards the north existing since Early Cretaceous time.

## *North Alpine Foreland Basin: western part (J.P.B.)*

The North Alpine Foreland Basin (NAFB) – often referred to as the Molasse Basin – was part of the Alpine-Carpathian Foredeep forming a west–east trending basin in front of the prograding nappes of the Alpine orogenic wedge. It can be traced from the Rhône Basin in the west via Switzerland and Bavaria to Austria (Fig. 17.13).

*Palaeogeography*
Several palaeogeographic reconstructions of the NAFB have been published (Berger 1996; Sissingh 1998; Schlunegger & Pfiffner 2001; Kuhlemann & Kempf 2002; Becker & Berger 2004; Berger *et al.* 2005*b*). During the Lutetian, the sea was located in the area of north Italy and southern Switzerland, with its northern shoreline about 70 km south of Bern (Sissingh 1998). The Alpine front was probably situated *c.* 300 km south of its present position (Dèzes *et al.* 2004). Most of the area of present-day Switzerland was affected by erosion (marked by local siderolithic deposits).

Subsequently, the sea transgraded along the northern front of the Alps. During the Late Rupelian, the Paratethys regressed towards the east. It is most likely that during this time a marine connection existed between the NAFB and the Upper Rhine

Graben (URG) (perhaps during NP23; see Berger 1996; Kuhlemann & Kempf 2002; Diem 1986; Berger 1995; Picot 2002). A marine connection between the URG and the NAFB was only possible via the central and eastern parts of the Swiss Foreland Basin, since its western part was covered by fluviatile sediments (Berger 1996) while in its eastern part (Bavaria), open marine conditions occurred. Following a regression during the Early Chattian, fluvial sedimentation prevailed in the Swiss part of the NAFB. Alluvial conglomeratic fans, derived from the Alps, were drained by a SW–NE orientated fluviatile system referred to as the 'Genferseeschüttung'. The fluvial drainage joined the marine development still present in Bavaria. Part of this system continued into the southern URG through the Jura Molasse, as evidenced by the heavy minerals of the 'Molasse Alsacienne' (Picot 2002).

The Late Chattian shows an important decrease in clastic supply to the western Swiss NAFB, resulting in the development of lacustrine and brackish conditions, as attested by the accumulation of lacustrine limestones and gypsiferous marls (Molasse à charbon, Grès et marnes gris à gypse). During the Aquitanian, the accumulation of alluvial clastic sediments continued in the Swiss Molasse Basin, with local lacustrine and brackish deposits dominating in its distal parts. The occurrence of a marine ingression in its western parts is evidenced by the presence of mammal faunas (MN2a) which were trapped in tidal deposits (Berger 1985). In Bavaria, the fluvial drainage entered the sea in the vicinity of Munich (Kuhleman & Kempf 2002). A marine ingression, originating from west and east, covered the entire NAFB in the Burdigalian. During the Late Burdigalian, the sea probably regressed towards the distal part of the basin, where brackish conditions prevailed (Marnes rouges, Helicidenmergel; see Becker 2003), and then towards the west (i.e. France). An important estuary is evident in NE Switzerland and SW Germany, the so-called 'Graupensandrinne' (see Reichenbacher *et al.* 1998). In the German part, brackish and lacustrine sedimentation prevailed.

During the Langhian a NE–SW fluviatile drainage system (= 'Glimmersand') drained the NAFB from Germany to Switzerland. Alluvial fans derived from the Alps (Napf, Hörnli and Bodensee-Pfander, Hochgrat, Nesselburg) are evident in central and eastern Switzerland and Bavaria (see Kuhlemann & Kempf 2002). All of these deposits form the so-called Upper Freshwater Molasse (Obere Süsswassermolasse) and contain several bentonite levels. Equivalent sediments are unknown for the western part of the Swiss NAFB, where 2000 m of Miocene sediments were probably eroded during the Plio-Pleistocene (Kuhlemann & Kempf 2002). Only relicts of marine middle Miocene deposits occur in the western Jura Molasse (NN4–NN5; see Kälin *et al.* 2001). During the Serravallian, fluviatile sedimentation continued, with an important clastic source located in the Vosges and Black Forest massifs, confirming continued uplift during this time.

The Tortonian drainage pattern is very difficult to reconstruct in Switzerland; a general west–east drainage of the Swiss NAFB has been proposed (Giamboni *et al.* 2004; Kuhlemann and Kempf 2002; Liniger 1966; Petit *et al.* 1996; Schlunegger *et al.* 1998). This pattern is based on the uplift of the western and central parts of the NAFB in conjunction with the folding of the Jura Mountains. In Germany, fluviatile sedimentation persisted until the Early Tortonian (11 Ma; Kuhleman & Kempf 2002).

*Sedimentary and stratigraphic development*

The NAFB is traditionally subdivided into four depositional groups (Fig. 17.9): (1) the Lower Marine Molasse (= 'Untere Meeresmolasse', UMM) commenced with the increase of subsidence leading to the creation of the foreland basin; (2) the Lower Freshwater Molasse (= 'Untere Süsswassermolasse', USM) is composed of freshwater and rare brackish sediments; (3) the Upper Marine Molasse ('Obere Meeresmolasse', OMM) represents general marine sedimentation occurring in the entire basin; and (4) the Upper Freshwater Molasse (= 'Obere Süsswassermolasse', OSM) represents freshwater sedimentation extending to the Tortonian. The NAFB is also traditionally subdivided into a Sub-Alpine (thrusted and folded units, originally deposited further to the south) and a 'Plateau' or 'Foreland' molasse, which is relatively autochthonous. The distal part of the Swiss NAFB is generally called 'Jura Molasse', representing the connection with the Upper Rhine Graben.

In the **Sub-Alpine Molasse**: the UMM deposits comprise the Meletta shales, the Taveyannaz and Aldorf sandstones, the Val d'Illiez Formation and the Vaulruz Formation (see Diem 1986; Kuhlemann & Kempf 2002; Lateltin 1988; Schlunegger *et al.* 1997). In the western part of the Swiss NAFB, marine sedimentation stopped earlier (not before NP22) than in the eastern part, where marine sediments are known until NP24 or even NP25 (Doppler *et al.* 2000). Marine sedimentation continued in Germany during the Rupelian (i.e. Bausteinschichten) and even until the Aquitanian in Bavaria.

Due to the general sea-level fall (corresponding with the Ch1 sequence; see Hardenbol *et al.* 1998) these deposits are overlain by the freshwater deposits of the USM, which consist of conglomeratic alluvial fan deposits, fluviatile sediments, and palustrine-lacustrine deposits, such as the Molasse à Charbon (see Berger 1998; Engesser *et al.* 1984; Fasel 1986; Schlunegger *et al.* 1996, 1997). In Germany, the Chattian sediments were essentially deposited in freshwater environments (Granitische Molasse), passing towards the east into brackish (Cyrenenschichten) and later fully marine conditions (Prombergerschichten; Schwerd *et al.* 1996). No Miocene sediments have been recorded in the Sub-Alpine Molasse of Western Switzerland. Some conglomeratic fans persist in eastern Switzerland until the Middle Aquitanian (Schlunegger *et al.* 1997). In Germany, the Aquitanian is characterized from west to east by the freshwater–marine transition (i.e. 'Aquitan Fischschiefer'; Schwerd *et al* 1996). The OMM and the OSM are only rarely present.

In the **Swiss Plateau Molasse**, continental deposits, rich in lateritic products (so-called Siderolithic, with 'Bohnerz' = iron ore nuggets and/or 'Hupper' = quartz sands), were deposited, some of them dated by mammals (Engesser & Mödden 1997; Hooker & Weidmann 2000). Few lacustrine deposits of Rupelian age are known from the Swiss Plateau Molasse (Calcaires inférieurs), which are generally dated by charophytes (Berger 1992). In the Early Chattian, fluviatile sediments (Untere Bunte Mergel) were deposited in the entire foreland basin. During the Middle and Late Chattian, lacustrine and brackish limestones, dolomites and gypsiferous marls occur. In the NE distal part of the basin, sedimentation probably did not begin before the middle Chattian (Müller *et al.* 2002; Schlunegger & Pfiffner 2001). All mentioned units are relatively well dated by mammals, charophytes, otolithes and magnetostratigraphy; see Berger *et al.* 2005*a*).

In Germany, the UMM is represented by the distal parts of the Tonmergelschichten and Bausteinschichten (Rupelian). During the Chattian, a freshwater to marine transition occurred (Doppler *et al* 2000; Schwerd *et al* 1996). A fluviatile facies characterizes the Aquitanian deposits of the Swiss Plateau Molasse (e.g. Molasse Grise de Lausanne, Obere Bunte Mergel, Granitische Molasse; Berger 1985; Keller *et al.* 1990). A marine transgression flooded the North Alpine

Foreland Basin during the late Aquitanian (MN2) and Burdigalian. Its typical deposits comprise the OMM (Berger 1985; Homewood & Allen 1981; Keller 1989; Kempf *et al.* 1997, 1999; Schoepfer 1989; Strunck & Matter 2002). In Germany, a freshwater–marine transition prevailed during the Aquitanian. Following reduced sedimentation during the early Burdigalian, the sea invaded the entire basin. In Switzerland, marine sediments were confined during the Langhian to the north and NE (Graf 1991); fluviatile sediments associated with alluvial fans are present in the south (OSM) and persisted until the Serravallian (MN7, ?MN8) (Bolliger 1992; Kälin 1993; Kälin & Kempf 2002; Kempf *et al.* 1999). The OSM is very well represented in Germany, with conglomerates alternating with fluvial and lacustrine sediments. The meteorite of the Nördlinger Ries impacted during the Early Serravallian (14.6 Ma). In Switzerland, no Upper Serravallian, Tortonian or Messinian sediments are recorded. However, several authors suggested that an additional 700 m and up to >2000 m of sediment were deposited in the east and west Swiss NAFB (see Kuhleman & Kempf 2002).

The Palaeogene to Neogene **Swiss Jura Molasse** is preserved in a number of synclines in the Jura Mountains (Picot 2002; Becker 2003). Eocene deposits are represented by siderolithic units. Even though it has not been precisely dated, a Lutetian, Bartonian and Priabonian age is suggested based on correlation with other siderolithic occurrences. The Swiss Jura Molasse was subdivided by Berger *et al.* (2005*a*) into five different areas. (1) SW Jura Molasse (Valserine, Joux, Auberson, Travers, Val de Ruz): deposits of the Lower Marine Molasse are absent. The USM is represented by the Chattian Calcaires inférieurs and the Aquitanian Calcaires de La Chaux (MN2b). OMM sediments are preserved as well, but the OSM is absent. (2) NW Jura Molasse (Verrières, Pont de Martel, Locle-Chaux de Fonds): only deposits of the OMM and of the OSM are present; the latter is represented by the famous Oeningian facies. (3) Central-South Jura Molasse (St. Imier, Pery-Reuchenette, Tramelan-Tavannes, Balstahl, Moutier): thick units of fluviatile and lacustrine sediments accumulated during the Oligocene (Calcaires inférieurs, Molasse alsacienne, Calcaires delémontiens). After a gap during the Aquitanian, the OMM commenced with classic tidal sandstones. The OSM is essentially lacustrine (Oeningian facies) and conglomeratic. (4) Central-North Jura Molasse (Soulce, Delémont, Laufen, Porrentruy, Liesberg): the UMM is represented by marine marls dated from NP22 to NP25, alternating with Oligocene freshwater deposits (e.g. conglomerates, Molasse Alsacienne, Calcaires delémontiens). A sedimentary gap during the Aquitanian is followed by the sedimentation of the OMM and lacustrine OSM deposits. (5) East Jura Molasse (Mummliswil, Waldenburg): essentially USM and OMM are developed. OSM is only partly preserved (Glimmersand).

The Pliocene is principally represented by conglomerates (Ältere Deckenschotter, Graf 1993) in the NE of Switzerland. The only dated Pliocene deposits in this area are the karstic filling of the Vue des Alpes (MN15; Bolliger *et al.* 1993), and the Höhere Deckenschotter from Irchels (MN17, Bolliger *et al.* 1996). In Germany, Pliocene sediments have been reported from the 'Hochflächenschotter' and the 'Hochschotter' (e.g. Schwäbische Alb, Naabtal).

## *North Alpine Foreland Basin: eastern part (M.H., R.R.)*

The Austrian part of the North Alpine Foreland Basin (NAFB) is bordered to the north by the passive margin of the Variscan Bohemian Massif and by the overriding Rhenodanubian Flysch Unit and Helvetic Unit of the Alpine-Carpathian thrust front in the south. The width of the *c.* 300 km long Austrian part of the NAFB in Lower and Upper Austria ranges from 5 to 50 km. The present basin is only a narrow remnant of the original basin (Fig. 17.13).

*Tectonic setting*

During the Oligocene, progradation of the Alpine-Carpathian nappe system resulted in the passive margin of the Bohemian Massif being transformed into a foreland molasse trough. In the south, emplacement of the Helvetic and Rhenodanunian Flysch units formed the southern slope of the basin. During the Late Oligocene, these units became integrated into the Alpine thrust front. The Calcareous Alps formed the shelf on which debris from the Central Alps accumulated. In the north a fault system of conjugate NW–SE and NE–SW trending faults in the southern part of the Bohemian Massif resulted in the formation of a triangular crystalline peninsula, which extended far south into the NAFB, separating the basin in the area into western and eastern parts. Tectonic activity within the thrust sheets and lateral movements of the basement along the eastern flank of the Bohemian Massif are still ongoing.

*Sedimentary and stratigraphic development*

The depositional history and stratigraphic development of the eastern NAFB differs considerably from that of its western part (see above) and may be subdivided into several stages. The oldest Cenozoic deposits in the NAFB are Upper Eocene fluvial and shallow-marine sandstones, shales and carbonates of the Perwang Group (Buchholz 1989; Rasser 2000) (Fig. 17.9). As a result of subduction of the European plate beneath the Peri-Adriatic plate and the weight of the advancing Alpine nappe system, the downwarping of the foreland crust accelerated during the Early Oligocene and the NAFB subsided rapidly into a deep pelagic area. Black shales were deposited in Switzerland, Bavaria and western Austria (= Fischschiefer). Towards the south, these shales graded into the deep-marine deposits of the Deutenhausen Formation. An upwelling current system might have been established during the Late Eocene, affecting deposition along the northern slope throughout the Early Oligocene, as suggested by the presence of nannoplankton ooze.

The Southern Bohemian Massif acted as the northern margin of the NAFB. During the Oligocene it was drained towards the south and east by fluvial systems, represented by the sands and gravels of the Freistadt-Kefermarkt Beds and the St. Marein-Freischling Formation. During the Early Oligocene (Kiscellian regional stage) vast mudflats and lagoonal embayments developed along the coast formed by the Bohemian Massif (e.g. mollusc-rich pelites, lignites of the Pielach Formation; Harzhauser & Mandic 2001). Sandy sediments of the coeval and overlying Linz-Melk Formation reflect the marine transgression during the Oligocene (Kiscellian and Egerian regional stages). These comprise lagoon, rocky shore, sandy shoreface and tide-influenced open-shelf environments. The interruption of this transgression by the marked Lower Egerian regression is evidenced by erosion surfaces, redeposition and intercalations of lagoonal dark coaly pelites (Roetzel 1983).

Along the western part of the northern margin of the NAFB, the Oligocene shallow-water deposits interfinger towards the south with offshore pelites of the Ebelsberg and Eferding formations. Due to the progressive Upper Oligocene transgression, these offshore pelites overlap the shallow-water deposits to the north. Along the southern slope of the NAFB, the Egerian

Puchkirchen Formation was deposited in a deep marine channel, comprising slumps, conglomeratic debris flows and turbidites, derived from both slopes of the NAFB (DeRuig 2002). Frequently strong bottom currents reworked the turbidites into contourites (Wagner 1996, 1998).

Continuous deep-marine sedimentation in the eastern NAFB is contrasted with the deposition of the Lower Freshwater Molasse in Vorarlberg (western Austria) and Bavaria during the Egerian (see section above). Here, brackish environments formed in the Late Oligocene and overlie the shallow-marine deposits of the Baustein Beds. A westward prograding limnic-fluvial facies of the 'Lower Coloured Molasse' developed and this grades into the brackish swampy environments of the 'Lower *Cyrena* beds'. A short-lived marine ingression (Promberg Beds) is followed by the limnic-fluvial conditions of the 'Upper Coloured Molasse' in the latest Oligocene and early Early Miocene. In the Early Miocene (Eggenburgian regional age) marine sedimentation was re-established, as evidenced by the deposition of the shallow marine sediments of the Upper Marine Molasse. In eastern Austria, however, deep-water sedimentation continued during the Late Egerian and Eggenburgian, and is typified by the debris flows, slumps and contourites of the Eggenburgian Hall Group. During the Eggenburgian and Ottnangian (Early Miocene), deltaic gravels and sands were transported from the south into the NAFB, forming the conglomerates of the Buchberg and Wachtberg, today partly located in the imbricated nappes of the NAFB.

Shallow-marine deposits are mostly absent in the western, Upper Austrian part of the NAFB due to both submarine and later Alpine erosion. Erosional relicts of the Eggenburgian are best preserved along the eastern margin of the Bohemian Massif in Lower Austria. There, the Lower Eggenburgian successions reflect a stepwise landward shift of the palaeoshoreline (Mandic & Steininger 2003). The marine sediments onlapped either directly onto a relief formed by crystalline rocks of the SE Bohemian Massif, as shown by the Fels Formation, or prograded towards the NW into the estuarine-fluvial systems of the St. Marein-Freischling Formation. Initial brackish-estuarine biotopes of the Mold Formation were gradually replaced by fully marine conditions, typified by the sandy Loibersdorf Formation, which includes the historical holostratotype of the Eggenburgian stage at Loibersdorf (Steininger 1971). Continuing transgression onto the Bohemian Massif in the late Eggenburgian led to the deposition of the mollusc-rich nearshore sands of the Burgschleinitz and Gauderndorf formations. Following a prominent regressional phase, the sandy bryozoan limestones of the Zogelsdorf Formation were deposited at the beginning of the new Ottnangian transgressional cycle. Towards the east these shallow-water deposits interfinger with the offshore clays of the Zellerndorf Formation. During the Ottnangian, due to further westward transgression of the sea onto the Bohemian Massif, these offshore clays were deposited above the nearshore sediments. Towards the west a transition of the marine clays to the brackish clays of the Weitersfeld Formation can be noted. In marginal areas brackish-estuarine sediments with coal seams were deposited (Langau Formation) during the Ottnangian and were followed by marine nearshore sands (Riegersburg Formation). In several of these marginal Ottnangian units, acidic volcaniclastics, derived from the Carpatho-Pannonian region, are present (Nehyba & Roetzel 1999).

In the Late Eggenburgian and Ottnangian the reopening of the NAFB towards the Rhône Basin in the west led to a distinct change in the depositional environments. Consequently, in the western part of the NAFB sands and silts of the Innviertel Group show evidence of strong tidal influence, ubiquitous reworking, and submarine erosion (Faupl & Roetzel 1988). Close to the margin of the Bohemian Massif, reworking of Egerian and Eggenburgian sediments is reflected in the presence of the phosphorite-bearing Plesching Formation (Faupl & Roetzel 1990). In the eastern part of the NAFB, basinal clays, silts and sands of the Robulus Schlier and the so-called Sandstreifenschlier represent Eggenburgian to Ottnangian offshore deposits. In the Ottnangian, at the margin of the Bohemian Massif, submarine debris flows occur (Mauer Formation). These interdigitate with tidal channel sands of the Prinzersdorf Formation (Krenmayr 2003*a*, *b*).

In the Late Ottnangian, the presence of the widespread *Rzehakia* ('*Oncophora*') beds reflects a major regression. These beds yield an endemic mollusc fauna with bivalves such as *Rzehakia* and *Limnopagetia*, which thrived in shallow brackish lakes. In the western NAFB, a pronounced phase of erosion took place up to the latest Early Miocene. Subsequently, deposition of limnic-fluvial sediments of the Upper Freshwater Molasse commenced. Its basal parts comprise lignite-bearing clays, sands and gravels (Trimmelkam and Munderfing beds), which are of Middle Miocene age. After another gap the 'Lignite bearing Freshwater beds', the Kobernausserwald gravels and the Hausruck gravels were deposited in limnic-fluvial environments during the Late Miocene.

In the eastern part of the NAFB shallow-marine conditions also prevailed in late Early Miocene times and are represented by the pelitic and sandy sediments of the Laa and Nový Přerov formations (Roetzel 2003). In the early Middle Miocene, similar sediments were deposited (Grund and Gaindorf formations). Sandy-gravelly and shelly intercalations within the predominantly pelitic Grund Formation are interpreted as storm-induced event deposits (Roetzel & Pervesler 2004). On topographic highs corallinacean limestone developed (Mailberg Formation). To the south these sediments are correlated with submarine deltaic conglomerates (Hollenburg-Karlstetten Formation). Foraminiferal data document an Early Badenian age (= Langhian) for these deposits and suggest that marine deposition in the eastern NAFB continued until *c*. 14.5 Ma, when Middle Miocene uplift caused the sea to retreat.

The very last marine ingression into the already dry basin took place during the Early Sarmatian (= late Serravallian). The marine Sarmatian is confined to a rather narrow, *c*. 40 km long west–east trending trough extending from the Bohemian Massif in the west to the Vienna Basin in the east. The location was controlled by an older incised valley which became flooded during the Early Sarmatian. Clays, silts and sands were deposited suggesting the formation of extended sandy to muddy tidal flats. The dating of the Ziersdorf Formation as Early Sarmatian is based on the occurrence of several species of the endemic gastropod *Mohrensternia* (Kowalke & Harzhauser 2004) and rare *Elphidium reginum* (Papp *et al.* 1974). Upper Sarmatian deposits are absent from the NAFB due to the final retreat of the Paratethys Sea from that area.

The early Late Miocene of the NAFB in Lower Austria is characterized by a huge fluvial system often referred to as the Palaeo-Danube. The corresponding deposits of the Hollabrunn-Mistelbach Formation indicate a dominant gravel-rich fluvial depositional environment, which grades into a braid-delta environment towards the east at the entrance to the Vienna Basin (Nehyba & Roetzel 2004). The mostly coarse-grained clastic fluvial to deltaic sediments, extend, on the surface, in a WSW–ENE direction from Krems in the NAFB towards the Steinberg Fault in the Vienna Basin over a distance of >86 km. The width of this sediment body is between 3 and 14 km, and up to 20 km in the delta area.

### *Austro-Alpine Gosau basins (M.W.)*

Palaeogene strata in the Austro-Alpine parts of the Eastern Alps (Northern Calcareous Alps (NCA) and Central-Alpine Zone (CAZ)) (Fig. 17.13) are partly continuous from the Upper Cretaceous successions. Following the work of Kühn (1930), Palaeogene-age strata have been recognized from the Gosau Group of the NCA. Most of the NCA Palaeogene deposits are deep-marine (Wagreich & Faupl 1994; Wagreich 2001); shallow-water sediments have only been reported from the southeastern part of the NCA (Kambühel and Hochschwab areas; Tragelehn 1996), and from the CAZ (Krappfeld area; Wilkens 1989; Rasser 1994). Shallow-water carbonates are also found as olistoliths in deep-water strata (Lein 1982; Moussavian 1984).

Outcrops of the Palaeogene Gosau Group comprise only erosional remnants of the widespread Palaeogene cover of the NCA and the CAZ as evidenced by the widespread redeposition of Palaeogene sediments into younger formations (e.g. Hagn 1981). The Palaeogene deposits of the Gosau Group record the geodynamic evolution of the Eastern Alpine orogenic wedge from a phase of deep-water sedimentation to renewed thrusting, which culminated in the meso-Alpine Orogeny related to compression between the European and the African-Adriatic plates during the Palaeogene (e.g. Dewey *et al.* 1989; see also Froitzheim *et al.* 2008).

*Palaeogeography*

The Palaeogene deposits of the Gosau Group of the NCA record deep-water sedimentation on top of the early orogenic wedge of the Eastern Alps, which evolved during Early to early Late Cretaceous Alpine deformation (Faupl & Wagreich 2000) (Fig. 17.14). Palaeogeographic reconstructions indicate a generally northward-deepening slope, dissected by depocentres and structural highs forming slope basins along an active continental margin. To the south of the NCA, exhumation of metamorphic complexes of the Austro-Alpine basement formed a rising source area for Palaeogene siliciclastics. This rising hinterland separated the depositional area of the Gosau Group of the NCA from southern CAZ basins such as the Krappfeld (Neubauer *et al.* 1995; Wagreich & Siegl-Farkas 1999). Palaeogene deep-water sediments, comparable to the Gosau Group, are also known from the eastward continuation of the NCA into the Western Carpathians (Wagreich & Marschalko 1995). Palaeogene deposition within the CAZ can be interpreted as a continuation of the 'Central Carpathian Palaeogene' deep-water trough from Slovakia (Wagreich 2001; Kázmér *et al.* 2003) into the Eastern Alps. Farther to the south, a marine seaway from the 'Central Alpine' Gosau Basin into the Southern Alps can be assumed, due to the occurrence of Palaeocene–Eocene deep-water strata, in, for example, the Lombardian Basin in northern Italy, where an Early Palaeocene hiatus is followed by the deposition of turbidites and marlstones of Palaeocene–Middle Eocene age (Bersezio *et al.* 1993).

*Sedimentary and stratigraphic development*

Formally defined lithostratigraphic subdivisions of Palaeogene deposits of the Austro-Alpine units have been established in the Gosau area (Fig. 17.15) (based on Weigel (1937) and Kollmann in Plöchinger (1982): Nierental Formation, Zwieselalm Formation), in the Gießhübl syncline (Gießhübl Formation; Plöchinger 1964; Wessely 1974; Sauer 1980) and in the Grünbach-Neue Welt area (Zweiersdorf Formation; Plöchinger 1961). Paleocene shallow-water carbonates of the Kambühel Formation, as defined by Tollmann (1976), were investigated by Tragelehn (1996) who distinguished two members (St. Lorenzen Member, Ragglitz Member). Biostratigraphic data for the deep-water successions are mainly based on planktonic foraminifera and calcareous nannoplankton (e.g. Hillebrandt 1962; Wille-Janoschek 1966; Wille 1968; Kollmann 1964; Wagreich & Krenmayr 1993; Hradecká *et al.* 1999; Egger *et al.* 2004).

The Palaeogene in the CAZ is subdivided into the Holzer Formation (Paleocene), the Sittenberg Formation (Ypresian/Lutetian) and the Dobranberg Formation (Lutetian; Wilkens 1991; Rasser 1994) which includes several members.

Four generalized facies associations have been distinguished within the Palaeogene part of the Gosau Group of the NCA (Wagreich 2001): siliciclastic and mixed siliciclastic/carbonate turbidites, hemipelagites and pelagites, debrites, and shallow-water carbonates of reef, lagoonal and forereef facies. The gravity-flow-dominated facies association suggests deposition on small submarine fans. Proximal fan areas are characterized by channels filled with conglomerates and pebbly sandstones, whereas classical turbidites indicate interchannel and distal fan depositional environments.

During the Early Palaeocene, turbidites and hemipelagites dominated the Gosau Group of the NCA, from the Tyrol in the west (Muttekopf area, Ortner 1994) to the Gießhübl Syncline in the east (Sauer 1980). Several localities (Gosau, Gams, Lattengebirge, Gießhübl Syncline) display a conformable succession of Maastrichtian to Palaeocene deep-water sediments, without major facies changes around the K/Pg boundary (Lahodynsky 1988; Krenmayr 1999). Several hundred metres of thick turbiditic

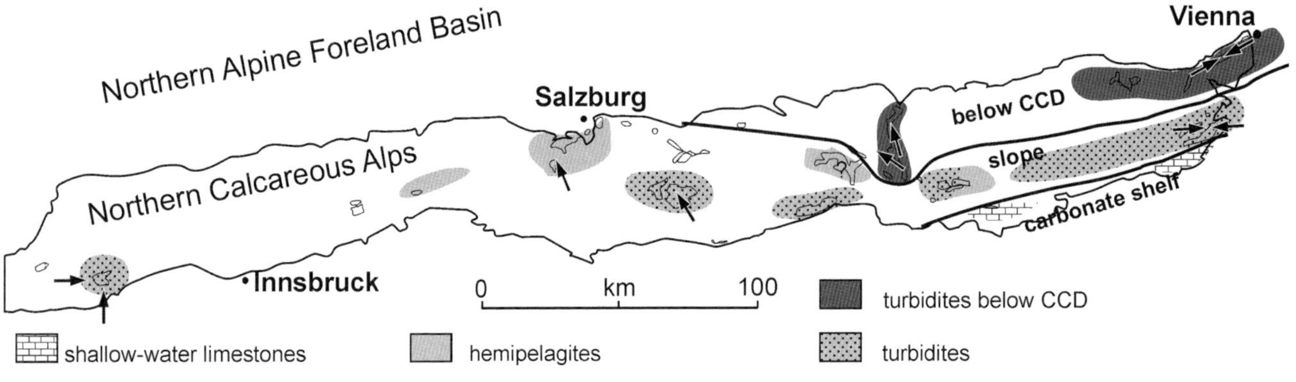


**Fig. 17.14.** Palaeogeographic sketch map for the Early Palaeocene (nannoplankton zones NP1–4) of the Northern Calcareous Alps with the main Gosau Basins. Arrows indicate palaeocurrent directions.

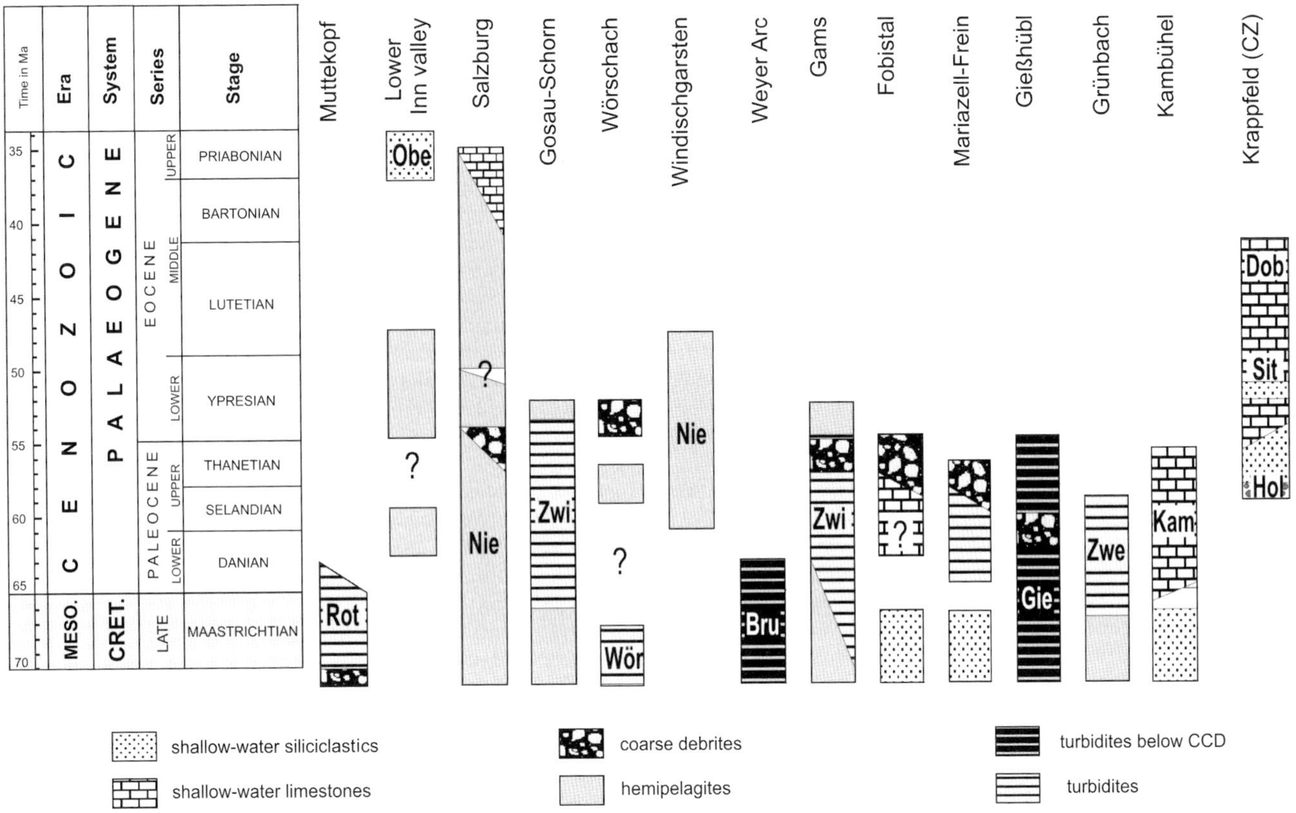


**Fig. 17.15.** Lithofacies, lithostratigraphy and chronostratigraphic correlation of main successions of Palaeogene sediments of the Gosau Group of the Northern Calcareous Alps and the Palaeogene of the Central Alpine Zone. Abbreviations: Bru, Brunnbach Formation; Dob, Dobranberg Formation; Gie, Gießhübl Formation; Hol, Holzer Formation; Kam, Kambühel Formation; Nie, Nierental Formation; Obe, Oberaudorf Formation; Rot, Rotkopf Formation; Sit, Sittenberg Formation; Wör, Wörschachberg Formation; Zwe, Zweiersdorf Formation; Zwi, Zwieselalm Formation.

successions are known from Gosau, Gams and the Gießhübl Syncline. Palaeocurrent data point to southern source areas for the turbidites (Faupl 1983), although basin-parallel, east–west trending flows are also recorded. Turbiditic sandstones can be classified as lithic arenites and display mixing of siliciclastic (mainly low- to medium-grade metamorphic clasts) and carbonate debris. Carbonate clasts include both extraclasts from the underlying strata of the NCA, and bioclasts from a contemporaneous carbonate shelf to the south. Ar/Ar dating of micas from pebbles suggests significant erosion of pre-Alpine, Permian metamorphic crystalline units of the Austro-Alpine basement to the south (Frank *et al.* 1998). Hemipelagites and pelagites (Nierental Formation; Krenmayr 1996, 1999) occur either as packages several tens to hundreds of metres thick or as thin intervals within turbidite-dominated successions. Thin- to medium-bedded marly limestones, marls and shales with a generally high degree of bioturbation (*Zoophycus* ichnofacies) predominate. The carbonate content consists mainly of calcareous nannoplankton and planktonic foraminifera. Intercalations of thin sandstone and debrite beds or slump deposits are common (e.g. Krenmayr 1999; Wagreich & Krenmayr 2005).

Within the Weyer Arc area, carbonate-free hemipelagic clays within the turbiditic succession of the Brunnbach Formation record deposition below the local carbonate compensation depth (CCD) (Faupl 1983). This deep-water basin received material from two sources, building a sand-rich and a sand-poor submarine fan (Faupl 1983). To the south and SE of this deep basin, the Gosau Group of Gams, deposited in a slope basin–trench–slope basin setting, records deposition in bathyal depths during the Early Palaeocene (Wagreich & Krenmayr 1993; Krenmayr 1996; Egger *et al.* 2004). South of Gams, in the Hochschwab area, shallow-water carbonates and limestone olistoliths are present. These remnants of shallow-water facies (Kambühel Formation) continue up to the eastern margin of the Alps (Kambühel near Ternitz). Palaeocene reef carbonates comprise bafflestones/boundstones/rudstones with abundant corallinacean and dasycladacean algae and corals. Forereef facies include packstones rich in corallinacean algae. Third-order transgression–regression cycles, marked by emersion horizons, have been reported by Tragelehn (1996). Reef growth stopped during the Middle Thanetian, probably due to a sea-level fall and tectonism (Tragelehn 1996).

During the Thanetian to Lower Ypresian coarse debrites, including olistoliths of Palaeocene shallow-water carbonates, are widespread in the NCA. They occur either as debrite layers several metre thick associated with mixed siliciclastic-carbonate turbiditic successions (e.g. Gießhübl Formation), or as isolated breccias including olistoliths, up to 50 m in diameter, in the Hochschwab area. Olistostromes, including metamorphic clasts, were reported from the lower 'Ilerdian' (P5) of the Salzburg-Reichenhall area and the Kaisergebirge/Tyrol (Moussavian *et al.* 1990). The southern carbonate platform was probably dissected by canyons, enabling the siliciclastics to bypass the carbonate environment.

The occurrence of bentonites, originating from airfall, in the Upper Palaeocene (NP10) of Salzburg and Gams (Egger *et al.* 1996, 2004) suggest that there was a close connection of the depositional areas of the Gosau Group and parts of the Rhenodanubian Flysch, where similar bentonites of basaltic composition are known (Egger *et al.* 2000).

In the CAZ a hiatus marks the top of the Late Maastrichtian to Early Palaeocene sequence. This is followed by a (Late?) Palaeocene succession of terrestrial conglomerates, sandstones and clays including coals (Holzer Formation; Wilkens 1991).

Eocene deposits of the Gosau Group are known from Gams (Kollmann 1964; Egger & Wagreich 2001), Windischgarsten, the Schorn area near Gosau and Abtenau (Wille 1968), the Salzburg-Untersberg area (Hillebrandt 1962, 1981), and the Lower Inn Valley (Hagn 1981). An Early to Middle Eocene age (NP12–15) for the end of sedimentation has been reported from most of these areas; only the succession in the Salzburg–Untersberg area displays a significantly younger interval up to the Late Eocene (P15–16, NP19). This unusually high stratigraphic range may be explained by a transition from the Gosau Group sedimentary cycle to the Late Eocene/Oligocene sedimentary cycle of the 'lower Inn valley Tertiary' (Ortner & Sachsenhofer 1996; Löffler & Nebelsick 2001; Nebelsick *et al.* 2001; Ortner & Stingl 2001), a complex pull-apart-piggyback basin which was connected to the foreland Molasse Basin. Major facies types of Eocene–Oligocene shallow-water carbonates of the circum-Alpine area were recently summarized by Nebelsick *et al.* (2003, 2005).

Due to renewed northward thrusting onto the Rhenodanubian Flysch Zone and Helvetic Units during the Middle/Late Eocene, large parts of the NCA were subaerially exposed and marine sedimentation terminated in most of the Gosau basins. At the tip of the NCA wedge, marine sedimentation continued within piggyback basins, which subsided during ongoing thrusting of the NCA.

In the CAZ, a transgression around the Palaeocene–Eocene boundary resulted in the deposition of marginal marine siliciclastics and carbonates. Late Palaeocene to Early Eocene clastics and nummulite marls are represented by the Sittenberg Formation. The overlying Dobranberg Formation marks a transition to pure larger foraminiferal limestones. Basal parts of this formation are characterized by intercalations of alveolinid and nummulitid limestones with local intercalations of orthophragminid foraminifera (Wilkens 1989, 1991; Hillebrandt 1993). The nummulitid foraminifera are Early Eocene in age (Hillebrandt 1993). Coralline algae and encrusting foraminifera dominate the middle part of the succession where they form huge accumulations of rhodoliths and acervulinid macroids (Rasser 1994) which are thought to be Ypresian to Lutetian in age (Wilkens 1989; see also Moussavian 1984).

## *Vienna Basin and its satellite basins (M.H., M.K., R.R.)*

The Vienna Basin covers large parts of eastern Austria (Lower Austria, Vienna and Burgenland) and extends into the Czech Republic in the north and the Slovak Republic in the east (Fig. 17.16). It is about 200 km long and 55 km wide, striking roughly SW–NE from Gloggnitz (Lower Austria) in the SSW to Napajedla (Czech Republic) in the NNE. As a classic Neogene basin it has been the subject of hundreds of geoscientific studies since the early nineteenth century.

### *Tectonic setting and development*

The Vienna Basin is a rhombic Neogene-age pull-apart basin. Its SW border is formed topographically by the Eastern Alps and to the NW by the Waschberg and Ždánice units. To the east it is bordered by the Rosalia, Leitha and Hainburg hills, and the Male Karpaty Mountains, all four of which are part of the Alpine-Carpathian Central Zone. The Pieniny Klippen Belt represents an internal boundary of the Outer Carpathian Flysch Belt; sediments of the Magura Unit form the northern margin of the basin. The basement of the basin is formed by Alpine-Carpathian nappes. The maximum thickness of the Neogene basin fill is 5500 m. Since the basin is subdivided by a morphological high, the Spannberg Ridge, into a northern and a southern part, marine sedimentation was restricted to the north (north of the Danube) during the Early Miocene and extended into the south only during the Middle and Late Miocene. Due to the complex fault system the basin was internally subdivided into a series of horst and graben systems. The uplifted blocks at the margins of the basin are separated from the deeper areas by major faults (e.g. Mistelbach Block and Steinberg Fault, Moravian central depression and Bulhary Fault in the northern basin, Mödling Block and Leopoldsdorf Fault in the southern basin; Láb-Malacky High and Leitha and Láb fault zones).

A detailed overview including all relevant literature used in the present section was presented by Kováč *et al.* (2004). The formation of the Vienna Basin began in the Early Miocene as an east–west trending piggyback basin on top of the Alpine thrust belt. It was initiated during the Eggenburgian and was active until the late Early Miocene (Early Karpatian). In the late Early Miocene thrusting was replaced by the lateral extrusion of the Western Carpathian lithospheric fragment from the Alpine Realm and depocentres originated by pull-apart processes. During the latest Early Miocene, NE–SW orientated deep sinistral strike-slip faults were formed along the eastern margin of the basin, together with north–south orientated normal faults. The Middle Miocene subsidence of the synrift stage of the Vienna Basin was controlled by a palaeostress field with NE–SW orientated compression (NW–SE extension). The development of the basin during the Middle Miocene was influenced by NE–SW orientated normal faults. A second phase of more rapid tectonic subsidence during the late Middle Miocene (Early Sarmatian) is related to ENE–WSW sinistral strike-slip faults and NE–SW orientated normal faults. These faults induced subsidence of the Zistersdorf–Moravian Central Depression. Synrift extension in the northern part of the Vienna Basin was enhanced by active elongation of the Western Carpathian Orogen during the Sarmatian due to subduction in front of the Eastern Carpathians. The Late Miocene represents the post-rift stage in basin evolution. In the Late Miocene (Pannonian) and Pliocene, the Vienna Basin was inverted and subsequently only minor amounts of sediment were deposited. Fault-controlled subsidence in grabens at the eastern margin of the basin (Zohor-Plavecký Mikuláš and Mitterndorf grabens) documents a sinistral transtensional regime of this zone, lasting up to recent times, and accompanied by seismic activity.

### *Sedimentary and stratigraphic development*

The initial phase of Miocene deposition in the present Vienna Basin (Fig. 17.9) was related to the Eggenburgian transgression and to the tectonic opening of depocentres in its northern part. Piggyback basin depocentres developed in the Outer Carpathian Flysch Belt zone, while in the Central Western Carpathians wrench fault basins opened. Deposition commenced with the clays and sands of the fluvial Stráže Formation. The onset of marine transgression is reflected by the boulder-sized Brezová conglomerates which pass into fine-grained conglomerates and shoreface sands. Upwards, sandy deposits containing a rich pectinid fauna are found. Laterally, to the south and east, the coastal facies passes into open-marine conditions marked by the upper part of the Lužice Formation. Neritic sands and clays (= 'Schlier') contain a rich deep-water foraminiferal assemblage, yielding taxa that tolerated low-oxygen bottom conditions. The

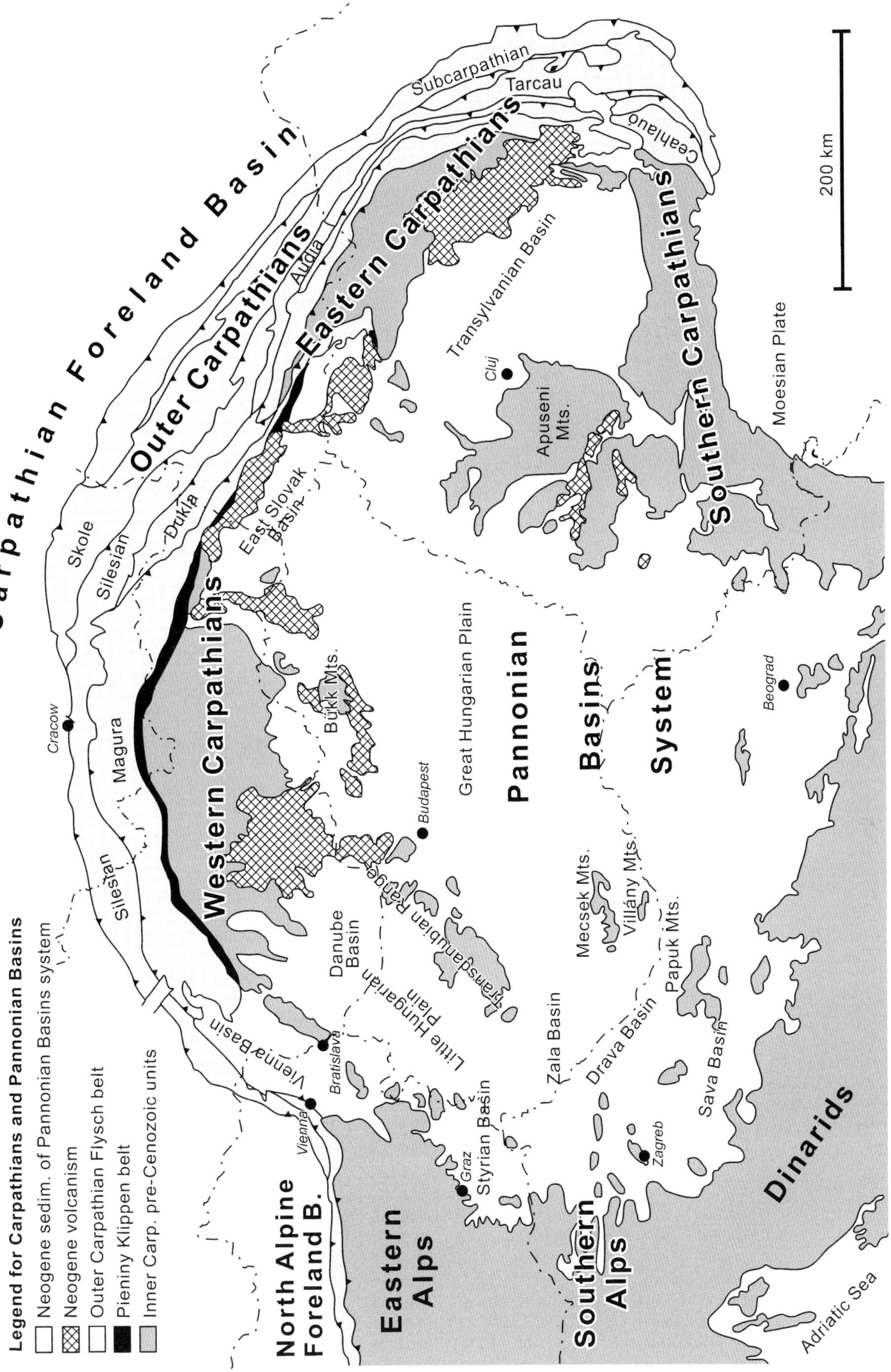
Legend for Carpathians and Pannonian Basins
Neogene sedim. of Pannonian Basins system
Neogene volcanism
Outer Carpathian Flysch belt
Pieniny Klippen belt
Inner Carp. pre-Cenozoic units
Carpathian Foreland Basin
Outer Carpathians
Eastern Carpathians
Western Carpathians
Southern Carpathians
Subcarpathian
Tarcau
Ceahlau
Audia
Dukla
Silesian
Skole
Magura
Cracow
East Slovak Basin
Bükk Mts.
Transylvanian Basin
Cluj
Apuseni Mts.
Moesian Plate
200 km
Great Hungarian Plain
Pannonian Basins System
Beograd
Budapest
Transdanubian Range
Danube Basin
Little Hungarian Plain
Vienna Basin
Bratislava
Vienna
Mecsek Mts.
Villány Mts.
Papuk Mts.
Zala Basin
Drava Basin
Sava Basin
Styrian Basin
Graz
Zagreb
Dinarids
North Alpine Foreland B.
Eastern Alps
Southern Alps
Adriatic Sea

**Fig. 17.16.** Geology of the Carpathians and the Pannonian Basins System.

Eggenburgian–Ottnangian boundary is marked by a relative sea-level fall and recorded by the basinward progradation of shallow-water sandy facies at the base of the Ottnangian. In the northern Vienna Basin, the sandy Štefanov Member (150 m) represents a deltaic body entering the basin from the SW during this regression. The overlying Ottnangian transgression is represented by the silts and silty sands of the upper Lužice Formation, which onlaps the slopes of topographic highs.

During the subsequent Karpatian a pull-apart basin began to open. Rapid subsidence and sea-level rise led to the development of offshore settings in the northern Vienna Basin, as reflected by the pelites of the Laa and Lakšáry formations. Sedimentation in the southern part of the basin differed significantly, due to the presence of a topographic barrier formed by the Spannberg Ridge in the central Vienna Basin. Thus, in the southern Vienna Basin, sedimentation started during the Early Miocene with the deposition of the alluvial Bockfliess Formation comprising lacustrine to brackish-littoral environments. After a regressive phase at the end of the Early Karpatian this formation was discordantly overlain by the lacustrine-terrestrial facies of the Gänserndorf Formation. At the same time, up to 400 m of sandy deltaic deposits (Šaštín Member) prograded into the Slovak part into the Vienna Basin. The top of the Gänserndorf Formation grades into the overlying Aderklaa Formation without a major unconformity. Sandstones, interbedded pelites and rare conglomerates characterize the deposits of the 1000 m thick Aderklaa Formation. Deposition took place in a limnic/fluvial environment as part of a meandering river system. The Gänserndorf and Aderklaa formations in the southern Vienna Basin can be correlated with the marine, brackish to freshwater Závod Formation in the northern Vienna Basin.

A major regressive event at the Lower–Middle Miocene (Karpatian–Badenian) boundary, found in many Paratethyan nearshore settings, is also recorded in the Vienna Basin by erosional truncations of up to 400 m. The Vienna Basin became subaerial during this time, as reflected by palaeosol formation. In the south, sedimentation recommenced during the early Middle Miocene with the deposition of the Aderklaa Conglomerate, which formed part of a braided river system. Similar conditions are documented by the Jablonica Conglomerate in the north. During the subsequent Badenian transgression offshore pelites (Baden Group) were deposited. This group consists of several formations, including the Lanžhot Formation in the Slovak part of the basin. Corallinacean limestones ('Leitha limestone') frequently formed in areas with little clastic input. The first occurrences of *Praeorbulina* and of *Orbulina suturalis* within the Baden Group are important biostratigraphic markers (Rögl *et al.* 2002).

During the early Badenian at *c.* 14.2 Ma a major sea-level fall occurred. Several small deltaic bodies developed (e.g. Andlersdorf, Zwerndorf and Auersthal members). A second Badenian sequence followed. Deltaic, fluvial and lagoonal settings developed in the northern part of the Vienna Basin (Žižkov Formation). This mostly freshwater and brackish formation consists of calcareous clays, containing lenses of cross-bedded sand bodies (*c.* 1200 m in the Moravian Central Depression). This deltaic succession passes upward into littoral sandy clays with a marine fauna. The following relative sea-level rise is expressed by the deposition of transgressive shelf sand bars and a backstepping of the deltaic sediments. The littoral sands were subsequently overlain by the calcareous clays of the neritic offshore Jakubov Formation.

A third Badenian succession includes littoral and sublittoral shoreface sands with coralline algal biostromes at their base. A distinct flooding surface is preserved near Devínska Nová Ves in Slovakia. In the central part of the basin, layers of Upper Badenian corallinacean limestones represent a shallow-marine shoal along the Spannberg Ridge that extended for more than 150 km$^2$ (Kreutzer 1978). This topographic high acted as a Late Badenian platform from which a bird-foot delta spread into the southern basin (Weissenbäck 1996). This delta was supplied with sediments from the continental North Alpine Foreland Basin. The offshore sediments consist of marine calcareous clays (Studienka Formation). Oxygen-depleted bottom conditions commonly occurred in basinal settings but also on the carbonate platforms (Schmid *et al.* 2001).

The Badenian–Sarmatian boundary is characterized by a major fall in sea level. Badenian-age corallinacean limestones were exposed and significant erosion took place along the margins of the basin. Renewed transgression in the Early Sarmatian filled incised valleys. This transgression is represented mainly by calcareous clays, silts, and rare acidic tuffs (Holíč Formation; Vass 2002). The lowermost Sarmatian deposits are recorded from the Kúty and Kopčany grabens in the northern Vienna Basin. Fluvial gravel was derived from the Northern Alpine Foreland Basin. In coastal settings unique bryozoan–serpulid–algal bioconstructions flourished, forming reefoid structures several metres high. These are well preserved along the Malé Karpaty and Leitha mountains in the eastern and southern Vienna Basin and along the Steinberg Ridge. A subsequent regressive phase in the Middle Sarmatian was characterized by the progradation of a huge delta complex in the Matzen area in the central Vienna Basin and by erosion of Lower Sarmatian bioherms. The renewed flooding during the Late Sarmatian is reflected by the various mixed siliciclastic/carbonate deposits of the Skalica Formation (Vass 2002). Extended oolite shoals (up to 30 m thick) and coquina shell beds formed in the entire Vienna Basin (Harzhauser & Piller 2004).

At the Sarmatian–Pannonian boundary, the Paratethys Sea retreated from the Pannonian Basin area and the brackish Lake Pannon was established. The Vienna Basin was dry and Middle Miocene deposits were eroded. Consequently, lowermost Pannonian fluvial facies penetrated far into the basin, reworking older Sarmatian strata. A rather uniform, 50–100 m thick, monotonous unit of marl and sand of prodelta- and basinal facies follows and includes a 20–50 m thick marker unit of ostracod-bearing marly clay at the top. The marly prodelta facies is followed by a sandy succession up to 200 m thick with rare gravels representing a prograding delta of the palaeo-Danube in the northwestern part of the Vienna Basin. The occurrence of the three-toed horse *Hippotherium* within those deposits is an important biostratigraphic marker.

A major transgression followed and the elevated highs along the western margin of the basin were flooded by Lake Pannon (Harzhauser *et al.* 2004). The Middle Pannonian deposits consist of *c.* 440 m of clays and sands (Bzenec Formation = Inzersdorf Tegel). The Upper Pannonian is characterized by the ubiquitous occurrence of thin lignite seams in its basal parts and by a 200 m thick sandy/marly upper part (Čáry Formation). During the Late Pannonian, the margin of Lake Pannon had retreated from the Vienna Basin. Floodplain deposits and freshwater lakes developed which were not connected to Lake Pannon. The basin fill terminates with a 450 m thick succession of marls, clays and silts with intercalations of sands, gravels, rare lignites and freshwater limestones (Pannonian Gbely and Pliocene Brodské formations). In the southern Vienna Basin, Miocene sedimentation terminates with the fluvial Rohrbach Conglomerate.

**The Korneuburg (Sub-)Basin** formed due to pull-apart

activity within the Alpine-Carpathian thrust belt. This asymmetric SSE–NNE orientated basin is *c*. 20 km long and attains a maximum width of 7 km, but is strongly narrowed in its northern extension. A central high separates the southern part (*c*. 880 m deep) from a shallower northern depocentre (*c*. 530 m deep).

The basin margins are formed in the north by the Waschberg Unit and towards the south by the Rhenodanubian Flysch Unit. These Alpine-Carpathian nappes are underlain by the autochthonous basement formed mainly by Upper Cretaceous and Jurassic units and by the crystalline basement of the Bohemian Massif. Sedimentation began during the early Miocene (Eggenburgian) and comprised shallow-marine marls and sands (Ritzendorf Formation). The main phase of deposition, however, began in the late Early Miocene (Karpatian), and is represented by marly silts and fine to medium sands (Korneuburg Formation).

A connection to the Paratethys was only warranted along the northern basin margin, where the sea extended into the Alpine-Carpathian Foredeep. This situation is also reflected in the internal facies patterns. Thus, the small, elongated basin was divided into a southern, estuarine part with extensive tidal mudflats and *Crassostrea* bioherms, and a northern shallow-marine part with depth of 20–30 m. No Middle or Upper Miocene deposits are known from the Korneuburg Basin (all data from Harzhauser *et al.* 2002; Harzhauser & Wessely 2003).

**The Eisenstadt-Sopron (Sub-)Basin** is more or less triangular in shape and measures about 20 km. In the north it is bounded by the NE–SW trending Leitha Mountains and the associated SE-dipping Eisenstadt Fault. In the east, the basin is bordered by the north–south trending Köhida Fault. The Rust-Fertörakos Mountains separate the basin from the Danube Basin in the east. A crystalline ridge, covered by Lower Miocene gravels, extending from the Rosalia Mountains to the Brennberg, defines the southern margin. This topographical barrier also separates the Eisenstadt-Sopron Basin from the Styrian Basin. The development of the Eisenstadt-Sopron Basin is closely linked with that of the Vienna Basin, although the thickness of the basin fill is much less (*c*. 1500 m).

The oldest Neogene deposits in the present Eisenstadt-Sopron Basin are of Early Miocene age. They comprise terrestrial, fluvial and lacustrine deposits which are genetically related to the fluvial system in the southern Vienna Basin. This suggests that the Leitha Mountains did not exist as a barrier at that time and that basin development was initiated not before the Middle Miocene. The onset of subsidence in the Early Badenian led to an initial marine ingression and the Leitha Mountains became a peninsula connected with the Alpine mainland in the east. Nearshore deposits of this transgression are represented along the SE margin of the Leitha Mountains by the Hartl Formation which grades from reworked gravel, through marine sandwaves into corallinacean debris. During periods of high sea level in the Middle and Late Badenian, the Leitha Mountains were completely covered by water allowing the growth of thick corallinacean limestones and coral carpets.

Following a sea-level fall at the Badenian–Sarmatian boundary, the Leitha Mountains and their Badenian sedimentary cover became exposed and the mountain ridge once again became an island again until the withdrawal of Lake Pannon during the Late Miocene. Incised valleys developed and intensively eroded the Middle Miocene limestone platforms. Lower Sarmatian deposits from the Eisenstadt-Sopron Basin consisting of pelites, sands and serpulid limestones can be correlated with the Holíč Formation of the Vienna Basin. Correspondingly, the Upper Sarmatian Skalica Formation of the Vienna Basin extends into the Eisenstadt-Sopron Basin. A mixed siliciclastic/carbonate succession comprising gravels, sands, oolitic sands and marls is typical throughout the basin. Lake Pannon covered the Eisenstadt-Sopron Basin during the Late Miocene, as shown by the presence of clayey marls and sands. During the middle Pannonian a small river formed on the Leitha Mountains supplying reworked Lower Miocene gravels into the basin. As in the Vienna Basin, the withdrawal of Lake Pannon allowed the establishment of floodplains and swamps during the latest Pannonian (all data from Schmid *et al.* 2001; Kroh *et al.* 2003).

## *Styrian Basin and Neogene intra-Alpine basins (M.H.)*

Although situated along the eastern margin of the Eastern Alps the Styrian Basin (SB) is a sub-basin of the Pannonian Basin System (Fig. 17.16). The SB, situated in SE Austria, is *c*. 100 km long and 60 km wide. It is bordered in the west, north, and east by Alpine mountains such as the Koralpe, the Gleinalpe and the Wechsel. The Southern Burgenland High, consisting on the surface of a SW–NE trending range of low hills, represents the southern border. In the Early and Middle Miocene, the eastern part of the basin was covered by the Paratethys and by Lake Pannon during the Late Miocene. In the western part of the basin, swamps formed during the Early Miocene, giving rise to thick lignites, which have been exploited up to recent times.

*Tectonic setting and development*

The SB is a small extensional basin located on top of an eastward-moving crustal wedge, which contains *c*. 4 km of Neogene sediments. Basement comprises crystalline and low-grade metamorphic Palaeozoic rocks of the Austro-Alpine nappe system. The tectonic evolution is divided into an Early Miocene (Ottnangian to Karpatian) synrift phase and a subsequent post-rift phase. The SW–NE trending South Burgenland High separates the SB from the Pannonian Basin. Internally, the SB is subdivided by the Middle Styrian and Auersbach highs into several small sub-basins, including the shallower Western Styrian Basin and the deeper Eastern Styrian Basin complex, which consists of the Mureck, Gnas and Fürstenfeld basins.

*Sedimentary and stratigraphic development*

Sedimentation commenced during the Early Miocene (Ottnangian) (Fig. 17.9). In the Western Styrian Basin fault-controlled limnic-fluvial deposits of the Eibiswald Member formed thick lignite deposits. In the Western Styrian Basin Miocene sedimentation ended with the Middle Miocene limnic-fluvial Stallhofen Formation.

In the Eastern Styrian Basin, Ottnangian floodplain and coastal-plain deposits were overlain by a thick Karpatian-age succession deposited following a marine ingression from the Pannonian Basin. Due to the extremely high subsidence rate (30 cm/100 a), related to synsedimentary fault tectonics, the shallow-marine setting evolved rapidly into a deep-marine one (Sachsenhofer 1996). The corresponding 'Steirscher Schlier', a deep-marine shale succession with intercalated turbiditic sandstones and tuffs, formed in the upper bathyal zone under dysaerobic conditions (Spezzaferri *et al.* 2002). Coastal areas along the emerging Alps were affected by strong fluvial input of coarse clastics. Synchronous with the synrift phase, andesitic island-arc volcanism commenced and formed huge shield volcanoes. The andesitic and shoshonitic volcanism continued into the early Middle Miocene.

Towards the end of the Early Miocene, uplift (i.e. Styrian Tectonic Phase) led to basin shallowing and finally to the tilting of older deposits. In marginal areas considerable erosion took place and Middle Miocene deposits are separated by a distinct unconformity from Lower Miocene ones. A renewed marine ingression during the Early Badenian led to the establishment of shallow-marine conditions with widespread development of patch-reefs and corallinacean limestones (Weissenegg Formation) (Friebe 1990). Corallinacean platforms developed along the shallow swells, and sublittoral to fairly deep-water marly and pelitic sediments were deposited in the deeper parts of the SB. According to Friebe (1993), the Badenian of the Styrian Basin can be subdivided into three marine sequences which are related to global sea-level cycles.

A major drop in the relative sea-level occurred at the Sarmatian–Badenian boundary. Fault-controlled subsidence rates increased during the Sarmatian with the extensive deposition of marls. On topographic highs (e.g. South Burgenland High) and along the coasts, bryozoan–serpulid bioconstructions formed isolated carbonate bodies (Grafenberg Formation). Marine sedimentation was interrupted in the middle Sarmatian by the deposition of up to 100 m of fluvial sands and gravels (Carinthian gravel). The overlying Upper Sarmatian units consist of the mixed siliciclastic/carbonate Gleisdorf Formation, which contains several oolitic beds. The upper part of the Upper Sarmatian is characterized by repeated intercalations of thin lignites and by a marker horizon with peneroplid foraminifera.

In the Late Miocene, the SB became flooded by Lake Pannon, and marls and silty sands of the Feldbach Formation were deposited. The overlying fluvial-limnic Paldau Formation represents a second Pannonian sequence. The Upper Pannonian follows discordantly and comprises fluvial and limnic deposits reflecting a total separation from Lake Pannon. A second magmatic phase is represented by tuff pipes and basaltic lava flows of Plio/Pleistocene age.

An overview of the tectonic evolution of the Styrian Basin has been provided by Sachsenhofer (1996); detailed overviews of stratigraphy and depositional environments have been published by Kollmann (1965), Friebe (1993), Gross (2003), Kosi *et al.* (2003) and Harzhauser & Piller (2004).

The **Fohnsdorf Basin**, 22 km long and 11 km wide, formed to the NW of the Styrian Basin at the junction of two strike-slip fault systems (Sachsenhofer *et al.* 2000; Strauss *et al.* 2003). These fault systems, the sinistral east–west trending Mur-Mürz-Fault System and the dextral NNW–SSE trending Pöls-Lavanttal-Fault System, form the border of the escaping crustal wedge which hosts the Styrian Basin. The evolution of the basin, with a Neogene basin-fill of about 3 km, was subdivided by Strauss *et al.* (2003) into three stages. The initial pull-apart phase (stage 1) lasted from the Late Karpatian to the Early Badenian and commenced with the deposition of the Fohnsdorf Formation. This is characterized by up to 800 m of alluvial sediments which terminate in a 15 m thick lignite seam which yields a typical '*Congeria*'-coquina. Lacustrine to brackish prodelta and fan sediments were deposited in the late pull-apart phase and constitute the overlying 2000 m thick Ingering Formation. The brackish conditions in the lower part of the Ingering Formation suggest a connection to the marine flooding of the Lavanttal Basin (see below) in the Early Badenian. During the Badenian, the basin experienced a half-graben stage (stage 2) and was covered by floodplain and lacustrine fan delta deposits. These immature conglomerates and sandstones constitute the Apfelberg Formation (Strauss *et al.* 2003). The final compressive phase (stage 3) began in the Late Miocene and was heralded by inversion and movement along the Pöls-Lavanttal Fault System.

The fault system controlling the Fohnsdorf Basin extends south to the **Lavanttal Basin**. This basin, situated west of the Styrian Basin, is a pull-apart basin located between the crystalline of the Sauaple and the Koralpe. Its development began in the Early Miocene with the formation of the *c.* 12 km long west–east trending Granitztal Sub-basin. Fluvial clastics and limnic clays of Ottnangian and Karpatian age were deposited. At the Early–Middle Miocene boundary the basin geometry changed considerably due to activation of the Pöls-Lavanttal Fault System resulting in the formation of a 27 km long NNW–SSE trending basin. A diverse mollusc and foraminifera fauna in the marls of the Lower Badenian Mühldorf Beds is indicative of a marine ingression. This short-lived connection to the Paratethys ended during the Middle and Upper Badenian when fluvial-lacustrine and continental environments became dominant. A final transgression from the east took place during the Early Sarmatian. Shallow-marine to paralic conditions prevailed; rare lignite seams within marls are typical deposits. Following a Middle Sarmatian hiatus, limnic pelites with lignites are found in the Upper Sarmatian, whilst the Pannonian is characterized by fluvial deposits. A Pliocene magmatic phase, represented by the Kollnitz basalt, would appear to be related to a synchronous volcanic phase in the Styrian Basin (Tollmann 1985; Strauss *et al.* 2003).

## Carpathians, Carpathian Foredeep and Pannonian Basins System: overview (M.K.)

Despite being a part of the Alpine-Carpathian Orogen (Figs 17.2 & 17.16), the Carpathians are very different from the Alps, mainly due to the presence of broad Neogene basins and extensive acidic to calc-alkaline volcanic activity. The difference is caused by the tectonic evolution of the Carpathians, with a transition from 'A-type' subduction during frontal collision with compressional regime during the earliest Miocene, to oblique collision with the European platform and 'B-type' subduction during the remainder of the Neogene (Tomek & Hall 1993; see also Froitzheim *et al.* 2008).

The subduction in front of the orogen caused folding and nappe thrusting, which resulted in the development of an accretionary wedge of the Outer Carpathians. In the foreland, the Carpathian Foredeep developed on the slopes of the European Platform, due to the deep subsurface load of the downgoing plate and the loading of the accretionary wedge. The foredeep shows a significant pattern of depocentre migration from NW to SE (Meulenkamp *et al.* 1996).

Subducting slab pull and the subsequent stretching of the overriding plates were followed by basin opening in the Pannonian backarc area under an extensional tectonic regime (Royden 1988). In addition to the pull of the sinking slab and the subsequent stretching of the overriding plate, the evolution of the Pannonian backarc basins system was influenced by asthenospheric mantle diapirism and by related deep structural unroofing of the basement units (Tari *et al.* 1992; Horváth 1993). During the initial rifting and synrift stage of the backarc system, two types of basins developed: pull-apart basins (Vienna Basin, East Slovakian Basin, Derecke Basin) and grabens or half-grabens (Danube Basin, North Hungarian–South Slovakian Basin, Styrian Basin). The youngest late Miocene to Pliocene period is characterized by thermal post-rift subsidence, but in many places fault-controlled basin subsidence also occurred (Horváth & Cloetingh 1996). During Pliocene times, tectonic inversion of the backarc basin began.

For a fuller understanding of the Neogene geodynamic evolution of the Carpathian Orogen it is necessary to understand that the Outer Carpathian belt is an external tectonic unit, while the internal units are parts of two consolidated, palaeo-Alpine lithospheric fragments or microplates (Alcapa and Tisza-Dacia microplates). These microplates have a very complex movement trajectory relative to their present-day positions (e.g. counterclockwise rotation and movement of *c.* 150–300 km of the Alcapa microplate and clockwise rotation of the southern Tisza-Dacia microplates (Csontos *et al.* 1992; M. Kováč *et al.* 1994; Kováč & Márton 1998).

Five orogenic and basin evolution stages have been recognized in the Western Carpathians, each of which is characterized by its own tectonic regime (Konečný *et al.* 2002). (1) The compressional regime is related to 'A-type' subduction at the Alpine-Western Carpathian orogenic front during the Early Miocene (Eggenburgian to Ottnangian). (2) The transpressive–transtensional tectonic regime is related to the escape of the Western Carpathian lithospheric fragment (microplate) from the Eastern Alpine area, accompanied by its oblique collision with the North European platform edge in the latest Early Miocene and initial Middle Miocene (Karpatian to Badenian); initial rifting of the Pannonian backarc basin occurred in a transtensional to extensional regime. (3) The extensional regime is related to 'B-type' subduction at the Carpathian orogenic front, accompanied by the synrift stage of the Pannonian backarc basin system during the Middle Miocene (Badenian to Sarmatian). (4) Post-rift extension of the Pannonian backarc basin system occurred due to thermal subsidence and the onset of isostatic uplift of the orogen during the Late Miocene (Pannonian to Pontian). (5) A Pliocene transtensional tectonic regime controlled isostatic uplift and tectonic inversion of the Western Carpathian basins; this was accompanied by the onset of a transpressional tectonic regime in the Pannonian backarc basin system.

## *Danube Basin (M.K.)*

The Danube Basin represents the NW part of the Pannonian backarc basin system (Fig. 17.16). In Slovakia it is geographically termed the Danube Lowland while in Hungary it is referred to as the Little Hungarian Plain. It is situated between the Eastern Alps, the Western Carpathians and the Transdanubian Range in Hungary.

### *Tectonic setting*

The Danube Basin is *c.* 240 km long and 100 km wide and strikes roughly NE-SW. The western border comprises units of the Central Eastern Alps, the Leitha, Hundsheim and Malé Karpaty mountains. The northern margin is represented by the Považský Inovec and Tribeč mountains belonging to the Central Western Carpathians. The Burda Mountains form the margin in the NE while the Hungarian Transdanubian Range Mountains represent the SE border of the basin. The pre-Cenozoic basement is built up by the Austro-Alpine and Slovako-Carpathian units in the western, northern and central part of the basin; the basement of the SE margin comprises units of the Transdanubicum (Fusán *et al.*1987; Fülöp *et al.* 1987).

The basin is divided into several depocentres. Along the northern margin these are from west to east: the Blatná, Rišňovce and Komjatice depressions (separated by the Považský Inovec and the Tribeč mountains). In the NE part, the Želiezovce Sub-basin is located between the Levice Horst and the Transdanubian Range Mountains (Lankreijer *et al.* 1995). The southern, Hungarian part of the basin is separated by the NNE–SSW trending Mihályi High into major sub-basins which parallel the Repce Fault in the west and the Raba Fault in the east. The deepest part of the Danube Basin is the Gabčíkovo Sub-basin (Vass *et al.* 1990) with a maximum thickness of Neogene sediments of >8500 m (Kilényi & Šefara 1989; Hrušecký *et al.* 1993, 1996).

The northern Vienna Basin and the northern Danube Basin shared a common tectonic evolution which is characterized by an Early Miocene palaeostress field with a NW–SE orientated principle compression. (P. Kováč & Hók 1993; P. Kováč *et al.* 1994). During this time, a wrench fault elongate basin developed in the northern part of the present Danube Basin.

An initial phase of rifting commenced during the late Early Miocene (Karpatian) following the extrusion of the Western Carpathians from the East Alpine domain (Csontos *et al.* 1992). In the northern Danube Basin pull-apart depocentres opened in the Blatná and the central Gabčíkovo depressions/sub-basins (Hrušecký *et al.* 1996; Kováč *et al.* 1999). In the southern part of the basin, north–south orientated normal faults were activated (Nemčok *et al.* 1989; Csontos *et al.* 1991; Tari *et al.* 1992; Royden 1993*a*, *b*; Hrušecký *et al.* 1996).

During the Middle Miocene (Badenian) the palaeostress field changed and NW–SE orientated extension prevailed (Csontos *et al.* 1991; Nemčok *et al.* 1989; Nemčok 1993; Vass *et al.* 1993*a*). The Badenian synrift stage of basin development was characterized by structural unroofing of the deeply buried basement units, especially along the western margin (Rechnitz-Sopron area). During the Late Badenian and Sarmatian, north–south, NNE–SSW and NE–SW normal faults were active in the northern Danube Basin (Peničková & Dvořáková 1985; Vass *et al.* 1993*a*). During the early late Miocene (early Pannonian), tectonic subsidence is documented only in the central and southern parts of the Danube Basin (Lankreijer *et al.* 1995). Predominantly low-angle normal faults were activated (Pogácsás *et al.* 1996). During the late Pannonian and Pontian, thermal post-rift subsidence commenced (Becker 1993; Horváth 1993) and was followed by Pliocene basin inversion, which was associated with minor compression from the SW during the Late Miocene and Pliocene (Horváth & Cloetingh 1996). Despite the Pliocene tectonic inversion, in some depocentres subsidence still occurred. Subsidence in the Danube Basin centre, in the Gabčíkovo Sub-basin, is interpreted as being related to secondary 'sag basins', which are not superimposed on the older Miocene basin depocentres (Wernicke 1985).

### *Sedimentary and stratigraphic development*

The Neogene sedimentation in the area of the present Danube Basin began during the Eggenburgian transgression. The sea flooded the northern margin of the Western Carpathians and penetrated from the Alpine and Carpathian foredeep into the Vienna Basin, the Dobrá Voda, Vad'ovce and Blatná sub-basins, the Váh river valley, the Bánovce Basin and the upper Nitra Basin. A connection with the North Hungary–South Slovakia and East Slovakia basins can be documented (Kováč *et al.* 1998). Coarse clastic littoral to shallow-marine deposits of the Dobrá Voda Conglomerate (Kovác *et al.* 1991) in the Blatná Sub-basin and the Klačno Conglomerate in the Bánovce Basin represent the basal part of the Eggenburgian Čausa Formation. Up-section, the 500 m thick Čausa Formation consists of calcareous and sandy clays and silts with some tuff layers deposited in a deeper neritic marine environment (Čechovič 1959; Brestenská 1980; Kováč *et al.* 1999; Hók *et al.* 1995).

Ottnangian and Karpatian terrestrial, fluvial and lacustrine sediments were deposited along the western margin of the Danube Basin and document the initial phase of rifting. These sediments are known from the Sopron area in Hungary where, on the slopes of the Eastern Alps, the coal-bearing Brennberg Formation. (Csaszár 1997) was deposited during the Ottnangian and was overlain by the fluvial to limnic gravels of the Ligeterdö Formation (Csaszár 1997). Ottnangian and Karpatian marine deposits are known from the Dobrá Voda and the Blatná sub-basins in the north and from the Transdanubian Range Mountains. along the southern margin of the Danube Basin. Calcareous siltstones of the Ottnangian to Lower Karpatian Planinka Formation were deposited in the Dobrá Voda Sub-basin (Kováč *et al.* 1992), and the Bánovce Formation represents this facies in the Bánovce Basin (Vass in Keith *et al.* 1994). In this latter basin, the Ottnangian part of the sedimentary succession is *c.* 300 m thick while the Karpatian part is *c.* 250 m thick. The lower part was deposited in a brackish environment, with lowered oxygen content, and the upper part in a marine, shallow to deep neritic environment. The marine pelites ('Schlier') are characterized by the appearance of foraminifer associations containing *Uvigerina graciliformis.*

At the Early–Middle Miocene boundary, rifting in the Danube Basin was accompanied by calc-alkaline volcanic activity. The stratovolcanoes are buried below the Middle–Upper Badenian sedimentary fill in the northern and central parts of the present-day basin and document crustal extension during basin formation (Hrušecký *et al.* 1996). From the Hungarian part of the Danube Basin younger Badenian, Sarmatian to early Pannonian trachyte volcanism is recorded in the Pástori Formation (Császar 1997).

Karpatian deposition commenced with terrestrial sediments in the central part of the basin (*c.* 500 m thick near Györ). The Bajtava Formation, at the eastern basin margin, contains Lower Badenian marginal transgressive conglomerates, sandstones and volcaniclastics, overlain by calcareous clays, siltstones and rare sandstones deposited in a neritic environment (Kováč *et al.* 1999). In the NW part of the basin calcareous clays and siltstones of the 3000 m thick Middle Badenian Špačince Formation were deposited. In the Blatné Sub-basin the delta-front sands of the Madunice Formation indicate shallowing in the latest Middle and Late Badenian (Adam & Dlabač 1969). The Upper Badenian part of Pozba Formation overlies the Špačince Formation. It is up to 2000 m thick. This consists of calcareous clays, siltstones and sandstones with volcaniclastics; in marginal areas algal limestones developed. In the southern (Hungarian) part of the basin, the Baden Clay Formation was deposited (Csaszár 1997). This consists of clays and marls of open-marine facies, with a rich thin-shelled mollusc fauna as well as foraminifers. Its maximum thickness is *c.* 1000 m. In the southern part of the basin coralline algal limestones of the Rákos Formation and marls of the Szilágy Formation were deposited; these have a combined thickness of up to 100 m. At the NW basin margin freshwater deposits with coal-bearing clays and lignite seams of Late Badenian age are also known (Vass *et al.* 1990).

The Badenian deposits are discordantly overlain by the Sarmatian Vráble Formation (Harčár *et al.* 1988). This offshore facies comprises calcareous clays, siltstones and sandstones up to 600 m thick (Adam & Dlabač 1969). In the nearshore areas conglomerates, sandstones, limestones, local lignites and tuffs were deposited. The maximum thickness (1300 m) of the Sarmatian strata is documented from the Rišňovce Subbasin (Biela 1978). In the southern, Hungarian part of the basin, the equivalent of the Sarmatian offshore facies is the Kozárd Formation with a maximum thickness of 150 m. Marginal development is here represented by the Tinnye Formation (100 m) with frequent occurrences of mollusc-bearing calcareous sands and sandstones (Császár 1997).

Pannonian and Pontian-age sediments of the Danube Basin were deposited along the northern margin of Lake Pannon. The northernmost part of the basin was shallow, while the central and southern parts were hundreds of metres deep (Kovač *et al.* 1999). The basin was gradually filled by deltaic deposits entering the basin from the NNW, transporting clastic material from the uplifting Alpine-Carpathian orogenic belt. The Upper Miocene and Pliocene deposits, containing clays, siltstones and sandstones, are up to 3500 m thick in the Gabčíkovo Depression/ Sub-basin (Adam & Dlabač 1969; Vass *et al.* 1990).

In the Hungarian part of the basin, Lower Pannonian deposition began with the open-water marls of the Endröd Formation (Vass 2002) indicating a water depth of up to 800 m. The overlying Middle to Upper Pannonian Újfalu Formation was deposited in delta-front to delta-plain settings. The Pontian to Lower Pliocene Zagyva Formation represents alluvial plain, fluvial to lacustrine environments, and comprises *c.* 1000 m of sands, silts and coal-bearing clays (Csaszár 1997). In the Slovak part of the Danube Basin the Lower and Middle Pannonian sediments are represented by the Ivánka Formation (Harčár *et al.* 1988), comprising calcareous clays, siltstones and sandstones. The Upper Pannonian/Pontian, *c.* 100 m thick Beladice Formation (Harčár *et al.* 1988) consists of calcareous clays and siltstones, with coal-bearing clays and lignite seams. The Lower Pliocene Volkovce Formation contains deltaic deposits of the palaeo-Hron river in Komjatice and the Gabčíkovo sub-basins. The Upper Pliocene Kolárovo Formation (Dlabač 1960) represents the palaeo-Váh river deposits in the Blatná Sub-basin. Quaternary deposits of the Danube Basin are represented by loess deposition (up to 150 m) and fluvial and alluvial deposits.

## *East Slovak Basin (M.K.)*

The East Slovak Basin (ESB) is situated between the Western and Eastern Carpathians (Fig. 17.16). The western border of the basin is formed by the Tatric and Veporic units of the Central Western Carpathians. The NE and eastern margins consist of units of the Pieniny Klippen Belt, and the Humenné Mountains. Towards the south the Neogene successions pass into the Hungarian Hernád Basin. The SW and SE margins are formed by the Slovak-Hungarian Zemplín area and the Ukrainian Seredné area (Rudinec 1978, 1989).

*Tectonic setting*

The ESB represents the NW part of the Transcarpathian Basin which covers parts of Slovakia, Ukraine and Romania, reaching 220 km in a NW–SE direction. The ESB is generally up to 9000 m deep, although the Ukrainian depocentres were only 2000–3000 m deep (Rudinec 1989). Various structural and geological units belonging to the Western and Eastern Carpathians form the basement of the ESB (Sviridenko 1976; Rudinec *et al.* 1981; Rudinec 1984; Vass *et al.* 1988; Soták *et al.* 1990 1993, 1994). The NE margin is represented by the Mesozoic and Palaeogene units of the Pienniny Klippen Belt which separates the units of the Outer Carpathians Flysch Belt from the Mesozoic complexes of the Humenné Mountains (Mahel 1986). The NW part of the basin basement comprises the Central Western Carpathian Mesozoic and Palaeozoic units of the Čierna Hora Complex, while the SW part consists of the Zemplín and Ptrukša complexes (Rudinec 1984; Vass *et al.* 1988; Soták *et al.* 1993).

The tectonic development of the ESB reflects changes both in terms of its geotectonic position, as well as due to changes in the palaeostress field orientation (Kováč *et al.* 1995). The Lower Miocene (Eggenburgian) sediments were deposited in a forearc basin position on the margin of the moving Central Western Carpathians. The palaeostress field reflects NE–SW to NNE–

SSW orientated main compression (Nemčok 1993). Compressive tectonics led to the disintegration of the Early Miocene basin and to the development of backthrusts in the Pieniny Klippen Belt (Seneš 1956; Roth 1980; Plašienka *et al.* 1998).

During the late Early Miocene (Karpatian), a palaeostress field with a north–south orientated main compression prevailed. NW–SE orientated normal and later right-lateral strike-slip faults were formed. During Karpatian and Early Badenian initial rifting, pull-apart depocentres opened in the central part of the ESB. Tectonically controlled subsidence shows a cyclic character, with periods of high sedimentation followed by periods of basin isolation and shallow-water evaporite deposition. Crustal extension was associated with updoming of a lithospheric mantle diapir leading to structural unroofing of the Iňačovo-Kritschevo Peninic Unit (Soták *et al.* 1993).

The Upper Badenian and Sarmatian tectonic regime of the ESB can be characterized as the development of an interarc/backarc type basin. The change from transtension, during initial rifting, to pure extension, during the synrift phase, resulted in tectonically controlled subsidence and a high sedimentation rate during the Early Sarmatian (Pereszlényi *et al.* 1991). The main depocentres shifted to the SE. The basin development coincided with increased volcanic activity at this time (Lexa *et al.* 1993).

During the Upper Miocene the thermal, post-rift phase began and the ESB became part of the Pannonian Basin System (Horváth *et al.* 1988; Mattick *et al.* 1988). Subsidence was controlled by north–south to NW–SE extension. The Pliocene was characterized by tectonic inversion and a palaeostress field with NE–SW orientated compression which led to folding of the Pannonian deposits (Kováč *et al.* 1995) and uplift of the youngest sediments in the East Slovak Lowlands (Mořkovský & Lukášová 1986, 1991).

*Sedimentary and stratigraphic development*

The Lower Miocene deposits are situated mainly in the NW part of the basin, Middle Miocene deposits fill its central part, and the late Middle Miocene and the Upper Miocene depocentres are in the SE part of the ESB (Janáček 1969; Rudinec 1978, 1989). The following summary is based mainly on Vass & Čvercko (1985), Zlinská (1992) and Rudinec (1978, 1989) for the Slovakian part and on Vialov (1986) and Andreyeva-Grigorovich *et al.* (1997) for the Ukraine.

The Eggenburgian open-marine sediments belong to the Prešov Formation and were deposited in a forearc basin environment. The succession, which is up to 1000 m thick, consists of clays, siltstones, sandstones and conglomerates. The end of Eggenburgian deposition is marked by the Čelovce Member where marine siltstones and clays grade into lagoonal and freshwater deltaic deposits consisting of conglomerates, sandstones, siltstones and lignites. Ottnangian deposits have not been recorded in the ESB. In the Ukrainian part of the Transcarpathian Basin the Burkalo Formation represents similar early Miocene deposits. In the ESB, 1600 m thick Karpatian-age sediments comprise the Teriakovce, Sol'ná baňa and Kladzany formations. The Teriakovce Formation is up to 500 m thick and grades from conglomerates and sandstones into siltstones and clays deposited in a deep-marine, neritic to shallow bathyal environment. The overlying Sol'ná baňa Formation (400 m) is represented by evaporite deposition which took place in a shallow-water environment as a result of basin isolation. Renewed latest Early Miocene tectonic subsidence is reflected by the deposition of clastic material via turbidity currents of the Kladzany Formation. The succession contains clays and siltstones with sandstone intercalations and attains a maximum thickness of 1000 m. In the Ukrainian part of the Transcarpathian Basin, the Tereshul Formation is the equivalent of the Karpatian deposits in the East Slovak Basin.

The Lower Badenian sediments in the eastern and central part of the ESB are represented by volcaniclastic deposits of the Nižný Hrabovec Formation. The formation is up to 600 m thick and consists of marine clays, siltstones with sandstone intercalation and rhyolite tuffs. In the western part of the basin the Lower Badenian is represented by the Mirkovce Formation with marked redeposition of Karpatian-age microfaunas in its basal parts. In the Ukrainian part of the Transcarpathian Basin the Lower Badenian is represented by the Novoselytsa Formation.

During the Middle Badenian, clays, siltstones, sandstones and rare tuffs of the 600 m thick Vranov Formation were deposited in the central part of the basin. The sands were derived from the uplifting Outer Carpathians in the NE. The sedimentary environment gradually changed from a deep-marine to a shallow-marine one and the end of deposition is represented by the lagoonal evaporites of the Zbudza Formation. In the Ukrainian part of the Transcarpathian Basin these evaporites are united in the Tereblya Formation and the lower part of the Solotvino Formation.

The Upper Badenian transgression reached the ESB from the south, from the Pannonian region. The deep-water pelitic facies in the basin centre pass into coarse clastic deltaic deposits prograding from the NW margin of the basin. The lower part of the Upper Badenian succession is represented by the Lastomír Formation, attaining a thickness of up to 2000 m in the SE part of the basin. The formation consists of calcareous clays with siltstone intercalations deposited in delta-slope and prodelta environments. The upper part of the succession is represented by the Kolčovo Formation (up to 1700 m thick), whose deposition extended up into early Sarmatian. In the Ukrainian part of the Transcarpathian Basin, the Upper Badenian is represented by the upper part of the Solotvino, the Teresva and the Baskhev formations.

In the Sarmatian, the depocentre of the ESB widened towards the SE in the region of the Vihorlat Mountains and towards the SW in the Košice Sub-basin. Fan deltas and braided river system deltas prevailed (Janočko 1993). The Lower to Middle Sarmatian Stretava Formation (1600 m thick) is a monotonous unit of calcareous clays with rhyolite tuff intercalations which was deposited in a deltaic environment. The delta prograded from the NW towards the SE. Its marginal facies are represented by the Košice Member (Kaličiak 1991). The overlying Upper Sarmatian Ptrukša Formation, consisting of calcareous sandstones and tuffs, is up to 300 m thick. In the western part of the basin freshwater systems prevailed, as indicated by the lignite-bearing Middle to Upper Sarmatian Kochanovce Formation. In the Ukrainian part of the Transcarpathian Basin the Sarmatian is represented by the Dorobrotiv, Lukiv and Almash formations.

The Upper Miocene of the ESB comprises up to 600 m of brackish to freshwater deposits. The Pannonian Sečovce Formation consists of calcareous clays, coal-bearing clays, coal seams and tuffs (Albínov tuff; Janáček 1969) whilst the Pontian Senné Formation was deposited initially in fluvial (Pozdišovce Member) and later in lacustrine, environments. Up to 200 m of clays, sands, gravels (with andesite pebbles) and tuffs comprise the Pliocene Čečehov Formation.

In the Ukrainian part of the Transcarpathian Basin the Pannonian Iza and the Pontian Koshelevo formations attain a joint thickness of up to 400 m and represent the Upper Miocene succession. The Pliocene is represented by the Dacian Ilnitsa Formation, up to 500 m thick, and the Pleistocene by the clays, sandstones and gravels of the Chop Formation (600 m).

*Volcanism*
The development of the East Slovak Basin was associated with voluminous volcanic activity related to backarc extension and subduction beneath the front of the Carpathian arc. Extension-related acid rhyolite volcanism is known from the Lower and Middle Miocene successions. The Middle to Upper Miocene is predominantly calc-alkaline andesite volcanism related to subduction processes. The Late Badenian and Early Sarmatian volcanic activity is of arc type (Vass *et al.* 1988; Kaličiak & Pospíšil 1990; Szabó *et al.* 1992; Lexa *et al.* 1993). During the Sarmatian, the basin evolved into an interarc basin and andesite volcanic activity culminated (Vass *et al.* 1988). The volcanic chains can be traced along the eastern margin of the basin towards the Gutin Mountains and along its southern border along a now-buried area between Zemplín and Beregovo (Slávik 1968).

## North Hungarian–South Slovak basins (M.K., D.V., L.S., A.N.)

The North Hungarian–South Slovak basin is bordered to the north by the Western Carpathians (Fig. 17.16). The western margin is represented by the Transdanubian Range Mountains, while the eastern margin consists of units of the Bükk Mountains. In the south, it is bordered by the Mid-Hungarian region which forms the boundary between the Alcapa and the Tisza-Dacia microplates.

*Palaeogeography and tectonic setting*
The pre-Cenozoic basement is formed in the north by units of the Central Western Carpathians (Veporicum, Gemericum, Silicicum, Meliaticum), in the west by units of the Transdanubicum and in the east by units of the Igal–Bükk Zone. The Slovak part is geologically not an individual basin but represents the northern margin of three basin complexes which overlie one another: the Buda Basin (= North Hungary Palaeogene Basin), the Fil'akovo-Pétervására Basin and the Novohrad-Nógrad Basin. A detailed overview including all relevant literature used in the present text was published by Kováč *et al.* (2002). The entire region rotated 50° counterclockwise during the Early to Middle Miocene (Márton *et al.* 1996).

The Buda Basin (North Hungary Palaeogene Basin) began to form following a long period of emersion of the Transdanubian Range Mountains (Transdanubicum units), as indicated by lateritic weathering and the creation of karst bauxite deposits (Báldi & Báldi-Béke 1985). Its evolution was terminated by the tectonic extrusion, post-late Oligocene, of the Alcapa Microplate from the Alpine-Dinaride domain towards the Carpathian-Pannonian realm. This led to the disintegration of the Palaeogene basin by right-lateral displacement along the Mid-Hungarian region. Two segments were created, Buda and Slovenia (Ljublana), which are at present 300 km distant from one another (Nagymarosy 1990; Csontos *et al.* 1992).

In the Early Miocene (Eggenburgian), the Fil'akovo-Pétervášára Basin was formed. Its extent was less then that of the Buda Basin and it lacked the southern connection to the open sea but opened towards the basins of the Outer and Inner Carpathians (Sztanó 1994; Halásová *et al.* 1996). At the end of the Eggenburgian, extensive felsic volcanism, related to asthenospheric mantle uplift associated with the uplift of the area (active rifting), occurred, together with a coeval marine regression. Initial backarc rifting resulted in the deposition of the Bukovina Formation which consists of continental deposits with rhyodacite tuffs (Zagyvápálfalva Formation (Császár 1997), rhyodacite tuffs in Gyulakeszi, Hungary).

During the late Early Miocene, the development of the backarc basin continued (Vass *et al.* 1993*a*) and the Novohrad-Nógrád Basin formed. Gradual marine transgressions from the south in the Ottnangian are documented by paralic sedimentation in Boršod (northern Hungary) and by marine ingressions in southern Slovakia. Basin subsidence reached a maximum during the Karpatian, followed by rapid regression. The area was uplifted and erosion was marked by latest Karpatian times. The final transgression extended into the area of south Slovakia, in the early Middle Miocene (Badenian). From Middle Badenian times onward the region was emergent and subjected to intense weathering.

*Sedimentary and stratigraphic development*
This section is largely based on the work of Báldi & Báldi-Beke (1985), Báldi (1986), Báldi-Beke & Báldi (1991), Vass (2002), Vass *et al.* (1979, 1983, 1987), Vass & Elečko (1982, 1992), and Hámor (1988).

**Zala Basin.** The southwesternmost Palaeogene deposits of the Transdanubian Range area occur in the Zala Basin (Fig. 17.17). The oldest member of the succession is the littoral to neritic Upper Lutetian Szőc Limestone (180 m). This formation is overlain up to 600 m of calcareous and sandy marls of the pelagic, epibathyal Padrag Marl, reflecting the period of maximum deepening during the Late Lutetian and Early Priabonian. In the upper part of the formation, andesitic tuffs of the Zalatárnok-Zalaszentmihály volcanic centre are interbedded (Szentmihály Andesite). Near the basin centre, a stratovolcanic complex more than 1000 m thick, has been penetrated. The Eocene deposits are covered by up to 2000 m of Neogene sediments (Kőrössy 1988).

**South Bakony Mountains.** In the southern Bakony the Palaeogene sequences begin with local bauxite deposits (Gánt Formation). Bauxite occurrences can be traced along the northern and southern margins of the Bakony Mountains. The bauxite is overlain by the Lower Lutetian Darvastó Formation (*c.* 40 m) comprising terrestrial clays and quartzitic conglomerates in its lower part. Its upper part consists of neritic limestones and marls with a rich *Alveolina* and *Nummulites* fauna (Kecskeméti 1998). The Darvastó Formation is conformably overlain by the Upper Lutetian to Lower Bartonian Szőc Limestone (*c.* 100 m). This biogenic limestone contains various shallow-marine organisms such as corallinaceans, bryozoans, echinoids and larger foraminifera. The Szőc Formation passes upwards into the pelagic, bathyal Padrag Marl (*c.* 250 m; Bartonian to Priabonian). Pebbly mudstones, sandy turbidites and tuffitic intercalations occur in its upper part. The top of the eroded Eocene is unconformably covered by the terrestrial and fluviatile gravels and clays of the Upper Oligocene Csatka Formation (*c.* 120 m).

**North Bakony Mountains.** In this region Eocene deposition in an archipelago landscape commenced during the latest Lutetian somewhat later than in the South Bakony Mountains. Basal clastics and redeposited bauxite are covered by the Dorog Coal Formation (*c.* 50 m) comprising paralic marls with diverse brackish and marine mollusc fauna. The coal is conformably overlain by neritic marls and by the epibathyal Padrag Marl (*c.* 200 m). Above a hiatus, the Upper Oligocene non-marine Csatka Formation follows (*c.* 800 m); this part of the succession is similar to that of the South Bakony Mountains. Terrestrial and freshwater deposits alternate; thin coal seams occur in the basal parts and fluviatile gravels and claystones are characteristic in the upper part.

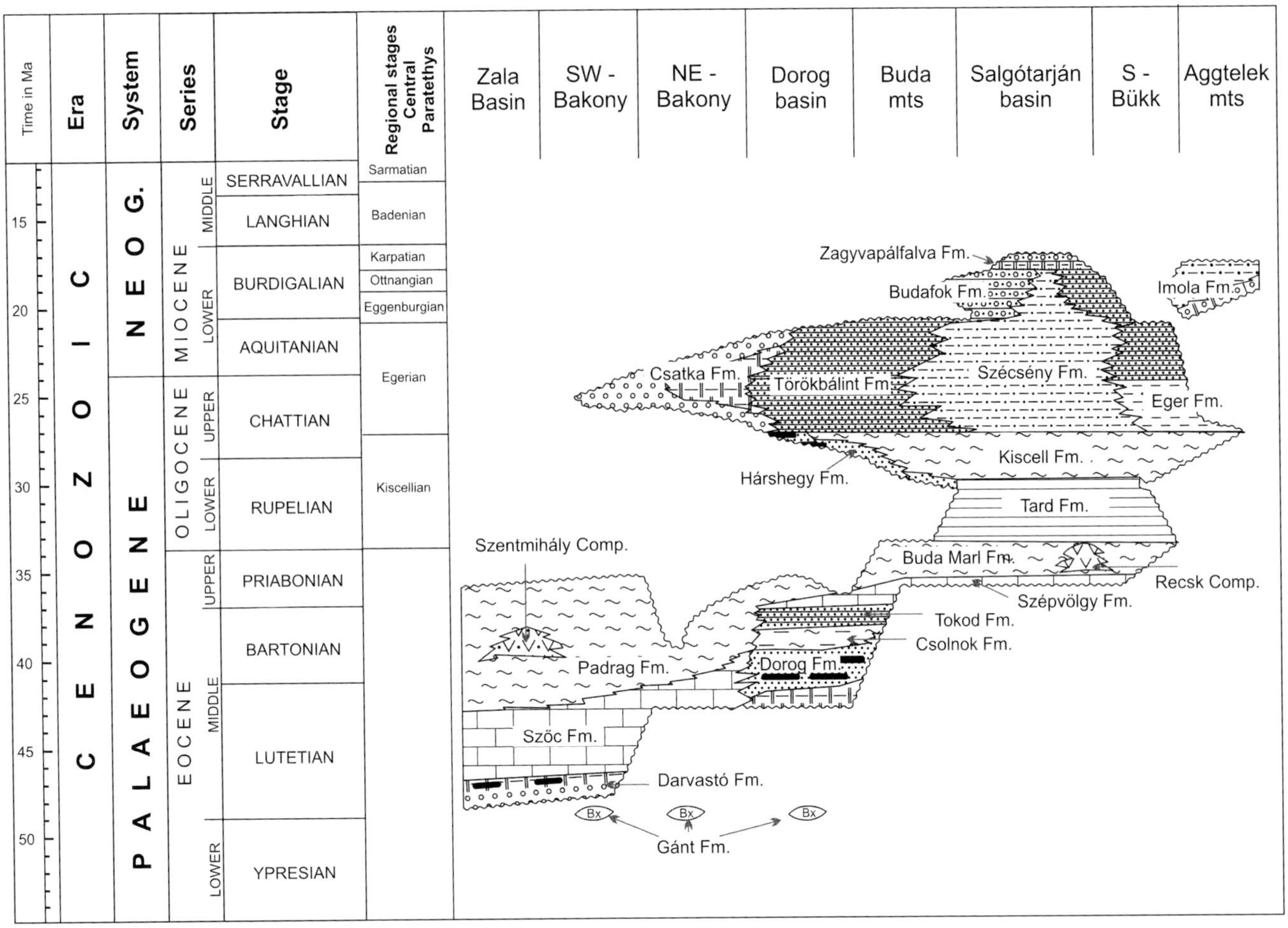


**Fig. 17.17.** Palaeogene and lower Neogene lithostratigraphy of the Hungarian basins. See Figure 17.18 for legend.

**Buda Basin.** The Lutetian transgression gradually flooded the Buda Basin (Fig. 17.17; North Hungary Palaeogene Basin) forming lagoons in which lignite deposition (Obid Member, Dorog Formation) occurred. Shallow-water carbonate sedimentation and deposition on the outer shelf is represented by the Priabonian limestones of the Szépvölgy Formation (Kázmér 1985) and the overlying marls of the Buda Formation. At the end of the Eocene, a regression in the Transdanubian region led to a shift of the depocentre eastwards into the region of the Buda Hills.

During the Oligocene, the Buda Basin rapidly deepened as indicated by the deposits of the Číž Formation in Slovakia and the equivalent Hárshegy and Kiscell formations in Hungary. The oldest Oligocene sediments are freshwater and fluvial deposits of the Skálnica Member (Kiscellian age) deposited in the Rimava and Lučenec sub-basins. These are overlain by the littoral deposits of the Hostišovce Member consisting of clays, silts and sandstones with thin coal seams. Ongoing transgression led to the formation of the sponge/bioclastic and intraclast limestones of the Batka Limestone Member deposited along the slopes of barrier islands. The subsequent isolation of the Central Paratethys is manifested by the euxinic facies of the Tard Clay Formation cropping out in the Budapest area. The development of new depositional centres in the Oligocene was accompanied by a transgression during the Kiscellian as marked by the clays of the Kiscell Formation (800 m) in Hungary and the upper Číž Formation in Slovakia. In the Late Oligocene (Egerian) the evolution of the Buda Basin continued with the deposition of the Lučenec Formation. Its lower part consists of up to 150 m of transgressive breccias, conglomerates and sandstones with a shallow-water marine fauna (i.e. Panica Member). Stratigraphic equivalents include the Hungarian Törökbálint Formation and the Slovak Budikovany Formation. The Egerian offshore facies is represented by shaly calcareous siltstones up to 1000 m thick (Szécsény Member = Lower part of Szécsény Schlier Formation). Limestones and conglomerates of the Bretka Member, containing *Miogypsina gunteri,* represent the nearshore facies in the upper part of the Lučenec Formation. The Egerian succession terminates with the regressive delta sediments of the 180 m thick Slovak Opatovce Member and the lignite-bearing, brackish, marshy-fluvial Becske Formation.

**Fil'akovo-Pétervášára Basin.** During the Eggenburgian, the short-lived Fil'akovo-Pétervášára Basin evolved. The Fil'akovo Formation concordantly overlies the Lučenc Formation in the Cerová vrchovina Mountains. Its Hungarian equivalent is the Pétérvásara Formation. The 500 m thick formation was deposited in shelf environments, often showing a strong tidal influence (Sztanó 1994). The Slovak Čakanovce Member and the upper part of the Hungarian Szécsény Formation (Császár 1997) represent the offshore facies. During the late Eggenburgian the 200 m thick, mainly fluvial deposits of the Bukovinka (Slovakia) and Zagyvapálfa formations (Hungary) were deposited. These comprise sandstones, clays and rhyodacite tuffs (in Hungary Gyulakészi tuff) with abundant remnants of warm subtropical to tropical flora. The Hungarian Zagyvapálfa formation contains the famous footprint sandstone at Ipolytarnóc with very well preserved traces of mammals and birds, and an enormous fossil trunk of *Pinus* sp. (Kordos 1985; Hably 1985).

**Novohrad-Nógrád Basin.** During the middle Early Miocene (Ottnangian), the Novohrad-Nógrád Basin began to form. In Slovakia the lacustrine Salgótarján Formation is up to 250 m thick. In its lower part it consists of 30–80 m of locally cross-bedded sands and clays with three characteristic coal seams (Pôtor Member). The overlying Plachtince Member comprises clays with rare coals and tuffs. Carbonate clays include foraminifera and nannoflora of zones NN3 and NN4 indicating marine ingressions during the Ottnangian. The Salgótarján Formation gradually passes into the Karpatian Modrý Kameň Formation, of which the Medokýš Member represents the basal part of the succession. It consists of *c.* 60 m of fine-grained laminated sandstones and siltstones, locally with convolute bedding (Vass & Beláček 1997) and tempestites with mixed marine and endemic-brackish fauna. The overlying Krtíš Member (40 m) represents littoral sediments. Deposition culminated with the 300 m thick Sečiance Member containing a rich bathyal marine fauna. Its equivalents in north Hungary include the Egyházasgerge and the Fót formations and the Garáb Schlier Formation (Csaszár 1997). At the end of the Early Miocene a major regression occurred in the entire Novohrad-Nógrád Basin leading to erosion.

A subsequent transgression in the early Middle Miocene (Badenian) led to the deposition of the Príbelce Member (Vass *et al.* 1979), which is an equivalent of the Hungarian Baden Clay Formation (Csaszár 1997). This transgression was accompanied by intense volcanic activity, represented by andesite volcaniclastics in the Krupinská planina Mountains. The Hrušovo Member comprises tuffaceous deposits with marine fauna and nannoflora of the Early Badenian. During the Middle Miocene the Novohrad-Nógrád Basin became continental. After a phase of emersion and denudation during the Middle and Late Miocene, some subsidence is recorded in the latest Miocene or Pliocene (Pontian). Fluvial and lacustrine deposits of the Poltár Formation (gravels, sands and kaolin clays) were deposited in the Lučenec, Rimava, Rožňava and Turňa sub-basins. Coeval basaltic volcanism (Podrečiany Formation) led to the formation of maars with laminated lacustrine deposits rich in organic matter (e.g. alginates at Pinciná; diatomic clays at Jelšovec) (Vass *et al.* 1998). Dacian to lowermost Quaternary volcanism is indicated by the basaltic Cerová Formation which includes various volcanic structures (cones, lava flows, lava plateaus, maars). As a consequence of the uplift of the Cerová vrchovina Mountains and due to the selective erosion of the softer deposits of the Fil'akovo Formation, the basaltic flows, originally filling palaeovalleys, now form the relief (relief inversion).

**Continental development.** South of the Mecsek Mountains more than 500 m of clastics of the Eocene Szentlőrinc Formation represent an isolated Palaeogene continental depositional environment in the Szigetvár area (Császár *et al.* 1990).

## *Pannonian Basins System (A.N.)*

The Pannonian Basins System (PBS) (Fig. 17.16) is a complex of several (sub-)basins that formed during the Neogene. Geographically, they form the Little Hungarian Plain and the Great Hungarian Plain. The PBS is surrounded by several Neogene basins (e.g. the Vienna and Styrian basins in the west, the Bánovce, Nitra and Transcarpathian basins in the north, the Transylvanian Basin in the east, and the Morava, Sava and Tuzla basins in the south). All of these basins formed in the Early–Middle Miocene and contain several thousand metres of sediment. Generally, a gradual shift in basin formation can be observed from the NW to the SE (see Csontos *et al.* 1992). Geologically, the major basins described below are the most important.

### *The Little Hungarian Plain Basin*

The Little Hungarian Plain Basin (LHPB) (Figs. 17.16 & 17.18) extends to the north of the Transdanubian Range and south of the Kőszeg, Sopron, Little Carpathian and Inovec mountains. In its initial, early Middle Miocene, stage of formation, the LHPB was not connected to the Vienna and Zala basins. During the Middle Miocene, it became connected with the Zala Basin but remained separated from the Vienna Basin by the Mihályi Ridge (Tanács & Rálisch 1990). The Tatricum in Slovakia (Fusán *et al.* 1987), the Bakony Unit in Hungary and the Alpine nappe systems form the basement of the LHPB. This basement is structured by tectonic highs (e.g. the Mosonszentjános and Mihályi highs) and deep sub-basins (e.g. the Csapod, Pásztori and Szigetköz sub-basins).

Subsidence of the LHPB began during the late Early Miocene. Initial deposits include terrestrial and freshwater clays, breccias and conglomerates (up to 400 m) deposited along the central axis of the basin, in a 25 to 30 km wide belt. The first Middle Miocene marine sediments (Badenian) are the sandstones and limestones deposited at the basin margins. Pelites with sandstone intercalations appear in the more basinal parts. These deposits are up to 300 m thick and include the Baden Clay Formation and the Rákos Limestone. Volcanic tuffs are frequent in the marine sequences and thick stratovolcanic successions occur to the NE in Slovakia. By the Badenian the entire LHPB had been flooded by the sea. Only a few NE–SW trending ridges formed islands. The thickest Badenian units are located in the NE of the basin. The Badenian–Sarmatian transition appears to be continuous in the deepest part of the LHPB. The Sarmatian successions, up to 450 m thick, consist of clayey marls, claystones, sandstones and tuffitic sandstones (Tinnye and Kozár Formations). Upper Miocene (Pannonian) successions of the Peremarton supergroup (up to 1200 m thick) overlie the Sarmatian. The lower part of this supergroup is mainly clayey (e.g. Endrőd Marl = Belezna Calcareous Marl, Lenti Marl, Nagylengyel Marl) while the Újfalu (= Tófej) Sandstone and Algyő (= Dráva) Formation occur in the upper part. The associated Late Pannonian transgression of Lake Pannon led to flooding of the entire area (Tanács & Rálisch 1990). The thickest units (*c.* 2100 m) of the LHPB were deposited during the latest Miocene and Pliocene. These include the Dunántúl Supergroup which is composed of the Újfalu Sandstone, the Rábaköz and the Hanság Red-bed formations (Jámbor 1989).

The **Hungarian Central Range** (HCR) represents a complex of small sub-basins extending in age from the Ottnangian to the Middle Badenian. During the Late Badenian it formed a slowly, but continuously, rising SW–NE striking ridge. The uplift is still ongoing. This ridge includes the Bakony, Vértes, Gerecse, Buda, Cserhát, Bükk and Aggtelek-Rudabánya mountains. Between the uplifting blocks, small sub-basins developed, while the later Neogene sedimentation was confined to the margins of the

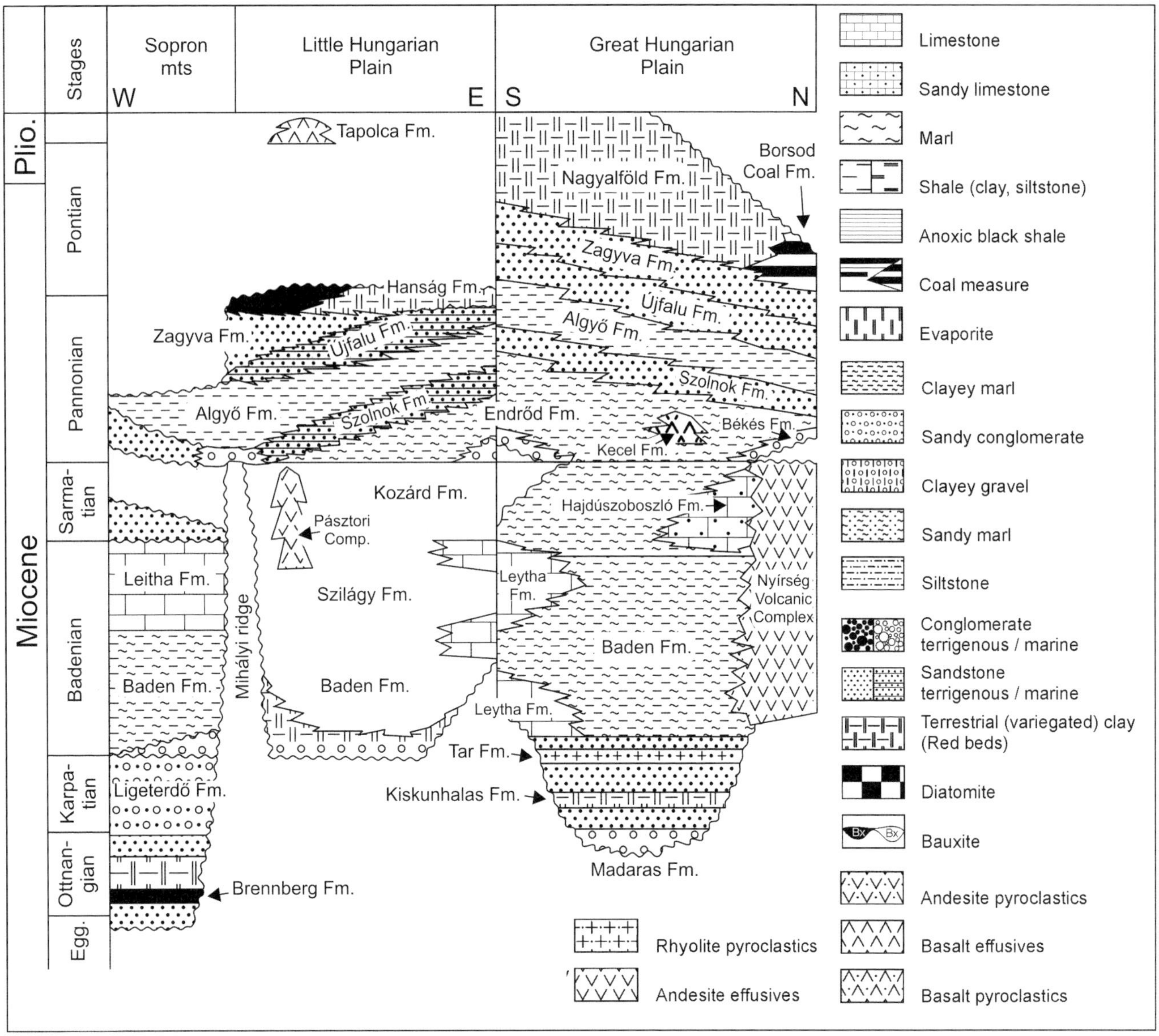


**Fig. 17.18.** Lithostratigraphy of the Sopron Mountains in Hungary, the Little Hungarian Plain and the Great Hungarian Plain.

uplifting mountains. The HCR comprises the Nagygörbő and the Varpalota basins, and the Budapest area.

The Nagygörbő Basin developed during the Early Miocene along the NW margin of the Bakony Mountains (Jámbor 1980; Hámor & Jámbor in Steininger *et al.* 1985). The Ottnangian deposition commenced with terrestrial clays and conglomerates, including the Lower Rhyolite Tuff (130 m). This member is overlain by Karpatian clayey marls, siltstones and sandstones (150 m) yielding marine fossils in the upper part. The Badenian sandy marls, limestones, sandstones and conglomerates are up to 420 m thick, unconformably followed by 40 m of Sarmatian conglomerates and limestones. The Pannonian is represented by 120 m of siltstones and gravels, while the Pontian and Pliocene comprise 200 m of sands, clays and lignites.

In the Várpalota Basin (North Bakony) 50 m of terrestrial clays (possibly Eggenburgian?) are overlain by the Ottnangian–Karpatian Bántapuszta Formation (250 m), a marine complex of conglomerates, calcareous gravels, sandy limestones and tuffaceous clays (Kókay 1973; Jámbor 1980). An Upper Badenian unit up to 350 m thick consists of brackish to freshwater clays, coal seams, diatomites and alginites and unconformably overlies this succession. The Sarmatian is characterized by tuffaceous sandstones and claystones. The upper part of the depositional succession of the Várpalota Basin is composed of 60 m of Pannonian clayey marls, 120 m of Pontian sandstones, siltstones and freshwater limestones.

In the Budapest area the Neogene succession begins with 100 m of Eggenburgian marine conglomeratic sands (Budafok Sand). This is the littoral equivalent of the Szécsény and Pétervására formations in northern Hungary. The conglomeratic sands are overlain by Ottnangian and Karpatian gravels, calcareous conglomerates and tuffitic siltstones of the Fót Formation (90 m). In the Middle Badenian non-marine beds and tuffs were deposited, and were subsequently overlain by corallinacean limestones and clays in the Late Badenian. The Sarmatian Sóskút Limestone lies conformably on the Badenian. The total thickness of the Middle Miocene is 200 m in this region. Pannonian clays and Pontian sands (up to 300 m) unconformably overlie the Middle Miocene deposits (compiled from Jámbor *et al.* 1966).

The **Somogy-Mecsek-Kiskunhalas Basin** (SMKB) consists of a series of sub-basins extending from south Transdanubia to the Danube-Tisza interfluve. The sub-basins of the SMKB have a SE–NW strike, and are bounded by two large fault systems: the Mecsekalja Lineament in the south and the Kapos Lineament in the north. The SMKB extends from Transdanubia to the southern part of the Great Hungarian Plain (Tanács & Rálisch 1990). An important feature of the sedimentation in this region is the early onset of subsidence (latest Eggenburgian to earliest Ottnangian) in contrast to the areas of Great Hungarian Plain and the Little Hungarian Plain.

The evolution of the SMKB can be related to three transgressions. Subsidence began in the Early Ottnangian but affected only the western part of the zone (i.e. the Somogy and the West Mecsek region). Terrestrial and fluvial sedimentation was mainly to the west and north of the Mecsek Mountains. No subsidence took place in the Kiskunhalas area during the Ottnangian and Early Karpatian. The next phase began in the Late Karpatian. The character of the sedimentation changed from terrestrial through brackish to marine. This transgression also invaded the Kiskunhalas area. Maximum sediment accumulation was to the north (Mecsek) and in the Kiskunhalas Sub-basin. During the third phase, the transgression covered the area from the SW. During the Pannonian and Pontian the Mecsek area was uplifted and formed an island in Lake Pannon. The area north and south of the Mecsek area subsided markedly during the Late Miocene (1500 to 2000 m thick units). In the southern part of the Kiskunhalas Sub-basin (Felgyő and Kömpöc areas) intense subsidence continued into the Pliocene. The sedimentary development in the SMKB is herein subdivided into four areas as described below.

1. In the West Somogy area of the SMKB the succession begins with the 1100 m thick Szászvár Formation, a series of terrestrial/fluviatile conglomerates, sandstones, clays, clayey marls and clays. It is overlain by the marine sandstones and clayey marls of the Budafa Formation of Karpatian to Early Badenian age (970 m). Up-section follows the 490 m thick Tekeres Schlier, a series of clayey marls and siltstones. A hiatus separates the lower part of the Lower Badenian and the overlying 690 m thick Middle and Late Badenian rocks, represented by the Rákos Limestone and *Turritella-Corbula*-bearing marls (Szilágy Formation). The next hiatus spans the Sarmatian and large parts of the Pannonian. The transgressive Újfalu Sandstone represents only the upper part of the Pannonian. These beds are followed by the Zagyva Formation. The total thickness of the Pannonian is only 330 m. The overlying Pontian comprises 250 m of sands and clays (Somló Formation) and 650 m of the Tihany Formation.

2. In the West Mecsek Mountains (compiled from Forgó *et al.* 1966 and Hámor 1970) the Neogene succession begins with a 500 m thick series of Ottnangian–Karpatian terrestrial/fluvial conglomerates, sandstones and siltstones (Szászvár Formation). The regressional upper part contains coal seams and clays. The Gyulakeszi ('Lower') Rhyolite Tuff is intercalated into the lowermost part of this formation. The second, Karpatian–Lower Badenian succession comprises limnic shales (Komló Member), the brackish and marine Budafa Formation, and the shallow marine Tekeres Schlier. The Middle–Late Badenian is represented by the 130 m thick Rákos Limestone. This littoral/shallow neritic lithofacies may be substituted by the Szilágy Marl (*Turritella-Corbula* beds) of more basinal character. The Sarmatian comprises 20–80 m of littoral limestones. Because of uplift during the Late Miocene and Pliocene, Neogene sedimentation ceased during the Sarmatian in the West Mecsek Mountains.

3. The development in the East Mecsek Mountains differs considerably in terms of the distribution and thicknesses of the formations (Forgó *et al.* 1966; Hámor 1970). The terrestrial/fluviatile Szászvár Formation (380 m) represents the initial period of sedimentation. It consists of clays, conglomerates, sandstones and coal seams in its upper part. The overlying Karpatian fish-shale (370 m) includes conglomerates, thin marine siltstones and an intercalation of the Tar ('Middle') Rhyolite Tuff in its upper part. The Badenian is represented by the corallinacean limestones of the Pécsszabolcs Formation. This is overlain by the paralic coal seams of the Hidas Formation. The Late Badenian transgression deposited the Szilágy Marl in the basinal parts and the Rákos Limestone in nearshore environments. The total thickness of the Badenian is 280 m. The conformably overlying Sarmatian limestones are 150 m thick.

4. The Kiskunhalas Basin is located in the southern part of the Danube-Tisza interfluve. Its depth may be >5000 m. The oldest Neogene sediments belong to the Kiskunhalas Formation, and comprise coarse-grained clastics, which correspond to the Szászvár Formation in the Mecsek Mountains. These beds, up to 800 m thick, are of Early Karpatian age in the deeper sub-basins or younger (Early Badenian?) in the shallower ones. The marine Middle Badenian conformably overlies these non-marine beds. It is represented by conglomerates, breccias and the offshore Szilágy Marl (*c.* 600 m). No Sarmatian deposits are known from this area. The transgressive pelitic and sandy Pannonian Peremarton Supergroup follows (850 m). Effusive lava beds of the Kiskörös-Kecel basalt are intercalated into the Lower Pannonian pelitic beds. The Pontian and Pliocene regressive sucession (*c.* 1800 m thick) is represented by the mainly sandy Dunántúl Supergroup. Clays occur in the upper part of the Pliocene.

The **Mid-Transdanubian Zone** is a deep Neogene basin located between the Balaton and Kapos lineaments in Hungary. The deepest part of the basin may be up to 5000 m. The oldest member of the Neogene comprises a few hundred metres of conglomerates with frequent red-bed intercalations. Its age may be pre-Badenian or Early Badenian. It is overlain by thin marine Badenian deposits and a thick Badenian volcanic complex. The younger part of the Neogene was cored by the Mezőcsokonya-4 borehole which recorded 2000 m of Neogene rocks, but did not drill the entire thickness of the Badenian volcanic complex. This was unconformably overlain by 450 m of the Pannonian Peremarton Supergroup and by 1200 m of the Pontian and Pliocene Dunántúl Supergroup.

## *Zala and Drava basins*

The Zala Basin is located in SW Hungary (Fig. 17.16) and is subdivided into a northern and a southern sub-basin (Körössy 1988; Szentgyörgyi & Juhász 1988). The adjoining Drava Basin is situated in the Drava lowlands, which partly cover SW Hungary and northern Croatia. These two basins are connected both geographically and also in terms of their depositional history. The main difference is the strike of the basins. While the axis of the Zala Basin is SW–NE, the Drava Basin is NW–SE (Körössy 1988, 1989; Tanács & Rálisch 1990). There are also differences in the sediment thicknesses between the basins, with the Neogene succession being somewhat thicker in the Dráva Basin. The Zala Basin formed parallel to the Rába Fault, which can be considered as a major low-angle fault (Rumpler & Horváth 1988). Seismic evidence indicates that the Budafa area, where the Dráva and Zala basins join, underwent very late compression resulting in folding of the uppermost Miocene/Pliocene strata (Körössy 1988), although the Quaternary units are undeformed. These folded structures can be considered as the west–east axial prolongation of the flat Sava folds which extend from Slovenia into Hungary. The maximum subsidence of the area took place in the Pannonian and Pontian. The thickness of the Pontian (probably including Pliocene parts) is up to 2500 m in the Dráva Basin.

The Zala Basin is subdivided into a northern and a southern sub-basin. The northern Zala sub-basin is characterized by the Transdanubian Range. Here, the Karpatian deposits are often missing, and the Badenian, Sarmatian, Pannonian and Pontian deposits are relatively thin and taper out towards the north and east. Coarse-grained conglomerates and breccias form the Lower Miocene (presumably Karpatian) unit. The upper part of this unit consists of poorly sorted conglomeratic sandstones and non-marine pebbly siltstones (215 m total thickness). Badenian deposits comprising 619 m of clays, silts and corallinacean-bearing sandstones of the Tekeres Schlier and the Szilágy Formation follow. The Sarmatian Kozárd Formation (344 m) conformably overlies the Badenian. It consists of clayey marls and sandstones. The 1049 m thick Late Miocene (Pannonian) Peremarton Supergroup comprises clayey marls in the lower part and the Újfalu Sandstone and Algyő Formation in the upper part. The Pontian (1471 m) consists of alternations of sandy-clayey marls and sandstones, with clays, conglomerates and coal seams in its upper part. The deeper southern Zala sub-basin formed above basement, which consists of older crystalline complexes and Mesozoic units, but is generally poorly known. Basin development was generally comparable with that of the northern sub-basin. In the deepest part (Budafa area), sedimentation began during the Karpatian with the deposition of conglomerates. The overlying marine Badenian is very thick (>2900 m) comprising clayey marls, rare sandstone intercalations and a 150 m thick stratovolcanic complex in its lower part. The Sarmatian, if preserved, comprises sandstones and bituminous, clayey marls with fish scales. As in the northern sub-basin, the Upper Miocene and Lower Pliocene are represented by the Peremarton Supergroup (1155 m) and the Dunántúl Supergroup (825 m).

In the Drava Basin the thickness of the Neogene in the Croatian segment is up to 7000 m. The basement consists of Palaeozoic and Mesozoic crystalline and sedimentary units. The Neogene succession, as presented here, is based on Velic & Sokac (in Steininger *et al.* 1985). Deposition commenced during the Ottnangian and Early Karpatian, represented by 2000 m of conglomerates, sandstones, limestones and clayey marls. During the latest Karpatian, the marine character of the basin became dominant, but fully marine conditions were typical only from the Badenian, when the marine transgression reached the Drava Basin. Corallinacean limestones are widespread along the basin margins, while marls and pelites were deposited in the deeper parts of the basin. The total thickness of the Badenian is 1200 m. In the 400 m thick Sarmatian units there are alternations of marls, laminated bituminous marls, rare sandstones and diatomites. Towards the top of the Sarmatian, the regressive trend resulted in an erosional unconformity between the Sarmatian and the Pannonian. Thus, the top part of the Sarmatian is missing. The Pannonian units (up to 1000 m thick) comprise marls, clayey marls and subordinately sandstones, which were deposited in freshwater to brackish water environments. The overlying Pontian units (2500 m) are lithologically very similar but have coal seams and clays in the uppermost part.

## *Great Hungarian Plain*

The Great Hungarian Plain (GHP) which forms part of the PBS covers parts of Hungary, Romania and the former Yugoslavia. The area of maximum subsidence in the GHP is situated in the valleys of the Danube and the Tisza (Fig. 17.16). Basement relief and sedimentary fill of the GHP are very heterogeneous (Nagymarosy 1981; Fig. 17.18). The area can be subdivided into extremely deep sub-basins (up to 7000 m), with a more or less complete Middle Miocene to Pliocene sedimentary sequence, and intrabasinal ridges and highs, with an incomplete sedimentary record (up to 2000 m and usually lacking the Middle Miocene). The sub-basins of the GHP include the Jászság Sub-basin (in the NW central zone), the Nyírség Sub-basin (in the NE), the Derecske Sub-basin (in the east central zone), and the Makó and Békés grabens (in the south). A further sub-basin located in the western part of the GHP (Kiskunhalas Sub-basin) is tectonically related to the South Transdanubian Mecsek Zone.

*Palaeogeography and tectonic setting*

The evolution of the GHP can be summarized as a history of gradual subsidence beginning in the latest Early Miocene and continuing through the Middle Miocene into the Pliocene or even Quaternary times. The rapid subsidence may have been related to the crustal attenuation of the area (Horváth *et al.* 1986), resulting in the formation of pull-apart basins located in strike-slip fault zones (e.g. the Balaton and the Mecsekalja lineaments). The sub-basins in the north subsided rapidly during the Middle Miocene and the Early Pannonian while in the south the main phase of subsidence took place during Late Pannonian, Pontian and Pliocene times (Tanács & Rálisch 1990). The oldest Neogene subsidence occurred in a zone extending from the Mecsek Mountains (Transdanubia) to the Kiskörös area where subsidence began in the middle Early Miocene (Ottnangian). Subsidence in the rest of the GHP commenced in the latest Early Miocene or Middle Miocene.

Marine transgression reached the GHP in Badenian times. During the Badenian and Sarmatian the GHP formed an archipelago of large islands, shallow and deep-marine basins. During the Sarmatian and Early Pannonian even the topographic highs (e.g. the Battonya-Pusztaföldvár and Algyő highs) were submerged. During the Early Pannonian the GHP attained its maximum depth. This event is documented first by the presence of the pelagic Endrőd-Tótkomlós Marl, an important potential source rock, and later by the turbidite-rich Szolnok Formation. At the end of the Pannonian, basin subsidence slowed down and gradual infilling of the basin began. Deltas prograded from the NNW to the SSW. While the northern part of the basin had already filled up and the paludal Bükkalja coal seams were deposited, in the Derecske, Makó and Békés sub-basins the deposition of delta-slope and delta-plain sediments continued. The youngest sub-basins, existing in the Pliocene, were in the Banat and Morava sub-basins located to the south in former Yugoslavia and in Romania.

*Sedimentary and stratigraphic development*

The pre-Badenian formations of the GHP are tentatively assigned to the Lower Miocene (Ottnangian and Karpatian). The oldest of the pre-Badenian formations is the terrestrial-limnic Madaras Formation (up to 100 m thick), which consists of conglomerates and thin tuff beds. The overlying Kiskunhalas Formation (80–

900 m) comprises sandy siltstones with conglomerates in limnic-terrestrial facies. The first Middle Miocene lithostratigraphic unit is the Tar ('Middle') Rhyolite Tuff and related volcanic complexes (e.g. Nyírség Volcanic Complex). The first marine event occurred in the Badenian and comprises the littoral/shallow neritic Abony Limestone with conglomerate intercalations, the Makó Formation (marls and siltstones) and the Ebes Limestone. In the Sarmatian both the brackish-water Hajduszoboszló Sandstone and the Dombegyháza Limestone were deposited in littoral to neritic settings.

The Pannonian and Pontian facies belts shifted in time and space due to the gradual infilling of the GHP (Pogácsás *et al.* 1990). Thus, separation of the Pannonian and Pontian units is difficult and the formations outlined below cannot be precisely dated (Jámbor 1989; Juhász 1991; Fig. 17.19). The oldest series of formations belongs to the transgressive Maros Group and include evidence of basaltic volcanism in some places (e.g. Kecel Formation). The basal Békés Conglomerate occurs mainly in the Makó and Békés grabens. The conglomeratic beds are overlain by the Endrőd Marl and the Tótkomlós Calcareous Marl Member, which were deposited in a deep offshore environment. Submarine fans (Dorozsma Marl Member) also occur. These were derived from steep slopes and occur only in the Makó and Derecske sub-basins. The Vásárhely Marl Member is a more pelitic variant of the Dorozsma Marl. The lava flows and tuffs of the Kecel Formation are interbedded with the sediments of the Dorozsma Marl.

The deposition of the overlying Jászkunság Group coincided with maximum deepening and the beginning of basin infill. The lower part of the group is represented by the offshore marls of the Nagykörü Member (Endrőd Formation) which is overlain by or interfingered with the turbidite-rich Szolnok Formation. Pontian sedimentation commenced with the deposition of the Csongrád Group comprising the Algyő and Törtel formations. The Algyő Formation (alternating clayey marls and sandstones) represents the delta slope of rivers filling the GHP. Delta-front and delta-plain environments are indicated by the sandy Újfalu (= Törtel) Formation. The overlying Heves Supergroup was deposited in the north during the Late Pontian and in the south during Pliocene times. The older unit of the supergroup is the sandy-clayey Zagyva Formation which represents an alluvial-plain environment and interfingers with the Bükkalja Lignite. The Pliocene succession ends with the clays of the lacustrine-paludal Nagyalföld Formation.

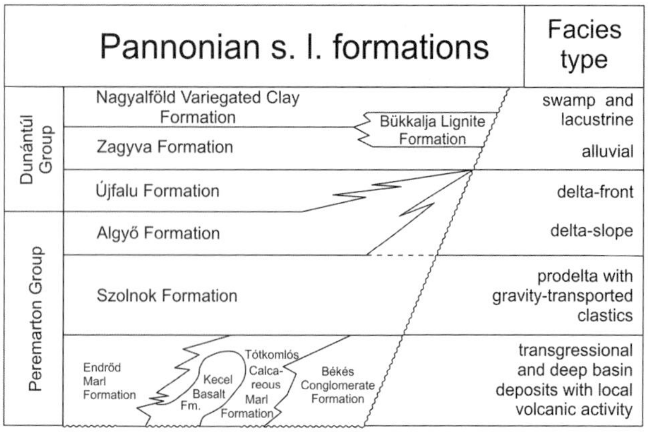


**Fig. 17.19.** Lithostratigraphy and facies types of the Pannonian in Hungary.

## *Szolnok 'Flysch' Basin (A.N.)*

The Szolnok Basin (= Szolnok Flysch Belt) is a 130 km long and 20 km (rarely 40 km) wide, SW–NE striking basin that extends beneath the Great Hungarian Plain from the town of Szolnok (Hungary) into the Maramures area of Romania (Fig. 17.20) (Dudich & Bombita 1983). The basin strikes parallel to an elevated crystalline ridge between Túrkeve and Körösszegapáti. It can be traced toward the east to Carei and Satu Mare in Romania and disappears beneath the Gutii Mountains. It is known from several boreholes, especially from Hungary, but also from eastern Romania. North of the ridge the basement drops and is overlain by the deep-marine deposits (flysch) of the Szolnok Basin (Körössy 1959) and this contact may be tectonic.

*Palaeogeography and tectonic setting*

The Szolonok Basin is located on the NE margin of the Tisza microcontinent. Together with the Mesozoic Tisza Nappes they form a tectonic unit and represent the basement of the Neogene Pannonian Basin. Körössy (1959, 1977) and Szepesházy (1973) emphasized the strongly tectonized character of the deposits of the Szolnok Basin, with dips of between 70° and 90°. Palaeontological investigations indicate that deposition was not continuous, but occurred over discrete time intervals with long hiatuses between them. The preservation and recent distribution of the Szolnok Basin deposits is strongly controlled by Early Miocene compressional tectonics and subsequent Miocene denudation. Tectonic imbrication and erosion is also suspected, which would explain the lack, or scarcity, of Palaeocene and Cretaceous units. Thus, the Szolnok Basin has an exotic position within the Carpathian arc, having no direct connection with any of the Carpathian or Dinaric units. In terms of its palaeogeographic position, the Szolnok Basin may represent either (1) the tectonically displaced continuation of one of the Outer Carpathian units, or (2) the continuation of the Inner Carpathian units (i.e. the Transcarpathian 'flysch' in the Marmures area).

*Stratigraphic development*

The Senonian to Oligocene turbidite-dominated succession of deposits of the Szolnok Basin is often referred to as 'Szolnok Flysch' in the literature (see Szepesházy 1973). The >1000 m thick unit is covered by up to 3000 m of Neogene and Quaternary sediments. The precise thickness of the turbidite dominated deposits is unknown, since boreholes did not reach basement. The lithological composition of the Szolnok Basin succession is incompletely known, but it is non-continuous and can be subdivided into discrete time slices. Studies of core materials (Báldi-Beke *et al.* 1981; Nagymarosy & Báldi-Beke 1993) have shown that only a few Cretaceous and Palaeogene nannoplankton zones can be recognized.

The Szolnok Basin deposits overlie clastic deposits with alkaline basaltic complexes of Early Cretaceous age. Deposition commenced during the Late Cretaceous and is represented by calcareous shales, marls, clayey and calcareous marls of the Izsák Marl. In the West Carpathians, the Upper Campanian to Lower Maastrichtian Puchov Formation represents an equivalent for these beds. Turbiditic sandstones with graded conglomerates, and rarely with breccias, are interbedded into the generally shaly unit. Based on the palaeoecology of foraminifers, a pelagic and bathyal depositional environment is suggested for the Puchov Formation (Majzon 1966; Szepesházy 1973). In some units, non-calcareous and non-fossiliferous shales may indicate deposition below or close to the CCD. The top part of the Cretaceous and almost the entire Palaeocene are missing from the core material.

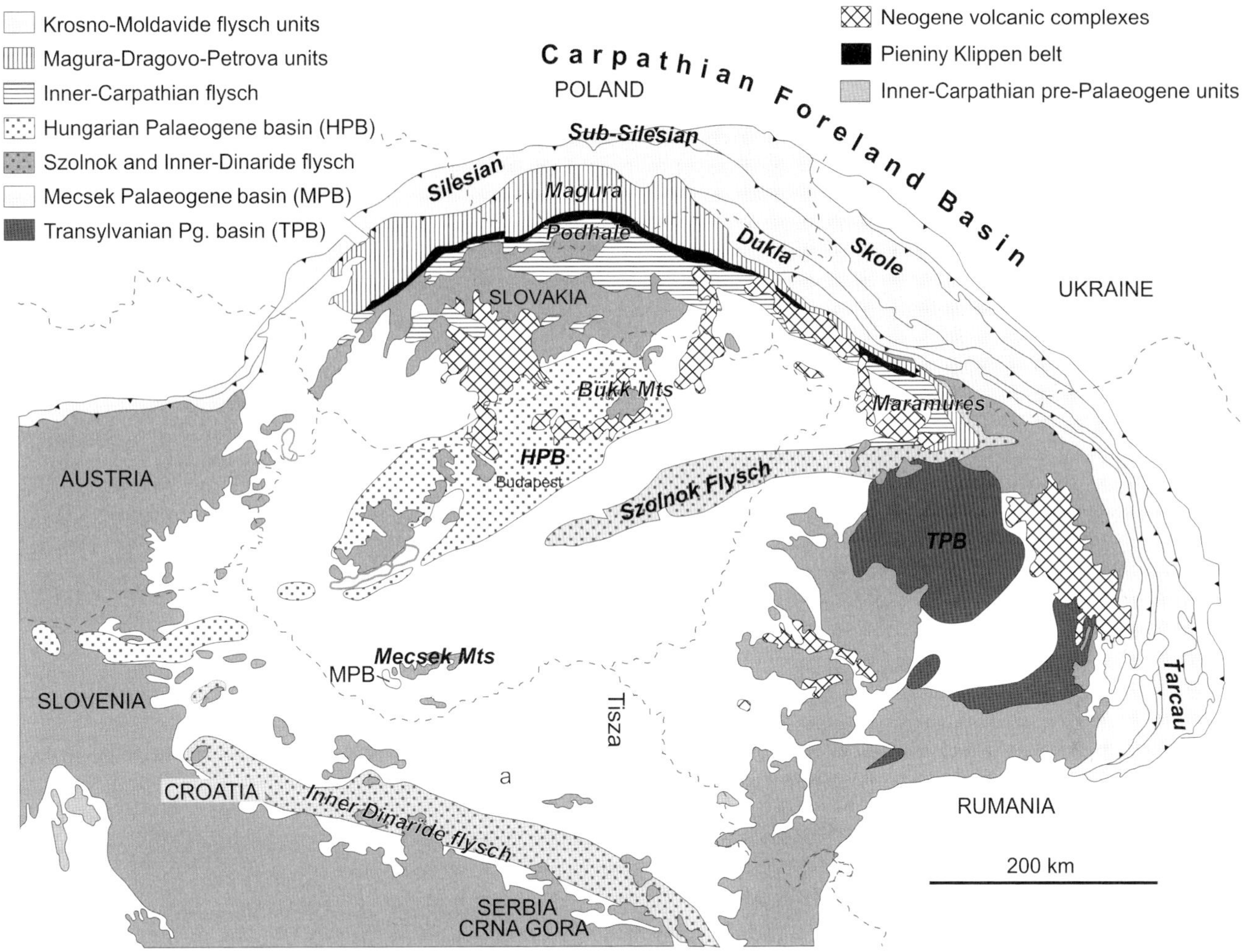


**Fig. 17.20.** Palaeogene basins in the Carpathian–Pannonian–Inner Dinarides region.

Some cores may cover the transition of the uppermost Palaeocene and Lower Eocene (NP9 nannoplankton zone: Nagymarosy & Báldi-Beke 1993; Szepesházy 1973; Majzon 1966).

The Middle and Upper Eocene part of the succession comprises shales, thin sandstones, polymictic conglomeratic sandstones, conglomerates and breccias. Rare nummulitid- and coralline algae-bearing limestones (with chaotic structure, probably redeposited) were observed. The Eocene calcareous nannoplankton assemblages indicate pelagic conditions and are fundamentally different from the coeval nearshore assemblages of the neighbouring epicontinental Transdanubian Palaeogene basin (Báldi-Beke 1984; Nagymarosy & Báldi-Beke 1993), proving the absence of a close palaeogeographic relation.

The presence of Early Oligocene sediments is uncertain. The Oligocene part of the sequence comprises clayey marls (similar to the Kiscell Clay) with sandstone intercalations. *Lepidocyclina*-bearing conglomerates are also recorded. The Oligocene nannoplankton assemblages are less pelagic and show more nearshore features than the Eocene ones, suggesting that the depositional environment gradually changed from pelagic deep-water to a shallower, nearshore one.

## *Transylvanian Basin (S.F.)*

The Transylvanian Basin (TSB) is surrounded by the Eastern and Southern Carpathians and the Apuseni Mountains, and represents a post-Cenomanian–Neogene intra-Carpathian sedimentary basin, locally preserving up to 5000 m of sediments (Fig. 17.16). The basin developed on basement consisting of metamorphic, ophiolitic and sedimentary units assembled during the Middle Cretaceous (Ciupagea *et al.* 1970; Săndulescu 1984).

*Palaeogeography and tectonic setting*

The history of the TSB basinfill was strongly influenced by the evolution of the Carpathians. Its sedimentary record is subdivided into four tectonostratigraphic megasequences: Upper Cretaceous, Palaeogene, Lower Miocene, and Middle–Upper Miocene (Krézsek & Bally 2006).

The Upper Cretaceous clastic sequence was deposited in a basin generated by the collapse of the Mid-Cretaceous Orogen (Sanders 1999; Willingshofer *et al.* 2001). The succession is up to 1000 m thick and consists of coarse and fine-grained siliciclastics and limestones deposited in continental and marine (both shallow and deep) settings. Deposition of the Palaeogene sediments was coeval with a compressional post-rifting phase (Krézsek 2005). The sedimentation rate was low but constant and the alternating marine and continental cycles are separated by two third-order sequence boundaries related to minor inversion of the Palaeogene basin. During the Early Miocene, the flexural sub-basin generated by the thrusting of the Pienides was developed almost exclusively in the northern part of the TSB (up to 1000 m of sediments). Several unconformities related to synsedimentary tectonic activity have been recorded in the shallow- to deep-marine sediments.

Major tectonic changes from the beginning of the Middle Miocene (Badenian) transformed the TSB into a backarc basin (Săndulescu 1984), characterized by a dominantly compressional regime and a high rate of subsidence between the Late Badenian and the Early Pannonian. Early Badenian hemipelagic to shallow-marine sedimentation (less than 100 m) was followed by an important phase of Middle Badenian evaporite deposition (300 m). Subsequent siliciclastic deposition (up to 3000 m) occurred in deep-marine (Late Badenian), outer-ramp (Early Sarmatian), shelf and delta (Late Sarmatian to Pannonian) settings (Krézsek & Filipescu 2005). Most of the Upper Miocene basin fill was eroded due to the post-Pannonian uplift and erosion.

*Sedimentary and stratigraphic development*

The **Palaeogene megasequence** (Fig. 17.21 MS1 & MS2) is divided by two unconformities (Hosu 1999) into three sedimentary phases, corresponding to the Danian(?)–Early Priabonian, the Late Priabonian–Early Rupelian and the Late Rupelian–Chattian (see also Filipescu 2001*a*). Close to the K/Pg boundary, tectonic compression led to a major change in the depositional environments, initiating erosion and a change to alluvial fan and fluvial sedimentation (Jibou Formation; Hosu 1999). Fossil vertebrates have been described from the lacustrine deposits in the vicinity of the Thanetian–Ypresian boundary (Gheerbrant *et al.* 1999), while deep-marine deposits with Danian foraminifera were identified in the northern part of the basin (Filipescu & Kaminski in press).

Beginning in Bartonian times, a marine transgression initiated the deposition of the Călata Group (= 'lower marine series'). Sea-level rise led to the onset of the supratidal to intertidal evaporitic facies of the Foidaş Formation, overlain by the shallow-marine inner-platform deposits of the Căpuş Formation, and finally the offshore deposits of the Mortănuşa Formation. In marginal areas, the low rate of basin subsidence led to the development of carbonate platforms (Rusu 1995; Proust & Hosu 1996), as represented by the Inucu Formation (mudstones with intercalations of bioclastic limestones, and *Crassostrea bersonensis* bioherms), the Văleni Limestone (bioclastic shoals with very diverse micro- and macrofaunas), the Ciuleni Formation (siliciclastics and bioclastic calcarenites dominated by bivalves such as *Crassostrea orientalis* and foraminifera), and the Viştea Limestone (bioclastic bars with Priabonian large foraminifera, molluscs, echinoids and crustaceans).

Compressional tectonics interrupted the shallow-marine sedimentation and changed the depositional environment to a coastal plain and fluvial system (e.g. Valea Nadăşului Formation; Hosu 1999). Its fossil record consists of freshwater gastropods, plants and mammals.

The Upper Priabonian–Lower Rupelian fill represents a new marine cycle (Turea Group = upper marine series) consisting mainly of shallow-marine sediments. Deposition commenced with a Priabonian transitional freshwater to evaporitic unit (Jebuc Formation), followed by a carbonate platform (Cluj Limestone) with *Crassostrea transilvanica* and *Nummulites fabianii*. Maximum flooding is indicated by offshore bryozoan marls (Brebi Formation) which also include the Priabonian–Rupelian boundary (*Pycnodonte gigantica* biohorizon). Progressive shallowing is recorded in the overlying Hoia Limestone (skeletal packstones) and the Mera Formation (siliciclastic and calcareous).

Tectonic events at the end of the Early Rupelian led to a progressive shift to fluvial and siliciclastic ramp environments (e.g. Moigrad Formation). The Upper Rupelian is strongly transgressive, including dysoxic environments (bituminous shales of the Ileanda Formation).

The Chattian is mainly siliciclastic with an overall progradational pattern and widespread continental deposition, probably generated by a eustatic sea-level fall and climate change. While most of the southern part of the basin was exposed, and continental deposits were dominant in the Gilău and Meseş area, marine inner shelf (Buzaş Formation) and offshore to slope (Vima Formation) deposits were dominant in the Preluca area.

The base of the **Lower Miocene megasequence** (MS3) is coincident with deposition of the marine Vima Formation which was continuous across the Oligocene–Miocene boundary. Subsequent retrogradation was coeval with the transgressive event which was generated by the onset of compressional tectonics and which created a flexural basin (Györfi *et al.* 1999). Microfaunas with Mediterranean affinities (Popescu *et al.* 1995) invaded the basin, and the overlying Eggenburgian littoral sands of the Coruş Formation preserve a typical assemblage of bivalves with *Oopecten gigas* (Moisescu & Popescu 1980). Early Miocene maximum flooding is associated with the deposition of the Eggenburgian Chechiş Formation, an offshore unit preserving diverse microfaunal assemblages with *Globigerinoides trilobus* (Popescu 1975). Following the deposition of the Chechiş Formation, the basin was filled during the remaining Early Miocene with deep-marine turbidites and coarse-grained fan deltas belonging to the Hida Formation.

The base of the **Middle to Upper Miocene megasequence** (MS4) coincides with the Middle Miocene (Badenian) transgression which was synchronous in all of the Paratethyan basins. Carbonate and clastic sedimentation dominated shallow ramp environments (Filipescu 1996), while hemipelagites were deposited in the deeper areas (less than 100 m thick). The Lower Badenian Dej Tuff testifies to the local intense volcanic activity (Seghedi & Szakács 1991) and represents a useful regional stratigraphic marker.

Initial transgressive conditions are documented by two important planktonic foraminfera invasions (*Praeorbulina glomerosa* and *Orbulina suturalis* biozones; Popescu 1975). Benthic assemblages show affinities to offshore and shoreface siliciclastic and carbonate environments. The upper part of the Lower Badenian succession indicates a progressively shallower facies, terminating in lowstand conditions (Krézsek & Filipescu 2005). At the beginning of the Middle Badenian, an important transgressive event renewed the planktonic and benthic assemblages, suggesting a deeper depositional environment when compared to the Early Badenian (Filipescu 2001*b*).

A major relative sea-level fall from the late Mid-Badenian (near the end of the Langhian) induced progressive restriction in basin circulation and created conditions for the deposition of sabkha to shallow-ramp gypsum in the west (Cheia Formation) and deep-ramp salt (Ocna Dejului Formation). The salt crops out along two major lineaments situated at the western and eastern margins of the basin as a result of its post-depositional tectonics (Krézsek 2004).

The marine flooding event at the beginning of the Late Badenian (Popescu 1972; Dumitrică *et al.* 1975) was probably both globally and regionally (increased subsidence rates due tectonic shortening in the Eastern Carpathians: Săndulescu 1988) controlled. Transgression resulted in the deposition of hemipelagic sediments, subsequently overlain by the highstand prograding submarine fans of the Pietroasa Formation (Filipescu 2004). By the end of the Late Badenian, increased regional compression resulted in a relative sea-level fall and lowstand deposition. Due

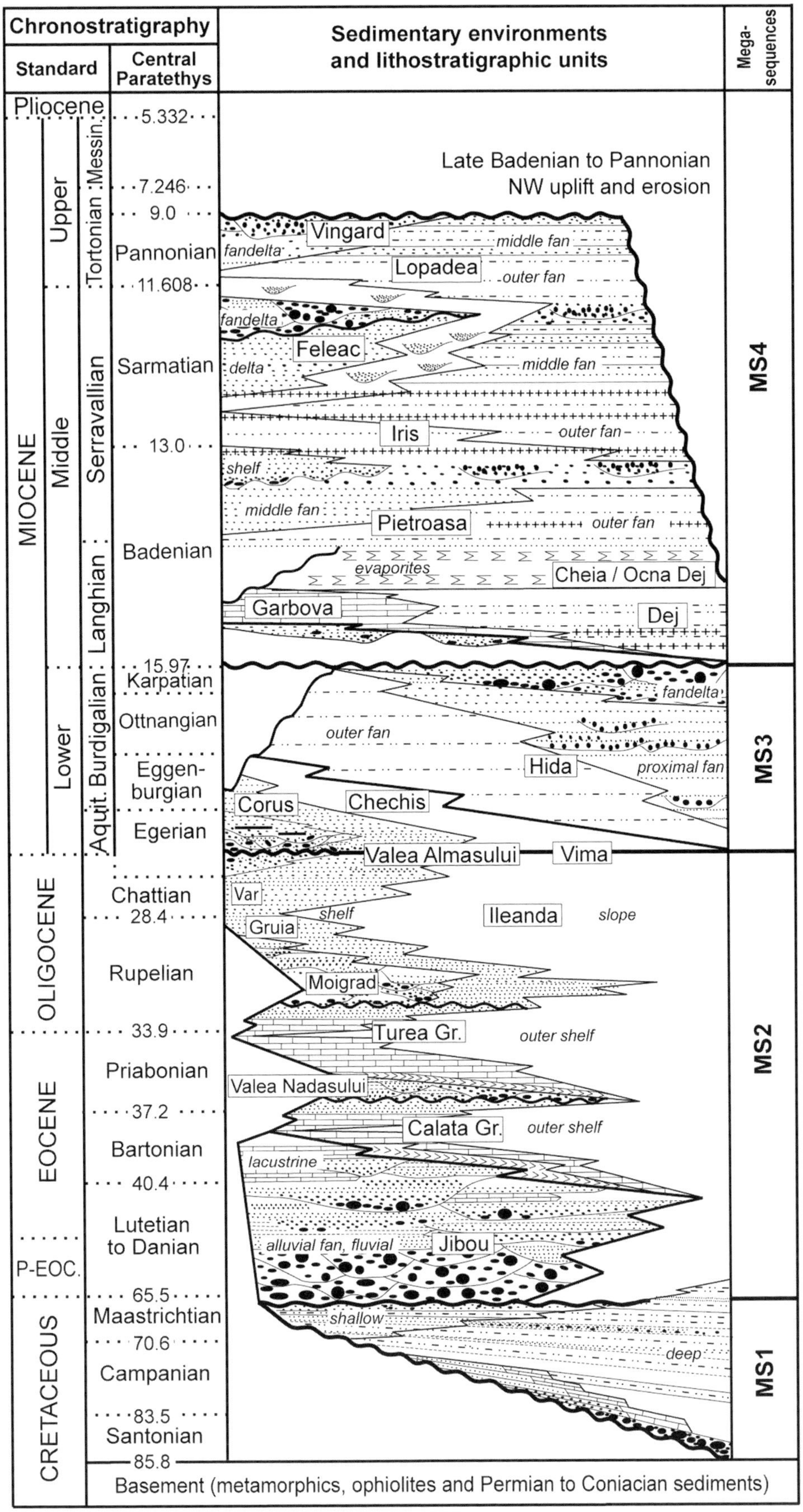


**Fig. 17.21.** Lithostratigraphy of the Transylvanian Basin (based on Krézsek & Bally 2006).

to the particular tectonic setting, the total thickness of the Upper Badenian ranges from a few metres (in the west) to >1500 m (in the SE).

The subsequent transgressive deposits near the Badenian–Sarmatian boundary (planktonic foraminifera and *Anomalinoides* biozones) were followed by prograding submarine fans (Sarmatian Iris Formation). The subsequent sea-level fall resulted in increased salinity in the basin (*Varidentella reussi* Biozone: Popescu 1995), and extensive erosion in the northern part of the basin. Another transgressive event (*Elphidium reginum* Biozone) was associated with deltaic progradation (*Dogielina sarmatica* Biozone) (Krézsek & Filipescu 2005). By Late Sarmatian times, the onset of uplift along the basin margins (Apuseni Mountains) resulted in the deposition of deltas, fan deltas, coarse submarine fans (Feleac Formation), and a major unconformity. Sarmatian deposits range in thickness between 300 m and >1000 m (in the basin centre).

The overlying shallow-ramp and deep-marine siliciclastic deposits are associated with a new transgression at the end of the Sarmatian (*Porosononion aragviensis* Biozone). This extended into the earliest part of the Pannonian (Lopadea Formation); outer-ramp condensed sedimentation predominated. Fan deltas, ramp and deep lacustrine sediments are typical of the subsequent prograding systems (Krézsek 2005). The brief re-establishment of connections with the outer Carpathian region can be inferred from a brackish marine ingression (*Ammonia* acme), generated by an extrabasinal relative sea-level rise. Fan deltas, proximal lacustrine fans, incised channels and alluvial fan systems were the most characteristic features of the middle part of the Lower Pannonian. The subsequent transgressive and highstand conditions are documented only in the eastern part of the TSB, and comprise an overall coarsening-upward succession (Vingard Formation). The thickness of the Pannonian deposits ranges from 300 m (SW) to 500 m (SE). The Pliocene to Holocene evolution of the TSB was characterized by uplift, erosion (Sanders 1999) and structural complications produced by salt tectonics (Krézsek & Bally 2006).

*Volcanism*

Mid- to Late Miocene Carpathian deformation was accompanied by intense magmatic activity in the volcanic arc covering most of the eastern margin of the TSB. Volcanic products sealed parts of the Pannonian sedimentary record. There are several well-known volcanic tuff lithohorizons in the Badenian–Pannonian sedimentary record of the TSB (Mârza & Mészáros 1991), which are related to Neogene calc-alkaline, subduction-related magmatic activity of the Carpathians and Apuseni Mountains (Pécskay *et al.* 1995).

## Outer Carpathians in Poland (N.O.)

The Polish Outer Carpathians (POC) are part of a mountainous arc that stretches for >1300 km from Vienna to the Iron Gate of the Danube River at the Serbian–Romania boundary (near Orsova) (Figs 17.16 & 17.22). In the west, the Carpathians are linked to the Eastern Alps and in the east they pass into the Balkan chain. The POC are *c.* 315 km long and 60–90 km wide, and are located in southern Poland.

*Tectonic setting*

Traditionally, the Western Carpathians are subdivided into two distinct ranges (Książkiewicz 1977; see also Froitzheim *et al.* 2008). The Inner Carpathians are considered to be the older range, while the Outer Carpathians represent the younger range. Between them, the Pieniny Klippen Belt represents a Cenozoic strike-slip boundary; this is a strongly tectonized terrain *c.* 600 km long and 1–20 km wide. The Outer Carpathians are formed by stacked nappes and thrust sheets, which show different lithostratigraphic and structural development. From south to north they include: the Magura, Fore-Magura-Dukla Group, and the Silesian, Sub-Silesian and Skole units. In the Outer Carpathians the main décollement surfaces are located at different stratigraphic levels. All of the Outer Carpathian nappes are flatly overthrust onto the Miocene deposits of the Carpathian Foredeep (Oszczypko 1998; Oszczypko & Tomaś 1985). However, along the frontal Carpathian thrust a narrow zone of folded Miocene deposits developed. In Poland these are represented mainly by the Zgłobice, and partially by the Stebnik units. The detachment levels of the folded Miocene units are usually connected with Lower and Middle Miocene evaporites.

*Palaeogeography*

The Outer Carpathian Basin occupied the northern margin of Neo-Tethys (Oszczypko 2004, 2006). Geomagnetics revealed that the boundary between the North European Plate and the Central West Carpathian Block was probably located 60–100 km south of the present-day position of the Carpathian margin (Oszczypko & Ślączka 1985; Żytko 1997; Oszczypko 2006). The Outer Carpathian sedimentary area can be regarded as the remnant of an oceanic basin transformed into a foreland basin (Oszczypko 1999). This basin developed between the colliding European continent and various intra-oceanic arcs. The important driving forces behind tectonic subsidence in the basin were syn- and post-rift thermal processes as well as the emplacement of the nappe loads related to subduction processes (Poprawa *et al.* 2002). Similar to other orogenic belts, the Outer Carpathians were progressively folded towards the continental margin. According to the reconstructions of Roure *et al.* (1993), Roca *et al.* (1995) and Behrman *et al.* (2000), the Early Oligocene Outer Carpathian Basin was at least 380 km wide.

*Palaeomagnetism*

According to Marton *et al.* (1995*b*) the Western Carpathians and its hinterland are characterized by a counterclockwise rotation of 80°. The first rotation of 50° took place during the Late Ottnangian to Early Karpatian and the second one (of 30°) occurred during the Badenian.

*Sedimentary and stratigraphic development*

The Outer Carpathians are composed of mainly Upper Jurassic to Lower Miocene deep-marine deposits ('flysch') (Fig. 17.23). The sedimentary successions of the main tectonic units differ in terms of facies development and thickness. The thickest sedimentary cover belongs to the Silesian unit, which varies from 3000 m in the west to >5000 m in the east. The thickness of the other tectonic units is markedly thinner and varies between 3000–3800 m in the Skole Unit, *c.* 1000 m in the Sub-Silesian Unit, 2300–2500 m in the Dukla Unit, and 2500–3500 m in the Magura Nappe (Poprawa *et al.* 2002). In terms of facies distribution, thickness of deposits, and palaeocurrent directions (only in the Magura area), the Silesian and Skole basins can be considered as independent sedimentary areas. The Magura and Silesian basins were separated by the Silesian Ridge, while the Sub-Silesian area formed a submarine high dividing the Skole and Silesian basins during the Late Cretaceous to Eocene (Książkiewicz 1962).

The sedimentary succession of the POC comprises four depositional megasequences, which reflect the main stages of basin development (Poprawa *et al.* 2002; Oszczypko 2004): Middle

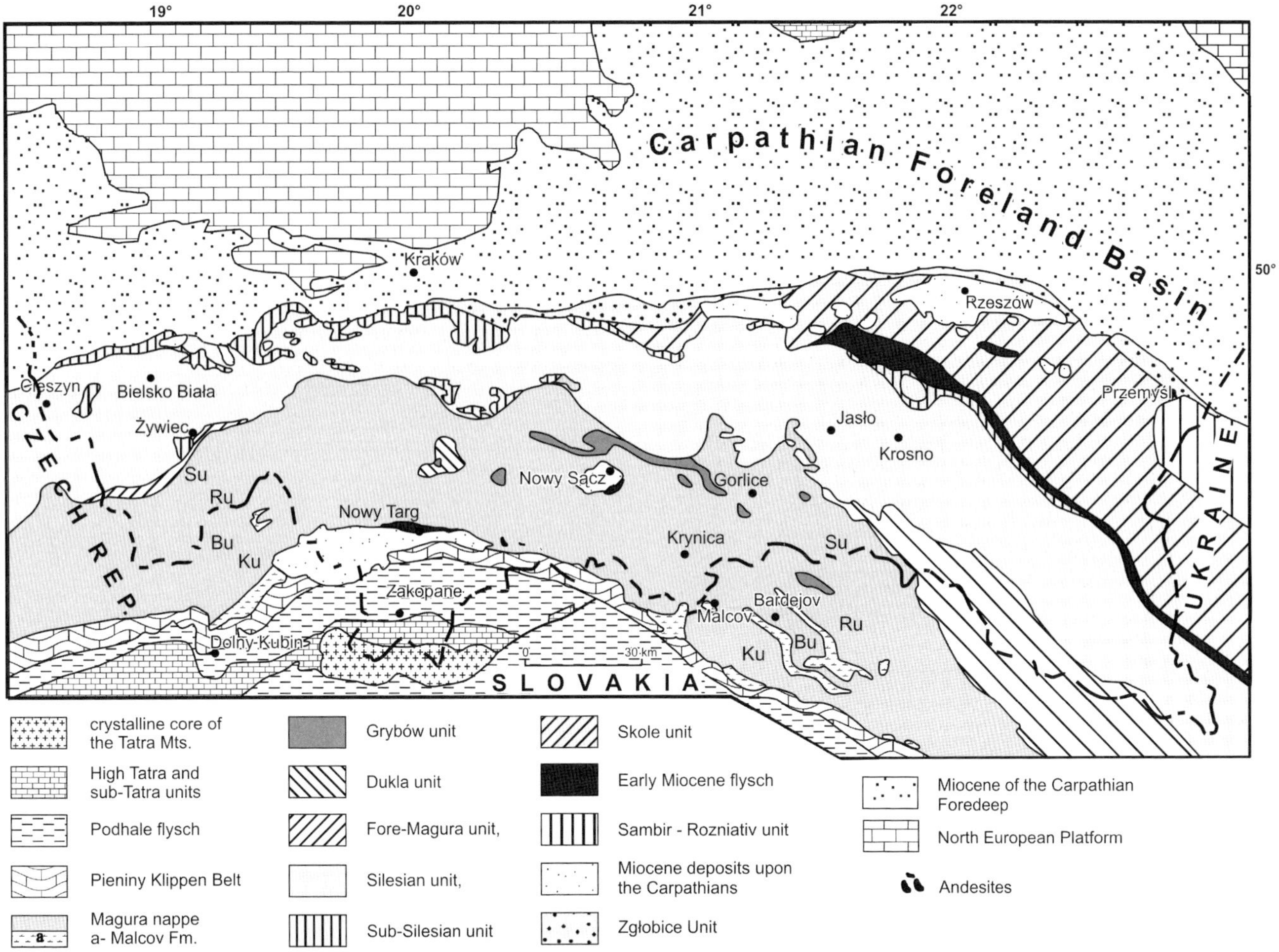


**Fig. 17.22.** Geological sketch map of the Polish Carpathians and their foreland basin. Abbreviations of facies-tectonic subunits of the Magura Nappe: Bu, Bystrica Subunit; Ku, Krunica Subunit; Ru, Rača Subunit; Su, Siary Subunit.

Jurassic–Early Cretaceous basin opening; Late Cretaceous–Palaeocene inversion; subsidence during Palaeocene to Middle Eocene times; and Late Eocene–Early Miocene synorogenic closing of the basins. In the Outer Carpathian area the K/Pg boundary is located within a continuous turbidite sequence.

The Palaeocene represents a time of major changes in sedimentary conditions in the Outer Carpathian basins, ranging from uplift of the intrabasinal source areas to general subsidence and a sea-level rise. These changes are marked by the deposition of thin- to medium-bedded turbidites, traditionally referred to as the 'Inoceramian Beds' (Bieda *et al.* 1963), and recorded from the Magura, Dukla and Skole successions. The 300–500 m thick units are characterized by calcareous, micaceous sandstones intercalated with clay shales. During this time the evolution of the Silesian Basin was still influenced by the Silesian Ridge, from which non-calcareous, thick-bedded turbidites and conglomerates (Istebna Beds) were shed into the basin. The upper part of the Istebna Beds comprises up to 200 m of shales. The Lower Eocene is characterized by the occurrence of thick-bedded turbidites and conglomerates (up to 500 m), which form elongated lenses (Ciężkowice Sandstones). The northern periphery of the Silesian Basin was dominated by marls with exotic pebbles (sub-Silesian succession).

During the Eocene, a broad connection between the Outer Carpathian basins and the world oceans was established (Golonka *et al.* 2000; Golonka 2004), resulting in the unification of facies, including the position of the CCD level, as well as low sedimentation rates. This general trend dominated the Early and Middle Eocene in the Skole, Sub-Silesian, Silesian and Dukla basins, as well as in the northern part of the Magura Basin. The deepest parts of these basins were occupied by hemipelagic, non-calcareous shales. During the Middle Eocene these shales passed up into shales with intercalations of thin-bedded sandstones (Hieroglyphic Beds).

In the Magura Basin, Palaeocene deposits are overlain by shales (up to 150 m), which pass upwards into the thin-bedded turbidites of the 200–600 m thick Beloveza Formation (Oszczypko 1991). The upper part of the Lower/Middle Eocene succession comprises the thick-bedded turbidites of the Magura Formation, which is 1000–2000 m thick (Birkenmajer & Oszczypko 1989). Eocene deposition in the Magura Basin was controlled by the activity of an accretionary wedge which developed on the southern margin of the basin during the Late Palaeocene collision between the Inner Western Carpathian block and the Pieniny Klippen Belt. During the Eocene the migrating load of the accretionary wedge led to further subsidence and a shift in the depocentres to the north. As a result, a long and narrow submarine fan developed. The northern, deepest part of the basin, often below the CCD, was dominated by basinal turbidites and hemipelagites. The sedimentation rate varied from 6–18 m/Ma on the abyssal plain to 103–160 m/Ma on the outer

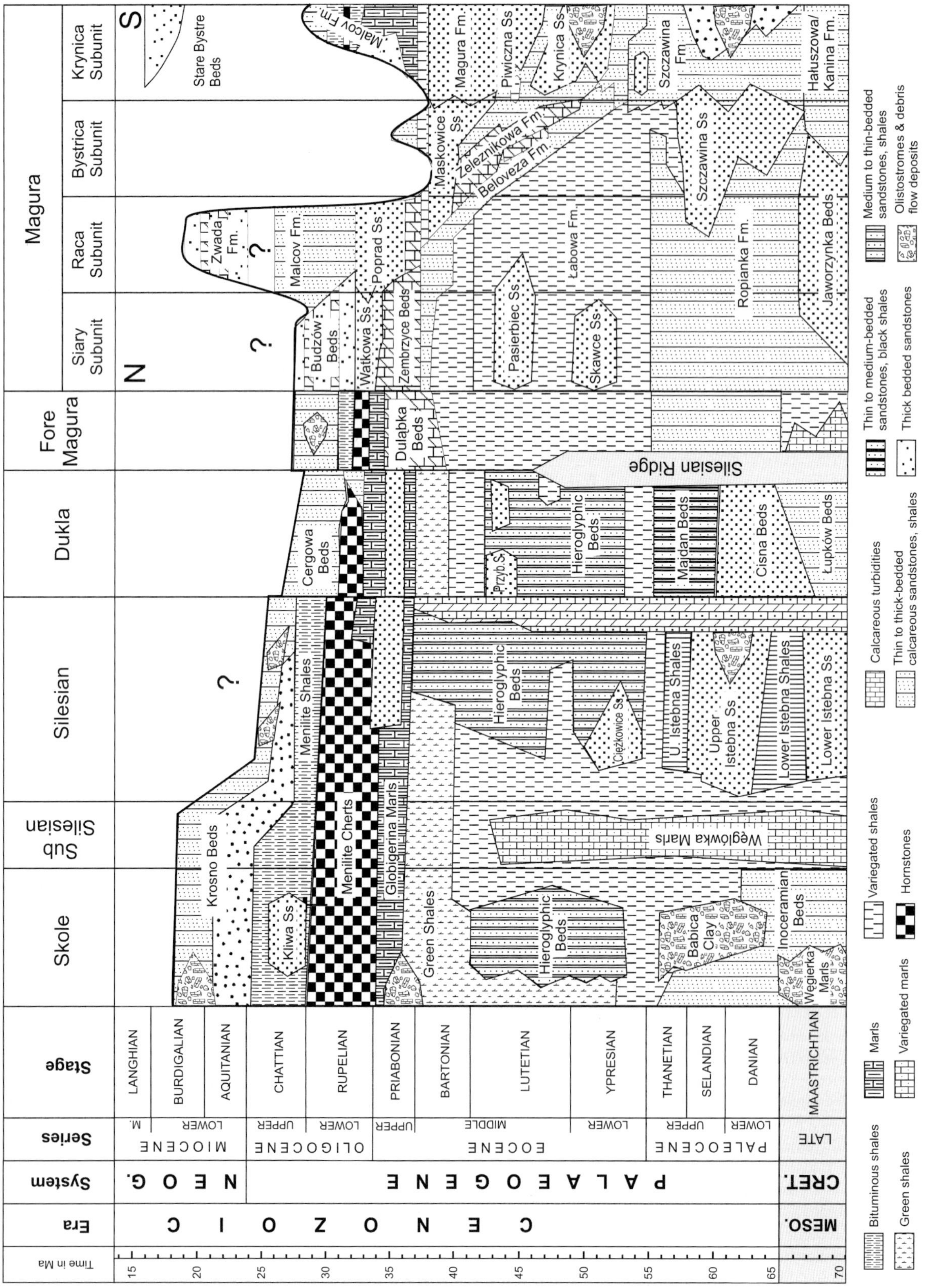


**Fig. 17.23.** Regional stratigraphic scheme of the Palaeogene and Lower Miocene deposits of the Polish Outer Carpathians (after Oszczypko 2004).

fan, and 180–350 m/Ma in the area affected by the middle fan-lobe systems (Oszczypko 2004). The fan was supplied from the SE, probably from the Inner Carpathian/Inner Dacide area.

During the Priabonian and Rupelian, uplift in the Outer Carpathian Basin (Poprawa *et al.* 2002; Oszczypko 2004) was accompanied by the transformation of the Outer Carpathian remnant oceanic basin into a foreland basin. This led to the replacement of deep-water shales and basinal turbidites by pelagic *Globigerina* Marls, followed by Oligocene bituminous Menilite shales deposited in the newly restricted basin. This type of deposition dominated all of the Outer Carpathian basins, except for the main part of the Magura Basin (Van Couvering *et al.* 1981). During that time, the pelagic *Globigerina* marls and Menilite shales of the Magura Formation, as well as the turbidites of the Malcov Formation (Middle/Upper Oligocene), were deposited in the SE part of the Magura Basin. The northernmost part of the Magura Basin, which was supplied from the NW (Silesian Ridge), is characterized by Middle Eocene shales that pass upwards into marls and thin-bedded turbidites (Zembrzyce Beds, Upper Eocene), thick-bedded glauconitic sandstones (Wątkowa Sandstone, Lower Oligocene), and finally into glauconitic sandstones and marls (Budzów Beds, Oligocene) (Oszczypko-Clowes 2001). In the marginal parts of the Outer Carpathian basins, *Globigerina* Marls pass into Menilite Shales (up to 250 m thick) with chert horizons at the base. The Menilite Shales, which contain lenses of thick-bedded sandstones (Cergowa and Kliwa Sandstones), gradually pass upwards into a complex of thick-bedded, medium-grained, calcareous sandstones (Lower Krosno Beds, up to 800–1000 m). Higher up in the succession, thin-bedded, fine-grained sandstones pass into marly shales (Upper Krosno Beds, Early Miocene, up to 3000 m). These lithofacies are diachronous across the Silesian, Sub-Silesian and Skole basins (Ślączka & Kamiński 1998).

Following the phase of Late Oligocene folding, the Magura Nappe was thrust northwards onto the terminal Krosno Basin. This resulted in the final phase of subsidence in the Outer Carpathian Basin (Late Oligocene–Early Miocene). Subsidence was accompanied by a progressive migration of the depocentre axes towards the north and increased depositional rates ranging from 350 m/Ma in the Rupelian (northern part of Magura basin) to 600 m/Ma at the end of the Oligocene (SE part of Silesian Basin). During the Eggenburgian a piggyback basin developed on the Magura Nappe (Zawada and Kremna formations, at least 550 m thick) and a marine connection with the Vienna Basin via Orava was established (Oszczypko *et al.* 1999, 2005; Oszczypko & Oszczypko-Clowes 2002, 2003).

*Volcanism*

The final stages of tectonic evolution of the Polish Outer Carpathians were associated with volcanic activity related to subduction beneath the front of the Carpathian arc. In the Krościenko-Szczawnica area small andesite intrusions are located along the northern margin of the Pieniny Klippen Belt. The time of the volcanic activity in this area has been dated as 11.35 ± 0.45 Ma (Birkenmajer & Pecskay 2000).

## Carpathian Foredeep in the Czech Republic (S.N., N.D., Š.H., P.P.)

The Carpathian Foredeep in the area of the Czech Republic (CCF) is limited to the NW by the passive margin of the Variscan Bohemian Massif and its Mesozoic platform cover and by the overriding nappes of the Western Carpathians in the SE. The CCF continues southwards into the Austrian part of the North Alpine Foreland Basin and northwards into the Polish Carpathian Basin. The basin is *c.* 210 km long and *c.* 6–40 km wide.

*Tectonic setting*

The CCF is a peripheral foreland basin that developed due to subsurface loading of the Alpine-Carpathian orogenic belt on the passive margin of the Bohemian Massif. The CCF exhibits striking lateral variations in terms of basin width, depth, and the stratigraphy of the sedimentary infill. There are also variations in pre-Neogene basement composition and tectonic subsidence. The main area of subsidence shifted from the south, in the Late Oligocene/Lower Miocene to the north in Middle Miocene times. This reflects the change in orientation of the main convergence direction and a generally eastward-directed lateral extrusion of the Carpathian blocks. The reactivation of NW–SE and NE–SW trending basement faults was also important for the basin shape and for its extent. The southern part of the CCF had a complicated evolution due to its position at the junction between the Eastern Alps and the Western Carpathians.

*Sedimentary and stratigraphic development*

Deposition in the CCF began in Egerian–Early Eggenburgian times (Fig. 17.24). Terrestrial (alluvial and fluvial, Žerotice Member) and deltaic sediments occur locally at the base of the succession in the SW of the basin. During the subsequent transgression from the south, SE and east, these deposits progressively passed into marine ones (clastic coast and shallow-marine environments). The shallow-marine facies (about 40 m palaeowater depth) was interdigitated with lagoonal and deltaic deposits (Nehyba *et al.* 1997). The upper part of this Lower Miocene succession comprises deltaic and clastic coast deposits (Čejkovice Sands). The source area was the deeply weathered margin of the Bohemian Massif. A distal rhyolite airfall tephra horizon occurs in the Upper Eggenburgian (Nehyba 1997). Dunajovice and Dyjákovice sandstones and the Dobré Pole Claystone (glauconitic sands and calcareous clays with rich foraminiferal fauna) were deposited under marine conditions in the SE part of the CCF during Early Miocene times (Adámek 2003; Chlupáč *et al.* 2002). Eggenburgian deposits also occur in the northern part of CCF in the area of Ostrava. Basal fluvial sands and gravels pass upwards into marine claystones, bryozoan limestones, sandstones and conglomerates (Jaklovec Conglomerate) (Chlupáč *et al.* 2002). Lower Miocene basaltic volcanism is known from the Opava region.

A second depositional cycle is confined to the middle Early Miocene (Ottnangian) and was related to the onset of thrusting, which led to markedly different depositional histories in the proximal and distal parts of the CCF. In the distal (western) part, the deposition was directed by the interplay of basement relief, sediment supply and eustasy, while Late Eggenburgian thrusting affected the deposition in the proximal parts of the basin. The deposition of a synorogenic clastic wedge, related directly to flexural subsidence due to the thrust loading, reflects this change (Nehyba 2004). At the base of the succession a typical basal forebulge unconformity occurs (Crampton & Allen 1995). Towards the passive margin, the unconformity is overlain by progressively onlapping sediments above an increasing stratigraphic gap. Changes in the heavy mineral spectra (Nehyba & Buriánek 2004) reflect the new situation. Brackish to fluvial sands and clays (Vítonice Clays), and sands and gravels of the Rzehakia Beds, comprise the Ottnangian deposits in the distal parts of the basin. These deposits (with the endemic bivalve *Rzehakia socialis*) were recognized in the Miroslav and Frýdek-

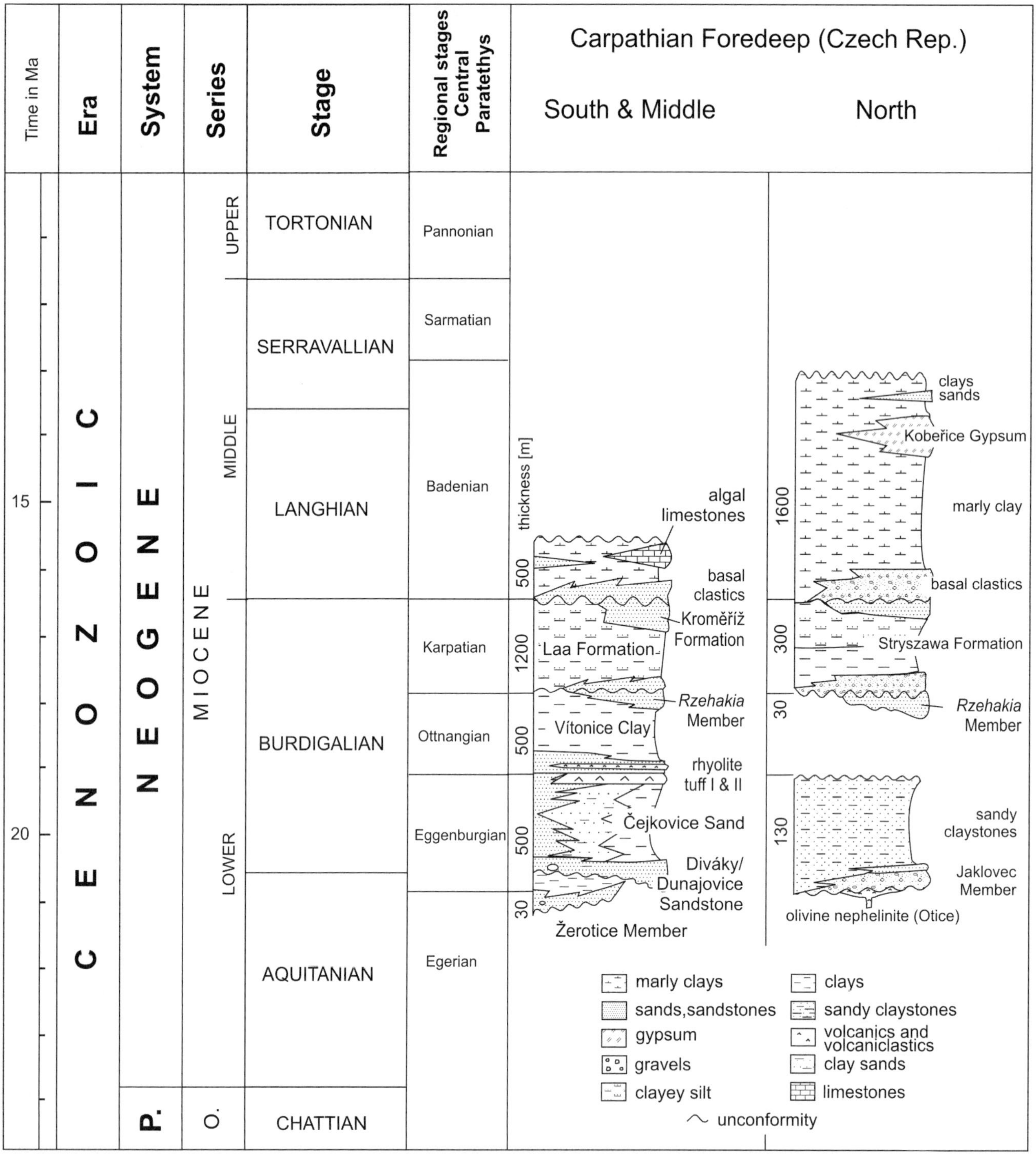


**Fig. 17.24.** Regional stratigraphic scheme of the Neogene of the Carpathian Foredeep in Moravia (Czech Republic) (after Brzobohatý in Chlupac *et al.* 2002; Adamek *et al.* 2003; Adamek 2003).

Místek areas (Čtyroký 1991). The flora indicates a humid climate (Doláková *et al.* 1999). Layers of acidic volcaniclastics (Ottnangian) were also deposited (Nehyba & Roetzel 1999). Fine-grained siltstones, claystones and fine sandstones (Late Eggenburgian and Ottnangian in age) were deposited in the proximal parts of the basin.

Continued compression along the Western Carpathian Front led to the progression of a westward-prograding and eastward-thickening clastic wedge during the late Early Miocene (e.g. Laa Formation; Adámek *et al.* 2003). Coastal, shallow-marine and deep-marine (bathyal) conditions alternate. Laminated silty clays (= Schlier) with abundant microfauna are typical (e.g. foraminifers; Petrová 2004). These were deposited on the deeper shelf under fluctuating oxygen contents. In the middle and southern parts of the CCF, the marine transgression covered an area of relatively flat relief and extended far across the Bohemian

Massif; marshes were established on the continental margin (Doláková & Slamková 2003). In the northern part of the CCF, the upper Lower Miocene (Karpatian) deposits are represented by the Stryszawa Formation comprising terrestrial basal conglomerates, sandstones and claystones, and lacustrine/lagoonal siltstones that pass into marine deposits (claystones and siltstones, and subordinate gravels and sandstones). Clays, silts, sandstones and conglomerates with gypsum form the uppermost part of the succession (Adámek *et al.* 2003).

Tectonic activity along the active margin affected the deposits of the CCF. Sediments in the foreland of the Carpathian nappes were shingled and stacked in the form of duplexes. Sandstones, conglomerates and clays (gravity current deposits) in front of the Ždánice Nappe in the middle part of the basin belong to the Kroměříž Member.

During the early Middle Miocene the CCF geometry was reorganized, because the NNW- and NW-directed compression of the Carpathian orogenic wedge changed to a NNE- and NE-directed compression during the Late Karpatian and Early Badenian. In the south, deposits are located in the central parts of the basin at some distance from the passive and active basin margins. The areas with the maximum sediment thickness are situated along the basin axis forming an almost symmetric basin with a SSW–NNE orientation. Deposits of coarse-grained Gilbert deltas, coastal environments, lagoonal deposits and deeper-marine deposits have been recognized. These are partly correlated with the Grund Formation in the North Alpine Foreland Basin. The maximum thickness of the deltaic gravels and gravelly sands is about 175 m. Deltas are located along both basin margins. Abundant intraclasts (sometimes several metres in diameter) reflect cannibalization of the older basin infill. In the northern part of the basin, the basal conglomerates and sandstones may have been deposited in marine environments (Chlupáč *et al.* 2002). The deeper-marine deposits (*c.* 600 m) comprise mudstones with silts, clays and shell debris. These are interpreted as outer-shelf deposits or hemipelagites. The presence of otoliths confirm a palaeowater depth of about 400 m in the central part of the basin (Brzobohatý 1997). Coastal and lagoonal deposits, as well as occurrences of algal and bryozoan limestones and calcareous sandstones, are restricted both areally and in thickness. Horizons of distal airfall tephra (Nehyba 1997) are related to the acidic calc-alcaline volcanism of a volcanic arc in the Carpatho-Pannonian area (Middle Rhyolite Tuff). Isolated relicts of Lower Badenian deposits can be found far to the west (e.g. Hostim, Kralice, Borač, Ústí nad Orlicí). Early Badenian terrestrial deposits (sands and clays with lignite seams) are developed in the Opava area in the northern part of the basin.

The subsequent cessation of marine sedimentation was largely due to the final stages of thrusting of the orogenic wedge along the NE part of the basin and to flexural uplift of the foreland in the SW. Middle and Upper Badenian deposits are known only from the north of the CCF in the Ostrava and Opava areas where the basin continued into Poland. Evaporites (Kobeřice Gypsum) and clays (*c.* 60 m), including a distal rhyolitic tephra horizon, are of Middle Badenian age (Nehyba 2000). Clays and claystones with abundant plant remnants and rare limestones represent the Upper Badenian (Cicha *et al.* 1985).

Fluvial and lacustrine deposition occurred during the Middle and Late Miocene. Moldavite-bearing sands and gravels are found in SW Moravia (Trnka & Houzar 1991). The reactivation of NW–SE trending faults led to the formation of brackish basins in the Mohelnice Graben and in the Upper Morava Valley. The Upper Miocene and Pliocene fluvial and lacustrine deposits have a thickness of about 200 m (Růžička 1989) in this area (= Lower and Upper Formation).

### *Carpathian Foredeep in Poland (N.O.)*

The *c.* 350 km long Polish Carpathian Foredeep Basin (PCFB) is part of a large sedimentary basin that stretches from the Danube in Vienna (Austria) to the Southern Carpathians in Romania (Fig. 17.22). Towards the west it is replaced by the North Alpine Foreland Basin. The width of the PCFB varies from 30–40 km in the west to 90 km in the Rzeszów area and 50 km at the Polish–Ukrainian border. It can be subdivided into an 'inner' and the 'outer' part. The boundary between them runs along the Carpathian Thrust.

*Palaeogeography*

The Early to Middle Miocene PCFB developed as a peripheral foreland basin and is related to the advancing Carpathian Front (Oszczypko 1998; Oszczypko *et al.* 2006, and references therein). During late Early Miocene times the Western Outer Carpathians overrode the European platform. The load of the Carpathian nappes resulted in the development of a 25–50 km wide Early Miocene flexural depression (inner foredeep). This basin developed both on the top of the advancing Carpathian Front and on the platform basement. The relatively narrow brackish or freshwater, moat-like basin was filled with coarse clastic sediments derived from the emergent front of the Outer Carpathians and from the platform. The Lower Miocene deposits of the inner foredeep formed a clastic wedge along the Northern Carpathians, comparable with the 'Lower Freshwater Molasse' of the western North Alpine Foreland Basin.

Latest Early Miocene times were characterized by the development of SW–NE and NW–SE trending grabens. Subsidence, which affected both the inner and outer foredeep, was accompanied by the Early Badenian transgression (Oszczypko 1998; Oszczypko *et al.* 2006) which flooded both the foredeep and the marginal part of the Carpathians. Simultaneously, the shoreline shifted northwards, from 30–40 km to 100 km in the western and eastern parts of the basin, respectively. The palaeobathymetry of the Early Badenian basin varied between upper bathyal depths in the axis of the basin, to neritic and littoral conditions in the marginal areas. The deepest part of the basin (inner foredeep), which reached mid-bathyal depth, was located about 20 km south of the present-day position of the Carpathian Front. In the Carpathian offshore area, Lower Badenian deposits onlapped, deformed and eroded deposits of the Skole and Silesian/Sub-Silesian nappes and this resulted in an angular unconformity. Middle Badenian shallowing in the PCFB caused partial isolation of the basin, and initiated a Badenian salinity crisis in shallow areas (inner–middle neritic? depths; see Kasprzyk 1993; Peryt 2001; Bąbel 2004; Oszczypko *et al.* 2006). A new period of intense subsidence was initiated during the Late Badenian and was confined to the inner and outer foredeep areas (Oszczypko 1998). Late Badenian subsidence continued into the Sarmatian. Depocentres shifted 40–50 km towards the NE and rotated clockwise by up to 20°.

*Tectonic setting*

The evolution of the PCFB was controlled by synsedimentary fault tectonics. The majority of the NW–SE and WNW–ESS trending faults were reactivated during the Late Cretaceous–Palaeogene inversion. These faults controlled Late Badenian and Sarmatian subsidence in the PCFB. The highest rate of Late Badenian subsidence was up to 2000 m/Ma in the SE part of the area. In the NW Rzeszów area, the rate of subsidence reached about 1200–1300 m/Ma, and was accompanied by a sedimentation rate of only 1000 m/Ma. Towards the NE margin of the PCFB, the subsidence and sedimentation rate decreased to 100–200 m/Ma. The area of maximum Sarmatian subsidence was the Wielkie Oczy Graben. The total subsidence in this zone varied from 1500 m in its NE part to 3000 m in the SE.

A relatively narrow belt of deformed Upper Badenian–Sarmatian foredeep deposits known as the Zgłobice Unit crops out at the front of the Polish Outer Carpathians (Kotlarczyk 1985; Książkiewicz 1977). This unit consists of several fault-and-fold structures with a maximum width of up to 10 km. To the west of Kraków, there is a narrow zone of folded Miocene deposits (Książkiewicz 1977). In the western part of the Carpathians (Andrychów-Kęty area) several thrust sheets of the Sub-Silesian Unit, covered by lower and upper Badenian deposits, are recorded. These sheets are thrust onto the Badenian deposits in the outer PCFB.

*Sedimentary and stratigraphic development*

The PCFB is asymmetric and filled with predominantly clastic Miocene sediments (Oszczypko *et al.* 2006) (Fig. 17.25). The outer foredeep is filled with Middle Miocene (Badenian and Sarmatian) marine deposits, which range from a few hundred metres thick in the northern part to 3500 m at the Carpathian Front. The inner foredeep, located beneath the Carpathian nappes, is composed of Lower to Middle Miocene autochthonous deposits. The Lower Miocene strata are mainly of terrestrial origin, whereas the Badenian and Sarmatian sediments are marine. The deposits of the Carpathian Foredeep are underlain by Permo-Mesozoic terrestrial and shelf sediments and locally by Palaeogene deposits. The platform basement, with a Neogene sediment cover, dips southward beneath the Outer Carpathian nappes for at least 50 km (Oszczypko & Ślączka 1985; Oszczypko 1998).

The oldest Miocene deposits were found in a sub-thrust position in a few boreholes in the western inner foredeep, and comprise marine mudstones of late Egerian–Eggenburgian age (Garecka *et al.* 1996; Oszczypko & Oszczypko-Clowes 2003). Higher up in the sequence, slide deposits attain a thickness of up to 370 m. The overlying Karpatian deposits comprise coarse- to medium-grained, polyimictic conglomerates and are followed by a conglomerate–sand–mudstone unit up to 650 m thick. The upper part of the succession may have been deposited in an alluvial fan setting. In the Cieszyn area, the Lower Miocene foreland deposits are overlapped by a 40–90 m thick unit of Late Karpatian transgressive conglomerates.

The Badenian sediments rest directly on the platform basement, except for the SE part of the inner foredeep, where they overlie Lower Miocene deposits. The thickness of the Lower Badenian deposits is variable, ranging from 1000 m in the western inner foredeep (Skawina Formation) to 30–40 m in other parts (Baranów Formation) (Ney *et al.* 1974). Sedimentation of the Skawina Formation (clays and sands) began during the *Praeorbulina glomerosa* Zone in the inner foredeep and during the *Orbulina suturalis* Zone in the outer foredeep (Garecka *et al.* 1996). The mid-Badenian evaporitic horizon (lower part of the NN6 zone; see Peryt 1997; Andreyeva-Grigorovich *et al.* 2003) either overlies these deposits or rests directly upon the platform basement. This evaporitic horizon consists of rock salt, claystones, anhydrite, gypsum and marls. Between Wieliczka and Tarnów, the thickness of the salts reaches 70–110 m (Garlicki 1968) and decreases towards the east to a few dozen metres. The mid-Badenian evaporites are overlain by thick (up to 1.5 km in the central part, and up to 2.5 km in the eastern part) Upper Badenian–Sarmatian sandstones and shales (Gaździcka 1994), which display large-scale clinoforms (Krzywiec 1997). During the early Sarmatian, littoral carbonates and clastics were deposited. After the Sarmatian the final northward thrust moved the Outer Carpathians onto the PCFB.

## *Carpathians in Western Ukraine (O.Y.A., V.V.A.)*

Four main structural units are recognized in the Western Ukraine from west to east (Figs 17.4 & 17.16): the Transcarpathian Basin, the Carpathians, the Carpathian Foredeep, and the Volhyno-Podolian Plate (i.e. the SW margin of the East European Platform). The Mukatchevo and Solotvino sub-basins are part of the Transcarpathian Basin which is separated from the Romanian Transylvanian Basin by the Maramures, Lepus, Rodna and Preluka mountains. To the SW the basin is bordered by the Great Hungarian Plain. The Mukatchevo and Solotvino sub-basins are divided by the volcanic Vyhorlat-Hutin Zone (Voznesensky 1988).

*Palaeogeography and tectonic setting*

The pre-Neogene basement of the Transcarpathian Basin consists of Palaeozoic to Palaeogene units. In Neogene times, the Solotvino Sub-basin underwent maximum subsidence during the Badenian and up to 2000 m of sediments were deposited, while the deposits in the Mukatchevo Sub-basin are >2500 m thick. Generally, the successions are comparable with those of the Great Hungarian Plain and the East Slovak Basin. The deposits are usually only slightly deformed. Close to the Chop-Vyschkovo Anticline, however, beds dip at up to 90° and displacements of *c.* 20 km are recorded in the northern part of the Solotvino depression (Voznesensky 1988).

The Carpathian Foredeep is situated to the NE of the Carpathians Front and is divided into an inner and an outer zone. The inner zone consists of the Boryslav-Pokuttya and Sambir nappes whose development was caused by the uplift of the Carpathians. The Boryslav-Pokuttya Nappe overthrusts the Sambir Nappe (Kulchytsky 1989). The flexural downbending of the outer zone commenced in the Badenian. The subsequent post-Sarmatian folding resulted in complex deformations in the inner zone, but did not affect the outer zone (Vialov 1986). The Sambir and Boryslav-Pokuttya nappes were detached from their basement and moved *c.* 25–30 km. Sedimentary cover attains a thickness of up to 6000 m.

*Sedimentary and stratigraphic development*

The lowermost deposits of the **Transcarpathian Basin** are of Eggenburgian age and comprise up to 90 m of sandstones, siltstones and sandy clays (Burkalo Formation, zone NN3; Andreyeva-Grigorovich *et al.* 2002). Karpatian deposits are represented by the Tereshul conglomerates (up to 100 m), comprising unsorted boulder–pebble conglomerates. The conglomerate components are slightly rounded and consist mainly of Jurassic and Cretaceous limestones, sandstones and claystones derived from the Palaeocene (Andreyeva-Grigorovich *et al.* 1997). The overlying Middle Miocene (Badenian) deposits are represented by the Novoselitsa and Tereblia formations, comprising rock salt (up to 270 m) which formed as a result of a marked regression (Vialov 1986; Voznesensky 1988). The marine Novoselitsa Formation and the lower parts of the Tereblia Formation have nannoplankton assemblages of the NN5 zone, while NN6 zone assemblages occur in the upper part of the Tereblia Formation (Andreyeva-Grigorovich *et al.* 2002). The Late Badenian transgression led to the establishment of

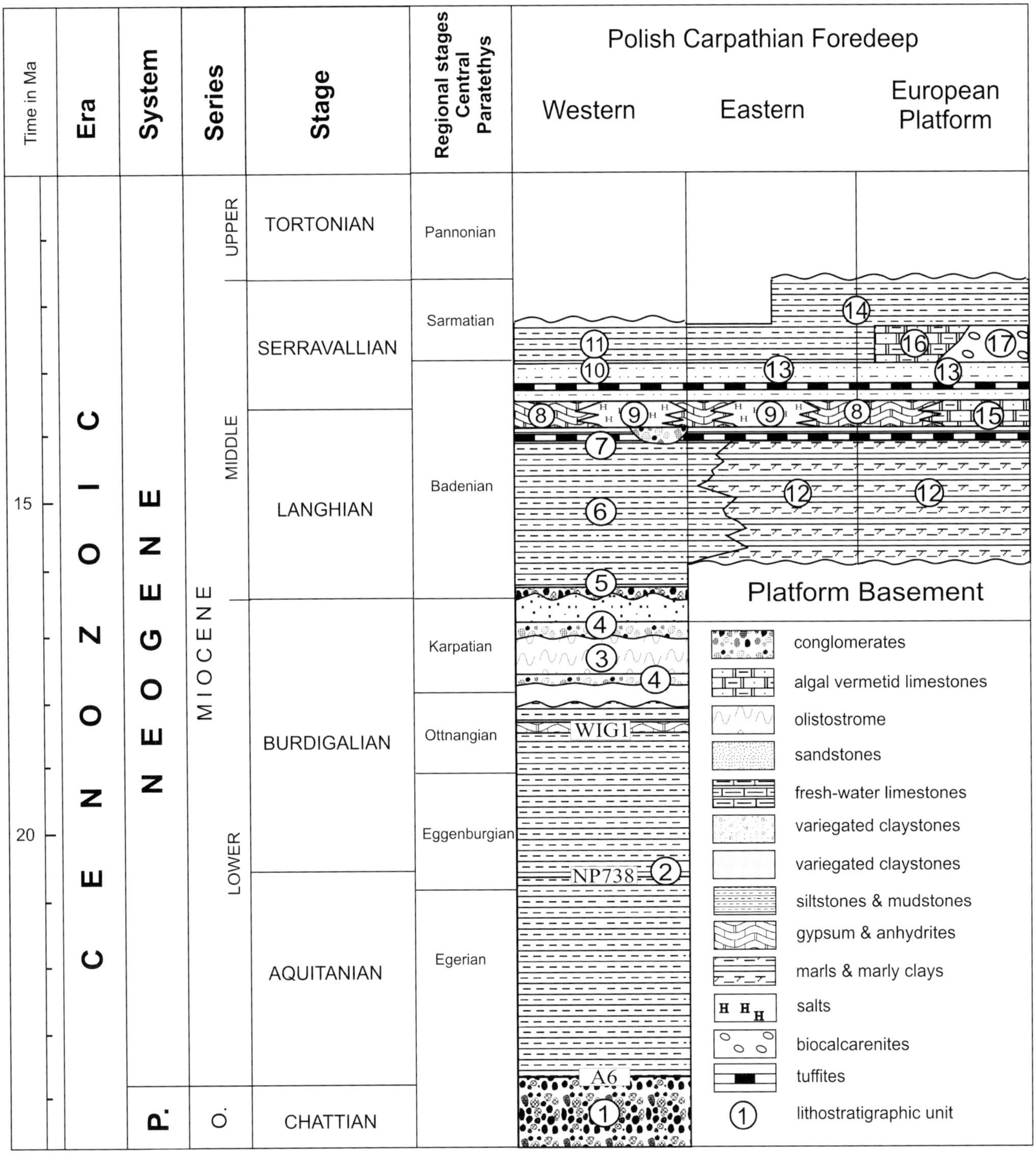


**Fig. 17.25.** Regional stratigraphic scheme of the Miocene deposits of the Polish Carpathian Foredeep (after Oszczypko 1998; Andreyeva-Grigorovich *et al.* 2003). Lithostratigraphic units: 1, Andrychów Formation; 2, Zebrzydowice Formation; 3, Sucha Formation-flysch olistoplaque; 4, Stryszawa Formation; 5, Debowiec Conglomerate; 6, Skawina Formation; 7, Sypka Góra conglomerates; 8, Krzyżanowice Formation; 9, Wieliczka Formation; 10, Gliwice beds; 11, Kedzierzyn beds; 12, Baranów beds; 13, Chodenice and Grabowiec beds; 14, Krakowiec beds; 15, sulphur-bearing limestones; 16, algal-vermetid reef limestones; 17, Biocalcarenite of the Chmielnik Formation.

marine environments as reflected by the deposits of the Solotvino, Teresva and Baskhev formations. During the Badenian, separation into the Mukatchevo and the Solotvino sub-basins occurred. Sarmatian units are represented by the clays, sands and tuffs of the Dorobratiy, Lukiv and Almash formations, which were mainly deposited in the Mukatchevo Sub-basin in lagoonal and terrestrial environments. Upper Miocene and Pliocene sediments are represented by the Iza, Koshelevo, Ilnitsa and Chop formations, which are restricted to the Mukatchevo Sub-basin. These are mainly volcanic and terrigenous deposits, including important lignite seams (Voznesensky 1988).

In the **Inner Carpathian Foredeep** the Boryslav-Pokuttya and Sambir nappes comprise the Polyanytsa, Vorotyshcha, Stebnyk and Balych formations (Vashchenko & Hnylko 2003) (Fig. 17.8). Calcareous clays, siltstones, sandstones, conglomerates and olistostromes are characteristic of the Polyanytsa and Vorotyshcha formations. The Polyanytsa Formation is absent in the Sambir Nappe and the Vorotyshcha Formation has only a restricted distribution. The Polyanytsa Formation is usually assumed to be of Eggenburgian age (Andreyeva-Grigorovich *et al.* 1997; Veklich *et al.* 1993), although there is some evidence that sedimentation commenced during the Oligocene (Vashchenko & Hnylko 2003). The boundary between the Polyanytsa and Vorotyshcha formations is diachronous and ranges from the Oligocene–Miocene boundary up to the Eggenburgian. Sedimentation of the Vorotyshcha Formation lasted until the Badenian, but its upper boundary is also diachronous (Vashchenko & Hnylko 2003). Sandy-argillaceous sediments characterize the Ottnangian to Lower Badenian Stebnyk Formation in the Boryslav-Pokuttya Nappe. In the Sambir Nappe the basal part of the Stebnyk Formation is cut by thrusting, and passes upwards into the sandy-argillaceous Karpatian to Lower Sarmatian Balych Formation. In the NW of the Sambir Nappe, the Balych Formation is overlain by the Radych Conglomerates (Vashchenko & Hnylko 2003).

The **Outer Carpathian Foredeep** was generated on the margin of the East Europaean Platform, where thick marine, brackish and continental Neogene sediments overlie Proterozoic, Palaeozoic and Mesozoic deposits (Kulchytsky 1989). The Middle Miocene (Badenian) succession begins with the Bogorodchany Formation (*c.* 100 m thick) which is characterized by marly-tuffacous sediments (up to 40 m). Its upper part consists of sandy clays with sandstones rich in pectinids. The overlying Tirass Formation (up to 40 m) is characterized by evaporites which are overlain by the laminated clays and siltstones of the Kosiv Formation (up to 700 m), including an important bed with radiolarians (20 m) (Vialov 1986). The Lower Sarmatian is represented by the Dashava Formation, up to 5000 m thick, comprising clays with sandstones and tuffs.

*Volcanism*

The Neogene magmatism of the Transcarpathian is characterized by intensive volcanic activity. It was associated with the flexural subsidence of the Transcarpathian region along deep faults, which acted as conduits for the upwelling magmas. The thickest accumulations of tuffaceous and effusive rocks were deposited (1) during the Early Badenian in the central part of Solotvino and the eastern part of the Mukatchevo basins, (2) during the Badenian and Sarmatian in the Beregovo and Vyshkovo areas, and (3) during the Pliocene in the Vyhorlat-Hutin Zone. Badenian volcanism was characterized by acid liparite-dacitic and dacitic lavas and their associated tuffs. From the Sarmatian to the Pliocene, the acid volcanism was replaced by intermediate, and later by alkaline, volcanism, i.e. andesites, andesite-basalts and basalts (Voznesensky 1988).

## Southern Alps and Dinarides: overview (D.B.)

The Southern Alps are separated from the Eastern Alps (i.e. Austro-Alpine units) by the Periadriatic Lineament (PAL) (Fig. 17.26). In terms of palaeogeography, both units are considered to represent the northern extension of the Adriatic Microplate which also includes the Po Plain and the adjacent Adriatic Sea. During the Palaeogene, when the Eastern Alps formed an archipelago,

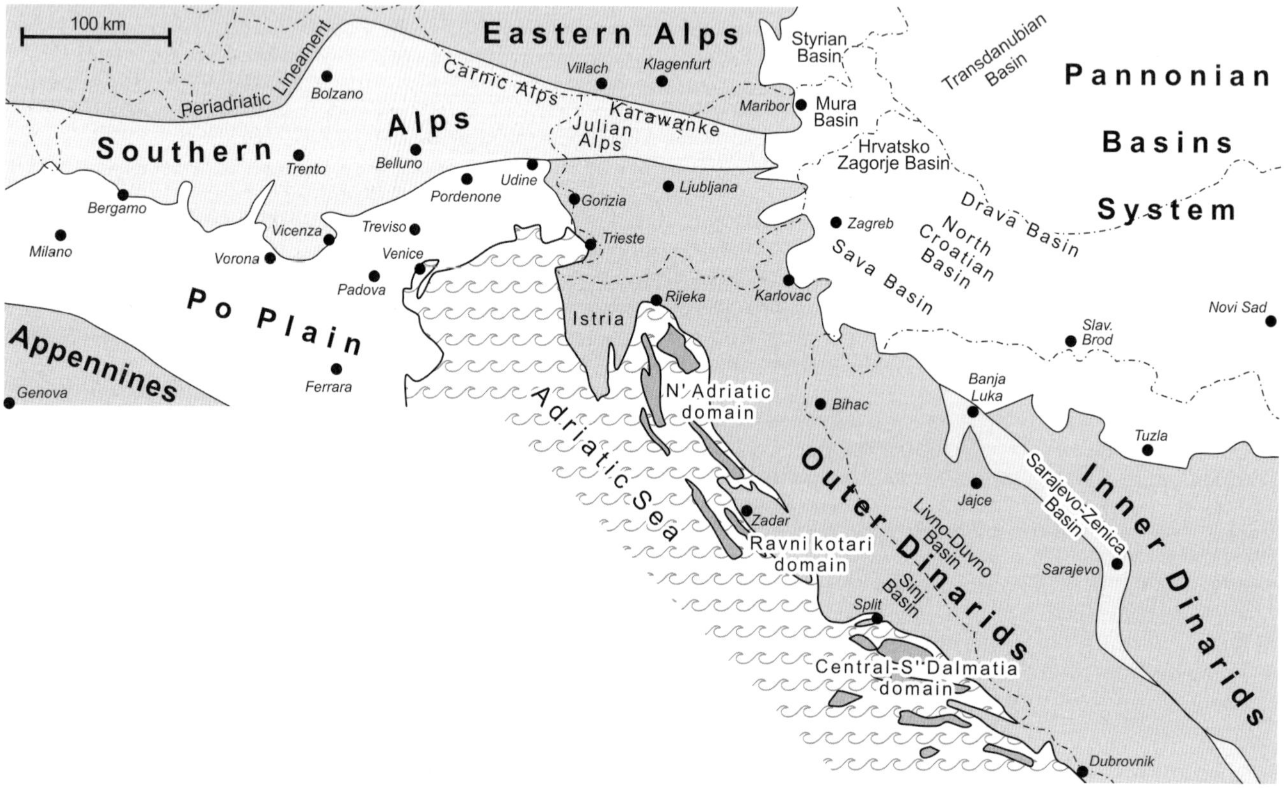


**Fig. 17.26.** Geology and main sedimentary basins of the Southern Alpine and Dinarides region.

the Southern Alps formed their southern continuation. Southern Alpine units in NE Italy include: (a) Palaeozoic basement; (b) Permian–Pliocene sedimentary cover, including continental, platform and basinal deposits; (c) volcanic and subvolcanic deposits, mostly occurring in the Dolomites–Recoaro (Mid-Triassic) and Colli Euganei–Monti Lessini areas (Palaeogene), and (d) a thick succession of Quaternary alluvial deposits filling the Po Plain. The Variscan and Alpine orogenic cycles are recorded in this area. The former involved pre-Permian thrusting, polyphased folding and metamorphic imprinting of the basement whereas the latter is recorded by the Dinaric (Palaeogene) SW-vergent thrusts and by the widely distributed décollement cover, basement nappes and transfer faults of the Neo-Alpine (Neogene) south-vergent episodes, prograding toward the Po Plain foreland.

The Friuli Platform and the Julian Basin continue southwards to the Adriatic and Dinaric platforms, and the Bosnian Basin, respectively (Cati *et al.* 1987; Herak 1987). Cati *et al.* (1987) have proposed a scenario with an additional Friuli Basin that subdivided the Friuli Platform into SW (SW of Pordenone) and NE (Udine area and south of Udine) sectors. This basin supposedly continued to the Outer (= External) Dinarides. As a consequence, the SW and NE Friuli platforms should be connected with the Adriatic (present-day Dalmatian zone) and Dinaric (present-day High Karst zone) platforms, respectively.

## *Southern Alps in Italy: Venetian Pre-Alps (D.B., G.B., P.M., J.H.N.)*

The Palaeogene of the Southern Alpine area of NW Italy encompasses parts of the Trentino-Alto Adige and Veneto regions. At the beginning of the Cenozoic, this area was subdivided into two basins which are roughly separated by the present-day north–south alignment of the Brenta River.

### *Palaeogeography and tectonic setting*

The western basin, encompassing the Monte Baldo and Monti Lessini, the Monti Berici and Colli Euganei as well as the Vincentin Pre-Alps, is characterized by widespread Palaeocene, Lower–Middle Eocene and Oligocene volcanic activity and by the deposition of shallow-water carbonates. The Eocene succession comprises series of shallow-marine platform systems and related basinal units. Some areas became emergent in the Early Oligocene, while others were sites of shallow-marine siliciclastic sedimentation, with an increasing carbonate sedimentation rate in Late Oligocene times. At the Oligocene–Miocene boundary, most of this western area was transgressed leading to the development of widespread marine sedimentary systems.

The Cenozoic of the eastern basin (Valsugana, Belluno, Feltre, Vittorio Veneto, Alpago areas) is characterized by the deposition of thick, mostly siliciclastic sediments including Scaglia- (Late Cretaceous to Early Eocene), deep-marine (Palaeogene) and continental (Neogene) successions, as well as a lack of volcanic activity. Basin development during the Chattian to Langhian was influenced by the rapidly rising axial zone of the Alps, which represented an important source of clastic sediments. This is indicated by the presence of clasts derived from the Penninic and Austro-Alpine successions (e.g. Massari *et al.* 1986*a*).

The present-day structure of the Venetian Southern Alps is the result of the superposition of two main Cenozoic compressive phases, designated as the Eo-Alpine and Neo-Alpine tectonic phases. Evidence for an Eo-Alpine (Late Cretaceous–Early Palaeogene) deformation phase, as present in the central-western part of the Southern Alps, is lacking in this area. From the Late Palaeocene onward, the Intraplacca rift became active, resulting in the development of the Cenozoic volcanism of the Venetian area (e.g. Doglioni & Bosellini 1987). In the NE Veneto, the Eo-Alpine phase produced overthrusts and WSW-verging folds which completely deformed the Permo-Cenozoic sedimentary cover.

The Neo-Alpine tectonic phase acted during the Neogene and reached its acme during Late Miocene–Pliocene times. Much of the uplift of the Venetian mountains, and the formation of a series of south-verging overthrusts which progressively migrated towards the Venetian plain, are due to this cycle. Although the Venetian and Trento area constitutes one of the lesser deformed regions of the Southern Alps, the geometry of the Neogene deformation is rather complex (Doglioni & Bosellini 1987).

In the Veneto region, Neo-Alpine tectonic activity is indicated mainly by south-verging overthrusts. Just south of the Dolomites, the overthrusts also involve the crystalline basement (Valsugana Lineament, Pieve di Cadore Lineament; e.g. Doglioni 1984). To the south, in the Venetian Pre-Alps, the sedimentary cover is deformed by folds and overthrusts. The presence of a basal décollement surface, consisting of Upper Permian evaporites, is still under debate. Neogene deformation in the SW part of the Venetian area (i.e. Monti Lessini, Monti Berici, Colli Euganei) is rare. Folds and overthrusts occur in the westernmost part of the Monti Lessini and in the Monte Baldo; these are SE-verging and are linked to the Late Miocene Giudicarie compression (Castellarin 1981, 1984; Grandesso *et al.* 2000). Diachronism in the deformation of the Southern Alps was noted by Castellarin & Vai (1981), who showed that the main shortening event in the western area of the Southern Alps occurred during the Late Oligocene to Early Miocene, as marked by the coarse-grained clastics of the Lower Gonfolite Group, whereby the eastern area experienced the climax of deformation during the Late Miocene and Pliocene.

From the Chattian to Langhian, the Lessini Block can be considered as the foreland basin of the Dinaric Range (Massari *et al.* 1986*a*). An important palaeogeographic and geodynamic change occurred in the Mid-Miocene with the onset of a major phase of extension in the Pannonian Basin and the Inner Dinarides (Horváth 1984). The ongoing northward convergence of Adria and Europe culminated in a major Upper Miocene compressional phase, whose effects were widespread across the Alps and Apennines. Major south-verging thrusting, uplift and southward tectonic progradation occurred in the Venetian area during this phase, concurrent with episodic subsidence and very high sedimentation rates in the Venetian Basin. Strike-slip faults outlined the basin and controlled sedimentation at this stage (Massari *et al.* 1986*b*). A further outward shifting of the depocentres occurred during the Pliocene to Quaternary in the foredeep belt of the Peri-Adriatic ranges (Po, Venetian and Adriatic basins), where subsidence, coupled with compressional deformation, continued. This was associated with the accumulation of a succession, several kilometres thick, in the Po Plain and in the Adriatic (Massari *et al.* 1986*a*).

The final phase of Neogene deformation began in the Pliocene and is still active, as demonstrated by the high seismic activity of some areas. The Aviano overthrust, buried beneath the alluvial deposits of the Upper Venetian Plain, delimits the southern hills of Marostica, Asolo, Montello and Conegliano (Costa *et al.* 1996).

### *Sedimentary and stratigraphic development*

**Western Veneto and southern Trentino–Alto Adige.** The Jurassic Trento Platform of the Southern Alps is a major structural and palaeogeographic domain of the Adria Plate continental margin (Winterer & Bosellini 1981). It was a region of shallow-marine carbonate accumulation until the uppermost Early Jurassic. The platform was drowned during the Bajocian to Kimmeridgian and formed a deeper shelf characterized by the famous 'Rosso Ammonitico Veronese'. Lower Cretaceous–Lower Eocene sediments ('Maiolica', 'Scaglia rossa') (Fig. 17.27) are of deeper-marine origin (Bosellini 1989). During the complex collision between Europe and the Adria Plate, the former Trento Plateau reacted rigidly and was block-faulted; the submerged Trento Platform was segmented into separate blocks, showing variable uplift, and was punctuated by several volcanic piles. Shallow-marine carbonate sedimentation was initiated on these topographic highs and eventually coalesced to form the Lessini Shelf (Luciani 1988; Bosellini 1989; Zampieri 2000; Beccaro *et al.* 2001).

The distribution of Palaeogene sediments in the Southern Alpine area of NE Italy was strongly influenced by the Alpone-Chiampo Graben (Barbieri *et al.* 1991; Barbieri & Zampieri 1992; Zampieri 1995). This graben was active during the Palaeogene and extends along a NNW–SSE axis in the central-eastern Lessini Shelf. The graben thus divides the Lessini Shelf into two areas which evolved separately, as shown by the different stratigraphic successions from earliest Late Palaeocene onwards (Antonelli *et al.* 1990). The eastern margin of the graben encompasses the eastern Lessini Shelf and the western Monti Berici and the succession comprises planktonic marls and resedimented calcarenites (P. Mietto, unpubl. data). Further to the west, in the western Lessini Shelf, shallow-marine carbonates predominate, including many of the famous fossiliferous localities found in the Monti Lessini (De Zanche & Conterno 1972; Mietto 1975; Beschin *et al.* 1998). The poorly studied western margin encompasses the central-eastern Lessini Shelf up to the San Bonifacio hills.

In the SE Monti Berici an important tectonic threshold, probably coincident with the Riviera Berica area, has been identified; commencing in middle Eocene times, this boundary separated the Berici-Lessini area, comprising mainly shallow-marine deposits, from the Euganean Basin characterized by deep open-water sedimentation (Piccoli *et al.* 1976). This threshold played a fundamental role in the Oligocene palaeogeography. During the Oligocene a new graben formed in the Marostica area (Barbieri *et al.* 1991; Zampieri 1995).

Thin and discontinuous Upper Palaeocene to Lower Eocene marly limestones are widely distributed in NE Italy, e.g. Monte Baldo (Luciani 1989), Lessini Shelf (Garavello & Ungaro 1996), Monti Berici (Massari & Medizza 1973) and Colli Euganei (Massari *et al.* 1976), as well as the southern Altopiano di Asiago areas (Ungaro & Garavello 1989). During the early to middle Eocene, sedimentation was differentiated into pelagic and neritic facies. The latter are widespread across the entire area from middle Eocene (Lutetian) times onwards. A representative area for Ypresian sedimentation is found near the village of

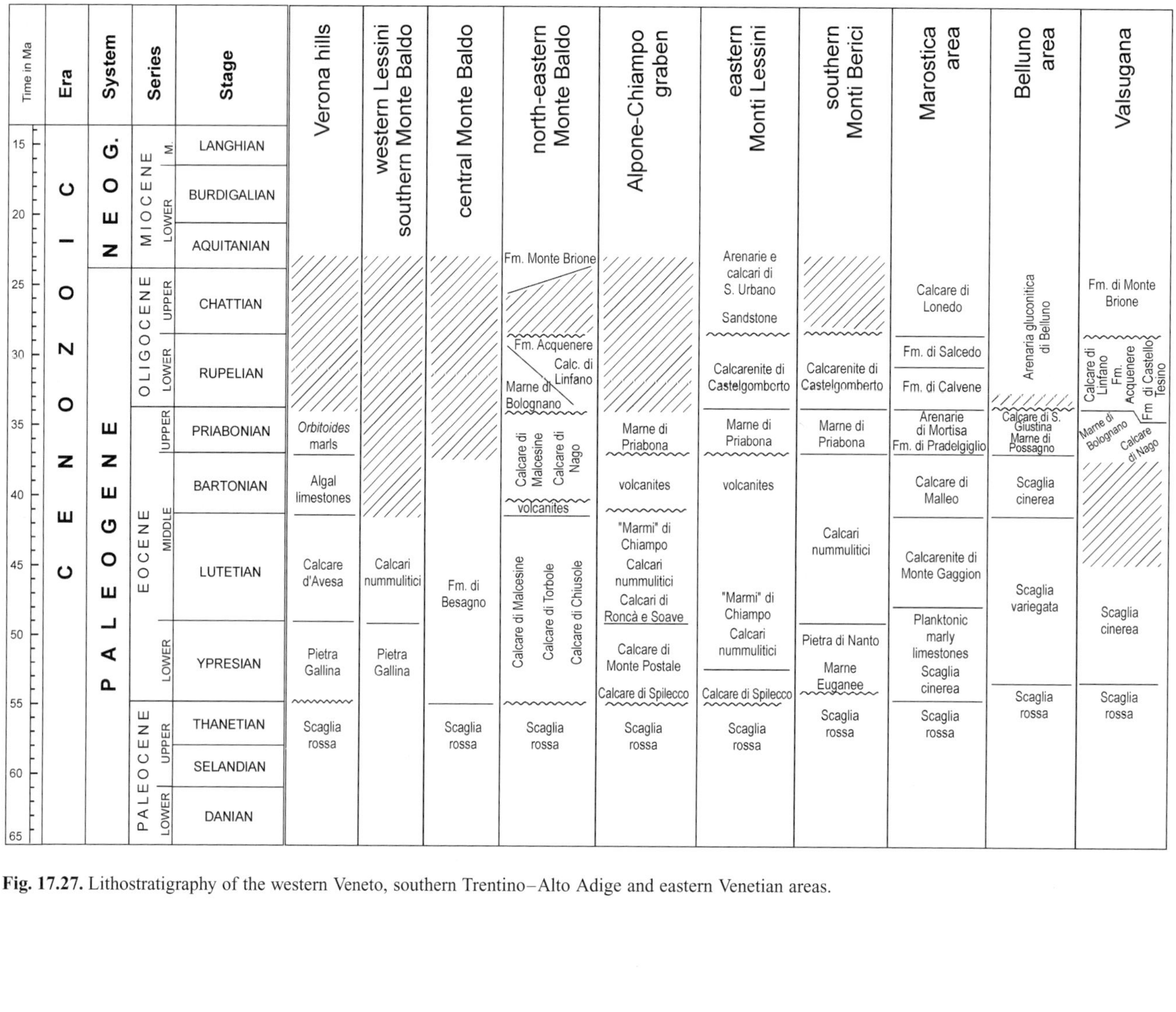


**Fig. 17.27.** Lithostratigraphy of the western Veneto, southern Trentino–Alto Adige and eastern Venetian areas.

Avesa in the Verona hills. Here, a 70 m thick succession of bedded marls and marly limestones (= Pietra Gallina; Hottinger 1960) is deposited above hardgrounds on top of the Scaglia rossa.

In the western Lessini Mountains (Fumane area), micritic and marly limestones with planktonic foraminifera range in age from Thanetian to Lutetian (Ungaro 1990; Garavello & Ungaro 1996). These limestones are overlain by *c.* 50 m of Middle Eocene nummulitic calcarenites (Formazione di Avesa; Sarti 1980; Ungaro 2001). In the western Monti Lessini area, near Verona and in the southern Monte Baldo area, the Lower Eocene succession consists of a few metres of muddy calcarenites and marls belonging to the Pietra Gallina; these are overlain by nummulitic calcarenites, which were deposited from Ypresian to Bartonian times (De Zanche *et al.* 1977).

In the central Monte Baldo area, Ypresian to Lutetian nummulitic calcarenites with coralline algae and corals (Formazione di Besagno, 50–70 m thick) overlie the Upper Cretaceous–Upper Palaeocene Scaglia rossa, or the lower Ypresian deposits. In the northern Monte Baldo area, Early to Middle Eocene sediments comprise shallow- and deep-water carbonates. These overlie the Scaglia rossa (Bosellini & Luciani 1985), the basinal deposits (Scaglia cinerea, Calcare di Chiusole) as well as the slope and platform carbonates (Calcare di Malcesine, Calcare di Torbole), which represent the initial platform sediments of the area (Bosellini *et al.* 1988; Luciani 1989).

Within the Alpone-Chiampo Graben, micritic and clayey limestones, apparently identical to the underlying Scaglia rossa, have been ascribed to the middle Thanetian (Barbieri & Medizza 1969). Malaroda (1967) grouped all of the sediments from the Upper Cretaceous Scaglia rossa (below) to the Lower to Middle Eocene Calcari nummulitici (above) into the Calcare di Spilecco. This unit consists of basal massive limestones overlying volcaniclastics, followed by larger foraminiferal limestones with brachiopods, crinoids and calcareous algae. These are considered to be Early–Middle Ilerdian (= Ypresian) in age by Papazzoni & Less (2000). Ungaro (2001) ascribed the Calcare di Spilecco cropping out in the Cavalo-Poiano area to the Palaeocene–Early Eocene. Volcanic layers (including basaltic flows, hyaloclastites and volcaniclastics) are often intercalated with these carbonates (Barbieri & Medizza 1969). The Lower–Middle Eocene succession differs markedly from other areas in having two main carbonate bodies which, towards the NE, coalesce into a *c.* 100 m thick succession (Valle dell'Agno; Beccaro *et al.* 2001).

In the Bolca area, the middle Eocene nummulite limestones (Marmi del Chiampo) are interbedded with 100–200 m thick hyaloclastites. Both the calcarenites and the biogenic carbonates of the Monte Postale area, as well as the laminated carbonates of the Monte Bolca area, are laterally equivalent with the lower member of the Marmi del Chiampo. According to Papazzoni (2000*a*), coralline and coral limestones of the Monte Postale area are Early Eocene in age, while the Calcari di Roncà e Soave, Marmi di Chiampo and the Pietra Gallina are middle Eocene in age. Locally, these data are confirmed by calcareous nannoplankton (Beccaro *et al.* 2001). Within the thick volcaniclastic deposits, some lignitic deposits are present, including the famous fossil Lagerstätten of the Purga di Bolca area (Sorbini 1989). At the top of the Calcari di Chiampo, a rich fossiliferous volcaniclastic horizon occurs (San Giovanni Ilarione horizon; Fabiani 1915; Mietto 1975). The thick overlying basalt flows show a rapid environmental change from marine to continental settings, linked with the accumulation of volcanic products which progressively infilled the Alpone-Chiampo Graben. This event occurred in the lowermost Bartonian and is marked by the deposition of paralic facies including the famous Roncà horizon (De Zanche & Conterno 1972). During the Bartonian, subaerial volcanic activity led to the formation of the Monte Calvarina and Monte Faldo, and the original Alpone-Chiampo Graben was replaced by an emergent volcanic ridge on which muddy and lignitic sediments were deposited (Valle dell'Agno; Barbieri *et al.* 1991).

The Bolca area has been studied since the end of the nineteenth century (Oppenheim 1894; Fabiani 1912, 1914, 1915; Schweighauser 1953; Malaroda 1954; Hottinger 1960; Cita & Bolli 1961). Barbieri & Medizza (1969) summarized the geological and stratigraphical setting. The famous Pesciara fish-beds have been known for more than four centuries (Sorbini 1989; Papazzoni 2000*b*).

In the Monti Berici, the Scaglia rossa is followed by a few metres of turbiditic tuffs, tuffaceous marls and marls, which pass upward into marly calcarenites (Pietra di Nanto; Fabiani 1915). This unit is Lutetian in age and grades upward into larger *Nummulites* calcarenites, up to 50–90 m thick, traditionally named the Calcari nummultici (e.g. Ungaro & Bosellini 1965; Mietto 1988; Bassi *et al.* 2000). In the SE part of the Monti Berici, Early Eocene pelagic limestones have been ascribed to the Scaglia rossa (Piccoli *et al.* 1976). In the eastern Monti Berici (Mossano area), outside the Alpone-Chiampo Graben, the Calcari nummulitici extend up the Bartonian–Priabonian boundary (Ungaro 1969; Papazzoni & Sirotti 1995; Bassi *et al.* 2000). In the western Colli Berici, this formation comprises only Lutetian rocks (Fabiani 1915); shallow-marine carbonate sedimentation was interrupted by the extrusion of basalt flows which led to the infilling and emersion of the Alpone-Chiampo Graben at the end of the middle Eocene (Ungaro & Bosellini 1965). At the Bartonian–Priabonian boundary, a general regressive phase has been recognized in the Monti Berici and Monti Lessini areas (e.g. Ungaro 1969; Luciani *et al.* 2002; Bassi *et al.* 2000). In the Colli Euganei, basinal conditions continued through the entire Early Eocene; Palaeocene sediments are absent in the Berici area (Massari *et al.* 1976). In the Colli Euganei, pelagic marls are deposited above the Ypresian Scaglia rossa (Massari *et al.* 1976; Lucchi Garavello 1980) and extend up to the basal Oligocene. Locally, calcarenites and basaltic pillow lavas occur (De Vecchi & Sedea 1995).

In the Marostica area (southern Altopiano di Asiago), the Palaeocene is represented by the Scaglia rossa facies, which is overlain by marly limestones and marls with planktonic foraminifera (Garavello & Ungaro 1982). Lower–Middle Eocene micritic, marly limestones with planktonic foraminifera (Scaglia cinerea) pass upwards into Lutetian–Bartonian larger foraminiferal calcarenites, glauconitic marls and massive calcarenites (Calcareniti di Monte Gaggion; Frascari Ritondale Spano 1969; Garavello & Ungaro 1982; Ungaro & Garavello 1989). The Lower–Middle Eocene deposits of the southern Altopiano di Asiago (Calvene-Pradipaldo area) were described by Garavello & Ungaro (1982), Trevisani (1994) and Papazzoni & Trevisani (2000).

An important transgression is recorded across the entire western Venetian area at the beginning of the Priabonian. In Calvene, a biogenic conglomerate (Conglomerato di Grumale) marks this transgression. This is overlain by massive calcarenites, with local bioherm calcarenites, *c.* 100 m thick (Formazione di Pradelgiglio; Garavello & Ungaro 1982; Ungaro & Garavello 1989; Trevisani 1994, 1997). Marly, arenaceous siltstones, sandstones and conglomerates (10 to 40 m thick) gradually overlie these calcarenites and represent the Priabonian Arenarie di Mortisa (Papazzoni & Trevisani 2000). This formation is overlain by the Lower Oligocene Formazione di Calvene. The Priabonian transgression is also evident on the elevated ridge of the former Alpone-Chiampo Graben, where the historical holostratotype of the Priabonian is located (Passo di Priabona, near Monte di Malo) (see Mietto 2000 for overview). The Priabonian succession transgresses altered Middle Eocene basalts and is characterized by the basal Conglomerato del Boro (Fabiani 1915; Antonelli *et al.* 1990).

In the western Monti Berici this conglomerate is not so evident and is known as the Conglomerato a *Cerithium diaboli* (Fabiani 1915; Ungaro & Bosellini 1965; Mietto 1988). The Marne di Priabona has a thickness of *c.* 90 m in the type area and can attain 170 m in the Mossano area (eastern Monti Berici; Bassi *et al.* 2000). The top of the succession is locally characterized by a marly horizon rich in bryozoans (e.g. Ungaro 1978; Marne di Brendola in Broglio Loriga 1968). This formation appears to decrease in thickness towards the centre of the elevated ridge of the former Alpone-Chiampo Graben; it is absent in the Valle dell'Agno, where the overlying Oligocene Calcareniti di Castelgomberto is transgressive over Middle Eocene volcanic units (Barbieri *et al.* 1980; Mietto 1992).

The basaltic units of the Monte Baldo area were subaerially exposed in the uppermost Bartonian. The overlying Middle to Upper Eocene succession comprises platform (Calcare di Nago), slope (Calcare di Malcesine) and basin (Scaglia cinerea) deposits (e.g. Castellarin & Cita 1969; Luciani 1989; Bassi 1998). The Calcare di Nago was subaerially exposed at the Eocene–Oligocene boundary (Luciani 1989).

In the southern Altopiano di Asiago, the Formazione di Pradelgiglio was deposited during the Priabonian between the Astico and Brenta rivers (Frascari Ritondale Spano 1970; Trevisani 1994). This formation consists of siliciclastic sediments which pass upwards into larger foraminiferal calcarenites with coralline algae and benthic macrofossils (Papazzoni & Trevisani 2000). The upper Priabonian Arenarie di Mortisa, overlying the Formazione di Pradelgiglio, consists of bioturbated marls with larger foraminifera, siltstones and sandstones, and foraminiferal calcarenites (Trevisani 1993).

The Oligocene is missing in the Monti Lessini area of the Verona Province (Antonelli *et al.* 1990). The presence of fossilized palaeokarstic cavities, filled by yellow soils (terra gialla di Verona), suggests intense erosion subsequent to emersion (Corrà 1977). Near Cavalo (North Verona), Oligocene beach sandstones transgress over Lower Eocene deposits (Castellarin & Farabegoli 1974). The Oligocene is well represented along the eastern Monti Lessini margin and in the Colli Berici (from Lumignano to Villaga), where an important shallow-water carbonate platform, characterized partly by hermatypic corals and patch-reefs developed (Geister & Ungaro 1977; Ungaro 1978; Frost 1981). These shallow-marine carbonates represent the Calcarenite di Castelgomberto (Bosellini 1967; Bosellini & Trevisani 1992) in which volcanodetrital lenses, rich in fossils, are locally present (e.g. Accorsi Benini 1974). On the opposite side of the Monti Berici, towards the Colli Euganei, the Marne Euganee were deposited in a pelagic basin (Piccoli *et al.* 1976). The temporary emersion of volcanic islands is documented by the formation of lignitic deposits, the most famous of which in Monteviale and Gazzo di Zovencedo (Monti Berici) contain an extraordinary land mammal fauna (e.g. Dal Piaz 1937; Bagnoli *et al.* 1997).

At the beginning of the Late Oligocene, the Calcareniti di Castelgomberto carbonate platform became emergent (Frost 1981; Gianolla *et al.* 1992); this event is documented by extreme palaeokarst formation (Bartolomei 1958; Mietto & Zampieri 1989; Dal Molin *et al.* 2001). In the Late Oligocene, following weak, local volcanic activity, this area emerged, as documented by the clays produced by the subaerial alteration of the volcanic sediments present at the top of the Calcareniti di Castelgomberto (Sovizzo; Bosellini 1964). In the northern Monti Berici (Valmarana, Col del Bosco), the Chattian succession is represented by sandstones and calcareous sandstones rich in larger foraminifera, which are overlain by coralline algal rudstones (Ungaro 1978; Bassi *et al.* 2007). Chattian sandstones and coralline algal rudstones are also present in the Monti Lessini area and are known as the Arenarie e calcari di S. Urbano (Bosellini 1967; Bassi *et al.* 2007); these are overlain by Lower Miocene marine marls (Marne argillose del M. Costi).

In the Monte Baldo area, the Early Oligocene is represented by shallow-water carbonates (Formazione Acquenere), siliciclastic carbonates (Calcare di Linfano) and marls (Marne di Bolognano) (Bosellini *et al.* 1988; Luciani 1989). Upper Oligocene sediments crop out in the Monte Brione and Monte Moscal areas; this succession is represented by conglomerates and larger foraminiferal and coralline algal calcarenites (Calcare di Incaffi; Luciani 1989) and by deep-water mixed siliciclastic-carbonate units (Formazione di M. Brione, Oligo-Miocene in age; Luciani & Silvestrini 1996).

In the southern Altopiano di Asiago area, the Oligocene units comprise siliciclastic sediments passing into paralic facies. The Arenarie di Mortisa formation is overlain by thick lower Oligocene siltstones and sandstones, often with conglomerates (Formazione di Calvene; Papazzoni & Trevisani 2000). The succession ends with the Formazione di Salcedo, a rhythmic alternation of volcanic deposits and fossiliferous units such as the Arenarie di Sangonini and the Marne di Chiavon. This area emerged in the uppermost Early Oligocene (Principi 1926; Frascari Ritondale Spano & Bassani 1973).

During the Aquitanian a new transgression led to the re-establishment of marine conditions in the western Venetian area. The Miocene successions are represented by sandstones and calcareous sandstones directly overlying the Marne di Priabona (Monti Lessini in the Verona Province), Oligocene limestones (Monti Lessini in the Vicenza Province), and submarine volcaniclastic sediments (Monti Berici; Ungaro & Bosellini 1965). In the Marostica area, the Aquitanian Calcare di Lonedo transgressed onto the Formazione di Salcedo, which comprises coralline calcarenites (Frascari Ritondale Spano 1969). The Burdigalian Molasse of Schio overlies the Calcare di Lonedo. In the Vicenza area, the Chattian Arenaria di S. Urbano is overlain by the Miocene Marne argillose del M. Costi, which are only a few metres thick (Bosellini & Dal Cin 1966; Bassi *et al.* 2007).

**Eastern Venetian part of the Brenta River.** During the Palaeocene–Early Eocene, pelagic units were deposited in the Belluno (Scaglia cinerea, Marna della Vena d'Oro) and in the western Treviso (Scaglia variegata) areas (Fig. 17.27). In the latter area, as in the Feltre area, sedimentation continued until the Middle Eocene (Scaglia cinerea). During the Late Eocene, a regressive succession evolved with the deposition of the Marna di Possagno and the Calcare di Santa Giustina units. In the SE Monte Grappa area (Treviso Province), the Possagno section (parastratotype of the Priabonian) is the thickest Priabonian succession in the Southern Alps. The section is *c.* 700 m thick and consists mainly of clay marls with planktonic and small benthic foraminifera (lower-middle Priabonian Marna di Possagno formation; Cita 1975; Grünig & Herb 1980). The Marna di Possagno is overlain by the upper Priabonian Calcare di Santa Giustina unit, consisting of larger foraminiferal calcarenites

(Braga 1972; Trevisani 2000).

The Belluno Flysch is a sedimentary body >1000 m thick, located between the Alpago and the Feltre areas, as well as in the Venetian foreland basin between Vittorio Veneto and Segusino. In the Alpago and Belluno areas, this unit contains only lower Eocene sediments, in the Feltre area it extends into the middle Eocene, and in the Follina area up to the late Eocene. North of Feltre, the middle-upper Eocene succession is characterized by alternations of biogenic calcarenites, marls and sandstones. The Marna di Possagno unit and the upper part of the Belluno Flysch are interpreted as slope deposits interfingering with the distal facies of the Belluno Flysch (e.g. Costa *et al.* 1996; Stefani & Grandesso 1991).

Across the eastern Venetian area, the Eocene deposits are unconformably overlain by the Chattian Molasse. The unconformity is the result of an important hiatus which becomes older towards the east (Middle Eocene–Early Oligocene in the Alpago and Belluno areas) and younger towards the west and south (Early Oligocene in the Feltre, Possagno and Follina areas). The Southern Alpine Molasse ranges from the Chattian to Recent (Massari *et al.* 1986*a*; Costa *et al.* 1996), and represents parts of the infilling of the Venetian Basin, restricted to the east by the Dinaride Mountains, and to the west by the Schio-Vicenza lineament. The Chattian–Messinian sediments form a clastic body with a maximum thickness of >4000 m at the Venetian foreland basin–plain boundary. The molasse consists mainly of sandstones, siltstones, marls and conglomerates. These are inner-platform carbonate deposits that are occasionally overlain by more distal sediments (Marna di Bolago, Marna di Monfumo, Marna di Tarzo; Massari *et al.* 1986*a*). Sedimentation commenced with shallow-marine deposits including a tide- and wave-dominated delta system, and a mixed siliciclastic-carbonate facies (Massari *et al.* 1986*a*, *b*). The Arenaria glauconitica di Belluno, up to 50 m thick, consists of fossiliferous sandstones rich in glauconite and represents the transgressive basal layer of the molasse succession. It is heteropic with the Conglomerato di M. Parei and the Calcarenite dell'Alpago (Massari *et al.* 1986*b*). The Conglomerato di M. Parei (Keim & Stingl 2000), which crops out in the Ampezzo area, contains Chattian to Aquitanian fossils in the matrix and unconformably overlies Mesozoic units. The Chattian Calcarenite dell'Alpago (Costa *et al.* 1996) comprises up to 50 m thick glauconitic calcarenites with larger foraminifera, rhodoliths and bryozoans. This is restricted to the Alpago area (Massari *et al.* 1986*b*). The Calcarenite di Castelcucco (Scudeler Baccelle & Reato 1988; Bassi *et al.* 2007) crops out in the Castelcucco and Vittorio Veneto area and is represented by larger foraminiferal and coralline algal calcarenites alternating with thin marly beds. This unit overlies the Siltite di Bastia and is disconformably overlain by the Aquitanian Siltite di Casoni (Massari *et al.* 1986*b*).

The northern margin of the Lessini Shelf is located in the Valsugana area (Borgo Valsugana to Pieve Tesino). The early to lowermost middle Eocene is represented by deep-water sediments (Scaglia cinerea) with planktonic foraminifera (Fuganti *et al.* 1965). The Late Eocene consists of shallow-marine foraminiferal and coralline algal calcarenites of the Calcare di Nago unit and deep-water sediments (Marne di Bolognano, Formazione di Castello Tesino; Luciani & Trevisani 1992). The Oligocene is represented by the Formazione Acquenere (marls and marly siltstones with *Nummulites*), the Calcare di Linfano (larger foraminiferal calcarenites: Schiavinotto 1978), the Formazione di Castello Tesino and the Formazione di M. Brione. The Priabonian to Rupelian deposits are generally characterized by a large amount of siliciclastics and a reduced thickness (Trevisani 1997).

The Neogene sediments of the Vittorio Veneto–Belluno area are mainly siliciclastics. Carbonate deposits with thick rhodolith accumulations are represented by the upper Chattian Calcarenite di Castelcucco unit in the Vittorio Veneto area, and by the coeval Calcarenite dell'Alpago unit in the Belluno–Alpago area. The Siltite di Bastia unit is overlain by the Calcarenite di Castelcucco and overlies the Calcarenite dell'Alpago. In the Alpago area the Siltite di Bastia is up to 250 m thick and decreases in thickness towards Feltre; in the Venetian foreland basin area it is a few metres thick (Ghibaudo *et al.* 1996). Between the Feltre and Alpago areas, two sandstone units with glauconite (Arenaria di Orzes and Arenaria di Libano) overlie the Siltite di Bastia, separated by a silty unit (Siltite di Casoni). Around Belluno these three formations are >100 m thick. The Arenaria di Orzes has been interpreted as an estuary shoal deposit, while the Siltite di Casoni and the Arenaria di Libano represent prodelta and delta-front facies (Massari *et al.* 1986*a*; Costa *et al.* 1996).

The Burdigalian is represented by a transgressive–regressive succession related to a eustatic event affecting the outer carbonate platform. The Marna di Bolago consists of marls and ranges in thickness from 100 m (Feltre) to 200 m (Venetian foreland basin area). The overlying Arenaria di S. Gregorio (up to 60 m of sandstones) represents a rapid transition from outer- to inner-platform environments with a fluvial influence (Costa *et al.* 1996).

The Langhian commenced with a rapid transgression, which followed the abrupt deepening of the Venetian Basin to bathyal conditions. The succession begins with the Marna di Monfumo which comprises a basal layer of fossil-rich glauconitic sandstones overlain by marls containing small bivalves (20–45 m thick). The Arenaria di Monte Baldo overlies the Marna di Monfumo and consists of coarse glauconitic-fossiliferous sandstones, and biocalcarenites alternating with grey marls. This unit represents shelf deposits with sand ridges (Massari *et al.* 1986*a*, *b*). The Arenaria di M. Baldo crops out in the Venetian foreland basin area (Vittorio Veneto, Crespano). Its thickness ranges from 50 to 300 m, with a maximum near Vittorio Veneto.

From the Serravallian to the Messinian, several important changes occurred in the Venetian basin: the axis of the foredeep shifted and the basin was incorporated into the South Alpine deformational system. In the initial stage, accelerated subsidence led to the deposition of epibathyal marls (Marna di Tarzo) overlying the Arenaria di M. Baldo, followed by organic-rich lower Tortonian mudstones. The subsequent stage was characterized by rapid slope progradation (middle Tortonian). Localized conglomerate bodies (Conglomerato di M. Piai) within this succession represent mass-flow deposits probably funnelled along a structural depression (Massari *et al.* 1986*a*). In the late Tortonian, subsidence slowed down and a stack of vertically aggrading fan-delta sequences (Arenaria di Vittorio Veneto) were deposited on the shelf created by the previous progradational episode (Massari *et al.* 1986*a*). The architecture of the Messinian alluvial system was largely controlled by tectonics. Palaeocurrent indicators and the composition of Tortonian–Messinian sandstones and conglomerates suggest a source area within the eastern South Alpine domain. The Messinian Conglomerato del Montello represents coarse fan-deltas passing upward into alluvial deposits (up to 200 m thick). Blue sandy clays, early–middle Pliocene in age, deposited above the Conglomerato del Montello crop out near Cornuda and represent a neritic setting (Massari *et al.* 1993).

### *Volcanism*

Palaeogene magmatism within the Eastern Alps is variable in time and space. This magmatism can be interpreted in terms of the changing geodynamic framework that is reflected in the different evolution of the related mantle sources (Wilson & Bianchini 1999). Two main tectonomagmatic associations can be recognized: orogenic (subduction-related) suites and anorogenic (intraplate) suites.

Magmatic rocks characterized by orogenic affinities, including both mafic and felsic dykes as well as granitoid intrusions, occurred mainly between 42 and 25 Ma (with a climax between 33 and 29 Ma) along the Insubric-Periadriatic Lineament. Major element composition of the basic rocks indicates a spectrum of magma compositions ranging from calc-alkaline and high-K calc-alkaline to shoshonitic types (Beccaluva *et al.* 1979, 1983; von Blanckenburg & Davies 1995; Macera *et al.* 2002). The most primitive mantle compositions appear to be mantle-derived melts relatively unaffected by shallow-level crustal contamination. Their trace element distribution displays enrichments in LILE (large ion lithophile elements, e.g. Cs, Rb, K) and depletion in HFSE (high field strength elements, e.g. Nb, Ta, Ti) as typically observed in magmas from active continental margins. These geochemical features, along with Sr–Nd isotopic evidence, indicate that magmatism was induced by partial melting of lithospheric mantle domains intensely metasomatized by subduction-related fluids/melts. The significant presence of shoshonites suggests that continental crustal components were also involved in subduction.

To the south, anorogenic volcanic rocks characterize the Veneto Volcanic Province (VVP). This is Late Palaeocene to Late Oligocene in age and is represented by a series of eruptive centres orientated NNW–SSE. Magma generation appears to have been triggered by decompressional effects related to extensional deformation which affected the South Alpine Foreland in response to the general north–south compression during the Alpine Orogeny (Beccaluva *et al.* 2003, 2005). VVP lavas are mainly basic and comprise a wide compositional spectrum of mantle-derived melts including (mela) M-nephelinites, basanites, alkali-basalts and tholeiites (De Vecchi & Sedea 1995), as typically observed in low-volcanicity rifts. The relative abundance of silica-undersaturated and silica-oversaturated products varies regionally, with more abundant nephelinites and basanites to the west (Val d'Adige and western Monti Lessini), and predominantly alkali-basalts, transitional basalts and tholeiites to the east (eastern Monti Lessini and Marostica area). The sodic character ($Na_2O/K_2O > 1$), and the incompatible element distribution (characterized by negative anomalies in Cs, Rb, K, and positive anomalies in Nb–Ta) of VVP volcanics show similarities with intraplate magmas. Recent studies on spinel-peridotites (mantle fragments) entrained as xenoliths in VVP basanites and nephelinites indicated that: (a) the local lithospheric mantle was extensively metasomatized by alkali-silicate melts; and (b) the area was characterized by an anomalously hot geotherm (Siena & Coltorti 1989, 1993; Beccaluva *et al.* 2001). These factors, coupled with the adiabatic decompression that was induced by extension, triggered magma-genesis and, thus, the observed volcanism (Beccaluva *et al.* 2005). Sr–Nd–Pb analyses of the volcanics, integrated with studies of the entrained mantle xenoliths, indicate that both lithospheric and sublithospheric (possibly plume-related) mantle sources were involved in their generation (Macera *et al.* 2003; Beccaluva *et al.* 2005).

## *Southern Alps in Italy: Friuli Pre-Alps and Karst (N.P., G.T.)*

The Palaeogene deposits of the Friuli-Venezia-Giulia region have been extensively studied (e.g. Stache 1889; Dainelli 1915; Martinis 1962; Auboin 1963; Bignot 1972; Cousin 1981; Cucchi *et al.* 1987). A short synthesis was given by Venturini & Tunis (2002). The Palaeogene scenario, inherited from the Mesozoic, consisted of the Friuli Platform, which bordered the Belluno Basin to the NW and the Julian Basin towards the NE (Venturini & Tunis 2002). Palaeogene deposits of the Friuli-Venezia-Giulia were part of the Friuli Platform and the Julian Basin. From a geographic point of view, the Friuli Platform corresponds to the present-day southern Pre-Alps and Karst, and the Julian Basin can be related to the Julian Pre-Alps. The Friuli Platform and the Julian Basin can be traced southwards to the Adriatic and Dinaric Platforms, and the Bosnian Basin, respectively (Cati *et al.* 1987; Herak 1989). Moreover, Cati *et al.* (1987) proposed a new scenario with an additional Friuli Basin that subdivided the Friuli Platform into SW (SW of Pordenone) and NE (Udine area and south of Udine) sectors. This new basin would then continue to the Outer Dinarides. As a consequence, the SW and NE Friuli platforms may be connected with the Adriatic (present-day Dalmatian Zone) and Dinaric (present-day High Karst Zone) platforms, respectively.

### *Tectonic setting*

The tectonic setting of the Palaeogene of the Friuli-Venezia-Giulia regions comprises a series of NW–SE overthrusts, which verge southwards (Castellarin & Vai 2002). Compression led to the establishement of a foreland basin which migrated from Slovenia towards the Veneto (Doglioni & Bosellini 1987). Drowning of parts of the Friuli Platform proceeded from east to west. This tectonic phase is mainly Early Eocene in age (Carulli *et al.* 1982; Poli & Zanferrari 1995) and can be linked to compressive activity during the Meso-Alpine collisional phase (Castellarin & Vai 2002). Following Oligocene extension, a neo-Alpine compressive phase occurred (Chattian-Burdigalian), as demonstrated by the formation of NW–SE orientated thrusts (Castellarin & Vai 2002; Ponton & Venturini 2002). Subsequently, two further compressive phases occurred during Langhian–Tortonian and ?Messinian–Pliocene–Quaternary times, as demonstrated by south-orientated thrusts.

### *Sedimentary and stratigraphic development*

The Palaeogene carbonate platform succession commences with Palaeocene sediments, which mostly overlie Late Cretaceous units; Maastrichtian is proven for some localities of the east Trieste Karst (Pugliese *et al.* 1995) and the south and north Gorizia Karst (Tentor *et al.* 1994). Maastricthian inner lagoonal sediments comprise the last rudist genera *Bournonia* and *Apricardia* as well as foraminifers (Caffau *et al.* 1998). The latest Cretaceous to early Danian succession contains several stratigraphic hiatuses, often associated with emergence and the development of peritidal cycles, such as in the eastern Trieste Karst (Pugliese *et al.* 2000). One of the basal peritidal cycles at Padriciano records the K/Pg boundary (Pugliese & Drobne 1995; Pugliese *et al.* 1995, 2000), which is also present elsewhere in the Slovenian Karst area (Drobne *et al.* 1988*a*; Ogorelec *et al.* 1995, 2001). The boundary is documented by palaeontological data (Pugliese *et al.* 1995, 2000), palaeomagnetism (Martón *et al.* 1995*a*), an iridium anomaly (Hansen *et al.* 1995), and a negative shift in $\delta^{13}C$ (Ogorelec *et al.* 1995).

After the K/Pg boundary crisis, pioneer biota (small foraminifers, thin shelled ostracods and gastropods) appeared in peritidal environments during the early Danian (Shallow Benthic Zone SBZ1 of Serra-Kiel *et al.* 1998). Characean algae indicate freshwater influence. The peritidal cycles are overlain by inner lagoonal limestones, which are Danian (SBZ1) to Thanetian

(SBZ3) in age. Alveolinid and nummulitid foraminifers, corals, corallinacean algae and sea-urchins appeared during SBZ4 (Pugliese *et al.* 1995, 2000). Sedimentation continues until the late Cuisian (SBZ12) with shallow-marine sediments containing larger foraminifera (Gozzi 2003). These Palaeogene deposits are mainly NW–SE directed (Drobne *et al.* 2000*b*) and preliminary larger foraminifera data suggest two main belts in the Trieste Karst (Drobne 2003*b*). The first one (zone 2 of Drobne 2003*b*) includes the localities Padriciano, Opicina and Duino. It is characterized by Danian to early Ypresian (SBZ1–9) carbonate ramp deposits, partly overlain by late Ypresian deep-marine sediments (Castellarin & Zucchi 1966; Pugliese *et al.* 1995; Gozzi 2003). The area of Colle of Medea (Udine) may also be part of this belt (Barattolo 1998). The second belt (zone 3 of Drobne 2003*b*) includes the Rosandra valley and is characterized by Danian to late Cuisian (SBZ1–12) carbonate ramp deposits overlain by deep-marine sediments.

Palaeogene terrigenous sedimentation took place in the Julian Basin, a narrow, elongate basin, which today is part of the SE Alps (eastern Friuli–western Slovenia). The basin had an internal margin in the north, which was subject to compression, and an external margin in the south, represented by the Friuli Carbonate Platform. The basin was characterized by mixed carbonate/siliciclastic sedimentation from late Campanian to Early Eocene times. Sediment distribution patterns are complex due to a combination of tectonics, relative sea-level changes, and subsidence (Tunis & Venturini 1992). During the main phase of turbidite deposition (Maastrichtian–early Eocene), >4000 m of sediments were deposited.

Most of the Maastrichtian units are interpreted as slope-apron environments located close to the margin of the Friuli Platform, while the Palaeocene and Eocene units reflect a position close to the outer side of the basin (Flysch di Calla, Flysch di Masarolis and Flysch di Grivò), followed by basin-plain environments and a deltaic system (Flysch di Cormons). The Flysch di Calla (early–middle Palaeocene) consists of reddish marls interbedded with thin sandstones and is a significant unit in eastern Friuli and western Slovenia (Pirini Radrizzani *et al.* 1986; Dolenec & Pavsic 1995). The Flysch di Masarolis (middle–upper Palaeocene) is mainly represented by thin siliciclastic turbidites, while the Flysch di Grivò (Late Palaeocene–Early Eocene) contains several carbonate megabreccias derived from the resedimentation of shallow-marine carbonates (Friuli Platform) as well as intercalated siliciclastic–carbonate turbidites. These extensive carbonate debris accumulations are explained by catastrophic resedimentation events in the deep-water basin. Some megabeds have a strike of more than 70 km and individual thicknesses of up to 200–260 m (Vernasso Megabed). Olistoliths can reach a length of several hundred metres.

The major megabreccia units were generated by the fault-controlled failure of the Friuli Platform margin, which became seismically active during the Late Palaeocene–Early Eocene. The Flysch di Cormons (Early Eocene–Mid Eocene) is characterized by basin-plain turbidites. Sea-level changes controlled basinal sedimentation from the latest Ypresian to the earliest Lutetian (Venturini & Tunis 1991). During the early Lutetian, a rapid progradation of prodelta, delta-front, and deltaic-plain deposits occurred in response to tectonic uplift. The prodelta deposits contain a rich and diverse macrofauna (corals, molluscs, echinids, alveolinids, nummulitids, etc.) (Maddaleni & Tunis 1993; Hottinger 1960). The corals formed patch-reefs in front of the advancing deltaic system. Together with the Slovensko Primorje, the Trieste area belongs to the Trieste-Koper Syncline. According to Pavšič & Pekmann (1996), the Trieste Flysch is characterized by interbedded siliciclastic sandstones and marlstones. The sedimentological features (probably basin plain turbidites) and the ichnofacies suggest a deep-marine environment (Tunis *et al.* 2002). In agreement with Pavšič & Pekmann (1996) and Tunis *et al.* (2002), the turbidity current flow was parallel to the WNW–ESE striking basin axis during the Mid-Eocene.

## *Slovenian Tethys basins (K.D., B.O., J.P., R.P.)*

Slovenia is situated at the contact of the Southern and Eastern Alps with the Pannonian Basin, the Dinarides and the Adriatic Sea (Figs 17.2, 17.26 & 17.29). Palaeogene sediments in SW Slovenia are delimited to the NE by the high plateaus of Trnovski gozd, Nanos and Snežnik, as well as Gorski Kotar in Croatia, and to the south by the Čičarija hills in the Croatian part of Istria. To the west, it passes along a narrow belt across the Trieste-Komen Plateau to the Soča valley, and further along it towards the north. In a wide arc the boundary encloses the hills of Goriška Brda. Further northward the boundary rises on the ridges between the Soča and Nadiža rivers. These deposits are heavily karstified and contain numerous caves, dolinas as well as several valleys with outcrops of deep-marine sediments. Palaeogene belts associated with the predominant Dinaric direction (NW–SE) continue to the east and south to Croatia, and to the west to Friuli. In the SE part of Slovenia, Palaeocene beds are exposed only as small erosional relics, e.g. between Ribnica and Novo mesto.

*Tectonic setting and palaeogeography*

Slovenia belongs to four large tectonic units: the Eastern Alps and the Southern Alps separated by the Peri-Adriatic Lineament; the Pannonian Basin in the east; and the Outer Dinarides extending to the south (Premru 1980, 1982, 2005; Placer 1981, 1999*a*). The Dinarides border the Adriatic Platform along the Dinaric Thrust. This series of overthrusts verges from the north towards the SE and includes Trnovski gozd, Nanos with Hrušica, Snežnik, and in Croatia, Gorski Kotar and Velebit (Rakovec 1956; Poljak 2000; Bigi *et al.* 1990; Blašković 2000). The Čičarija Zone is presumably a deformed intermediate zone between the Dinaric Thrust and the Istria autochthon (Placer & Vrabec 2004). The tectonic relationship between the Dinarides and the Southern Alps was described by Herak (1985, 1986, 1987, 1999). He subdivided the region into three tectogenetic units, namely Dinaricum, Adriaticum and Epiadriaticum, the first two of which represent carbonate platforms and the third one an intermediate pelagic zone. This subdivision is widely used (Blašković 2000; Biondić *et al.* 1997; Carulli *et al.* 1990; Drobne & Trutin 1997; Mioč 2003; Drobne *et al.* 2000*a*, *b*), but it is still under discussion. Other studies have suggested a separation of the Karst Dinarides, or a single Adriatic Carbonate Platform (AdCP) instead of the Dinaric Platform (Tišljar *et al.* 2002; Vlahović *et al.* 2002; Dragičević & Velić 2002). During the Cenozoic, most parts of the Adriatic and Dinaric platforms were emerged, and only small areas of the Adriatic Platform remained below sea level. This occurred during the Palaeocene in Slovenia, the Trieste region (Pugliese *et al.* 1995) and Hercegovina. Sedimentation continued, with interruptions, up to the end of the Middle Eocene. The development of the Palaeogene in SW Slovenia commenced either in the central part of the Western Tethys (after Golonka 2004) or, as proposed by Channell *et al.* (1979), as an African promontory along a submarine belt. This structural unit, known as the Apulian Plate or Adriatic (Micro)-Plate consisted of large carbonate platforms: in the west the

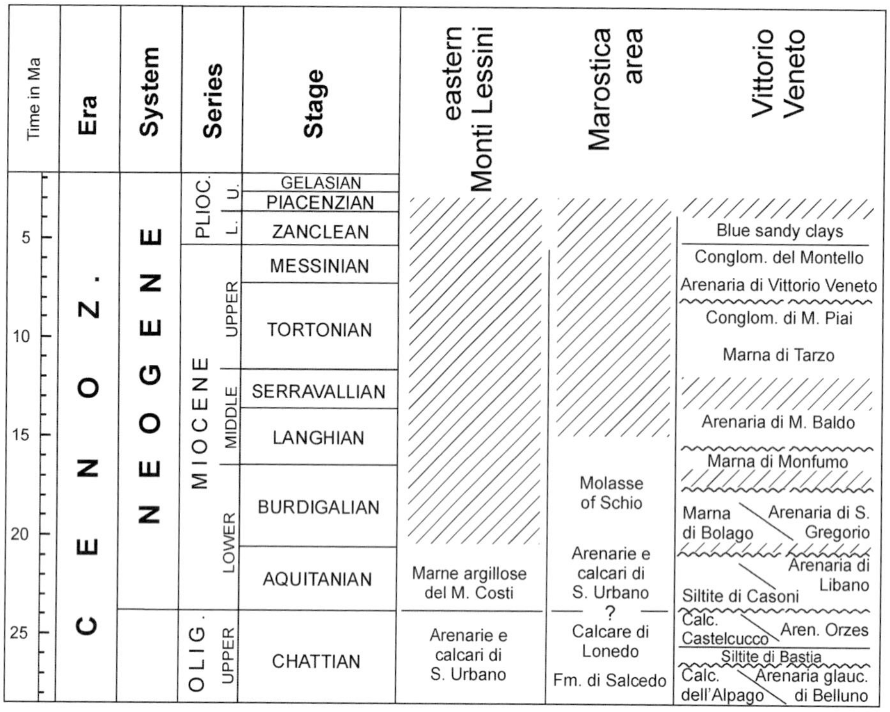
Time in Ma
Era
System
Series
Stage
eastern Monti Lessini
Marostica area
Vittorio Veneto
5
10
15
20
25
C E N O Z.
N E O G E N E
PLIOC.
L.
U.
MIOCENE
UPPER
MIDDLE
LOWER
OLIG.
UPPER
GELASIAN
PIACENZIAN
ZANCLEAN
MESSINIAN
TORTONIAN
SERRAVALLIAN
LANGHIAN
BURDIGALIAN
AQUITANIAN
CHATTIAN
Marne argillose del M. Costi
Arenarie e calcari di S. Urbano
Molasse of Schio
Arenarie e calcari di S. Urbano
?
Calcare di Lonedo
Fm. di Salcedo
Blue sandy clays
Conglom. del Montello
Arenaria di Vittorio Veneto
Conglom. di M. Piai
Marna di Tarzo
Arenaria di M. Baldo
Marna di Monfumo
Marna di Bolago
Arenaria di S. Gregorio
Arenaria di Libano
Siltite di Casoni
Calc. Castelcucco
Aren. Orzes
Siltite di Bastia
Calc. dell'Alpago
Arenaria glauc. di Belluno

**Fig. 17.28.** Lithostratigraphy of selected localities in the western and eastern Venetian areas.

Apennines with Apulia, in the east the Adriatic-Dinaric Carbonate Platform (or Adriatic Carbonate Platform), alternating with deep-marine basins (e.g. Belluno, Friuli basin; Cati *et al.* 1987).

*Palaeomagnetism*

At the Dolenja Vas section, which crosses the K/Pg boundary, reversed polarity has been observed in the Polarity Chron C29R, with a rotation angle of 28° in a clockwise direction (Dolenec *et al.* 1995; Marton in Drobne *et al.* 1996*a*, *b*). Investigations from this zone both towards the north into the Vipava valley and south to Savudrija, indicate rotation in a counterclockwise (CCW) direction of 30°. The polarity chrons between C29R and C21 have been described by Marton *et al.* (1995*a*, 2000*a*, *b*). New interpretations indicate that the imbricated Čičarija Zone and Istria have rotated by 30° CCW in relation to Africa and Europe during the Cenozoic. The most recent data for the last rotation is late Miocene to early Pliocene (Marton *et al.* 2003*a*, *b*). These dates may be valid for the entire AdCP as well as for the Adriatic Plate (cf. Mantovani *et al.* 1990).

*Sedimentary and stratigraphic development*

Palaeogene rocks in SW and southern Slovenia occur in three sedimentary units that co-existed parallel to each other: the deep trench, the deep-marine (flysch) basin, and the carbonate platform (Fig. 17.30). The succession begins with the Liburnian Formation, separated into the Maastrichtian Lower Miliolid Beds, the Danian to Selandian Kozina Beds, and the Thanetian Upper Miliolid Beds. The Liburnian Formation passes into the Ypresian to mid-Lutetian Alveolinid-Nummulitid Limestone (Alveolinsko Numulitni Apnenec in Slovenian literature). The lithostratigraphic terminology is inconsistent (e.g. Delvalle & Buser 1990; Jurkovšek *et al.* 1996*a*, *b*; Košir 1997, 2004; Ćosović *et al.* 2004*a*, *b*). Locally, the Cretaceous part of the Liburnian Formation is known as the Vreme Beds, and the Upper Palaeocene part as the Trstelj Beds (Pavlovec 1963; Pleničar & Pavlovec 1981). Other terms used include Slivje Beds for the first appearance of larger foraminifers in the Upper Miliolid Beds (Delvalle & Buser 1990), or Operculinid Limestone for nummulitid accumulations at the base of the Alveolinid-Nummulitid Limestone (Pavlovec 1963).

Based on underlying sediments (deep-marine clastics or shallower- to deeper-marine carbonate platform) and the distribution of larger foraminifera, Drobne (2000, 2003*b*) defined four biosedimentary zones for the area of SW Slovenia and Istria (Fig. 17.30). They were supported by various studies (e.g. Hottinger & Drobne 1980; Hottinger 1990; Drobne & Trutin 1997; Drobne & Ćosović 1998; Drobne & Hottinger 1999; Drobne *et al.* 2000*b*, 2002; Ćosović *et al.* 2004*a*, *b*; Serra-Kiel *et al.* 1998). The following description is arranged according to these biosedimentary zones (BSZ). References for the Palaeogene stratigraphy and palaeontology are presented by Pavlovec *et al.* (1989) and Pignatti *et al.* (1998).

**Biosedimentary Zone 1** (BSZ 1; includes clastic sediments from Goriška Brda, the Vipava Valley, and Kališe to the east, and Ilirska Bistrica to the south). Clastic sediments of the Scaglia and flysch beds are exposed in the Epiadriaticum between the thrust front of the Dinaricum in the north and the Cretaceous–Palaeogene platform of the Adriaticum in the SW. Deep-trench pelagic sediments are termed Scaglia or Podsabotin beds in the Slovenian terminology. They consist of red marls interbedding with limestone sheets, and were deposited before and after the K/Pg boundary, with sedimentation extending through the Palaeocene (Šribar 1965, 1967; Pavšič 1977, 1979). They can be traced along the thrust front separating the Dinaricum and Adriaticum in the line from north Gorica to Ilirska Bistrica.

Deep-marine sedimentation is continuous from the Cretaceous to the Palaeogene (Pavšič & Horvat 1988). The Palaeocene–Eocene boundary is recorded in the Nozno section (Pavšič & Dolenec 1995; Pavšič 1997; Dolenec *et al.* 2000*a*, *b*). The northernmost exposures of middle Palaeocene age (e.g. Banjšice Plateau, Soča Valley) comprise characteristic chaotic breccias (Pavšič 1995). The Upper Palaeocene to Upper Cuisian in Goriška

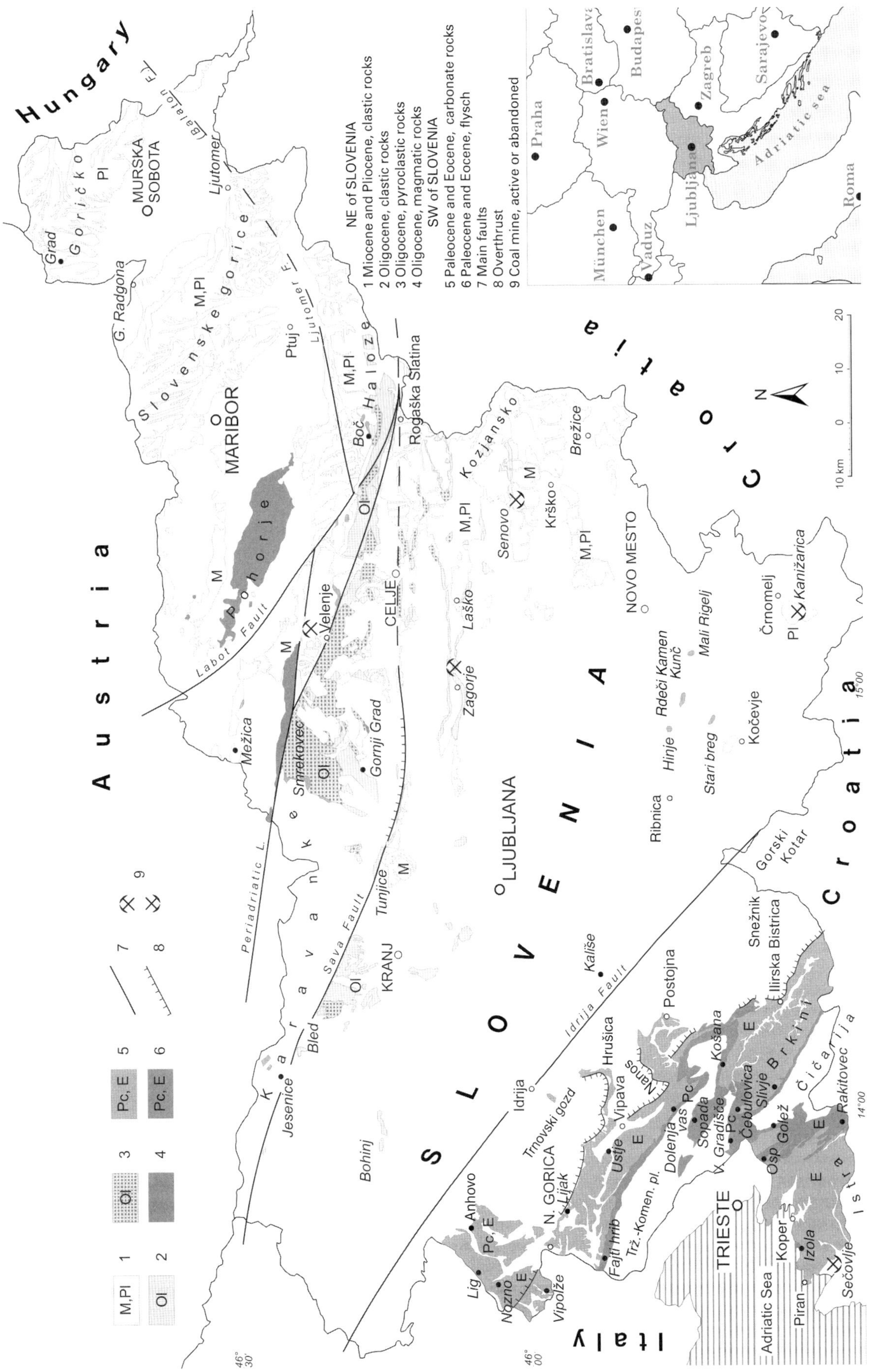


**Fig. 17.29.** Palaeogene and Neogene rocks in Slovenia.

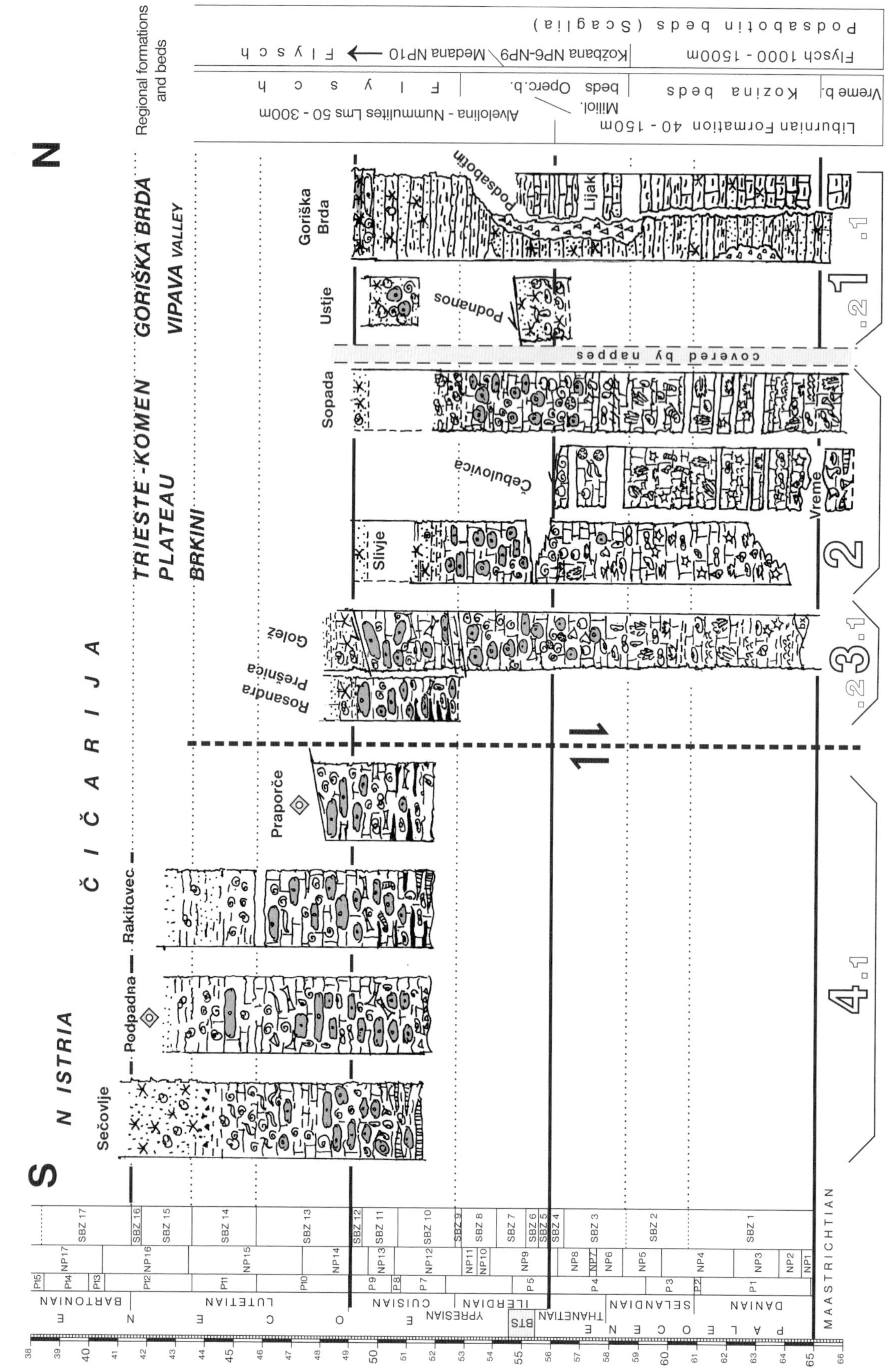


**Fig. 17.30.** Palaeogene sections in SW Slovenia: lithology, index fossils and biosedimentary zones 1–4 (larger foraminifera zonation SBZ after Serra-Kiel *et al.* 1998).

Brda include the Palaeocene Kožbana Beds (with megaclasts), and the more marly Eocene Medana Beds (Pavlovec 1966; Drobne & Pavšič 1991). Cuisian (SBZ12) clastic sediments in Goriška Brda are mostly developed as proximal turbidites and contain intercalations with pebbles of Cretaceous and Palaeogene limestones. They are particularly rich in nannoplankton and plankton assemblages (Cimerman *et al.* 1974) with abundant corals, gastropods and larger foraminifers (Cimerman *et al.* 1974; Drobne & Bačar 2003; Pavlovec 2004; Mikuž & Pavlovec 2002).

West of Goriška Brda, submarine slides and megaturbidites were described (Tunis & Venturini 1984; Skaberne 1989). Near Nova Gorica, a 1500 m deep borehole records a depression filled with deep-marine sediments (Marinko 1992). In the Gorica area, conglomerates with a source area to the NW and SW (i.e. Friuli platform) were deposited in several phases from Maastrichtian to Middle Eocene times (cf. Venturini & Tunis 1992).

Deep-marine sediments of the Vipava Valley syncline and its SE extension may overlie Scaglia beds. They are either concordant at the platform–basin transition, or follow after a hiatus (Engel 1970). Locally, megaturbidite beds with nummulitic breccias predominate (Engel 1974; Mikuž & Pavlovec 2002), and larger foraminifers of Middle Cuisian age (SBZ11) can occur in upper beds (De Zanche *et al.* 1967; Drobne & Bačar 2003). In the Vipava Valley, the Middle/Late Palaeocene (NP7, Lijak) to Middle Eocene development is well established (Krašeninikov *et al.* 1968; Buser & Pavšič 1976, 1978; Pavšič 1994; Rižnar 1997). At Postojna, deep-marine sediments with conglomerates containing nummulites indicate a Middle Cuisian transgression (Pavlovec 1981).

Separated from the Gorica area and Vipava Valley, several isolated exposures of deep-marine sediments occur in southern Slovenia. They are mostly erosional remnants (Premru 1982; Pavšič 1994, 1995).

**Biosedimentary Zone 2** (BSZ 2; includes platform and deep-marine sediments from the southern edge of Vipava Valley, Brkini with border areas, and southwards to the northern slopes of Čičarija). The deep-marine basins of Brkini and Trieste-Komen Plateau are part of the Adriaticum. The Brkini Flysch (Cuisian age: Khan *et al.* 1975; Drobne & Pavšič 1991; Pavlovec *et al.* 1991; Pavšič & Premec-Fuček 2000) was deposited in an elongated syncline with gently uplifted limbs of Palaeocene and Eocene limestones. At the NE margin, there is a gradual transition from limestones to deep-marine sedimentation (Drobne 1977; Pavlovec *et al.* 1991; Knez 1992). At the SW side, this change is more rapid and partly tectonically induced. Deep-marine sediments of the Trieste-Komen plateau (Kras area) are only known from a few isolated localities. The entire belt of deep-marine sediments (flysch) was dated as Cuisian (NP12 to NP14), and is underlain by mostly Ilerdian (partly Lower Cuisian) limestones (Pavlovec 1963; Drobne *et al.* 1991*a*, *b*, *c*).

In this biosedimentary zone, Maastrichtian limestones (Vreme Beds) are overlain by K/Pg boundary breccias, followed by Danian to Ilerdain limestones. They were deposited in shallow-marine environments characterized by occasional emersion events. The inner part of the shelf is typified by the formation of coal prior to, and after, the K/Pg boundary (Hamrla 1959, 1988; Hötzl & Pavlovec 1991). The overlying lagoonal and brackish environments were occasionally affected by emersion. Carbonate sedimentation was coeval with a Late Palaeocene transgression, and persisted until the Early Eocene. Carbonate microfacies and palaeontology have been investigated in several studies (Castellarin & Zucchi *et al.* 1966; Drobne 1977, 1991*a*, *b*, 1996*a*, *b*, 2000*a*, *b*, 2003; Pugliese 1995; Brazzatti *et al.* 1996; Accordi *et al.* 1998; Barattolo 1998; Turnšek & Drobne 1998; Gozzi 2003; Sirel 2004).

**Biosedimentary Zone 3** (BSZ 3; includes platform and deep-marine sediments from the SE slopes of Čičarija, Rosandra (Glinščica) valley, eastward to Krk Island). Carbonate platform sediments of this zone occur in a narrow belt extending along the Čičarija Brkini and the karst plateau to the NE, and Golež to the SW and towards the coast along the river Rosandra (Glinščica). To the SE, it extends to the NE margin of Krk Island. These sediments were deposited on a carbonate platform subsequent to Cretaceous–Palaeogene emersion. A pecularity of this development was the continued deposition of the Alveolinid-Numulitid Limestones during the Ilerdian and Cuisian as well as a transition into deeper-marine sediments, with glauconite-bearing strata, at the Cuisian–Lutetian boundary (NP14). Alveolinids predominate, especially those of *Alveolina histrica* (i.e. *Alv. rakoveci*), in addition to nummulitids (Drobne 1977; Drobne & Pavlovec 1991; Drobne & Ćosović 1998; Drobne & Trutin 1997).

**Biosedimentary Zone 4** (BSZ 4; includes carbonate platform and deep-marine sediments located along the oldest vertical faults on the SW slopes of Čičarija to Savudrija ridge, to Podpićan, and between Krk and Cres islands). The deep-marine sediments of Čičarija and Slovenian Istria can be subdivided into two complexes of different ages, both of which were part of the Adriaticum. The older one includes the NP14 zone and passes from Alveolinid-Nummulitid Limestone into deep-marine sediments with glauconite beds or with macrofossils (SBZ12?; Mikuž & Pavlovec 2004). At Gračišče, crabs, nummulites and nannoplankton revealed an Early Lutetian (NP15) age (Pavlovec & Pavšič 1987). The coastal belt comprises four sedimentary complexes, passing from limestones with alveolinids and nummulitids (Early to Middle Lutetian, NP15–NP16 boundary) into basinal sediments. Sedimentation continued until the NP16 zone (Pavšič & Peckmann 1996).

Alveolinid-Nummulitid Limestones were deposited from the Middle Cuisian to the Middle Lutetian (SBZ11–SBZ14). They overlie deeply eroded rudist limestones, bauxite, coal and bituminous beds and represent restricted shallow-water environments. At the transition to the Lutetian, foraminiferal associations were part of a larger Central Proto-Tethyan fauna, including species typical for SBZ13 and SBZ14 (Serra-Kiel *et al.* 1998). At the transition from the Middle to the Late Lutetian (NP15–NP16), a subsiding deep-marine basin developed (Drobne 1977; Ćosović & Drobne 1998; Krivic 1982, 1988; Marinko *et al.*1994).

*Significant stratigraphic boundaries*

In the Slovenian Karst region, the K/Pg boundary is present at several localities (Drobne *et al.* 1988*a*, *b*, 1989, 1995, 1996*a*; Pugliese *et al.* 1995; Dolenec *et al.* 1995; Ogorelec *et al.* 1995, 2001, 2005; Delvalle & Buser 1990). Close to the K/Pg boundary the Maastrichtian lagoonal limestone becomes darker and a freshwater influence is indicated by the presence of ostracods and characeans. The K/Pg boundary itself is characterized by a 20 cm (Dolenja Vas) to 2 m (Čebulovica) thick intraformational breccia of intertidal and supratidal origin, indicated by shrinkage pores and the occurrence of *Microcodium*. This short-lived emersion phase lasted, in Dolenja Vas, for at least 40 ka (Hansen *et al.* 1995). In some sections (Sopada) the breccia is less distinct, and only some plasticlasts and mud-cracked laminae are present (Jurkovšek *et al.* 1996*a*).

Extreme depletion in $\delta^{13}C$ (up to 10‰, from +2 to −8‰ PDB in the Dolenja Vas and Sopada sections) suggests global climatic changes caused by an impact body, followed by the destruction and combustion of terrestrial plants. At Dolenja Vas, the iridium values rise from 0.2 ppb below the boundary up to 5.8 ppb (Hansen *et al.* 1995). Mercury enrichment was reported by

Palinkaš *et al.* (1996) and Hansen & Toft (1996). In the deep-marine basins the K/Pg boundary is known from several locations where it is developed as ooze deposits (scaglia) or within the Podsabotin Formation. The hiatus spans the lowermost Palaeogene (Šribar 1965, 1967; Pavšič 1977, 1981, 1994; Perch-Nielsen & Pavšič 1979).

The Palaeocene–Eocene boundary is documented in the deep-marine sediments of Goriška Brda (Pavšič & Dolenec 1995, 1996; Pavšič 1997). The boundary was defined below the first occurrence date of *Rhomboaster bramlettei* (Bronnimann & Stradner). Anomalous contents of various elements, including iridium, occur somewhat below the biostratigraphically defined Palaeocene–Eocene boundary (Dolenec *et al.* 2000*a*, *b*).

The analyses of $\delta^{13}C$ stable isotopes at the Sopada section (part of BSZ2) reveal an excursion at the K/Pg boundary (depletion of 8‰ $\delta^{13}C$) and a longer-lasting event at the Palaeocene–Eocene boundary with a reduction from +2‰ to −4‰ PDB (Drobne *et al.* 2006), which is supposed to correspond to the global carbon isotope excursion. The excursion is situated within the transitional beds between SBZ4 and SBZ5 (Fig. 17.28). It is characterized by *Lacazina blumenthali, Thomasella labyrinthica* and also by a change from Operculina to Alveolinid-Nummulitid limestones. A $\delta^{18}O$ excursion was found in younger beds of SBZ6. It reveals a decrease from −2‰ to −8‰ (PDB), and corresponds with the Palaeocene–Eocene thermal maximum (Pujalte *et al.* 2003).

## *Slovenian Paratethys basins (B.J., H.R., D.S., M.Po., P.K.)*

The Paratethyan deposits of Slovenia (Figs 17.29 & 17.31) are preserved in the Alpine and Dinaric foothills in the central and SE part of the country, in the rolling hills and plains in the east and NE, as well as in some Alpine valleys in the north and NW of the country. From the margin of the Pannonian Basins System in the east, several long, narrow depressions, filled by Cenozoic deposits up to 2 km thick, extend towards the Alpine and the Dinaric mountain chains in the west. The westernmost Paratethyan deposits are found in the valleys of the Julian Alps. The Dinaric chain separates the Mediterranean from the Paratethyan deposits.

*Tectonic setting and palaeogeography*

From the middle Late Eocene to the Pliocene, depositional basins were continuously created, deformed and destroyed by extensional and compressional tectonic regimes (Jelen & Rifelj 2005*a*, *b*). The area under consideration was subaerially exposed after the suturing of Apulia and the Austro-Alpine units. It underwent extension and flooding during the middle Late Eocene. Block faulting is evidenced by scarp breccias, isolated small carbonate platforms, grabens of different depths, and the diachronous drowning of carbonate platforms. The termination of extension is not known, but the architecture of Early Egerian sediments overlying the Kiscellian deposits is interpreted as a tectonic load-flexural basin sequence.

After Egerian times, the process of post-collisional tectonic escape (Ratschbacher *et al.* 1991) controlled the development of the area. The lateral extrusion process of the Alcapa crustal block from the Eastern Alpine orogenic belt along the Periadriatic Lineament (PAL) fault system and the NW part of the Dinaric orogenic belt (Haas & Kovács 2001; Jelen *et al.* 2001) along the Zagreb-Zemplin Lineament (ZZL) deformed and offset the presumably uniform Palaeogene basin into the present-day Slovenian Palaeogene Basin and the Hungarian Palaeogene Basin (Csontos *et al.* 1992; Jelen *et al.* 1992, 1998; Fodor *et al.* 1998).

Subsequent continental extension (rifting) in a backarc setting resulted in the formation of rapidly subsiding grabens/sub-basins from Karpatian until Middle Badenian times. Synrift subsidence ceased near the Middle–Late Badenian boundary. This was followed by subsidence, which was caused by the post-rift collapse of the extensional basins.

The area to the east of the Julian Alps and NW Dinarides is the western margin of the Pannonian backarc rift. The Venetian Basin to the west of the Dinarides underwent a low rate of ENE–WSW Dinaric compression from the Chattian to the Langhian and was not incorporated into the NNW–SSE South Alpine compression prior to the Serravallian (Massari *et al.* 1986*a*).

Towards the end of the Middle Miocene, minor compression occurred, resulting in uplift and erosion. In the early Late Miocene, the change from uplift and erosion to flooding coincided with extensional reactivation of the Karpatian and Badenian normal faults. In the Pliocene, the climax of compressional activity caused intense folding, accompanied by basin inversion, and strike-slip faulting, accompanied by the formation of small pull-apart and transtensional basins.

*Sedimentary and stratigraphic development*

Jelen *et al.* (1992) defined four tectonostratigraphic units that correspond to the sedimentary units used herein. These are described from north to south (Fig. 17.31). (1) Unit A1 extends over a wide area north of the PAL (Northern Karavanke mountain range, Pohorje Mountains, Pannonian plain of NE Slovenia) and continues in the Styria (Austria) and in the Zala area and Little Hungarian plain. (2) Unit A2 extends in a very narrow belt between the PAL and the Donat Tectonic Zone (Southern Karavanke mountain range and the Haloze Hills towards the Čakovec area in Croatia). (3) Unit B1 extends in a narrow belt from the Julian Alps in the west and eastwards between the Donat Tectonic Zone and the Sava-Celje Tectonic Zone into the Varaždin area in Croatia. (4) Unit B2 occupies a wide area of central and SE Slovenia between the Sava-Celje Tectonic Zone and the ZZL and continues eastward to Croatia.

**Palaeogene Tethys.** The oldest Cenozoic deposits developed prior to the creation of the Paratethys Sea in the area under consideration are described above. Other pre-Paratethys remnants are situated to the north of the PAL in unit A1. Two small tectonic enclosures inside the Northern Karavanke overthrust, and south of Kotlje, contain bedded Middle Cuisian to Lower Lutetian limestones (Drobne *et al.* 1977; Mioč 1983). Two further remnants are preserved west of Zreče. There, the Late Cretaceous Gosau beds are unconformably overlain by coal-bearing platy and laminated marly limestones grading into shales (Hamrla 1988). This deeply eroded sequence is covered by fluvial conglomerates, which are interbedded with finer-grained clastic sediments and coal up-section. Alveolinid and nummulitid limestone pebbles indicate a post-Middle Eocene age of formation. These deposits correlate with the Early and Middle Eocene sequences of the Guttaring Group of the Eastern Alps.

**Palaeogene Paratethys.** Following the suturing of Apulia and the Austro-Alpine units, the area under consideration underwent subaerial weathering, and some bauxites were deposited. Subsequently, depositional basin developments began in Unit A2 within the nannoplankton zone NP19–20 (Jelen *et al.* 2000). These deposits crop out sporadically between the area north of

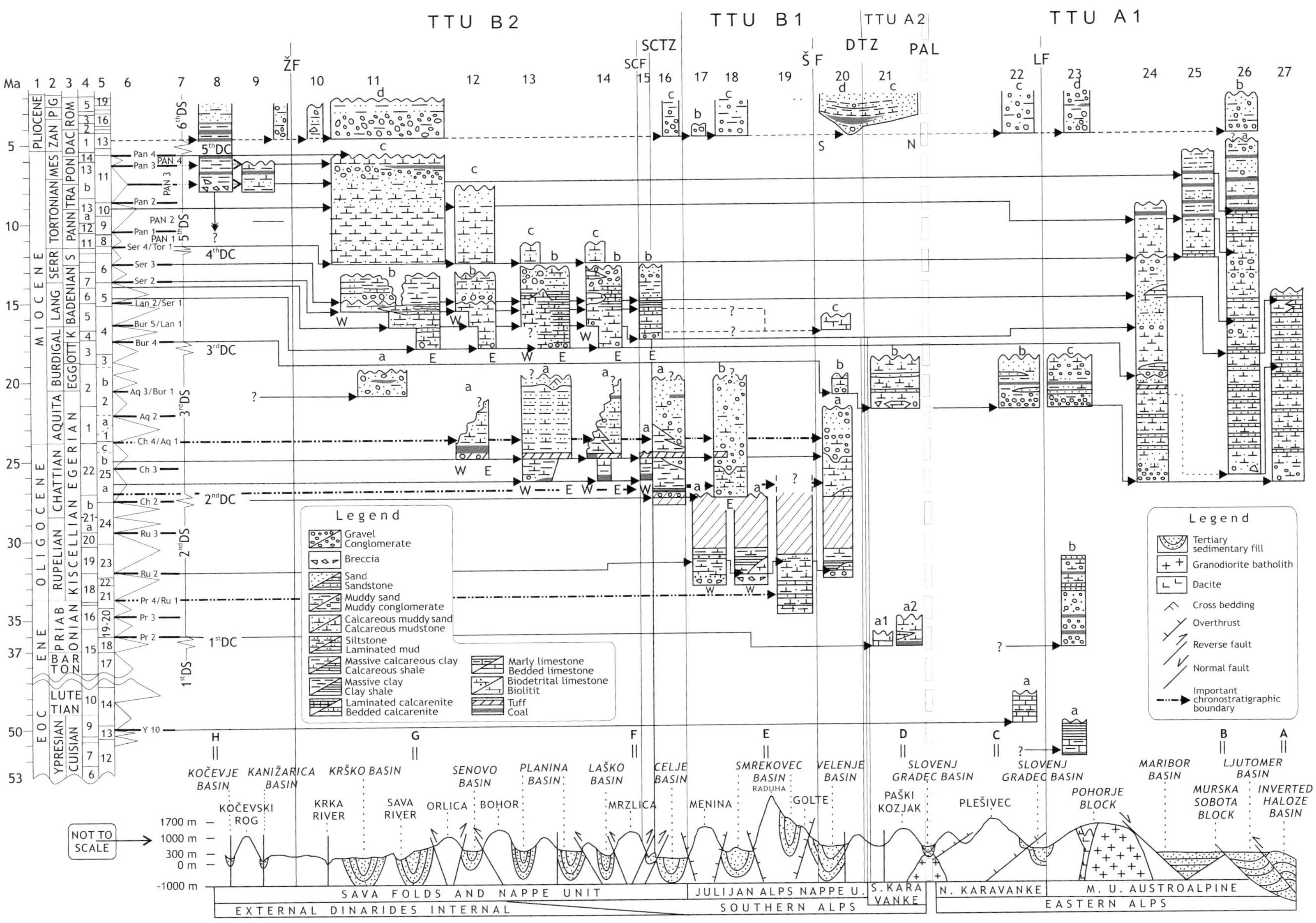


**Fig. 17.31.** Model of the stratigraphic relations in the Paratethys sedimentary area in Slovenia. TTU, Tertiary tectonostratigraphic units as defined by Jelen *et al.* (1992), corresponding to sedimentary units described in the text. Columns 1–6, chronostratigraphic subdivisions. 1, 2, Standard subdivisions (AQUITA, Aquitanian; LANG, Langhian; SERR, Serravallian; MES, Messinian; ZAN, Zanclean; P, Piacenzian; G, Gelasian). 3, Paratethyan subdivision (EGG, Eggenburgian; OTT, Ottnangian; K, Karpatian; BADEN, Badenian; S, Sarmatian; PANNON, Pannonian; TRA, Transdanubian; PON, Pontian; DAC, Dacian; ROM, Romanian). 4, Planktonic foraminifera biozones. 5, Nannoplankton biozones. 6, Chronosequences after Hardenbol *et al.* (1998), for the Late Miocene after Sacchi (2001); Ru 2, chronosequence boundary. 7, Stratigraphical development stages (DS) and changes in development (DC). Other abbreviations: DTZ, Donat transpressive fault; LF, Labot (Lavantal) fault; PAL, Periadriatic line; SCF, Sava-Celje fault; SCTZ, Sava-Celje tectonic zone; ŠF, Šoštanj fault; ŽF, Žužemberk fault.

Jesenice and the Slovenian–Croatian border (Mikuž 1979; Drobne *et al.* 1985; Šimunić *et al.* in Jelen *et al.* 2000; Jelen & Rifelj 2002). For the Socka area, the co-existence of a platform and a basin can be assumed. To the north, the sedimentary environments changed rapidly up-section, from freshwater to marginal-marine, to outer-shelf, and finally to bathyal environments. The freshwater, coal-bearing strata and brackish calcareous mudstones termed the Socka beds are well-known for their rich flora (Unger 1850). They are overlain by calcareous mudstones deposited on the shelf and slope. Nummulitid-discocyclinid limestones were deposited on the platform to the south, (Jelen *et al.* 2000). During tectonic escape, the basins were inverted and incorporated into the Southern Karavanke shear zone between the PAL and the Donat Tectonic Zone (Fodor *et al.* 1998).

During the latest Priabonian (earliest NP21 or latest NP19–20 zone; Baldi-Beke in Jelen & Rifelj 2002), the extensional basin-forming processes reached unit B1. Unit B1 deposits crop out in various locations between the Julian Alps in Slovenia and the Ravna gora in Croatia (Jelen & Rifelj 2002). The succession of the Smrekovec Basin, with a depocentre in the Luče area, begins with algal-miliolid, nummulitid and discocyclinid limestones. These were suffocated by the oxygen minimum zone. Carbonate-depleted mud was deposited on the outer shelf and upper slope during the Eocene–Oligocene transition. Frequent deep-marine carbonate gravity flows interrupted the low suboxic slope calcareous mud deposition. The latter changed, within the Oligocene part of NP21 zone, to suboxic basin-plain deposition with rare distal calcarenitic turbidites. Its topmost part belongs to NP22. The deepest sediments are the non-calcareous siltstones of the early NP23, in which deep-water agglutinated foraminifera faunas dominate (Jelen & Rifelj 2002).

South of the Luče depocentre, in the Gornji Grad area, delta-plain deposition occurred before late NP22, when a transgression commenced (Báldi-Beke in Jelen & Rifelj 2002). The Gornji Grad Beds (= Oberburg Beds) comprise brackish siliciclastics and marine limestones rich in coralline algae, bryozoa, corals, larger foraminifera and molluscs (e.g. Hauer & Morlot 1848; Reuss 1864; Barta-Calmus 1973; Nebelsick *et al.* 2000). They are overlain by shelf-muds and bathyal turbiditic muds (Scherbacher 2000; Schmiedl *et al.* 2002, and references therein). East of the depocentre, in the Mozirje area, the transgression began in early NP23 (Báldi-Beke in Jelen & Rifelj 2002). Massive calcareous mudstones, in places rich in molluscs, as well as laterally adjacent nummulite limestones, are overlain by a black laminated mud containing fish and plant remains (fish slates of Teller 1896). In the shallower oxygenated grabens, a mud similar to the Kiscell Clay of Hungary was deposited. In the deep sub-sill grabens, deposition of black laminated muds, interrupted by carbonate gravity flows, continued. The locality is historically known for its endemic fauna (Rolle 1858), which is now considered important for the biostratigraphic correlation of the central and eastern Paratethys (Báldi 1984). In the depocentre, non-calcareous silts were interbedded with volcaniclastics derived from the Smrekovec volcanism which occurred within the earliest NP23. The Smrekovec volcaniclastic deposits originate mostly from gravity flows and reach an estimated thickness of 800–1000 m (Mioč 1983; Mioč *et al.* 1986).

The Rupelian foraminifera fauna (Herlec 1985; Drobne *et al.* 1985; Pavlovec 1999), and its position within the Julian Alps nappe structure, suggested that unit B1 continues in the sporadic Cenozoic deposits in the Julian Alps nappe. These deposits, with a total thickness of more than 600 m, consist mainly of alternating various siliciclastics, freshwater limestones and coal lenses. The freshwater succession is topped by a *c.* 20 m thick succession of calcareous siliciclastics and limestones with a rich shallow-water fauna (Herlec 1985; Pavlovec 1999).

**Egerian to Eggenburgian Paratethys.** Within units B1 and B2, a complex tectonic load-flexural basin, with an inner thrust sheet within the present-day Sava-Celje Tectonic Zone, was formed during the Early Egerian. On the surface, these deposits extend continuously from the Ljubljana Basin to the Slovenia–Croatia border to the east and SE and continue to Croatia. The Celje foredeep basin, in front of the thrust sheet, reached an upper bathyal depth within less than one million years. The basal filling shows that flexure began while the Smrekovec volcanism was still active. The succession grades into marsh, brackish, shallow- and deep-marine environments. The transition to marine mud, (several hundred metres thick) of the underfilling stage took place near the Kiscellian–Egerian boundary (P21–P22 boundary) (Rögl in Jelen & Rifelj 2002). These muds are similar to the Kiscell Clay in Hungary, and are occasionally interrupted by submarine fans. A second volcaniclastic sequence within the mudstones was dated as late Early Egerian age (late NP25) (Báldi-Beke in Jelen & Rifelj 2002).

The Laško back-bulge basin contains economically important coal deposits that have been intensively studied since the middle of the nineteenth century (Ettingshausen 1872, 1877, 1885; Bittner 1884; Papp 1955, 1975; Kuščer 1967; Mihajlović & Jungwirth 1988; Placer, 1999*b*). Volcaniclastic intercalations in coal were dated to 25 ± 1 Ma (Odin *et al.* 1994) and are therefore correlatable with the second volcaniclastic sequence.

A basin north of the inner thrust sheet (i.e. in unit B1) also underwent tectonic load subsidence. Lenses of corallinacean limestones in the shallower part of the inner thrust sheet, and submarine gravel fans in the deeper part, were deposited on the Smrekovec volcanics. Further to the north, there is a transition from volcaniclastic to siliciclastic sedimentation. During the underfilled stage, the northern basin was filled by about 600 m of Early Egerian sediments similar to the Egerian Szécsény Schlier in the Hungarian Palaeogene Basin.

Channel formation occurred prior to the deposition of the second volcaniclastic sequence. They indicate a change in the flexural basin development. Subsequently, the sedimentation rate increased relative to the rate of subsidence and an overfilled basin developed. The interplay of subsidence, sea-level fluctuations and sediment supply resulted in the accumulation of >300 m of sediments. These deposits are best preserved to the east of Celje and Laško. The delta-front shelf tilted towards the north and alternations of sand and mud accumulated rapidly. At the shelf break, glauconitic sand accumulated. Cross-bedding and coal occur at the top of the stacking.

The Adria push and the clockwise rotation of the Tisza Unit, led to inversion, dextral strike-slip faulting and displacement in the Eocene and Oligocene basins. The premise for this displacement is that the NW strike of the Sava-Vardar ophiolite zone changes to a NE strike along the Zagreb–Zemplin Lineament and crops out again in NE Hungary (Bükk Mountains) along with the Szépvölgy Limestone, the Buda Marl, the Tard Clay, the Recsk volcanics and Egerian deposits, all similar to deposits in the Slovenian Palaeogene Basin (Jelen *et al.* 1998, 2001; Haas & Kovács 2001).

**Karpatian to Sarmatian Paratethys.** A phase of east–west to NE–SW directed backarc extension (rifting) created accommodation space in unit A1 and a NNE–SSW oriented extension created space in unit A2. This resulted in the formation of the

Mura-Zala Basin (Fodor *et al.* 2002), which was part of the Styrian extensional wedge of Ratschbacher *et al.* (1991) and of the Raba extensional corridor of Tari (1994). It includes the Radgona-Vas, the Mureck (Cmurek), the Slovenj Gradec, the Maribor, the Eastern Mura-Örség and the Haloze-Ljutomer-Budafa grabens/sub-basins as well as the Pohorje and the Murska Sobota extensional blocks.

During the first phase of extension in the Karpatian, benthic and planktonic foraminifers indicate deep-marine, restricted environments. Proxy equations of van der Zwaan *et al.* (1990) suggest that a water depth of 840 m (±20%) was reached very quickly in the grabens. They were filled by a mud/sand-rich system of gravity flows, and by dacite/andesite volcaniclastics, with a sedimentation rate of 1000–2000 m/Ma. Sediments were derived from a fluviodeltaic system of muddy flooding rivers and alluvial fans. These processes coincided with the formation of a significantly high relief in the Eastern Alps and the activity of a number of strike-slip and normal faults (Kuhlemann *et al.* 2002). We assume that towards the end of this first phase, the extension established a connection between the Paratethys and the Mediterranean. This happened during the falling stage systems tract between the Bur4 and Bur5/Lan1 sequence boundaries of Hardenbol *et al.* (1998) as indicated by the contemporaneous leap in abundance of the benthic and planktonic foraminifera and the first appearance of species immigrating from the Mediterranean (Jelen & Rifelj 2003). The Karpatian marine sediments are limited to the Styrian extensional wedge and to the marginal basins/feeding canyons south of the Donat Tectonic Zone. The Karpatian age of the brackish water, fluvial and mire deposits west of the wedge has been assumed on the basis of the observed interdigitation (Mioč & Žnidarčič 1989).

The Karpatian–Badenian boundary in Slovenia corresponds with the Styrian unconformity (Mioč & Žnidarčič 1989) and thus with the Bur5/Lan1 sequence boundary. Recent studies (Rögl & Rifelj, unpublished data) suggest, however, a position beneath the Styrian unconformity, corresponding with the increasing abundance of foraminifera and Mediterranean invaders. This finding is in accordance with the observation that the cooling events Mi-2 and MLi-1 are younger than the proposed age of the Burdigalian–Langhian boundary at the first occurrence of *Praeorbulina sicana* (Abreu & Haddad 1998). The Styrian unconformity in this area is a product of tectonic activity and a eustatic sea-level fall.

The Early Badenian was a time of significant paleogeographic changes caused by a second, strong extensional pulse and the Langhian eustatic sea-level rise of Hardenbol *et al.* (1998). Between the Donat Tectonic Zone and the ZZL, the Kozjansko crustal block underwent normal faulting and present-day east–west trending faults were reactivated as scissors faults. During the concurrent range zone of *Orbulina suturalis* and *Preorbulina circularis*, flooding created accommodation space along the boundary-normal faults in the eastern part of the Kozjansko Block and westward along the deep graben, following the central scissor transfer fault. The subsidence rate was very high and the water depth may have reached 500 m. The late Early Badenian transgression was accompanied by the formation of organic buildups composed of corallinacean algae, bryozoans and corals. Rhodoliths with diameters of up to 15 cm occur (Aničić & Ogorelec 1995). The short-lived carbonate platforms were soon tectonically tilted and destroyed (Kázmér *et al.* 2005), followed by the deposition of bathyal mud and calcareous/siliciclastic turbidites.

Continuous extension, which masked the eustatic signal, was followed by the late Middle Badenian transgression. The Late Badenian extensional collapse (near the Middle–Late Badenian boundary) and the Late Badenian flooding of Hardenbol *et al.* (1998) resulted in the maximum extension of the Badenian sea. Its westernmost remnant was found at Kamnik (Premru 1983). The collapse produced confined basins, calciruditic submarine fans, turbidites and laminated muds, with blooms of benthic foraminifera tolerant to oxygen depletion.

Most of the Senovo and Krško basins comprise Late Badenian mainly shallow-subtidal limestones and some calcareous mudstones. From the Krško Basin, Mikuž (1982, 2000) described a rich gastropod fauna. The succession could be dated by diatoms and silicoflagellates (Horvat 2003).

In the Mura-Zala Basin, the combination of the second, strong extensional pulse and a major eustatic flood resulted in water depths of 880 m (±20%) during the late Early Badenian. The lowstand wedge is overlain by transgressive coralline algal limestones with *Orbulina suturalis* and *Preorbulina circularis*, followed by deep-water calcareous muds and rare turbidites. A sudden change to sand-rich turbidites close to the final occurrence of *Preorbulina circularis* may have been related to the eustatic sea-level fall at the Lan2–Ser1 boundary of Hardenbol *et al.* (1998); this was followed by an extensional collapse creating confined basins.

A sea-level fall at the Badenian–Sarmatian boundary, which is correlated with the Ser3 sequence boundary of Hardenbol *et al.* (1998) and the MSi-3 isotopic event (Abreu & Haddad 1998), caused further facies differentiation. On the Kozjansko Block, shelf areas were temporarily subaerially exposed and subsequently flooded by the Early Sarmatian eustatic sea-level rise (Rižnar *et al.* 2002; Horvat 2003; Rifelj *et al.* in press). Various muds and laminated to bedded calcarenites contain diatoms, silicoflagellates, molluscs and plant remains (Horvat 2003, and references therein). In shallow basins, discrete occurrences of Badenian/Sarmatian limestones of various thicknesses, and rich in coralline algae, conformably overlie Badenian mudstones. Limestones and mudstones are overlain by laminated calcareous shales or calcareous mudstones and calcarenites. Sandstones, conglomerates, clays and corallinacean limestone, containing brackish molluscs (Bittner 1884), and in the deepest basins turbiditic sandstones, cover the calcareous mudstones and calcarenites. During the Sarmatian, episodes of marine/brackish conditions alternate with brackish/freshwater conditions (Horvat 2003; Rifelj *et al.* in press). The westernmost Sarmatian deposits are known from Kamnik (Premru 1983), where calcareous mudstones with brackish-water molluscs (Kühnel 1933) and diatoms (Horvat 2003) are overlain by poorly consolidated siliciclastics.

In the shallow parts of the Mura-Zala sub-basins, lowstand coarse clastics are overlain by sporadic corallinacean limestones, mudstones and siltstones with molluscs and plant remains. In the upper part of the succession, poorly consolidated sandstones and conglomerates predominate (Mioč & Žnidarčič 1989). Fan deposits and distal turbidites are the dominant sediment types in the deeper parts of the sub-basins. During the Late Sarmatian, the Neogene sedimentary sequence was locally deeply eroded due to tectonic uplift and a major eustatic sea-level fall at the Ser4/Tor1 boundary of Hardenbol *et al.* (1998).

**Pannonian *sensu stricto* to Pontian Paratethys.** The Late Sarmatian uplift and erosion was followed by the Early Pannonian subsidence and flooding. On the flanks of the Mura-Zala sub-basins, Pannonian mudstones interspersed with sandstones onlap eroded Sarmatian and Badenian rocks and the metamorphic basement of the Murska Sobota extensional block. Turbidite deposition continued in deeper parts of the basins. On the

Kozjansko Block, Early Pannonian deposits transgrade over Sarmatian, Badenian, or pre-Cenozoic rocks (Poljak 2004; Aničić 1991). Sediments of the Kozjansko Block are well studied in the Krško Basin (Poljak 2004; Škerlj 1985; Stevanović & Škerlj 1985, 1990) and the succession can be correlated with the seismic sequences of Sacchi (2001) as follows. Aggradational calcareous muds containing *Congeria czjzeki* and progradational sands containing *C. praerhomboidea* are equivalent to the PAN-2 (Fig. 17.31) seismic sequence of Sacchi (2001). The overlying aggradational sandy calcareous muds with *C. rhomboidea* and the following progradational calcareous muddy sands with a coal deposit on the top is equivalent to the PAN-3 seismic sequence. The youngest deposits are calcareous muds containing brackish-water ostracods and are equivalent to the PAN-4 seismic sequence. The *C. czjzeki* aggradational unit corresponds with the Pannonian *sensu stricto (sensu* Stevanović 1951, 1990). The *C. praerhomboidea* progradational and the *C. rhomboidea* aggradational units correlate with the Transdanubian (*sensu* Sacchi 2001). The second progradational unit plus PAN-4 are correlatable to the Pontian *sensu stricto* (*sensu* Sacchi 2001). Other remnants along the Slovenia–Croatia border are Pannonian marls and marly clays interspersed with sands and sandstones (Aničić 1991).

In the Mura-Zala Basin, the delta began to prograde into the basin during the Sarmatian, and in the Krško Basin during the early Transdanubian. By the end of the Pontian, the delta plain extended over both basins. Transdanubian sediments attain a thickness of 350 m in the Krško Basin and 500 m in the Mura-Zala Basin; the thickness of Pontian sediments in the two basins is 1100 m and 1700 m, respectively. It is not clear, whether this was the result of post-rift subsidence or post-rift activity coupled with the increasing intraplate stress caused by the Adria microplate CCW rotation (Márton *et al.* 2003*b*). This movement began at *c.* 9 Ma, which is the time of the opening of the Tyrrhenian Sea (Jelen & Rifelj 2005*a*, *b*).

**Pliocene.** Intense folding and the development of pop-up structures supplied material to alluvial fans and fluvial systems; e.g. the Haloze part of the Ljutomer-Haloze-Budafa sub-basin was positively inverted and about 2000 m of sediments were eroded (Sachsenhofer *et al.* 2001; Fodor *et al.* 2002; Márton *et al.* 2002*a*). Coeval strike-slip faulting created small pull-apart and transtensional basins (Vrabec 1994, 1999) filled by lake sediments.

The Velenje Basin includes some of the best studied lake sediments in the region. The basin was presumably formed during the Middle Pliocene as a transtensional basin with a half-graben geometry (Brezigar *et al.* 1987; Vrabec 1999). Pliocene sediments of this basin include basal silts with boulders, marsh and mire lignite, shallow lake marls and clays as well as massive and laminated clays with pebbly sands. At the depocentre, near the Šoštanj Fault, these sediments are about 1000 m thick.

A change from the *Taxodium* to *Fagus* palynoflora in the laminated clays represents the Middle–Late Pliocene boundary. The Pliocene–Pleistocene boundary is transitional within the transitional shallow lake/terrestrial silts and sands. Shallow-water lake deposits are rich in molluscs, mammals and plants (Brezigar *et al.* 1987). Lamination is interpreted as being related to planktonic diatom stratification in a eutrophic lake. The geology and petrology of the 160 m thick uniform lignite seam was studied by Brezigar (1987) and Markič & Sachsenhofer (1997).

*Volcanism*

Cenozoic volcanic activity in NE Slovenia is closely related to the tectonic evolution of the Pannonian Basin within the Alpine–Dinarides–Carpathian orogenic belt. This commenced with the subduction of the European Plate below Africa and continued with the collision, post-syncollisional transpression, separation and eastward escape of the Pannonian fragment, and finally basin extension. Calc-alkaline volcanism apparently commenced in the Eocene and reached its climax during the Late Oligocene and the earliest Miocene. It ceased during the Badenian. The youngest volcanic rocks are alkaline basalts that extruded after the main extension of the Pannonian Basin during the Upper Pliocene–Romanian.

The Oligocene to Early Miocene magmatic period along the easternmost sector of the PAL was very intense. It yielded Karavanke and Pohorje tonalite and granodiorite intrusions (Altherr *et al.* 1995; Pamić & Palinkaš 2000) and volcanic rocks of the Smrekovec suite which encompass the Smrekovec volcanic complex and the occurrences of pyroclastic and volcaniclastic rocks extending from NW Slovenia (Peračica) via Sava Folds to the Celje, Laško and Mura basins (Hinterlechner-Ravnik & Pleničar 1967; Kralj 1996, 1999). Volcanic rocks of the Smrekovec suite range in composition from basaltic andesite to rhyolite, and mainly exhibit a medium-K affinity.

Three main volcanic lithofacies groups were recognized: coherent, autoclastic and volcaniclastic types (Kralj 1996). Coherent rocks are developed as lavas, shallow intrusive bodies or volcanic vent fillings. Marginal parts of lavas and shallow intrusive bodies are commonly autobrecciated with a tendency to grade into hyaloclastite breccias and peperitic breccias. Peperites are less common.

Volcaniclastic deposits are the most widespread lithofacies group. Submarine pyroclastic flow deposits of dacitic to rhyolitic composition can be >100 m thick, and consist of pumice and volcanic glass shard-rich tuffs (Kralj 1999). Secondary volcaniclastic deposits are abundant in the Smrekovec volcanic complex and comprise volcaniclastic debris flows and turbidity flows. They form internally stratified, fining-upward sequences.

Late Pliocene alkaline basaltic volcanism occurred in the northwesternmost margin of the Mura Basin in the Late Pliocene (Romanian). This volcanism is related to the extension of the Pannonian fragment and upwelling of the asthenosphere (Embey-Isztin & Kurat 1996). Alkali basaltic volcanism occurred in a fluvial environment characterized by rapid sedimentation (Kralj 1995). Initial magmatic eruptions created a cinder cone with minor lava flows. Occasionally, the style of eruptions became essentially hydrovolcanic, producing pyroclastic surge deposits, and in the final stage, large lahar deposits. Alkali basaltic volcanism can be correlated with the final stage of volcanic activity in the neighbouring Styrian Basin (Poulditis 1981; Poschl 1991), Little Hungarian Plain and the Bakony–Balaton highland (Martin & Németh 2004). Palaeogene volcanism of the Smrekovec Basin was recently studied by Hanfland *et al.* (2004).

## *Dinarides in north Croatia and Bosnia (D.P., M.B.)*

The area of Croatia can be divided into three major units (Fig. 17.26). (1) The Pannonian and Peri-Pannonian area comprises the lowland and hilly parts of east and NW Croatia. (2) The hilly and mountainous Dinarides separate the Pannonian Croatia from the coastal region. (3) The Adriatic Area includes a narrow coastal belt separated from the hinterland by high mountains. This is predominantly a karst area.

*Tectonic setting*

The geological evolution of the areas of central and northern Croatia and Bosnia and Herzegovina differed during the Palaeogene and Neogene. The Palaeogene basin development was mainly controlled by compressional events, which resulted in closure of the Western Tethys and uplift of the Dinarides, while extension, interrupted by minor compressional events, controlled sedimentation in the Neogene. The area of north Croatia and north Bosnia was characterized by changing marine connections, typical for the Central Paratethys.

The formation of the Palaeogene basin in the area of north Croatia and north Bosnia was related to Jurassic/Cretaceous subduction along the north Tethyan margin. This initiated the gradual closure and shortening of the Dinaridic Tethys and the development of a magmatic arc. In the trench associated with this magmatic arc, Late Cretaceous–Palaeogene deep-marine sequences accumulated. Compression at the end of the Eocene was accompained by uplift of the Dinarides (Pamić *et al.* 1998, 2000*a*). This caused the formation of local alluvial environments in eastern Croatia (Halamić *et al.* 1993).

The Neogene basins of north Croatia and north Bosnia were part of the south Pannonian Basins System (PBS), and were formed due to the collision of the European (Tisia-Moesia) and the African plates (Horváth & Royden 1981; Horváth 1995; Kováč *et al.* 1998). Following separation of the Western Tethys into the Paratethys and Mediterranean during the Late Eocene, the northern part of the uplifted Dinarides became emergent. During the Oligocene transpressional phase, a Periadriatic dextral strike-slip fault, controlling the formation of the SW margin of the PBS along relicts of the previous subduction zone, was generated. The passive, lithosphere-generated rifting processes led to the formation of elongated half-grabens during the synrift phase. This began during the Ottnangian and lasted until the Middle Badenian. At the end of the Karpatian, uplift commenced as a consequence of the rotation of fault blocks around a horizontal axis. The uplift was contemporaneous with sinistral NE–SW strike-slip faulting, which was transverse to oblique to the master WNW–ESE elongated structures causing CCW rotation and the destruction of the elongate half-graben structures. This locally reduced the effects of uplift (Jamičić 1983; Pavelić *et al.* 1998, 2003; Márton *et al.* 1999*b*, 2002*b*; Pavelić 2001).

The post-rift phase lasted from the Middle Badenian to Recent, and was characterized by thermal subsidence, which was interrupted by two compressional phases generated by intraplate stress. The onset of the first period of intraplate stress took place at the end of the Sarmatian and may have initiated the uplift of blocks, resulting in base-level fall and partial basin inversion. The second intraplate stress phase affected the basin during the Pliocene, causing overall compression and structural inversion across the North Croatian Basin and north Bosnia. In these areas it was characterized by the formation of several compressional structures, subsidence, the uplift of basement blocks, CCW rotations, and erosion (Márton *et al.* 1999*b*, 2002*b*; Pavelić 2001; Tomljenović & Csontos 2001; Pavelić *et al.* 2003; Saftić *et al.* 2003).

Tectonic activity was the main external control on sedimentation in the Neogene intramontane basins of the Dinarides and it can be assumed that both compressional and extensional events influenced basin evolution. The Dinaridic intramontane basins were formed after the uplift of the Dinarides due to compression. Most of the Dinarides became emergent during the Palaeogene and normal faulting may have caused the formation of small tectonic depressions during the Oligocene and Neogene. Tectonically-controlled subsidence facilitated high sedimentation rates, although Pleistocene tectonics may have generated differential uplift of the Dinarides (Soklić 1970; Herak 1986). In addition to compression, extension was also active during the Pleistocene (Jamičić & Novosel 1999). In the Pleistocene, the uplift of the Dinarides to Recent elevations caused erosion of the Neogene sediments and reduced the dimensions of the freshwater basins. Frequent earthquakes along the eastern Adriatic coast suggest that compressional tectonics is still active today (Prelogović & Kranjec 1983; Papeš 1985; Herak 1986; Blašković 1999; Dragičević *et al.* 1999).

*Sedimentary and stratigraphic development*

**Palaeogene.** In the north Dinarides (i.e. north Bosnia), Palaeogene sediments form part of a Late Senonian–Palaeogene sedimentary sequence. The K/Pg boundary is frequently characterized by a significant biostratigraphic discontinuity (Polšak 1985). The uppermost Cretaceous–Palaeogene sedimentary sequence consists mainly of turbidites deposited in a narrow basin (Jelaska 1978). The deep-marine sedimentation, starting in the Maastrichtian, consists of individual graded sequences. It is dominated by sandstones and shales during the Maastrichtian and Palaeocene, while calcareous shales and sandstones, sandy limestones and limestones prevail during the Early and Middle Eocene. These deep-marine sediments are conformably overlain by late Middle Eocene limestones. This succession reflects the Palaeogene termination of subduction and the convergence of stable Africa and Eurasia in the area of the northern Dinarides (Jelaska 1978; Polšak 1985; Pamić *et al.* 1998). Tectonic uplift and erosion of the Dinarides took place at the end of the Late Eocene and Early Oligocene.

The Palaeogene sediments occur in scattered outcrops and in the subsurface of NW and central Croatia. Palaeocene sediments include marine clastics and limestones such as algal and coral limestones (Jelaska *et al.* 1970; Šikić *et al.* 1979; Pikija 1987). At the beginning of the Eocene, sedimentation of the Cretaceous–Palaeogene deep-marine succession was interrupted, and initial emergence occurred in NW Croatia. The emergence phase lasted until the Middle Eocene, when terrestrial clast accumulations were flooded by a marine transgression (Šimunić *et al.* 2000). Several Eocene sediment types occur in NW Croatia: Early Eocene limestone breccias, calcarenites, shales and conglomerates pass upward into reddish-brown gravels, sands and tuffitic clays, and Early Eocene bauxites; Middle Eocene coarse-grained clastic limestone breccias and limestone-dolomite breccias; shallow-marine Middle to Late Eocene limestones (coral biolithites, algal-foraminiferal biomicrites and biomicrudites) (Šimunić *et al.* 2000).

Marine sediments are also known from the Oligocene of NW Croatia. They are characterized by marls with sand intercalations (Šimunić 1992). At Mount Požeška (east Croatia), Oligocene coarse-grained clastics were deposited in an alluvial environment, thus reflecting the existence of continental conditions (Halamić *et al.* 1993).

**Neogene of north Croatia and north Bosnia.** Neogene rocks cover a large area of north Croatia and north Bosnia (Fig. 17.32). The thickness of Neogene deposits is highly variable and is more that 6500 m in the Drava depression. Egerian–Eggenburgian brackish-water to marine sedimentation was restricted to the Hrvatsko Zagorje Basin, i.e. to the area of the PAL (Šimunić *et al.* 1990; Pavelić *et al.* 2001). Marine deposition continued into Ottnangian times.

South and SE of the Hrvatsko Zagorje Basin (i.e. south Pannonian Basins System), alluvial and lacustrine sedimentation commenced in the earliest synrift phase (Pavelić & Kovačić 1999; Pavelić 2001; Saftić *et al.* 2003). The occurrence of

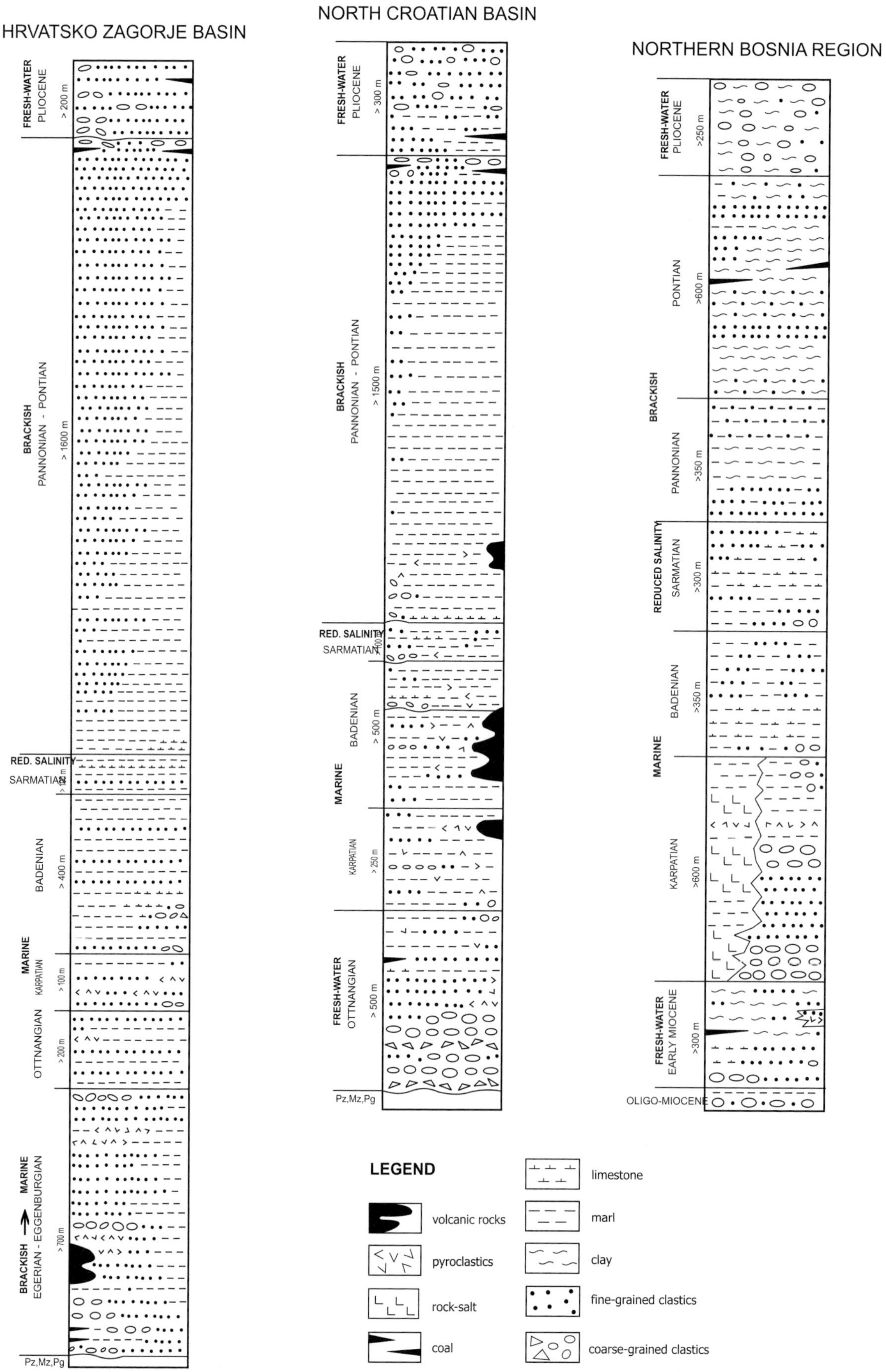


**Fig. 17.32.** Geological columns of the southern Pannonian Basins System.

*Mastodon angustidens* indicates a non-marine development during the Early Miocene of the Tuzla Basin (Soklić & Malez 1969). During the Late Ottnangian, a hydrologically open lake covered the whole area. Lacustrine sedimentation was accompanied by explosive rhyolitic volcanism (Mutić 1980; Vrabac 1999; Pavelić 2001). Marine environments commenced during the Karpatian (Pavelić 2001; Bajraktarević & Pavelić 2003; Saftić *et al*. 2003). They are characterized by calcareous siltstones with intercalations of clastics. The Karpatian sediments in the Tuzla sub-basin contain rock-salt and pyroclastic layers (Vrabac *et al*. 2003).

Due to a relative sea-level fall at the end of the Karpatian, some blocks were exposed, which locally resulted in the complete erosion of Early Miocene deposits and the exposure of basement rocks. The eroded siliciclastics were transported into high-energy, shallow-marine environments (Pavelić *et al*. 1998; J. Velić *et al*. 2000), and also into the relatively deeper sea (Pavelić *et al*. 1998). A deepening event during the Early Badenian caused the deposition of marls and gravelly calcarenites in the offshore areas (Pavelić *et al*. 1998). During the Late Badenian, the transgression flooded the peaks of the exposed blocks, which had formed isolated islands during the Early Badenian. Marine sedimentation commenced with the deposition of gravels, which are overlain by coralline algal beds. Further deepening resulted in the deposition of marls. In the Early Sarmatian, the salinity of the sea decreased, and the environment became mesohaline. The isolation of the basin caused a sea-level fall during the latest Badenian, which resulted in the resedimentation of older Badenian faunas (Pavelić 2001; Saftić *et al*. 2003). A subsequent transgression resulted in widening of the basin. Laminated marls (similar to varves) and massive marls dominated in this period, and the episodic input of sands took place by sediment gravity flows. The excellent preservation of the lamination may reflect anoxic conditions (Pavelić 2001).

The ecological conditions changed during the Early Pannonian. The environments became brackish (oligohaline) and locally freshwater, which caused the development of endemic molluscs and ostracods. Early Pannonian deposits overlie Sarmatian sediments almost conformably and include lacustrine platy and thin-bedded, littoral limestones. Resedimented Badenian fossils are abundant in the middle Pannonian deposits, reflecting a short-lived latest Sarmatian period of emergence and erosion. A subsequent lake-level rise affected the dominance of marls with occasional siliciclastic influx. During the Pontian, gradual shallowing is reflected by the increased terrigenous sedimentation within a prodelta environment. Sedimentation terminated during the Pontian with sandy delta progradation and the formation of peat bogs (Vrsaljko 1999; Pavelić 2001; Saftić *et al*. 2003; Kovačić *et al*. 2004).

Late Miocene deposits are overlain by Pliocene siliciclastic sediments accumulated in small freshwater lakes, swamps and rivers. Pleistocene deposits are comparable to those of the Pliocene, except for the remarkable amounts of aeolianites (J. Velić & Durn 1993; J. Velić & Saftić 1999; Saftić *et al*. 2003).

**Neogene intramontane basins of the Dinarides.** In the Dinarides, sedimentation of Neogene freshwater sediments began within intramontane depressions that had started to form during the Late Palaeogene (Fig. 17.33). Neogene sediments overlie the pre-Neogene basement or Oligocene deposits, and are characterized by frequent lateral and vertical facies variations as a result of independent local basin developments. Throughout Bosnia and Herzegovina as well as central and south Croatia, earliest Miocene sedimentation was restricted to freshwater basins, except for the SE part, which was probably flooded from the Adriatic Sea. The thicknesses of the Neogene deposits in these basins vary from a few hundred to 1900 m in the Livno-Duvno Basin and more than 2400 m in the Sarajevo-Zenica Basin. However, the stratigraphy of these freshwater deposits is still problematic (Pavelić 2002).

The oldest Neogene sediments belong to the upper part of the Oligo-Miocene series. Siliciclastics include conglomerates, sandstones, marls and clays. Characaean limestones and coal beds are sometimes found. Similar conditions occurred in the Early Miocene, and were followed by sporadic volcanic activity. Freshwater endemic bivalves *(Congeria)* had their main phase of evolution at this time (Kochansky-Devidé & Slišković 1978). Middle Miocene deposits are similar to those of the Early Miocene. Marls, limestones, sandstones, clays and conglomerates predominate. Pyroclastics occur in some areas. Thick marly limestone units with occasional coal seams are Middle and Late Miocene in age. The Upper Miocene and Pliocene deposits are characterized by marls, clays, siltstones, sandstones, conglomerates, limestones and coal seams. Pliocene sediments are known from a few localities, such as a series with lignite in the Livno-Duvno Basin and the Sarajevo-Zenica Basin. The youngest Pliocene to Pleistocene sediments are found in the intramontane basin in the NW Dinarides (Jurišić-Polšak *et al*. 1997).

*Volcanism*

Palaeogene magmatic rocks in north Croatia and north Bosnia were generated by the collision of the NE parts of the Apulian Plate and the SW margin of the Eurasian Plate. The final stage of this subduction is recorded by the sedimentary, magmatic and metamorphic units of the Prosara and Motajica mountains in north Bosnia, which are interpreted as remnants of a subduction-related magmatic arc (Pamić 1977, 1993; Lanphere & Pamić 1992). In north Bosnia, granitoids occur both on the surface and the subsurface. They occur as veins and small- to medium-sized synkinematic plutons in medium-pressure metamorphic rocks. Isotopic ages of Mesoalpine granitoids, which are associated with andesites and dacites, range from 48 to 30 Ma. In the basement of the Neogene of the north Croatian Basin, rhyolites of the ophiolite complex yielded ages of 67–47 Ma (Pamić 1993; Tari & Pamić 1998).

Neogene volcanism is generally related to extensional processes, except for the oldest volcanic units. Volcanic rocks occur mostly in the area of the Hrvatsko Zagorje Basin, and in the northern part of the North Croatian Basin, i.e. in the Drava depression. These rocks are divided into several volcanic formations: the Egerian–Eggenburgian dacite–andesite formation, the Ottnangian pyroclastics, the Karpatian trachyandesite (latite) formation, the Badenian andesite–basalt formation with subordinate dacites and rhyolites, and the post-Badenian basalt–alkali basalt formation (Pamić 1997; Pavelić 2001).

The rocks of the Egerian–Eggenburgian dacite–andesite formation are known only from the Hrvatsko Zagorje Basin and from neighbouring Slovenia. They may be associated with brackish-water and marine sands, sandstones, marls, breccias and conglomerates (Šimunić & Pamić 1993). The main phase of Alpine deformation (i.e. the Pyrenean phase), which was followed by a transpressional phase, controlled this magmatic activity (Laubscher 1983; Pamić 1997).

The Ottnangian was characterized by very low rates of volcanic activity. Lacustrine sedimentation was accompanied by explosive volcanism, resulting in the deposition of tuffs and tuffites, reflecting the commencement of rifting (Mutić 1980; Šćavničar *et al*. 1983; Pavelić 2001).

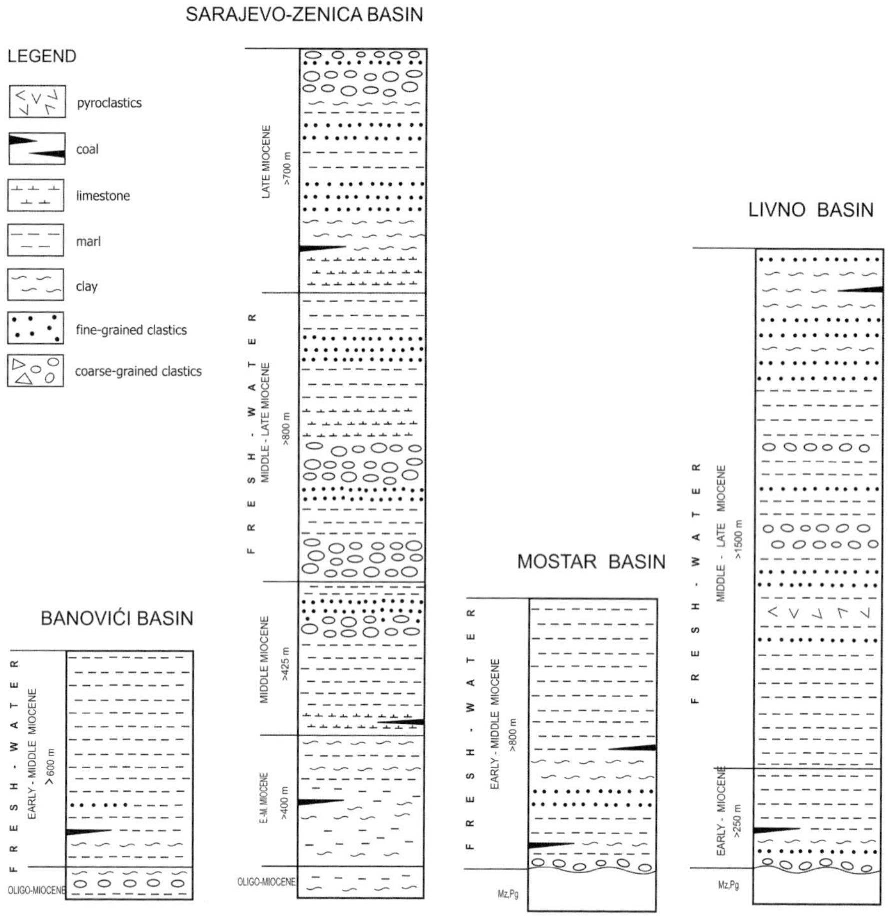


**Fig. 17.33.** Geological columns of the Dinarides intramontane freshwater basins.

The Karpatian volcanics are known only from east Croatia. They comprise a volcanic body of 5 km$^2$ on Mount Krndija made up of trachyandesites and tuffs interlayered with marine clastic sediments. These volcanics may have originated from the partial melting of upper mantle rocks enriched in MgO (Golub & Marić 1968; Pamić *et al.* 1992/1993; Pamić 1997).

The Early Badenian is characterized by a climax in volcanic activity. The rocks of the Badenian andesite–basalt formation, with subordinate dacites and rhyolites, are the most widespread volcanics in the North Croatian Basin (Lugović *et al.* 1990; Pamić 1992). Peperites and pillow lava also occur (Belak *et al.* 2000). The thickness of the volcanics varies and is more than 1000 m in some parts of the Drava depression. They are also found in the Hrvatsko Zagorje Basin. The volcanics are frequently intercalated with marine clastics and marls. In some places pyroclastics occur within algal limestones (Belak *et al.* 1991). The rocks of this formation probably originated from the partial melting of the heterogeneous lower crust (Pamić 1997), and are a result of the final stage of the synrift phase of basin evolution (Pavelić 2001).

The rocks of the post-Badenian basalt–alkali basalt formation are known only from a few wells in the Drava depression. K–Ar measurements carried out on basalts yielded isotopic ages of 11.6–9.4 Ma (Pamić 1997). The occurrence of these rocks has been interpreted as being related to a short-lasting period of volcanic reactivation during a post-rift phase of basin evolution (Pavelić 2001).

In the southern Dinarides, dacite–andesite tuff beds found in the Sinj Basin are interpreted as being derived from volcanic sources in Bosnia (Šušnjara & Šćavničar 1974).

### *Outer Dinarides: eastern Adriatic coast (V.Ć., T.M., K.D., A.M.)*

The eastern Adriatic coast includes two units: the autochthonous part (Adriatic carbonate platform) and the overthrust nappe system (Dinaric thrust front), which is situated between the Dinaric Mountains and the Apennines, and includes convergent major structural units. Four particular domains can be distinguished (Figs 17.24 & 17.34): (1) Istria with the Ćićarija Mountains at the NW part of the coast; (2) the northern Adriatic (the coast with the islands of Krk, Cres, Lošinj, Rab, and Pag); (3) Ravni kotari (northern Dalmatia with the island of Dugi Otok and the Kornati archipelago); and (4) central to southern Dalmatia (the coast and the islands of Hvar, Brač and Korčula).

*Palaeogeography*

In terms of palaeogeography, the studied region belongs to two different tectonic settings: the Adriatic Carbonate Platform (AdCP) (*sensu* Herak 1986, 1999; Tari 2002) and the Dinaric nappe realm (Herak 1986, 1999; or frontal thrust of the western thrust belt of Tari 2002). According to the Eocene palaeogeographic reconstruction of Butterlin *et al.* (1993), the AdCP was situated at the northern fringe of the global desert belt, where

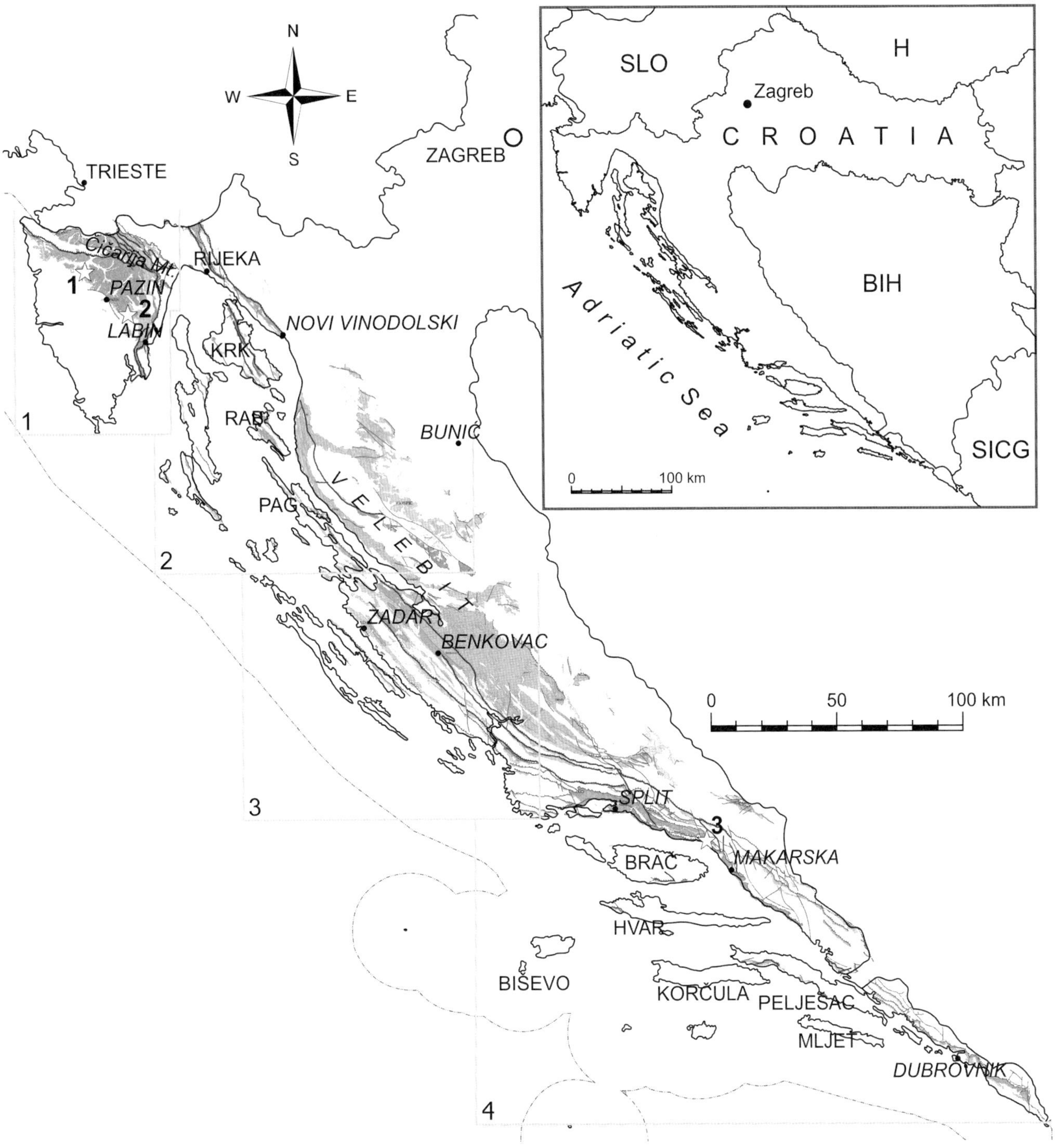


**Fig. 17.34.** Geological sketch map of the Croatian Outer Dinarides showing the location of principal Cenozoic zones (modified after Geologic map of Croatia 1:300 000, 1995). Zones of the Outer Dinarides: 1, Istrian peninsula and Ćićarija Mountains; 2, northern Adriatic coastal region with adjacent larger islands Krk, Cres, Lošinj, Rab and Pag; 3, Ravni kotari region with adjacent Kornati islands and Dugi Otok; 4, central to southern Dalmatian coastal area with adjacent islands Hvar, Brač and Biševo.

continental runoff was low. Larger benthic foraminifers indicate oligotrophic, warm-water conditions during Early–Middle Eocene times, and their development reflects the Eocene to Oligocene 'greenhouse'/'icehouse' transition (Moro & Ćosović 2002) The global Middle to Late Eocene cooling trend is shown by the planktonic foraminiferal associations of the deep-water deposits (Premec-Fućek & Živković 2005). Fossil flora (Jungwirth 2003) and coals from the Promina beds (Eocene–Oligocene) indicate wet vegetation conditions on land.

Carbonate platforms, such as the extensive AdCP, are an important element in the Outer Dinarides. Shallow-marine carbonate deposition commenced in the Late Triassic and lasted until the Lutetian transgression (Velić *et al.* 2003; Drobne 2003*b*, Vlahović *et al.* 2005). Carbonate deposition was terminated by the Eo-Alpine tectonic phase, which caused uplift and emergence of the Dinarides, resulting in the formation of significant bauxite accumulations (Istria, Ravni kotari). Post-Eo-Alpine sedimentation commenced diachronously from Ilerdian to Cuisian times (Bignot 1972; Drobne 1977; Ćosović *et al.* 1994; Matičec *et al.* 1996; Marjanac *et al.* 1998).

The Cenozoic history of the east Adriatic coast reflects the transition from a Cretaceous passive-margin setting (Dercourt *et al.* 1993) to a foreland basin evolution (Tari 2002). During the Early Eocene, a homoclinal carbonate ramp, the AdCP, developed. Palaeogene carbonate ramps were subject to short-term tectonic controls, including subsidence and sea-level changes. Inner and middle ramp deposits (Liburnian formations and foraminiferal limestones) are widespread along the coast, while outer ramp deposits are rare in the north Adriatic region and north Dalmatia. Deep-marine sedimentation commenced after a significant drowning of the Eocene carbonate platforms.

*Tectonic setting*

Numerous studies have examined the present-day structural architecture, tectonic evolution, and palaeogeography of the east Adriatic coastal region (Kossmat 1924; Petković 1958; Grubić 1975; Dimitrijević 1982; Pamić *et al.* 1998; Herak 1986, 1999; Picha 2002; Tari 2002). Although there is general agreement that the east Adriatic coast consists of (an) autochthonous platform(s) overthrust by nappes, the tectonic evolution is controversial. For instance, Pamić *et al.* (1998) assumed a uniform Adriatic–Dinaridic carbonate platform, while Herak (1986, 1999) distinguished the Adriatic and Dinaric platforms, and this is supported by biostratigraphic data (Drobne 1977, 2003*b*). Tari (2002) distinguished a gently tectonized Adriatic carbonate platform (Istria) with an imbricated margin (the so-called imbricated Adria) and the Dinaric nappe pile.

The Palaeogene development was characterized by several tectonic events. The first of these caused an unconformity between the Upper Cretaceous and Palaeogene strata (Pamić *et al.* 1998), and period of tectonic movements must have been responsible for the SW vergence at the east Adriatic coast. According to Pamić *et al* (1998), the second period of deformation took place during the latest Eocene to Early Oligocene. Picha (2002) related NW–SE trending strike-slip faults to the opening of the post-Messinian Albanian foredeep in the Pliocene–Holocene (the third deformational event), which indicates the existence of escape tectonics in the region. Tari (2002) suggested that folding and thrusting began in the Oligocene, when collision and progressive underthrusting of Adria beneath the Dinaric carbonate platform created imbricated structures at the margin of Adria; this process continued during the Miocene and thereafter. The typical NW–SE striking Dinaric structures were refolded as a result of neotectonic deformation (Marinčić 1997), producing west–east orientated structures, which are most prominent in the Central Dalmatian islands.

*Palaeomagnetism*

Palaeomagnetic studies were performed on Cuisian to Lutetian platform carbonates from Istria and central to south Dalmatia (Márton *et al.* 1995*a*, 2003*b*) as well as on deep-marine sediments from Istria. These proved the existence of an Adriatic microplate and demonstrate counterclockwise (CCW) rotation with respect to both the African and European plates in post-Eocene times. Istria must have rotated by 30° CCW, relative to Africa and stable Europe. The latest Miocene to early Pliocene CCW rotations observed in the Adriatic region were driven by that of the Adriatic foreland. This implies that the studied regions were rigidly connected and together participated in post-Eocene CCW rotation.

*Sedimentary and stratigraphic development*

Generally, the oldest Palaeogene deposits of the area (Fig. 17.35) are breccias overlain by freshwater or brackish and paralic limestones (Kozina-type limestones, part of the Liburnian Formation; Drobne & Pavlovec 1991) with local coal accumulations (Hamrla 1959). Fully marine conditions were established during the Ilerdian to Lutetian (Drobne 1974, 1977), when foraminiferal limestones were deposited on carbonate platforms (Magaš & Marinčić 1973; Korolija *et al.* 1977; Košir 1997; Ćosović & Drobne 1998; Marjanac *et al.* 1998; Drobne 2000; Velić *et al.* 2003; Ćosović *et al.* 2004*a*). These are overlain by the so-called Transitional Beds with the basal Marls with crabs and the overlying *Globigerina* ('*Subbotina*') marls. These sediments reflect the regionally diachronous deepening, which commenced during the Early to Middle Lutetian in Istria (Šikić 1965; Bignot 1972; Drobne 1977; Benić 1991; Ćosović & Drobne 1995, 1998; Ćosović *et al* 2004*a*) and during the Late Lutetian in Dalmatia (Pavšič & Premec Fuček 2000). Varying thicknesses were caused by orogenic processes (Šikić 1965, 1968, 1969). Clastic Eocene sediments of this area are traditionally referred to as flysch deposits (e.g. Marinčić 1981; Marjanac *et al.* 1998). The onset of deep-marine (flysch) sedimentation is diachronous, ranging from Cuisian–Middle/Late Lutetian (Živković 2004; Schweitzer *et al.* 2005) to Late Lutetian (Benić 1983), Bartonian (Benić 1983), Bartonian–Priabonian boundary (Kraševinikov *et al.* 1968; Marinčić 1981; Marjanac *et al.* 1998) and to Priabonian (Pavšič & Premec Fuček 2000). Sedimentation lasted until the Priabonian (NP18; Benić 1991), Bartonian (Benić 1983) and Late Oligocene–Early Miocene (Puškarić 1987; De Capoa *et al.* 1995). Deep-marine sediments are mostly overlain by the Eocene–Oligocene continental to shallow-marine sediments of the Promina Beds (Šikić 1965; Komatina 1967; Babić & Zupanič 1983), which are overlain by the Jelar breccia (Oligocene and younger) (Bahun 1974; Herak & Bahun 1979; Vlahović *et al.* 1999). During the Miocene, lacustrine sediments were deposited (Jurišić-Polšak 1979; Jurišić-Polšak *et al.* 1993; Šušnjara & Sakač 1988).

**Istria.** The geological literature on Istria (part of the AdCP) is plentiful, including two complex reviews by Bignot (1972) and Drobne (1977), and many overviews (Drobne 1979; Drobne *et al.* 1979; Hagn *et al.* 1979; Drobne & Pavlovec 1991; Drobne & Pavšič 1991; Ćosović 1991, Benić 1991, Marjanac 1991; Velić *et al.* 1995, 2002, 2003; Šparica *et al.* 2000). The carbonate depositional regime, which prevailed throughout the Mesozoic, terminated during the Early to Late Cretaceous (Drobne 1977; Matičec *et al.* 1996). Different Eocene successions transgraded over various Cretaceous units, which resulted in a high degree of lateral and vertical facies variability. The Liburnian Formation was deposited in the deepest parts of the palaeorelief. It is characterized by alternating freshwater to brackish, lagoonal Early Eocene deposits up to 80 m thick (Ilerdian to Cuisian; Drobne 1977). These are thin-bedded mudstones rich in organic matter and/or clayey mudstones, sporadically with stromatolites and coal intercalations (Labin Basin). Their fossil content, well-known since Stache (1889), includes Charophyta and molluscs.

The early Eocene to Middle Lutetian foraminiferal limestones in Istria (up to 200 m thick) were deposited in environments ranging from the restricted inner parts of the carbonate platform/

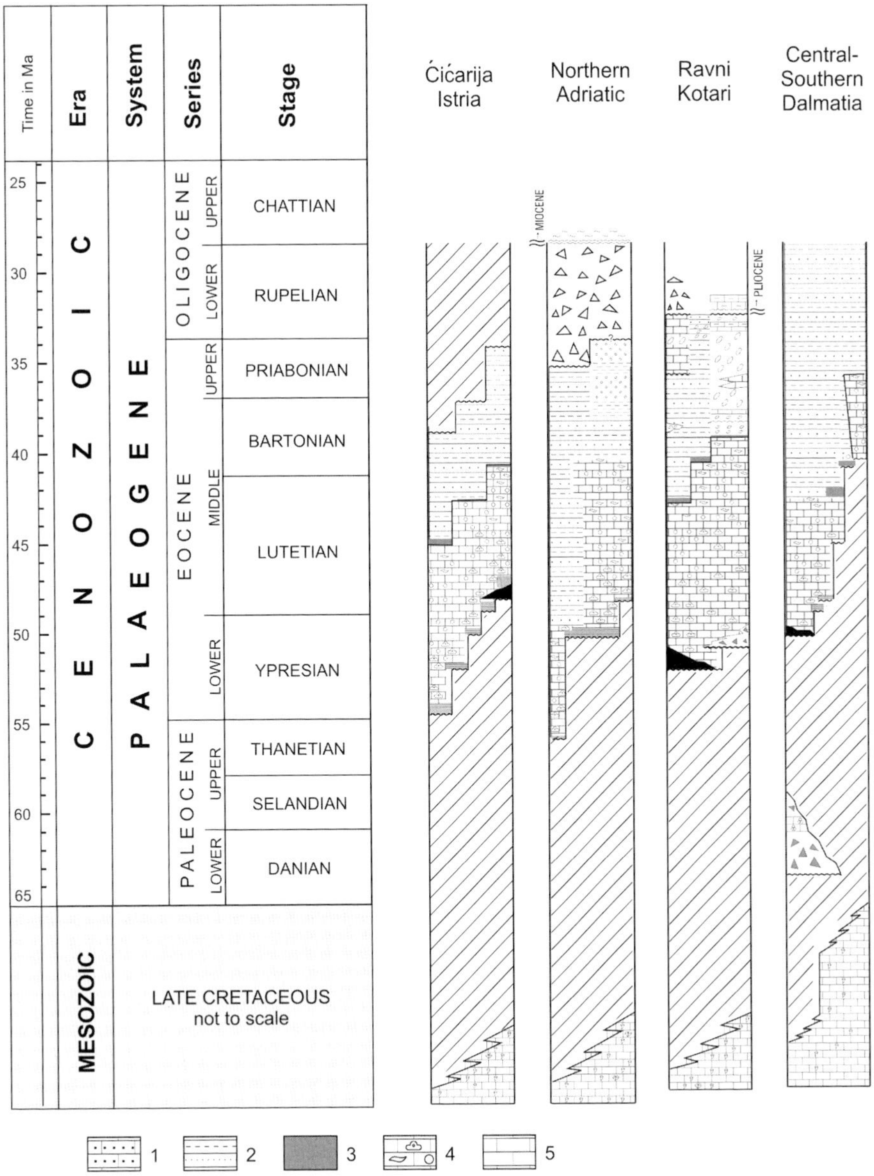


**Fig. 17.35.** Correlation chart of lithostratigraphic units from the Palaeocene to Pliocene in the different zones of the Croatian Outer Dinarides. Columns correspond to the zones of Figure 17.34. 1, Promina beds; 2, Flysch; 3, Transitional beds; 4, Shallow-marine carbonates (including Kozina-type of limestones, Foraminiferal limestones); 5, Shallow-marine limestones (zone 1 after Bignot 1972; Drobne 1977; Drobne *et al.* 1979; Benić 1991; Drobne & Pavlovec 1991; Ćosović *et al.* 2004*a*; Živković 2004; zone 2 according to Magaš 1968; Mamužić 1968; Mamužić *et al.* 1969; Bignot 1972; Drobne 1974; Benić 1983; Márton *et al.* 1995*a*; zone 3 according to Mamužić *et al.* 1970; Ivanović *et al.* 1973; Benić 1983; Drobne *et al.* 1991*c*; zone 4 according to Magaš & Marinčić 1973; Borović *et al.* 1976, 1977; Korolija *et al.* 1977; Benić 1983; Šušnjara & Sakač 1988; De Capoa *et al.* 1995; Marjanac *et al.* 1998; Pavšič & Premec Fuček 2000; Jelaska *et al.* 2003; Ćosović *et al.* 2004*b*).

ramp (Miliolid limestones), to shallower and deeper shoreface environments (with conical agglutinated foraminiferal, *Alveolina* and *Nummulites* limestones), and to deeper parts of relatively open carbonate ramps (Orthophragminae limestones). Facies patterns reflect a general deepening-upward trend. This was the consequence of intense synsedimentary tectonics providing appropriate accommodation space and a relatively low sedimentation rate. Sedimentation commenced during the Middle Ilerdian (SBZ7; Serra-Kiel *et al.* 1998) in the Ćićarija region, during the Cuisian (SBZ10–SBZ12) throughout Istria, and during the Early Lutetian (SBZ13) in its eastern part (Labin Basin; Bignot 1972).

The Transitional Beds range from shallow to deep-marine deposits. The basal Marls with crabs comprise <5 m thick nodular clayey limestones and calcitic marls (Schweitzer *et al.* 2005; Tarlao *et al.* 2005), and the upper parts consist of thick (a few to several tens of metres), massive *Globigerina* (*Subbotina*) marls with occasional intercalations of thin sandstone beds. These marls are rich in planktonic foraminifera and glauconite grains. They were deposited in Middle to Late Lutetian deeper-marine environments (bathyal hemipelagic deposits) (Ćosović *et al.* 2004*a*).

Deep-marine deposits crop out in the Trieste-Pazin Basin, Labin Basin, Mount Učka, and partly at Mount Ćićarija. These bathyal deposits (600 to 1200 m water depth; Živković & Babić 2003; Živković 2004) are up to 350 m (Marinčić *et al.* 1996). They were deposited in a structurally controlled basin, which was fed from the NW, NE, south and SE. The palaeotransport pattern was complex, although the central Pazin Basin shows a predominantly longitudinal transport direction with respect to the basinal axis (Babić & Zupanič 1996). The deposits are characterized by an alternation of hemipelagic marls and gravity flow deposits (Magdalenić 1972). The prevailing turbidite succession of hybrid carbonate/siliciclastic sandstones and marls is randomly intercalated with thick carbonate beds of debrite origin, i.e. megabeds (Hagn *et al.* 1979). The succession is characterized by two distinct stratigraphic units: the lower marl-rich unit with subordinate arenite interbeds, and an upper sandstone-rich unit. The deep-marine sediments have a stratigraphic range covering the Middle to Upper Eocene planktonic foraminiferal zones P11 to P15 (Berggren *et al.* 1995) or E9 to E15 (Berggren & Pearson 2005).

**Northern Adriatic.** The north Adriatic region (AdCP and Dinaric thrust front) includes the north Adriatic islands (Krk, Rab, Pag) and the adjacent coastal region (Rijeka hinterland and Vinodol area). Geological overviews are given in the geological maps of Ilirska Bistrica (Šikić *et al.* 1972), Delnice (Savić & Domazet 1984), Labin (Šikić *et al.* 1969), Crikvenica (Šušnjar *et al.* 1970), Cres (Magaš 1968), Rab (Mamužić *et al.* 1969), Lošinj (Mamužić 1968), Silba (Mamužić *et al.* 1970) and Gospić (Sokač *et al.* 1974).

The oldest Palaeogene sediments are the Liburnian deposits, followed by foraminiferal limestones and marly limestones with crabs. The Liburnian deposits, and the freshwater and brackish to marine limestones, are of Palaeocene age (Thanetian, SBZ 4 in Klana environs; Drobne 1974; Drobne & Ćosović 1998) and show a gradual transition to carbonate platform limestones composed of alveolinids, nummulitids, assilinids, operculinids and orthophragminids (SBZ11–SBZ13; Krk island and environs of Rijeka: Bignot 1972; Drobne 1977; Schaub 1981; Ibrahimpašić & Gušić 2000; Klepač 2003). They are overlain by mainly deep-marine sediments, the deposition of which started diachronously in Early Eocene (Rijeka hinterland; Bignot 1972), and Late Lutetian (P12 or E11, Rab and Krk islands; Benić 1983) times. The Lopar (Rab) sandstones are unique in the east Adriatic realm, because they represent shallow-marine siliciclastics. The facies patterns document sea-level changes and comprise sandy marls, heterolithic packages (sandstone–marl alternation), sandstones, calcarenites, conglomerates and slumps. The age of this succession is uncertain, because specimens resedimented from older strata prevail among the nannofossils (Benić 1983). The deep-marine sediments are overlain by the Jelar breccia of unknown age (Oligocene and younger) and by the Promina beds.

Towards the mainland, in the Lika region, Palaeogene outcrops are rare. The largest occurrence of Eocene limestones and deep-marine sediments is located at Bunić village (tectonic window after Herak 1986). Studies on alveolinids show a Middle to Late Cuisian age (SBZ11 and SBZ12; Drobne & Trutin 1997). Lacustrine sediments of Miocene age are found in the north Adriatic region (Pag island, Krbavsko polje; Jurišić-Polšak 1979; Jurišić-Polšak *et al.* 1993).

**Northern Dalmatia.** The area of Ravni kotari in north Dalmatia (AdCP and Dinaric thrust front) comprises Mesozoic platform carbonates transgressively overlain by Eocene foraminiferal limestones (Middle Cuisian to Middle Lutetian, SBZ10–SBZ14; Drobne *et al.* 1991*c*). Their contact is marked by breccias and locally by bauxite accumulations (Marković 2002). They are overlain by Transitional Beds, which are overlain by *c.* 850 m of deep-marine sediments (Ivanović *et al.* 1973). The Ravni kotari deep-marine deposits are Late Lutetian (NP16) to Bartonian (NP17; Benić 1983). The Bekovac section indicates that deposition extended from the Bartonian (plankton zone P13, E12) to the Priabonian (P16/17, E16: Drobne *et al.* 1991*c*) and was deposited in a deep-marine basin with mainly transversal palaeocurrent patterns. A close relationship of sandstone bodies (depositional lobes) with channels indicates a lower-slope or base-of-slope environment (Babić & Zupanič 1983). The latter is also indicated by the presence of olistolite-bearing megabeds with huge shallow-marine limestone clasts. The deep-marine sediments of north Dalmatia are overlain by the Promina Beds (sometimes referred to as a 'formation'; Ivanović *et al.* 1976) which are characterized by progressive shallowing of the basin. Babić & Zupanič (1983) located its base in a deep-marine olistostrome, and assumed an Eocene–Oligocene age for the entire formation. The lower part of the Promina Beds is characterized by an alternation of marls, sandstones, conglomerates, limestones and cherts, with freshwater to brackish-water fauna. Sedimentation of the upper Promina Beds is characterized by significant shallowing, which caused progradation of coarse alluvial sediments. These conglomerates contain marly beds with coal and plant remains. The Jelar breccia is interpreted as the youngest Cenozoic sedimentary unit in the area, but there are no direct contacts between the deep-marine units, the Promina Beds and the Jelar breccia. The age of the latter is uncertain, being possibly Middle Eocene–Early Oligocene (Herak & Bahun, 1979), Palaeogene–Neogene (Ivanović *et al.* 1973) or Late Lutetian–Bartonian (Sakač *et al.* 1993). Palaeogeographically, the Jelar breccia is an element of the Dinaric thrust front.

**Central and Southern Dalmatia.** Palaeogene deposits of this region (AdCP and Dinaric thrust front) primarily occur in tectonic contact with Mesozoic units, except for a few localities (Solin and Trogir hinterland). Previous studies were conducted in the framework of regional mapping (Borović *et al.* 1976, 1977; Herak *et al.* 1976; Korolija *et al.* 1977), stratigraphy and tectonics (Blanchet 1972, 1974; Chorowitz 1969, 1975, 1977; Šikić 1965) as well as sedimentology and stratigraphy (Benić 1983; Drobne *et al.* 1988*b*; Puškarić 1987; De Capoa *et al.* 1995; Marjanac 1996; Marjanac *et al.* 1998, Drobne *et al.* in press).

The oldest Palaeogene deposits are known from the Split–Makarska hinterland. These are Danian to Early Thanetian (P1–P3) limestones (Chorowicz 1977; Jelaska *et al.* 2003; Ćosović *et al.* 2006) which are overlain by Early–Middle Eocene (Ypresian to Lutetian) clast-supported breccias and limestones with larger planktonic foraminifers.

The Kozina-type limestones were deposited in more-or-less brackish, protected lagoons and bays during the Middle Cuisian (SBZ11), which were partly affected by severe subaereal exposure causing karstification. They comprise discorbidal limestones, miliolid limestones, stromatolites and breccias. Discorbidal limestones and stromatolites predominate in Hvar, while miliolid limestones are prominent on the Pelješac Peninsula.

The Kozina-type limestones were transgressively overlain by low-energy, open-shelf foraminiferal limestones. Their age ranges from Middle to Late Cuisian (SBZ11–12) in the central Dalmatian coastal region (Drobne 1985; Hottinger & Drobne 1980), from early Middle Lutetian (SBZ14) to early Late Lutetian (SBZ16) in the central Dalmatian islands, and from Early Lutetian (SBZ13) to Late Lutetian/Bartonian (SBZ17) in south Dalmatia. Massive Nummulite–Orthophragmina limestones indicate deposition in a quiet, well-aerated subtidal environment. Cross-bedded skeletal sands and imbricated larger foraminifers indicate the influence of major storm events.

The foraminiferal limestones are overlain by the so-called Transitional Beds, which comprise Marls with crabs and *Globigerina* (*Subbotina*) marls. Their thickness ranges from 11 m (central Dalmatian islands) to 15 m (south Dalmatia). The deposition of the Transitional Beds extends from the Late Middle Lutetian to the Late Lutetian and reflects a progressive deepening of the sedimentary environment.

Several hundred metres of deep-marine sediments were deposited above the Transitional Beds. The contact can be transgressive or transitional (Marinčić 1981; Šikić 1965). The stratigraphic range is probably from the Bartonian (NP17: Benić 1983) up to the Upper Miocene (De Capoa *et al.* 1995). A Priabonian age has been proven for the south Dalmatian deposits (Pavšič & Premec Fuček 2000). In central Dalmatia, the sediments are divided into Lower, Middle and Upper Flysch zones. The Lower Flysch Zone is about 750 m thick and dominated by megabeds. The Middle Flysch Zone is a *c.* 200 m thick olistostrome (Marjanac 1996). Within the 850 m thick Upper Flysch Zone, megabeds are restricted to the lower part; conglomerates interfingering with turbidites and alternations of thin-bedded calcarenites and calcirudites and marls occur throughout this unit. Coeval with the upper parts of the Upper Flysch Zone are Miocene lacustrine sediments on the island of Pag and inland in most of the karst poljes (Jurišić-Polšak 1979; Kochansky-Devidé & Slišković 1981; Šušnjara & Sakač 1988; Jurišić-Polšak *et al.* 1993).

Biševo Island extends far out into the Adriatic Sea and its fossil content represents a geological peculiarity. The Cretaceous–Cenozoic stratigraphy and fossil content of the island differs from those of the AdCP; instead the transgressive Oligocene sediments of the island (Drobne *et al.* 2000*a*) are similar to those of Cephalonia, Greece (Accordi *et al.* 1998). The Cenozoic succession of the island begins with a characteristic interval of reddish to yellowish clayey marls, alternating with thin layers of nodular limestones. The marls are overlain by limestones with *Nummulites fichteli* (SBZ 22, Rupelian–Chattian, *sensu* Cahuzac & Poignant 1997).

### Dinarides and South Pannonian Basin in Bosnia and Herzegovina (S.Č., R.Red., H.H.)

The area of Bosnia and Herzegovina (Figs 17.2 & 17.26) is mostly mountainous, encompassing the central Dinarides. The NE parts extend into the Pannonian Basin, while the south partly borders the Adriatic Sea. Isolated Cenozoic sediments crop out all across the region. Sedimentary rocks prevail, but eruptive masses of dacite–andesite rocks occur in east Bosnia. During the Palaeogene, shallow-marine carbonates were dominant. They occur in two separate regions: in the Herzegovina area (Outer Dinarides) to the south and in Bosnia to the north. The Inner Dinarides (Bosnia) are composed of deeply weathered clastic, metasedimentary, metamorphic and igneous rocks. They included mostly Palaeozoic–Triassic rocks and the Dinaride Ophiolite Zone. The South Pannonian Basin (SPB) covers the Tuzla area (north Bosnia), while the Pannonian Basin *sensu lato* covers a large area at the southern margin of the Posavina area.

#### *Palaeogeography and tectonic setting*

The evolution of the region is related to the Palaeogene Eo-Alpine, Pyrenean and Sava orogenic phases, and subsequent Neogene neotectonic phases. Marine sedimentation prevailed until the earliest Oligocene in the Inner and Outer Dinarides, and was probably terminated by the orogenically induced rise of the middle Dinarides. A good example for the tectonic control is the synorogenic Promina Formation (Late Eocene–Early Oligocene) of Herzegovina, which developed during the Pyrenean Orogeny. The Eocene final deformation of the Dinarides resulted from underplating of Apulia beneath Tisia (the present-day Pannonian Basin terrains), which began during an Oligocene (32–28 Ma) period of transpression. This deformation gave rise to the final structure of the Dinarides. To the north of the uplifted Dinarides, strike-slip faulting produced a system of smaller and larger transpressional depressions, mainly orientated NE and ESE. During the Oligocene, shallow- to deep-water, marine and brackish to freshwater sedimentation took place in these depressions. Along the northern Dinarides margin, this dextral strike-slip faulting is seen in the incipient Sava and Drava transpressional faults, which apparently represent the ESE prolongation of the PAL (Pamić *et al.* 1998). Strike-slip faulting was accompanied by Early Oligocene volcanic activity, which took place in the northern Oligocene transpressional basins and along the northern margin of the Dinarides (e.g. area of Maglaj and Srebrenica). Oligocene strike-slip faulting was very active across the Dinarides area and is evident in the presence of transpressional depressions as precursors of Neogene freshwater basins. The largest transpressional faults are the Bosovača Fault, which controlled the origin of the Sarajevo-Zenica depression, and the Vrbas-Voljevac Fault, which controlled the origin of some smaller Cenozoic depressions. Within the AdCP, the Oligocene strike-slip faulting produced several larger and smaller karst valleys.

In the SPB, NE of the uplifted Dinarides, geodynamic processes changed fundamentally after the Oligocene transpressional deformation. Diapirism of the upper mantle and resulting attenuation of the lower continental crust are manifest in the extensional processes that gave rise to the evolution of the Pannonian Basin (18–17 Ma; Royden 1988). The extensional evolution of the SPB was mainly predisposed by the original Drava and Sava fault system, created during the Oligocene transpression. As a result of the extension, marine transgression occurred, and the first phases of the evolution of the Pannonian Basin took place under rift-related, mainly marine environments. This rift-related Early/Middle Miocene filling of the Pannonian Basin was accompanied by synsedimentary volcanic activity, which took place during the Karpathian and Badenian. The first rift-related stage of the evolution of the Pannonian Basin terminated by the end of the Sarmatian. This was followed by the second evolutionary stage, when continuous Late Miocene and Pliocene freshwater sedimentation occurred in the Pannonian Basin.

#### *Palaeogene of the Outer Dinarides*

In this zone, the Palaeogene rocks are found around Bihać, in Dinara, and between Livno, Mostar and Trebinje. Palaeocene sediments are restricted to the syncline core of Čardak Livada, in the Votorog Mountains (Papeš 1985). They are up to 400 m thick, contain characteristic Palaeocene foraminifers and algae, and are composed of breccias, marls, conglomerates and thick-bedded calcirudites.

Palaeocene–Eocene carbonates of the 50–300 m thick Liburnian Formation (= Liburnian Limestone; Čičić 1977) occur in the vicinity of Bihać, between Livno and Mostar, and from Stolac and Čapljina up to Trebinje. They are dark grey to black coloured beds. Locally, basal breccia limestones and calcarenites occur, while the upper levels are characterized by marly and platy, compact limestones. They discordantly overlie Senonian rudist limestones, separated by a bauxite unit.

Early and Middle Eocene sediments appear in Dinara, in the vicinity of Duvno and Lip Mountain, as well as in the area of Mostar and further towards the east. Sediments in the area of Duvno and Lip Mountain comprise *c.* 400 m of thick deep-marine sediments with larger planktonic foraminifers (Papeš 1985). At other localities, 100–600 m thick alveolinid-nummulitid limestones of the same age overlie the Liburnian Formation. Both of these successions are found in narrow zones related to reverse faulting and block overthrusting.

Middle and Late Eocene sediments of Herzegovina can be separated into two distinct successions: (1) marls, conglomerates, sandy stones, clays, slates, breccia limestones and limestones; and (2) limestone breccias, marls and sandstones with a thickness of 100–600 m and mainly deep-marine. Sediments of the first type are known from large areas on both sides of the Neretva river, from Posušje and Čitluk to Dabrica, and in the area of Lukavičko. They discordantly overlie the Liburnian Formation. Bauxite deposits of significant economical importance occur in the areas of Posušje and Dabrice. Mollusc lumachelles containing larger foraminifera are also found (Čičić 1977). Sediments of the second type are typically developed around Posušje, Tribistovo and Konjovac. They discordantly overlie alveolitid-nummulitid limestones and bauxites, and contain a rich mollusc, coral and echinid fauna. The succession is up to 200 m thick and considered as being coeval with the first succession.

Eocene–Oligocene units comprise conglomerates, calcarenites and marls. According to their typical development in the Promina Mountains (Dalmatia) they are called the Promina Beds (see above). They lie discordantly on Late Cretaceous and early Palaeogene sediments and are interpreted as terrestrial. The age of the Promina Beds is assumed to be Late Eocene to Early Oligocene. Their thickness decreases from Livno (1300 m), towards Posušje and Tihaljina (900 m), and to Nevesinje and Gacko (200–600 m).

*Palaeogene of the Inner Dinarides*

Various types of igneous rocks are known from the Dinarides (Katzer 1926; Varićak 1966; Pamić 1996). In Motajica, granites create the central part of the mountain. Six types of granite can be recognized: (1) massive, medium-grain-sized normal granite; (2) fine-grained granite with 'frozen edges'; (3) leucocratic granite; (4) greisenized; (5) aplicoide; and (6) kaolinized granites. Isotopic analyses suggested a Cretaceous–Palaeogene age, although Palaeocene–Eocene metamorphosis of the sediment cover suggests an Eocene–Oligocene age. Granite massifs also form significant parts of the base of the Pannonian Basin close to the Sava River.

Carbonate sediments dominate during Palaeocene to Early Eocene times. They are known from the broad area of Doboj and Tešanj, Derventa as well as in the areas of Trebovac and Majevica (Stojčić 1968). The microfauna of this 50–200 m thick succession comprises planktonic, benthic and larger foraminifera. In NE Majevica, sediments of this age are characterized by a 700–1500 m thick succession of slates, sandstones, marls and limestones. Sections from Tavna and north Majevica suggest that these sediments are part of a continuous Maastrichtian to Palaeogene deep-marine succession. The succession was dated by means of foraminifera and algae (e.g. Radoičić 1992). Over large parts of north Bosnia, deep-marine sedimentation continues up into the Middle Eocene. The thickness of these sediments is highly variable, ranging from 550 m (Kozara) to 1100 m (Majevica, Trebovac).

On Majevica and Trebovac, the lower part of these units is characterized by an alternating series of sandstones, slates and marls, with subordinate conglomerates and limestones. Marly sandstones, sandy limestones and limestones prevail at the top of the succession. The macrofauna was studied by Oppenheim (1908), Katzer (1918) and Čičić (1964).

Between the rivers Una and Vrbas, in the crest of Kozara and surrounding terrains, the so-called Kozara Flysch occurs. Palynological data (Čičić 1977) suggests an age of Early to Middle Eocene. It is composed of arkose and subarkose sandstones, as well as quartz-mica siltstones and rare conglomerates.

The Majevica Mountains comprise a 100 m thick Middle Eocene series of deep-marine sandstones, marls and limestones, which are overlain by marls that include a mixed marine and freshwater fauna (Čičić 1964), as well as slates and sandstones with limestone beds. The thickness of this succession in north Majevica is up to 200 m. Coal seams in these sediments are of local economic importance.

During the Middle and Late Eocene, the Majevica and Trebovac mountains comprise a series of 400–1200 m thick flysch-like sediments (Čičić 2002*b*). The lower parts are composed of sandstones and alevrolite, the middle parts comprise siltstones, marls, slates and rare limestones. The upper parts are characterized by thick-bedded marls, slates and sandstones, locally with conglomerate lenses. Sediments from the Vučjak and Trebovac mountains comprise thick-bedded sandstones, siltstones, conglomerates and slates with larger foraminifera, pollen and spores suggesting a continuous succession from the Late Eocene to the Oligocene (Ercegovac & Čičić 1968; Čičić 1977).

*Miocene freshwater basins*

A large number of lakes existed during the Miocene, which were initiated by tectonic movements during the Sava Phase. These created depressions, in which swamps and lakes formed due to the change from an arid to a humid climate. Milojević (1964) separated the lacustrine basins of Bosnia and Herzegovina into three regions: (1) north Bosnian region (Ugljevik, Mezgraja-Tobut, Priboj, Prnjavor, Lješljani, Banovići, Đurđevik, Seona and Jasenica basins); (2) middle Bosnian region (Miljevina-Rogatica, Sarajevsko-Zenički, Žepački, Teslić, Kotor Varoš, Banja Luka and Kamengrad basin); and (3) Outer Dinarides (Gacko, Mostar, Livno, Duvno and Cazin basins).

The largest lacustrine basins of Bosnia and Herzegovina were created within the main fault zones, e.g. Sarajevo-Zenica Basin in Busovača, Tuzla Basin in Spreča, Kamengrad Basin between the Grmeč and Sana fault, Mostar Basin in the zone of the Neretva Fault. Terrestrial sediments filling these basins have thicknesses of 1000–4500 m. Sedimentation in the larger basins began during the Egerian, but the exact age is unclear in many cases. In Ugljevik and other lacustrine basins of north Bosnia, the lacustrine regime lasted until the Karpatian marine ingression from the Pannonian Sea. In other basins, lacustrine sedimentation continued until the Pontian. In addition to coal seams, these basins contain marls, limestones, clays and conglomerates, and individual units of freshwater limestone can be more than 300 m thick.

Palaeontological information on the lacustrine sediments is sparse, but several biostratigraphic conclusions based mainly on mammals can be drawn, (Laskarev 1925; Milojković 1929; Malez & Slišković 1964 Pamić-Sunarić 1977; Malez & Thenius 1985). A palaeontological overview on Bosnia and Herzegovina has been published by Soklić (2001).

## *The Tuzla Basin*

The Tuzla Basin is part of the South Pannonian Basin, which is situated to the north of the Dinarides mountain chain. This section summarizes the most important papers (Katzer 1918; Soklić 1955, 1959, 1964, 1977, 1982, 2001; Stevanović & Eremija 1960, 1977; Čičić 1977, 2002*b*; Čičić & Papeš 1970; Čičić & Milojević 1975; Čičić & Jovanović 1987; Čičić *et al.* 1988; Čičić & Redžepović 2003; Vrabac 1989, 1991, 1999; Ferhatbegović 2004).

Hydrocarbon exploration between 1934–50 provided data on the pre-Neogene basement of the Tuzla Basin. This consists of: (1) Upper Cretaceous clastics and carbonates; (2) Maastrichtian–Palaeocene–Lower Eocene deep-marine deposits; (3) Middle Eocene with foraminifers, molluscs and corals; and (4) Upper Eocene quartz sandstones and marls. Early Miocene sediments comprise the Slavinovići limestones, the Red and Mottled suites, and the Salt Formation. They are Aquitanian and Burdigalian in age (i.e. Late Egerian, Eggenburgian, Ottnangian and Karpatian).

The 60 m thick Slavinovići Limestone is characterized by desiccation cracks of dry lake-mud and the occurrence of freshwater gastropods. It is overlain by the Red suite, composed of redeposited tropical soils, derived from the peneplanated Dinarides. Silty sediments with secondary conglomerates with chert, peridotite and other silicate pebbles. The overlying Mottled suite, genetically related to renewed tectonic activity, was derived from the same source area. In addition to ophiolite rocks, pebbles of Tithonian–Valanginian limestones also occur. Volcanic activity in the adjacent Podrinje area caused the occurrence of ash layers. Sediments of the Mottled suite are rich in fossils, particularly gastropods. Pelite sediments of the suite are irregularly reddish, greenish and flaky, which is characteristic of muds flooded by alluvial fans. In the area of Soline, both the Red and Mottled suites are about 300 m thick. The *c.* 600 m thick Salt Formation was deposited within a marine lagoonal environment and shows a distinct cyclicity. The cycles begin with banded marls, followed by anhydrite and finally salt (halite and tenardite). Occasional volcanic ash layers can be up to 14 m thick. The Salt Formation is exploited at Tušanj (Tuzla town).

The overlying Karpatian sediments (>300 m thick) were deposited after a marine transgression from the Pannonian Basin (Central Paratethys). In the Ravna Trešnja-1 well near Tuzla, rocks of the Mottled suite comprise coarse-grained marine conglomerates with intercalations of clayey and slightly bituminous marls.

Karpatian sediments are conformably overlain by deep-marine Badenian marls intercalated with fine-grained sandstones. The marls contain foraminifers, pteropods and other molluscs, nautilids and echinoids, while Late Badenian coarse-grained sediments contain larger, thick-shelled, shallow-marine fossils. The total thickness of the Badenian sediments is about 500 m (e.g. deep-well Bukinje). They are covered by up to 300 m of Sarmatian brackish-water sediments comprising marls intercalated with sandstones and conglomerates. In contrast to the Badenian marine fauna, the brackish Sarmatian fauna comprises a low species diversity but a large number of individuals. The Pannonian fossils are characteristic of brackish environments.

In the Kreka Basin, six cyclothems with coal seams were deposited during the Pannonian. The cycles were caused by regressions within the Pontian Sea, which resulted in sandy sequences with increasing compositional maturity up-section. These processes continued until the final filling of the basin, after which freshwater swamps developed. Subsequently, these areas were covered by swampy forests, which were predisposed to coal generation. The accumulation of lignite and cellulose continued until the following marine ingression, which occurred as a result of sudden subsidence or, alternatively, of penetration of the barrier separating the basin from the Pontian Sea.

### *Pannonian Basin sensu lato*

The Pannonian Basin *sensu lato* covers a large area in north Bosnia, between the rivers Una in the NW and Drina in the SE. The Late Miocene to Pontian period contains 200–300 m of brackish and limnic sediments rich in molluscs. The *c.* 100 m thick Pannonian sediments of the Sarmatian Sea comprise molluscs and ostracods. Sediments (170 m thick) of the brackish Sarmatian Sea show a characteristic succession: reefal olithic and sandy limestones, sandy marls, clayish marls with molluscs, foraminifers and ostracods (Soklić 1977, 2001). Further proven ages are Early Miocene–Ottnangian (sandstones and marls), Karpatian (marls and sandstones with Globigerinid foraminifers) and Badenian (sandstones and marls with foraminifers, molluscs and reefal limestones; Soklić 2001).

## Summary

Geologically, the Cenozoic represents the period when Africa and Europe were converging, with seafloor spreading taking place in the Atlantic only as far north as the Labrador Sea (between Greenland and North America). Additionally, numerous microplates in the Mediterranean area were compressed as a direct result of Africa–Europe convergence, gradually fusing together. This resulted in a shift in the palaeogeography of Europe from a marine archipelago to more continental environments; this change was also related to the rising Alpidic mountain chains. Around the Eocene–Oligocene boundary, Africa's movement and subduction beneath the European plate led to the final disintegration of the ancient Tethys Ocean. In addition to the emerging early Mediterranean Sea another relict of the closure of the Tethys was the vast Eurasian Paratethys Sea. At the beginning of the Cenozoic, mammals replaced reptiles as the dominant vertebrates.

Central Europe is composed of two tectonically contrasting regions, namely a northern Variscan, and a southern Alpine Europe. The European Plate, a broad area of epicontinental sedimentation, essentially represented the stable European continent during the Cenozoic. The area, extending from the Atlantic shelves of Norway and the Shetland Islands through to eastern Poland and beyond, was separated from the Alpine-Carpathian chain by the Alpine-Carpathian Foreland Basin (= Molasse Basin) and its precursors as a part of the Palaeogene Tethys or Oligocene–Miocene Paratethys. The region encompasses the North Sea Basin, the Polish Lowlands, the Volhyno-Podolian Plate, the Upper Rhine Graben and the Helvetic units. To the south lay the Alps, a chain of mountains which formed during the multiphase Alpine Orogeny (see Froitzheim *et al.* 2008), and which can be traced eastwards into the Carpathians; this latter area is very different from the Alps mainly due to the presence of broad Neogene basins and extensive acidic to calc-alkaline volcanic activity. During the Palaeocene and Eocene, the Alpine system formed an archipelago. The North Alpine Foreland Basin was part of the Alpine-Carpathian Foredeep, a west–east trending basin located in front of the prograding nappes of the Alpine orogenic wedge. The Southern Alps, to the south of the Periadriatic Lineament, represent the northern extension of the Adriatic Microplate (together with the Eastern Alps, i.e. Austro-Alpine units). In Palaeogene times, they constituted the southern continuation of the Eastern Alps archipelago.

The Cenozoic history of Central Europe is chronicled in a series of Palaeogene and Neogene basins present across the region. In addition to the more stable North Sea Basin, the majority of these basins were strongly influenced by compressive forces related to the ongoing evolution of the Alpine chain. These forces resulted in general uplift of Europe during the Cenozoic. The marginal position of the seas covering the region of Central Europe and the considerable synsedimentary geodynamic control resulted in incomplete stratigraphic successions with frequent unconformities, erosional surfaces and depositional gaps. Additionally, during the Palaeocene, Europe–Africa convergence paused and a major hot-spot developed in the Faeroe–Greenland area. This mantle plume caused thermal uplift and associated volcanism across a broad area extending from Great Britain to the west coast of Greenland. At the Palaeocene–Eocene boundary, continental rupture occurred across this thermal bulge and ocean-floor spreading commenced between Greenland and Europe. Thus from Eocene times onwards, NW Europe became part of a thermally subsiding passive continental margin which moved progressively away from the hot-spot that continues today under Iceland.

Cenozoic times were characterized by a gradual long-term fall in global sea levels. This broad pattern was overlain by high-frequency and high-amplitude short-term changes related to polar glaciations and the repeated development of continental icesheets in subpolar areas of the northern hemisphere, which were broadly related to the closure of the Panama Isthmus (Ziegler 1990). Glaciation commenced in Miocene times, with regional icesheets present from the Pliocene. These eustatic changes are broady reflected in the sedimentary record of western and Central Europe. The Oligocene and Miocene deposits of the region are mainly found in the North Sea area in the north, the Mediterranean Sea region in the south and the intermediate Paratethys Sea and its late Miocene to Pliocene successor Lake Pannon. At its maximum extent, Paratethys extended from the Rhône Basin in France towards Inner Asia. Subsequently, it was partitioned into a smaller western part, consisting of the Western and Central Paratethys, and the larger Eastern Paratethys. The Western Paratethys comprises the Rhône Basin and the Alpine Foreland Basin of Switzerland, Bavaria and Austria. The Central Paratethys extends from the Vienna Basin in the west to the Carpathian Foreland in the east where it abuts the area of the Eastern Paratethys. Eurasian ecosystems and landscapes were impacted by a complex pattern of changing seaways and landbridges between the Paratethys, the North Sea and the Mediterranean, as well as the western Indo-Pacific. The geodynamic evolution of the region in Cenozoic times has resulted in marked biogeographic differentiation across the region. This has necessitated the establishment of different chronostratigraphic and geochronologic scales in order to facilitate cross-regional correlation.

O. and V. Anistratenko are grateful to M. Paszkowski (Cracow) for proof-reading. D. Bassi was financially supported in part by local research funds at the University of Ferrara. V. Ćosović was supported by national research projects nos. 1–09–084 and 119402. K. Drobne and co-authors thank S. Pirc and H. Glenn for translations as well as M. Herak and F. Rögl for discussion; their work was supported by the Slovenian Research Agency and by the UNESCO IGCP Project No. 286. B. Jelen and co-authors wish to thank S. Pirc for correcting the English; their work was supported by the Slovenian Ministry for Science and Technology, the Slovenian Research Agency and the Slovenian Ministry of Environment and Spatial Planning. The research was carried out in the framework of several intergovernmental Slovenian–Hungarian research projects, German SFB 275 project and Austrian Science Foundation projects. T. Marjanac was supported by national research projects Nos. 1–09–084 and 119303. A. Moro was supported by national research project No. 119402. A. Nagymarosy was supported by OTKA project no. 47 107.

## References

ABREU, V. S. & HADDAD, G. A. 1998. Glacioeustatic fluctuations. The mechanism linking stable isotope events and sequence stratigraphy from the Early Oligocene to Middle Miocene. *In*: DE GRACIANSKY, P.-C., HARDENBOL, J., JACQUIN, T. & VAIL, R. P. (eds) *Mesozoic and Cenozoic Sequence Stratigraphy of European Basins*. SEPM, Special Publications, **60**, 245–259.

ACCORDI, G., CARBONE, F. & PIGNATTI, J. 1998. Depositional history of a Palaeogene carbonate ramp (Western Cephalonia, Ionian Islands, Greece). *Geologica Romana*, **34**, 131–205.

ACCORSI BENINI, C. 1974. I fossili di Case Soghe-M. Lungo (Colli Berici, Vicenza). 2. Lamellibranchi. *Memorie Geopaleontologiche dell'Università di Ferrara*, **3**, 61–80.

ACKERMANN, K. 1986. Le flysch de la nappe du Niesen. *Eclogae Geologicae Helvetiae*, **79**, 641–684.

ADAM, Z. & DLABAČ, M. 1969. Erklärungen zur Mächtigkeitskarte und zur lithofaziellen Entwicklung der Donau - Niederung. *Západne Karpaty*, **11**, 156–171.

ADÁMEK, J. 2003. Miocén karpatské předhlubně na jižní Moravě, geologický vývoj a litostratigrafické členění. *Zprávy o geologických výzkumech v roce*, **2002**, 9–11 [English summary].

ADÁMEK J., BRZOBOHATÝ R., PÁLENSKÝ P. & ŠIKULA J. 2003. The Karpatian in the Carpathian Foredeep (Moravia). *In:* BRZOBOHATÝ, R., CICHA, I., KOVÁČ, M. & RÖGL, F. (eds) *The Karpatian. A Lower Miocene Stage of the Central Paratethys*. Masaryk University, Brno, 75–92.

ADAMOVA, M. & SCHNABEL, G. W. 1999. Comparison of the East Alpine and West Carpathian Flysch Zone - A Geochemical Approach. *Abhandlungen der Geologischen Bundesanstalt*, **56**(2), 567–584.

AHRENDT, H., KÖTHE, A., LIETZOW, A., MARHEINE, D. & RITZKOWSKI, S. 1995. Lithostratigraphie, Biostratigraphie und radiometrische Datierung des Unter-Eozäns von Helmstedt (SE-Niedersachsen). *Zeitschrift der deutschen geologischen Gesellschaft*, **146**, 450–457.

ALTHERR, R., LUGOVIĆ, B., MEYER, H.-P. & MAJER, V. 1995. Early Miocene post-collisional calc-alkaline magmatism along the easternmost segment of the Periadriatic fault system (Slovenia and Croatia). *Mineralogy and Petrology*, **54**, 225–247.

ANDERSON, H. J. 1964. Die miocäne Reinbek-Stufe in Nord- und Westdeutschland und ihre Mollusken-Fauna. *Fortschritte in der Geologie von Rheinland und Westfalen*, **14**, 31–368.

ANDREYEVA-GRIGOROVICH, A. S., KULTCHYTSKY, Y. O., *et al.* 1997. Regional stratigraphic scheme of Neogene Formations of the Central Paratethys in the Ukraine. *Geologica Carpathica*, **48**, 123–136.

ANDREYEVA-GRIGOROVICH, A. S., LOZYNYAK, P. & PETRASHKEVICH, M. 2002. Miocene nannoplankton from the Burkalo crook (Transcarpathian). *Paleontological Collection*, **34**, 87–96 [in Ukrainian].

ANDREYEVA-GRIGOROVICH, A. S., OSZCZYPKO, N., ŚLĄCZKA, A., SAVITSKAYA, N. A. & TROFIMOVICH, N. A. 2003. Correlation of Late Badenian salt of the Wieliczka, Bochnia and Kalush areas (Polish and Ukrainian Carpathian Foredeep). *Annales Societatis Geologorum Poloniae*, **73**, 67–89.

ANIČIĆ, B. 1991. Geological setting of the Orlica mountain. *Geologija*, **33**, 233–287.

ANIČIĆ, B. & OGORELEC, B. 1995. Badenian rhodolith in Kozjansko (E Slovenia). *Geologija*, **37/38**, 225–249.

ANISTRATENKO, O. YU. 2000. Mollusks of the family Tecturidae (Gastropoda Cyclobranchia) from the Sarmatian deposits of the Ukraine. *Vestnik zoologii, Suppl.* **14**, 33–39 [in Russian].

ANISTRATENKO, O. YU. & ANISTRATENKO, V. V. 2005. A recent survey of Sarmatian Molluscs of the *Trochus podolicus* Group (Gastropoda, Trochoidea). *Vestnik zoologii*, **38**, 3–15.

ANTONELLI, R., BARBIERI, G., *et al.* 1990. *Carta geologica del Veneto 1.250.000, una storia di cinquecento milioni di anni.* Regione del Veneto, Segreteria Regionale per il Territorio.

AUBOIN, J. 1963. Essai sur la paléogéographie post-triasique et l'évolution secondaire et tertiare du versant sud des Alpes orientales (Alpes méridionales, Lombardie et Vénétie, Italie, Slovénie occidentale, Yugoslavie). *Bulletin Societé géologique France*, **5**, 730–766.

BĄBEL, M. 2004. Badenian evaporite basin of the northern Carpathian Foredeep as a drawdown salina basin. *Acta Geologica Polonica*, **54**(3), 313–337.

BABIĆ, LJ. & ZUPANIČ, J. 1983. Paleogene Clastic Formations in Northern Dalmatia. *In:* BABIĆ, LJ. & JELASKA, V. (eds) *Contribu-*

*tions to Sedimentology of Some Carbonate and Clastic Units of the Coastal Dinarides*. Excursion Guide Book, 4th IAS Regional Meeting Split, 37–61.

BABIĆ, LJ. & ZUPANIČ, J. 1996. Coastal Dinaric flysch belt. Paleotransport model for the the Pazin Basin, and the role of a foreland uplift (Istria, Croatia). *Natura Croatica*, **5**(4), 317–327.

BAGNOLI, C., BESCHIN, C., DAL LAGO, A., MIETTO, P., PIVA, E. & QUAGGIOTTO, E. 1997. *Solo a Vicenza. Gli endemismi della provincia*. Blended edizioni, Vicenza.

BAHUN, S. 1974. The tectonogenesis of Mt. Velebit and the formation of Jelar deposits. *Geološki vjesnik*, **27**, 35–51.

BAJRAKTAREVIĆ, Z. & PAVELIĆ, D. 2003. The Karpatian in Croatia. *In:* BRZOBOHATÝ, R., CICHA, I., KOVÁČ M. & RÖGL, F. (eds) *The Karpatian. A Lower Miocene Stage of the Central Paratethys*. Masaryk University, Brno, 141–144,.

BALDI, T. 1984. The terminal Eocene and Early Oligocene events in Hungary and the separation of an anoxic, cold Paratethys. *Eclogae Geologicae Helvetiae*, **77**, 1–27.

BALDI, T. 1986. *Mid-Tertiary Stratigraphy and Paleogeographic Evolution of Hungary*. Akadémiai Kiadó, Budapest.

BALDI, T. & BÁLDI-BÉKE, M. 1985. The evolution of the Hungarian Paleogene basin. *Acta Geologica Hungarica*, **28**, 5–28.

BÁLDI T. & SENES, J. 1975. OM Egerien. Die Egerer, Pouzdraner, Puchkirchener Schichtengruppe und die Bretkaer Formation. *Chronostratigraphie und Neostratotypen, Miozän der Zentralen Paratethys*, **5**, 1–577.

BÁLDI-BEKE, M. 1984. The nannoplankton of the Transdanubian Paleogene formations. *Geologica Hungarica, Serie Palaeontologia*, **43**, 1–307.

BÁLDI-BEKE, M. & BÁLDI, T. 1991. Paleobathymetry and paleogeography of the Bakony Eocene basin in W Hungary. *Palaeogeography, Palaeoclimatology, Palaeoecology*, **88**, 25–52.

BÁLDI-BEKE, M., HORVÁTH, M. & NAGYMAROSY, A. 1981. Biostratigraphic investigations of flysch formations in the Great Hungarian Plain. *Annales Institute Geologica Hungarica*, **1979**, 143–158.

BARATTOLO, F. 1998. Dasycladacean green algae and microproblematica of the uppermost Cretaceous–Paleocene in the Karst area (NE Italy and Slovenia). *In:* HOTTINGER, L. & DROBNE, K. (eds) Paleogene shallow benthos of the Tethys. *Opera Dela Slovenske akademije znanosti in umetnosti (SAZU), Ljubljana*, **34**(2), 65–127.

BARBIERI, G. & MEDIZZA, F. 1969. Contributo alla conoscenza geologica della regione di Bolca (Monti Lessini). *Memorie dell'Istituto di Geologia e Mineralogia, Università di Padova*, **27**, 1–36.

BARBIERI, G. & ZAMPIERI, D. 1992. Deformazioni sinsedimentarie eoceniche con stile a domino e relativo campo di paleostress (Monti Lessini). *Atti Ticinensi di Scienze della Terra*, **35**, 25–31.

BARBIERI, G., DE VECCHI, G., DE ZANCHE, V., DI LALLO, E., FRIZZO, P., MIETTO, P. & SEDEA, R. 1980. Note illustrative della Carta Geologica dell'area di Recoaro alla scala 1.20.000. *Memorie di Scienze Geologiche*, **34**, 23–52.

BARBIERI, G., DE ZANCHE, V. & SEDEA, R. 1991. Vulcanismo paleogenico ed evoluzione del semigraben Alpone-Agno (Monti Lessini). *Rendiconti della Società geologica Italiana*, **14**, 5–12.

BARTA-CALMUS, S. 1973. *Revision de collections de Madreporares provenant du Nummulitique du Sud-Est de la France, de l'Italie et de la Yugoslavie septentrionales*. Doctoral thesis, University of Paris.

BARTOLOMEI, G. 1958. Resti di un carsismo terziario nei Colli Berici. *Atti 12 Congrès Iternationale de Spéléologie in Putignano*, **1**, 216–219.

BASSI, D. 1998. Coralline algal facies and their palaeoenvironments in the Late Eocene of Northern Italy (Calcare di Nago). *Facies*, **39**, 179–202.

BASSI, D., COSOVIC, V., PAPAZZONI, C. A. & UNGARO, S. 2000. The Colli Berici. *In:* BASSI, D. (ed.) Field trip guide book. Shallow water benthic communities at the Middle-Upper Eocene boundary. *Annali dell'Università di Ferrara, Scienze della Terra, supplemento*, **8**, 43–57.

BASSI, D., HOTTINGER, L. & NEBELSICK, J.H. 2002. First record of large benthic porcelaneous foraminifera (Archaiasininae) in the Upper Oligocene shallow water carbonate deposits of north-eastern Italy. *In:* REVETS, S. A. (ed.) *Forams 2002, International Symposium on Foraminifera, Abstracts Volume*. The University of Western Austalia, Perth, 4–8 February 2002, 83–84.

BASSI, D., HOTTINGER, L. & NEBELSICK, J. H. 2007. Larger foraminifera of the Late Oligocene of the Venetian area, north-eastern Italy. *Palaeontology*, **50**, 845–868.

BECCALUVA, L., GATTO, G. D, GREGNANIN, A., PICCIRILLO, E. M. & SCOLARI, A. 1979. Geochemistry and petrology of dyke magmatism in the Alto Adige (Eastern Alps) and its geodynamic implications. *Neues Jahrbuch für Geologie Paläontology Monatshefte*, **6**, 321–339.

BECCALUVA, L., BIGIOGGERO, B., *et al.* 1983. Post collisional orogenic dike magmatism in the Alps. *Memorie della Società Geologica Italiana*, **26**, 341–359.

BECCALUVA, L.,BONADIMAN, C., COLTORTI, M., SALVINI, L. & SIENA, F. 2001. Depletion events, nature of metasomatizing agent and timing of enrichment processes in lithospheric mantle xenoliths from the Veneto Volcanic Province. *Journal of Petrology*, **42**, 173–188.

BECCALUVA, L., BIANCHINI, G., *et al.* 2003. Tertiary nephelinite to tholeiite magma generation in the Veneto volcanic province, Southern Alps. *FIST-Geoitalia 2003 (4° Earth Sciences forum), Abstract Volume*, 189.

BECCALUVA, L., BIANCHINI, G., BONADIMAN, C., COLTORTI, M., MACCIOTTA, G., SIENA, F. & VACCARO, C. 2005. Within-plate Cenozoic volcanism and lithospheric mantle evolution in the western-central mediterranean area. *In:* FINETTI, I. (ed.) *Deep Seismic Exploration of the Mediterranean Region (CROP Project.)*. Elsevier, Amsterdam, 641–664

BECCARO, L., FORNACIARI, E., MIETTO, P. & PRETO, N. 2001. Analisi di facies e ricostruzione paleambientale dei "Calcari nummulitici" (Eocene, Monti Lessini orientali - Vicenza). dati preliminari. *Studi Trentini di Scienze Naturali, Acta Geologica*, **76** (1999), 1–16.

BECKER, A. 1993. An attempt to define a "neotectonic period" for central and northern Europe. *Geologische Rundschau*, **82**, 67–83.

BECKER, D. 2003. Paléoécologie et paléoclimats de la Molasse du Jura (Oligo-Miocène): apport des Rhinoceratoidea (Mammalia) et des minéraux argileux. *Geofocus*, **9**, 1–327

BECKER, D. & BERGER, J-P. 2004. Paleogeography of the Swiss Molasse basin and the Upper Rhine graben during the HRI 3 (between 17–14 ma). *Proceedings volume EEDEN Project, Courier Forschungsinstitut Senckenberg*, **249**, 1–14.

BEHRMANN, J. H., STIASNY, S., MILICKA, J. & PERESZLENYI, M. 2000. Quantative reconstruction of orogenic convergence in the northeast Carpathians. *Tectonophysics*, **319**, 111–127.

BELAK, M., SARKOTIĆ ŠLAT, M. & PAVELIĆ, D. 1991. An occurence of Badenian rhyolitic volcanoclastic rocks from middle parts of Mt. Dilj (northeastern Croatia). *Geološki vjesnik*, **44**, 151–159.

BELAK, M., MIKNIĆ, M., KRUK, B., KASTMÜLLER. Ž. & KRUK, LJ. 2000. Basalt-clayey limestone peperites: lithofacies and chronostratigraphic contribution to the knowledge of the volcanites of the Mt.Budim near Voćin. *In:* VLAHOVIĆ, I. & BIONDIĆ, R. (eds) *Second Croatian Geological Congress,* Cavtat-Dubrovnik, 17–20 May 2000, 109–113.

BENIĆ, J. 1983. *Calcareous nannoplankton and its application in biostratigraphy of the Cretaceous and Paleogene deposits in Croatia*. Doctoral thesis, University of Zagreb.

BENIĆ, J. 1991. The age of Istrian flysch deposits based on calcareous nannofossils. *In:* DROBNE, K. & PAVLOVEC, R. (eds) *Introduction to the Paleogene SW Slovenia and Istria, Field-trip Guidebook IGCP 286 "Early Paleogene Benthos", 2nd Meeting Postojna*, 25.

BERGER, J.-P. 1985. La transgression de la Molasse marine supérieure (OMM) en Suisse occidentale. *Münchner geowissenschaftliche Abhandlungen*, **A5**, 1–207.

BERGER, J.-P. 1992. *Paléontologie de la Molasse de Suisse occidentale*. Doctoral thesis, University of Fribourg.

BERGER, J.-P. 1995. Des nannofossiles calcaires aux rhinocéros: déplacés au remaniés? *Eclogae Geologicae Helvetiae*, **88**, 657–680.

BERGER J.-.P. 1996. Cartes paléogéographiques-palinspastiques du bassin molassique Suisse (Oligocène inférieur-Miocène moyen). *Neues Jahrbuch Mineralogie Geologie Paläontologie, Abhandlungen*, **202**(1),1–44.

BERGER J.-.P. 1998. "Rochette" (Late Oligocene, Swiss Molasse), a strange example of a fossil assemblage. *In:* FERGUSON, D. (ed.) Case studies in the cenophytic paleobotany of Central Europe. *Review of Paleobotany & Palynology*, **101**, 95–110

BERGER, J.-P., REICHENBACHER, B., *et al.* 2005*a*. Paleogeography of the Swiss Molasse Basin and the URG from Late Eocene to Pliocene.

*International Journal of Earth Sciences*, **94**, 697–710.

Berger J.-P., Reichenbacher, B., *et al.* 2005*b*. Eocene-Pliocene time scale and stratigraphy of the Upper Rhine Graben (URG) and the Swiss Molasse Basin (SMB). *International Journal of Earth Sciences*, **96**, 711–731.

Berggren, W. A. & Pearson, P. N. 2005. A revised tropical to subtropical Paleogene Planktonic Foraminiferal zonation. *Journal of Foraminiferal Research*, **35**(4), 279–298.

Berggren, W. A., Kent, D. V., Swisher, C. C. III & Aubry, M-P. 1995. A revised Cenozoic geochronology and chronostratigraphy. *In:* Berggren, W. A., Kent, D. V., Aubrey, M.-P. & Hardenbol, J. (eds) *Geochronology, Time Scales, and Global Stratigraphic Correlation*. SEPM, Special Publications, **54**, 129–212.

Bernecker, M. and Weidlich, O. 1990. The Danian (Paleocene) coral limestone of Fakse, Denmark. A model for ancient aphotic, azooxanthellate coral mounds. *Facies*, **22**, 103–138.

Bersezio, R., Fornaciari, M., Gelati, R., Napolitano, A. & Valdisturlo, A. 1993. The significance of the Upper Cretaceous to Miocene clastic wedges in the deformation history of the Lombardian southern Alps. *Geologie Alpine*, **69**, 3–20.

Besse, J. & Courtillot, V. 2002. Apparent and true polar wander and the geometry of the geomagnetic field over the last 200 Myr. *Journal of Geophysical Research*, **107**(B11), EPM6-1–EPM6-31.

Besse, J. & Courtillot, V. 2003. Correction to "Apparent and true polar wander and the geometry of the geomagnetic field over the last 200 Myr". *Journal of Geophysical Research*, **108**(B10), EPM3-1–EPM3-2.

Beschin, C., Busulini, A., De Angeli, A., Tessier, G. & Ungaro, S. 1998. Crostacei eocenici di "Cava Rossi" presso Monte di Malo (Vicenza-Italia settentrionale). *Studi Trentini di Scienze Naturali Acta Geologica*, **73**(1996), 7–34.

Bieda, F., Geroch, S., Koszarski, L., Książkiewicz, M. & Żytko, K. 1963. Stratigraphie des Karpates externes polonaises. *Biuletyn Państwowego Instytutu Geologicznego*, **181**, 5–174.

Biela, A. 1978. Deep drillings in the Western Carpathian basins. *Regional Geology*, **10**, 1–224.

Bigi, G., Cosentino, D., Parotto, M., Sartori, R. & Scandoni, P. 1990. *Structural Model of Italy, 1:500.000*. Consiglio nazionale delle ricerche (CNR), Progetto finalizzato geodinamica, Roma.

Bignot, G. 1972. Recherces stratigraphiques sur les calcaires du Crétacé supérieur et del'Eocene d'Istrie et de region voisines. Essai de revision du Liburnien. *Travaux du laboratoire de Micropaleontologie*, **2**, 1–355.

Biondíć, B., Dukarić, H., Kuhta, M. & Biondić, R. 1997. Hydrogeological exploration of the Rječina River Spring in the Dinaric Karst. *Geologia Croatica*, **50**, 279–288.

Birkenmajer, K. & Oszczypko, N. 1989. Cretaceous and Palaeogene lithostratigraphic units of the Magura Nappe, Krynica Subunit, Carpathians. *Annales Societatis Geologorum Poloniae*, **59**(1–2), 145–181.

Birkenmajer, K. & Pecskay, Z. 2000. K-Ar dating of the Miocene andesite intrusions, Pieniny Mts, West Carpathians: a supplement. *Studia Geologica Polonica*, **11**, 7–25.

Birklund, T. & Bromley, R. G. 1979. Cretaceous–Tertiary Boundary Events. I. The Maastrichtian and Danian of Denmark. University of Copenhagen.

Bittner, A. 1884. Die Tertiär-Ablagerungen, von Trifail und Sagor. *Jahrbuch der Kaiserlich-Königlichen Geologischen Reichsanstalt*, **34**, 433–596.

Blanchet, R. 1972. Sur un profil des Dinarides, de l'Adriatique (Split - Omiš, Dalmatie) au bassin Pannonique (Banja Luka - Doboj, Bosnie). *Bulletin Societé géologique de France.* (7), **12**(6) (1970), 1010–1027.

Blanchet, R. 1974. De l'Adriatique au bassin Pannonique. Essai d'un modèle de chaîne alpine. *Mémoire Societé Géologique de France, n.s.* **53**(120), 1–172.

Blašković, I. 1999. Tectonics of part of the Vinodol Valley within the model of the continental crust subduction. *Geologia Croatica*, **52**, 153–189.

Blašković, I. 2000. Subsurface tectonic relations – a basis for delimitation of the zones of petroleum-geological prospectivety. *2nd International Symposium on Petroleum Geology, Probability Approach to Petroleum Exploration. Nafta, Special Issue,* 157–167.

Blumenstengel, H. & Krutzsch, W. 2008 (in press). Tertiär. *In:* Bachmann, G. H., Ehling, B.-C., Eichner, R. & Schwab, M. (eds). *Geologie von Sachsen-Anhalt*. Schweizerbart, Stuttgart.

Blumenstengel, H., Koch, B., Martiklos, M. & Volland, L. 1999. Beitrag zur Strukturgeologie und Stratigraphie des Tertiärs im Raum Halle-Merseburg. *Mitteilungen. Geologie Sachsen-Anhalt,* **5**, 31–44.

Bolliger, T. 1992. Kleinsäugerstratigraphie in der miozänen Hörnlischüttung (Ostschweiz). *Documenta naturae*, **75**, 1–296

Bolliger, T., Engesser, B. & Weidmann, M. 1993. Première découverte de mammifères pliocènes dans le Jura neuchâtelois. *Eclogae Geologicae Helvetiae*, **86**(3), 1031–1068.

Bolliger, T., Fejfar, O., Graf, H. & Kaelin, D. 1996. Vorläufige Mitteilung über Funde von pliozänen Kleinsäugern aus den höheren Deckenschottern des Irchels (Kt. Zürich). *Eclogae Geologicae Helvetiae*, **89**(3),1043–1048.

Bonde, N. 1979. Palaeoenvironment in the 'North Sea' as indicated by the fish bearing Mo-clay deposit (Paleocene/Eocene), Denmark. *Mededelingen van de Werkgroep voor Tertiaire en Kwartaire Geologie*, **16**(1), 3–16.

Borović, I., Marinčić, S. & Majcen, Ž. 1976. *Osnovna geološka karta SFRJ 1.100000, list Vis K33–33*. Institute of Geology Zagreb, Federal Geological Survey Beograd.

Borović, I., Marinčić, S., Majcen, Ž. & Magaš, N. 1977. *Osnovna geološka karta SFRJ 1.100000. Tumač za list Vis K33–33*. Institute of Geology Zagreb, Federal Geological Survey Beograd, 5–57.

Bosellini, A. 1964. Nuovi affioramenti miocenici nei Lessini orientali. *Bollettino del Servizio Geologico d'Italia*, **85**, 35–40.

Bosellini, A. 1967. Calcareniti di Castelgomberto. Arenarie e calcari di S. Urbano. *In:* Bosellini, A., Carraro, F., *et al.* (eds) *Note Illustrative della carta geologica d'Italia alla scala 1.100.000, Foglio 49 Verona*. Servizio Geologico d'Italia, Nuova Tecnica Grafica, Roma, 25–27.

Bosellini, A. 1989. Dynamics of tethyan carbonate platforms. *In:* Crevello, P. D., Wilson, J. L., Sarg, J. F. & Read, J. F. (eds) *Controls on Carbonate Platform and Basin Platform*. SEPM, Special Publications, **44**, 3–13.

Bosellini, A. & Dal Cin, R. 1996. Analisi sedimentologica delle Arenarie di S. Urbano" (Miocene inferiore, Lessini vicentini). *Bollettino della Società Geologica Italiana*, **85**, 739–765.

Bosellini, A. & Luciani, V. 1985. Contributo alla conoscenza dell'hardground di Nago. *Rendiconti della Società Geologica Italiana*, **8**, 61–64.

Bosellini, A. & Trevisani, E. 1992. Coral facies and cyclicity in the Castelgomberto Limestone (Early Oligocene, Eastern Lessini Moutains, Northern Italy). *Rivista Italiana di Paleontologia e Stratigrafia*, **98**, 339–352.

Bosellini, F. R., Luciani, V., Russo, A. & Sirotti, A. 1988. Emendamenti alla stratigrafia paleogenica del Monte Baldo (Alpi meridionali, Italia). *Bollettino della Società Paleontologica Italiana*, **27**, 361–366.

Braga, G. 1972. Calcare di S. Giustina. *Servizio Geologico d'Italia, Studi Illustrati, Carta Geologica d'Italia, formazioni geologiche*, **1**, 87–99.

Brause, H. 1990. Beiträge zur Geodynamik des Saxothuringikums. *Geoprofil*, **2**, 1–88.

Brazzatti, T., Caffau, M., Cozzi, A., Cucchi, F., Drobne, K. & Pugliese, N. 1996. Padriciano Section (Karst of Trieste, Italy). *In:* Drobne, K., Goričan, Š. & Kotnik, B. (eds). *International workshop Postojna '96: The Role of Impact Processes in the Geological and Biological Evolution of Planet Earth*. Scientific Research Centre SAZU, Ljubljana, 189–198.

Brestenská, E. 1980. *Geological map and explanatory notes to region of the Bánovská kotlina Basin 1:50 000*. Geofond, Bratislava.

Brezigar, A. 1987. Coal seam of the Velenje coal mine. *Geologija*, **28/29**, 319–336.

Brezigar, A., Kosi, G., Vrhovšek, D. & Velkovrh, F. 1987. Paleontological investigations of the Plio-Quaternary beds of the Velenje depression. *Geologija*, **28/29**, 93–119.

Broglio Loriga, C. 1968. La coupe de Brendola (M. Castello). *Mémoires du Bureau des Recherches géologiques et Minières, Colloque sur l'Éocène*, **69**, 6–10.

Brzobohatý R. 1997. Paleobathymetry of the Lower Badenian (Middle Miocene, Carpathian Foredeep, South Moravia) based on otoliths. *In:* Hladilová, Š. (ed.) *Dynamika vztahů marinního a kontinentálního prostředí, Grantový projekt GAČR* **205/95/1211.** Masarykova univerzita, Brno, 37–45.

Buchardt, B. 1978. Oxygen isotope palaeotemperatures from the Tertiary period in the North Sea area. *Nature*, **5676**, 121–123.

Buchholz, P. 1989. Der Lithothamnienkalk Südostbayerns. Sedimentologie und Diagenese eines Erdgasträgers. *Geologica Bavarica*, **93**, 5–97.

Bülow, W. v. 2000. Geologische Entwicklung Südwest-Mecklenburgs seit dem Ober-Oligozän. *Schriftenreihe für Geowissenschaften*, **11**, 1–413.

Bülow, W. v. & Müller, S. 2004. Tertiär. *In:* Katzung, G. (ed.) *Geologie von Mecklenburg-Vorpommern*, 197-216. Schweizerbart, Stuttgart.

Burger, A. 2001. Heavy minerals in the Nieder Ochtenhausen Borehole. *Geologisches Jahrbuch*, **152**, 141–157.

Buser, S.& Pavšič, J. 1976. Paleocene Flysch beneath the Nanos (Western part of Slovenia). *Bulletin Scientifique*, **21**, 198–200.

Buser, S. & Pavšič, J. 1978. Migration of the Upper Cretaceous and Paleogene Flysch basin in the Western Slovenia. *Zbornik radova*, **9**, 74–81.

Butterlin, J., Vrielynck, B., *et al.* 1993. Lutetian paleoenvironments (46 to 40 Ma). *In:* Dercourt, J., Ricou, L. E. & Vrielynck, B. (eds) *Atlas Tethys Paleoenvironmental Maps*. BEICIP – FRANLAB, Gauthiers – Villars, Paris.

Cahuzac, B. & Poignant, A. 1997. Essai de biozonation de l'Oligo-Miocene dans les basins européens a l'aide des grandes foraminifers néritiques. *Bulletin de la Société Geologique de France*, **168**, 155–169.

Caron, C. 1976. La nappe du Gurnigel dans les Préalpes. *Eclogae Geologicae Helvetiae*, **69**(2), 297–308.

Caron, C., Homewood, P., Morel, R. & Van Stuijvenberg, J. 1980. Témoins de la nappe du Gurnigel sur les Préalpes médianes: une confirmation de son origine ultrabriançonnaise. *Bulletin Société fribourgeoise des Sciences naturelles*, **69**(1), 64–79.

Caron, C., Homewood, P. & Wildi, W. 1989. The original Swiss flysch: a reappraisal of the type deposits in the Swiss Prealps. *Earth-Science Reviews*, **26**, 1–45.

Carulli, G. B., Pirini Radrizzani, C. & Zucchi Stolfa, M. L. 1982. L'Eocene di Monte Forcella (Gruppo del Monte Amariana, Carnia Orientale). *Memorie della Società Geologica Italiana*, **24**, 65–70.

Carulli, G. B., Nicolich, R., Rebez, A. & Slejko, D. 1990. Seismotectonics of the northwest External Dinarides. *Tectonophysics*, **179**, 11–25.

Castellarin, A. 1981. *Carta tettonica delle Alpi Meridionali alla scala 1.200.000*. Centro Nazionale delle Ricerche CNR, **441**.

Castellarin, A. 1984. Schema delle deformazioni tettoniche sudalpine. *Bollettino di Oceanologia teorica ed applicata*, **2**, 105–114.

Castellarin, A. & Cita, M. B. 1969. Étude de quelques coupe priabonienne dans le Monte Baldo (Prov. Verona et Trento) et discussion de limite de l'étage. *Mémoires du Bureau des Recherches géologiques et Minières, Colloque sur l'Éocène*, **69**, 119–140.

Castellarin, A. & Farabegoli, E. 1974. Cicli sedimentari di spiaggia nell'Oligocene di Cavalo (M. Lessini - Verona). *Giornale di Geologia*, **39**, 393–346.

Castellarin, A. & Vai, G. B. 1981. Importance of Hercynian tectonics within the framework of the Southern Alps. *Journal of Structural Geology*, **3**, 477–486.

Castellarin, A. & Vai, G. B. 2002. Tettonica. Le Alpi meridionali centro-orientali nella catena alpina. *In:* Vai, G.B., Venturini, C., Carulli, G.B. & Zanferrari, A. (eds) *Guide geologiche regionali. Alpi e Prealpi Carniche e Giulie. Friuli Venezia Giulia*. Società Geologica Italiana, BE-MA, **9**, 62–67.

Castellarin, A. & Zucchi, M. L. 1966. La successione stratigrafica paleocenica ed eocenica nei dintorni di Opicina. *Studi Trentini di Scienze Naturali, sez. A*, **43**, 275–325.

Cati, A., Sartorio, D. & Venturini, S. 1987. Carbonate platforms in the subsurface of the northern Adriatic area. *Memorie della Società Geologica Italiana,* **40**, 295–308.

Čechovič, V. 1959. Geológia treťohorných vrstiev severného okraja handlovskej uhoľnej panvy. *Geologice Práce*, **53**, 5–58.

Channell, J. E. T., Brandner, R., Spieler, A. & Stoner, J. 1992. Paleomagnetism and paleogeography of the Northern Calcareous Alps (Austria). *Tectonics*, **11**, 792–810.

Channell, J. E. T., D'Argenio, B. & Horváth, F. 1979. Adria, the African promontory, in Mesozoic Mediterranean Palaeogeography. *Earth Science Reviews*, **15**, 213–292.

Chlupáč, I., Brzobohatý, R., Kovanda, J. & Stráník, Z. 2002. *Geologická minulost České republiky*. Academia, Praha.

Chorowitz, J. 1969. Stratigraphie et teqtonique d'un secteur de la Dalmatie moyenne, près de Split (Yougoslavie). *Bulletin de la Société Geologique de France*, **11**(6), 862–870.

Chorowitz, J. 1975. Le devenir de la zone de Budva vers le Nord-Ovest de la Yougoslavie. *Bulletin de la Société Geologique de France* (7), **17**(5), 699–707

Chorowitz, J. 1977. Etude geologique des Dinarides le long de la structure transverale Split - Karlovac (Yougoslavie). *Societé Géologique du Nord,* **1**, 3–331.

Cicha I. *et al.* 1985. Neogén v opěrných vrtech OS-1 Kravaře a OS-2 Hať v opavské pánvi. *Sborník geologických věd, Geologie*, **40**, 189–229.

Čičić, S. 1964. Geološki sastav i tektonika sjeveroistočnog dijela planine Majevice s naročitim osvrtom na geološko-ekonomski značaj ležišta mrkog uglja. *Geološki glasnik*, **6**, 3–173.

Čičić, S. 1977. *Paleogen. Geologija Bosne i Hercegovine, 3, Kenozojske periode*. Geoinženjering, Sarajevo.

Čičić, S. 2002*a*. *Geološka karta Bosne i Hercegovine 1.300 000.* Earth Science Institute, Sarajevo.

Čičić, S. 2002*b*. *Geološki sastav i tektonika Bosne i Hercegovine*. Monografija, Earth Science Institute, Sarajevo.

Cimerman, F., Pavlovec, R., Pavšič, J., & Todesco, L. 1974. Biostratigraphy of the Paleogene beds of Goriška Brda. *Geologija*, **17**, 8–130.

Cita, M. B. 1975. Stratigrafia della Sezione di Possagno. *In:* Bolli, H. M. (ed.) Monografia micropaleontologica sul Paleocene e l'Eocene di Possagno, Provincia di Treviso, Italia. *Schweizerische Paläontologische Abhandlungen*, **97**, 9–32.

Cita, M. B. & Bolli, H. M. 1961. Nuovi dati sull'età paleocenica dello Spilecciano di Spilecco. *Rivista Italiana di Paleontologia e Stratigrafia*, **67**, 369–392.

Ciuk, E. 1970. Schematy litostratygraficzne trzeciorzędu Niżu Polskiego. *Geological Quarterly*, **14**, 754–771.

Ciuk, E. 1973. Szczegółowy profil litologiczno-stratygraficzny. Trzeciorzęd, Wyniki badań litologicznych i stratygraficznych. Trzeciorzęd. Charakterystyka litologiczno-stratygraficzna. *In:* Jaskowiak-Schoeneichowa, M. (ed.) *Profile głębokich otworów Instytutu Geologicznego*. Szczecin, Warszawa.

Ciuk, E. 1974. Schematy litostratygraficzne paleogenu Polski poza Karpatami i zapadliskiem przedkarpackim. *Biuletyn Państwowego Instytutu Geologicznego*, **281**, 7–48.

Ciuk, E. 1975. Rozwój litologii i sedymentacji utworów trzeciorzędowych w rejonie Tanowa na północny zachód od Szczecina. *Biuletyn Państwowego Instytutu Geologicznego*, **284**, 133–169.

Ciuk, E. & Pożaryska, K. 1982. On paleogeography of the Tertiary of the Polish Lowland. *Prace Muzeum Ziemi*, **35**, 81–88.

Ciupagea, D., Păucă, M., Ichim, T. 1970. *Geologia Depresiunii Transilvaniei*. Editura Academiei R.S.R., Bucureşti.

Clausen, O. R., Gregersen, U., Michelsen, O., Sorensen, J. C. 1999. Factors controlling the Cenozoic sequence development in the eastern parts of the North Sea. *Journal of the Geological Society London*, **156**, 809–816.

Corrà, G. 1977. Osservazioni su fenomeni paleocarsici terziari nei calcari eocenici delle Colline di Verona. Studi Trentini di Scienze Naturali, *Acta geologica*, **54**, 123–141.

Ćosović, V. 1991. Discocyclina from Istria. *In:* Drobne, K. & Pavlovec, R. (eds) *Introduction to the Paleogene SW Slovenia and Istria Field-trip Guidebook, 2nd Meeting IGCP Project 286*, 19–27 October 1991, Postojna, 23–24.

Ćosović, V. & Drobne, K. 1995. Paleoecological significance of morphology of orthophragminids from the Istrian peninsula (Croatia and Slovenia). *Geobios*, **18**, 93–99.

Ćosović, V. & Drobne, K. 1998. Lutetian Orthophragminae from the Istrian Peninsula (Adriatic Sea, -Croatia and Slovenia). *Dela - Opera SAZU 4 razreda*, **34**(2), 173–181.

Ćosović, V., Balončić, D., Koić, M., Marjanac, T., Moro, A., Gušić, I. & Jelaska, V. 1994. Paleontological evidence of Paleogene transgression on Adriatic carbonate platform. *Géologie Mediterranee*, **21**(3–4), 49–53.

Ćosović, V., Drobne, K. & Moro, A. 2004*a*. Paleoenvironmental model for Eocene foraminiferal limestones of the Adriatic carbonate platform (Istrian Peninsula). *Facies*, **50**, 61–75.

Ćosović, V., Premec Fuček, V., Jelaska, V., Gušić, I. & Moro, A. 2004*b*. Updating of the biostratigraphy of the Central Dalmatia (Adriatic Sea, Croatia). *In:* Bice, K., Aubry, M.-P. & Ouda, K. (eds), *Climate and Biota of the Early Paleogene CBEP V,* 8–12 February 2004, Luxor, Egypt, Abstract and Program Book, C 11.

Ćosović, V., Premec Fuček, V., Gušić, I., Jelaska, V. & Moro, A. 2006. The age of the Tilovica Breccias in the Central Dalmatia, Croatia. *Micropaleontology*, **52**, 281–286.

Costa, L. I. & Manum, S. B. 1988. Dinoflagellates. The description of the interregional zonation of the Paleogene (D1–D15) and the Miocene (D16–D20). *In:* Vinken, R. (ed.) The Northwest European Tertiary Basin. *Geologisches Jahrbuch*, A100, 321–330.

Costa, V., Doglioni, C., Grandesso, P., Masetti, D., Pellegrini, G. B. & Tracanella, E. 1996. *Note illustrative del Foglio 063 Belluno alla scala 1.50.000.* Istituto Poligrafico e Zecca dello Stato, Roma.

Cousin, M. 1981. *Les rapports Alpes-Dinarides; les confins de l'Italie et de la Yugoslavie.* Societé Géologique du Nord, **5**.

Crampton, S. L. & Allen, P. A. 1995. Recognition of forebulge unconformities associated with early stage foreland basin development: example from the North Alpine foreland basin. *AAPG Bulletin*, **79,** 1495–1514.

Csaszár, G. (ed.) 1997. *Basic Lithostratigraphic Units of Hungary.* Geological Institut of Hungary.

Császár, G., Galacz, A., *et al.* 1990. Paleogeography of the Pannonian Basin. *Societe Geologique de France, Memoires, NS*, **154**, 63–89.

Csontos, L., Tari, G., Bergerat, F. & Fodor, L. 1991. Evolution of the Stress fields in the Carpatho- Pannonian area during the Neogene. *Tectonophysics*, **199**, 73–91.

Csontos, L., Nagymarosy, A., Horváth, F. & Kováč, M. 1992. Tertiary evolution of the intra-Carpathian area. A model. *Tectonophysics*, **208**, 221 - 241.

Čtyroký, P. 1991. Division and correlation of the Eggenburgian and Ottnangian in the southern Carpathian Foredeep in southern Moravia. *Západné Karpaty, sér. Geológia*, **15**, 67–109, Bratislava.

Cucchi, F., Pirini Radrizzani, C. & Pugliese, N. 1987. The carbonate stratigraphic sequence of the Karst of Trieste (Italy). *Memorie della Società Geologica Italiana*, **40**, 35–44.

Czerwonka, J. A. & Krzyszkowski, D. 2001. Preglacial (Pliocene – Early Middle Pleistocene) deposits in Southwestern Poland: lithostratigraphy and reconstruction of drainage pattern. *In*: Krzyszkowski, D. (ed.) *Late Cainozoic stratigraphy and palaeogeography of the Sudetic Foreland.* Wind, Wrocław, 147–195.

Dainelli, G. 1912. *L'Eocene Friulano. Monografia geologica e paleontologica.* Editrice Le Memorie geografiche.

Dal Molin, L., Mietto, P. & Sauro, U. 2001. Considerazioni sul paleocarsismo terziario dei Monti Berici. la Grotta della Guerra a Lumignano (Longare - Vicenza). *Natura Vicentina*, **4**(2000), 33–48.

Dal Piaz, Gb. 1937. I Mammiferi dell'Oligocene veneto. Archaeopteropus transiens. Memorie dell'Istituto di Geologia Regia Università di Padova, **11**, 1–8.

Darga, R. 1992. Geologie, Paläontologie und Palökologie der südostbayerischen unter-priabonen (Ober-Eozän) Riffkalkvorkommen des Eisenrichtersteins bei Hallthurm (Nördliche Kalkalpen) und des Kirchbergs bei Neubeuern (Helvetikum). *Münchner Geowissenschaftliche Abhandlungen* (A), **23**, 1–166.

De Capoa, P., Radoicic, R. & D'Argenio, B. 1995. Miocene deformation of the External Dinarides (Montenegro and Dalmatia). *New biostratigraphic evidence. Memorie di Scienze Geologiche Università di Padova*, **47**, 157–172.

Delvalle, D. & Buser, S. 1990. Mikrofacies analysis of limestone from the Upper Cretaceous to the Lower Eocene of SW Slovenia (Yugoslavia). *Geologija*, **31/32**, 351–394.

Dercourt, J., Ricou, L. E. & Vrielynch, B. (eds). 1993. *Atlas Tethys, Paleoenvironmental Maps.* Gauthiers – Villars, Paris.

DeRuig, M. J. 2002. Landscape evolution: architectural element analysis of 3D seismic data from the Puchkirchen Submarine Channel Belt (Upper Austrian Molasse) – implications for depositional process and reservoir distribution. *Pangeo Austria: Erdwissenschaften in Österreich,* 28–30 June 2002, Salzburg: Programm und Kurzfassungen, 38.

De Vecchi, G. & Sedea, R. 1995. The Paleogene basalts of the Veneto region (NE Italy). *Memorie di Scienze Geologiche Università di Padova,* **47**, 253–274.

Dewey, J. F., Helman, M. L., Turco, E., Hutton, D. H. W. & Knott, S. D. 1989. Kinematics of the western Mediterranean. *In:* Coward, M. P., Dietrich, D. & Park, R. G. (eds) *Alpine Tectonics.* Geological Society, London, Special Publications, **45**, 265–283.

De Zanche, V. & Conterno, T. 1972. Contributo alla conoscenza geologica dell'orizzonte eocenico di Roncà nel veronese e nel vicentino. *Atti Memorie dell'Accademia Patavina delle Scienze, Lettere ed Arti*, **84**, 287–295.

De Zanche, V., Pavlovec, R. & Proto-Decima, F. 1967. Microfauna and microfacies of the Eocene flysch series near Ustje in the Vipava valley, Vipavska dolina, SW Slovenia. *Razprave 4. razreda, SAZU,* **10**, 205–263.

De Zanche, V., Sorbini, L. & Spagna, V. 1977. Geologia del territorio del Comune di Verona. *Memorie del Museo civico di Storia Naturale di Verona*, **1**, 1–52.

Dèzes, P., Schmid, S. & Ziegler, P. A. 2004. Evolution of the European Cenozoic Rift System: interaction of the Alpine and Tyrenean orogens with their foreland lithosphere. *Tectonophysics*, **389**, 1–33.

Diem, B. 1986. Die Untere Meeresmolasse zwischen der Saane und Ammer. *Eclogae Geologicae Helvetiae*, **79**(2), 493–559.

Dill, H. G., Köthe, A., Gramann, F. & Botz, R. 1996., A palaeoenvironmental and palaeoecological analysis of fine grained Paleogene estuarine deposits of North Germany. *Palaeogeography, Palaeoclimatology, Palaeoecology*, **124**, 273–326.

Dimitrijević, M. D. 1982. Dinarides. An outline of the tectonics. *Earth Evolution Sciences*, **2**, 4–23.

Dlabač, M. 1960. Poznámky ke vzt'ahu medzi tvarem povrchu a geologickou stavbou Podunajské nížiny. *Geologicke Práce*, **59**, 69–101.

Doglioni, C. 1984. *I sovrascorrimenti nelle Dolomiti. Sistemi di ramp-flat.* Tecnoprint, Bologna.

Doglioni, C. & Bosellini, A. 1987. Eoalpine and mesoalpine tectonics in the Southern Alps. *Geologische Rundschau*, **77**, 734–754.

Doláková, N., Hladilová, Š. & Nehyba, S. 1999. Development of Sedimentation, molluscs and palynospectra in the Lower Miocene of the south-western Part of the Carpathian Foredeep in Moravia (Czech Republic). *Acta Palaeobotanica, Suppl.*, **2**, 269–278.

Doláková, N. & Slamková, M. 2003. Palynological characteristics of Karpatian sediments. *In:* Brzobohatý, R., Cicha, I., Kováč, M. & Rögl, F. (eds) *The Karpatian. A Lower Miocene stage of the Central Paratethys.* Masaryk University, Brno, 325–346.

Dolenec, T. & Pavsic, J. 1995. Elemental and stable isotope variations in the Cretaceous–Tertiary boundary sediments from the Soca Valley, NW Slovenia. *Terra Nova*, **7**, 630–635.

Dolenec, T., Cucchi, F., Giacomich, R., Marton, E. & Ogorelec, B. 1995. Abiotic characteristics of carbonate rocks from the K/T boundary on the Karst area (isotops, geochemistry, geochronology and paleomagnetism). *4th International Workshop ESF Sci. Network "Impact Cratering and Evolution of Planet Earth",* Ancona, May 1995, Abstracts and Field Trips, 68–69.

Dolenec, T., Pavšič, J. & Lojen, S. 2000*a*. Ir anomalies and other elemental markers near the Paleocene – Eocene boundary in a flysch sequence from the Western Tethys (Slovenia). *Terra Nova*, **12**(5), 129–204.

Dolenec, T., Pavšič, J. & Lojen, S. 2000*b*. The Paleocene – Eocene boundary in a flysch sequence from Goriška Brda (Western Slovenia): Oxygen and carbon stable isotope variations. *Geologija*, **43**(1), 37–42.

Doppler, G., Pürner, T. & Seidel, M. 2000. Zur Gliederung und Kartierung der bayerischen Vorlandmolasse. *Geologica Bavarica*, **105**, 217–241.

Dorobek, S. L. 1995. Synorogenic carbonate platforms and reefs in foreland basins: controls on stratigraphic evolution and platform/reef morphology. *In*: Dorobek, S. L. & Ross, G. M. (eds) *Stratigraphic Evolution of Foreland Basins.* SEPM, Special Publications, **52**, 127–147.

Dragičević, I. & Velić, I. 2002. The northeastern margin of the Adriatic carbonate platform. *Geologia Croatica*, **55**, 185–232.

Dragičević, I., Prelogović, E., Kuk, V. & Buljan, R. 1999. Recent tectonic activity in the Imotsko Polje area. *Geologia Croatica*, **52**, 191–196.

Drobne, K. 1974. Les grandes miliolides des couches paleocenes de la

Yougoslavie du Nord-Ouest (Idalina, Fabularia, Lacazina, Periloculina). *Razprave SAZU 4. razreda*, **17**(3), 125–184.

DROBNE, K. 1977. Alvéolines paléogenes de la Slovénie et de l'Istrie. *Schweizerische Paläontologische Abhandlungen*, **99**, 1–132.

DROBNE, K. 1979. Paleogene and Eocene beds in Slovenia and Istria. *16th European Micropaleontology Colloquium, Ljubljana*, 49–64.

DROBNE, K. 1984. *Periloculina slovenica* B form from the Paleocene of Majevica Mt. (Yugoslavia) and the new family Fabulariidae. *Razprave 4. razreda, SAZU*, **25**, 1–32.

DROBNE, K. 1985. *Periloculina dalmatina*, a new trematophorid miliolid from the Cuisian of Yugoslavia. *Opera SAZU IV Classis*, **26**, 159–176.

DROBNE, K. 2000. The north-western part of the Adriatic Carbonate platform from the K/T boundary to the Flysch deposition during Paleocene-Eocene. *In:* CARULLI, G. B. & LONGO SALVADOR, G. (eds) *Riassunti delle comunicazioni orali e dei poster. 80a Riunione Estiva,* Trieste, 6–8 settembre 2000, 231–232.

DROBNE, K. 2003*a*. Larger Foraminifera at the Paleocene /Eocene boundary on the Adriatic Carbonate Platform. *Symposium on the Paleogene. Preparing for Modern Life and Climate. Abstract & Program book.* International Subcommittee on Paleogene Stratigraphy, Leuven.

DROBNE, K. 2003*b*. Paleogene biota from the sedimentary zones 1–4 on the Adriatic Carbonate Platform (ACP). *In:* VLAHOVIĆ, I. (ed.) *22nd IAS Meeting Sediment, Opatija, Abstract Book,* Zagreb, 47.

DROBNE, K. & BAČAR, S. 2003. Vallée de la Vipava. *In:* DROBNE, K., PUGLIESE, N. & TAMBAREAU, Y. (eds) *De la mer Adriatique aux Alpes Juliennes (Italie Nord-Orient et Slovénie occidentale) un parcours géologique sans frontieres*, Scientific Research Centre SAZU, Ljubljana 54–62, 69–71.

DROBNE, K. & ĆOSOVIĆ, V. 1998. Repetitive order of appearance of Larger Foraminifera and the ecological gradients preserved in Paleogene shallow benthic carbonate deposits. *In:* THOMPSON, P. R. (ed.), *Tertiary to Recent Larger Foraminifera. Their Depositional Environments and Importance as Petroleum Reservoirs.* Conference – Workshop – Fieldtrip, Kingston, 10.

DROBNE, K. & HOTTINGER. L. 1999. The taxon *Coskinolina liburnica* Stache, and its 124 years of geological use. *Convegno internationale di studi Buie e il suo Carso nella geologia dell' Istria*, 11–15.

DROBNE, K. & PAVLOVEC, R. 1991. Paleocene and Eocene beds in Slovenia and Istria. *In:* DROBNE, K. & PAVLOVEC, R. (eds) *Introduction to the Paleogene SW Slovenia and Istria Field-trip Guidebook, 2nd Meeting IGCP Project 286*, 19–27 October 1991 Postojna, 7–18.

DROBNE, K. & PAVŠIČ, J. 1991. Clastic carbonate deposits in SW Slovenia and Istria. *In:* DROBNE, K. & PAVLOVEC, R. (eds) *Introduction to the Paleogene SW Slovenia and Istria Field-trip Guidebook, 2nd Meeting IGCP Project 286*, 19–27 October 1991 Postojna, 19–21.

DROBNE, K. & TRUTIN, M. 1997. Alveolinas from the Bunić section (Lika, Croatia). *Geologia Croatica*, **50**(2), 215–223.

DROBNE, K., PAVLOVEC, R. & DROBNE, F. 1977. Paleogene Larger Foraminifera from the area between Mežica and Slovenj Gradec (NW Yugoslavia). *Razprave, 4. razreda SAZU*, **20**, 1–88.

DROBNE, K., PAVLOVEC, R., ŠIKIĆ, L. & BENIĆ, J. 1979. Excursion F, Pićan, Istria - Cuisian, Lutetian. *Guidebook of the 16th European Micropaleontology Colloquium*, Ljubljana.

DROBNE, K., PAVLOVEC, R., DROBNE, F., CIMERMAN, F. & ŠIKIĆ, L. 1985. Some larger foraminifera from the Upper Eocene and the basal Oligocene beds in North Slovenia. *Geološki glasnik*, **28**, 77–117.

DROBNE K., OGORELEC B., PLENIČAR M., ZUCCHI-STOLFA M. L. & TURNŠEK, D. 1988*a*. Maastrichtian, Danian and Thanetian Beds in Dolenja Vas (NW Dinarides, Yugoslavia), microfacies, foraminifers, rudists and corals. *Razprave SAZU 4*, **29**, 147–224.

DROBNE, K., PAVLOVEC, R., TRUTIN, M. & MARJANAC, T. 1988*b*. Paleogene transgression on the Adriatic carbonate platform. *Abstracts 4th International Symposium on Benthic Foraminifera*, Sorrento, 21.

DROBNE, K., OGORELEC, B., PLENIČAR, M., BARATTOLO, F., TURNŠEK, D. & ZUCCHI-STOLFA, M. L. 1989. The Dolenja Vas section, a transition from Cretaceous to Paleocene in the NW Dinarides, Yugoslavia. *Memorie della Società geologica Italiana*, **40** (1987), 73–84.

DROBNE, K., OGORELEC, B., PAVLOVEC, R. & PAVŠIČ, J. 1991*a*. Golež: Danian – Cuisian. *In:* DROBNE, K. & PAVLOVEC, R. (eds), *Paleocene and Eocene beds in Slovenia and Istria.* 2nd Meeting of IGCP 286 – Early Paleogene Benthos, Postojna (Slovenia), 61–68.

DROBNE, K., PAVLOVEC, R. & PAVŠIČ, J. 1991*b*. Section Veliko Gradišče-Thanetian, Ilerdian. *In:* DROBNE, K. & PAVLVOEC, R. (eds) *Paleocene and Eocene beds in Slovenia and Istria.* 2nd Meeting of IGCP 286 – Early Paleogene Benthos, Postojna (Slovenia), 55–60.

DROBNE, K., VLAHOVIĆ, I., *et al.* 1991*c*. Ecxursion B - Ravni kotari Paleogene. *In:* VLAHOVIĆ, I. & VELIĆ, I. (eds) *Some Aspects of the Shallow Water Sedimentation on the Adriatic Carbonate Platform (Permian to Eocene).* Excursion Guide-Book, Second International Symposium on the Adriatic carbonate platform, Relation with adjacent regions, Zadar, 12–18 May 1991, 53–105.

DROBNE, K., OGORELEC, B., *et al.* 1995. The Dolenja Vas section (Upper Maastrichtian, Lower and Upper Danian, Thanetian). Atti Mus. Geol. Paleont. *Quaderno Spec.*, **3**, 99–115.

DROBNE, K., GORIČAN, Š. & KOTNIK, B. (eds) 1996*a*. *The role of impact processes in the geological and biological evolution of planet Earth.* International workshop, Paleontology Institute of ZRC-SAZU, Ljubljana.

DROBNE, K., OGORELEC, B., DOLENEC, T., MARTON, E. & PALINKAŠ, L. 1996*b*. Biota and abiota at the K/T boundary in the Dolenja vas section, Slovenia. *In:* DROBNE, K., GORIČAN, Š. & KOTNIK, B. (eds) *The role of impact processes in the geological and biological evolution of planet Earth.* International workshop, Palaeontology Institue of ZRC-SAZU, Ljubljana, 163–181.

DROBNE, K., ĆOSOVIĆ, V. & HOTTINGER, L. 2000*a*. Oligocene shallow benthic foraminifera from Biševo Island (Croatia) in the Adriatic Sea. *In:* VLAHOVIĆ, I. & BIONDIĆ, R. (eds) *Proceedings of the 2nd Croatian Geological Congress*, Cavtat - Dubrovnik, 501.

DROBNE, K. PUGLIESE, N. & TRUTIN, M. 2000*b*. Correlation of Paleocene Biota of the North Adriatic Karst Area and Hercegovina. *2nd Croatian Geological Congress, Zagreb, Zbornik radova Proceedings*, 167–170.

DROBNE, K., ĆOSOVIČ, V. & ROBINSON, E. 2002. Larger miliolids of the Late Cretaceous and Paleogene seen through space and time. *Geologija*, **45**(2), 359–366.

DROBNE, K., GOZZI, E., MELIS, R. & PUGLIESE, N. 2003. Belvedere San Lorenzo. *In:* DROBNE, K., PUGLIESE, N. & TAMBAREAU, Y. (eds) *De la mer Adriatique aux Alpes Juliennes*, Scientific Research Centre SAZU, Ljubljana, 9–12.

DROBNE, K., PREMEC-FUĆEK, V., *et al.* 2006. The lower Paleogene in SW Slovenia (Adria plate). *In:* CABALLERO, E. *et al.* (eds) *Climate and Biota of the Early Paleogene 2006. Volume of Abstracts, Bilbao,* 37–38.

DROBNE, K., TRUTIN, M. & PAVLOVEC, R. (in press). The Paleogene carbonates on the Adriatic platform. *Dela – Opera SAZU 4. razreda*, **34/3**.

DUDICH, E. & BOMBITA, G. 1983. Étude minerali-petrographique et géochemique de quelques roches sedimentaires d'age Crétacé supérieur et Paléogene de la zone du Flysch de Szolnok-Maramure. *Anuarul Institutului de Geologie si Geofizica*, **62**, 217–228.

DUMITRICĂ, P., GHEȚA, N. & POPESCU, G. 1975. New data on the biostratigraphy and correlation of the Middle Miocene in the Carpathian area. *Dări de Seamă, Institutul de Geologie și Geofizică*, **61**, 65–84.

DUPUIS, C., DE CONINCK, J. & ROCHE, E. 1984. Remise en cause du rôle Paléógéographic du horst de l'Artois à l'Ypresien inférieur. Mise en évidence de l'entervention du Môle Bray-Artois. *Comptes Rondus de l'Académie des Sciences, II, (2)*, **298**, 53–56.

DURINGER, P. 1988. *Les conglomérats des bordures du rift cénozoïque rhénan. Dynamique sédimentaire et contrôle climatique.* Doctoral thesis, Université Louis Pasteur, Strasbourg.

DYBKJAER, K. 2004*a*. Morphological and abundance variations in Homotryblium-cyst assemblages related to depositional environments; uppermost Oligocene–Lower Miocene, Jylland, Denmark. *Palaeogeography, Palaeoclimatology, Palaeoecology*, **206**, 41–58

DYBKJAER, K. 2004*b*. Dinocyst stratigraphy and palynofacies studies used for refining a sequence stratigraphic model – uppermost Oligocene to lower Miocene, Jylland, Denmark. *Review of Palaeobotany and Palynology*, **131**, 201–249.

DYJOR, S. 1966. Wiek serii białych żwirów i glin kaolinowych w zachodniej części przedpola Sudetów. *Przeglad Geologiczny*, **14**, 478–480.

EGGER, H. 1990. Zur paläogeographischen Stellung des Rhenodanubischen Flysches (Neokom-Eozän) der Ostalpen. *Jahrbuch der Geologischen Bundesanstalt*, **133**(2), 147–155.

EGGER, H. 1992. Zur Geodynamik und Paläogeographie des Rhenodanubischen Flysches (Neokom-Eozän) der Ostalpen. *Zeitschrift der Deutschen Geologischen Gesellschaft*, **143**, 51–65.

EGGER, H. 1995. Die Lithostratigraphie der Altlengbach-Formation und der Anthering-Formation im Rhenodanubischen Flysch (Ostalpen, Penninikum). *Neues Jahrbuch für Geologie und Paläontologie, Abhandlungen*, **196**, 69–91.

EGGER, H. & WAGREICH, M. 2001. Upper Paleocene – Lower Eocene nannofossils from the Gosau Group of Gams/Styria (Austria). *In:* PILLER, W. E. & RASSER, M. W. (eds) *Paleogene of the Eastern Alps*. Österreichische Akademie der Wissenschaften, Schriftenreihe der Erdwissenschaftlichen Kommissionen, **14**, 465–472.

EGGER, H., BICHLER, M., HOMAYOUN, M., KIRCHNER, E. C. & SURENIAN, R. 1996. Spätpaleozäne Bentonite aus der Gosau-Gruppe des Untersberg-Vorlandes (Nördliche Kalkalpen, Salzburg). *Jahrbuch der Geologischen Bundesanstalt*, **139**, 13–20.

EGGER, H., BICHLER, M., *et al.* 1997. Mudturbidites, black shales and bentonites from the Paleocene/Eocene boundary: the Antering Formation of the Rhenodanubian Flysch (Austria). *Jahrbuch der Geologischen Bundesanstalt*, **140**(1), 29–45.

EGGER, H., HEILMANN-CLAUSEN, C. & SCHMITZ, B. 2000. The Paleocene/Eocene-boundary interval of a Tethyan deep-sea section (Austria) and its correlation with the North Sea basin. *Bulletin Société géologique de France*, **171**, 207–216.

EGGER, H., RÖGL, F. & WAGREICH, M. 2004. Biostratigraphy and facies of Paleogene deep-water deposits at Gams (Gosau Group, Austria). *Annalen des Naturhistorischen Museums Wien*, **106A**, 281–307.

EISSMANN, L. 1970. Geologie des Bezirkes Leipzig – Eine Übersicht. *Natura regionis Lipsiensis*, **1**, 1–174.

EISSMANN, L. & LITT, T. 1994. Das Quartär Mitteldeutschlands. Ein Leitfaden und Exkursionsführer. Mit einer Übersicht über das Präquartär des Saale-Elbe-Gebietes. *Altenburger naturwissenschaftliche Forschungen*, **7**, 1–458.

EMBEY-ISZTIN, A. & KURAT, G. 1996. Young alkali basalt volcanism from the Graz Basin to the Eastern Carpathians. *In:* DUDICH, E. & LOBITZER, H. (eds) *Austrian-Hungarian Joint Geological Research*. Geological Survey Vienna, 159–175.

ENGEL, W. 1970. Die Nummuliten – breccien im Flyschbecken von Ajdovščina in Slowenien als Beispiel karbonatische Turbidite. *Verhandlungen Geologische Bundesanstalt*, **1970**(4), 570–582.

ENGEL, W. 1974. Sedimentologische Untersuchungen im Flysch des Beckens von Ajdovščina (Slovenien). *Göttinger Arbeiten Geologie Paläontologie*, **16**, 1–65.

ENGESSER, B. & MÖDDEN, C. 1997. A new version of the biozonation of the Lower Freshwater Molasse (Oligocene and Agenian) of Switzerland and Savoy on the basis of fossil mammals. *In:* AGUILAR, J. P., LEGENDRE, S. & MICHAUX, J. (eds) *Actes du Congrès Biochrom'97. Mémoires et Travaux, EPHE, Institut de Montpellier*, **21**, 475–499.

ENGESSER, B., MAYO, N. A. & WEIDMANN, M. 1984. Nouveaux gisements de mammifères dans la molasse subalpine vaudoise et fribourgeoise. *Mémories suisses de Paléontologie,* **107**, 83–110.

ENGESSER, B., SCHÄFER, P., SCHWARZ, J. & TOBIEN, H. 1993. Paläontologische Bearbeitung des Grenzbereichs Obere Cerithienschichten/Corbicula-Schichten (= Schichten mit *Hydrobia inflata*) im Steinbruch Rüssingen mit Bemerkungen zur Oligozän/Miozän-Grenze im Kalktertiär des Mainzer Beckens. *Mainzer geowissenschaftliche Mitteilungen*, **22**, 247–274.

ERCEGOVAC, M. & ČIČIĆ, S. 1968. Rezultati palinoloških ispitivanja eocenskih sedimenata između Sapne i Rožnja (istočna Majevica). *Geološki glasnik*, **12**, 113–124.

ETTINGSHAUSEN, C. 1872. Die Fossile Flora von Sagor in Krain, 1. *Denkschriften der Kaiserlichen Akademie der Wissenschaften, Mathematisch-Naturwissenschaftliche Classe*, **32**, 159–202.

ETTINGSHAUSEN, C. 1877. Die Fossile Flora von Sagor in Krain, 2. Denkschriften der Kaiserlichen Akademie der Wissenschaften, Mathematisch-Naturwissenschaftliche Classe, **37**, 161–216.

ETTINGSHAUSEN, C. 1885. Die Fossile Flora von Sagor in Krain, 3. Denkschriften der Kaiserlichen Akademie der Wissenschaften, Mathematisch-Naturwissenschaftliche Classe, **50**, 1–55.

FABIANI, R. 1912. Nuove osservazioni sul Terziario fra il Brenta e l'Astico. *Atti dell'Accademia delle Scienze Veneta-Trentino-Istriana*, **5**, 7–36.

FABIANI, R. 1914. La serie stratigrafica del Monte Bolca e dei suoi dintorni. *Memorie dell'Istituto di Geologia Regia Università di Padova*, **2** (1913), 223–235.

FABIANI, R. 1915. Il Paleogene del Veneto. Memorie dell'Istituto di Geologia Regia Università di Padova, **3**, 1–336.

FASEL, J. M. 1986. *Sédimentologie de la Molasse d'eau douce subalpine entre le Léman et la Gruyère*. Thesis, University of Fribourg, **907**.

FAUPL, P. 1977. Untersuchungen an terrigenen Gesteinen der paläogenen Buntmergelserie der östlichen Ostalpen (Vorbericht). *Verhandlungen der Geologischen Bundesanstalt,* **1977**, 13–15.

FAUPL, P. 1983. Die Flyschfazies in der Gosau der Weyerer Bögen (Oberkreide, Nördliche Kalkalpen, Österreich). *Jahrbuch der Geologischen Bundesanstalt*, **126**, 219–244.

FAUPL, P. & ROETZEL, R. 1988. Gezeitenbeeinflußte Ablagerungen der Innviertler Gruppe (Ottnangien) in der oberösterreichischen Molassezone. *Jahrbuch der Geologischen Bundesanstalt*, **130**, 415–447.

FAUPL, P. & ROETZEL, R. 1990. Die Phosphoritsande und Fossilreichen Grobsande: Gezeitenbeeinflußte Ablagerungen der Innviertler Gruppe (Ottnangien) in der oberösterreichischen Molassezone. *Jahrbuch der Geologischen Bundesanstalt*, **133**, 157–180.

FAUPL, P. & WAGREICH, M. 2000. Late Jurassic to Eocene palaeogeography and geodynamic evolution of the Eastern Alps. *Mitteilungen der Österreichischen Geologischen Gesellschaft*, **92**, 79–94.

FERAZZINI, B. 1981. *Zur Geologie des Ultrahelvetikums zwischen Adelboden und Lenk, Berner Oberland*. Doctoral thesis, University of Bern.

FERHATBEGOVIĆ, Z. 2004. *Geološke karakteristike središnjeg dijela Tuzlanskog basena*. Doctoral thesis, University of Tuzla.

FILIPESCU, S. & KAMINSKI, M. A. (in press). Paleocene deep-water agglutinated foraminifera in the Transylvanian Basin. *In:* KAMINSKI M.A., COCCIONI R. & MARSILI A. (eds), 2007. *Proceedings of the Seventh International Workshop on Agglutinated Foraminifera*, Urbino, 13.

FILIPESCU, S. 1996. Stratigraphy of the Neogene from the western border of the Transylvanian Basin. *Studia Universitatis Babeş-Bolyai, seria Geologia*, **41**, 3–78.

FILIPESCU, S. 2001*a*. Cenozoic Lithostratigraphic units in Transylvania. *In:* BUCUR, I. I., FILIPESCU, S. & SASARAN, E. (eds) *Algae and Carbonate Platforms in Western Part of Romania*. 4th Regional Meeting of IFAA Cluj-Napoca 2001 - Field Trip Guidebook. Cluj University Press, 75–92.

FILIPESCU, S. 2001*b*. Wielician Foraminifera at the Western border of the Transylvanian Basin. *Studia Universitatis Babeş-Bolyai, seria Geologia*, **46**, 115–123.

FILIPESCU, S. 2004. *Bogdanowiczia pocutica pishvanova* in the Middle Miocene of Transylvania – Paleoenvironmental and stratigraphic implications. *Acta Palaeontologica Romaniae*, **4**, 113–117.

FODOR, L., JELEN, B., MÁRTON, E., SKABRNE, D., ČAR, J. & VRABEC, M. 1998. Miocene – Pliocene tectonic evolution of the Slovenian Periadriatic Line and surroundings area – implications for the Alpine-Carpathian extrusion models. *Tectonics*, 17, 690–709.

FODOR, L., JELEN, B., *et al.* 2002. Miocene to Quaternary deformation, stratigraphy and paleogeography in Northeastern Slovenia and Southwestern Hungary. *Geologija*, **45**(1), 103–114.

FORGÓ, L., MOLDVAY, L., STEFANOVICS, P. & WEIN, G. 1966. *Explanatory notes to the 1:200000 scale geological map of Hungary*. Hungarian Geological Survey, Budapest [In Hungarian].

FÖRSTERLING, G. & REICHENBACHER, B. 2002. Lithofazies und Fischfaunen der Mittleren und Oberen Cerithienschichten (Oberoligozän-Unter Miozän) im Mainzer Becken - Paläoökologische und paläogeographische Implikationen. *Courier Forschungsintitut Senckenberg*, **237**, 293–317

FRANK, W., SCHUSTER, R. & FAUPL, P. 1998. Permisch metamorphe Kristallingerölle aus der höheren Gosau der Weyerer Bögen (Oberösterreich). *Mitteilungen der Österreichischen Mineralogischen Gesellschaft*, **143**, 273–275.

FRASCARI RITONDALE SPANO, F. 1969. Serie paleogeniche nell'area pedemontana a Sud dell'Altopiano di Asiago (Vicenza, Italia). *Mémoires du Bureau des Recherches géologiques et Minières*, **69**, 173–182.

FRASCARI RITONDALE SPANO, F. 1970. Formazione di Pradelgiglio. Servizio Geologico Italiano, Studi Illustrati Carta Geologica Italiana, Formazioni Geologiche, **4**, 93–101.

Frascari Ritondale Spano, F. & Bassani, P. 1973. Ricerche geologiche nei dintorni di Bassano del Grappa. *Memorie del Museo Tridentino di Scienze Naturali*, **19**, 63–107.

Freimoser, M. 1972. Zur Stratigraphie, Sedimentpetrographie und Faziesentwicklung der Südostbayerischen Flyschzone und des Ultrahelvetikums zwischen Bergen/Obb. und Salzburg. *Geologica Bavarica*, **66**, 7–91.

Friebe, J. G. 1990. Lithostratigraphische Neugliederung und Sedimentologie der Ablagerungen des Badenium (Miozän) um die Mittelsteirische Schwelle (Steirisches Becken, Österreich). *Jahrbuch der Geologischen Bundesanstalt,* **133**, 223–257.

Friebe, J. G. 1993. Sequence stratigraphy in a mixed carbonate-siliciclastic depositional system (Middle Miocene; Styrian Basin, Austria). *Geologische Rundschau,* **82**, 281–294.

Fromm, K. 1986. Der paläomagnetische Befund an der Pliozän-/Pleistozängrenze in Mainz-Weisenau. *Bericht des niedersächsischen Landesamtes für Bodenforschung*, 1–17.

Frost, S. H. 1981. Oligocene reef coral biofacies of the Vicentin, northeastern Alps. *In:* Toomey, D.F. (ed.) *European Fossil Reef Model.* SEPM, Special Publications, **30**, 483–539.

Froitzheim, N., Plasienka, D & Schuster, R. 2008. Alpine tectonics of the Alps and Western Carpathians. *In:* McCann, T. (ed.) *The Geology of Central Europe. Volume 2: Mesozoic and Cenozoic.* Geological Society, London, 1141–1232

Fuganti, A., Morteani, G. & Ungaro, S. 1965. Studio seimentologico e micropaleontologico dei sedimenti terziari di Castel Tesino (Trento) con riferimento al tettonismo del "cristallino di Cima d'Asta". *Studi Trentini di Scienze Naturali*, **42**, 274–300.

Fuhrmann, U. & Lippolt, H. J. 1987. K-Ar-Datierungen an Maintrapp-Basalten nach der 40 Ar-3/39 Ar-Stufenentgasungstechnik. *Geologisches Jahrbuch Hessen*, **115**, 245–257.

Fülöp, J., Bresznyánszky, K. & Haas, J. 1987. The new map of the Pannonian basin basement in the Hungary. *Acta Geologica Hungarica*, **30**, 3–20.

Fusán, O., Biely, A., Ibrmajer, J., Plančár, J. & Rozložník, L. 1987. Basement of the Tertiary of the Inner West Carpathians. *GUDŠ, Bratislava,* 1–103.

Garavello, A. M. & Ungaro, S. 1982. Studio biostratigrafico e paleoecologico della serie eocenica di Pradipaldo nella zona pedemontana meridionale dell'Altipiano di Asiago (Vicenza). *Geologica Romana,* **21**, 655–675.

Garavello, A. M. & Ungaro, S.1996. Biostratigrafia del Paleocene ed Eocene inferiore dei M. Lessini. sezione stratigrafica di Gazzo (Verona). *Annali dell'Università di Ferrara, sezione Scienze della Terra,* **7**, 23–34.

Garecka, M., Marciniec, P, Olszewska, B. & Wójcik, A. 1996. New biostratigraphic data and attempt to correlation of the Miocene deposits in the basement of the Western Carpathians. *Przegląd Geologiczny,* **44**(5), 495–501.

Garlicki, A. 1968. Autochthonous salt series in the Miocene of the Carpathian Foredeep, between Skawina and Tarnów. *Biuletyn Państwowego Instytutu Geologicznego*, **215**, 5–77.

Gaździcka, E. 1994. Nannoplankton stratigraphy of the Miocene deposits in Tarnobrzeg area (northeastern part of the Carpathian Foredeep). *Geological Quarterly,* **38**, 553–570.

Geister, J. & Ungaro, S. 1977. The Oligocene coral formations of the Colli Berici (Vicenza, northern Italy). *Eclogae geologicae Helvetiae*, **70**, 811–823.

Gheerbrant, E., Codrea, V., Hosu, Al., Sen, S., Guernet, C., de Lapparent de Broin, F. & Riveline, J. 1999. Découverte de vertébrés dans les Calcaires de Rona (Thanétien ou Sparnacien), Transylvanie, Roumanie. les plus anciens mammiferes cénozoiques d'Europe Orientale. *Eclogae Geologicae Helvetiae*, **92**, 517–535.

Ghibaudo, G., Grandesso, P., Massari, F. & Stefani, C. 1996. Use of trace fossils in delineating sequence stratigraphic surfaces (Tertiary, Venetian Basin, north-eastern Italy). *Palaeogeography Palaeoclimatology Palaeoecology,* **120**, 261–279.

Giamboni, M., Ustaszewski, K., Schmid, S. M., Schumacher, M. E. & Wetzel, A. 2004. Plio-Pleistocene trasnpressional reactivation of Paleozoic and Paleogene structures in the Rhine-Bresse transform zone (northern Switzerland and eastern France). *Eclogae Geologicae Helvetiae*, **97**, 17–31.

Gianolla, P., Mietto, P. & Zampieri, D. 1992. Lower Oligocene carbonate platform margins in the Berici Hills (Venetian Prealps-NE Italy). *Platform Margins International Symposium in Chichilianne, Abstracts*, 46–47.

Global Palaeomagnetic Database. 2005. World Wide Web address: www.ngu.no/dragon/Palmag/paleomag.htm

Gohrbandt, K. 1963. Zur Gliederung des Paläogen im Helvetikum nördlich Salzburg nach planktonischen Foraminiferen. *Mitteilungen der Geologischen Gesellschaft Wien*, **56**(1), 1–116.

Golonka, J. 2004. Plate tectonic evolution of the southern margin of Eurasia in the Mesozoic and Cenozoic. *Tectonophysics*, **381**, 235–273.

Golonka, J., Oszczypko, N. & Ślączka, A. 2000. Late Carboniferous – Neogene geodynamic evolution and paleogeography of the circum-Carpathian region and adjacent areas. *Annales Societatis Geologorum Poloniae*, **70**, 107–136.

Golub, Lj. & Marić, L. 1968. Kvarcni trahiandeziti s Lončarskog visa, Krndija. *Geološki vjesnik*, **21**, 255–271.

Gozzi, E. 2003. *Le alveoline nelle biozone eoceniche del Carso Triestino.* Doctoral thesis, University of Trieste.

Gradstein, F. M. & Ogg, J. G. 2004. Geologic time scale 2004 – why, how, and where next! *Lethaia*, **37**, 175–181.

Graf, H. R. 1991. Die OMM und OSM im Gebiet des Kleinen Randen (südlicher badischer Klettgau). *Mitteilungen der naturforschenden Gesellschaft Schaffhausen,* **36**, 1–44.

Graf, H. R. 1993. *Die Deckenschotter der zentralen Nordschweiz.* Doctoral thesis, ETH Zürich, Nr 10205.

Gramann, F. & Kockel, F. 1988. Palaeogeographical, lithological, palaeoecological and palaeoclimatic development of the Northwest European Tertiary Basin. *In:* Vinken, R. (ed.) The Northwest European Tertiary Basin. *Geologisches Jahrbuch*, **A100**, 428–441.

Gramann, F. & von Daniels, C. H. 1988. Biostratigraphy. Foraminifera. *In:* Vinken, R. (ed.) The Northwest European Tertiary Basin. *Geologisches Jahrbuch*, **A100**, 145–151.

Grandesso, P., Stefani, C. & Tunis, G. 2000. La successione neogenica. Guida alle escursioni, 80° *Riunione Estiva della Società Geologica Italiana*, Trieste, 6–8 settembre 2000, 25–27.

Gregory, J. M., Dixon, K.W., Stouffer, R.J. *et al.* 2005. A model intercomparison of changes in the Atlantic thermohaline circulation in response to increasing atmospheric $CO_2$ concentration. *Geophysical Research Letters*, **32**, 1–5.

Griessemer, T. 2002. The Bolboforma signal: a distinct level for correlating Lower Oligocene deposits (NP22), the Melania Clay formation of Northern Hesse (Hessian Depression) with the Middle Pechelbronn Formation of the Mainz Basin (Rhineland-Palatinate, Germany). *Northern European Cenozoic Stratigraphy.* Proceedings of the 8th biannual joint meeting of RCNNS/RCNPS, Landesamt fur Natur und Umwilt Schlerswig-Holstein (Flintbek), 57–66.

Grimm, K. 2002. Paläobiogeographische Untersuchungen an rupelischen Foramniferenfaunen aus der Bayerischen Molasse, dem Inntaltertiär, dem Mainzer Becken und dem Oberrheingraben. *Neues Jahrbuch für Geologie und Paläontologie, Abhandlungen,* **223**, 183–199.

Grimm, K. & Grimm, M. 2003. Die fossilen Wirbellosen des Mainzer Tertiärbeckens, Teil 1–1. Geologischer Führer durch das Mainzer Tertiärbecken. *Mainzer Naturwissenschaftliches Archiv, Beiheft*, **26**, 1–165.

Grimm, M. & Hottenrott, M. 2002. Oberrheingraben. *In:* Deutsche Stratigraphische Kommission (ed.) *Stratigraphische Tabelle von Deutschland 2002.*

Grimm, K., Grimm, M. & Schindler, T. 2000. Lithostratigraphische Gliederung im Rupelium/Chattium des Mainzer Beckens, Deutschland. *Neues Jahrbuch für Geologie und Paläontologie, Abhandlungen,* **218**, 343–397.

Gripp, K. 1958. Erdgeschichtliche Aussagen der Korallen des niederrheinischen Oberoligozäns und Mittelmiozäns. *In:* Ahrens, W. (ed.) Die Niederrheinische Braunkohlenformation. *Fortschritte in der Geologie von Rheinland und Westfalen,* 1, 239–253.

Grischkevich, G. N. 1970. Buglov layers and their stratigraphical position. *In:* Vialov, O. S. (ed.) *Buglovskije sloi miocena.* Naukova dumka, Kiev, 19–68 [in Russian].

Gross, M. 2003. Beitrag zur Lithostratigraphie des Oststeirischen Beckens (Neogen/Pannonium; Österreich). *Österreichische Akademie der Wissenschaften, Schriftenreihe der Erdwissenschaftlichen Kommissionen,* **16**, 11–62

GRUBIĆ, A. 1975. Tectonics of Yugoslavia. *Acta Geologica*, **8**(20), 365–385.

GRÜNIG, A. & HERB, R. 1980. Paleoecology of late Eocene benthonic Foraminifera from Possagno (Treviso-northern Italy). *Cushman Foundation Special Publication*, **18**, 68–85.

GÜMBEL, C. W. 1861. Geognostische Beschreibung des bayerischen Alpengebirges und seines Vorlandes. Justus Perthes, Gotha.

GÜRS, K. 2002. Miocene nassariid zonation. A new tool in North Sea Basin Neogene biostratigraphy. *In:* GÜRS, K. (ed.) *Northern European Cenozoic Stratigraphy.* Proceedings of the 8th biannual joint meeting of the RCNPS/RCNNS, Landesamt für Natur und Umwelt Schleswig-Holstein (Flintbek), 91–106.

GÜRS, K. 2005. Das Tertiär von Nordwestdeutschland in der Stratigraphischen Tabelle von Deutschland 2002. *In:* MENNING, M. & DEUTSCHE STRATIGRAPHISCHE KOMMISSION. Erläuterungen zur Stratigraphischen Tabelle Deutschland 2002. *Newsletters on Stratigraphy*, **41**(1–3), 313–322.

GÜRS, K. & JANSSEN, A.W. 2002. Revised Pteropod biostratigraphy for the Miocene of the North Sea Basin. *In*: GÜRS, K. (ed.) *Northern European Cenozoic Stratigraphy.* Proceedings of the 8th biannual joint meeting of the RCNPS/RCNNS, Landesamt für Natur und Umwelt Schleswig-Holstein (Flintbek), 117–131.

GÜRS, K. & JANSSEN, A.W. 2004. Sea level related molluscan plankton Eevents (Gastropoda, Euthecosomata) during the Rupelian (Early Oligocene) of the North Sea Basin. Netherlands *Journal of Geosciences*, **83**(3), 199–208.

GÜRS, K. & SCHNETLER, K. I. 2004. *Aquilofusus klugorum* n. sp. (Gastropoda, Buccinidae) from late Miocene of the North Sea Basin and stratigraphical implications of the genus *Aquilofusus* Kautsky 1925. *Meyniana*, **56**.

GÜRS, K. & SPIEGLER, D. 2000. Kalkige Mikrofossilien aus dem Miozän der Bohrung Lübtheen 27/82 (SW Mecklenburg). *In:* BÜLOW, W. VON (ed.) Geologische Entwicklung Südwest-Mecklenburgs seit dem Ober-Oligozän. *Schriftenreihe für Geowissenschaften*, **11**, 135–155.

GÜRS, K. & WEINBRECHT, F. 2001. Die Gattung *Alvania* (Gastropoda, Rissoidae) im norddeutschen Miozän. *Meyniana*, **53**, 75–88.

GYÖRFI, I., CSONTOS, L. & NAGYMAROSI, L. 1999. Early Tertiary structural evolution of the border zone between the Pannonian and Transylvanian Basins. *In:* DURAND, B., KOLIVET, L., HORVÁTH, F. & SÉRANNE, M. (eds) *The Mediterranean Basins. Tertiary Extension within the Alpine Orogene.* Geological Society, London, Special Publications, **156**, 251–268.

HAAS, J. & KOVÁCS, S. 2001. The Dinaric-Alpine connection – as seen from Hungary. *Acta Geologica Hungarica*, **44**(2–3), 345–362.

HABLY, L. 1985. Early Miocene Plant fossils from Ipolytarnóc, N Hungary. *Geologica Hungaria ser. Pal.*, **45**, 73–256.

HAGN, H. 1954. Geologisch-paläontologische Untersuchungen im Helvetikum und Flysch des Gebietes von Neubeuern am Inn (Oberbayern). *Geologica Bavarica,* **22**, 1–136.

HAGN, H. 1960. Die stratigraphischen, paläogeographischen und tektonischen Beziehungenzwischen Molasse und Helvetikum im östlichen Oberbayern. *Geologica Bavarica*, **44**, 1–208.

HAGN, H. 1967. Das Alttertiär der Bayerischen Alpen und ihres Vorlandes. *Mitteilungen der Bayerischen Staatssammlung für Paläontologie und Historische Geologie*, **7**, 245–320.

HAGN, H. 1981. Die Bayerischen Alpen und ihr Vorland in mikropaläontologischer Sicht. *Geologica Bavarica*, **82**, 1–408.

HAGN, H. & DARGA, R. 1989. Zur Stratigraphie und Paläogeographie des Helvetikums im Raum von Neubeuern am Inn. *Mitteilungen der Bayerischen Staatssammlung für Paläontologie und Historische Geologie*, **29**, 257–275.

HAGN, H. & WELLNHOFER, P. 1973. Der Kressenberg - eine berühmte Fossillagerstätte des bayerischen Alpenvorlandes. *Jahrbuch des Vereins zum Schutze der Alpenpflanzen und -Tiere*, **38**, 1–35.

HAGN, H., PAVLOVEC, R. & PAVŠIČ, J. 1979. Excursion G, Gračišće near Pićan, Istria - Eocene. *Excursions Guidebook, 16th European Micropalaeontology Colloquium*, Ljubljana, 185–190.

HALAMIĆ, J., BELAK, M. & PAVELIĆ, D. 1993. The sedimentological significance and stratigraphic position of coarse-grained red beds (?Oligocene) of the northwestern margin of Mt. Požeška gora (North Croatia). *Geologia Croatica*, **46**, 137–143.

HALÁSOVÁ, E., HUDÁČKOVÁ, N., HOLCOVÁ, K., VASS, D,. ELEČKO, M. & PERESZLÉNYI, M. 1996. Sea ways connecting the Filakovo - Petervasara Basin with the Eggenburgian/Burdigalian open sea. *Slovak Geological Magazine*, **2**, 125–136.

HÁMOR, G. 1970. Das Miozän des östliches Mecsek Gebirges. *Annales Institute Geologica Hungarica*, **53**, 1–483.

HÁMOR, G. (ed.) 1988. *Neogene Palaeographic Atlas of Central and Eastern Europe*. Hungarian Geological Institute.

HAMRLA, M. 1959. On the conditions of origin of the coal beds in the Karst region. *Geologija*, **5**, 180–264.

HAMRLA, M. 1988. Contribution to the geology of coal deposits in the Zreče area and reflectance-based ranking of its coal. *Geologija*, **30**, 343–390.

HANFLAND, C., LÄUFER, A. L., NEBELSICK, J. H. & MOSBRUGGER, V. 2004. The Paleogene Smrekovec Basin and related volcanism (Slovenia): Sedimentology, Geochemistry, and Tectonic Evolution. *Neues Jahrbuch für Geologie und Paläontologie, Abhandlungen*, **232**, 77–125.

HANSEN, H. J. & TOFT, P. 1996. Dolenja Vas and its carbon isotopes. *In:* DROBNE, K., GORIČAN, Š. & KOTNIK, B. (eds) *The role of Impact processes in the geological and biological evolution of Planet Earth.* International workshop, Palaeontology Institute of ZRC-SAZU, Ljubljana, 31–32.

HANSEN, H.J., DROBNE, K. & GWOZDZ, R. 1995. The K/T boundary in Slovenia. dating by magnetic susceptibility, stratigraphy and iridium-anaomaly in a debris-flow. *In:* MONTANARI A. & COCCIONI R. (eds) *ESF 4th International Workshop*, Ancona, 84–85.

HARČÁR, J., PRIECHODSKÁ, Z., KAROLUS, K., KAROLUSOVÁ, E. REMŠÍK, A. & ŠUCHA, P. 1988. *Vysvetlivky ku geologickej mape severovýchodnej časti Podunajskej nížiny 1:50 000.* GUDŠ.

HARDENBOL, J., THIERRY, J., FAIRLEY, M. B., JACQUIN, TH., DE GRACIANSKY, P.-C. & VAIL, P. R. 1998. Cenozoic sequence chronostratography. *In:* DE GRACIANSKY, P.-C., HARDENBOL, J., JACQUIN, TH. & VAIL, P. R. (eds) *Mesozoic and Cenozoic Stratigraphy of European Basins.* SEPM, Special Publications, **60**, Chart 2.

HARMS, F. J. 2001. Eozänzeitliche Ölschiefer-Vorkommen auf dem Sprendlinger Horst (Süd-Hessen): ein Modell zu ihrer Entstehung. *Natur und Museum*, **131**, 86–94.

HARZHAUSER, M. & MANDIC, O. 2001. Late Oligocene Gastropods and Bivalves from the Lower and Upper Austrian Molasse Basin. Österreichische Akademie der Wissenschaften. *Schriftenreihe der Erdwissenschaftlichen Kommissionen*, **14**, 671–774.

HARZHAUSER, M. & PILLER W. E. 2004. Integrated stratigraphy of the Sarmatian (Upper Middle Miocene) in the western Central Paratethys. *Stratigraphy*, **1**, 65–86.

HARZHAUSER, M. & WESSELY, G. 2003. The Karpatian of the Korneuburg Basin (Lower Austria). *In*: BRZOBOHATÝ, R. CICHA, I., KOVÁC, M. & RÖGL, F. (eds) *The Karpatian - A Lower Miocene Stage of the Central Paratethys*. Masaryk University, Brno, 107–110.

HARZHAUSER, M., BÖHME, M., MANDIC, O. & HOFMANN, CH.-CH. 2002. The Karpatian (Late Burdigalian) of the Korneuburg Basin - A palaeoecological and biostratigraphical synthesis. *Beiträge zur Paläontologie*, 27, 441–456.

HARZHAUSER M., DAXNER-HÖCK G. & PILLER W. E. 2004. An integrated stratigraphy of the Pannonian (Late Miocene) in the Vienna Basin. *Austrian Journal of Earth Sciences,* **95/96**, 6–19.

HAUER, F. & MORLOT, A. 1848. Neue Fossilenfundorte aus den südlichen Alpen im westlichen Theile des Cillyer Kreises. *Berichte über die Mitteilungen von Freunden der Naturwissenschaften in Wien (= Heidingers Berichte)*, **6**, 39–42.

HEILMANN-CLAUSSEN, C., VAN SIMAEYS, S., KING, C., NIELSEN, O.B., THOMSEN, E., ABRAHAMSEN, N. & LYKKE-ANDERSEN, H. 2001. Stratigraphy and facies in the Middle and Upper Eocene of the Kysing 4 borehole, Denmark. *Northern European Cenozioc Stratigraphy.* Abstracts of the 8th biannual meeting of the RCNNS/RCNPS, Flintbek-Salzau.

HERAK, M. 1985. On the relation of Adriatic and Dinaric structures. *Razprave 4. razreda SAZU*, **26**, 401–414.

HERAK, M. 1986. A new concept of geotectonics of the Dinarides. *Acta Geologica,* **16**(1), 1–42.

HERAK, M. 1987. Relationship between Adriatic and Dinaric carbonate platforms. *Memorie della Società Geologica Italiana*, **40**, 289–293.

HERAK, M. 1999. Tectonic interrelation of the Dinarides and the Southern Alps. *Geologia Croatica*, **52**(1), 83–98.

HERAK, M. & BAHUN, S. 1979. The role of calcareous breccias (Jelar Formation) in the tectonic interpretation of the High Karst Zone of the Dinarides. *Geološki vjesnik*, **31**, 49–59.

HERAK, M., MARINČIĆ, S. & POLŠAK, A. 1976. Geology of the island of Hvar. *Acta Geologica*, **9**(1), 5–14.

HERB, R. 1988. Eocäne Paläogeographie und Paläotektonik des Helvetikums. *Eclogae Geologicae Helvetiae*, **81**(3), 611–657.

HERB, R., HUGUENEY, M., LANGE-BADRE, B. & WEIDMANN, M. 1984. Données nouvelles sur les mammifères et les nummulites de l'Eocène supérieur sudalpin (synclinaux du Charbon, d'Entrevernes, Bauges et Haute-Savoie). *Geobios*, **17**, 221–234.

HERLEC, U. 1985. Oligocene beds in the Bohinj valley. *Geološki glasnik*, **28**, 185–191.

HERM, D., VON HILLEBRANDT, A. & PERCH-NIELSEN, K. 1981. Die Kreide/Tertiärgrenze im Lattengebirge (Nördliche Kalkalpen) in mikropaläontologischer Sicht. *Geologica Bavarica*, **82**, 319–344.

HILLEBRANDT, A. VON 1962. Das Alttertiär im Becken von Reichenhall und Salzburg (Nördliche Kalkalpen). *Zeitschrift der deutschen Geologischen Gesellschaft*, **113**, 339–358.

HILLEBRANDT, A. VON 1981. Das Alttertiär zwischen Bad Reichenhall und Salzburg. *In*: HAGN, H. (ed) *Die Bayerischen Alpen und ihr Vorland in mikropaläontologischer Sicht*. Geologica Bavarica, **82**, 26–28.

HILLEBRANDT A VON 1993. Nummuliten und Assilinen aus dem Eozän des Krappfeldes in Kärnten (Österreich). *Zitteliana*, **20**, 277–293

HINSCH, W. 1986*a*. Lithologie, Stratigraphie und Paläogeographie des Neogens. *In:* TOBIEN (ed.) Nordwestdeutschland im Tertiär. *Beiträge zur regionalen Geologie der Erde*, **18**, 22–38.

HINSCH, W. 1986*b*. Der Leitwert miozäner Molluskenfaunen im Nordseebecken. *In:* TOBIEN (ed.) Nordwestdeutschland im Tertiär. *Beiträge zur regionalen Geologie der Erde,* **18**, 342–369.

HINSCH, W. 1988. Section M-M'. *In:* VINKEN, R. (comp.). The Northwest European Tertiary Basin. Results of the International Geological Correlation Programme Project no. 124. *Geologisches Jahrbuch,* **A100**, 127–128.

HINSCH, W. 1994. Biostratigraphy and paleogeography of Vierlandian and Hemmoorian (Early Miocene) in the Flensburg-Schleswig and North Frisia Region. *Bulletin de la Société Belge de Géologie,* **102**, 117–145.

HINSCH, W., KAEVER, M. & MARTINI, E. 1978. Die Fossilführung des Erdfalls von Nieheim (SE-Westfalen) und seine Bedeutung für die Paläogeographie im Campan und Miozän. *Paläontologische Zeitschrift,* **52**, 219–245.

HINSCH, W., JAKUBOWSKI, G., JANSSEN, A. W., JANSSEN, R. & KING, C. 1988. Biostratigraphy. Molluscs. Benthic molluscs (Pelecypods, Gastropods). The description of the interregional zonation (BM zones) and its correlation with the regional lithostratigraphy. *In:* VINKEN, R. (ed.) The Northwest European Tertiary Basin. *Geologisches Jahrbuch*, **A100**, 344–356.

HINSKEN, S. 2003. Geologische Untersuchungen an Synriftsedimenten des südlichen Oberrheingrabens. Master Thesis, Universität Basel.

HINTERLECHNER-RAVNIK, A. & PLENIČAR, M. 1967. The smrekovec Andesite and ist Tuff. *Geologija*, **10**, 219–237.

HÓK, J., ŠIMON, L., KOVÁČ, P., ELEČKO, M., VASS, D., HALMO, J., & VERBICH, F. 1995. Tectonics of the Hornonitrianska kotlina depression in the Neogene. *Geologica Carpathica*, **46**, 191–196.

HOMANN, M. 1991. Die Diatomeen der Fur-Formation (Alttertiär, Limfjord/Dänemark). *Geologisches Jahrbuch,* **A 123**, 1–285.

HOMEWOOD, P. 1974. Le flysch du Meilleret (Prealpes romandes) et ses relations avec les unités l'encadrant. *Eclogae Geologicae Helvetiae*, **67**, 349–401.

HOMEWOOD, P. & ALLEN, P. 1981. Wave-, tide-, and current-controlled sandbodies of Miocene Molasse, Western Switzerland. *Bulletin of the American Association of Petroleum Geologists*, **65**, 2534–2545.

HOMEWOOD, P. & LATELTIN, K. 1988. Classic Swiss clastics, the alpine connections. *Geodinamica Acta*, **2**, 1–12.

HOOKER, J. J. & WEIDMANN, M. 2000. The Eocene mammal fauna of Mormont, Switzerland. Systematic revision and resolution of dating problems. *Memoires Suisse Paléontologie*, **120**, 1–143.

HOOYBERGHS, H., MOORKENS, T. & WOUTERS, K. 2002. Ypresian Biostratigraphy based on Foraminifera, Ostracoda and other Biota of the Ampe Outcrop Section at Egem (NW Belgium). *In:* GÜRS, K. (ed.) *Northern European Cenozoic Stratigraphy.* Proceedings of the 8th biannual joint meeting of the RCNPS/RCNNS. Landesamt für Natur und Umwelt Schleswig-Holstein (Flintbek). 67–81.

HORVAT, A. 2003. *Paleontologija, biostratigrafija in paleoekologija miocenskih diatomej (Bacillariophyta) Slovenije*. Doctoral thesis, University of Ljuljana.

HORVÁTH, F. 1984. Neotectonics of the Pannonian basin and the surrounding mountain belts. Alps, Carpathians and Dinarids. *Annales des Géophysique*, **2**, 147–154.

HORVÁTH, F. 1993. Towards a mechanical model for the formation of the Pannonian basin. *Tectonophysics*, **226**, 333–357.

HORVÁTH, F. 1995. Phases of compression during the evolution of the Pannonian Basin and its bearing on hydrocarbon exploration. *Marine and Petroleum Geology,* **12**, 837–844.

HORVÁTH, F. & CLOETINGH, S. 1996. Stress-induced late-state subsidence anomalies in the Pannonian Basin. *Tectonophysics*, **266**, 287–300.

HORVÁTH, F. & ROYDEN, L. H. 1981. Mechanism for the formation of the Intra-Carpathian Basins. A Review. *Earth Science Review,* **3–4**, 307–316.

HORVÁTH, F., SZALAY, Á., DÖVÉNYI, P. & RUMPLER, J. 1986. Structural and thermal evolution of the Pannonian basin: An overview. *In*: BURRUS, J. (ed.) *Thermal Modelling in Sedimentary Basins*. Éditions Technip, Paris, 339–358.

HORVÁTH, F., DOVENYI, P., SZALAY, S. & ROYDEN, L. H. 1988. Subsidence, thermal and maturation history of the Great Hungarian Plain. *In:* ROYDEN, L. H. & HORVÁTH F. (eds) *The Pannonian Basin*. AAPG Memoir, **45**, 355–372.

HÖSCH, K. 1985. *Zur lithofaziellen Entwicklung der Greifensteiner Schichten in der Flyschzone des Wienerwaldes*. Doctoral thesis, University of Vienna.

HOSU, A. 1999. Arhitectura sedimentației depozitelor eocene din nord-vestul Depresiunii Transilvaniei. Presa Universitară Clujeană, Cluj-Napoca.

HOTTENROTT, M., KAERCHER, T. & SCHILL, I. 1995. Zur Pliozän-Pliostozän Grenze im nördlichen Oberrheingraben bei Eich (Bl. 6216 Gernsheim) anhand neuer Bohrergebnisse. *Jahrbuch Nassauer. Verein Naturkunde Wiesbaden,* **116**, 41–64.

HOTTINGER, L. 1960. Recherches sur les Alvéolines du Paléocène et de l'Eocène. *Schweizerische Paläontologische Abhandlungen*, **75/76**, 1–243.

HOTTINGER, L. 1990. Significance of diversity in shallow benthic foraminifera. *In:* ROBBA, E. (ed.) *Proceedings 4th Symposium on Ecology and Paleoecology of Benthic Communities*, Sorrento, 1988, Museo Regionale Scienza Naturale, Torino, 35–51.

HOTTINGER, L. & DROBNE, K. 1980. Early Tertiary imperforate conical foraminifera. *Razprave 4 razreda SAZU,* **22**, 187–276.

HÖTZL, M. & PAVLOVEC, R. 1991. Excursion L, Vremski Britof – Cretacous/Danian. *In:* DROBNE, K. (ed.) *Guidebook of 16th European Micropaleontology Colloquium*, Ljubljana, 225–228.

HRADECKÁ, L., LOBITZER, H., OTTNER, F., SVÁBENICKÁ, L. & SVOBODOVÁ, M. 1999. Biostratigraphy and facies of selected exposures in the Grünbach-Neue Welt Gosau-Group (Coal-bearing series, Inoceramus-Marl, and Zweiersdorf-Formation, Late Cretaceous and Paleocene, Lower Austria). *Abhandlungen der Geologischen Bundesanstalt,* **56**, 519–551.

HRUŠECKÝ, I., PERESLÉNYI, M., HÓK, J., ŠEFARA, J. & VASS, D. 1993. The Danube Basin geological pattern in the light of new and reinterpretation of old geophysical data. *In:* RAKÚS, M. & VOZÁR, J. (eds) *Geodynamický model a hlbinná stavba Západných Karpát.* GUDŠ, Bratislava, 291–296.

HRUŠECKÝ, I., ŠEFARA, J., MASARYK, P. & LINTNEROVÁ, O. 1996. The structural and facies development and exploration potential of the Slovak part of the Danube Basin. *In:* WESSELY, G. & LIEBL, W. (eds) *Oil and Gas in Alpidic Thrustbelts and Basins of Central and Eastern Europe*. EAGE Special Publications, **5**, 417–429.

IBRAHIMPAŠIĆ, H. & GUŠIĆ, I. 2000. Biotratigraphical correlation of the deposits of the southeastern part of the Krk island. *In:* VLAHOVIĆ, I. & BIONDIĆ, R. (eds) *Proceedings of the 2nd Croatian Geological Congress*, Zagreb, 213–217.

IVANOVIĆ, A., SAKAČ, K., MARKOVIĆ, S., SOKAČ, B., ŠUŠNJAR, M., NIKLER, L. & ŠUŠNJARA, A. 1973. *Osnovna geološka karta SFRJ 1.100000, List Obrovac. L33–140.* Institute of Geology Zagreb, Federal Geological Survey Beograd.

IVANOVIĆ, A., SAKAČ, K., SOKAČ, B., VRSALOVIĆ-CAREVIĆ, I. & ZUPANIČ, J. 1976. *Osnovna geološka karta SFRJ 1.100000, Tumač za list Obrovac L33–140.* Institute of Geology Zagreb, Federal Geological Survey Beograd, 5–61.

JÁMBOR, Á. 1980. A Dunántúli-középhegység pannon képződményei-

Pannonian in the Transdanubian Central Mountains. *Annales Institute Geologica Hungarica*, **62**, 1–259.

JÁMBOR, Á. 1989. Review of the geology of the s. l. Pannonian formations of Hungary. *Acta Geologica Hungarica*, **32**, 269–324.

JÁMBOR, Á., MOLDVAY, L. & RÓNAI, A. 1966. *Explanatory notes to the 1:200000 scal geological map of Hungary, L-34-II, Budapest.* Hungarian Geological Institute, Budapest.

JAMIČIĆ, D. 1983. O tangencijalnim kretanjima u području slavonskih planina. *Nafta*, **34**(12), 685–691.

JAMIČIĆ D. & NOVOSEL T. 1999. The dynamics of tectonic modelling of some caves in the Karst Region (Croatia). *Geologia Croatica*, **52**, 197–202.

JANÁČEK, J. 1969. Stratigrafie, tektonika a paleogeografie neogénu východního Slovenska. *Geolgicke Práce,* **52**, 71–182.

JANOČKO, J. 1993. *Development of braid depositional system, Lower Sarmatian, Neogene East Slovakian Basin.* Manuscript, Archív GUDŠ.

JANSSEN, A. W. 2001. The age of the North Sea Basin Hemmoorian (Miocene); holoplanktonic molluscan evidence. *Aardkundige Mededelingen,* **11**, 45–50.

JANSSEN, A. W. & GÜRS, K. 2002. Notes on the systematics, morphology and biostratigraphy of fossil holoplanktonic Mollusca, 12. On the identity of *Hyalea perovalis* Von Koenen, 1882 (Mollusca, Gastropoda, Euthecosomata) from the Early Miocene of the North Sea Basin. *Basteria*, **66**, 143–148.

JANSSEN, A. W. & KING, C. 1988. Planktonic molluscs (Pteropods). *In:* VINKEN R. (ed.) The northwest European Tertiary Basin. Results of the International Geological Correlation Programme Project no. 124. *Geologisches Jahrbuch*, **A100**. 356–368.

JANSSEN, A. W. & ZORN, I. 1993. Revision of Middle Miocene Pteropoda (Mollusca, Euthecosomata) published by W. Krach. *In:* JANSSEN, A. W. & JANSSEN, R. (eds) Proceedings Symposium 'Mollusca Palaeontology', 11th International Malacalogical Congress, Siena 1992. *Scripta Geologica*, Special Issue **2**, 155–236.

JANSSEN, R. 1979. Die Mollusken des Oberoligozäns (Chattium) im Nordseebecken. 2. Neogastropoda, Euthyneura, Cephalopoda. *Archiv für Molluskenkunde*, **109**, 277–376.

JELASKA, V. 1978. Stratigrafski i sedimentološki odnosi senonsko-paleogenskog fliša šireg područja Trebovca (sjev. Bosna). *Geološki vjesnik*, **30**, 95–118.

JELASKA, V., BULIĆ, J. & OREŠKI, E. 1970. Stratigrafski model eocenskog fliša Banije. *Geološki vjesnik*, **23**, 81–94.

JELASKA, V., BENČEK, D., *et al.* 2003. Platform dynamics during the Late Cretaceous and Early Paleogene - External Dinarides, Dalmatia. *In:* VLAHOVIĆ, I. & TIŠLJAR, J. (eds) *Evolution of Depositional Environments from the Palaeozoic to the Quaternary in the Karst Dinarides and the Pannonian Basin.* 22nd IAS Meeting of Sedimentology, Opatija, 17–19 September 2003, Field Trip Guidebook, 101–107.

JELEN, B. & RIFELJ, H. 2002. Stratigraphic structure of the B1 Tertiary tectonostratigraphic unit in eastern Slovenia. *Geologija*, **45**, 115–138.

JELEN, B. & RIFELJ, H. 2003. The Karpatian in Slovenia. *In:* BRZOBOHATÝ, R., CICHA, I., KOVAČ, M. & RÖGL, F. (eds) *The Karpatian, A Lower Miocene Stage of the Central Paratethys.* Masaryk University, Brno, 133–139.

JELEN, B. & RIFELJ, H. 2005*a*. On the dynamics of the Paratethys Sedimentary Area in Slovenia. *7th Workshop on Alpine Geological Studies, Abstract Book.* Croatian Geological Society, Zagreb, 45–46.

JELEN, B. & RIFELJ, H. 2005*b*. Patterns and processes in the Neogene of the Mediterranean region. *12th Congress*, Regional Committee on Mediterranean Neogene Stratigraphy, Vienna, Abstract Book, 116–118.

JELEN, B., ANIČIĆ, B., *et al.* 1992. Model of positional relationships for Upper Paleogene and Miocene strata in Slovenia. *In:* MONTANARI, A., COCCIONI, R. & ODIN, G. S. (eds) *Interdisciplinary Geological Conference on the Miocene Epoch with Emphases on the Umbria – Marche – Sequence.* International Union of Geological Sciences, Subcommission on Geochronology, Ancona, 71–72.

JELEN, B., BÁLDI-BEKE, M. & RIFELJ, H. 1998. Recent improvements in Slovenian Upper Paleogene and Lower Miocene Time-rock Stratigraphy. *Carpathian-Balkan Geological Association, 16th Congress 1998, Abstracts.* Geological Survey of Austria, 248.

JELEN, B., ŠIMUNIĆ, A., *et al.* 2000. Eocene in NE Slovenia and NW Croatia. 5th Meeting of the IUGS – UNESCO IGCP 393. *Annali Universita di Ferrara, Sci Terra, Suppl.*, **8**, 97–147.

JELEN, B., BÁLDI-BEKE, M. & RIFELJ, H. 2001. Oligocenske klastične kamenine v tektonostratigrafskem modelu terciarja vzhodne Slovenije. *Geološki zbornik*, **16**, 34–37.

JOVANOVIĆ, Č. 1980. Geneza pretortonskih miocenskih sedimenata između Drine i Une. *Geološki glasnik,* **15**, 3–159.

JUHÁSZ, G. 1991. Lithostratigraphical and sedimentological framework of the Pannonian (s. l.) sedimentary sequence in the Hungarian Plain(Alföld), Eastern Hungary. *Acta geologica Hungarica*, **34**, 53–72.

JUNGWIRTH, E. 2003. Paleogene flora of Slovenia, Croatia and Bosnia and Herzegovina. *Natura Croatica*, **12**, 151–156.

JURIŠIĆ-POLŠAK, Z. 1979. Miocenske i pliocenske neritide u Hrvatskoj. *Paleontologia jugoslavica*, **22**, 1–50.

JURIŠIĆ-POLŠAK, Z., KRIZMANIĆ, K. & HAJEK-TADESSE, V. 1993. Freshwater Miocene of Krbavsko Polje in Lika (Croatia). *Geologia Croatica*, **46**(2), 213–228.

JURIŠIĆ-POLŠAK, Z., SAKAČ, K. & POJE, M. 1997. New Pliopleistocene gastropods from Lika, Croatia. *Natura Croatica*, **6**, 91–111.

JURKOVŠEK, B., TOMAN, M.,OGORELEC, B., ŠRIBAR, L.,DROBNE K., POLJAK, M. & ŠRIBAR, L. 1996*a*. *Formacijska geološka karta južnega dela Tržaško-komenske planote - Kredne in paleogenske kamnine 1:50.000.* GZL, Ljubljana.

JURKOVŠEK, B., OGORELEC, B., ŠRIBAR, L & DROBNE, K. 1996*b*. New results of the geological researches of the Trieste-Komen plateau and comparison with other areas of the Dinaric Carbonate Platform. *In:* DROBNE, K., GORIČAN, Š. & KOTNIC, B. (eds) *The role of impact processes in the geological and biological evolution of planet Earth.* International workshop, Palaeontology Institute of ZRC-SAZU, Ljubljana, 125–132.

KÄLIN, D. 1993. *Stratigraphie und Säugetierfaunen der Oberen Süsswassermolasse der Nordschweiz.* Doctoral thesis, ETH-Zürich.

KÄLIN, D. & KEMPF, O. 2002. High-resolution mammal biostratigraphy in the Middle Miocene continental record of Switzerland (Upper Freshwater Molasse, MN4-MN9, 17–10 Ma). *Abstract, EEDEN-Meeting*, Frankfurt, November 2002.

KÄLIN, D., WEIDMANN, W., ENGESSER, B. & BERGER, J-P. 2001. Paléontologie et âge de la Molasse d'eau douce supérieure (OSM) du Jura neuchâtelois. *Mémoires suisses de paléontologie*, **121**, 65–99.

KALIČIAK, M. 1991. Explanatory notes to the geological map of the Košice depression and of the Slánske vrchy Mts. southern part. GÚDŠ, Bratislava.

KALIČIAK, M. & POSPÍŠIL, L. 1990. Neogene magmatism in Transcarpathian depression: geological and geophysical evaluation. *Mineralia Slovaca,* **22**, 481–498.

KASIŃSKI, J. R. 1989. Lacustrine sedimentary sequences in the Polish Miocene lignite-bearing basins - Facies distribution and sedimentary development. *In:* TALBOT, M. R. & KELTS K. (eds) The Phanerozoic record of lacustrine basins and their environmental signals. *Palaeogeography Palaeoclimatology Palaeoecology*, **70**, 287 304.

KASIŃSKI, J. R. & TOŁKANOWICZ, E. 1999. Amber in the northern Lublin Region – origin and occurrence. *In:* KOSMOWSKA-CERANOWICZ, B. & PANER, H. (eds) *Investigations into Amber.* Proceedings of International Interdisciplinary Symposium 'Baltic amber and other fossil resins' , Muzeum Archeologiczne, Gdańsk, 41–52.

KASIŃSKI, J. R., CZAPOWSKI, G. & GĄSIEWICZ, A. 2002. Marine-influenced and continental settings of the Poznań Formation (Upper Neogene, Central and SW Poland). *In:* GÜRS, K. (ed.) *Northern European Cenozoic Stratigraphy.* Proceedings of the 8th Biannual Meeting of the RPCSS/RNCSS. Landesamt für Natur und Umwelt des Landes Schleswig-Holstein, Flintbek, 162–184.

KASPRZYK, A. 1993. Lithofacies and sedimentation of the Badenian (Middle Miocene) gypsum in the northern part of the Carpathian Foredeep, southern Poland. *Annales Societatis Geologorum Poloniae*, **63**, 33–84.

KATZER, F. 1918. *Die Fossilen Kohlen Bosniens und der Hercegovina.* Erster und Zweiter Band, Wien (also published in Sarajevo, 1921).

KATZER, F. 1926. *Geologie Bosniens und der Hercegovina.* Direktion der Staatlichen Bergbauunternehmungen, Sarajevo.

KAZMER M. 1985. Microfacies pattern of the Upper Eocene limestones at Budapest, Hungary. *Annales Universitatis Scientiarum Budapestinensis, Sectio Geologica*, **25**, 139–152.

KÁZMÉR, M., DUNKL., I., FRISCH, W., KUHLEMANN, J. & OSZVART, P.

2003. The Paleogene forearc basin of the Eastern Alps and Western Carpathians. subduction erosion and basin evolution. *Journal of the Geological Society, London*, **160**, 413–428.

Kázmér, M., Jelen, B., Rifelj, H. & Zágoršek, K. 2005. Badenian (Middle Miocene) bryomol carbonate sedimentation in the Slovenian corridor. *12th Regional Committee on Mediterranean Neogene Stratigraphy Congress*, Vienna, Abstracts, 123–124.

Kecskeméti, T. 1998. *Magyarország epikontinentális eocén képződményeinek rétegta*. MOL-MÁFI. Hungarian Geological Survey, Budapest, 403–417.

Keim, L. & Stingl, V. 2000. Lithostratigraphy and facies architecture of the Oligocene conglomerates at Monte Parei (Fanes, Dolomites, Italy). *Rivista Italiana di Paleontologia e Stratigrafia*, **106**, 123–132.

Keith, J. F., Vass, D. & Kováč, M. 1994. The Danube Lowland Basin. *In: Slovakian Geology*. ESRI, Occasional Publications, **11A**, 63–87.

Keller, B. 1989. Fazies und Stratigraphie der Oberen Meeresmolasse zwischen Napf und Bodensee. Doctoral thesis, University of Bern.

Keller, B., Bläsi, H., Platt, N., Mozley, P. & Matter, A. 1990. *Sedimentäre Architektur der distalen Unteren Süsswassermolasse und ihre Beziehung zur Diagenese und der Petrophysik. Eigenschaften am Beispiel der Bohrungen Langenthal*. Nagra Technische Berichte, **90–41**.

Kempf, O., Bolliger, T., Kälin, D., Engesser, B. & Matter, A. 1997. New magnetostratigraphic calibration of Early to Middle Miocene mammal biozones of the north alpine foreland basin. *In:* Aguilar, J. P., Legendre, S. & Michaux, J. (eds) *Actes du Congrès Biochrom'97, Mémoires et Travaux, EPHE, Institut de Montpellier*, **21**, 547–561.

Kempf, O., Matter, A., Burbank, D. W. & Mange, M. 1999. Depositional and structural evolution of a foreland basin margin in a magnetostratigraphic framework: The Eastern Swiss Molasse basin. *International Journal of Earth Sciences*, **88**, 253–275.

Khan, M. R., Pavlovec, R. & Pavšič, J. 1975. Eocene microfossils from Podgrad. *Geologija*, **18**, 9–60.

Kilényi, E. & Šefara, J. 1989. Pre-Tertiary basement contour map of the Carpathian basin beneath Austria, Czechoslovakia and Hungary. Eotvos Lóránd Geophysical Institute, Budapest.

King, C. 1982. Cainozoic micropaleontological biostratigraphy of the North Sea. *Institute of Geology, Scientific Reports*, **82**, 1–37.

Klepač, K. 2003. *Fossil fauna of the Island of Krk*. Atlas, Natural History Museum, Rijeka.

Knez, M. 1992. *Paleoekološke značilnosti vremskih in kozinskih plasti v okolici Škocjasnskih jam*. Master Thesis, University of Ljubljana.

Kochansky-Devidé, V. & Slišković, T. 1978. Miocenske kongerije Hrvatske, Bosne i Hercegovine. *Palaeontologia Jugoslavica*, **19**, 1–98.

Kochansky-Devidé, V. & Slišković, T. 1981. Mlađe miocenske kongerije Livanjskog, Duvanjskog i Kupreškog polja u jugozapadnoj Bosni i Hudova u Hercegovini. *Paleontologia Jugoslavica*, **25**, 1–25.

Kockel, F. 1988. The palaeogeographical maps. *In:* Vinken, R. (ed.) The Northwest European Tertiary Basin. *Geologisches Jahrbuch*, **A100**, 423–427.

Kockel, F. 1995. Structural and Palaeogeographical Development of the German North Sea Sector. *Beiträge zur regionalen Geologie der Erde*, **26**, 1–96.

Kockel, F., Baldschuhn, R. & Frisch, U. 1996. *Geotektonischer Atlas von NW-Deutschland 1.300,000*. Bundesanstalt für Geowissenschaften und Rohstoffe, Hannover.

Kollmann, H. A. 1964. Stratigraphie und Tektonik des Gosaubeckens von Gams (Steiermark, Österreich). *Jahrbuch der Geologischen Bundesanstalt*, **107**, 71–159.

Kollmann, K. 1965. Jungtertiär im Steirischen Becken. *Mitteilungen der Geologischen Gesellschaft in Wien*, **57**, 479–632.

Komatina, M. 1967. Stratigraphic composition and tectonic framework. *Memoires du service Geologique et geofisique*, **15**, 1–77.

Konečný, V., Kováč, M., Lexa, J. & Šefara, J. 2002. Neogene evolution of the Carpatho – Pannonian region: an interplay of subduction and back-arc diapiric uprise in the mantle. *EGS Stephan Mueller Special Publications Serie*, **1**, 105–123.

Kókay, J. 1973. Faziostratotypen der Bántapusztaer Schichtengruppe. *In:* Papp, A., Rögl, F. & Senes, J. (eds) *M2 Ottnangien. Die Innviertler, Salgótarjáner, Bántapusztaer Schichtengruppe und die Rzehakia Formation*. Chronostratigraphie und Neostratotypen, Miozän der Zentralen Paratethys, **3**, 227–243.

Kordos, L. 1985. Footprints in Lower Mioecene Sandstone at Ipolytarmóc, N Hungary. *Geologica Hungaria ser. Pal.*, **46**, 261–415.

Korolija, B., Borović, I., Grimani, I., Marinčić, S., Jagačić, T., Magaš, N. & Milanović, M. 1977. *Osnovna geološka karta SFRJ 1.100000, Tumač za listove Lastovo K33–46, Korčula K33–47 i Palagruža K33–5*. Institute of Geology Zagreb, Federal Geological Survey Beograd, 5–53.

Körössy, L. 1959. The flysch-like formations of the Great Hungarian Basin. *Földtani Közlöny*, **89**, 115–124 [in Hungarian].

Körössy, L. 1977. Flysch formations of Hungary: structural position and connections. *Földtani Közlöny*, **107**, 398–405 [in Hungarian].

Körössy, L. 1988. Hydrocarbon geology of the Zala Basin in Hungary. *Általános Földtani Szemle*, **23**, 3–162.

Körössy, L. 1989. Hydrocarbon geology of SE Transdanubia, Hungary. *Általános Földtani Szemle*, **24**, 3–122.

Kosi, W., Sachsenhofer, R. F. & Schreilechner, M. 2003. High resolution sequence stratigraphy of Upper Sarmatian and Pannonian Units in the Styrian Basin, Austria. *Österreichische Akademie der Wissenschaften, Schriftenreihe der Erdwissenschaftlichen Kommissionen*, **16**, 63–86.

Košir, A. 1997. Eocene platform-to-basin depositional sequence, southwestern Slovenia. *Gaea heidelbergensis, 18th IAS Regional European Meeting of Sedimentology*, Heidelberg, 205.

Košir, A. 2004. *Microcodium* revisited: root calcification products of terrestrial plants on carbonate-rich substrates. *Journal of Sedimentary Research*, **74**, 845–857.

Kossmat, F. 1924. Geologie der zentralen Balkanhalbinsel. Mit einer Übersicht des dinarischen Gebirgsbattes. Die Kriegsschauplätze 1914–1916. Gebrüder Borntraeger, Berlin.

Köthe, A. 1988. Nannoplankton of Denmark. *In:* Vinken, R. (ed.) The Northwest European Tertiary Basin. *Geologisches Jahrbuch*, **A100**, 280–283.

Köthe, A. 2003. Dinozysten-Zonierung im Tertiär Norddeutschlands. *Revue Paléobiologique*, **22**, 895–923.

Kotlarczyk, J. 1985. An outline of the stratigraphy of Marginal Tectonic Units of the Carpathian Orogene in the Rzeszów-Przemysl area. *Guide to excursion 4, XIII Congress of the Carpathian-Balkan Geological Assiciation*, Cracow, Poland, 1985, 21–32.

Kováč, M. & Márton, E. 1998. To rotate or not to rotate. Palinspastic reconstruction of the Carpatho - Pannonian area during the Miocene. *Slovac Geological Magazine*, **4**, 75–85.

Kováč, M., Michalík, J., Plašienka, D. & Putiš, M. 1991. *Malé Karpaty Mts. Geology of the Alpine - Carpathian Junction*. Excursion guide, Bratislava, 61–74.

Kováč, M., Šutovská, K., Nemčok, M. & Fordinál, K. 1992. Planinka Formation - Ottnangian to Lower Badenian sediments in the northern part of the Malé Karpaty Mts. *Geologické Práce, Správy*, **96**, 47–50.

Kováč, M., Král', J., Márton, M., Plašienka, D. & Uher, P. 1994. Alpine uplift history of the Central Western Carpathians. geochronological, paleomagnetic, sedimentary and structural data. *Geologica Carpathica*, **45**, 83–96.

Kováč, M., Kováč, P., Marko F., Karoli, S. & Janočko, J. 1995. The East Slovakian Basin - A complex back arc basin. *Tectonophysics*, **252**, 453–466.

Kováč, M., Nagymarosy, A., *et al.* 1998. Palinspastic reconstruction of the Carpathian-Pannonian region during the Miocene. *In:* Rakús, M. (ed.) *Geodynamic Development of the Western Carpathians*. Mineralia Slovaca Monograph, 189–217.

Kováč, M., Holcová, K. & Nagymarosy, A. 1999. Paleogeography, paleobathymetry and relative sea-level changes in the Danube Basin and adjacent areas. *Geologica Carpathacia*, **50**, 325–338.

Kováč, M., Vass, D., *et al.* 2002. North Hungarian - South Slovak Paleogene and Miocene Basins of the Central Paratethys. *17th Congress of Carpathian-Balkan Geological Association. Guide to Geological Excursions, ŠGÚDŠ*, 47–52.

Kováč, M., Barath, I., Harzhauser, M., Hlavaty, I. & Hudackova, N. 2004. Miocene depositional systems and sequence stratigraphy of the Vienna Basin. *Courier Forschungsinstitut Senckenberg*, **246**, 187–212.

Kováč, P. & Hók, J. 1993. The Central Slovak Fault System – field evidence of a strike-slip. *Geologica Carpathica*, **44**, 155–160.

KOVÁČ, P., VASS, D., JANOČKO, J., KAROLI, S. & KALIČIAK, M. 1994. Tectonic history of the East Slovakian Basin during the Neogene. *In: Slovakian Geology*. ESRI, Occasional Publications, **11A**, 1–15.

KOVAČIĆ, M., ZUPANIČ, J., *et al.* 2004. Lacustrine basin to delta evolution in a Pannonian sub-basin (Pontian, NW Croatia). *Facies*, **50**, 19–33.

KOWALKE, T. & HARZHAUSER, M. 2004. Early ontogeny and palaeoecology of the Mid-Miocene rissoid gastropods of the Central Paratethys. *Acta Palaeontologica Polonica*, **49**, 111–134.

KRALJ, P. 1995. *Gornjepliocenski fluvialni i vulkanoklastični sedimenti područja Grada u sjeveroistočnoj Sloveniji*. Doctoral Thesis, University of Zagreb.

KRALJ, P. 1996. Lithofacies characteristics of the Smrekovec volcaniclastics, northern Slovenia. *Geologija*, **39**, 159–191.

KRALJ, P. 1999. Volcanic rocks in borehole Tdp-1/84 Trobni Dol, Eastern Slovenia. *Geologija*, **41**, 135–155.

KRAŠENINIKOV, V. A., MULDINI-MAMUŽIĆ, S. & DŽODŽO-TOMIĆ, R. 1968. Značaj planktonskih foraminifera za podjelu paleogena Jugoslavije i poredba s drugim istraženim područjima. *Geološki vjesnik*, **21**, 117–146.

KRENMAYR, H. G. 1996. Hemipelagic and turbiditic mudstone facies associations in the Upper Cretaceous Gosau Group of the Northern Calcareous Alps (Austria). *Sedimentary Geology*, **101**, 149–172.

KRENMAYR, H. G. 1999. Die Nierental-Formation der Oberen Gosau-Gruppe (Oberkreide-Paleozän, Nördliche Kalkalpen) in Berchtesgaden: Definition, Fazies und Environment. *Jahrbuch der Geologischen Bundesanstalt,* **141**, 409–447.

KRENMAYR, H. G. 2003*a*. Bericht 2000 über geologische Aufnahmen im Tertiär und Quartär auf Blatt 55 Obergrafendorf. *Jahrbuch der Geologischen Bundesanstalt,* **143**, 351–353.

KRENMAYR, H. G. 2003*b*. Bericht 2001 und 2002 über geologische Aufnahmen im Tertiär und Quartär auf Blatt 55 Obergrafendorf. *Jahrbuch der Geologischen Bundesanstalt,* **143**, 461–464.

KREUTZER N. 1978. Die Geologie der Nulliporen (Lithothamnien)-Horizonte der miozänen Badener Serie des Ölfeldes Matzen (Wiener Becken). *Erdöl-Erdgas-Zeitschrift,* **94**, 129–145.

KRÉZSEK, C. 2004. Salt-related gravitational gliding in Transylvania. *Extended Abstract, AAPG Prague Conference 2004*, 8.

KRÉZSEK, C. 2005. *Sedimentology and architecture of the Pannonain deposits from the eastern Transylvanian Basin*. Doctoral Thesis, Babeș-Bolyai University, Cluj-Napoca.

KRÉZSEK, C. & BALLY, A.W. 2006. The Transylvanian Basin (Romania) and its relation to the Carpathian fold and thrust belt: insights in gravitational salt tectonics. *Marine and Petroleum Geology*, **23**, 405–442.

KRÉZSEK, C. & FILIPESCU, S. 2005. Middle to late Miocene sequence stratigraphy of the Transylvanian Basin (Romania). *Tectonophysics*, **410**, 437–463.

KRIVIC, P. 1982. *Vrtina Podpadna, Sektor za geotehniko in hidrogeologijo*. Arhiv GZS, Ljubljana.

KRIVIC, P. 1988. *Vrtina Podgorje P 30, Praproče P 29, vrtina Rižana P 27, sektor za geotehniko in hidrogeologijo*. Arhiv GZS, Ljubljana.

KROH, A., HARZHAUSER, M., PILLER, W. E. & RÖGL, F. 2003. The Lower Badenian (Middle Miocene) Hartl Formation (Eisenstadt-Sopron Basin, Austria). *Österreichische Akademie der Wissenschaften, Schriftenreihe Erdwissenschaftliche Kommissionen*, **16**, 87–109.

KRUTZSCH, W. 1992. Paläobotanische Klimagliederung des Alttertiärs (Mitteleozän bis Oberoligozän) in Mitteldeutschland und das Problem der Verknüpfung mariner und kontinentaler Gliederungen (klassische Biostratigraphien – paläobotanisch-ökologischer Klimastratigraphie – Evolutions-Stratigraphie der Vertebraten). *Neues Jahrbuch Geologie Paläontologie, Abhandlung,* **186**, 137–253.

KRUTZSCH, W. 2000*a*. Die Mikrofloren SW-Mecklenburgs aus dem Bereich Laupiner bis Loosener Schichten. *In:* BÜLOW, W. VON (ed.). Geologische Entwicklung Südwest-Mecklenburgs seit dem Ober-Oligozän. *Schriftenreihe für Geowissenschaften*, **11**, 219–270.

KRUTZSCH, W. 2000*b*. Stratigraphische Tabelle Oberoligozän und Neogen (marin-kontinental). *Berliner geowissenschaftliche Abhandlungen*, **E 34**, 153–164.

KRZYWIEC, P. 1997. Large-scale tectono-sedimentary Middle Miocene history of the central and eastern Polish Carpathian Foredeep Basin - results of seismic data interpretation. *Przegląd Geologiczny*, **10**(2), 1039–1053.

KSIĄŻKIEWICZ, M. (ed.). 1962. *Atlas Geologiczny Polski. Zagadnienia stratygraficzno-facjalne*. Kreda i starszy trzeciorzęd w polskich Karpatach zewnętrznych z. 13. Instytut Geologiczny, Warszawa.

KSIĄŻKIEWICZ, M. 1977. The tectonics of the Carpathians. *In:* POŻARYSKI, W. (ed.) *Geology of Poland, IV. Tectonics*, Wydawnictwa Geologiczne, Warszawa. 476–620.

KUHLEMANN, A. & KEMPF, O. 2002. Post-eocene evolution of the North Alpine Foreland Basin and its response to Alpine tectonics. *Sedimentary Geology*, **152**, 45–78.

KUHLEMANN, J., FRISCH, W. & DUNKL, I. 2002. Post-collisional sediment budget history of the Alps. tectonic versus climatic control. *International Journal of Earth Sciences*, 91, 818–837.

KUHLMANN, G. 2004. High resolution stratigraphy and paleoenvironmental changes in the southern North Sea during the Neogene. *Geologica Ultraiectina*, **245**, 1–205.

KÜHN, O. 1930. Das Danian der Äußeren Klippenzone bei Wien. *Geologisch-Paläontologische Abhandlungen, Neue Folge*, **17**(5), 495–496.

KUHN, W. 1992. Paleozäne und untereozäne Benthos-Foraminiferen des bayerischen und salzburgischen Helvetikums - Systematik, Stratigraphie und Palökologie. *Münchner Geowissenschaftliche Abhandlungen*, 24/A, 1–224.

KUHN, W. & WEIDICH, K. F. 1987. Neue mikropaläontologische Ergebnisse aus dem Haunsberg-Helvetikum (Salzburg, Österreich). *Paläontologische Zeitschrift*, **61**(3/4), 181–201.

KÜHNEL, W. 1933. Zur Stratigraphie und Tektonik der Tertiärmulden bei Kamnik (Stein) in Krain. *Prirodoslovne razprave*, 2, 61–124.

KULCHYTSKY, A. J. 1989. The scheme of comparison of the Neogene deposits Precarpathian and Transcarpathian foredeeps, Carpathians and Volhyno-Podolia. *Paleontological collection*, **26**, 65–71 [in Russian].

KURZ, W., FRITZ, H., PILLER, W. E., NEUBAUER, F. & GENSER, J. 2001. Overiew of the Paleogene of the Eastern Alps. *In:* PILLER, W. E. & RASSER, M. W. (eds) *Paleogene of the Eastern Alps*. Österreichische Akademie der Wissenschaften Schriftenreihe der Erdwissenschaftlichen Kommissionen, **14**, 11–56.

KUŠČER, D. 1967. Tertiary formations of Zagorje. *Geologija*, **10**, 5–85.

LAHODYNSKY, R. 1988. Lithostratigraphy and sedimentology across the Cretaceous/Tertiary boundary in the Flyschgosau (Eastern Alps, Austria). *Revista Espanola Paleontologia Extraord.*, **1988**, 73–82.

LANGE, G., SÖLLIG, A. & RIPPEL, J. 1990. *Geologische Karte der Deutschen Demokratischen Republik, Tektonische Karte 1:500 000.* Zentrales Geologisches Institut, Berlin.

LANKREIJER A., KOVÁČ, M., CLOETINGH, S., PITONÁK, P., HLÔŠKA, M. & BIERMANN, C. 1995. Quantitative subsidence analysis and forward modelling of the Vienna and Danube Basins: thin skinned versus thick skinned extension. *Tectonophysics*, **252**, 433–451.

LANKREIJER, A., BIELIK, M., CLOETINGH, S. & MAJCIN, D. 1998. Rheology predictions across the Western Carpathians, Bohemian Massif and Pannonian basin: Implication for tectonic scenarios. *Tectonics*, **18**, 1139–1153.

LANPHERE, M. & PAMIĆ, J. 1992. K-Ar and Rb-Sr Ages of Alpine Granite-Metamorphic Complexes in the Northwestern Dinarides and the Southwestern Part of the Pannonian Basin in Northern Croatia. *Acta Geologica,* **22**, 97–111.

LASKAREV, V. 1925. Sur la trouvaille des Anthracothérides en Serbie et en Bosnie. *Annales géologique de la Péninsula balkanique*, **8**, 85–92

LATELTIN, O. 1988. *Les dépôts turbiditiques oligocènes d'avant-pays entre Annecy (Haute-Savoie) et le Sanetsch (Suisse)*. Doctoral thesis, University of Fribourg, **949**.

LAUBSCHER, H. 1983. The late Alpine (Periadriatic) intrusions and the Insubric Line. *Memorie della Societá Geoogica. Italiana*, **26**, 21–30.

LEIN, R. 1982. Vorläufige Mitteilung über ein Vorkommen von flyschoider Gosau mit Komponenten paleozäner Riffkalke in den Mürztaler Alpen. *Mitteilungen der Gesellschaft der Geologie- und Bergbaustudenten Österreichs*, **28**, 121–132.

LEXA, J., KONEČNÝ, V., KALIČIAK, M. & HOJSTRIČOVÁ, V. 1993. Space-time distribution of volcanics in the Carpatho-Pannonian region. *In:* RAKÚS, M. & VOZÁR, J. (eds) *Geodynamický model a hlbinná stavba Západných Karpát*. Geologický ústav D. Štúra, Bratislava, 57–70.

LINIGER, H. 1966. Das plio-altpleistozäne Flussnetz der Nordschweiz. *Regio Basiliensis,* **7**(2), 158 -177.

Litt, T., Wansa, S., Ellwanger, D. & Jerz, H. 2002. Subkommission Quartär. Das Quartär in der Stratigraphischen Tabelle von Deutschland 2002. *In:* Menning, M. & Deutsche Stratigraphische Kommission (eds) *Die Stratigraphische Tabelle von Deutschland 2002*. Deutsche Stratigraphische Kommission.

Litt, T., Schmincke, H.-U., Frechen, M. & Schlüchter, C. 2008. Quaternary. *In:* McCann, T. (ed.) *The Geology of Central Europe. Volume 2: Mesozoic and Cenozoic*. Geological Society, London, 1287–1340.

Löffler, S.-B. & Nebelsick, J.H. 2001. Palaeoecological Aspects of the Lower Oligocene "Zementmergel" Formation based on Molluscs and Carbonates. *In*: Piller, W. E. & Rasser, M. W. (eds) *The Paleogene of the Eastern Alps*. Verlag der Österreichishcen Akademie der Wissenschaften, Vienna, 641–670.

Lotsch, D. 1969. Stratigraphisches Korrelationsschema für das Tertiär der Deutschen Demokratischen Republik. *Abhandlungen Zentrales Geologisches Institut Berlin*, **12**, 1–438.

Lotsch, D. 1981. *TGL 25234/08 Geologie, Stratigraphie, Stratigraphische Skala der DDR, Tertiär.* Zentrales Geologisches Institut, Berlin.

Louwye, S., De Coninck, J. & Verniers, J. 2000*a*. Shallow marine Lower and Middle Miocene deposits at the southern margin of the North Sea Basin. Dinoflagellate cyst biostratigraphy and depositional history. *Geological Magazine*, **137**, 381–394.

Louwye, S., Head, M.J. & de Schepper, S. 2000*b*. Dinoflaggelate cyst stratigraphy and palaeoecology of the Pliocene in northern Belgium, southern North Sea Basin. *Geological Magazine*, **141**, 353–378.

Lucchi Garavello, A. M. 1980. Età ed ambienti dele Marne Euganee nei Colli Berici orientali. *Annali dell'Università di Ferrara, Nuova Serie, sez. 9*, **6**, 47–62.

Luciani, V. 1988. La dorsale paleogenica M. Baldo-M. Bondone (Trentino Meridionale). significato paleogeografico e paleotettonico. *Rivista Italiana di Paleontologia e Stratigrafia*, **93**, 507–520.

Luciani, V. 1989. Stratigrafia sequenziale del Terziario nella catena del Monte Baldo (Provincie di Verona e Trento). *Memorie di Scienze Geologiche*, **41**, 263–351.

Luciani, V. & Silvestrini, A. 1996. Planktonic foraminiferal biostratigraphy and paleoclimatology of the Oligocene/Miocene transition from the Monte Brione Formation (northern Italy, Lake Garda). *Memorie di Scienze Geologiche*, **48**, 155–169.

Luciani, V. & Trevisani, E. 1992. Evoluzione paleogeografica del Paleogene della Valsugana (Trentino sud-orientale). *Annali dell'Università di Ferrara, sezione Scienze della Terra*, **3**, 83–99.

Luciani, V., Negri, A. & Bassi, D. 2002. The Bartonian-Priabonian transition in the Mossano section (Colli Berici, north-eastern Italy). a tentative correlation between calcareous plankton and shallow-water benthic zonations. *In:* Monegatti, P., Cecca, F. & Raffi, S. (eds) *Proceedings of the International Conference Paleobiogeography and Paleoecology.* Geobios, 35, Mém. Spec. **24**, 140–149.

Łuczkowska, E. & Dyjor, S. 1971. Mikrofauna utworów trzeciorzędowych serii poznańskiej Dolnego Śląska. *Annales Societatis Geologorum Poloniae*, **41**, 337–358.

Lugović, B., Majer, V. & Strumpfl, E. W. 1990. Geochemical characteristics of basaltic andesites from Baranja (Croatia, Yugoslavia). *Geološki vjesnik,* **43**, 135–142.

McCann, T., Kiersnowski, H., *et al.* 2008. Permian. *In:* McCann, T. (ed.) *The Geology of Central Europe. Volume 1: Precambrian and Palaeozoic*. Geological Society, London, 531–597.

Macera, P., Gasperini, D., Maffei, K., Martin, S. & Piromallo, C. 2002. Tertiary magmatism in the Eastern Alps. *Memorie della Società Geologica Italiana*, **54**, 119–122.

Macera, P., Gasperini, D., Piromallo, C., Blichert-Toft, J., Bosch, D., Del Moro, A. & Martin, S. 2003. Geodynamic implications of HIMU mantle in the source of Tertiary volcanics from the Veneto region (South-Eastern Alps). *Journal of Geodynamics*, **36**, 563–590.

Maddaleni, P. & Tunis, G. 1993. Il litosoma conglomeratico ad echinidi di Buttrio (Udine, NE Italia). *Gortania-Atti del Museo Friulano di Storia Naturale*, **15**, 35–48.

Magaš, N. 1968. *Osnovna geološka karta SFRJ 1.100000, list Cres L33–113.* Institute of Geology Zagreb, Federal Geological Survey Beograd.

Magaš, N. & Marinčić, S. 1973. *Osnovna geološka karta SFRJ 1.100000. Tumač za listove Split i Primošten, K 33–20 i K 33–21.* Institute of Geology Zagreb, Federal Geological Survey Beograd.

Magdalenić, Z. 1972. Sedimentology of Central Istria flysch deposits. *Acta Geologica*, **7**, 71–100.

Mahel, M. 1986. *Paleoalpine Units*. Veda, Bratislava.

Mai, D. H. 1995. *Tertiäre Vegetationsgeschichte Europas. Methoden und Ergebnisse*. Gustav Fischer Verlag, Jena.

Mai, D. H. 1999. Die untermiozänen Floren aus der Spremberger Folge und dem 2. Flözhorizont in der Lausitz. Teil I–III. *Palaeontographica Abt. B*, **250**, 1–76, **251**, 1–70, **253**, 1–106.

Mai, D. H. 2000. Die untermiozänen Floren aus der Spremberger Folge und dem 2. Flözhorizont in der Lausitz. Teil IV. *Palaeontographica Abt. B*, **254**, 65–176.

Majzon, L. 1966. *Foraminifera vizsgálatok*. Academic Press, Budapest.

Malaroda, R. 1954. Il Luteziano del Monte Postale. Memorie degli Istituti di Geologia e Mineralogia Università di Padova, **19**, 1–108.

Malaroda, R. 1967. Calcari nummulitici. *In:* Bosellini, A., Carraro, F., *et al.* (eds) *Note Illustrative della Carta geologica d'Italia, Foglio 49, "Verona"*. Servizio Geologico d'Italia, Roma, 21–23.

Malez, M. & Slišković, T. 1964. Neue Fundorte tertiärer Wirbeltiere in Bosnien und Herzegowina. *Bulletin scientifique, Conseil des Academies de la R.P.F., Yougoslavie*, **9(1–2)**, 2–4.

Malez, M. & Thenius, E. 1985. Über das Vorkommen von Amynodonten (Rhinocerotoidea, Mammalia) im Oligo-Miozän von Bosnien. *Paleontologia Jugoslavica*, **34**, 1–26

Mamužić, P. 1968. *Osnovna geološka karta SFRJ, List Lošinj L33–125.* Institute of Geology Zagreb, Federal Geological Survey Beograd.

Mamužić, P., Milan, A., Korolija, B., Borović, I. & Majcen, Ž. 1969. *Osnovna geološka karta SFRJ 1.100000, List Rab L33–114.* Institute of Geology Zagreb, Federal Geological Survey Beograd.

Mamužić, P., Sokač, B. & Velić, I. 1970. *Osnovna geološka karta SFRJ 1.100000, List Silba L33–126.* Institute of Geology Zagreb, Federal Geological Survey Beograd.

Mandic, O. & Steininger, F. F. 2003. Computer-based mollusc stratigraphy – a case study from the Eggenburgian (Lower Miocene) type region (NE Austria). *Palaeogeography, Palaeoclimatology, Palaeoecology*, **197**, 263–291.

Mantovani, E., Babbucci, D., Albarello, D. & Mucciarelli, M. 1990. Deformation pattern in the central Mediterranean and behavior of the African/Adriatic promontory. *Tectonophysics*, **179**, 63–79.

Marinčić, S. 1981. Eocenski fliš jadranskog pojasa (Eocene flysch of the Adriatic realm). *Geološki vjesnik*, **34**, 27–38.

Marinčić, S. 1997. Tectonic structure of the Island of Hvar (Southern Croatia). *Geologia Croatica*, **50**(1), 57–77.

Marinčić, S., Šparica, M., Tunis, G. & Uchman, A. 1996. The Eocene flysch deposits of the Istrian peninsula in Croatia and Slovenia. regional, stratigraphic, sedimentological and ichnological analyses. *Annales*, **9**, 136–156.

Marinko, M. 1992. *Vrtina Šempeter pri Novi Gorici.* Arhiv Oddelek za hidrogeologijo GZS, Ljubljana.

Marinko, M., Šribar, L. & Veselič, M. 1994. *Vrtina Lucija*. Arhiv, Oddelek za hidrogeologijo GZS, Ljubljana.

Marjanac, T. 1991. Paleotransport of Istrian flysch. *In:* Drobne, K. & Pavlovec, R. (eds) *Introduction to the Paleogene SW Slovenia and Istria Field-trip Guidebook, 2nd Meeting IGCP Project 286*, 19–27 October 1991 Postojna, 33–34.

Marjanac, T. 1996. Deposition of megabeds (megaturbidites) and sea-level change in a proximal part of Eocene-Miocene flysch of central Dalmatia (Croatia). *Geology*, **24**(6), 543–546.

Marjanac, T., Babac, D., *et al.* 1998. Eocene carbonate sediments and sea-level changes on the NE art of Adriatic Carbonate Platform (Island of Hvar and Pelješac Peninsula, Croatia). *Dela - Opera SAZU 4 razreda*, **34**(2), 243–254.

Markič, M. & Sachsenhofer, R. F. 1997. Petrographic composition and depositional environments of the Pliocene Velenje lignite seam (Slovenia). *International Journal of Coal Geology*, **33**, 229–254.

Marković, S. 2002. *Hrvatske mineralne sirovine (Croatian mineral sources)*. Institut za geološka istraživanja, Zagreb.

Marquet, R. 2004. The Neogene Bivalvia (Heterodonta and Anomalodesmata) and Scaphopoda from Kallo and Doel (Oost-Vlaanderen, Belgium). *Palaeontos*, **6**.

Martin, U. & Németh, K. 2004. Phreatomagmatic volcanic fields in a Mio/Pliocene fluvio-lacustrine basin, Western Pannonian Basin, Hungary: a review. *Geologica Hungarica*, **26**, 11–49.

Martini, E. 1973. Nannoplankton-Massenvorkommen in den Mittleren Pechelbronner Schichten (Unter-Oligozän). *Oberrheinische geolo-*

*gische Abhandlungen*, **22**, 1–12.

MARTINI, E. 1981. Sciaeniden (Pisces) aus dem Basisbereich der Hydrobien-Schichten des Oberrheingrabens, des Mainzer Beckens und des Hanauer Beckens (Miozän). *Senckenbergiana lethaea*, **62**, 93–123.

MARTINI, E. 1991. Biostratigraphie des Eozäns am "Hohen Ufer" bei Heiligenhafen/Holstein (Nannoplankton). *Senckenbergiana Lethaea*, **71**, 319–337.

MARTINIS, B. 1962. Ricerche geologiche e paleontologiche nella regione compresa tra Il T. Iudrio e il F. Timavo (Friuli orientale). *Memorie della Rivista Italiana di Paleontologi e Stratigrafia*, **8**, 1–246.

MÁRTON, E. 2001. Tectonic implications of Tertiary paleomagnetic results from the PANCARDI area (Hungarian contribution). *Acta Geologica Hungarica*, **44**(2), 135–144.

MÁRTON, E. 2005. Paleomagnetic evidence for Tertiary counterclockwise rotation of Adria with respect to Africa. *In:* PINTER, N., GRENERCZY, GY., WEBER, J., STEIN, S. & MEDAK , D. (eds) *The Adria Microplate: GSP Geodesy, Tectonics and Hazards*. Kluwer, Dordrecht, 55–64.

MÁRTON, E. & FODOR, L. 2003. Tertiary paleomagnetic results and structural analysis from the Transdanubian Range (Hungary); sign for rotational disintegration of the Alcapa unit. *Tectonophysics*, **363**, 201–224.

MÁRTON, E. & MÁRTON, P. 1996. Large scale rotations in North Hungary during the Neogene as indicated by palaeomagnetic data. *In:* MORRIS, A. & TARLING, D. H. (eds) *Palaeomagnetism and Tectonics of the Mediterranean Region*. Geological Society, London, Special Publications, **105**, 153–173.

MÁRTON, E. & PÉCSKAY, Z. 1998. Correlation and dating of the Miocene ignimbritic volcanics in the Bükk foreland, Hungary: complex evaluation of paleomagnetic and K/Ar isotope data. *Acta Geologica Hungarica*, **41**, 467–476.

MÁRTON, E., DROBNE, K., CIMERMAN, F., ĆOSOVIĆ, V. & KOŠIR, A. 1995*a*. Paleomagnetism of Latest Maastrichtian Through Oligocene Rocks in Istria (Croatia), the Karst Region, and S of the Sava Fault (Slovenia). *First Croatian Geological Congress Proceedings, Opatija*, **2**, 355–360.

MÁRTON, E., VASS, D. & TÚNYI, I. 1995*b*. Early Tertiary rotations of the Pelso megaunit and neighbouring Central West Carpathians. *In*: HAMRŠNÍD, E. (ed.) *New Results in Tertiary of West Carpathians II.* MND Hodonín, KZPN, **16**, 97–108.

MÁRTON, E., VASS, D. & TÚNYI, I. 1996. Rotation of the South Slovak Paleogene and Lower Miocene rocks indicated by paleomagnetic data. *Geologica Carpathica*, **47**, 31–41.

MÁRTON, E., MASTELLA, L. & TOKARSKI A. K. 1999*a*. Large counterclockwise rotation of the Inner West Carpathian Paleogene Flysch – evidence from paleomagnetic investigation of the Podhale Flysch (Poland). *Physics and Chemistry of the Earth (A)*, **8**, 645–649.

MÁRTON, E., PAVELIĆ, D., TOMLJENOVIĆ, B., PAMIĆ, J. & MÁRTON, P. 1999*b*. First paleomagnetic results on Tertiary rocks from the Slavonian Mountains in the Southern Pannonian Basin, Croatia. *Geologica Carpathica*, **50**, 273–279.

MÁRTON, E., KUHLEMANN, J., FRISCH, W. & DUNKL, I. 2000*a*. Miocene rotations in the Eastern Alps - Paleomagnetic results from intramontane basin sediments. *Tectonophysics*, **323**, 163–182.

MÁRTON, E., VASS, D. & TÚNYI, I. 2000*b*. Counterclockwise rotations of the Neogene rocks in the East Slovak Basin. *Geologica Carpathica*, **51**, 159–168.

MÁRTON, E., TOKARSKI, A. K. & NEMCOK, M. 2000*c*. Paleomagnetic constraints for the accretion of the tectonic units at the stable European margin, north of the Western Carpathians. *EGS 25th General Assembly, Nice, Geophysical Research Abstracts, 2, SE1.02*, 80.

MÁRTON, E., FODOR, L., JELEN, B., MÁRTON, P., RIFELJ, H. & KEVRIĆ, R. 2002*a*. Miocene to Quaternary deformation in NE Slovenia: complex paleomagnetic and structural study. *Journal of Geodynamics*, **34**, 627–651.

MÁRTON, E., PAVELIĆ, D., TOMLJENOVIĆ, B., AVANIĆ, R., PAMIĆ, J. & MÁRTON, P. 2002*b*. In the wake of a counterclockwise rotating Adriatic microplate: Neogene paleomagnetic results from Northern Croatia. *International Journal of Earth Sciences*, **91**, 514–523.

MÁRTON, E., SCHOLGER, R., MAURITSCH, H.J., TOKARSKI, A.K., THÖNY, W. & KREJČÍ, O. 2003*a*. Counterclockwise rotated Miocene molasse at the southern margin of Stable Europe indicated by palaeomagnetic data. *6th Alpine Workshop, Sopron. Annale Universitatis Scientiarum Budapestinensis de Rolando Eötvös nominatae, sectio geologica*, **35**, 96–97.

MÁRTON, E., DROBNE, K., ĆOSOVIĆ, V. & MORO, A. 2003*b*. Palaeomagnetic evidence for Tertiary counterclockwise rotation of Adria. *Tectonophysics*, **377**, 143–156.

MÂRZA, I. & MÉSZÁROS, M. 1991. Les tuffs volcaniques de Transylvanie. historique, valeur théorique et pratiqe dans le développement de la géologie Transylvaine. *In:* BEDELEAN, I., GHERGARI, L., MÂRZA, I., MÉSZÁROS, M., NICORICI, E. & PETRESCU, I. (eds) *The Volcanic Tuffs from the Transylvanian Basin, Romania, University of Cluj-Napoca, Cluj Napoca*, 11–21.

MASSARI, F. & MEDIZZA, F. 1973. Stratigrafia e paleogeografia del Campaniano-Maastrichtiano nelle Alpi Meridionali (con particolare riguardo agli hard grounds della Scaglia rossa veneta. *Memorie degli Istituti di Geologia e Mineralogia, Università di Padova*, **28**, 1–62.

MASSARI, F., MEDIZZA, F. & SEDEA, R. 1976. L'evoluzione geologica dell'area euganea tra il Giurese superiore e l'Oligocene inferiore. *In:* PICCOLI, G. *et al.* (eds) Il sistema idrotermale euganeo-berico e la geologia dei Colli Euganei. *Memorie degli Istituti di Geologia e Mineralogia, Università di Padova*, **30**, 174–197.

MASSARI, F., GRANDESSO, P., STEFANI, C. & JOBSTRAIBIZER, P. G. 1986*a*. A small polyhistory foreland basin evolving in a context of oblique convergence: the Venetian basin (Chattian to Recent, Southern Alps, Italy). *In*: ALLEN, P. A. & HOMEWOOD, P. (eds) *Foreland basins*. Association of Sedimentologists, Special Publications, **8**, 141–168.

MASSARI, F., GRANDESSO, P., STEFANI, C. & ZANFERRARI, A. 1986*b*. The Oligo-Miocene Molasse of the Veneto-Friuli region, Southern Alps. *Giornale di Geologia*, **48**, 235–255.

MASSARI, F., MELLERE, D. & DOGLIONI, C. 1993. Cyclicity in non-marine foreland-basin sedimentary fill. the Messinian conglomerate-bearing succession of the Venetian Alps (Italy). *In*: MARZO, M. & PUIGDEFABREGAS, M. (eds) *Alluvial Sedimentation*. International Association of Sedimentologists, Special Publications, **17**, 501–520.

MATIČEC, D., VLAHOVIĆ, I., VELIĆ, I. & TIŠLJAR, J. 1996. Eocene limestones overlying Lower Cretaceous deposits of Western Istria (Croatia). Did some parts of present Istria form land during the Cretaceous? *Geologia Croatica*, **49**(1), 117–126.

MATTICK, R., LAWRENCE, E., PHILLIPS, R. & RUMPLER, J. 1988. Seismic stratigraphy and depositional framework of sedimentary rocks in the Pannonian Basin in southeastern Hungary. *In*: ROYDEN, L. H. & HORVÁTH, F. (eds) *The Pannonian Basin*. American Association of Petroleum Geologists, Memoirs, **45**, 117–146.

MENKFELD-GFELLER, U. 1994. Die Wildstrubel-, die Hohgant- und die Sanetsch-Formation: Drei neue lithostratigraphische Einheiten des Eocaens der helvetischen Decken. *Eclogae Geologicae Helvetiae*, **87**, 789–809.

MENKFELD-GFELLER, U. 1995. Stratigraphie, Fazies und Palaeogeographie des Eocaens der helvetischen Decken der Westschweiz (Diablerets und Wildhorn-Decke). *Eclogae Geologicae Helvetiae*, **88**, 115–134.

MENKFELD-GFELLER, U. 1997. Die Bürgen-Fm. und die Klimsenhorn-Fm.: Formelle Definition zweier lithostratigraphischer Einheiten des Eozäns der helvetischen Decken. *Eclogae Geologicae Helvetiae*, **90**, 245–261.

MEULENKAMP, J. E., KOVÁČ, M. & CICHA, I. 1996. On Late Oligocene to Pliocene depocentre migrations and the evolution of the Carpathian - Pannonian system. *Tectonophysics*, **266**, 301–317.

MICHELSEN O. & NIELSEN, L. H. 1993. Structural development of the Fennoscandian border zone, offshore Denmark. *Marine and Petroleum Geology*, **10**, 124–134.

MICHELSEN, O., THOMSEN, E., DANIELSEN, M., HEILMANN-CLAUSEN, C., JORDT, H., & LAURSEN, G. V. 1998. Cenozoic sequence stratigraphy in the eastern North Sea. *In:* GRACIANSKY, P.-C., HARDENBOL, J., JACQUIN, T. & VAIL, P. R. (eds) *Mesozoic and Cenozoic Sequence Stratigraphy of European Basins*. SEPM, Special Publications, **60**, 91–118.

MIETTO, P. 1975. La Collezione paleontologica "Dal Lago" e le località fossilifere di Grola e Rivagra nell'Eocene vicentino. *Memorie degli Istituti di Geologia e Mineralogia dell'Università di Padova*, **31**, 1–28.

MIETTO, P. 1988. Aspetti geologici dei Monti Berici. *AA.VV. I Colli Berici natura e civiltà. Signum ed., Padova,* 12–23.

MIETTO, P. 1992. *Monte di Malo Aspetti Geologici*. Tipografia Operaia Menin, Schio.

MIETTO, P. 2000. The Priabonian in the type locality (Vicentinian Prealps, NE Italy). *In:* BASSI, D. (ed.) *Field Trip Guide Book. Shallow Water Benthic Communities at the Middle-Upper Eocene Boundary.* Annali dell'Università di Ferrara, Scienze della Terra, supplemento, **8**, 66–75.

MIETTO, P. & ZAMPIERI, D. 1989. Fenomeni paleocarsici nei Monti Berici, un problema da approfondire. *Atti XIV Congresso Nazionale di Speleologia in Castellana Grotte*, 763–774.

MIHAJLOVIĆ, D. & JUNGWIRTH, E. 1988. Ologocene aged Flora from Novi Dol (Slovenia, Yugoslavia). *Revue de Paléobiologie*, **7**, 435–447.

MIKUŽ, V. 1979. Middle Eocene molluscan fauna from Lepena. *Geologija*, **22**(2), 189–224.

MIKUŽ, V. 1982. *Miocenske Turritellidae Slovenije*. Doctoral thesis, University of Ljubljana.

MIKUŽ, V. 2000. *Pereiraea gervaisi* (Vézian) from Miocene beds south of Šentjernej in Lower Carniola, Slovenia. *Geologija*, **42**, 123–140.

MIKUŽ, V. & PAVLOVEC, R. 2002. The first finding of gastropod Velates in Eocene flysch from Slovenia. *Razprave 4. razreda SAZU,* **43**(1), 91–107.

MIKUŽ, V. & PAVLOVEC, R. 2004. Sea urchin Amblypygus dilatatus from Lower Eocene limestone in the Griže quarry in the Rižana river valley, Western Slovenia. *Geologija*, **47**(1), 15–21.

MILOJEVIĆ, R. 1964. Geološki sastav i tektonski sklop Srednjebosanskog basena. *Geološki glasnik, posebno izdanje*, **7**, 3–120.

MILOJKOVIĆ, M. 1929. Stratigrafski pregled geoloških formacija u Bosni i Hercegovini. Geološki zavod. Posebno izdanje.

MIOČ, P. 1983. Basic geological map SFRJ 1.100 000, Geology of the sheet Ravne on Koroška. Savezni geološki zavod, Beograd.

MIOČ, P. 2003. Outline of the geology of Slovenia. *Acta Geologica Hungarica*, **46**(1), 3–27.

MIOČ, P. & ŽNIDARČIČ, M. 1989. Basic geological map of SFRJ 1.100 000, Geology of the sheet Maribor and Leibnitz. Savezni geološki zavod, Beograd.

MIOČ, P., ANIČIĆ, B. & ŽNIDARČIČ, M. 1986. Sedimentation of the Smrekovec sedimentary – volcanic series in the Northern Slovenia (NW Yugoslavia). *5th Yugoslav Meeting of Sedimentologists, Abstracts,* 61–66.

MOISESCU, V. & POPESCU, GH. 1980. Chattian - Badenian biochronology in Romania by means of mollusks. *Anuarul Institutului de Geologie şi Geofizică, Bucureşti*, **56**, 205–224.

MOREL, R. 1980. Géologie du massif du Niremont (Préalpes romandes) et de ses abords. *Bulletin Société fribourgeoisedes Sciences naturelles*, **69**, 99–207.

MOŘKOVSKÝ, M. & LUKÁŠOVÁ, R. 1986. Tectonogenesis of the SE part of the East Slovakian Basin. *Mineralia Slovaca*, **18**, 421–433.

MOŘKOVSKÝ, M. & LUKÁŠOVÁ, R. 1991. The geological structure of the eastern margin of the Pannonian basin in East Slovakia. *Perspektívy naftového priemyslu, Luhačovice*, 1–12.

MORO, A. & ĆOSOVIĆ, V. 2002. Rudists and larger benthic foraminifers as relative indicators of water depth- an example from the Istrian (Upper Cretaceous to Eocene) part of the Adriatic carbonate platform. *Memorie della Società Geologica Italiana,* **57**, 203–208.

MOUSSAVIAN, E. 1984. Die Gosau- und Alttertiär-Gerölleder Angerberg-Schichten (Höheres Oligozän, Unterinntal, Nördliche Kalkalpen). *Facies*, **10**, 1–86.

MOUSSAVIAN, E., HERM, D. & HÖFLING, R. 1990. Olisthostromatische Umlagerungen im Paläogen des Salzburg-Reichenhaller Beckens als Ausdruck verstärkter orogener Geodynamik. *Zentralblatt für Geologie und Paläontologie, Teil I,* **1989**, 1383–1398.

MULDER, E. F. J., GELUK, M. C., RITSEMA, I., WESTERHOFF, W. E. & WONG, T. E. 2003. *De ondergrond van Nederland.* NITG-TNO, Utrecht.

MÜLLER, A. 1983. Fauna und Palökologie des marinen Mitteloligozäns der Leipziger Tieflandsbucht (Böhlener Schichten). *Altenburger Naturwissenschaftliche Forschungen*, **2**, 1–152.

MÜLLER, C. & SPIEGLER, D. 1993. Revision of late/middle Miocene boundary on the Voering Plateau (ODP Leg 104). *Newsletter Stratigraphy,* **28**, 171–178.

MÜLLER, W. H., NAEF, H. & GRAF, H. R. 2002. Geologische Entwicklung der Nordschweiz, Neotektonik und Langzeitszenarien Zürcher Weinland. *NAGRA technischer Bericht*, **99**, 1–237.

MUTIĆ, R. 1980. Tufovi u donjohelvetskim naslagama na području Brestika i Bojne (Banija, Hrvatska). *Geološki vjesnik*, **31**, 253–266.

MUTTI, E. & RICI LUCCHI, F. 1972. Le torbiditi dell'Appennino settentrionale: introduzione all'analisi di facies. *Memorie della Società Geologica Italiana*, **11**, 161–199.

NAGYMAROSY, A. 1981. Chrono- and biostratigraphy of the Pannonian basin: a review based mainly on data from Hungary. *Earth Evolution Science*, **1**, 183–194.

NAGYMAROSY, A. 1990. Paleogeographical and paleotectonical outlines of some Intracarpathian Paleogene basins. *Geologica Carpathica*, **41**, 259–274.

NAGYMAROSY, A. & BÁLDI-BEKE, M. 1993. The Szolnok unit and its probable paleogeographic position. *Tectonophysics*, **226**, 457–470

NEBELSICK, J., BASSI, D. & DROBNE, K. 2000. Microfacies Analysis and Paleoenvironmental Interpretation of Lower Oligocene, Shallow-water Carbonates (Gornji Grad Beds, Slovenia). *Facies*, **43**, 157–176.

NEBELSICK, J. H., STINGL, V. & RASSER, M. 2001. Autochthonous Facies and Allochthonous Debris Flows Compared: Early Oligocene Carbonate Facies Patterns of the Lower Inn Valley (Tyrol, Austria). *Facies*, **44**, 31–46.

NEBELSICK, J. H., RASSER. M. & BASSI, D. 2003. The marine Eocene-Oligocene transition as recorded in shallow water, circumalpine carbonates. *In:* PROTHERO, D. R., IVANY, L. C. & NESBITT, E. (eds) *From Greenhouse to Icehouse: The Marine Eocene–Oligocene Transition.* Columbia University Press, New York, 471–491.

NEBELSICK, J. H., RASSER, M. W. & BASSI, D. 2005. Facies dynamics in Eocene to Oligocene circumalpine carbonates. *Facies*, **51**, 197–216.

NEHYBA, S. 1997. Miocene volcaniclastics of the Carpathian Foredeep in Czech Republic. *Věstník ČGÚ,* **72**, 311–327.

NEHYBA, S. 2000. Middle Badenian volcaniclastics in the drill hole OS-2 Hat' near Hlučín (Silesia). *Geologické výzkumy na Moravě a ve Slezsku v roce 1999, Masarykova univerzita*, 69–72 [In Czech, English summary].

NEHYBA, S. 2004. Sedimentary architecture of the southern part of the Carpathian Foredeep. *23rd IAS Meeting of Sedimentology*, Coimbra, Abstract Book, 206.

NEHYBA, S. & BURIÁNEK, D. 2004. Chemistry of garnet and tourmaline – contribution to provenance studies of fine grained Neogene deposits of the Carpathian Foredeep. *Acta Musei Moraviae, Sci. Geol.*, **LXXXIX**(1), 149–159 [In Czech].

NEHYBA, S. & ROETZEL, R. 1999. Lower Miocene Volcaniclastics in South Moravia and Lower Austria. *Jahrbuch der Geologischen Bundesanstalt, Wien*, **141**, 473–490.

NEHYBA, S. & ROETZEL, R. 2004. The Hollabrunn - Mistelbach Formation (Upper Miocene, Pannonian) in the Alpine-Carpathian Foredeep and the Vienna Basin in Lower Austria – An example of a coarse-grained fluvial system. *Jahrbuch der Geologischen Bundesanstalt*, **144**, 191–221.

NEHYBA, S., HLADILOVÁ, Š. & DOLÁKOVÁ, N. 1997. Sedimentary evolution and changes of fossil assemblages in the sw. part of the Carpathian Foredeep in Moravia during the Lower Miocene. *In:* HLADILOVÁ, Š. (ed.) *Dynamika vztahů marinního a kontinentálního prostředí.* Grantový projekt, Masarykova univerzita, Brno, 47–58.

NEMČOK, M. 1993. Transition from convergence to escape: field evidence from the West Carpathians, *Tectonophysics*, **217**, 117–142.

NEMČOK, M., MARKO, F., KOVÁČ, M. & FODOR, L. 1989. Neogene tectonics and paleostress changes in the Czechoslovakian part of the Vienna Basin. *Jahrbuch der Geologischen Bundesanstalt*, **132**, 443–458.

NEUBAUER, F., DALLMEYER, R. D., DUNKL, I. & SCHIRNIK, D. 1995. Late Cretaceous exhumation of the metamorphic Gleinalm dome, Eastern Alps: kinematics cooling history and sedimentary response in a sinistral wrench corridor. *Tectonophysics*, **242**, 79–98.

NEY, R., BURZEWSKI, W., BACHLEDA, T., GÓRECKI, W., JAKÓBCZAK, K. & SŁUPCZYŃSKI, K. 1974. Outline of paleogeography and evolution of lithology and facies of Miocene layers in the Carpathian Foredeep. *Prace Geologiczne Oddział PAN Kraków,* **82**, 1–65.

O'CONNOR, J. M., STOFFERS, P., WIJBRANS, J. R., SHANNON, P. M. & MORRISSEY, T. 2000. Evidence from episodic seamount volcanism for pulsing of the Iceland plume in the past 70 Myr. *Nature*, **408**, 954–958.

OBERHAUSER, R. 1980. Das Altalpidikum (Die geologische Entwicklung von der Mittleren Kreide bis an die Wende Eozän - Oligozän). *In:* OBERHAUSER, R. (ed.) *Der geologische Aufbau Österreichs*. Springer, Wien, 35–48.

OBERHAUSER, R. 1991. *Erläuterungen zur Geologischen Karte 110 und 111, Süd*. Geologische Bundesanstalt, Wien.

OBERHAUSER, R. 1995. Zur Kenntinis der Tektonik und der Paläogeographie des Ostalpenraumes zur Kreide-, Paleozän- und Eozänzeit. *Jahrbuch der Geologischen Bundesanstalt*, **138**(2), 369–432.

ODRZYWOLSKA-BIEŃKOWA, E., POŻARYSKA, K. & MARTINI, E. 1978. Middle Oligocene microfossils from the Polish Lowlands: their stratigraphical and paleogeographical significance. *Acta Palaeontologica Polonica*, **23**, 249–291.

ODRZYWOLSKA-BIEŃKOWA, E., KOSMOWSKA-CERANOWICZ, B., *et al.* 1981. The Polish part of the NW-European Tertiary Basin: a generalization of its stratigraphic section. *Bulletin of the Polish Academy of Science, Earth Sciences*, **29**, 3–17.

OGORELEC, B., DOLENEC, T., CUCCHI, F., GIACOMICH, R., DROBNE, K. & PUGLIESE, N. 1995. Sedimentological and geochemical characteristics of carbonate rocks from the K/T boundary to Lower Eocene on the Karst area (NW Adriatic platform). *First Croatian Geological Congress Proceedings*, *Opatija* **2**, 415–422.

OGORELEC, B., DROBNE, K., JURKOVŠEK, B., DOLENEC, T. & TOMAN, M. 2001. Paleocene beds of the Liburnia Formation in Ćebulovica (Slovenia, NW Adriatic-Dinaric platform). *Geologija*, **44**, 15–65.

OGORELEC B., BARATTOLO, F. & DROBNE, K. 2005. Paleocene marine algae of SW Slovenia (Dolenja Vas and Čebulovica). Studi Trentini Sci. Nat., Field Excursion Guide Book. *Acta Geologica, Suppl.* **80**, 45–58.

OPPENHEIM, P. 1894. Über die Nummuliten des Venetianischen Tertiärs. Friendländer, Berlin.

OPPENHEIM, P. 1908. Über ein Eocänfauna von Ostbosnien und einige Eocänfossilien der Herzegowina. *Jahrbuch der kk Geologischen Reichsanstalt*, **58**, 311–344.

ORTNER, H. 1994. Die Muttekopfgosau (Lechtaler Alpen, Tirol/Österreich): Sedimentologie und Beckenentwicklung. *Geologische Rundschau*, **83**, 197–211.

ORTNER, H. & SACHSENHOFER, R. F. 1996. Evolution of the Lower Inn Valley Tertiary and constraints on the development of the source area. *In:* WESSELY, G. & LIEBL, W. (eds) *Oil and Gas in Alpidic Thrustbelts and Basins of Central and Eastern Europe*. EAGE, Special Publications, **5**, 237–247.

ORTNER, H., & STINGL, V. 2001. Facies and basin development of the Oligocene in the Lower Inn Valley, Tyrol/Bavaria. *In:* PILLER, W. E. & RASSER, M. W. (eds) *Paleogene of the Eastern Alps*. Österreichische Akademie der Wissenschaften Schriftenreihe der Erdwissenschaftlichen Kommissionen, **14**, 153–196.

OSIJUK, D. 1979. Cechy sedymentacji mioceńskich osadów węglonośnych na podstawie wybranych przykładów z zachodniej i środkowej Polski. *Biuletyn Państwowego Instytutu Geologicznego*, **320**, 57–131.

OSZCZYPKO, N. 1991. Stratigraphy of the Palaeogene deposits of the Bystrica Subunit (Magura Nappe, Polish Outer Carpathians). *Bulletin Polish Academy of Sciences, Earth Sciences*, **39**(4), 415–431.

OSZCZYPKO, N. 1998. The Western Carpathian foredeep-development of the foreland basin in front of the accretionary wedge and its burial history (Poland). *Geologica Carpathica*, **49**(6), 1–18.

OSZCZYPKO, N. 1999. From remnant oceanic basin to collision-related foreland basin-a tentative history of the Outer Western Carpathians. *Geologica Carpathica, special issue*, **50**, 161–163.

OSZCZYPKO, N. 2004. The structural position and tectonosedimentary evolution of the Polish Outer Carpathians. *Przegląd Geologiczny*, **8**(2), 780–791.

OSZCZYPKO, N. 2006. Late Jurassic-Miocene evolution of the Outer Carpathian fold-and thrust belt and its foredeep basin (Western Carpathians, Poland). *Kwartalnik Geologiczny*, **50**, 169–194.

OSZCZYPKO, N. & OSZCZYPKO-CLOWES, M. 2002. Newly discovered Early Miocene deposits in the Nowy Sącz area (Magura Nappe, Polish Outer Carpathians). *Geological Quarterly*, **46**, 117–133.

OSZCZYPKO, N. & OSZCZYPKO-CLOWES, M. 2003. The Aquitanian arine deposits in the basement of Polish Western Carpathians and its paleogeographical and paleotectonic implications. *Acta Geologica Polonica*, **53**(2), 101–122.

OSZCZYPKO, N. & ŚLĄCZKA, A. 1985. An attempt to palinspastic reconstruction of Neogene basins in the Carpathian Foredeep. *Annales Societatis Geologorum Poloniae*, **55**(1–2), 55–76.

OSZCZYPKO, N. & TOMAŚ, A. 1985. Tectonic evolution of marginal part of the Polish Flysch Carpathians in the Middle Miocene. *Kwartalnik Geologiczny*, **29**(1), 109–128.

OSZCZYPKO, N., ANDREYEVA-GRIGOROVICH, A., MALATA, E. & OSZCZYPKO-CLOWES, M. 1999. The Lower Miocene deposits of the Rača Subunit near Nowy Sącz (Magura Nappe, Polish Outer Carpathians). *Geologica Carpathica*, **50**, 419–433.

OSZCZYPKO, N., OSZCZYPKO-CLOWES, M., GOLONKA, J. & MARKO, F. 2005. Oligocene-Lower Miocene sequences of the Pieniny Klippen Belt and adjacent Magura Nappe between Jarabina and Poprad River (East Slovakia and South Poland): their tectonic position and paleogeographical implications. *Kwartalnik Geologiczny*, **49**, 379–402.

OSZCZYPKO, N., KRZYWIEC, P., POPADYUK, I. & PERYT, T. 2006. Carpathian Foredeep Basin (Poland and Ukraine): its sedimentary, structural, and geodynamic evolution. *In:* GOLONKA, J. & PICHA, F. J. (eds) *The Carpathians and their foreland: Geology and hydrocarbon resources*. AAPG Memoirs, **84**, 293–350.

OSZCZYPKO-CLOWES, M. 2001. The nannofossils biostratigraphy of the youngest deposits of the Magura nappe (East of the Skawa river, Polish flysch Carpathians) and their palaeoenviromental conditions. *Annales Societatis Geologorum Poloniae*, **71**(3), 139–188.

OVEREEM, I. 2002. *Process-response simulation of fluvio-deltaic stratigraphy*. Doctoral thesis, Delft University of Technology.

PALIENKO, V. P. 1990. Reflection of the fundament blocks dynamic in the latest tectonics and modern relief. *In:* CHEBANENKO, I. I. (ed.) *Geotectonic of the Volhyno-Podolia*. Naukova, Dumka, 203–209 [in Russian].

PALINKAŠ, A. L., DROBNE, K., DURN, G. & MIKO, S. 1996. Mercury anomaly at the Cretaceous – Tertiary boundary, Dolenja vas, Slovenia. *In:* DROBNE, K., GORIČAN, Š. & KOTNIK, B. (eds) *The role of impact processes in the geological and biological evolution of planet Earth*, International Workshop, Palaeontology Institute of ZRC-SAZU, Ljubljana, 57–60.

PAMIĆ, J. 1977. Alpski magmatsko-metamorfni procesi i njihovi produkti kao indikatori geološke evolucije terena sjeverno Bosne. *Geološki glasnik*, **22**, 257–291.

PAMIĆ, J. 1992. Trijaske i tercijarne vulkanske piroklastične stijene iz Murske depresije u Hrvatskoj. *Nafta*, **43**, 259–304.

PAMIĆ, J. 1993. Eoalpine to Neoalpine magmatic and metamorphic processes in the northwestern Vardar Zone, the easternmost Periadriatic Zone and the southwestern Pannonian Basin. *Tectonophysics*, **226**, 503–518.

PAMIĆ, J. 1996. Magmatske formacije Dinarida Vardarske zone i južnih dijelova Panonskog bazena. *Časopis Nafta Zagreb*.

PAMIĆ, J. 1997. Vulkanske stijene Savsko-dravskog međurječja i Baranje (Hrvatska). *Časopis Nafta Zagreb*.

PAMIĆ, J. & PALINKAŠ, L. 2000. Petrology and geochemistry of Paleogene tonalites from the easternmost parts of the Periadriatic Zone. *Minerology and Petrology*, **70**, 121–141.

PAMIĆ, J., GUŠIĆ, I. & JELASKA, V. 1998. Geodynamic evolution of the Central Dinarides. *Tectonophysics*, **297**, 251–268.

PAMIĆ, J., BELAK, M., BULLEN, T. D., LANPHERE, M. A. & MCKEE, E. H. 2000*a*. Geochemistry and geodynamics of a late Cretaceous bimodal volcanic association from the southern part of the Pannonian Basin in Slavonija (North Croatia). *Mineralogy and Petrology*, **68**, 271–296.

PAMIĆ, J., BALEN, D. & HERAK, M. 2002. Origin and geodynamic evolution of Late Paleogene magmatic associations along the Periadriatic – Sava – Vardar magmatic belt. *Geodynamica Acta*, **15**, 209–231.

PAMIĆ-SUNARIĆ, O. 1977. Kamengradski ugljeni basen. *Ležišta mineralnih sirovina BiH, 1, "Geoinženjering"*, Sarajevo.

PANAIOTU, C. 1998. Paleomagnetic constrains on the geodynamic history of Romania. *In:* SLEDZINSKI, J. (ed.) *Monograph of Southern Carpathians*, Reports on Geodesy, **7**, 205–216.

PAPAZZONI, C. A. 2000*a*. Stratigraphy. *In:* BASSI, D. (ed.) Field trip guide book. Shallow water benthic communities at the Middle–Upper Eocene boundary. *Annali dell'Università di Ferrara, Scienze della Terra, supplemento*, **8**, 60.

PAPAZZONI, C. A. 2000*b*. The Early Eocene (Early-Late Cuisian) of Bolca. *In:* BASSI, D. (ed.) Field trip guide book. Shallow water benthic communities at the Middle-Upper Eocene boundary. *Annali* *dell'Università di Ferrara, Scienze della Terra, supplemento*, **8**, 61–62.

Papazzoni, C. A. & Less, G. 2000. Stop 2. the type "Spileccian". *In:* Bassi, D. (ed.) Field trip guide book. Shallow water benthic communities at the Middle-Upper Eocene boundary. *Annali dell'Università di Ferrara, Scienze della Terra, supplemento*, **8**, 64–65.

Papazzoni, C. A. & Sirotti, A. 1995. Nummulite biostratigraphy at the Middle/Upper Eocene boundary in the northern Mediterranean area. *Rivista Italiana di Paleontologia e Stratigrafia*, **101**, 63–80.

Papazzoni, C. A. & Trevisani, E. 2000. The southern Altopiano di Asiago. *In:* Bassi, D. (ed) Field trip guide book. Shallow water benthic communities at the Middle-Upper Eocene boundary. *Annali dell'Università di Ferrara, Scienze della Terra, supplemento*, **8**, 77–85.

Papeš, J. 1985. Geologija jugozapadne Bosne. *Geološki glasnik*, **19**, 1–197.

Papp, A. 1955. Lepidocyclinen aus Zagorje und Tuhinjska dolina östlich von Kamnik (Slowenien). *Geologija*, **3**, 209–215.

Papp, A. 1975. Die Grossforaminiferen des Egerien *In:* Báldi, T. & Seneš, J. (eds) *Chronostratigraphie und Neostratotypen*, 5, 289–307.

Papp, A., Marinescu, F. & Seneš, J. 1974. M5 Sarmatien (sensu E. Suess, 1866). Die Sarmatische Schichtengruppe und ihr Stratotypus. *Chronostratigraphie und Neostratotypen*, **4**, 1–707.

Paramonova, N. P. 1994. History of Sarmatian and Aktchagylian Bivalve molluscs. *Trudy Paleontologiceskogo instituta*, **260**, 1–212 [in Russian].

Pavelić, D. 2001. Tectonostratigraphic model for the North Croatian and North Bosnian sector of the Miocene Pannonian Basin System. *Basin Research*, **13**, 359–376.

Pavelić, D. 2002. The south-western boundary of Central Paratethys. *Geologia Croatica*, **55**, 83–92.

Pavelić, D. & Kovačić, M. 1999. Lower Miocene alluvial deposits of the Požeška Mt. (Pannonian Basin, Northern Croatia). cycles, megacycles and tectonic implications. *Geologia Croatica*, **52**, 67–76.

Pavelić, D., Miknić, M. & Sarkotić Šlat, M. 1998. Early to Middle Miocene facies succession in lacustrine and marine environments on the southwestern margin of the Pannonian basin system. *Geologica Carpathica*, **49**, 433–443.

Pavelić, D., Avanić, R., Kovačić, M., Vrsaljko, D. & Miknić, M. 2003. An outline of the evolution of the Croatian part of the Pannonian Basin System. *In:* Vlahović, I. & Tišljar, J. (eds) *Evolution of depositional environments from the Palaeozoic to the Quaternary in the Karst Dinarides and the Pannonian Basin.* 22nd IAS Meeting of Sedimentology, Opatija, 17–19 September 2003, Field Trip Guidebook, 155–161.

Pavlovec, R. 1963. Die stratigraphische Entwicklung des älteren Paläogens im südwestlichen Teil Sloweniens. *Razprave SAZU, 4. razreda*, **7**, 421–556.

Pavlovec, R. 1966. Taxonomie der Nummulitinae. Operculina exiliformis n.sp. aus dem Palaeogen in südlichen Slowenien. *Razprave 4. razreda SAZU*, **9**, 255–297.

Pavlovec, R. 1981. Flysch from Postojna. *Geologija*, **24**, 285–301.

Pavlovec, R. 1999. Oligocene nummulitines in rock specimens from glacial drift in Bohinj, Slovenia. *Rudarsko-metalurški zbornik*, **46**(3), 549–554.

Pavlovec, R. 2004. Some interesting features about nummulitins from Vipolže 2 in Brda, west Slovenia. *Geologija*, **47**(1), 29–40.

Pavlovec, R. & Pavšič, J. 1987. Biostratigraphy of beds with crabs in Istria. *Geologija*, **28/29**, 55–68.

Pavlovec, R., Pleničar, M., Drobne, K., Ogorelec, B. & Šušteršič, F. 1989. History of geological investigations of the Karst (Kras) region and the neighbouring territory (western Dinarides). *Memorie della Società Geologica Italiana*, **40**, 9–20.

Pavlovec, R., Knez, M., Drobne, K. & Pavšič, J. 1991. Profiles: Košana, Sv.Trojica and Leskovec: the desintegration of the carbonate platform. *In:* Drobne, K. & Pavlovec, R. (org.) *Paleocene and Eocene beds in Slovenia and Istria.* 2nd Meeting of IGCP 286 – Early Paleogene Benthos, 69–72.

Pavšič, J. 1977. Nannoplankton from the Upper Cretaceous and Paleocene beds in the Gorica region. *Geologija*, **20**, 33–64.

Pavšič, J. 1979. *Nanoplanktonska biostratigrafija krednih in paleocenskih plasti Slovenije*. Doctoral thesis, University of Ljubljana.

Pavšič, J. 1981. The nannoplankton biostratigraphy of Cretaceous and Paleogene beds in Slovenia. *Rudarsko-metalurški zbornik*, **28**(4), 369–382.

Pavšič, J. 1994. Biostratigraphy of Cretaceous, Paleocene and Eocene clastics of Slovenia. *Razprave 4. razreda SAZU*, **35**, 65–84.

Pavšič, J. 1995. Nannoplankton stratigraphy of clastic Upper Cretaceous and Paleogene beds in the Kočevje area, Slovenia. *Razprave 4. razreda SAZU*, **36**, 135–177.

Pavšič, J. 1997. Nannoplankton from the Paleocene/Eocene boundary in Goriška Brda. *Razprave 4. razrreda SAZU*, **18**, 83–95.

Pavšič, J. & Dolenec, T. 1995. Floristic and isotopic changes at the Paleocene–Eocene boundary in Slovenia. *Journal of Nannoplankton Research*, **17**(2), 79.

Pavšič, J. & Dolenec, T. 1996. Floristic and isotopic changes at the Paleocene–Eocene boundary in the flysch of Goriška Brda, W Slovenia. *Early Paleogene Stage Boundaries, International Meeting Field Conference*, Zaragoza, 38–39.

Pavšič, J. & Horvat, A. 1988. The Cretaceous/Tertiary boundary interval in the flysch of Slovenia. *Razprave 4. razreda SAZU*, **29**, 129–146.

Pavšič, J. & Pekmann, J. 1996. Stratigraphy and sedimentology of the Piran flysch area (Slovenia). *Annales*, **9**, 123–138.

Pavšič, J. & Premec Fuček, V. 2000. Calcareous nannoplankton and planktonic foraminiferal zones during the Middle and Upper Eocene of the "Transitional beds" of the Adriatic platform. *Annalis di Museo Civice di Storia naturali Ferrara*, **3**, 22–23.

Pécskay, Z., Lexa, J., *et al.* 1995. Space and time evolution of the Neogene-Quaternary volcanism in the Carpatho-Pannonian Region. *Acta Vulcanologica*, **7**, 15–28.

Pěničková, M. & Dvořáková, V. 1985. Final report of the hydrocarbon prospection in Danube basin during 1973–1983. Geophysical Institute, Brno.

Perch-Nielsen, K. & Pavšič, J. 1979. Calcareous nannofossils from the Cretaceous/Tertiary boundary in Slovenia. *Cretaceous/Tertiary Boundary events symposium II Proceedings*, Copenhagen, University of Copenhagen, 179–184.

Pereszlényi, M., Trgiňa, P. & Vitáloš, R. 1991. Možnosti predikcie termálnej zrelosti uhľovodíkov vo východoslovenskej neogénnej panve. Geofond, Bratislava.

Peryt, D. 1997. Calcareous nannoplankton stratigraphy of the Middle Miocene in the Gliwice area (Upper Silesia, Poland). *Bulletin of the Polish Academy of Sciences, Earth Sciences*, **45**, 119–131.

Peryt, T. M. 2001, Gypsum facies transitions in basin-marginal evaporites: middle Miocene (Badenian) of West Ukraine. *Sedimentology*, **48**, 1103–1119.

Petit, C., Campy, M., Chaline, J. & Bonvalot, J. 1996. Major paleogeographic changes in Alpine Foreland during the Pliocene - Pleistocene. *Boreas*, **25**,131–143.

Petković, K. 1958. Neue Erkentnisse über den Bau der Dinariden. *Jahrbuch der Geologischen Bundesantalt*, **H1**, 1–101.

Petrová, P. 2004. Foraminiferal assemblages as an indicator of foreland basin evolution (Carpathian Foredeep, Czech Republic). *Bulletin of Geosciences*, **79**(4), 231–242.

Piccoli, G., Bellati, R., *et al.* 1976. Il sistema idrotermale euganeo-berico e la geologia dei Colli Euganei. *Memorie degli Istituti di Geologia e Mineralogia, Università di Padova*, **30**, 1–276.

Picha, F. J. 2002. Late orogenic strike-slip faulting and escape tectonics in frontal Dinarides- Hellenides, Croatia, Yugoslavia, Albania, and Greece. *AAPG Bulletin*, **86**(9), 1659–1671.

Picot, L. 2002. *Le Paléogène des synclinaux du Jura et de la bordure sud-rhénane: paléontologie (Ostracodes), paléoécologie, biostratigraphie et paléogéographie.* Thesis, University of Fribourg, *Geofocus*, **5**.

Pignatti, J. *et al.* 1998. Reference list. Paleogene shallow benthos of the Tethys, 1. *Dela-Opera 4. razreda SAZU*, **34**(1).

Pikija, M. 1987. Osnovna geološka karta SFRJ 1.100000. *Tumač za list Sisak.* Institute of Geology, Zagreb, Federal Geological Survey, Beograd.

Pirini Radrizzani, C., Tunis, G. & Venturini, S. 1986. Biostratigrafia e paleogeografia dell'area sud-occidentale dell'anticlinale M. Mia-M. Matajur (Prealpi Giulie). *Rivista Italiana di Paleontologia e Stratigrafia*, **92**, 327–382.

Pischvanova, L. S., Dzodzo-Tomic, R. & Dikova P. 1970. Micro-faunistic characteristic of the Buglov layers. *In:* VIALOV, O. S. (ed.) *Buglovskie sloi miocena.* Naukova dumka, Kiev, 75–85 [in Russian].

PIWOCKI, M. 1998. Charakterystyka dolnomioceńskiej IV dąbrowskiej grupy pokładów węgla brunatnego w Polsce. *Przegląd Geologiczny*, **46**, 55–61.

PIWOCKI, M. 2002. Stratygrafia bursztynonośnych osadów północnej Lubelszczyzny. *Przegląd Geologiczny*, **50**, 561–574.

PIWOCKI, M. & KASIŃSKI, J. R. 1995. Outline of development of the Lower Oligocene transgression in northern Poland. *Geosynoptyka. i Geotermia*, **34**, 47–52.

PIWOCKI, M. & OLKOWICZ-PAPROCKA, I. 1987. Litostratygrafia paleogenu, perspektywy i metodyka poszukiwań bursztynu w północnej Polsce. *Biuletyn Państwowego Instytutu Geologicznego*, **356**, 7–28.

PIWOCKI, M., OLKOWICZ-PAPROCKA, I., KOSMOWSKA-CEARNOWICZ, B., GRABOWSKA, I. & ODRZYWOLSKA-BIEŃKOWA, E. 1985. Stratygrafia trzeciorzędowych osadów bursztynonośnych okolic Chłapowa koło Pucka. *Prace Muzeum Ziemi*, **37**, 61–77.

PIWOCKI, M., OLSZEWSKA, B. & GRABOWSKA, I. 1996. Korelacja biostratygraficzna paleogenu Polski z innymi obszarami. *In:* MALINOWSKA, L. & PIWOCKI, M. (eds) *Budowa geologiczna Polski. Atlas skamieniałości przewodnich i charakterystycznych. Kenozoik – Trzeciorzęd – Paleogen*, 3:3a, Panstwowego Instytutu Geologicznego, Warszawa, 25–36.

PLACER, L. 1981. Geological structure of Southwestern Slovenia. *Geologija*, **24**, 27–60.

PLACER, L. 1999*a*. Contribution to the macrotectonic subdivision of the border region between Southern Alps and External Dinarides. *Geologija*, **41**, 223–255.

PLACER, L. 1999*b*. Structural meaning of the Sava folds. *Geologija*, **41**, 191–221.

PLACER, L. & VRABEC, M. 2004. Neogene structural evolution of the Northwestern external Dinarides and Istria peninsula (Adriatic foreland). *32 nd IGC Florence, Scientific Sessions, abstract (part 1)*, 248.

PLAŠIENKA, D., SOTÁK, J. & PROKEŠOVÁ, R. 1998. Structural profiles across the Šambron - Kamenica Periklippen Zone of the Central Carpathian Paleogene Basin in NE Slovakia. *Mineralia Slovaca*, **30**, 173–184.

PLENIČAR, M. & PAVLOVEC, R. 1981. New views of the development of Maastrichtian in Slovenia. *Rudarsko-metal. zbornik*, **28**, 383–386.

PLÖCHINGER, B. 1961. Die Gosaumulde von Grünbach und der Neuen Welt (N.Ö.). *Jahrbuch der Geologischen Bundeanstalt*, **104**, 359–441.

PLÖCHINGER, B. 1964. Die Kreide-Paleozän-Ablagerungen in der Gießhübler Mulde zwischen Perchtoldsdorf und Sittendorf (Nö.). *Mitteilungen der Österreichischen. Geologischen Gesellschaft*, **56**, 469–501.

PLÖCHINGER, B. 1982. *Erläuterungen zu Blatt 95 Sankt Wolfgang im Salzkammergut.* Geologische Bundesanstalt, Vienna.

POGÁCSÁS, G., JÁMBOR, Á., MATTICK, R. E., *et al.* 1990. Chronostratigraphic relations of Neogene formations of the great Hungarian Plain based on interpretation of seismic and paleomagnetic data. *International Geological Review*, **32**, 449–467.

POGÁCSÁS, G., SZALAY, Á., BÉRSZY, I., BARDÓCZ, B., SZALÓKI, I. & KONCZ, I. 1996. Hydrocarbons in Hungary, exploration and developments (extended abstracts). *In:* WESSELY, G. & LIEBL, W. (eds) *Oil and Gas in Alpidic Thrust Belts and Basins of Central and Eastern Europe.* EAGE, Special Publications, **5**, 37–39.

POLI, M.E. & ZANFERRARI, A. 1995. Dinaric thrust tectonics in the southern Julian Prealps (Eastern-Southern Alps, NE Italy). *Proceedings of 1st Croatian Geological Congress, Opatija*, **2**, 465–468.

POLŠAK, A. 1985. The boundary between the Cretaceous and Tertiary in terms of the stratigraphy and sedimentology of the biolithitic complex in The Mt. Medvednica (Northern Croatia). *Acta Geologica, Yugoslav Academy of Sciences and Arts*, **15**(1), 1–23.

POLJAK, M. 2000. *Structural-tectonic map of Slovenia, 1:250.000.* Geological Survey of Slovenia, Ljubljana.

POLJAK, M. 2004. *Geological map of the Krško basin 1. 25 000.* Geological Survey of Slovenia, Ljubljana.

PONTON, M. & VENTURINI, C. 2002. Il ciclo alpino. *In:* VAI, G. B., VENTURINI, C., CARULLI, G. B. & ZANFERRARI, A. (eds) *Guide geologiche regionali. Alpi e Prealpi Carniche e Giulie. Friuli Venezia Giulia.* Società Geologica Italiana, **9**, 76–81.

POPESCU, GH. 1972. Biostratigraphy of the Oligocene - Miocene deposits from south of Preluca based on planctonic formanifera. *Dări de Seamă, Institutul de Geologie și Geofizică, București*, **58**, 105–127.

POPESCU, GH. 1975. Etudes des foraminiferes du Miocene inferieur et moyen du nord-ouest de la Transylvanie. *Memoriile Institutului de Geologie și Geofizică, București*, **23**, 1–121.

POPESCU, GH. 1995. Contributions to the knowledge of the Sarmatian foraminifera of Romania. *Romanian Journal of Paleontology, București*, **76**, 85–98.

POPESCU, GH., MĂRUNȚEANU, M. & FILIPESCU, S. 1995. Neogene from Transylvania Depression - Guide to excursion A1 (pre-Congress) (X-th Congress RCMNS, București, 1995), Romanian Journal of Stratigraphy, **76**(3).

POPOV, S. V., RÖGL, F., ROZANOV, A. Y., STEININGER, F. F., SHCHERBA, I. G. & KOVÁČ, M. 2004. Lithological-Paleogeographic maps of Paratethys. 10 Maps Late Eocene to Pliocene. *Courier Forschungsinstitut Senckenberg*, **250**, 1–46.

POPRAWA, P., MALATA, T. & OSZCZYPKO, N. 2002. Tectonic evolution of the Polish part of Outer Carpathian's sedimentary basins – constraints from subsidence analysis. *Przegląd Geologiczny*, **11**, 1092–1108.

POSCHL, I. 1991. A model for the depositional evolution of the volcaniclastic succession of a Pliocene maar volcano in the Styrian basin (Austria). *Jahrbuch der Geologischen Bundesanstalt*, **134**, 809–843.

POULDITIS, CH. 1981. *Petrologie und Geolochimie basaltischer Gesteine der steirischen Vulkanbogens in der Steiermark und im Burgenland.* Doctoral thesis, University of Vienna.

POŻARYSKA, K. & SZCZECHURA, J. 1968. Foraminifera from the Paleocene of Poland, their ecological and biostratigraphical meaning. *Palaeontologia Polonica*, **20**, 1–107.

PRELOGOVIĆ, E. & KRANJEC, V. 1983. Geološki razvitak područja Jadranskog mora. *Pomorski zbornik*, **21**, 387–405.

PREMEC-FUĆEK, V. & ŽIVKOVIĆ, S. 2005. Paleoecological and paleogeographical controls on the Middle to Late Eocene planktonic foraminiferal assemblages of southwestern Croatia. *In:* VELIĆ, I., VLAHOVIĆ, I. & BIONDIĆ, R. (eds) *Abstracts Book, Third Croatian Geological Congress, Opatija*, 163–164.

PREMRU, U. 1980. Geological structure of Central Slovenia. *Geologija*, **23**, 227–278.

PREMRU, U. 1982. Geological structure of Southern Slovenia. *Geologija*, **25**, 95–126.

PREMRU, U. 1983. Basic geological map of SFRJ 1. 100 000, Geology of the sheet Ljubljana. Savezni geološki zavod, Beograd.

PREMRU, U. 2005. *Tectonic and Tectogenesis of Slovenia.* Monograph Series, Geological Survey of Slovenia, Ljubljana.

PREY, S. 1980. Erläuternde Beschreibung des Nordteiles der geologischen Karte der Umgebung der Stadt Salzburg, 1:50.000. - Flyschzone, Walserbergserie, Gosau im Nordrand der Kalkalpen und Quartär. *Verhandlungen der Geologischen Bundesanstalt*, **1980**(3), 281–325.

PREY, S. 1984. Das Helvetikum von Ohlsdorf-Oberweis an der Traun nördlich Gmunden (O.Ö.). *Jahrbuch der Geologischen Bundesanstalt*, **126**, 497–511.

PRINCIPI, P. 1926. La flora oligocenica di Chiavon e Salcedo. *Memorie per servire alla descrizione della Carta Geologica d'Italia*, **10**, 1–124.

PROTHERO, D. R., IVANY, L. C. & NESBITT, E. A. (eds) 2003. *From Greenhouse to Icehouse. The Marine Eocene–Oligocene Transition.* Columbia University Press, New York.

PROUST, J. N. & HOSU, A. 1996. Sequence stratigraphy and Paleogene tectonic evolution of the Transylvanian Basin (Romania, eastern Europe), *Sedimentary Geology*, **105**, 117–140.

PUGLIESE, N. & DROBNE, K. 1995. Paleontological and paleoenvironmental events at the K/T boundary in the Karst area. *In:* MONTANARI, A. & COCCIONI, R. (eds) *ESF 4th International Workshop*, Ancona, 137–140.

PUGLIESE, N., DROBNE, K., *et al.* 1995. Micro and macrofossils from the K/T boundary through Paleocene in the Northern Adriatic Platform. *First Croatian Geological Congress Proceedings, Opatija*, **2**, 415–422.

PUGLIESE, N., ARBULLA, D., CAFFAU, M. & DROBNE, K. 2000. Strategia di vita nel biota daniano (SBZ 1) del Carso Triestino (Italia). *Crisi biologiche, radiazioni adattative e dinamica delle piattaforme carbonatiche.* Accademia Nazionale delle Scienze Lettere ed Arti di

Modena, Collana di Studi, **21**, 215–220.

PUJALTE, V., ORUE-EXTEBARRIA, X., *et al.* 2003. Basal Ilerdian (earliest Eocene) turnover of larger foraminifera; Age constraints based on calcareous plankton and $\delta^{13}C$ isotopic profiles from new southern Pyrenean sections (Spain). *In:* WING, S. L., GINGERISH, P. D., SCHMITZ, B. & THOMAS, E. (eds) *Causes and Consequences of Globally Warm Climates in the Early Paleogene.* Geological Society of America, Special Papers, **369**, 205–221.

PUŠKARIĆ, S. 1987. Calcareous nannoplankton from clastic sediments of the island of Hvar. *Rad Jugoslavenske Akademije Znanosti i Umjetnosti*, **22**(431), 7–16.

RADOIČIĆ, R. 1992. Paleocene microflora of Kamenjak limestone, E Majevica (4th note). *Radovi Geoinstituta,* **26**, 201–230.

RAKOVEC, I. 1956. A survey of the tectonic structure of Slovenia. *1st Geological Congress, Bled 1954*, 73–83.

RASCHER, J., ESCHER, D., FISCHER, J., DUTSCHMANN, U. & KÄSTNER, S. 2005. *Geologischer Atlas Tertiär Nordwestsachsen 1: 250 000.* Sächsisches Landesamt für Umwelt und Geologie.

RASMUSSEN, E. S. 2004. Stratigraphy and depositional evolution of the uppermost Oligocene – Miocene succession in western Denmark. *Bulletin Geological Society Denmark*, **51**, 89–109.

RASMUSSEN, L. B. 1966. Molluscan Faunas and Biostratigraphy of the Marine Younger Miocene Formations of Denmark, Part II. Geology and Biostratigraphy. Danmarks Geologiske Undersøgelse, II, Række.

RASSER, M. 1994. Facies and palaeoecology of rhodoliths and acervilinid macroids in the Eocene of the Krappfeld (Austria). *Beiträge zur Paläontologie Österreichs*, **19**, 191–217.

RASSER, M. W. 2000. Coralline red algal limestones of the Late Eocene Alpine Foreland Basin in Upper Austria: component analysis, facies and palecology. *Facies*, **42**, 59–92.

RASSER, M. W. & PILLER, W. E. 1999*a*. Lithostratigraphische Neugliederung im Paläogen des österreichisch-bayerischen Südhelvetikums. *Abhandlungen der Geologischen Bundesanstalt*, **56**(2), 699–712.

RASSER, M. W. & PILLER, W. E. 1999b. Kroisbachgraben und Frauengrube: Lithostratigraphische Typuslokalitäten für das paläogene Helvetikum Salzburgs. *Abhandlungen der Geologischen Bundesanstalt,* **56**(2), 713–722.

RASSER, M. W. & PILLER, W. E. 2001. Facies patterns, subsidence and sea-level changes in ferruginous and glauconitic environments: The Paleogene Helvetic Shelf in Austria and Bavaria. *In:* PILLER, W. E. & RASSER, M. W. (eds) *Paleogene of the Eastern Alps.* Österreichische Akademie der Wissenschaften, Schriftenreihe der Erdwissenschaftlichen Kommission, Wien, **14**, 77–110.

RATSCHBACHER, L., FRISCH, W. & LINZER, H.-G. 1991. Lateral extrusion in the Eastern Alps, Part 2. structural analysis. *Tectonics*, **10**, 257–271.

REICHENBACHER, B. 2000. Das brackish-lakustrine Oligozän und UnterMiozän im Mainzer Becken und Hanauer Becken: Fischfaunen, Paläoökologie, Biostratigraphie, Paläogeographie. *Courier Forschungsinstitut Senckenberg,* **222**, 1–143.

REICHENBACHER, B. & KELLER, T. 2002. Neudefinition von stratigraphischen Einheiten im Tertiär des Mainzer und Hanauer Beckens (Deutschland, Oligozän-Miozän). Teil 2: Wiesbaden-Formation [= Untere Hydrobien-Schichten]. *Mainzer geowissenschaftliche Mitteilungen*, **31**, 99–122.

REICHENBACHER, B., BÖTTCHER, R., *et al.* 1998. Graupensandrinne - Ries-Impakt: Zur Stratigraphie der Grimmelfinger Schichten, Kirchberger Schichten und Oberen Süsswassermolasse (nördliche Vorlandmolasse, Süddeutschland). *Zeitschrift der deutschen geologischen Gesellschaft,* **149**, 127–161.

REICHERTER, K., FROITZHEIM, N., *et al.* 2008. Alpine tectonics north of the Alps. *In:* MCCANN, T. (ed.) *The Geology of Central Europe. Volume 2: Mesozoic and Cenozoic.* Geological Society, London, 1233–1285.

REIS, O. M. 1926. Die Nummulitenschichten im Grüntener Bogen. *Geognostische Jahreshefte*, **39**, 22–24.

REUSS, A. E. 1864. Die Fossilen Foraminiferen, Anthozoen und Bryozoen von Oberburg in Steiermark. Ein Beitrag zur Fauna der Oberen Nummulitenschischten. *Denkschriften der Kaiserlichen Akademie der Wissenschaften, Mathematisch-Naturwissenschaftliche Classe*, **23**, 1–38.

RICHTER, M. 1978. Vorarlberger Alpen. *Sammlung Geologischer Führer*, **49**, 1–171.

RIFELJ, H., JELEN, B., POLJAK, M. & SKABERNE, D. in press. Stratigraphic interpretations of some Badenian and Sarmatian sedimentary deposits in the Krško basin. *Geologija.*

RITZKOWSKI, S. 1987. Lower and Middle Oligocene deposits from the Doberg near Bünde (Westfalia, F.R.G.) – bathymetric interpretation of the ostracod fauna. *Mededelingen van de Werkgroep voor Tertiaire en Kwartaire Geologie,* **24**, 181–190.

RITZKOWSKI, S. 1999*b*. Latdorf-Schichten (Oligozän) auf dem Süd-Kamm des Hildesheimer Waldes nördlich Almstedt (Südliches Niedersachsen. *Mitteilungen des Roemer-Museums Hildesheim, Neue Folge,* **7**, Appendix.

RIŽNAR, I. 1997. *Geologija okolice Postojne.* Geoloski oddelek NTF, Univerza, Ljubljana.

RIŽNAR, I., MILETIĆ, D., VERBIČ, T. & HORVAT, A. 2002. Srednjemiocenske kamnine severnega pobočja Gorjancev med Čatežem in Kostanjevico. *Geologija*, **45**(2), 531–536.

ROCA, E., BESSEREAU, G., JAWOR, E., KOTARBA, M. & ROURE, F. 1995. Pre-Neogene evolution of the Western Carpathians: Constrains from the Bochnia - Tatra Mountains section (Polish Western Carpathians). *Tectonics*, **14**(4), 855–873.

ROETZEL, R. 1983. Die Faziesentwicklung des Oligozäns in der Molassezone zwischen Krems und Wieselburg (Niederösterreich). *Jahrbuch der Geologischen Bundesanstalt*, **126**, 129–179.

ROETZEL, R. 2003. The Karpatian Sediments in the Alpine-Carpathian Foredeep in Austria. *In*: BRZOBOHATÝ, R., CICHA, I., KOVÁČ, M. & RÖGL, F. (eds) *The Karpathian – A Lower Miocene Stage of the Central Paratethys.* Masaryk University, Brno, 97–100.

ROETZEL. R. & PERVESLER, P. 2004. Storm-induced event deposits in the type area of the Grund Formation (Middle Miocene, Lower Badenian) in the Molasse Zone of Lower Austria. *Geologica Carpathica,* **55**, 87–102.

RÖGL, F. 1998. Paleogeographic considerations for Mediterranean and Paratethys seaways (Oligocene to Miocene). *Annalen Naturhistorisches Museum Wien*, 99A, 279–310.

RÖGL F., SPEZZAFERRI S. & CORIC S. 2002. Micropaleontology and biostratigraphy of the Karpatian-Badenian transition (Early-Middle Miocene boundary) in Austria (Central Paratethys). *Courier Forschungsinstitut Senckenberg*, **237**, 47–67.

ROLL, A. 1979. Versuche einer Volumenbilanz der Oberhreingrabens und seiner Schultern. *Geologisches Jahrbuch*, **A52**, 1–82.

ROLLE, F. 1858. Über die geologische Stellung der Sotzka-Schichten. Sitzungsberichte der Akademie der Wissenschaften, Matematisch-Naturwissenschaftliche Classe, **30**, 3–33.

ROTH, Z. 1980. *The Western Carpathians – a Tertiary structure of the Central Europe.* Knihovňa UUG, Geological Survey Prague, **55**.

ROTHAUSEN, K. & SONNE, V. 1984. Mainzer Becken. *Sammlung geologischer Führer*, **79**, 1–203.

ROURE, F., ROCA, E. & SASSI, W. 1993. The Neogene evolution of the outer Carpathians flysch units (Poland, Ukraine and Romania): Kinematics of a foreland/fold-and-thrust belt system. *Sedimentary Geology*, **86**, 177–201.

ROYDEN, L. H. 1988. Late Cenozoic tectonics of the Pannonian basin system. *In:* ROYDEN, L. & HORVÁTH, F. (eds) *The Pannonian Basin. A Study in Basin Evolution.* AAPG, Memoirs, **45**, 27–48.

ROYDEN, L. H. 1993*a*. The tectonic expression of slab pull at continental convergent boundaries. *Tectonics*, **12**, 303–325.

ROYDEN, L. H. 1993*b*. Evolution of retreating subduction boundaries formed during continental collision. *Tectonics*, **12**, 629–638.

RUDINEC, R. 1978. Paleogeographical, lithofacial and tectonic development of the Neogene in eastern Slovakia and its relation ti volcanism and deep tectonic. *Geologica Carpathica*, **29**, 225–240.

RUDINEC, R. 1984. *Petroleum Industry in Czechoslovakia.* Knihovnička zem. plyn. a nafty, Special Publications, **5**, 1–368.

RUDINEC, R. 1989. New view on the paleogeographic development of the Transcarpathian depression during the Neogene. *Mineralia Slovaca*, **21**, 27–42.

RUDINEC, R., TOMEK, Č. & JIŘÍČEK, R. 1981. Sedimentary and structural Evolution of the Transcarpathian Depression. *Earth Evolutionary Sciences*, **3–4**, 205–211.

RUSU, A. 1995. Eocene formations in the Călata region (NW Transylvania). A critical review. *Romanian Journal of Tectonics and Regional Geology*, **76**, 59–72.

RŮŽIČKA, M. 1989: Pliocén Hornomoravského úvalu a Mohelnické brázdy. *Sborník geologických věd, Antropozoikum*, **19**, 129–151.

SACCHI, M. 2001. *Late Miocene evolution of the western Pannonian basin, Hungary.* Doctoral thesis, Eötvös Loránd University, Budapest.

SACHSENHOFER, R. F. 1996. The Neogene Styrian Basin: An overview. *Mitteilungen der Gesellschaft der Bergbaustudenten Österreichs*, **41**, 19–32.

SACHSENHOFER, R. F., KOGLER, A., POLESNY, H., STRAUSS, P. & WAGREICH, M. 2000. The Neogene Fohnsdorf Basin: basin formation and basin inversion during lateral extrusion in the Eastern Alps. *International Journal of Earth Science*, **89**, 415–430.

SACHSENHOFER, R. F., JELEN, B., HASENHÜTTL, CH., DUNKL, I. & RAINER, T. 2001. Thermal history of Tertiary basins in Slovenia (Alpine-Dinaride-Pannonian junction). *Tectonophysics*, **334**, 77–99.

SAFTIĆ, B., VELIĆ, I., SZTANÓ, O., JUHÁSZ, G. & IVKOVIĆ, Ž. 2003. Tertiary subsurface facies, source rocks and hydrocarbon reservoirs in the SW part of the Pannonian Basin (Northern Croatia and South-western Hungary). *Geologia Croatica*, **56**, 101–122.

SAKAČ, K., BENIĆ, J., BAHUN, S. & PENCINGER, V. 1993. Stratigraphic and tectonic position of Paleogene Jelar beds in the Outer Dinarides. *Natura Croatica*, **2**(1), 55–72.

SANDERS, C. A. E. 1999. *Tectonics and erosion. Competitive forces in a compressive orogen. A fission track study of the Romanian Carpathians.* Doctoral thesis, Vrije Universiteit, Amsterdam.

SĂNDULESCU, M. 1984. *Geotectonica României.* Editura Academiei R.S.R., Bucureşti.

SĂNDULESCU, M. 1988. Cenozoic tectonic history of the Carpathians. *In:* ROYDEN L. & HORVÁTH F. (eds) *The Pannonian Basin. A Study in Basin Evolution.* AAPG, Memoirs, **45**, 17–25.

SAUER, R. 1980. *Zur Stratigraphie und Sedimentologie der Gießhübler Schichten im Bereich der Gießhübler Gosaumulde (Nördliche Kalkalpen).* Doctoral thesis, Univiversity of Vienna.

SAVIĆ, D. & DOMAZET, S. 1984. *Osnovna geološka karta SFRJ 1.100000, List Delnice L33–90.* Institute of Geology Zagreb, Federal Geological Survey Beograd.

ŠĆAVNIČAR, S., KRKALO, E., ŠĆAVNIČAR, B., HALLE, R. & TIBLJAŠ, D. 1983. Naslage s analcimom u Poljanskoj. *Rad Jugosl. akad. znan. umjetn.*, **404**, 137–169.

SCHÄFER, P. & KADOLSKY, D. 2002. Neudefinition von stratigraphischen Einheiten im Tertiär des Mainzer und Hanauer Beckens (Deutschland, Oligozän-Miozän) Teil 1: Oberrad-Formation [= Obere Cerithienschichten, oberer Teil] und Rüssingen-Formation [= Inflata-Schichten]. *Mainzer geowissenschaftliche Mitteilungen,* **31**, 73–98.

SCHÄFER, A., UTESCHER, T. & MÖRS, T. 2004. Stratigraphy of the Cenozoic Lower Rhine Basin, northwestern Germany. *Newsletter on Stratigraphy,* **40**, 73–110.

SCHAUB, H. 1981. Nummulites et Assilines de la Tethys paléogène. Taxinomie, phylogenèse et biostratigraphie. *Mémoires suisses de Paléonotologie*, **104**, 1–236.

SCHERBACHER, M. 2000. Rekonstruktion der oligozänen Umweltentwicklung im Ostalpenraum anhand von Foraminiferen, *Tübinger Mikropaläontologische Mitteilungen*, **23**.

SCHIAVINOTTO, F. 1978. Nephrolepidina nella Valle del Maso (Borgo Valsugana-Italia settentrionale). *Rivista Italiana di Paleontologia*, **81**, 729–750.

SCHLOSSER, M. 1925. Die Eocaenfaunen der bayrischen Alpen, I. Teil: die Faunen des Unter- und Mitteleocaen. II. Teil: Die Obereocaenfauna. *Abhandlungen der Bayerischen Akademie der Wissenschaften, mathematisch-naturwissenschaftliche Klasse*, **30**(7), 1–206.

SCHLUNEGGER, F. & PFIFFNER, A. 2001. The sedimentary response of the North Alpine Foreland basin to changes in erosional processes in the Alps. *IAS 2001, 21st Meeting*, Davos, 3–5 September 2001, Excursion guides, 85–99.

SCHLUNEGGER, F., BURBANK, D. W., MATTER, A., ENGESSER, B. & MÖDDEN, C. 1996. Magnetostratigraphic calibration of the Oligocene to Middle Miocene (30–15 MA) mammal biozones and depositional sequences of the Swiss Molasse basin. *Eclogae Geologicae Helvetiae*, **89**, 753–788.

SCHLUNEGGER, F., MATTER, A., BURBANK, D. W. & KLAPER, E. M. 1997. Magnetostratigraphic constraints on relationships between evolution of the central Swiss Molasse Basin and Alpine orogenic events. *GSA Bulletin*, **109**, 225–241.

SCHLUNEGGER, F., SLINGERLAND, R. & MATTER, A. 1998. Crustal thickening and crustal extension as controls on the evolution of the drainage network of the central Swiss Alps between 30 Ma and the present: constraints from the stratigraphy of the North Alpine Foreland Basin and the structural evolution of the Alps. *Basin Research*, **10**, 197–212.

SCHMID, H. P., HARZHAUSER, M. & KROH, A. 2001. Hypoxic events on a middle Miocene carbonate platform of the central Paratethys (Austria, Badenian, 14 Ma). *Annalen des Naturhistorischen Museums in Wien*, **102A**, 1–50.

SCHMIEDL, G., SCHERBACHER, M., *et al.* 2002. Paleoenvironmental evolution of the Paratethys in the Slovenian Basin during the Late Paleogene. *International Journal of Earth Sciences*, **91**, 123–132.

SCHMITZ, B., HEILMANN-CLAUSEN, C., KING, C., STEURBAUT, E., ANDREASSON, F. P., CORFIELD, R. M. & CARTLIDGE, J. E. 1996. Stable isotope and biotic evolution in the North Sea during the early Eocene Albaeck Hoved section, Denmark. *In:* KNOX, R. W. O'B., CORFIELD, R. M. & DUNAY, R. E. (eds) *Correlation of the Early Paleogene in Northwest Europe.* Geological Society, London, Special Publications, **101**, 275–306.

SCHOEPFER, P. 1989. *Sédimentologie et stratigraphie de la Molasse Marine supérieure (OMM) entre le Gibloux et l'Aar (Suisse).* Doctoral thesis, University of Fribourg.

SCHOLGER, R. & STINGL, K. 2003. Paleomagnetic reconstruction of geodynamic events in the Eastern Alpine Neogene. *EGS-AGU-EUG Joint Assembly, Nice, Geophysical Research Abstracts*, **5**, 05311.

SCHOLGER, R. & STINGL, K. 2004. New paleomagnetic results from the middle Miocene (Karpatian and Badenian) in Northern Austria. *Geologica Carpathica*, **55**, 1–8.

SCHOLGER, R., STINGL, K. & MAURITSCH, H. J. 2003. New palaeomagnetic results from the Eastern Alpine Neogene basins indicate rotations of micro-plates during the Miocene. 6th Alpine Workshop, Sopron. *Annale Universitatis Scientiarum Budapestinensis de Rolando Eötvös nominatae, sectio geologica,* **35**, 89–90.

SCHULER, M. 1990. Palynologie et biostratigraphie de l'Eocene et de l'Oligocene inférieur dans les fossés rhénan, rhodanien, et de Hesse. *Doc BRGM*, 1–190.

SCHULTZ, O. 1998. *Tertiärfossilien Österreichs: Wirbellose, niedere Wirbeltiere und marine Säugetiere.* Goldschneck-Verlag, Korb.

SCHWARZ, J. 1997. Charophyten aus dem Tertiär des Oberrheingrabens (Mitteleozän-Untermiozän). *Palaeontographica*, **B243**, 1–84.

SCHWEIGHAUSER, J. 1953. Mikropaläontologische und stratigraphische Untersucungen im Paleocaen und Eocaen des Vicentin (Norditalien) mit besonderer Berücksichtingun der Discocyclinen und Asterocyclinen. *Schweizerische Paläontologische Abhandlungen*, **70**, 1–97.

SCHWEITZER, C., ĆOSOVIĆ, V. & FELDMANN, R. 2005. *Harpactocarcinus* from the Eocene of Istria, Croatia, and the paleoecology of the Zanthopsidae VIA, 1959 (Crustacea: Decapoda: Brachyura). *Journal of Paleontology*, **79**(4), 663–669.

SCHWERD, K., DOPPLER, H. & UNGER, H.-J. 1996. Gesteinsfolge des Molassebeckens und der inneralpinen Tertiärbecken. *In:* FREUDENBERGER, W. & SCHWERD, K. (eds) *Erläuterungen zur Geologischen Karte von Bayern 1:500'000.* Bayerrisches Geologisches Landesamt, Munich, 141–149.

SCUDELER BACCELLE, L. & REATO, S. 1988. Cenozoic algal biostromes in the eastern Veneto (northern Italy): a possible example of nontropical carbonate sedimentation. *Sedimentary Geology*, **60**, 197–206.

SEGHEDI, I. & SZAKÁCS, A. 1991. The Dej tuff from Dej-Ciceu area. some petrographical, petrochemical and volcanological aspects. *In:* BEDELEAN, I., GHERGARI, L., MÂRZA, I., MÉSZÁROS, M., NICORICI, E. & PETRESCU, I. (eds) *The Volcanic Tuffs from the Transylvanian Basin, Romania.* Cluj Napoca, 135–146.

SEMMEL, A. 1983. Die plio-pleistozänen Deckschichten im Steinbruch Mainz-Weisenau. *Geologisches Jahrbuch Hessen,* **111**, 219–233.

SENEŠ, J. 1956. Remarks to geotectonic and paleogeographic development of the Eastern Slovakia Neogene. *Geologicke Práce*, **7**, 75–88.

SERRA-KIEL, J., HOTTINGER, L., *et al.* 1998. Biostratigraphy of the Tethyan Paleocene and Eocene. *Bulletin de la Societé géologique de France,* **169**, 281–299.

SHEVENELL, A. E., KENNETT, J. P. & LEA, D. W. 2004. Middle Miocene Southern Ocean cooling and Antarctic cryosphere expansion. *Science,* **305**, 1766–1770.

SIENA, F. & COLTORTI, M. 1989. Lithospheric mantle evolution. evidences from ultramafic xenoliths in the Lessinian volcanics (Northern Italy). *Chemical Geology*, **77**, 347–364.

SIENA, F. & COLTORTI, M. 1993. Thermobarometric evolution and metasomatic processes of upper mantle in different tectonic settings.

Evidence from spinel peridotite xenoliths. *European Journal of Mineralogy*, **5**, 1073–1090.

Šikić, D. 1965. Geologija područja s naslagama paleogena Istre, Hrvatskog primorja I Dalmacije. Doctoral thesis, University of Zagreb.

Šikić, D. 1968. Istarsko-dalmatinska orogenetska faza i stratigrafija eocena u Dinaridima. *1st Colloqium on Geology of Dinarides*, **1**, 135–142.

Šikić, D. 1969. O razvoju paleogena i lutetskim pokretima u Dalmaciji. *Geološki vjesnik*, **22**, 309–331.

Šikić, D., Polšak, A. & Magaš, N. 1969. *Osnovna geološka karta SFRJ 1.100000, List Labin L33–101*. Institute of Geology Zagreb, Federal Geological Survey Beograd.

Šikić, D., Pleničar, M. & Šparica, M. 1972. *Osnovna geološka karta SFRJ 1.100000, List Ilirska Bistrica L83–89*. Institute of Geology Zagreb, Federal Geological Survey Beograd.

Šikić, K., Basch, O. & Šimunić, An. 1979. *Osnovna geološka karta SFRJ 1.100000. Tumač za list Zagreb.* Institute of Geology Zagreb, Federal Geological Survey, Beograd.

Šimunić, A. 1992. *Geološki odnosi središnjeg dijela Hrvatskog zagorja*. Doctoral thesis, University of Zagreb.

Šimunić, A. & Pamić, J. 1993. Geology and petrology of Egerian-Eggenburgian andesites from the easternmost parts of the Periadriatic zone in Hrvatsko Zagorje (Croatia). *Acta Geologica Hungarica*, **36**, 315–330.

Šimunić, A., Avanić, R. & Šimunić, A. 1990. "Maceljski pješčenjaci" i vulkanizam zapadnog dijela Hrvatskog zagorja (Hrvatska, Jugoslavija). *Rad JAZU*, **449**, 179–194.

Šimunić, A., Avanić, R. & Ćosović, V. 2000. Eocene sediments from north-western part of Croatia. *In:* Bassi, D. (ed.) *5th Meeting of the IUGS-UNESCO, IGCP 393, July 18th–31st, 2000. Shallow water benthic communities at the Middle-Upper Eocene boundary. Southern and North-Eastern Italy, Slovenia, Croatia, Hungary. Field Trip Guidebook*, 135–139.

Sirel, E. 2004. *Türkiye'nin Mesozoyik ve Senozoyik Yeni Bentik Foraminiferleri*. TMMOB Jeoloki mühendisleri Odasi, Ankara.

Sissingh, W. 1998. Comparative Tertiary stratigraphy of the Rhine graben, Bresse graben and Molasse basin: correlation of Alpine foreland events. *Tectonophysics*, **300**, 249–284.

Sissingh, W. 2003. Tertiary paleogeographic and tectonostratigraphic evolution of the Rhenish Triple Junction. *Palaeogeography, Palaeoclimatology, Palaeoecology*, **196**, 229–263.

Skaberne, D. 1989. Megaturbidits in the Paleogene flysch in the region of Anhovo (W Slovenia, Yugoslavia). *Memorie della Socuetà Geoligica Italiana*, **40** (1987), 231–239.

Škerlj, Ž. 1985. Ablagerungen des Pannonien in Slowenien (Jugoslawien). *In:* Papp, Á., Jámbor, A. & Steininger, F. F. (eds) *Pannonien M6, Chronostratigraphie und Neostratotypen, Miozän der Zentralen Paratethys*, Akadémiai Kiadó, Budapest. 7, 85–89.

Ślączka, A. & Kaminski, M. A. 1998. *Guidebook to excursions in the Polish Flysch Carpathians*, Grzybowski Foundation, Special Publications, **6**.

Slávik, J. 1968. Chronology and tectonic background of the Neogene volcanism in Eastern Slovakia. *Geologicke Práce*, **44**, 199–214.

Sliggers, B. C. & van Leeuwen, R. J. W. 1987. Mollusc biozonation of the Miocene in the south-eastern Netherlands and correlation with the foraminiferal Biostratigraphy. *Mededelingen van de Werkgroep voor Tertiaire en Kwartaire Geologie*, **24**, 41–57.

Słodkowska, B. 2000. Paleocene in the Polish Palynological Research. *In:* Wand, W., Ouyang, S., Su, X. & Yu, G. (eds) *Abstracts 10th International Palynological Congress*, June 24–30, 2000, Nanjing, 153–154.

Sokač, B., Nikler, L., Velić, I. & Mamužić, P. 1974. *Osnovna geološka karta SFRJ 1.100000, List Gospić L33–127*. Institute of Geology Zagreb, Federal Geological Survey Beograd.

Soklić, I. 1955. Fauna molusaka sarmata sjeveroistočne Bosne i njen stratigrafski značaj. *Geološki glasnik*, **1**, 61–145.

Soklić, I. 1959. Paleogeografija tuzlanskog miocena i postanak sonog ležišta. *III kongres geologa Jugoslavije, Budva.*

Soklić, I. 1964. Postanak i struktura Tuzlanskog basena. *Geološki glasnik*, **10**, 5–26.

Soklić, I. 1970. Stratigrafija kvartara sjeveroistočne Bosne. *Geološki glasnik*, **14**, 57–77.

Soklić, I. 1977. Od ponta do danas – srednji i gornji pliocen, kvartar. *Geološki glasnik*, 217–239.

Soklić, I. 1982. Stratigrafija i starost sononosnih naslaga grada Tuzle. *Radovi Akademija nauka i umjetnosti Bosne i Hercegovine*, **7**, 135–151

Soklić, I. 2001. Fosilna flora i fauna Bosne i Hercegovine. *Monografija, ANU Bosne i Hercegovine*, **74**, 5–585.

Soklić, I. & Malez, M. 1969. Ein Fund der Art *Mastodon angustidens* in der Bunten Folge bei Tuzla (Mittleres Miozän). *Bulletin Scientes*, **14**, 380–382.

Sorbini, L. 1989. *I fossili di Bolca*. Museo Civico di Storia Naturale di Verona, Verona.

Soták, J., Križáni, I. & Spišiak, J. 1990. On position and material composition of the Merník conglomerates (the Central Carpathian Paleogene). *Acta Geologica et Geographica Universitatis Comenianae, Geoligica*, **45**, 117–125.

Soták, J., Biroň, A. & Spišiak, J. 1993. The Penninic "pull apart" dome in the pre-Neogene basement of the Transcarpathian depression (Eastern Slovakia). *Geologica Carpathica*, **44**, 11–16.

Soták, J., Spišiak, J. & Biroň, A. 1994. Metamorphic sequences with "Bundnerschiefer" lithology in the pre Neogene basement of the East Slovakian Basin. *Mitteilungen der Österreichischen Geologischen Gesellschaft*, **86**, 111–120.

Šparica, M., Drobne, K., Tunis, G., Bergant, S., Hajek-Tadesse, V. & Bačani, A. 2000. Stop 11 e 12. Sezioni Sterna/Šterna e Momiano/Momjan. Il Flysch Eocenico dell'Istria centrale (Croazia). *In:* Carulli, G. B. (ed.) *Guida alle escursioni 80° Riunione Estiva*, Trieste, 6–8 settembre 2000, 281–288.

Spezzaferri S., Coric S., Hohenegger, J. & Rögl, F. 2002. Basin-scale paleobiogeography and paleoecology: An example from Karpatian (Latest Burdigalian) benthic and planktonic foraminifera and calcareous nannoplankton from the Central Paratethys. *In:* Monegatti, P., Cecca, F. & Raffi, S. (eds) International Conference "Paleobiogeography & Paleoecology 2001", *GeoBios*, **35/24**, 241–256.

Spiegler, D. 1999. *Bolboforma* Biostratigraphy from the Hatton-Rockall Basin (North Atlantic). *Procceedings of the ODP, Scientific Results*, **162**, 35–49.

Spiegler, D. 2002. Correlation of Marine Miocene Bolboforma Zonation and Uvigerina Zonation in Northern Germany. *In:* Gürs, K. (ed.) *Northern European Cenozoic Stratigraphy.* Proceedings of the 8th biannual joint meeting of the RCNPS/RCNNS. Landesamt für Natur und Umwelt Schleswig-Holstein (Flintbek), 133–141.

Šribar, L. 1965. The boundary between Cretaceous and Tertiary in Goriška Brda. *Geologija*, **8**, 121–129.

Šribar, L. 1967. About the sediments in the Cretaceous-Tertiary boundary in southern Slovenia. *Geologija*, **10**, 161–166.

Stache, G. 1889. Die Liburnische Stufe und deren Grenz-Horizonte. *Abhandlungen der Geologischen Reichsanstalt*, **13**, 1–170.

Standke, G. 1997. Die Hainer Sande im Tagebau Witznitz – Ergebnisse der geologischen Aufschlußdokumentation stillgelegter Braunkohlentagebaue in Sachsen. *Mauritiana*, **16**, 241–259.

Standke, G. 1998. Die Tertiärprofile der samländischen Bernsteinküste bei Rauschen. *Schriftenreihe für Geowissenschaften*, **7**, 93–133.

Standke, G. 2001. Thierbacher Schichten und Hainer Sande (Oligozän – Eozän) im ehemaligen Braunkohlentagebau Bockwitz südlich von Leipzig. *Mauritiana*, **18**, 61–89.

Standke, G. 2002. Das Tertiär zwischen Leipzig und Altenburg. *Beiträge zur Geologie von Thüringen, Neue Folge*, 9, 41–73.

Standke, G. 2004. *Paläogeographisch-fazielle Modellierung des Unter-/Mittelmiozän-Grenzbereichs in der Lausitz (Briesker Folge/Formation)*. Doctoral thesis, TU Bergakademie Freiberg.

Standke, G., 2006. Paläogeographisch-fazielle Modellierung des Unter-/Mittelmiozän-Grenzbereichs in der Lausitz (Briesker Folge/Formation). *Schriftenreihe für Geowissenschaften*, **14**, 1–130.

Standke, G., 2008*a*. Paläogeografie des älteren Tertiärs (Paleozän bis Untermiozän) im mitteldeutschen Raum. Zeitschrift der Deutschen Gesellschaft für Geowissenschaften, **159**, 87–109.

Standke, G., 2008*b* (in press). Tertiär. *In*: Pälchen, W. & Walter, H. (eds): *Geologie von Sachsen*. Schweizerbart, Stuttgart.

Standke, G. & Suhr, P. 1998. Vulkane-Flüsse-Küstenmoore. Die fazielle Vielfalt am Südrand der Nordwest-Europäischen Tertiärsenke. Exkursion A10, GEO-Berlin'98. *Terra Nostra*, 98, 79–98.

Standke, G., Rascher, J. & Strauss, C. 1993. Relative sea-level fluctuations and brown-coal formation around the Early-Middle

Miocene boundary in the Lusatian Brown-Coal District. *Geologische Rundschau,* **82**, 295–305.

Standke, G., Rascher, J. & Volkmann, N. 2002. Lowstand cycles and coal formation in paralic environments. New aspects in sequence stratigraphy. *In:* Gürs, K. (ed.) *Northern European Cenozoic Stratigraphy.* Proceedings of the 8th biannual joint meeting of the RCNPS/RCNNS. Landesamt für Natur und Umwelt Schleswig-Holstein (Flintbek). 153–161.

Standke, G., Blumenstengel, H. & von Bülow, W. 2005. Das Tertiär Ostdeutschlands in der Stratigraphischen Tabelle von Deutschland 2002. *In:* Menning, M. & Deutsche Stratigraphische Kommission (eds) Erläuterungen zur Stratigraphischen Tabelle Deutschland 2002. *Newsletters on Stratigraphy,* **41**(1–3), 323–338.

Stefani, C. & Grandesso, P. 1991. Studio preliminare di due sezioni di Flysch bellunese. *Rendiconti della Società geologica Italiana,* **14**, 157–162.

Steininger, F. 1971. Holostratotypus und Faziostratotypen der Eggenburger Schichtengruppe im Raume von Eggenburg in Niederösterreich (Österreich). *In:* Steininger, F. & Senes, J. (eds) M1 Eggenburgien. Die Eggenburger Schichtengruppe und ihr Stratotypus. *Chronostratigraphie und Neostratotypen,* **2**, 104–166.

Steurbaut, E. & Verbeek, J. 1988. The nannoplankton distribution in sediments of the Antwerpen – Northern Kempen area (Belgium). *In:* Vinken, R. (ed.) The northwest European Tertiary Basin. Results of the International Geological Correlation Programme Project no. 124. *Geologisches Jahrbuch,* **A100**.

Stevanović, P. 1951. Pontische Stufe im engeren Sinne – Obere Congerien schichten Serbiens und der angrenzend Gebiete. Special issues, *Srpska akademija nauka*, 187, 1–366.

Stevanović, P. 1990. Discussion on the Pontian in the Pannonian Basin of the Western (Central) Paratethys. *In:* Malez, M. & Stevanović, P. (eds) *Chronostratigraphie und Neostratotypen, Neogen der Westlichen (»Zentrale«) Paratethys*, **8**, 31–40.

Stevanović, P. & Eremija, M. 1960. *Miocen Donje Tuzle. Annales géologique de la Péninsula balkanique*, **27**, 34–78.

Stevanović, P. & Eremija, M. 1977. Geološke karakteristike panona i ponta Bosne i Hercegovine. *Geologija BiH, Kenozojske periode*, **3**, 163–216.

Stevanović, P. & Škerlj, Ž. 1985. Beitrag zur Biostratigraphie der Pannon-Pontischen Ablagerungen in der Umgebung von Videm-Krško. *Razprave, 4. razreda Slovenske akademije znanosti in umetnosti,* 26, 281–304.

Stevanović, P. & Škerlj, Ž. 1990. The Pontian sediments in Slovenia. *In*: Stevanović, P., Nevesskaja, L.A., Marinescu, F., Sokac, A. & Jámbor, A. (eds) *Pontien, Pl 1. Chronostratigraphie und Neostratotypen, Neogen der Westlichen (Zentrale) Paratethys*, **8**, 458–462.

Stojčić, B. 1968. The first identification of Paleocene in the Inner Dinarides (the neighbourhood of Tešanj in Bosnia). *Geološki glasnik*, **12**, 85–87.

Storni, A. 2002. *Etude paléontologique et sédimentologique de la carrière d'Altkirch (Alsace, Paléogène) et cartographie des sédiments tertiaires et quaternaires de la région de Porrentruy.* Diploma thesis, University of Fribourg.

Strauss, P., Daxner-Höck, G. & Wagreich, M. 2003. Lithostratigraphie, Biostratigraphie und Sedimentologie des Miozäns im Fohnsdorfer Becken (Österreich). *Schriftenreihe der Erdwissenschaftlichen Kommissionen,* **16**, 111–140.

Strunck, P. & Matter, A. 2002. Depositional evolution of the western Swiss Molasse. *Eclogae Geologicae Helvetiae,* **95**,197–222.

Stuchlik, L. 1987. Przegląd badań paleobotanicznych osadów plioceńskich i wczesnoplejstoceńskich Polski środkowej i południowej. *In:* Jahn, A. & Dyjor, S. (eds) *Problemy młodszego neogenu i eoplejstocenu w Polsce*. Ossolineum, Wrocław, 53–63.

Studer, B. 1827. Remarques geognostiques sur quelques parties de la chaîne septentrionale des Alpes. *Annales Scientes Naturales Paris,* **11**, 1–47.

Stuijvenberg van, J. 1979. Geology of the Gurnigel area (Prealps, Switzerland). *Matériaux carte géologique Suisse, N.S.,* **151**, 1–111.

Stuijvenberg van, J. 1980. Stratigraphie et structure du Gurnigel aux Voirons, Haute-Savoie. *Bulletin Société fribourgeoise des Sciences Naturelles,* **69**, 80–96.

Stuijvenberg van, J., Morel, R. & du Chene, J. R. 1976. Contribution à l'étude du flysch de la région des Fayaux (Préalpes externes vaudoises). *Eclogae Geologicae Helvetiae*, **69**, 309–326.

Suhr, P. 2003. The Bohemian Massif as a Catchment Area for the NW European Tertiary Basin. *Geolines*, **15**, 147–159.

Šušnjar, M., Bukovac, J., *et al.* 1970. *Osnovna geološka karta SFRJ 1.100000, List Crikvenica L33–102.* Institute of Geology Zagreb, Federal Geological Survey Beograd.

Šušnjara, A. & Sakač, K. 1988. Miocenski slatkovodni sedimenti područja Sinja u srednjoj Dalmaciji (Miocene freshwater sediments in the vicinity of Sinj, Central Dalmatia). *Geološki vjesnik*, **41**, 51–74 [with English summary].

Šušnjara, A. & Šćavničar, B. 1974. Tufovi u neogenskim naslagama srednje Dalmacije (južna Hrvatska). *Geološki vjesnik*, **27**, 239–253.

Sviridenko, V. G. 1976. Geological structure of the Pre-Neogene substratum of the Transcarpathian Depression. *Mineralia Slovaca*, **8**, 395–406.

Szabó, C., Harangi, S. & Csontos, L. 1992. Review of Neogene and Quaternary volcanism of the Carpathian - Pannonian region. *Tectonophysics*, **208**, 243–256.

Szentgyörgyi, K. & Juhász, G. K. 1988. Sedimentological characteristics of the Neogene sequences in SW Transdanubia, Hungary. *Acta Geologica Hungarica*, **31**, 209–225.

Szepesházy, K. 1973. *A Tiszántúl északi részének felsőkréta és paleogén korú képződményei*. Akadémiai Kiadó, Budapest.

Sztanó, O. 1994. The tide-influenced Pétervására sandstone, Early Miocene, Northern Hungary: sedimentology, paleogeography and basin development. *Geologica Ultraiectina*, **120**, 1–153.

Tanács, J. & Rálisch, E. 1990. *Kainozoós képződmények alulnézeti térképe*. [Worm-eye map of the Cenozoic formations of Hungary] Hungarian Geological Institute, Budapest.

Tari, G. 1994. *Alpine tectonics of the Pannonian Basin.* Doctoral thesis, Rice University, Houston.

Tari, G., Horváth, F. & Rumpler, J. 1992. Styles of extension in the Pannonian Basin. *Tectonophysics*, **208**, 203–219.

Tari, V. 2002. Evolution of the northern and western Dinarides. a tectonostratigraphic approach. *EGS Stephan Mueller Special Publisher Series,* **1**, 1–21.

Tari, V. & Pamić, J. 1998. Geodynamic evolution of the northern Dinarides and the southern part of the Pannonian Basin. *Tectonophysics,* **297**, 269–281.

Tarlao, A., Tunis, G. & Venturini, S. 2005. Dropstones, pseudoplanktonic forms and deep-water decapod crustaceans within a Lutetian condensed succession of central Istria (Croatia): relation to palaeoenvironmental evolution and paleogeography. *Palaeogeography, Palaeclimatology, Palaeoecology,* **218**(3–4), 325–345.

Teller, F. 1896. *Erläuterungen zur Geologischen Karte der östlichen Ausläufer der Karnischen und Julischen Alpen (Ostkarawanken und Steier Alpen).* Geologische Reichsanstalt, Vienna.

Tentor, M., Tunis, G. & Venturini, S. 1994. Schema stratigrafico e tettonico del Carso Isontino. *Natura Nascosta,* **9**, 1–32.

Tišljar, J., Vlahović, I., Velić, I. & Sokač, B. 2002. Carbonate platform megafacies of the Jurassic and Cretaceous. Deposits of the Dinarides. *Geologica Croatica*, **55**(2), 139–170.

Tobien, H. 1987. The position of the "Grande Coupure" in the Paleogene of the upper Rhine Graben and the Mainz Basin. *Münchner geowissenschaftliche Abhandlungen*, **A10**, 197–202.

Tobien, H. 1988. Mammals: the Rhinegraben and the Mainz Basin *In:* Vinken, R. (ed.) The Northwest European Tertiary basin. *Geologisches Jahrbuch*, **A100**, 395–398.

Tollmann, A. 1964. Zur alpidischen Phasengliederung in den Ostalpen. *Anzeiger der Österreichischen Akademie der Wissenschaften,* **1964**(10), 237–246.

Tollmann, A. 1976. *Analyse des klassischen nordalpinen Mesozoikums: Stratigraphie, Fauna und Fazies der Nördlichen Kalkalpen.* Deuticke, Vienna.

Tollmann, A. 1985. *Geologie von Österreich. Band II: Außerzentralalpiner Anteil.* Deuticke, Wien.

Tomek, Č. & Hall, J. 1993. Subducted continental margin imaged in the Carpathians of Czechoslovakia. *Geology,* **21**, 535–538.

Tomljenović, B. & Csontos, L. 2001. Neogene – Quaternary structures in the border zone between Alps, Dinarides and Pannonian Basin (Hrvatsko zagorje and Karlovac basins, Croatia). *International Journal of Earth Sciences*, **90**, 560–578.

Tragelehn, H. 1996. *Maastricht und Paläozän am Südrand der Nördlichen Kalkalpen (Niederösterreich, Steiermark).* Doctoral thesis, Univiversity of Erlangen.

TRAUB, F. 1953. Die Schuppenzone im Helvetikum von St. Pankraz am Haunsberg, nördlich von Salzburg. *Geologica Bavarica*, **15**, 1–38.

TRAUB, F. 1990. Zur Geologie und Stratigraphie der paläozänen Oichinger Schichten im Helvetikum des Haunsberges, nördlich von Salzburg, Österreich. *Mitteilungen der Bayerischen Staatssammlung für Paläontologie und Historische Geologie*, **30**, 137–147.

TRAUTWEIN, B., DUNKL, I., KUHLEMANN, J. & FRISCH, W. 2001. Geodynamic evolution of the Rhenodanubian Flysch Zone - evidence from apatite and zircon fission-track geochronology and morphology studies on zircon. *In:* PILLER, W. E. & RASSER, M. W. (eds) *Paleogene of the Eastern Alps.* Österreichische Akademie der Wissenschaften, Schriftenreihe der Erdwissenschaftlichen Kommission, **14**, 111–128.

TREVISANI, E. 1993. Analisi di facies e ciclicità delle Arenarie di Mortisa (Priaboniano superiore, Prealpi Venete). *Memorie di Scienze Geologiche*, **45**, 57–65

TREVISANI, E. 1994. Evoluzione paleogeografica e stratigrafia sequenziale del margine orientale del Lessini Shelf durante l'Eocene inferiore-medio (Prealpi Venete). *Memorie di Scienze Geologiche*, **46**, 1–15.

TREVISANI, E. 1997. Il margine settentrionale del Lessini Shelf. evoluzione paleogeografica e dinamica deposizionale del Paleogene della Valsugana (Trentino sud-orientale). *Atti Ticinensi di Scienze della Terra, serie speciale,* **5**, 115–127.

TREVISANI, E. 2000. The southern Monte Grappa massif. In: Bassi D. (ed) Field trip guide book. Shallow water benthic communities at the Middle-Upper Eocene boundary. *Annali dell'Università di Ferrara, Scienze della Terra, supplemento,* **8**, 87–93.

TRNKA, M. & HOUZAR, S. 1991. Moravian Moldavites. *Vlastivědná knihovna moravská*, **76**, 1–115.

TRÜMPY, R. 1980. *Geology of Switzerland*. Wepf & Co, Basel.

TUNIS, G. & VENTURINI, S. 1984. Stratigrafia e sedimentologia del flysch Maastrichtiano - Paleocenico del Friuli orientali. *Gortania, Atti del Museo Friulare de Storia Naturale*, **5**, 5–58.

TUNIS, G. & VENTURINI, S. 1992. Evolution of the southern margin of the Julian basin with emphasis on the megabeds and turbiditic sequence of the Southern Julian Prealps. *Geologia Croatica*, **45**, 127–150.

TUNIS, G., UCHMAN, A., CAFFAU, M., FAVARIN, S. & PICCOLI, C. 2002. Stop 6. Bagnoli della Rosandra. *In:* HOHENEGGER, J., MELIS, R., PERVESLER, P. & PUGLIESE, N. (eds) *3rd International Congress "Environmental Micropaleontogy, Microbiology and Meiobenthology", Field Excursion Guide*, 37–41.

TURNŠEK, D. & DROBNE, K. 1998. Paleocene corals from the northern Adriatic platform. *In:* HOTTINGER, L. & DROBNE, K. (eds). Paleogene shallow benthos of the Tethys, 2. *Contributions IGCP 286. Dela-Opera 4. razreda SAZU,* **34**(2), 129–154.

UNGARO, S. 1969. Étude micropaléontologique et stratigraphique de l'Éocène supérieur (Priabonien) de Mossano (Colli Berici). *Mémoires du Bureau des Recherches géologiques et Minières*, **69**, 267–280.

UNGARO, S. 1978. L'Oligocene dei Colli Berici. *Rivista Italiana di Paleontologia*, **84**, 199–278.

UNGARO, S. 1990. Microfaune e biozone dell'Eocene inferiore (M. Lessini meridionali, Verona). *Annali dell'Università di Ferrara, sezione Scienze della Terra*, **2**, 37–45.

UNGARO, S. 2001. Le biofacies paleoceniche ed eoceniche dei Monti Lessini (Veneto, Italia). *Annali dell'Università di Ferrara, sezione Scienze della Terra*, **9**, 1–40.

UNGARO, S. & BOSELLINI, A. 1965. Studio micropaleontologico e stratigrafico sul limite Eocene-Oligocene nei Colli Berici occidentali. *Annali dell'Università di Ferrara (Nuova Serie), sezione 9*, **3**, 157–183.

UNGARO, S. & GARAVELLO, A. 1989. Biostratigrafia e paleoambienti del Paleogene nella zona pedemontana meridionale dell'Altipiano di Asiago (Vicenza). *Atti 3° Simposio di Ecologia e Paleoecologia delle Comunità Bentoniche, Catania-Taormina 1985*, 773–801.

UNGER, F. 1850. Die Fossilen Flora von Sotzka. *Denkschriften der Kaiserlichen Akademie der Wissenschaften, Mathematisch-Naturwissenschaftliche Classe*, **2**, 130–197.

VAN COUVERING, J. A., AUBRY, M.-P., BERGGREN, W. A., BUJAK, C. W., NAESER, C. W. & WIESER, T. 1981. The Terminal Eocene Event and the Polish connection. *Palaeography, Palaeoclimatology, Palaeoecology,* **36**, 321–362.

VAN DER VOO, R. 1993. *Paleomagnetism of the Atlantic, Tethys and Iapetus Oceans*. Cambridge University Press, Cambridge.

VAN LEEUWEN, R. J. W. 2001. Calcareous foraminiferal micropaleontology of Nieder Ochtenhausen and correlation with the Standard Zonation of The Netherlands. *In:* MEYER, K.-J. (coord.) Forschungsbohrung Nieder Ochtenhausen. Ein Beitrag zur Miozän-Stratigraphie in NW-Deutschland. *Geologisches Jahrbuch*, **A152**, 159–173.

VAN VLIET-LANOË, B., VANDENBERGHE, N., *et al.* 2002. Palaeogeographic evolution of northwestern Europe during the Upper Cenozoic. *Geodiversitas,* **24**, 511–541.

VANDENBERGHE, N., LAGA, P., STEURBAUT, E., HARDENBOL, J. & VAIL, P. R. 1998. Tertiary sequence stratigraphy at the southern border of the North Sea Basin. *In:* GRACIANSKY, P.-C., HARDENBOL, J., JACQUIN, T. & VAIL P. R. (ed) *Mesozoic and Cenozoic Sequence Stratigraphy of European Basins*. SEPM, Special Publications, 60, 119–154.

VANDENBERGHE, N., HERMAN, J. & STEURBAUT, E. 2002. Detailed analysis of the Rupelian Ru-1 transgressive surface in the Type Area (Belgium). *In:* GÜRS, K. (ed.) *Northern European Cenozoic Stratigraphy*. Proceedings of the 8th biannual joint meeting of the RCNPS/RCNNS. Landesamt für Natur und Umwelt Schleswig-Holstein (Flintbek), 67–81.

VANDENBERGHE, N., BRINKHUIS, H. & STEURBAUT, E. 2003. The Eocene/Oligocene boundary in the North Sea area. A sequence stratigraphic approach. *In:* PROTHERO, D. R., IVANY, L. C. & NESBITT, E. A. (eds) *From Greenhouse to Icehouse. The Marine Eocene–Oligocene Transition*. Columbia University Press, New York, 419–437.

VARIĆAK, D. 1966. Petrološka studija Mozajičkog granitskog masiva. *Geološki glasnik*, **9**, 15–129

VASHCHENKO, V.O. & HNYLKO, O. M. 2003. About stratigraphy and sedimentary features of the Neogene molasses of the Boryslav-Pokuttya and Sambir nappes of the Ukrainian Fore-Carpathians. *Geology & Geochemistry of Combustible Minerals*, **1**, 87–101 [in Ukrainian].

VASS, D. 2002. Lithostratigraphy of Western Carpathians: Neogene and Buda Paleogene. *Štàny geologický ústav Dionýza Štúra*, Budapest, 1–202.

VASS, D. & BELÁČEK, B. 1997. Konvolútne deformácie v medokýšskych vrstvách Ipel'skej kotliny. *Mineralia Slovaca*, **6**, 391–400.

VASS, D. & ČVERČKO, J. 1985. Neogene lithostratigraphic units in the East Slovakian Lowlands. *Geologicke Práce*, **82**, 111–126.

VASS, D. & ELEČKO, M. 1982. Litostratigrafické jednotky kišcelu až egenburgu Rimavskej kotliny a cerovej vrchoviny (južné Slovesnko). *Geologicke Práce*, **77**, 111–124.

VASS, D. & ELEČKO, M. 1992. Explanations to geological map of the Lučenecká kotlina Basin and the Cerová vrchovina Upland 1:50000. GUDŠ, Bratislava.

VASS, D., KONEČNÝ, V., ŠEFARA, J., PRISTAŠ, J., ŠKVARKA, L. & FILO, M. 1979. *Geologická stavba Ipel'skej kotliny a Krupinskej planiny.* GUDŠ, Bratislava

VASS, D. KONEČNÝ, V. & PRISTAŠ, J. 1983. Explanations to geological map of the Ipel'ská kotlina Basin and the Krupinská planina Upland 1:50 000. GUDŠ, Bratislava

VASS, D., ELEČKO, M., KANTOROVÁ, V., LEHOTAYOVÁ, R. & KLUBERT, J. 1987. The first finding of marine Ottnangian in the South Slovak Basin. *Mineralia Slovaca*, **19**, 417–422.

VASS, D., KOVÁČ, M., KONEČNÝ, V. & LEXA, J. 1988. Molasse basins and volcanic activity in Western Carpathian Neogene - its evolution and geodynamic chracter. *Geologica Carpathica*, **39**, 539–561.

VASS, D., PERESZLÉNYI, M., KOVÁČ, M. & KRÁL, M. 1990. Outline of Danube basin geology. Foldtani Kozlony. *Bulletin Hungarian Geological Society,* **120**, 193–214.

VASS, D., HÓK, J., KOVÁČ, P. & ELEČKO, M. 1993*a*. The Paleogene and Neogene tectonic events of the Southern Slovakia depressions in the light of the stress-field analyses. *Mineralia Slovaca*, **25**, 79–92.

VASS, D., ELEČKO, M., *et al.* 1998. *Geology of Rimavská kotlina depression*. Slovak Geological Survey, 5–160.

VEKLICH, M. F., VELIKANOV, V. A., *et al.* 1993. *Stratigraphic schemes of the Phanerozoic and Precambrian of the Ukraine.* Interdepartmental Stratigraphic Committee of the Ukraine, Ukrainian State Commitee on Geology and Utilization of Bowels of the Earth, Academy of Sciences of Ukraine, Kiev [in Russian].

VELIĆ, I., TIŠLJAR, J., MATIČEC, D. & VLAHOVIĆ, I. 1995. Opći prikaz geološke građe Istre (A review of the geology of Istria). *In:* Vlahović, I. & Velić, I. (eds) *1st Croatian Geological Congress, Excursion Guide-Book,* Zagreb, 5–30.

Velić, I., Tišljar, J., Vlahović, I., Matičec, D., Korbar, T., Moro, A. & Ćosović, V. 2002. Geological evolution of Istria (NW Part of the Adriatic Carbonate Platform, Croatia). *In:* Vlahović, I. & Korbar, T. (eds), *6th International Congress on Rudists, Rovinj. Abstracts and Excursion Guidebook,* Zagreb, 83–93.

Velić, I., Tišljar, J., Vlahović, I., Matičec, D., & Bergant, S. 2003. Evolution of the Istrian part of the Adriatic carbonate platform from the Middle Jurassic to the Santonian and formation of the Flysch Basin during the Eocene. Main events and regional comparison. *In:* Vlahović, I. & Tišljar, J. (eds) *Evolution of depositional environments from the Palaeozoic to the Quaternary in the Karst Dinarides and the Pannonian Basin.* 22nd IAS Meeting of Sedimentology, Opatija, 17–19 September 2003, Field Trip Guidebook, 3–17.

Velić, J. & Durn, G. 1993. Alternating lacustrine-marsh sedimentation and subaeral exposure phases during Quaternary. Prečko, Zagreb, Croatia. *Geologia Croatica*, **46**, 71–90.

Velić, J. & Saftić, B. 1999. Subsurface spreading and facies characteristics of Middle Pleistocene deposits between Zaprešić and Samobor. *Geološki vjesnik*, **44**, 69–82.

Velić, J., Tišljar, J., Dragičević, I. & Blašković, I. 2000. Shoreline cross-bedded biocalcarenites (Middle Miocene) in the Podvrško - Šnjegavić area, Mt. Psunj, and their petroleum significance (Požega subdepression - Eastern Croatia). *Geologica Croatica*, **53**, 281–293.

Venturini, S. & Tunis, G. 1991. Nuovi dati stratigrafici, paleoambientali e tettonici sul Flysch di Cormons (Friuli orientale). *Gortania, Atti del Museo Friulano di Storia Naturale*, **11**, 5–24.

Venturini, S. & Tunis, G. 1992. La composizione dei conglomerati cenozoici del Friuli: dati preliminari. *Studi Geologici Camerti, Vol. spec. (1992/2), CROP I-1A*, 285–295.

Venturini, S. & Tunis, G. 2002. La sequenza giurassico-paleogenica. *In:* Vai, G. B., Venturini, C., Carulli, G. B. & Zanferrari, A. (eds) *Guide geologiche regionali. Alpi e Prealpi Carniche e Giulie. Friuli Venezia Giulia*. Società Geologica Italiana, **9**, 49–55.

Vialov, O. S. 1986. The Carpathians, Subcarpathian and Transcarpathian Foredeepes and Volhyno-Podolian Plate. *In:* Muratov, M. V. & Nevesskaja, L. A. (eds) *Stratigraphy of the USSR Neogene system*, Nedra, Moscow, **1**, 54–96 [in Russian].

Vlahović, I., Velić, I, Tišljar, J. & Matičec, D. 1999. Lithology and origin of Tertiary Jelar Breccia within the framework of tectogenesis of Dinarides. *In: Some Carbonate and Clastic Successions of the External Dinarides. Velebit Mt., Island of Rab. Harold Reading's IAS Lecture Tour '99 (Croatia), Fieldtrip Guidebook*, 23–25.

Vlahović, I., Tišljar, J., Velić, I. & Matičec, D. 2002. The Karst Dinarides are composed of relics of a single Mesozoic platform: Facts and consequences. *Geologia Croatica*, **55**(2), 171–183.

Vlahović, I., Tišljar, J., Velić, I. & Matičec, D. 2005. Evolution of the Adriatic Carbonate Platform: Palaeogeography, main events and depositional dynamics. *Palaeogeography, Palaeoclimatology, Palaeoecology*, **220**, 333–360.

Vogeltanz, R. 1970. Sedimentologie und Paläogeographie eines eozänen Sublitorals im Helvetikum von Salzburg (Österreich). *Verhandlungen der Geologischen Bundesanstalt*, **1970**(3), 373–451.

Von Blanckenburg, F. & Davies, J. W. 1995. Slab breakoff. a model for syncollisional magmatism and tectonics in the Alps. *Tectonics,* **14**, 120–131

Voznesensky, A. I. 1988. History of formation of Neogene deposits in the Trans-Carpathian foredeep. Nauka, Moscow [in Russian].

Vrabac, S. 1989. *Paleogeografija juznog oboda Panonskog basena u badenu i sarmatu.* Doctoral thesis, University of Tuzla.

Vrabac, S. 1991. O nalasku marinskih fosila u sonoj formaciji tuzlanskog basena sa osvrtom na starost i genezu ležišta kamene soli. *Geol. anali Balk. Pol.*, **55**.

Vrabac, S. 1999. Facijalne i biostratigrafske odlike badena i sarmata Sjeverne Bosne.Univerzitet u Tuzli, Tuzla.

Vrabac, S., Ćorić, S. & Ferhatbegović, Z. 2003. The Karpatian in Bosnia and Herzegovina. *In:* Brzobohatý, R., Cicha, I., Kováč, M. & Rögl, F. (eds) *The Karpatian. A Lower Miocene Stage of the Central Paratethys*, Masaryk University, Brno, 145–147.

Vrabec, M. 1994. Some thoughts on the pull-apart origin of Karst Poljes along the Idrija strike-slip fault zone in Slovenia. *Acta Carsologica, Classe 4*, **23**, 155–167.

Vrabec, M. 1999. Style of postsedimentary deformation in the Plio-Quaternary Velenje basin, Slovenia. *Neues Jahrbuch für Geologie und Paläontologie, Monatshefte*, **8**, 449–463.

Vrsaljko, D. 1999. The Pannonian palaeoecology and biostratigraphy of molluscs from Kostanjek - Medvednica Mt., Croatia. *Geologia Croatica*, **52**(1), 9–27.

Wagner, L. R. 1996. Stratigraphy and hydrocarbons in Upper Austrian Molasse Foredeep (Active margin). *In:* Wessely, G. & Liebl, W. (eds) *Oil and Gas in Alpidic Thrustbelts and Basins of Central and Eastern Europe*. European Association of Geoscientists and Engineers, Special Publications, **5**, 217–235.

Wagner, L. R. 1998. Tectono-stratigraphy and hydrocarbons in the Molasse Foredeep of Salzburg, Upper and Lower Austria. *In*: Mascle, A., Puigdefàbregas, C., Luterbacher, H. P. & Fernàndez, M. (eds) *Cenozoic Foreland Basins of Western Europe*. Geological Society, London, Special Publications, **134**, 339–369.

Wagreich, M. 1993. Subcrustal tectonic erosion in orogenic belts - A model for the Late Cretaceous subsidence of the Northern Calcareous Alps (Austria). *Geology,* **21**, 941–944.

Wagreich, M. 1995. Subduction tectonic erosion and Late Cretaceous subsidence along the northern Austroalpine margin (Eastern Alps, Austria). *Tectonophysics*, **242**, 63–78.

Wagreich, M. 2001. Paleocene - Eocene paleogeography of the Northern Calcareous Alps (Gosau Group, Austria). *In:* Piller, W. E. & Rasser, M. W. (eds) *Paleogene of the Eastern Alps*. Österreichische Akademie der Wissenschaften, Schriftenreihe der Erdwissenschaftlichen Kommissionen, **14**, 57–75.

Wagreich, M. & Faupl, P. 1994. Palaeogeography and geodynamic evolution of the Gosau Group of the Northern Calcareous Alps (Late Cretaceous, Eastern Alps, Austria). *Paleogeography, Paleoclimatology, Paleoecology*, **110**, 235–254.

Wagreich, M. & Krenmayr, H.-G. 1993. Nannofossil biostratigraphy of the Late Cretaceous Nierental Formation, Northern Calcareous Alps (Bavaria, Austria). *Zitteliana*, **20**, 67–77.

Wagreich, M. & Krenmayr, H.-G. 2005. Upper Cretaceous Oceanic Red Beds (CORB) in the Northern Calcareous Alps (Nierental Formation, Austria): slope topography and clastic input as primary controlling factors. *Cretaceous Research*, **26**, 57–64.

Wagreich, M. & Marschalko, R. 1995. Late Cretaceous to Early Tertiary palaeogeography of the Western Carpathians (Slovakia) and the Eastern Alps (Austria): implications from heavy mineral data. *Geologische Rundschau*, **84**, 187–199.

Wagreich, M. & Siegl-Farkas, A. 1999. Subsidence analysis of Upper Cretaceous deposits of the Transdanubian Central Range (Hungary). *Abhandlungen der Geologischen Bundesanstalt*, **56**(2), 435–438.

Weber, H. 1977. *Salzstrukturen, Erdöl und Kreidebasis in Schleswig-Holstein, 1.500,000.* Übersichtskarten zur Geologie von Schleswig-Holstein.

Weidmann, M., Homewood, P., Caron, C. & Baud, A. 1976. Réhabilitation de la « Zone submédiane » des Préalpes. *Eclogae Geologicae Helvetiae*, **69**, 265–277.

Weidmann, M., Franzen, E. & Berger, J-P. 1991. Sur l'âge des Couches à Cérithes ou Couches des Diablerets de l'Eocène alpin. *Eclogae Geologicae Helvetiae*, **84**, 893–919.

Weigel, O. 1937. Stratigraphie und Tektonik des Beckens von Gosau. *Jahrbuch der Geologischen Bundeanstalt,* **87**, 11–40.

Weissenbäck, M. 1996. Lower to Middle Miocene sedimentation model of the central Vienna Basin. *In:* Wessely, G. & Liebl, W. (eds) *Oil and Gas in Alpidic Thrustbelts and Basins of the Central and Eastern Europe*. European Association of Geoscientists and Engineers, Special Publications, **5**, 355–363.

Wernicke, G. 1985. Uniform sense simple shear of contonental lithosphere. *Canadian Journal of Earth Science,* **22**, 108–125.

Wessely, G. 1974. Rand und Untergrund des Wiener Beckens - Verbindungen und Vergleiche. *Mitteilungen der Österreichischen Geologischen Gesellschaft*, **66–67**, 265–287.

Wierzchołowski, B. 1993. Stanowisko systematyczne i geneza sudeckich skał wulkanicznych. *Archiwum Mineralogiczne*, **49**, 199–235.

Wildi, G. 1985. Heavy mineral distribution and dispersal pattern in penninic and ligurian flysch basins (Alps, northern Apennines). *Giornale di Geologia*, 3, **47**(1–2), 77–99.

Wilkens, E. 1989. Entstehung von Großforaminiferen-Akkumulationen, Biofabric-Entwicklung und Bioklastaggregaten im Alttertiär des

Sonnberges. *Arbeitstagung der Geologischen Bundesanstalt*, 100–106.

Wilkens, E. 1991. *Das zentralalpine Paläogen der Ostalpen: Stratigraphie, Sedimentologie und Mikrofazies Großforaminiferen-reicher Sedimente*. Doctoral thesis, University of Hamburg.

Wille, U. 1968. Die Foraminiferenfauna des Eozäns von Schorn bei Abtenau (Salzburg, Österreich). *Jahrbuch der Geologischen Bundeanstalt*, **111**, 213–291.

Wille-Janoschek, U. 1966. Stratigraphie und Tektonik der Schichten der Oberkreide und des Alttertiärs im Raume von Gosau und Abtenau (Salzburg). *Jahrbuch der Geologischen Bundeanstalt*, **109**, 91–172.

Willingshofer, E., Andriessen, P., Cloetingh, S. & Neubauer, F. 2001. Detrital fission track thermochronology of Upper Cretaceous synorogenic sediments in the South Carpathians (Romania): inferences on the tectonic evolution of a collisional hinterland. *Basin Research*, **13**, 379–395.

Wilson, M. & Bianchini, G. 1999. Tertiary-Quaternary magmatism within the Mediterranean and surrounding regions. *In:* Durand, B., Jolivet, L., Horváth, F. & Séranne, M. (eds) *The Mediterranean Basin. Tertiary Extension within the Alpine Orogen*. Geological Society, London, Special Publications, **156**, 141–168.

Winkler, W. 1983. Stratigraphie, Sedimentologie und Sedimentpetrographie des Schlieren-Flysches (Zentralschweiz). *Beitrag zur geologischen Karte der Schweiz, N. F.*, **158**, 1–105.

Winterer, E. L. & Bosellini, A. 1981. Subsidence and sedimentation on Jurassic passive continental margin, southern Alps, Italy. *AAPG Bulletin*, **65**, 394–421.

Wold, C. N. 1995. Palaeobathymetric reconstruction on a gridded database. the northern North Atlantic and southern Greenland-Iceland-Norwegian sea. *In*: Scrutton R. A., Stoker, M. S., Shimmield, G. B. & Tudhope, A. W. (eds) *The Tectonics, Sedimentation and Palaeoceanography of the North Atlantic Region*. Geological Society, London, Special Publications, **90**, 271–302.

Zachos, J., Pagani, M., Sloan, L., Thomas, E. & Billups, K. 2001. Trends, rhythms, and aberrations in global climate 65 ma to present. *Science*, **292**, 686–693.

Zagwijn, W. H. & Hager, H. 1987. Correlations of continental and marine Neogene deposits in the south-eastern Netherlands and the Lower Rhine District. *Mededelingen van de Werkgroep voor Tertiaire en Kwartaire Geologie*, **24**, 59–78.

Zampieri, D. 1995. Tertiary extension in the southern Trento Platform, Southern Alps, Italy. *Tectonics*, **14**, 645–657.

Zampieri, D. 2000. Segmentation and linkage of the Lessini Mountains normal faults, Southern Alps, Italy. *Tectonophysics*, **319**, 19–31.

Ziegler, J. H. 1975. Alttertiäre Eisenerze am bayerischen Alpenrand. *Geologisches Jahrbuch* (D), **10**, 239–270.

Ziegler, J. H. 1983. Die alttertiären Eisenerze des Achtal-Kressenberger Bergbaureviers. *Geologisches Jahrbuch* (D), **61**, 5–22.

Živković, S. 2004. *Male bentičke foraminifere u eocenskim klastitima zapadne Hrvatske. Paleoekologija taložnog bazena*. Doctoral thesis, University of Zagreb.

Živković, S. & Babić, Lj. 2003. Paleoceanographic implications of smaller benthic and planktonic foraminifera from the Eocene Pazin Basin (Coastal Dinarides, Croatia). *Facies*, **49**, 49–60.

Zlinská, A. 1992. Zur biostratigraphischen Gliederung des Neogens des Ostslowakischen Beckens. *Geologiche Práce*, **96**, 51–57.

Zwaan der vaan, G., Jorissen, F. & de Stigter, H. 1990. The depth dependency of planktonic/benthic foraminiferal ratios. Constraints and applications. *Marine Geology*, **95**, 1–16.

Żytko K. 1997. Electrical conductivity anomaly of the northern Carpathians and the deep structure of the orogen. *Annales Societatis Geologorum Poloniae*, **67**, 25–44.

# 18 Alpine tectonics of the Alps and Western Carpathians

NIKOLAUS FROITZHEIM (co-ordinator),
DUŠAN PLAŠIENKA & RALF SCHUSTER

The Alps and Western Carpathians constitute that part of the Alpine-Mediterranean orogenic belt which advances furthest to the north into Central Europe. They were formed by a series of Jurassic to Tertiary subduction and collision events affecting several Mesozoic ocean basins, continental margins, and continental fragments. The Western Alps form a pronounced, westward-convex arc around which the strike of the tectonic units changes by almost 180° (Fig. 18.1). The Western Carpathians are a northward-convex arc of similar size but with minor curvature. The two arcs are connected by an almost straight, WSW–ENE striking portion including the Eastern Alps

Stresses produced by tectonic processes in the Alps also influenced the tectonics of large parts of central and northern Europe, leading, for example, to basin inversion and strike-slip faulting. In this chapter, we will discuss the present-day structure of the different tectonic units in the Alps and Western Carpathians in relation to their palaeotectonic history in order to illustrate the plate tectonic evolution using geological data. Many tectonic problems of the Alps and Western Carpathians are still unsolved, although dramatic progress has been made, especially over the last *c*. 20 years. Therefore, some of the interpretations presented below are still controversial and do not always express the opinion of all three authors. Given that the main theme of this book is Central Europe, the Southern and Western Alps are discussed in less detail than those parts of the Alps which belong to Central Europe: the Central Alps, the Eastern Alps and the Western Carpathians.

## The Alps (N.F., R.S.)

### *Geographic outline*

The Alps form an arcuate mountain chain *c*. 1000 km long and between 120 and 250 km wide. The eastern end of the Alps follows approximately a north–south orientated line from Vienna towards the south. Along this line, the Alpine tectonic units disappear beneath the sediment fill of Cenozoic basins, the Vienna Basin to the north and the Styrian Basin further south. Additionally, various Alpine tectonic units reappear in the Western Carpathians and this chain represents the continuation of the northern part of the Alps. To the SE, there is no clear limit between the Southern Alps and the Dinarides, either morphologically or geologically. Hence the Dinarides represent the continuation of the Southern Alps, just as the Western Carpathians prolongate the northern part of the Alps. South of the Alps, on the inner side of the arc, is the Cenozoic Po Basin. This is the foreland basin of the Southern Alps, since this part of the Alps forms a south-directed thrust-and-fold belt. The Po Basin is closed in the west by the westward-convex arc of the Western Alps. At the southern end of this arc, the Alps continue into the Apennines located south of the Po Basin. A complex north–south orientated fault zone, the Sestri-Voltaggio Zone, is taken as the boundary between the Alps and the Apennines. Across this line, the direction of tectonic transport changes: the main thrusts on the Alpine side are SW-directed, whereas the younger thrusts on the Apenninic side (i.e. from late Middle Eocene onward; Marroni *et al.* 2002) are NE-directed, so that the Po Basin also serves as the foreland basin for the Apennines. On its outer, western side, the arc of the Western Alps is in contact with the Provençal chains, a series of east–west striking ridges which represent, in a structural sense, an eastern continuation of the Pyrenees. North of these chains, the Alps are bordered by the Cenozoic fill of the Rhone-Bresse graben, and still further north, the chain of the Jura Mountains diverges in a northwesterly direction from the westernmost part of the Alps. This arcuate, outward-vergent fold-and-thrust belt is often treated as part of the Alps because the folds branch off from the external zone of the Western Alps, and because its basal thrust is probably rooted at depth under the Alps. In a topographic sense, however, the Jura Mountains are distinct from the Alps and form an independent range, enclosing, together with the Alps, the Swiss Molasse Basin, which is the westernmost part of the northern foreland basin of the Alps.

### *Geographic subdivision of the Alps*

A large-scale geographic subdivision of the Alps distinguishes between the Western, Central, Eastern, and Southern Alps (Fig. 18.1). (In the German and Austrian literature, the Central Alps are included in the Western Alps.) The boundary between the Southern Alps and the other parts of the Alps is defined by a system of important east–west orientated valleys (e.g. Valtellina, Pustertal, Gailtal). These valleys are the morphological expression of the Periadriatic Fault, a major fault of Tertiary age. Therefore, this boundary is both a geographic and a structural one.

The geographic boundary between the Eastern and Central

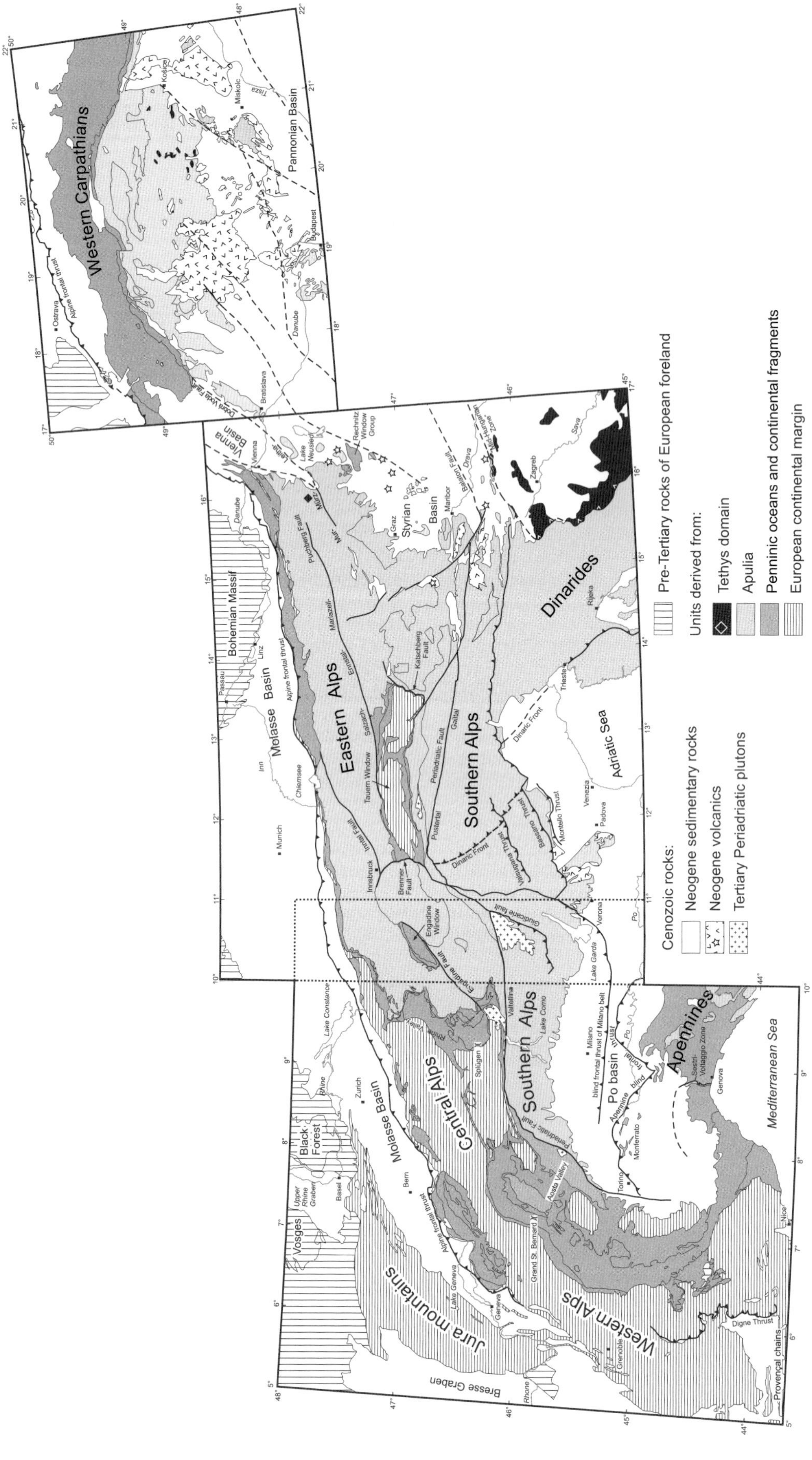


**Fig. 18.1.** Tectonic map of the Alps and Western Carpathians. After Schmid *et al.* (2004*a*) and other sources.

Alps is drawn from Lake Constance southward along the Rhine Valley and over the Splügen Pass to Lake Como, the boundary between the Central and Western Alps from Lake Geneva south along the Rhone Valley, over the Grand St. Bernard Pass, and along the Aosta Valley to the Po Plain.

### *Tectonic subdivision*

In terms of tectonics, the Alps are subdivided into structural zones, termed Helvetic, Penninic, Austro-Alpine and South Alpine, each of which is again subdivided into smaller units (e.g. Sub-Penninic, Lower, Middle and Upper Penninic; Fig. 18.2). This subdivision coincides with the geographical one only in the case of the South Alpine Zone which is identical with the Southern Alps. The South Alpine Zone is the part of the Alpine edifice to the south of the Periadriatic Line. It forms a south-directed thrust-and-fold belt (a 'retro-wedge' since the formation of the Alps is related to southward subduction). The South Alpine Zone is characterized by the almost complete absence of an Alpine metamorphic overprint. In contrast, the Austro-Alpine, Penninic and Helvetic zones are partly metamorphosed and constitute the north-directed (or, in the Western Alps, west-directed) 'pro-wedge' of the Alps. They form three groups of thrust sheets or nappes, of which the Austro-Alpine is structurally highest, the Penninic is in a middle position, and the Helvetic is at the base. Thrusting and metamorphism in the Austro-Alpine Zone are mainly Cretaceous in age whereas they are Tertiary in the Penninic and Helvetic zones. All of these zones have distinct sedimentary facies in the Mesozoic. The facies boundaries, however, are not always strictly parallel to the later tectonic boundaries (thrusts). Furthermore, these terms were introduced long before plate tectonics and, hence, do not denote plate tectonic entities such as oceans or continental margins. Only the Austro-Alpine–Penninic boundary coincides with a plate tectonic boundary: the boundary between the Apulian continental crust and the Piemont-Ligurian oceanic crust.

### *Palaeogeographic subdivision*

In terms of Mesozoic palaeogeography, the Alps were constructed by units which developed from a range of continental and oceanic domains. From NW to SE, these include (Fig. 18.3): (1) the European shelf and continental margin (Helvetic nappes and External massifs, Sub-Penninic nappes); (2) a northern ocean basin, the Valais Ocean (Lower Penninic nappes); (3) the Briançonnais Terrane, representing a northeastern prolongation of Iberia (Middle Penninic nappes); (4) a southern ocean basin, the Piemont-Liguria Ocean (Upper Penninic ophiolite nappes); (5) the Cervinia terrane, a narrow, elongate continental fragment within the Piemont-Liguria Ocean (Upper Penninic continental nappes); (6) the Apulian continental margin (Austro-Alpine nappes and South Alpine units); and (7) a southeastern ocean basin, the Meliata Ocean (only present as small slivers in the Austro-Alpine Zone but more broadly exposed in the Western Carpathians).

Both the opening and closure of the oceanic basins, as indicated by radiometric ages of oceanic magmatites and high-pressure metamorphism, respectively, show a broad trend towards younger ages from SE to NW (Fig. 18.4).

### *Outline of palaeogeographic evolution*

During the Triassic, a sedimentary prism representing a typical passive continental margin developed in the future Alps. A wide carbonate platform developed in the Austro-Alpine and South Alpine zones and was bordered to the NW by more terrestrially influenced sedimentation in the Penninic and Helvetic zones. The ocean to which this continental margin belongs must have been located to the east or SE of the Alpine area. An association of deep-marine Ladinian- to Carnian-age sediments (radiolarite), basalts partly overprinted by blueschist-facies metamorphism of middle Jurassic age, and Jurassic deep-marine clastics cropping out at Meliata (Slovakia) in the southern foothills of the Western Carpathians, is interpreted to be a remnant of this Triassic ocean which is therefore called the Meliata Ocean (Kozur & Mock 1973). Similar associations are present in the mélange zones of the Dinarides and occur as slivers in the Eastern Alps, within the Austro-Alpine nappe pile (Kozur & Mostler 1992; Mandl & Ondrejickova 1993). The Meliata Ocean is interpreted as a marginal basin of Tethys (Stampfli & Borel 2004). The exact geometry of the Mesozoic-age continents and oceans in south-eastern Europe, however, is still controversial.

The closure of the Triassic Meliata Ocean commenced at the end of the Triassic (Kozur 1991), probably at a SE-dipping, intra-oceanic subduction zone. Backarc spreading above the subduction zone created Jurassic oceanic crust (Vardar Ocean). The collision of the northwestern (Apulian) continental margin with the arc, above the subduction zone, during the Jurassic led to obduction of ophiolite sheets onto the Apulian margin in the Dinarides and probably also in the Austro-Alpine Zone. By that time the Piemont-Ligurian Ocean had opened farther to the NW. Ophiolites from this basin can be traced along the strike of the Alps. The first oceanic crust in the Piemont-Ligurian Ocean was formed during the Middle Jurassic. The Piemont-Ligurian Ocean was kinematically linked to the Middle Atlantic that opened at the same time, in that the Middle Atlantic continental breakup propagated northward only as far as the latitude of Gibraltar from where a strike-slip or transtensional zone extended eastward into the future western Mediterranean region, transferring the east–west separation from the Middle Atlantic into the SW–NE striking Piemont-Ligurian Ocean. It is not clear if and how the Piemont-Ligurian Ocean continued east of the Alps and into which basin of the SE European Tethyan realm it finally merged. The Cervinia terrane (Pleuger *et al.* 2007) was an elongate fragment of continental crust, separated from the Apulian continental margin by serpentinitic and basaltic ocean floor (Fig. 18.3). It has been proposed that this fragment is an extensional allochthon which rifted away from the Apulian margin by top-to-the-NW detachment faulting (Froitzheim & Manatschal 1996). Alternatively, the fragment may have resulted from a ridge jump or the simultaneous opening of two sub-basins during an early phase of opening of the Piemont-Ligurian Ocean.

The second oceanic basin of the Penninic Zone, the Valais Ocean, opened in the Early Cretaceous to the NW of the Piemont-Ligurian Ocean (Fig. 18.3). Ophiolites and sediments from this basin are well developed in Switzerland and can be traced to the SW into France as far as the town of Moutiers, from whence they disappear to the south. The continental fragment between the Valais and Piemont-Liguria ocean basins is termed the Briançonnais fragment, after a system of cover nappes derived from this continent cropping out around the town of Briançon in the Western Alps. In the Eastern Alps the ophiolites of the Valais and Piemont-Ligurian oceans are separated by nappes of the Briançonnais fragment only in the Engadine Window. Towards the east, in the Tauern Window and the Rechnitz Window Group, the Briançonnais fragment is missing. This suggests that the Briançonnais fragment wedged out towards the east and that the two oceanic basins merged into

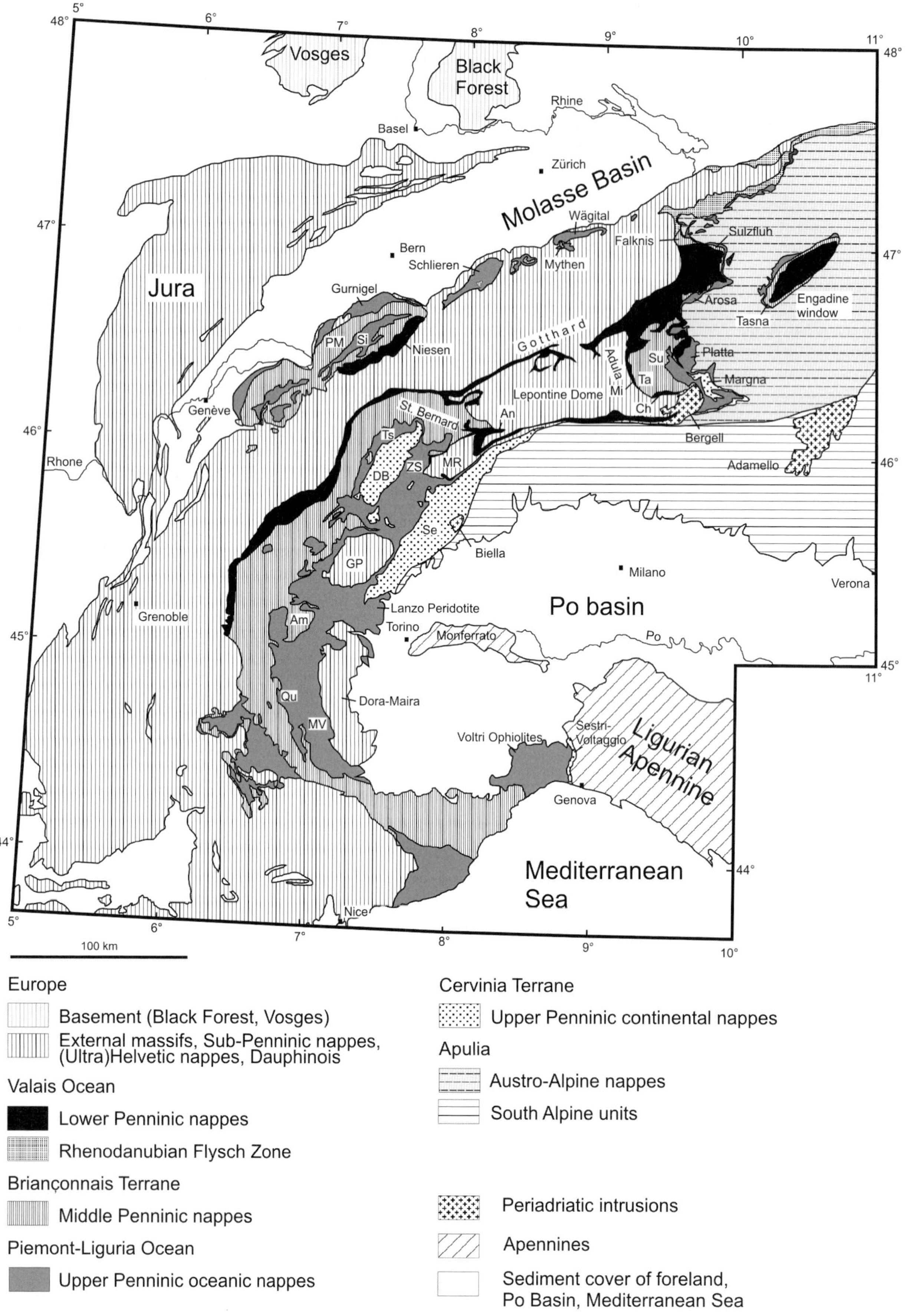
Vosges
Black Forest
Rhine
Basel
Zürich
Molasse Basin
Wägital
Falknis
Sulzfluh
Bern
Schlieren
Mythen
Jura
Gurnigel
Arosa
Engadine window
Tasna
PM
Si
Niesen
Gotthard
Adula
Su
Platta
Ta
Margna
Lepontine Dome
Mi
Genève
St. Bernard
An
Ch
Bergell
Rhone
Ts
DB
ZS
MR
Adamello
Se
Biella
GP
Milano
Verona
Grenoble
Am
Lanzo Peridotite
Torino
Po basin
Monferrato
Po
Qu
Dora-Maira
MV
Voltri Ophiolites
Sestri-Voltaggio
Ligurian Apennine
Genova
Mediterranean Sea
Nice
100 km
5°
6°
7°
8°
9°
10°
11°
44°
45°
46°
47°
48°
Europe
Basement (Black Forest, Vosges)
External massifs, Sub-Penninic nappes, (Ultra)Helvetic nappes, Dauphinois
Valais Ocean
Lower Penninic nappes
Rhenodanubian Flysch Zone
Briançonnais Terrane
Middle Penninic nappes
Piemont-Liguria Ocean
Upper Penninic oceanic nappes
Cervinia Terrane
Upper Penninic continental nappes
Apulia
Austro-Alpine nappes
South Alpine units
Periadriatic intrusions
Apennines
Sediment cover of foreland, Po Basin, Mediterranean Sea

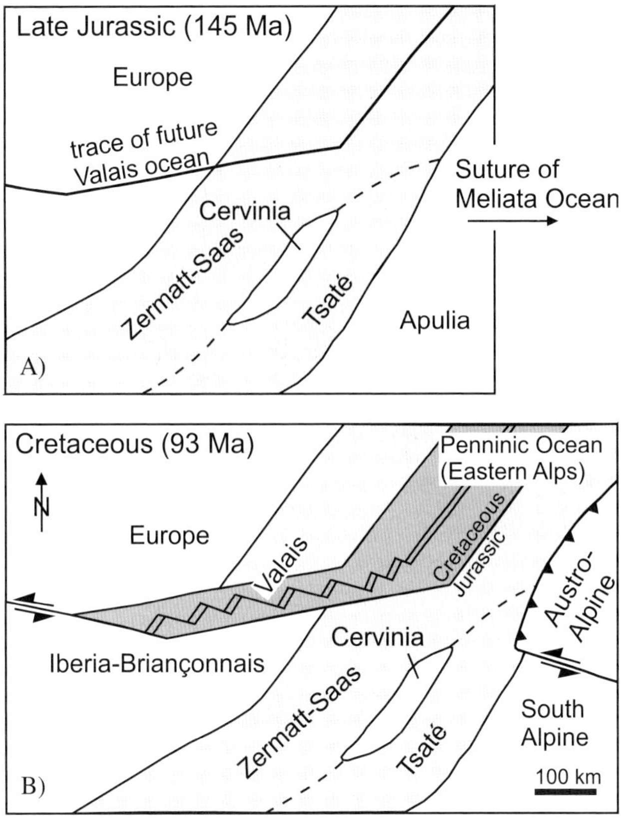


**Fig. 18.3.** Palaeogeographic reconstruction of Penninic oceans in Late Jurassic (A) and Late Cretaceous time (B). (**A**) Jurassic crust formed in the Piemont-Ligurian Ocean; the Cervinia terrane represents either a microcontinent or an extensional allochthon isolated from the Apulian margin during rifting. (**B**) Sinistrally transtensive opening of the Valais Ocean between Iberia and Europe during the Cretaceous. Towards the east Jurassic crust was re-rifted in the Cretaceous. Note that the Valais Ocean contains both Cretaceous crust (dark grey) and Jurassic crust (light grey) originally formed in the Piemont-Ligurian ocean.

one. However, in these areas the subdivision of the Valais and Piemont-Ligurian basins is problematic and several interpretations exist (e.g. Tollmann 1987; Froitzheim *et al.* 1996).

The Valais Ocean is related to Atlantic Ocean opening in a similar way to the Piemont-Ligurian Ocean (Frisch 1979; Stampfli 1993). The continental breakup in the Atlantic propagated towards the north during the Lower Cretaceous as far as the Bay of Biscay, from where a transtensional basin extended eastwards through the later Pyrenees and joined the Valais Ocean of the Alps, a connection which was later obliterated by Alpine deformation. Accordingly, the Briançonnais fragment formed a peninsular prolongation of Iberia into the Alpine realm. Recent dating of metagabbroic rocks from the Penninic Zone (Liati *et al.* 2003; Liati & Froitzheim 2006) yielded ages as young as 93 Ma for oceanic crust of the Valais Ocean, but also Jurassic ages of around 155 to 160 Ma, suggesting that Cretaceous opening of the Valais Ocean involved renewed rifting of Jurassic oceanic crust (Figs 18.3 & 18.4).

The closure of the Penninic oceans began in the Cretaceous with the southeastward subduction of Piemont-Ligurian lithosphere beneath the southern continental margin represented by the Austro-Alpine and South Alpine zones. The precise timing is, however, still uncertain. According to Wagreich (2001*a*) subduction began in the Late Aptian/Albian (*c.* 112 Ma). Thrust imbrication in the most internal parts of the Austro-Alpine Zone had commenced earlier in the Late Jurassic and continued prograding towards the NW during the Early Cretaceous. Thrusting within the Austro-Alpine Zone can, therefore, not have resulted from Penninic subduction, but was related to the collisional closure of the Meliata Ocean and post-collisional shortening. In this collision, parts of the Austro-Alpine Zone represented the lower plate. These were affected during the Cretaceous by thrusting and a metamorphic cycle including locally high-pressure (Hoinkes *et al.* 1999) and ultrahigh-pressure (Janák *et al.* 2004, 2006) metamorphism. During the Late Cretaceous, the Austro-Alpine nappe stack was extended in a west–east to NW–SE direction, leading to ductile deformation and normal faulting. Large parts subsided below sea level and were covered by clastic marine sediments (deposition of the Gosau Group from Turonian to Paleogene). At the same time, Piemont-Ligurian oceanic lithosphere was subducted from the north and NW beneath the Austro-Alpine and South Alpine zones of the Apulian continent.

The Penninic oceans were completely subducted by Eocene times (*c.* 40 Ma). An uncertainty exists about the kinematics of consumption of the Penninic oceans. Some authors assume that there was only one slab descending towards the south, which brought first the Piemont-Ligurian, then the Briançonnais, and finally the Valaisan crust to the foot of the accretionary wedge (Schmid *et al.* 1996). Others, however, assume that there were two subduction zones, one in the Piemont-Ligurian and one in the Valais Ocean (Frisch 1979; Froitzheim *et al.* 2003).

## *Tectonic units derived from the European margin*

The European margin of the Penninic oceans was affected by Alpine tectonics in a progression from internal to external zones. It is represented by basement and cover units that have been deformed and metamorphosed to varying degrees, from moderate folding and thrusting in the external parts to high-grade metamorphism and complete transposition in the most internal parts. The sedimentary units have been partly detached from their basement and accumulated in the external parts. The following units are, in our view, derived from the European margin: the External massifs and their cover, the Dauphinois Zone, and the Helvetic, Ultra-Helvetic and Sub-Penninic nappes.

*External massifs*

The External massifs (Fig. 18.5) are structural culminations where Variscan basement of the European plate is exposed in the external part of the Alps. The basement consists predominantly of various gneisses, amphibolites and granitoids. The following massifs occur from SW to NE along the strike of the Alps: Argentera, Pelvoux, Belledonne, Aiguilles Rouges, Mont Blanc and Aare. In addition, some smaller basement lamellae occur on the internal side of the larger massifs, such as the Mont Chetif Massif to the SE of Mont Blanc and the Tavetsch massifs to the

**Fig. 18.2.** Palaeogeographic units of the Western and Central Alps (after Froitzheim *et al.* (1996) and Schmid *et al.* (2004*a*), modified). Abbreviations: Am, Ambin; An, Antrona Ophiolites; Ch, Chiavenna Ophiolites; DB, Dent Blanche Nappe; GP, Gran Paradiso Nappe; MV, Monte Viso; PM, Préalpes Médianes Nappe; Qu, Queyras; Se, Sesia Nappe; Si, Simme Nappe; Su, Suretta Nappe; Ta, Tambo Nappe; Ts, Tsaté Nappe; ZS, Zermatt-Saas Zone.

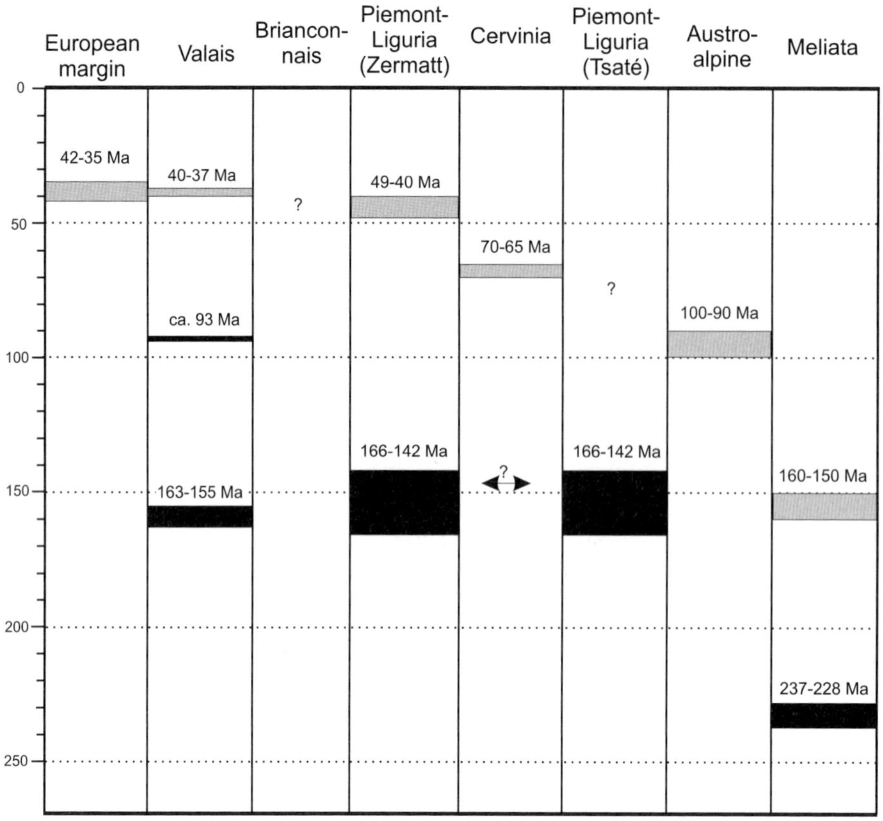


**Fig. 18.4.** Age data for oceanic spreading (black bars) and high-pressure metamorphism during subduction (grey bars) of Alpine palaeogeographic units. All ages are radiometric data, except for spreading of the Meliata ocean which is based on stratigraphic data (Channell & Kozur 1997). For oceanic spreading ages of the Piemont-Ligurian ophiolites, affiliation to the Zermatt-Saas or Tsaté sub-basin is in some cases unclear. If possible, preference was given to U–Pb, Sm–Nd and Lu–Hf ages. Sources: Dallmeyer *et al.* (1996), Duchêne *et al.* (1997), Faryad & Henjes-Kunst (1997), Gebauer (1996), Gebauer *et al.* (1997), Lapen *et al.* (2003, 2007), Liati *et al.* (2003, 2005), Liati & Froitzheim (2006), Miller *et al.* (2005), Rubatto *et al.* (1998, 1999), Stucki *et al.* (2003), Tilton *et al.* (1991).

SE of the Aare Massif. The Gotthard Nappe (Figs 18.6 & 18.7; Gotthard Massif of older authors) is now generally included in the Sub-Penninic nappes (as suggested by Milnes 1974) and is no longer treated as an External massif. The Alpine metamorphism of the External massifs reaches the greenschist facies in the more internal parts.

The position of the massifs is controlled by thrust geometry. The Aare, Mont Blanc and Aiguilles Rouges massifs are ramp anticlines above thrust faults cutting the upper crustal basement (Fig. 18.6 & 18.7). These thrusts formed during the Miocene, leading to uplift and cooling of the external massif basement and to antiformal bending of the earlier (Oligocene to Miocene) basal thrusts of the Helvetic nappes. On the external sides of the massifs, the outward dip of thrusts that results from this bending has often been misinterpreted as indicating gravitational emplacement of the Helvetic nappes. The position of the Pelvoux Massif (Fig. 18.5), in contrast, results from an interference of Oligocene–Miocene west-directed thrusting with structures formed during two older, pre-Priabonian, thrusting and folding events that are related to the Pyrenean collision (Ford 1996; Sue *et al.* 1997). The northern limit of the area affected by the Pyrenean shortening runs along the NW border of the Pelvoux Massif (Fig. 18.5). The geometry of the Pelvoux and Belledonne massifs was also strongly predetermined by Jurassic rift tectonics. Half-grabens formed during Jurassic east–west directed extension were transformed into pinched cover synclines during Alpine shortening, and the east-dipping master normal faults of these grabens were partly transformed into thrust faults.

*Cover of the External massifs, Dauphinois Zone*

The autochthonous and parautochthonous sedimentary cover crops out in Switzerland only in the vicinity of the External massifs, below the Helvetic nappes. Towards the west, into France, the displacement of the overlying Helvetic nappes decreases and they become indistinct, so that the area constituted by the autochthonous and parautochthonous cover units widens considerably. In this sense, the Dauphinois Zone in France (Fig. 18.5), also known as the Chaînes Subalpines, is the continuation of the autochthonous and parautochthonous cover units in Switzerland. However, the shortening of the Dauphinois Zone is important and is accommodated by outward-directed thrust systems, for example, the Digne Thrust (Fig. 18.5).

In Switzerland, the autochthonous/parautochthonous cover comprises locally Upper Carboniferous and Permian graben fill, followed by Triassic to Eocene, predominantly shallow-water sediments, and by the late Eocene to Oligocene North Helvetic Flysch (Fig. 18.7). An important member of the latter is the 32–29 Ma (Boyet *et al.* 2001) Taveyannaz Sandstone with detritus including 32 Ma andesite, providing evidence for the existence of andesitic volcanoes at that time. This sandstone also occurs in

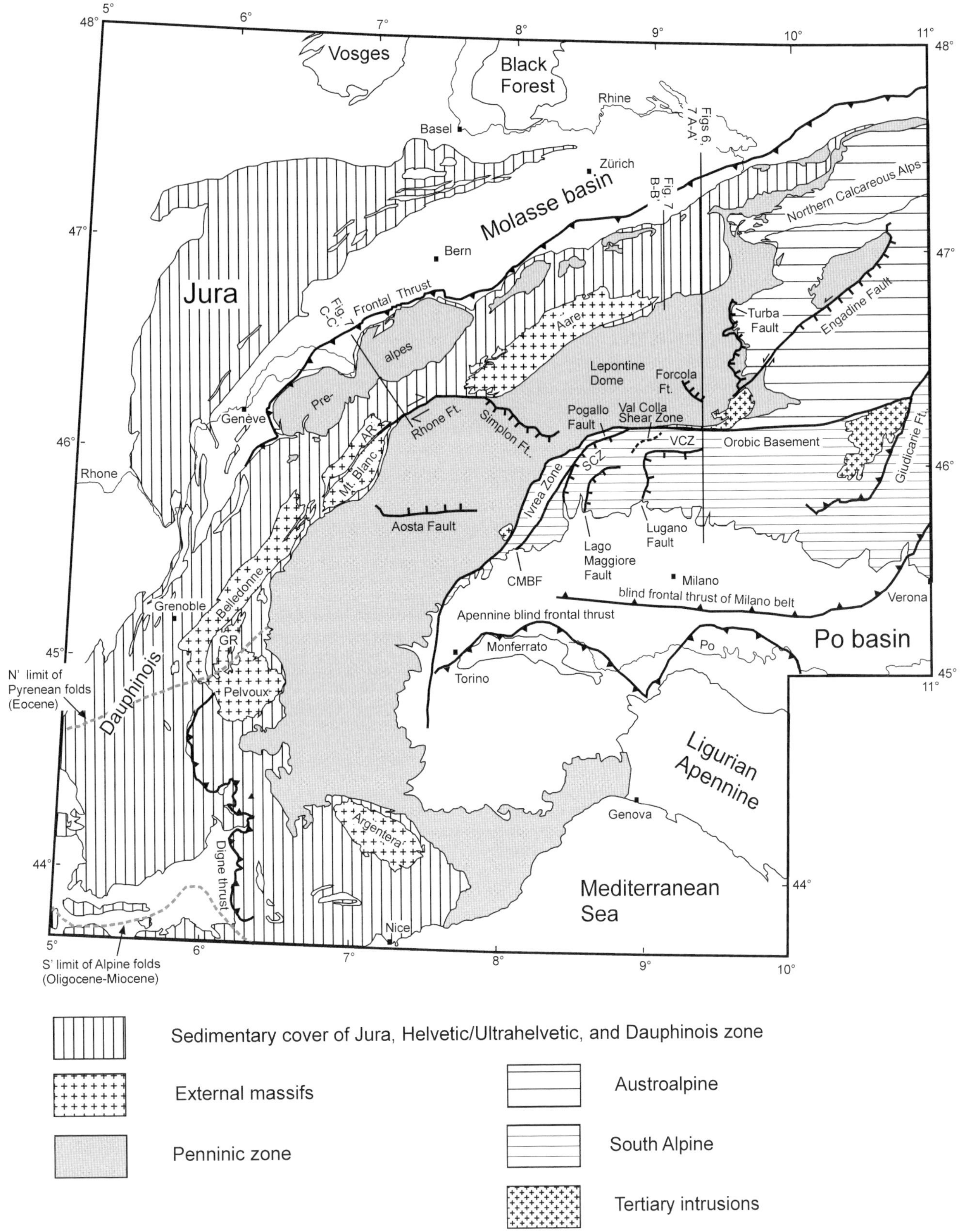


**Fig. 18.5.** Map of the Western and Central Alps with some important faults indicated. Abbreviations: AR, Aiguilles Rouges Massif; CMBF, Cossato-Mergozzo-Brissago Fault; GR, Grandes Rousses Massif; SCZ, Strona-Ceneri Zone; VCZ, Val Colla Zone.

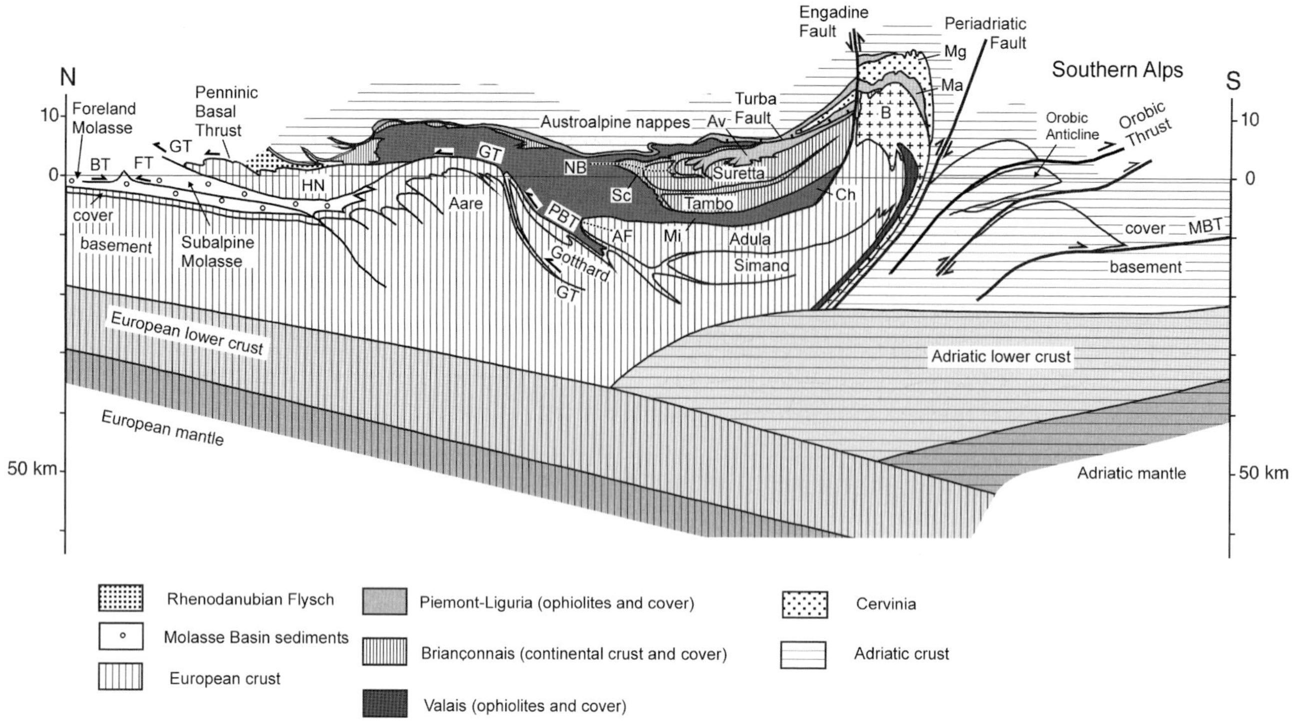


**Fig. 18.6.** Cross-section through the Central Alps (modified after Schmid *et al.* 1996). Abbreviations: AF, axial trace of the frontal fold of the Adula Nappe; Av, Avers Bündnerschiefer Nappe; B, Bergell granitoids; BT, backthrust in the Molasse Basin; Ch, Chiavenna Ophiolite; FT, frontal thrust of the Alps; GT, Glarus Thrust; HN, Helvetic Nappes; Ma, Malenco Ultramafic Complex; Mg, Margna Nappe; MBT, basal thrust of Milano belt (Miocene); Mi, Misox Zone; NB, axial trace of the Niemet-Beverin Fold; PBT, Penninic Basal Thrust; Sc, Schams Nappes. See Figure 18.5 for location of cross-section.

the Helvetic Nappes (Wildhorn Nappe in western Switzerland). The equivalents of the North Helvetic Flysch in the Western Alps are the Champsaur (also andesite-bearing) and Annot sandstones in the Dauphinois Zone and the Aiguilles d'Arves Flysch in a position similar to the Helvetic nappes.

The Morcles Nappe in western Switzerland represents the cover of the external part of the Mont Blanc Massif, partly detached from the massif and folded into a recumbent anticline with a thick normal limb and an extremely thinned inverted limb. The thin Ardon Nappe on top of the Morcles Nappe is the parautochthonous cover of the internal Mont Blanc Massif (Fig. 18.7, profile C–C′).

In the northern foreland of the Eastern Alps, the eastward continuation of the autochthonous and parautochthonous sedimentary cover units is buried beneath sediments of the Molasse Basin. In the Waschberg Zone near Vienna, however, shallow-marine Malm-age limestones are visible at the surface.

*Helvetic nappes*

The Helvetic nappes are classically developed in the Central Alps of Switzerland. They are cover nappes without a pre-Permian basement. The sedimentary succession locally comprises the clastic and volcanic fill of Permian rift basins (e.g. Glarus Verrucano in Eastern Switzerland; Fig. 18.7, profile B–B′), followed by thin Triassic sediments in a Germanic facies, Jurassic deposits with variable thickness due to rift tectonics, Cretaceous to Palaeogene shelf deposits, and locally Eocene to Early Oligocene deep-marine clastics. Some of the Helvetic nappes are thrust nappes lacking an inverted limb, for example, the Glarus Nappe in eastern Switzerland. This nappe is floored by the most famous thrust fault of the Alps, the Glarus Thrust (Figs 18.6 & 18.7), along which Permian-age Verrucano sedimentary and volcanic rocks overlie Jurassic- to Tertiary-age sediments of the Infra-Helvetic Complex (see below). Others are fold nappes with a well-developed inverted limb such as the Wildhorn Nappe in western Switzerland. The sequence of the Helvetic nappes in eastern Switzerland comprises (from base to top) the Glarus Nappe, the Mürtschen Nappe, the Axen Nappe and the Säntis-Drusberg Nappe (Fig. 18.7, profile B–B′). The first three of these are not independent nappes; their bounding thrusts become less important towards the south and die out in the internal parts of the Helvetic nappes. In western Switzerland, the Helvetic nappes are represented by the lower Diablerets Nappe and the higher Wildhorn Nappe. The Ardon and Morcles nappes, underlying the Diablerets Nappe, are not Helvetic nappes in the strict sense but are parautochthonous cover units of the internal and external parts, respectively, of the Mont Blanc Massif (see above).

The basement from which the eastern Helvetic nappes were detached is more internal than the Aare Massif since the latter has its own sediment cover in an autochthonous to parautochthonous position. The basement for the eastern Helvetic nappes is represented by the Tavetsch 'Zwischenmassif' which is a narrow, strongly deformed basement complex SE of the Aare Massif, and by the Sub-Penninic Gotthard Nappe (Fig. 18.7, profile B–B′). Other parts of this basement have disappeared at depth, between the Aare Massif and the Tavetsch Massif, and between the latter and the Gotthard Nappe.

In the Western Alps, the Aiguilles d'Arves Unit (Ceriani *et al.* 2001; Ceriani & Schmid 2004) occupies a similar position

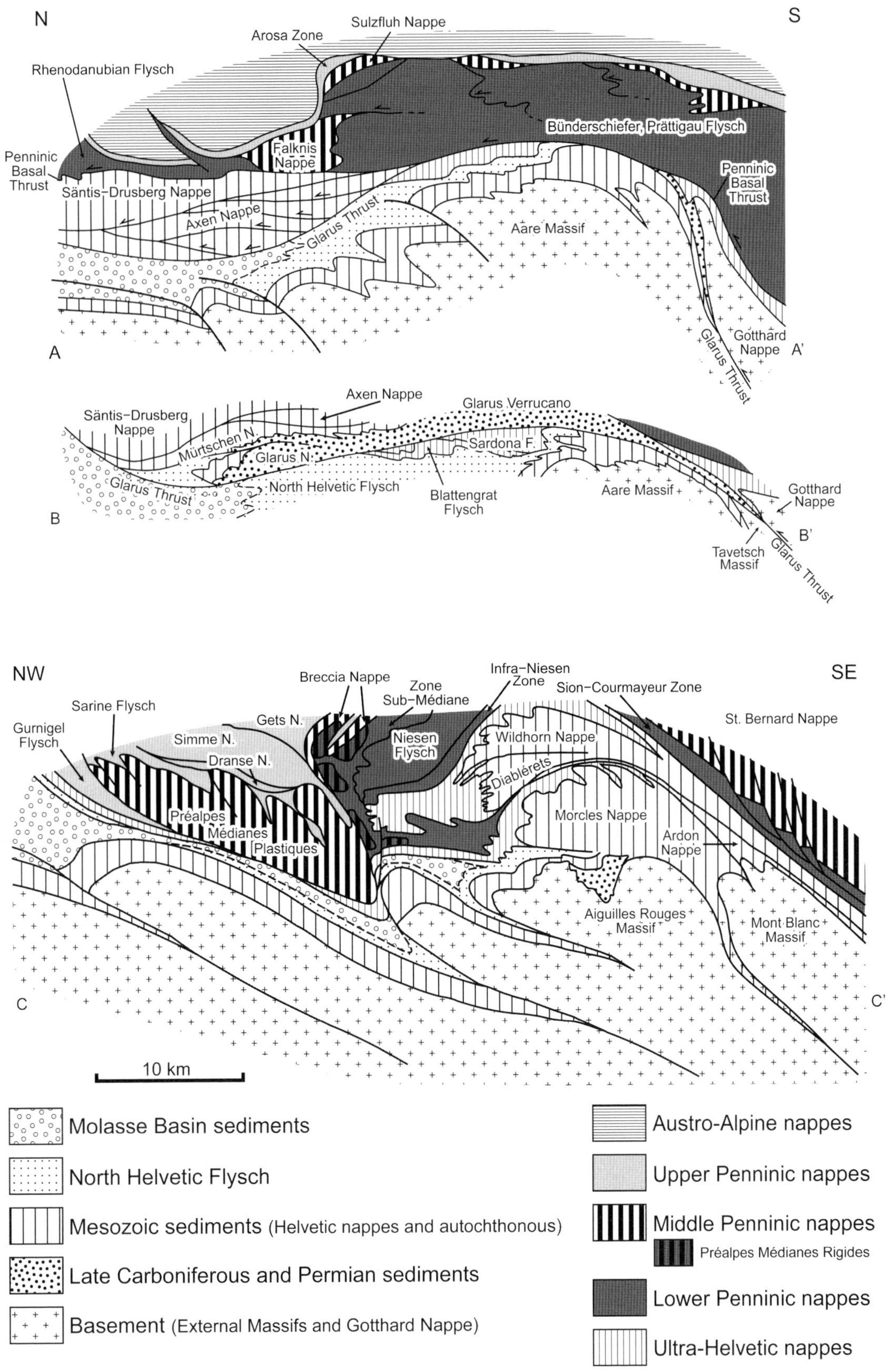


**Fig. 18.7.** Three profiles through the Helvetic Zone in Switzerland. After Schmid *et al.* (1996; profile A–A′), Schmid (1975; profile B–B′) and Escher *et al.* (1997, profile C–C′), modified. See Figure 18.5 for locations of cross-sections.

to the Helvetic nappes. It comprises basement (Combeynot Massif) and Triassic and Jurassic carbonates, unconformably overlying nummulitic limestone and Late Eocene (Priabonian) deep-marine clastics (Aiguilles d'Arves Flysch). In the older literature, the Aiguilles d'Arves Unit and the lowermost of the Lower Penninic nappes, the Cheval Noir Unit, were termed 'Ultradauphinois'.

*Ultra-Helvetic nappes*

This term encompasses a group of tectonic units which were structurally situated above the Helvetic nappes after initial thrusting, but which have locally become enveloped under Helvetic nappes in the course of out-of-sequence thrusting and nappe refolding. The palaeogeographic origin of these nappes was the Cretaceous continental rise between the Valais Ocean to the SE and the European shelf (Helvetic units) to the NW. Therefore, the facies of the Cretaceous sediments in the Ultra-Helvetic nappes is, in general, more pelagic (marly) than in the Helvetic nappes. Their youngest sediments are Eocene to Early Oligocene deep-marine clastics. Locally, for example, in western Switzerland, the Ultra-Helvetic units represent a mélange of various blocks of older rocks in a matrix of these clastic sediments. The Ultra-Helvetic units were emplaced on the Helvetic realm, that is, the later Helvetic nappes to the south and the autochthonous/parautochthonous cover of the External massifs to the north, by early thin-skinned thrusting during the Oligocene, before the Helvetic nappes formed. When these formed, the Ultra-Helvetic units acted like the 'youngest sediment layer' and became enveloped between and below the Helvetic nappes. In eastern Switzerland, such enveloping beneath the Glarus Thrust (i.e. the basal thrusts plane of the Helvetic Glarus Nappe) affected not only the Ultra-Helvetic Sardona Flysch but also the Blattengrat Flysch, the origin of which is assumed to be in the southern part of the subsequently-formed Helvetic nappes (Fig. 18.7, profile B–B′).

The Gotthard Nappe has only thin remnants of its own cover. The main part of the present sedimentary cover of this nappe is allochthonous and in an upside-down position (Etter 1987). This allochthonous Gotthard cover can be regarded as belonging to the Ultra-Helvetic nappes (Fig. 18.7, profile B–B′). It was emplaced on the Gotthard Nappe in an event of north-directed 'cover substitution' thrusting, when the original cover of the nappe, which is now part of the Helvetic nappes, was detached and replaced by the Ultra Helvetic sediments.

*Helvetic and Ultra-Helvetic nappes along the front of the Eastern Alps*

Helvetic units cropping out along the northern front of the Alps in western Austria (Vorarlberg) and Bavaria form the eastward continuation of the Säntis-Drusberg Nappe of eastern Switzerland. Deeper Helvetic nappes are not exposed but were encountered in the Hindelang 1 borehole in western Bavaria (Schwerd *et al.* 1995), namely the Hindelang Nappe and the still deeper Hohenems Nappe. In addition, another Helvetic imbricate, the Grünten Nappe, locally occurs at the surface above the Säntis-Drusberg Nappe. The sequence is then, from base to top: Hohenems, Hindelang, Säntis-Drusberg and Grünten nappes (Schwerd *et al.* 1995). The Helvetic units comprise sediments of Upper Jurassic to Middle Eocene age, detached from the older rocks and thrust northward over the fill of the Molasse Basin. In Vorarlberg and western Bavaria, the Helvetic Säntis-Drusberg Nappe is overlain by the Ultra-Helvetic Liebenstein Nappe which includes sediments of Aptian to Middle Eocene age, predominantly marls and pelagic limestones. The basal thrust of the Liebenstein Nappe is folded together with the sedimentary succession of the Säntis-Drusberg Nappe.

True Helvetic units with the shelf facies occur approximately as far east as Salzburg,. Further to the east, the shelf facies is replaced in the Helvetic units by a more basinal facies resembling the Ultra-Helvetic nappes of Switzerland, with pelagic marls (Buntmergel) of Late Cretaceous to Early Tertiary age. These units have the structural position of the Helvetic nappes but exhibit the facies of the Ultra-Helvetic nappes. This situation arises because the thrust front of the Helvetic nappes is oblique to the facies boundaries. To the west, the thrust front formed on the shelf, and to the east, on the continental rise. The pre-Late Cretaceous succession of these units is developed in the so-called Gresten Facies with sandy, shallow-marine sediments of Jurassic age.

Between Salzburg and Vienna, the Helvetic units – in 'Ultra-Helvetic' facies – form an imbricate fan together with the tectonically overlying nappes of the Rhenodanubian Flysch. Initially, the Rhenodanubian Flysch was emplaced from the south onto the Helvetic units, and then onto the imbricate fan formed by northward thrusting over the fill of the Molasse Basin. The Helvetic units are exposed in the immediate hanging-walls of the individual thrusts, from whence they disappear towards the south under the Rhenodanubian Flysch.

*Sub-Penninic nappes*

The Sub-Penninic nappes (Milnes 1974) comprise elements of the distal European continental margin, dominated by basement but also including Permo-Mesozoic cover rocks. In contrast to the External massifs, the Sub-Penninic nappes have been completely detached from the lithospheric mantle. Sub-Penninic nappes occur in the Lepontine area of the Central Alps and in the Tauern Window of the Eastern Alps. In contrast to the original definition of Milnes (1974) which excluded the Adula Nappe, this nappe is now also termed 'Sub-Penninic' (Schmid *et al.* 2004*a*). We also include the Monte Rosa, Gran Paradiso and Dora-Maira nappes because they are in a similar structural position to the Adula Nappe, representing the most distal part of the European margin (Gebauer 1999; Froitzheim 2001).

The most external parts of the Sub-Penninic units, e.g. the Gotthard Nappe, formed the basement from which the Ultra-Helvetic and parts of the Helvetic cover nappes were detached. The lower Sub-Penninic nappes are eclogite-free whereas the uppermost and most internally derived nappes (Adula, Monte Rosa, Dora-Maira) were affected by eclogite-facies, partly ultra-high-pressure metamorphism during the Eocene.

The classical gneiss nappes of the Lepontine Dome (Fig. 18.2) belong to the Sub-Penninic nappes. The bulk of these nappes contain no eclogites. The uppermost tectonic unit, the Adula Nappe, however, includes Alpine eclogites and garnet peridotites (Heinrich 1986). The lower, eclogite-free nappes are the Simano, Lucomagno-Leventina, Maggia, Antigorio, Lebendun and Monte Leone nappes. The Gotthard Nappe (former Gotthard Massif) is the structurally deepest Sub-Penninic nappe in the area and crops out to the north of the other units (Figs 18.2 & 18.6). The Maggia Nappe has sometimes been correlated with the Briançonnais units because it locally overlies the Adula Nappe (e.g. Froitzheim *et al.* 1996; Schmid *et al.* 2004*a*), but other authors (Grujic & Mancktelow 1996; Maxelon 2004) explained this geometry as being related to post-nappe recumbent folding and they correlated the Maggia Nappe with the Sub-Penninic nappes, an interpretation followed herein. Towards the SW, the Moncucco and Camughera (Fig. 18.8) nappes also belong, in our view, to the Sub-Penninic system.

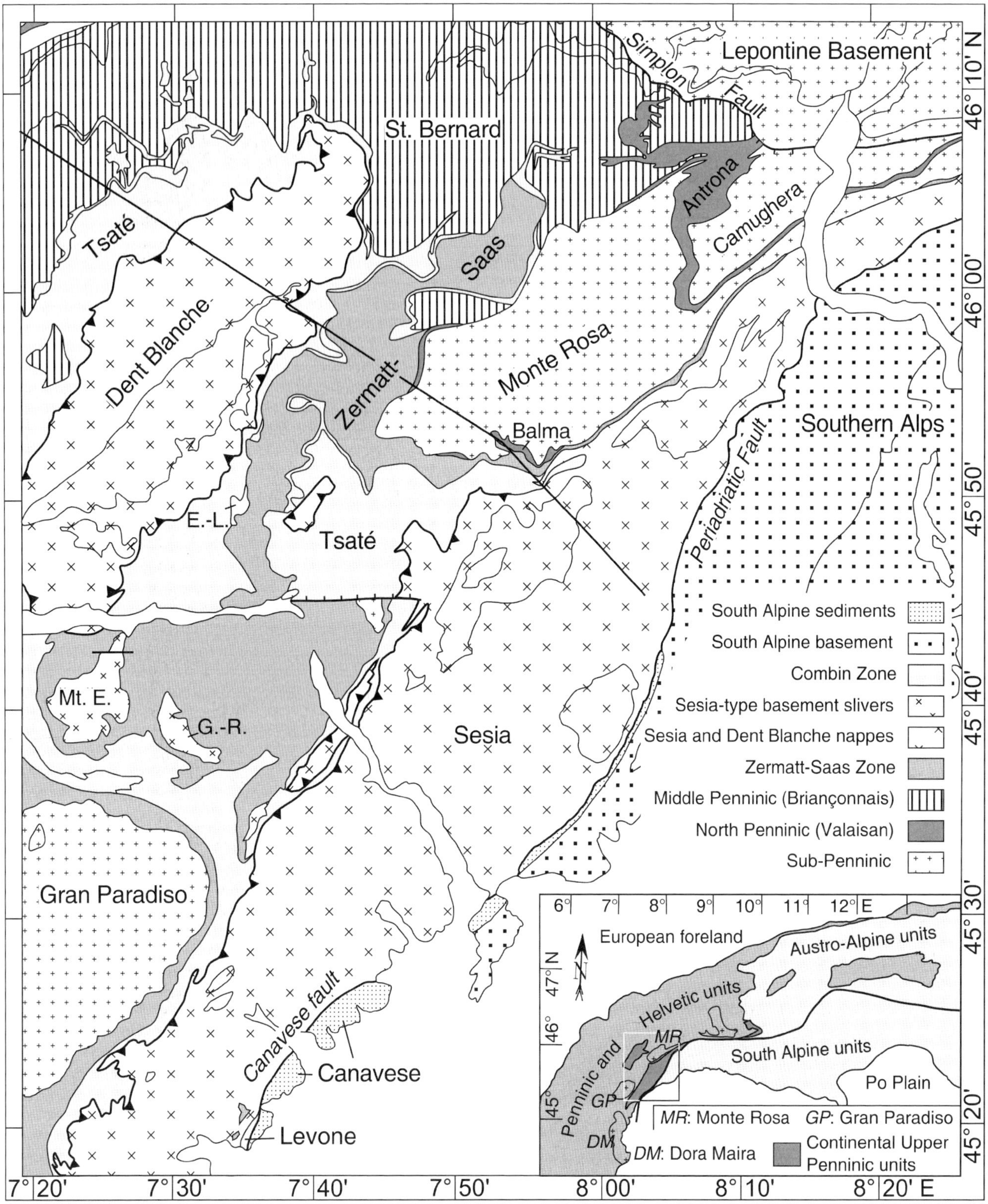


**Fig. 18.8.** Tectonic map of the Penninic Alps. Ophiolites from the Piemont-Ligurian Ocean occur in a deeper level (Zermatt-Saas Zone) and a higher level (Tsaté Nappe). In between are slivers of basement (E.-L., Etirol-Levaz; G.-R., Glacier-Rafray; Mt. E., Monte Emilius) and sedimentary rocks (C.B., Cimes Blanches Nappe), interpreted here to have been derived from the Cervinia terrane. A second, much thicker thrust sheet derived from Cervinia is on top of the Tsaté nappe, forming the Dent Blanche and Sesia nappes. It was emplaced by a NW-directed out-of-sequence thrust. Trace of cross-section in Figure 18.9 is indicated. After Steck *et al.* (1999) and Pleuger *et al.* (2007).

The eclogite-free Sub-Penninic nappes of the area are recumbent folds with a basement core (orthogneiss, paragneiss, amphibolite) and a thin sedimentary cover. The latter forms nappe-separating synclines pinching out mostly towards the south. Ophiolites and associated 'Bündnerschiefer' derived from the Valais Ocean also locally occur in these synclines. They were thrust over the Sub-Penninic units before the recumbent folds formed. As the folding occurred after initial thrusting, the stacking order of the recumbent folds, in many cases, does not reflect their original palaeogeographic arrangement, which led to the controversy concerning the origin of the Maggia Nappe.

The Adula Nappe (Figs 18.2 & 18.6) is the uppermost Sub-Penninic unit of the Lepontine Dome. It is not a coherent basement sheet but a stack of thin basement sheets separated by even thinner layers of Mesozoic quarzites, marbles and calcareous schists. Abundant lenses and boudins of eclogite and, in the southern part, garnet peridotite are also found in the Adula Nappe. For the Cima Lunga Unit, i.e. the southwestern part of the Adula Nappe, an Alpine age of high-pressure equilibration (40 to 35 Ma) is well established (Becker 1993; Gebauer 1996). A garnet peridotite body at Monte Duria in the southeastern Adula Nappe was rapidly exhumed from eclogite-facies conditions at 34 to 33 Ma (Hermann *et al.* 2006). An additional, pre-Alpine high-pressure event may have affected part of the Adula Nappe (Biino *et al.* 1997). An early Palaeozoic age was determined for some eclogite protoliths in the Adula Nappe (Santini 1992).

*Monte Rosa, Gran Paradiso and Dora-Maira nappes*

The palaeogeographic origin of these units is controversial. We have assigned them to the Sub-Penninic nappes (Gebauer 1999; Froitzheim 2001) whereas many other authors have favoured an origin from Briançonnais crust (Escher *et al.* 1997; Schmid *et al.* 2004*a*). The Monte Rosa Nappe (Figs 18.8 & 18.9) comprises para- and orthogneisses, the latter representing Carboniferous and Permian intrusions into the paragneisses. Albite-rich micaschists at the northern rim of the Monte Rosa Nappe may represent remnants of the Permo-Carbonferous cover, although generally, the cover was sheared off during subduction. Metabasic boudins in the paragneiss of the Monte Rosa Nappe record eclogite-facies metamorphism, the age of which is Eocene (*c.* 42 Ma; Lapen *et al.* 2007). In the interpretation outlined here, the Monte Rosa Nappe is a post-nappe recumbent anticline similar to the other Sub-Penninic nappes, and the Antrona Ophiolites that occur below the Monte Rosa Nappe do not represent an oceanic suture but are situated in a post-thrusting synform, the Antrona synform (Fig. 18.9; Froitzheim 2001). The geometric analysis of the Lepontine nappes by Maxelon (2004) demonstrates that the Monte Rosa Nappe is at the same structural level of the nappe stack as the Adula Nappe, which would support our interpretation.

The Gran Paradiso Nappe is very similar to the Monte Rosa Nappe in most respects. It was affected by Alpine eclogite-facies metamorphism in the Eocene (Meffan-Main *et al.* 2004). In contrast to the Monte Rosa Nappe, the Gran Paradiso Nappe has a Mesozoic metasedimentary cover. The Dora-Maira Nappe is composed of several sheets of Variscan basement (ortho- and paragneisses and metabasites) separated by Permo-Mesozoic metasediments and locally minor ophiolites. The nappe experienced blueschist- to eclogite-facies metamorphism, and one of the basement sheets even reached ultrahigh-pressure (UHP) conditions. Indeed, this is the famous coesite locality (Chopin 1984). UHP metamorphism is dated at *c.* 35 Ma (Gebauer *et al.* 1997). The Pinerolo Unit is exposed in a window beneath the Dora-Maira Nappe and contains metamorphic Permo-Carboniferous sediments in a facies similar to the Briançonnais units, and late Variscan granitic to dioritic bodies. The Pinerolo Unit underwent only blueschist metamorphism. The same lithological association, as in the Pinerolo Unit, also crops out in the Money Window, a small tectonic window through the Gran Paradiso Nappe (Compagnoni *et al.* 1974). If these rocks indeed belong to the Middle Penninic (Briançonnais) nappes, our interpretation implies major out-of-sequence thrusting of the 'European' Gran Paradiso and Dora-Maira nappes over the more internally derived Briançonnais nappes.

*Sub-Penninic nappes in the Tauern window*

Of the three large tectonic windows where Penninic units crop out in the Eastern Alps (Engadine Window, Tauern Window,

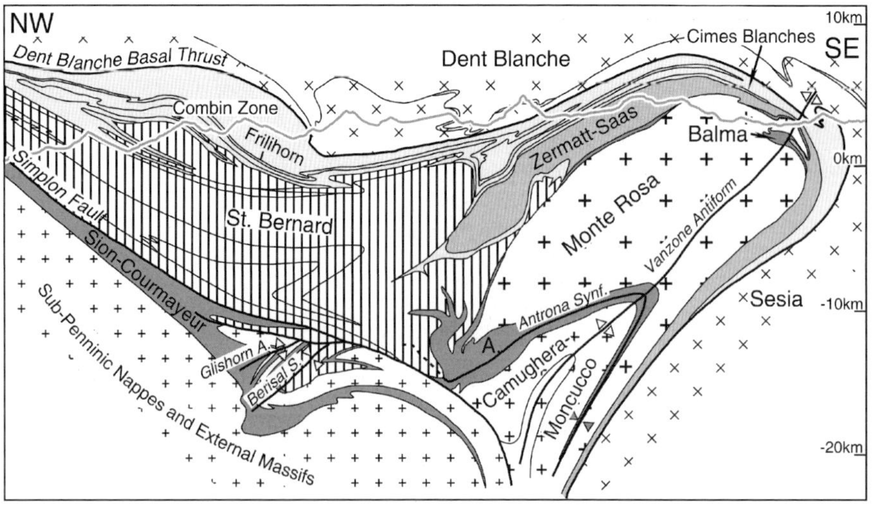


**Fig. 18.9.** Cross-section of the Penninic Alps. Note intensive, polyphase refolding of nappes and out-of-sequence thrusting, leading to the situation that originally deeper, more externally derived nappes (Monte Rosa Nappe, Dent Blanche Nappe) overlie originally higher, more internally derived nappes (Antrona Ophiolites and Tsaté Nappe, respectively). Glishorn A., Glishorn Antiform; Berisal S., Berisal Synform. For legend and location of section see Figure 18.8. After Escher *et al.* (1993) and Pleuger *et al.* (2007).

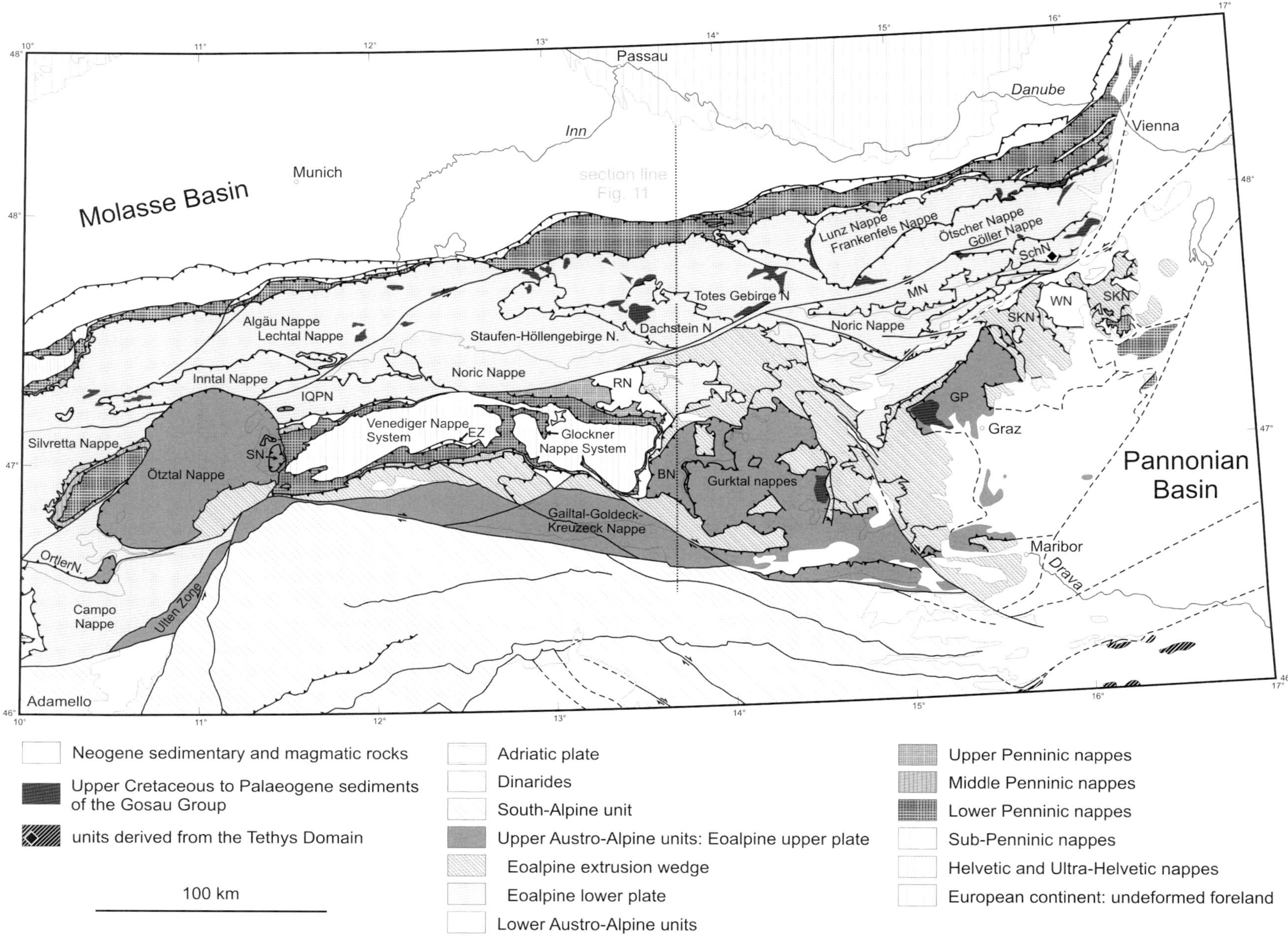


**Fig. 18.10.** Tectonic units of the Eastern Alps. Abbreviations: BN, Bundschuh Nappe; EZ, Eclogite Zone; GP, Graz Palaeozoic nappes; IQPN, Innbruck Quartz Phyllite Nappe; MN, Mürzalpen Nappe; RN, Radstadt nappes; SchN, Schneeberg Nappe; SKN, Stuhleck-Kirchberg Nappe; SN, Steinach Nappe; WN, Wechsel Nappe.

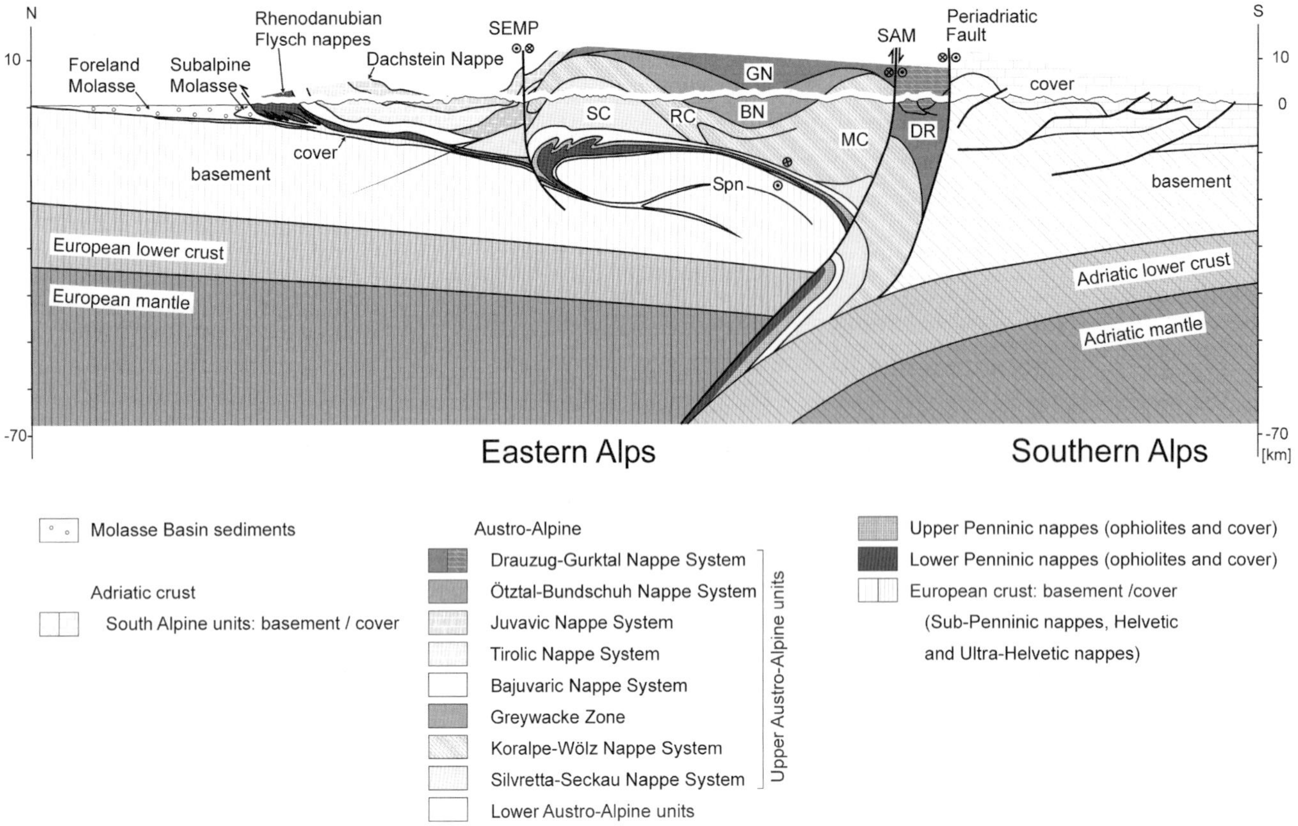


**Fig. 18.11.** Cross-section through the Eastern Alps. Abbreviations: BN, Bundschuh Nappe; DR, Drau Range; GN, Gurktal Nappe; MC, Millstatt Complex; RC, Radenthein Complex; SAM, Southern limit of Alpine metamorphism, coinciding with the Mölltal Fault in this cross-section; SC, Seckau Complex; SEMP, Salzach-Ennstal-Mariazell-Puchberg Fault; SPN, Sub-Penninic nappes. SEMP and Periadriatic Fault accommodate eastward extrusion of crustal units in the central part of the profile. Neogene switch in subduction polarity has led to north-dipping subduction zone at depth.

Rechnitz Window Group; Fig. 18.1), only the Tauern Window exposes Sub-Penninic nappes. These are represented by the Venediger Nappe System (Fig. 18.10 & 18.11; Frisch 1976), the lowermost unit exposed in the Tauern Window. It comprises continental crust from the European margin: Variscan granitoids (Zentralgneis) intruded into partly migmatized, pre-existing Palaeozoic sequences (e.g. Habach Complex) and possibly even older country rocks, and Permo-Mesozoic cover rocks. Within the nappe system a transition in the sediment facies and degree of allochthony can be recognized: in the palaeogeographically northern parts, Upper Jurassic carbonates represent a shelf environment and are still partly attached to thick basement. For example, the large gneiss nappes of the Tux and Ahorn massifs are covered by the Upper Jurassic Hochstegen Marble, and the Hochalm Massif in the eastern part of the Tauern Window is covered by the Silbereck Marble (Höfer & Tichy 2005). In contrast, successions derived from the slope towards the oceanic basin in the south have been sheared off completely, or together with thin basement lamellae, and displaced towards the north. One of these is the Wolfendorn Nappe. It was derived from the proximal slope and is characterized by a Triassic succession overlain by the Hochstegen Marble and Cretaceous clastic sediments including black shales, quartzites and meta-arkoses (Kaserer Formation). The cover sequences of the Seidlwinkl Nappe (Cornelius & Clar 1939) and the Rote Wand-Modereck Nappe (Kober 1922) were deposited on the distal slope. These include Permian siliciclastic rocks (Wustkogel Formation; lying on a Variscan basement lamella in the Rote Wand-Modereck Nappe), Triassic shallow-marine sedimentary rocks (Seidlwinkl Formation) and Jurassic to Cretaceous phyllites and carbonatic quartzites (Brennkogel Formation). The central part of the Venediger Nappe System (central with respect to the boundaries of the Tauern Window) was metamorphosed under amphibolite-facies conditions, whereas the outer parts reached greenschist-facies conditions during Tertiary metamorphism ('Tauernkristallisation') (Schuster *et al.* 2004). Typical cooling ages of the Venediger Nappe System range from 30 to 17 Ma (Oxburgh *et al.* 1966; Frank *et al.* 1987).

The Eclogite Zone (Fig. 18.10) is a south-dipping thrust sheet near the southern border of the central Tauern Window, intercalated between the 'Zentralgneis' and its Mesozoic cover to the north, and the Rote Wand-Modereck Nappe to the south. It is either a mixed or a transitional continental-oceanic unit. It comprises eclogite-facies metabasites, serpentinites and metamorphosed sedimentary rocks of probable Permian to Late Cretaceous age (quartzite, marble, calcareous schist). The age of the metabasite protoliths is not known. The eclogite metamorphism is probably Eocene in age (Zimmermann *et al.* 1994; Ratschbacher *et al.* 2005) and pre-dates the 'Tauernkristallisation'. Kurz *et al.* (1998) assumed that the Eclogite Zone was derived from the continent–ocean transition, thrust northward over the Sub-Penninic nappes, and then buried under the Rote Wand-Modereck Nappe by an out-of-sequence thrust.

The internal structure of the Venediger Nappe System reflects a polyphase evolution (Braumüller & Prey 1943; Kurz *et al.* 2001*b*). During the period of subduction in the Eocene, the structurally higher nappes of the system were formed from the distal margin and thrust over the more proximal parts, together with the units of the overlying Glockner Nappe System derived from the Penninic Ocean (see below). Parts of the Glockner and Venediger nappe systems were isoclinally interfolded during this process (e.g. Seidlwinkl Nappe and Glockner Nappe *sensu stricto*). In the Miocene the entire nappe pile was refolded by an east–west trending fold system with steeply dipping axial planes, and at the same time stretched east–west. Stretching became progressively localized in a west-dipping normal fault at the western end of the Tauern Window (Brenner Fault; Behrmann 1988; Selverstone 1988) and an east-dipping one at the eastern end (Katschberg Fault; Genser & Neubauer 1989). This period of deformation was related to the indentation of the South-Alpine block into the Eastern Alps (Rosenberg *et al.* 2004).

In the Engadine Window, the Sub-Penninic nappes are not exposed but occur at depth under the Lower Penninic (Valaisan) Bündnerschiefer, according to reflection-seismic interpretation (Pfiffner & Hitz 1997).

To summarize, the Sub-Penninic nappes represent the southern continental margin of the European plate which was subducted in the Eocene. Accordingly, Eocene high-pressure and ultrahigh-pressure metamorphic rocks occur in the originally most distal parts of the continental margin which were subducted to the greatest depths and now form the structurally highest nappes (from east to west): the Eclogite Zone of the Tauern Window, the Adula Nappe, the Monte Rosa Nappe, the Gran Paradiso Nappe, and the Dora-Maira Nappe. The Ultra-Helvetic nappes represent parts of the sedimentary cover of the Sub-Penninic nappes which were sheared off and frontally accreted to the orogenic wedge.

## *Lower Penninic (Valaisan) nappes*

*Valaisan nappes in the Central Alps*

Sedimentary rocks and ophiolites from the Valais Ocean crop out in a narrow zone from Graubünden in the NE to Savoie in the SW. To the NE, these units plunge under the Austro-Alpine nappes and reappear in the Engadine Window. To the SW, the Valais units pinch out near the town of Moutiers in Savoie. In the Lepontine Dome area, the Valaisan rocks interdigitate with the Sub-Penninic nappes, due to the post-thrusting recumbent folding. The typical sediments of the Valais Ocean are calcareous schists of Cretaceous age ('Bündnerschiefer'). These pass upwards into calcareous to siliciclastic turbidites in the latest Cretaceous and Early Tertiary. The Valais Ocean floor (serpentinite, gabbro and basalt) is preserved as isolated slivers in the Bündnerschiefer and locally as coherent ophiolite bodies several kilometres in length.

The suture of the Valais Ocean, between the Middle Penninic (Briançonnais) nappes above and the Sub-Penninic nappes below, is exposed in two areas, to the west and east of the Lepontine area. In the east, it comprises the east-dipping Misox Zone (Fig. 18.2) above the Adula Nappe. At the same structural level, the Chiavenna ophiolites are exposed farther to the south (Fig. 18.2). Oceanic gabbros in the Chiavenna ophiolite were dated at *c.* 93 Ma (Liati *et al.* 2003). A metagabbro in the Misox Zone was dated at 161 Ma (Liati *et al.* 2005). Hence, both Jurassic and Cretaceous ocean floor existed in the Valais Ocean (Fig. 18.4), as predicted by Stampfli (1993). The Jurassic seafloor originally belonged to the Piemont-Ligurian Ocean and was captured in the Valais Ocean when the Briançonnais fragment rifted away from Europe during the Earliest Cretaceous and moved to the east. This implies renewed rifting of Jurassic oceanic lithosphere (Fig. 18.3; Liati *et al.* 2005).

To the west, the suture of the Valais Ocean is represented by the eclogite-facies (Colombi & Pfeifer 1986) Antrona Ophiolites. These are folded-in below the Monte Rosa Nappe, but were originally at a higher structural level (Fig. 18.9). The Valais suture can be traced from the Antrona Ophiolites through discontinuous slivers at the front of the Monte Rosa Nappe towards the SW, and over the top of the Monte Rosa Nappe towards the SE into the Balma Unit (Pleuger *et al.* 2005; Fig. 18.9). Protolith ages of metagabbros are between 155 and 163 Ma in the Antrona Ophiolites (Liati *et al.* 2005), and *c.* 93 Ma in the Balma Unit (Liati & Froitzheim 2006). Hence, in this part of the Valaisan suture both Jurassic and Late Cretaceous ocean floor occurs.

In the French part of the Valaisan, eclogite-facies metabasics occur in the Versoyen Complex. A Late Carboniferous age (*c.* 309 Ma) for a leucogabbro dyke in the Versoyen Complex (Schärer *et al.* 2000) was interpreted as indicating a Palaeozoic age for the ophiolite complex. This is in marked contrast to the Jurassic and Cretaceous ages from the Swiss-Italian Valais ophiolites (see above). In the Préalpes klippe, the Valaisan is represented by the Zone Submediane, a mélange zone below the floor thrust of Briançonnais-derived nappes, and by the underlying Niesen Nappe with thick Late Cretaceous to Eocene deep-marine clastics (Niesen Flysch; Fig. 18.7).

*Valaisan nappes in the Engadine Window*

Rocks from the Valais Ocean are exposed in the central part of the Engadine Window. The lowermost unit in the window is the Pfunds Zone, a thick pile of probably Cretaceous calcareous schists (Bündnerschiefer) with intercalated ophiolites (e.g. at Piz Mundin; Oberhauser 1980). The Pfunds Zone may be subdivided into a lower part (Mundin Unit) containing blueschist-facies assemblages (Mg-carpholite and glaucophane) and a higher part (Arina Unit) which experienced lower greenschist-facies metamorphism (Bousquet *et al.* 1999). The overlying tectonic mélange including Bündnerschiefer, deep-marine clastics, and ophiolite slices is referred to as the Roz-Champatsch-Pezid Zone (Oberhauser 1980, 1998). Slivers of Mesozoic sedimentary rocks, in a typical Austro-Alpine facies, are tectonically intercalated at the boundary between the Pfunds and the Roz-Champatsch-Pezid zones (Stammerspitze). In the southwestern part of the Engadine Window, the Roz-Champatsch-Pezid Zone is overlain by the Prutz-Ramosch Zone which includes pillow basalts and fragments of serpentinized mantle lherzolite. These are, in turn, overlain by a sheet of granitic/gneissic basement with a cover of Triassic to Palaeogene-age sediments (Tasna Nappe, derived from the Briançonnais fragment). Florineth & Froitzheim (1994) suggested that Lower Cretaceous sediments of the Tasna Nappe onlap both the granitic/gneissic basement and a lherzolite body belonging to the Prutz-Ramosch Zone (Piz Nair serpentinite). Hence, this location preserves a former ocean–continent transition between the Briançonnais continental crust to the south and the Valais Ocean to the north (Florineth & Froitzheim 1994.). These relationships support the assumption of Early Cretaceous opening of the Valais Ocean kinematically linked with the opening of the Bay of Biscay and transtensional basin formation in the Pyrenees (Frisch 1979; Stampfli 1993; see Manatschal *et al.* 2006 for a different interpretation). Towards the NE, the Tasna Nappe is replaced by an Alpine tectonic mélange, the Fimber Zone (Oberhauser 1998).

### *Middle Penninic (Briançonnais-derived) nappes*

The Briançonnais fragment was a block of continental crust, wider in the SW and tapering out to the NE, that existed during the Cretaceous between the Piemont-Ligurian Ocean and the Valais Ocean (Fig. 18.3). Frisch (1979) and Stampfli (1993) interpreted the Briançonnais fragment as a prolongation of the Iberian continent into the Alpine realm, a hypothesis that is today widely accepted. The southward pinching-out of the Valais units in France may be explained by omission through Alpine faults (Fügenschuh *et al.* 1999) or, alternatively, may reflect the primary termination of the oceanic basin. The term Briançonnais, as used here, comprises not only the Briançonnais *sensu stricto* as exposed in the type area, but also the Sub-Briançonnais units derived from a Jurassic to Cretaceous basin on continental crust along the northwestern margin of the Briançonnais fragment. It also comprises the Pre-Piemontais units. These sedimentary successions were probably deposited on the SE margin of the Briançonnais fragment (although some of the Pre-Piemontais units may have been derived from a more internal continental fragment, Cervinia). The Middle Penninic nappes are partly sedimentary nappes, partly composite sediment/basement nappes. The sedimentary successions are characterized by Early to Middle Jurassic rift tectonics related to the opening of the Piemont-Ligurian Ocean, leading to the emergence of the Briançonnais *sensu stricto* as the rift shoulder and the formation of the Sub-Briançonnais rim basin NW of it (Stampfli *et al.* 1998). Rifting and opening of the Valais Ocean are also recorded in the sediments (e.g. Tithonian-age, rift-related Falknis Breccia in the Falknis Nappe of eastern Switzerland).

The Middle Penninic nappes escaped Alpine eclogite-facies metamorphism, except in the most internal Briançonnais units of the Western Alps (Acceglio Unit; Schwartz *et al.* 2000). Briançonnais nappes in internal positions show a blueschist-facies overprint (e.g. the Suretta and Tambo nappes in eastern Switzerland and the Vanoise and Ambin units in the western Alps).

*Middle Penninic nappes in the eastern Central and Eastern Alps*

The Tambo Nappe and the overlying Suretta Nappe (Fig. 18.6) are basement nappes with a thin overlying cover of Permo-Triassic clastic sediments which follow an important hiatus with equally thin Cretaceous (or Jurassic?) breccias and calcareous schists. This sedimentary cover is, in the case of both the Tambo Nappe and the Suretta Nappe, overlain by an allochthonous Triassic to Cretaceous sedimentary succession, again showing an important hiatus in the Middle to Upper Triassic and Liassic (Baudin *et al.* 1995; Stampfli *et al.* 1998). This allochthonous cover, the Starlera Nappe, was emplaced on the Tambo and Suretta nappes by thin-skinned thrusting before the Suretta Nappe was thrust towards the north over the Tambo Nappe, leading to the duplication of the Starlera Nappe. All of this occurred during the Palaeogene. The Starlera Nappe is derived from the southeastern part of the Briançonnais fragment (Baudin *et al.* 1995) and the Suretta and Tambo nappes from a palaeogeographic high in the central part of the fragment. However, the existence of the Starlera Nappe is controversial because, due to the lack of fossils, the interpretation of Baudin *et al.* (1995) is based on lithostratigraphy alone. Other authors assume that the succession which forms the Starlera Nappe, according to Baudin *et al.* (1995), belongs rather to the autochthonous sediment cover of the Suretta and Tambo nappes (e.g. Schmid *et al.* 1996).

The Schams Nappes (Fig. 18.6), which are extremely deformed sediment nappes with various facies evolutions during the Jurassic and Cretaceous, were probably derived from the northwestern margin of the Briançonnais fragment (Schmid *et al.* 1990). They are probably rooted below the Tambo Nappe, at the top of the Misox Zone, and were folded back around the front of the Tambo and Suretta nappes by a north-closing recumbent fold (the Niemet-Beverin fold, Fig. 18.6; Milnes & Schmutz 1978; Schmid *et al.* 1990) of late Eocene to Early Oligocene age (35 to 31 Ma). Above the Suretta Nappe, a south-closing recumbent fold brings the Schams Nappes back into their proper position in the nappe stack, between the Piemont-Ligurian units above and the Valaisan units below (Schmid *et al.* 1990; Schreurs 1993; Weh & Froitzheim 2001). In this area, the Schams Nappes are omitted due to a top-to-the-east low-angle normal fault of the same age (35 to 31 Ma), the Turba Fault (Fig. 18.6; Nievergelt *et al.* 1996). Further to the north, where the Turba Fault dies out, sedimentary nappes equivalent to the Schams Nappes reappear at the same structural position, in the form of the Falknis Nappe and the Sulzfluh Nappe (Figs 18.2 & 18.7).

The Late Jurassic to Cretaceous sediment succession of the Falknis Nappe was deposited in a basin similar to that of the Sub-Briançonnais. After deposition of the youngest sediments in the Palaeocene to possibly Early Eocene (Allemann 1957), the sedimentary succession was spectacularly folded. Two generations of folds may be distinguished. The Sulzfluh Nappe overlies the Falknis Nappe and is derived from a Late Jurassic carbonate platform south of the basin from which the Falknis Nappe was derived. It forms an antiformal stack of imbricated Upper Jurassic limestone sheets.

The Tasna Nappe in the Engadine Window (see above) had a sedimentary evolution similar to that of the Falknis Nappe. It was situated at the immediate transition from the Briançonnais continental fragment to the Valais Ocean (Florineth & Froitzheim 1994). No unequivocal Briançonnais elements occur further to the east, either in the Tauern Window or at the northern border of the Alps. Therefore it may be assumed that the Tasna Nappe marks the eastern end of the Briançonnais fragment where the Valais and Piemont-Ligurian basins merged into one Penninic Ocean.

*Middle Penninic nappes in the western Central Alps*

Briançonnais-derived nappes occur both in the internal part of the Alpine chain, in the Pennine Alps, and close to the front of the Alps in the Préalpes, a large outlier of the Penninic nappes, and minor klippen further to the east (e.g. the Mythen, Fig. 18.2). The main Briançonnais unit in the Préalpes is the Préalpes Médianes Nappe, also termed Klippen Nappe, comprising Triassic to Middle Eocene sediments. Its external part (Préalpes Médianes Plastiques) is deformed by large-scale thrust-related folds (Mosar *et al.* 1996; Wissing & Pfiffner 2002) whereas the internal part (Préalpes Médianes Rigides) is present as large fault-bounded blocks and slices (Fig. 18.7, profile C–C′). This reflects the different stratigraphies in each part. In the Préalpes Médianes Rigides, Jurassic platform carbonates rest with an erosional unconformity (due to the Middle Jurassic emersion) directly on Triassic ones. In the Préalpes Médianes Plastiques, in contrast, Lower and Middle Jurassic shale horizons exist and allow flexural flow. The Préalpes Médianes Plastiques are stratigraphically comparable to the Sub-Briançonnais in France, the Préalpes Médianes Rigides to the Briançonnais *sensu stricto* (Trümpy 1980). The Préalpes Médianes Nappe is unmetamorphosed in the NW changing to anchizonal in the area of the Préalpes Médianes Rigides. To the south, the Préalpes Médianes Rigides are overlain by the Breccia Nappe (Fig. 18.7, profile C–C′; Upper Triassic to Palaeocene) characterized by thick, rifting-related breccias of Jurassic age which may have been shed from fault scarps at the transition from the Briançonnais to the Piemont-Ligurian Ocean. The Breccia Nappe may be included in the Pre-Piemontais units.

In the Pennine Alps, the Briançonnais is represented by the St. Bernard Nappe (or Bernhard Nappe, Figs 18.8 & 18.9). This composite basement/sediment nappe has been subdivided into several sheets, including, from base to top and from originally external to internal (Escher *et al.* 1997; Sartori *et al.* 2006): (1) the Zone Houillière, a detached, coal-bearing Permo-Carboniferous graben fill, overlain by Triassic cover rocks; (2) the Ruitor Zone, a basement unit which is present only in the western part; (3) the Siviez-Mischabel Nappe, containing basement with a cover ranging from Late Carboniferous to Eocene; and (4) the Mont Fort Nappe, comprising basement and Permo-Carboniferous to Liassic cover rocks. The cover of the Siviez-Mischabel Nappe is best preserved in the Barrhorn area where the typical Briançonnais facies was recognized by Ellenberger (1953). The metamorphism of the St. Bernard Nappe is in the greenschist facies, increasing from base to top. Only the Mont Fort Nappe shows blueschist-facies metamorphism. Deformation and metamorphism commenced in the Eocene.

*Middle Penninic (Briançonnais and Sub-Briançonnais) nappes in the Western Alps*

The Briançonnais of the Western Alps comprises basement and cover nappes. The main Variscan basement complexes are (from north to south) the Ruitor, Vanoise and Ambin 'massifs' (they are in fact completely allochthonous and underlain by Lower Penninic nappes). These are formed by paraschists and gneisses with Variscan and older, greenschist- to amphibolite-facies metamorphism (Desmons 1977). Similar Briançonnais basement complexes crop out further SE in the Ligurian Alps. The Briançonnais cover is still partly attached to the basement and partly forms detached cover nappes.

Thick Upper Carboniferous to Permian clastic units comprise the Zone Houillière, the continuation of the same zone described above for the western Central Alps. Lower Triassic sandstones are overlain by Triassic platform carbonates with intercalated evaporites. During the Liassic to Middle Jurassic, the platform broke up into fault blocks along rift-related normal faults and was uplifted, partly above sea level, as evidenced by karst and bauxite formation (Faure & Mégard-Galli 1988; Goffé 1977). Large parts of the prerift cover were eroded. In the Bathonian, the area subsided again below sea level and during the Late Jurassic it was covered by pelagic limestones.

In the internal part of the Briançonnais, sedimentation continued until the Early Eocene; in the external parts, until the Late Eocene (Jaillard 1999). Breccia and olistolith deposition during the Late Cretaceous and earliest Tertiary, particularly in the internal part, provide evidence of tectonic activity at this time, but not yet leading to accretion of the nappes.

The most internal part of the Briançonnais in the Western Alps is the Acceglio Zone (= 'Ultra-Briançonnais'). The Alpine metamorphic grade is blueschist facies in the internal part (eclogite facies in the Acceglio Zone; Schwartz *et al.* 2000) to unmetamorphosed in the external part. Lemoine *et al.* (1986) interpreted the sedimentary nappes in the classic Briançon profile as assembled by simple east-over-west stacking and retrodeformed them accordingly. Claudel & Dumont (1999), however, found evidence for early north-directed thrusting and later west-directed out-of-sequence thrusting. Still later, the area was affected by dramatic top-to-the-east shearing and backfolding (Platt *et al.* 1989). The blueschist-metamorphic, Permo-Carboniferous metasediments of the Pinerolo Unit, underlying the Sub-Penninic Dora-Maira Nappe along its eastern contact, and similar rocks exposed in the Money Window below the Gran Paradiso Nappe, may also belong to the Briançonnais. As stated above, we assume a more external, European origin for the Gran Paradiso and Dora Maira nappes than for the Briançonnais. If the Pinerolo and Money units are indeed Briançonnais, they would have been overthrust by the Gran Paradiso and Dora-Maira nappes along out-of-sequence thrusts.

The Sub-Briançonnais underlies the Briançonnais *sensu stricto* along its western margin. This unit comprises unmetamorphosed Triassic and Jurassic carbonates and marls, detached along the Carnian evaporites. During the Early and Middle Jurassic, the Sub-Briançonnais represented a rim basin located to the NW of the Briançonnais rift shoulder on the northwestern margin of the Piemont-Liguria Ocean. In the Early Cretaceous it became part of the Iberia-Briançonnais microcontinent, separated from Europe by the Valais Ocean.

*Pre-Piemontais nappes*

The Pre-Piemontais nappes comprise several units that are generally found in two different structural positions: (1) between the Briançonnais (below) and Upper Penninic ophiolite nappes (above); and (2) intercalated between the Upper Penninic ophiolite nappes. The Breccia Nappe of the Préalpes is an example of the first situation, while an example of the second is the Cimes-Blanches Nappe (Fig. 18.9) at the boundary between the Zermatt-Saas Zone (below) and the Tsaté Nappe (above), two ophiolite-bearing Upper Penninic nappes (see below).

The Pre-Piemontais nappes are mostly formed by sedimentary successions originally deposited on, and detached from, continental basement. Some slivers of Variscan basement are also present, particularly in the Ligurian Alps, at the base of the Pre-Piemontais nappes (Seno *et al.* 2005). The Pre-Piemontais stratigraphy does not show the hiatus resulting from Early to Middle Jurassic uplift and erosion which is typical for the Briançonnais. Characteristic for the Pre-Piemontais are evaporites and dolomites in the Upper Triassic, Lower to Middle Jurassic rift breccias (e.g. in the Breccia Nappe), and Upper Jurassic radiolarites. The youngest sediments are early (to Middle?) Eocene turbidites (Seno *et al.* 2005).

It is generally assumed that the Pre-Piemontais units originated from the passive margin between the Briançonnais and the Piemont-Ligurian Ocean. However, this is probably not the case for all of the Pre-Piemontais units. In particular, the Cimes-Blanches Nappe was probably detached from Cervinia and emplaced by top-to-the-NW thrusting over the Zermatt-Saas Zone (Pleuger *et al.* 2007). It is, therefore, likely that the Pre-Piemontais is of heterogeneous origin, being partly derived from the internal Briançonnais margin and partly from Cervinia.

## Upper Penninic (Piemont-Ligurian) nappes

The Upper Penninic nappes include oceanic crust and sedimentary cover of the Piemont-Ligurian Ocean, also known as the Alpine Tethys. In addition, they include several continental nappes, the Sesia Nappe (= Sesia-Lanzo Zone), the Dent Blanche Nappe and the Margna Nappe (Upper Penninic continental nappes). These are derived from a continental fragment or microcontinent, Cervinia (Pleuger *et al.* 2007) or the Margna-Sesia fragment (Schmid *et al.* 2004*a*), within the Piemont-Ligurian Ocean. The Sesia and Dent Blanche nappes were originally treated as Penninic (Argand 1909) but later correlated with the Lower Austro-Alpine Err and Bernina nappes in the

Eastern Alps (Staub 1938) and, therefore, termed Austro-Alpine. More recent work has raised serious doubts about this correlation (e.g. Trümpy 1992; Froitzheim & Manatschal 1996; Froitzheim *et al.* 1996; Pleuger *et al.* 2007). Since the Penninic–Austro-Alpine boundary is defined as the top of the uppermost (palaeogeographically southernmost) Piemont–Ligurian ophiolites (Trümpy 1975), we adopt the view of Argand (1909) and treat the Sesia, Dent Blanche and Margna nappes as Upper Penninic continental nappes.

Oceanic Upper Penninic nappes are found all along the Alpine chain, from Liguria to eastern Austria. In the Central and Western Alps, radiometric ages of oceanic gabbros and their more acidic differentiates yielded ages of between $142 \pm 5$ and $166 \pm 1$ Ma, indicating oceanic spreading in the late Middle to Late Jurassic (Fig. 18.4; Liati *et al.* 2003, and references therein; Stucki *et al.* 2003). The Piemont-Liguria-derived nappes are of two types: ophiolite nappes and deep-marine clastic ('flysch') nappes. The characteristic sediment cover of the ophiolite nappes consists of radiolarites (Bathonian–Late Jurassic), Calpionella limestones (Tithonian–Berriasian) and Argille a Palombini Formation (shale with limestone layers; Neocomian), overlain by shales (often with ophiolite detritus), calcareous schists (Schistes lustrés) and various units of deep-marine clastics that are Late Cretaceous in age. Biostratigraphic ages from the radiolarite confirm that oceanic spreading began in the Bajocian (Bill *et al.* 2001).

The ophiolite nappes are subdivided in the Western Alps and western Central Alps into structurally deeper ones with eclogite-facies metamorphism (Voltri Ophiolites, Monte Viso Ophiolites, Lanzo Peridotite, Zermatt-Saas Zone) and higher ones with blueschist- to greenschist-facies metamorphism (Queyras area, Tsaté Nappe; Figs 18.2, 18.8 & 18.9). An important pressure gap occurs at the boundary of the two groups of nappes, between high pressure below and lower pressure above (Ballèvre & Merle 1993; Dal Piaz *et al.* 2001; Bousquet *et al.* 2004). (The Tsaté Nappe and the Cimes-Blanches Nappe are collectively termed the Combin Zone; see Fig. 18.8.) The uppermost ophiolite-bearing nappes in the Western Alps are unmetamorphosed (Montgenèvre or Chenaillet Ophiolite).

In the eastern Central Alps, Piemont-Ligurian ophiolites and their sediment cover form the greenschist-facies Platta Nappe. Towards the south, the Platta Nappe is prolongated by two layers of ophiolites, above and below the continental Upper Penninic Margna Nappe (see below). The structurally deeper ophiolite layer includes the Malenco Ultramafic Complex, comprising mostly mantle rocks exhumed by rifting (Fig. 18.6; Trommsdorff *et al.* 1993; Hermann *et al.* 1997). At a still deeper structural level, Piemont-Ligurian ophiolites also occur in the Avers Bündnerschiefer Nappe which underwent blueschist-facies metamorphism (Oberhänsli 1978). The Avers Bündnerschiefer Nappe is separated from the structurally higher Piemont-Ligurian ophiolite nappes by the Turba Fault, an east-dipping, Palaeogene normal fault (Nievergelt *et al.* 1996). Towards the north, the Platta Nappe continues into the Arosa Zone, a strongly dismembered unit along the base of the Austro-Alpine nappes which records a complicated history of Cretaceous and Tertiary subduction (Ring *et al.* 1988; Nagel 2006). The Arosa Zone contains Piemont-Ligurian ophiolites, their sedimentary cover, and slivers of basement and sediments of Austro-Alpine provenance. The Cenomanian–Turonian-age Verspala Flysch (part of the Arosa zone) contains abundant chromite, suggesting erosion of already accreted Piemont-Ligurian oceanic crust at that time (Burger 1978; Oberhauser 1983). The Arosa Zone is also exposed in the Engadine Window where it forms the uppermost structural unit. It comprises Jurassic-age ophiolites (e.g. Idalpe Ophiolite) with a cover of radiolarite, which experienced a blueschist-facies metamorphic imprint (Höck & Koller 1987).

The flysch nappes derived from the Piemont-Ligurian Ocean lack an ophiolite basement. They comprise the Helminthoid Flysch nappes, of Campanian to locally Middle Eocene age and including characteristic light-coloured, fine-grained calciturbidites ('Alberese'). Such nappes include the San Remo and Alassio nappes in the Ligurian Alps, the Parpaillon and Autapie nappes in the external part of the Western Alps, the Gurnigel Flysch Nappe in the frontal part of the Préalpes (Fig. 18.7), the Dranse Nappe on top of the Préalpes, and the Schlieren and Wägital Flysch nappes further to the east. (However, Trümpy (2006) proposed that the Gurnigel, Schlieren and Wägital nappes may be derived from the Valais Ocean.) Some of these nappes lie in a very external position, for example, the Parpaillon and Autapie nappes which travelled over the Briançonnais nappes transporting slivers of Briançonnais at their base. They were later overthrust by the main mass of the Briançonnais along a top-to-the-west out-of-sequence thrust. Some klippen of the Helminthoid Flysch nappes are also found in the Western Alps on the Briançonnais nappes themselves. The Gets Nappe, the uppermost unit of the Préalpes, consists of Cretaceous deep-marine clastics containing olistoliths of both oceanic (166 Ma gabbro; Bill *et al.* 1997) and continental provenance. The underlying Simme Nappe consists of chromite-bearing (ophiolite-fed) deep-marine clastics of Cretaceous age. Assigning certain depositional areas in the Piemont-Ligurian ocean basins to these tectonic units is still rather speculative. It is often assumed that the Helminthoid Flysch units were deposited close to the Apulian margin, since the Late Cretaceous calciturbidites required a carbonate shelf source area which can only have been the Apulian shelf at that time.

The Sesia and Dent Blanche nappes in the western Central Alps and the Margna Nappe in the Eastern Alps were derived from a continental fragment or microcontinent (i.e. Cervinia) between two branches of the Piemont-Ligurian Ocean. The Sesia Nappe and the Dent Blanche Nappe (Figs 18.8 & 18.9) represent the rear and frontal part, respectively, of one originally continuous thrust sheet. Both units lie on top of the Tsaté Nappe (Piemont-Ligurian ophiolites, see above). Both comprise three different types of basement: (1) Variscan basement with a Permian granulite-facies overprint (Valpelline Series in the Dent Blanche Nappe, Seconda Zona Dioritico-Kinzigitica or '2DK' in the Sesia Nappe); (2) Variscan upper-crustal basement; and (3) Permian gabbros. In addition, thin slivers of Mesozoic cover rocks are present. The Alpine-age overprint comprises eclogite-facies metamorphism in the Sesia Nappe, dated at *c.* 65 Ma (Rubatto *et al.* 1999), to blueschist-facies metamorphism in the Dent Blanche Nappe. Basement rocks with the typical characteristics of the Sesia and Dent Blanche nappes occur not only within these but also at deeper structural levels (Ballèvre *et al.* 1986), either immediately below the contact between the Zermatt-Saas Zone and the Tsaté Nappe (Fig. 18.8) or deeper within the Zermatt-Saas Zone. The slivers underwent eclogite-facies metamorphism, together with the Zermatt-Saas ophiolites, at 45 to 40 Ma (Dal Piaz *et al.* 2001).

Along the Periadriatic Fault, thin lenses of ophiolite occur between the Sesia Nappe to the NW and the Canavese Zone to the SE, e.g. at Levone (Fig. 18.8). The Canavese Zone represents the distal passive continental margin of the Apulian continent, characterized by rifting-related breccias in the Jurassic (Ferrando *et al.* 2004). This led several authors (Aubouin *et al.* 1977; Mattauer *et al.* 1987) to place the suture of the Piemont-Ligurian

Ocean between the South Alpine units and the Sesia Nappe, and not NW of Sesia. New structural work (Pleuger *et al.* 2007) suggests that the Tsaté Nappe represents an accretionary prism formed during the subduction of the internal basin of the Piemont-Ligurian Ocean, between Cervinia and the Apulian margin, and that the Zermatt-Saas Zone is a remnant of the external basin. Following closure of the internal basin, the Tsaté Nappe was thrust over the Sesia and Dent Blanche nappes and came to lie on the – already partly exhumed – Zermatt-Saas Zone. The Tsaté and Zermatt-Saas units were subsequently overthrust by the Sesia and Dent Blanche nappes along an out-of-sequence thrust.

The Margna Nappe at the western border of the Eastern Alps comprises the same lithological association as the Sesia and Dent Blanche Nappes (see above) but was only affected by elevated-pressure greenschist-facies metamorphism during the Alpine Orogeny (Liniger & Guntli 1988). It is sandwiched between Piemont-Ligurian ophiolites above (Platta Nappe) and below (Malenco Ultramafic Complex).

## *Penninic nappes in the Eastern Alps*

Since the Brianconnais probably ended in the Engadine Window, oceanic series found further east in the Tauern Window, the Rechnitz window group, and along the northern border of the Alps were derived from one large Penninic ocean. A subdivision into Valaisan and Piemont-Ligurian-derived units is, therefore, not necessary. Nevertheless, structurally deeper units in the Tauern Window (Glockner Nappe System) resemble the Valais units in the Central Alps, and structurally higher units (Matrei Zone) the Piemont-Ligurian units. In Figure 18.10, the units were correlated in this way.

### *Glockner Nappe System in the Tauern Window*

The Glockner Nappe System (Fig. 18.10) overlies the Sub-Penninic Venediger Nappe System and comprises slices of ophiolites (mostly greenschists, prasinites to amphibolites, and some serpentinites) and a thick mass of calcareous schists, phyllites and mica-rich marbles (Bündnerschiefer) which were deposited on the ophiolites. Permo-Triassic sedimentary rocks directly beneath the Glockner Nappe System, partly with underlying continental basement lamellae, were previously interpreted as forming the pre-Jurassic part of the Glockner Nappe System (e.g. Tollmann 1977). However, it is now thought that they originated at the European continental margin (Kurz *et al.* 1998) and, thus, belong to the Sub-Penninic nappes (see above). In the Glockner Nappe System several nappes can be distinguished based on their facies and structural position. The lower nappes are rich in ophiolite fragments ('Glockner facies') whereas structurally higher nappes lack ophiolitic material ('Fusch facies').

The Glockner Nappe System underwent a subduction-related high-pressure metamorphism (reaching blueschist-facies conditions in some parts) and was overprinted by an Oligocene to Miocene greenschist- to amphibolite-facies metamorphism ('Tauernkristallisation') (Frank 1987; Schuster *et al.* 2004).

### *Matrei Zone and equivalents in the Tauern Window*

In the Tauern Window the Glockner Nappe System is overlain by units representing a tectonic and sedimentary mélange with a characteristic lithological content. These comprise the Matrei Zone in the south and the 'Nordrahmenzone' (Northern frame zone) in the east, north and west. Slices of oceanic crust consisting of serpentinite, in contact with radiolarite and Aptychus limestone, are similar to the Piemont-Ligurian ophiolite nappes of the Central and Western Alps (Koller & Pestal 2003). Olistoliths of material from the Austro-Alpine continental margin are also found (Frisch *et al.* 1989). The matrix consists of Cretaceous to Jurassic calcareous schists or phyllites and mica-rich marbles (Bündnerschiefer). The Matrei Zone and its equivalents formed during the subduction of the Penninic Ocean below the Austro-Alpine continental margin in an accretionary wedge setting. The ophiolite components are derived from Jurassic oceanic crust in the southern part of that ocean. The Reckner Complex, overlying the adjoining Austro-Alpine units at the NW corner of the Tauern Window, also represents an ophiolite sequence with Jurassic radiolarites. Its present tectonic position is a result of complex tectonics in this region which are not yet fully understood.

The Reckner Complex and parts of the Matrei Zone underwent a blueschist-facies metamorphism with conditions of *c.* 1.0 GPa and 350°C, dated at *c.* 50 Ma (Dingeldey *et al.* 1997; Koller & Pestal 2003). Together with the 'Nordrahmenzone' they were overprinted under greenschist-facies conditions ('Tauern-Kristallisation').

### *Penninic nappes of the Rechnitz Window Group*

At the eastern margin of the Eastern Alps, Penninic units occur in several tectonic windows (Fig. 18.1; e.g. Rechnitz, Eisenberg Window). They comprise slices of ophiolites and a pile of metasediments several kilometres thick, including calcareous mica schists, quartz phyllites, graphite phyllites, rare breccias and a few horizons of cargneule (Pahr 1980). Microfossils indicate a late Lower Cretaceous to Upper Cretaceous age for parts of the metasediments (Schönlaub 1973). During the Alpine metamorphic cycle, parts of the unit were metamorphosed under blueschist-facies conditions (330–370°C at a minimum pressure of 600–800 MPa), whereas the entire unit was affected by a greenschist-facies imprint with cooling ages ranging from 22 to 19 Ma (Koller 1985).

### *Rhenodanubian Flysch Zone and Ybbsitz Klippen Zone*

The Rhenodanubian Flysch Zone (Figs 18.10, 18.11) along the northern border of the Eastern Alps is formed by predominantly deep-marine clastic sediments. Their age is Early Cretaceous to Maastrichtian (in the western part) or to Eocene (in the eastern part). In both parts, the Rhenodanbian Flysch Zone is subdivided into several nappes (Oberstdorf, Sigiswang and Üntschen nappes in the west, Laab, Greifenstein and Kahlenberg nappes in the east). These nappes were stacked by north- to NW-directed thrusts (Decker 1990). However, out-of-sequence thrusting led to the situation that the more northerly derived units (Oberstdorf Nappe in the west, Laab Nappe in the east) locally lie on top of more southerly derived units (Sigiswang Nappe in the west, Greifenstein and Kahlenberg nappes in the east; Fuchs 1985; Oberhauser 1995; Mattern 1999; Trautwein *et al.* 2001).

The Rhenodanubian Flysch was deposited at least partly on Jurassic oceanic crust which is preserved in the Ybbsitz Klippen Zone (Decker 1990; Schnabel 1992). This unit is structurally above the Rhenodanubian Flysch, directly at the base of the Austro-Alpine nappes. Similar to the Matrei Zone of the Tauern Window, the Ybbsitz Klippen Zone contains serpentinites in contact with Jurassic radiolarites and Aptychus limestones which correspond to the Piemont-Ligurian ophiolite nappes of the Central and Western Alps. The Ybbsitz Klippen Zone also includes Cretaceous deep-marine clastics which are developed in a similar facies to the Rhenodanubian Flysch nappes. Therefore, it probably represents a piece of the former basement of the Rhenodanubian Flysch nappes (Schnabel 1992).

Other parts of the basin floor may have been Cretaceous-age oceanic crust (see Fig. 18.3). The Rhenodanubian Flysch was detached from its oceanic basement during subduction and formed part of an accretionary wedge at the front of the Austro-Alpine nappes.

## *Austro-Alpine nappes*

The Austro-Alpine nappes represent a crustal fragment with a complex Phanerozoic history, documented by their (meta)sedimentary successions and the large variety of magmatic rocks. Due to imprints during the Variscan, Permo-Triassic, Eo-Alpine (Cretaceous) and Alpine (Tertiary) metamorphic events, large parts of the Austro-Alpine nappes consist of crystalline rocks. These rocks show different metamorphic histories, different relations to Permo-Mesozoic cover series, and occur in different tectonic positions within the nappe stack which formed during the Eo-Alpine and Alpine events. Other Austro-Alpine nappes are formed entirely from Permo-Mesozoic sedimentary rocks.

There has been a long-standing controversy about the tectonic correlation of the different nappes and their palaeogeographic restoration (Tollman 1959; Frank 1987; Neubauer *et al.* 2000). The subdivision provided below follows the one of Schmid *et al.* (2004*a*). The Austro-Alpine nappes are subdivided into Lower and Upper Austro-Alpine, and the Upper Austro-Alpine nappes themselves are grouped into several nappe systems (Figs 18.10, 18.11 & 18.12). This subdivision is an attempt to reflect not only the distribution of the sedimentary units of various ages and facies but also the internal tectonic style as well as the distribution and timing of metamorphism in the crystalline units.

### *Lower Austro-Alpine units*

The Lower Austro-Alpine units are defined as that part of the Austro-Alpine units which formed the northern margin of Apulia towards the Piemont-Ligurian Ocean in Jurassic to Early Tertiary times. For this reason they were affected by both the opening and closure of this oceanic realm. Preceding the opening in the Jurassic, the Lower Austro-Alpine units underwent extension, as demonstrated by the formation of tilted blocks, half-grabens and extensional detachment faults, as well as the deposition of breccias (Häusler 1987; Eberli 1988; Froitzheim & Eberli 1990; Manatschal & Nievergelt 1997). When the Penninic oceans closed in Late Cretaceous to Tertiary times, the Lower Austro-Alpine nappes were involved in the subduction-related deformation and underwent anchizonal to greenschist-facies metamorphism (Schuster *et al.* 2004).

Most of the Lower Austro-Alpine nappes contain a Variscan metamorphic basement and a Permo-Mesozoic cover series. Late Carboniferous sedimentary rocks occur between these in some nappes. The Permo-Mesozoic cover commences with Permian-age metaconglomerates and acidic metavolcanics, Lower Triassic quartzites (Semmering and Lantschfeld quarzites) and Middle Triassic shallow-marine carbonates (e.g. Wetterstein limestones and dolomites). A Keuper facies with gypsum and shales is characteristic of the Upper Triassic strata of the eastern part, whereas in the western part shales, sandstones and evaporites of Carnian age are followed by dolomite (Hauptdolomit) in the Norian. Fossil-rich marls (Kössen Formation) were deposited in the Rhaetian. Jurassic sediments include Liassic and early Middle Jurassic syntectonic breccias and Upper Jurassic radiolarites. The youngest sediments in the western Lower Austro-Alpine nappes are Late Cretaceous deep-marine clastics (Furrer 1985). The successions are tectonically truncated at different stratigraphic levels (Tollmann 1977).

The Lower Austro-Alpine units are widespread in eastern Switzerland, particularly along the western margin of the Austro-Alpine nappes. They comprise the structurally deeper Err Nappe System and the higher Bernina Nappe System (Froitzheim *et al.* 1994) in the southern part of that margin, as well as slivers of Lower Austro-Alpine nappes further north. As mentioned above, slivers of Austro-Alpine origin also occur within some Upper Penninic ocean-derived units, e.g. in the Engadine Window and the Matrei Zone and 'Nordrahmenzone' of the Tauern Window (Frisch *et al.* 1989). These may have been emplaced either as olistoliths, by tectonic mélange formation, or as extensional allochthons during rifting and continental breakup.

The Sadnig and Zaneberg complexes to the south of the Tauern Window, consisting of crystalline basement and Late Palaeozoic metasediments (Fuchs & Linner 2005), are interpreted to represent Lower Austro-Alpine units, as are the Radstadt Nappe System and the Katschberg Zone at the eastern margin of the Tauern Window, and the Reckner and Hippold nappes at the northwestern margin. In the easternmost part of the Alps, the Wechsel Nappe and the Semmering Nappe (with the exception of the Grobgneiss Nappe) can be correlated with the Lower Austro-Alpine units.

The Upper Austro-Alpine units comprise the remaining major part of the Austro-Alpine nappes. They represent a complex nappe stack formed by the Eo-Alpine tectonometamorphic events. During the Tertiary Alpine events, the nappe stack stayed in an upper-plate position and Tertiary deformation is mostly restricted to brittle faulting.

### *Bajuvaric, Tirolic, and Juvavic nappe systems (Northern Calcareous Alps)*

The Northern Calcareous Alps are composed of, from bottom to top, the Bajuvaric, Tirolic and Juvavic nappe systems (Figs 18.11 & 18.12). All three consist of Permian- to Palaeocene-age sediments. However, the Triassic facies evolution of the individual nappe systems shows significant differences and, furthermore, the tectonically controlled Jurassic and Cretaceous sediments are variable (Tollmann 1985). Additionally, these nappe systems were mobilized at different times during the Eo-Alpine orogeny. The nappe systems are described below in the context of the geodynamic evolution from Permian to Palaeocene times, closely following the more detailed descriptions in Mandl (2000) and Faupl & Wagreich (2000).

In Permian times, fluviatile red-beds (e.g. Prebichl Formation) and, locally, shallow-marine evaporitic sediments were deposited in the area of the three nappe systems. Subsequently, a shallow-marine basin developed, broadly silicilastic-filled with limestone layers intercalated in the upper part (Werfen schists, Alpiner Buntsandstein). In the Early Anisian, bituminous micritic carbonates were deposited under restricted shallow-water conditions (Gutenstein Formation). These pass laterally into Dasycladacean-bearing carbonates (Steinalm Formation). During the Middle Anisian rapid deepening and contemporaneous block faulting resulted in the formation of a seafloor relief and the deposition of nodular limestones (Reifling Formation). Most probably the tectonic activity was related to the rifting and breakup of the Meliata Ocean to the SE. Subsequently, extensive carbonate platforms (Wetterstein limestone and dolomite) developed in the proximal shelf area with lateral slope sediments (Raming limestone) deposited towards the intervening basins. These basins were filled by nodular limestones (Reifling Formation) and shales (Partnach Formation). On the deeper, outer shelf area closer to the Meliata Ocean, pelagic limestones were deposited (Hallstatt limestone). The transition from the pelagic limestones towards

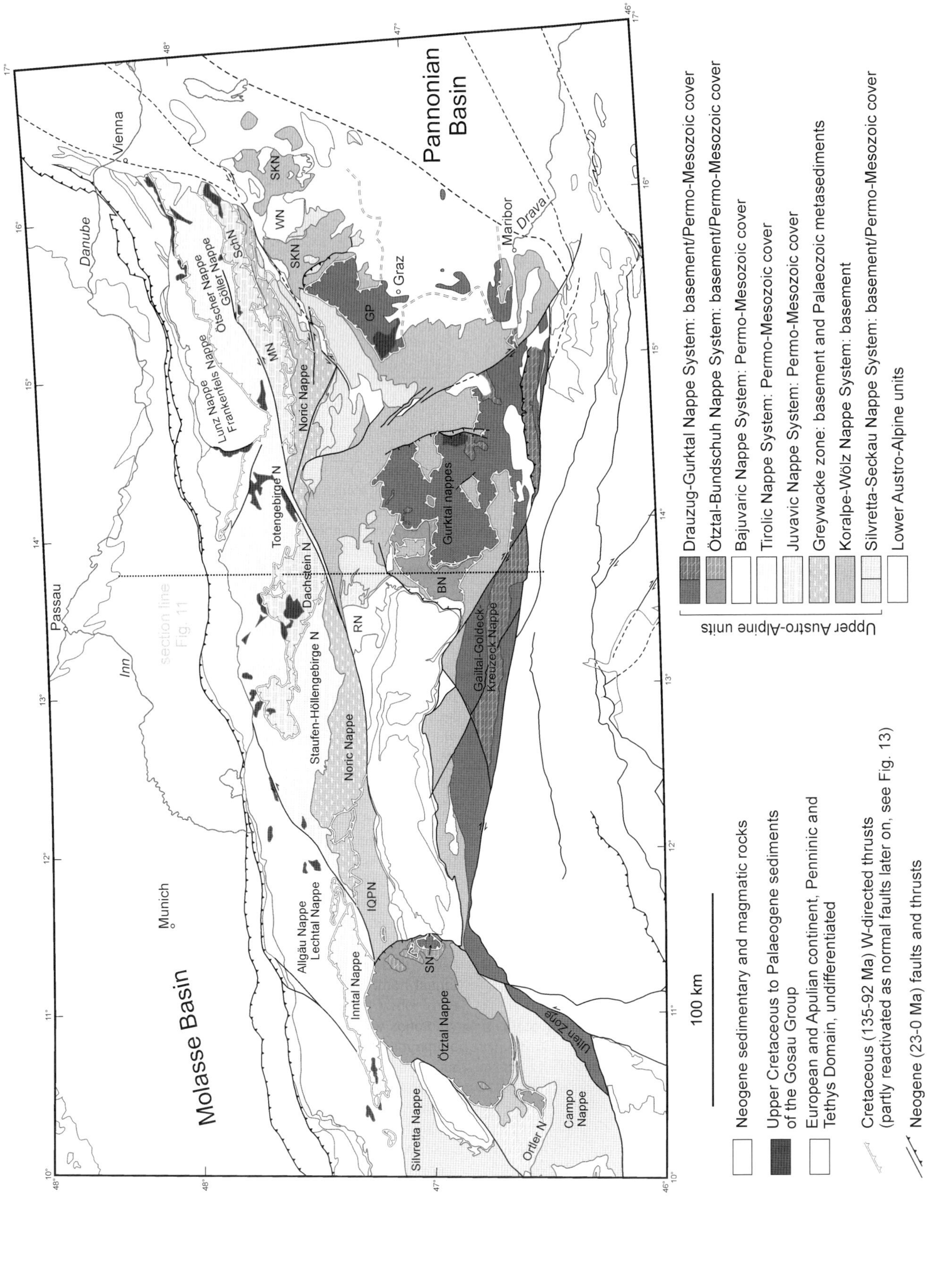


**Fig. 18.12.** Subdivision of the Austro-Alpine units into nappe systems. Abbreviations: see caption to Figure 18.10.

the radiolarites of the oceanic realm is not preserved in the Northern Calcareous Alps. In general, the Wetterstein carbonate platforms prograded onto the adjacent basinal sediments until earliest Carnian times. A subsequent sea-level lowstand resulted in a rapid decrease in carbonate production. The platforms became partly emergent and the remaining interplatform basins were completely filled by siliciclastic material from the European hinterland and intercalated carbonates (Raibl Group). Brackish-water sandstones with coals formed the Lunz Formation, whereas on the slopes and the deeper shelf the regression event can be recognized by the siliciclastic influx in the Reingraben schists.

In the Late Carnian, sea level began to rise and flooded the platform areas where both lagoonal carbonates (Waxeneck limestone and dolomite) and carbonates intercalated with gypsum (Opponitz limestone and dolomite) were now deposited. A transgressive pulse at the end of the Carnian resulted in the onlap of pelagic limestones onto the former platforms, and initial reef growth within the remaining shallow-marine areas. Subsequently a second extensive carbonate platform was established. In the central part of the Northern Calcareous Alps its reefs (Dachstein limestone) are situated on top of the Wetterstein reefs and are connected to the Hallstatt-facies basinal sediments (e.g. Hallstatt limestone, Pötschen limestone) of the deeper shelf by allodapic limestones (Gosausee limestone). In the eastern part of the Northern Calcareous Alps, in contrast, the reefs are located above the former platform interior, several kilometres behind the former Wetterstein reef front. Pelagic sediments were deposited on top of the latter until late Norian times (Aflenz Formation, Hallstatt limestone). A large lagoonal area extended behind (to the NW of) the Dachstein reefs. Bedded limestones (Dachstein limestone) were deposited directly behind the reefs, and dolomites (Hauptdolomit) more to the NW. In the most proximal (northwestern) part of the lagoonal area the dolomites contain evidence of siliciclastic influx derived from the siliciclastic shelf (Keuper facies) located further to the north. This influx increased in Rhaetian times and large parts of the lagoonal area were covered by dark marly sediments with small patch-reefs, indicating a restricted facies (Kössen Formation). Coevally, the marls of the Zlambach Formation were deposited in the deeper shelf areas. The total thickness of the Permo-Triassic succession in the Northern Calcareous Alps is up to *c*. 3 km.

At the beginning of the Jurassic, the Austro-Alpine shelf was drowned and synsedimentary faulting resulted in the formation of a complex seafloor topography. Strongly condensed nodular limestones with Fe/Mn hardgrounds and ammonoids (e.g. Adnet and Klaus formations) or crinoids (Hierlatz limestone) were deposited in elevated areas, whereas marly and cherty limestones (Allgäu Formation) were deposited in the intervening troughs. The water depths were greatest in the Callovian and Oxfordian, when radiolarites were deposited (Ruhpolding radiolarite). At this time, tectonically induced mass-transport complexes (i.e. breccias, olistoliths, and sliding blocks and nappes, several kilometres in size, in a radiolarite matrix) were deposited (e.g. Strubberg Formation). Initially, this material was derived from mobilized units of the Triassic deeper shelf (Hallstatt facies), and later from the Triassic platform margins which had been imbricated by a system of ramp faults (Gawlick & Suzuki 1999; Mandl 2000).

The material which became mobilized during the Jurassic tectonic event forms the Juvavic Nappe System. Ongoing sedimentation sealed the contacts along which the Juvavic nappes were emplaced on the units which later formed the Tirolic Nappe System. In the Kimmeridgian and Tithonian the new seafloor topography aided the growth of reefs (Plassen and Tressenstein limestones) on elevated parts of large sliding blocks and nappes of the Juvavic Nappe System, whereas pelagic limestones were deposited in deeper areas and to the north (Oberalm Formation). The Oberalm Formation extends up into the earliest Cretaceous, when deepening and increasing terrigeneous input led to a gradual transition into the Early Cretaceous marly Aptychus limestones of the Schrambach Formation.

In the Valanginian, shortening and nappe stacking propagated from SE to NW and resulted in the renewed deposition of mass-transport complexes. The nappes of the Tirolic Nappe System were detached from their basement. They represent southeastern parts of the Norian lagoonal area and carried the sealed Juvavic mass transport complexes on top. At their southern margins the Tirolic nappes remained in transgressive contact with their basement, which is formed by Palaeozoic-age metasediments of the Noric Nappe (belonging to the Greywacke Zone, see below). The Tirolic Nappe System was thrust onto the northwestern parts of the lagoonal area, which later became the Bajuvaric Nappe System.

During thrusting, large parts of the Tirolic and Juvavic nappe systems were elevated above sea level, but at the front of the individual Tirolic nappes the deep-marine clastics of the Rossfeld Formation were deposited. In the Aptian, the deposition of deformation-related mass-transport complexes shifted further to the NW. The deep-water marly Aptychus limestones passed up into a marl-rich succession with black shales (Tannheim Formation, Late Aptian to Albian) which was overlain by silty marls, turbidites and deep-marine conglomerates (Losenstein Formation, Albian to Cenomanian). The Tannheim-Losenstein Basin, located in the area of the Bajuvaric Nappe System, was filled with material from the south and from the north. According to Wagreich (2001*a*), local material of the arriving nappes was carried into the basin from the south whereas 'exotic' material was deposited from the north (e.g. metamorphic basement rocks, serpentinites, Jurassic and Cretaceous limestone of 'Urgonian' type).

In some areas of the Bajuvaric Nappe System, Cenomanian to Santonian marine sediments (including turbidites and shales) were deposited (Branderfleck Formation). They lie unconformably on older rocks. At this time detritus was still partly derived from the north and included phengites with Variscan cooling ages and glaucophane (von Eynatten & Gaupp 1999).

Large parts of the Northern Calcareous Alps became terrestrial in the Turonian. In the Late Turonian a new sedimentary cycle began with the deposition of the Gosau Group. The Gosau Group of the Northern Calcareous Alps can be subdivided into two subgroups (Faupl *et al.* 1987). The Lower Gosau Subgroup (Turonian to Campanian/Maastrichtian) consists of terrestrial, mainly fluviatile conglomerates which pass into a shallow-marine succession. Detritus from Permian quartz porphyries and from ophiolites is present, in addition to local detritus from the surrounding Mesozoic rocks. Sedimentation occurred in pull-apart-type basins in a predominantly transpressional regime (Wagreich & Faupl 1994).

By this time the entire Bajuvaric Nappe System had been detached from its basement. Typically the sedimentary profiles in the Bajuvaric nappes commence in the Middle or Upper Triassic. Permian-age strata are generally missing and may have remained attached to the basement.

The Upper Gosau Subgroup (Campanian–Palaeocene) is characterized by deep-water sediments such as marl-rich slope sediments with slumps (Nierental Formation) and breccias (Spitzenbach Formation, Zwieselalm Formation) which were deposited on a north-facing slope, partly below the carbonate compensation depth (CCD). The terrigenous material of the Upper Gosau Subgroup is characterized by metamorphic detritus eroded from an area to the south of the Northern Calcareous Alps. The sudden change in facies from the Lower to the Upper Gosau Subgroup took place diachronously, earlier in the NW of the Northern Calcareous Alps (Santonian) and progressively later in the SE (Palaeocene). In several localities the deep-water sediments unconformably rest upon deformed deposits of the Lower Gosau Subgroup (Faupl & Wagreich 2000).

During the Eo-Alpine Orogeny the Tirolic Nappe System underwent anchizonal to lowermost greenschist-facies metamorphism along its southern margin, whereas the rest of the Northern Calcareous Alps remained in the zone of diagenesis (Fig. 18.13; Kralik *et al.* 1987).

*Greywacke Zone*

The nappe system of the Greywacke Zone (Figs 18.11 18.12) underlies the Tirolic Nappe System and includes, from bottom to the top, the Veitsch, Silbersberg, Vöstenhof-Kaintaleck and Noric nappes (Neubauer *et al.* 1994*b*). The lowermost Veitsch Nappe mainly comprises Carboniferous clastic and carbonaceous metasediments with metamorphosed coal intercalations and magnesite. Permian clastic sediments are locally present. The overlying Silbersberg Nappe consists of phyllites with intercalations of chlorite schists and the Gloggnitz riebeckite gneiss. The latter represents alkaline metavolcanics, possibly Jurassic in age (Koller & Zemann 1990). The Vöstenhof-Kaintaleck Nappe is formed by a basement of paragneisses, mica schists and amphibolites with overlying post-Mid-Devonian clastic metasediments (e.g. Kalwang conglomerate). The crystalline rocks of this nappe show a Variscan amphibolite-facies imprint with remarkably old Variscan cooling ages of more than 350 Ma (Neubauer *et al.* 1994*b*).

The largest and uppermost Noric Nappe (including the western part of the Greywacke Zone) comprises a Lower Palaeozoic to Upper Carboniferous succession of phyllites, acidic and basic metavolcanics, quartzites and carbonates (marbles, dolomites, siderite and magnesite deposits). This is transgressively overlain by the Permian-age strata of the Tirolic Nappe System.

Within the nappe pile of the Greywacke Zone the Eo-Alpine metamorphic grade increases downward to upper greenschist facies in parts of the lowermost nappe. Only the uppermost Noric Nappe is in stratigraphic contact with the Tirolic Nappe System of the Northern Calcareous Alps; the other nappes are not.

*Silvretta-Seckau Nappe System*

This is the structurally lowermost Upper Austro-Alpine nappe system, directly overlying the Lower Austro-Alpine units. It includes in the west the Languard, Campo-Sesvenna and Silvretta nappes, to the south of the Tauern Window the Lasörling Complex, and to the east the Schladming, Seckau-Troiseck, Speik, Waldbach and Kulm complexes.

The Silvretta-Seckau Nappe System comprises biotite-plagioclase gneisses and mica schists, typical hornblende gneisses, layered amphibolites, and a wide spectrum of orthogneisses. In some units ultramafic complexes occur (Ulten peridotite, Speik Complex), as well as migmatites and eclogites (Ulten Zone, Silvretta Nappe, Speik Complex; Hauzenberger *et al.* 1996; Melcher *et al.* 2002).

According to Neubauer (2002), the magmatic rocks of the Silvretta-Seckau Nappe System reflect Precambrian to Ordovician collision, subduction and rifting processes. Orthogneisses from Variscan protoliths also occur. The eclogites formed during the Variscan orogenic cycle. Age determinations range from 397 ± 8 Ma in the Speik Complex (Faryad *et al.* 2002) to 351 ± 22 Ma in the Silvretta Nappe (Ladenhauf *et al.* 2001) and 336 ± 4 Ma in the Ulten Zone (Thöni 2006). The peak of Variscan metamorphism, which reached up to high-amphibolite-facies conditions and local anatexis, occurred at *c.* 330 Ma. Typical cooling ages are *c.* 310 Ma (Thöni 1999; Tumiati *et al.* 2003). Schlingen folds (regional-scale folds with steep axes) are a typical structural element of the Variscan deformation.

In the structurally lowermost parts of the Silvretta-Seckau Nappe System in the west (Languard, Campo-Sesvenna and Silvretta nappes), Permian pegmatites and gabbros are also present (Benciolini 1994). For these areas a Permo-Triassic thermal imprint up to amphibolite-facies conditions has been suggested (Schuster *et al.* 2001). The Eo-Alpine metamorphism reached uppermost-anchizonal to amphibolite-facies conditions (Fig. 18.13).

Most of the units show remnants of transgressive Permo-Mesozoic cover successions. The northwestern margin of the Silvretta Nappe is locally covered by Upper Carboniferous strata and transgressively overlain by Permo-Mesozoic sediments of the Lechtal Nappe, belonging to the Bajuvaric Nappe System (Amerom *et al.* 1982; Rockenschaub *et al.* 1983). Further to the south, transgressive Permo-Mesozoic sediments are preserved in the Landwasser and Ducan synclines on top of the Silvretta Nappe.

*Koralpe-Wölz Nappe System*

This comprises a series of basement nappes which lack Permo-Mesozoic cover. Within the nappe system several groups of units with special lithological compositions and a distinct metamorphic grade can be traced over long distances. The northernmost parts consist of lower-greenschist-facies units (e.g. Ennstal quartz phyllite). The southerly adjacent Wölz Complex and its equivalents are characterized by garnet mica schists with a dominant Eo-Alpine metamorphic imprint of upper-greenschist- to amphibolite-facies grade. Locally a Permo-Triassic greenschist-facies imprint has been documented (Schuster *et al.* 2001). The overlying Rappold Complex and its equivalents underwent Variscan, Permo-Triassic and Eo-Alpine amphibolite-facies metamorphism. Kyanite- and garnet-bearing two-mica gneisses with kyanite pseudomorphs after andalusite (so-called 'Disthenflasergneis') and Permian pegmatites are characteristic of this complex. Permian-age granites (e.g. Wolfsberg granite) occur in several places whereas pre-Permian orthogneisses have not been documented.

The southern part of the Koralpe-Wölz Nappe System is formed by units bearing Cretaceous-age eclogites. These units are also characterized by 'Disthenflasergneis' and Permian pegmatites. From west to east they include the Texel, Polinik-Prijakt, Millstatt, Saualpe-Koralpe-Pohorje and Sieggraben complexes. Most of the eclogites developed from amphibolites but some developed from Permian MORB-type gabbros and basalts (Miller & Thöni 1997). In the eclogite-bearing units some pre-Permian orthogneisses have been reported, although thus far not from the Saualpe-Koralpe-Pohorje Complex. An ultramafic body in the Pohorje area probably represents a fragment from the lithospheric mantle (Hinterlechner-Ravnik *et al.* 1991; Janák *et al.* 2006). The metasedimentary rocks of the Saualpe-Koralpe-Pohorje Complex record a Permo-Triassic amphibolite-facies imprint and an eo-Alpine eclogite-facies and subsequent amphibolite-facies overprint.

The Plankogel Complex overlies the eclogite-bearing units in the Saualpe-Koralpe area and is characterized by the presence of garnet-bearing mica schists which also show kyanite pseudo-

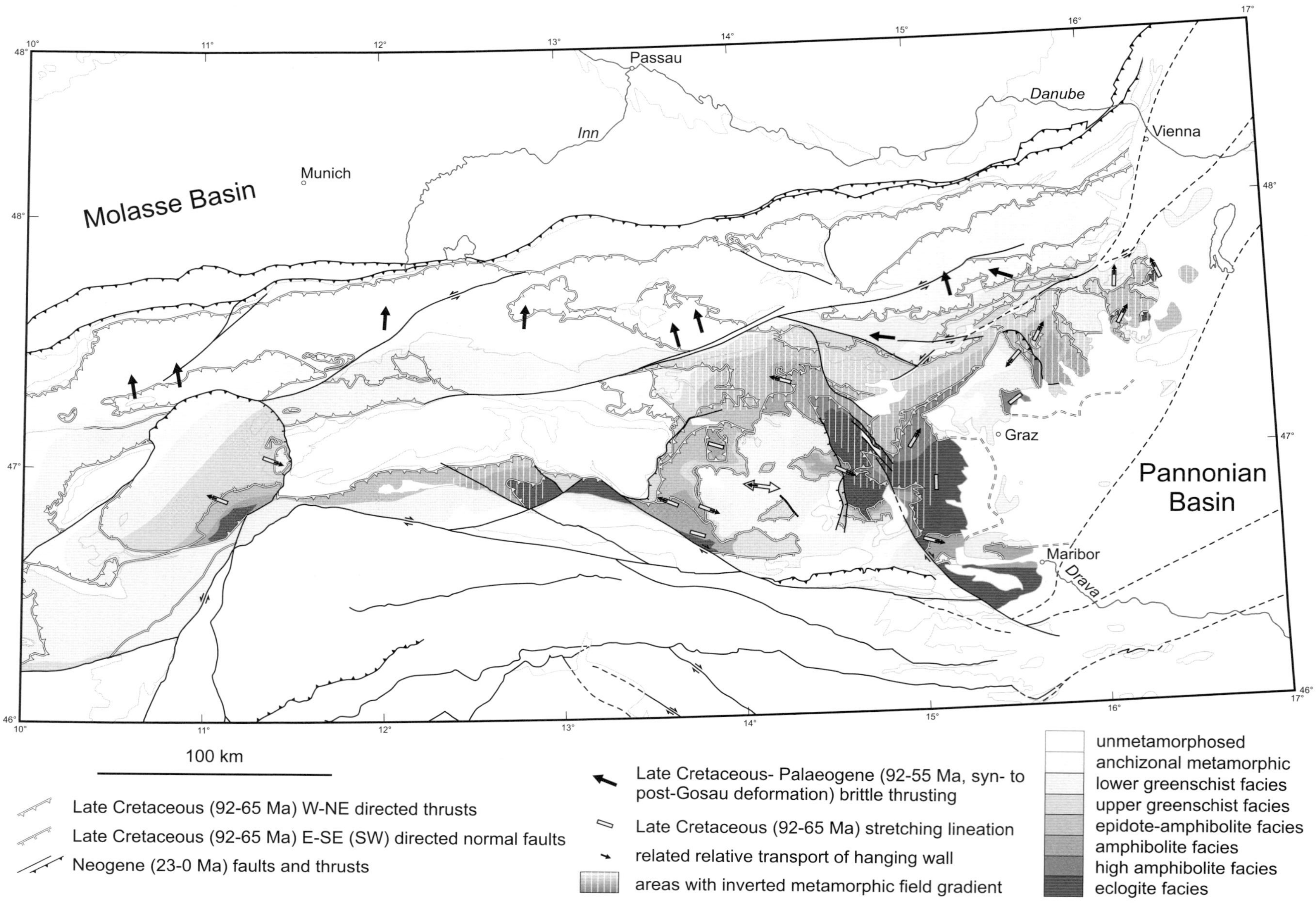


**Fig. 18.13.** Areal distribution of Cretaceous-age metamorphism in the Austro-Alpine units, age and character of major tectonic contacts, and directions of tectonic transport. Late Cretaceous top-to-the-SE low-angle normal faults have emplaced lower-grade on higher-grade metamorphic units.

morphs after andalusite. Intercalations of Mn-quartzites, serpentinites, amphibolites, marbles, and Permian pegmatites also occur. The Plankogel Complex is characterized by a Permo-Triassic imprint which reached up to amphibolite-facies conditions, and an Eo-Alpine amphibolite-facies overprint. The uppermost part of the Koralpe-Wölz Nappe System consists of several units rich in garnet-bearing mica schists. Some of these (e.g. Radenthein Complex) are very similar to the Wölz Complex. In all of them eo-Alpine upper-greenschist- to amphibolite-facies metamorphism is the predominant crystallization phase.

*Ötztal-Bundschuh Nappe System*

The Ötztal-Bundschuh Nappe System (Figs 18.11 & 18.12) overlies the Koralpe-Wölz Nappe System. It consists of the Ötztal Nappe including the 'Brenner Mesozoics' and the Bundschuh Nappe including the lower part of the 'Stangalm Mesozoics' (Stangnock Scholle; Tollmann 1977). Its lithological composition and pre-Alpine metamorphic history are quite similar to that of the Silvretta-Seckau Nappe System. The predominant lithologies include biotite-plagioclase gneisses, mica schists, amphibolites, and a wide range of orthogneisses. Migmatites and eclogites also occur. Remnants of transgressive Permo-Triassic cover sequences are present on top of the pre-Alpine basement and are characterized by successions quite similar to those of the western part of the Bajuvaric Nappe System, including the Norian Hauptdolomite.

Cambrian and Ordovician ages have been determined for some of the magmatic rocks as well as the migmatites in the Ötztal Nappe (Klötzli-Chowanetz *et al.* 1997; Thöni 1999). The eclogites developed during the Variscan tectonometamorphic cycle at *c.* 350 Ma (Miller & Thöni 1995) and the peak of Variscan amphibolite-facies metamorphism occurred at *c.* 340 Ma (Hoinkes *et al.* 1997). Schlingen folds are typical of the Variscan deformation. Cooling ages (Ar/Ar and Rb–Sr, muscovite and biotite) range between 315 and 300 Ma (Thöni 1999). According to Habler & Thöni (2005) the Matsch Unit in the southwestern part of the Ötztal Nappe belongs to the basal part of the nappe which was steepened up during the Eo-Alpine event. It shows an amphibolite-facies Permian metamorphic imprint and contains Permian pegmatites. The Eo-Alpine metamorphic imprint decreases upwards within the Ötztal Nappe from amphibolite- to greenschist-facies conditions (Schuster *et al.* 2004).

*Drauzug-Gurktal Nappe System*

This is structurally the highest of the nappe systems south of the Northern Calcareous Alps (Figs 18.11 & 18.12). It comprises units bordered by steeply dipping Alpine faults (tectonic blocks), located directly to the north of the Periadriatic Fault, as well as nappes overlying the Koralpe-Wölz and Ötztal-Bundschuh nappe systems.

The tectonic blocks consist of crystalline basement (e.g. Meran-Mauls basement, Defferegen, Strieden, Gaugen complexes), Palaeozoic metasediments (e.g. Thurntal quartz phyllite and Goldeck complexes), and Permo-Mesozoic sedimentary successions of the Drau Range (Lienz Dolomites, Gailtal Alps, Dobratsch, North Karawanken). The Permo-Mesozoic strata show a characteristic facies evolution similar to that of the western parts of the Southern Alps and the western parts of the Bajuvaric Nappe System (Bechstädt *et al.* 1976; Tollmann 1987; Lein *et al.* 1997), suggesting that all of these blocks were in a more westerly position during the Triassic than today. In the Jurassic and Early Cretaceous, they moved eastwards along a system of strike-slip faults, with respect to their former neighbouring units. The basement of these blocks consists of orthogneisses from pre-Variscan protoliths and metasedimentary rocks with a Variscan metamorphic imprint up to amphibolite-facies grade. A Permo-Triassic high-temperature/low-pressure overprint reached upper-amphibolite-facies conditions with local anatexis and formation of pegmatites in the lowermost parts (Schuster *et al.* 2001). This overprint becomes weaker towards higher levels of the basement. An Eo-Alpine overprint reached greenschist facies only at the base; the uppermost parts of the units stayed under conditions of diagenesis. Therefore, the pre-Alpine structures and metamorphic assemblages are well preserved.

The above-mentioned nappes comprise the Steinach Nappe, Gurktal Nappes, and the nappes of the Graz Palaeozoic. The Gurktal Nappes (including the Murau, Ackerl and Stolzalpen nappes) and the Steinach Nappe on the eastern and western sides, respectively, of the Tauern Window show many similarities indicating that they were parts of one continuous thrust sheet prior to the Tertiary exhumation of the Penninic rocks in the Tauern Window. The Murau, Stolzalpen and Steinach nappes are composed of Lower Palaeozoic rocks metamorphosed under greenschist-facies conditions. Additionally, the latter two include remnants of Carboniferous clastic sediments and coals of a Variscan intramontane basin (Krainer 1993). In contrast, the Ackerl Nappe comprises mica schists and paragneisses with a Variscan metamorphism (Neubauer 1980). Permo-Mesozoic sedimentary cover is present on top of the Gurktal Nappes. As in the case of the Mesozoic cover of the tectonic blocks described above, the facies of these cover rocks indicates a westerly position during the Triassic and later eastward translation relative to the Bajuvaric Nappe System and the Southern Alps. The nappes of the Graz Palaeozoic (Schöckel, Hochlantsch and Rannach nappes) are formed by Lower Palaeozoic to lowermost Upper Carboniferous sequences with various patterns of facies evolution (Flügel & Hubmann 2000). Upward-decreasing Eo-Alpine metamorphic conditions, from greenschist facies at the base to diagenesis at the top, affected the Gurktal and Graz Palaeozoic nappes (Hoinkes *et al.* 1999). Sediments of the Gosau Group (Late Cretacous) rest unconformably on top of the Gurktal Nappes and the Graz Palaeozoic.

## South Alpine units

The South Alpine units comprise the part of the Alps located to the south of the Periadriatic Fault. They are characterized by the absence of (or a weak) Alpine metamorphic overprint. The South Alpine units may be subdivided, from a tectonic point of view, into the Lombardic-Giudicaric fold-and-thrust belt to the west, and the eastern South Alpine units (Dolomites, Carnio and Julian Alps) to the east.

The Lombardic-Giudicaric fold-and-thrust belt (Milano Belt; Fig. 18.5) is a south-vergent thrust belt affecting basement and sedimentary cover rocks. It evolved from Late Oligocene to Late Miocene times. It affected an area which had previously been stretched in an east–west direction during Liassic rifting preceding the opening of the Piemont-Ligurian Ocean. The resultant north–south trending normal faults were reactivated in Tertiary times as transverse zones with a transpressional character. Thrusts pre-dating the Adamello intrusion (i.e. older than 43 Ma) are observed in the northern part of the thrust belt. These are also directed towards the south. The various parts of the fold-and-thrust belt are briefly described below.

*Canavese Zone*

This is a narrow belt of crystalline basement and Permo-Mesozoic sedimentary rocks directly to the east of the westernmost part of the Periadriatic Fault (the Canavese Fault; Fig. 18.8). The Mesozoic sedimentary succession is very similar to that in the most distal parts of the Lower Austro-Alpine Jurassic-age passive continental margin, in particular the Err Nappe in Graubünden, and is characterized by the presence of rift-related polymict breccias in the Early and Middle Jurassic (Ferrando *et al.* 2004). In the Jurassic, the Canavese Zone and the Err Nappe were adjacent areas on the southeastern passive margin of the Piemont-Ligurian Ocean. The Canavese Zone is separated from the Ivrea Zone to the east by an Alpine fault contact (Internal Canavese Line; Biino & Compagnoni 1989).

*Ivrea Zone*

The Ivrea Zone (or Ivrea-Verbano Zone; Fig. 18.5) represents Variscan basement, comprising mainly paragneiss, metabasic rocks and some marbles, with a Permian-age high-temperature metamorphic overprint of granulite facies in the northwestern part, to amphibolite facies in the SE. The Permian-age (*c.* 285 Ma; Boriani & Villa 1997) metamorphism was associated with voluminous gabbro intrusions (magmatic underplating; Voshage *et al.* 1990).

The Ivrea Zone forms an upright, strongly asymmetric antiform (Proman antiform), with the hinge very close to the northwestern boundary. Peridotite bodies are found in the core of this antiform (Schmid *et al.* 1987) at Finero, Balmuccia and Baldissero. These represent former subcontinental mantle. In most of the Ivrea Zone the layering is steep, forming the southeastern limb of the antiform. Schmid *et al.* (1987) interpreted the Proman antiform as an Alpine structure deforming the entire (but already strongly thinned) crust, so that the top of the mantle is exposed in the core of the antiform, and is flanked by the steepened former lower crust to the SE. The crust, according to these authors, had been thinned by Early Jurassic rift extension. Other authors, however, assume that much of the crustal thinning and exhumation of the Ivrea Zone is Permian in age and attribute less importance to Jurassic and Alpine deformation (e.g. Brodie *et al.* 1989; Boriani & Villa 1997).

The Ivrea Zone is underlain by the Ivrea geophysical body, a shallow-seated mass of mantle material resulting in a strong positive gravity anomaly. The emplacement of this body at shallow depth is explained by a combination of extensional exhumation in the Permian and/or Mesozoic, Alpine forethrusting, and Late Alpine backthrusting (Schmid *et al.* 1987).

The contact between the Ivrea Zone and the southeasterly adjacent Strona-Ceneri Zone is formed by two different tectonic features: the Pogallo Shear Zone to the NE, and the Cossato-Mergozzo-Brissago Shear Zone to the SW. Both of these shear zones are steeply orientated. The Cossato-Mergozzo-Brissago shear zone was interpreted by Handy *et al.* (1999) as an Early Permian sinistrally transtensional shear zone (285 to 275 Ma; Mulch *et al.* 2004). According to Hodges & Fountain (1984) and Schmid *et al.* (1987), the Pogallo Shear Zone, which is younger and offsets the Cossato-Mergozzo-Brissago Shear Zone, was originally active as an east-dipping, extensional, rift-related shear zone during the Early Jurassic, exhuming the Ivrea Zone relative to the Strona-Cenri Zone. It was later steepened by Alpine shortening. In contrast to this, Boriani & Villa (1997), using $^{39}Ar/^{40}Ar$ dating (mostly on amphibole), suggested that there was no significant differential exhumation between the Ivrea and Strona-Ceneri zones after 270 Ma.

*Strona-Ceneri Zone*

The Strona-Ceneri Zone, the Val Colla Zone, and the Orobic basement (Fig. 18.5) represent upper crustal basement units of the Lombardic-Giudicaric fold-and-thrust belt. The Strona-Ceneri Zone was formed by amphibolite-facies metasediments and amphibolites intruded by Ordovician granitoids. The peak of the Variscan amphibolite-facies metamorphism occurred at *c.* 340 Ma (Boriani & Villa 1997) or 320 Ma (Handy *et al.* 1999). Schlingen folds (regional-scale folds with steep axes) formed at *c.* 320 Ma (Zurbriggen *et al.* 1998) or at *c.* 290 Ma (Boriani & Villa 1997). There is also evidence for earlier (Ordovician) metamorphism. In the Early Permian, the basement was intruded by granitoids (Baveno granite) approximately coeval with, and genetically related to, granulite-facies metamorphism and gabbroic underplating in the Ivrea Zone.

*Val Colla Zone*

The Val Colla Zone is separated from the Strona-Ceneri Zone by a mylonite belt, the Val Colla Shear Zone (Fig. 18.5), which is of Carboniferous age according to Handy *et al.* (1999). The Val Colla Zone comprises mica schists, phyllites, and characteristic leucocratic granitoid gneisses with mylonitic and cataclastic deformation features (Gneiss Chiari). Towards the SE, the Val Colla Zone is separated from the sedimentary cover rocks of the Generoso Basin by the Monte Grona Fault, a steeply dipping, east–west striking fault and shear zone which forms the northeastern extension of the Early Jurassic, east-dipping, rift-related Lugano Fault (Bertotti 1990; Fig. 18.5). This portion of the fault was originally shallowly inclined but was steepened and exhumed during Tertiary compression. To the east, the fault may be traced into the Orobic Basement as the Valgrande Mylonite Zone.

*Orobic Basement*

East of Lake Como, the basement of the Southern Alps is exposed as a west–east striking belt, the Orobic Basement, between the Periadriatic (Tonale) Fault to the north and the Permo-Mesozoic cover to the south. In addition, basement rocks are exposed in the cores of Alpine ramp anticlines further south, including, from west to east, the Orobic (Fig. 18.6), Trabuchello-Cabianca, Cedegolo and Camuna anticlines. Most of the Orobic basement underwent Variscan amphibolite-facies metamorphism but the easternmost part reached only greenschist facies and contains Ordovician–Silurian palynomorphs (Colombo & Tunesi 1999). The basement was locally intruded by Early Permian granitoids, e.g. the Val Biandino Pluton in the western part of the Orobic Anticline (285 ± 20 Ma; Thöni *et al.* 1992). In addition to polyphase Variscan deformation, the Orobic basement also underwent Permian normal faulting related to the formation of the Collio Basin (Sciunnach 2003; Frotzheim *et al.* 2008). Furthermore, the basement was affected by Mesozoic extensional shearing, e.g. along the Valgrande line, the intrabasement continuation of the Lugano-Monte Grona normal fault (see above) east of Lago di Como.

*Post-Variscan cover of the Lombardic-Giudicaric belt*

Deposition of the post-Variscan succession of the western Southern Alps locally commenced with Upper Carboniferous clastic sediments unconformably overlying the basement. These were followed by the mixed volcanic/sedimentary Collio Formation of Early Permian age (Sakmarian to Artinskian), with a thickness of up to 1250 m in the area of the Orobic Anticline (Sciunnach 2001). These rocks were deposited in rift grabens, the most important being the Collio Basin between Lake Como and the Eocene- to Oligocene-age Adamello intrusion. Deposition was contemporaneous with granitoid intrusion in the upper crustal basement and gabbroic underplating in the lower crust (Ivrea

Zone). The Collio Formation is overlain with an angular unconformity by Late Permian fluvial clastics of the Verrucano Lombardo, followed by a Triassic shelf succession similar to the one in the Austro-Alpine nappes. The westernmost portions are similar to the successions in the Lower Austro-Alpine nappes (relatively thin and marginal-marine), while the more easterly successions are thicker and more open-marine.

Rifting related to the formation of the Piemont-Ligurian Ocean began in the latest Triassic and was associated with the development of significant facies and thickness variations within the Rhaetian sediments. Rifting was most pronounced during the Early Jurassic. Prominent east-dipping normal faults active at this stage include the Lago Maggiore Fault at the western border of the Monte Nudo Basin and the Lugano Fault at the western border of the Generoso Basin (Bernoulli 1964). The basins were filled with up to 3 km of hemipelagic limestones and marls of Liassic age (Moltrasio limestone) whereas the coeval sediments on the graben shoulders are extremely thin. The former northern extension of the Monte Nudo Basin is found in the Ela Nappe (Lower Austro-Alpine nappes, Graubünden), while the Generoso Basin can be extended into the Ortler Nappe (Upper Austro-Alpine nappes, Graubünden) (Bernoulli *et al.* 1990), indicating that these areas were directly adjacent and were not separated by an ocean basin (Froitzheim *et al.* 1996).

The Late Jurassic–Early Cretaceous succession is mostly pelagic. In Late Cenomanian to Campanian times, siliciclastic deep-marine sediments were derived from source areas to the north (later Austro-Alpine nappes). Pelagic sedimentation was re-established in the Maastrichtian and continued until the Middle Eocene, interfingering with bioclastic turbidites (Schumacher *et al.* 1997). These sediments were unconformably overlain by the Late Oligocene to Middle Miocene deep-water clastics of the Gonfolite Lombarda Group. These represent the onset of the infilling of the South Alpine foreland basin.

The eastern part of the Lombardic-Giudicaric fold-and-thrust belt was intruded by the Adamello granitoids, of Eocene to Oligocene age. Intrusions are oldest in the southern part (43 Ma; Del Moro *et al.* 1983) and youngest in the north (34 to 32 Ma; Stipp *et al.* 2004).

*Dolomites*

The area of the Dolomites lies to the east of the Lombardic-Giudicaric fold-and-thrust belt and is characterized by Middle to Late Triassic carbonate edifices forming spectacular mountains. The basement is formed by Cambrian- to Silurian-age sedimentary and volcanic rocks deformed and metamorphosed to greenschist facies during the Variscan Orogeny. This is unconformably overlain by thin Lower Permian conglomerates and Lower Permian, predominantly rhyolitic volcanic rocks (Bozen quartz porphyry). The latter are up to 2000 m thick in the caldera structure near Bozen. Plutonic equivalents of this complex are found within the basement (Brixen granitoids close to the Periadriatic Fault, Cima d'Asta granitoids further south). The cover succession continues with red-beds (Gardena/Gröden sandstone, Upper Permian), evaporites and carbonates (Bellerophon Formation, Upper Permian) and shallow-water carbonates and terrigenous deposits (Werfen Formation, Lower Triassic). Early Middle Triassic (Pelsonian) block faulting and local erosion, followed by strong subsidence, were contemporaneous with the main rifting phase of the Meliata Ocean (Kozur 1991). This rifting event initiated the formation of carbonate platforms with pronounced lateral facies heterogeneities during the Middle Triassic (e.g. Ladinian Sciliar/Schlern dolomite). In the Ladinian, important volcanism is represented by shoshonitic basalt dykes cutting the older rocks and by pillow lavas and hyaloclastites filling the basins between the reef platforms. The Predazzo and Monzoni diorite, monzonite, monzodiorite and monzogabbro bodies intruded Permian and Triassic carbonates and represent plutonic equivalents of the volcanics. In the Late Ladinian, following the volcanic event, carbonate platform growth resumed. In the late Carnian, terrigeneous, evaporite and carbonate sediments of the Raibl Group were deposited. Subsequently, the area became part of the extensive Dolomia Principale/Hauptdolomit platform of Norian age. In the Rhaetian, Jurassic and Cretaceous, the Dolomites formed part of the relatively stable Venetian platform. Limestones were deposited during the Rhaetian and Jurassic, and marls during the Cretaceous.

The Lower Miocene, marine Monte Parei conglomerate overlies folded and eroded Jurassic rocks. These had been deformed in the course of SW-directed, Palaeogene thrusting. The conglomerates were themselves deformed by the second phase of Alpine deformation in the Dolomites, is Neogene NNW–SSE shortening leading to the formation of bivergent thrusts (Doglioni 1987).

*Carnic Alps and South Karawanken Mountains*

The belt of Variscan basement at the northern border of the Southern Alps continues eastward into the Carnic Alps. Further east, it is hidden beneath Permo-Mesozoic sediments, to be exposed again in the South Karawanken. Continuing the trend of the eastward-decreasing grade of Variscan metamorphism in the Southern Alps, the Variscan part of the Carnic Alps and the South Karawanken are formed by unmetamorphosed to low-grade metamorphic successions of Late Ordovician to Early Carboniferous sediments, affected by Carboniferous, south-directed nappe stacking. The Variscan unconformity lies in the Westphalian C to D and is overlain by continental to shallow-marine clastic sediments of Late Carboniferous age (Auernig Group). Marine shelf sedimentation began in the Early Permian (e.g. Trogkofel limestone) and was interrupted by a phase of uplift and erosion, in the Early Permian, after which a new transgressive series commenced with the Gröden Formation (red-beds) and the Bellerophon Formation (dolomites and evaporites) in the Late Permian, followed by a similar Mesozoic succession as described above for the Dolomites (Schönlaub & Histon 2000*b*; see also McCann *et al.* 2008*b*). In the Carnic Alps, metamorphism increases in grade from anchizonal to epizonal, in a direction from east to west but also from south to north towards the Periadriatic Fault. Variscan and Alpine metamorphism were approximately of the same grade (Rantitsch 1997). The fact that levels with epizonal Alpine metamorphism reach the surface can be explained by the action of Tertiary-age dextral transpression along the Periadriatic Fault, leading to the development of a pop-up structure and erosional exhumation. The metamorphic zonation is offset by NW-trending dextral and NE-trending sinistral strike-slip faults interpreted as synthetic and antithetic Riedel shears, related to the motion along the Periadriatic Fault (Rantitsch 1997).

## *Remnants of the Meliata Ocean*

In the Alps, remnants of basement and cover of the Meliata Ocean are present only within some small tectonic slivers. Similar units are more extensively exposed in the Western Carpathians (Meliaticum, see below). The Meliata Ocean existed from the Middle Triassic to Jurassic or possibly into Cretaceous times. It was bordered by the Western Carpathian and Austro-Alpine domains to the north and NW, by the South Alpine Domain to the west, and the Dinaride domain to the SW. The exact geometry of this ocean and its relations to other sub-basins of Tethys are the subject of discussion (Channell & Kozur 1997; Stampfli & Borel 2004).

Remnants of the Meliata Ocean occur in the eastern part of the Northern Calcareous Alps, in a strongly sheared zone below the base of the Schneeberg Nappe (Juvavic Nappe System), partly overlying the Permian cover of the Noric Nappe (Greywacke Zone), and partly the Göller Nappe (Tirolic Nappe System) (Kozur & Mostler 1992; Mandl & Ondrejickova 1993; Fig. 18.10). Lithologically, these units include serpentinites, basic volcanic rocks, and Jurassic metasediments. The latter comprise upper Callovian mass-flow deposits with components of Triassic radiolarites and limestones, radiolarian-bearing cherty shales, and dark shales and sandstones at the top. These rocks can be correlated with the Meliaticum in the Western Carpathians. They show an upper anchizonal metamorphic imprint but no indications of subduction-related high-pressure/low-temperature metamorphism.

Basic volcanic rocks and serpentinites also occur in mélanges with a matrix of Permian-age evaporites at the base of the Juvavic Nappe System. They were interpreted as dismembered Triassic ophiolites from the Meliata Ocean tectonically introduced into the mélanges (Kozur & Mostler 1992). Detritus of serpentinite and chrome spinel with a presumed origin from the Meliata Ocean occurs in many Cretaceous synorogenic sediments from the Berriasian onwards (Faupl & Wagreich 2000). Additionally, pebbles of Triassic radiolarite, together with basic volcanic rocks, greenschists and partly garnet-bearing amphibolites occur in some Late Cretaceous sediments of the Lower Gosau Subgroup (Gruber *et al.* 1992). In the garnet-bearing amphibolites, $^{40}Ar/^{39}Ar$ hornblende dating yielded Early Jurassic ages (Schuster *et al.* 2003). This material may have been eroded from the metamorphic sole of obducted ophiolites from the Meliata-Vardar oceanic realm.

The tectonic evolution of the Alps is described in chronological order in the following sections.

## Permian and Triassic tectonics in the Alps

Graben structures and sedimentation of post-Variscan continental sediments in the area of the future Alps indicate thinning of the thickened Variscan crust by orogenic collapse and erosion during Late Carboniferous to Early Permian time (Wopfner 1984; Ziegler 1993; Bonin *et al.* 1993). Extension is also recorded by magmatic rocks and by high-temperature/low-pressure metamorphism. These features are particularly widespread in the South Alpine and Austro-Alpine units, but similar processes also affected the Penninic and Helvetic units. In the Mid-Permian, marine transgressions in parts of the Austro-Alpine and South Alpine units were accompanied by the deposition of fine-grained clastic, evaporitic and carbonate sediments, whereas fluvial sediments were deposited in continental areas. The distribution and facies of the sediments argue for a relatively flat topography, a low altitude and a normal crustal thickness.

In the Early Permian, lithospheric extension resulted in the formation of basaltic melts in the mantle. The melts mainly underplated the crust while some rose into the crust, crystallizing as gabbros with ages of *c.* 290 Ma (Quick *et al.* 1992; Thöni 1999). The resultant heating was responsible for high-temperature/low-pressure metamorphism and melting in the lower crust.

In the Ivrea Zone (Southern Alps), where the Mesozoic mantle–crust boundary was exhumed during the Alpine event, gabbros are interlayered with kinzigites which are restites from the molten lower crust. Due to high melting rates, the melts generated from the lower crust have calc-alkaline signatures. They reached the surface at *c.* 275–285 Ma and are present mostly as rhyolitic volcanic rocks, e.g. the Bozen quartz porphyry in the area of the Dolomites (Klötzli *et al.* 2003), volcanites of the Collio Basin in the western Southern Alps (Schaltegger & Brack 1999), rhyolites within the Permian succession of the Helvetic nappes (Glarus Nappe) and Penninic nappes (e.g. St. Bernard Nappe; Sartori *et al.* 2006), and as layers and pebbles in the Lower Permian clastic sediments of the Austro-Alpine nappes.

Thinning due to extension and additional advective heat from the mantle and lower crustal melts led to a high-temperature/low-pressure metamorphic event in the middle and upper crust and the development of anatectic granitic melts and pegmatoids. Based on andalusite- and sillimanite-bearing assemblages, the geothermal gradient in the middle crust was typically >40°C/km (Diella *et al.* 1992; Habler & Thöni 2001). Pegmatoides which are partly spodumen-bearing are frequent in granulite- and upper amphibolite facies metamorphic rocks, whereas they have not been found in the overlying lower amphibolite and greenschist facies rock series (Schuster *et al.* 2001). Sm–Nd dating of garnets from the pegmatoides as well as from metapelitic rocks indicates that the thermal peak occurred at 270 to 245 Ma (Thöni & Miller 2000; Schuster *et al.* 2001). These ages correspond to those of the Permian gabbroic and granitic intrusions in the Koralpe-Wölz Nappe System (Miller & Thöni 1997). The Permian sediments show evidence of a diastathermal metamorphic imprint due to the high heat flow near the surface (Ferreiro Mählmann 1995).

Following thermal subsidence in the Early Triassic, a further rifting event took place in the Early Middle Triassic, leading to the opening of the Meliata Ocean. Crustal extension recommenced in the Late Triassic and continued into the Jurassic (Bertotti *et al.* 1993). Through these processes, the metamorphic rocks were covered by Triassic sedimentary sequences up to 3 km thick. This resulted in slow cooling from the high geothermal gradient to a gradient of about 25°C/km at *c.* 200 Ma. This thermal history can be studied in the Gailtal-Goldeck-Kreuzeck Nappe (Drauzug-Gurktal Nappe System) and the Silvretta Nappe (Silvretta-Seckau Nappe System). There the $^{40}Ar/^{39}Ar$ muscovite ages decrease continuously in a downward direction from typical Variscan cooling ages of c. 310 Ma close to the top of the Variscan basement, to about 210 Ma in the andalusite-bearing, and 190 Ma in the sillimanite-bearing rocks (Schuster *et al.* 2001).

The slow cooling and the episodic extension of the lithosphere during the Triassic led to subsidence and the accumulation of shallow-marine sediments. In the Lower Triassic almost the entire Alpine area was transgressed. The change from restricted to open-marine conditions in the Ladinian and the accompanying facies differentiation into lagoonal, reef (Wetterstein dolomite and limestone) and deep-water sediments indicates the existence of a nearby ocean at that time. This Triassic-age ocean was the Meliata Ocean which may have been a backarc ocean related to subduction of the Palaeotethys Ocean (Stampfli & Borel 2004). Following a phase of regression in the Carnian, due to a global sea-level fall (Brandner 1984), a second stage of carbonate platform growth produced the classic facies succession with the proximal Hauptdolomit, Dachsteinkalk reef, and deep-water Hallstatt facies developed along the passive continental margin (Tollmann 1977; Mandl 2000).

## Jurassic tectonics

### *Rifting and break-up of the Piemont-Liguria Ocean*

A distinct change in tectonic regime and sedimentation can be recognized at the beginning of the Jurassic. The extensive shallow-water shelf area NW of the Meliata Ocean was affected by rifting. The Triassic carbonate platforms were drowned and the input of tectonically controlled mass-flow deposits became increasingly important. Rifting eventually led to the opening of the Piemont-Ligurian Ocean in the Middle Jurassic, cutting obliquely across the Triassic-age shelf. Also during Middle Jurassic times, compressional tectonics affected the southeasternmost part of the Austro-Alpine units.

Fault systems related to the breakup of the Piemont-Ligurian Ocean are well-preserved in the Austro-Alpine nappes in Graubünden (Froitzheim & Manatschal 1996), in the western Southern Alps (Bernoulli *et al.* 1990), and in the Briançonnais and Dauphinois zones of the Western Alps (Lemoine *et al.* 1986). Rifting was most intense in two phases, early Liassic and late Liassic–Middle Jurassic. During the first phase, the upper crust was fragmented by normal faults which dipped predominantly to the east, but the overall geometry of lithospheric stretching was probably close to symmetric. During the second phase, a west-dipping normal fault cut through the already strongly thinned crust and into the remaining mantle lithosphere, and developed into a sequence of top-to-the-west low-angle detachment faults that tectonically denuded the upper mantle in the Austro-Alpine–Penninic transition zone (Froitzheim & Manatschal 1996; Manatschal & Nievergelt 1997; Manatschal 2004). On the Austro-Alpine–South Alpine side of the Piemont-Ligurian Ocean, rifting produced a basement high with thin sediment cover in the distal part of the passive continental margin. This high can be followed from the western Southern Alps, where it was located immediately east of the Canavese zone (Ferrando *et al.* 2004), to the Lower Austro-Alpine Bernina Nappe in Graubünden. A similar position is occupied by the Tatric/Inovec basement nappe in the Western Carpathians (Plašienka 1995*a*).

In asymmteric rifting models (e.g. Lemoine *et al.* 1987; Froitzheim & Manatschal 1996; Manatschal 2004), the Austro-Alpine and South Alpine units were interpreted as representing the lower-plate margin, and the Briançonnais the upper-plate margin with respect to a detachment fault cutting through the entire lithosphere. This hypothesis is supported by the observed top-to-the-west detachment faults, and it explains the Middle Jurassic emergence of the Briançonnais units in terms of an isostatic response to non-uniform stretching, where the thickness of the mantle lithosphere was markedly reduced beneath the Briançonnais. The asymmetric hypothesis was recently challenged by a numerical modelling study (Nagel & Buck 2004) where two conjugate continental margins with the characteristics of the Austro-Alpine–Penninic boundary (mantle exhumation, top-to-the ocean detachment fault, blocks tilted towards the continent) were produced by a symmetric rifting process. If this model were applied to the opening of the Piemont-Ligurian Ocean, a different explanation for the Briançonnais emersion would be required.

During the process of continental breakup, the Cervinia Terrane was isolated from the Austro-Alpine–South Alpine continental margin. According to Froitzheim & Manatschal (1996), this terrane represented an extensional allochthon close to the Austro-Alpine–South Alpine margin, that is, a fault block of continental crust that was left behind during extensional unroofing of the mantle. Alternatively, the Cervinia Terrane may represent a microcontinent between two branches of the Piemont-Ligurian Ocean (Fig. 18.3).

In contrast to the approximately orthogonal, east–west to SE–NW directed stretching in the Central and Western Alps, Jurassic rifting occurred in a framework of sinistral transtension further east in the Eastern Alps. In this regime, half-grabens along the northern margin of the Austro-Alpine units (Lower Austro-Alpine domain) were filled with marine, breccia-rich successions (Häusler 1987).

*Compressional tectonics in the internal Austro-Alpine units*

Beginning in Mid-Jurassic times, the southeastern part of the Austro-Alpine units, close to the Meliata Ocean, was affected by compressional deformation. In general, this deformation commenced in the SE and propagated northwestward, as documented by the presence of mass-transport complexes in the upper Jurassic deep-water sediments of the Juvavic and Tirolic nappe systems (Gawlick *et al.* 1999; Mandl 2000). In the initial stage, ophiolites of the Meliata-Vardar oceanic realm were obducted onto the Austro-Alpine continental margin, probably resulting from the collision of this margin with an east- or south-dipping, intra-oceanic subduction zone. In contrast to the Dinarides where the obducted ophiolite sheets are exposed over large areas (Pamić 2002), the obduction is poorly documented in the Eastern Alps. It is, however, suggested by the presence of redeposited detritus of ophiolitic material and Triassic radiolarites within syntectonic sediments (Faupl & Wagreich 2000). Any obducted ophiolite sheets which may have existed on top of the Austro-Alpine nappes have since been completely eroded.

The oldest sediments containing redeposited Triassic radiolarites are Callovian mass-transport complexes in the Meliata-derived slivers of the Northern Calcareous Alps (Mandl & Ondrejickova 1993). Callovian to Early/Middle Oxfordian mass-transport complexes in the Strubberg Formation of the Tirolic Nappe System (Gawlik & Suzuki 1999) record the initial detachment of the most distal Triassic shelf sediments from their basement and their stacking as thrust sheets. These complexes contain up to kilometre-sized olistoliths of Triassic sediments developed in the pelagic Hallstatt facies. In the Oxfordian, northwestward-propagating thrusting affected the Triassic-age carbonate platforms, creating the large Juvavic nappes (Dachstein Nappe and Mürzalpen Nappe). The Dachstein Nappe was thrust over Jurassic mass-transport complexes containing olistoliths of pelagic Hallstatt limestones. On the other hand, it carried similar mass-transport complexes on its back. The basal thrust of the Dachstein Nappe, of Oxfordian age, was reactivated during the Tertiary.

Rare fragments of metamorphosed and ductilely deformed Triassic-age limestones occur in the Jurassic-age, unmetamorphosed to anchizonal metamorphic mass-transport complexes. They indicate a thermal imprint during Early to Mid-Jurassic times (Gawlick *et al.* 1999) which may be related to ophiolite obduction.

These tectonic processes coeval with sedimentation of chert-rich deep-water deposits in the Callovian to Oxfordian. Following this phase of intensive deformation, a period of reduced tectonic activity continued until the end of the Jurassic. The tectonic contacts were sealed by Tithonian-age basinal (Oberalm Formation) and carbonate platform sediments (Plassen Formation).

The regional framework of Jurassic tectonics in the internal Austro-Alpine units is still under discussion. Obduction of Meliata oceanic crust over the Austro-Alpine continental margin units is suggested by, among other lines of evidence, the occurrence of Early Jurassic amphibolites, probably derived from the metamorphic sole of such ophiolites, as clasts in Upper Cretaceous-age Gosau sediments (Schuster *et al.* 2003). Some authors (e.g. Gawlick & Höpfer 1999) have suggested that the Jurassic tectonism resulted from the collision of the Austro-Alpine margin with another continental terrane. In this collision, the Austro-Alpine margin represented the lower plate which was partly subducted towards the south or SE. Gawlick & Höpfer (1999) found evidence for high-pressure/low-temperature metamorphism in the Pailwand Complex, a part of the Juvavic Nappe System, and dated this metamorphism as Jurassic. This appeared analogous to the blueschist-facies metamorphism of ophiolites in the Meliaticum of the Western Carpathians, which proves Jurassic subduction of the Meliata Ocean there (Maluski *et al.* 1993; Dallmeyer *et al.* 1996; Faryad & Henjes-Kunst 1997). According to Gawlick *et al.* (1999), the rocks in the Pailwand Complex were metamorphosed when the Austro-Alpine continental margin entered the south-dipping subduction zone following the closure of the Meliata Ocean and was subducted below a continental element. There is, however, no agreement in the literature as to which continental fragment formed the overriding plate. In some articles it is unspecified (Gawlick & Höpfner 1999), others favour Tisia (Tizia), a terrane largely hidden under the Pannonian Basin (Froitzheim *et al.* 1996; Channell & Kozur 1997), or a continental fragment comprising the South Alpine units and the upper Juvavic nappes (Schweigl & Neubauer 1997; Neubauer *et al.* 2000). This leads to different positions for a proposed Meliata suture, e.g. between the Austro-Alpine and the South Alpine units, or within the Austro-Alpine units between the Tirolic Nappe System and the upper Juvavic nappes (Schweigl & Neubauer 1997).

Several lines of evidence, however, make a Jurassic continent collision unlikely. The proposed oceanic Meliata suture has not been found in the Alps. The slices of the Meliata zone occur in a structurally high position and there is no evidence of continuation at deeper levels. The proposed Jurassic high-pressure/low-temperature metamorphism in the Juvavic nappes is not generally accepted, because no pressure data exist for metamorphic olistoliths in the Jurassic mass-transport complexes, and, on the other hand, the age of the elevated-pressure metamorphic imprint in the Pailwand Complex is not Jurassic but Cretaceous, according to Frank & Schlager (2005).

Alternatively, it may be assumed that the Austro-Alpine margin did not collide with another continent but entered an intra-oceanic subduction zone, leading to ophiolite obduction onto the continental margin in a similar way as in the Dinarides (e.g. Pamić *et al.* 2002; Stampfli & Borel 2004). After that a system of east–west striking, sinistral strike-slip faults may have developed (Schmid *et al.* 2004*a*; Frank & Schlager 2005). The Juvavic and Tirolic nappe systems, which came from the distal part of the Austro-Alpine margin and carried the Meliata remains, were on the northern side of this fault system. They were transferred towards the west and emplaced to the north of other Austro-Alpine units which represented more proximal parts of the Triassic continental margin. Such elements include the Drauzug-Gurktal Nappe System (Bechstädt *et al.* 1976; Kázmér & Kovać 1985; Tollmann 1987), the Ötztal-Bundschuh Nappe System, the Pelson Unit (Transdanubian Range) and the Southern Alps. The activity of this fault system would have post-dated the Triassic and pre-dated the onset of Mid-Cretaceous thrust tectonics. This is a viable hypothesis explaining the lack of a Meliata suture in the Alps. It is, however, only based on indirect evidence such as the distribution of Triassic facies. Jurassic strike-slip faults have not been identified thus far (in contrast, for example, to Jurassic rift-related detachment faults in the Lower Austro-Alpine units).

## *Cretaceous tectonics*

### *Austro-Alpine units*

Following a period of relative quiescence, tectonic shortening in the Austro-Alpine units recommenced in the Valanginian (*c.* 137 Ma). This was the beginning of the Cretaceous orogenic cycle, often referred to as Eo-Alpine. As noted above, there are various opinions concerning the arrangement of the tectonic units at the time when Eo-Alpine tectonics began. The model of Schmid *et al.* (2004*a*) and Schuster (2004) suggests that a SE- to east-dipping, intracontinental subduction zone developed along the hypothetical Jurassic strike-slip fault, that is, to the north of the future Drauzug-Gurktal and Ötztal-Bundschuh nappe systems. These units formed the upper plate with respect to the subduction zone, whereas the lower plate to the NW can be subdivided into a number of units; Lower Austro-Alpine units represent the most external part. An intermediate area comprised the rocks of the future Bajuvaric Nappe System, underlain by the rocks that later formed the lower nappes of the Greywacke Zone (Vöstenhof-Kaintaleck, Silbersberg and Veitsch nappes). The Silvretta-Seckau Nappe System followed to the SE. Close to the initial position of the subduction boundary was an area that comprised the future Tirolic Nappe System, lying with a stratigraphic contact on Palaeozoic rocks of the Noric Nappe, and already carrying the Juvavic Nappe System on top, which had been emplaced during the Jurassic. The middle and lower crust of this area later formed the Koralpe-Wölz Nappe System.

During early stages of convergence, the Ötztal-Bundschuh and Drauzug-Gurktal nappe systems formed from the upper crust of the subduction zone's upper plate. This thick nappe pile (more than 10 km in the southeastern part) moved westward (Ratschbacher *et al.* 1989) relative to the units of the lower plate. The upper part of the lower plate (Noric Nappe, Tirolic Nappe System, Juvavic Nappe System) was detached from the deeper basement (future Koralpe-Wölz Nappe System). The latter was subducted towards the SE. The detached units formed an orogenic wedge whose early evolution is recorded by synorogenic sediments of the Rossfeld Formation (Hauterivian–Aptian, 120–135 Ma), which were deposited in basins in front and on top of the Tirolic nappes. In the Albian, the southern (upper) nappes of the Bajuvaric Nappe System (Upper Bajuvaric Nappes) and, probably, also the lower nappes of the Greywacke Zone were stripped off from their basement and incorporated into the wedge. At this stage, the Tannheim-Losenstein Basin formed in the northern part of the future Lower Bajuvaric nappes in front of the wedge (Upper Aptian–Lower Cenomanian, 97–105 Ma). The Tannheim-Losenstein basin was partly filled with material from a ridge to the north, where metamorphic basement rocks and serpentinites were exposed ('Rumunic Ridge'; Faupl 1979). Wagreich (2001*a*) suggested that the fomation of this ridge along the northern margin of the Austro-Alpine units against the Penninic Ocean resulted from oblique subduction and the related dextrally transpressive deformation, and that the onset of subduction of the Penninic oceans below the Austro-Alpine units began at that time.

Geochronology suggests that the Eo-Alpine eclogites formed around 92 Ma, i.e. in Turonian times (Thöni 2006). Middle and lower crustal material of the Austro-Alpine units, which had been subducted since Valanginian times, reached a maximum depth at that time. The pressure and temperature data on the Eo-Alpine eclogites show a distinct distribution. The greatest depths were reached in the Saualpe-Koralpe-Pohorje Complex. Up to 2 GPa at 700°C (Miller 1990; Thöni & Miller 1996; Habler 1999) were reached in its northern part, whereas ultrahigh-pressure conditions of 3 GPa at 800°C have been reported by Janàk *et al.* (2004) from the Porhorje mountains in the south. The eclogites formed from Permian-age, N-MORB gabbroic rocks and from metabasalts. Garnet peridotite associated with the eclogites in the

Pohorje mountains yielded up to 4 GPa at 900°C (Hinterlechner-Ravnik *et al.* 1991; Janák *et al.* 2006). To the east and west of the Saualpe-Koralpe-Pohorje Complex the metamorphic peak conditions decrease (Hoinkes *et al.* 1999; Schuster *et al.* 2004) and here the eclogites are derived from metabasite interlayers within pre-Alpine metamorphic complexes.

A major tectonic change can be recognized in the Turonian (*c.* 92 Ma). The eclogite-bearing parts of the Austro-Alpine units were rapidly exhumed to middle crustal levels and formed the central part of the Koralpe-Wölz Nappe System. Cooling of the rocks is dated by Rb–Sr, K–Ar and Ar/Ar ages measured on hornblendes, muscovites and biotites. These are generally in the range of 90 to 60 Ma (Thöni 1999), whereas those of the southern part of the Saualpe-Koralpe-Pohorje Complex in the Pohorje Mountains are Miocene (see below). Exhumation is assumed to have occurred in a tectonic wedge regime (Fig. 18.10) with thrusting in the lower part and normal faulting in the upper part of the wedge (Schuster *et al.* 2004; Schmid *et al.* 2004*a*; Wiesinger *et al.* 2006). In the eastern part of the Eastern Alps a pro-wedge geometry with respect to a SE-directed subduction was established. NW- to north-directed thrusting is documented in the lower part of the wedge, below and within the eclogite-bearing complexes (Krohe 1987), and SE-directed normal faulting in the upper part of the wedge (Fig. 18.13). Several ductile deformed Austro-Alpine nappes of the extrusion wedge exhibit an east- to ESE-trending extensional stretching lineation which may indicate a component of extension oblique to the general extrusion direction. In the southwestern part of the Austro-Alpine units (Texel Mountains and southern Nockberge area), on the other hand, SE-directed extrusion has been suggested (Sölva *et al.* 2001).

Whereas most authors assume exhumation of the Austro-Alpine eclogite-bearing units by buoancy-driven wedge extrusion (Sölva et al 2001; Wiesinger *et al.* 2006), Janák *et al.* (2004, 2006) suggested that slab extraction (Froitzheim *et al.* 2003) was the dominant exhumation mechanism.

The units of the tectonic upper plate, positioned on top of the extruding wedge, were affected by normal faulting. Extensional basins, partly associated with extensional detachment faults (Neubauer *et al.* 1994*a*; Rantitsch *et al.* 2005), developed on top of the Gurktal Nappes and the Graz Palaeozoic Nappes (Krappfeld, St. Paul and Kainach Basins) and were filled with sediments of the Gosau Group (Santonian to Eocene). The clastic material is mainly derived from the surroundings. In addition to detritus of Austro-Alpine provenance, detritus of South Alpine provenance also occurs in the Kainach Basin. This material indicates a close spatial relationship of this basin to the South Alpine units or, alternatively, the existence of klippen with that kind of material on top of the Austro-Alpine nappes during the time of sedimentation (Gollner *et al.* 1987).

At the northern front of the orogen, the basal detachment jumped down to deeper structural levels. The Lower Bajuvaric nappes and the lower nappes of the Greywacke Zone were now incorporated into the orogenic wedge, and this wedge overrode the 'Rumunic Ridge'. In the Turonian (90 Ma), large parts of the Northern Calcareous Alps emerged, resulting in erosion and the formation of bauxite. Subsequently, the Gosau basins developed and were filled with conglomerates and clastic shallow-marine sediments derived from the local surroundings (Lower Gosau Subgroup, Upper Turonian to Campanian).

The Gosau basins of the Northern Calcareous Alps have been interpreted as extensional (Ortner 1994), but most authors assume that they formed in compressional, transpressional or strike-slip regimes (Wagreich 1995; Ortner 2001), in contrast to the extensional Gosau basins on the Drauzug-Gurktal Nappe System. Following a short phase of deformation and erosion, the sedimentation of slope and deep-water clastics of the Upper Gosau Subgroup (Upper Santonian to Eocene) commenced. This was governed by the rapid subsidence of the Bajuvaric and Tirolic nappe systems into bathyal and abyssal depths (Faupl & Wagreich 1996). This facies change took place diachronously from the NW (Santonian) to the SE (Palaeocene). The subsidence pulse has been attributed to an event of tectonic erosion triggered by the subduction of a topographic high of the Penninic oceanic plate (ocean ridge) below the Austro-Alpine margin (Wagreich 1995). An alternative interpretation would be that the frontal part of the Austro-Alpine tectonic wedge passed over the Austro-Alpine–Penninic continental margin and moved onto the accretionary wedge in the oceanic basin to the north. A further alternative suggests that the subsidence resulted from westward retreat (roll-back) of the Piemont-Ligurian subduction zone (Froitzheim *et al.* 1997; Stampfli & Borel 2004).

As mentioned above, most authors assume exhumation of the eclogite-bearing Austro-Alpine units by wedge extrusion following the model of Chemenda *et al.* (1995). This model implies voluminous erosion of metamorphic rocks during exhumation. Larger amounts of Eo-Alpine metamorphic detritus, however, are only documented in Cenomanian- to Turonian-age deep-marine clastic sediments of the Reiselsberg Formation (Rhenodanubian Flysch Zone; Neubauer *et al.* 2007), whereas such detritus is absent in the Late Cretaceous sediments of the Austro-Alpine and South Alpine units prior to the Maastrichtian. In the Maastrichtian and Palaeogene, sandstones rich in detrital white mica, with Eo-Alpine cooling ages, occur in the Upper Gosau Subgroup of several localities (Schuster *et al.* 2003). The late input of this Eo-Alpine upper-greenschist- to eclogite-facies material may be explained as follows. The P-T-t paths of the Eo-Alpine eclogite-bearing units were characterized by rapid (in some cases isothermal: Hoinkes *et al.* 1999) exhumation from eclogite facies to amphibolite facies and a subsequent slow cooling (Thöni 1999). This may indicate that the rocks were exhumed rapidly by 'blind' wedge extrusion in the Late Cretaceous and then stored in an upper crustal position without reaching the surface. The later exhumation to the surface would have been controlled by other processes, including erosion and block tilting (see below). The slab extraction model as proposed by Janák *et al.* (2004, 2006), on the other hand, does not necessitate erosion of metamorphic rocks during exhumation.

As noted above, subduction of the Penninic Ocean beneath the Austro-Alpine units probably commenced in Albian time (Wagreich 2001*a*). Between the downgoing Penninic slab and the Upper Austro-Alpine nappes, the Lower Austro-Alpine nappes represent slices of continental crust which entered the subduction zone at different times and reached different depths. A decrease in metamorphic grade from lower greenschist facies at the top to anchizonal conditions at the base can be recognized in the Radstadt Nappe System. The formation ages of white micas that formed during the metamorphic event decrease from Cretaceous to Miocene in the same direction (Slapansky & Frank 1987; Liu *et al.* 2001). At the eastern border of the Alps an inverted metamorphic field gradient can also be established. In the lowermost Wechsel Nappe (Lower Austro-Alpine), only newly formed white micas within shear bands yield Cretaceous ages, whereas in the overlying Semmering Nappe (Lower Austro-Alpine) at least partly rejuvenated Ar/Ar ages are found in pre-Alpine metamorphic rocks, and muscovite and biotite from greenschist facies metamorphic Mesozoic rocks yield formation ages of about 82 Ma (Müller *et al.* 1999; Dallmeyer *et al.* 1998).

In this area, the Upper Austro-Alpine nappes were emplaced on the Lower Austro-Alpine Wechsel Nappe by north-directed out-of-sequence thrusting (Willingshofer & Neubauer 2002).

In the westernmost part of the Austro-Alpine nappes (Silvretta Nappe and units to the south of it), Cretaceous tectonics commenced with west-directed thrusting (*c.* 100 to 90 Ma), followed by sinistral transpressive shearing in an east–west striking corridor, and by top-to-the-ESE extensional faulting (*c.* 80–67 Ma) (Froitzheim 1992; Froitzheim *et al.* 1994; Handy 1996). This deformation affected not only the Austro-Alpine units, but also the underlying Upper Penninic nappes (Platta Nappe and Margna Nappe). Thrusting may have been diachronous to some extent, older in the structurally higher units and younger in the deeper ones. The Late Cretaceous episode of extensional faulting affected the entire nappe stack from the Ötztal Nappe at the top to the Margna Nappe at the base. Some of the top-to-the-ESE extensional faults are detachment faults with large offsets, e.g. the Schlinig Fault at the western border of the Ötztal Nappe (Froitzheim *et al.* 1997) which had previously been regarded as a thrust (Schmid & Haas 1989). At deep levels of the nappe stack, recumbent folds formed during Late Cretaceous extension as a result of the collapse of initially steeply orientated layers (Froitzheim 1992; Handy 1996).

*South Alpine units*

South-directed, thick-skinned thrusting and folding in the internal part of the Lombardic-Giudicaric thrust belt pre-dates the oldest part of the Adamello intrusion and must therefore be older than *c.* 43 Ma (De Sitter & De Sitter Koomans 1949; Brack 1981). The 64 Ma K–Ar amphibole/groundmass age of a dyke cutting one of the thrusts (Zanchi *et al.* 1990) suggests a Cretaceous age, older than 64 Ma, for the thrusting event. However, in view of the many K–Ar ages published in the Alpine literature which have turned out to be geologically meaningless, thrusting prior to the intrusion of the Adamello pluton could also be Palaeocene to Early Eocene and could thus be correlated with the Dinaric thrusting observed in the Dolomites. Hence, there is no unequivocal evidence for Cretaceous thrusting in the Southern Alps. There is some evidence from sediment facies distribution, however, that narrow elongate horsts and grabens formed in a transpressional setting in the area of the Giudicarie Fault (Doglioni & Bosellini 1987).

*Penninic nappes*

It has long been assumed that the high-pressure metamorphism in the Penninic units of the Alps was Cretaceous in age and, consequently, that subduction-related thrusting affected these units during the Cretaceous. This belief was mostly based on K–Ar and $^{40}Ar/^{39}Ar$ data affected by excess argon. The application of U–Pb, Sm–Nd and Lu–Hf dating resulted in Tertiary ages (e.g. Tilton *et al.* 1991; Becker 1993; Gebauer 1996; Duchêne *et al.* 1997). It is now generally accepted that the high- and ultrahigh-pressure metamorphism in the Penninic nappes is Tertiary in age. The only exception to the Tertiary age is the Cervinia Terrane, where eclogite-facies metamorphism occurred at *c.* 65 Ma and prograde metamorphism preceded the eclogite facies at c. 76 Ma (Sesia Nappe; Rubatto *et al.* 1999). Hence, the Cervinia fragment entered the Piemont-Ligurian subduction zone at *c.* 76 Ma. The accretionary prism of the Tsaté Nappe would thus have formed between *c.* 100 Ma, when subduction of the Piemont-Ligurian Ocean began, and 76 Ma, when the Cervinia Terrane arrived at the trench. However, there is still no geochronological proof for this assumption.

In the Valais Basin, oceanic spreading took place during the Cenomanian and Turonian, as evidenced by metagabbros with an age of *c.* 93 Ma in the Chiavenna Ophiolite (eastern Central Alps; Liati *et al.* 2003) and in the Balma Unit (western Central Alps; Liati & Froitzheim 2006). Spreading may also have occurred earlier in the Cretaecous, as Lower Cretaceous (Barremian or older) sediments seal the transition between thinned continental crust and exhumed mantle material in the Tasna Nappe derived from the southern margin of the Valais Ocean (Florineth & Froitzheim 1994), indicating that continental break-up took place there in the Early Cretaceous. Late Cretaceous oceanic spreading was strongly transtensional, related to sinistral displacement of the Iberia-Briançonnais microcontinent relative to Europe.

It is not totally clear when the subduction of the Valais Ocean began. In the Western and Central Alps, the Valais Ocean was consumed during the Palaeogene in its own subduction zone which dipped southeastward, under the Briançonnais fragment. In Eocene times, the Iberia-Briançonnais microcontinent was an independent tectonic plate and the northeastern spur of this plate (the Briançonnais fragment) was bordered by SE-dipping subduction zones on both sides (Stampfli & Borel 2004). The Valais subduction zone was connected to the west across the Pyrenees with the subduction zone that consumed the southern part of the Bay of Biscay oceanic crust beneath Iberia. Subduction of the Valais Ocean may have commenced in the Late Cretaceous, if it is assumed that the Upper Cretaceous Niesen Flysch, in the external part of the Valaisan, was deposited in a subduction-related trench. However, the Valais Ocean cannot have been completely consumed in the Cretaceous, because marine sedimentation in the Valais Basin extends into the Eocene (Ziegler 1956; Bagnoud *et al.* 1998). Thus the question of Cretaceous subduction of the Valais Ocean is still open. We prefer to assume that subduction began in the Palaeogene, because of the lack of direct evidence for Cretaceous subduction, that is, radiometric ages for subduction-related metamorphism. Radiometric evidence exists only for Eocene subduction of the Valais Ocean (Liati *et al.* 2005; Liati & Froitzheim 2006).

Stratigraphic evidence from the Briançonnais and Valais units indicates tectonic activity in the Late Cretaceous. This was the case for the internal Briançonnais in the western Alps, where Late Cretaceous breccias and olistoliths occur (Jaillard 1999), as well as for the Tasna Nappe in the Engadine Window. In the latter area, the Cretaceous succession from the Tristel Formation (Barremian-Lower Aptian) through the 'Gault' sandstones and shales up to the Late Cretaceous–Palaeogene 'Couches Rouges' received coarse-grained clastic input, including both basement and sediment clasts, from a nearby escarpment that was located to the south. Olistoliths, several tens of metres in size, were shed down the escarpment in Late Cretaceous–Palaeogene times. This escarpment was probably related to a strike-slip fault, since a thrust fault would have led to the closure of the sedimentary basin after a certain time. Breccias of probable Cretaceous age have also been reported from the Schams Nappes (Schmid *et al.* 1990), but their exact age is unclear. Similar lithological associations are observed in the Valaisan of the Western Alps. There, the Upper Cretaceous sediments contain subaqueous mass-flow deposits (Brèche de Tarentaise) shed from a rapidly eroding source area to the west (Lomas 1992).

*European margin*

During the Cretaceous, a series of folds trending approximately east–west developed in the Diois, Baronnies and Dévoluy areas of the Chaînes Subalpines, SW of the Pelvoux Massif. The folds are overlain by Late Cretaceous sediments along a spectacular unconformity which was itself later deformed by folds and thrusts reflecting east–west shortening in the external part of the Western Alpine arc. The age of folding has been suggested to be Turonian (Mercier 1958) or Coniacian (Flandrin 1966). The north–south orientated contraction is associated with NE–SW striking, sinistral strike-slip faults (Arnaud 1973). The folding preceded the Pyrenean-Provençal deformation resulting from the collision of Iberia with Europe.

In conclusion, Cretaceous tectonics in the Penninic units and more external zones was characterized by oceanic subduction in the southeastern sub-basin of the Piemont-Ligurian Ocean, probably beginning at *c.* 100 Ma (Albian), by the collision of the Cervinia Terrane with the upper plate of this subduction zone at *c.* 76 Ma (Campanian), by strike-slip faulting in the Briançonnais, by sinistrally transtensive oceanic accretion in parts of the Valais Ocean until 93 Ma (Cenomanian–Turonian), and by north–south shortening in the southwestern part of the European margin at *c.* 90 to 85 Ma.

## *Tertiary tectonics*

The Tertiary period was characterized by the consumption of the remaining oceanic spaces and continental collision in the Alps. Following collision, extensional faulting and strike-slip faulting, alternating or coeval with crustal shortening, took place during ongoing continent convergence.

### *Central Alps*

The southeastern sub-basin of the Piemont-Ligurian Ocean (Tsaté sub-basin, Fig. 18.3) had, at least partly, been consumed in the Cretaceous. Subduction in the Zermatt-Saas sub-basin occurred during the Palaeocene to Eocene and is constrained by radiometric ages for the eclogite-facies and locally ultrahigh-pressure metamorphism in the Zermatt-Saas Zone ranging between 49 and 40 Ma (Ypresian-Lutetian; Rubatto *et al.* 1998; Lapen *et al.* 2003). The Zermatt-Saas sub-basin was subducted towards the SE beneath the upper plate, which included the Cervinia Terrane and Apulia.

As noted above, it is not clear when the Valais Ocean began to be subducted. At 40 to 37 Ma, ophiolites of this ocean had reached eclogite-facies depth. Ages in this range were determined for eclogite-facies metamorphism of Valaisan ophiolites in the Central Alps (Fig. 18.4; Liati *et al.* 2003, 2005; Liati & Froitzheim 2006). The subduction zone dipped below the Briançonnais fragment (Fig. 18.14). Rocks of the distal European margin must have arrived at the subduction zone a few million years before 40 Ma, in order to leave sufficient time for distal European margin units such as the Adula Nappe and the Monte Rosa Nappe to reach eclogite-facies conditions at *c.* 40 Ma (Figs 18.4 & 18.14). There is some evidence that the subduction zone was not located directly at the boundary between the Valais Ocean and the Briançonnais fragment, but was rather intra-oceanic, within the Valais Ocean (Fig. 18.14). This evidence comes from two sources. Firstly, the ocean–continent transition between the Briançonnais fragment and the Valais Ocean preserved in the Tasna Nappe was not disrupted by subduction but preserved within this nappe until the present day, and subduction-related shearing and metamorphism are only found at a deeper level in the Bündnerschiefer of the Engadine Window (Bousquet *et al.* 1999). Secondly, Bagnoud *et al.* (1998) reported late Middle Eocene fossils in sediments from the transition area between the Briançonnais fragment and the Valais Ocean in western Switzerland, indicating that this area was still open at *c.* 40 Ma when the distal European margin had already entered the subduction zone.

Tertiary deformation in the Penninic units was dominated by thrusting until about 35 Ma. This thrusting was initially thin-skinned, when sedimentary cover sheets were detached from their oceanic or continental basement, and subsequently thick-skinned, when the continental basement was shortened. Thrusting, both thin- and thick-skinned, was generally directed towards the European foreland. Overprinting of early thin-skinned by thick-skinned, out-of-sequence thrusting led to an earliest phase of nappe refolding. Examples of this include the folding of the Valaisan Bündnerschiefer, representing the detached sediment cover of the Valais Ocean, around the frontal fold of the Adula Nappe in the eastern Central Alps (Schmid *et al.* 1996), and the analogous folding of the Valaisan Antrona Ophiolites around the front of the Monte Rosa Nappe in the western Central Alps (Fig. 18.9; Froitzheim 2001). According to a new interpretation (Froitzheim *et al.* 2006; Pleuger *et al.* 2007), the basal thrust of the Sesia and Dent Blanche nappes over the Tsaté Nappe is also out of sequence, and the Tsaté Nappe was originally in a higher structural position than the Sesia and Dent Blanche nappes.

At about 35 Ma, the kinematics of the Penninic nappes changed from foreland-directed thrusting to extension. The extension direction was initially parallel to the orogen, as in the case of top-to-the-east normal shearing along the Turba Normal Fault (Figs 18.5 & 18.15) at the eastern border of the Lepontine Dome (Nievergelt *et al.* 1996). Orogen-parallel extension is also reflected by top-to-the-SW shearing in the area of the Monte Rosa Nappe (Steck 1990; Pleuger *et al.* 2007) and other parts of the Penninic nappe stack to the west of the Lepontine Dome. These two large-scale shear zones with opposite dips and shear senses accommodated early exhumation of the Lepontine Dome between them. The Lepontine nappes themselves were also affected by this orogen-parallel stretching. This was mainly expressed by the formation or modification of large-scale isoclinal recumbent folds with hinges parallel to the stretching lineation. Examples are the Antigorio Nappe (D2 of Grujic & Mancktelow 1996) and the modification of the frontal fold of the Adula Nappe during pronounced ENE–WSW orientated stretching in the 'Leis phase' (Löw 1987).

During this process of extensional shearing, a slight change in the extension direction occurred in the Swiss-Italian part of the Penninic nappes (Fig. 18.15). The direction of extension became top-to-the-SE, oblique to the strike of the chain. In the Monte Rosa region, orogen-parallel top-to-the-SW shearing was followed by top-to-the-SE shearing (Pleuger *et al.* 2007). The latter was most pronounced along the Gressoney Shear Zone (Reddy *et al.* 1999; Wheeler *et al.* 2001) where it reactivated an earlier top-to-the-NW thrust which had emplaced the Tsaté Nappe on the Zermatt-Saas Zone. The shear zone dips to the SE beneath the Sesia Nappe; its geometry is extensional. Towards the east, the shear zone followed the southern border of the Lepontine Dome whose southern parts were penetratively affected by top-to-the-SE shearing (e.g. the southern parts of the Adula and Simano nappes; Nagel *et al.* 2002). The shear zone thus acted as an oblique normal fault in a south-dipping orientation. Hence, part of the exhumation of the Lepontine Dome was not accommodated by backthrusting but by normal faulting. Later, beginning at *c.* 30 Ma, the normal fault was rotated into the orientation of a backthrust and pervasively overprinted by ongoing mylonitic shearing until *c.* 26 Ma (Schärer *et al.* 1996). Further east, the 'Insubric normal fault' curved away from the Periadriatic Fault towards the north (33 to 30 Ma Preda Rossa Shear Zone; Berger *et al.* 1996) and was probably connected

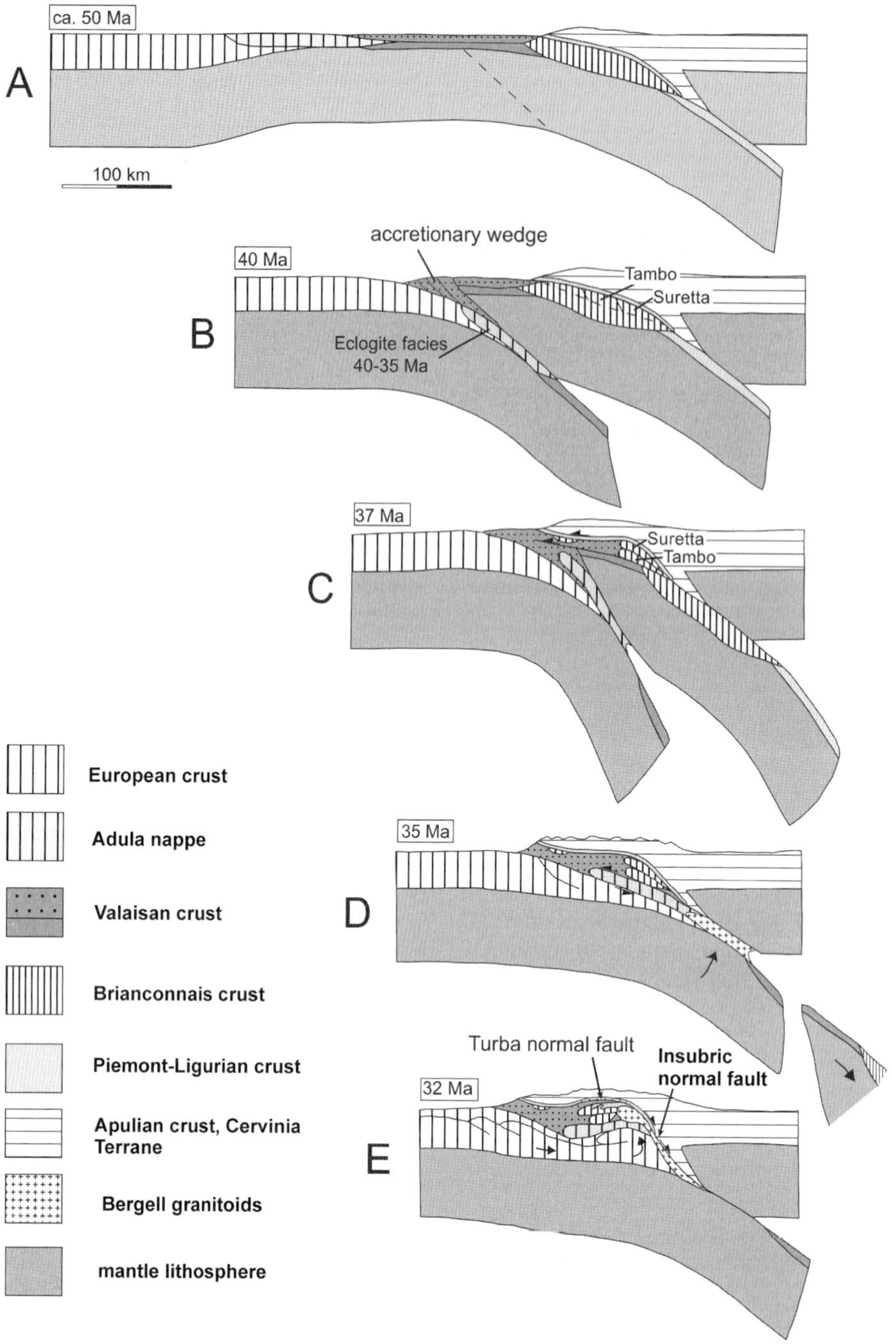


**Fig. 18.14.** Reconstructed kinematic evolution of the Central Alps along the cross-section of Figure 18.6. Exhumation of the Adula nappe high-pressure rocks was achieved by subduction of the overlying microplate including the Briançonnais Terrane (slab extraction) between steps B and D.

with the Turba Normal Fault. This connection was interrupted by the intrusion of the 30 Ma Bergell granodiorite which truncates the Turba Normal Fault (Nievergelt *et al.* 1996) and, thereby, sets a lower age limit to the top-to-the-SE extensional shearing.

Although the geometry of top-to-the-SE shearing is extensional in the Penninic nappes, it does not reflect plate divergence across the Alps but rather it occurred contemporaneously with shortening and foreland-directed thrusting in the more external units (Helvetic units; Milnes & Pfiffner 1980; Weh & Froitzheim 2001). Therefore, it may reflect corner flow during plate convergence. Important backfolds formed during the extensional event, most notably the Niemet-Beverin Fold (Fig. 18.6) in the eastern, and the Mischabel Fold in the western Central Alps. These are not related to compressional 'backthrusting' along the Insubric line but to extensional 'backshearing' since the Insubric Fault was not yet a backthrust at that time but rather a south-dipping normal fault (Figs 18.6, 18.10 & 18.14; Nagel *et al.* 2002).

The Helvetic units of the Central Alps evolved in a similar fashion to the Penninic units, with an early phase of thin-skinned

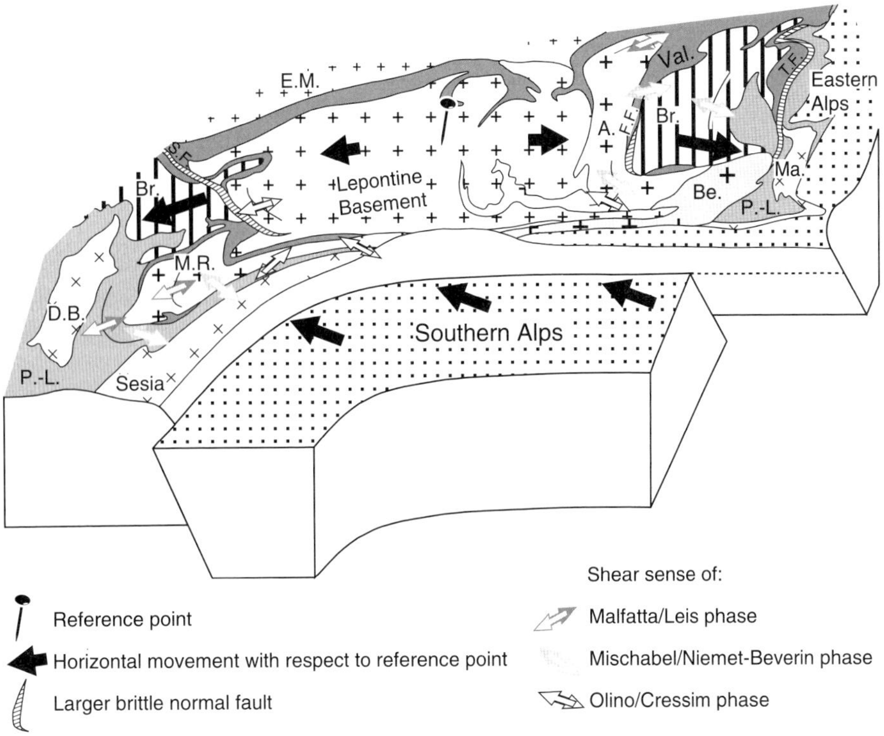


**Fig. 18.15.** Schematic block diagram illustrating kinematics of the Central Alps and the Insubric Fault during Oligocene to Miocene times. Black arrows indicate overall motions with respect to a reference point in the Lepontine Dome. Double arrows indicate shear sense during Oligocene to Miocene phases of extensional deformation in the Penninic units: orogen-parallel extension during the Malfatta/Leis phase (*c.* 35–33 Ma), SE- to east-directed extension during the Mischabel/Niemet-Beverin phase (*c.* 33–30 Ma), again orogen-parallel extension during the Olino/Cressim phase (after 30 Ma), progressively localized in normal faults (Simplon and Forcola faults). Extensional deformation of the Penninic units occurred during convergence of Europe and Adria and accommodated exhumation of the Penninic units relative to the Southern Alps. Abbreviations: A., Adula Nappe; Be., Bergell intrusion; Br., Briançonnais units; D.B., Dent Blanche Nappe; E.M., External Massifs; F.F., Forcola Fault; Ma., Margna Nappe; M.R., Monte Rosa Nappe; T.F., Turba Fault; P.-L., units derived from Piemont-Ligurian Ocean; Val., units derived from Valais Ocean. After Pleuger *et al.* (2008).

thrusting followed by later phases of thick-skinned thrusting. However, the entire sequence began later and lasted longer. Synorogenic extension, as observed in the Penninic nappes, is either absent or at least weaker. In the eastern Central Alps, thrusting in the Helvetic units began in the latest Eocene to earliest Oligocene (*c.* 35 Ma) with the emplacement of the Ultra-Helvetic and South Helvetic units (Sardona Flysch, Blattengrat Flysch) on top of the units that would later form the Helvetic nappes and the Infra Helvetic Complex. This emplacement was coeval with extension in the Penninic nappes. The contemporaneity may be interpreted as indicating gravitational spreading at the scale of the orogen as suggested by Milnes & Pfiffner (1980).

In the Penninic units, the extensional phase lasted from *c.* 35 Ma to 30 Ma (Schreurs 1993; Schmid *et al.* 1996). It was followed by NW–SE to north–south compression associated with orogen-parallel extension, creating folds with steep axial planes like the Vanzone Antiform (east of Monte Rosa) and the Cressim Antiform (southern Adula Nappe) (Nagel *et al.* 2002). The formation of these folds was related to the development of the Southern Steep Belt adjacent to the Periadriatic Fault (Milnes 1974). Dextral shearing along the Periadriatic Fault (Schmid *et al.* 1987) began at *c.* 30 Ma in the Central Alps.

At this time, the thrusts that define the Helvetic nappes, such as the Glarus Thrust, also formed. North-directed thrusting along the Glarus Thrust must have begun after 30 Ma because the 32 to 29 Ma Taveyannaz sandstone (Boyet *et al.* 2001) is present in the footwall of this thrust. To the north, the thrust continues into the frontal thrust of the Helvetic nappes which buried Miocene sediments of the Molasse Basin in its footwall. The activity of the Glarus Thrust must therefore have continued during the Miocene. Further south, the Glarus Thrust buried the earlier-emplaced Blattengrat and Sardona Flysch units in its footwall; hence it is an out-of-sequence thrust. It is rooted to the south in the boundary zone between the Aare Massif and the Gotthard Nappe. During the Miocene, the Glarus Thrust was deformed into its present antiformal shape by the updoming of the Aare Massif. This updoming was the result of underthrusting from the north. The Aare Massif can be viewed as an antiformal stack of basement units imbricated during this stage.

In Miocene times, a second phase of extensional tectonics affected the internal part of the Central Alps, south of the Helvetic units. This led to the development of normal faults with slip direction parallel to the orogen. Typical examples include the Simplon Fault (Fig. 18.5; Mancktelow 1985), the Forcola Fault (Meyre *et al.* 1998; Ciancaleoni & Marquer 2006), and the Engadine Fault (Schmid & Froitzheim 1993). These faults are related to the exhumation of Penninic metamorphic domes: the Lepontine Dome in the case of the Simplon and Forcola faults, and the Engadine Window in the case of the Engadine Fault.

The Simplon Fault is a large-scale normal fault with a wide

zone of greenschist-facies mylonitic shearing in the footwall, evolving upwards into cataclasites and finally into a discrete fault. Top-to-the-SW normal faulting along the Simplon Fault was contemporaneous with NW–SE shortening. This is demonstrated from slightly older, but already Simplon-Fault-related mylonites in the footwall that were deformed into SW–NE striking folds and truncated by younger mylonites of the Simplon Fault (Mancktelow 1992). The main extensional movements along the Simplon Fault occurred at *c.* 18 to 15 Ma but displacement went on at a lower rate until 3 Ma (Grasemann & Mancktelow 1993). The extension direction of the Simplon Fault is parallel to the direction of Early Oligocene orogen-parallel extension (see above). Top-to-the-SW greenschist-facies mylonites found in the hanging wall of the Simplon Fault, which are related to the Early Oligocene orogen-parallel extension, were therefore interpreted by Steck (1990) to be part of the wider 'Simplon Shear Zone', assuming continuity between Early Oligocene and Miocene extensional faulting.

Although it seems logical from map view that the Simplon Fault is connected with the Insubric Fault through the Centovalli, a west–east striking zone of cataclasite, this is in fact not the case. Instead, the Simplon Fault becomes a ductile shear zone towards the east, then turns to the NE into the Lepontine Dome and becomes indistinct (Mancktelow 1985). The Simplon and Insubric faults are not directly linked (Mancktelow 1985; Schmid *et al.* 1987). Towards the west, the Simplon Fault is connected with a dextral strike-slip fault in the Rhone Valley. This fault is assumed to continue into the Western Alps as a shear zone between the Aiguilles Rouges and Mont Blanc massifs (Hubbard & Mancktelow 1992).

The east-dipping Forcola Fault (Meyre *et al.* 1998) is the symmetrical counterpart of the Simplon Fault on the eastern side of the Lepontine Dome but the amount of displacement is smaller. At its southern termination, Forcola-Fault-related shearing affected the 24 Ma old (Liati *et al.* 2000) Novate leucogranite intrusion, probably soon after its intrusion (Ciancaleoni & Marquer 2006). Together, the Simplon and Forcola faults accommodated Miocene exhumation of the Lepontine Dome by east–west extension.

The SW–NE striking Engadine Fault (Fig. 18.5) shows a combination of strike-slip and normal-fault motion (Schmid & Froitzheim 1993). In the Lower Engadine, towards the NE, it has a SE-dipping normal-fault orientation and accommodated relative uplift and exhumation of the Penninic nappes of the Engadine Window in its footwall. Its vertical component in this area amounts to at least 4 km. Towards the SW in the Upper Engadine, it becomes vertical and acted as a sinistral strike-slip fault with a vertical component opposite to the one in the Lower Engadine. Here, it is the southeastern block which was uplifted relative to the northwestern one. Activity of the Engadine Fault post-dates the emplacement of the Bergell granodiorite at 30 Ma (Von Blanckenburg 1992), since it truncates the contact metamorphic aureole of the Bergell intrusion. The continuations of the Engadine Fault towards the NE and SW are still unclear. Towards the NE, it may continue into the fault that separates the Ötztal Nappe to the south from the Northern Calcareous Alps to the north.

During the Miocene, shortening of the European crust prograded towards the north. The basement of the Aare Massif was progressively shortened by ductile to brittle thrust faults; the lowermost of these is probably connected with the frontal thrust fault of the Alps, which is the thrust of the Subalpine Molasse over the Foreland Molasse. The Subalpine Molasse forms a stack of imbricates dipping towards the south under the Helvetic nappes. Movement of the frontal thrust lasted at least until the end of the Burdigalian (*c.* 16 Ma) since the Burdigalian Upper Marine Molasse is affected by thrust-related deformation. Seismic and geological field studies suggest the existence of a south-directed backthrust at depth to the north of the frontal thrust and cropping out a short distance to the north of the frontal thrust. Together, this backthrust and the frontal thrust form a triangle structure (Fig. 18.6; Stäuble & Pfiffner 1991; Berge & Veal 2005). The backthrust was active at *c.* 15 to 13 Ma (Kempf *et al.* 1999).

The Jura Mountains are kinematically linked to the Alps and represent the youngest part of the north-directed Alpine thrust belt. The age of folding and thrusting in the Jura Mountains is Late Miocene to Pliocene. Younger, Pleistocene to recent shortening has been observed in the foreland of the Jura frontal thrust to the west of Basel. At its southwestern end, the Jura folds and thrusts continue into the most external folds and thrusts of the Western Alps. At its eastern termination, the Jura shortening dies out and the Jura Mountains end without a connection to the Alps, at least at the surface. The Jura folds represent classic detachment folds; they were detached along Middle and Upper Triassic evaporites. Although it is clear that shortening in the Jura Mountains is part of the Alpine Orogeny, there is a long-standing controversy about whether the basal thrust is rooted in the basement below the Jura Mountains or runs within the Mesozoic-age sediments below the fill of the Molasse Basin and is rooted below the Alps ('Fernschubhypothese', e.g. Laubscher 1961). Based on seismic sections of the Molasse Basin, Pfiffner *et al.* (1997) suggested that the Jura basal thrust is indeed rooted in the basement under the Jura Mountains, and continues southward at a shallow level within the basement beneath the Molasse Basin. Thrusting in the Jura Mountains also involved inversion of Late Carboniferous to Permian basins.

### *Eastern Alps*

The tectonic evolution of the Eastern Alps during Tertiary times was governed by four major processes: closure of remaining parts of the Penninic Ocean by subduction (until *c.* 47–40 Ma; Kurz *et al.* 2001*a*); thrusting of Austro-Alpine and Penninic units over the European continental margin and imbrication of the latter (from *c.* 47 to *c.* 17 Ma); Oligocene synintrusive shearing along the Periadriatic Fault (*c.* 35 to 28 Ma); east–west extension and eastward extrusion of Austro-Alpine crustal fragments, coeval with north–south shortening (from 25–20 Ma to *c.* 9 Ma; Decker & Peresson 1996) (Fig. 18.16).

Subduction of the Penninic Ocean continued from the Late Cretaceous into the Palaeogene, and parts of this ocean remained open until the middle Eocene when the youngest sediments were deposited. Sedimentation ended in the Penninic units of the Engadine Window in the western part of the Eastern Alps at *c.* 49–48 Ma (Ypresian–Lutetian boundary; Bertle 2002), and in the Laab Nappe, one of the Rhenodanubian Flysch nappes in the eastern part of the Eastern Alps, at *c.* 40 Ma (end of Lutetian; Piller *et al.* 2004). This indicates eastward-propagating closure of the Penninic Ocean and accretion of the oceanic units under the Austro-Alpine nappes. Subduction of the distal European margin may have begun earlier, since $^{40}Ar/^{39}Ar$ geochronology on high-pressure rocks from the Eclogite Zone (Sub-Penninic) of the Tauern Window yielded middle Eocene ages (*c.* 42 Ma) for early exhumation after the pressure peak (Ratschbacher *et al.* 2005). However, a much younger age has also been proposed for the high-pressure metamorphism in the Eclogite Zone (*c.* 31.5 Ma using Rb/Sr; Glodny *et al.* 2005).

The Austro-Alpine units in the upper plate of the subduction

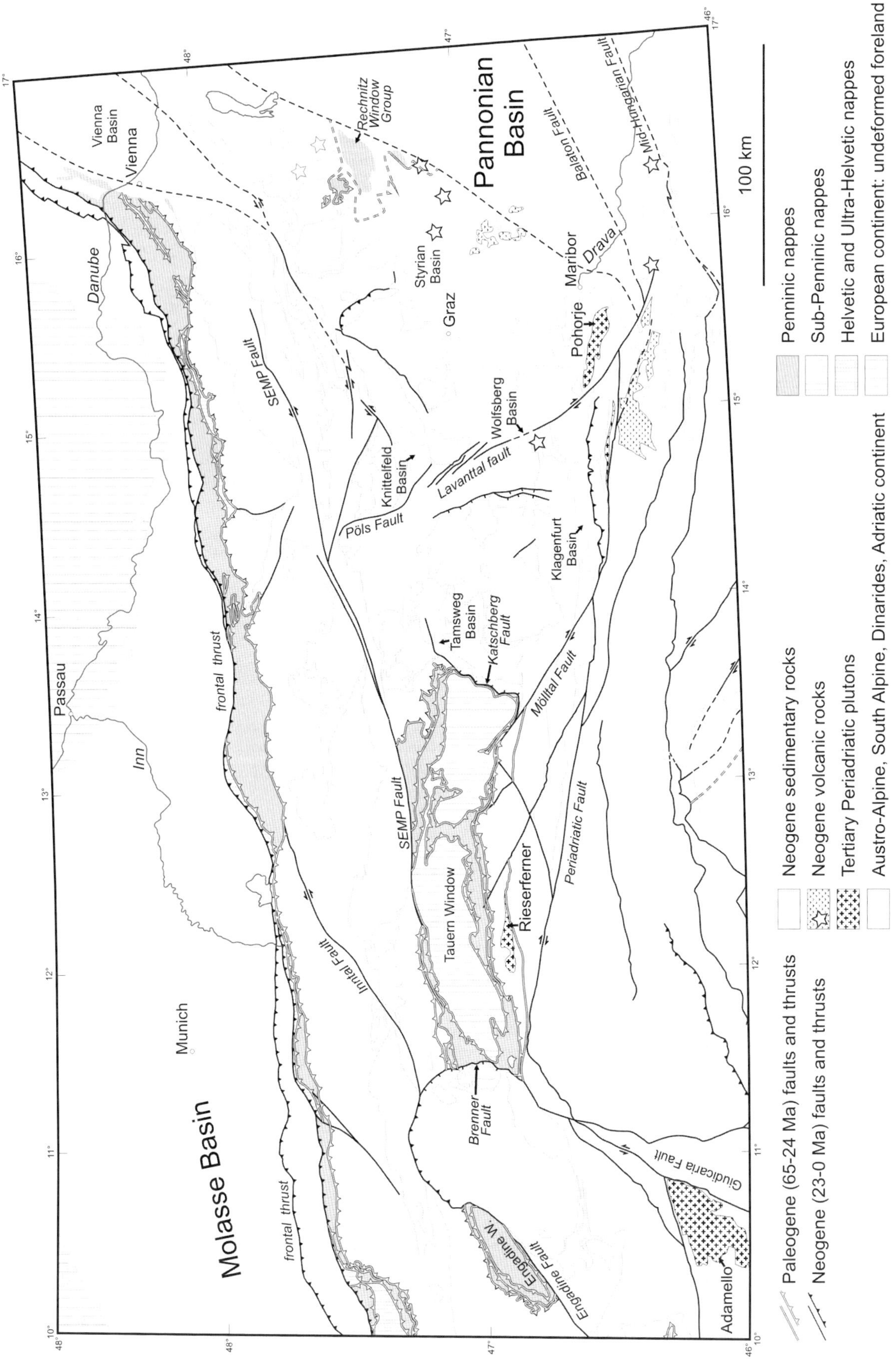


**Fig. 18.16.** Main Tertiary-age structures in the Eastern Alps.

zone represented a flooded (and, in the southern part, extended) mountain belt where the highest peaks formed belts of islands. Between these islands and on the northern slope towards the subduction zone, sedimentation of the Gosau Group continued until the Early Eocene (Wagreich 2001*b*). The collision with the European continental margin resulted in uplift of the upper plate and the termination of marine sedimentation of the Gosau Group. As noted above, Eo-Alpine metamorphic crystalline detritus can be observed in mica-rich sandstones of the Gosau Group from the uppermost Cretaceous onward (Schuster *et al.* 2003). The oldest apatite fission track data from the Austro-Alpine basement units are over 60 Ma (Dunkl 1992; Hejl 1992; Fügenschuh *et al.* 2000). Hence, the metamorphic cycle and pervasive deformation of most of the Austro-Alpine units was completed at that time, with the exception of some parts located to the south, which were significantly exhumed during the Tertiary. Examples for this include the Austro-Alpine basement hosting the Rieserferner Pluton between the Defereggen-Antholz-Vals Fault and the southern border of the Tauern Window (Steenken *et al.* 2002) and the basement in the Pohorje Mountains (Fodor *et al.* 2003).

The sedimentary succession of the Ultra-Helvetic Liebenstein Nappe, representing the distal European continental margin in the western part of the Eastern Alps, ends at *c.* 47 Ma (Piller *et al.* 2004). This datum approximately marks the beginning of continental collision in the Eastern Alps. After that time, the Ultra-Helvetic units were accreted to the nappe stack consisting of Rhenodanubian Flysch nappes and Austro-Alpine nappes. In the eastern part of the Eastern Alps, sedimentation in the Helvetic/Ultra-Helvetic units continued until *c.* 38 Ma, which reflects oblique, eastward-propagating collision (Piller *et al.* 2004). When the Helvetic units were detached from their basement, beginning at *c.* 38 Ma in the western part, thrust-related folds in the Helvetic units deformed the older basal thrusts of the Ultra-Helvetic and Rhenodanubian Flysch nappes. Finally, thrusting propagated into the southern part of the Molasse Basin (Folded Molasse) beginning at *c.* 24 Ma (Oberhauser 1998). The Folded Molasse is formed by northward-overthrust synclines; the intervening anticlines are cut by the thrust faults. This structure represents closely spaced fold-propagation folds. At the southern rim of the Foreland Molasse, i.e. the part of the Molasse Basin located north of the Folded Molasse, the strata dip to the north and are floored by a north-dipping backthrust. Together with the southward-dipping basal thrust of the Folded Molasse, this backthrust forms a triangle structure (Berge & Veal 2005) which can be followed over 350 km from eastern Switzerland through Bavaria into Austria. Thrusting along the northern rim of the Eastern Alps continued until *c.* 17 Ma, the age of the youngest overthrust sediments (Decker & Peresson 1996). Blind thrusts at depth may still have been active after this time.

In the eastern part of the Alps, several tonalitic, granodioritic and granitic intrusions are found in the vicinity of, or directly at, the Periadriatic Fault including: Adamello Pluton, Rensen Pluton, Rieserferner Pluton, Karawanken Pluton, Pohorje Pluton and several smaller fault-parallel tonalite lamellae intruded into the middle and upper crust. Subvolcanic dykes and extrusive volcanics with tonalitic and basaltic compositions reached the uppermost crust and the surface. The basaltic rocks show alkaline and calc-alkaline signatures (Deutsch 1984; Müller *et al.* 1992). Except for the southern part of the Adamello Pluton (45 Ma) and the Pohorje Pluton, all granitoid intrusions occurred in a rather short timespan between 34 and 28 Ma (Rosenberg 2004). The intrusion of the Pohorje Pluton was dated by K–Ar at 18 to 16.5 Ma (Marton *et al.* 2002); U–Pb or other data from high-retentivity systems are not yet available for this pluton.

There is obviously a close relationship between the Periadriatic Fault and the intrusions (this is also the case for the Periadriatic intrusions in the Western and Central Alps). Either there was a linear magma source (von Blanckenburg & Davies 1995), or the magma rising from a wider source area was channelled into the fault zone (Rosenberg 2004). Von Blanckenburg & Davies (1995) suggested that the Periadriatic magmatism resulted from break-off of the subducted Penninic Ocean slab at 45 Ma, leading to melting of supra-subduction-zone lithosphere. Although many authors have adopted the slab break-off hypothesis, there is no consensus about the timing. Slab break-off events have been proposed to have taken place in the Alps at 100 Ma and 45 Ma (Von Blanckenburg & Davies 1995, 1996), 35 to 30 Ma (Schmid *et al.* 1996), 25 Ma (Michon *et al.* 2003), and 5 Ma (Schmid *et al.* 2004*b*). This inflation of events sheds serious doubt on the testability of the slab break-off hypothesis in the case of the Alps. On the other hand, slab break-off is still an elegant model to explain short-time, intense magmatism in a long and narrow zone. Froitzheim *et al.* (2003) suggested slab extraction as a cause of the Periadriatic magmatism, which would be quite similar to slab break-off regarding the thermal consequences.

Along the Periadriatic Fault System in the Eastern Alps, important movements took place in the Oligocene, contemporaneously with Periadriatic magmatism. At the northern end of the Adamello Pluton, dextral strike-slip shearing occurred at 35 to 32 Ma, coeval with the intrusion, and probably continued until *c.* 20 Ma (Stipp *et al.* 2004). Along the northern part of the SW–NE striking Giudicarie Fault, which formed a restraining bend in the dextral Periadriatic Fault, Austro-Alpine units were backthrust over South Alpine ones around 32 Ma according to Viola *et al.* (2001). This is in contrast to other interpretations (e.g. Frisch *et al.* 1998; Fig. 18.17) which assume that the Periadriatic Fault was initially straight and only offset by the northern Giudicarie Fault during the Miocene.

In the area south of the Tauern Window, displacement along steeply orientated shear zones north of the Periadriatic Fault, such as the Defereggen-Antholz-Vals Fault and the southern border of the Tauern Window, was sinistrally transtensive in Early Oligocene times, with a north-side-up vertical component (Mancktelow *et al.* 2001). This is similar to the top-to-the-SE extensional faulting along the Periadriatic (Insubric) Fault in the Central Alps during the same time interval. A change to dextrally transpressive kinematics occurred at *c.* 30 Ma, and dextral movement along the Periadriatic Fault continued at least until 13 Ma (Mancktelow *et al.* 2001), in the framework of east-directed extrusion of the Eastern Alps (see below). Although the Periadriatic Fault is a first-order tectonic boundary in this area, it was not imaged by the TRANSALP reflection seismic experiment (Lüschen *et al.* 2004).

According to Frisch *et al.* (1998) the western parts of the Eastern Alps formed a mountainous region after the Oligocene, whereas the eastern part was characterized by hilly to peneplane topography with a north-directed drainage system. On the low-lying northeastern part (Northern Calcareous Alps) sands and conglomerates, rich in quartz pebbles eroded from a greenschist-facies metamorphosed hinterland, were deposited by braided rivers (Augenstein Formation of Late Oligocene to Early Miocene age), probably passing into marine sediments of the Molasse Basin to the north. The difference in the topography is also expressed in the Oligocene sediments of the Molasse Basin, where coarse-grained material, including detritus from Periadriatic volcanoes and plutons, is frequent in the western part.

During the Miocene, continued north–south shortening of the Eastern Alps ceased to be primarily accommodated by thrust

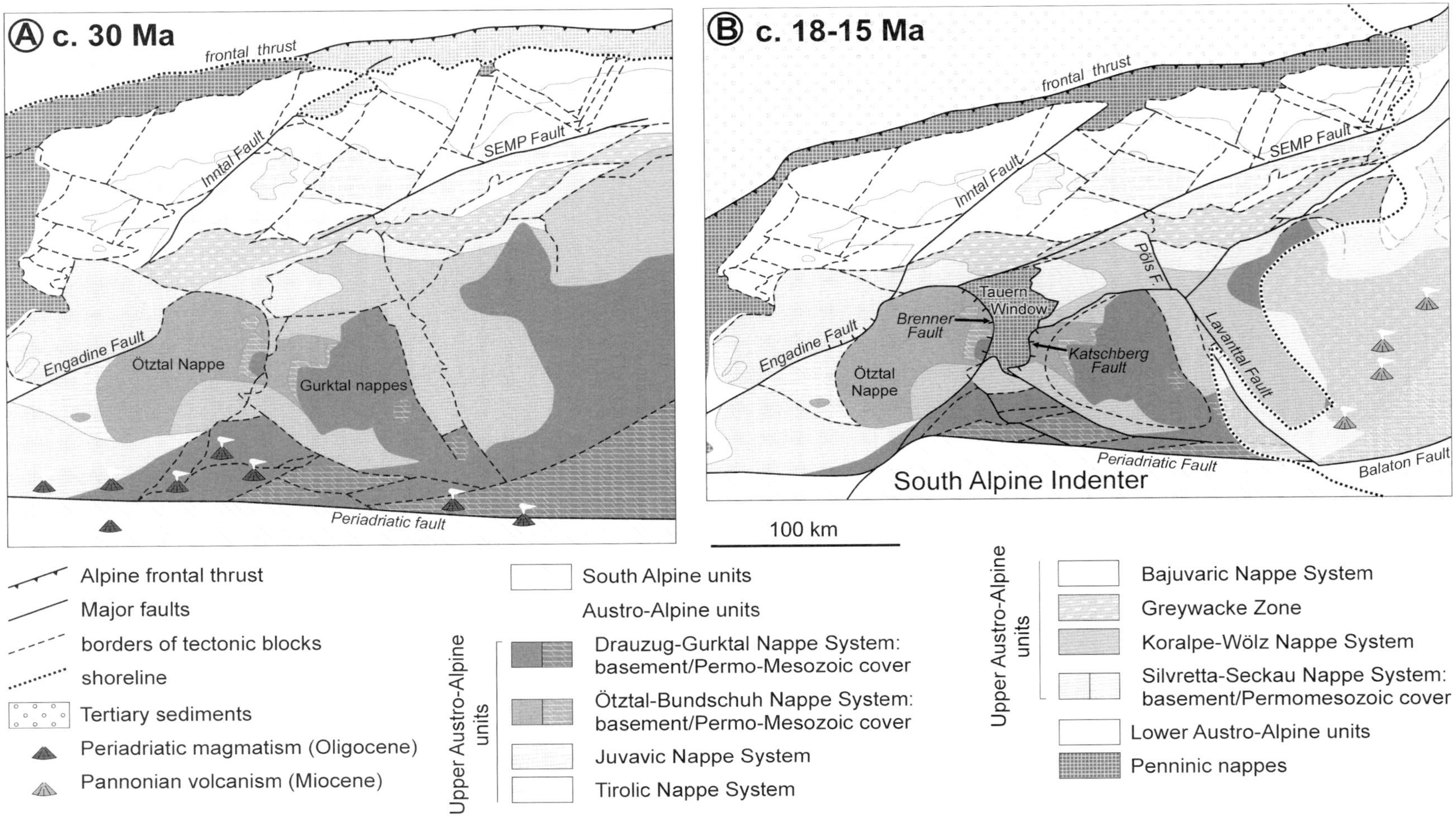


**Fig. 18.17.** Reconstructions of the Eastern Alps during (**A**) Oligocene (*c*. 30 Ma) and (**B**) Miocene times (*c*. 18 to 15 Ma). Miocene reconstruction shows beginning of east–west extension and eastward extrusion of lozenge-shaped blocks. Tauern Window begins to form by east–west extension and north–south shortening in front of the northward-advancing South Alpine indenter. After Frisch *et al*. (1998), modified.

imbrication of the European margin, but increasingly by eastward extrusion of the units located between the front of the Alps and the Periadriatic Fault (Ratschbacher *et al.* 1989; Decker & Peresson 1996; Linzer *et al.* 2002). This eastward extrusion was responsible for, or at least accentuated, the elongate shape of the Eastern Alps. It led to disintegration of the Austro-Alpine nappes above the ductilely deformed Penninic and Sub-Penninic units, cropping out in several windows (Engadine Window, Tauern Window and Rechnitz Window Group), by a system of strike-slip and normal faults. Sinistral, WSW–ENE striking faults developed in the northern part (e.g. Inntal-Salzburg-Amstetten and Salzach-Ennstal-Mariazell-Puchberg faults) whereas WNW–ESE striking dextral faults dominated in the southern part (Periadriatic, Isel, Mölltal and Lavanttal faults). Major normal faults border the western and eastern end of the Tauern Window (Brenner and Katschberg faults) and the Rechnitz Window Group (Behrmann 1988; Selverstone 1980; Genser & Neubauer 1989; Grasemann & Dunkl 1996; Fügenschuh *et al.* 1997). The new fault system had a strong influence on the topography and the drainage pattern which has been east-directed in the eastern part of the Eastern Alps since that time (Frisch *et al.* 2000). Along the faults Miocene basins developed mostly in a pull-apart regime (e.g. Tamsweg, Knittelfeld, and Vienna basins). In the case of the Vienna Basin, the evolution began with the formation of a piggyback basin on top of the Austro-Alpine nappes (Strauss *et al.* 2006). To the SE the Pannonian Basin and the related Styrian Basin formed in the interior of the Alpine-Carpathian arc. This process was associated with Miocene volcanism.

The Klagenfurt Basin formed in the Late Miocene to Pliocene as a flexural basin in front of the NW-directed overthrust of the Karawanken Mountains (Nemes *et al.* 1997). This overthrust was probably related to dextral shearing along the Periadriatic Fault (Polinski & Eisbacher 1992).

The extension and eastward extrusion of the Eastern Alps during the Miocene may be explained in different ways. Ratschbacher *et al.* (1991) suggested that it was driven by a combination of forces applied to the boundaries of wedge-shaped blocks (tectonic escape) and gravitational spreading away from a topographic high in the area of the Tauern Window (extensional collapse). This topographic high resulted from the northward motion of the South Alpine indenter bounded by the Giudicarie Fault to the NW and the Pustertal Fault to the NE, which caused strong north–south shortening, antiformal stacking and uplift of the Sub-Penninic basement nappes in the Tauern Window (Lammerer & Weger 1998). Rosenberg *et al.* (2004, 2007) emphasized the tectonic escape part and assumed extensional collapse to be less important. In addition to these 'intra-Alpine' forces, subduction retreat (roll-back) in the Eastern Carpathians, where oceanic lithosphere was probably subducted in a west-dipping subduction zone, exerted a pull force on the upper-plate lithosphere in the Pannonian Basin and Eastern Alps which contributed to the extension and extrusion (Peresson & Decker 1997).

The extension was terminated by an east–west compressional event between 9 Ma and 5.3 Ma which may have resulted from the entrance of thick European continental crust into the Eastern Carpathians subduction zone and the ensuing termination of subduction (Peresson & Decker 1997). The extrusion, however, appears to have continued until the present. GPS data suggest that eastward extrusion of the Eastern Alps is presently taking place within the framework of north–south convergence between the Adria microplate and Europe (Grenerczy *et al.* 2005; Vrabec *et al.* 2006).

*Southern Alps*

In the Lombardic-Giudicaric thrust belt, i.e. the western part of the Southern Alps, thrusting evolved in two major phases: before the Adamello intrusion and after it. Important south-vergent basement thrusts (Gallinera, Porcile, Orobic thrusts; Schönborn 1992) and related folds are truncated by the oldest part of the Adamello intrusion and are, therefore, older than 43 Ma (Brack 1981). As discussed above, these 'pre-Adamello' structures may be Late Cretaceous or Early Tertiary (Palaeocene–Eocene) in age. These structures were later passively transported southward in the hanging walls of Miocene-age thrusts. The direction of shortening in the Palaeogene (or Late Cretaceous) was north–south to NE–SW. This implies that the Alps were already a bivergent orogen in the Palaeogene (if not already in the Late Cretaceous).

Thrusting after the Adamello intrusion began in the Chattian and lasted, possibly with interruptions, until the Tortonian. Over this time, a thrust system evolved whose frontal, southern part is hidden beneath sediments of the Po Basin but is known from drilling (Pieri & Groppi 1981). According to Picotti *et al.* (1995), post-Adamello thrusting culminated in three phases: Chattian-Burdigalian, Serravallian-Tortonian, and (?)Late Tortonian. The thrusts in the subsurface were sealed by Messinian sediments. In the most external foreland area, Alpine compression came to an end after the Early Messinian. In contrast, east of the Lombardic-Giudicaric fold-and-thrust belt, Alpine deformation lasted until the Pleistocene (Fantoni *et al.* 2004).

The thrust front of the Lombardic-Giudicaric fold-and-thrust belt strikes east–west but towards the eastern termination it swings around into a SSW–NNE strike parallel to the Giudicarie Fault. This fault lies inside the belt, to the NW of the thrust front. The Giudicarie Fault approximately coincides with the eastern border of the Lombardian rift basin (of Jurassic age) against the Venetian Platform, so that the western part of the Venetian Platform was also affected by thrusting (Picotti *et al.* 1995). The southern part of the Giudicarie Fault (south of the junction with the Tonale Fault) separates uplifted Adamello granitoids, Variscan basement, and Permo-Triassic rocks of the northwestern block from mainly Mesozoic rocks of the southeastern block. It represented a sinistrally transpressive fault active after 20 to 18 Ma (Viola *et al.* 2001).

In the central and eastern Dolomites, Palaeogene, NE–SW orientated compression produced a SW-vergent thin-skinned thrust belt (Doglioni & Bosellini 1987). The thrusts typically form ramps on the northeastern slopes of the Triassic carbonate platforms and flats on top. Spectacular west-facing folds occur in the Jurassic sediments above the flats ('Gipfelfaltung': summit folding). This thrust belt is the northwestern extension of the Eocene thrust system in the Dinarides. The thrust front (Dinaric Front in Fig. 18.1) is displaced towards the west relative to its position further SE in the Dinarides; this offset results from younger, Neogene, southward thrusting along the east–west striking Bassano Thrust (see below) and similar thrusts in the eastward continuation of the Bassano Thrust.

In the Neogene, a new, thick-skinned, south- to SE-vergent thrust belt formed. The thrusts are almost at right angles to the Palaeogene ones. Two main, basement-involving, south-directed thrust zones occur: the Serravallian-Tortonian Valsugana Thrust to the north, and the Messinian to Recent Bassano and Montello thrusts to the south (Fig. 18.1; Schönborn 1999; Castellarin & Cantelli 2000). The Valsugana Thrust forms the southern limit of the Dolomites and the Bassano Thrust runs close to the northern border of the Po Plain, whereas the blind Montello Thrust is kinematically linked to the Bassano Thrust and represents the frontal element of the Neogene thrust system. Quaternary terraces have been deformed by a ramp anticline related to the Montello Thrust (Benedetti *et al.* 2000), showing that this thrust is presently active. Antithetic, north-directed thrusts also occur. The Dolomites are in the structural position of a wide, open synform between the Periadriatic Fault to the north and the Valsugana Thrust to the south. The basement crops out on both sides in the vicinity of these faults.

*Western Alps*

Subduction of oceanic units in the Western Alps probably lasted until the Early Eocene and was followed by continental subduction of the European margin leading to high- to ultrahigh-pressure metamorphism of European margin units in the Late Eocene (Dora-Maira Nappe, Gran Paradiso Nappe; Lardeaux *et al.* 2006). Ongoing continental collision in the Oligocene resulted in the thrusting of the internal zones (Penninic) of the Western Alps on the external zones (External Massifs, Dauphinois Zone) along the Penninic Frontal Thrust, coeval with rapid exhumation of the high-pressure units in the internal zone (*c.* 35 to 32 Ma; Rubatto & Hermann 2001). During the Neogene and up to the present day, the strain is partitioned into widespread extension in the internal part of the Western Alps, with the extension direction initially parallel and later perpendicular to the strike of the orogen, and shortening in the western, external part. The boundary between external and internal zones, the Penninic frontal thrust, was reactivated as an east-dipping extensional detachment fault during the Neogene (Sue & Tricart 1999, 2003). Miocene-age, orogen-parallel extension of the inner Western Alps has been interpreted as reflecting extrusion of the inner part of the Western Alps towards the south (Champagnac *et al.* 2006).

Based on palaeomagnetic evidence, the internal part of the Western Alps (Penninic units) experienced strong counterclockwise vertical-axis rotation after the Oligocene (Collombet *et al.* 2002). The amount of this rotation increases dramatically from north to south (from *c.* 25° NW of Torino to *c.* 117° in Liguria). This increase in rotation angle approximately parallels the change in the strike of the orogen around the arc of the Western Alps, suggesting that the arcuate shape of the internal zones of the Western Alps resulted from the bending of an initially straighter orogen during its post-collisional interaction with Europe. The counterclockwise rotation of the internal zones is probably closely related to the Miocene and younger southwestward thrusting of the Dauphinois Zone along the Digne Thrust (Fig. 18.5).

Other authors (Schmid & Kissling 2000) suggested that the formation of the Western Alpine arc resulted from the two-stage motion of the Adriatic microplate relative to Europe: 195 km northward motion of Adria between 50 and 35 Ma, leading to sinistral transpression in the already north–south striking Western Alps, followed by 124 km northwestward motion with 18° anticlockwise rotation between 35 Ma and the present, leading to outward-directed thrusting. This model predicts little or no rotation of the internal zones of the western Alps.

## *Present-day kinematics of the Alps*

GPS data suggest that the Adriatic microplate is presently rotating anticlockwise with respect to stable Europe around a pole in the Po Basin near Milan at an angular rate of 0.52°/Ma (Calais *et al.* 2002). This movement implies that there is an eastward-increasing north–south convergence between Adria and Europe along the northern boundary of Adria, reaching 2–3 mm/a in the eastern Alpine region, and this is taken up by contraction in the Eastern Alps and concomitant eastward extrusion of the Eastern Alps into the Pannonian Basin (Grenerczy *et al.* 2005). The southern boundary of the eastward-extruding block is the Periadriatic Fault System where dextral displacements of *c.* 1 mm/a exist on individual faults (Vrabec *et al.* 2006).

High-resolution teleseismic tomography suggests that a NE-dipping, Adriatic, lithospheric slab is present under the Eastern Alps, in contrast to the Central and Western Alps where only a European slab dipping under the Adriatic microplate is imaged (Lippitsch *et al.* 2003). This suggests that the present north–south convergence in the Eastern Alps is accommodated at a lithospheric scale by the northward subduction of Adria. Hence, the polarity of subduction appears to have changed in the Neogene, from the southward subduction of Europe to the northward subduction of Adria (Fig. 18.11). This northward subduction may be kinematically linked to the presently active southward thrusting at the front of the Southern Alps in their eastern part (Montello thrust; Fig. 18.1).

Towards the west, the rate of north–south convergence across the Alps diminishes due to the rotation of Adria. The northwestern corner of the Adriatic microplate, west of the rotation pole, even moves southward with respect to Europe (Calais *et al.* 2002), which leads to north–south compression on the south side of this corner, i.e. in the Ligurian Alps (Calais *et al.* 2002).

In the Western and Central Alps, the present-day strain field is modified by stresses resulting from topography and crustal thickness. These have a much larger effect on the local strains than the relative motions of the foreland plates. The analysis of earthquake focal mechanisms from the Western and Central Alps revealed a continuous area of extensional strain which closely follows the topographic crest line of the Alps and the axis of thickest crust. In contrast, a thrusting regime is observed locally near the border of the Alpine chain. In addition, strike-slip faults occur in both the internal and external zones (Delacou *et al.* 2004). In the Western Alps, the directions of both $\sigma_3$ in the internal, extending zone and $\sigma_1$ in the external, shortening zone are perpendicular to the orogen, which results in a radial arrangement of these principal stresses. At present, the extension direction in the inner Western Alps is orogen-perpendicular and the Western Alps are in a state of gravitational spreading, in contrast to the Eastern Alps where lateral (eastward) extrusion caused by convergence of the bounding plates is more important.

# The Western Carpathians (D.P.)

## *Geographic outline*

The Western Carpathians are the northernmost segment of the European Alpides. They form a northward-convex arc *c.* 500 km long in the west–east direction and 300 km across (Fig. 18.18). Taking into consideration the pre-Tertiary units, the Western Carpathian area includes not only the mountainous regions mostly in its northern part, but also the subsurface of the wide flat lowlands of the Pannonian Basin to the south. The western limit of the Western Carpathians next to the Eastern Alps is conventionally located in the basement of the Vienna and Danube basins. On the narrow horst dividing these two basins, the boundary is located in the so-called Carnuntum Gate between the Leitha Gebirge (Mountains) and the Malé Karpaty Mountains. North of Vienna this boundary roughly corresponds to the

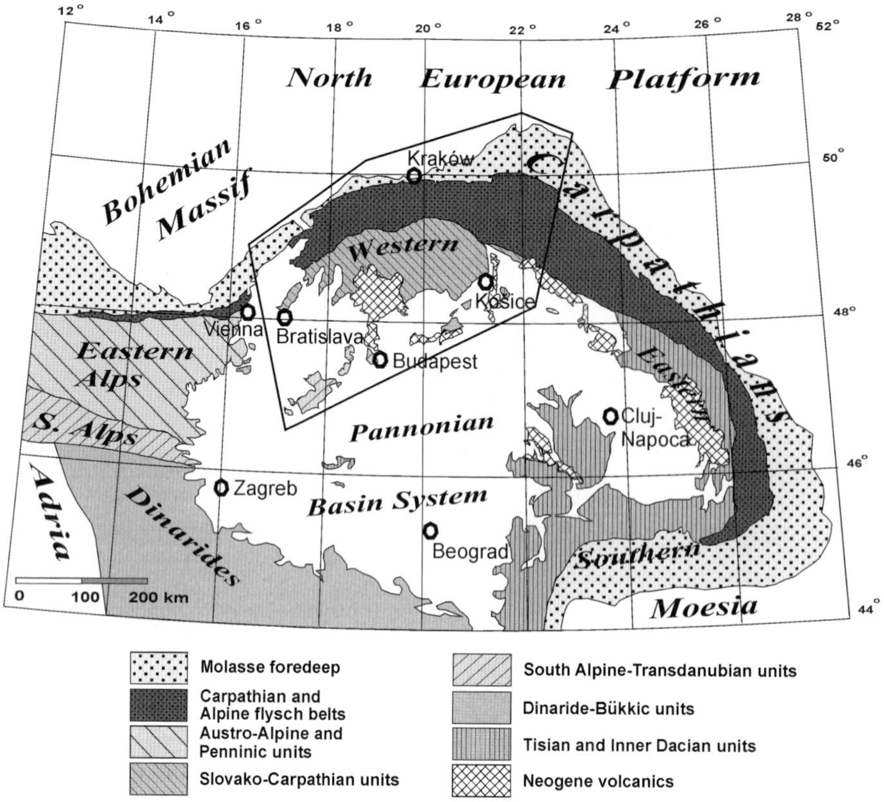


**Fig. 18.18.** Outline of the Alpine-Carpathian-Pannonian-Dinaride region. Outlined area delineates the extent of the Western Carpathians.

Rhenodanubian Flysch/Waschberg Zone division. The arcuate northern limit of the Western Carpathians follows the boundary between the most external Western Carpathian units (including the foredeep) and the foreland North European Platform composed of various pre-Alpine units and their Meso-Cenozoic sedimentary cover.

The eastern boundary of the Western against the Eastern Carpathians is the most problematic of the various boundaries, since it is not distinct either from a geographical or a geological point of view. Conventionally the boundary approximately follows the north–south trending Polish and Slovakian border with the Ukraine. However, the official geographic boundary of the Western and Eastern Carpathians is located further to the west. The extensive Rhenodanubian-Magura Superunit of the Alpine-Carpathian Flysch Belt and the Austro-Alpine–Slovako-Carpathian system wedge out in this area. In contrast, the outermost, typically Eastern Carpathian Stebnik, Sambor-Rozniatov and Borislav-Pokuty units first appear in this area and these widen to the east of the 'Przemyśl sigmoid'. However, some other large Western Carpathian units (Skole-Skiba-Tarcău, Silesian-Chornohora and Dukla units, Pieniny Klippen Belt) continue eastwards without any considerable changes. The conventional SE boundary of the pre-Tertiary Western Carpathian units follows the SW–NE trending, broad Mid-Hungarian Fault Zone (Zagreb–Zemplín Fault System). This complex Tertiary fault zone juxtaposes the southernmost Western Carpathian elements against the largely subsurface Tisza (Tisia) block in the SE part of the Pannonian Basin. However, all along this line the contact is buried beneath a thick Neogene sedimentary cover.

### *Geographic subdivision of the Western Carpathians*

The Western Carpathian area is geomorphologically divided into two principal parts: the mountainous Western Carpathians proper and the lowlands of the NW part of the Pannonian backarc basin system, i.e. the Vienna and Danube (Kisalföld) basins and the NW part of the Great Hungarian Plain (Alföld). The mountainous Western Carpathians are subdivided into the Outer Western Carpathians (mainly the Tertiary Flysch Belt) and the Inner Western Carpathians (mainly formed by pre-Tertiary complexes and Tertiary volcanic edifices), but their geographic boundary only partly corresponds to the major tectonic divide in the Western Carpathians, the Pieniny Klippen Belt. The Inner Western Carpathians are split into numerous horst blocks (so-called core mountains) separated by small Late Tertiary intramontane basins and embayments of the Pannonian Basin.

### *Tectonic subdivision*

With the exception of the unconformable Tertiary formations, the Western Carpathians can be longitudinally subdivided into three major zones, namely, the External, Central and Internal Western Carpathians (Plašienka 1999*a*; Figs 18.19, & 18.20).

The External Western Carpathians cover the territories of northeasternmost Austria, SE Moravia (Czech Republic), NW and NE Slovakia and SE Poland. They include the Carpathian foredeep, which is the eastern prolongation of the Alpine Molasse Basin, and the Carpathian Flysch Belt. Both continue along the entire Carpathian arc. The Carpathian Flysch Belt represents the Tertiary accretionary complex and consists of two

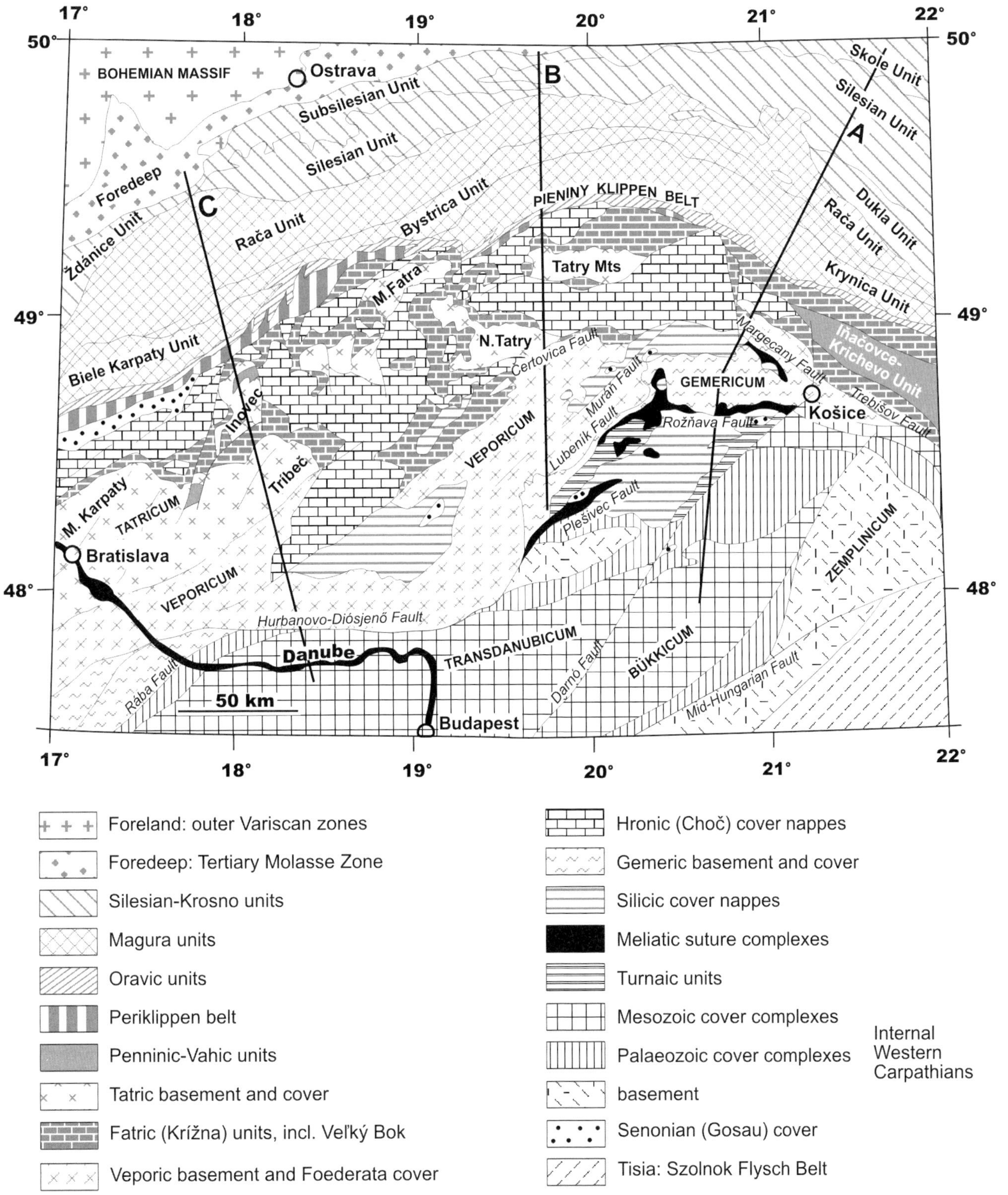


**Fig. 18.19.** Tectonic sketch of the Western Carpathians stripped off the Tertiary overstep complexes. Cross-sections A, B and C are shown in Figure 18.20.

groups of nappes (Figs 18.19 & 18.20). (1) The outer Moldavide tectonic system (Silesian-Krosno units) has no connections westwards into the Alps, but includes a substantial part of the Eastern Carpathian Flysch Belt with the exception of the Outer Dacides (Săndulescu 1988). (2) The inner Magura Superunit is considered to be a direct prolongation of the Rhenodanubian Flysch of the Eastern Alps (e.g. Schnabel 1992). It wedges out at the Western/Eastern Carpathian boundary. Palaeogeographically, the Magura Superunit represents the (northern) Penninic realm.

The Central Western Carpathians, covering much of Slovakia,

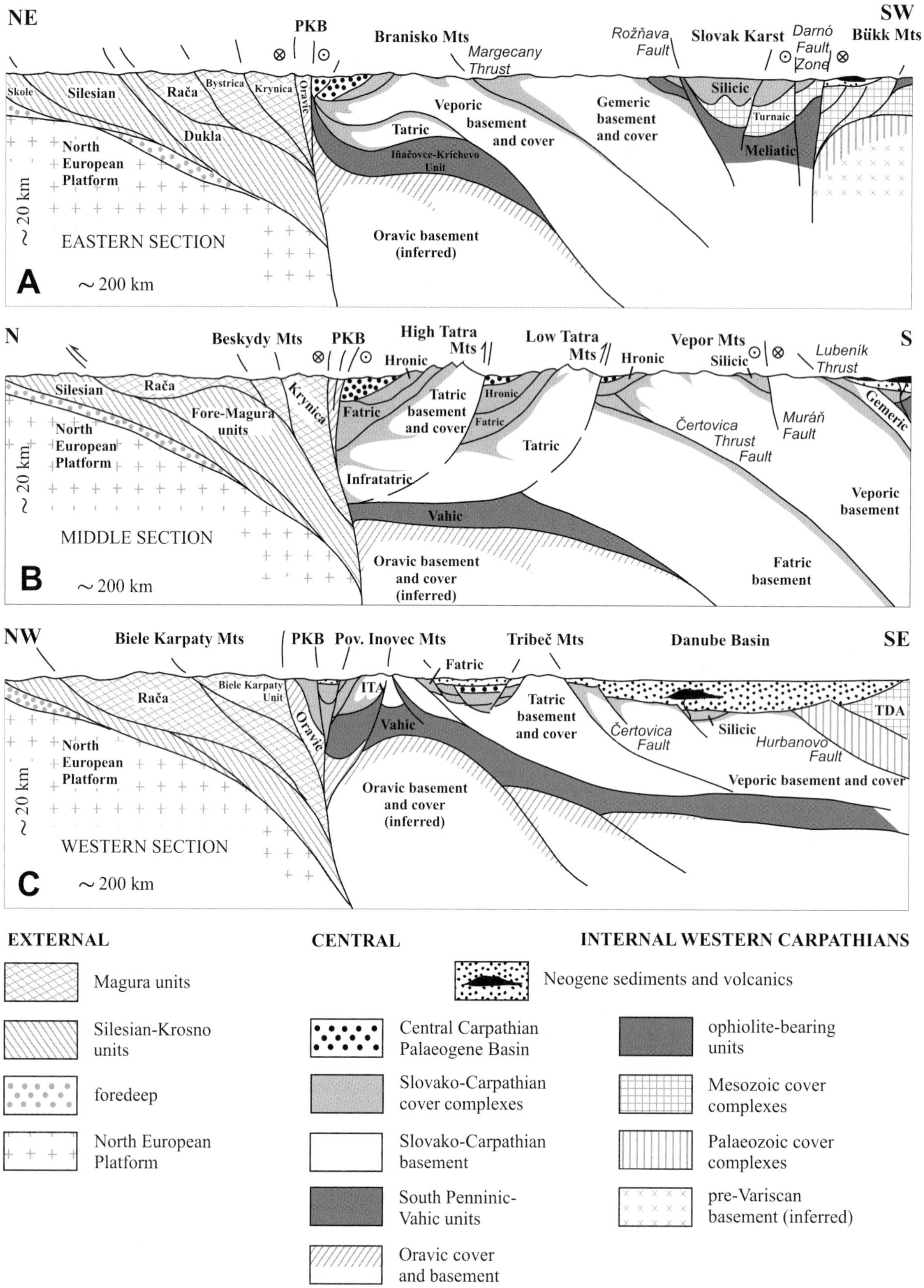


**Fig. 18.20.** Conceptual cross-sections through the Western Carpathians. Sections are vertically exaggerated; their approximate positions are shown in Figure 18.19. Abbreviations: PKB, Pieniny Klippen Belt; ITA, Infratatric Inovec nappe; TDA, Transdanubian Superunit.

include various pre-Tertiary units and the unconformable Cenozoic sedimentary and volcanic complexes. The former are distributed in several longitudinal morphotectonic belts (Plašienka *et al.* 1997). The narrow Pieniny Klippen Belt represents the boundary between the External and Central Western Carpathians. It includes units of (Middle) Penninic provenance (Oravic Superunit) and units probably derived from the Austro-Alpine–Slovako-Carpathian tectonic system (Plašienka 1995*a*). However, the Oravic Continental Fragment, from which the Oravic Superunit was derived, is only geometrically analogous to the Middle Penninic Briançonnais High of the Western Alps, since there is no connection between these units in the Eastern Alps (Trümpy 1988; Froitzheim *et al.* 1996). Areas to the south of the Pieniny Klippen Belt are composed of numerous Cretaceous nappe units which represent a continuation of the Austro-Alpine units of the central Eastern Alps and are collectively termed the Slovako-Carpathian tectonic system (Fig. 18.20). The Tatra-Fatra belt of core mountains includes the lowermost Tatric Superunit composed of (1) pre-Alpine basement and its Mesozoic sedimentary cover and (2) detached cover nappes of the Fatric and Hronic thrust systems. The former (1) is partially related to the Lower Austro-Alpine (*sensu* Tollmann 1977), while the latter (2) mainly correspond to the Upper Austro-Alpine nappes of the Northern Calcareous Alps (e.g. Häusler *et al.* 1993). The Vepor-Gemer Belt to the south corresponds to the central Eastern Alpine (Middle Austro-Alpine *sensu* Tollmann 1977) stack of basement-dominated nappes (Fig. 18.21). It is formed by the north-verging thick-skinned Veporic and Gemeric basement/cover thrust sheets and the Silicic cover nappes. The Vepor-Gemer Mountains gradually disappear towards the south under the Tertiary sediments and volcanics, making it difficult to follow the boundary between the Central and Internal Western Carpathians.

The Internal Western Carpathians are represented by the so-called Pelso Megaunit exposed mostly in isolated mountains (inselbergs) in northern Hungary (Transdanubian Range, the Bükk and surrounding mountains and the Aggtelek-Rudabánya Mountains; cf. Kovács *et al.* 2000). The supposed Central–Internal Western Carpathian boundary is represented by the oceanic complexes of the Meliata Unit, but this suture is mostly obliterated by superimposed nappe units and unconformable cover rocks. The Internal Western Carpathians mainly comprise unmetamorphosed Palaeozoic and Mesozoic complexes that form a south-directed fold-and-thrust belt (Figs 18.19, 18.20 & 18.21). In terms of palaeogeography, the Pelso Megaunit is closely related to the southern Austro-Alpine or to the South Alpine facies realm (Transdanubian Range), or even to that of the Dinarides (Bükk Mountains).

In plate tectonic terms, the External Western Carpathians correspond to a Tertiary accretionary complex related to the southward subduction of the North Penninic (Magura), and possibly also the Moldavide, oceanic realms. The Pieniny Klippen Belt forms a narrow steep transpressional zone between the accretionary wedge and the Central Western Carpathians representing the backstop. It is also the boundary between the Penninic and Austro-Alpine-related units in the Western Carpathians. Accordingly, it is a fossil plate boundary (i.e. suture), although surface evidence for ophiolite complexes is lacking. The Central and Internal Western Carpathians represent the stacks of crustal-scale units within the late Mesozoic collisional pro- and retro-wedge, respectively, shaped by the latest Jurassic to mid-Cretaceous subduction–collision processes related to the closure of the Triassic–Jurassic Meliata Ocean. The ophiolite-bearing Meliata Suture is approximately located in a central position between the pro- and the retro-wedge.

### *Palaeogeographic subdivision*

From the point of view of Mesozoic–Cenozoic palaeogeography, two principal evolutionary periods can be distinguished in the Western Carpathians. During the first (Triassic–Jurassic), units of the External and Central Western Carpathians were located on the northern, rifted, passive European margin of the Meliata Ocean. In contrast, the Internal Western Carpathian elements formed the southern (in present co-ordinates) passive (Triassic) and later active (Jurassic) margin of the ocean, corresponding to the NE part of Apulia-Adria. The Central and Internal Western Carpathians were welded together by the time of the Jurassic–Cretaceous boundary following closure of the Meliata Ocean. From this time onward, the Western Carpathian Cretaceous palaeogeography generally corresponds to that of the Alps, including the following zones from north to south: European continental margin, largely overridden by the Western Carpathians units during the Tertiary; Moldavide basins (partly oceanic?) in the north to NE only, and widening eastwards; elongated continental fragment (the Silesian Ridge); the North Penninic–Magura Oceanic Basin; rifted continental fragment in a Middle Penninic position (the Oravic or Czorsztyn Ridge); the South Penninic–Vahic Oceanic Zone; and the broad and dissected Adria-related continental margin including the Slovako-Carpathian (Austro-Alpine) and Pelso (Upper Austro-Alpine–South Alpine–Dinaridic) units.

### *Outline of the palaeogeographic and palaeotectonic evolution*

The Alpine edifice of the Western Carpathians was constructed on the remnants of the Variscan orogenic belt of Central Europe. The Variscan Orogeny culminated with the late Early to early Late Carboniferous collision processes (Putiš 1992; Plašienka *et al.* 1997; see also Kroner *et al.* 2008; McCann *et al.* 2008*a*). Post-Variscan unconformable successions include marine Pennsylvanian and continental Permian clastic units. During the Permian, several narrow rift basins formed, which were filled with continental red-beds (Vozárová & Vozár 1988; Vozárová 1996). Some of these were accompanied by alkaline to calc-alkaline, acid to intermediate (locally also basic) volcanism (Dostal *et al.* 2003). Permian to Lower Triassic granitoid intrusions include late-orogenic S-type granites in the Gemeric Superunit and several small, post-orogenic A-type intrusions in the southern zones of the Western Carpathians (e.g. Broska & Uher 2001). In the Early Triassic, the region had become a peneplain and most of the Western Carpathians area was covered by mature continental to beach siliciclastics (Mišík & Jablonský 2000), subsequently overlain by lagoonal or sabkha deposits. However, the site of the later Meliata Rift was already marked by the presence of much thicker Scythian-age deposits (Hips 2001).

Gradual subsidence of the European shelf during the Anisian is reflected by the deposition of widespread carbonate ramp and platform deposits, with intervening narrow intrashelf basins (e.g. Michalík 1994*a*). Early Mesozoic Tethyan rifting culminated in the opening of the Meliata Ocean in the early Middle Triassic (as indicated by the Pelsonian breakup unconformity in adjacent areas; cf. Kozur 1991). The Meliata Ocean has been interpreted as a backarc basin related to the northward subduction of Palaeotethys (Stampfli *et al.* 1998). This ocean subsequently separated the stable European shelf in the north from the mobile Adria-related continental fragments in the SW (Figs 18.22 & 18.23). The broad northern shelf exhibited only restricted

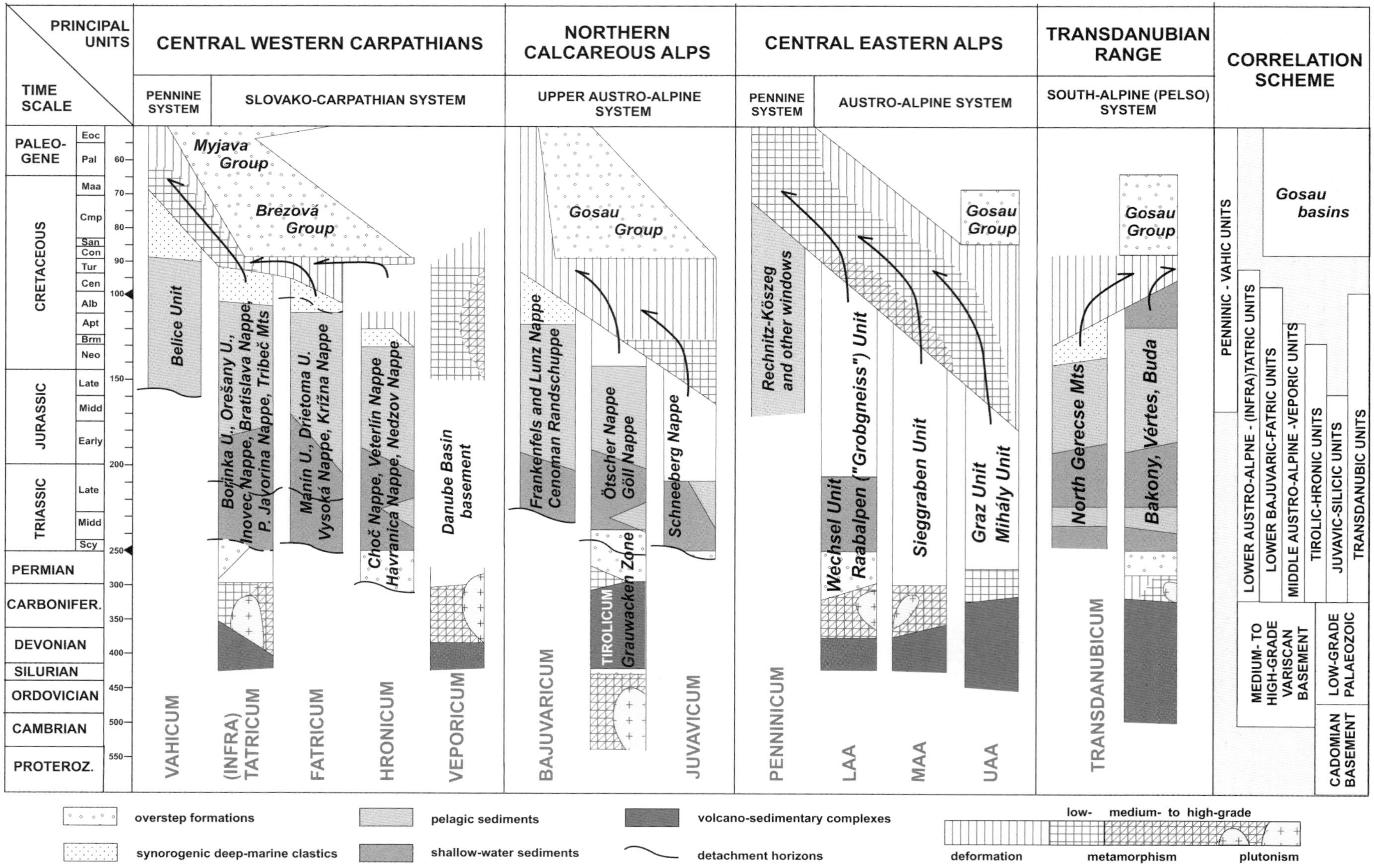


**Fig. 18.21.** Synoptic correlation table of pre-Tertiary units at the Alpine–Carpathian–Pannonian junction area (east Austria, SW Slovakia, NW Hungary), after Plašienka (1999*b*), modified. Nomenclature of Alpine units is mainly according to Tollmann (1977) and Wessely (1992).

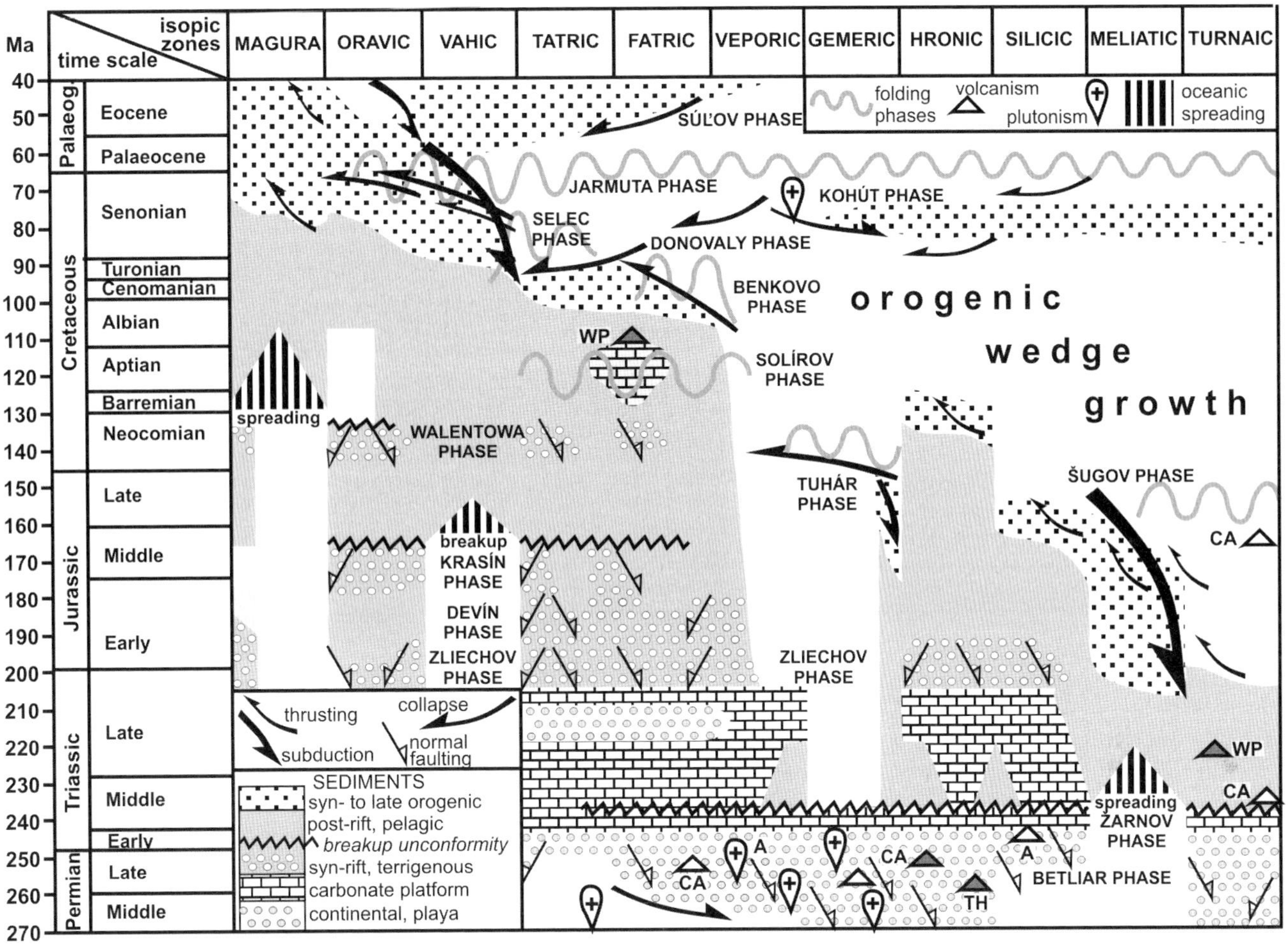

**Fig. 18.22.** Synoptic overview of the principal early Alpine orogenic processes and regional tectonic phases defined in the Central Western Carpathians and adjacent zones.

subsidence during the Triassic. Epicontinental successions similar to those of the German Basin were deposited, e.g. the Upper Triassic Carpathian Keuper Formation. Along the edge of the northern shelf, however, extensive, reef-cored Middle–Upper Triassic carbonate platforms developed. These reflect the thermal subsidence of the Meliata Ocean flanks. In contrast, the southern Meliata margin records Tethyan-type, mostly deep-water pelagic sedimentation, since deposition did not keep pace with subsidence (Haas *et al.* 1995; Csontos 2000). In the axial zones of the Meliata Ocean, sedimentation below the CCD predominated. Ladinian and Upper Triassic radiolarites today occur as blocks within the Jurassic olistostromes and mélanges, together with dismembered ophiolite fragments (Mock *et al.* 1998).

From the Triassic–Jurassic boundary onwards, important palaeogeographic changes occurred. The northern shelf experienced several strong rifting phases that led to the disintegration of the Triassic carbonate platform and ultimately resulted in the opening of new, Penninic-related oceanic basins (Plašienka 1995*a*, 2003*a*). The Slovako-Carpathian domain was separated from the North European Platform by the, probably Bathonian, breakup of the South Penninic–Vahic ocean, and was dissected into several longitudinal, wide, subsiding basins, floored by extended lithosphere and filled with deep-water, predominantly calcareous pelagic sediments (Figs 18.22 & 18.23b). These Jurassic–Lower Cretaceous basins were separated by narrow, occasionally emergent ridges with shallower and/or condensed sedimentation (e.g. Wieczorek 2001).

The southward subduction of the Meliata Ocean probably commenced during the Early Jurassic and its closure occurred in the latest Jurassic (Kozur 1991; Kovács 1992; Haas *et al.* 1995; Csontos 1999; Kovács *et al.* 2000). Subsequent shortening migrated from the collision zone to both sides (Figs 18.22 & 18.23a,b). During the Early Cretaceous, the Internal Western Carpathian retro-wedge (Pelso Megaunit) was formed by generally southward thrusting and obduction of a small Upper Jurassic backarc oceanic basin, as indicated by the presence of the Szarvaskő ophiolites of the Bükk Mountains (Csontos 1999, 2000) and by backthrusting and formation of a retro-arc, ophiolite-detritus-bearing deep-marine clastic basin in the Transdanubian Range (Császár & Árgyelán 1994). Subsequently, the Pelso units were unconformably overlain by the Senonian (Gosau Group) and by Eocene to Lower Miocene epicontinental deposits of the North Hungarian (Buda) Basin.

The Central Western Carpathian pro-wedge grew significantly during the late Early and early Late Cretaceous. Considerable shortening of the Central Western Carpathian crust, attenuated by previous Jurassic rifting, took place and the principal thick- and thin-skinned nappe sheets were thrust northward (e.g. Plašienka *et al.* 1997). Mid-Cretaceous deep-marine clastic basins developed in front of the advancing basement thrust wedges. The

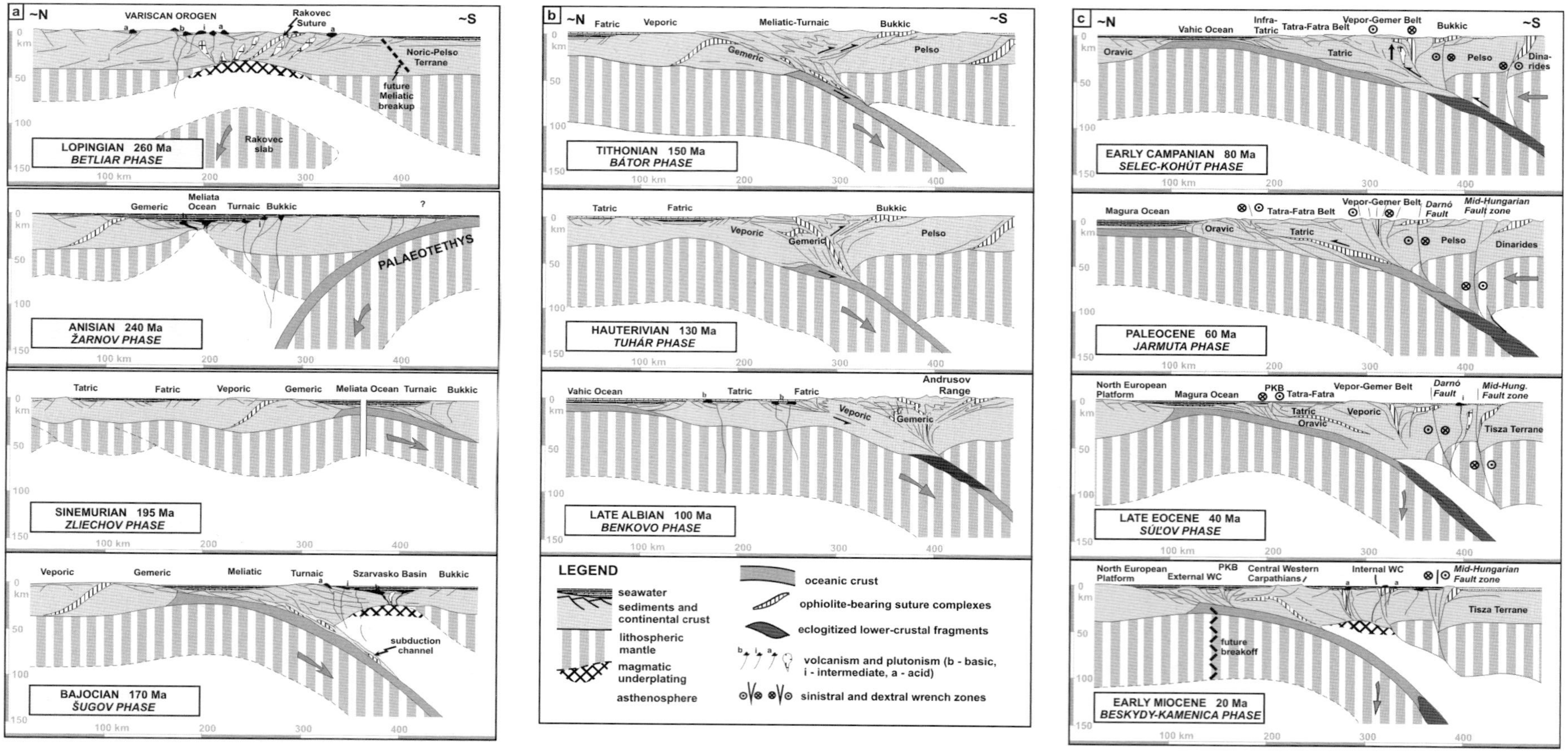


**Fig. 18.23.** Tentative palaeogeodynamic sections of the Western Carpathian orogen during (**a**) Late Permian to Middle Jurassic; (**b**) Late Jurassic to mid-Cretaceous; (**c**) Late Cretaceous to Early Miocene.

Cretaceous nappe stack in the Central Western Carpathians was completed by the Turonian, and is unconformably overlain by the Senonian deposits, although these are only locally preserved (Wagreich & Marschalko 1995). The thickened crust collapsed in the southern zones of the Central Western Carpathians in the Late Cretaceous, when the Veporic metamorphic core complex was exhumed by an orogen-parallel, extensional unroofing (Janák *et al.* 2001).

Deep-water clastic deposits, several thousand metres thick, of the Central Carpathian Palaeogene Basin form the main seal in the Central Western Carpathians. These indicate the rapid collapse of the northern part of the Central Western Carpathian following the eastward-migrating Eocene transgression (Wagreich 1995; Soták *et al.* 2001; Kázmér *et al.* 2003). The Central Western Carpathian Palaeogene deposits are generally undeformed and the Central–Internal Western Carpathian orogenic wedge functioned as a relatively rigid buttress for the developing accretionary wedge of the External Western Carpathians during the late Palaeogene and Miocene (Figs 18.22 & 18.23c).

North of the Slovako-Carpathian domain, Penninic rifting occurred in three main phases. The first Early Jurassic phase affected broad areas, but did not yet lead to continental breakup. The Middle Jurassic localized asymmetric rifting led to opening of the South Penninic–Vahic ocean basin, while the onset of oceanic crust production in the North Penninic–Magura Ocean probably began as late as the earliest Cretaceous (Plašienka 2003*a*). There is, however, no direct evidence for the oceanic nature of these basins, since no ophiolites are found. Southward-directed subduction of the Vahic oceanic crust commenced in Senonian times (Plašienka 1995*a*, *b*). The Oravic continental fragment began to collide with the Slovako-Carpathian orogenic wedge at the Cretaceous–Palaeogene boundary (Figs 18.22 & 18.23c). Only detached Vahic, Oravic and Magura sediments were frontally accreted to the orogenic wedge, while the entire Penninic lithosphere, either oceanic or continental, was subducted. Subduction of the Magura Ocean probably began during the Eocene and lasted until the earliest Miocene. The eastward-migrating subduction of the basement of the Moldavian units, followed by underthrusting of the European margin below the External Western Carpathian accretionary wedge, commenced in the Late Oligocene and ended by the Early Miocene in the west and by the Middle Miocene further to the east (Nemčok *et al.* 1998, 2000).

The Middle to Late Miocene retreat (roll-back) of the subduction zone in the External Western Carpathians had crucial consequences for the evolution of the Central and Internal Western Carpathians in the upper plate position (Figs 18.22 & 18.23c). From the Middle Miocene onwards, the Pannonian Basin System formed in a backarc position (e.g. Royden *et al.* 1982; Csontos *et al.* 1992; Horváth 1993; Csontos 1995; Kováč *et al.* 1998; Bada & Horváth 2001). Initially, small pull-apart basins opened, followed by widespread rifting and thermal subsidence that unified numerous small depocentres into the extensive Pannonian Basin. In the Western Carpathians, this backarc rifting was also associated with the uplift of small horsts, forming mountains from the Late Miocene up until the present (Kováč *et al.* 1994). The peaks of the High Tatra Mountains are the highest in the entire Carpathians, though the highest point (Gerlachovský štít) is only 2654 m above sea level. Marine conditions in the Pannonian Basin System were replaced by brackish and then by freshwater conditions during the Late Miocene to Pliocene, as the connections with the Mediterranean and Black seas were closed (Kováč *et al.* 1993; Kováč 2000). Lithospheric stretching and asthenospheric upwelling were associated with voluminous calc-alkaline andesitic volcanism, which culminated during the Middle and Late Miocene and was terminated by minor basanitic extrusions during the Pliocene and Quaternary (e.g. Konečný *et al.* 2002).

### *Carpathian foredeep*

The Carpathian foredeep is the eastward lateral prolongation of the East Alpine Molasse Basin. It is the outermost element of the Carpathian Orogen which developed at the orogenic front of the Carpathian arc from the area north of Vienna to the Iron Gate of the Danube in Romania i.e. near Orşova (Fig. 18.18). It is *c.* 1500 km long with a curvature of nearly 270°. In the Western Carpathian sector, the foredeep is filled with marine to brackish sediments and with some continental sediments of Lower to Middle Miocene age. It represents the peripheral flexural foreland basin formed in response to the loading of the lower, subducted plate by the advancing nappes of the accretionary wedge (Carpathian Flysch Belt). The main phases of the foredeep subsidence and depocentre migration were closely related to the thrusting phases in the Carpathian Flysch Belt (Meulenkamp *et al.* 1996; Oszczypko 1998). Due to the oblique, eastward-migrating soft collision of the frontal part of the West Carpathian orogenic system with the North European Platform, the foredeep exhibits a conspicuous eastward younging. Forming during the terminal stages of the orogeny, the foredeep reflects the gradual frontal and lateral cessation of convergence between the stable platform foreland and the mobile Alpine-Carpathian Orogen.

The sedimentary infill of the Carpathian foredeep forms a characteristic clastic wedge thinning towards the foreland, and is subdivided into: (1) the lower and outer autochthonous part directly overlying various pre-Tertiary basement and cover rock complexes of the Bohemian Massif and Malopolska Block of the North European Platform; and (2) the parautochthonous inner and upper part, which is partly incorporated into the Outer Carpathian accretionary wedge (Carpathian Flysch Belt). Three lateral sectors can be identified in the Western Carpathian foredeep, differing both in terms of the character and the age of the sedimentary filling.

The westernmost, **Moravian sector,** extending from NE Austria to south-central Moravia (Czech Republic) is <20 km wide and comprises sediments predominantly of Lower Miocene age (e.g. Brzobohatý & Cicha 1993). However, two deep, buried, NW–SE orientated canyons (Nesvačilka, Vranovice), filled with Palaeocene–Eocene clastic sediments, have been encountered by drilling below the foredeep deposits and the nappe front of the Carpathian Flysch Belt in southern Moravia (Pícha 1979). These presumably represent the channels that fed the Outer Carpathian deep-marine clastic basins.

The oldest (Egerian–Eggenburgian, i.e. Aquitanian to Early Burdigalian) deposits consist of reworked material from the weathered crystalline rocks of the underlying Bohemian Massif. The subsequent Eggenburgian marine transgression resulted in the deposition of thick clastic units. During the Ottnangian (Middle Burdigalian), older sediments were partly eroded and brackish, lagoonal and freshwater sediments developed locally. A new, Carpathian (Late Burdigalian) sedimentary cycle began with the deposition of basal clastics, followed by up to 1200 m of deep-marine calcareous clays, turbiditic siltstones, and sandstones. During the Carpathian, the foredeep width was laterally reduced due to the advance of the Flysch Belt nappes. Some of the older sediments were buried or detached to create transitional parautochthonous elements at the boundary between the foredeep and the accretionary wedge (the Pouzdřany Unit in southern Moravia). The final marine transgression, which extended far into the foreland (Bohemian Massif) along tectonically predisposed zones, took place in the Early Badenian (Langhian). Hundreds of metres of shallowing-upward, terrigenous clastics and calcareous clays were deposited in the axial zones of the foredeep. From the Middle Badenian (Serravalian) onwards, the foredeep depocentres migrated to the NE. The youngest, uppermost Miocene and Pliocene continental clastic sediments are mainly found in wide grabens orientated perpendicular to the foredeep axis, thus reflecting their post-convergence formation.

The middle, **Silesian sector** of the foredeep in northern Moravia and southern Poland (west of Kraków) is *c.* 30–40 km wide and is filled with deposits of Badenian to Sarmatian age. Lower Miocene sediments are known only from boreholes that extend through the Carpathian Flysch Belt nappes. The Middle to Late Badenian (Serravalian) foredeep is filled with characteristic evaporitic deposits (e.g. famous salt mines at Wieliczka near Kraków and sulphur pits at Tarnobrzeg). The decline in subsidence (or even uplift) was associated with a phase of decreased Carpathian convergence (Oszczypko 1998). The latest Badenian and Sarmatian are represented by pelitic and psammitic sediments reflecting decreasing salinity.

The eastern, **Galician sector** of the Western Carpathian foredeep between the Kraków and Przemyśl at the Polish–Ukrainian border is younger still, and filled with thick (up to 3500 m) units of marine sediments of Late Badenian to Sarmatian (Serravalian to Early Tortonian) age. The foredeep reaches its greatest width in this area (>80 km at the surface). Its inner part, composed of Lower to Middle Miocene units, mainly terrestrial sediments >1.0 km thick, is overridden by the Carpathian Flysch Belt nappes. Folded Badenian- and Sarmatian-age sediments are also partially incorporated into the outermost parts of the Carpathian Flysch Belt (narrow Zgłobice Unit in front of the Silesian and Skole nappes).

## *Carpathian Flysch Belt*

The Carpathian Flysch Belt extends from the area north of Vienna up to the Vrancea region at the boundary between the Eastern and Southern Carpathians (Fig. 18.18). It represents the frontal Tertiary accretionary wedge of the Carpathian Orogen and forms a crescent-shaped arc around the various pre-Tertiary units, blocks or terranes in the inner part of the orogen, which have complex, and sometimes ambiguous, mutual relationships (e.g. Csontos *et al.* 1992; Kováč *et al.* 1994; Csontos & Vörös 2004). Its inner arc is *c.* 1000 km and the outer arc >1200 km long. The width of the belt varies between 60 and 120 km. It is composed exclusively of Jurassic to Miocene sediments that were scraped off the subducted, presumably at least partly oceanic, basement of the Carpathian embayment. However, no ophiolite remnants are found at the surface in the Carpathian Flysch Belt.

### *Silesian-Krosno units (Moldavides)*

The Carpathian Flysch Belt consists of numerous elongate tectonic units though none of these is continuous all along the belt. Two first-order, large-scale tectonic systems can be discerned. The outer one, the Moldavian system (Silesian-Krosno units), comprises most of the Eastern Carpathian Flysch Belt, but narrows westward and is progressively replaced by the more internal Magura Superunit of the (North) Penninic tectonic system (Fig. 18.19). Hence, in the External Western Carpathians both Moldavian and Penninic units are present, the former first appearing at the front of the Carpathian Orogen in the hinge area between the Eastern Alps and Western Carpathians, the latter gradually wedging out in the area of the Western–Eastern Carpathian boundary.

The Silesian-Krosno (or Krosno-menilite) units form a thin-skinned fold-and-thrust belt that overlies the foredeep sediments and autochthonous cover and basement of the North European Platform (Tomek 1993; Tomek & Hall 1993; see Fig. 18.20). The outermost **Pouzdřany Unit** appears as a narrow belt of deformed Oligocene to Lower Miocene clays, marls and silts at the boundary between the foredeep and the Carpathian Flysch Belt proper in southern Moravia. The **Ždánice Unit** in south-central Moravia overrides the Pouzdřany Unit and includes sediments of a much wider stratigraphic range. It extends to the SW into Austria where it is known as the **Waschberg Zone**. Upper Jurassic platform limestones form isolated tectonic slices at the nappe front. The Senonian- to Eocene-age succession is only a few hundred metres thick and contains mainly hemipelagic claystones with occasional bodies of sandstones and conglomerates. The Oligocene Menilite Formation, which is typical of all of the Silesian-Krosno units, is composed of deep-water, anoxic bituminous shales with characteristic fish remains and black cherts ('menilites'), overlain by >1200 m of Egerian (Chattian–Aquitanian) synorogenic, turbiditic sediments. The Eggenburgian and Carpathian (Burdigalian) sediments were deposited in localized piggyback basins. The Ždánice Unit extends northeastwards into the **Sub-Silesian Unit** of Silesia which comprises a Senonian to Oligocene, hemipelagic and partly turbiditic succession.

The **Skole Unit** in SE Poland is detached along the mid-Cretaceous black shale horizon and ranges stratigraphically up to the Lower Miocene (Oszczypko 2004). It contains Upper Cretaceous siliciclastic and calcareous turbidites, Palaeocene–Eocene shales and distal turbidites, Lower Oligocene 'Globigerina' marls and black shales and the Egerian Krosno Flysch Formation. The Skole Unit is the areally extensive and internally tightly imbricated thrust sheet that extends from the NE part of the Western Carpathians for more than 700 km up to the Eastern/Southern Carpathian hinge. Its prolongation is known as the Skiba Unit in the Ukraine and the Tarcău Unit in Romania.

The **Silesian Unit** is one of the largest in the Carpathian Flysch Belt. It extends from Silesia to the Ukrainian Eastern Carpathians north of the Marmarosh Massif (here termed the Chornohora Unit) and comprises a continuous stratigraphic succession up to 6000 m thick from the Late Jurassic through to the Egerian. Maximum thicknesses are typical in the dominant basinal ***Godula succession*** while other successions, representing slope and ridge environments, are much thinner and occur only in Silesia. Pre-Tertiary beds crop out mainly in the west in Silesia, while Palaeogene deposits are widespread further to the east. The oldest sediments are Oxfordian to Berriasian hemipelagic marlstones and allodapic detrital limestones, overlain by Valanginian–Aptian, proximal to distal, calcareous deep-marine clastics with interdigitated submarine lava flows and dykes (known as 'teshenites') which are rift-related alkaline basalts. Mid-Cretaceous sediments are partly anoxic hemipelagic shales, passing upwards into thick Cenomanian–Senonian deep-marine clastics. The Palaeocene and Eocene are dominated by deep-marine shales and distal turbidites. The Lower Oligocene Menilite Formation is overlain by the turbiditic Krosno Formation of Egerian age which attains a thickness of >1000 m in SE Poland. The latter was deposited immediately prior to the onset of thrusting and folding. The ridge facies (***Baška succession***) is represented mainly by blocks and slices of Tithonian platform limestones (Stramberg Formation) which are found in the frontal part of the Silesian nappe.

The **Dukla Unit** first appears on the surface between the Silesian and Magura units near the Polish–Slovakian border and then widens to the SE from NE Slovakia to the Ukrainian Eastern Carpathians. The Dukla Unit is composed of mid-Cretaceous shales, Senonian to Eocene turbidites and the Lower Oligocene Menilite Formation which passes upwards into distal turbidites (e.g. Oszczypko 2004). The Dukla and related units (e.g. Grybów, Obidowa-Slopnice) are extensive in the subsurface below the frontal Magura nappes in Poland and NE Slovakia, as recorded by deep wells and tectonic windows (e.g. Mszana Dolna, Smilno). Balanced cross-sections reveal that the Dukla Unit and its equivalents (sometimes referred to as the Fore-Magura group of nappes; Oszczypko 2004) are volumetrically the largest unit of the entire External Western Carpathians (Roca *et al.* 1995; Nemčok *et al.* 2000). The **Fore-Magura Unit** *sensu stricto*. in Silesia is the western counterpart of the Dukla Unit. It is restricted to narrow tectonic slices in front of the Magura Superunit.

*Magura Superunit*

The Magura Superunit, which overthrusts the Silesian-Krosno units, emerges from the pre-Neogene units of the Vienna Basin in southern Moravia and western Slovakia and continues in a belt up to 50 km wide as far as the Western–Eastern Carpathian boundary in SW Ukraine, where it wedges out eastwards (Fig. 18.19). Its southern boundary follows the northward-convex arcuate Pieniny Klippen Belt for c. 400 km. Four principal units are generally recognized within the Magura Superunit (Figs 18.19 & 18.20): from north to south the Rača, Bystrica and Krynica subunits can be distinguished. These are broadly related, whereas the innermost and westernmost Biele (Bílé) Karpaty Unit at the Slovakian–Moravian border has some special features and is sometimes considered to be an independent unit. The various Magura units comprise detached sediments of Late Cretaceous to Early Oligocene age dominated by deep-marine clastic lithologies (e.g. Oszczypko 1992, 2004).

The outer **Rača Subunit** (including the Siary Subunit recognised in Poland; Oszczypko 2004) is the areally most extensive of the Magura subunits. Its sole thrust is moderately south-dipping and overrides the Silesian and Fore-Magura units in the west and the Dukla and related units in the north and east. Fragments of Lower Cretaceous basinal sediments occur sporadically in front of the Magura Superunit. The Rača Subunit is composed of mid-Cretaceous non-calcareous shales, Senonian thick-bedded turbiditic sandstones, Lower Eocene deep-water shales (Beloveža Formation), and Middle–Upper Eocene and locally Oligocene synorogenic turbidites (Magura and Malcov formations). Rare Lower Miocene sediments also occur in remnants of small piggyback basins.

The Rača Subunit is deformed into numerous imbricates and tight north-vergent asymmetric macrofolds formed by fault propagation. Fold axes are subhorizontal and parallel, hence the regional strike directions are quite uniform. Based on data from tectonic windows of the Fore-Magura units, borehole data and section balancing, it is clear that the Magura basal overthrust is folded due to the duplexing of underlying units.

The **Bystrica Subunit** comprises a narrow (5–10 km), but long and continuous band of Senonian- to Oligocene-age sediments similar to the Rača Subunit. It represents the axial zone of the Magura Basin with Eocene deep-marine clastics attaining a thickness of *c.* 1000 m.

The inner **Krynica Subunit** (also called the Oravská Magura Unit in NW Slovakia) is restricted to the central segment of the Western Carpathian Flysch Belt. The Eocene thick-bedded sandstones (Magura Formation) of this subunit form the morphologically most prominent part of the Magura Superunit. The Lower Oligocene Menilite Formation is overlain by the turbiditic Malcov Formation deposited in a small ponded basin. Lower Miocene deposits occur in restricted piggyback basins. In some places, mainly in Poland, narrow slices of basinal Jurassic and Cretaceous sediments known as the **Grajcarek Unit** occur along the boundary between the Krynica Subunit and the Pieniny Klippen Belt. These are considered to represent the innermost part of the Magura Basin incorporated into the Pieniny Klippen Belt structure (Birkenmajer 1986; Oszczypko 2004). Partial synonyms for the Grajcarek Unit include the Hulina Unit (Sikora 1974), and the Fodorka succession of western Slovakia.

Lithological complexes within the Bystrica and Krynica subunits are often steeply dipping (or even overturned) and tightly folded with steep axial planes, and affected by transpressional deformation. The southernmost elements are locally backthrust onto the Pieniny Klippen Belt. These features suggest that the southernmost part of the accretionary wedge of the Carpathian Flysch Belt plunges to great depth at the contact of the colliding North European Platform and Carpathian Orogen (Fig. 18.20).

The **Biele Karpaty Unit** (Bílé Karpaty in the Czech literature) comprises sediments of Cretaceous to earliest Eocene age (e.g. Švábenická *et al.* 1997). Lower Cretaceous deep-water siliceous shales pass into distal and then, during the latest Cretaceous and Palaeocene, into proximal calcareous turbidites similar to the Jarmuta Formation of the Pieniny Klippen Belt. This succession is dominated by carbonate terrigenous material derived from the areas of the Pieniny Klippen Belt and the Central Western Carpathians to the south, unlike other units of the Carpathian Flysch Belt which contain predominantly siliciclastic material derived from more distant sources. In contrast to the underlying and more external, imbricated Magura thrust stack, the Biele Karpaty Unit forms a flat-lying and comparatively less deformed, thin thrust sheet that was most probably emplaced out of sequence.

The structural styles of the Outer Carpathian nappes include piggyback thrusting, the formation of imbricated duplexes, fault-bend and fault-propagation folding, ramp and flat geometry in frontal parts, and oblique out-of-sequence thrusting of the Magura Superunit (Nemčok *et al.* 2000). Internal shortening of the Magura Superunit was estimated to be 50%, while that of the Silesian-Krosno units was 60%. The overall shortening attains at least *c.* 160–180 km in the Polish part (Nemčok *et al.* 2000; Roca *et al.* 1995), resulting in a shortening rate of 1.1–1.4 cm/a during the Oligocene–Sarmatian. According to Behrmann *et al.* (2000), the cumulative shortening of the Carpathian Flysch Belt in the eastern West Carpathians was 260 km, resulting in a convergence rate of 2.2 cm/a. The amount of shortening in the Carpathian Flysch Belt closely matches estimates of the total extension in the Pannonian Basin.

## *Pieniny Klippen Belt*

The Pieniny Klippen Belt is probably the most famous, and doubtlessly also the most complicated and enigmatic, of the Western Carpathian units. It typically follows the boundary between the external and central Carpathian zones for *c.* 500 km (from the eastern margin of the Vienna Basin to Novoselica in SW Ukraine), or for nearly 700 km if its lateral counterparts, with similar positions and structures, are taken into account (i.e.

the St. Veit Klippenzone in the Vienna Forest and the Poiana Botizei Zone in northern Romania). In contrast, the width of the belt is just several kilometres, and it may be as narrow as several tens of metres in some areas (Fig. 18.19).

Several deep boreholes and seismic lines indicate a nearly vertical subsurface dip for the Pieniny Klippen Belt down to depths of at least 5 km (e.g. Birkenmajer 1986; Tomek 1993; Vozár *et al.* 1998; Bielik *et al.* 2004; Hrušecký *et al.* 2006). The surface trend of the Pieniny Klippen Belt largely coincides with the course of the 'Peri-Pieniny Lineament' at greater depths (Máška & Zoubek in Buday *et al.* 1960); this is a deep crustal-scale fault associated with several geophysical anomalies (gravity minimum, change in polarity of the Wiese vectors, Moho steps). This fault has been assumed to coincide with the boundary between the subducted margin of the North European Platform and the Carpathian orogenic stack (Fig. 18.20). However, it is rather improbable that the units of the Pieniny Klippen Belt extend along this fault into the lower crust. It is more likely that they become inclined to the south at a depth of 5 to 10 km and extend southwards below the outer part of the Central Western Carpathians (Bielik *et al.* 2004). In the middle to lower crust, the Peri-Pieniny Lineament may represent the contact between the North European Platform and the original basement of most of the Pieniny Klippen Belt units (the underthrust Oravic continental fragment).

The present surface structure of the Pieniny Klippen Belt can be best explained as resulting from extensive and complex transpressional to transtensional movements (e.g. Ratschbacher *et al.* 1993; Nemčok & Nemčok 1994; Kováč & Hók 1996) that affected an originally shallow fold-and-thrust belt. In most areas, the Pieniny Klippen Belt forms the axial part of a broad flower structure which also includes the inner units of the Carpathian Flysch Belt and the frontal units of the Central Western Carpathians (Fig. 18.24). In NW Slovakia (Kysuce and Orava regions) the axis of the flower strucure is located north of the Pieniny Klippen Belt and, therefore, its structure is here dominated by oblique backthrusts. Additionally, the Zázrivá-Párnica sigmoid, the only important transversal structure in the Pieniny Klippen Belt, is located in this area. This is an abrupt dextral offset of *c.* 5 km affecting the otherwise linear trend of the Pieniny Klippen Belt. Its formation was related to the Late Miocene activity of a north–south trending wrench fault zone which affected the entire Central Western Carpathians (Central Slovakian Fault System; Kováč & Hók 1993).

The rock complexes cropping out in the Pieniny Klippen Belt are exclusively non-metamorphic sediments of Jurassic (very rarely also Triassic) to Palaeogene age. These are usually subdivided into morphologically positive forms (called 'klippen') formed by comparatively hard rocks (mostly Jurassic to Lower Cretaceous limestones), surrounded by less competent Upper Creaceous to Palaeogene 'klippen mantle' (marlstones, deep-marine clastics). The typical klippen structure was compared to a megabreccia, a mélange, or a chaotic mixture of lens-shaped, or often nearly isometric, rigid inclusions, several metres to kilometres in size, floating within an incompetent, highly deformed matrix. The complex internal structure of the Pieniny Klippen Belt units developed in several stages, from shallow, downward-propagating (piggyback) thrusting through tight upright folding, out-of-sequence thrusting, and imbrication, to transpression associated with the pop-up of blocks (i.e. klippen) (Fig. 18.25). However, there are some parts of the Pieniny Klippen Belt where the structure is less disintegrated and instead is dominated by tight linear folds which are generally orientated parallel to the

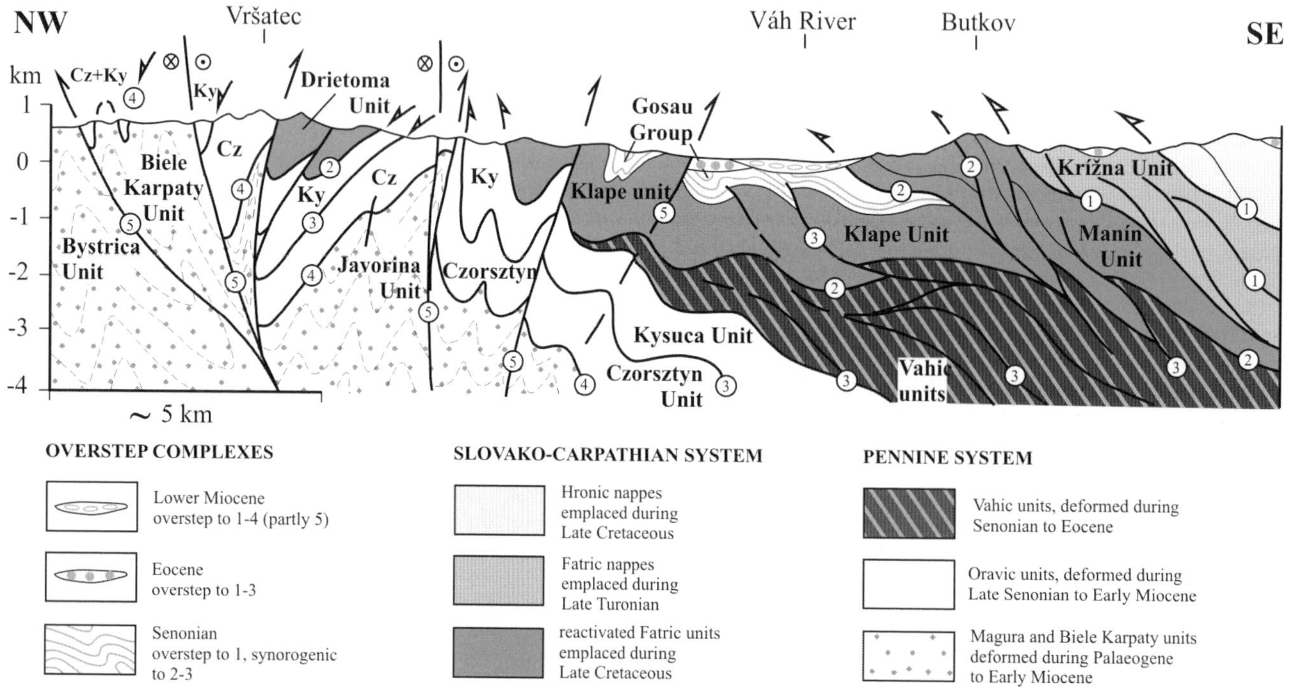


**Fig. 18.24.** Schematic cross-section through the Pieniny Klippen Belt and adjacent zones in western Slovakia (middle Váh Valley). Note that the Vršatec area represents the Pieniny Klippen Belt *sensu stricto* with tight imbricate flower structure, whereas the Váh Valley represents the Peri-Klippen Belt as a mixture of Penninic and Slovako-Carpathian units and several unconformably overlying formations. Abbreviations: Cz, Czorsztyn Unit; Ky, Kysuca-Pieniny Unit. Numbers in circles refer to the age of principal fault and fold structures: 1, late Turonian; 2, late Turonian, reactivated during Senonian; 3, Senonian to Palaeocene; 4, Palaeocene to Eocene; 5, Oligocene to Early Miocene.

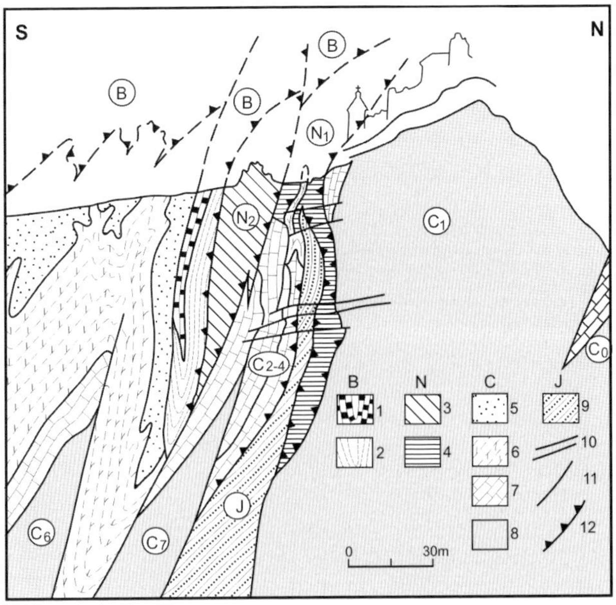


**Fig. 18.25.** A detailed profile of the Pieniny Klippen Belt illustrating its tight, imbricated small-scale structure. Niedzica castle hill, Polish Pieniny Mountains (after Birkenmajer (1999), slightly modified). Legend: B, Branisko Unit; $N_1$–$N_2$, scales of the Niedzica Unit; $C_1$–$C_6$, scales of the Czorsztyn Unit; J, Jarmuta Formation. 1, Oxfordian radiolarites; 2, Middle Jurassic shales; 3, Bajocian–Berriasian limestones; 4, Toarcian–Aalenian shales and turbidites; 5, Senonian deep-marine clastics; 6, Albian–Turonian marlstones; 7, Bajocian–Berriasian limestones; 8, Bajocian massive crinoidal limestones; 9, Maastrichtian–Palaeocene deep-marine clastics; 10, Upper Miocene transversal strike-slip faults; 11, Lower Miocene reverse faults; 12, Lower Palaeogene overthrusts.

boundaries of the Pieniny Klippen Belt. In these parts, the stratigraphic successions can also be precisely reconstructed and the relationships between the klippen and their mantle can be studied. Based on these sections, and thanks to the mainly excellent preservation of fossils in the Pieniny Klippen Belt deposits, numerous individual formations, successions or tectonic units have been defined over the last c. 150 years of intensive research (e.g. Stur 1860; Neumayr 1871; Uhlig 1903; Andrusov 1938, 1968; Scheibner in Buday *et al.* 1967; Birkenmajer 1977, 1986; Marschalko 1986; Mišík 1994). The most characteristic of these, the Oravic units, occur (at least rudimentarily) in all parts of the Pieniny Klippen Belt.

The western Slovakian sector of the Pieniny Klippen Belt is the broadest and, at the same time, the most complex part. It can be subdivided parallel to strike into the 'Klippen Belt *sensu stricto*', which is a very narrow outer strip bounding the Magura units, and the 'Periklippen Zone', which is a much wider zone (up to 15 km) with less intricate structure. The former zone only includes units derived from an independent palaeogeographic region which is designated as the **Oravic** area (Pieninic or Pienidic in older literature) and is thought to represent the (Middle) Penninic tectonic element in the Western Carpathians. The latter zone, however, also incorporates cover units undoubtedly derived from the frontal parts of the Slovako-Carpathian–Austro-Alpine tectonic system (Fig. 18.24). The tectonic mixture of both types of units leads to many uncertainties and misunderstandings which still provoke lively discussion on the origin, evolution and tectonic significance of the Pieniny Klippen Belt. Although it has often been considered to represent a suture, it should be pointed out that no ophiolite or blueschist units have been encountered. On the other hand, the deep-marine clastic formations from the klippen mantle often include boulder beds and conglomerates which are designated as exotic, since the provenance of many rock types occurring as pebbles (including ophiolites and blueschists) is not known.

*Oravic Superunit*

The Oravic Superunit is composed of two palaeogeographically contrasting units – the Czorsztyn and the Pieniny – which are interconnected by several 'transitional' successions. Both units comprise sedimentary successions whose deposition commenced in the Early Jurassic. Triassic dolomites occur only in the Maríková Klippe in western Slovakia. However, frequent dolomite clasts are present in Jurassic synrift sediments, indicating that a carbonate platform formed the original Triassic substratum of the Oravic units.

The **Czorsztyn Unit** (or Subpieniny in older literature; e.g. Uhlig 1903) represents a former ridge or high environment and was characterized by prevailing shallow-water facies during the Jurassic and Early Cretaceous (Mišík 1979*a*, 1994). It is interpreted as having been derived from a subducted continental ribbon in a Middle Penninic position (Fig. 18.26). Due to the marked dissection of the ridge as a result of several rifting events, the sedimentary formations show considerable lateral and vertical variations. Several sedimentary successions can be distinguished. The Czorsztyn succession is generally composed of (Birkenmajer 1977): (1) Middle Liassic to Aalenian deep-water, partly anoxic bioturbated marlstones and black shales ('Fleckenmergel', Allgäu Group); (2) Bajocian–Bathonian very shallow-water, sandy-crinoidal limestones (Smolegowa and Krupianka formations), or in places scarp breccias (Krasín Breccia; Aubrecht & Szulc 2006); (3) following the Upper Bathonian breakup unconformity, a thick complex of condensed 'Ammonitico rosso' nodular limestones (Czorsztyn Formation); (4) Tithonian–Berriasian coquinas, breccias, Maiolica-type Calpionella limestones and Neocomian crinoidal limestones, only locally preserved. After a hiatus indicated by numerous Neptunian dykes and partial erosion down to the Dogger deposits (Barremian–Aptian gap), the locally karstified surface was covered by an Albian hardground followed by; (5) deepening Upper Cretaceous 'couches rouges', Globotruncana-bearing marlstones (Púchov Formation); and (6) Maastrichtian–Eocene deep-marine clastics (Jarmuta and Proč formations).

Other successions related to the Czorsztyn Unit represent dissected slope environments. The ***Pruské succession*** (analogous to the ***Niedzica succession*** of the Polish sector of the Pieniny Klippen Belt, Fig. 18.27) contains mostly redeposited (allodapic/turbiditic) Dogger crinoidal limestones, intercalations of Oxfordian radiolarites within the Czorsztyn Formation, and a poorly developed Lower Cretaceous hiatus. In the ***Czertezik succession*** of the Polish Pieniny Klippen Belt, the Oxfordian radiolarites directly overlie the crinoidal limestones.

Since the Czorsztyn Unit is mainly composed of massive or thickly bedded competent limestones, it forms block- or plate-shaped klippen of various sizes (metre- to kilometre-scale) which are often in a subvertical or overturned position. These mostly occur along the outer limit of the Pieniny Klippen Belt, but in places also in a more internal position, in tectonic windows surrounded by other units of the Pieniny Klippen Belt (Fig. 18.24). Therefore, the Czorsztyn Unit is regarded as the lowermost tectonic unit, and is in a subautochthonous position with respect to all of the other Pieniny Klippen Belt units (Birkenmajer 1986). Locally it clearly overrides the innermost Magura

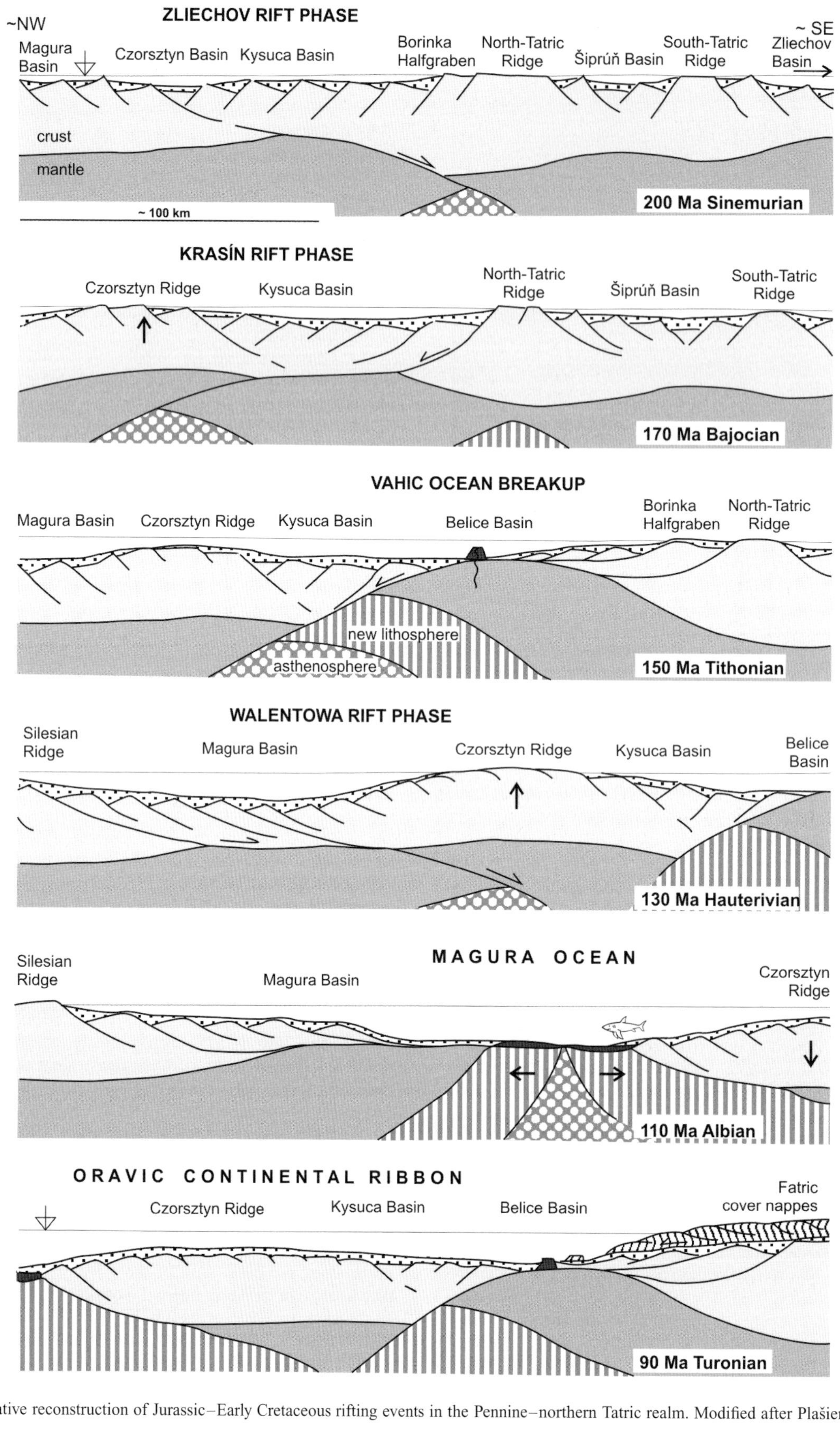


**Fig. 18.26.** Tentative reconstruction of Jurassic–Early Cretaceous rifting events in the Pennine–northern Tatric realm. Modified after Plašienka (2003*a*).

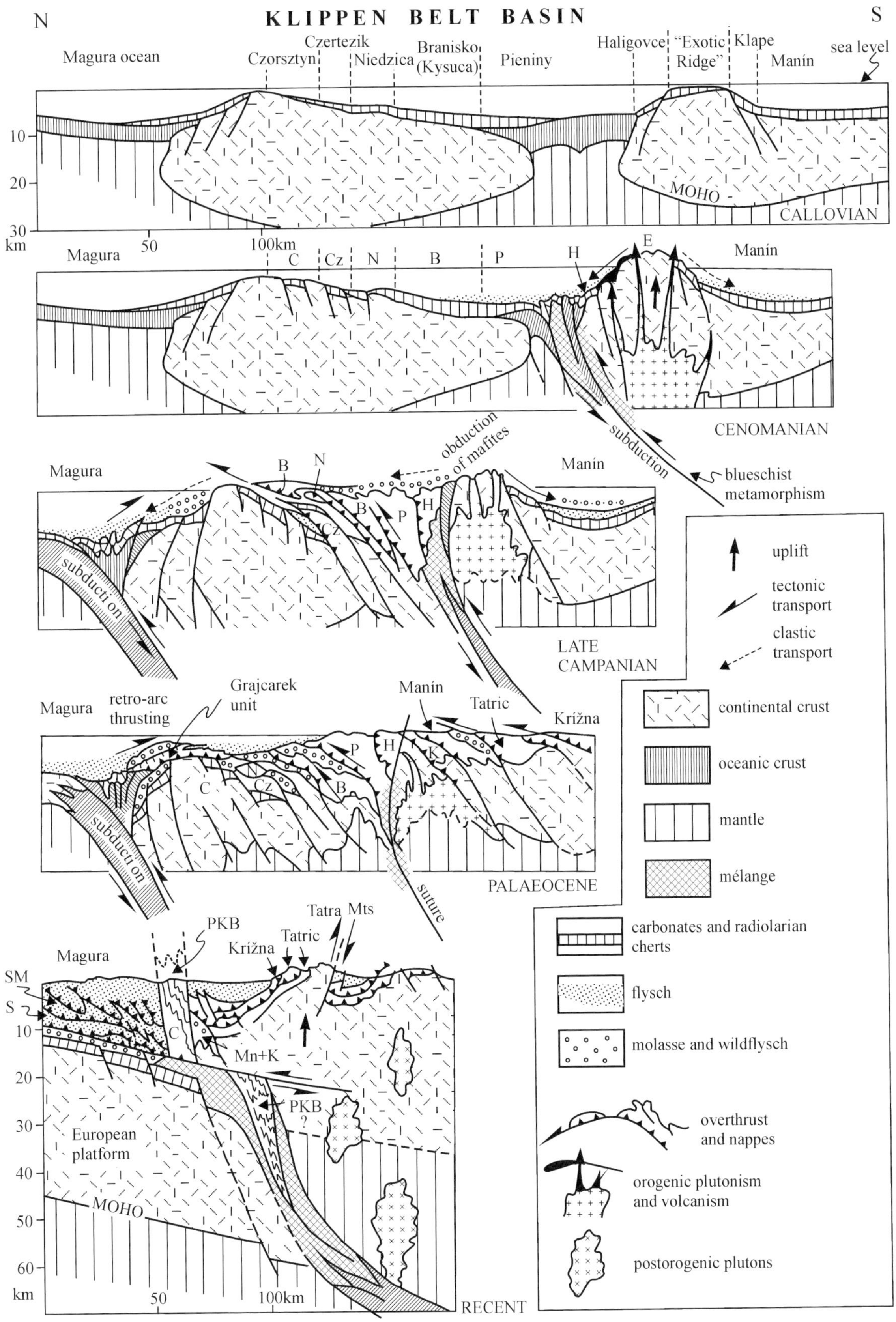


**Fig. 18.27.** Birkenmajer's concept of the tectonic evolution of the Pieniny Klippen Belt. Modified after Birkenmajer (1986).

elements (Jurewicz 1997). In places the slope successions were thrust over the ridge-derived Czorsztyn succession (Niedzica Nappe; Jurewicz 1994), indicating that the Pieniny Klippen Belt represents a former fold-thrust belt.

The **Pieniny Unit** includes basinal successions with continuous stratigraphic successions ranging from the Lias to the Late Cretaceous. The most widespread of these, the ***Kysuca succession*** (analogous to the ***Branisko succession*** in Poland), consists of: (1) lowermost Jurassic synrift siliciclastics (Gresten Formation); (2) Liassic to Aalenian hemipelagic marlstones (Allgäu Formation); (3) Middle Jurassic 'Posidonia' (*Bositra buchi*) marlstones, in places with synrift siliciclastic turbidites ('Aalenian flysch', Szlachtowa Formation), passing gradually into; (4) Callovian–Oxfordian radiolarites (Sokolica and Czajakowa formations); (5) Kimmeridgian red nodular limestones; (6) Tithonian–Neocomian Biancone- and Maiolica-type cherty limestones (Pieniny Formation); (7) various mid-Cretaceous hemipelagic marlstones; (8) Turonian–Santonian upward-coarsening, deep-marine clastics with conglomerates containing exotic pebbles (Snežnica and Sromowce formations); and (9) Campanian red pelagic 'Globotruncana' marls (Púchov Formation).

The ***Pieniny succession*** is nearly identical to the Kysuca-Branisko succession, but was deposited in even deeper waters, with radiolarites passing into the Kimmeridgian and with a very thick complex of Tithonian–Neocomian pelagic cherty limestones (Pieniny Formation). The ***Nižná succession,*** recognized from the Orava region in NW Slovakia, is marked by the presence of Barremian–Aptian platform, Urgonian-type limestones within an otherwise deep-water succession. The ***Orava (Podbiel) succession,*** of problematic affiliation, also includes Toarcian red nodular limestones (Adnet Formation).

In contrast to the Czorsztyn Unit, the klippen of the Pieniny Unit are composed of well-bedded strata that are generally folded rather than faulted. Consequently, there are long sections in this unit with continuous stratigraphic successions and quite simple macrofold structures (e.g. in the Kysuce region of NW Slovakia). Some smaller klippen of the Pieniny Unit represent disrupted cores of major folds.

### *Peri-Klippen Zone*

The Peri-Klippen Zone is typically well-developed in western Slovakia and includes several units of problematic affiliation. In the area of the westernmost Pieniny Klippen Belt it comprises the Drietoma Unit, with a succession that closely resembles the Upper Triassic–mid-Cretaceous formations of the deep-water Zliechov succession of the Krížna Nappe System (Fatricum) of the Central Western Carpathians. This unit is, therefore, considered to represent a frontal Fatric element incorporated into the Pieniny Klippen Belt following its emplacement as a nappe during the Turonian. The Manín Unit, cropping out in the inner part of the Pieniny Klippen Belt in the middle Váh valley, may also be derived from the Fatric Nappe System and may represent its shallow-water Jurassic–Lower Cretaceous Vysoká succession (the second alternative is that it corresponds to a frontal Tatric element; e.g. Rakús & Hók 2005; Birkenmajer 1986; Fig. 18.27). Generally, the 'klippen style' is poorly developed in this area and the Manín klippen are in fact brachyantiforms with more or less continuous stratigraphic successions. The most characteristic members of the Manín succession are the Barremian–Aptian (Urgonian) platform limestones and Albian pelagic marls (Butkov Formation). Along the internal boundary of the Manín Unit, the Kostolec Unit, of uncertain position, is found as a narrow strip. Its klippen are now interpreted as olistoliths of shallow-water Jurassic limestones derived from the frontal parts of the Central Western Carpathian cover nappes (Hronicum?).

In addition to all of these complications, the western part of the Pieniny Klippen Belt contains another large and most puzzling element, the **Klape Unit**. This unit crops out mainly in the middle Váh valley in western Slovakia between the Manín Unit and the Oravic units of the 'Klippen Belt *sensu stricto*' (Fig. 18.24). The Klape Unit is composed of prisms several thousand metres thick of mostly proximal deep-marine clastic to mélange ('wildflysch') complexes, which are Albian–Senonian in age. The Klape Klippe, formed by shallow-water Jurassic limestones, has recently been interpreted as a large olistolith embedded in Cretaceous deep-marine clastics (Marschalko 1986). In addition, the deep-marine clastics of the Klape Unit also contain olistoliths of Triassic carbonates. However, the most conspicuous feature of the Klape Unit is the presence of 'exotic' conglomerates and chaotic boulder beds.

The exotic, so-called Upohlav conglomerates occur in two stratigraphic levels: Albian–Lower Cenomanian and Coniacian–Santonian, and are separated by the Upper Cenomanian–Turonian shallowing-upward sequence of massive sandstones with tempestites and oyster banks (Orlové Formation). The conglomerates show a wide range of composition with numerous rock types, which have been thoroughly studied and described (e.g. Mišík *et al.* 1977, 1981, 1991; Mišík & Sýkora 1981; Marschalko 1986; Mišík & Marschalko 1988; Birkenmajer *et al.* 1990; Faryad & Schreyer 1996). In addition to many common rock types, the most noticeable exotic material includes Triassic basinal limestones, Upper Jurassic platform limestones, Urgonian limestones with serpentinite clasts, Permian A-type granites with Lower Cretaceous fission-track cooling ages (Uher & Pushkarev 1994; Kissová *et al.* 2005), large amounts of calc-alkaline volcanics of uncertain age (Permian, Upper Jurassic?), Upper Jurassic glaucophanites (e.g. Dal Piaz *et al.* 1995), and heavy-mineral spectra rich in Cr-spinel (Mišík *et al.* 1980). To explain the source of these exotic clasts, which cannot have been derived from successions in the Pieniny Klippen Belt and neighbouring zones, the concept of a short-lived Cretaceous 'exotic ridge' (Fig. 18.27), the 'Klape ridge' or 'Pieniny (ultra-Pieninic) cordillera', has been developed over many decades. Birkenmajer (1988) renamed this structure as the **Andrusov Ridge** in honour of Dimitrij Andrusov, the outstanding twentieth-century Carpathian geologist and leading expert on the geology of the Pieniny Klippen Belt.

Following the advent of plate tectonics, the exotic ridge has been interpreted as a compressional tectonic structure in an active margin setting: a complex of imbricated, obducted oceanic material or a subduction mélange temporarily cropping out on the outer structural high of an accretionary prism (Mišík 1979*b*), a subduction complex exhumed in the rear part of the South Penninic–Vahic accretionary wedge (Klape Unit; Mahel' 1989) or a magmatic island arc (Birkenmajer 1986, 1988; Fig. 18.27). The exotic pebble material would suggest that the corresponding ocean basin opened during the Triassic and was closed during the Late Jurassic–Early Cretaceous (e.g. Birkenmajer 1988; Dal Piaz *et al.* 1995). However, this is in marked contradiction to the geological record of all of the other Pieniny Klippen Belt and neighbouring units, where no such events can be documented. On the other hand, these events are documented from the southern zones of the Western Carpathians, where they were associated with the opening and closing of the Meliata Ocean. The problem remains, however, as to how this material could have been transported across the Central Western Carpathian zones (with their rugged morphology) and be deposited in the neighbourhood of the Pieniny Klippen Belt zones, where an extensional tectonic regime was active during the entire Jurassic–Early Cretaceous period (cf. Plašienka 1995*a*, 2003*a*). Therefore, Plašienka (1995*b*) proposed a hypothetical solution which considers the Klape Unit to have been derived from the Fatric Zliechov Basin, which was adjacent to the Meliatic collisional stack in mid-Cretaceous times and received exotic material from it. During the Turonian, the Klape Unit (as a part of the Fatric Krížna Nappe System) moved far to the north to occupy a position in the neighbourhood of the subsequently-formed Pieniny Klippen Belt, and was then incorporated into its structure. The Lower Senonian conglomerates with a similar composition to the Albian exotic deep-marine clastics would contain, at least partly, recycled material. If this is correct, the Klape Unit and its exotic conglomerates record important tectonic events in completely different tectonic zones in the Carpathians, which have nothing in common with events occurring in the broad area of the present-day Pieniny Klippen Belt.

Moving further east, the Pieniny Klippen Belt has a constant, *c.* 5 km width and comprises just the Oravic units, with the exception of the **Haligovce Unit** which is found in one large klippe in the Pieniny Mountains at the Polish–Slovakian border NE of the High Tatra Mountains. The presence of Urgonian limestones and some additional features make the Haligovce Unit comparable with the Manín Unit of the western sector of the Pieniny Klippen Belt. It also includes Triassic dolomites.

The structure of the Pieniny Klippen Belt in its key area in the Polish–Slovakian Pieniny Mountains was influenced by pronounced dextral transpression (Ratschbacher *et al.* 1993). Transpression also affected the adjacent Krynica Unit to the north, as well as the narrow peri-Klippen Šambron-Kamenica Zone of the Central Carpathian Palaeogene Basin (Podhale Basin in the Polish literature) to the south. This zone was formed by several en-echelon, east–west trending, slightly asymmetric, south-vergent brachyanticlines (Plašienka *et al.* 1998). Further to the east, close to the Slovakian–Ukrainian border, the backthrusts in the southern limb of the flower structure centred on the Pieniny Klippen Belt create a local antiformal thrust stack in the Humenné Mountains comprising Mesozoic (Krížna-Fatric units from the outermost part of the Central Western Carpathians; Gosau deposits) as well as Palaeogene deposits (Soták *et al.* 1997).

In many areas, especially in western Slovakia, the southern boundary of the Pieniny Klippen Belt against the Central Western Carpathians cannot be precisely defined. It often coincides with deformed Palaeocene–Lower Eocene sediments referred to as the 'Peri-Klippen Palaeogene' (currently designated as the Myjava-Hričov Group). In the westernmost parts of the Pieniny Klippen Belt and the Central Western Carpathians (Malé Karpaty Mountains), these form the upper part of the Gosau Supergroup in a position similar to that of the Gosau sediments in the Northern Calcareous Alps (e.g. Wagreich & Marschalko 1995). In sections close to the Pieniny Klippen Belt, the transition from the Senonian to the Palaeocene does not contain a stratigraphic gap, and Palaeogene deposits seem to form a continuation of the 'klippen mantle'. To the south, however, the Cretaceous–Tertiary boundary is marked by an unconformity (Salaj & Began 1983). There, the Senonian Brezová Group rests transgressively on Triassic carbonates of the Hronic Nappe System (analogous to the Upper Bajuvaric and Lower Tyrolic nappes of the Northern Calcareous Alps). Gosau sediments in the Northern Calcareous Alps and Malé Karpaty Mountains are connected by the prolongation of the Giesshübl Syncline which was drilled in the substratum of the Neogene Vienna Basin (e.g. Wessely 1992). Further to the NE in the central Váh Valley, Palaeocene to Lower Eocene sediments of the Myjava-Hričov Group are closely related to those of the Central Carpathian Palaeogene Basin which extends far to the south, overlying the cover nappes of the Central Western Carpathians. In the areas close to the Pieniny Klippen Belt, the transgressive base of the Central Carpathian Palaeogene Basin is formed by exceptionally thick Eocene dolomite breccias (Súl'ov Conglomerates; Marschalko & Samuel 1993). In general, the Gosau-type Brezová and Myjava-Hričov groups are dominated by pelagic marls and calcareous deep-marine clastic formations with shallow-water biogenic detritus and reef-derived olistoliths. They were presumably deposited in narrow compressional or transpressional basins within the rear part of the developing Vahic-Oravic accretionary wedge along the northern edge of the Central Western Carpathian units.

In inner zones of the Central Western Carpathians, south of the Pieniny Klippen Belt, only rare occurrences of the Senonian-age Gosau sediments are known (Šumiac village and Dobšiná Ice Cave in central Slovakia). These represent remnants of an originally extensive marine channel which crossed the Central Western Carpathian area from northern Hungary. This interpretation is based on drilling of the pre-Tertiary basement in southern Slovakia (Mišík 1978). Other occurrences of Senonian sediments are known from the Slovak Karst area (Gombasek, Miglinc) and from the Uppony Mountains in NE Hungary.

In the Polish sector of the Pieniny Klippen Belt, carbonate conglomerates of the Jarmuta Formation transgressively overlie various klippen successions with an angular discordance, thus suggesting that there was an important phase of pre-Palaeogene ('Laramian') deformation within the Pieniny Klippen Belt (Birkenmajer 1970, 1986). This concept has been questioned, however, by some workers who emphasized that there was a record of continuous sedimentation through the Senonian and across the Cretaceous–Palaeogene boundary (e.g. Sikora 1974). However, this continuous record is probably applicable only to some 'marginal' Pieniny Klippen Belt successions (Hulina and Zlatna according to Sikora 1974). In eastern Slovakia, there are several localities where carbonate conglomerates containing olistoliths of klippen successions (Gregorianka Breccia; Nemčok *et al.* 1989) occur as olistostromes within the Palaeocene–Eocene deep-marine clastic sequence (Proč Formation). Indeed, Nemčok (1980) regards the entire Pieniny Klippen Belt as a gigantic olistostrome body, although this opinion is not accepted by any other workers in the area.

### *Vahic Superunit*

The origin and evolution of the Pieniny Klippen Belt are closely related to the long-term problem of the continuation of the South Penninic (Piemont-Liguria) Ocean into the ancient Western Carpathian realm. Since there are no surface exposures of ophiolites or Bündnerschiefer complexes in the Western Carpathians, such a continuation has been considered speculative. Some authors have assumed that the deep-water Fatric (Krížna-Zliechov) Trough represented this continuation (Tollmann 1978; Kozur & Mock 1996), but this is obviously a Slovako-Carpathian–Austro-Alpine element that was underlain by thinned continental crust and its tectonic history is very different from that of the Penninic zones. Since the Slovako-Carpathian units of the Central Western Carpathians clearly form a lateral continuation of the Austro-Alpine system, and the Oravic units have many common features with the Middle Penninic zones (Briançonnais), the majority of authors consider that this hypothetical ocean was located between the present Pieniny Klippen Belt and the Central Western Carpathians, where its suture is obliterated by superimposed nappe units and unconformably overlying sedimentary complexes. This ocean has been named 'Ocean X' (Birkenmajer 1986, 1988) or the Vahic Ocean, and its vestiges were referred to as the Vahicum (Mahel' 1981). However, there has never been any general agreement as to which particular unit represents relicts of the Vahic Ocean (for Mahel' (1981) it was the Klape Unit).

Tomek (1993) interpreted a series of seismic reflections on the Carpathian deep seismic profile 2T, which underlie the Tatric basement sheet in the northern parts of the Central Western Carpathians, to represent the shallow-dipping Piemont-Ligurian suture. Plašienka (1995*a*, *b*) assigned the **Belice Unit** to the Vahicum and assumed that this unit is the only Vahic element cropping out at the surface. It is exposed in small tectonic windows in the Považský Inovec Mountains (some 10 km south of the Pieniny Klippen Belt). The Belice Unit is composed of a thin (only several tens of metres) but strongly imbricated pelagic succession of Upper Jurassic red radiolarites and Lower Cretaceous siliceous slates (closely resembling the 'Palombini Shales' of the Ligurian Alps) with thin intercalations of Calpionella-bearing limestones in the lower part. This is overlain by a thicker, coarsening-upward Senonian deep-marine clastic succession which is topped by chaotic breccias composed of material from the Tatric basement thrust sheet that overrides the Belice Unit. Thus, the Belice Unit is positioned below the Tatric thrust sheet and its Infra-Tatric elements, representing the most external Slovako-Carpathian units. Volcanic material possibly derived from oceanic crust of the Vahic Ocean is present only as small fragments and olistoliths in the Senonian deep-marine clastics. The Belice Unit crops out in the northern and southernmost parts of the Považský Inovec Moutains. The outcrops in the north formed as a result of antiformal thrust stacking, and those in the south resulted from extensional exhumation during Miocene formation of the Danube Basin (Fig. 18.28).

The **Iňačovce-Krichevo Unit** is another element possibly representing the Carpathian analogue of the (South?) Penninic Ocean (Fig. 18.20A). This is known solely from deep boreholes that extended into the pre-Neogene substratum of the East Slovakian Basin south of the Pieniny Klippen Belt. The unit comprises Triassic carbonates and slates (similar to the Quartenschiefer in the Helvetic units), thick low-grade metasediments strongly resembling the Bündnerschiefer of the Tauern Window, Eocene deep-marine clastics, and serpentinite bodies (Soták *et al.* 1993, 1994, 2000).

## *Tectonic evolution of the Pieniny Klippen Belt*

Based on the existing data, mostly from western Slovakia, a series of evolutionary stages can be reconstructed for the Magura, Oravic, Vahic and other units involved in the Pieniny Klippen Belt and adjacent zones (Plašienka, 1995*a*, 2003*a*; Figs 18.26 & 18.27).

1. Triassic: establishment of a carbonate platform in the Oravic domain.
2. Liassic to Aalenian: broad symmetric rifting and related tectonic subsidence, resulting in the formation of a series of half-grabens with sedimentation under mainly anoxic conditions.
3. Bajocian: strongly asymmetric rifting phase with development of the Czorsztyn Ridge due to thermal uplift above a lithospheric-scale, north-dipping detachment fault.
4. Bathonian: continental breakup on the internal side of the Czorsztyn Ridge, resulting in the opening of the South Penninic-Vahic Ocean with the Kysuca-Pieniny Basin being located on its northern (in present-day coordinates) flank.
5. Callovian to Tithonian: thermal subsidence of the entire Oravic domain.
6. Early Neocomian: renewed asymmetric rifting and thermal uplift of the Czorsztyn Ridge; development of a south-dipping detachment fault on the northern side of the Czorsztyn Ridge.
7. Late Neocomian: breakup of the North Penninic-Magura Ocean to the north of the Czorsztyn Ridge.
8. Mid-Cretaceous to Senonian: thermal subsidence, resulting in the transformation of the Czorsztyn Ridge into a pelagic high.
9. Turonian: nappe emplacement of frontal elements of the Krížna (Fatric) Nappe System of the Central Western Carpathians (Drietoma, Klape, Manín units) onto the southern parts of the Vahic Ocean.
10. Early Senonian: onset of subduction of the Vahic Ocean lithosphere below the Central Western Carpathians; deformation of the Krížna elements in the position of a 'false' accretionary complex, erosion and resedimentation of Albian conglomerate material, including exotic pebbles, from the Klape Unit into deep-marine clastic deposits of the Pieniny Unit.
11. Late Senonian: gradual closure of the Vahic Ocean; partial inversion of the Magura Ocean.
12. Maastrichtian to Palaeocene: final closure (still ongoing) of the Vahic Ocean with the formation of numerous narrow remnant and piggyback deep-marine clastic basins; collision of the accretionary complex with the Czorsztyn Ridge; detachment and thrusting of the internal Oravic units along Liassic black shale horizons and formation of a foreland fold-and-thrust belt.
13. Eocene: onset of subduction of the Magura Ocean; detachment of the Czorsztyn Unit from its basement which was underthrust beneath the Central Western Carpathians; duplexing, recumbent folding, and thrusting of the Czorsztyn Unit over the southern Magura elements.
14. Oligocene to earliest Miocene: closure of the Magura Ocean; dextral transpression and oroclinal bending in the Pieniny Klippen Belt due to counterclockwise rotation of the Central Western Carpathian block; development of a positive flower structure usually centred by a narrow, generally vertical zone within the Pieniny Klippen Belt *sensu stricto*, in which strike-slip movement predominated, leading to the formation of the typical 'klippen' tectonic style as a result of pervasive brittle faulting.
15. Middle to Late Miocene: sinistral transtension along the western, SW–NE trending sector of the Pieniny Klippen Belt; the NW–SE trending eastern Slovakian sector underwent only dextral wrenching: initial transpression during the Early–Middle Miocene, followed by transtension and later extension during the Late Miocene and Pliocene (leading to the opening of the Transcarpathian Basin); volcanic activity in the so-called Pieniny andesite line along the eastern Pieniny Klippen Belt, which extends from the Polish Pieniny Mountains (Mount Wżar) to the eastern Slovakian–Ukrainian chain of Sarmatian–Pannonian subduction related stratovolcanoes.

## *Central Western Carpathians*

### *Regional subdivision*

The Central Western Carpathian region forms the core of the Carpathian Orogen which underwent a complex evolution and

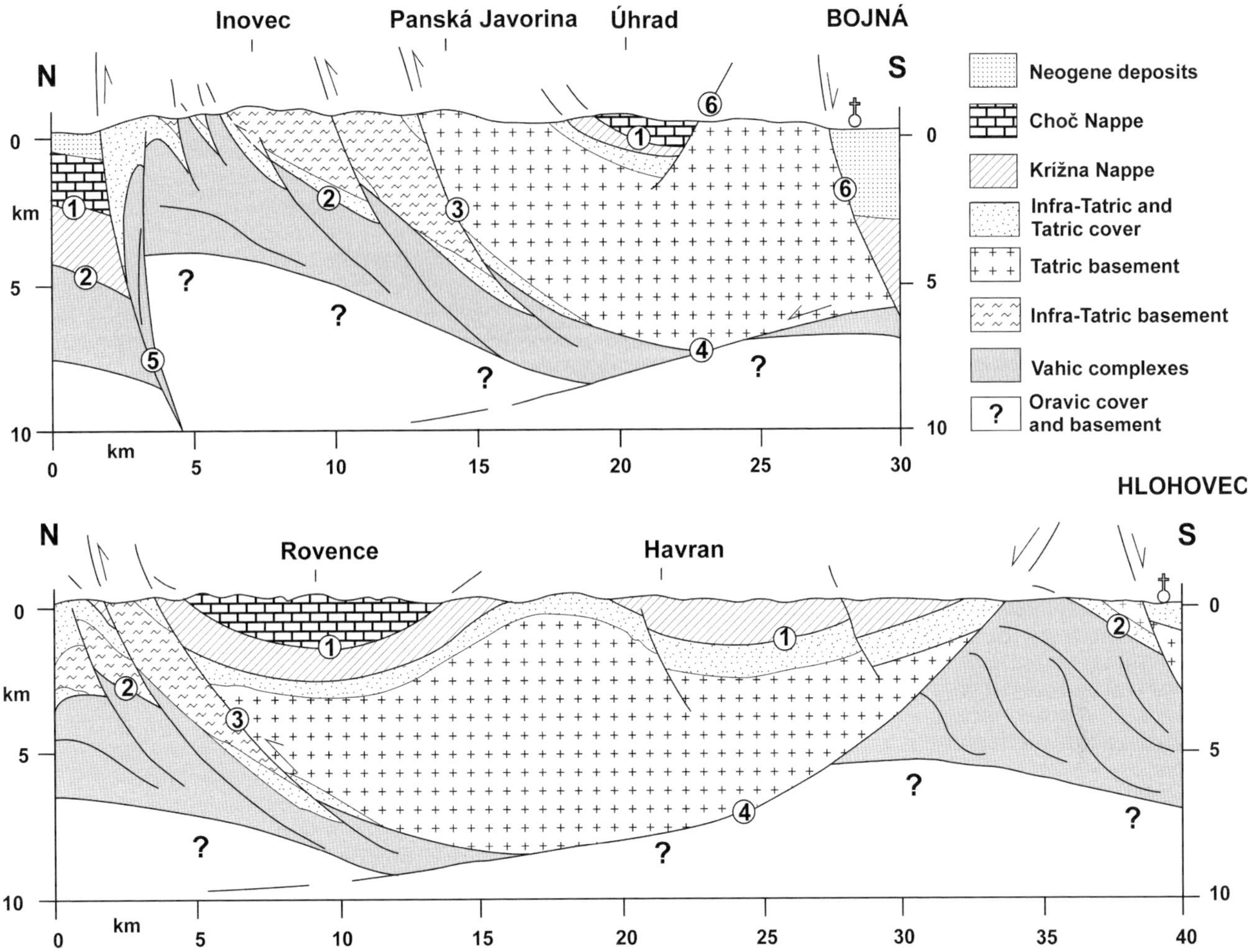


**Fig. 18.28.** Deep profiles of the Považský Inovec Mountains horst (after Plašienka 1999*b*). Numbered fault structures: 1, upper Turonian overthrust planes of the Fatric (Krížna) and Hronic (Choč) cover nappe systems; 2, uppermost Cretaceous overthrust of the Slovako-Carpathian (Infratatric–Tatric and overlying) units onto the Vahic Belice Unit; 3, early Palaeogene out-of-sequence reverse faults; 4, Middle Miocene low-angle normal faults; 5, Upper Miocene rotational oblique reverse faults; 6, Upper Miocene normal faults.

contains a number of nappe units of various orders and ages. Two main types of tectonic units are present: thick-skinned thrust sheets which comprise the pre-Alpine crystalline basement along with its Late Palaeozoic–Mesozoic sedimentary cover (the Tatric, Veporic and Gemeric superunits), and detached cover nappe systems containing Late Palaeozoic to Mesozoic sedimentary rocks with rare volcanics (the Fatric, Hronic and Silicic superunits) (e.g. Andrusov 1968, 1975; Andrusov *et al.* 1973; Mahel' 1986; Biely 1989; Plašienka *et al.* 1997).

The Southernmost Central Western Carpathian zones were overridden by nappe units belonging to the Internal Western Carpathians (Meliatic and partly Turnaic Superunits). The main phase of crustal shortening and nappe formation took place during the early Late Cretaceous in the Central Western Carpathians. Deformation processes reflect an outward (northward) vergence of the orogen. Regionally, the Central Western Carpathians are divided into two principal morphostructural zones: the Tatra-Fatra Belt and the Vepor-Gemer Belt.

The **Tatra-Fatra Belt** includes so-called core mountains in western and northern Slovakia with a Tatric-type (see below) crystalline basement and the classic 'Sub-Tatra' nappes (in the sense of Uhlig 1907; Andrusov 1936). These mountains represent mainly asymmetric, northward-tilted horst structures (*c.* 40–50 km long and 15–20 km wide on average) resulting from Late Tertiary uplift, surrounded by cover nappe units and Tertiary sedimentary basins. There are nine principal core mountains, namely, from west to east: the Malé Karpaty (Lesser Carpathians), Považský Inovec, Tribeč, Strážovské vrchy, Žiar, Malá Fatra, Vel'ká Fatra, Nízke Tatry (Low Tatra), and Tatry (High Tatra) mountains (Figs 18.19 & 18.29).

The core mountains comprise the Tatric Superunit including Variscan high-grade crystalline basement and its Late Palaeozoic and Mesozoic sedimentary cover, overridden by the superficial nappe systems: the Fatric Superunit (Krížna nappe *sensu lato*) and the Hronic Superunit (Choč nappe *sensu lato*) (Fig. 18.30). The post-nappe cover is formed by Palaeogene (Central Carpathian Palaeogene Basin), Neogene and Quaternary rocks. The northern boundary of the Tatra-Fatra Belt is formed by the above-noted, locally ill-defined contact with the Pieniny Klippen Belt. The southern boundary, against the Vepor-Gemer Belt, is the contact between the Tatric sheet and the overriding Veporic crystalline basement, which is a crustal-scale thrust fault (the

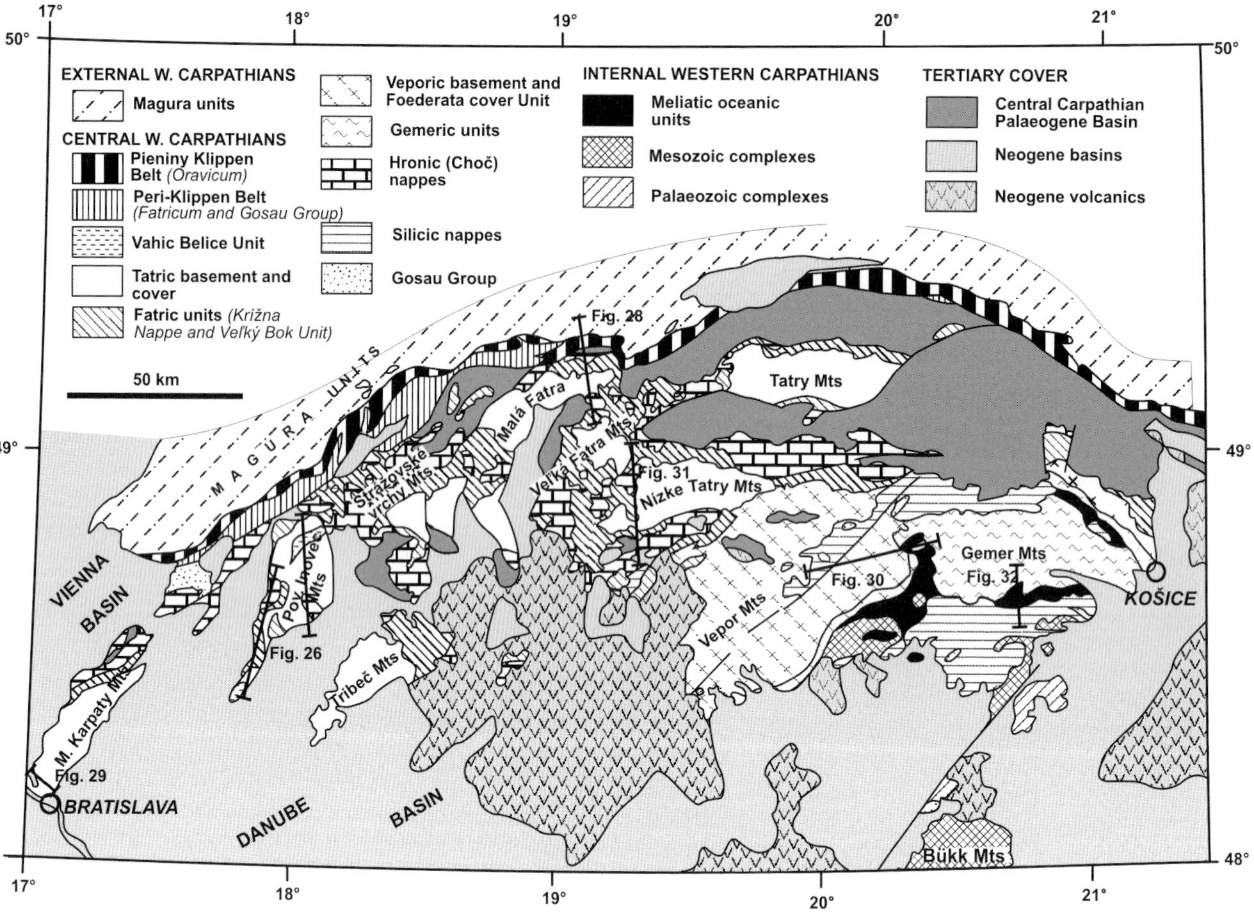


**Fig. 18.29.** Simplified geological map of the Central and Internal Western Carpathians. All boundaries of pre-Tertiary units are tectonic in origin.

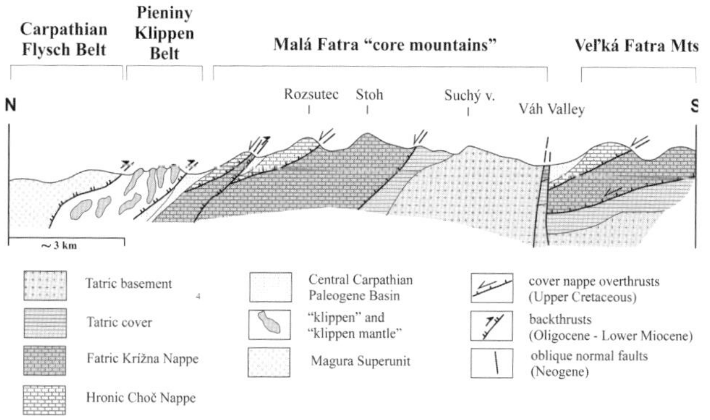


**Fig. 18.30.** Cross-section of typical 'core mountains' – the Malá Fatra Mountains of NW Slovakia (modified after Polák 1979). Note backthrusting that modified the nappe structures in the proximity of the Pieniny Klippen Belt.

Čertovica Fault). However, this fault is precisely defined only in the Nízke Tatry Mountains, where it is exposed over a short distance.

The westward continuation of the Čertovica Fault is beneath the Central Slovakian neovolcanic area and to the south of the Tribeč Mountains, where it was reactivated as a Neogene extensional normal fault system (Mojmírovce faults; Hrušecký *et al.* 1996; Hók *et al.* 1999). A further possible SW prolongation of this fault below the Neogene fill of the Danube Basin has not been verified (see Fig. 18.19). In the subsurface of the western part of the Danube Basin, only the basement units in the vicinity of the Malé Karpaty Mountains and the Hainburg Hills (and possibly the Leitha Mountains in the easternmost part of the Alps) can be considered to be Tatric. No typical Tatric elements occur in the Eastern Alps; here they are replaced by the Lower Austro-Alpine units. These are equivalent to the Infra-Tatric units in the Western Carpathians, a frontal, imbricated part of the Tatric Superunit. East of the Nízke Tatry Mountains, the Čertovica Fault is covered by the Hronic Nappes and Palaeogene sediments of the Central Carpathian Palaeogene Basin, and somewhere to the north of the Branisko Mountains it probably joins the Pieniny Klippen Belt.

The **Vepor-Gemer Belt** is the metamorphic core of the Western Carpathian Orogen and is predominantly built up of basement complexes, which were exhumed from deeper crustal levels early in the Alpine Orogeny. The Vepor-Gemer Belt includes the Král'ovohol'ské Nízke Tatry Mountains, the Slovak Ore Mountains (Veporské, Stolické and Volovské vrchy mountains), and the Branisko and Čierna Hora mountains to the NW of Košice. These areas are constituted either by Veporic or Gemeric basement and cover complexes. In addition to the dominant underlying Veporic Superunit, the northern Vepor Sub-belt also includes remnants of the overriding Gemeric Superunit and large nappe outliers of the Silicic Superunit (Drienok, Muráň, Vernár and Stratená nappes). Unconformable cover complexes include Senonian Gosau sediments, Palaeogene sedimentary, and Neogene sedimentary and volcanic complexes.

The contact of the Vepor Sub-belt with the Gemer Sub-belt to the south is represented by the Lubeník-Margecany Fault. This is a complex, arcuate fault zone that underwent a complex kinematic evolution. Its precursor was a thrust plane along which the Gemeric Superunit was thrust over the Veporic Superunit, probably during the Early Cretaceous. During the Late Cretaceous, the SW–NE striking Lubeník sector of the Lubeník-Margecany Fault acted as a sinistral transpressional zone. Simultaneously, its presently NNW–SSE striking part was reactivated as a low-angle normal fault which accommodated top-to-the-east unroofing of a metamorphic core complex constituted by the Veporic Superunit (Plašienka *et al.* 1999).

The Vepor Sub-belt plunges to the SW beneath the Central Slovakian volcanic complexes and then continues in the subsurface of the southeastern part of the Neogene Danube Basin between the Mojmírovce faults in the north (reactivated Čertovica Fault) and the Rába-Hurbanovo Fault Zone (Figs 18.19 & 18.20). According to the borehole data, the Vepor Sub-belt in this area is dominantly composed of basement complexes. It continues westward into the Central Eastern Alps.

The Gemer Sub-belt includes the eastern part of the Slovak Ore Mountains and comprises mainly rocks belonging to the Gemeric Superunit: Palaeozoic, mainly low-grade metamorphic volcanosedimentary complexes with possible Mesozoic-age cover. It is overlain by remnants of the Jaklovce and Bôrka nappes belonging to the Meliatic Superunit and by cover nappes belonging to the Silicic Superunit (Stratená and Galmus nappes along the northern margin, Radzim and Opátka outliers in the central part, and the northern margin of the Silica Nappe *sensu stricto* at the boundary with the Slovak Karst Mountains). Tertiary cover rocks are present only at the peripheries of the exposed part of the sub-belt. The southern boundary of the sub-belt is poorly defined but it is herein considered to coincide with the course of the Meliatic suture separating the Central Western Carpathians and the Internal Western Carpathians. This suture was probably reactivated by fault zones such as the Rožňava Fault Zone, continuing toward the west and SW into the Plešivec, Diósjenő, Hurbanovo and Rába fault zones (Plašienka 1999*a*).

## *Slovako-Carpathian tectonic system*

*Tatric Superunit*

The Tatric Superunit (or Tatricum) represents the most external and lowermost component of the Slovako-Carpathian tectonic system. Its internal structure is dominated by pre-Alpine crystalline basement complexes, though Mesozoic cover rocks are common at the surface. As revealed by deep seismic transects, the Tatric Superunit forms a tabular, slightly convex, >10 km thick upper-crustal body, rooted in the lower crust below the wedge-shaped Veporic Superunit (Tomek 1993; Bielik *et al.* 2004; see Fig. 18.20). At depth, the Tatric Superunit presumably overrides the Vahic Superunit. It is overlain by thin-skinned nappes of the Fatric and Hronic superunits, as well as by unconformably overlying Tertiary sediments and volcanics.

Compared to the overlying Veporic Superunit, the Tatric Superunit is internally less differentiated. Late Tertiary extensional faults (mainly the bounding faults of the horsts forming the core mountain), and minor north-vergent overthrusts along

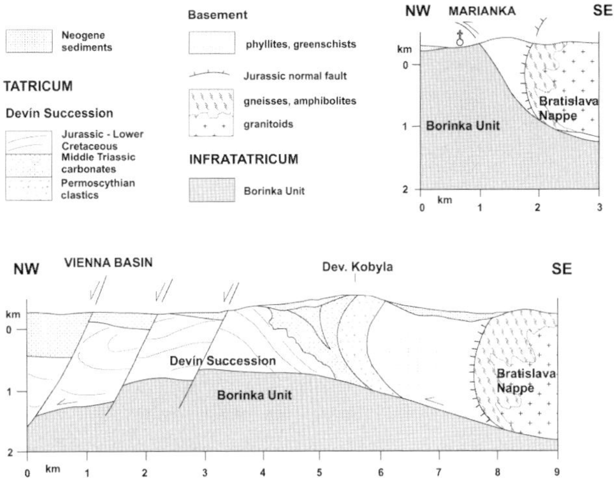


**Fig. 18.31.** Large-scale recumbent fold at the tip of the Tatric Bratislava nappe in the southern part of the Malé Karpaty Mountains (after Plašienka 1999*b*).

the northern edges of some of the core mountains (Tribeč, Ďumbierske Nízke Tatry, High Tatra) are also documented. The latter formed as a result of Cretaceous inversion of Jurassic extensional faults (Dumont *et al.* 1996; Plašienka 2003*b*). Major overthrusts are present along the northern edge of the Tatric Superunit, where Tatric units were thrust over various complexes of the so-called Infra-Tatricum (e.g. the Tatric Bratislava Nappe overriding the Infra-Tatric Borinka Unit in the Malé Karpaty Mountains; Plašienka 1990; Plašienka *et al.* 1991; Fig. 18.31).

The mid-crustal suture between the rigid Tatric basement sheet and the underlying Vahic complexes represents a crustal inhomogeneity coinciding with the ductile–brittle transition. It was, therefore, reactivated during Palaeogene and Miocene extension. Listric extensional faults flattening into the ductile middle crust were imaged by seismic profiling particularly in the Danube Basin area (Tomek *et al.* 1987; Tari *et al.* 1992; Tari 1996; Horváth 1993; Hrušecký 1999). The weak mid-crustal layer probably also controlled the dissection of the Tatric sheet in Tertiary times into a system of uplifted horsts (forming the core mountains) and subsiding grabens in the areas of Neogene extension (mainly in western Slovakia) and the rotation of these blocks (Kováč *et al.* 1994, 1997; Hrouda *et al.* 2002*a*).

The Tatric Superunit consists of pre-Alpine crystalline basement complexes and their Upper Palaeozoic–Mesozoic sedimentary cover. Upper Palaeozoic rocks are mainly present in the Infra-Tatric units. The Tatric crystalline basement was only slightly affected by Alpine deformation and metamorphism; it commonly retains Variscan structures and isotopic ages. The Tatric sedimentary cover is autochthonous to parautochthonous with respect to the basement.

The pre-Alpine, generally Variscan crystalline basement includes medium- to high-grade, rarely low-grade metamorphic volcanosedimentary complexes which were intruded by numerous differentiated Variscan granitoid plutons (Petrík *et al.* 1994; Petrík 2000; Broska & Uher 2001). In the western High Tatra Mountains, a Variscan nappe structure was documented (Kahan 1969; Janák 1994). It has been suggested that this nappe structure controls the distribution of metamorphic complexes within the Tatric and also the Veporic basement (Putiš 1992; Bezák *et al.* 1997).

The Tatric sedimentary cover is largely of Mesozoic age (Lower Triassic–Lower Turonian), although immature terrestrial clastics of probable Late Permian age are found locally (Vozárová & Vozár 1988). Triassic sediments are comparable to the record in the German Basin. Scythian strata are continental siliciclastics. Lower Scythian quartz sandstones (Lúžna Formation) usually directly overlie the pre-Alpine basement. The Upper Scythian Werfen Formation is composed of sandstones, siltstones, shales and, in the upper part, evaporites (dolomite, gypsum, cargneule). The Middle Triassic Gutenstein Formation represents a shallow carbonate ramp and includes evidence of hypersaline environments and submarine slumping. It is overlain by a partly hypersaline dolomitic complex (Ramsau Formation) with shale intercalations in its upper part. The maximum thickness of the Middle Triassic carbonate complex is *c.* 500 m. The Upper Carnian–Norian Carpathian Keuper Formation includes shales, quartz sandstones, rare conglomerates, and minor evaporites. Due to erosion associated with Lower Jurassic rifting, Rhaetian-age shallow-marine sediments are rarely preserved. Rhaetian limnic sediments with dinosaur footprints (Tomanová Formation) occur in the High Tatra Mountains.

The Jurassic sediments of the Tatric area were deposited on two bounding structural highs (south and north Tatric ridges) and in the intervening Šiprúň Basin (Fig. 18.26). The synrift Lower Jurassic sediments are represented by biodetritic and sandy limestones and sandstones and, in the Šiprúň Basin, also by the hemipelagic Allgäu Formation. While the ridges maintained their elevated position up into the Late Jurassic, the Middle and Upper Jurassic strata in the Šiprúň Basin are chiefly represented by a deep-water pelagic facies (cherty and siliceous limestones to radiolarites). The Upper Jurassic–Lower Cretaceous succession comprises limestones with chert nodules. Bioclastic limestones were widespread during the Barremian. Terrigenous allodapic sandy limestones of that age surround the north Tatric ridge (Jablonský *et al.* 1993). In the area of the south Tatric ridge (High Tatra Mountains), Urgonian platform limestones and related slope deposits occur. Small bodies of basanitic lavas locally occur within the Barremian and Aptian sediments (Spišiak & Hovorka 1997). Synorogenic turbidite sediments dominated by terrigenous siliciclastic material, together with bodies of exotic conglomerates (Poruba Formation), were deposited during the Late Albian and Cenomanian. Hemipelagic sedimentation ceased as late as the Early Turonian.

The **Infra-Tatric units** comprise the lower and frontal, imbricated parts of the Tatric sheet and crop out in the western part of the Tatra-Fatra Belt. The Borinka Unit of the Malé Karpaty Mountains (Fig. 18.31), the Inovec Nappe of the northern part of Považský Inovec Mountains, and the Kozol Unit in the Malá Fatra Mountains can be regarded as Infra-Tatric units (Plašienka *et al.* 1997). Units underlying the Infra-Tatric units crop out only in the Považský Inovec Mountains (Belice Unit of supposed Vahic provenance; Plašienka 1995*b*). Substantial portions of the Lower Austro-Alpine complexes occurring in the easternmost part of the Eastern Alps (Wechsel, Grobgneis and Semmering nappes) can be considered to form a westward prolongation of the Infra-Tatric units (Pahr 1991; Häusler *et al.* 1993). The Infra-Tatric units represent a system of recumbent fold nappes. They are exposed in uplifted areas forming tectonic windows and half-windows. The thrust planes of the nappes are accompanied by ductile/brittle shear zones formed under low-grade metamorphic conditions (*c.* 250–300°C; Putiš 1991; Plašienka *et al.* 1993; Korikovsky *et al.* 1997).

The Infra-Tatric basement is exposed only within the Inovec Nappe, and is composed mainly of mica schists and rarer amphibolites and metagranotoids. It is covered by the thick Upper Palaeozoic Kálnica Group, consisting principally of Permian continental clastics; similar sediments occur in the Kozol Unit of the Malá Fatra Mountains. The Permian sediments are overlain by Scythian-age clastics and by a Middle Triassic-age carbonate complex. Upper Triassic-age formations are often missing due to erosion associated with Early Jurassic rifting. Jurassic synrift sediments consist of prisms up to 1000 m thick of marine terrigenous clastics (Borinka Unit of the Malé Karpaty Mountains, interpreted as the infill of an extensional half-graben; Plašienka 1987; Plašienka *et al.* 1991; Fig. 18.26).

*Veporic Superunit*

The Veporic Superunit (or Veporicum) is the central of the three crustal-scale thick-skinned thrust sheets of the Central Western Carpathians. Based on the 2T and G1 deep seismic profiles (Tomek 1993; Vozár *et al.* 1998; Bielik *et al.* 2004), it can be characterized as a wedge-shaped, partly imbricated crustal slice. It is *c.* 15–20 km thick in its central part and up to 30 km thick in the rear part, where it occupies almost the entire crustal profile (profile 2T). Towards the east (profile G1), the Veporic Superunit is only *c.* 5 km thick in the northern part and 8–10 km thick in the southern part (see Fig. 18.20). In seismic profiles, the inner structure of the Veporic Superunit is complex, with numerous reflective zones, roughly paralleling its boundaries. These reflectors are interpreted as mylonitic zones created during the palaeo-Alpine (Cretaceous) collision and subsequent post-collisional extension (e.g. Hrouda *et al.* 2002*b*). Some of the reflections (i.e. the subhorizontal or slightly northward-dipping ones) can be considered as pre-Alpine, related to Variscan thrusting and collisional processes (Bezák *et al.* 1997; Bielik *et al.* 2004).

At the surface, the Veporic Superunit mainly comprises pre-Alpine crystalline basement, with a similar composition and pre-Alpine history to that of the Tatric Superunit. Its Upper Palaeozoic–Mesozoic cover is only locally preserved. The basement is, for the most part, composed of probable Lower Palaeozoic volcanosedimentary complexes with a low- to medium-grade Variscan metamorphic overprint. High-grade migmatitic and amphibolite complexes occur in the northern and central parts of the Veporic Superunit, where they are intruded by the Vepor Pluton and smaller granitoid massifs (Hrončok, Rimavica and Cretaceous Rochovce granitoid massifs; Putiš *et al.* 2000; Poller *et al.* 2001). In contrast to the Tatric Superunit, the basement of the southern Veporicum was considerably influenced by palaeo-Alpine tectonometamorphic processes, especially by low- to medium-grade metamorphism and the development of a penetrative subhorizontal mylonitic structure that superimposed the Variscan metamorphic features and tectonic relationships of the pre-Alpine complexes (Hók *et al.* 1993; Madarás *et al.* 1996; Plašienka *et al.* 1999; Janák *et al.* 2001).

The sedimentary cover of the northern part of the Veporic Superunit, the **Vel'ký Bok Unit**, represents the southern slope of the Fatric Basin. The Vel'ký Bok Unit crops out on the northern slopes of the Král'ovohol'ské Nízke Tatry Mountains, in the NW part of the Slovenské rudohorie Mountains, and in the Branisko and Čierna Hora Mountains. It is composed of a Permian–Lower Cretaceous sedimentary succession similar to that of the Zliechov succession of the Fatric Superunit (see below), and is subdivided into several partial units, commonly forming large recumbent folds (Plašienka 1995*c*, 2003*b*).

Thick (>1000 m in places) Permian clastics, including a volcanic horizon (L'ubietová Group), directly overlie the northern Veporic crystalline basement and grade up into Scythian quartzites and shales. The Middle Triassic carbonate complex comprises limestones and dolomites. The Upper Triassic is represented by the Carpathian Keuper Formation. The Jurassic commences with synrift sandy limestones, with local gaps in sedimentation and occasional erosion of the underlying Triassic. The post-rift units are mainly Middle Jurassic to Lower Cretaceous pelagic sediments (i.e. marly, cherty and siliceous limestones, locally also radiolarites). The Neocomian–Lower Albian pelagic marlstones attain a thickness of >1000 m. Younger sediments are not known from the Vel'ký Bok Unit.

The **Foederata Unit** represents the cover of the southern and central zones of the Veporicum. However, it is poorly preserved. In the southernmost part of the Veporic Superunit, along the Lubeník Fault, only Upper Palaeozoic and Scythian-age units are preserved (Revúca Group; Vozárová & Vozár 1988). The Foederata Unit in the central Veporicum comprises Permian–Triassic metamorphosed sedimentary complexes made up of Permian–Scythian-age clastics and a Middle to Upper Triassic carbonate succession. All of the rocks of the Foederata Unit are metamorphosed to greenschist facies and underwent ductile deformation (Plašienka 1993; Lupták *et al.* 2000). However, they remained in a parautochthonous position with respect to their basement.

The structural association of the central and southern parts of the Veporic Superunit is dominated by a flat, or moderately NE-dipping, metamorphic/mylonitic $S_1$ foliation that is penetrative in both the topmost parts of the basement granitoids and the cover (Foederata Unit). The foliation planes exhibit a distinct stretching lineation $L_1$ plunging generally to the east. The association of this first Alpine deformation stage $D_1$ is completed by moderately east- to NE-dipping shear bands which are mesoscopically penetrative in the vicinity of the NW–SE trending sector of the Lubeník line (C′-type shear bands). Shear bands and other shear-sense criteria indicate top-to-the-east kinematics (Fig. 18.32) (i.e. orogen-parallel extension). The growth of new metamorphic minerals (micas, chloritoid, kyanite) within the cover rocks is generally syn- to early post-kinematic with respect to the $S_1$ foliation, and pre- to synkinematic with respect to the C' planes (Lupták *et al.* 2000).

The $D_1$ structural association represents a large-scale subhorizontal ductile shear zone. This shear zone is interpreted as a low-angle detachment fault that parallels the basement–cover interface and lithological boundaries within the Foederata Unit, as well as the original Veporicum/Gemericum overthrust contact (Plašienka 1993; Hók *et al.* 1993; Madarás *et al.* 1996). Basement complexes in the footwall of the detachment exhibit abruptly downward-decreasing strain and increasing metamorphic grade due to vertical thinning and the telescoping of isograds within the shear zone. The maximum P-T conditions reach the lower amphibolite facies along a prograde loop, up to 620°C at about 1 GPa (Janák *et al.* 2001) in the deepest exposed unit (garnetiferous mica schists). The Foederata Unit indicates metamorphic conditions of 530–560°C at 600–800 MPa for Permian metasediments (chloritoid-kyanite schists; Lupták *et al.* 2000) and only 330–380°C at *c.* 400 MPa for Mesozoic metasediments (Lupták *et al.* 2003). Rocks in the hanging wall of the detachment fault, i.e. extensional allochthons of the Gemeric and Silicic superunits, are only anchizonal to unmetamorphosed. The cataclastic shear zone along their base was formed under considerable fluid overpressure (Milovský *et al.* 2003).

The detachment fault at the top of the Veporic Superunit was active during the Late Cretaceous unroofing of the Veporic metamorphic core complex as suggested by $^{40}Ar/^{39}Ar$ data (Maluski *et al.* 1993; Dallmeyer *et al.* 1996; Kováčik *et al.* 1997; Janák *et al.* 2001), which record cooling ages of various mineral phases between 110 and 75 Ma (Fig. 18.32). The extension and exhumation of the southern part of the Veporicum culminated in the intrusion of the Rochovce Granite at 81 to 76 Ma (Hraško *et al.* 1999; Poller *et al.* 2001). Apatite fission-track ages from Variscan granitoids suggest that cooling took place from the Late Cretaceous to the Palaeogene (Král' 1977).

Orogen-parallel extension was accompanied, and followed, by orogen-normal contraction resulting in superimposed deformation stages (Plašienka 1993; Plašienka *et al.* 1999). The $D_2$ structural association is dominated by steep cleavage and related tight upright folds that are associated with several SW–NE to

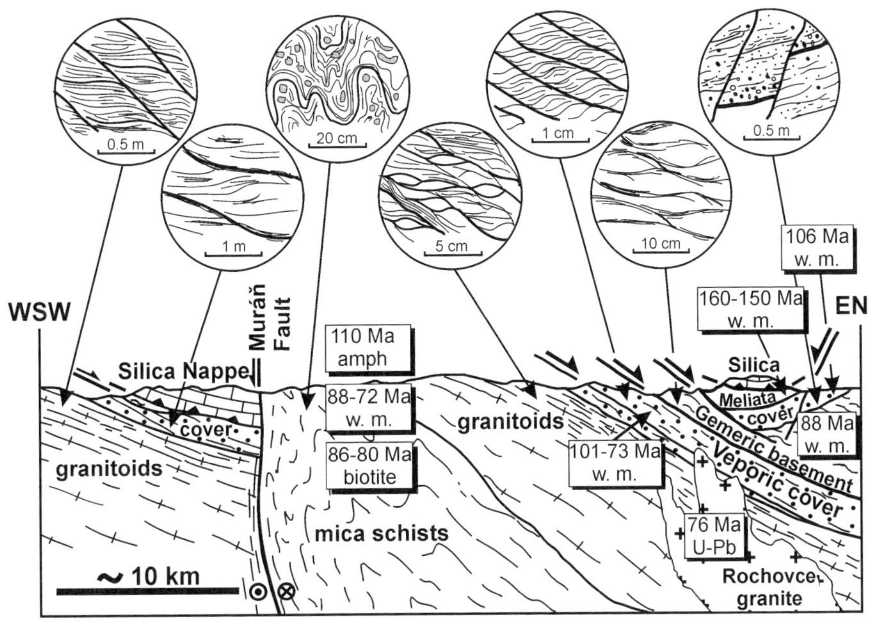


**Fig. 18.32.** Geological cross-section across the eastern margin of the Veporicum parallel to the regional trend of the stretching lineation (modified after Plašienka *et al.* 1999*b*). Typical structures related to east-vergent unroofing and important radiometric (mostly $^{40}Ar/^{39}Ar$) data are shown.

WSW–ENE trending high-strain zones. These are interpreted as deep-seated sinistral transpressional belts (e.g. Lexa *et al.* 2003). They dissect the exposed part of the Veporicum in central Slovakia into individual zones. The Osrblie Fault System separates the L'ubietová Zone from the Kraklová Zone, while the Pohorelá Fault divides the Kraklová and the Král'ova Hol'a zones (Hók & Hraško 1990; Putiš 1991; Madarás *et al.* 1994), and the Muráň Fault (Marko 1993) separates the Král'ova Hol'a Zone from the Kohút Zone. All of these fault systems, together with the Čertovica Fault (e.g. Siegl 1978) which separates the Veporic and Tatric superunits, and the Lubeník Fault at the boundary between the Veporic and Gemeric superunits, are latest Cretaceous–earliest Palaeogene in age. Outcrop data suggest that there was no reactivation of these faults in Neogene times. The same is true for conjugate transversal fault systems with a NW–SE direction (e.g. the Mýto-Tisovec Fault; Marko & Vojtko 2006).

*Gemeric Superunit*

The Gemeric Superunit (or Gemericum) is the uppermost basement-cover superunit of the Central Western Carpathians. It is volumetrically smaller than the Tatric and the Veporic superunits and, moreover, it wedges out laterally. Partial analogues of the Gemeric Superunit can be found in the Upper Austro-Alpine units of the Eastern Alps which include Palaeozoic formations, such as the Greywacke Zone (Noric nappe), the Graz Palaeozoic, the Gurktal nappes, and some units in the basements of the Styrian and Danube basins (e.g. Mihályi Ridge; Neubauer & Vozárová 1990; Balla 1994; Ebner 1992; Tari 1995).

During the Variscan cycle, the Gemeric Superunit represented the southern, external parts of the orogen, whereas during the Alpine cycle it formed the innermost zone of the Central Western Carpathians. Palaeogeographically, it represents the southern marginal zone of the Slovako-Carpathian system, abutting the Meliata Ocean which was located to the south. Following closure of the ocean, the Gemericum was thrust northward over the Veporic Superunit. According to data from the G1 deep-seismic profile (Vozár *et al.* 1998), the Gemeric sheet is a wedge-shaped, southward-thickening upper crustal body in its central part. Its lower limiting plane, dipping at *c.* 20°, can be traced downward along the Lubeník-Margecany Fault which merges with the steeply dipping Rožňava Fault Zone at at *c.* 15 km depth (Fig. 18.20).

The Gemeric Superunit comprises a series of northward-verging thrust imbricates and partial nappes, the number and terminology of which varies from author to author. Most frequently, the North Gemeric (Klátov, Rakovec, Črmel' and Ochtiná units) and South Gemeric (Volovec and Štós units) units are distinguished.

The North Gemeric basement is represented by the Rakovec and Klátov units with an oceanic affinity. The **Rakovec Unit** (phyllite–diabase complex) comprises low-grade metasediments and basic volcanics, of probable Devonian age. Together with the higher-metamorphosed **Klátov Unit** (gneiss–amphibolite complex) it probably represents a Variscan oceanic suture.

The North Gemeric Mississippian cover is represented by the **Ochtiná and Črmel' units** (the former to the west, the latter to the east; both are *c.* 1000 m thick). They comprise low-grade metamorphosed marine clastics and metasomatized carbonates (magnesites), together with basic volcanics and, in places, ultrabasics. Their age is Late Visean–Serpukhovian (Vozárová 1996). The Pennsylvanian Dobšiná Group lies transgressively on the Lower Palaeozoic substratum in the northern part of the Gemeric area. Basal clastics are overlain by shallow-marine fossiliferous carbonates, basic volcanics and a regressive paralic succession. The Permian Krompachy Group rests transgressively on various North Gemeric complexes. Its basal part consists of unsorted coarse clastics deposited in a terrestrial environment. These pass up into Upper Permian and Lower Triassic lagoonal-sabkha sediments, accompanied by subalkaline rhyolitic volcanism. These sediments are tectonically overlain by carbonate complexes considered to be part of the Silicic Superunit (Stratená Nappe; Mello 2000). Previously, the carbonates were assumed to be part of the cover of the Gemericum ('North-Gemeric Mesozoic'). Indeed, the tectonic contact cannot be convincingly documented in many places.

The largest unit of the Gemericum is the **Volovec Unit**, comprising low-grade metamorphosed Lower Palaeozoic volcanosedimentary complexes (Gelnica Group, several thousand metres thick), intruded by the Late Variscan (Permian) Spiš-Gemer granitoids (Finger & Broska 1999; Poller *et al.* 2002). The sedimentary units consist of upward-thickening deep-marine clastic megacycles containing abundant terrigenous and volcanogenic material. The bases of the megacycles comprise pelagic chert (lydites), anoxic shales, and locally carbonates (e.g. Grecula 1973, 1982; Ivanička *et al.* 1989). The age of the Gelnica Group ranges from Cambrian to Early Devonian. The volcanics (mostly volcaniclastics) are acidic to intermediate, and rarely basic. The **Štós Unit** is the uppermost imbricate of the Gemeric Superunit, composed of monotonous phyllites of uncertain, but possibly Mississippian age. The sedimentary cover of the Volovec and Štós units comprises the Permian–Scythian clastic Gočaltovo Group, including the continental, Verrucano-type Lower Permian Rožňava Formation and the Upper Permian–Lower Triassic, partly shallow-marine Štítnik Formation (Reichwalder 1973; Vozárová & Vozár 1988; Vozárová 1996). Some erosional remnants of Middle Triassic carbonates locally occur below the Meliatic Bôrka Nappe and are also probably part of the Gemeric sedimentary cover (Mello 1997).

The internal structure of the Gemeric Superunit formed as a result of the interaction of Variscan and Alpine deformation. Distinguishing between these two deformation events is a matter of much controversy (e.g. Reichwalder 1973; Ivanička *et al.* 1989; Grecula 1982; Jacko *et al.* 1996; Németh *et al.* 1997; Lexa *et al.* 2003). The most conspicuous feature of the Gemeric structure is the presence of a tight, isoclinally folded and imbricated fabric associated with a large-scale cleavage fan transversally cut by transpressional shear zones (Grecula *et al.* 1990) which were possibly caused by the indentation of a still-unrecognized basement block from the south (Lexa *et al.* 2003).

*Fatric Superunit*

The term Fatric Superunit, or Fatricum, is used to refer to units composed mainly of detached sedimentary cover, which were derived from zones between the present-day Tatric Superunit in the north and the Veporic Superunit in the south (Fig. 18.33) (i.e. this term is used both in a tectonic and a palaeogeographic sense). The term was introduced by Andrusov *et al.* (1973) for the 'Lower Sub-Tatra Nappe' (i.e. the Krížna and analogous units). However, the Fatricum includes not only the detached complexes of the Krížna nappe proper, but also their original (mostly underthrust) basement, although this basement is only rarely exposed at the surface.

Three types of tectonic units occur in the Fatric Superunit: (1) units with basement and cover; (2) cover nappes (Krížna Unit); and (3) detached units in the Peri-Klippen Zone. The first type is represented by units comprising pre-Alpine basement and its Permian–Scythian sedimentary cover, which form duplexes in

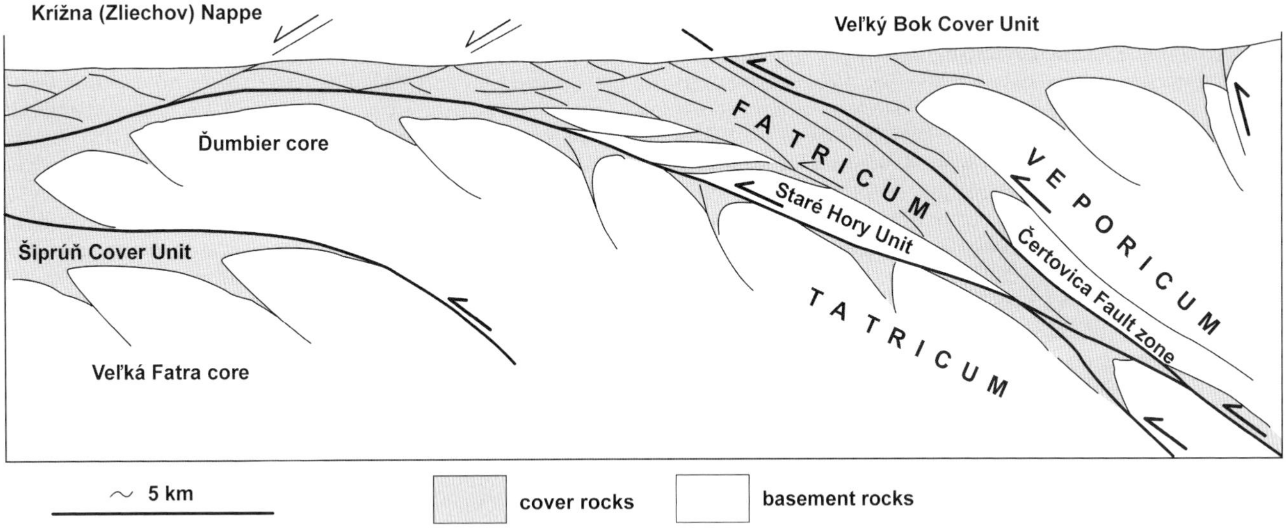


**Fig. 18.33.** Schematic section through the rear Fatric elements showing their relationships to the underlying Tatric and overlying Veporic units (after Plašienka 1999*b*).

the internal part of the Fatric nappe system (Jaroš 1971; Hók *et al.* 1994; Plašienka 2003*b*). The **Rázdiel Unit** in the Tribeč Mountains includes pre-Alpine basement composed of phyllites, mica schists, amphibolites, and mylonitized granitoids. The cover consists of Late Permian coarse-clastic and shaly sediments. An analogous, imbricated basement duplex (**Staré Hory Unit**, Fig. 18.33) is found in the Starohorské vrchy Mountains (western part of the Nízke Tatry Mountains) and contains an orthogneiss basement overlain by Permian and Triassic sediments. In the **Smrekovica Unit** of the Branisko Mountains, the basement comprises a pre-Alpine, high-grade metamorphosed crystalline complex, covered by Permian and Scythian clastics.

The second type of tectonic units is typified by the **Krížna Unit**, which is one of the fundamental units of the Tatra-Fatra Belt. This unit is composed of several detached partial nappes containing mainly Middle Triassic–mid-Cretaceous sedimentary successions of several lithotectonic types (e.g. Andrusov 1968; Mahel' 1983, 1986). These are in an allochthonous position above the Tatric cover and are tectonically overlain by the Hronic nappes (Fig. 18.33). The nappe sole is formed by incompetent Upper Scythian shales and evaporites and by carbonatic tectonic breccias (cargneule) (Jaroszewski 1982; Plašienka & Soták 1996). The overlying Middle Triassic carbonates form the rigid, mechanically dominating element of the nappe. As in the Tatric Superunit, the lower Middle Triassic strata are represented by the Gutenstein Formation, overlain by sabkha-type Ramsau dolomites. However, unlike the Tatric Superunit, the upper part of the Ladinian–Carnian dolomite complex includes a thin package of quartz sandstones and shales (Lunz Formation). The Norian-age Carpathian Keuper Formation (up to 300 m) contains fewer clastics than the stratigraphic equivalent in the Tatric Superunit and is composed of claystones, siltstones, rare sandstones, and in places gypsum, with the upper part dominated by evaporitic dolomites deposited in supratidal lagoons (Al-Jaboury & Ďurovič 1996). Secondary detachment zones were generated along this incompetent horizon. The Kössen Formation comprises shallow-marine fossiliferous limestones and reflects the Rhaetian marine transgression as well as the onset of rifting of the European shelf (Michalík 1977, 1978; Tomašových 2000).

The Jurassic–Lower Cretaceous deposits are found in two distinct lithotectonic units showing differing facies development. Substantial parts of the Krížna Unit (Krížna Nappe *sensu stricto* = Zliechov partial unit) comprise the deep-water ***Zliechov succession***, up to 2000 m thick, which begins with the Hettangian–Sinemurian, terrigenous, littoral to neritic Kopienec Formation. This passes up into the synrift, hemipelagic Allgäu Formation represented by bioturbated marlstones and limestones ('Fleckenmergel', up to 500 m thick). In marginal areas to the south (***Il'anovo succession***), originally close to the North Veporic Vel'ký Bok Unit, the Kopienec and Allgäu formations are replaced by swell facies of oolitic, crinoidal and nodular limestones (Hierlatz and Adnet formations). Nodular and marly limestones represent the entire Middle and Upper Jurassic. In the Zliechov succession, the Middle to Late Jurassic sediments reflect post-rift thermal subsidence. They are pelagic cherty and siliceous limestones, overlain by Oxfordian-age radiolarites (Ždiar Formation; Polák *et al.* 1998). During the Middle and Late Malm, siliceous, cherty and marly limestones were deposited in the axial zones of the Zliechov Basin (Jasenina and Osnica formations). The proportion of terrigenous clayey material increased during the Early Cretaceous (Mráznica and Párnica formations; e.g. Borza *et al.* 1980; Michalík *et al.* 1993*a*; Reháková 2000). Allodapic calciturbidite and slump breccia intercalations occur in several horizons (Michalík & Reháková 1995; Michalík *et al.* 1996). The Párnica Formation also includes numerous, though small bodies of submarine basanitic lavas (Hovorka & Spišiak 1988, 1993; Spišiak & Hovorka 1997) and olistostromes (Jablonský & Marschalko 1992). Sedimentation in all of the Krížna units terminated with the deposition of the mid-Cretaceous (Albian–Cenomanian), synorogenic, turbiditic Poruba Formation (Jablonský 1978). Following deposition of the Poruba Formation, in the Late Turonian, the main phase of nappe thrusting took place.

While the Zliechov succession builds up a substantial part of the Krížna Unit (the Krížna nappe *sensu stricto*), the ***Vysoká succession*** forms several smaller, partially independent subunits situated at the front and sole of the Krížna nappe *sensu stricto* (i.e. Vysoká, Beckov, Belá, Ďurčiná and Havran partial nappes). The Vysoká succession is characterized by the dominance of Jurassic sediments deposited in comparatively shallow water. Liassic strata are represented by bioclastic (crinoidal) and sandy cherty limestones, while the Dogger and Malm comprise massive crinoidal limestones (Vils Formation), as well as cherty, siliceous and nodular limestones (Koša 1998). The Lower Cretaceous deposits are similar to those of the Zliechov succession but allodapic limestones are more frequent, especially in the Barremian and Aptian (allodapic bioclastic limestones derived from adjacent Urgonian carbonate platforms; Michalík & Soták 1990; Michalík 1994*b*).

The third type of Fatric unit includes detached units containing mostly Lower Jurassic–Middle Cretaceous sedimentary successions, located in the Peri-Klippen Zone of the Pieniny Klippen Belt. These also include Upper Cretaceous, post-overthrust sedimentary sequences. The Drietoma, Manín, Klape and Haligovce units and, perhaps, some other 'non-Oravic' units of the Pieniny Klippen Belt belong to this subdivision.

The evolutionary tectonic model of the Krížna Unit (Plašienka & Prokešová 1996; Plašienka 1995*c*, 1999*b*, 2003*b*) assumes that the Zliechov partial unit (Krížna Nappe *sensu stricto*) was formed by underthrusting of an extensive basin floored by continental crust which had been strongly stretched and thinned during Early Jurassic rifting. The lithological variability of the cover in the Krížna Unit resulted in a mechanical stratification of the nappes. They contain three important décollement horizons: Upper Scythian, Keuper, and the base of the Poruba Formation. The first décollement horizon is the most important, since almost all of the nappes of the Krížna Unit were detached along it. The importance of the other two increases towards the frontal parts of the Krížna Unit. Cover units below the Upper Scythian décollement remained mostly attached to the underlying basement (Jaroš 1971). Massive Triassic carbonates form the relatively rigid basal part, and the well-bedded Jurassic to Lower Cretaceous sequences the incompetent middle part of the nappes. The uppermost Poruba Formation was the most incompetent; it is mostly absent in the rear and accumulated in the frontal parts of the nappes.

The structural evolution of the Fatric Superunit and the closely related, southerly adjacent Vel'ký Bok Unit (Veporic Superunit) is subdivided into several deformational stages, the first two of which occurred during the generation and emplacement of the Fatric Superunit. The Vel'ký Bok Unit (Fig. 18.33) displays complex structures formed under low- to very-low-grade metamorphic conditions (Plašienka 1995*c*, 2003*b*). The first stage involved the formation of bedding-parallel foliation, stretching lineation and flow folds in calcite-rich rocks. Macrostructures of this stage include large-scale recumbent to northward-plunging folds, all with top-to-the-north to NW kinematics. These structures originated at the northern tip of the Veporic Superunit overriding the underthrust Fatric basement. The second deformation stage involved the development of crenulation cleavage and upright folds during the collision of the Veporic Superunit with the northern, Tatric margin of the Zliechov Basin. In the Krížna Unit, these two stages are represented by compressional structures, such as intrastratal detachment zones, mesofolds, and imbricated duplexes formed during initial décollement and shortening of the Zliechov Basin fill. These contractional structures were passively transported during the gravitationally driven final emplacement of the Krížna Unit. Structures related to this gliding event are extensional and presumably formed synchronously with the second (shortening) deformation stage in the Vel'ký Bok Unit.

The inversion of the Zliechov Basin and the generation of the Krížna Unit occurred in mid-Cretaceous times. The Zliechov Basin was progressively shortened through underthrusting of its basement complexes below the Veporic thrust wedge (Plašienka 2003*b*). The sedimentary fill was detached along the lower décollement horizon and formed an initial fold-and-thrust stack prograding outwards. Simultaneously, deep-marine clastic prisms (Poruba Formation, Klape Unit) fed by rising hinterland units were deposited in piggyback basins as well as in the foreland (Tatric Superunit). Following the complete closure of the Zliechov Basin by southward underthrusting of its basement, the Tatric and Veporic basin margins collided and the detached Krížna Nappe *sensu stricto* was pushed over the frontal South Tatric ramp, from which the frontal Fatric elements (Vysoká- and Manín-type), with slope- and ridge-related sedimentary successions, were detached. In the late Turonian, the nappes of the Fatric Superunit moved northwards under the force of gravity from an uplifted area in the southern part of the Tatricum and over the basinal areas in the northern Tatricum. The Klape Unit, composed of a mid-Cretaceous deep-marine clastic complex, was the lowermost and most frontal sheet. Some frontal, mostly Manín- and Vysoká-type units, were emplaced above it as the second sheet. The Klape and Manín units glided furthest, and were emplaced on the (later-subducted) oceanic crust of the Vahic domain north of the Tatric Superunit. In the overlying main sheet, which is the Krížna nappe *sensu stricto* with its dominant basinal Zliechov succession, the emplacement event is recorded by extensional structures superimposed on older, compressional structures (Prokešová 1994). Finally, the frontal elements of the Veporic basement wedge overrode the southern Tatric basement and cover (the former northern margin of the Zliechov Basin), along with local imbricated basement duplexes detached from the original substratum of the Zliechov Basin (Plašienka 2003*b*).

### *Hronic Superunit*

The Hronic Superunit (or Hronicum) represents the structurally highest nappe system in the Tatra-Fatra Belt where it forms numerous nappe outliers resting on the Fatric units. Hronic units also occur in the northern part of the Malé Karpaty Mountains (Veterlín, Havranica, Jablonica and Nedzov nappes). Upper Austro-Alpine nappes in the Northern Calcareous Alps (Upper Bajuvaric and Tirolic units: Lunz, Göll and Ötscher nappes), and beneath the fill of the Vienna Basin, are analogous to the Hronicum. In the Northern Calcareous Alps, however, the typical Hronic member, the Upper Palaeozoic Ipoltica Group, is absent.

The Hronic Superunit is a large system of unmetamorphosed sedimentary cover nappes which originated in the southern zones of the Slovako-Carpathian system, i.e. on the northern passive margin of the Meliata Ocean. They were detached at the base of the Upper Palaeozoic detrital succession, but in the northern parts of the Central Western Carpathians the Triassic carbonate complex is detached along the horizon of Upper Scythian shales and marlstones. The nappes underwent exclusively brittle deformation and represent thin-skinned, décollement cover nappes. Originally, during the Cretaceous, they formed thin tabular bodies subhorizontally covering (probably) the entire Tatra-Fatra Belt. Internally, they are not very deformed, but the portions containing rigid reef bodies usually form independent partial nappes (e.g. the Strážov nappe; Kováč & Havrila 1998). Along the northern margin of the Central Western Carpathians, in the vicinity of the Pieniny Klippen Belt, the Hronic nappes were largely affected by superimposed transpressional and transtensional deformation together with their syn- to post-tectonic sedimentary cover (Gosau Supergroup).

The basal part of the Hronic nappe system in the southern zones of the Tatra-Fatra Belt is represented by the thick (several thousand metres) Upper Palaeozoic–Scythian Ipoltica Group.

The Upper Pennsylvanian Nižná Boca Formation consists of a regressive lacustrine-deltaic succession including sandstones, conglomerates, sandy shales, and dacitic volcaniclastics (50–500 m thick). The overlying, synrift, fluvial-lacustrine and alluvial Malužiná Formation includes extensive basaltic volcanism and probably represents the entire Permian. This unit is up to 2000 m thick. Synsedimentary basaltic and andesitic volcanics, forming extensive lava flows, were generated during two major eruption phases (Vozár 1997; Dostal *et al.* 2003). Chemically, the basalts represent continental tholeiites suggesting a continental rift environment. The Lower Triassic strata comprise Lower Scythian quartz sandstones and Upper Scythian shales and sandstones, alternating with marlstones and sandy limestones in the upper part.

The Middle Triassic succession is comparatively thick and includes a wide range of sedimentary facies, representing various parts of the shelf environment, from tidal flats and reef platforms up to pelagic intrashelf basins. There were several subsiding and elevated zones within the Hronic sedimentary area during the Middle Triassic (e.g. Dobrá Voda Basin, Nedzov-Strážov Platform, Biely Váh Basin, Čierny Váh Platform; Kováč & Havrila 1998), which were later inverted to create numerous partial units within the Hronic Superunit. The Anisian-age carbonate ramp (Gutenstein and Annaberg formations) with restricted platforms (Steinalm Formation) was partly destroyed during the Pelsonian rifting event. This event ultimately led to the formation of a series of subsiding pelagic basins (Reifling Formation; e.g. Masaryk *et al.* 1993) rimmed by carbonate clastic aprons where the sediments were derived from adjoining, reef-cored prograding platforms (e.g. Wetterstein Formation, up to 1000 m thick; Michalík *et al.* 1993*b*; Polák *et al.* 1996). During the middle Carnian, the intrashelf basins were completely filled with up to 600 m of shales and siliciclastic turbidites (Lunz Formation). In the Norian and Rhaetian, carbonate platform conditions were re-established (Hauptdolomit and Dachstein formations). Locally, Rhaetian fossiliferous limestones infilled channels in tidal flats.

Two successions have been distinguished within the Middle and Upper Triassic part of the Hronic Superunit: the Čierny Váh and the Biely Váh successions. The ***Čierny Váh succession*** is characterized by a predominance of ramp and platform carbonates, now mainly dolomites, while the ***Biely Váh succession*** is more diverse, with predominantly basinal facies from late Anisian to early Carnian and shallow-water facies during the late Carnian to Rhaetian. This latter succession represents the fill of intrashelf depressions which originated due to late Anisian rifting (Michalík 1994*a*), probably related to the opening of the Meliata Ocean. The Middle to Upper Triassic carbonate platform complexes attain a thickness of 2000–3000 m.

In Early Liassic times, a hiatus has been noted in the Hronic Superunit and this was followed by the deposition of the Upper Lias and Dogger successions which are partly condensed (e.g. Hierlatz, Adnet, Klaus and Vils formations). The Upper Jurassic stage is represented by pelagic basinal limestones (Oberalm Formation) with intercalations of allodapic calciturbidites (Barmstein Formation; Mišík & Sýkora 1982). During the Early Cretaceous, a pelagic marly and cherty limestone succession was deposited, and this was overlain by the Hauterivian siliciclastic turbiditic Schrambach and Rossfeld formations (Michalík *et al.* 1996). These are the youngest sediments in the Hronic Superunit.

The Hronic nappes are typical 'rootless' nappes with no connection to their original basement. Circumstantial evidence suggests that this basement corresponded to the Veporic or an analogous palaeogeographic zone. Nevertheless, structural studies suggest that the Hronic nappes were not derived from the presently exposed part of the Veporic basement nor from the Lubeník-Margecany Fault (Plašienka & Soták 2001).

*Silicic Superunit*

The Silicic Superunit (Silicicum) includes the structurally highest, unmetamorphosed nappes of the region. They are restricted to the Vepor-Gemer Belt of the Central Western Carpathians and the Slovak-Aggtelek Karst area at the boundary between the Central Western Carpathians and the Internal Western Carpathians (i.e. Drienok, Muráň, Vernár, Stratená and Silica-Aggtelek nappes, Szőlősardó and Bódva nappes in the Aggtelek Karst and Rudabánya Mountains of northern Hungary). Based on their lithostratigraphy, the Silicic nappes can be correlated with the Upper Tirolic and/or Juvavic nappes of the Northern Calcareous Alps. The palinspastic position of the Silicic Superunit is uncertain. The facies relationships support a proposed original position along the northern passive margin of the Meliata Ocean. However, the structural position of the Silicic Superunit at the top of the nappe stack would suggest an origin from the southern margin of the Meliata Ocean (see discussion in Frisch & Gawlick 2003; Mello 1997).

The Silicic units form internally little-deformed thrust nappes, detached at the basis of a thick Triassic carbonate platform complex, usually located along the Upper Permian–Lower Scythian evaporitic horizon. In places, however, slivers of Meliatic oceanic rocks were found at the base of the Silicic nappes, incorporated into evaporite mélanges (Réti 1985; Havrila & Ožvoldová 1996; Horváth 2000; Vojtko 2000). In the Slovak Karst and Slovenský raj (Stratenská hornatina, Galmus) areas, the Silicic nappes were dissected by later transpressional movements along deep-seated wrench faults (e.g. the Rožňava and Muráň faults; Mello 1997, 2000).

The Silicic units contain sedimentary complexes of Late Permian to Late Jurassic age and dominated by extensive Middle to Upper Triassic carbonate platforms. The soles of the Silicic nappes are formed by the Upper Permian, evaporite-bearing Perkupa Formation, overlain by Lower Triassic sandstones and shales (Bódvaszilas Formation) and marlstones to limestones (Szin Formation), with a total thickness of 400–800 m. Rhyolite volcanics occur in the latter formation in the northern parts of the Silicic nappe system. The Anisian carbonate ramp (Gutenstein Formation) and platform (Steinalm Formation) are *c.* 500–600 m thick and were partly destroyed by a marked Pelsonian rifting event, which led to the formation of intrashelf basins filled with hemipelagic nodular limestones and resedimented carbonates (Schreyeralm, Reifling, Nádaska, Raming formations). Carnian-age siliciclastic turbidites also occur locally (Lunz and Reingraben formations). Thin intercalations of altered tuffites are known from the Ladinian succession. However, thick Middle–Upper Triassic carbonate platform complexes with extensive, prograding, 1000–2000 m thick reef bodies surrounded by perireef bioclastic aprons (Steinalm, Wetterstein, Tisovec-Waxeneck, Furmanec formations) predominate in the Silicic units. Barrier reefs grade into backreef lagoonal flats (Dachstein, Hauptdolomit, Bleskový Prameň formations; e.g. Mello 1997, 2000). Toward the south (Slovak-Aggtelek Karst), Middle Triassic platform carbonates are overlain by Upper Triassic basinal and slope pelagic limestones and marlstones (Aflenz, Pötschen, Hallstatt, Zlambach formations). The southernmost units, presumably belonging to the Silicic system (Szőlősardó and Bódva nappes in northern Hungary), are already marked by the prevalence of pelagic facies already in the Middle Triassic (subsequent to the Pelsonian rift event), such as the Ladinian Hallstatt-type Bódvalenke limestone and cherts deposited near the CCD (Szárhegy Formation). This facies indicates an area of transition to the Meliata Ocean (e.g. Kovács 1992).

Following the earliest Jurassic hiatus, limestones of the Hierlatz and Adnet formations were deposited on basin highs on top of the Upper Triassic platform sediments. In basinal areas, hemipelagic sediments of the Allgäu Formation were deposited (Rakús 1996; Rakús & Sýkora 2001; Mello 1997). Middle to Late Jurassic subsidence led to the deposition of deep-water shales and radiolarites with some terrigenous input. In the Slovak Karst area, bodies of chaotic breccias (olistostromes) are also found (Sýkora & Ožvoldová 1996). The youngest dated sediments of the Silicic Superunit are Oxfordian radiolarites. The Jurassic members are, however, poorly preserved; their overall thickness is only several tens of metres. Shallow-water Upper Jurassic limestones are found as clasts in Senonian and Tertiary conglomerates.

Relicts of Senonian-age Gosau Group sediments, related to the Silicic nappes, occur in several locations (e.g. Poniky, Šumiac, Dobšiná Ice Cave, Gombasek, Miglinc), and are preserved along younger fault structures. They comprise freshwater limestones, conglomerates, rudist limestones, pelagic marlstones (Campanian) and the clayey infill of palaeokarst cavities (Mello 1997, 2000).

#### *Meliatic Superunit*

Tectonic units belonging to the Meliatic Superunit (Meliaticum) represent the structurally deepest elements of the Slovak Karst Mountains. Parts of the Meliaticum which were thrust northward over the Gemeric basement form the Jaklovce Unit (unmetamorphosed ophiolite mélange; Mock *et al.* 1998), and the low-temperature, high-pressure (12 kbar) metamorphosed Bôrka Unit. The latter is a transitional Gemeric–Meliatic element (Faryad 1995*a*, *b*, 1997, 1999; Mello *et al.* 1998). The Meliata Unit *sensu stricto*. (Jurassic deep-water clastic complexes with radiolarites, olistostromes, mélanges and ophiolitic bodies; Kozur & Mock 1973, 1995, 1997; Kozur 1991; Mello 1997; Mock *et al.* 1998) crops out in tectonic windows from below the Tornaic and Silicic nappes in the western parts of the Slovak Karst area (Figs 18.19, 18.29 & 18.34). The most distinctive feature of the Meliata Superunit is the presence of slivers and olistoliths of ophiolites, blueschists and Triassic sediments. These latter include Lower Anisian platform carbonates showing evidence of a Pelsonian unconformity, and Upper Anisian and younger pelagic deposits (Upper Anisian red cherty limestones, Ladinian and Upper Triassic radiolarites, Norian nodular limestones etc.).

The original assumption of a Triassic Meliata Ocean was based on these pelagic Triassic strata which were thought to represent a continuous stratigraphic succession. Although the olistolith character of the Triassic sediments was later recognized, they still provide evidence, along with other features, for the existence of a Triassic oceanic realm that persisted up to Late Jurassic times. Hence, the Meliata Ocean in the Western Carpathian realm is assumed to have existed from the Middle Triassic to the early Late Jurassic.

Based on sparse biostratigraphic data, the deformation of the Meliatic units occurred after the closure of the Meliatic Ocean. This occurred before the Kimmeridgian (Kozur 1991; Rakús 1996). Blueschist-facies metamorphic basalts from the base of the Meliatic accretionary complex (Bôrka Nappe), overridding the southern, Gemeric, margin of the Slovako-Carpathian system, yielded Late Jurassic ages for the high-pressure/low-temperature metamorphism (150–160 Ma, $^{40}Ar/^{39}Ar$ on phengites; Maluski *et al.* 1993; Dallmeyer *et al.* 1996; Faryad & Henjes-Kunst 1997).

### *Central Carpathian Palaeogene Basin*

The Central Carpathian Palaeogene Basin (= Podhale Basin in Poland) most likely originally covered the entire Tatra-Fatra Belt as well as much of the Vepor Sub-belt in the Eocene and Oligocene. However, in western Slovakia only erosional remnants of its sediments are preserved in small basins between the 'core mountains'. In northern and northeastern Slovakia, the basin sediments (Podtatra Group) are more widespread, 3000–5000 m thick and subdivided into four formations (e.g. Soták *et al.* 2001; Fig. 18.29). The basal, transgressive Borové Formation consists of carbonate conglomerates and nummulitic limestones, as well as extensive prisms of the Súl'ov dolomitic breccia in areas close to the Pieniny Klippen Belt. The age of the Borové Formation decreases from the north (Pieniny Klippen Belt) towards the south and from the west (Early to Middle Eocene in the Malé Karpaty Mountains) to the east (Late Eocene to Early Oligocene in the Levoča Mountains). This reflects the direction of the Eocene transgression. The overlying Huty Formation is composed of shales and distal turbidites, locally with conglomeratic slump bodies. The siliciclastic turbiditic Zuberec Formation forms much of the basin fill. Thick bodies of massive, amalgamated sandstones (Biely Potok Formation) form the highest member (Egerian).

The Senonian and Palaeogene basins (Gosau Supergroup basins, Central Carpathian Palaeogene Basin) in the northern part of the Central Western Carpathians originated in a forearc position at the outer edge of the Central Western Carpathians. Their subsidence may have been caused by tectonic erosion during subduction of the South Penninic (Vahic) Ocean and later of the North Penninic (Magura) Ocean (Wagreich 1995; Kázmér *et al.* 2003).

### *Palaeotectonic evolution of the Central Western Carpathians*

The Central Western Carpathians represent a complex tectonic system that evolved from Late Palaeozoic times onward. This evolution can be summarized as follows (Plašienka 1995*a*, 2003*a*; Fig. 18.22 & 18.23).

1. Late Carboniferous to Permian: collapse and erosion of the Variscan Orogen accompanied by the formation of several grabens filled with immature continental red-beds; alkaline to calc-alkaline rift-related volcanism and plutonism, persisting until the Early Triassic.
2. Triassic: period of gradual subsidence; marked Late Anisian rifting related to breakup of the Meliata Ocean.
3. Early to Middle Jurassic: rifting proceeding in three phases; destruction of the Triassic carbonate platform; subsequent thermal subsidence during Middle and Late Jurassic.
4. Late Jurassic: closure of the Meliata Ocean; formation of a collisional belt in the southern zones of the Central Western Carpathians.
5. Early Cretaceous: thrusting (Gemericum over Veporicum) in zones adjoining the Meliata suture; extension and subsidence in foreland zones.
6. Mid-Cretaceous: northward (in present-day co-ordinates) progradation of crustal shortening (Veporicum over Tatricum); detachment and emplacement of cover nappe systems (Fatricum and Hronicum).

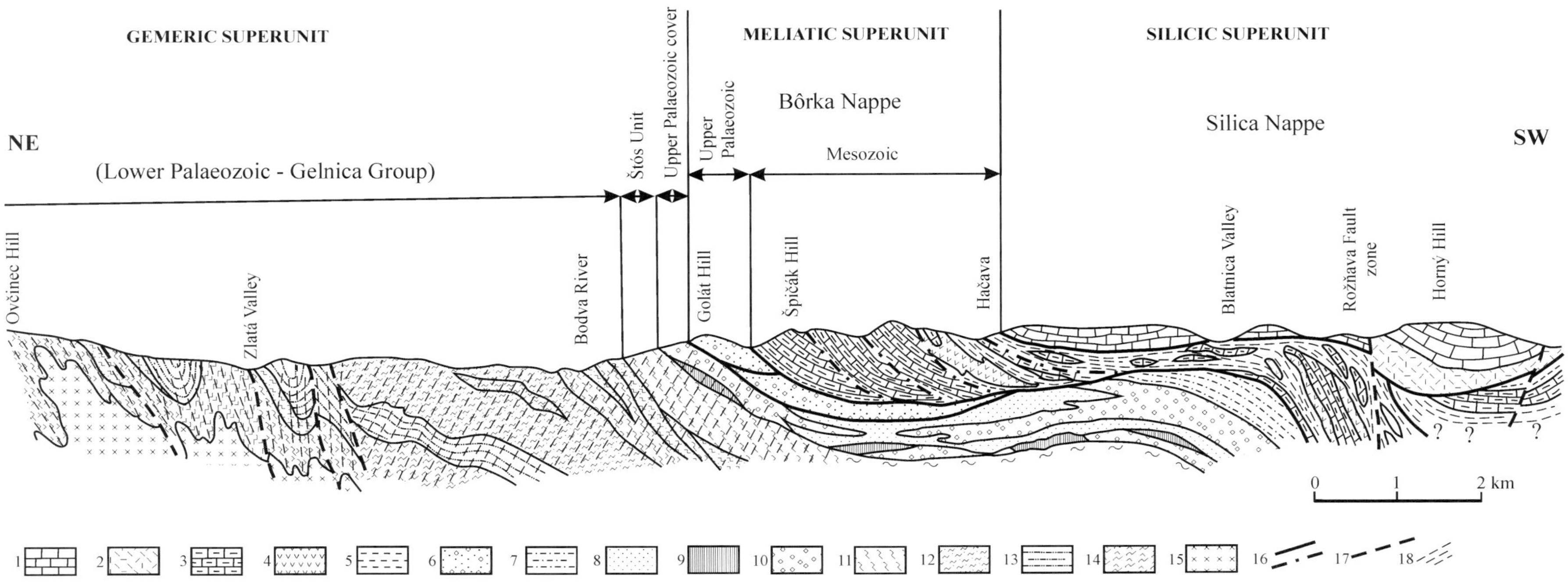


**Fig. 18.34.** Cross-section of the Slovak Karst Mountains and southern part of the Gemeric Superunit (modified after Reichwalder 1982). Note the cleavage fan in the Gemericum, imbrication in the Meliatic Bôrka Nappe and structural discordance at the base of the Silica Nappe above the steepened part of the Meliaticum within the Rožňava Fault Zone (suture?). Legend: Silica Nappe: 1, Triassic carbonates; 2, Scythian marls, shales and sandstones. Meliaticum: 3, crystalline limestone; 4, glaucophanized basalts; 5, phyllite, slates (Jurassic?); 6, metasandstones, metaconglomerate (Permian?). Gemericum, Permian cover: 7–10, conglomerates, sandstones, shales, rhyolites. Gemericum, Lower Palaeozoic metavolcanosedimentary complexes (Gelnica Group): 11–15, phyllites, metasandstones, porphyroids. Structures: 16, major overthrusts, 17, steep faults, 18, cleavage.

7. Senonian: extensional collapse of the southern zones of the Central Western Carpathians; exhumation of the Veporic metamorphic core complex; emplacement of the Silicic cover nappes.
8. Early Palaeogene: renewed shortening; sinistral transpression.
9. Eocene to Oligocene: extensional collapse of the northern zones of the Central Western Carpathians (Eocene) and subsidence of the Central Carpathian Palaeogene Basin.
10. Early Miocene: crustal shortening.
11. Middle Miocene: backarc extension leading to formation of the Pannonian Basin System and widespread calc-alkaline volcanism.
12. Late Miocene to Pliocene: gradual slowing of the rate of subsidence in the various basins of the region; uplift of 'core mountains'.

## *Internal Western Carpathians*

The term Inner (Mahel' 1986) or Internal Western Carpathians (Plašienka 1999*a*) is used for the units extending south of the inferred suture resulting from the closure of the Meliata Ocean. These units have many features in common with units of the Southern Alps and/or the Dinarides. The position of the suture of the Meliata Ocean plays a key role in the separation of the Internal Western Carpathians from the Central Western Carpathians. Since part of the Meliatic Superunit was emplaced on the Gemericum as a north-vergent nappe (Bôrka Unit), the main suture should be placed immediately south of the Gemericum. This area is designated the 'Rožňava Suture' (Rožňava-Šugov according to Kozur & Mock 1997). An almost identical structure was termed by Grecula (1973) the 'Carpathian-Pannonian Suture'. This author assumed that the Gemericum was expelled from it during the Alpine (Cretaceous) Orogeny; the Rožňava Fault Zone represents its surficial expression. The Rožňava Suture is, however, largely covered by the Tornaic and Silicic nappes in the Slovak Karst Mountains (Fig. 18.34) and covered by unconformably overlying Tertiary complexes elsewhere. The Rožňava Suture can be tentatively extended towards the west along the geophysically defined, deep-seated Plešivec, Diósjenő, Hurbanovo and Rába faults (Plašienka *et al.* 1997).

The Rožňava Suture marks the boundary between the Central and Inner Western Carpathians. The rock complexes within the Rožňava Suture are mainly composed of sheared-off slivers of oceanic sediments and dismembered ophiolites occurring within an ancient accretionary complex which separates crustal blocks of varying development, composition and structure. However, this boundary between the Central and Internal Western Carpathians is a conceptual one and cannot be drawn precisely, due to the many uncertainties in the exact position and lateral prolongation of the Meliatic Superunit and related units.

Regionally, the Internal Western Carpathians include the Slovak Karst Mountains and the north Hungarian mountains (i.e. Aggtelek, Rudabánya, Szendrő, Bükk, Uppony, Darnó, and Transdanubian Range), possibly also the Zemplínske Vrchy Mountains in SE Slovakia. The southern limits of the Internal Western Carpathians coincide with the Mid-Hungarian Lineament which separates them from the microcontinent Tisia (or Tisza-Dacia; Csontos 1995).

### *Pelso Megaunit*

The definition of the Internal Western Carpathians given above broadly corresponds to the original definition of the Pelso Megaunit by Fülöp *et al.* (1987). Subsequently, the 'Gemer-Bükk Unit' was also assigned to the Pelso Megaunit (e.g. Kovács 1992), and the entire megaunit was considered as a Tertiary block which was expelled, or escaped, from the Eastern Alps during collision and was welded to the Western Carpathians as late as the Oligocene–Lower Miocene. However, this interpretation does not conform with the observed surface structures of the Central Western Carpathians where a pre-Tertiary contact between the Veporicum and the Gemericum can be documented. Moreover, the northern boundary of the Pelso Megaunit (the Rába–Hurbanovo–Diósjenő Lineament) cannot, based on structural and palaeomagnetic investigations, be considered as a large-scale Tertiary sinistral strike-slip fault as would be expected if the Pelso Megaunit represented an escaping block. The Miocene escape included not only the Pelso Megaunit but also the Central Western Carpathians, i.e. the entire 'North Pannonian Unit' of Csontos *et al.* (1992), subsequently renamed the 'Alcapa' microcontinent (Csontos 1995; Fodor *et al.* 1999). These considerations support the idea of a Cretaceous-age welding of the Central Western Carpathians with the Pelso Megaunit, and suggest that the Pelso Megaunit is part of the Western Carpathians, a concept favoured here, despite the fact that the Central Western Carpathian (Slovako-Carpathian) units and the Pelso Megaunit were derived from very different Mesozoic palaeogeographic zones. A more recent definition of the Pelso Megaunit or 'Pelsonia Composite Terrane' by Kovács *et al.* (2000) includes only units occurring in Hungary, which implies a return, to some extent, to the original definition.

### *Tornaic Superunit*

The Tornaic Superunit (Tornaicum in the Hungarian, Turnaicum in the Slovak literature, South Rudabányaicum according to Kozur & Mock 1997) is defined as a rootless nappe system consisting of several partial units comprising sediments of Lower Pennsylvanian to Upper Triassic (probably up to Jurassic) age, overlying the Meliaticum and underlying the Silicicum (Mello 1997). In the western part of the Slovak Karst Mountains, it comprises the Slovenská skala Unit. The Turňa (Torna) Unit crops out from below the Silicicum in the Turňa Valley. In Hungary, the Tornaicum occurs mainly in the northern part of the Rudabánya Mountains (Mártonyi Unit; Fodor & Koroknai 2000; Less 2000). It has been suggested that Tornaic elements are present in the Alps, together with the Meliatic Florianikogel Unit (Kozur & Mostler 1992).

The stratigraphic succession of the Tornaicum includes the Bashkirian Turiec Formation (Vozárová & Vozár 1992), which is related to the Szendrő Phyllite Formation and the Hochwipfel Flysch of the Carnic Alps (e.g. Ebner 1992; Ebner *et al.* 2006). Permian continental sediments and Scythian clastics are overlain by Middle to Upper Triassic units. These are crucial for the definition of the Tornaicum and include Lower Anisian platform carbonates (mainly Steinalm Formation) and exclusively pelagic limestones from the Late Anisian on (= Žarnov, Nádaska, Reifling and Pötschen limestones). Carnian sediments, including shales, marlstones, sandstones and, locally, volcanics are also typical of the Tornaic Superunit.

The Tornaic Superunit displays a complex fold-and-thrust structure, forming a Jurassic accretionary complex together with the underlying Meliatic Superunit. Consequently, the boundaries between the Meliaticum and Tornaicum are sometimes uncertain. In most places, the Tornaicum shows evidence of low-grade, but relatively high-pressure metamorphism (about 7 kbar; Árkai & Kovács 1986).

*Bükk Superunit*
The Bükk Superunit (Bükkicum and Bükkium in the Slovak and Hungarian literature, respectively) comprises the eastern part of the Pelso Megaunit. It crops out in the Bükk, Uppony and Szendrö mountains. Some units in the Rudabánya Mountains probably also belong to the Bükk Superunit. Typically, the Bükk Superunit includes Palaeozoic and Triassic–Jurassic sedimentary and volcanic complexes which are lithologically similar to Dinaridic units and which underwent a low-grade Alpine, Cretaceous-aged metamorphism.

The structure of the Bükk Mountains is controversial. Csontos (1999, 2000) proposed that the Bükk Superunit consists of two fundamental units, the Bükk 'Parautochthon' and the Mónosbél-Szarvaskő nappe system (Mónosbél Unit and Szarvaskő Unit). This is the currently accepted model (albeit with some modifications).

The **Bükk Parautochthon** (Fennsíkum in terminology of Kozur & Mock 1997) consists of a Palaeozoic–Jurassic passive continental margin succession. The complexes of the Uppony Mountains and the 'North-Bükk Anticlinorium' include Silurian shales, Devonian–Lower Carboniferous platform carbonates, Middle Carboniferous deep-marine clastics, Lower Permian continental sediments, and Upper Permian and Lower Triassic shallow-water carbonates. Younger rocks, including Middle Triassic platform carbonates and calc-alkaline volcanics, Carnian clastics (Raibl Beds), and Upper Triassic platform carbonates only occur in the Bükk Mountains. Jurassic deep-water shales and radiolarites crop out in several synclines in the southern part of the Bükk Mountains.

The **Mónosbél Unit** and the **Szarvaskő Unit** are nappes (partly corresponding to the Bátor Nappe of Kozur 1991) and contain only Jurassic rocks: dismembered ophiolitic complexes, deep-water shales, radiolarites, and olistostromes with blocks of Triassic oceanic rocks. It is presumed that these south-vergent nappes were derived from a Jurassic backarc basin which formed to the north of the Bükk Parautochthon due to southward subduction of the Meliata Ocean (Balla *et al.* 1980, 1983; Kozur 1991). The nappes were thrust over the Bükk Parautochthon most likely during the Late Jurassic/Early Cretaceous.

There are no Cretaceous sediments in the entire area, with the exception of Gosau-type Senonian-age conglomerates in the Uppony Mountains. According to radiometric dating, the low-grade Alpine metamorphism in the Bükk Superunit is of Early Cretaceous age (Árkai *et al.* 1995). This metamorphism accompanied penetrative ductile deformation with several tight fold and cleavage sets. This deformation resulted in the overall south-vergent imbricated structure of the Bükk Mountains (Csontos 1999, 2000).

*Transdanubian Superunit*
The Transdanubian Superunit (= Transdanubicum or Bakonyicum) is a large tectonic complex occupying the western part of the Pelso Megaunit, and cropping out in the Transdanubian Range (Balaton Hills, Bakony Forest, Gerecse Mountains, Vértes Mountains, Buda Hills and Csővár Hills east of the Danube). Below the Tertiary cover, this superunit extends as far as the Hurbanovo-Diósjenő Fault to the north, the Rába Fault to the NW, and the Balaton Fault to the south. The superunit comprises weakly metamorphosed Lower Palaeozoic and unmetamorphosed Upper Palaeozoic and Mesozoic complexes overlain by Tertiary rocks. The Transdanubian Superunit is commonly considered to be analogous to the Upper Austro-Alpine nappe units, with facies links also to the South-Alpine realm (e.g. Tari 1995).

Palaeozoic rocks crop out locally near Lake Balaton and also occur below the Danube Basin in the vicinity of the Rába Fault. They consist of low-grade metamorphosed slates and phyllites with intercalations of metavolcanics and limestones. The age of the succession is Ordovician to Mississippian, the age of the metamorphism Variscan. In the Velence Mountains, late-Variscan granitoids also occur, showing a subalkaline geochemical trend. This succession is overlain by Pennsylvanian conglomerates.

The Upper Permian to Neocomian sediments represent a passive continental margin succession (e.g. Haas & Budai 1995, 1999; Császár & Haas 1984; Trunkó 1996; Haas *et al.* 2001). The Upper Permian sediments consist of terrestrial clastics and lagoonal evaporites, with marine dolomites occurring in the east. A general transgression at the Permian–Triassic boundary led to the deposition of shallow-marine carbonates followed by platform carbonates in the Middle Triassic. Anisian rifting resulted in the differentiation of the platform into subsiding intrashelf basins with Ladinian thin-bedded, cherty, sometimes bituminous limestones with thin tuffaceous 'Pietra Verde' intercalations (Buchenstein Formation), and elevated highs characterized by platform dolomites. The thickness of the Lower–Middle Triassic succession varies between 2000 and 2400 m.

Significant palaeogeographic changes occurred during the Late Triassic. The influx of fine-grained terrigenous material resulted in the deposition of Carnian marls which occur mainly above the basinal limestones, and are up to 800 m thick. In the Upper Carnian and Norian, almost the entire Transdanubian Range was the site of shallow-water carbonate platform sedimentation. The most widespread formation is the 1000–1500 m thick Hauptdolomit Formation. This is overlain by the Upper Triassic (Norian–Rhaetian) Dachstein Limestone Formation. In the eastern Csővár–Buda area, platform carbonates are replaced by basinal cherty limestones and dolomites. The total thickness of the Upper Triassic strata is up to 2000–2300 m.

The Triassic–Jurassic boundary is not reflected by a facies change within the Dachstein Limestone Formation. In the Jurassic, the sedimentary environments were differentiated into highs with comparatively thin, discontinuous and condensed lithofacies, and deeper-water areas with thicker, continuous successions showing less condensation.

Throughout the Liassic, nodular, cherty limestones, with interbedded Hierlatz Limestone and 'Ammonitico Rosso'-type limestones and marls (Adnet Formation) are found. Pelagic carbonate sedimentation continued up to the Middle Jurassic when it was replaced by siliceous marls and bedded radiolaritic cherts. Calcareous sediments reoccur in the Upper Jurassic ('Ammonitico Rosso'-type limestone and white pelagic cherty limestone and marls). The thickness of the Jurassic strata ranges from a few tens of metres up to 400–420 m. In the Bakony Mountains, the deposition of cherty limestones and marls was continuous from the Jurassic into the Lower Cretaceous. In contrast, the Lower Cretaceous strata in the Gerecse Mountains (northern part of the Transdanubian Range) represent a siliciclastic deep-marine succession including marls, turbiditic sandstones and conglomerates with ophiolitic detritus (e.g. Császár & Árgyelán 1994). Following the first Mesozoic phase of compressional deformation during the Albian, a new sedimentary cycle began with the deposition of freshwater and brackish marlstones, locally with bauxite lenses. Reef limestones (Zirc Formation) deposited on basin highs were overlain by shallow-marine marls extending up to the Cenomanian.

The surface structure of the Transdanubian Superunit appears to be rather simple and is dominated by a large syncline with some reverse faults along its flanks (e.g. the south-vergent Litér Thrust), which formed prior to the deposition of the Upper

Cretaceous sedimentary cover (Balla & Dudko 1993) and was overprinted by Tertiary transversal faults. However, according to Horváth (1993) and Tari (1995), the Transdanubian Superunit consists of nappes. The original thrust planes were reactivated during Miocene extension as low-angle normal faults (e.g. the Rába Fault). In contrast, other authors have interpreted the Rába Fault as a deep-reaching, steep crustal boundary of strike-slip character (Balla 1994). The Transdanubian Superunit, though influenced by Palaeogene back-thrusts and Neogene transtensional tectonics, represented a comparatively rigid block within the Pannonian Basin system.

*Zemplín Unit*

The Zemplín Unit is represented by pre-Tertiary strata of the Zemplín Mountains (southern part of the Neogene East Slovakian Basin, Fig. 18.19). The precise position of this unit is controversial, with some authors suggesting that it belongs to the Veporic Superunit while others derive it from Tisia (Tizia). The Zemplin Unit consists of high-grade crystalline basement of probably Variscan age, overlain by thick post-Variscan complexes including Pennsylvanian coal-bearing strata, Permian to Scythian continental sediments, and minor Middle Triassic carbonates. Along its NE boundary, the Zemplin Unit has a subsurface contact either with the Ptrukša Zone (= possible continuation of the Fatric Superunit), or directly with the Iňačovce-Krichevo Unit (Vozár *et al.* 1998).

## *Senonian to Lower Miocene complexes of the Internal Western Carpathians*

Large areas covered by Senonian-age, Gosau-type sediments occur in the western part of the Transdanubian Range (Bakony Mountains). These represent a new sedimentary cycle which began following Albian deformation and the Late Cenomanian–Late Santonian hiatus. The Senonian succession is more than 1000 m thick and commences with bauxites and terrestrial clastics with fluvial, limnic and paralic coal measures. Overlying marls are found in the basin lows while rudist-bearing platform limestones developed on basin highs. In the latest Cretaceous, the platforms were buried by pelagic pelitic-carbonatic sediments.

The **North Hungarian–South Slovakian Palaeogene–Lower Miocene Basin (Buda Basin)** had an elongate, SW–NE orientated shape. Palaeogene deposition began in the southern Bakony area with continental bauxite deposits during the Palaeocene to Early Eocene. The bauxites were overlain by Upper Eocene neritic nummulitic limestones and marls. In northern parts of the basin, coeval coal measures were deposited. Upper Eocene andesites occur near Recsk.

In most parts of the Transdanubian Range, Eocene sedimentation was followed by an erosional event ('infra-Oligocene denudation'). In the western part of the area, eroded Eocene rocks are unconformably overlain by brackish and freshwater Upper Oligocene deposits. The Oligocene transgression reached this area in the Late Kiscellian. Initially, coal beds were deposited, and these were overlain by littoral sandstones and subsequently by deep-water clays. During the Egerian, deep-water deposition continued (marls, calcareous siltstones and sandstones up to 700 m thick). Late Eggerian uplift and regression are recorded by prograding delta fans. During the Eggenburgian (Early Burdigalian), a new sedimentary cycle began in a sub-basin which was located further to the east (Fil'akovo-Pétervásara Partial Basin). This was a short-lived sub-basin filled with shallow-marine sandstones that ended with terrestrial clastics, uplift and erosion during the Late Eggenburgian. This uplift was associated with the first widespread evidence of explosive rhyolitic volcanism in the Pannonian area which recorded the onset of backarc lithospheric extension, asthenospheric upwelling and crustal melting. During the Ottnangian the deposition of coal measures was widespread, while basinal marls were again deposited during the Karpatian (Novohrad-Nógrád Partial Basin). Sedimentation was terminated in the Early Badenian (Langhian) due to regional uplift and erosion of the underlying strata. This was followed by rifting of the Pannonian Basin System and widespread andesitic volcanism.

## *Palaeotectonic evolution of the Internal Western Carpathians*

As shown in Figures 18.22 and 18.23, the tectonic history of Internal Western Carpathians can be summarized as follows.

1. Early Palaeozoic to Mississippian: Internal Western Carpathians located in the external and foreland zones of the Variscan Orogen.
2. Pennsylvanian: marine transgression; Permian to Scythian: shallow sea.
3. Triassic: gradual subsidence; marked Upper Anisian (Pelsonian) rifting event related to the breakup of the Meliata Ocean.
4. Early to Middle Jurassic: rifting; destruction of the Triassic carbonate platform.
5. Upper Jurassic: closure of the Meliata Ocean; formation of a collisional belt.
6. Early Cretaceous: backthrusting in the Bükk Superunit; deposition of synorogenic deep-marine clastics with input from obducted ophiolites in the NW part of the Transdanubian Superunit, probably adjoining the suture of the Meliata Ocean.
7. Mid-Cretaceous: southward (in present-day co-ordinates) thrusting in the Transdanubian Superunit.
8. Senonian: extension and shallow-marine deposition (Gosau Supergroup).
9. Eocene to Early Miocene: formation and subsidence of the Buda Basin.
10. Middle to Late Miocene: backarc extension (Pannonian Basin System) and widespread calc-alkaline volcanism.

## *Pannonian Basin System and Neogene volcanics*

During Miocene times, there was thrusting in the External Western Carpathians, the Central and Internal Western Carpathians were largely influenced by lithospheric stretching, basin formation and volcanism (see reviews by Kováč *et al.* 1997, 1998; Kováč 2000). These processes resulted in the formation of the Pannonian Basin System, including, among others, the Danube Basin and the Transcarpathian Basin. The Vienna Basin is also part of the Pannonian Basin System but occupies a slightly different position, partly covering the External Western Carpathians.

Remnants of Lower Miocene (dominantly Eggenburgian) sediments are found in the northern parts of the present Vienna and Danube basins, where they were deposited in a transpressional, wrench-fault dominated setting. The lozenge-shaped **Vienna Basin** is a pull-apart basin formed by late Early Miocene (Karpatian) sinistral wrenching along the Mur-Mürz-Leitha-Láb-Dobrá Voda Fault System trending SW–NE. The basin subsided during the Middle–Upper Miocene and in Pliocene–Quaternary times.

Large basins within the Central and Internal Western Carpathians include the Danube Basin and the Transcarpathian Basin. The **Danube Basin** formed during the Middle–Late Miocene by NW–SE extension, accommodated by NE–SW to NNE–SSW striking listric normal faults and detachment faults. The detachment faults partly reactivated Cretaceous-age thrusts (e.g. Horváth 1993).

The **Transcarpathian Basin** to the east had a complicated history. Lower Miocene (Eggenburgian) basinal sediments found in the NW part of the basin were deposited in a remnant forearc compressional depression, while the Transcarpathian Basin itself was formed as a result of Karpatian–Early Badenian dextral transtension along NW–SE orientated oblique-slip faults. Transtension was followed by general extension during the Late Badenian to Sarmatian, accompanied by extensive volcanism. Compressional inversion characterizes the basin evolution during the Pliocene.

Several smaller intramontane Neogene basins are restricted to western and central Slovakia, located between the 'core mountains' of the Fatra-Tatra Belt. Their evolution was controlled by block rotation, tilting and the uplift of adjacent highs.

Tertiary volcanics related to subduction in the External Western Carpathians and to backarc extension connected with asthenospheric updoming, are mainly found in the Internal and Central Western Carpathians, and more rarely in the External Western Carpathians. These calc-alkaline and alkaline volcanics include basaltic, intermediate and acidic lavas, subvolcanic complexes, and pyroclastic rocks of Neogene to Pleistocene age. Based on their age, spatial distribution and geochemical/petrological character, four stages of volcanism can be distinguished (Konečný & Lexa 1984; Konečný *et al.* 2002; Lexa & Konečný 1998). These are:

(1) *Areally extensive dacitic to rhyolitic volcanism* (Eggenburgian–Early Badenian). This stage involved the widespread deposition of tuffs and ignimbrites and the formation of extrusive domes in the source areas. Thickness varies from tens to hundreds of metres, exceeding 1000 m in the central part of the Pannonian Basin System. The rocks were derived from crustal anatectic melts that originated due to overheating of the continental crust as a result of mantle updoming in an extensional regime.

(2) *Areally extensive andesitic volcanism* (Early Badenian–Early Pannonian). Products of this stage are most widespread. Several stratovolcanoes formed which exhibit alternating effusive and extrusive activity. Additional stratovolcanoes are buried below the younger sediments of the Danube Basin. This stage commenced during the Early Badenian in the west and NW part of the Pannonian Basin System. In the Central Slovakian volcanic area (Fig. 18.29) it continued intermittently through to the Early Pannonian. Pyroxene-amphibole andesites (sometimes with garnet) and their pyroclastic products are dominant. Beginning in the Sarmatian, acidic volcanic rocks of rhyolite to rhyodacite composition also occur. This calc-alkaline, mainly intermediate magmatism represents mantle-derived melts that were significantly contaminated by crustal material. Magmatic activity can be genetically related to asthenosphere upwelling and lithospheric stretching due to the subduction of the oceanic basement of the Magura Zone (External Western Carpathians) beneath the continental Tatric-Veporic plate margin.

(3) *Arc-type andesitic volcanism* (Late Badenian–Sarmatian). Rare products of this stage are found along the Pieniny Klippen Belt (Horné Sŕnie, Pieniny Andesite Line in Poland). In Moravia they are also found in the Carpathian Flysch Belt (Uherský Brod). More significant occurrences are in eastern Slovakia (Slanské vrchy Mountains, Vihorlat Mountains) where they form a chain of stratovolcanoes continuing into the Ukraine and Romania. Basaltic and pyroxene andesites (with trachybasalts) originated due to the subduction of the Silesian-Krosno-Moldavian oceanic crust of the External Western Carpathians.

(4) *Post-orogenic alkaline-basaltic to basanitic volcanism* (Pannonian–Pleistocene). This stage is represented by relatively small occurrences of basaltic volcanics and involved the formation of diatremes, maars, scoria cones and lava flows. This type of volcanic activity began in the west (SE part of Austria) during the Pannonian and extended through the Danube Basin and the Transdanubian Range as far as the South Slovakian–North Hungarian Basin. Lava flows and a scoria cone overlying the Hron river terrace near Nová Baňa appear to be the youngest products of this stage of volcanic activity (Šimon & Halouzka 1996). Their age was determined as *c.* 100 ka (Šimon & Maglay 2005). The volcanics are interpreted as the products of post-orogenic extension which was characterized by asthenospheric mantle updoming and the ascent of basaltic magmas through fault-weakened zones of the thinned crust.

## *Permian and Triassic tectonics of the Western Carpathians*

The Variscan Orogeny in Central Europe terminated in a phase of gravitational collapse associated with rifting and extensive magmatism (regional **Betliar Phase**, see Figs 18.22 & 18.23a). Thus, the Early Mesozoic rifting was preceded by significant extensional tectonic events during the Permian (Vozárová & Vozár 1988; see also McCann 2008*b*). A particularly thick, rift-related, continental succession (Ipoltica Group) forms the sole of the Hronic cover nappe system. In this succession, the Permian continental sediments are associated with voluminous calc-alkaline to continental tholeiitic, andesitic and basaltic volcanism, which erupted in two distinct phases during the Early and Late Permian (Vozárová & Vozár 1988; Vozár 1997; Dostal *et al.* 2003). The original palaeogeographic position of this mature rift sequence is not precisely known. Other deep, but comparatively narrow Permian rift basins filled with immature continental clastics originated in the North Tatric, Veporic and Gemeric zones. Their formation was usually accompanied by calc-alkaline and/or subalkaline volcanism and A-type (Uher & Broska 1996, Broska & Uher 2001) as well as specific S-type (Poller *et al.* 2002) granitic plutonism. This rift-related silicic magmatism probably extended up into the Middle Triassic (*c.* 240 Ma; Kotov *et al.* 1996; Putiš *et al.* 2000; Uher & Broska 2000). The site of the future Meliata oceanic rift was characterized by strong Scythian subsidence and shallow-marine terrigenous sedimentation accompanied by alkaline rhyolitic volcanism (Uher *et al.* 2002). These features indicate that the terminal Variscan events (i.e. orogenic collapse and lithospheric attenuation) could have been genetically related to the early Alpine rifting in the southern zones of the Central Western Carpathians, which ultimately led to the opening of the Meliata Ocean.

At *c.* 240 Ma (Upper Anisian) the breakup of the Meliata Ocean occurred (Kozur 1991). This ocean formed probably as a backarc basin related to the northward subduction of Palaeotethys under the Eurasian continent (e.g. Stampfli 1996). Middle Triassic rifting was accompanied by widespread calc-alkaline volcanism in the Internal Western Carpathian zones (Buchenstein Formation in the Transdanubian and Bükk superunits). In contrast, the axial zones of the Meliatic superunit were marked by backarc-basin- and mid-ocean-ridge-type basalts (Ivan 2002).

The oldest deep-sea sediments, radiolarites, are of Ladinian age (Mock *et al.* 1998).

The Upper Anisian (Pelsonian) rifting and initial opening of the Meliata Ocean is termed the **Žarnov Phase** (Figs 18.22 & 18.23a). In the areas adjacent to the Meliaticum, this event was recorded by a breakup unconformity between the Lower Anisian ramp and platform carbonates and Pelsonian pelagic limestones. The younger Triassic pelagic facies include deep-water, partially condensed nodular limestones and Ladinian–Norian radiolarites. In more northern Slovako-Carpathian superunits (Tatricum, Fatricum) the evidence of Anisian rifting is much weaker, although slumps, tempestites and tsunamites occur within the carbonate ramp or platform complexes (e.g. Michalík 1997).

## *Jurassic tectonics*

The regional geodynamic situation changed considerably by the earliest Jurassic. The broad northern shelf of the Meliata Ocean underwent widespread rifting and, contemporaneously, subduction of Meliata oceanic lithosphere commenced. Most probably these processes were related to a change in the large plate movement kinematics (i.e. the beginning of southeastward drift of Africa and Adria relative to Europe during the opening of the Central Atlantic). The Western Carpathian orogenic wedge began to form by accretion of material scraped off from the subducted Meliata lithosphere to the tip of the upper plate. Thus the Jurassic period represents a nascent stage of the Western Carpathian orogenic wedge growth. Based on the timing of marked changes in the bathymetric evolution and on the character and distribution of syn- and post-rift sedimentary sequences, four main Jurassic–Cretaceous rifting phases can be identified within the Western Carpathian area (Plašienka 2003*a*): two Early Jurassic rifting phases resulting from lithospheric stretching and leading to the fragmentation of the Triassic platform (Zliechov Phase and Devin Phase); one rifting phase that led to the breakup of the South Penninic-Vahic Ocean in the late Middle Jurassic (Krasín Phase); and one rifting phase resulting in the breakup of the North Penninic-Magura Ocean in the Early Cretaceous (Walentowa Phase).

The Hettangian–Sinemurian-age **Zliechov Phase** of the 'wide rift' type is well recorded especially in the Tatric, Fatric and Hronic domains (Figs 18.22 & 18.23a). It involved overall uniform stretching of the continental lithosphere and resulted in the formation of broad subsiding intracontinental basins (Zliechov, Šiprúň, Kysuca-Czorsztyn-Magura), which were separated by subaerial highs (i.e. South Tatric and North Tatric ridges). For *c.* 100 Ma following the Zliechov Phase, sediment-starved basins within the Tatricum (Šiprúň Basin) and the Fatricum (Zliechov Basin) were subjected to slow thermal subsidence with accompanying deep-water pelagic sedimentation.

The Toarcian-age **Devín Phase** was more localized in terms of its effects. The area of the North Tatric Ridge (partly analogous to the Lungau Swell of Tollmann 1977) underwent Lower Jurassic uplift and erosion of the pre-rift Triassic successions, so that Upper Liassic–Lower Dogger clastic limestones were deposited on deeply eroded Triassic strata or on pre-Alpine basement complexes (Michalík *et al.* 1993*c*; Plašienka 1999*a*). The Devín Phase was probably also the main stage of extensional block tilting as indicated by the increasing contrast between the hemipelagic, partly anoxic sedimentation in the half-grabens (Allgäu Formation) and the deposition of 'Ammonitico Rosso'-type limestones (Adnet Formation) in well-aerated environments on the elevated edges of the tilted fault blocks (Soták & Plašienka 1996; Wieczorek 2000, 2001).

The Bajocian-age **Krasín Phase** strongly affected areas to the north of the North Tatric Ridge. Simple shear extension along a lithospheric detachment fault dipping towards the NW resulted in additional stretching in the Kysuca Basin and the late Bajocian to early Bathonian breakup and opening of the Vahic (South Penninic) Ocean (Plašienka 2003*a*). The breakaway fault of the detachment was the bounding fault of the Infra-Tatric Borinka half-graben (Malé Karpaty Mountains) where exceptionally thick Middle Jurassic scarp breccias were deposited (Somár Formation; Plašienka 1987). These were derived from the North Tatric Ridge which at that time formed the lower plate. The Czorsztyn Ridge formed at this time (e.g. Aubrecht & Szulc 2006), probably as a result of thinning of the lithosphere under the distal upper-plate margin by the detachment fault. Coeval subsidence of the basinal areas (i.e. Magura, Vahic, Šiprúň, Zliechov) to abyssal depths below the CCD is indicated by widespread deposition of radiolarites from Callovian through to Kimmeridgian times.

Collision between the Slovako-Carpathian continental margin and the Pelso Megaunit, following the closure of the Meliata Ocean, commenced during the late Middle Jurassic. Subsequently, the Slovako-Carpathian margin was overridden by the Meliatic accretionary complex in the Late Jurassic (**Šugov Phase**). Subsequently, the Gemeric Superunit was stacked over the Veporic Superunit (**Tuhár Phase**). An extensional tectonic regime and low-energy pelagic sedimentation still prevailed in the foreland of the convergent system (Figs 18.22 & 18.23a, b).

## *Cretaceous tectonics*

The Berriasian–Hauterivian **Walentowa Phase** represents the migration of rifting into the foreland area and is interpreted as recording the breakup of the Magura Ocean. This breakup was preceded by asymmetric rifting. Unlike the Krasín Phase, the detachment fault in this case dipped to the SE (Plašienka 2003*a*). Lithospheric extension and mantle upwelling triggered the second uplift event of the upper plate (Czorsztyn Ridge), which was manifested through the shallowing of depositional environments and the deposition of synrift debris flows and carbonate scarp breccias (Walentowa Breccia; Birkenmajer 1977; Krobicki & Słomka 1999). This was followed by widespread uplift, karstification, erosion and non-deposition extending into Albian times (Aubrecht *et al.* 2006). The Tatricum and Fatricum (including the basin highs) were characterized by generally uniform pelagic sedimentation during the Neocomian, interrupted by occasional incursions of turbidites (Michalík *et al.* 1996).

Marked subsidence of the Magura Basin to abyssal depths following the Walentowa Phase and the breakup of the Magura Ocean is evidenced by the presence of hemipelagic and turbiditic sedimentation commonly below the CCD, beginning in the Barremian and continuing throughout the Cretaceous. The Walentowa Phase was also accompanied, and followed, by submarine extrusion of primitive, mantle-derived alkaline basalts. This magmatic activity commenced in the Berriasian and continued up into the Lower Albian. Volcanic products occur in the Fatric Superunit, Tatric Superunit and the Silesian-Krosno units (e.g. Spišiak & Hovorka 1997; Lucińska-Anczkiewicz *et al.* 2002; Dostál & Owen 1998).

The above-noted extensional tectonic phases were followed by the **Solírov Phase** (Barremian–Early Albian) which is marked by the growth of the Urgonian carbonate platforms on the former South-Tatric Ridge and by syntectonic sedimentation around the North Tatric Ridge (calciturbiditic Solírov Formation; Jablonský *et al.* 1993). Following the Solírov Phase, in the Middle Albian, synorogenic, coarsening-upward deep-marine clastic sedimentation commenced in the Fatric and Tatric domains (Poruba Formation). These mid-Cretaceous successions are interpreted as reflecting underthrusting of the Fatricum beneath the northern part of the Veporicum (**Benkovo Phase**; Figs 18.22 & 18.23b). This epoch ended with the emplacement of extensive Fatric and Hronic cover nappes on the Tatricum (**Donovaly Phase**).

Changes in both the kinematics and dynamics of tectonic activity in the western Tethyan realm during the Late Cretaceous were related to changing relative motions of large plates, particularly the onset of convergence between Africa-Adria and Europe (e.g. Dewey *et al.*, 1989; Savostin *et al.* 1986). The advance of the Adriatic indenter, represented by the Pelso Megaunit, led to shortening and modification of the central, thermally-weakened parts of the original collisional wedge and triggered transpressional exhumation of the Veporic metamorphic dome in the Senonian (**Kohút Phase**). In upper structural levels, this exhumation was achieved by orogen-parallel, extensional unroofing (Plašienka *et al.* 1999; Janák *et al.* 2001). At the same time, the compressional stresses were transmitted from the indenter towards the front of the rigid Tatricum where subduction of the Vahic Ocean lithosphere commenced (**Selec Phase**; Figs. 18.22 & 18.23c). Moreover, the contractional regime affected the entire Alpine-Carpathian foreland with far-field effects extending into the distant interior of the North European Platform, where it initiated transpressional inversion of basins (see Reicherter *et al.* 2008).

### *Tertiary tectonics*

Late Cretaceous lateral extension reduced the angle of taper of the Western Carpathian orogenic wedge. Consequently, the collision of the wedge tip with the Oravic continental fragment generated a strong contraction event within the wedge (Maastrichtian–Danian **Jarmuta Phase**; Figs 18.22 & 18.23c). Similarly, the gravitational collapse of the wedge during the Eocene (**Súl'ov Phase**, formation of the Central Carpathian Palaeogene Basin) was replaced by compression during the Late Oligocene–Early Miocene collision of the External Carpathian accretionary wedge with the North European Platform (**Beskydy Phase**). This compressional event migrated backward into the entire wedge (**Kamenica Phase**).

During the final Middle–Late Miocene tectonic phases, the roll-back rate of the subduction zone of oceanic domains of the External Western Carpathians (first Magura, then Silesian-Krosno and Moldavian) exceeded the rate of advance of the indenter. Consequently, the convergent system changed from advancing to retreating (Royden 1993). As a result, the Western Carpathian orogenic system began to be governed by a general extensional regime (**Alföld Phase**). The compressional regime persisted only in the most easterly areas. There, the wedge continued to grow by frontal accretion of sedimentary units scraped off the subducting Moldavian lithosphere and the passive margin of the North European Platform.

### *Present-day crustal structure and neotectonics*

The present knowledge about the deep structure of the Western Carpathians is based on an extensive database of geophysical measurements. The structure of the Western Carpathian lithosphere and crust has been investigated using a wide range of geophysical methods, including seismic refraction and reflection profiling, seismology, gravimetry, magnetotellurics, geothermics and magnetometrics. The section is largely based on the review papers of Bielik & Šefara (2002) and Bielik *et al.* (2004), which summarize the results of various geophysical studies.

The complicated structure of the Western Carpathians resulted from the interference of the pre-Alpine, early Alpine and, predominantly, the late Alpine deep-seated tectonic activity. The fundamental role of the youngest lithosphere-scale collisional processes associated with the formation of the backarc Pannonian Basin System has been emphasized by many authors (e.g. Lillie *et al.* 1994; Lenkey 1999; Kováč 2000). Geophysical studies in this region have clearly shown that tectonic units differing in thermotectonic age, lithologic/rheologic stratification and crustal thickness produce important variations in the structure and geodynamics of the lithosphere (Horváth 1993; Lillie *et al.* 1994; Šefara *et al.* 1996; Lenkey 1999; Bada 1999; Szafián 1999).

### *The Western Carpathian lithosphere*

Recent estimates of the lithosphere thickness in the Carpathians have been made by Zeyen *et al.* (2002) using integrated lithosphere modelling. They presented 2D numerical models based on a combined interpretation of heat flow, gravity data and absolute topographic elevation. Unlike older models, this integrated modelling shows important differences in lithosphere thickness along the strike of the Western Carpathian Orogen. In contrast to the western part of the orogen, the lithosphere increases in thickness to a maximum of 140–150 km beneath the central and eastern parts of the Western Carpathians. To explain this lithospheric root, Zeyen *et al.* (2002) suggested that during the relatively short time following collision and slab break-off, convergence continued and resulted in lithospheric thickening of *c.* 40 km over a period of 2–4 Ma assuming a convergence rate of 1–2 cm/a.

Based on the results of this integrated modelling, critical analysis of earlier models and new interpolation of older data, the approximation of the lithosphere thickness in the Carpathian region was modified. The estimated total error of lithosphere thickness is not greater than 20 km. The hinterland of the Western Carpathians in the backarc Pannonian Basin System is characterized by a thin lithosphere. Based on the seismic and magnetotelluric surveys, the lithosphere may be as thin as 40–60 km beneath some of the sub-basins of the Pannonian Basin System (Posgay *et al.* 1995; Ádám *et al.* 1996). It has been suggested that stretching of the plate and asthenospheric mantle updoming caused this extreme lithospheric thinning (e.g. Bielik 1988; Lillie *et al.* 1994; Kováč 2000; Konečný *et al.* 2002).

The surface heat flow density in the Pannonian Basin System is one of the highest terrestrial heat flows measured. Additionally, a very strong blanketing effect was determined (up to 32%) in the central part of the basin system (Lenkey 1999), which emphasizes its temperature abnormality. The high present-day heat flow in this region may be attributed to the phase of Early–Middle Miocene lithospheric extension (Royden *et al.* 1983*a*, *b*). Thus, the areas characterized by high heat flow are underlain by a thin lithosphere.

The Carpathian–Pannonian area represents one of the key areas for studying the influences of various mechanical parameters on lithospheric rheology since it is possible to simultaneously observe several thermotectonic regimes in a relatively small area. Results of pioneering studies dealing with the prediction of lithospheric rheological behaviour in the Western Carpathians and in the surrounding tectonic units have been presented by Lankreijer *et al.* (1999) and Bielik *et al.* (2000). These indicate a general decrease in the mechanical strength of the lithosphere beneath the Western Carpathians from north to south. The effective elastic thickness varies between 15 and 23 km. In comparison with the older European platform, the rheological strength of the lower crust is strongly reduced in the Western Carpathians. This is a consequence of the increased temperature of the crust. The lithosphere strength further decreases and eventually completely disappears in the Pannonian Basin System.

The Bohemian Massif represents a mechanically rigid block extending down to a depth of *c.* 60 km. The predicted effective elastic thickness values for this region are 20–40 km. Based on this result, Lankreijer *et al.* (1999) assumed that, as a consequence of the high strength, that the Bohemian Massif blocked the northward movement of the colliding Alpine region. This was, possibly, the main reason for the Miocene-age sinistral strike-slip movement in a NE–SW direction in the Eastern Alps and its continuation into the Western Carpathians (Mur-Mürz-Leitha-Láb-Dobrá Voda Fault Zone). The result of this process was the opening of the Vienna Basin at the East Alpine–Western Carpathian junction by a pull-apart mechanism during the Karpatian (17.5–16.4 Ma).

The Pannonian Basin System, including the Danube and East Slovakian Basins, is characterized by only one, relatively thin rigid layer located in the uppermost 10 km of the crust. Thus, there is no strength in the lower crust or lithosphere in this region. The extreme flexibility of the Pannonian lithosphere is a direct result of the high values of heat flow and the very shallow and warm asthenosphere. The predicted effective elastic thickness is only 0–10 km. The calculations of Lankreijer (1998) also indicate that the peripheral parts of the Pannonian Basin are, at present, more resistant to deformation than the central depressions, which suggests that the effective elastic thickness decreases from the margins to the central part of the Pannonian Basin System.

The rheological prediction that only a thin layer of upper crust carries most of the strength of the lithosphere in the Carpathian–Pannonian area is in good agreement with the earthquake hypocentres which occur only to a depth of 15–17 km (e.g. Kováč *et al.* 2002).

## *The Western Carpathian crust*

The crust of the Western Carpathians and neighbouring areas has a complicated structure and is composed of fragments formed during the Variscan, palaeo-Alpine and neo-Alpine orogenic events. The accretionary wedge of the External Western Carpathians originated in the Tertiary. The Central and Internal Western Carpathians are composed of tectonic units that originated during the palaeo-Alpine Orogeny in the Mesozoic. The main, crustal-scale Alpine tectonic units of the Central Western Carpathians (Tatric, Veporic and Gemeric superunits) consist of pre-Alpine crystalline basement and its Upper Palaeozoic–Mesozoic cover. The tectonic units of the Variscan Orogeny form the crystalline basement.

The crustal thickness varies considerably across the Western Carpathians. Initial data on the regional Moho depth were based on deep seismic surveys. However, these incorporate large uncertainties. A more accurate determination of the Moho depth in the Western Carpathians and Bohemian Massif was achieved by the common depth point method (e.g. Tomek *et al.* 1987, 1989; Tomek & Hall 1993).

Crustal thickness (Moho depth) clearly tends to increase from west to east along the Carpathian Orogen. The Western Carpathians are characterized by crustal thicknesses of *c.* 30–35 km, while in regions influenced by Tertiary extension such as the Pannonian Basin System the Moho rises up to *c.* 25 km depth.

The present-day internal crustal structure of the Western Carpathians is a complex combination of structures originated during the Variscan and Alpine orogenies. A dominant role has been played by the Late Alpine, Tertiary extensional tectonics. This was documented for the entire Central Western Carpathian region (Bezák *et al.* 1993; Plašienka *et al.* 1997; Kováč 2000). On the deep seismic transect 2T (Tomek *et al.* 1987; Tomek 1993; Vozár *et al.* 1998; Bielik *et al.* 2004), a northerly inclined package of reflections is observed in the upper crust in the northern part of the profile (Pieniny Klippen Belt and adjacent areas). This package is interpreted as resulting from backthrusts related to Tertiary collision. In the southern part of the profile the reflectors are inclined towards the south or SE and are interpreted as palaeo-Alpine faults (Cretaceous). In the southernmost part (Pannonian Basin System) reflectors appear to cross not only the lower crust, but also the Moho. In the continuation of one of the reflectors a zone of low resistivity in the upper mantle (down to a depth of about 50 km) was modelled based on magnetotelluric measurements. This was interpreted as partially molten asthenospheric material, the probable source for the youngest Plio-Quaternary volcanic rocks (alkaline basalts) found on the surface (Šefara *et al.* 1998).

The fragmentation of the crust is more pronounced in the western part of the Western Carpathians (3T profile; Tomek *et al.* 1987; Vozár *et al.* 1998). The subsurface of the Danube Basin shows seismic reflectors which are interpreted as a low-angle normal fault system unroofing the basin floor during the formation of the basin (Šefara *et al.* 1998). The final phase of sedimentation (starting from the lower Pannonian) is related to a period of thermal subsidence in this area (Royden *et al.* 1983*a*, *b*; Lankreijer 1998).

The crustal structure in the basement of the East Slovakian Basin is characterized by three main features (Kováč *et al.* 1995; Bielik 1998): (1) down-bending of the North European Platform margin in the collision area into a steep orientation; (2) flower structure developed by transpression along the Pieniny Klippen Belt; (3) tectonic unroofing under transtensional/extensional conditions in the basement of the East Slovakian Basin. Unroofing of the Penninic-related Iňačovce-Krichevo Unit (Soták *et al.* 1993) and associated crustal thinning and increase of heat flow were related to Middle Miocene extension.

## *Neotectonics*

Ongoing neotectonic processes in the Western Carpathians are characterized by generally constant stress field characteristics and corresponding tectonic regimes for the Pliocene to Holocene, i.e. for the last approximately 5.3 Ma (e.g. Hók *et al.* 2000). The main source of the contemporaneous stress field in the Carpatho-Pannonian area is the counterclockwise rotation of Adria microplate ('Adriatic push'). Secondary sources are compressions generated by collisions in the Vrancea region of the Eastern Carpathians and at the southern corner of the Bohemian Massif in the Western Carpathians (Bada 1999). Variations in the effective elastic thickness of the lithosphere and topography-related sources have only a local significance.

Data on the recent stress field in the Western Carpathians are comparatively scarce, and are derived from focal mechanisms, structural analyses and *in situ* measurements (Pospíšil *et al.* 1992; Jarosiński 1998; Bada 1999; Hók *et al.* 2000; Kováč *et al.* 2002). These data suggest ongoing, albeit very slow, convergence between the North European Platform and the Carpathian orogen with the maximum horizontal stress axis being perpendicular to the orogen front along the arc. On the other hand, the interior regions of the Pannonian Basin are undergoing general extension and subsidence.

Moving from north to south, several provinces with differing structural regimes can be distinguished (Hók *et al.* 2000; Kováč *et al.* 2002): (1) the External Western Carpathian area which is characterized by a general NW–SE to north–south compression generating thrust faulting and uplift; (2) the Pieniny Klippen Belt which exhibits ongoing sinistral strike-slip movements; (3) the Central Western Carpathian area which is dominated by NW–SE compression, although NE–SW extension also occurs.

Important north-trending wrench-fault zones separate regions with differing vertical movements. The Central Slovakian Fault System separates western Slovakia, dominated by block rotation, uplift of 'core mountains' and subsidence of intramontane basins, from central Slovakia showing general uplift. The Hornád Fault System delineates the western boundary of the subsiding area in eastern Slovakia. The transition zone between the mountainous Central Western Carpathians and the Pannonian Basin shows predominantly orogen-parallel extension and subsidence.

Recent seismic activity in the Western Carpathians is concentrated into several zones that are interpreted to be a result of the interference of the actual stress field and the pre-existing crustal discontinuities (Šefara *et al.* 1998; Kováč *et al.* 2002). The most notable is the Pieniny Klippen Belt, which represents the deep-seated contact of the North European Platform with the Central Western Carpathians. The Mur-Mürz-Leitha-Láb-Dobrá Voda Fault Zone, trending SW–NE along the southern margin of the Vienna Basin, is the still-active sinistral wrench zone that accommodated the eastward extrusion of the Alcapa plate out of the collision zone in the Eastern Alps during the Neogene. The extensionally reactivated Čertovica and Rába-Hurbanovo-Diósjenő low-angle fault zones generate occasional earthquakes. The expected maximum epicentral intensity in these zones has been estimated as $I_{max} = 7–9$ (Šefara *et al.* 1998).

## References


Ádám, A., Szarka, L., Prácser, E. & Varga, G. 1996. Mantle plumes or EM distortions in the Pannonian Basin? (Inversion of the deep magnetotelluric (MT) soundings along the Pannonian geotraverse). *Geophysical Transactions*, **40**, 45–78.

Al-Jaboury, A. I. & Ďurovič, V. 1996. Supratidal origin of Carpathian Keuper dolostones. *Mineralia Slovaca*, **28**, 12–20.

Allemann, F. 1957. Geologie des Fürstentums Liechtenstein (Südwestlicher Teil) unter besonderer Berücksichtigung des Flyschproblems. *Jahrbuch des Historischen Vereins für das Fürstentum Liechtenstein*, **56**, 1–244.

Amerom, H. W. J., Angerer, H. & Mostler, H. 1982. Über eine Autuno-Stephanische Flora aus den Kristbergschichten im Montafon, Vorarlberg (Österreich). *Jahrbuch der Geologischen Bundesanstalt (Wien)*, **124**, 283–323.

Andrusov, D. 1936. Les nappes subtatriques des Carpathes occidentales. *Carpatica*, **1**, 3–50.

Andrusov, D. 1938. *Étude géologique de la zone des Klippes internes des Carpathes Occidentales, III$^E$ partie: Tectonique*. State Geological Survey, Prague.

Andrusov, D. 1968. *Grundriss der Tektonik der nördlichen Karpaten*. Verlag der Slowakischen Akademie der Wissenschaften, Bratislava.

Andrusov, D. 1975. *Aperçu bref du bâti des Carpathes Occidentales*. Proceedings X Congress CBGA, D. Štúr Institute of Geology, Bratislava, 95–108.

Andrusov, D., Bystrický, J. & Fusán, O. 1973. *Outline of the structure of the West Carpathians*. Guide book, X Congress CBGA, D. Štúr Institute of Geology, Bratislava.

Argand, E. 1909. L'exploration géologique des Alpes Pennines Centrales. *Bulletin des laboratoires de géologie, géographie physique, minéralogie et paléontologie de l'Université de Lausanne*, **14**, 1–64.

Árkai, P. & Kovács, S. 1986. Diagenesis and regional metamorphism of the Mesozoic of Aggtelek-Rudabánya mountains (Northeast Hungary). *Acta Geologica Hungarica*, **29**, 349–373.

Árkai, P., Balogh, K. & Dunkl, I. 1995. Timing of low-temperature metamorphism and cooling of the Paleozoic and Mesozoic formations of the Bükkium, innermost Western Carpathians, Hungary. *Geologische Rundschau*, **84**, 334–344.

Arnaud, H. 1973. Mise en évidence d'un important décalage antémiocène de sens senestre le long de la faille de Presles (Vercors occidental). *Comptes-Rendus de l'Académie des Sciences Paris*, **276**, 2245–2248.

Aubouin, J., Blanchet, R., Labesse, B. & Wozniak, J. 1977. Alpes occidentales et Alpes orientales : la zone du Canavese existe-t-elle? *Comptes rendus sommaires de la Société géologique de France*, **1977**, 155–158.

Aubrecht, R. & Szulc, J. 2006. Deciphering of the complex depositional and diagenetic history of a scarp limestone breccia (Middle Jurassic Krasin Breccia, Pieniny Klippen Belt, Western Carpathians). *Sedimentary Geology*, **186**, 265–281.

Aubrecht, R., Krobicki, M., *et al.* 2006. Early Cretaceous hiatus in the Czorsztyn Succession (Pieniny Klippen Belt, Western Carpathians): submarine erosion or emersion? *Annales Societatis Geologorum Poloniae*, **76**, 161–196.

Bada, G. 1999. *Cenozoic stress field evolution in the Pannonian Basin and surrounding orogens. Inferences from kinematic indicators and finite element stress modeling*. PhD Thesis, Vrije University, Amsterdam.

Bada, G. & Horváth, F. 2001. On the structure and tectonic evolution of the Pannonian Basin and surrounding orogens. *Acta Geologica Hungarica*, **44**, 301–327.

Bagnoud, A., Wernli, R. & Sartori, M. 1998. Discovery of Paleogene foraminifers in the Sion-Courmayeur zone at Sion (Valais, Switzerland). *Eclogae geologicae Helvetiae*, **91**, 421–429.

Balla, Z. 1994. Basement tectonics of the Danube Lowlands. *Geologica Carpathica*, **45**, 271–281.

Balla, Z. & Dudko, A. 1993. Tectonics of the Transdanubian Range. *In:* Balla Z. (ed.) *Geological problems of the East Alpine-West Carpathian-Pannonian junction area*. Guide to pre-workshop excursion in the Transdanubian Range. Hungarian Geological Survey, Budapest, 3–24.

Balla, Z., Baksa, Cs., Földessy, J., Havas, L. & Szabó, I. 1980. The tectonic setting of the ophiolites in the Bükk Mountains (north Hungary). *Geologický Zborník Geologica Carpathica*, **31**, 465–493.

Balla, Z., Hovorka, D., Kuzmin, M. & Vinogradov, V. 1983. Mesozoic ophiolites of the Bükk Mountains (north Hungary). *Ofioliti*, **8**, 5–46.

Ballèvre, M. & Merle, O. 1993. The Combin Fault : compressional reactivation of a Late Cretaceous-Early Tertiary detachment fault in the Western Alps. *Schweizerische Mineralogische und Petrographische Mitteilungen*, **73**, 205–227.

Ballèvre, M., Kienast, J.-R. & Vuichard, J.-P. 1986. La "nappe de la Dent-Blanche" (Alpes occidentales): Deux unités austroalpines indépendantes. *Eclogae geologicae Helvetiae*, **79**, 57–74.

Baudin, T., Marquer, D., Barfety, J. C., Kerckhove, C., Persoz, F. 1995. A new stratigraphical interpretation of the Tambo and Suretta nappes. Evidence for early thin-skinned tectonics. *Comptes Rendus de l'Academie des Sciences*, série II a, **321**, 401–408.

Bechstädt, T., Brandner, R. & Mostler, H. 1976. Das Frühstadium der alpinen Geosynklinalentwicklung im westlichen Drauzug. *Geologische Rundschau*, **65**, 616–648.

Becker, H. 1993. Garnet peridotite and eclogite Sm-Nd mineral ages from the Lepontine Dome (Swiss Alps): New evidence for Eocene high-pressure metamorphism in the central Alps. *Geology*, **21**, 599–602.

Behrmann, J. H. 1988. Crustal-scale extension in a convergent orogen: the Sterzing-Steinach mylonite zone in the Eastern Alps. *Geodynamica Acta*, **2**, 63–73.

Behrmann, J. H., Stiasny, S., Milička, J. & Pereszlényi, M. 2000. Quantitative reconstruction of orogenic convergence in the northeast Carpathians. *Tectonophysics*, **319**, 111–127.

Benciolini, L. 1994. Metamorphic evolution of the Silvretta gabbro and related rocks (Upper Austroalpine, Central Alps). Its bearing on the pre-Mesozoic history of the Alpine area basement. *Memorie di Scienze Geologiche (Padova)*, **46**, 353–371.

Benedetti, L., Tapponier, P., King, G. C. P., Meyer, B. & Manighetti, I. 2000. Growth folding and active thrusting in the Montello region, Veneto, northern Italy. *Journal of Geophysical Research*, **105**, 739–766.

Berge, T. B. & Veal, S. L. 2005. Structure of the Alpine foreland. *Tectonics*, **24**, TC5001.

Berger, A., Rosenberg, C. & Schmid, S. M. 1996. Ascent, emplacement and exhumation of the Bergell pluton within the Southern Step Belt of the Central Alps. *Schweizerische Mineralogische und Petrographische Mitteilungen*, **76**, 357–382.

Bernoulli, D. 1964. Zur Geologie des Monte Generoso (Lombardische Alpen). *Beiträge zur Geologischen Karte der Schweiz*, N.F., **118**, 1–134.

Bernoulli, D., Bertotti, G. & Froitzheim, N. 1990. Mesozoic faults and associated sediments in the Austroalpine – South Alpine continental margin. *Memorie della Societá Geologica Italiana*, **45**, 25–38.

Bertle, R. J. 2002. Kreide und Paläogen in der Fimber-Zone (Unterengadiner Fenster, Schweiz - Österreich). Neue Mikrofossilfunde und deren paläogeographische Bedeutung. *Eclogae geologicae Helvetiae*, **95**, 153–167.

Bertotti, G. 1990. The deep structure of the Generoso basin: an extensional basin in the south-Alpine Mesozoic passive continental margin. *Mémoires de la Société Géologique de France*, **156**, 303–308.

Bertotti, G., Picotti, V., Bernoulli, D. & Castellarin, A. 1993. From rifting to drifting: tectonic evolution of the South-Alpine upper crust from the Triassic to the Early Cretaceous. *Sedimentary Geology*, **86**, 53–76.

Bezák, V., Hók, J., Kováč, P. & Madarás, J. 1993. Možnosti tektonickej interpretácie seizmického profilu 2T (English summary: Alternative of tectonic interpretation on the seismic line 2T). *In:* Rakús, M. & Vozár, J. (eds) *Geodynamic Model and Deep Seated Structures of the Western Carpathians*. Konferencie Sympóziá Semináre, D. Štúr Institute of Geology, Bratislava, 287–290.

Bezák, V., Jacko, S., Janák, M., Ledru, P., Petrík, I. & Vozárová, A. 1997. Main Hercynian lithotectonic units of the Western Carpathians. *In:* Grecula, P., Hovorka, D. & Putiš, M. (eds) *Geological Evolution of the Western Carpathians*. Monograph, Mineralia Slovaca, Bratislava, 261–268.

Bielik, M. 1988. A preliminary stripped gravity map of the Pannonian Basin. *Physics of the Earth and Planetary Interiors*, **51**, 185–189.

Bielik, M. 1998. Analysis of the gravity field in the Western and Eastern Carpathian junction area: density modelling. *Geologica Carpathica*, **49**, 75–83.

Bielik, M. & Šefara, J. 2002. Deep structure of the Western Carpathians. *Krystalinikum*, **28**, 7–62.

Bielik, M., Lankreijer, A. & Zoetemeijer, R. 2000. Using of gravity and geothermal fields to rheological study in the Western Carpathians and the surrounding tectonic units. *Österreichische Beiträge zur Meteorologie und Geophysik*, **26**, 47–60.

Bielik, M., Šefara, J., Kováč, M., Bezák, V. & Plašienka, D. 2004. The Western Carpathians – interaction of Hercynian and Alpine processes. *Tectonophysics*, **393**, 63–86.

Biely, A. 1989. The geological structure of the West Carpathians. *In:* Rakús, M., Dercourt, J. & Nairn, A. E. M. (eds) *Evolution of the Northern Margin of Tethys, Vol. II*. Mémoire de la Société Géologique de France, Nouvelle Série No. 154 (II), Paris, 51–57.

Biino, G. & Compagnoni, R. 1989. The Canavese Zone between Serra d'Ivrea and the Dora Baltea River (Western Alps). *Eclogae geologicae Helvetiae*, **82**, 413–427.

Biino, G. G., Marquer, D. & Nussbaum, C. 1997. Alpine and pre-Alpine subduction events in polycyclic basements of the Swiss Alps. *Geology*, **25**, 751–754.

Bill, M., Bussy, F., Cosca, M., Masson, H. & Hunziker, J. C. 1997. High-precision U-Pb and $^{40}Ar/^{39}Ar$ dating of an Alpine ophiolite (Gets nappe, French Alps). *Eclogae geologicae Helvetiae*, **90**, 43–54.

Bill, M., O'Dogherty, L., Guex, J., Baumgartner, P. O. & Masson, H. 2001. Radiolarite ages in Alpine-Mediterranean ophiolites: Constraints on the oceanic spreading and the Tethys-Atlantic connection. *Geological Society of America Bulletin*, **113**, 129–143.

Birkenmajer, K. 1970. Pre-Eocene fold structures in the Pieniny Klippen Belt (Carpathians) of Poland. *Studia Geologica Polonica*, **31**, 1–77 [In Polish with English summary].

Birkenmajer, K. 1977. Jurassic and Cretaceous lithostratigraphic units of the Pieniny Klippen Belt, Carpathians, Poland. *Studia Geologica Polonica*, **45**, 1–158.

Birkenmajer, K. 1986. Stages of structural evolution of the Pieniny Klippen Belt, Carpathians. *Studia Geologica Polonica*, **88**, 7–32.

Birkenmajer, K. 1988. Exotic Andrusov Ridge: its role in plate-tectonic evolution of the West Carpathian foldbelt. *Studia Geologica Polonica*, **41**, 7–37.

Birkenmajer, K. 1999. Stages of structural evolution of the Niedzica Castle tectonic window, Pieniny Klippen Belt, Carpathians, Poland. *Studia Geologica Polonica*, **115**, 117–130.

Birkenmajer, K., Kozur, H. & Mock, R. 1990. Exotic Triassic pelagic limestone pebbles from the Pieniny Klippen Belt of Poland: a further evidence for Early Mesozoic rifting in West Carpathians. *Annales Societatis Geologorum Poloniae*, **60**, 3–44.

Bonin, B., Brändlein, P., *et al.* 1993. Late Variscan Magmatic Evolution of the Alpine Basement. *In:* Neubauer, F. & Von Raumer, J. F. (eds) *The Pre- Mesozoic Geology of the Alps*. Springer, Berlin, 172–201.

Boriani, A. C. & Villa, I. M. 1997. Geochronology of regional metamorphism in the Ivrea-Verbano Zone and Serie dei Laghi, Italian Alps. *Schweizerische Mineralogische und Petrographische Mitteilungen*, **77**, 381–401.

Borza, K., Gašpariková, V., Michalík, J. & Vašíček, Z. 1980. Upper Jurassic – Lower Cretaceous sequence of the Krížna-nappe (Fatric) in the Strážovce section, Strážovské vrchy Mts. (Western Carpathians). *Geologický Zborník Geologica Carpathica*, **31**, 541–562.

Bousquet, R., Oberhänsli, R., Goffe, B., Jolivet, L. & Vidal, O. 1999. High-pressure - low-temperature metamorphism and deformation in the "Bündnerschiefer" of the Engadine window: implications for the regional evolution of the Central Alps. *Journal of Metamorphic Geology*, **17**, 657–674.

Bousquet, R., Engi, M., *et al.* 2004. Explanatory notes to the map: metamorphic structure of the Alps Transition from the Western to the Central Alps. *Mitteilungen der Österreichischen Mineralogischen Gesellschaft*, **149**, 145–156.

Boyet, M., Lapierre, H., Tardy, M., Bosch, D, Maury, R. 2001. Sources of the andesitic components in the Taveyannaz Sandstones and Champsaur Sandstones: implications for the Paleogene geodynamic evolution of the Alps. *Bulletin de la Société Géologique de France*, **172**, 487–501.

Brack, P. 1981. Structures in the southwestern border of the Adamello intrusion (Alpi bresciane, Italy). *Schweizerische Mineralogische und Petrographische Mitteilungen*, **61**, 37–50.

Brandner, R. 1984. Meeresspiegelschwankungen und Tektonik in der Trias der NW-Tethys. *Jahrbuch der Geologischen Bundesanstalt (Wien)*, **126**, 435–475.

Braumüller, E. & Prey, S. 1943. Zur Tektonik der mittleren Hohen Tauern. *Berichte des Reichsamts für Bodenforschung (Wien)*, **1943**, 113–140.

Brodie, K. H., Rex, D. & Rutter, E. H. 1989. On the age of deep crustal extensional faulting in the Ivrea zone, northern Italy. *In:* Coward, M. P., Dietrich, D. & Park, R. G. (eds) *Alpine Tectonics*. Geological Society, London, Special Publication, **45**, 203–210.

Broska, I. & Uher, P. 2001. Whole-rock chemistry and genetic typology of the West-Carpathian Variscan granites. *Geologica Carpathica*, **52**, 79–90.

Brzobohatý, R. & Cicha, I. 1993. Karpatská předhlubeň (English summary: The Carpathian foredeep). In: Přichystal, A., Obstová, V. & Suk, M. (eds) *Geology of Moravia and Silesia*. Moravské Zemské Muzeum & Sekce Geologických Věd PřF MU, Brno, 123–128.

Buday, T., Kodym, O., Mahel', M., Máška, M., Matějka, A., Svoboda, J. & Zoubek, V. 1960. *Tectonic Development of Czechoslovakia*. Nakladatelství ČSAV, Praha.

Buday, T., Cicha, I., *et al.* 1967. *Regional Geology of ČSSR*. Díl II – Západní Karpaty, sv. 2. Academia, Praha.

Burger, H. 1978. Arosa- und Madrisa-Zone im Gebiet zwischen dem Schollberg und der Verspala (Osträtikon). *Eclogae geologicae Helvetiae*, **71**, 255–266.

CALAIS, E., NOCQUET, J.-M., JOUANNE, F. & TARDY, M. 2002. Current strain regime in the Western Alps from continuous Global Positioning System measurements, 1996–2001. *Geology*, **30**, 651–654.

CASTELLARIN, A. & CANTELLI, L. 2000. Neo-Alpine evolution of the Southern Eastern Alps. *Journal of Geodynamics*, **30**, 251–274.

CERIANI, S. & SCHMID, S. M. 2004. From N-S collision to WNW-directed post-collisional thrusting and folding: Structural study of the Frontal Penninic Units in Savoie (Western Alps, France). *Eclogae geologicae Helvetiae*, **97**, 347–369.

CERIANI, S., FÜGENSCHUH, B. & SCHMID, S. M. 2001. Multi-stage thrusting at the "Penninic Front" in the Western Alps between Mont Blanc and Pelvoux massifs. *International Journal of Earth Sciences*, **90**, 685–702.

CHAMPAGNAC, J. D., SUE, C., DELACOU, B., TRICARD, P., ALLANIC, C. & BURKHARD, M. 2006. Miocene lateral extrusion in the inner western Alps revealed by dynamic fault analysis. *Tectonics*, **25**, TC3014.

CHANNELL, J. E. T. & KOZUR, H. W. 1997. How many oceans? Meliata, Vardar, and Pindos oceans in the Mesozoic alpine palaeogeography. *Geology*, **25**, 183–186.

CHEMENDA, A. I., MATTAUER, M., MALAVIEILLE, J. & BOKUN, A. N. 1995. A mechanism for syn-collisional deep rock exhumation and associated normal faulting: results from physical modelling. *Earth and Planetary Science Letters*, **132**, 225–232.

CHOPIN, C. 1984. Coesite and pure pyrope in high-grade blueschists of the western Alps: a first record and some consequences. *Contributions to Mineralogy and Petrology*, **86**, 107–118.

CIANCALEONI, L. & MARQUER, D. 2006. Syn-extension leucogranite deformation during convergence in the Eastern Alps: example of the Novate intrusion. *Terra Nova*, **18**, 170–180.

CLAUDEL, M.-E. & DUMONT, T. 1999. A record of multistage continental break-up on the Briançonnais marginal plateau (Western Alps): Early and Middle-Late Jurassic rifting. *Eclogae geologicae Helvetiae*, **92**, 45–61.

COLLOMBET, M., THOMAS, J. C., CHAUVIN, A., TRICART, P., BOUILLIN, J. P. & GRATIER, J. P. 2002. Counterclockwise rotation of the wewstern Alps since the Oligocene: New insights from paleomagnetic data. *Tectonics*, **21**, DOI: 10.1029/2001TC901016.

COLOMBI, A. & PFEIFER, H.-R. 1986. Ferrogabbroic and basaltic meta-eclogites from the Antrona mafic-ultramafic complex and the Centovalli-Locarno region (Italy and Southern Switzerland) – first results. *Schweizerische Mineralogische und Petrographische Mitteilungen*, **66**, 99–110.

COLOMBO, A. & TUNESI, A. 1999. Pre-Alpine metamorphism of the Southern Alps west of the Giudicarie Line. *Schweizerische Mineralogische und Petrographische Mitteilungen*, **79**, 63–77.

COMPAGNONI, R., ELTER, G. & LOMBARDO, B. 1974. Eterogeneità stratigrafica del complesso degli "Gneiss minuti" nel massiccio cristallino del Gran Paradiso. *Memorie della Società Geologica Italiana*, **13**, 227–239.

CORNELIUS, H. P. & CLAR, E. 1939. Geologie des Großglocknergebietes (1. Teil). *Abhandlung der Zweigstelle Wien der Reichsstelle für Bodenforschung (früher Geologische Bundesanstalt)*, **25**, 1–305.

CSÁZSÁR, G. & ÁRGYELÁN, G. B. 1994. Stratigraphic and micromineralogic investigations on Cretaceous formations of the Gerecse Mountains, Hungary and their palaeogeographic implications. *Cretaceous Research*, **15**, 417–434.

CSÁZSÁR, G. & HAAS, J. 1984. The Cretaceous in Hungary: A review. *Acta Geologica Hungarica*, **27**, 417–428.

CSONTOS, L. 1995. Tertiary tectonic evolution of the Intra-Carpathian area: a review. *Acta Vulcanologica*, **7**, 1–13.

CSONTOS, L. 1999. Structural outline of the Bükk Mts (N Hungary). *Földtani Közlöny*, **129**, 611–651 [English abstract].

CSONTOS, L. 2000. Stratigraphic reevaluation of the Bükk Mts (N Hungary). *Földtani Közlöny*, **130**, 95–131 [English abstract].

CSONTOS, L. & VÖRÖS, A. 2004. Mesozoic plate-tectonic reconstruction of the Carpathian region. *Palaeogeography, Palaeoclimatology Palaeoecology*, **210**, 1–56.

CSONTOS, L., NAGYMAROSY, A., HORVÁTH, F. & KOVÁČ, M. 1992. Tertiary evolution of the intracarpathian area: a model. *Tectonophysics*, **208**, 221–241.

DALLMEYER, R. D., NEUBAUER, F., HANDLER, R., FRITZ, H., MÜLLER, W., PANA, D. & PUTIŠ, M. 1996. Tectonothermal evolution of the internal Alps and Carpathians: Evidence from $^{40}Ar/^{39}Ar$ mineral and whole-rock data. *Eclogae geologicae Helvetiae*, **89**, 203–227.

DALLMEYER, R. D., HANDLER, R., NEUBAUER, F. & FRITZ, H. 1998. Sequence of thrusting within a thick-skinned tectonic wedge: evidence from 40Ar/39Ar and Rb-Sr ages from the Austroalpine nappe complex of the Eastern Alps. *Journal of Geology*, **106**, 71–86.

DAL PIAZ, G. V., MARTIN, S., VILLA, I. M., GOSSO, G. & MARSCHALKO, R. 1995. Late Jurassic blueschist facies pebbles from the Western Carpathian orogenic wedge and paleostructural implications for Western Tethys evolution. *Tectonics*, **14**, 874–885.

DAL PIAZ, G. V., CORTIANA, G., DEL MORO, A., MARTIN, S., PENNACCHIONI, G. & TARTAROTTI, P. 2001. Tertiary age and paleostructural inferences of the eclogitic imprint in the Austroalpine outliers and Zermatt-Saas ophiolite, western Alps. *International Journal of Earth Sciences*, **90**, 668–684.

DECKER, K. 1990. Plate tectonics and pelagic facies: Late Jurassic to Early Cretaceous deep sea sediments of the Ybbsitz ophiolite unit (Eastern Alps, Austria). *Sedimentary Geology*, **67**, 85–99.

DECKER, K. & PERESSON, H. 1996. Tertiary kinematics in the Alpine-Carpathian-Pannonian system: links between thrusting, transform faulting and crustal extension. *In:* WESSELY, G. & LIEBL, W. (eds) *Oil and Gas in Alpidic Thrustbelts and Basins of Central and Eastern Europe*. EAGE, Special Publication, **5**, 69–77.

DELACOU, B., SUE, C., CHAMPAGNAC, J. D. & BURKHARD, M. 2004. Present-day geodynamics in the bend of the western and central Alps as constrained by earthquake analysis. *Geophysical Journal International*, **158**, 753–774.

DEL MORO, A., PARDINI, G., QUERCIOLI, C., VILLA, I. M. & CALLEGARI, E. 1983. Rb/Sr and K/Ar chronology of Adamello granitoids, Southern Alps. *Memorie della Societá geologica Italiana*, **26**, 285–299.

DE SITTER, L. U. & DE SITTER KOOMANS, C. M. 1949. The geology of the Bergamasc Alps, Lombardia, Italy. *Leidse geologische Mededelingen*, **14**, 1–257.

DESMONS, J. 1977. Mineralogical and petrological investigations of Alpine metamorphism in the internal French western Alps. *American Journal of Science*, **277**, 1045–1066.

DEUTSCH, A. 1984. Young Alpine dykes south of the Tauern Window (Austria): a K-Ar and Sr isotope study. *Contributions to Mineralogy and Petrology*, **85**, 45–57.

DEWEY, J. F., HELMAN, M. L., TURCO, E., HUTTON, D. H. W. & KNOTT, S. D. 1989. Kinematics of the Western Mediterranean. *In:* COWARD, M. P., DIETRICH, D. & PARK, R. G. (eds) *Alpine Tectonics*. Geological Society, London, Special Publications, **45**, 265–283.

DIELLA, V., SPALLA, M. I. & TUNESI, A. 1992. Contrasting thermo-mechanical evolutions in the Southalpine metamorphic basement of the Orobic Alps (Central Alps, Italy). *Journal of Metamorphic Geology*, **10**, 203–219.

DINGELDEY, C., DALLMEYER, R. D., KOLLER, F. & MASSONNE, H.-J. 1997. P-T-t history of the Lower Austroalpine Nappe Complex NW of the Tauern Window: Implications for the geodynamic evolution of the central Eastern Alps. *Contributions to Mineralogy and Petrology*, **129**, 1–19.

DOGLIONI, C. 1987. Tectonics of the Dolomites (Southern Alps, Northern Italy). *Journal of Structural Geology*, **9**, 181–193.

DOGLIONI, C. & BOSELLINI, A. 1987. Eoalpine and Mesoalpine tectonics in the Southern Alps. *Geologische Rundschau*, **76**, 735–754.

DOSTAL, J. & OWEN, J. V. 1998. Cretaceous alkaline lamprophyres from northeastern Czech Republic: geochemistry and petrogenesis. *Geologische Rundschau*, **87**, 67–77.

DOSTAL, J., VOZÁR, J., KEPPIE, J. D. & HOVORKA, D. 2003. Permian volcanism in the Central Western Carpathians (Slovakia): Basin-and-range type rifting in the southern Laurussian margin. *International Journal of Earth Sciences*, **92**, 27–35.

DUCHÊNE, S., BLICHERT-TOFT, J., LUAIS, B., TÉLOUK, P., LARDEAUX, J.-M. & ALBARÈDE, F. 1997. The Lu-Hf dating of garnets and the ages of Alpine high-pressure metamorphism. *Nature*, **387**, 586–589.

DUMONT, T., WIECZOREK, J. & BOUILLIN, J.-P. 1996. Inverted Mesozoic rift structures in the Polish Western Carpathians (High-Tatric units). Comparison with similar features in the Western Alps. *Eclogae geologicae Helvetiae*, **89**, 181–202.

DUNKL, I. 1992. Final episodes of the cooling history of eastern termination of the Alps. *ALCAPA Field Guide*. IGP/KFU, Graz, 137–139.

EBERLI, G. P. 1998. The evolution of the southern continental margin of the Jurassic Tethys Ocean as recorded in the Allgäu Formation of the Austroalpine nappes of Graubünden (Switzerland). *Eclogae geologicae Helvetiae*, **81**, 175–214.

Ebner, F. 1992. Correlation of marine Carboniferous sedimentary units of Slovakia, Hungary and Austria. *In:* Vozár, J. (ed.) *The Paleozoic Geodynamic Domains: Western Carpathians, Eastern Alps, Dinarides*. Conferences Symposia Seminars, D. Štúr Institue of Geology, Bratislava, 37–47.

Ebner, F., Rantitsch, G., Russenegger, B., Vozárová, A. & Kovács, S. 2006. A three component (organic carbon, pyritic sulphur, carbonate content) model as a tool for lithostratigraphic correlation of Carboniferous sediments in the Alpine-Carpathian-North Pannonian realm. *Geologica Carpathica*, **57**, 243–256.

Ellenberger, F. 1953. Sur l'extension des faciès briançonnais en Suisse, dans les Préalpes médianes et les Pennides. *Eclogae geologicae Helvetiae*, **45**, 285–286.

Escher, A., Masson, H. & Steck, A. 1993. Nappe geometry in the Western Swiss Alps. *Journal of Structural Geology*, **15**, 501–509.

Escher, A., Hunziker, J.-C., Marthaler, M., Masson, H., Sartori, M. & Steck, A. 1997. Geological framework and structural evolution of the western Swiss-Italian Alps. *In:* Pfiffner, O. A., Lehner, P., Heitzmann, P., Mueller, S. & Steck, A. (eds) *Deep Structure of the Swiss Alps: Results of NRP 20*. Birkhäuser, Basel, 205–221.

Etter, U. 1987. *Stratigraphische und strukturgeologische Untersuchungen im Gotthardmassivischen Mesozoikum zwischen dem Lukmanierpass und der Gegend von Ilanz*. PhD Thesis, University of Bern.

Fantoni, R., Bersezio, R. & Forcella, F. 2004. Alpine structure and deformation chronology at the Southern Alps-Po Plain border in Lombardy. *Bollettino della Societá geologica Italiana*, **123**, 463–476.

Faryad, S. W. 1995*a*. Phase petrology and P-T conditions of mafic blueschists from the Meliata unit, West Carpathians, Slovakia. *Journal of Metamorphic Geology*, **13**, 701–714.

Faryad, S. W. 1995*b*. Petrology and phase relations of low-grade high-pressure metasediments of the Meliata Unit, Western Carpathians, Slovakia. *European Journal of Mineralogy*, **7**, 71–87.

Faryad, S. W. 1997. Lithology and metamorphism of the Meliata unit high-pressure rocks. *In:* Grecula, P., Hovorka, D. & Putiš, M. (eds) *Geological Evolution of the Western Carpathians*. Monograph, Mineralia Slovaca, Bratislava, 131–144.

Faryad, S. W. 1999. Exhumation of the Meliata high-pressure rocks (Western Carpathians): petrological and structural records in blueschists. *Acta Montanistica Slovaca*, **4**, 137–144.

Faryad, S. W. & Henjes-Kunst, F. 1997. Petrological and K-Ar and $^{40}Ar$-$^{39}Ar$ age constraints for the tectonothermal evolution of the high-pressure Meliata unit, Western Carpathians (Slovakia). *Tectonophysics*, **280**, 141–156.

Faryad, S. W. & Schreyer, W. 1996. Petrology and geological significance of high-pressure metamorphic rocks occurring as pebbles in the Cretaceous conglomerates of the Klippen Belt (West Carpathians, Slovakia). *European Journal of Mineralogy*, **9**, 547–562.

Faryad S. W., Melcher, F., Hoinkes, G., Puhl, J., Meisel, T. & Frank, W. 2002. Relics of eclogite-facies metamorphism in the Austroalpine basement, Hochgrössen (Speik Complex), Austria. *Mineralogy and Petrology*, **74**, 49–73.

Faupl, P. 1979. Zur räumlichen und zeitlichen Entwicklung von Breccien- und Turbiditserien in den Ostalpen. *Mitteilungen der Gesellschaft der Geologie- und Bergbaustudenten in Österreich*, **25**, 81–110.

Faupl, P. & Wagreich, M. 1996. Basin analysis of the Gosau Group of the Northern Calcareous Alps (Turonian-Eocene, Eastern Alps). *In:* Wessely, G. & Liebl, W. (eds) *Oil and Gas in Alpidic Thrustbelts and Basins of Central and Eastern Europe*. EAGE, Special Publication, **5**, 127–135.

Faupl, P. & Wagreich, M. 2000. Late Jurassic to Eocene palaeogeography and geodynamic evolution of the Eastern Alps. *Mitteilungen der Österreichischen Geologischen Gesellschaft*, **92**, 79–94.

Faupl, P., Pober, E. & Wagreich, M. 1987. Facies development of the Gosau Group of the eastern parts of the Northern Calcerous Alps during the Cretaceous and Paleogene. *In*: Flügel, H.W. & Faupl, P. (eds) *Geodynamics of the Eastern Alps*. Deuticke, Wien, 142–155.

Faure, J.-L. & Mégard-Galli, J. 1988. L'émersion jurassique en Briançonnais: sedimentation continentale et fracturation distensive. *Bulletin de la Société géologique de France*, **1988**(4), 681–692.

Ferrando, S., Bernoulli, D. & Compagnoni, R. 2004. The Canavese zone (internal Western Alps): a distal margin of Adria. *Schweizerische Mineralogische und Petrographische Mitteilungen*, **84**, 237–256.

Ferreiro Mählmann, R. 1995. Das Diagenese-Metamorphose-Muster von Vitrinitreflexion und Illit-"Kristallinität" in Mittelgraubünden und im Oberhalbstein Teil 1: Bezüge zur Stockwerktektonik. *Schweizerische Mineralogische und Petrographische Mitteilungen*, **75**, 85–122.

Finger, F. & Broska, I. 1999. The Gemeric S-type granites in southeastern Slovakia: Late Palaeozoic or Alpine intrusions? Evidence from electron-microprobe dating of monazite. *Schweizerische Mineralogische und Petrographische Mitteilungen*, **79**, 439–443.

Flandrin, J. 1966. Sur l'âge des principaux traits structuraux du Diois et des Baronnies. *Bulletin de la Société Géologique de France, (7)*, **8**, 376–386.

Florineth, D. & Froitzheim, N. 1994. Transition from continental to oceanic basement in the Tasna nappe (Engadine window, Graubünden, Switzerland): evidence for Early Cretaceous opening of the Valais ocean. *Schweizerische Mineralogische und Petrographische Mitteilungen*, **74**, 437–448.

Flügel, H. W. & Hubmann, B. 2000. Das Paläozoikum von Graz: Stratigraphie und Bibliographie. *Schriftenreihe der Erdwissenschaftlichen Kommissionen /Österreichische Akademie der Wissenschaften*, **13**, 1–118.

Fodor, L. & Koroknai, B. 2000. Ductile deformation and revised lithostratigraphy of the Martonyi subunit (Torna Unit, Rudabánya Mts.), northeastern Hungary. *Geologica Carpathica*, **51**, 355–369.

Fodor, L., Csontos, L., Bada, G., Györfi, I. & Benkovics, L. 1999. Tertiary tectonic evolution of the Pannonian Basin system and neighbouring orogens: a new synthesis of paleostress data. *In:* Durand, B., Jolivet, L., Horváth, F. & Séranne, M. (eds) *The Mediterranean Basins: Tertiary Extension within the Alpine Orogen*. Geological Society, London, Special Publications, **156**, 295–334.

Fodor, L., Koroknai, B., Balogh, K., Dunkl, I. & Horváth, P. 2003. Nappe position of the Transdanubian Range Unit ("Bakony") based on structural and geochronological data from NE Slovenia. *Földtani Közlöny*, **133**, 535–546.

Ford, M. 1996. Kinematics and geometry of early Alpine, basement-involved folds, SW Pelvoux Massif, SE France. *Eclogae geologicae Helvetiae*, **89**, 269–295.

Frank, W. 1987. Evolution of the Austroalpine Elements in the Cretaceous. *In:* Flügel, H. W. & Faupl, P. (eds) *Geodynamics of the Eastern Alps*. Deuticke, Wien, 379–406.

Frank, W. & Schlager, W. 2005. Jurassic strike slip versus subduction in the Eastern Alps. *International Journal of Earth Sciences*, **95**, 431–450.

Frank, W., Höck, V. & Miller, C. 1987. Metamorphic and tectonic history of the Central Tauern Window. *In:* Flügel, H. W. & Faupl, P. (eds) *Geodynamics of the Eastern Alps*. Deuticke, Wien, 34–54.

Frisch, W. 1976. Ein Modell zur alpidischen Evolution und Orogenese des Tauernfensters. *Geologische Rundschau*, **65**, 375–393.

Frisch, W. 1979. Tectonic progradation and plate tectonic evolution of the Alps. *Tectonophysics*, **60**, 121–139.

Frisch, W. & Gawlick, H.-J. 2003. The nappe structure of the central Northern Calcareous Alps and its disintegration during Miocene tectonic extrusion – a contribution to understanding the orogenic evolution of the Eastern Alps. *International Journal of Earth Sciences*, **92**, 712–727.

Frisch, W., Gommeringer, K., Kelm, U. & Popp, F. 1989. The Upper Bündner Schiefer of the Tauern Window – A key to understanding Eoalpine orogenic processes in the Eastern Alps. *In:* Flügel, W. & Faupl, P. (eds) *Geodynamics of the Eastern Alps*. Deuticke, Wien, 55–69.

Frisch, W., Kuhlemann, J., Dunkl, I. & Brügel, A. 1998. Palinspastic reconstruction and topographic evolution of the Eastern Alps during late Tertiary tectonic extrusion. *Tectonophysics*, **297**, 1–15.

Frisch, W., Székely, B., Kuhlemann, J. & Dunkl, I. 2000. Geomorphological evolution of the Eastern Alps in response to Miocene tectonics. *Zeitschrift für Geomorphologie*, N. F., **44**, 103–138.

Froitzheim, N. 1992. Formation of recumbent folds during synorogenic crustal extension (Austroalpine nappes, Switzerland). *Geology*, **20**, 923–926.

FROITZHEIM, N. 2001. Origin of the Monte Rosa nappe in the Pennine Alps – A new working hypothesis. *Geological Society of America Bulletin*, **113**, 604–614.

FROITZHEIM, N. & EBERLI, G. P. 1990. Extensional detachment faulting in the evolution of a Tethys passive continental margin, Eastern Alps, Switzerland. *Geological Society of America Bulletin*, **102**, 1297–1308.

FROITZHEIM, N. & MANATSCHAL, G. 1996. Kinematics of Jurassic rifting, mantle exhumation, and passive-margin formation in the Austroalpine and Penninic nappes (eastern Switzerland). *Geological Society of America Bulletin*, **108**, 1120–1133.

FROITZHEIM, N., SCHMID, S. M. & CONTI, P. 1994. Repeated change from crustal shortening to orogen-parallel extension in the Austroalpine units of Graubünden. *Eclogae geologicae Helvetiae*, **87**, 559–612.

FROITZHEIM, N., SCHMID, S. M. & FREY, M. 1996. Mesozoic paleogeography and the timing of eclogite-facies metamorphism in the Alps: A working hypothesis. *Eclogae geologicae Helvetiae*, **89**, 81–110.

FROITZHEIM, N., CONTI, P. & VAN DAALEN, M. 1997. Late Cretaceous, synorogenic, low-angle normal faulting along the Schlinig fault (Switzerland, Italy, Austria) and its significance for the tectonics of the Eastern Alps. *Tectonophysics*, **280**, 267–293.

FROITZHEIM, N., PLEUGER, J., ROLLER, S. & NAGEL, T. 2003. Exhumation of high- and ultrahigh-pressure metamorphic rocks by slab extraction. *Geology*, **31**, 925–928.

FROITZHEIM, N., PLEUGER, J. & NAGEL, T. J. 2006. Extraction faults. *Journal of Structural Geology*, **28**, 1388–1395.

FROITZHEIM, N., DERKS, J. F., WALTER, J. M. & SCIUNNACH, D. 2008. Evolution of an Early Permian extensional detachment fault from synintrusive, mylonitic flow to brittle faulting (Grassi Detachment Fault, Orobic Anticline, southern Alps, Italy). *In*: SIEGESMUND, S., FÜGENSCHUH, B. & FROITZHEIM, N. (eds) *Tectonic Aspects of the Alpine-Dinaride-Carpathian System*. Geological Society, London, Special Publications, **298**, 69–82.

FUCHS, W. 1985. Großtektonische Neuorientierung in den Ostalpen und Westkarpathen unter Einbeziehung plattentektonischer Gesichtspunkte. *Jahrbuch der Geologischen Bundesanstalt (Wien)*, **127**, 571–631.

FUCHS, G. & LINNER, M. 2005. Die geologische Karte der Sadnig-Gruppe: Ostalpines Kristallin in Beziehung zur Matreier Zone. *Jahrbuch der Geologischen Bundesanstalt (Wien)*, **145**, 293–301.

FÜGENSCHUH, B., SEWARD, D. & MANCKTELOW, N. 1997. Exhumation in a convergent orogen: the western Tauern window. *Terra Nova*, **9**, 213–217.

FÜGENSCHUH, B., LOPRIENO, A., CERIANI, S. & SCHMID, S. M. 1999. Structural analysis of the Subbriançonnais and Valais units in the area of Moûtiers (Savoy, Western Alps): paleogeographic and tectonic consequences. *International Journal of Earth Sciences*, **88**, 201–218.

FÜGENSCHUH, B., MANCKTELOW, N. S. & SEWARD, D. 2000. Cretaceous to Neogene cooling and exhumation of the Oetztal-Stubai basement complex, eastern Alps: A structural and fission track study. *Tectonics*, **19**, 905–918.

FÜLÖP, J., BRESZNYÁNSZKY, K. & HAAS, J. 1987. The new map of the Pannonian basin basement in the Hungary. *Acta Geologica Hungarica*, **30**, 3–20.

FURRER, H. (ed.) 1985. Field workshop on Triassic and Jurassic sediments in the Eastern Alps of Switzerland. *Mitteilungen aus dem Geologischen Institut der ETH und der Universität Zürich, N.F.*, **248**, 1–81.

GAWLICK, H.-J. & HÖPFER, N. 1999. Stratigraphie, Fazies und Hochdruck-Mitteltemperatur-Metamorphose der Hallstätter Kalke der Pailwand (Nördliche Kalkalpen, Österreich). *Zeitschrift der Deutschen Geologischen Gesellschaft*, **150**, 641–671.

GAWLICK, H.-J. & SUZUKI, H. 1999. Zur stratigraphischen Stellung der Strubbergschichten in den Nördlichen Kalkalpen (Callovium-Oxfordium). *Neues Jahrbuch für Geologie und Paläontologie*, **211**, 233–263.

GAWLICK, H.-J., FRISCH, W., VECSEI, A., STEIGER, T. & BÖHM, F. 1999. The change from rifting to thrusting in the Northern Calcareous Alps as recorded in Jurassic sediments. *Geologische Rundschau*, **87**, 644–657.

GEBAUER, D. 1996. A P-T-t path for an (ultra?-) high-pressure ultramafic/mafic rock-association and its felsic country-rocks based on SHRIMP-dating of magmatic and metamorphic zircon domains. Example: Alpe Arami (Central Swiss Alps). *In:* BASU, A. & HART, S. (eds) *Earth Processes: Reading the Isotopic Code*. American Geophysical Union, Geophysical Monographs, **95**, 307–329.

GEBAUER, D. 1999. Alpine geochronology of the Central and Western Alps: new constraints for a complex geodynamic evolution. *Schweizerische Mineralogische und Petrographische Mitteilungen*, **79**, 191–208.

GEBAUER, D., SCHERTL, H.-P., BRIX, M. & SCHREYER, W. 1997. 35 Ma old ultrahigh-pressure metamorphism and evidence for very rapid exhumation in the Dora Maira Massif, Western Alps. *Lithos*, **41**, 5–24.

GENSER, J. & NEUBAUER, F. 1989. Low angle normal faults at the eastern margin of the Tauern window (Eastern Alps). *Mitteilungen der Österreichischen Geologischen Gesellschaft*, **81**, 233–243.

GLODNY, J., RING, U., KUHN, A., GLEISSNER, P. & FRANZ, G. 2005. Crystallization and very rapid exhumation of the youngest Alpine eclogites (Tauern Window, Eastern Alps) from Rb/Sr mineral assemblage analysis. *Contributions to Mineralogy and Petrology*, **149**, 699–712.

GOFFÉ, B. 1977. Succession de subfaciès métamorphiques en Vanoise méridionale (Savoie). *Contributions to Mineralogy and Petrology*, **62**, 23–41.

GOLLNER, H., SCHIRNIK, D. & TSCHELAUT, W. 1987. The Problem of the Southalpine Clasts in the "Mittelsteirische Gosau". *In:* FLÜGEL, H. W. & FAUPL, P. (eds) *Geodynamics of the Eastern Alps*. Deuticke, Wien, 156–163.

GRASEMANN, B. & DUNKL, I. 1996. Thermal effects of the exhumation of metamorphic core complex on syn-rift sediments: an example from the Rechnitz Window (Austria). *Mitteilungen der Gesellschaft der Geologie- und Bergbaustudenten in Österreich*, **41**, 108–109.

GRASEMANN, B. & MANCKTELOW, N. S. 1993. 2-dimensional thermal modeling of normal faulting – The Simplon fault zone, Central Alps, Switzerland. *Tectonophysics*, **225**, 155–165.

GRECULA, P. 1973. Domovská oblast' gemerika a jeho metalogenéza (English summary: Homeland of the Gemericum and its metalogenesis). *Mineralia Slovaca*, **5**, 221–316.

GRECULA, P. 1982. Gemericum – segment of the Paleotethyan riftogenous basin. Monografia, Mineralia Slovaca, Alfa, Bratislava [English summary].

GRECULA, P., NÁVESŇÁK, D., BARTALSKÝ, B., GAZDAČKO, L'., NÉMETH, Z., IŠTVÁN, J. & VRBATOVIČ, P. 1990. Shear zones and arc structure of Gemericum, the Western Carpathians. *Mineralia Slovaca*, **22**, 97–110.

GRENERCZY, G., SELLA, G., STEIN, S. & KENYERES, A. 2005. Tectonic implications of the GPS velocity field in the northern Adriatic region. *Geophysical Research Letters*, **32**, L16311.

GRUBER, P., FAUPL, P. & KOLLER, F. 1992. Zur Kenntnis basischer Vulkanitgerölle aus Gosaukonglomeraten der östlichen Kalkalpen - ein Vergleich mit Vulkaniten aus dem Haselgebirge. *Mitteilungen der Österreichischen Geologischen Gesellschaft*, **84**, 77–100.

GRUJIC, D. & MANCKTELOW, N. S. 1996. Structure of the northern Maggia and Lebendun Nappes, Central Alps, Switzerland. *Eclogae geologicae Helvetiae*, **89**, 461–504.

HAAS, J. & BUDAI, T. 1995. Upper Permian – Triassic facies zones in the Transdanubian Range. *Rivista Italiana di Paleontologia e Stratigrafia*, **101**, 249–266.

HAAS, J. & BUDAI, T. 1999. Triassic sequence stratigraphy of the Transdanubian Range (Hungary). *Geologica Carpathica*, **50**, 459–475.

HAAS, J., KOVÁCS, S., KRYSTYN, L. & LEIN, R. 1995. Significance of Late Permian – Triassic facies zones in terrane reconstructions in the Alpine-North Pannonian domain. *Tectonophysics*, **242**, 19–40.

HAAS, J., HÁMOR, G., JÁMBOR, Á., KOVÁCS, S., NAGYMAROSY, A. & SZEDERKÉNYI, T. 2001. *Geology of Hungary*. Eötvös University Press, Budapest.

HABLER, G. 1999. Die polyphase Metamorphose- und Strukturprägung der Eklogit-führenden ostalpinen Kristallineinheiten im Raum Knappenberg (NW Saualpe, Kärnten). *Diploma Thesis Formal- und Naturwissenschaftliche Fakultät Universität Wien*, Wien.

HABLER, G. & THÖNI, M. 2001. Preservation of Permo-Triassic low-pressure assemblages in the Cretaceous high-pressure metamorphic Saualpe crystalline basement (Eastern Alps, Austria). *Journal of Metamorphic Geology*, **19**, 679–697.

HABLER, G. & THÖNI, M. 2005. The Variscan and Permian tectonometamorphic imprint of the S Ötztal-Stubai Complex (Eastern Alps): petrographical, geochronological and structural constraints. *Abstract Book, 7th Workshop on Alpine Geological Studies* (Opatija/Croatia), 43–44.

HANDY, M. R. 1996. The transition from passive to active margin tectonics: a case study from the Zone of Samedan (eastern Switzerland). *Geologische Rundschau*, **85**, 832–851.

HANDY, M. R., FRANZ, L., HELLER, F., JANOTT, B. & ZURBRIGGEN, R. 1999. Multistage accretion and exhumation of the continental crust (Ivrea crustal section, Italy and Switzerland). *Tectonics*, **18**, 1154–1177.

HÄUSLER, H. 1987. The northern Austroalpine margin during the Jurassic: breccias from the Radstädter Tauern and the Tarntaler Berge. *In:* FLÜGEL, H. W. & FAUPL, P. (eds) *Geodynamics of the Eastern Alps*. Deuticke, Wien, 103–111.

HÄUSLER, H., PLAŠIENKA, D. & POLÁK, M. 1993. Comparison of Mesozoic successions of the Central Eastern Alps and the Central Western Carpathians. *Jahrbuch der Geologischen Bundesanstalt (Wien)*, **136**, 715–739.

HAUZENBERGER, C. A., HÖLLER, W. & HOINKES, G. 1996. Transition from eclogite to amphibolite-facies metamorphism in the Austroalpine Ulten Zone. *Mineralogy and Petrology*, **58**, 11–130.

HAVRILA, M. & OŽVOLDOVÁ, L. 1996. Meliaticum in the Stratenská hornatina Hills. *Slovak Geological Magazine*, **96**(3–4), 335–339.

HEINRICH, C. A. 1986. Eclogite facies regional metamorphism of hydrous mafic rocks in the Central Alpine Adula nappe. *Journal of Petrology*, **27**, 123–154.

HEJL, E. 1997. 'Cold spots' during the Cenozoic evolution of the Eastern Alps: thermochronological interpretation of apatite fission-track data. *Tectonophysics*, **272**, 159–173.

HERMANN, J., MÜNTENER, O., TROMMSDORFF, V., HANSMANN, W. & PICCARDO, G. B. 1997. Fossil crust-to-mantle transition, Val Malenco (Italian Alps). *Journal of Geophysical Research – Solid Earth*, **102**, 20123–20132.

HERMANN, J., RUBATTO, A. & TROMMSDORFF, V. 2006. Sub-solidus Oligocene zircon formation in garnet peridotite during fast decompression and fluid infiltration (Duria, Central Alps). *Mineralogy and Petrology*, **88**, 181–206.

HINTERLECHNER-RAVNIK, A., SASSI, F. P. & VISONA, D. 1991. The Austridic eclogites, metabasites and metaultrabasites from the Pohorje area (Eastern Alps, Yugoslavia): 2. The metabasites and metaultrabasites, and concluding considerations. *Rendiconti Fisiche Accademia Lincei*, **2**, 175–190.

HIPS, K. 2001. The structural setting of Lower Triassic formations in the Aggtelek-Rudabánya Mountains (northeastern Hungary) as revealed by geological mapping. *Geologica Carpathica*, **52**, 287–299.

HÖCK, V. & KOLLER, F. 1987. The Idalp Ophiolote (Lower Engadine Window, Eastern Alps) its Petrology and Geochemistry. *Ofioliti*, **12**, 179–192.

HODGES, K. V. & FOUNTAIN, D. M. 1984. Pogallo Line, South Alps, northern Italy: An intermediate crustal level, low-angle normal fault? *Geology*, **12**, 151–155.

HÖFER, C. G. & TICHY, G. 2005. Fossilfunde aus dem Silbereckmarmor des Silberecks, Hafnergruppe (Hohe Tauern, Salzburg). *Journal of Alpine Geology*, **47**, 145–158.

HOINKES, G., THÖNI, M., *et al.* 1997. Metagranitoides and associated metasediments as indicators for the pre-Alpine magmatic and metamorphic evolution of the western Austroalpine Ötztal Basement (Kaunertal, Tyrol). *Schweizerische Mineralogische und Petrographische Mitteilungen*, **77**, 299–314.

HOINKES, G., KOLLER, F., RANTITSCH, G., DACHS, E., HÖCK, V., NEUBAUER, F. & SCHUSTER, R. 1999. Alpine metamorphism of the Eastern Alps. *Schweizerische Mineralogische und Petrographische Mitteilungen*, **79**, 155–181.

HÓK, J. & HRAŠKO, L. 1990. Deformation analysis of the western part of the Pohorelá line. *Mineralia Slovaca*, **22**, 69–80 [English summary].

HÓK, J., KOVÁČ, P. & MADARÁS, J. 1993. Extensional tectonic of the western part of the contact area between Veporicum and Gemericum, Western Carpathians. *Mineralia Slovaca*, **25**, 172–176 [English abstract].

HÓK, J., IVANIČKA, J. & KOVÁČIK, M. 1994. Geological structure of the Rázdiel part of the Tríbeč Mts., Western Carpathians: new knowledge and discussion. *Mineralia Slovaca*, **26**, 192–196 [English summary].

HÓK, J., KOVÁČ, M., KOVÁČ, P., NAGY, A. & ŠUJAN, M. 1999. Geology and tectonics of the NE part of the Komjatice Depression. *Slovak Geological Magazine*, **5**, 187–199.

HÓK, J., BIELIK, M., KOVÁČ, P. & ŠUJAN, M. 2000. Neotectonic character of the Slovak territory. *Mineralia Slovaca*, **32**, 459–470 [English summary].

HORVÁTH, F. 1993. Towards a mechanical model for the formation of the Pannonian basin. *Tectonophysics*, **226**, 333–357.

HORVÁTH, P. 2000. Metamorphic evolution of gabbroic rocks of the Bódva Valley ophiolite complex, NE Hungary. *Geologica Carpathica*, **51**, 121–129.

HOVORKA, D. & SPIŠIAK, J. 1988. *Mesozoic Volcanism of the Western Carpathians*. Veda, Bratislava.

HOVORKA, D. & SPIŠIAK, J. 1993. Mesozoic volcanic activity of the Western Carpathian segment of the Tethyan Belt: diversities in space and time. *Jahrbuch der Geologischen Bundesanstalt*, **136**, 769–782.

HRAŠKO, L'., HATÁR, J., HUHMA, H., MÄNTÄRI, I., MICHALKO, J. & VAASJOKI, M. 1999. U/Pb zircon dating of the Upper Cretaceous granite (Rochovce type) in the Western Carpathians. *Krystalinikum*, **25**, 163–171.

HROUDA, F., PLAŠIENKA, D. & GREGOROVÁ, D. 2002*a*. Assumed Neogene deformation in the Central Western Carpathians as inferred from magnetic anisotropy investigations. *In:* BERTOTTI, G., SCHULMANN, K. & CLOETINGH, S.A.P.L. (eds) *Continental Collision and the Tectono-Sedimentary Evolution of Forelands*. EGS Stephan Mueller Special Publication Series, **1**, 125–136.

HROUDA, F., PUTIŠ, M. & MADARÁS, J. 2002*b*. The Alpine overprints of the magnetic fabrics in the basement and cover rocks of the Veporic Unit (Western Carpathians, Slovakia). *Tectonophysics*, **359**, 271–288.

HRUŠECKÝ, I. 1999. Central part of the Danube basin in Slovakia: geophysical and geological model in regard to hydrocarbon prospection. *Exploration Geophysics Remote Sensing and Environment*, **6**, 2–55.

HRUŠECKÝ, I., ŠEFARA, J., MASARYK, P. & LINTNEROVÁ, O. 1996. The structural and facies development and exploration potential of the Slovak part of the Danube Basin. *In:* WESSELY, G. & LIEBL, W. (eds) *Oil and Gas in Alpidic Thrustbelts and Basins of Central and Eastern Europe*. EAGE, Special Publications, **5**, 417–429.

HRUŠECKÝ, I., PLAŠIENKA, D. & POSPÍŠIL, L. 2006. Identification of the North-European Platform below the eastern part of the West Carpathian Flysch Belt. *In:* GOLONKA, J. & PÍCHA, F. J. (eds) *The Carpathians and their Foreland: Geology and Hydrocarbon Resources*. American Association of Petroleum Geologists, Memoirs, **84**, 717–728.

HUBBARD, M. & MANCKTELOW, N. S. 1992. Lateral displacement during Neogene convergence in the Western and Central Alps. *Geology*, **2**, 943–946.

IVAN, P. 2002. Relics of the Meliata Ocean crust: geodynamic implications of mineralogical, petrological and geochemical proxies. *Geologica Carpathica*, **53**, 245–256.

IVANIČKA, J., SNOPKO, L., SNOPKOVÁ, P. & VOZÁROVÁ, A. 1989. Gelnica Group – lower unit of Spišsko-gemerské rudohorie Mts. *Geologický Zborník Geologica Carpathica*, **40**, 483–501.

JABLONSKÝ, J. 1978. A contribution to knowledge of Albian Zliechov succesion of Strážovské Vrchy Mts. *In:* VOZÁR, J. (ed.) *Paleogeographical Evolution of Western Carpathians*. Konferencie Sympóziá Semináre, D. Štúr Institute of Geology, Bratislava, 175–187 [English summary].

JABLONSKÝ, J. & MARSCHALKO, R. 1992. Pre-flysch olistostromes in Central Western Carpathians, Barremian – Aptian of Krížna Nappe, Slovakia. *Geologica Carpathica*, **43**, 15–20.

JABLONSKÝ, J., MICHALÍK, J., PLAŠIENKA, D. & SOTÁK, J. 1993. Sedimentary enviroments of the Solírov Formation and correlation with Lower Cretaceous turbidites in Central West Carpathians, Slovakia. *Cretaceous Research*, **14**, 613–621.

JACKO, S., SASVÁRI, T., ZACHAROV, M., SCHMIDT, R. & VOZÁR, J. 1996. Contrasting styles of Alpine deformations at the eastern part of the Veporicum and Gemericum units, Western Carpathians. *Slovak Geological Magazine*, **96**(2), 151–164.

JAILLARD, E. 1999. The Late Cretaceous – Eocene sedimentation in the internal Briançonnais units of Vanoise (French Alps): Witnesses of early Alpine movements. *Eclogae geologicae Helvetiae*, **92**, 211–220.

Janák, M. 1994. Variscan uplift of the crystalline basement Tatra Mts., Central Western Carpathians: Evidence from $^{39}$Ar /$^{40}$Ar laser probe dating of biotite and P-T-t paths. *Geologica Carpathica*, **45**, 293–300.

Janák, M., Plašienka, D., Frey, M., Cosca, M., Schmidt, S. T., Lupták, B. & Méres, Š. 2001. Cretaceous evolution of a metamorphic core complex, the Veporic unit, Western Carpathians (Slovakia): P-T conditions and in situ $^{40}$Ar/$^{39}$Ar UV laser probe dating of metapelites. *Journal of Metamorphic Geology*, **19**, 197–216.

Janák, M., Froitzheim, N., Lupták, B., Vrabec, M. & Krogh Ravna, E. J. 2004. First evidence for ultrahigh-pressure metamorphism of eclogites in Pohorje, Slovenia: Tracing deep continental subduction in the Eastern Alps. *Tectonics*, **23**, TC5014.

Janák, M., Froitzheim, N., Vrabec, M., Krogh Ravna, E. J. & De Hoog, J. C. M. 2006. Ultrahigh-pressure metamorphism and exhumation of garnet peridotite in Pohorje, Eastern Alps. *Journal of Metamorphic Geology*, **24**, 19–31.

Jaroš, J. 1971. Tectonic styles of the homelands of superficial nappes. *Rozpravy Československé Akademie Věd, Řada Matematických a Přírodních Věd*, **81**(6), 1–59.

Jarosiński, M. 1998. Contemporary stress field distortion in the Polish part of the Western Outer Carpathians and their basement. *Tectonophysics*, **297**, 91–119.

Jaroszewski, W. 1982. Hydrotectonic phenomena at the base of the Krížna nappe, Tatra Mts. *In:* Mahel', M. (ed.) *Alpine Structural Elements: Carpathian-Balkan-Caucasus-Pamir Orogene Zone.* Veda, Bratislava, 137–148.

Jurewicz, E. 1994. Structural analysis of the Pieniny Klippen Belt at Jaworki, Carpathians, Poland. *Studia Geologica Polonica*, **106**, 7–87 [English summary].

Jurewicz, E. 1997. The contact between the Pieniny Klippen Belt and Magura Unit (the Małe Pieniny Mts.). *Geological Quarterly*, **41**, 315–326.

Kahan, Š. 1969. Eine neue Ansicht über den geologischen Aufbau des Kristalinikums der West-Tatra. *Acta Geologica et Geographica Universitatis Comenianae, Geologica*, **18**, 19–78.

Kázmér, M. & Kovać, S. 1985. Permian-Paleogene paleogeography along the eastern part of the Insubric-Periadriatic lineament system: evidence for continental escape of the Bakony-Drauzug unit. *Acta Geologica Hungarica*, **28**, 71–84.

Kázmér, M., Dunkl, I., Frisch, W., Kuhlemann, J. & Ozsvárt, P. 2003. The Palaeogene forearc basin of the Eastern Alps and Western Carpathians: subduction erosion and basin evolution. *Journal of the Geological Society (London)*, **160**, 413–428.

Kempf, O., Matter, A., Burbank, D. W. & Mange, M. 1999. Depositional and structural evolution of a foreland basin margin in a magnetostratigraphic framework: the eastern Swiss Molasse Basin. *International Journal of Earth Sciences*, **88**, 253–275.

Kissová, D., Dunkl, I., Plašienka, D., Frisch, W. & Marschalko, R. 2005. The Pieniny exotic cordillera (Andrusov Ridge) revisited: new zircon FT ages of granite pebbles from Cretaceous flysch conglomerates of the Pieniny Klippen Belt (Western Carpathians, Slovakia). *Slovak Geological Magazine*, **11**, 17–28.

Klötzli, U., Mair, V. & Bargossi, G. M. 2003. The "Bozener Quarzporphyr" (Southern Alps, Italy): single zircon U/Pb age evidence for 10 Million years of magmatic activity in the Lower Permian. *Mitteilungen der Österreichischen Mineralogischen Gesellschaft*, **148**, 187–188.

Klötzli-Chowanetz, E., Klötzli, U., & Koller, F. 1997. Lower Ordovician migmatisation in the Ötztal crystalline basement (Eastern Alps, Austria): linking U-Pb and Pb-Pb dating with zircon morphology. *Schweizerische Mineralogische und Petrographische Mitteilungen*, **77**, 315–324.

Kober, L. 1922. Regionalgeologische Gliederung des mittleren Teiles der ostalpinen Zentralzone. *Sitzungsberichte Akademie der Wissenschaften in Wien Mathematisch-Naturwissenschaftliche Klasse Abteilung I*, **130**, 375–381.

Koller, F. 1985. Petrologie und Geochemie der Ophiolithe des Penninikums am Alpenostrand. *Jahrbuch der Geologischen Bundesanstalt (Wien)*, **128**, 85–150.

Koller, F. & Pestal, G. 2003. Die ligurischen Ophiolite der Tarntaler Berge und der Matreier Zone. *Arbeitstagung Geologische Bundesanstalt, (Wien)*, 2003, 65–76.

Koller, F. & Zemann, J. 1990. Neues zu den Riebeckitgneisen des Ostendes der nordalpinen Grauwackenzone. *Anzeiger der Akadademie der Wissenschaften (Österreich), math.-naturwiss. Klasse*, **1990**(1), 1–4.

Konečný, V. & Lexa, J. 1984. Structure and evolution of the Neogene volcanism in Central Slovakia. *In:* Vozár. J. (ed.) *Magmatism of the Molasse-forming Epoch.* Konferencie Sympóziá Semináre, D. Štúr Institute of Geology, Bratislava, 125–129.

Konečný, V., Kováč, M., Lexa, J. & Šefara, J. 2002. Neogene evolution of the Carpatho-Pannonian region: an interplay of subduction and back-arc diapiric uprise in the mantle. *In:* Bertotti, G., Schulmann, K. & Cloetingh, S. A. P. L. (eds) *Continental Collision and the Tectono-sedimentary Evolution of Forelands*. EGS Stephan Mueller Special Publication Series, **1**, 105–123.

Korikovsky, S. P., Putiš, M., Plašienka, D., Jacko, S. & Ďurovič, V. 1997. Cretaceous very low-grade metamorphism of the Infratatric and Supratatric domains: an indicator of thin-skinned tectonics in the central Western Carpathians. *In:* Grecula, P., Hovorka, D. & Putiš, M. (eds) *Geological Evolution of the Western Carpathians.* Monograph, Mineralia Slovaca, Bratislava, 89–106.

Koša, E. 1998. Lithostratigraphy and depositional environment of Lower – Middle Jurassic crinoidal limestone formations of the Vysoká Nappe Unit (Malé Karpaty Mts., Western Carpathians). *Geologica Carpathica*, **49**, 329–339.

Kotov, A. B., Miko, O., Putiš, M., Korikovsky, S. P., Bereznaya, N. G., Král', J. & Krist, E. 1996. U/Pb dating of zircons of postorogenic acid metavolcanics and metasubvolcanics: a record of Permian – Triassic taphrogeny of the West-Carpathian basement. *Geologica Carpathica*, **47**, 73–79.

Kováč, M. 2000. *Geodynamic, Palaeogeographical and Structural Evolution of the Carpathian-Pannonian Region during the Miocene: New View on the Neogene Basins of Slovakia*. Veda, Bratislava [English summary].

Kováč, M., Nagymarosy, A., Soták, J. & Šutovská, K. 1993. Late Tertiary paleogeographic evolution of the Western Carpathians. *Tectonophysics*, **226**, 401–416.

Kováč, M., Král', J., Márton, E., Plašienka, D. & Uher, P. 1994. Alpine uplift history of the Central Western Carpathians: geochronological, paleomagnetic, sedimentary and structural data. *Geologica Carpathica*, **45**, 83–96.

Kováč, M., Kováč, P., Marko, F., Karoli, S. & Janočko, J. 1995. The East Slovakian Basin – a complex back arc basin. *Tectonophysics*, **252**, 453–466.

Kováč, M., Baráth, I. & Nagymarosy, A. 1997. The Miocene collapse of the Alpine-Carpathian-Pannonian junction: an overview. *Acta Geologica Hungarica*, **40**, 241–264.

Kováč, M., Nagymarosy, A., *et al.* 1998. Palinspastic reconstruction of the Carpathian-Pannonian region during the Miocene. In: Rakús, M. (ed.) *Geodynamic Development of the Western Carpathians.* Geological Survey of Slovak Republic, D. Štúr Publishers, Bratislava, 189–217.

Kováč, M., Bielik, M., *et al.* 2002. Seismic activity and neotectonic evolution of the Western Carpathians (Slovakia). In: Cloetingh, S.A.P.L., Horváth, F., Bada, G. & Lankreijer, A.C. (eds) *Neotectonics and Seismicity of the Pannonian Basin and Surrounding Orogens.* EGS Stephan Mueller Special Publication Series, **3**, 167–184.

Kováč, P. & Havrila, M. 1998. Inner structure of Hronicum. *Slovak Geological Magazine*, **4**, 275–280.

Kováč, P. & Hók, J. 1993. The Central Slovak Fault System – field evidence of a strike slip. *Geologica Carpathica*, **44**, 155–159.

Kováč, P. & Hók, J. 1996. Tertiary development of the western part of Klippen Belt. *Slovak Geological Magazine*, **96**(2), 137–149.

Kováčik, M., Král', J. & Maluski, H. 1997. Alpine reactivation of the southern Veporicum basement: metamorphism, $^{40}$Ar/$^{39}$Ar dating, geodynamic model and correlation aspects with the Eastern Alps. *In:* Grecula, P., Hovorka, D. & Putiš, M. (eds). *Geological Evolution of the Western Carpathians*. Mineralia Slovaca, Monograph, 163–174.

Kovács, S. 1992. Tethys "western ends" during the Late Paleozoic and Triassic and their possible genetic relationships. *Acta Geologica Hungarica*, **35**, 329–369.

Kovács, S., Haas, J., Császár, G., Szederkényi, T., Buda, Gy. & Nagymarosy, A. 2000. Tectonostratigraphic terranes in the pre-

Neogene basement of the Hungarian part of the Pannonian area. *Acta Geologica Hungarica*, **43**, 225–328.

KOZUR, H. 1991. The evolution of the Meliata-Hallstatt ocean and its significance for the early evolution of the Eastern Alps and Western Carpathians. *Palaeogeography Palaeoclimatology Palaeoecology*, **87**, 109–135.

KOZUR, H. & MOCK, R. 1973. Zum Alter und zur tektonischen Stellung der Meliata-Serie des Slowakischen Karstes. *Geologický Zborník Geologica Carpathica*, **24**, 365–374.

KOZUR, H. & MOCK, R. 1995. First evidence of Jurassic in the Folkmar Suture Zone of the Meliaticum in Slovakia and its tectonic implications. *Mineralia Slovaca*, **27**, 301–307.

KOZUR, H. & MOCK, R. 1996. New paleogeographic and tectonic interpretations in the Slovakian Carpathians and their implications for correlations with the Eastern Alps. Part I: Central Western Carpathians. *Mineralia Slovaca*, **28**, 151–174.

KOZUR, H. & MOCK, R. 1997. New paleogeographic and tectonic interpretations in the Slovakian Carpathians and their implications for correlations with the Eastern Alps. Part II: Inner Western Carpathians. *Mineralia Slovaca*, **29**, 164–209.

KOZUR, H. & MOSTLER, H. 1992. Erster paläontologischer Nachweis von Meliaticum und Süd-Rudabanyaicum in den Nördlichen Kalkalpen (Österreich) und ihre Beziehungen zu den Abfolgen in den Westkarpaten. *Geologisch-Paläontologische Mitteilungen Innsbruck*, **18**, 87–129.

KRAINER, K. 1993. Late- and Post-Variscian Sediments of the Eastern and Southern Alps. *In:* NEUBAUER, F. & RAUMER, J. F. (eds) *The Pre-Mesozoic Geology of the Alps*. Springer, Berlin, 537–564

KRÁL', J. 1977. Fission track ages of apatites from some granitoid rocks in West Carpathians. *Geologický Zborník Geologica Carpathica*, **28**, 269–276.

KRALIK, M., KRUMM, W. & SCHRAMM, J.-M. 1987. Low grade and very low grade metamorphism in the Northern Calcareous Alps and in the Greywacke Zone: illite crystallinity data and isotopic ages. *In:* FLÜGEL, H. W. & FAUPL, P. (eds) *Geodynamics of the Eastern Alps*. Deuticke, Wien, 164–178.

KROBICKI, M. & SŁOMKA, T. 1999. Berriasian submarine mass movements as results of tectonic activity in the Carpathian basins. *Geologica Carpathica*, **50**(special issue), 42–44.

KROHE, A. 1987. Kinematics of Cretaceous nappe tectonics in the Austroalpine basement of the Koralpe region (eastern Austria). *Tectonophysics*, **136**, 171–196.

KRONER, U., MANSY, J.-L. *et al.* 2008. Variscan tectonics. *In:* MCCANN, T. (ed.) *The Geology of Central Europe. Volume 1: Precambrian and Palaeozoic*. Geological Society, London, 599–664.

KURZ, W., NEUBAUER, F., GENSER, J. & DACHS, E. 1998. Alpine geodynamic evolution of passive and active continental margin sequences in the Tauern Window (eastern Alps, Austria, Italy): a review. *Geologische Rundschau*, **87**, 225–242.

KURZ, W., FRITZ, H., PILLER, W. E., NEUBAUER, F. & GENSER, J. 2001*a*. Overview of the Paleogene of the Eastern Alps. *In:* PILLER, W. E. & RASSER, M. (eds) *Paleogene of the Eastern Alps*. Schriftenreihe der Erdwissenschaftlichen Kommissionen /Österreichische Akademie der Wissenschaften, **14**, 11–56.

KURZ, W., UNZOG, W., NEUBAUER, F. & GENSER, G. 2001*b*. Evolution of quartz microstructures and textures during polyphase deformation within the Tauern Window (Eastern Alps). *International Journal of Earth Sciences*, **90**, 361–378.

LADENHAUF, C, ARMSTRONG, R, KONZETT, J & MILLER, C. 2001. The timing of pre-Alpine high-pressure metamorphism in the Eastern Alps: constraints from U-Pb SHRIMP dating of eclogite zircons from the Austroalpine Silvretta nappe. *Journal of Conference Abstracts* (EUG XI), **6**, 600.

LAMMERER, B. & WEGER, M. 1998. Footwall uplift in an orogenic wedge: The Tauern Window in the Eastern Alps of Europe. *Tectonophysics*, **285**, 213–230.

LANKREIJER, A. C. 1998. *Rheology and Basement Control on Extensional Basin Evolution in Central and Eastern Europe. Variscan and Alpine-Carpathian-Pannonian Tectonics*. NSG publication No. 980101, Amsterdam.

LANKREIJER, A., BIELIK, M., CLOETINGH, S. & MAJCIN, D. 1999. Rheology predictions across the Western Carpathians, Bohemian Massif and the Pannonian basin: implications for tectonic scenarios. *Tectonics*, **18**, 1139–1153.

LAPEN, T. J., JOHNSON, C. M., BAUMGARTNER, L. P., MAHLEN, N. J., BEARD, B. L. & AMATO, J. M. 2003. Burial rates during prograde metamorphism of an ultra-high-pressure terrane: an example from Lago di Cignana, western Alps, Italy. *Earth and Planetary Science Letters*, **215**, 57–72.

LAPEN, T. J., JOHNSON, C. M., BAUMGARTNER, L. P., DAL PIAZ, G. V., SKORA, S. & BEARD, B. L. 2007. Coupling of oceanic and continental crust during Eocene eclogite-facies metamorphism: evidence from the Monte Rosa nappe, western Alps. *Contributions to Mineralogy and Petrology*, **153**, 139–157.

LARDEAUX, J. M., SCHWARTZ, S., TRICART, P., PAUL, A., GUILLOT, S., BÉTHOUX, N. & MASSON, F. 2006. A crustal-scale cross-section of the south-western Alps combining geophysical and geological imagery. *Terra Nova*, **18**, 412–422.

LAUBSCHER, H. P. 1961. Die Fernschubhypothese der Jurafaltung. *Eclogae geologicae Helvetiae*, **52**, 221–282.

LEIN, R., GAWLICK, H.-J. & KRYSTYN, L. 1997. Paläogeographie und tektonische Herkunft des Drauzuges - Eine Diskussion auf der Basis von Fazies- und Conodont Colour Alteration Index (CAI)-Untersuchungen. *Zentralblatt für Geologie und Paläontologie*, Teil I, **5/6**, 471–483.

LEMOINE, M., BAS, T., *et al.* 1986. The continental margin of the Mesozoic Tethys in the Western Alps. *Marine and Petroleum Geology*, **3**, 179–199.

LEMOINE, M., TRICART, P. & BOILLOT, G. 1987. Ultramafic and gabbroic ocean floor of the Ligurian Tethys (Alps, Corsica, Apennines): In search of a genetic model. *Geology*, **15**, 622–625.

LENKEY, I. 1999. *Geothermics of the Pannonian Basin and its Bearing on the Tectonics of Basin Evolution*. NSG Publication No. 990112, Vrije Universiteit Amsterdam.

LESS, G. 2000. Polyphase evolution of the structure of the Aggtelek-Rudabánya mountains (NE Hungary), the southernmost element of the Inner Western Carpathians – a review. *Slovak Geological Magazine*, **6**, 260–268.

LEXA, J. & KONEČNÝ, V. 1998. Geodynamic aspects of the Neogene to Quaternary volcanism. *In:* RAKÚS, M. (ed.) *Geodynamic Development of the Western Carpathians*. Geological Survey of Slovak Republic, D. Štúr Publishers, Bratislava, 219–240.

LEXA, O., SCHULMANN, K. & JEŽEK, J. 2003. Cretaceous collision and indentation in the West Carpathians: View based on structural analysis and numerical modeling. *Tectonics*, **22**(6), 1066.

LIATI, A. & FROITZHEIM, N. 2006. Assessing the Valais ocean, Western Alps: U-Pb SHRIMP zircon geochronology of eclogite in the Balma unit, on top of the Monte Rosa nappe. *European Journal of Mineralogy*, **18**, 299–308.

LIATI, A., GEBAUER, D. & FANNING, M. 2000. U-Pb SHRIMP dating of zircon from the Novate granite (Bergell, Central Alps): evidence for Oligocene-Miocene magmatism, Jurassic/Cretaceous continental rifting and opening of the Valais trough. *Schweizerische Mineralogische und Petrographische Mitteilungen*, **80**, 305–316.

LIATI, A., GEBAUER, D. & FANNING, C. M. 2003. The youngest basic oceanic magmatism in the Alps (Late Cretaceous; Chiavenna unit, Central Alps): geochronological constraints and geodynamic significance. *Contributions to Mineralogy and Petrology*, **146**, 144–158.

LIATI, A., FROITZHEIM, N. & FANNING, C. M. 2005. Jurassic ophiolites within the Valais domain of the Western and Central Alps: geochronological evidence for re-rifting of oceanic crust. *Contributions to Mineralogy and Petrology*, **149**, 446–461.

LILLIE, J. R., BIELIK, M., BABUŠKA, V. & PLOMEROVÁ, J. 1994. Gravity modelling of the lithosphere in the Eastern Alpine - Western Carpathian - Pannonian Basin region. *Tectonophysics*, **231**, 215–235.

LINIGER, M. & GUNTLI, P. 1988. Bau und Geschichte des zentralen Teils der Margna-Decke. *Schweizerische Mineralogische und Petrographische Mitteilungen*, **68**, 41–54.

LINZER, H.-G., DECKER, K., PERESSON, H., DELL'MOUR, R. & FRISCH, W. 2002. Balancing lateral orogenic float of the Eastern Alps. *Tectonophysics*, **354**, 211–237.

LIPPITSCH, R., KISSLING, E. & ANSORGE, J. 2003. Upper mantle structure beneath the Alpine orogen from high-resolution teleseismic tomography. *Journal of Geophysical Research*, **108**. DOI: 10.1029/2002JB002016.

LIU, Y, GENSER, J., HANDLER, R., FRIEDL, G. & NEUBAUER, F. 2001.

40Ar/39Ar muscovite ages from the Penninic-Austroalpine plate boundary, Eastern Alps. *Tectonics*, **20**, 526–547.

LOMAS, S. 1992. Submarine mass-flow conglomerates of the Tarentaise zone, Western Alps – sedimentation processes and depositional setting. *Sedimentary Geology*, **81**, 269–287.

LÖW, S. 1987. Die tektono-metamorphe Entwicklung der nördlichen Adula-Decke. *Beiträge zur geologischen Karte der Schweiz* (Neue Folge), **161**, 1–83.

LUCIŃSKA-ANCZKIEWICZ, A., VILLA, I. M., ANCZKIEWICZ, R. & ŚLĄCZKA, A. 2002. $^{40}Ar/^{39}Ar$ dating of alkaline lamprophyres from the Polish Western Carpathians. *Geologica Carpathica*, **53**, 45–52.

LUPTÁK, B., JANÁK, M., PLAŠIENKA, D., SCHMIDT, S. T. & FREY, M. 2000. Chloritoid-kyanite schists from the Veporic unit, Western Carpathians, Slovakia: implications for Alpine (Cretaceous) metamorphism. *Schweizerische Mineralogische und Petrogrographische Mitteilungen*, **80**, 213–223.

LUPTÁK, B., JANÁK, M., PLAŠIENKA, D. & SCHMIDT, S. T. 2003. Alpine low-grade metamorphism of the Permian-Triassic sedimentary rocks from the Veporic superunit, Western Carpathians: phylosilicate composition and "crystallinity" data. *Geologica Carpathica*, **54**, 367–375.

LÜSCHEN, E., LAMMERER, B., GEBRANDE, H., MILLAHN, K., NICOLICH, R. & TRANSALP WORKING GROUP 2004. Orogenic structure of the Eastern Alps, Europe, from TRANSALP deep seismic reflection profiling. *Tectonophysics*, **388**, 85–102.

MCCANN, T., SKOMPSKI, S., *et al.* 2008*a*. Carboniferous. *In*: MCCANN, T. (ed.) *The Geology of Central Europe. Volume 1: Precambrian and Palaeozoic*. Geological Society, London, 411–529.

MCCANN, T., KIERSNOWSKI, H., *et al.* 2008*b*. Permian. *In*: MCCANN, T. (ed.) *The Geology of Central Europe. Volume 1: Precambrian and Palaeozoic*. Geological Society, London, 531–597.

MADARÁS, J., PUTIŠ, M. & DUBÍK, B. 1994. Structural characteristic of the middle part of the Pohorelá tectonic zone; Veporicum, Western Carpathians. *Mineralia Slovaca*, **26**, 177–191 [English summary].

MADARÁS, J., HÓK, J., SIMAN, P., BEZÁK, V., LEDRU, P. & LEXA, O. 1996. Extension tectonics and exhumation of crystalline basement of the Veporicum unit (Central Western Carpathians). *Slovak Geological Magazine*, **96**(3–4), 179–183.

MAHEL', M. 1981. Island character of Klippen Belt; Vahicum – continuation of Southern Penninicum in West Carpathians. *Geologický Zborník Geologica Carpathica*, **32**, 293–305.

MAHEL', M. 1983. Krížna nappe, example of polyfacial and polystructural unit. *Mineralia Slovaca*, **15**, 193–216 [English summary].

MAHEL' M. 1986. *Geological Structure of Czechoslovak Carpathians. Part 1: Paleoalpine Units*. Veda, Bratislava [English summary].

MAHEL', M. 1989. Klippen Belt from the aspect of the geodynamic model. *Mineralia Slovaca*, **21**, 99–108 [English summary].

MALUSKI, H., RAJLICH, P. & MATTE, P. 1993. $^{40}Ar$-$^{39}Ar$ dating of the Inner Carapthians Variscan basement and Alpine mylonitic overprinting. *Tectonophysics*, **223**, 313–337.

MANATSCHAL, G. 2004. New models for evolution of magma-poor rifted margins based on a review of data and concepts from West Iberia and the Alps. *International Journal of Earth Sciences*, **93**, 432–466.

MANATSCHAL, G. & NIEVERGELT, P. 1997. A continent-ocean transition recorded in the Err and Platta nappes (Eastern Switzerland). *Eclogae geologicae Helvetiae*, **90**, 3–27.

MANATSCHAL, G., ENGSTRÖM, A., DESMURS, L., SCHALTEGGER, U., COSCA, M., MÜNTENER, O. & BERNOULLI, D. 2006. What is the tectono-metamorphic evolution of continental break-up: The example of the Tasna Ocean-Continent Transition. *Journal of Structural Geology*, **28**, 1849–1869.

MANCKTELOW, N. S. 1985. The Simplon Line: a major displacement zone in the western Lepontine Alps. *Eclogae geologicae Helvetiae*, **78**, 73–96.

MANCKTELOW, N. S. 1992. Neogene lateral extension during convergence in the Central Alps – evidence from interrelated faulting and backfolding around Simplonpass (Switzerland). *Tectonophysics*, **215**, 295–317.

MANCKTELOW, N. S., STÖCKLI, D. F., *et al.* 2001. The DAV and Periadriatic fault systems in the Eastern Alps south of the Tauern window. *International Journal of Earth Sciences*, **90**, 593–622.

MANDL, G. 2000. The Alpine sector of the Tethyan shelf - Examples of Triassic to Jurassic sedimentation and deformation from the Northern Calcareous Alps. *Mitteilungen der Österreichischen Geologischen Gesellschaft*, **92**, 61–77.

MANDL, G. & ONDREJICKOVA, A. 1993. Radiolarien und Conodonten aus dem Meliatikum im Ostabschnitt der NKA (A). *Jahrbuch der Geologischen Bundesanstalt (Wien)*, **136**, 841–871.

MARKO, F. 1993. Kinematics of Muráň fault between Hrabušice and Tuhár village. *In:* RAKÚS, M. & VOZÁR, J. (eds) *Geodynamic model and deep structure of the Western Carpathians*. Conferences Symposia Seminars, D. Štúr Institute of Geology, Bratislava, 253–261.

MARKO, F. & VOJTKO, R. 2006. Structural record and tectonic history of the Mýto-Tisovec fault (Central Western Carpathians). *Geologica Carpathica*, **57**, 211–221.

MARRONI, M., MOLLI, G., MONTANINI, A., OTTRIA, G., PANDOLFI, L. & TRIBUZIO, R. 2002. The external Ligurian units (Northern Apennine, Italy): From rifting to convergence of a fossil ocean-continent transition zone. *Ofioliti*, **27**, 119–131.

MARSCHALKO, R. 1986. *Evolution and Geotectonic Significance of the Klippen Belt Cretaceous Flysch in the Carpathian Megastructure*. Veda, Bratislava [English summary].

MARSCHALKO, R. & SAMUEL, M. 1993. Sedimentology of Súl'ov Conglomerates eastern branch. *Západné Karpaty, Séria Geológia*, **17**, 7–38 [English summary].

MARTON, E., ZUPANCIC, N., PECSKAY, Z., TRAJANOVA, M. & JELEN, B. 2002. Paleomagnetism and new K-Ar ages of the Pohorje igneous rocks. *Geologica Carpathica*, **53**(special issue published on CD).

MASARYK, P., LINTNEROVÁ, O. & MICHALÍK, J. 1993. Sedimentology, lithofacies and diagenesis of the sediments of the Reifling intraplatform basins in the Central Western Carpathians. *Geologica Carpathica*, **44**, 233–249.

MATTAUER, M., MALAVIEILLE, J. & MONIÉ, P. 1987. Une coupe lithosphérique des Alpes occidentales dans l'hypothèse ou Sesia n'est pas d'origine sud-alpine. *Comptes Rendus de l'Académie des Sciences (Paris), série IIa*, **304**, 43–48.

MATTERN, F. 1999. Mid-Cretaceous basin development, paleogeography, and paleogeodynamics of the western Rhenodanubian flysch (Alps). *Zeitschrift der Deutschen Geologischen Gesellschaft*, **150**, 89–132.

MAXELON, M. 2004. *Developing a three-dimensional structural model of the lower Lepontine nappes*. PhD thesis No. 15598, ETH Zürich..

MEFFAN-MAIN, S., CLIFF, R. A., BARNICOAT, A. C., LOMBARDO, B. & COMPAGNONI, R. 2004. A tertiary age for Alpine high-pressure metamorphism in the Gran Paradiso massif, Western Alps: a Rb-Sr microsampling study. *Journal of Metamorphic Geology*, **22**, 267–281.

MELCHER, F., MEISEL, T., PUHL, J. & KOLLER, F. 2002. Petrogenesis and geotectonic setting of ultramafic rocks in the Eastern Alps: constraints from geochemistry. *Lithos*, **65**, 69–112.

MELLO, J. (ed.) 1997. *Explanations to the Geological Map of the Slovak Karst*. Geologická služba SR, Vydavatel'stvo D. Štúra, Bratislava.

MELLO, J. (ed.) 2000. *Explanations to the Geological Map of the Slovenský raj Mts., Galmus and Hornádska Kotlina Valley*. Geologická služba SR, Vydavatel'stvo D. Štúra, Bratislava.

MELLO, J., REICHWALDER, P. & VOZÁROVÁ, A. 1998. Bôrka nappe: high-pressure relic from the subduction-accretion prism of the Meliata ocean (Inner Western Carpathians, Slovakia). *Slovak Geological Magazine*, **4**, 261–273.

MERCIER, J. 1958. Sur l'age de la phase tectonique 'ante-senonienne' a l'ouest du Dévoluy (Drôme). *Bulletin de la Société Géologique de France, (6)*, **8**, 689–97.

MEULENKAMP, J. E., KOVÁČ, M. & CICHA, I. 1996. On Late Oligocene to Pliocene depocenter migrations and the evolution of the Carpathian – Pannonian system. *Tectonophysics*, **266**, 301–317.

MEYRE, C., MARQUER, D. & SCHMID, S. M. 1998. Syn-orogenic extension along the Forcola fault: Correlation of Alpine deformations in the Tambo and Adula nappes (Eastern Penninic Alps). *Eclogae geologicae Helvetiae*, **91**, 409–420.

MICHALÍK, J. 1977. Paläogeographische untersuchungen der Fatraschichten des nördlichen Teiles des Fatrikums in der Westkarpaten. *Geologický Zborník Geologica Carpathica*, **28**, 71–94.

MICHALÍK, J. 1978. To the paleogeographic, paleotectonic and paleoclimatic development of the West Carpathian area in the uppermost Triassic. *In:* VOZÁR, J. (ed.) *Paleogeographical Evolution of the West Carpathians*. D. Štúr Institute of Geology, Bratislava, 189–211.

MICHALÍK, J. 1994*a*. Notes on the paleogeography and paleotectonics of the Western Carpathian area during the Mesozoic. *Mitteilungen der Österreichischen Geologischen Gesellschaft*, **86**, 101–110.
MICHALÍK, J. 1994*b*. Lower Cretaceous carbonate platform facies, Western Carpathians. *Palaeogeography Palaeoclimatology Palaeoecology*, **111**, 263–277.
MICHALÍK, J. 1997. Tsunamites in a storm-dominated Anisian carbonate ramp (Vysoká Formation, Malé Karpaty Mts., Western Carpathians). *Geologica Carpathica*, **48**, 221–229.
MICHALÍK, J. & REHÁKOVÁ, D. 1995. Sedimentary records of Early Cretaceous tectonic activity in the Alpine-Carpathian region. *Slovak Geological Magazine*, **95**(2), 159–164.
MICHALÍK, J. & SOTÁK, J. 1990. Lower Cretaceous shallow marine buildups in the Western Carpathians and their relationship to pelagic facies. *Cretaceous Research*, **11**, 211–227.
MICHALÍK, J., VAŠÍČEK, Z. & BORZA, V. 1993*a*. The Upper Jurassic – Lower Cretaceous biostratigraphy and microfacies of a basin sequence in the Krížna Nappe of the Fatric. *Geologické Práce, Správy*, **97**, 105–112 [English summary].
MICHALÍK, J., MASARYK, P., LINTNEROVÁ, O., SOTÁK, J., JENDREJÁKOVÁ, O., PAPŠOVÁ, J. & BUČEK, S. 1993*b*. Facies, paleogeography and diagenetic evolution of the Ladinian/Carnian Veterlín reef complex, Malé Karpaty Mts. (Western Carpathians). *Geologica Carpathica*, **44**, 17–34.
MICHALÍK, J., REHÁKOVÁ, D. & ŽÍTT, J. 1993*c*. Upper Jurassic and Lower Cretaceous facies, microplancton and crinoids in the Kuchyňa unit, Malé Karpaty Mts. *Geologica Carpathica*, **44**, 161–176.
MICHALÍK, J., REHÁKOVÁ, D. & JABLONSKÝ, J. 1996. Geodynamic setting of fluxoturbidites in West Carpathian Upper Jurassic and Lower Cretaceous sedimentary basins. *Slovak Geological Magazine*, **96** (3–4), 325–329.
MILLER, C. 1990. Petrology of the type locality eclogites from the Koralpe and Saualpe (Eastern Alps), Austria. *Schweizerische Mineralogische und Petrographische Mitteilungen*, **70**, 287–300.
MICHON, L., VAN BALEN, R.T., MERLE, O. & PAGNIER, H. 2003. The Cenozoic evolution of the Roer Valley Rift System integrated at a European scale. *Tectonophysics*, **367**, 101–126.
MILLER, C. & THÖNI, M. 1995. Origin of eclogites from the Austroalpine Ötztal basement (Tirol, Austria): geochemistry and Sm-Nd vs. Rb-Sr isotope systematics. *Chemical Geology (Isotope Geoscience Section)*, **122**, 199–225.
MILLER, C. & THÖNI, M. 1997. Eo-Alpine eclogitisation of Permian MORB-type gabbros in the Koralpe (Eastern Alps, Austria): new geochronological, geochemical and petrological data. *Chemical Geology*, **137**, 283–310.
MILLER, C., MUNDIL, R., THÖNI, M. & KONZETT, J. 2005. Refining the timing of eclogite metamorphism: a geochemical, Sm-Nd and U-Pb case study from the Pohorje Mountains, Slovenia (Eastern Alps). *Contributions to Mineralogy and Petrology*, **150**, 70–84.
MILNES, A. G. 1974. Structure of the Pennine zone (Central Alps): a new working hypothesis. *Geological Society of America Bulletin*, **85**, 1727–1732.
MILNES, A. G. & PFIFFNER, O. A. 1980. Tectonic evolution of the Central Alps in the cross section St.Gallen-Como. *Eclogae geologicae Helvetiae*, **73**, 619–633.
MILNES, A. G. & SCHMUTZ, H.-U. 1978. Structure and history of the Suretta nappe (Pennine zone, Central Alps) – a field study. *Eclogae geologicae Helvetiae*, **71**, 19–33.
MILOVSKÝ, R., HURAI, V., PLAŠIENKA, D. & BIROŇ, A. 2003. Hydrotectonic regime at soles of overthrust sheets: textural and fluid inclusion evidence from basal cataclasites of the Muráň nappe (Western Carpathians, Slovakia). *Geodynamica Acta*, **16**, 1–20.
MIŠÍK, M. 1978. Continental, brakish and hypersaline facies in the Mesozoic of the Central Western Carpathians and the problem of emerged areas. *In:* VOZÁR, J. (ed.) *Paleogeographic Evolution of the Western Carpathians*. Konferencie Sympóziá Semináre, D. Štúr Institute of Geology, Bratislava, 35–48 [English summary].
MIŠÍK, M. 1979*a*. Sedimentological and microfacial study in the Jurassic of the Vršatec castle klippe (neptunic dykes, Oxfordian bioherm facies). *Západné Karpaty, séria Geológia*, **5**, 7–56 [English summary].
MIŠÍK, M. 1979*b*. Pieniny Klippen Belt and the global tectonics model. *In:* MAHEL', M. & REICHWALDER, P. (eds) *Czechoslovak Geology and Global Tectonics*. Veda, Bratislava, 89–101.
MIŠÍK, M. 1994. The Czorsztyn submarine ridge (Jurassic – Lower Cretaceous, Pieniny Klippen Belt): An example of a pelagic swell. *Mitteilungen der Österreichischen Geologischen Gesellschaft*, **86**(1993), 133–140.
MIŠÍK, M. & JABLONSKÝ, J. 2000. Lower Triassic quartzites of the Western Carpathians: transport directions, source of clastics. *Geologica Carpathica*, **51**, 251–264.
MIŠÍK, M. & MARSCHALKO, R. 1988. Exotic conglomerates in flysch sequences: Examples from the West Carpathians. *In:* RAKÚS, M., DERCOURT, J. & NAIRN, A. E. M. (eds) *Evolution of the Northern Margin of Tethys, Vol. I*. Mémoire de la Société Géologique de France, Nouvelle Série No. **154**, 95–113.
MIŠÍK, M. & SÝKORA, M. 1981. Pieninský exotický chrbát rekonštruovaný z valúnov karbonátových hornín kriedových zlepencov bradlového pásma a manínskej jednotky. *Západné Karpaty, séria Geológia*, **7**, 7–111.
MIŠÍK, M. & SÝKORA, M. 1982. Allodapische Barmsteinkalke im Malm des Gebirges Čachtické Karpaty. *Geologický Zborník Geologica Carpathica*, **33**, 51–78.
MIŠÍK, M., MOCK, R. & SÝKORA, M. 1977. Die Trias der Klippen-Zone der Karpaten. *Geologický Zborník Geologica Carpathica*, **28**, 27–69.
MIŠÍK, M., JABLONSKÝ, J., FEJDI, P. & SÝKORA, M. 1980. Chromian and ferrian spinels from Cretaceous sediments of the West Carpathians. *Mineralia Slovaca*, **12**, 209–228.
MIŠÍK, M., JABLONSKÝ, J., MOCK, R. & SÝKORA, M. 1981. Konglomerate mit exotischen Material in dem Alb der Zentralen Westkarpaten – paläogeographische und tektonische Interpretation. *Acta Geologica et Geographica Universitatis Comenianae, Geologica*, **37**, 5–55.
MIŠÍK, M., SÝKORA, M., MOCK, R. & JABLONSKÝ, J. 1991. Paleogene Proč conglomerates of the Klippen belt in the west Carpathians, material from Neopieninic exotic ridge. *Acta Geologica et Geographica Universitatis Comenianae, Geologica*, **46**, 9–101.
MOCK, R., SÝKORA, M., AUBRECHT, R., OŽVOLDOVÁ, L., KRONOME, B., REICHWALDER, P. & JABLONSKÝ, J. 1998. Petrology and stratigraphy of the Meliaticum near the Meliata and Jaklovce Villages, Slovakia. *Slovak Geological Magazine*, **4**, 223–260.
MOSAR, J., STAMPFLI, G. M. & GIROD, F. 1996. Western Préalpes Médianes Romandes: timing and structure. A review. *Eclogae geologicae Helvetiae*, **89**, 389–425.
MULCH, A., ROSENAU, M., DORR, W. & HANDY, M. R. 2004. The age and structure of dikes along the tectonic contact of the Ivrea-Verbano and Strona-Ceneri Zones (southern Alps, Northern Italy, Switzerland). *Schweizerische Mineralogische und Petrographische Mitteilungen*, **82**, 55–76.
MÜLLER, D., STUMPFL, E. F. & TAYLOR, W. R. 1992. Shoshonitic and Alkaline Lamprophyres with Elevated Au and PGE Concentrations from the Kreuzeck Mountains, Eastern Alps. *Mineralogy and Petrology*, **46**, 23–42.
MÜLLER, W., DALLMEYER, R. D., NEUBAUER, F. & THÖNI, M. 1999. Deformation-induced resetting of Rb/Sr and 40Ar/39Ar mineral systems in a low-grade, polymetamorphic terrane (Eastern Alps, Austria). *Journal of the Geological Society*, **156**, 261–278.
NAGEL, T. J. 2006. Structure of Austroalpine and Penninic units in the Tilisuna area (Eastern Rätikon, Austria): Implications for the paleogeographic position of the Allgäu and Lechtal nappes. *Eclogae geologicae Helvetiae*, **99**, 223–235.
NAGEL, T. J. & BUCK W. R. 2004. Symmetric alternative to asymmetric rifting models. *Geology*, **32**, 937–940.
NAGEL, T., DE CAPITANI, C., FREY, M., FROITZHEIM, N., STÜNITZ, H. & SCHMID, S. M. 2002. Structural and metamorphic evolution during rapid exhumation in the Lepontine dome (southern Simano and Adula nappes, Central Alps, Switzerland). *Eclogae geologicae Helvetiae*, **95**, 301–321.
NEMČOK, J. 1980. Non-traditional view of East-Slovakian Klippen Belt. *Geologický Zborník Geologica Carpathica*, **31**, 563–568.
NEMČOK, M. & NEMČOK, J. 1994. Late Cretaceous deformation of the Pieniny Klippen Belt, West Carpathians. *Tectonophysics*, **239**, 81–109.
NEMČOK, J., KULLMANOVÁ, A. & ĎURKOVIČ, T. 1989. Development and stratigraphic position of the Gregorianka breccia in eastern Slovakia. *Geologické Práce, Správy*, **89**, 11–37 [English summary].
NEMČOK, M., POSPÍŠIL, L., LEXA, J. & DONELICK, R. A. 1998. Tertiary subduction and slab break-off model for the Carpathian-Pannonian region. *Tectonophysics*, **295**, 307–340.

NEMČOK, M., NEMČOK, J., *et al.* 2000. Results of 2D balancing along 20° and 21°30' longitude and pseudo-3D in the Smilno tectonic window: implications for shortening mechanisms of the West Carpathian accretionary wedge. *Geologica Carpathica*, **51**, 281–300.

NEMES, F., NEUBAUER, F., CLOETINGH, S. & GENSER, J. 1997. The Klagenfurt Basin in the Eastern Alps: an intra-orogenic decoupled flexural basin? *Tectonophysics*, **282**, 189–203.

NÉMETH, Z., GAZDAČKO, L'., NÁVESŇÁK, D. & KOBULSKÝ, J. 1997. Polyphase tectonic evolution of the Gemericum (the Western Carpathians) outlined by review of structural and deformational data. *In:* GRECULA, P., HOVORKA, D. & PUTIŠ, M. (eds) *Geological Evolution of the Western Carpathians*. Monograph, Mineralia Slovaca, Bratislava, 215–224.

NEUBAUER, F. 1980. Zur tektonischen Stellung des Ackerlkristallins (Nordrand der Gurktaler Decke). *Mitteilungen der Österreichischen Geologischen Gesellschaft*, **73**, 39–53.

NEUBAUER, F. 2002. Evolution of late Neoproterozoic to early Palaeozoic tectonic elements in Central and Southeast European Alpine mountain belts: review and synthesis. *Tectonophysics*, **352**, 87–103.

NEUBAUER, F. & VOZÁROVÁ, A. 1990. The Noetsch-Veitsch-North Gemeric zone of Alps and Carpathians: correlation, paleogeography and significance for Variscan orogeny. *In:* MINAŘÍKOVÁ, D. & LOBITZER, H. (eds) *Thirty Years of Geological Cooperation between Austria and Czechoslovakia*. Federal Geological Survey Vienna, Geological Survey Prague, 167–171.

NEUBAUER, F., DALLMEYER, R. D., DUNKL, I. & SCHIRNIK, D. 1994*a*. Late Cretaceous exhumation of the metamorphic Gleinalm dome, Eastern Alps: kinematics, cooling history and sedimentary response in a sinistral wrench corridor. *Tectonophysics*, **242**, 79–98.

NEUBAUER, F., HANDLER, R., HERMANN, S. & PAULUS, G. 1994*b*. Revised lithostratigraphy and structure of the Eastern Graywacke Zone (Eastern Alps). *Mitteilungen der Österreichischen Geologischen Gesellschaft*, **86**, 61–74.

NEUBAUER, F., GENSER, J. & HANDLER, R. 2000. The Eastern Alps: Result of a two-stage collision process. *Mitteilungen der Österreichischen Geologischen Gesellschaft*, **92**, 117–134.

NEUBAUER, F., FRIEDL, G., GENSER, J., HANDLER, R., MADER, D. & SCHNEIDER, D. 2007. Origin and tectonic evolution of the Eastern Alps deduced from dating of detrital white mica: a review. *Austrian Journal of Earth Sciences*, **100**, 8–25.

NEUMAYR, M. 1871. Jurastudien 5. Der pienninische Klippenzug. *Jahrbuch der Kaiserlich-Königlichen Geologischen Reichsanstalt (Wien)*, **21**.

NIEVERGELT, P., LINIGER, M., FROITZHEIM, N. & FERREIRO MÄHLMANN, R. 1996. Early to mid Tertiary crustal extension in the Central Alps: The Turba mylonite zone (Eastern Switzerland). *Tectonics*, **15**, 329–340.

OBERHÄNSLI, R. 1978. Chemische Untersuchungen an Glaukophanführenden basischen Gesteinen aus den Bündnerschiefern Graubündens. *Schweizerische Mineralogische und Petrographische Mitteilungen*, **58**, 139–156.

OBERHAUSER, R. 1980. Das Unterengadiner Fenster. *In:* OBERHAUSER, R. (ed.) *Der geologische Aufbau Österreichs*. Springer, Wien, 291–299.

OBERHAUSER, R. 1983. Mikrofossilfunde im Nordwestteil des Unterengadiner Fensters sowie im Verspalaflysch des Rätikon. *Jahrbuch der Geologischen Bundesanstalt (Wien)*, **126**, 71–93.

OBERHAUSER, R. 1995. Zur Kenntnis der Tektonik und der Paläogeographie des Ostalpenraums zur Kreide-, Paleozän- und Eozänzeit. *Jahrbuch der Geologischen Bundesanstalt (Wien)*, **138**, 369–432.

OBERHAUSER, R. 1998. *Erläuterungen zur Geologisch-Tektonischen Übersichtskarte von Vorarlberg 1 : 200 000*. Geologische Bundesanstalt, Wien.

ORTNER, H. 1994. Die Muttekopfgosau (Lechtaler Alpen, Tirol/Österreich): Sedimentologie und Beckenentwicklung. *Geologische Rundschau*, **83**, 197–211.

ORTNER, H. 2001. Growing folds and sedimentation of the Gosau Group, Muttekopf, Northern Calcareous Alps, Austria. *International Journal of Earth Sciences*, **90**, 727–729.

OSZCZYPKO, N. 1992. Late Cretaceous through Paleogene evolution of Magura Basin. *Geologica Carpathica*, **43**, 333–338.

OSZCZYPKO, N. 1998. The Western Carpathian foredeep – development of the foreland basin in front of the accretionary wedge and its burial history (Poland). *Geologica Carpathica*, **49**, 415–431.

OSZCZYPKO, N. 2004. The structural and tectonosedimentary evolution of the Polish Outer Carpathians. *Przegład Geologiczny*, **52**, 780–791.

OXBURGH, E. R., LAMBERT, R. S. J., BAADSGAARD, H. & SIMONS, J. G. 1966. Potassium-Argon age studies across the southeast margin of the Tauern window, the East Alps. *Verhandlungen der Geologischen Bundesanstalt (Wien)*, **1966**, 17–33.

PAHR, A. 1980. Die Fenster von Rechnitz, Bernstein und Möltern. *In:* OBERHAUSER, R. (ed.) *Der geologische Aufbau Österreichs*. Springer, Wien, 320–326.

PAHR, A. 1991. Ein Diskussionbeitrag zur Tektonik des Raumes Alpenostende – Kleine Karpaten – Pannonisches Becken. *In:* LOBITZER, H. & CSÁSZÁR, G. (eds) *Jubiläumsschrift 20 Jahre Zusammenarbeit Österreich – Ungarn*. Teil 1, Wien, 297–305.

PAMIĆ, J. 2002. The Sava-Vardar Zone of the Dinarides and Hellenides versus the Vardar ocean. *Eclogae geologicae Helvetiae*, **95**, 99–113.

PAMIĆ, J., TOMLJENOVIĆ, B. & BALEN, D. 2002. Geodynamic and petrogenetic evolution of Alpine ophiolites from the central and NW Dinarides: an overview. *Lithos*, **65**, 113–142.

PERESSON, H. & DECKER, K. 1997. Far-field effect of late Miocene subduction in the eastern Carpathians: E-W compression and inversion of structures in the Alpine-Carpathian-Pannonian region. *Tectonics*, **16**, 38–56.

PETRÍK, I. 2000. Multiple sources of the West-Carpathian Variscan granitoids: a review of Rb/Sr and Sm/Nd data. *Geologica Carpathica*, **51**, 145–158.

PETRÍK, I., BROSKA, I. & UHER, P. 1994. Evolution of the Western Carpathian granite magmatism: Age, source rock, geotectonic setting and relation to the Variscan structure. *Geologica Carpathica*, **45**, 283–291.

PFIFFNER, O. A. & HITZ, L. 1997. Geologic interpretation of the seismic profiles of the Eastern Traverse (lines E1-E3, E7-E9): eastern Swiss Alps. *In:* PFIFFNER, O. A., LEHNER, P., HEITZMANN, P., MUELLER, S. & STECK, A. (eds.) *Deep Structure of the Swiss Alps: Results of NRP 20*. Birkhäuser, Basel, 73–100.

PFIFFNER, O. A., ERARD, P.-F. & STÄUBLE, M. 1997. Two cross sections through the Swiss Molasse Basin (lines E4-E6, W1, W7-W10). *In:* PFIFFNER, O. A., LEHNER, P., HEITZMANN, P., MUELLER, S. & STECK, A. (eds) *Deep Structure of the Swiss Alps: Results of NRP 20*. Birkhäuser, Basel, 64–72.

PÍCHA, F. 1979. Ancient submarine canyons of Tethyan continental margins, Czechoslovakia. *American Association of Petroleum Geologists Bulletin*, **63**, 67–86.

PICOTTI, V., PROSSER, G. & CASTELLARIN, A. 1995. Structures and kinematics of the Giudicarie – Val Trompia fold and thrust belt (Central Southern Alps, northern Italy). *Memorie della Societá geologica Italiana*, **47**, 95–109.

PIERI, M. & GROPPI, G. 1981. *Subsurface Geological Structure of the Po Plain, Italy*. Progetto Finalizzato Geodinamica, Publication No. 414.

PILLER, W. E. *et al.* 2004. *Die stratigraphische Tabelle von Österreich 2004 (sedimentäre Schichtfolgen)*. Österreichische Stratigraphische Kommission.

PLAŠIENKA, D. 1987. Lithological, sedimentological and paleotectonic pattern of the Borinka Unit in the Little Carpathians. *Mineralia Slovaca*, **19**, 217–230 [English summary]

PLAŠIENKA, D. 1990. Regional shear and transpression zones in the Tatric unit of the Little Carpathians. *Mineralia Slovaca*, **22**, 55–62 [English summary].

PLAŠIENKA, D. 1993. Structural pattern and partitioning of deformation in the Veporic Foederata cover unit (Central Western Carpathians). *In:* RAKÚS, M. & VOZÁR, J. (eds) *Geodynamic Model and Deep Structure of the Western Carpathians*. Conferences Symposia Seminars, D. Štúr Institute of Geology, Bratislava, 269–277.

PLAŠIENKA, D. 1995*a*. Passive and active margin history of the northern Tatricum (Western Carpathians, Slovakia). *Geologische Rundschau*, **84**, 748–760.

PLAŠIENKA, D. 1995*b*. Mesozoic evolution of Tatric units in the Malé Karpaty and Považský Inovec Mts.: Implications for the position of the Klape and related units in western Slovakia. *Geologica Carpathica*, **46**, 101–112.

PLAŠIENKA, D. 1995*c*. Cleavages and folds in changing tectonic regimes: the Vel'ký Bok Mesozoic cover unit of the Veporicum (Nízke Tatry Mts., Central Western Carpathians). *Slovak Geological Magazine*, **95**(2), 97–113.

PLAŠIENKA, D. 1999*a*. *Tectonochronology and Paleotectonic Evolution of* *the Central Western Carpathians during the Jurassic and Cretaceous*. Veda, Bratislava [English summary].

Plašienka, D. 1999*b*. Definition and correlation of tectonic units with a special reference to some Central Western Carpathian examples. *Mineralia Slovaca*, **31**, 3–16.

Plašienka, D. 2003*a*. Dynamics of Mesozoic pre-orogenic rifting in the Western Carpathians. *Mitteilungen der Österreichischen Geologischen Gesellschaft*, **94**(2001), 79–98.

Plašienka, D. 2003*b*. Development of basement-involved fold and thrust structures exemplified by the Tatric-Fatric-Veporic nappe system of the Western Carpathians (Slovakia). *Geodinamica Acta*, **16**, 21–38.

Plašienka, D. & Prokešová, R. 1996. Towards an evolutionary tectonic model of the Krížna cover nappe (Western Carpathians, Slovakia). *Slovak Geological Magazine*, **97**(3–4), 279–286.

Plašienka, D. & Soták, J. 1996. Rauhwackized carbonate tectonic breccias in the West Carpathian nappe edifice: introductory remarks and preliminary results. *Slovak Geological Magazine*, **96**(3–4), 287–291.

Plašienka, D. & Soták, J. 2001. Stratigraphic and tectonic position of Carboniferous sediments in the Furmanec Valley (Muráň Plateau, Central Western Carpathians). *Mineralia Slovaca*, **33**, 29–44 [English summary].

Plašienka, D., Michalík, J., Gross, P. & Putiš, M. 1991. Paleotectonic evolution of the Malé Karpaty Mts. – an overview. *Geologica Carpathica*, **42**, 195–208.

Plašienka, D., Korikovsky, S. P. & Hacura, A. 1993. Anchizonal Alpine metamorphism of Tatric cover sediments in the Malé Karpaty Mts. (Western Carpathians). *Geologica Carpathica*, **44**, 365–371.

Plašienka, D., Grecula, P., Putiš, M., Kováč, M. & Hovorka, D. 1997. Evolution and structure of the Western Carpathians: an overview. *In:* Grecula, P., Hovorka, D. & Putiš, M. (eds) *Geological Evolution of the Western Carpathians*. Monograph, Mineralia Slovaca 1–24i.

Plašienka, D., Soták, J. & Prokešová, R. 1998. Structural profiles across the Šambron-Kamenica Periklippen Zone of the Central Carpathian Paleogene Basin in NE Slovakia. *Mineralia Slovaca*, **29**, 173–184.

Plašienka, D., Janák, M., Lupták, B., Milovský, R. & Frey, M. 1999. Kinematics and metamorphism of a Cretaceous core complex: The Veporic unit of the Central Western Carpathians. *Physics and Chemistry of the Earth (A)*, **24**, 651–658.

Platt, J. P., Lister, G.S, Cunningham, P., Weston, P., Peel, F., Baudin, T. & Dondey, H. 1989. Thrusting and backthrusting in the Briançonnais domain of the western Alps. *In:* Coward, M. P., Dietrich, D. & Park, R. G. (eds) *Alpine Tectonics*. Geological Society, London, Special Publications, **45**, 135–152.

Pleuger, J., Froitzheim, N. & Jansen, E. 2005. Folded continental and oceanic nappes on the southern side of Monte Rosa (western Alps, Italy): Anatomy of a double collision suture. *Tectonics*, **24**, TC4013.

Pleuger, J., Roller, S., Walter, J. M., Jansen, E. & Froitzheim, N. 2007. Structural evolution of the contact between two Penninic nappes (Zermatt-Saas zone and Combin zone, Western Alps) and implications for the exhumation mechanism and palaeogeography. *International Journal of Earth Sciences*, **96**, 229–252.

Pleuger, J., Nagel, T. J., Walter, J. M., Jansen, E. & Froitzheim, N. (2008). On the role and importance of orogen-parallel and -perpendicular extension, transcurrent shearing, and backthrusting in the Monte Rosa nappe and the Southern Steep Belt of the Alps (Penninic zone, Switzerland and Italy). *In:* Siegesmund, S., Fügenschuh, B. & Froitzheim, N. (eds) *Tectonic Aspects of the Alpine-Dinaride-Carpathian System*. Geological Society, London, Special Publications, 257–280.

Polák, M. 1979. Geological profiles of the Krivánska Malá Fatra Mts. *In:* Mahel', M. (ed.). *Tectonic Profiles of the Western Carpathians*. Konferencie Sympóziá Semináre, D. Štúr Institute of Geology, Bratislava, 77–84 [English summary].

Polák, M., Havrila, M., Filo, I. & Pevný, J. 1996. Gader limestones – a new lithostratigraphic unit of the Hronicum in the Vel'ká Fatra Mts. and its extension in the Western Carpathians. *Slovak Geological Magazine*, **96**(3–4), 293–310.

Polák, M., Ondrejičková, A. & Wieczorek, J. 1998. Lithobiostratigraphy of the Ždiar Formation of the Krížna nappe (Tatry Mts.). *Slovak Geological Magazine*, **4**, 35–52.

Polinski, R. K. & Eisbacher, G. H. 1992. Deformation partitioning during polyphase oblique convergence in the Karawanken Mountains, southeastern Alps. *Journal of Structural Geology*, **14**, 1203–1213.

Poller, U., Uher, P., Janák, M., Plašienka, D. & Kohút, M. 2001. Late Cretaceous age of the Rochovce granite, Western Carpathians, constrained by U–Pb single-zircon dating in combination with cathodoluminiscence imaging. *Geologica Carpathica*, **52**, 41–47.

Poller, U., Uher, P., Broska, I., Plašienka, D. & Janák, M. 2002. First Permian – Early Triassic zircon ages for tin-bearing granites from the Gemeric unit (Western Carpathians, Slovakia): connection to the post-collisional extension of the Variscan orogen and S-type granite magmatism. *Terra Nova*, **14**, 41–48.

Posgay, K., Bodogy, T., *et al.* 1995. Asthenospheric structure beneath a Neogene Basin in SE Hungary. *Tectonophysics*, **252**, 467–484.

Pospíšil, L., Buday, T. & Fusán, O. 1992. Neotectonic movements in the Western Carpathians. *Západné Karpaty, Geológia*, **16**, 65–84 [English summary].

Prokešová, R. 1994. Structural analysis of the Krížna nappe in its near-root and superficial position). *Mineralia Slovaca*, **26**, 347–354 [English summary].

Putiš, M. 1991. Geology and petrotectonics of some shear zones in the West Carpathian crystalline complexes. *Mineralia Slovaca*, **23**, 459–473.

Putiš, M. 1992. Variscan and Alpidic nappe structures of the Western Carpathian crystalline basement. *Geologica Carpathica*, **43**, 369–380.

Putiš, M., Kotov, A.B., Uher, P., Salnikova, E. B. & Korikovsky, S. P. 2000. Triassic age of the Hrončok pre-orogenic A-type granite related to continental rifling: a new result of U-Pb isotope dating (Western Carpathians). *Geologica Carpathica*, **51**, 59–66.

Quick, J., Sinigoi, S., Negrini, L., Demarchi, G. & Mayer, A. 1992. Synmagmatic deformation in the underplated igneous complex of the Ivrea-Verbano zone. *Geology*, **20**, 613–616.

Rakús, M. 1996. Jurassic of the innermost Western Carpathian zones – its importance and influence on the geodynamic evolution of the area. *Slovak Geological Magazine*, **96**(3–4), 311–317.

Rakús, M. & Hók, J. 2005. The Manín and Klape units: Lithostratigraphy, tectonic classification, paleogeographic position and relationship to Vahicum. *Mineralia Slovaca*, **37**, 9–26 [English summary].

Rakús, M. & Sýkora, M. 2001. Jurassic of Silicicum. *Slovak Geological Magazine*, **7**, 53–84.

Rantitsch, G. 1997. Thermal history of the Carnic Alps (Southern Alps, Austria) and its paleogeographic implications. *Tectonophysics*, **272**, 213 232.

Rantitsch, G., Sachsenhofer, R. F., Hasenhüttl, C., Russegger, B. & Rainer, T. 2005. Thermal evolution of an extensional detachment as constrained by organic metamorphic data and thermal modeling: Graz Paleozoic Nappe Complex (Eastern Alps). *Tectonophysics*, **411**, 57–72.

Ratschbacher, L., Frisch, W., Neubauer, F., Schmid, S.M. & Neugebauer, J. 1989. Extension in compressional orogenic belts: The Eastern Alps. *Geology*, **17**, 404–407.

Ratschbacher, L., Frisch, W., Linzer, H. G. & Merle, O. 1991. Lateral extrusion in the eastern Alps, part II: structural analysis. *Tectonics*, **10**, 257–271.

Ratschbacher, L., Frisch, W., *et al.* 1993. The Pieniny Klippen Belt in the Western Carpathians of northeastern Slovakia: structural evidence for transpression. *Tectonophysics*, **226**, 471–483.

Ratschbacher, L., Dingeldey, C., Miller, C., Hacker, B. R. & McWillams, M. O. 2005. Formation, subduction, and exhumation of Penninic oceanic crust in the Eastern Alps: time constraints from $^{40}Ar/^{39}Ar$ geochronology. *Tectonophysics*, **394**, 155–170.

Reddy, S. M., Wheeler, J. & Cliff, R. A. 1999. The geometry and timing of orogenic extension: an example from the Western Italian Alps. *Journal of Metamorphic Geology*, **17**, 573–589.

Reháková, D. 2000. Calcareous dinoflagellate and calpionelid bioevents versus sea-level fluctuations recorded in the West-Carpathian (Late Jurassic/Early Cretaceous) pelagic environments. *Geologica Carpathica*, **51**, 229–243.

Reicherter, K., Froitzheim, N., *et al.* 2008. Alpine tectonics north of the Alps. *In*: McCann, T. (ed.) *The Geology of Central Europe. Volume 2: Mesozoic and Cenozoic*. Geological Society, London, 1233–1285.

REICHWALDER, P. 1973. Geologické pomery mladšieho paleozoika jv. časti Spišsko-gemerského rudohoria. *Zborník Geologických Vied, Západné Karpaty*, **18**, 99–139.

REICHWALDER, P. 1982. Structural characteristic of root zones of some nappes in innermost parts of West Carpathians. *In:* MAHEL', M. (ed.) *Alpine Structural Elements: Carpathian-Balkan-Caucasus-Pamir Orogene Zone*. Veda, Bratislava, 43–56.

RÉTI, Z. 1985. Triassic ophiolite fragments in an evaporitic melange, northern Hungary. *Ofioliti*, **10**, 411–422.

RING, U., RATSCHBACHER, L. & FRISCH, W. 1988. Plate-boundary kinematics in the Alps – motion in the Arosa suture zone. *Geology*, **16**, 696–698.

ROCA, E., BESSEREAU, G., JAWOR, E., KOTARBA, M. & ROURE, F. 1995. Pre-Neogene evolution of the Western Carpathians: Constraints from the Bochnia-Tatra Mountains section (Polish Western Carpathians). *Tectonics*, **14**, 855–873.

ROCKENSCHAUB, M. J., THEINER, U. & FRANK, W. 1983. Die Struktur von Phyllit- und Phyllitglimmergneiszone bei Landeck. - Die frühalpine Geschichte der Ostalpen. *Jahresbericht 1982 Hochschulschwerpunkt S 15*, Leoben, 223–237.

ROSENBERG, C. L. 2004. Shear zones and magma ascent: A model based on a review of the Tertiary magmatism in the Alps. *Tectonics*, **23**, TC3002.

ROSENBERG, C. L., BRUN, J. P. & GAPAIS, D. 2004. Indentation model of the Eastern Alps and the origin of the Tauern window. *Geology*, **32**, 997–1000.

ROSENBERG, C. L., BRUN, J. P., CAGNARD, F. & GAPAIS, D. 2007. Oblique indentation in the Eastern Alps: Insights from laboratory experiments. *Tectonics*, **26**, TC2003.

ROYDEN, L. H. 1993. The tectonic expression slab pull at continental convergent boundaries. *Tectonics*, **12**, 303–325.

ROYDEN, L., HORVÁTH, F. & BURCHFIELD, B. C. 1982. Transform faulting, extension and subduction in the Carpathian-Pannonian region. *Geological Society of America Bulletin*, **93**, 717–725.

ROYDEN, L. H., HORVÁTH, F. & RUMPLER, J. 1983*a*. Evolution of the Pannonian Basin system. 1. Tectonics. *Tectonics*, **2**, 63–90.

ROYDEN, L. H., HORVÁTH, F., NAGYMAROSY, A. & STEGENA, L. 1983*b*. Evolution of the Pannonian Basin system. 2. Subsidence and thermal history. *Tectonics*, **2**, 91–137.

RUBATTO, D. & HERMANN, J. 2001. Exhumation as fast as subduction? *Geology*, **29**, 3–6.

RUBATTO, D., GEBAUER, D. & FANNING, M. 1998. Jurassic formation and Eocene subduction of the Zermatt-Saas Fee ophiolites: implications for the geodynamic evolution of the Central and Western Alps, *Contributions to Mineralogy and Petrology*, **132**, 269–287.

RUBATTO., D., GEBAUER, D. & COMPAGNONI, R. 1999. Dating of eclogite-facies zircons : the age of Alpine metamorphism in the Sesia-Lanzo Zone (Western Alps). *Earth and Planetary Science Letters*, **167**, 141–158.

SALAJ, J. & BEGAN, A. 1983. Senonian to Paleogene paleogeographic and tectonic development of the Myjavská pahorkatina Upland (West Carpathians – Czechoslovakia). *Zitteliana*, **10**, 173–181.

SĂNDULESCU, M. 1988. Cenozoic tectonic history of the Carpathians. *In;* ROYDEN, L. H. & HORVÁTH, F. (eds) *The Pannonian Basin. A Study in Basin Evolution*. American Association of Petroleum Geologists, Memoirs, **45**, 17–25.

SANTINI, L. 1992. *Geochemistry and geochronology of the basic rocks of the Penninic nappes of east-central Switzerland*. PhD thesis, Lausanne University.

SARTORI, M., GOUFFON, Y. & MARTHALER, M. 2006. Harmonisation et définition des unités lithostratigraphiques briançonnaises dans les nappes Penniques du Valais. *Eclogae geologicae Helvetiae*, **99**, 363–407.

SAVOSTIN, L. A., SIBUET, J. C., ZONENSHAIN, L. P., LE PICHON, X. & ROULET, M. J. 1986. Kinematic evolution of the Tethys belt from the Atlantic Ocean to the Pamirs since the Triassic. *Tectonophysics*, **123**, 1–35.

SCHALTEGGER, U. & BRACK, P. 1999. Short-Lived Events of Extension and Volcanism in the Lower Permian of the Southern Alps, (Northern Italy, Southern Switzerland). *EUG10 Strasbourg, Journal of Conference Abstracts*, **4**(1), 296–297.

SCHÄRER, U., COSCA, M., STECK, A. & HUNZIKER, J. 1996. Termination of major ductile strike-slip shear and differential cooling along the Insubric line (Central Alps): U-Pb, Rb-Sr and $^{40}Ar/^{39}Ar$ ages of cross-cutting pegmatites. *Earth and Planetary Science Letters*, **142**, 331–351.

SCHÄRER, U., CANNIC, S. & LAPIERRE, H. 2000. Preliminary evidence for a Hercynian age of the Versoyen complex, western Alps. *Comptes Rendus de l'Academie des Sciences, série II a*, **330**, 325–332.

SCHMID, S. M. 1975. The Glarus overthrust: Field evidence and mechanical model. *Eclogae geologicae Helvetiae*, **68**, 247–280.

SCHMID, S. M. & FROITZHEIM, N. 1993. Oblique slip and block rotation along the Engadine line. *Eclogae geologicae Helvetiae*, **86**, 569–593.

SCHMID, S. M. & HAAS, R. 1989. Transition from near-surface thrusting to intrabasement décollement, Schlinig thrust, Eastern Alps. *Tectonics*, **8**, 697–718.

SCHMID, S. M. & KISSLING, E. 2000. The arc of the western Alps in the light of geophysical data on deep crustal structure. *Tectonics*, **19**, 62–85.

SCHMID, S. M., ZINGG, A. & HANDY, M. 1987. The kinematics of movements along the Insubric Line and the emplacement of the Ivrea Zone. *Tectonophysics*, **135**, 47–66.

SCHMID, S. M., RÜCK, P. & SCHREURS, G. 1990. The significance of the Schams nappes for the reconstruction of the paleotectonic and orogenic evolution of the Penninic zone along the NFP-20 East traverse (Grisons, eastern Switzerland). *Mémoires de la Société Géologique de France*, **156**, 263–287.

SCHMID, S. M., PFIFFNER, O. A., FROITZHEIM, N., SCHÖNBORN, G. & KISSLING, E. 1996. Geophysical-geological transect and tectonic evolution of the Swiss-Italian Alps. *Tectonics*, **15**, 1036–1064.

SCHMID, S. M., FÜGENSCHUH, B., KISSLING, E. & SCHUSTER, R. 2004*a*. Tectonic map and overall architecture of the Alpine orogen. *Eclogae geologicae Helvetiae*, **97**, 93–117.

SCHMID, S. M., FÜGENSCHUH, B., KISSLING E. & SCHUSTER R. 2004*b*. Transects IV, V and VI: the Alps and their Foreland. *In:* CAVAZZA, W., ROURE, F. M., SPAKMAN, W., STAMPFLI, G. M. & ZIEGLER, P. A. (eds) *The TRANSMED Atlas—the Mediterranean Region from Crust to Mantle*. Springer, Berlin, 108–114.

SCHNABEL, W. 1992. New data on the Flysch zone of the Eastern Alps in the Austrian sector and new aspects concerning the transition to the Flysch Zone of the Carpathians. *Cretaceous Research*, **13**, 405–419.

SCHÖNBORN, G. 1992. Alpine tectonics and kinematic models of the central Southern Alps. *Memorie di Scienze Geologiche (Padova)*, **44**, 229–393.

SCHÖNBORN, G. 1999. Balancing cross sections with kinematic constraints: The Dolomites (northern Italy). *Tectonics*, **18**, 527–545.

SCHÖNLAUB, H.-P. 1973. Schwamm-Spiculae aus dem Rechnitzer Schiefergebirge und ihr stratigraphischer Wert. *Jahrbuch der Geologischen Bundesanstalt (Wien)*, **116**, 35–49.

SCHÖNLAUB, H. P. & HISTON, K. 2000. The Paleozoic evolution of the Southern Alps. *Mitteilungen der Österreichischen Geologischen Gesellschaft*, **92**, 15–34.

SCHREURS, G. 1993. Structural analysis of the Schams nappes and adjacent tectonic units: implications for the orogenic evolution of the Penninic zone in eastern Switzerland. *Bulletin de la Société géologique de France*, **164**, 415–435.

SCHUMACHER, M. E., SCHÖNBORN, G., BERNOULLI, D. & LAUBSCHER, H. P. 1997. Rifting and collision in the Southern Alps. *In:* PFIFFNER, O. A., LEHNER, P., HEITZMANN, P., MUELLER, S. & STECK, A. (eds) *Deep Structure of the Swiss Alps: Results of NRP 20*. Birkhäuser, Basel, 186–204.

SCHUSTER, R. 2004. The Austroalpine crystalline units in the Eastern Alps. *Abstract Volume PANGEO 2004*, Berichte des Instituts für Erdwissenschaften der Karl-Franzens-Universität Graz, **9**, 30–36.

SCHUSTER, R., SCHARBERT, S., ABART, R. & FRANK, W. 2001. Permo-Triassic extension and related HT/LP metamorphism in the Austroalpine - Southalpine realm. *Mitteilungen der Gesellschaft der Geologie- und Bergbaustudenten in Österreich*, **44**, 111–141.

SCHUSTER, R., FAUPL, P. & FRANK, W. 2003. Metamorphic detritus in the Cretaceous Gosau Group (Eastern Alps). *Annales Universitatis Scientiarum Budapestinensis, Sectio Geologica*, **35**, 100–101.

SCHUSTER, R., KOLLER, F., HOECK, V., HOINKES, G. & BOUSQUET, R. 2004. Explanatory notes to the map: Metamorphic structure of the Alps - Metamorphic evolution of the Eastern Alps. *Mitteilungen der Österreichischen Mineralogischen Gesellschaft*, **149**, 175–199.

SCHWARTZ, S., LARDEAUX, J.-M. & TRICART, P. 2000. La zone d'Acceglio (Alpes cottiennes): un nouvel exemple de croûte continentale éclogitisée dans les Alpes occidentales. *Comptes Rendus de l'Academie des Sciences (Paris), Sciences de la Terre et des planètes*, **330**, 859–866.

Schweigl, J. & Neubauer, F. 1997. Structural development of the central Northern Calcareous Alps: Significance for the Jurassic to Tertiary geodynamics of the Alps. *Eclogae geologicae Helvetiae*, **60**, 303–323.

Schwerd, K., Huber, K. & Müller, M. 1995. Tektonik und regionale Geologie der Gesteine in der Tiefbohrung Hindelang 1 (Allgäuer Alpen). *Geologica Bavarica*, **100**, 75–115.

Sciunnach, D. 2001. The Lower Permian in the Orobic anticline (Southern Alps, Lombardy): A review based on new stratigraphic and petrographic data. *Rivista Italiana di Paleontologia e Stratigrafia*, **107**, 47–68.

Sciunnach, D. 2003. Fault-controlled stratigraphic architecture and magmatism in the Western Orobic Basin (Lower Permian, Lombardy Southern Alps). *Bollettino della Società Geologica Italiana*, **2**(special volume), 49–58.

Šefara, J., Bielik, M., Konečný, P., Bezák, V. & Hurai, V. 1996. The latest stages of development of the Western Carpathian lithosphere and its interaction with asthenosphere. *Geologica Carpathica*, **47**, 339–347.

Šefara, J., Kováč, M., Plašienka, D. & Šujan, M. 1998. Seismogenic zones in the Eastern Alpine - Western Carpathian - Pannonian junction area. *Geologica Carpathica*, **49**, 247–260.

Selverstone, J. 1988. Evidence for east-west crustal extension in the Eastern Alps: Implications for the unroofing history of the Tauern window. *Tectonics*, **7**, 87–105.

Seno, S., Dallagiovanna, G. & Vanossi, M. 2005. A kinematic evolutionary model for the Penninic sector of the central Ligurian Alps. *International Journal of Earth Sciences*, **94**, 114–129.

Siegl, K. 1978. Faults in the contact area of the Ďumbier and Kraklová crystalline complexes (West Carpathians). *Geologický Zborník Geologica Carpathica*, **29**, 147–160.

Sikora, W. J. 1974. The Pieniny Klippen Belt (Polish Carpathians). *In:* Mahel', M. (ed.) *Tectonics of the Carpathian-Balkan Regions*. D. Štúr Institute of Geology, Bratislava, 177–180.

Šimon, L. & Halouzka, R. 1996. Pútikov vŕšok volcano – the youngest volcano in the Western Carpathians. *Slovak Geological Magazine*, **96**(2), 103–123.

Šimon, L. & Maglay, J. 2005. Dating of sediments from the footwall of the lava flow of the Pútikov vrch volcano using method of optically stimulated luminiscence. *Mineralia Slovaca*, **37**, 279–281.

Slapansky, P. & Frank, W. 1987. Structural evolution and geochronology of the northern margin of the Austroalpine in the northwestern Schladming Crystalline (NE Radstädter Tauern). *In:* Flügel, H. W. & Faupl, P. (eds) *Geodynamics of the Eastern Alps*. Deuticke, Wien, 244–262.

Sölva, H., Thöni, M., Grasemann, B. & Linner, M. 2001. Emplacement of eo-Alpine high-pressure rocks in the Austroalpine Ötztal complex (Texel group, Italy/Austria). *Geochimica Acta*, **14**, 345–360.

Soták, J. & Plašienka, D. 1996. Upper Triassic – Lower Jurassic sediments of the Lučatín unit in the Northern Veporicum: facial diversity and tectonic stacking. *Slovak Geological Magazine*, **96** (3–4), 273–277.

Soták, J., Rudinec, R. & Spišiak, J. 1993. The Penninic "pull-apart" dome in the pre-Neogene basement of the Transcarpathian Depression (Eastern Slovakia). *Geologica Carpathica*, **44**, 11–16.

Soták, J., Michalík, J., Reháková, D. & Hamršmíd, B. 1997. Paleogene sediments below the base of a Mesozoic nappe in the Humenské vrchy Mts. (Podskalka borehole): Stratigraphic constraints for Tertiary thrust tectonics. *Geologica Carpathica*, **48**, 193–203.

Soták, J., Biroň, A., Prokešová, R. & Spišiak, J. 2000. Detachment control of core complex exhumation and back-arc extension in the East Slovakian Basin. *Slovak Geological Magazine*, **6**, 130–132.

Soták, J., Pereszlényi, M., Marschalko, R., Milička, J. & Starek, D. 2001. Sedimentology and hydrocarbon habitat of the submarine-fan deposits of the central Carpathian Paleogene Basin (NE Slovakia). *Marine and Petroleum Geology*, **18**, 87–114.

Spišiak, J. & Hovorka, D. 1997. Petrology of the Western Carpathians Cretaceous primitive alkaline volcanics. *Geologica Carpathica*, **48**, 113–121.

Stäuble, M. & Pfiffner, O. A. 1991. Processing, interpretation and modeling of seismic-reflection data in the Molasse Basin of eastern Switzerland. *Eclogae geologicae Helvetiae*, **84**, 151–175.

Stampfli, G. M. 1993. Le Briançonnais, terrain exotique dans les Alpes? *Eclogae geologicae Helvetiae*, **86**, 1–45.

Stampfli, G. M. 1996. The Intra-Alpine terrain: A Paleotethyan remnant in the Alpine Variscides. *Eclogae geologicae Helvetiae*, **89**, 13–42.

Stampfli, G. M. & Borel, G. D. 2004. The Transmed transects in space and time: constraints on the paleotectonic evolution of the Mediteranian Domain. *In:* Cavazza, W., Roure, F., Spakman, W., Stampfli, G. M. & Ziegler, P. A. (eds). *The TRANSMED Atlas: the Mediterranean Region from Crust to Mantle*. Springer Verlag, Berlin.

Stampfli, G. M., Mosar, J., Marquer, D., Marchant, R., Baudin, T. & Borel, G. 1998. Subduction and obduction processes in the Swiss Alps. *Tectonophysics*, **296**, 159–204.

Staub, R. 1938. Einige Ergebnisse vergleichender Studien zwischen Wallis und Bünden. *Eclogae geologicae Helvetiae*, **31**, 345–353.

Steck, A. 1990. Une carte des zones de cisaillement ductile des Alpes Centrales. *Eclogae geologicae Helvetiae*, **83**, 603–627.

Steck, A., Bigioggero, B., Dal Piaz, G. V., Escher, A., Martinotti, G. & Masson, H. 1999. *Carte tectonique des Alpes de Suisse occidentale et des régions avoisinantes, 1:100000*. Service Hydrologique et Géologique National, Bern, Carte spéciale no. **123**.

Steenken, A., Siegesmund, S., Heinrichs, T. & Fügenschuh, B. 2002. Cooling and exhumation of the Rieserferner Pluton (Eastern Alps, Italy/Austria). *International Journal of Earth Sciences*, **91**, 799–817.

Stipp, M., Fügenschuh, B., Gromet, L. P., Stünitz, H. & Schmid, S. M. 2004. Contemporaneous plutonism and strike-slip faulting: A case study from the Tonale fault zone north of the Adamello pluton (Italian Alps). *Tectonics*, **23**, TC3004.

Strauss, P., Harzhauser, M., Hinsch, R. & Michael, W. 2006. Sequence stratigraphy in a classic pull-apart basin (Neogene, Vienna Basin). A 3D seismic basis integrated approach. *Geologica Carpathica*, **57**, 185–197.

Stucki, A., Rubatto, D. & Trommsdorff, V. 2003. Mesozoic ophiolite relics in the Southern Steep Belt of the Central Alps. *Schweizerische Mineralogische und Petrographische Mitteilungen*, **83**, 285–299.

Stur, D. 1860. Bericht über die geologische übersicht-Aufnahme des Wassergebietes der Waag und Neutra. *Jahrbuch der Kaiserlich-Königlichen Geologischen Reichsanstalt (Wien)*, **11**.

Sue, C. & Tricart, P. 1999. Late alpine brittle extension above the Frontal Penninic Thrust near Briancon, western Alps. *Eclogae geologicae Helvetiae*, **92**, 171–181.

Sue, C. & Tricart, P. 2003. Neogene to ongoing normal faulting in the inner western Alps: a major evolution of the late alpine tectonics. *Tectonics*, **22**, TC1050.

Sue, C., Tricart, P., Dumont, T. & Pecher, A. 1997. Racourcissement polyphasé dans le massif du Pelvoux (Alpes occidentales):exemple du chevauchement de socle de Villard-Notre-Dame. *Comptes Rendus de l'Académie des Sciences (Paris), série II*, **324**, 847–854.

Švábenická, L., Bubík, M., Krejčí, O. & Stráník, Z. 1997. Stratigraphy of Cretaceous sediments of the Magura group of nappes in Moravia (Czech Republic). *Geologica Carpathica*, **48**, 179–191.

Sýkora, M. & Ožvoldová, L. 1996. Lithoclasts of Middle Jurassic radiolarites in debris flow sediments from Silica nappe (locality Bleskový prameň, Slovak Karst, Western Carpathians). *Mineralia Slovaca*, **28**, 21–25.

Szafián, P. 1999. *A case study in the Pannonian Basin and the surrounding mountain belt*. Vrije Universiteit Amsterdam, NSG Publication No. **990102**.

Tari, G. 1995. Phanerozoic stratigraphy of the Hungarian part of the NW Pannonian Basin. *In:* Horváth, F., Tari, G. & Bokor, Cs. (eds) *Hungary: extensional collapse of the Alpine orogene and hydrocarbon prospects in the basement and basin fill of the western Pannonian Basin*. Guidebook to Fieldtrip No. 6, AAPG International Conference and Exhibition, Nice, 21–46.

Tari, G. 1996. Extreme crustal extension in the Rába River extensional corridor (Austria/Hungary). *Mitteilungen der Gesellschaft der Geologie- und Bergbaustudenten in Österreich*, **41**, 1–17.

Tari, G., Horváth, F. & Rumpler, J. 1992. Styles of extension in the Pannonian Basin. *Tectonophysics*, **208**, 203–219.

Thöni, M. 1999. A review of geochronological data from the Eastern

Alps. *Schweizerische Mineralogische und Petrographische Mitteilungen*, **79**, 209–230.

THÖNI, M. 2006. Dating eclogite-facies metamorphism in the Eastern Alps – approaches, results, interpretations: a review. *Mineralogy and Petrology*, **88**, 123–148.

THÖNI, M. & MILLER, C. 1996. Garnet Sm–Nd data from the Saualpe and the Koralpe (Eastern Alps, Austria): chronological and P–T constraints on the thermal and tectonic history. *Journal of Metamorphic Geology*, **14**, 453–466.

THÖNI, M. & MILLER, C. 2000. Permo-Triassic pegmatites in the eo-Alpine eclogite-facies Koralpe complex, Austria: age and magma source constraints from mineral chemical, Rb-Sr and Sm-Nd isotopic data. *Schweizerische Mineralogische und Petrographische Mitteilungen*, **80**, 169–186.

THÖNI, M., MOTTANA, A., DELITALA, M. C., DECAPITANI, L. & LIBORIO, G. 1992. The Val Biandino composite pluton /a Late Hercynian intrusion into the South-Alpine metamorphic basement of the Alps (Italy). *Neues Jahrbuch für Mineralogie - Monatshefte*, **12**, 545–554.

TILTON, G. R., SCHREYER, W. & SCHERTL, H.-P. 1991. Pb-Sr-Nb isotopic behaviour of deeply subducted crustal rocks from the Dora Maira Massif, Western Alps, Italy-II: what is the age of the ultrahigh-pressure metamorphism? *Contributions to Mineralogy and Petrology*, **108**, 22–33.

TOLLMANN, A. 1959. Der Deckenbau der Ostalpen auf Grund der Neuuntersuchung des zentralalpinen Mesozoikums. *Mitteilungen der Gesellschaft der Geologie- und Bergbaustudenten in Wien*, **10**, 1–62.

TOLLMANN, A. 1977. *Geologie von Österreich. Band 1: Die Zentralalpen.* Deuticke, Wien.

TOLLMANN, A. 1978. Plattentektonische Fragen in den Ostalpen und der plattentektonische Mechanismus des mediterranen Orogens. *Mitteilungen der Österreichischen Geologischen Gesellschaft*, **69**, 291–351.

TOLLMANN, A. 1985. *Geologie von Österreich. Band 2: Außerzentralalpiner Anteil.* Deuticke, Wien.

TOLLMANN, A. 1987. Neue Wege in der Ostalpengeologie und die Beziehungen zum Ostmediterran. *Mitteilungen der Österreichischen Geologischen Gesellschaft*, **80**, 47–113.

TOMAŠOVÝCH, A. 2000. Lagoonal-peritidal sequences in the Fatra Formation (Rhaetian): an example from the Vel'ká Fatra Mountains (Western Carpathians). *Slovak Geological Magazine*, **6**, 256–259.

TOMEK, Č. 1993. Deep crustal structure beneath the central and inner West Carpathians. *Tectonophysics*, **226**, 417–431.

TOMEK, Č. & HALL, J. 1993. Subducted continental margin imaged in the Carpathians of Czechoslovakia. *Geology*, **21**, 535–538.

TOMEK, Č., DVOŘÁKOVÁ, L., IBRMAJER, I., JIŘÍČEK, R. & KORÁB, T. 1987. Crustal profiles of active continental collision belt: Czechoslovak deep seismic reflection profiling in the West Carpathians. *Geophysical Journal of the Royal Astronomical Society*, **89**, 383–388.

TOMEK, Č., IBRMAJER, I., KORÁB, T., BIELY, A., DVOŘÁKOVÁ, L., LEXA, J. & ZBOŘIL, A. 1989. Crustal structures of the West Carpathians on deep reflection seismic line 2T. *Mineralia Slovaca*, **21**, 3–26 [in Czech, English summary].

TRAUTWEIN, B., DUNKL, I. & FRISCH, W. 2001. Accretionary history of the Rhenodanubian Flysch zone in the Eastern Alps – evidence from apatite fission-track dating. *International Journal of Earth Sciences*, **90**, 703–713.

TROMMSDORFF, V., PICCARDO, G. B. & MONTRASIO, A. 1993. From magmatism through metamorphism to sea floor emplacement of subcontinental Adria lithosphere during pre-Alpine rifting (Malenco, Italy). *Schweizerische Mineralogische und Petrographische Mitteilungen*, **73**, 191–203.

TRÜMPY, R. 1975. Penninic-Austroalpine boundary in the Swiss Alps: a presumed former continental margin and its problems. *American Journal of Science*, **275**, 209–238.

TRÜMPY, R. 1980. *Geology of Switzerland – A Guide-book. Part A: An Outline of the Geology of Switzerland.* Wepf & Co, Basel.

TRÜMPY, R. 1988. A possible Jurassic – Cretaceous transform system in the Alps and the Carpathians. *In:* CLARK, S. P. JR., BURCHFIEL, B. C. & SUPPE, J. (eds) *Processes in Continental Lithospheric Deformation.* Geological Society of America, Special Papers, **218**, 93–109.

TRÜMPY, R. 1992. Ostalpen und Westalpen – Verbindendes und Trennendes. *Jahrbuch der Geologischen Bundesanstalt (Wien)*, **135**, 875–882.

TRÜMPY, R. 2006. Geologie der Iberger Klippen und ihrer Flysch-Unterlage. *Eclogae geologicae Helvetiae*, **99**, 79–121.

TRUNKÓ, L. 1996. *Geology of Hungary.* Gebrüder Borntraeger, Berlin,.

TUMIATI, S., THÖNI, M., NIMIS, P., MARTIN, S. & MAIR, V. 2003. Mantle-crust interaction during Variscan subduction in the Eastern Alps (Nonsberg-Ulten zone): geochronology and new petrological constraints. *Earth and Planetary Science Letters*, **210**, 509–526.

UHER, P. & BROSKA, I. 1996. Post-orogenic Permian volcanic rocks in the Western Carpathian-Pannonian area: geochemistry, mineralogy and evolution. *Geologica Carpathica*, **45**, 375–378.

UHER, P. & BROSKA, I. 2000. The role of silicic magmatism in the Western Carpathians: from Variscan collision to Early-Alpine extension. *Slovak Geological Magazine*, **6**, 278–280.

UHER, P. & PUSHKAREV, Y. 1994. Granitic pebbles of the Cretaceous flysch of the Pieniny Klippen Belt, Western Carpathians: U/Pb zircon ages. *Geologica Carpathica*, **45**, 375–378.

UHER, P., ONDREJKA, M., SPIŠIAK, J., BROSKA, I. & PUTIŠ, M. 2002. Lower Triassic potassium-rich rhyolites of the Silicic unit, Western Carpathians, Slovakia: geochemistry, mineralogy and genetic aspects. *Geologica Carpathica*, **53**, 27–36.

UHLIG, V. 1903. Bau und Bild der Karpaten. *In:* DIENER, C. *et al.* (eds) *Bau und Bild Österreichs.* Tempsky Wien, 651–911.

UHLIG, V. 1907. *Über die Tektonik der Karpaten.* Sitzungsberichte der Akademie der Wissenschaften, mathematisch-naturwissenschaftliche Klasse, **116** Abt. 1, Wien.

VIOLA, G., MANCKKTELOW, N. S. & SEWARD, D. 2001. Late Oligocene-Neogene evolution of Europe-Adria collision: New structural and geochronological evidence from the Giudicarie fault system (Italian Eastern Alps). *Tectonics*, **20**, 999–1020.

VOJTKO, R. 2000. Are there tectonic units derived from the Meliata-Hallstatt trough incorporated into the tectonic structure of the Tisovec Karst? (Muráň karstic plateau, Slovakia). *Slovak Geological Magazine*, **6**, 335–346.

VON BLANCKENBURG, F. 1992. Combined high-precision chronometry and geochemical tracing using accessory minerals: applied to the Central-Alpine Bergell intrusion (central Europe). *Chemical Geology*, **100**, 19–40.

VON BLANCKENBURG, F. & DAVIES, H. J. 1995. Slab breakoff: A model for syncollisional magmatism and tectonics in the Alps. *Tectonics*, **14**, 120–131.

VON BLANCKENBURG, F. & DAVIES, H. J. 1996. Feasibility of double slab breakoff (Cretaceous and Tertiary) during the Alpine convergence. *Eclogae geologicae Helvetiae*, **89**, 111–127.

VON EYNATTEN, H. & GAUPP, R. 1999. Provenance of Cretaceous synorogenic sandstones in the Eastern Alps; constraints from framework petrography, heavy mineral analysis and mineral chemistry. *Sedimentary Geology*, **124**, 81–111.

VOSHAGE, H., HOFMANN, A.W., MAZZUCCHELLI, M., RIVALENTI, G., SINIGOI, S., RACZEK, I. & DEMARCHI, G. 1990. Isotopic evidence from the Ivrea zone for a hybrid lower crust formed by magmatic underplating. *Nature*, **347**, 731–736.

VOZÁR, J. 1997. Rift-related volcanics in the Permian of the Western Carpathians. *In:* GRECULA, P., HOVORKA, D. & PUTIŠ, M. (eds) *Geological Evolution of the Western Carpathians.* Monograph, Mineralia Slovaca, Bratislava, 225–234.

VOZÁR, J., SZALAIOVÁ, V. & ŠANTAVÝ, J. 1998. Interpretation of the Western Carpathian deep structures on the basis of gravimetric and seismic sections. *In:* RAKÚS, M. (ed.) *Geodynamic Development of the Western Carpathians.* Geological Survey of Slovak Republic, D. Štúr Publishers, 241–257.

VOZÁROVÁ, A. 1996. Tectono-sedimentary evolution of late Paleozoic basins based on interpretation of lithostratigraphic data (Western Carpathians, Slovakia). *Slovak Geological Magazine*, **96**(3–4), 251–271.

VOZÁROVÁ, A. & VOZÁR, J. 1988. *Late Paleozoic in West Carpathians.* D. Štúr Institute of Geology, Bratislava.

VOZÁROVÁ, A. & VOZÁR, J. 1992. Tornaicum and Meliaticum in borehole Brusník BRU-1, Southern Slovakia. *Acta Geologica Hungarica*, **35**, 97–116.

VRABEC, M., PAVLOVCIC PRESEREN, P. & STOPAR, B. 2006. GPS study (1996–2002) of active deformation along the Periadriatic fault system in northwestern Slovenia: tectonic model. *Geologica Carpathica*, **57**, 57–65.

Wagreich, M. 1995. Subduction tectonic erosion and Late Cretaceous subsidence along the northern Austroalpine margin (Eastern Alps, Austria). *Tectonophysics*, **242**, 63–78.

Wagreich, M. 2001*a*. A 400-km-long piggyback basin (Upper Aptian-Lower Cenomanian) in the Eastern Alps. *Terra Nova*, **13**, 401–406.

Wagreich, M. 2001*b*. Paleogene – Eocene paleogeography of the Northern Calcareous Alps (Gosau Group, Austria). *In:* Piller, W. E. & Rasser, M. (eds) *Paleogene of the Eastern Alps*. Schriftenreihe der Erdwissenschaftlichen Kommissionen /Österreichische Akademie der Wissenschaften, **14**, 57–76.

Wagreich, M. & Faupl, P. 1994. Paleogeographic and geodynamic evolution of the Gosau Group of the Northern Calcaeous Alps (Late Cretaceous, Eastern Alps, Austria). *Palaeogeography, Palaeoclimatology, Palaeoecology*, **110**, 235–254.

Wagreich, M. & Marschalko, R. 1995. Late Cretaceous to Early Tertiary palaeogeography of the Western Carpathians (Slovakia) and the Eastern Alps (Austria): implications from heavy mineral data. *Geologische Rundschau*, **84**, 187–199.

Weh, M. & Froitzheim, N. 2001. Penninic cover nappes in the Prättigau half-window (Eastern Switzerland): Structure and tectonic evolution. *Eclogae geologicae Helvetiae*, **94**, 237–252.

Wessely, G. 1992. The Calcareous Alps below the Vienna Basin in Austria and their structural and facial development in the Alpine-Carpathian border zone. *Geologica Carpathica*, **43**, 347–353.

Wheeler, J, Reddy, S. M. & Cliff, R. A. 2001. Kinematic linkage between internal zone extension and shortening in more external units in the NW Alps. *Journal of the Geological Society*, **158**, 439–443.

Wieczorek, J. 2000. Mesozoic evolution of the Tatra Mountains (Carpathians). *Mitteilungen der Gesellschaft der Geologie- und Bergbaustudenten in österreich*, **44**, 241–262.

Wieczorek, J. 2001. Condensed horizons as turning events in passive margin evolution: the Tatra Mts. examples. *Zentralblatt für Geologie und Paläontologie, Teil I*, **2000**, 199–209.

Wiesinger, M., Neubauer, F. & Handler, R. 2006. Exhumation of the Saualpe eclogite unit, Eastern Alps: constraints from $^{40}Ar/^{39}Ar$ ages and structural investigations. *Mineralogy and Petrology*, **88**, 149–180.

Willingshofer, E. & Neubauer, F. 2002. Structural evolution of an antiformal window: the Scheiblingkirchen Window (Eastern Alps, Austria). *Journal of Structural Geology*, **24**, 1603–1618.

Wissing, S. B. & Pfiffner, O. A. 2002. Structure of the eastern Klippen nappe (BE, FR): Implications for its Alpine tectonic evolution. *Eclogae geologicae Helvetiae*, **95**, 381–398.

Wopfner, H. 1984. Permian deposits of the Southern Alps as product of initial alpidic taphrogenesis. *Geologische Rundschau*, **73**, 259–277.

Zanchi, A., Chiesa, S. & Guillot, P.-Y. 1990. Tectonic evolution of the Southern Alps in the Orobic chain: structural and geochronological indications for pre-Tertiary compressive tectonics. *Memorie della Societá Geologica Italiana*, **45**, 77–82.

Zeyen, H., Dérerová, J. & Bielik, M. 2002. Determination of the continental lithospheric thermal structure in the Western Carpathians: integrated modelling of surface heat flow, gravity anomalies and topography. *Physics of the Earth and Planetary Interiors*, **134**, 89–104.

Ziegler, P. A. 1993. Late Palaeozoic–Early Mesozoic plate reorganisation: evolution and demise of the Variscan Fold Belt. *In:* Neubauer, F. & Von Raumer, J. F. (eds.) *The Pre-Mesozoic Geology of the Alps*. Springer, Berlin, 203–216.

Ziegler, W. 1956. Geologische Studien in den Flyschgebieten des Oberhalbsteins (Graubünden). *Eclogae geologicae Helvetiae*, **49**, 1–78.

Zimmermann, R., Hammerschmidt, K. & Franz, G. 1994. Eocene high pressure metamorphism in the Penninic units of the Tauern Window (Eastern Alps): evidence from 40Ar-39Ar dating and petrological investigations. *Contributions to Mineralogy and Petrology*, **117**, 175–186.

Zurbriggen, R., Kamber, B., Handy, M. R. & Nägler, R. 1998. Dating syn-magmatic folds: A case study of Schlingen structures in the Strona-Ceneri Zone (southern Alps, northern Italy). *Journal of Metamorphic Geology*, **16**, 403–414.

# 19 Alpine tectonics north of the Alps

KLAUS REICHERTER, NIKOLAUS FROITZHEIM, MAREK JAROSIŃSKI (co-ordinators), JANUSZ BADURA, HANS-JOACHIM FRANZKE, MARTIN HANSEN, CHRISTIAN HÜBSCHER, RAINER MÜLLER, PAWEŁ POPRAWA, JOHN REINECKER, WERNER STACKEBRANDT, THOMAS VOIGT, HILMAR VON EYNATTEN & WITOLD ZUCHIEWICZ

The Cenozoic tectonic evolution of Central Europe was governed over long periods of time by far-field stresses resulting from continent collision in the Alps (which is still ongoing) ridge push in the Atlantic Ocean, and other sources. Such far-field stresses interfered with more local stresses related to processes such as the rise of mantle plumes, leading to the Cenozoic volcanism of Central Europe, and glaciation. Alpine tectonics north of the Alps began with the effects, of Late Cretaceous–Early Palaeogene continent collision in the Pyrenees, on the European crust. During Tertiary times, the stress field was unstable and repeatedly changed both in terms of magnitude and orientation. Notably, an episode of ESE–WNW to east–west directed extension during the late Eocene to Oligocene created the European Cenozoic Rift System (Rhône-Bresse Graben, Upper Rhine Graben, Lower Rhine Basin, and others) which up to the present is tectonically the most active zone of Central Europe. Flexural basins formed in the southernmost part of the Alpine-Carpathian foreland. The Jura Mountains also form part of the Alpine foreland, although they could, from a tectonic point of view, also be regarded as part of the Alps. They represent the most external foreland fold-and-thrust belt of the Alps. Folding and thrusting in the Jura Mountains took place during the Middle Miocene to Pliocene, and the thrust front presently propagates northward into the Upper Rhine Graben. The Alpine tectonics of southern Germany may best be described in terms of reactivation of older inherited, mainly Variscan, basement structures. This is also the case for the central Leine Graben, the Harz Mountains and parts of the North German Basin. Because of the frequent reactivation of faults, the following sections include some remarks on pre-Alpine deformation and sedimentation history.

The general episodes of Alpine deformation north of the Alps can be subdivided into three main phases: (1) the period of Late Cretaceous–Early Palaeogene inversion tectonics, when far-field effects of continent collision and the formation of the Pyrenees resulted in deformation extending as far north as the Danish North Sea, including the large-scale uplift of the Harz Mountains; (2) Eocene to Miocene extensional tectonics with the formation of large graben systems, for example the Upper Rhine Graben; and (3) the phase of tectonics related to the reorganization of the stress field during the Late Miocene, which coincides with the initiation of the 'neotectonic period' and the present-day stress field in Central Europe, which is characterized by SE–NW compression and NE–SW extension.

The Neogene to recent evolution of northern Central Europe, including the North German Basin and the Polish Basin, which are parts of the Central European Basin System, was partly affected by glacial loading and unloading during the Pleistocene. Presently, these regions are areas of low seismicity (macroseismic intensities III–IV EMS; Grünthal & Mayer-Rosa 1998). Major stresses acting within the North German Basin and the Polish Basin were induced by the North Atlantic ridge push forces (east–west, or NW–SE directed), the ongoing Alpine collision (north–south directed), and, from the late Pleistocene onwards, the post-glacial rebound of Fennoscandia (mainly vertical, but also with a horizontal, west–east directed component). Present-day maximum horizontal stresses within the North German Basin are generally directed NW–SE (Röckel & Lempp 2003), but fan and bend towards the NNE, north of 52°N and east of 11°E, especially in the Polish Basin. The present-day stress field in the Central European Basin System is influenced by the decoupling of two crustal units (Roth & Fleckenstein 2001), which are separated by Zechstein evaporites (the Pre-Zechstein formations together with the older units are decoupled from the overlying Mesozoic and Cenozoic sediments). The general stress orientation, with NE–SW maximum horizontal stress, was regionally modified or disturbed (Röckel & Lempp 2003). In areas of salt movement and the formation of salt pillows, salt walls and diapirs, the resultant local increase or decrease in salt thickness had a marked effect on stresses and tectonic structures (e.g. in the western Baltic Sea (Hansen *et al.* 2005) and in the Glückstadt Graben area (Maystrenko *et al.* 2005).

Major basement faults within the intracratonic Central European Basin System are orientated NW–SE, while minor faults trend NE–SW and NNE–SSW, and are clearly visible in shaded relief and satellite images (Reicherter *et al.* 2005). The northern rim of the Central European Basin System is bounded by the Tornquist Zone, which consists of the Teisseyre-Tornquist Zone from Poland to Bornholm Island, and the Sorgenfrei-Tornquist Zone from southern Sweden to Denmark (Fig. 19.1). Additionally, the drainage pattern and the distribution of lakes in northern Germany parallel the block boundaries and, hence, mark zones

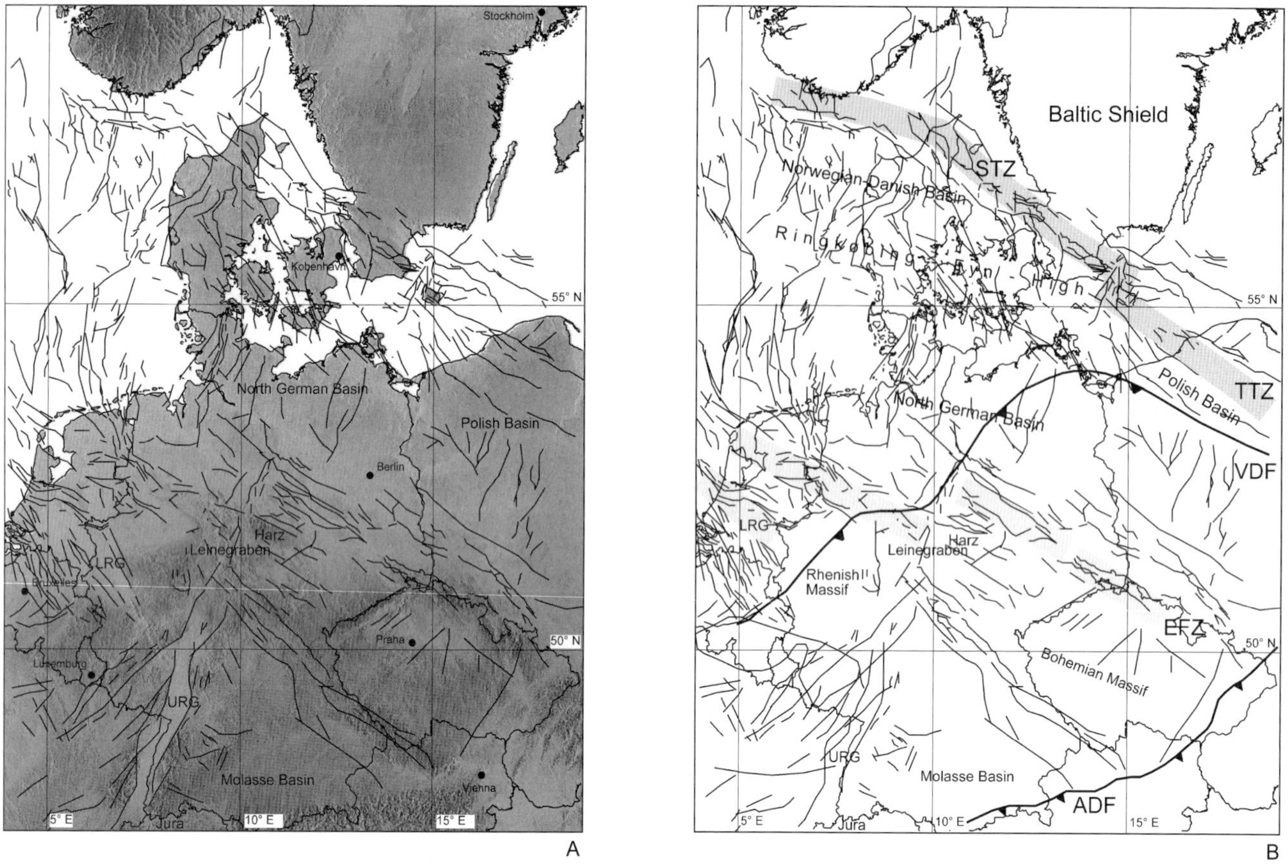


**Fig. 19.1.** (**A**) Shaded relief map of Central Europe, with the North German Basin and the Polish Basin. Abbreviations: A, Austria; B, Belgium; CZ, Czech Republic; D, Germany; DK, Denmark; F, France; HU, Hungary; LUX, Luxemburg; N, Norway; NL, Netherlands; PL, Poland; S, Sweden; SL; Slovakia. (**B**) Structural map of Central Europe, with major faults and faults systems. Abbreviations: ADF, Alpine Deformation Front; EFZ, Elbe Fault Zone; LRG, Lower Rhine Basin; STZ, Sorgenfrei-Tornquist Zone; TTZ, Teisseyre-Tornquist Zone; URG, Upper Rhine Graben; VDF, Variscan Deformation Front. Shaded areas indicate the Elbe Fault Zone and the Tornquist Zone, which is composed of the TTZ and the STZ.

of present-day subsidence (Mörner 1979; Stackebrandt 2004; Reicherter *et al.* 2005). A broad zone of subsidence extends from Hamburg to Berlin and onto Wroclaw (Poland) and is delineated by the depth to the base of the Rupelian Clay (Oligocene; Garetzky *et al.* 2001). This zone shows relatively minor faulting in the near-surface layers. The depocentre axes also had a NW–SE trend during the Mesozoic.

Understanding the post-glacial morphology and reactivation of faults of the North German Basin requires study of the very heterogeneous crust and upper mantle beneath the basin in Germany (Schwab 1985; Bayer *et al.* 1999, 2002; Stackebrandt 2004; Reicherter *et al.* 2005) and in Poland (Guterch *et al.* 1999) as well as the Mesozoic tectonosedimentary evolution (see also Scheck-Wenderoth *et al.* 2008). The readjustment of individual fault blocks during post-glacial relaxation of the lithosphere has led to differential, crust-dependent uplift and, probably, to the formation of Urstrom valleys. These valleys and terminal moraines in northern Germany and northern Poland appear to parallel the major tectonic lineaments and lithospheric 'block' boundaries. Large recent river systems clearly follow the trend of Palaeozoic basement structures. Indeed, correlation of the drainage pattern with 'Hercynian forms' was already recognized by Hennig (1906).

The Cenozoic evolution in Poland was governed by the presence of two major tectonic and facies domains. The northern Tethyan domain was restricted to the Carpathian Mountains in southern Poland. In the Outer Carpathians and the Central Carpathian Palaeogene Basin, the Cenozoic accumulation of sediments terminated in middle Miocene times. The second domain was the Peri-Tethyan domain which developed on the East European Platform. The transitional position between the two areas was occupied by the flexural foredeep of the Outer Carpathian fold-and-thrust belt, which was filled with Miocene-age sediments, predominantly continental.

Neotectonic studies in Poland are mainly concerned with geological indicators of tectonic movement. These include the development of neotectonically induced depocentres and young faults that were active in Late Neogene and Quaternary times, geodetically measured recent vertical and horizontal crustal motions and their relationship to photolineaments, salt tectonics, and the role of tectonic reactivation of fault zones due to human activity.

## Western Central Europe (N.F.)

Cenozoic tectonic activity in western Central Europe is concentrated in the Upper Rhine–Lower Rhine rift system. The Upper Rhine Graben is kinematically connected with the Lower Rhine Basin through the Rhenish Massif. The Jura Mountains represent the most external foreland fold-and-thrust belt of the Alps. Their thrust front presently propagates northward into the Upper Rhine Graben.

## *Jura Mountains*

The Jura Mountains represent a classic thin-skinned, frontal fold-and-thrust belt related to the formation of the Alps. The peculiarity of the Jura is that it is connected with the Alps only at one end, to the south, but is everywhere else separated from the Alps by an apparently undeformed foreland basin, the Swiss Molasse Basin (Fig. 19.2).

### *Structural architecture*

The Jura is subdivided into external and internal parts (Fig. 19.2). The internal or High Jura is characterized by spectacular, often faulted, detachment folds in its eastern part (Faltenjura: folded Jura) whereas thrusts are predominant in the western part. The external Jura is also known as the Plateau Jura. The plateaus are lozenge-shaped, wide, flat synclines, separated by narrow, faulted anticlinal zones (faisceaux). In the west, the external Jura is thrust a distance of about 7 km over the Tertiary fill of the Bresse Graben (Ricour 1956; Chauve *et al.* 1988). Important outward-(NW-)directed thrusts were also identified by drilling within the Jura. Recent shortening occurs in a marginal zone north of the Jura Mountains proper, especially at the southern end of the Upper Rhine Graben (Nivière & Winter 2000; Giamboni *et al.* 2004). In the southward continuation of the Upper Rhine Graben, synclines filled with Oligocene marine and brackish sediments occur within the Jura Mountains indicating that originally, prior to Jura folding, a structural depression (Rauracian depression) extended south of Basel. This was, however, less pronounced than the Upper Rhine Graben proper.

The folding and thrusting of the Jura took place in the Middle Miocene to Pliocene (11 to 3 Ma), as indicated by the age of the pre- and post-tectonic sediments (Kälin 1997). Deformation affected a stratigraphic succession of Middle Triassic to Miocene age. Older rocks, including the crystalline basement, the fill of the Late Carboniferous–Permian grabens, and the Early Triassic Buntsandstein, remained largely unaffected by the Jura shortening. Evaporites (anhydrite and salt) in the Middle Triassic (Middle Bunter) and Late Triassic (Keuper) serve as décollement horizons for the Jura tectonics. The Middle Triassic evaporites constitute the décollement horizon in the major part of the Swiss Jura, and the Keuper in the western Jura in France. The borders of the Jura Mountains were predetermined by the occurrence of these evaporites. Where the Muschelkalk salt wedges out towards the east, the Jura folding also dies out (Fig. 19.2; Philippe *et al.* 1996). The Triassic sediments were deposited in a basin (Burgundy Trough) whose depocentre coincides approximately with the Jura Mountains. The Jurassic to Early Cretaceous sedimentary succession above the décollement horizon comprises alternating competent (limestone) and incompetent (shale, marl) layers. This strong anisotropy favoured folding of the detached sequence. The thickness of the Jurassic units decreases from the internal to the external part. Cretaceous sediments are present only in the southern Jura Mountains; to the north, they have been eroded during the Palaeogene. Many of the folds of the Jura Mountains are detachment folds (Jamison 1987) belonging to the subtypes of disharmonic detachment folds and lift-off folds (Mitra 2003). The formation of these was facilitated by the extremely weak décollement horizon which allowed movement of the ductile material (salt) from the synclines to the anticlines. Attempts to construct a cross-section geometry of Jura folds under the assumption of only fold-bend and fault-propagation folding were prompted by the availability of cross-section balancing software, but these led to partly unrealistic results (Bitterli 1990; Laubscher 2003). In comparison, interpretations based on the detachment fold concept (Mitra 2003) were more realistic and quite similar to the original cross-sections by Buxtorf (1907, 1916) and Laubscher (1965) (Fig. 19.2, cross-sections 1 and 2). In the southernmost part of the Jura Mountains, where the Jura branches off from the Sub-Alpine Chains of the Western Alps, no significant salt horizon is present and, therefore, the geometry of the belt is dominated by west-directed thrusts associated with fault-bend and fault-propagation folds (Philippe *et al.* 1996).

The chain of the Jura Mountains has a pronounced arc shape, curving from a SSE–NNW orientated strike at the southern end to almost west–east strike at the eastern end. This is also the approximate strike of the main folds in the respective areas. The width of the chain decreases towards both ends, resulting in a crescent shape. In many parts of the Jura, folds and associated thrusts follow two different strike directions which results in the establishment of a lozenge pattern, as is typical for the plateaus in the external Jura. A similar pattern is also observed in the internal Jura. For example, the Val de Ruz syncline in the internal Swiss Jura is framed by ENE- and NNE-striking anticlines. This reflects the structural inheritance in that the NNE-striking structures probably nucleated along normal faults formed during the Oligocene WNW–ESE extension related to the Upper Rhine Graben (Homberg *et al.* 2002). In addition to these two fold-and-thrust sets, the Jura is cut by NNW-striking (in the west) to north-striking (in the east) sinistral strike-slip faults, or en-echelon fault systems (e.g. Accident de Pontarlier). Different fold-and-thrust geometries on both sides of these strike-slip faults reveal that they acted as transfer faults during the main phase of Jura folding, accommodating variable kinematic evolutions on both sides. The shortening perpendicular to the strike of the Jura amounts to more than 25 km in the central and western parts of the Jura and decreases to 0 km towards the eastern end (Laubscher 1965).

The Swiss Molasse Basin between the Jura and the Alpine front was uplifted and partly eroded following the cessation of deposition at *c.* 13 Ma. The uplift and erosion increase from east to west; an amount of >2000 m of uplift has been estimated for the western Swiss Molasse Basin (Laubscher 1974). This increase in uplift is parallel to the increase in shortening of the Jura. Therefore, Laubscher (1974) assumed that the uplift was partly driven by the northwestward translation of the fill of the Molasse Basin over a thrust following its base. Furthermore, the Swiss Molasse Basin was rotated clockwise by *c.* 16° to 17° after the Middle Miocene, that is, probably contemporaneous with Jura folding (Kempf *et al.* 1998). A clockwise rotation of the Jura by 7° had been predicted by Laubscher (1961) in order to explain the eastward decrease of shortening across the Jura. Except for a folded and thrusted strip close to the Alps (Sub-Alpine Molasse), the Swiss Molasse Basin is only gently deformed. This changes towards the southwestern end of the Molasse Basin where the Mesozoic rocks crop out as ramp anticlines (e.g. Montagne de Salève) within the Molasse Basin.

### *Large-scale kinematics*

A long-standing controversy exists concerning the 'Fernschub hypothesis' (Laubscher 1961), that is, the assumption that the Jura shortening does not affect the basement beneath the Jura but is kinematically linked to Alpine thrusting by a décollement under the Jura Mountains and the Swiss Molasse Basin (Fig. 19.2, cross-section 3). This hypothesis was already implicit in

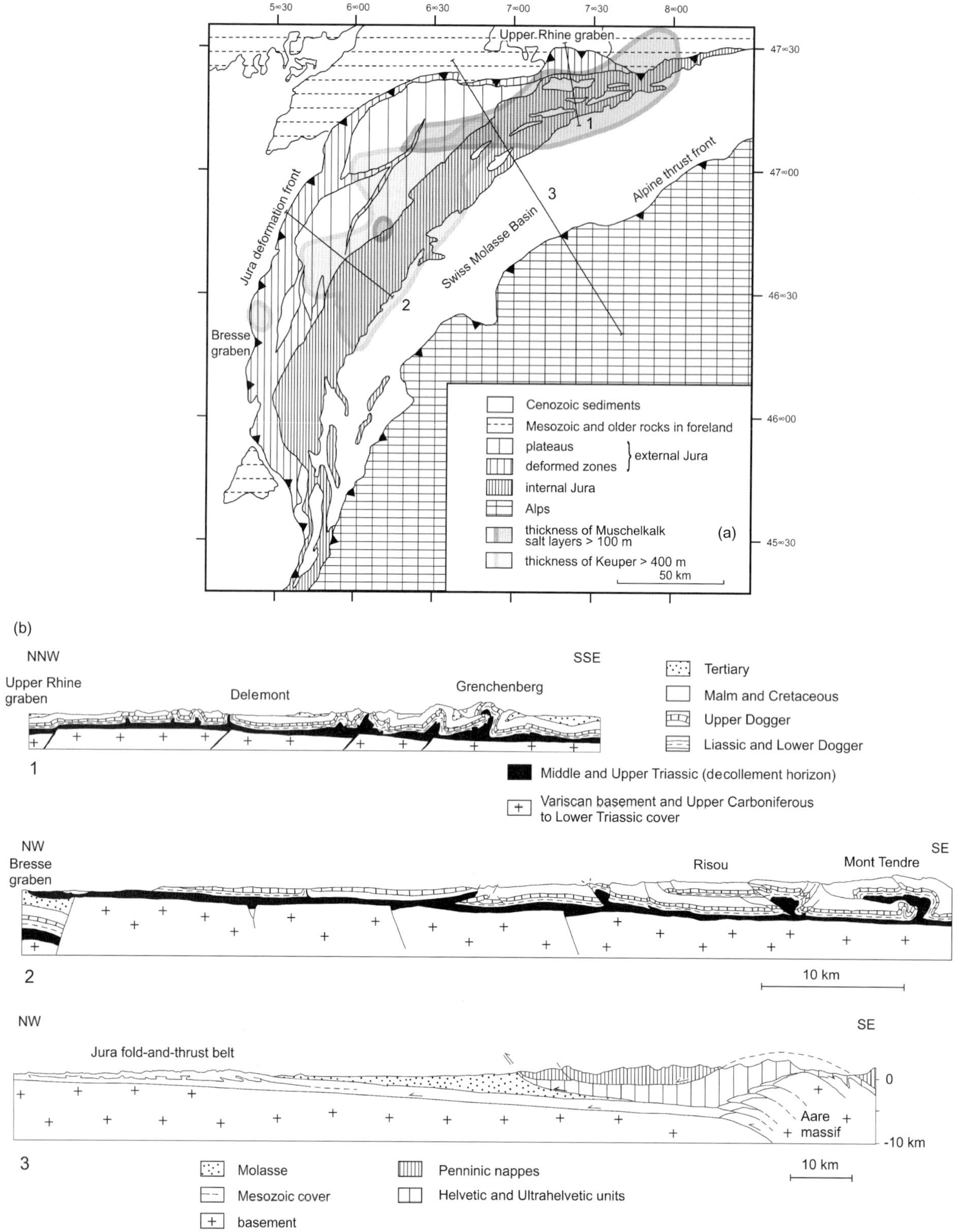


**Fig. 19.2.** (**A**) Tectonic sketch map of the northwestern foreland of the Alps and (**B**) three profiles across the Jura Mountains. Note the rough coincidence between thickness maxima of Triassic evaporites and the Jura Mountains in (A). In profiles 1 and 2 (B), the Jura folds are interpreted as detached folds, that is, movement of the ductile evaporite-bearing layers (black) from synclinal areas into anticlinal cores is assumed. Profile 3 shows the kinematic connection of the Jura fold-and-thrust belt with a crustal thrust below the Aare massif, along a hypothetic décollement below the Molasse basin. Map after Philippe *et al.* (1996), profile 1 after Buxtorf (1916) and Trümpy (1980), profile 2 after Laubscher (1965) and Trümpy (1980), profile 3 after Burkhard (1990).

the work of Buxtorf (1907, 1916) and was developed in a classic paper by Laubscher (1961). The model is now widely accepted, although some authors still have doubts (Ziegler 1990; Gorin *et al.* 1993; Pfiffner *et al.* 1997). The hypothesis has two major components: (1) the independence of cover and basement tectonics in the Jura during the main folding and thrusting phase; and (2) the existence of a thrust plane in the Mesozoic succession beneath the Molasse Basin (i.e. the allochthony of the Molasse Basin).

The independence of cover and basement tectonics within the Jura is not observable at the surface since the basement is not exposed. On the other hand, the construction of balanced cross-sections almost inevitably leads to the assumption of such independence (Buxtorf 1907, 1916; Laubscher 1965). There are, however, some observations that shed doubt on the complete independence. In reflection seismic profiles, the Ferrette and Glaserberg anticlines in the external Jura west of Basel appear to be related to thrust faults that do not shallow out in a basal décollement but instead cut across the entire sedimentary sequence into the basement (Rotstein & Schaming 2004). These two folds are the most frontal ones in this part of the Jura (Fig. 19.2, cross-section 1). Further to the north, in that part of the Upper Rhine Graben which forms the immediate foreland of the Jura Mountains, embryonic anticlines developed during the Plio-Pleistocene and may be interpreted as the propagation of Jura tectonics into the foreland. These are also connected with faults in the crystalline basement (Giamboni *et al.* 2004). These faults are reactivated Palaeozoic structures, related to the formation of Late Carboniferous to Permian grabens, as well as Palaeogene faults related to the Rhine–Rhône transform zone (Giamboni *et al.* 2004). Therefore, it would appear that the decoupling is not complete but that some shortening may be accommodated in the basement, especially as a result of compressional reactivation of Late Palaeozoic faults. The Late Carboniferous to Permian Konstanz-Frick Trough underlies the northern Jura (see also Laubscher 1987), and some reactivation of the graben-bounding faults during Neogene compression is likely.

As to the second component of the Fernschub hypothesis, i.e. the existence of a thrust plane below the Tertiary fill of the Molasse Basin, the available data are inconclusive. Several drillholes have encountered mylonitized anhydrite and, in one case, halite in the Triassic strata beneath the Molasse Basin (Jordan 1992). This would support the presence of a décollement (as depicted on Fig. 19.2, cross-section 3). On the other hand, reflection seismic profiles show that the evaporite-bearing layers do not form a smooth surface beneath the Molasse Basin but are dissected by steep faults (e.g. Pfiffner *et al.* 1997). A structural cross-section across the central Swiss Molasse Basin based on unpublished seismic profiles (Ziegler 1990) shows normal faults cutting across both the basement and the Mesozoic succession and dying out up-section in the Cenozoic sediments. These normal faults are interpreted to be Oligocene to Miocene in age and to pre-date Jura folding. The faults should have been dismembered by any northwestward displacement of the Molasse Basin along the décollement. If this observation were correct, it would contradict the Fernschub hypothesis. Similar observations were made in seismic sections from the western Swiss Molasse Basin (Gorin *et al.* 1993). For these reasons, Ziegler (1990) and Pfiffner *et al.* (1997) have suggested that the Jura shortening was accommodated by a thrust within the basement, dipping shallowly to the south from the Jura Mountains. Such a thrust could also have accommodated clockwise rotation and uplift of the Molasse Basin. However, it is hard to understand how a thrust fault could form in the basement almost parallel to, and only a short distance below, the basement–sediment interface, as proposed by Pfiffner *et al.* (1997), instead of ramping up into the evaporite layers at the base of the cover succession. An unequivocal answer to this problem could only be found by deep drilling at the internal border of the Jura.

If the 'Fernschub hypothesis' is accepted, several possibilities exist as to how the Jura shortening was accommodated in the Alps. Laubscher (1965) proposed that Jura shortening could be balanced by extension above the Aare Massif. Based on this view, the Jura shortening was not rooted but rather represents gravitational gliding. This model has been abandoned like most of the other attempts to explain thrust-and-fold belt formation by gravitational gliding. Alternatively, the Jura Thrust may have been rooted, together with the Helvetic nappes, SE of the Aare Massif (Laubscher 1973). This is unlikely since it would require uplift of the Aare Massif to post-date Jura thrusting and folding, which is not the case (see Burkhard 1990, and references therein). The final, and today generally accepted, possibility is that the Jura Thrust was rooted at the foot of the Aare Massif (e.g. Burkhard 1990; Fig. 19.2, cross-section 3). Thus, the Aare Massif represents an antiformal stack related to the passage of the Jura Thrust through the upper layer of the basement.

### *Cenozoic tectonic evolution*

According to a microtectonic analysis of Homberg *et al.* (2002), Late Miocene Jura folding was preceded by three distinct tectonic phases in the Palaeogene to Early Miocene. During the Eocene to Early Oligocene (phase 1) the area of the Jura was faulted in a stress regime of the strike-slip type where $\sigma_1$ was mostly subhorizontal and north–south, $\sigma_2$ subvertical, and $\sigma_3$ subhorizontal and east–west. This stress field is assumed to have been controlled by the Pyrenean collision between the Iberian and the European continents. It produced some NNE-trending sinistral strike-slip faults and east–west striking reverse faults. Some folding probably also occurred; these folds were eroded and unconformably covered by Late Oligocene to Middle Miocene strata (Aubert 1958). During the Oligocene, the area was affected by the ESE–WNW extension that also created the Upper Rhine Graben (phase 2), resulting in the formation of NE–SW striking normal faults. Phase 3 comprises minor NE–SW extension and the formation of NW–SE normal faults. The timing of this event is unclear but was prior to the Jura folding. The structures formed during these three phases were transported northwestward during the phase of Jura folding and thrusting and were, in part, reactivated during this process.

In the main Jura phase (Late Miocene to Pliocene), the sedimentary cover was detached, imbricated by thrusts, and folded. Palaeostress analysis for this phase using stylolite peaks and calcite twins yielded a pattern of radially diverging $\sigma_1$ trajectories; in the south, $\sigma_1$ is SW–NE to west–east, in the centre, NW–SE, and in the east, north–south (Plessmann 1972; Tschanz 1990; Philippe *et al.* 1996; Hindle & Burkhard 1999). Jura folding and thrusting fit a thrust-wedge model (e.g. Laubscher 1974; Philippe *et al.* 1996). The fill of the Molasse Basin and the units of the Jura Mountains above the décollement together constitute the thrust wedge. The possible décollement horizon in the Triassic beneath the Molasse Basin dips at *c.* 3.5° to the SE (Pfiffner *et al.* 1997). In the Jura Mountains, the décollement is almost horizontal. The angle of taper of the wedge at the beginning of thrusting was, therefore, higher beneath the Molasse Basin than under the Jura Mountains. Underthrusting of the foreland under the front of the External Massifs produced a relative outward (northwest-ward) displacement of the thrust wedge. In the Molasse Basin, the angle of taper was such that it facilitated sliding of the wedge without internal deformation, whereas the very low angle of taper in the Jura resulted in thickening by internal thrusting and folding. In three dimensions, the evolution of the fold-and-thrust belt was controlled by the limited occurrence of Triassic salt. The wedging-out of the salt towards the NE and SW contributed to the arc shape of the Jura and the divergence of the $\sigma_1$ trajectories, in that the thrust front could advance furthest towards the NW in the centre of the 'salt basin'. At some stage in the Pliocene(?), thin-skinned thrusting gave way to a new style of tectonics where the basement was shortened together with the sediment cover. This type of deformation is still active as indicated by *in situ* stress measurements (Becker 2000) and earthquake focal mechanisms (Lopes Cardoso & Granet 2003). The present-day stress field is markedly different from that of the main Jura phase as registered by stylolites and calcite twins in the Jura Mountains (Becker 2000), reflecting the change from thin- to thick-skinned thrusting.

## Upper Rhine Graben

The course of the river Rhine follows two important graben structures which differ in their tectonic evolution but, together, form a continuous belt of important present-day seismic activity, and hence a kinematic entity, namely, the Upper Rhine Graben and the Lower Rhine Basin. The Upper Rhine Graben is an elongate lowland flanked by uplifted plateaus. The Lower Rhine Basin forms a normal-fault-controlled embayment in the northern flank of the Rhenish Massif (Rheinisches Schiefergebirge). Its structures continue towards the NW in the subsurface of the Dutch–North German plain.

### *Structural architecture*

The Upper Rhine Graben is *c.* 300 km long, *c.* 40 km wide on average, and strikes NNE–SSW (Fig. 19.3). The southern termination of the graben is formed by the west–east striking frontal thrusts and thrust-bound flexures of the Jura Mountains, and its northern termination is the WSW–ENE striking southern boundary fault of the Rhenish Massif. Formation of the Upper Rhine Graben commenced in the Late Eocene, with the main rifting phase in the Oligocene. Variscan and post-Variscan faults were repeatedly reactivated during the Cenozoic evolution of the graben (Schumacher 2002; Lopes Cardozo & Granet 2005).

The Cenozoic graben-filling sediments unconformably overlie Palaeozoic to Late Jurassic sedimentary rocks with an overall increase in age towards the north (Late Jurassic at the southern end of the graben, Permian at the northern end; Pflug 1982). The angular nature of the unconformity indicates that the graben was formed following southward tilting and peneplanation of the area. However, the northward increase of the subcrop age is not uniform. Late Jurassic sediments underlie the graben fill not only at the southern end, but also reappear in the area to the north of Strasbourg. In the area in between, Middle Jurassic sediments form the subcrop. This indicates the existence of a very gentle anticline, prior to graben formation, which coincides with the present-day Black Forest (Schwarzwald) and Vosges graben shoulders. Hence, the Black Forest–Vosges uplift, although essentially of much younger (Miocene) age, had a precursor prior to graben formation, probably in the Late Cretaceous to Palaeocene. In the area of this uplift, erosion removed the Late Jurassic sediments.

The graben-filling sediments record the polyphase tectonic evolution of the Upper Rhine Graben (Sissingh 1998). They are subdivided by an unconformity in the Burdigalian at *c.* 18 Ma, following deposition of the Hydrobia marl (Roll 1979; Sissingh 2003*b*). This unconformity marks a turning point in the evolution of the Upper Rhine Graben. Before this time, the main depocentre was located in the southern part of the graben. Subsequent to 18 Ma, the southern part of the graben became the site of uplift and erosion, removing parts of the earlier accumulated graben fill and locally cutting down into the Lower Oligocene Pechelbronn Beds. Only in the Pliocene–Pleistocene did deposition resume in the southern part of the graben. The northern part, in contrast, was the site of major subsidence and deposition during the Upper Miocene and Pliocene–Pleistocene. Pleistocene to Holocene normal slip along the Western Border Fault in the northern upper Rhine Graben has been evidenced by trenching and geomorphology (Peters *et al.* 2005). The uplift and erosion of the southern part of the graben coincided with the uplift of the Black Forest and Vosges graben shoulders bordering this part of the Upper Rhine Graben. As a result of this deformation, the Vosges and Black Forest form a dome with an amplitude of 2.5 km and a wavelength of 200 km in geological profiles parallel to the graben, with a steeper southern and a gentler northern flank (Dèzes *et al.* 2004). Erosional denudation of the Black Forest and Vosges adjacent to the Upper Rhine Graben since the Late Eocene is in the range of 1 to 2.2 km (Timar-Geng *et al.* 2006).

The Upper Rhine Graben is bounded by major normal faults, inclined at 55° to 80°, with vertical displacements of up to 5000 m. Interpretation of seismic reflection profiles suggests that the fault dips decrease with depth (Brun *et al.* 1992; Fig. 19.3). Normal faults are also present within the graben, including both eastward- and westward-dipping faults. There is, however, a degree of asymmetry within the Upper Rhine Graben, depending on the extent of displacement of the border faults. In the northern part of the graben, the eastern border fault shows the greatest displacement and, accordingly, the greatest sediment thickness is located along the eastern margin of the graben. Further south, near Strasbourg, the western border fault was most active and the depocentre is close to the western border. Upper crustal extension across the Upper Rhine Graben amounts to *c.* 7 km (Dèzes *et al.* 2004). So-called 'Vorbergzonen' are formed by blocks with an intermediate position between the uplifted graben shoulders and the lowland of the graben fill. The rocks that crop out in these zones are mainly Mesozoic in age (Fig. 19.3). To the south of Mulhouse, the graben is subdivided into two sub-basins (Dannemarie Basin in the west, Sierentz Basin in the east) separated by a central high (Mulhouse High). Here, the boundary faults are often developed as extensional flexures in the Mesozoic cover rocks (Ustaszewski *et al.* 2005). In the southernmost part of the Upper Rhine Graben, close to the deformation front of the Jura fold-and-thrust belt, the geometry of the graben was strongly modified by Miocene to recent compressional and transpressional tectonics (Laubscher 2001; Giamboni *et al.* 2004; Rotstein *et al.* 2005).

Although most faults in the Upper Rhine Graben are normal, horizontal striations on fault planes, indicating sinistral displacement, are frequently observed. Furthermore, transpressional thrust faults are found in the southern part of the graben, and these are partly associated with diapirs of Lower Oligocene evaporites.

### *Extensions of the graben*

The southern termination of the Upper Rhine Graben is presently formed by younger (Late Miocene to Pliocene) frontal structures of the Jura. This coincides approximately with the original termination of the graben, as indicated by the presence of marginal sediment facies (Berger *et al.* 2005). However, a

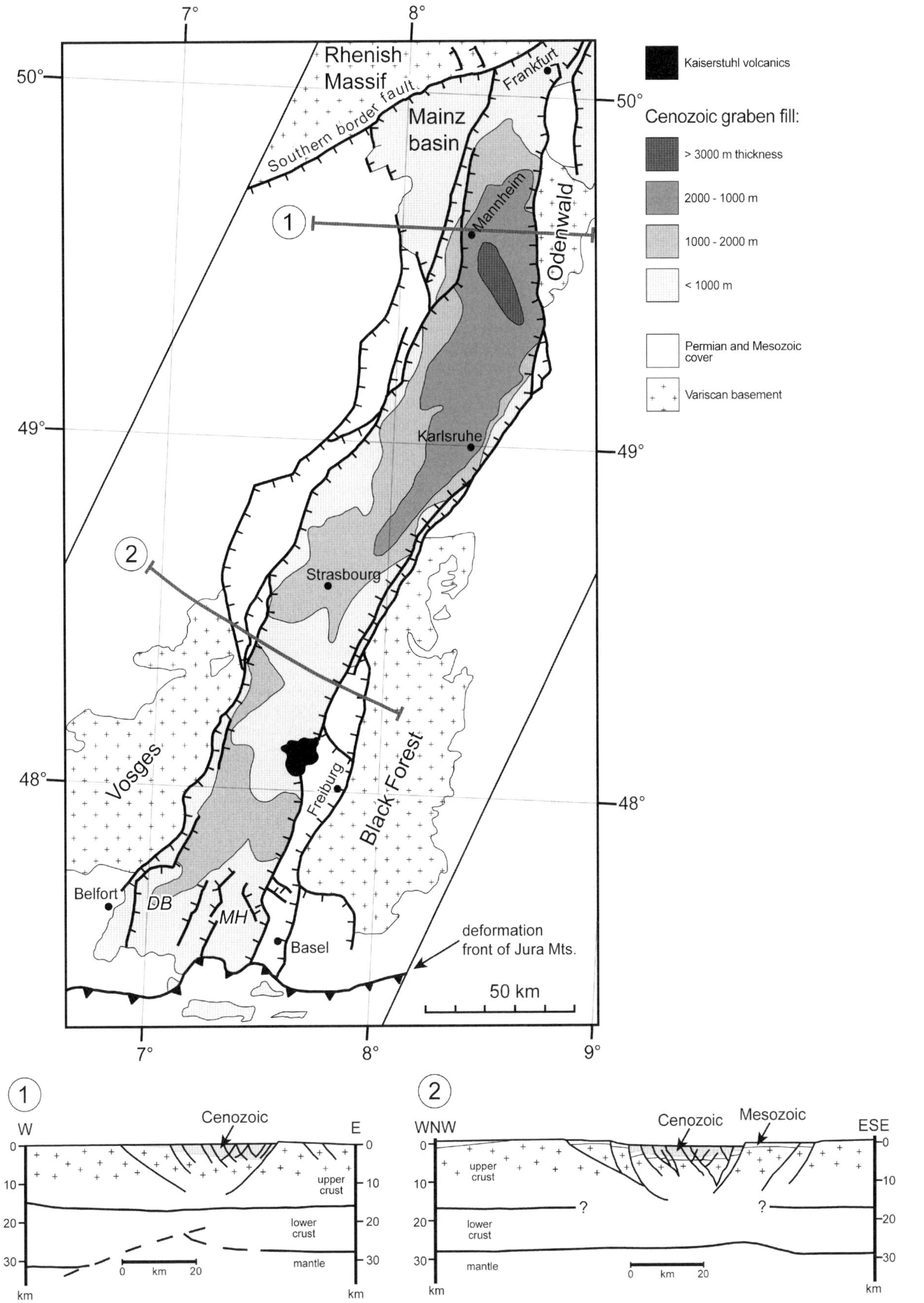


**Fig. 19.3.** Geological sketch map and sections across the Upper Rhine Graben. Thickness contours after Doebl & Olbrecht (1974), cross-sections after Brun *et al.* (1992). In the cross-sections, the thickness of Cenozoic sediments is exaggerated.

shallow depression formerly extended from the southern end of the Upper Rhine Graben into the area of the present-day Jura Mountains (Rauracian depression), the remainders of which are found in synclinal basins (Fig. 19.3).

An east–west striking, sinistral transfer zone extending from the southern end of the Upper Rhine Graben to the northern end of the Rhône-Bresse Graben is assumed for the area between the Vosges and the Jura Mountains. This may have been active during the main stage of graben formation in the Oligocene (e.g. Laubscher 2001), and this assumption is consistent with the observed fault pattern in the area (Contini & Théobald 1974). A close relationship between the Southern Upper Rhine Graben and the Rhône-Bresse Graben is documented by the stratigraphic record of these areas (Sissingh 1998, 2003*a*, *b*).

A northeastward branch of the Upper Rhine Graben extended into the Hessian Depression and the Leine Graben during the Oligocene (e.g. Ziegler 1994; Dèzes *et al.* 2004), as suggested by offsets of the base of Tertiary-age sediments and volcanics in this area (Schenk 1974). During the Early Rupelian, the Hessian Depression formed a narrow marine connection between the Upper Rhine Graben and the North German Basin (Murawski *et al.* 1983; Berger *et al.* 2005).

A northwestward extension from the Upper Rhine Graben into the Lower Rhine Basin was established during the Late Oligocene. However, the subsequent uplift of the Rhenish Massif, which occurred mainly during the Pleistocene to Recent (Meyer & Stets 2002), resulted in the erosional removal of the sediment fill of a possible connecting graben. Relicts of Rupelian to Chattian brackish and marine sediments in the Neuwied Basin and in the Eifel area suggest that there was a marine connection between the Lower Rhine Basin and the Upper Rhine Graben in mid-Oligocene times (Meyer *et al.* 1983; Negendank 1983). Today, the Upper Rhine Graben, Lower Rhine Basin and the part of the Rhenish Massif located between the two basins form a continuous zone of seismic activity whereas the Hessian Depression is seismically quiet.

*Moho structure*

A Moho dome is located beneath the Upper Rhine Graben. This dome is much wider than the actual graben and shows two components: an elongated, shallow bulge striking SW–NE from the Rhône-Bresse Graben through the Upper Rhine Graben area to the Hessian Depression, and a circular, more pronounced bulge centred beneath the southern part of the Upper Rhine Graben where the Moho rises up to <24 km depth (Dèzes *et al.* 2004). The centre of the latter bulge coincides with the Kaiserstuhl volcanic field, suggesting that there is a relationship between the Moho bulge and the Kaiserstuhl volcanism. This bulge also coincides with the uplift of the Black Forest and Vosges area.

*Seismicity and present-day deformation*

Earthquake hypocentres in the area of the Upper Rhine Graben occur beneath the graben and its elevated shoulders. Their depth range extends down as far as the Moho and ends abruptly there (Bonjer 1997). The largest historical earthquake in Central Europe, the Basel 1356 earthquake, occurred at the southern end of the Upper Rhine Graben. The epicentre was located south of Basel, approximately where the eastern border fault/flexure of the Upper Rhine Graben meets the front of the folded Jura. Meghraoui *et al.* (2001) suggested that a NNE–SSW striking, linear hill slope on the western side of the Birs valley represents the surface break of the seismic fault.

Stress inversion from earthquake focal mechanisms in the Upper Rhine Graben (Plenefisch & Bonjer 1997) yields a generally NE–SW (235°) orientated $\sigma_3$. $\sigma_1$ is distributed on a girdle between vertical orientation, implying NE–SW extensional tectonics, and horizontal, NNW–SSE (150°) orientation, implying sinistral strike-slip kinematics along graben-parallel faults and dextral strike-slip kinematics along west–east faults. Reconstruction of local crustal velocities from GPS data in central and western Europe (Tesauro *et al.* 2005) results in oblique, NW–SE directed compressional deformation across the Upper Rhine Graben. Sinistral shear is found along both borders of the graben.

*Volcanism*

Minor volcanic eruptions in the shoulder areas of the Upper Rhine Graben occurred in the Palaeocene, as indicated by $^{40}$Ar/$^{39}$Ar single crystal laser dating of an olivine melilite dyke in the Vosges (60.9 ± 0.6 Ma; Keller *et al.* 2002). Cretaceous K–Ar whole-rock ages for volcanic rocks in the shoulder areas (Lippolt *et al.* 1974) are probably geologically meaningless (Keller *et al.* 2002). The Kaiserstuhl volcanic field is located within the southern Upper Rhine Graben. The volcanism was active in the Miocene (18–16 Ma; Kraml *et al.* 1999) in a strike-slip stress regime (see below) subsequent to rifting of the Southern Rhine Graben and coincident with the onset of its uplift and partial erosion. The Palaeocene as well as the Miocene volcanics in the area of the Upper Rhine Graben are of melilitic to nephelinitic composition.

*Evolution of the stress field in the Upper Rhine Graben area*

The changing stress field in the Upper Rhine Graben area has been studied using microtectonic analyses in rocks of different ages (e.g. Buchner 1981; Bergerat 1983; Villemin & Bergerat 1987; Larroque & Laurent 1988). Villemin & Bergerat (1987) identified four different phases of brittle deformation. The oldest (phase I) is a strike-slip regime with $\sigma_1$ orientated horizontal and north–south, and $\sigma_3$ orientated horizontal and east–west. This activated the border faults of the graben as sinistral strike-slip faults. Villemin & Bergerat (1987) assumed that this deformation occurred in the Late Eocene, during the first stage of graben formation. However, as stated by themselves and Michon & Merle (2005), this age is uncertain since the measurements were made in Jurassic and older rocks, and thus the deformation may also be pre-Eocene (i.e. Cretaceous or Palaeocene). Villemin & Bergerat (1987) assumed a Late Eocene age because similar deformation has been reconstructed for this time in other parts of the European platform. Michon & Merle (2005), in contrast, assumed that phase I is Cretaceous to Palaeocene and that the initial rifting stage in the Late Eocene occurred under the same stress field as the main rifting stage in the Oligocene.

Phase II in the Oligocene, during the main stage of graben formation, occurred in an extensional regime with $\sigma_1$ vertical and $\sigma_3$ horizontal and east–west (Villemin & Bergerat 1987). The change from phase I to phase II represents a permutation of $\sigma_1$ and $\sigma_2$, with $\sigma_3$ maintaining its orientation (Villemin & Bergerat 1987; Larroque & Laurent 1988). Phase III occurred during the Late Oligocene to Early Miocene and was a strike-slip period of deformation with $\sigma_1$ horizontal and NE–SW, and $\sigma_3$ horizontal and NW–SE, which caused dextral strike-slip along the main graben-bounding faults (Villemin & Bergerat 1987). Larroque & Laurent (1988) did not find evidence for phase III and assumed that the same stress field as in phase II persisted until the Late Miocene. Finally, phase IV (Miocene to present), was again a strike-slip regime with $\sigma_1$ orientated NW–SE and $\sigma_3$

NE–SW, so that the main graben-bounding faults were reactivated as sinistral strike-slip faults.

*Dynamics of graben formation*
The dynamics of the Upper Rhine Graben are controversial (e.g. Dèzes *et al.* 2004; Michon & Merle 2005). It is obvious that the stress fields which controlled the formation and evolution of the graben resulted from the combination of different forces related to processes in the underlying mantle, plate boundary processes in the Alps and Pyrenees, and spreading in the Atlantic. The relative importance of these forces, however, is unclear. Dèzes *et al.* (2004) suggested that the main rifting phase during the Oligocene was controlled by north-directed compressional stresses, originating in the Pyrenean and Alpine collision zones, interfering with the load of an upwelling mantle plume. Michon & Merle (2005) argued that this is unlikely since marine sedimentation during the Oligocene contradicts the existence of an upwelling mantle plume beneath the Upper Rhine Graben at that time. They suggested that the graben formed as a result of east–west stretching of the European plate (i.e. passive rifting). Merle & Michon (2001) and Michon *et al.* (2003) explained the Late Eocene–Oligocene rifting as related to slab pull exerted by the Alpine lithospheric root, and the sudden change in graben dynamics around the Oligocene–Miocene transition (end of subsidence in the southern Upper Rhine Graben) by slab detachment below the Western Alps. However, there is little evidence for slab detachment at that time (Dèzes *et al.* 2004).

Another possible explanation for graben formation was suggested by Le Pichon *et al.* (1988) who noted that there is a difference between the Oligocene motion of Europe as determined from magnetic lineations in the North Atlantic, and its motion as determined from magnetic lineations in the Arctic Ocean. Assuming that this difference represents different motions of the main part of Eurasia and western Europe, an east–west divergent motion of these two parts of Eurasia results. This may have led to the formation of the Rhine–Rhône graben system. In this scenario, the formation of the Upper Rhine Graben would reflect far-field stresses related to global plate kinematics, whereas in the two other hypotheses discussed above, the stresses were connected to more local processes.

Despite the ongoing controversy, it can be stated that most authors assume passive rifting for the formation of the Upper Rhine Graben (e.g. Ziegler 1994; Dèzes *et al.* 2004). Active rifting, that is rifting caused by a rising mantle plume, is very unlikely because of the low elevation (as evidenced by marine sedimentation) during the main phase of rifting in the Oligocene.

## Lower Rhine Basin

The Lower Rhine Basin is a rift system active from Tertiary times to the present day and comprising several fault-bounded, SE–NW elongate blocks (Fig. 19.4). The southeastern part of the Lower Rhine Basin is morphologically expressed by the Lower Rhine Embayment (Niederrheinische Bucht), an area of low relief surrounded to the east, south and west by the uplifted plateau of the Rhenish Massif. The northwestern part of the Tertiary rift system is beneath the Dutch–North German plain. Many authors refer to the Lower Rhine Basin as the Roer Valley Rift System (e.g. Michon *et al.* 2003).

*Evolution and architecture*
The deepest graben structure of the Lower Rhine Basin is the Roer Valley Graben (Fig. 19.4). It was initiated in Late Permian–Early Triassic times and was again active in the Middle Jurassic (Zijerveld *et al.* 1992). During the Late Cretaceous and Early Palaeocene, this graben was inverted (Michon *et al.* 2003). Two periods of subsidence, in the Late Palaeocene and in the Oligocene to Recent, followed and these were separated by a further inversion phase in the Late Eocene (Michon *et al.* 2003). The present-day architecture and sediment fill of the Lower Rhine Basin developed mainly during the Late Oligocene to Recent (Schäfer *et al.* 2005). Along the margins of the Lower Rhine Embayment, the Oligocene sediments rest unconformably on Palaeozoic and Mesozoic strata. During the Quaternary, the subsidence rates in the Lower Rhine Basin significantly increased (Houtgast & Van Balen 2000) as did the rate of displacement along the main block-bounding normal faults. In the inner part of the Lower Rhine Embayment, the main faults are morphologically clearly expressed. The southernmost part of the Lower Rhine Embayment together with the Rhenish Massif, has been uplifted since the Pleistocene (Meyer & Stets 2002). The faults of the Lower Rhine Basin are generally almost pure dip-slip (see below) normal faults and follow two trends, the predominant SE to SSE (135–160°) trend and the subordinate ESE (110–120°) trend (Fig. 19.4). The intersection of these faults in map view leads to the formation of lozenge-shaped blocks which are mostly elongate in a NW–SE direction. In the Lower Rhine embayment, most tectonic blocks are half-grabens tilted to the NE, and the main normal faults accordingly dip to the SW (Fig. 19.4, section C–D). The maximum thickness of Cenozoic sediments, up to 2000 m, is found in the 20 km wide and 130 km long, NW–SE striking Roer Valley Graben. Within this graben, the thickness of the Cenozoic sediments decreases to the SE as well as to the NW. To the SE, the decrease in thickness is partly compensated by a thickness increase on the Erft Block which is the deepest half-graben in the inner part of the Lower Rhine Embayment (Fig. 19.4).

*Seismicity and present-day deformation*
The Lower Rhine Basin is seismically active and earthquakes of estimated magnitudes of >5 have repeatedly occurred. The strongest historical event was the Düren earthquake of 1756 with an estimated magnitude ($M_L$) of 6.1 (Ahorner 1994). The last major event, the 1992 Roermond earthquake with a local magnitude of 5.9, occurred at a depth of 14 to 18 km on or close to the Peel Boundary normal fault (i.e. the NE boundary fault of the Roer Valley Graben). This was an almost pure dip-slip earthquake; the ruptured fault plane trended NW–SE (124°) and dipped to the SW, towards the graben, at an angle of 68° (Ahorner 1994; Camelbeeck & van Eck 1994).

The present-day stress field in the shallow crust, as determined from earthquake focal mechanisms, is characterized by a subvertical $\sigma_1$ and a subhorizontal $\sigma_3$ orientated SW–NE (42°; Hinzen 2003). This probably grades into a strike-slip stress regime ($\sigma_1$ horizontal SE–NW) in the lower crust (Hinzen 2003). Results from a regional GPS net in the southern part of the Lower Rhine Basin suggest ongoing east–west directed separation of the basin shoulders (Campbell *et al.* 2002). An extensional regime in the Lower Rhine Basin is also indicated by analysis of GPS data in western and central Europe on a larger scale (Tesauro *et al.* 2005).

*Evolution of the stress field in the Lower Rhine Basin*
During the Late Eocene, the Lower Rhine Basin and the Upper Rhine Graben evolved in different ways. While rifting and subsidence shaped the Upper Rhine Graben, the Lower Rhine Basin was inverted and eroded. In the western part of the Lower Rhine Basin, 200 to 600 m of Late Eocene uplift have been

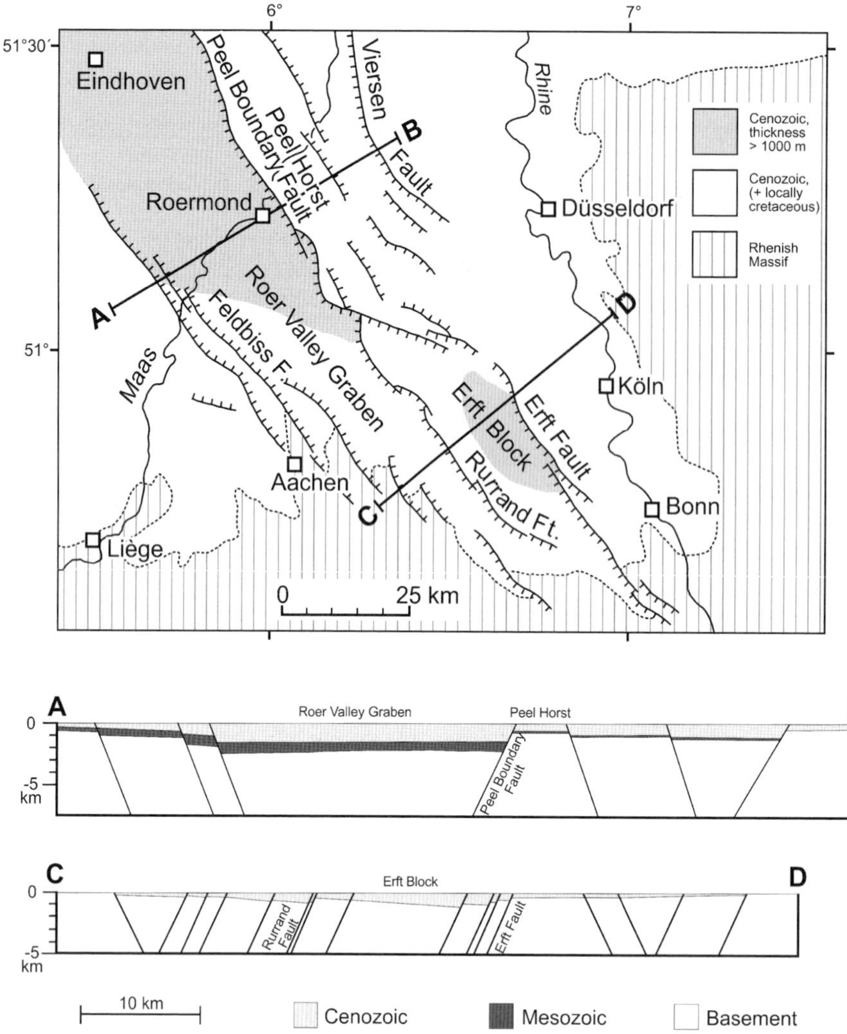


**Fig. 19.4.** Geological sketch map with major active normal faults and two schematic cross-sections (no vertical exaggeration) of the Lower Rhine Basin. After Ahorner (1994) and Schäfer (1994).

estimated from apatite fission track studies (Van Balen *et al.* 2002*a*). This inversion is consistent with the stress field assumed by Villemin & Bergerat (1987) for the Late Eocene in the area of the Upper Rhine Graben, a strike-slip regime with $\sigma_1$ orientated horizontal and north–south. (However, the timing of this stress field is uncertain; see above.) For the Oligocene, Michon *et al.* (2003) assumed a WNW–ESE direction of extension ($\sigma_3$). This is strongly oblique to the main faults which trend NW–SE, and would have resulted in dextrally transtensive opening. The late Oligocene–Early Miocene phase of strike-slip tectonics with $\sigma_1$ orientated NE–SW, identified by Villemin & Bergerat (1987) for the Upper Rhine Graben (but doubted by Larroque & Laurent 1988), is not seen in the Lower Rhine Basin. Such a stress field would have reactivated the Lower Rhine Basin faults in compression, for which there is little evidence. Instead, strong subsidence occurred in the Late Oligocene. From Early Miocene times, the stress field was probably similar to the present-day stress field as determined from earthquake focal mechanisms, characterized by a steep $\sigma_1$ and a shallow $\sigma_3$ orientated SW–NE (42°; Hinzen 2003). Continuity between the Miocene and the present day is suggested by the presence of down-dip slickensides on normal fault planes and by the offset of marker lines across normal faults in lignite open pit mines (Knufinke & Kothen 1997) which both indicate pure SW–NE dip-slip movement. The Miocene to present-day stress field in the Lower Rhine Basin is thus similar to the one in the Upper Rhine Graben, the different style of deformation (strike-slip in the Upper Rhine Graben, extension in the Lower Rhine Basin) resulting from the different orientations of the main graben-bounding faults which were inherited from earlier stages.

### *Rhenish Massif*

The Rhenish Massif (Rhenisches Schiefergebirge) is an uplifted area where Palaeozoic (mainly Devonian) rocks crop out. Although the uplift responsible for the present-day relief occurred during the Cenozoic, the NW and SE boundaries of the Rhenish Massif are partly inherited from Variscan tectonics. The NW boundary roughly corresponds to the NW limit of intense Variscan deformation, and the SE boundary to the boundary between the Rhenohercynian fold-and-thrust belt and the Mid-German Crystalline Zone (see also McCann *et al.* 2008*a*). Towards the SW, the Rhenish Massif plunges beneath the Mesozoic sediments of the Paris Basin, and towards the NE, beneath the Mesozoic of the Hessian Depression.

*Uplift*
Oligocene rifting of the Lower Rhine Basin probably also affected the central part of the Rhenish Massif, because the normal faults of the Lower Rhine Basin continue towards the SE into the Rhenish Massif. However, the distribution of coastal facies in the adjacent basins indicates that the Rhenish Massif was an uplifted area between the Lower Rhine Basin and the Upper Rhine Graben throughout most of the Oligocene and Miocene. The area was flooded by the sea for only a short period in mid-Oligocene times and possibly a second time in the Early Miocene (Murawski *et al.* 1983; Sissingh 2003*b*). The Rhenish Massif has been undergoing uplift from the Miocene to the present day. Analysis of fluvial terraces of the Lower Maas River indicates that the uplift of the Ardennes area strongly accelerated at *c.* 3 Ma (Van den Berg 1994). The uplift rate at the south-western flank of the Roer Valley Graben was 0.003 mm/a from 14 to 3 Ma, and on average 0.06 mm/a from 3 Ma to the present day (Van den Berg 1994). An episode of particularly strong uplift occurred in the early Middle Pleistocene at *c.* 0.7 Ma contemporaneously with the onset of the youngest phase of volcanism in the Eifel (Van Balen *et al.* 2002*b*; see also Litt *et al.* 2008). Uplift of up to 250 m over 800 000 years (>0.31 mm/a) in the central part of the Rhenish Massif was determined from the analysis of fluvial terraces along the Rhine, Lahn and Mosel rivers and their tributaries (Meyer & Stets 1998, 2002). The maximum of this young uplift is located between the West and East Eifel volcanic districts, suggesting a relationship between uplift and volcanism (Meyer & Stets 2002). A ridge of marked uplift (>200 m over the last 800 000 years) extends from the Eifel volcanic region towards the WNW into the Hohes Venn area. Present-day uplift rates determined from precision levelling are *c.* 0.6 mm/a in the Eifel volcanic region and up to *c.* 1.6 mm/a at the northern margin of the Rhenish Massif in the area of the Hohes Venn (Mälzer *et al.* 1983). Pleistocene vertical displacement between the northern end of the Upper Rhine Graben and the uplifted Rhenish Massif was mainly localized along the southern boundary fault of the Rhenish Massif (Peters & van Balen 2007).

The Rhenish Massif was not uplifted as a single block or plateau but rather as several blocks with marked differences in the rate of uplift. Whereas the Pleistocene uplift maximum in the Eifel volcanic region can be related to volcanism, the zone of marked uplift in the Hohes Venn area is devoid of Cenozoic volcanics and uplift here may be related to crustal shortening, as suggested by the occurrence of thrust earthquakes in this area (see below).

*Seismicity and stress field*
The distribution of historical and present-day earthquakes forms a continuous belt of seismicity from the Lower Rhine Basin through the Rhenish Massif to the northern end of the Upper Rhine Graben (e.g. Ahorner 1983). Branching off from this belt towards the west is a zone of seismicity that approximately follows the northern margin of the Rhenish Massif (Stavelot-Venn Massif). In the Middle Rhine Zone (between the Lower Rhine Basin and Upper Rhine Graben), fault-plane solutions suggest a stress regime of normal-faulting character with $\sigma_3$ orientated NE–SW, as in the Lower Rhine Basin (Ahorner 1983; Hinzen 2003). The Middle Rhine Zone is today a NW–SE striking rift forming a continuation of the Lower Rhine Basin. The rift has no Cenozoic sediment fill, except in the Neuwied Basin, because rifting occurs contemporaneously with regional uplift.

For the Stavelot-Venn Massif, a strike-slip stress regime is indicated with $\sigma_1$ orientated subhorizontal and NW–SE (316°), and $\sigma_3$ subhorizontal and SW–NE (225°) (Hinzen 2003). Some earthquakes in the Hohes Venn area have compressional (reverse) dip-slip focal mechanisms. For these, one of the two possible fault planes dips shallowly towards the SSE, as does the Variscan Aachen Thrust, the frontal thrust of the Rhenohercynian fold-and-thrust belt which underlies the Hohes Venn area. For this reason, Ahorner (1983) suggested a reactivation of the Aachen Thrust by SE–NW compression. This may explain the relatively strong present-day uplift of the area, and also the rough coincidence, in this area, of the NW margin of the Rhenish Massif with the NW front of Variscan deformation.

*Eifel plume*
P- and S-wave tomography revealed a low-velocity structure in the upper mantle beneath the Eifel volcanic field. This structure extends down to at least 400 km and is interpreted as a plume (Eifel plume; Ritter *et al.* 2001; Keyser *et al.* 2002). This plume was most likely the cause of the Pleistocene to Recent volcanism in the Eifel area (see also Litt *et al.* 2008). The geochemical similarity between the Quaternary and Tertiary volcanism in the Rhenish Massif (e.g. Haase *et al.* 2004) suggests that a mantle plume may have existed under the Rhenish Massif from Palaeogene times onward.

*Summary*
The Miocene to Recent tectonics of the Rhenish Massif were controlled by three processes: rifting in the Middle Rhine Zone (i.e. the prolongation of the Lower Rhine Basin), the rise of a mantle plume during the Pleistocene but probably also in Tertiary times, and regional NW–SE compression within the European plate. These three processes combined in a complex manner to produce the current situation.

## Western part of the South German Triangle (K.R., J.R.)

### *Geological framework*

Southern Germany consists of several tectonostratigraphic units (Fig. 19.5). The Upper Rhine Graben forms the western tectonic boundary, and is mainly characterized by Tertiary and Quaternary sediments. The eastern boundary comprises the crystalline basement of the Bohemian Massif. To the south the Molasse Basin of the Alps frames the area in a triangular shape. Herein, we concentrate on the main tectonic features of the area between the rivers Rhine (Rhein) and Danube (Donau) in the south as far as the city of Heidelberg and the river Neckar, and the Rhine in the west and the Ries impact crater in the east.

The so-called South German Triangle (e.g. Wurster 1986), or the Süddeutsche Großscholle (Carlé 1955), is characterized by extensive outcrops of Mesozoic rocks (Fig. 19.4), which do not exceed *c.* 1000 m in thickness above the crystalline basement of the Black Forest area (Schwarzwald). The sedimentary cover forms a typical cuesta landscape (Figs. 19.6 & 19.7; dipping 5–10° towards the SE or east) with major escarpments built up by resistant carbonates of the Late Jurassic (Albtrauf) and the Middle Triassic (Muschelkalk) as well as the sandstones of the Buntsandstein or Bunter (Early Triassic). Minor escarpments are formed by the sandstones in the Keuper (Late Triassic) and the Dogger (Middle Jurassic) as well as by thick individual carbonate sequences in the Early Liassic (Arietenkalk) and the Keuper (Acrodus-Corbula horizon). Generally, the Mesozoic cover dips gently towards the SE and is cut by several large fault systems, which are detectable in the present-day topography (Fig. 19.7).

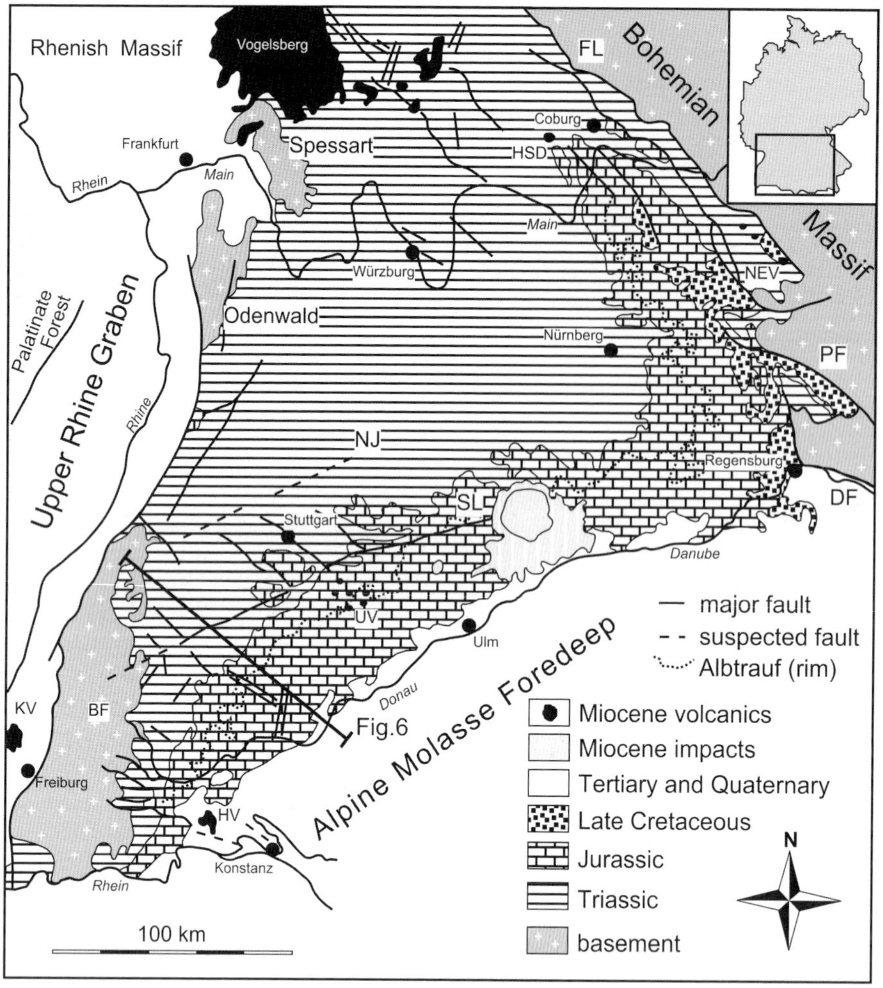


**Fig. 19.5.** Simplified geological map of southern Germany with the main structural elements. 'Albtrauf' means the cuesta formed by the Upper Jurassic limestones of the Swabian and Franconian Albs. Basement includes Precambrian and Palaeozoic, mainly metamorphosed sediments and magmatic rocks. The vertical striped pattern surrounding the Ries impact marks the ejecta blanket. Late Cretaceous is restricted to NE Bavaria. Abbreviations: BF, Black Forest; DF, Danube Fault; FL, Franconian Line; HSD, Heldburg Swarm Dykes; HV, Hegau volcanics; KV, Kaiserstuhl volcanics; NEV, Northeastern Bavarian Volcanics; NJ, Neckar-Jagst Fault Zone; PF, Pfahl Fault; SL, Swabian Lineament; UV, Urach volcanic area.

Middle Triassic (salt, gypsum and anhydrite) and Keuper (mainly anhydrite and gypsum) evaporites control the formation of more gentle landforms. The evaporite successions are up to 50 m thick and are subject to subrosion with the formation of caves, dolinas and sink holes. The evaporitic units can probably decouple the hanging wall sequence from the tectonic stress field of the underlying rocks and the basement. Claystone units form unstable slopes permanently prone to landslides, such as the Knollenmergel of the latest Triassic or the Opalinuston of the lowermost Middle Jurassic (Fig. 19.6).

From the Late Jurassic onwards, a hiatus of probable non-deposition extends far into the Tertiary and Cretaceous, and Lower Tertiary successions are absent. However, the existence of bedding-parallel stylolites in the Upper Jurassic (Tithonian) related to compaction suggests that there must have been at least 100 m of cover above the present-day landscape in order to generate the necessary pressure conditions. Bergerat (1994) assumed up to 200–450 m of erosion after the formation of vertical stylolites, and the eroded sediments may have included parts of the Late Jurassic, Cretaceous and Tertiary. It is, however, still doubtful if the Cretaceous and Tertiary were ever deposited in SW Germany. Some clay (e.g. the Feuersteinlehm on the top of the Swabian Alb, Fig. 19.6) and sand relicts of possibly older sediments are found in karstic caves and fissures. Their origin and stratigraphic position, however, are unclear.

Limonitic or ferruginous deposits (Bohnerze) formed as a result of lateritic alteration of the clay-rich Hangenden Bankkalke (Late Jurassic), and these are predominantly found in association with Palaeogene karstic forms. However, age determinations based on vertebrates and molluscs also suggested Pliocene ages for the formation of the Bohnerz. Karstification of the limestone plateau of the Swabian Alb was initiated in the Oligocene, and intensified during the Late Miocene. The entire Mesozoic succession is cut by Miocene volcanics. There are three main volcanic areas in southern Germany: the Kaiserstuhl volcano in the Upper Rhine Graben, the Hegau volcanoes near Lake Constance (Bodensee) and the Urach volcanic field south of Stuttgart (Figs. 19.7 & 19.8). Furthermore, the eastern part of the Swabian Alb was hit by a large meteorite, forming the Ries and Steinheim impact craters, *c.* 14.3 ± 0.2 Ma ago (Buchner *et al.* 2003; Figs 19.5, 19.7 & 19.8). Extensive parts of the impact area are covered by impact breccias (Suevit), while the craters are filled by clastic and carbonate lake sediments.

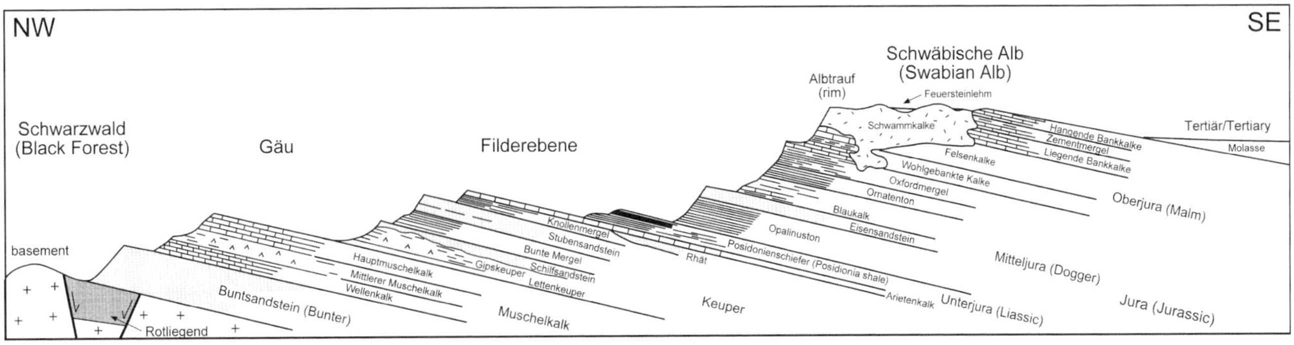


**Fig. 19.6.** Cuesta landscape of southern Germany (modified from Wagner 1961). Not to scale. Location of the section is shown in Figure 19.5.

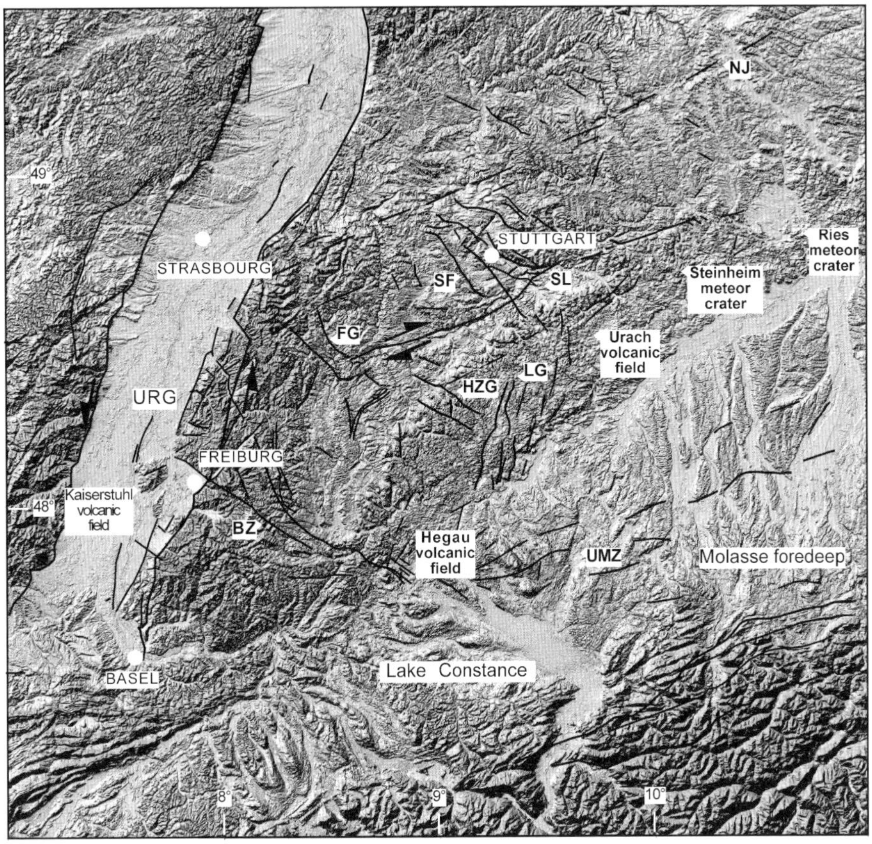


**Fig. 19.7.** Shaded relief map of southern Germany based on SRTM data (3 arc seconds) with faults and lineations. Abbreviations: BZ, Bonndorf Graben Zone; FG, Freudenstadt Graben; HZG, Hohenzollern Graben; LG, Lauchert Graben; NJ, Neckar-Jagst Fault Zone; SF, Sindelfingen and Filder Graben; SL, Swabian Lineament; UMZ, Lake Constance-Memmingen Fault Zone; URG, Upper Rhine Graben.

## *Structural framework*

*Recent seismicity in southern Germany*

Generally, southwestern Germany is a zone of low to moderate seismicity (Fig. 19.9). In contrast to the Upper Rhine Graben, where the seismic activity is distributed over a large area, earthquakes cluster in southwestern Germany around the Hohenzollern Graben (HZG) system and the Albstadt Shear Zone (ASZ). The earthquake activity and neotectonics of the HZG have recently been revised by Reinecker & Schneider (2002). The seismic activity is characterized by small to moderate earthquakes with local magnitudes of up to 6.2. Focal depths for the larger events are in the range of 6 to 13 km. Shallow earthquakes (<4 km) are very rare. The average seismic dislocation rates along the ASZ are of the order of 0.1 mm/a (Schneider 1993). The geometry is defined by the trend of aftershocks and focal mechanism solutions displaying a steep NNE to SSW trending (280/75, dip direction/dip) structure with sinistral strike-slip movement. From historical and instrumental recorded events,

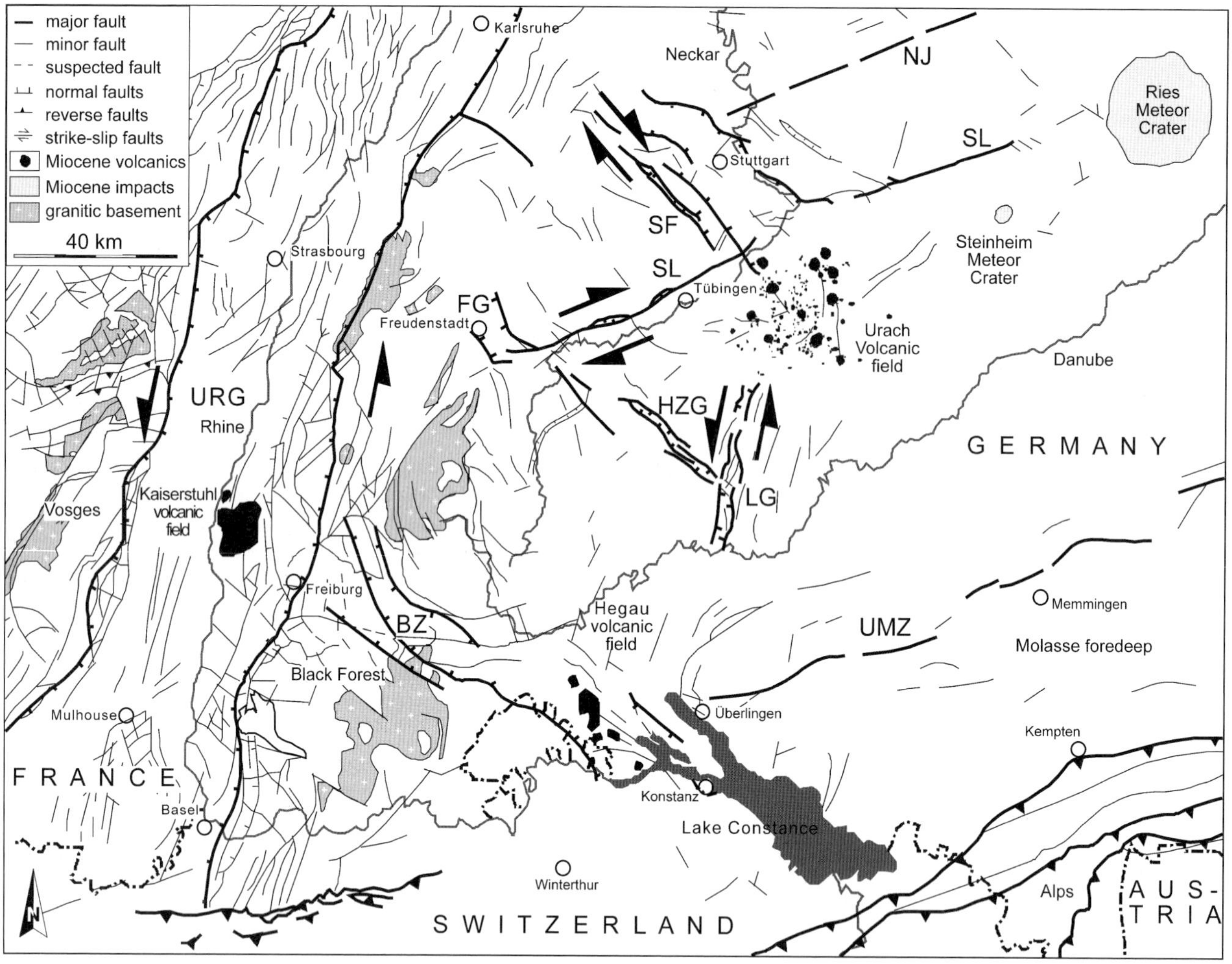


**Fig. 19.8.** Tectonic sketch map of southwestern Germany (modified after Meschede *et al.* 1997). Note that Miocene volcanic activity occurs predominantly at intersection points of three major fault or lineation directions (NW–SE, NNE–SSW and ENE–WSW). For abbreviations see Figure 19.7.

the ASZ can be traced from Stuttgart in the north to Switzerland in the south.

The largest measured earthquake occurred in the ASZ, on 3 September 1978 with a magnitude of M 5.7, causing damage to houses and Hohenzollern castle estimated at 50 million euros. The penultimate event took place on 16 November 1911, near Ebingen (Fig. 19.10), and was of comparable magnitude, with building damage estimated at about 200 million euros. Surface ruptures were observed, and landslides triggered by seismic shock in the epicentral area and close to Lake Constance. Slope instabilities developed both in the superficial Quaternary deposits and Tertiary Molasse sediments (Sieberg & Lais 1925) demonstrating the potential of hazardous secondary earthquake effects.

Minor seismic activity has been reported from the Freudenstadt Graben over the last 250 years with moderate shocks in 1784, 1822 and 1871 (Regelmann 1907). The return period of earthquakes with a magnitude of 5 has been estimated to be of the order of 1000 years, together with a possible migration of hypocentres towards the north along north–south striking deep-seated fault zones (Schneider 1979, 1980). Furthermore, NW–SE striking faults are regarded as potentially active, especially in areas where they intersect with north–south striking faults. This may be due to the reduced shear resistance and accompanied by aseismic creep (Schneider 1979, 1993; Wetzel & Franzke 2003). Rare, and up to now poorly understood, earthquakes also occur along ENE–WSW striking fault systems (Überlingen-Memmingen Zone, UMZ in Fig. 19.8), for example the 27 June 1935 earthquake in (Bad) Buchau, where the church in Kappel was heavily damaged due to roof collapse (Hiller 1936; Jung 1953). The isoseist map shows an ENE–WSW trending elliptical shape parallel to the Danube river with maximum European Macroseismic Scale (EMS) intensities of VII to VIII (equivalent to a maximum magnitude of *c.* 5.5; after Karnik 1971).

*Faults and recent stresses*

The regional stress field of southern Germany has been derived from focal mechanism solutions of earthquakes (Schneider 1979; Turnovsky 1981; Kunze 1982; Ahorner *et al.* 1983), by overcoring (Baumann 1986), borehole breakouts and hydraulic fracturing (Becker 1993). It is characterized by an average maximum horizontal stress orientation ($S_H$) of 150° and a strike-slip regime (Müller *et al.* 1992; Reinecker *et al.* 2004; Fig. 19.11). Close to and within the HZG the stress field $S_H$ rotates 20° counterclockwise into the strike direction of the HZG (130°;

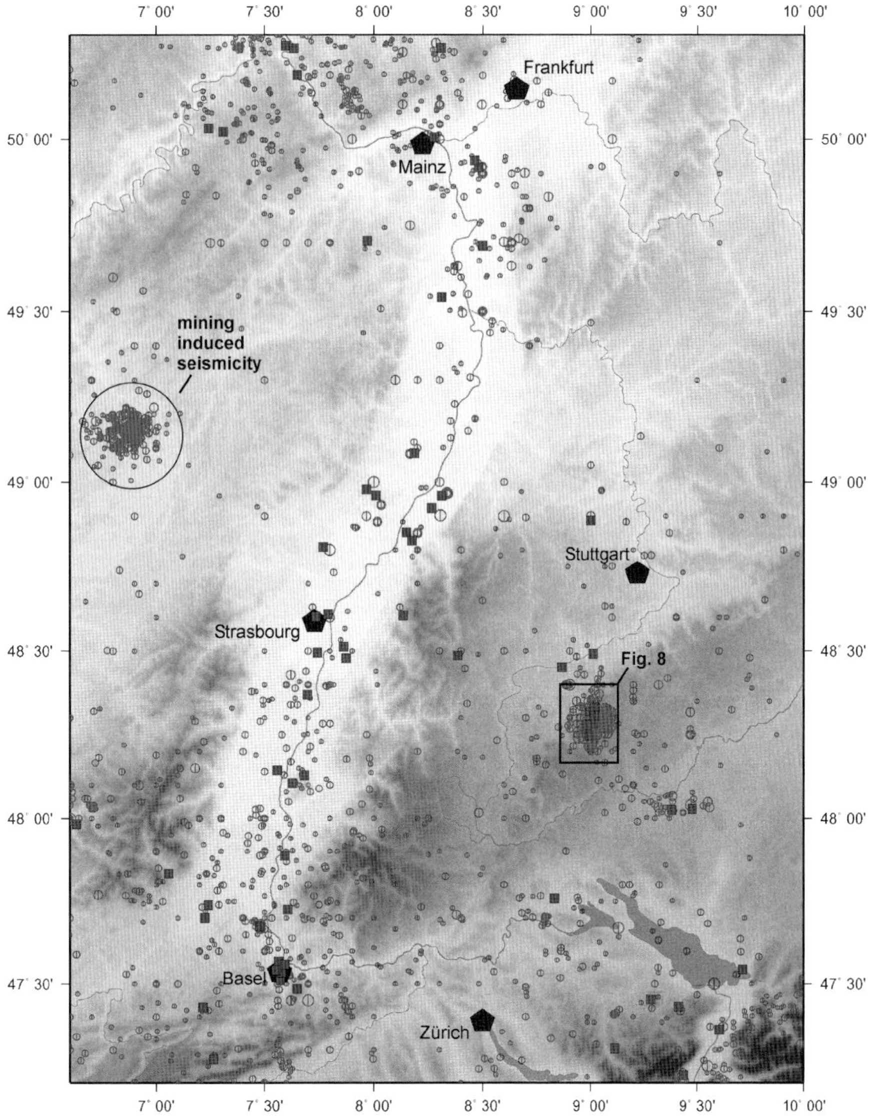


**Fig. 19.9.** Epicentral map of SW Germany and neighbouring countries. Size of circles is proportional to local magnitude; grey squares represent destructive earthquakes. Two major seismic clusters are observed: (1) south of Stuttgart due to tectonic activity in the Hohenzollern Graben/Albstadt Shear Zone area; and (2) in the Saar-Nahe Basin due to coal-mining activity (data compilation from various regional earthquake catalogues).

Baumann 1986), probably due to reduced marginal shear resistance. In recent years several attempts have been made to model past and recent stress fields in Central Europe (Grünthal & Stromeyer 1992; Gölke & Coblentz 1996; Kaiser *et al.* 2005). Most models incorporated plate boundary forces, such as the Mid-Atlantic ridge push and collisional forces within the Alpine Mobile belt and its foreland. A reference velocity along the Alpine Front of 0.1 cm/a is considered to be sufficient to produce the forces for the present state of stress (Marotta *et al.* 2001, 2002; Kaiser *et al.* 2005; calculations based on an average velocity since the beginning of the Alpine collision *c.* 32 Ma), resulting in an overall compressional regime.

It is important to note that Becker (1993) defined the neotectonic period as commencing during the Late Miocene. However, regional variations of the present-day NE–SW directed stress field occur. From structural analysis of stylolites, fault-slip data, joints and shear fractures a palaeostress history throughout southwestern Germany can be deduced. During the Permian, post-Variscan, orogen-parallel extension with predominant normal faulting is observed, for example the formation of the Rotliegend grabens (Fig. 19.6). Subsequently, rifting and opening of the Central Atlantic resulted in NE–SW extension during the Late Triassic which later rotated to an east–west direction in the Jurassic and Early Cretaceous. The far-field impact of the Pyrenean Orogeny (or Eo-Alpine phase) in the Late Cretaceous (Santonian) resulted in large-scale inversion of the area north of the Alps ($S_H$ directed SW–NE). During the main Alpine orogenic phase in the Oligo-Miocene, the $S_H$ was initially orientated north–south (Illies 1975; Illies & Greiner 1976; Illies *et al.* 1981) rotating counterclockwise during the Late Miocene–Pliocene into the present-day NW–SE direction (Grünthal & Stromeyer 1992; Müller *et al.* 1992).

Southern Germany is presently characterized by normal faulting (therefore major structures have been termed 'grabens').

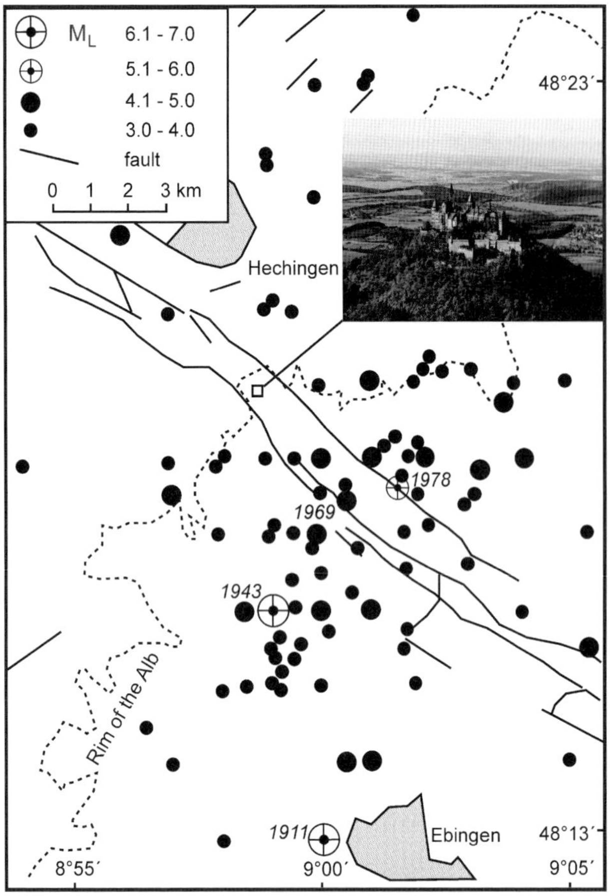


**Fig. 19.10.** Seismicity of the Hohenzollern Graben area between 1911 and 1979 (from Schneider 1980). Note the epicentres of the four major earthquakes in 1911, 1943, 1969 and 1978 (northward migration).

However, palaeostress analysis often reveals different phases of strike-slip movements along graben-bounding faults (e.g. Kazmierczak *et al.* 1999) and minor strike-slip faults are also observed. The Mesozoic cover is dissected by brittle fault zones which are grouped into three populations: (1) ENE–WSW striking dextral strike-slip faults and a transtensional stress field; (2) NW–SE striking normal and transtensional faults partly with a dextral sense of movement as well as graben structures; and (3) north–south to NNE–SSW striking sinistral strike-slip faults which parallel the Rhine Graben where a sinistral displacement of >30 km is observed (Carlé 1955; Edel & Weber 1995). Most prominent are the ENE–WSW trending faults (Figs 19.7 and 19.8) which coincide with major basement faults and inherited structures or block boundaries of the Variscan basement. The Neckar-Jagst Fault Zone (NJ, Fig. 19.8) is situated above the Variscan suture zone separating the Saxothuringian Zone in the north from the Moldanubian Zone in the south. The NJ forms the central part of the 'Fränkische Senkungszone' (Franconian Zone), which has been characterized as a region of enhanced subsidence since the Triassic. The zone of crustal and lithospheric weakness is smoothly folded with several synclines (Kraichgau Syncline, Stromberg Syncline) and anticlines (Hessigheim Anticline) and has undergone repeated reactivation, as demonstrated by evidence of differential vertical motions and significant strike-slip faulting. This suggests that there has been reactivation of Variscan basement structures, and large-scale crustal or lithospheric folding (Wurster 1986; Cloetingh *et al.* 2005). Important intersecting fault zones demonstrate (a) repeated fault activity under changing stress fields, and (b) Quaternary tectonic movement on discrete fault planes.

The intersection of the NJ with the Sindelfingen Graben (striking NW–SE; Fig. 19.8) close to Pforzheim is characterized by fluorite/baryte mineralization (Käfersteige mine). Cataclasis and remobilization of fluorite and repeated phases of mineralization on megaslickensides, as well as age dating, constrain reactivation (various phases of fluorite generation from 160 Ma to 100 Ma), the youngest of which yields baryte of 30–35 Ma. The second economically interesting fluorite mineralization, the Grube Clara near Freudenstadt, is also found at the intersection of the Swabian Lineament and the Freudenstadt Graben. The mineralization matches the radiometric and structural data obtained from clayey fault gouges in the Schauinsland mine by Werner *et al.* (2002). They also observed Jurassic and Cretaceous tectonic phases between 190 Ma (Early Jurassic) and 70 Ma (Late Cretaceous) on NW–SE (dextral) and NNE–SSW or NNW–SSE (dextral) striking shear zones. Satellite and aerial photographs show lineations striking predominantly north–south, NW–SW, ENE–WSW, similar to the trends of the mapped faults, although they are longer (Wetzel & Franzke 2003). Along the 9 East line of longitude, a 5–10 km wide zone of concentrated lineations is traceable between Stuttgart and Lake Constance (Wetzel & Franzke 2003). North of Stuttgart, the Quaternary course of the river Neckar was strongly influenced by the intersection of north–south striking faults and the NJ. River terraces are tilted and faulted (Brunner & Hinkelbein 1987). Leaching of the Middle Muschelkalk evaporites provides evidence for movement of the fault zones.

Another important ENE–WSW striking element is the Swabian Lineament (SL in Fig. 19.8). This extends from the Ries impact crater to the WSW into the Black Forest area. The ejecta of the Ries impact were not significantly faulted due to activity of the SL, and hence we regard it as an older structural feature. The lineament runs partly parallel to the cuesta of the Swabian Alb and forms an important tectonogeomorphological feature (Fig. 19.7). The sense of movement along the Swabian Lineament and the Neckar-Jagst Fault Zone is dextral. A restraining bend along the transpressive dextral NJ has resulted in the formation of a push-up structure, the Ellenweiler Horst, which displaces Triassic against Jurassic strata (Brunner *et al.* 1988; Dürr 1982).

The NW–SE striking faults (i.e. Variscan orientation) limit several important graben structures, for example the Hohenzollern, the Haigerloch, the Sindelfingen, the Filder, the Freudenstadt and the Bonndorf grabens (Fig. 19.8). The Miocene to present-day stress field provides dextral strike-slip on the fault planes; however, older kinematic indicators (stylolites, fibre tension gashes) suggest the sinistral initiation of these grabens during a phase of NE–SW directed maximum horizontal compression in Late Cretaceous–Palaeogene times.

The third major structural element in the region is the NNE–SSW or NNW–SSE striking fault zones, for example the Lauchert Graben (LG in Fig. 19.8) which parallel the Upper Rhine Graben. The relatively recent activity of the faults in the Lauchert Graben is proven by the displaced Plio-Quaternary terraces of the River Danube and the presence of the so-called Jura-Nagelfluh sediments (Miocene conglomerates and breccias). The sense of displacement of these faults is sinistral.

In areas where ENE–WSW directed faults, north–south and NW–SE trending fault zones intersect, Miocene volcanic centres,

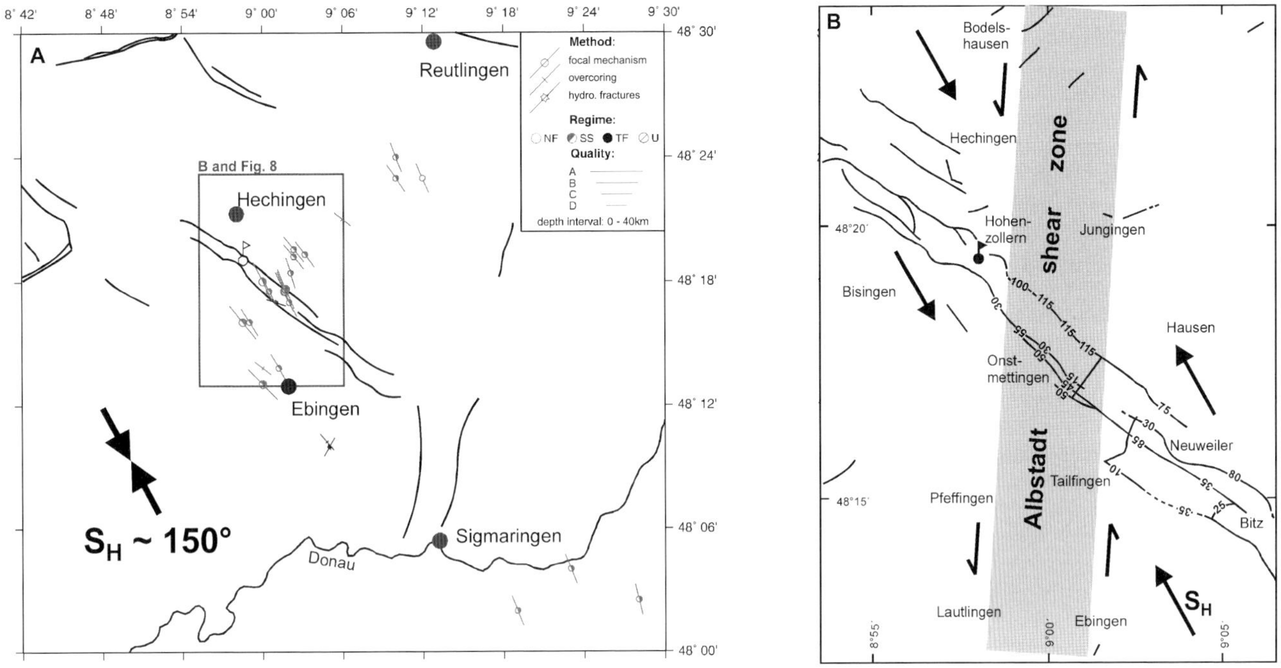


**Fig. 19.11.** (**A**) Stress map of the Hohenzollern area. The regional maximum horizontal stress orientation is 150° (Reinecker *et al.* 2004). Strike-slip stress regime prevails, accompanied by normal faulting. Abbreviations: NF, normal faulting; SS, strike-slip faulting; TF, thrust faulting; U, unkown; lines A to D represent quality ranking, A = best, D = worst. (**B**) Tectonic map of the Hohenzollern Graben. The Albstadt Shear Zone was deduced from seismicity and fault mechanism solutions (Reinecker & Schneider 2002). Total vertical displacements (in metres) at the border faults of the Hohenzollern Graben are indicated (from Kriele 1968).

for example the Urach Volcanic Field, the Hegau and the Kaiserstuhl in the Upper Rhine Graben, are located (Fig. 19.8).

Faults and faults zones in southwestern Germany are mainly characterized by moderate vertical and horizontal displacements; maximum values of vertical offset in the Hohenzollern Graben or the Freudenstadt Graben are on the order of 100–150 m. The horizontal displacements are difficult to establish, but are significantly lower. In the following sections, some peculiarities of individual fault zones will be illustrated, focusing on the seismically most active, the Albstadt Shear Zone.

*Freudenstadt Graben*

This graben is part of a NW–SE striking fault system in the Mesozoic cover of SW Germany, about 70 km SW of Stuttgart (Fig. 19.8). The graben structure was first recognized in 1866, when Paulus published the first geological description of the Freudenstadt area. Towards the SE the graben-bounding faults curve into the Swabian Lineament. The NW-trending main graben fault has a vertical displacement of *c.* 150 m (Carlé 1950) and juxtaposes the Trochitenkalk of the Muschelkalk against the Upper Bunter Formation. The faults were mineralized with baryte and fluorite.

The hanging wall of the Freudenstadt Graben forms a roll-over anticline associated with second-order roll-over structures as well as synthetic and antithetic faults (Fig. 19.12). The decrease of the dip angle of the graben-bounding fault is interpreted as being related to listric faults that continue into the marlstones and evaporites of the Middle Muschelkalk, and act as a shear horizon for the second-order structures in the Freudenstadt Graben. The local palaeostress history has been reconstructed by field methods (Meschede *et al.* 1997). Evidence from overprinting criteria indicates that fault planes, which trend NNE–SSW to north–south, are mostly sinistral strike-slip faults and are older than the NW–SE trending extensional faults, which parallel the Freudenstadt Graben (Meschede *et al.* 1997). Both fault systems coincide with the present-day crustal stress field with a NE–SW orientated minimum horizontal stress as proposed by Grünthal & Stromeyer (1992) and Müller *et al.* (1992).

*Sindelfingen Graben*

The Sindelfingen Graben (SF) forms a narrow fault zone *c.* 100–300 m wide and 24 km long and orientated NW–SE (130–140°), parallel to the Filder Graben (Fig. 19.8). In the area of Böblingen a *c.* 5 km long segment bends in a ESE–WNW direction (100–110°). The maximum vertical displacement on graben-bounding faults is *c.* 150 m juxtaposing the Ceratiten beds of the Late Muschelkalk against the Stubensandstein of the late Middle Keuper. However, displacement varies significantly along strike (Pöschl & Schweizer 1977). The individual graben-bounding faults are aligned in an en-echelon pattern, suggesting a component of dextral strike-slip. Moreover, asymmetric graben structures and pull-apart basins, bounded by normal faults and flexures, have also been described (Reicherter *et al.* 1994). The main fault splays in parts into a horse-tail array of faults which are associated with thrust faults (Wurm 1985, 1992), and show surface expression as small scarps (Ströbel 1953).

The tectonic style of the SF is very different from that of the Freudenstadt Graben. The thickness of the Triassic succession is significantly reduced, for example the Gipskeuper, which has a normal thickness of *c.* 80–100 m, is here reduced to a thickness of only 15 m. Several steeply NE-dipping domino-like step faults form the southern fault zone (Fig. 19.13) and are associated with antithetic faults, open to isoclinal folds and small-scale thrusts. NE-directed normal faulting was followed by a phase of dextral

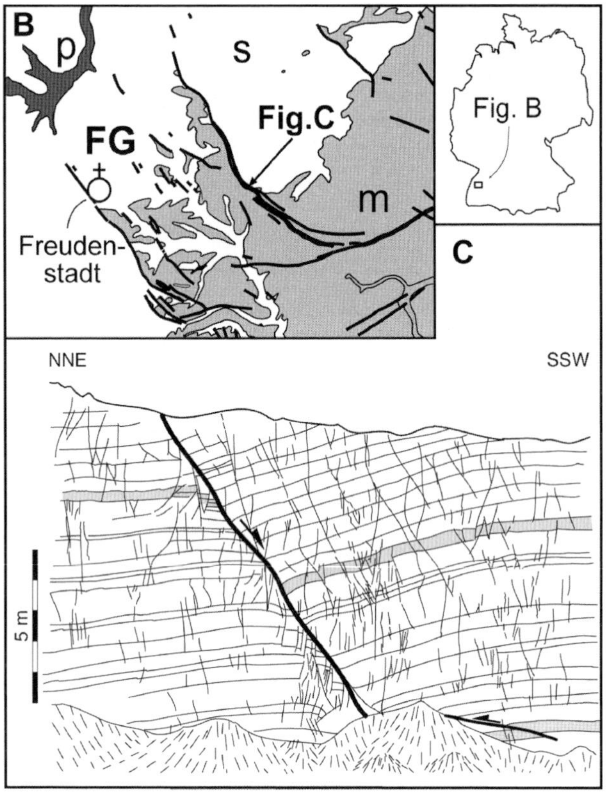


**Fig. 19.12.** (**A**) Location of the Freudenstadt Graben (FG, see Fig. 19.7). (**B**) Geological sketch map: m, Muschelkalk; p, Rotliegend; s, Buntsandstein; (**C**) Secondary normal fault in the Upper Muschelkalk formation at the northern graben-bounding fault; note roll-over structure in the hanging wall.

strike-slip faulting. Pöschl & Schweizer (1977) and Wurm (1985, 1992) suggest multiple stages of graben evolution, caused not only by extensional tectonics (Carlé 1955; Geyer & Gwinner 1986) but also by transpression (Reicherter *et al.* 1994) acting on an inherited structural pattern originating in the Late Cretaceous–Palaeogene stress field.

*Hohenzollern Graben*

The Hohenzollern Graben (HZG) is a NW–SE striking, 30 km long and up to 1.5 km wide extensional feature dissecting the Mesozoic successions of the Swabian Alb and its foreland (Fig. 19.10). Morphologically, the HZG is not recognized by a depression due to relief inversion of the Upper Jurassic formations (Fig. 19.7). The border faults of the HZG dip at *c.* 60–70° towards the centre of the graben. The northeastern boundary comprises a single fault, whereas the southwestern margin is marked by a series of domino-style faults (step faults, Staffelbrüche). Displacements along the border faults are up to 115 m in the central part of the fault, decreasing towards the ends of the graben (Kriele 1968; Fig. 19.11). Structural investigations revealed mainly dip-slip movements but a considerable dextral strike-slip component has also been observed (Hoffers 1974; Illies & Greiner 1976; Baumann 1984; Reinecker & Schneider 2002). Geodetic surveys demonstrate that these movements are still ongoing. Repeated precise levelling across the HZG indicates subsidence rates of the order of 0.5 mm/a (Mälzer 1988; van Mierlo & Hartmann 1989; van Mierlo *et al.* 1992).

The formation age of the HZG is much debated. The youngest formation offset by the border faults is Tithonian in age. No river system developed in the HZG, although the adjacent Lauchert Graben has a river (Figs 19.8 & 19.14). Reinecker & Schneider (2002) have argued that this river system was established prior to graben formation and had average denudation rates of 0.02 mm/a over the last 5 Ma (Abel *et al.* 2000). This would reflect the average rate of graben subsidence.

*The Albstadt Shear Zone*

The Albstadt Shear Zone (ASZ) is mainly defined in terms of its seismic activity and its areal distribution (Figs 19.10 & 19.11). The seismic activity is characterized by small to moderate earthquakes with local magnitudes of up to 6.2. Focal depths for the larger events are in the range of 6–13 km. Shallow (<4 km) earthquakes are very rare. The average seismic dislocation rate

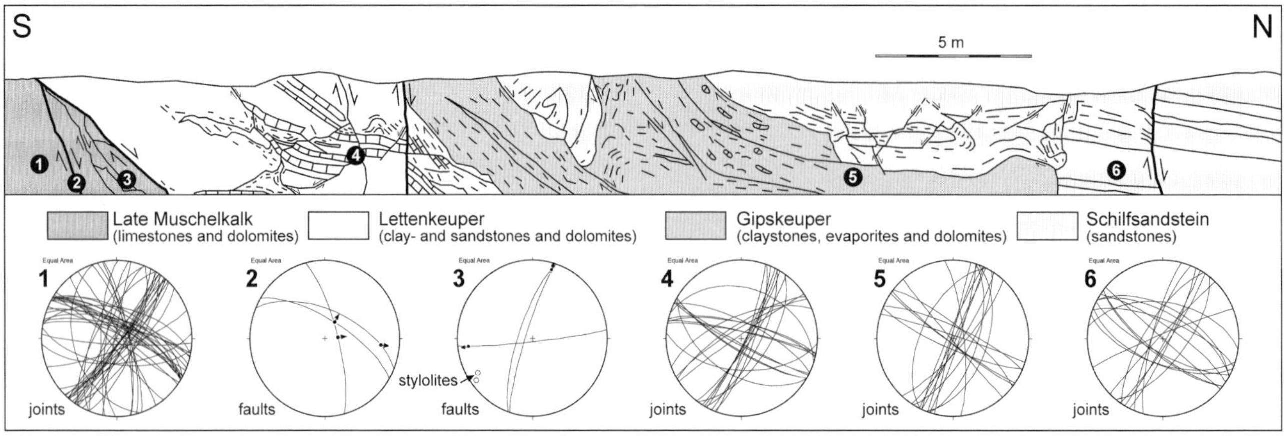


**Fig. 19.13.** Southern marginal fault of the Sindelfingen Graben near Magstadt; note tectonically reduced stratigraphic section (Lettenkeuper *c.* one-fifth and Gipskeuper *c.* one-sixth of undisturbed thickness), and synthetic drag (modified from Reicherter *et al.* 1994). 1, 4, 5 and 6 are great circles of joints (lower-hemisphere projection); 2 and 3 are fault planes and striations. The joints are trending NW–SW and NE–SW and show little horizontal axis rotation (tilting) in the different tectonic blocks and stratigraphic units. The main fault plane is striking NW–SE (2) and shows oblique dextral strike-slip after normal dip-slip faulting. Secondary fault planes (NNW–SSE) are sinistral strike-slip faults. Stylolites (3) indicate an older phase of NE–SW compression, which preceded both of the above-mentioned stress fields as a typical example of multiphase deformation of the Mesozoic cover of SW Germany.

along the ASZ is of the order of 0.1 mm/a (Schneider 1993). The geometry is defined by the trend of aftershocks and focal mechanism solutions displaying a steep NNE- to SSW-trending (280/75, dip direction/dip) structure with sinistral strike-slip movement. The ASZ can be traced from Stuttgart in the north to Lake Constance in the south (Fig. 19.15). Wetzel & Franzke (2003) have defined the ASZ as an up to 5 km broad and 150 km long zone characterized by the increased density of north–south trending satellite lineations, including linear morphological features and vegetation and soil humidity anomalies related to fractures and fracture density variations. A distinct fault zone exists only to the south of Ebingen (Reinecker & Schneider 2002).

Neotectonic models have been proposed to explain the HZG in relation to the observed seismic activity (e.g. Illies 1978, 1982; Stellrecht & Moelle 1980; Schneider 1993; Reinecker & Schneider 2002). According to the model of Reinecker & Schneider (2002) the Filder Graben (see Sindelfingen Graben), the Rottenburg flexure zone, the HZG, and the Bodensee (Lake Constance) normal faults are interpreted as tension structures orientated in an en-echelon system along the ASZ (Fig. 19.15), that is, all of these structures are of the same age and have been active over the last 3–5 Ma. Furthermore, Reinecker & Schneider (2002) proposed mechanical decoupling between the HZG, within the Mesozoic cover, and the ASZ in the crystalline basement below. The Middle Muschelkalk evaporite formation (Mittlerer Muschelkalk in Fig. 19.6) and the Gipskeuper (Late Triassic) are two possible decoupling horizons; both comprise evaporitic layers up to 50 to 70 m thick.

*Summary and palaeostress history*

The relationship between the palaeostress fields and the different stages of the Africa–Eurasia collision as outlined by Bergerat (1987) can also be observed in southwestern Germany. Tertiary volcanism and Late Mesozoic to Cenozoic mineralization (e.g. Werner & Franzke 2001; see also Dill *et al.* 2008) in southwestern Germany seem to be strongly related to the inherited Variscan fault pattern, and the reactivation of these structures during the Alpine Orogeny (beginning in the Late Cretaceous and culminating in the Miocene).

Several kinematic indicators on fault planes suggest that deformation took place on the same fault planes during the Cenozoic, and on into the Quaternary, suggesting repeated reactivation (Fig. 19.16). Presently, fault planes can be divided into three main groups: (1) faults striking NNE–SSW to north–south that show predominantly sinistral strike-slip – these coincide with the major faults observed in the Upper Rhine Graben area (Larroque & Laurent 1988); (2) NW–SE orientated faults, which are both normal and dextral strike-slip; and (3) faults orientated ENE–WSW, which are more or less inactive, although some of these faults show dextral strike-slip movement or evidence of reverse movement and folding. The recent stress field developed during the Late Miocene (Becker 1993) and is characterized by NW–SE horizontal compression and NE–SW extension (Fig. 19.17). Locally, an earlier north–south directed compressional phase has also been noted (Illies & Greiner 1976; Kazmierczak *et al.* 1999).

The reconstructed palaeostress fields of southwestern Germany

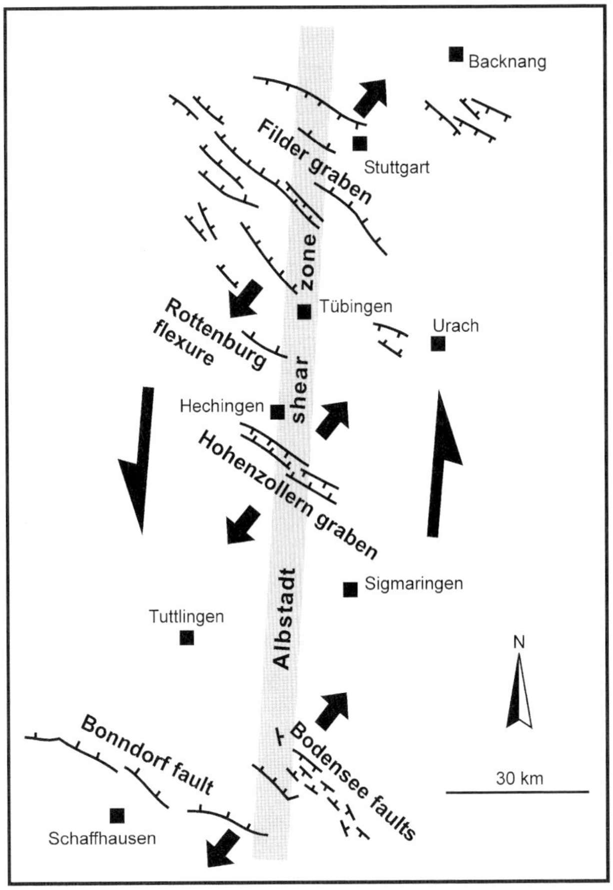


**Fig. 19.15.** Model of en-echelon orientated tension structures for the Albstadt Shear Zone. Due to continued sinistral shear the gashes rotate counterclockwise. The Filder Graben, the Hohenzollern Graben and the Bodensee Normal Faults are orientated in an en-echelon manner along the Albstadt Shear Zone.

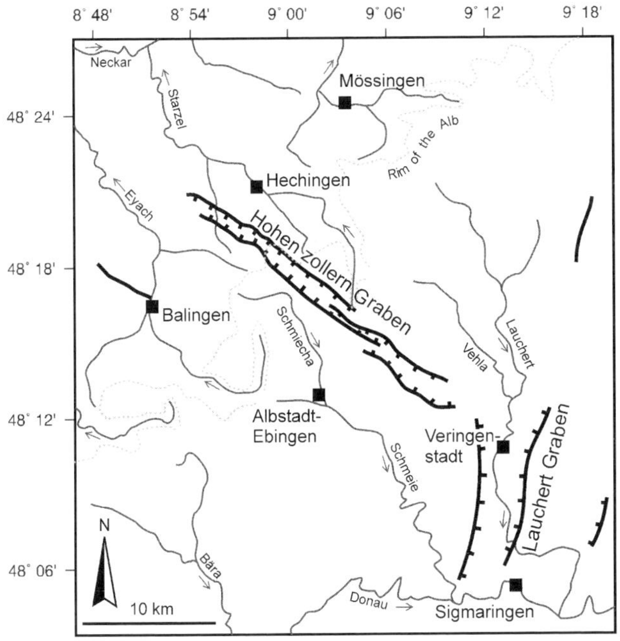


**Fig. 19.14.** Drainage pattern around the Hohenzollern Graben (from Reinecker & Schneider 2002). The HZG has never been involved in the main drainage, in contrast to the Lauchert Graben (Reinecker & Schneider 2002).

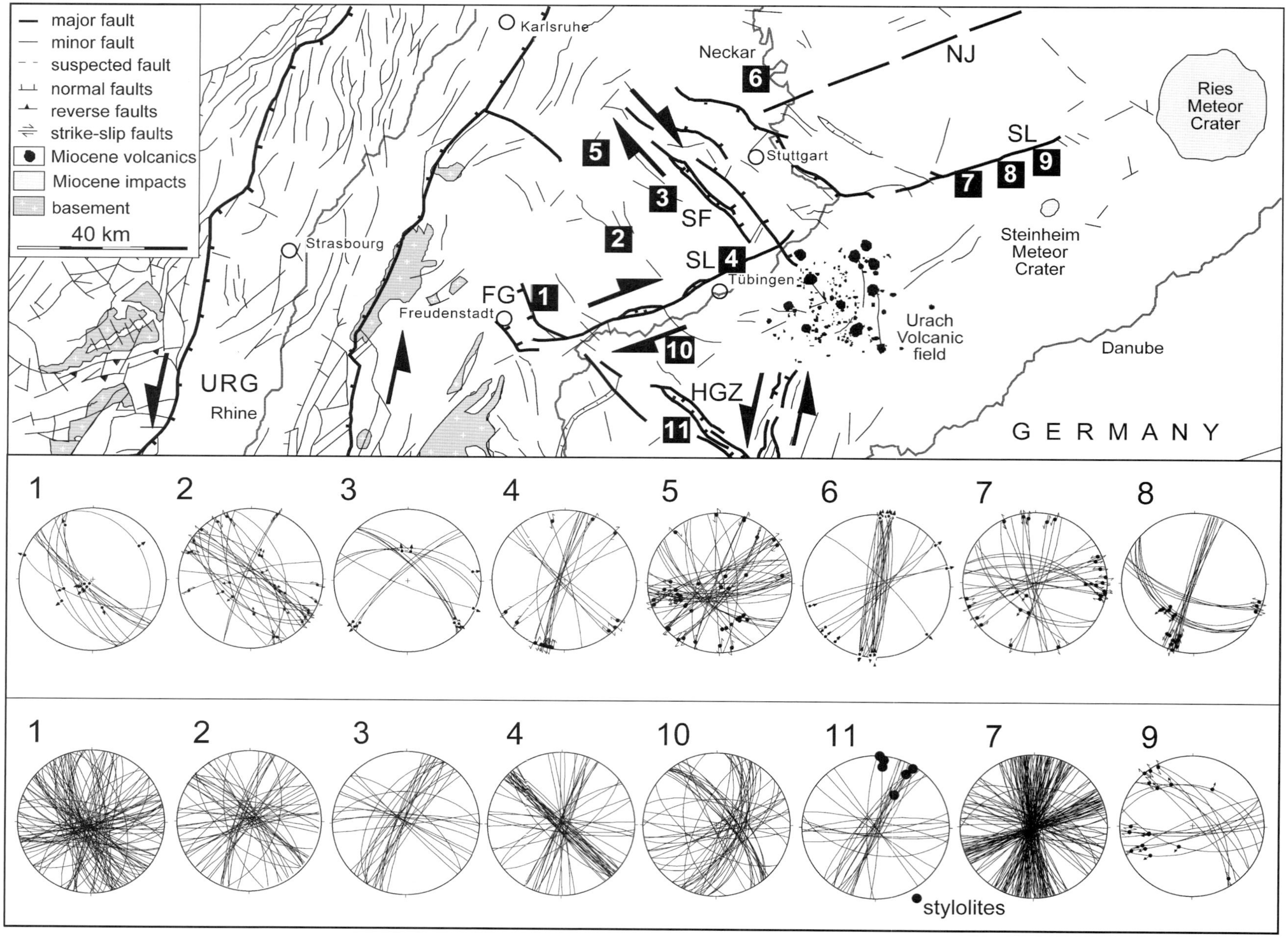


**Fig. 19.16.** Joint and fault-slip data along major fault zone in southern Germany; great circles of joints in lower-hemisphere projection. Numbers refer to numbers in map; 1–9 are fault slip data; numbers in the lower part refer to joint system at the same outcrops. Three major fault and fracture systems are observed throughout southern Germany: NW–SE, NNE–SSW and ENE–WSW. Stylolites point to an older deformation phase coincident with a NE–SW compression. Localities: 1, Dornstetten; 2, Haslach-Herrenberg; 3, Darmsheim; 4, Pfrondorf-Tübingen; 5, Käfersteige fluorite mine; 6, Marbach/Neckar; 7, Bettringen; 8, Heubach; 9, Lauterburg; 10, Fischingen; 11, Onstmettingen. For kinematic interpretation see also Figures 19.13 & 19.17 and text.

from Permian times as well as the kinematics of faulting are summarized in Figure 19.17. After the Variscan Orogeny, post-orogenic collapse and orogen-parallel extension led to the formation of the NE–SW trending Rotliegend graben systems (Schramberg Trough, Überlingen Trough). Later, during the Middle to Late Triassic, normal faulting affected the entire Eurasian Platform from the North Sea to southern Germany. NE–SW orientated extension in the Keuper was related to rifting in the Central Atlantic, and led both to the initiation and also reactivation of NW–SE striking graben structures. Extension and subsidence continued throughout the Jurassic and Early Cretaceous. North–south extension dominates in southern Germany (Bergerat & Geyssant 1983), although it is difficult to bracket this period due to an incomplete stratigraphic record. During the late Cretaceous (Santonian and Campanian), basin inversion occurred in the European Foreland and this was related to rifting in the South Atlantic and the Pyrenean Orogeny (NE–SW compression). In southern Germany inversion led to regional tilting of the Mesozoic cover rocks (Fig. 19.6). The NE–SW compressional stress field was followed by a period of basin-wide extension and subsidence in the late Palaeogene (Fig. 19.17). Normal reactivation of faults predominates (Becker 1993); NW–SE extension (Bergerat 1987) and east–west extension were observed (Bergerat & Geyssant 1983). During the late Palaeogene, initial extension occurred in the Upper Rhine Graben area, with the main rift phase continuing to the Oligocene. Subsidence in the Alpine Molasse Basin began as early as the Late Eocene and continued into the Middle/Late Miocene (Bachmann *et al.* 1987). The neotectonic period in southern Germany began in the Late Miocene and is still ongoing.

### Bohemian Massif (N.F.)

The Bohemian Massif (Fig. 19.18) is the most extensive uplifted area with exposed basement rocks in Central Europe. Like the Rhenish Massif and the Massif Central (western Europe), it was also an area of Cenozoic volcanism. The Cenozoic tectonic

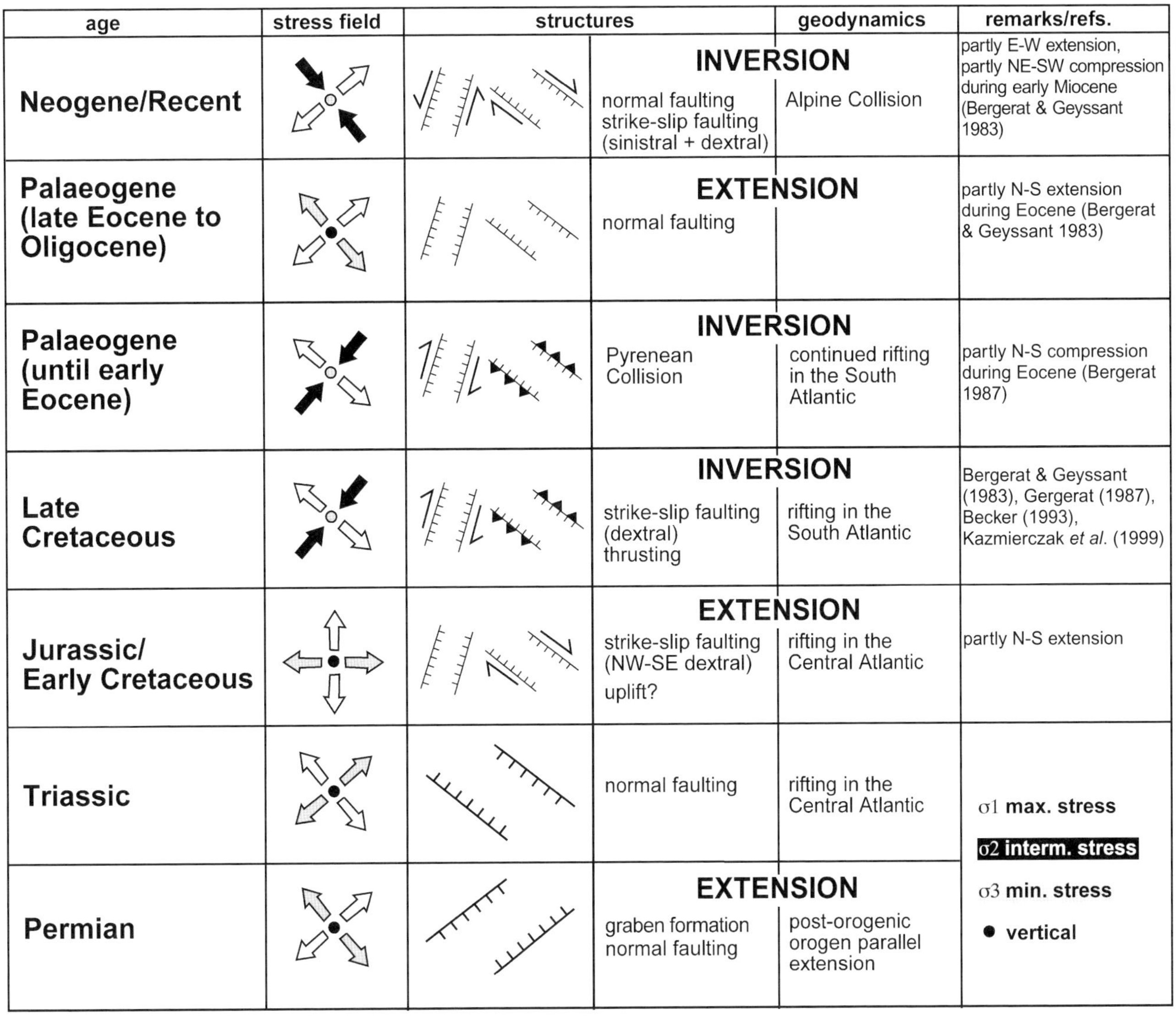

age
stress field
structures
geodynamics
remarks/refs.
Neogene/Recent
INVERSION
normal faulting
strike-slip faulting
(sinistral + dextral)
Alpine Collision
partly E-W extension, partly NE-SW compression during early Miocene (Bergerat & Geyssant 1983)
Palaeogene (late Eocene to Oligocene)
EXTENSION
normal faulting
partly N-S extension during Eocene (Bergerat & Geyssant 1983)
Palaeogene (until early Eocene)
INVERSION
Pyrenean Collision
continued rifting in the South Atlantic
partly N-S compression during Eocene (Bergerat 1987)
Late Cretaceous
INVERSION
strike-slip faulting (dextral)
thrusting
rifting in the South Atlantic
Bergerat & Geyssant (1983), Gergerat (1987), Becker (1993), Kazmierczak et al. (1999)
Jurassic/ Early Cretaceous
EXTENSION
strike-slip faulting (NW-SE dextral)
uplift?
rifting in the Central Atlantic
partly N-S extension
Triassic
normal faulting
rifting in the Central Atlantic
σ1 max. stress
σ2 interm. stress
σ3 min. stress
● vertical
Permian
EXTENSION
graben formation
normal faulting
post-orogenic orogen parallel extension


**Fig. 19.17.** Deformation history of southern Germany deduced from fault slip data, stratigraphic observation and, partly, compiled from literature. The individual tectonic phases correlate with major plate tectonic events. Reactivation of fault systems is commonly observed.

evolution of the Bohemian Massif was characterized by the reactivation of Late Variscan and post-Variscan faults, often striking NW–SE. The Alpine tectonics of the Sudetes and the Fore-Sudetic Block (NE part of Bohemian Massif) are discussed in the section 'Cenozoic geodynamic evolution of the Carpathian foreland in Poland' (see below).

### *SW Bohemian Border Zone*

Along its southwestern margin, the uplifted basement of the Bohemian Massif is separated from the Molasse Basin to the south and the Mesozoic strata of the South German Triangle to the north by a system of important, mainly SE–NW striking faults (SW Bohemian Border Zone; Schröder *et al.* 1997). These faults are arranged in a right-stepping en-echelon pattern. They include the Danube Fault, the Pfahl Fault and the Franconian Fault, among others. All of these were active in the Cretaceous and Cenozoic, but were initiated much earlier. The Pfahl Fault is localized in a Variscan shear zone (Bavarian Pfahl Shear Zone) of Early Carboniferous age (*c.* 330 Ma; Siebel *et al.* 2005). Mylonitization along the Danube Fault took place in the Early Permian (Brandmayr *et al.* 1995).

The SW Bohemian Border Zone is superimposed on a NW–SE striking, Stephanian to Early Permian rift basin system containing up to 2000 m of continental clastics which underwent a phase of transpressional deformation at the transition from the Early to the Middle Permian (Schröder 1987, 1988). From Triassic to Late Jurassic times the area remained relatively stable. In the Early Cretaceous, the Franconian and other faults were reactivated as reverse faults in a framework of north–south compression (Schröder 1987; Zulauf 1993). Data from the subsurface of the Molasse Basin suggest that this inversion took place in two subphases, Berriasian to Hauterivian, and Aptian (Nachtmann & Wagner 1987; Bachmann *et al.* 1987). Relative uplift of the Bohemian Massif across the Franconian Fault during the Early Cretaceous amounted to *c.* 1500 m (Schröder 1987). Following erosion of the Early Cretaceous relief and deposition of non-marine and marginally marine sediments from Cenomanian to Campanian (Regensburg Basin), the SW Bohemian Border Zone was affected by a second major phase of fault reactivation during the latest Cretaceous and Palaeocene, within a framework of dextral transpression which is interpreted to result from continent collision in the Alps. A late stage of multidirectional crustal extension with $\sigma_1$ vertical and $\sigma_2 = \sigma_3$ (Zulauf 1993) occurred in the Miocene, during the formation of the SW–NE striking Ohře (Eger) Graben.

The Franconian Fault dips at about 60° NE and accommodated thrusting of Variscan basement rocks over Permo-Mesozoic cover, combined with dextral strike-slip. At a depth of 7300 m, the KTB borehole (Continental Deep Drilling Project; Fig. 19.18) penetrated a series of brittle faults which is interpreted to represent the intrabasement part of the Franconian Fault (Zulauf & Duyster 1997). The main activity of the Franconian Fault is attributed to the Latest Cretaceous to Palaeocene. Apatite fission track studies on basement rocks from the KTB pilot hole (Coyle *et al.* 1997) suggest cooling from 120°C at 85–75 Ma to 40–50°C at *c.* 25 Ma.

### *Bohemian Cretaceous Basin*

The Bohemian Cretaceous Basin contains Cenomanian to Santonian, partly marine sediments with a thickness of up to >1000 m. Compressional and strike-slip tectonics from the Santonian to Eocene deformed the basin fill. The most prominent

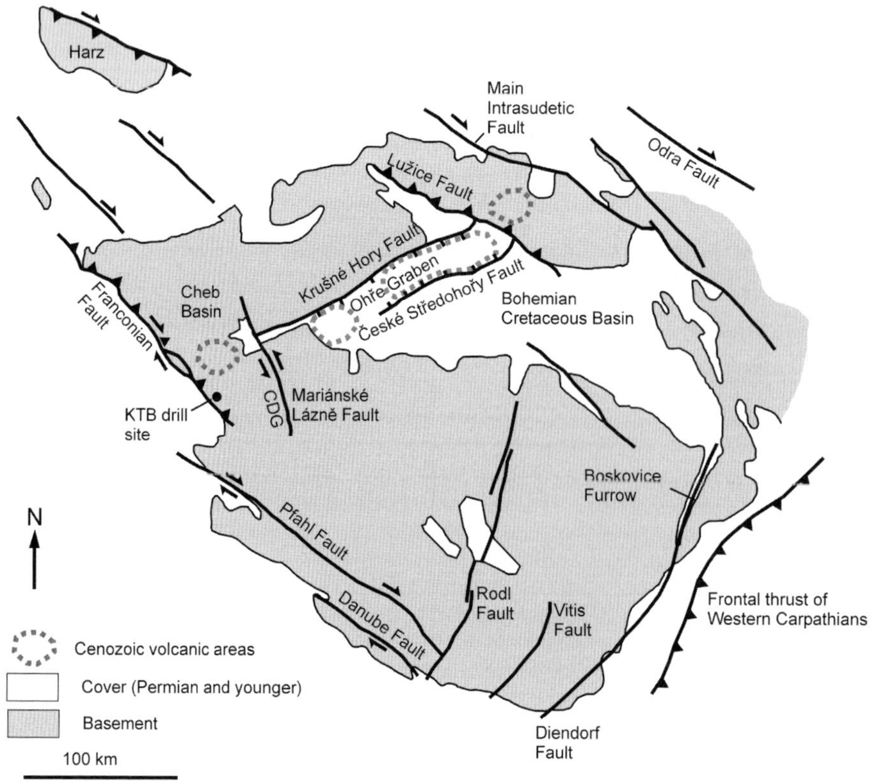


**Fig. 19.18.** Structural sketch map of the Bohemian Massif. After Zulauf (1993) and other sources.

structure from this period is the Lužice (Lausitz) Fault, a NE-dipping reverse fault along the NE border of the Bohemian Cretaceous Basin. The basement units of the NE block were uplifted by up to *c.* 1000 m (Coubal 1990). The style of faulting is similar to the contemporaneous processes along the Franconian Fault and along several other NE-dipping reverse faults in the Bohemian Massif (Malkovsky 1987).

### *Ohře (Eger) Graben*

The WSW–ENE striking Ohře Graben is a major tectonic and magmatic feature in Central Europe. It comprises several sedimentary basins and has been the site of intense alkaline intraplate volcanism. The Ohře Graben roughly coincides with the boundary between the Moldanubian and Saxothuringian zones of the Variscan Orogen. The main faults of the Ohře Graben are the subvertical Krušne Hory (Erzgebirge) Fault to the north and the north-dipping České Středohoři Fault to the south. The graben was opened in a framework of north–south to NNE–SSW orientated extension during the Oligocene and Miocene (Špičáková *et al.* 2000). Individual depocentres filled with Oligocene–Miocene clastic sediments, within the main rift, strike approximately east–west, oblique to the strike of the graben. In a second, Late Pliocene, phase of sedimentation, the NW–SE striking Cheb-Domažlice Graben formed at right angles to the Ohře Graben as a consequence of sinistral displacement along the Marianske Lazne Fault which is the eastern border fault of the Cheb-Domazlice Graben (Fig. 19.18). The Cheb Basin is located at the intersection of the Cheb-Domazlice Graben and the Ohře Graben. Alkaline volcanic activity in the western part of the Ohře Graben (western Bohemia) developed in three phases (Ulrych *et al.* 2003): Early Oligocene to Early Miocene (31–20 Ma), Middle to Late Miocene (16.5–8.3 Ma), and Pleistocene (0.43–0.11 Ma).

The area of the western Ohře Graben is a presently active $CO_2$ emanation area, Quaternary volcanic field, and earthquake swarm region (Geissler *et al.* 2005). The $CO_2$ is released from isolated melt reservoirs at a depth range of 60 to 30 km at the top of a mantle plume (Weinlich *et al.* 1999; Geissler *et al.* 2005) and emanates preferentially from fault zones, such as the Marianske Lazne Fault and the border faults of the Ohře Graben (Weinlich *et al.* 2003). The swarm earthquakes occur in a NNW–SSE trending zone following the Cheb-Domazlice Graben from the Vogtland in Germany to the Cheb Basin in the Czech Republic. The most intensive swarm earthquake activity occurs along the northern part of the Marianske Lazne Fault. Earthquakes induce changes in the composition of gas emanating from the fault zones, suggesting a close relationship between degassing and earthquake activity (Weinlich *et al.* 2006). The Moho is domed up to 27 km depth beneath the western Ohře Graben.

### *SE part of Bohemian Massif*

Several SW–NE to SSW–NNE striking fault zones occur in the SE part of the Bohemian Massif (Rodl Fault, Vitis Fault, Boskovice Furrow). These were initiated as ductile shear zones accommodating sinistral strike-slip in the Early Permian (Brandmayr *et al.* 1995) and, at least in the case of the Boskovice Furrow, also normal slip since the Boskovice Furrow formed an asymmetric half-graben during the Permian (see also McCann *et al.* 2008*b*). These shear zones were later overprinted by brittle faults with sinistral motion (Brandmayr *et al.* 1995), probably still in the Early Permian. Alpine reactivation also occurred and this involved structural inversion in the case of the Boskovice Furrow, so that at the northern end of the structure, the Permian fill of the related half-graben was uplifted above the Cretaceous rocks of the Bohemian Cretaceous Basin.

## Tectonic elements of central Germany

In northern Germany, the prominent Northern Harz Boundary Fault (Harz-Nordrandstörung), the Ahlsburg Thrust (near Göttingen) and the Lužice (Lausitz) Thrust in eastern Germany developed due to far-field compression. This inversion period was associated with dextral strike-slip along north–south trending faults (e.g. the Leine Graben developed as a prolongation of the Upper Rhine Graben).

### *The Leine Graben in the Hessian Depression (K.R.)*

The Leine Graben is one the most prominent north–south striking structures in Central Europe (Figs 19.19 & 19.20) and is related to far-field effects of the Alpine deformation (Late Cretaceous to Late Tertiary) influenced by salt movement (Saxonian tectonics or 'Bruchfaltentektonik'; Lotze 1937). Brittle deformation structures within Mesozoic sediments allow the trend, character and timing of the faulting to be established. The Leine Graben is a tectonic structure *c.* 50 km long and c. 8 km wide, bounded by an en-echelon array of normal and strike-slip faults (Figs 19.19 & 19.21). The total throw of the border faults on both sides of the graben is of the order of 600 m (Murawski 1955). Minor graben structures parallel the major boundary faults. The post-Pliocene vertical throw has been estimated to be *c.* 120 to 150 m (Brinkmann 1932; Murawski 1955).

The north–south striking Leine Graben connects with the Vogelsberg Lineament and the Upper Rhine Graben. The Leine Graben extends southward into the Altmorschen-Lichtenauer Graben and onward into the Miocene Vogelsberg Volcano Complex (Fig. 19.19).

Palaeostress data suggest that a phase of dextral transtension initiated graben formation during the Late Cretaceous. Subsequently, Early Tertiary extension was the main phase of graben formation. Rifting ended in the Eocene as evidenced by the presence of Oligocene marine sediments, deposited at the same level as the graben margins. Strike-slip movements modified the graben form and Alpine reactivation caused sinistral movements on north–south trending faults, and dextral slip on east–west striking faults. Structural relationships between the uplift of the Rhenish Massif, the Neogene basaltic volcanism in the southern Solling area and the formation of the Upper Rhine and Leine graben systems have been described by Murawski (1955).

The present-day stress orientation in the Leine Graben suggests a (N)NW–(S)SE directed maximum horizontal stress $S_{Hmax}$, whereas $\sigma_1$ is mainly vertical and $\sigma_3$ is horizontal in a NE–SW direction (Roth & Fleckenstein 2001; Röckel & Lempp 2003; Reinecker *et al.* 2004). However, the stress field in the area is heterogeneous as documented by permutations of the stress axes. Essentially, NE–SW extension and NW–SE subhorizontal compression are observed; the latter is parallel to the regional tectonic stress field, and it was probably influenced by the underlying salt. Recent seismological data point to a very low level of seismicity in the Leine Graben area.

### *Harz Mountains (H.J.F., R.M., T.V., H.V.E.)*

In the Harz Mountains a thick complex of Palaeozoic sediments deformed by SW–NE trending Variscan-age folds and thrusts is exposed (Fig. 19.22). The region forms part of the Rhenohercy-

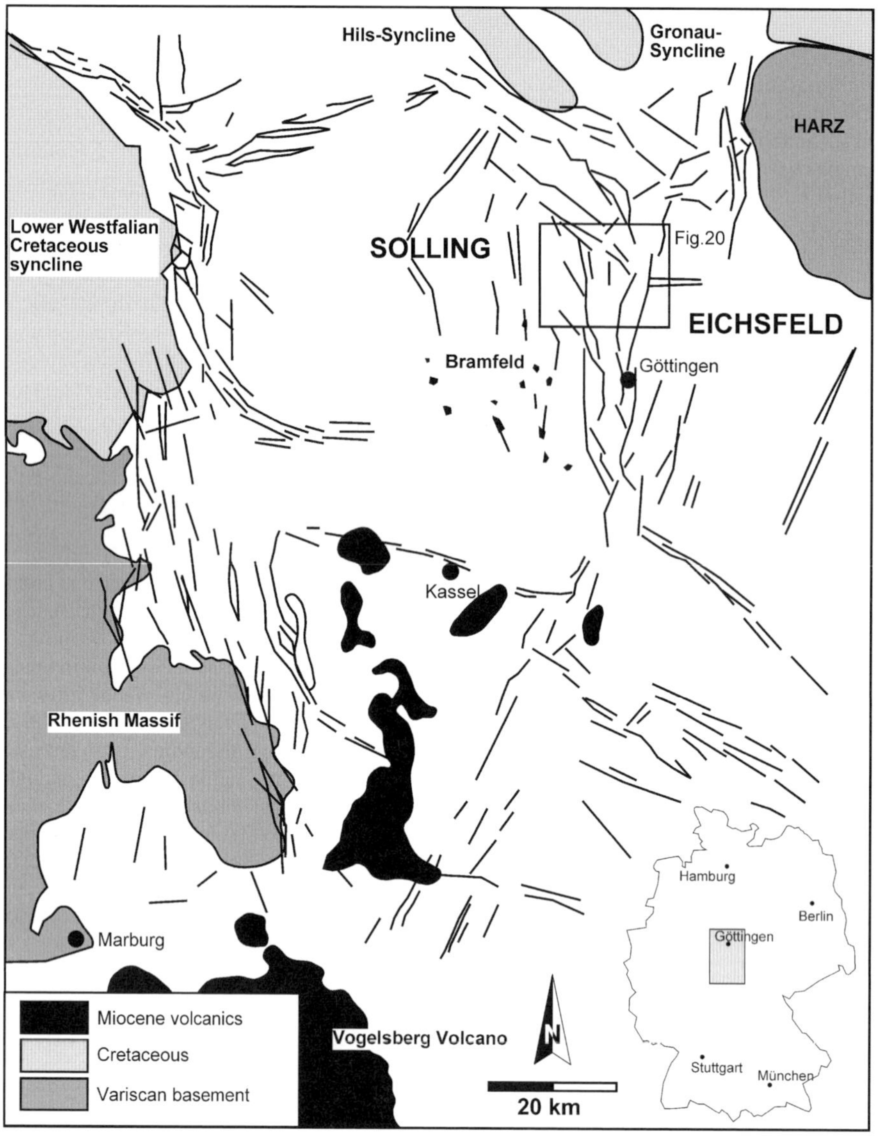


**Fig. 19.19.** Geological and structural overview map of the Leine Graben fault system in Central Germany. Frame indicates position of Figure 20.

nian Zone of the Central European Variscides. Following peak metamorphism (*c.* 360–320 Ma) and the termination of convergent tectonics (320–310 Ma), the stacked crust was rebalanced by vertical block movements (Late Variscan inversion stage). Early Permian (Rotliegend) sediments were deposited in intramontane basins. Early Permian intrusions (*c.* 295 Ma) and volcanic activity occurred along variously striking fracture zones.

Mesozoic deformation of the Harz region was characterized by brittle fracturing of the consolidated Variscan basement and the brittle–ductile fracturing of the younger sequences. Thus, studies of Mesozoic tectonic activities of the region also need to evaluate the brittle fracture pattern.

Fracture tectonics within Palaeozoic rocks commenced with the dissipation of the SE–NW trending convergent Variscan stress field (herein termed stage 1) and equilibration of the stacked crust by uplift as well as erosion under an extensional stress field (stage 2). Palaeozoic rocks were elevated to higher crustal levels (i.e. lower pressure/temperature conditions), as evidenced by the fact that the Late Carboniferous brittle deformation became the governing tectonic mechanism. Time markers are rare but swarms of volcanic dykes of Lower Permian age (stage 3, 290 Ma; Lippolt & Hess 1996) intruded the active fracture pattern in north–south, NW–SE, NNW–SSE and east–west directions. Subsequent Rotliegend continental sedimentation ended abruptly with the Zechstein marine transgression. A long period of shallow-marine and continental sedimentation then commenced, extending up to the Late Mesozoic. In total, more than 2 km of sediments accumulated in a period of over 250 Ma (stage 4) which was characterized by extensional tectonics until the Late Cretaceous.

During Triassic and Jurassic times sedimentary basins (Hessian Depression, Thuringian and Gifhorn Troughs) and highs (Hunte High, Eichsfeld-Altmark High) formed in the Harz area. These trend in a SSW–NNE direction, indicating east–west orientated minimum principal stresses, which later rotated towards the SW–NE. NW–SE striking listric normal faults devel-

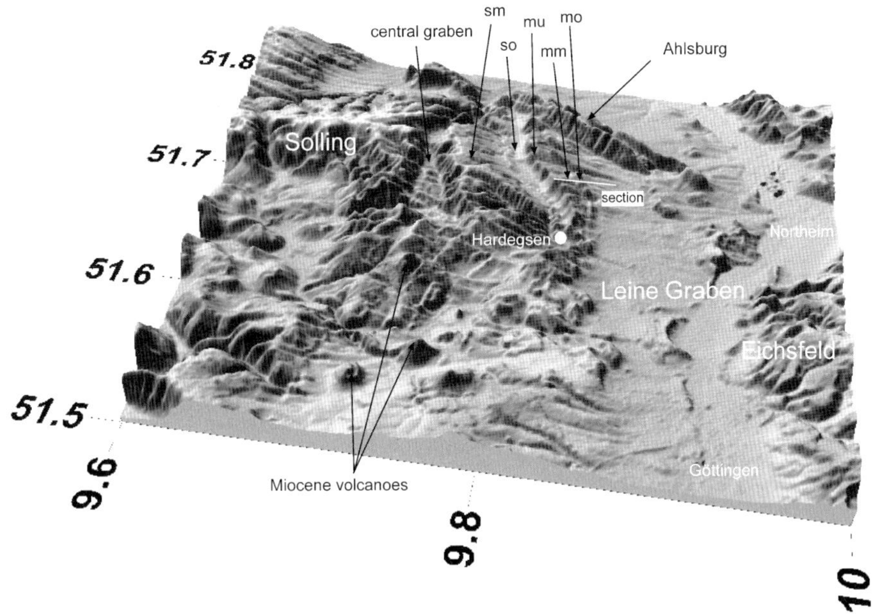


**Fig. 19.20.** Shaded relief of the Central Leine Graben, with the cuesta landscape, Miocene volcanic cones, crestal graben above the Solling salt pillow, and position of the section in Figure 19.21. Abbreviations: mu, Lower Muschelkalk; mm, Middle Muschelkalk; mo, Upper Muschelkalk; sm, Middle Bunter; so, Upper Bunter.

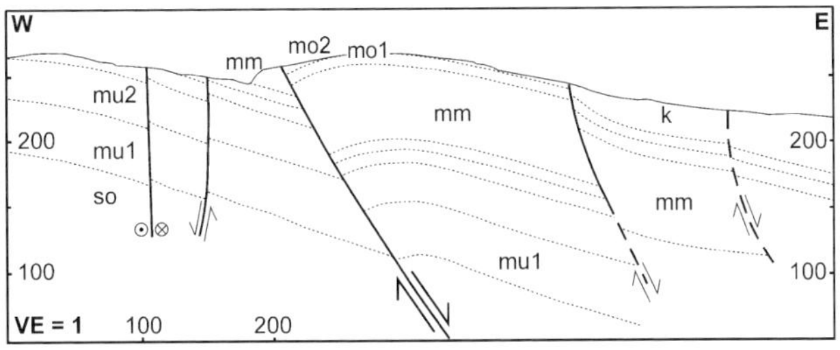


**Fig. 19.21.** Geological cross-section of the western margin of the Leine Graben (position is shown in Fig. 19.20). For abbreviations see Figure 19.20; k, Keuper (Late Triassic); VE, vertical exaggeration. Note fault-dependent relief inversion and formation of a roll-over structure in the hanging wall.

oped. The controlling fault zones are located above the detachment of evaporitic units of the Late Permian and comprise domino-style fault zones. Fluid circulation cells developed in the blocks and precipitation of fault-bounded polysulphidic mineralization (early stage 4, Late Triassic–Jurassic) below the evaporitic/pelitic barrier of the cover rocks occurred. Mineral precipitation took place in the course of pressure and temperature decreases caused by uplift and erosion in the area of the Harz Block resulting in fault movements and fluid circulations. In the Cretaceous, the Subhercynian Basin in the northern foreland of the Harz Block was formed along synsedimentary NW–SE trending faults ('Randtrog'; Voigt 1963), and this was subsequently partly inverted to form the Quedlinburg anticline (Fig. 19.22) later in Cretaceous times (stage 5).

During uplift of the Harz Block, the pre-tectonic sediments (Zechstein–Lower Coniacian) were progressively rotated and partly overturned along a 2 km wide flexural strip in front of the Northern Harz Boundary Fault ('Aufrichtungszone', Fig. 19.23). Accelerated uplift of the Harz Block began in the early Coniacian and syntectonic sedimentary successions disconformably overlie tilted older sediments. Five or more individual angular unconformities have been observed (Voigt *et al.* 2006). These unconformities also became progressively tilted during the on-going uplift of the Harz Block and were overlain by transgressively onlapping Late Cretaceous successions. The youngest exposed sediments of the early Campanian are also tilted along the contact to the border fault. The previous subdivision in different 'Subhercynian' phases of the 'Saxonian' tectonics is obsolete because sedimentation in the basins was not subject to tectonic movements (Voigt *et al.* 2004, 2006). Outcrop studies by Franzke *et al.* (2004) indicated that fault sets in the flexure zone were initially active as normal faults (Fig. 19.24) and later became rotated and transformed into convergent structures (Fig. 19.25) by north–south directed compression, partly beginning in the Late Santonian–Early Campanian (Harz Block), and partly in the Coniacian (Lower Saxony Basin; Kockel 2003). The gap in the stratigraphic record begins in the Middle Campanian and extends up to the Palaeocene (Early Tertiary).

In Late Cretaceous times, the Harz Block was subject to rapid uplift over a relatively short timespan of *c.* 10 Ma (83–73 Ma). The rates of uplift and erosion were approximately in balance and were up to 4–5 km (Thomson *et al.* 1997). The former platform sediments were completely eroded from the rising Harz Block and older Variscan folded rocks were exposed (Fig. 19.22 & 19.23).

During Cenozoic times, the Rupelian marine transgression (Lower Oligocene, 'Rupelton') forms a useful marker for the calculation of vertical crustal movements in the Tertiary. Marine sediments of the Lower Oligocene are preserved in the middle Harz close to Elbingerode at an altitude of 512 m. König & Blumenstengel (2005) noted a vertical displacement of 300 m between the rising Harz Block and its forelands between the

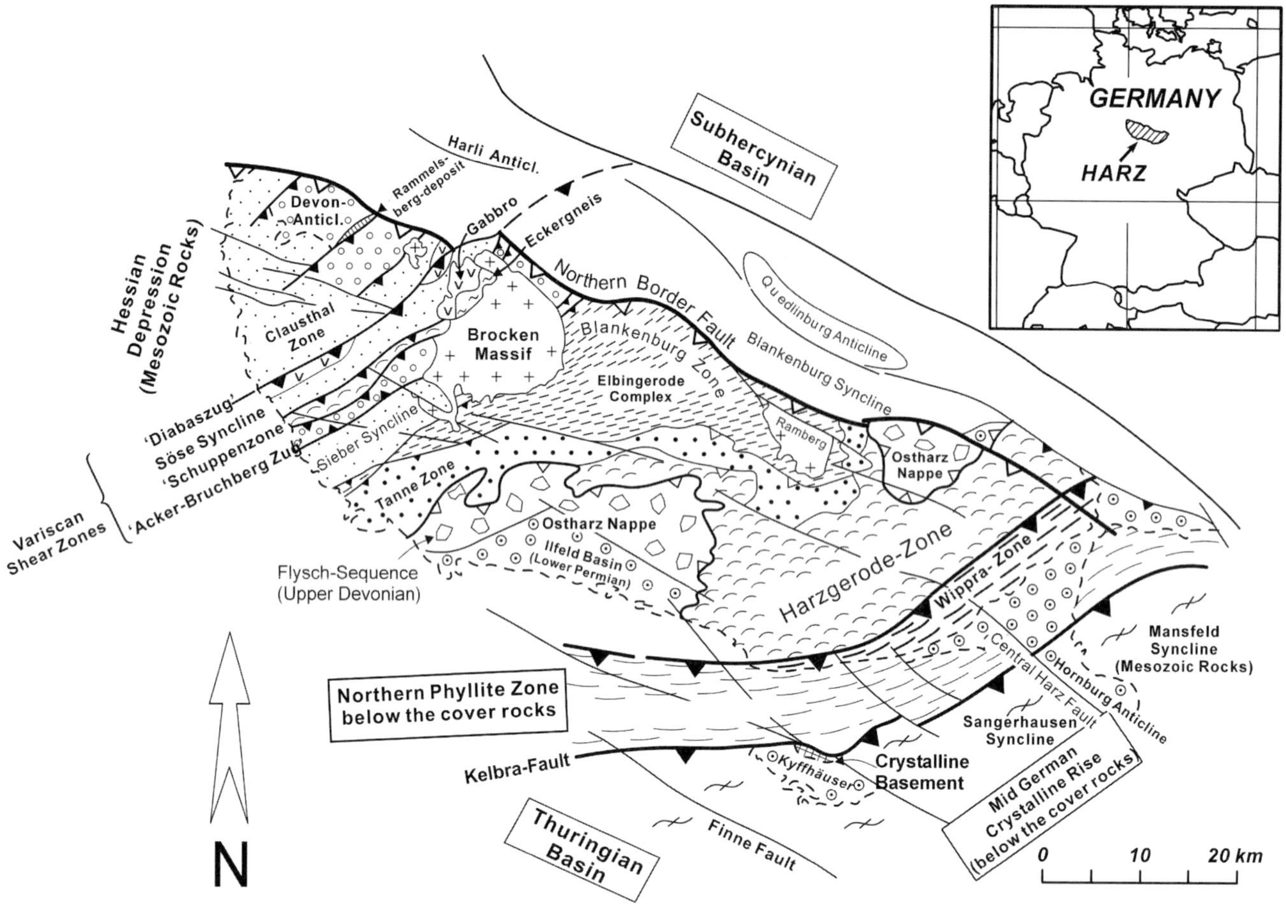


**Fig. 19.22.** Structural map of the Harz Mountains, the Kyffhäuser and surrounding basinal areas.

Lower Oligocene and the present day, although Quaternary and Holocene sediments were not affected by any fault activity along the Northern Harz Boundary Fault.

The kinematics of tectonic inversion on the Northern Harz Boundary Fault are controversial (e.g. Flick 1986; Wrede 1988; Kockel 2003; Franzke *et al.* 2004) with both dextral transpression and thrusting, both probably generated by compressive stresses from the Alpine-Carpathian Orogen, being proposed. These compressional phases are well documented in older publications as 'Subhercynian tectonic movements'.

The palaeostress fields reconstructed in the Harz Mountains can be subdivided into six deformation stages (Fig. 19.26): Variscan convergence (stage 1), Variscan uplift (stage 2), crustal stretching and magmatism/volcanism during the Permian (stage 3), Mesozoic extension and hydrothermal mineralization (stage 4 and various substages), Late Mesozoic compression/inversion (stage 5) and, finally, Cenozoic rifting (stage 6). These latter phases correlate with the palaeostress history of southwestern Germany as outlined in the previous section.

## Cenozoic geodynamic evolution of the Carpathian foreland in Poland (M.J., W.Z., P.P., J.B.)

### *General structural setting and subsidence pattern*

Cenozoic deposits in Poland are generally divided into two major tectonic and facies domains. The northern Tethyan domain is restricted to the Outer Carpathians and Central Carpathian Palaeogene Basin where the Cenozoic accumulation of mainly deep-marine sediments continues the pattern established on the Jurassic–Cretaceous passive margin and related deep-marine successions. The stratigraphic thickness of the Cenozoic succession attains a few thousand metres. Deposition in this area terminated in the Middle Miocene during folding of the Outer Carpathians. The second domain, the Peri-Tethyan, developed on the northern part of the European continental plate, and is described in more detail below. The transitional position between the two domains is occupied by the flexural foredeep of the Outer Carpathian fold-and-thrust belt filled with Miocene sediments of predominantly continental character. The Western Carpathians and their flexural foredeep have been described in the previous chapter.

A specific feature of the European plate in Poland is the presence of two contrasting types of crust (e.g. Guterch *et al.* 1994, 1999): the East European Platform (comparable to the Fenno-Scandian or Baltic shields) and the Epi-Palaeozoic Platform. These are subdivided by a relatively broad tectonic zone of Neoproterozoic and Palaeozoic accretion, the Trans-European Suture Zone (TESZ; e.g. Dadlez 1995; Pharaoh 1999). These old structures played an important role in the Palaeogene and Neogene evolution of the Polish Lowlands. Characteristic for the TESZ is its long-lasting tectonic activity, which was well expressed by the development of Neoproterozoic–Phanerozoic sedimentary basins and multiphase tectonic deformation. The

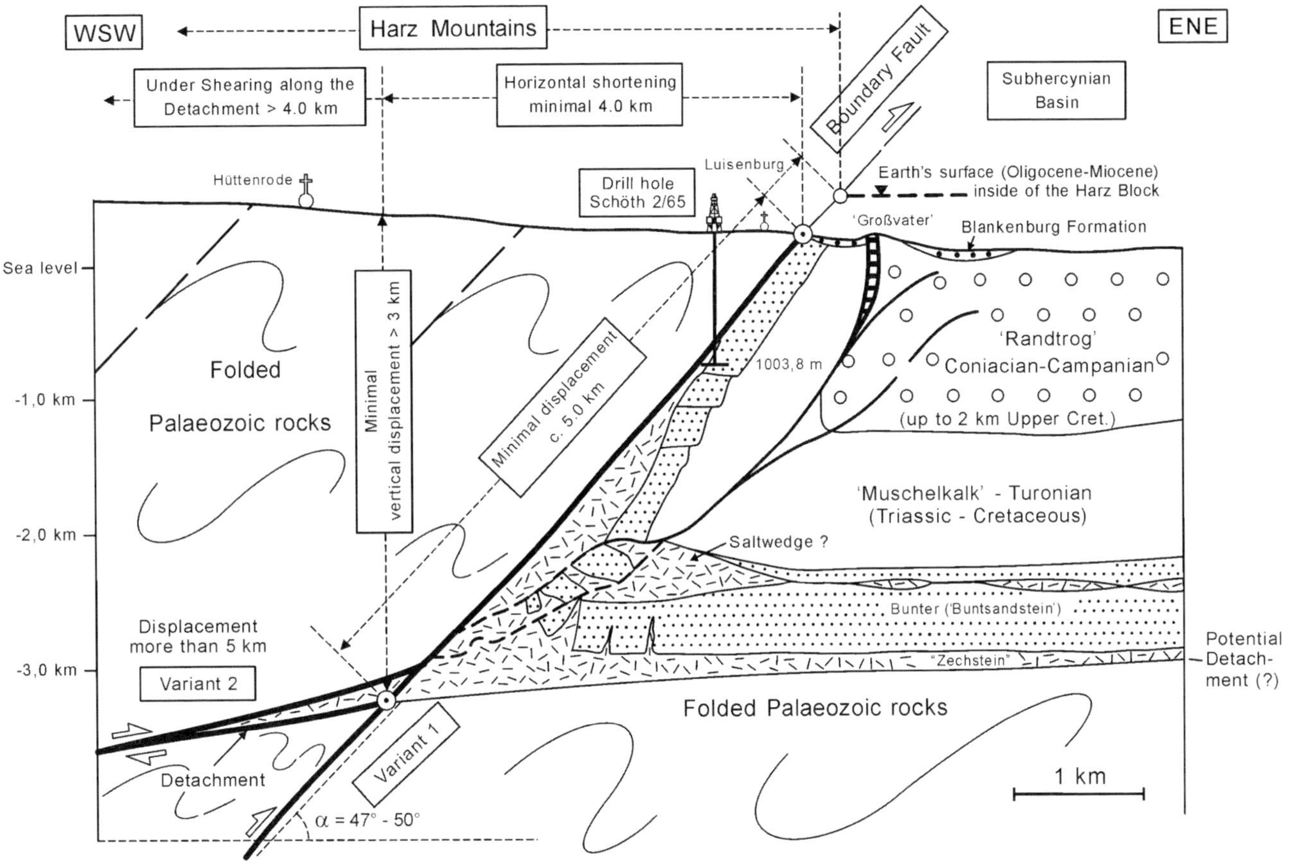


**Fig. 19.23.** Section across the northern border fault zone of the Harz Mountains along the eastern rim of Blankenburg. Variant 1 indicates the minimum horizontal displacement (4 km) and the minimal fault throw (>3 km); variant 2 describes enlarged horizontal displacements when the salt seams of the Late Permian are incorporated as detachment zone. In the acute segment between the border fault and the base of the Late Permian, disharmonic bending and fracturing is assumed. Invaded salt of the Late Permian at the level of the Late Buntsandstein may form a salt wedge. Thrust tectonics spread out from the main fault to its branches.

final major tectonic event in this area was the Late Cretaceous–Early Palaeogene inversion, accompanied by uplift and erosion of the Mid-Polish Trough (i.e. the main depocentre of the Polish Basin).

Following the cessation of the inversion-related deformation, the geodynamic arrangement of the area changed significantly. From the Late Palaeocene–Early Eocene until the present, the Carpathian foreland, which is located northward of the Outer Carpathian flexural foredeep and a forebulge, has not shown any evidence of significant vertical movement. As a consequence, over the last 50–60 Ma only a thin sedimentary cover has developed (*c.* 100–200 m), and this is characterized by relatively uniform facies showing little evidence of lateral change. The only exceptions are restricted to narrow grabens, where up to 100–200 m of sediments were accumulated.

The lowermost part of the Palaeocene sedimentary cover north of the Outer Carpathian foredeep (i.e. Danian chalk sediments) forms part of the Late Cretaceous sedimentary complex of the Polish Basin. The Palaeocene succession is unconformably covered by Eocene to Pleistocene sediments consisting of continental to shallow-marine fine-grained siliciclastics (Fig. 19.27). In the Neogene succession two major facies domains can be distinguished: the Carpathian foredeep sediments, and the sedimentary infill of the Central European Basin located to the north of the flexural forebulge. The forebulge divided the two domains from Miocene times onward. However, the Meta-Carpathian High played a similar role to an earlier topographic barrier, but located further to the south. The existence of these highs was the main reason for the development of exotic faunal provinces, leading to subsequent difficulties in precise stratigraphic correlation between the two domains (e.g. Olszewska *et al.* 1996). The upper part of the Cenozoic succession comprises the glacial Pleistocene deposits, typically a few tens of metres thick and extending almost continuously southwards as far as the Carpathians and the Sudetes (see also Litt *et al.* 2008). It must, however, be stressed that much of the Cenozoic is represented by hiatuses due to the lack of deposition and/or erosion.

### *Late Cretaceous to Palaeogene uplift of the Polish Trough*

The uplift history of the Mid-Polish Swell (Figs 19.28 & 19.29), an inversion ridge which developed along the former depocentre of the Mid-Polish Trough, is recorded by the presence of unconformities and, to some extent, by syninversion sediments. Very little sedimentary input was derived from the Mid-Polish

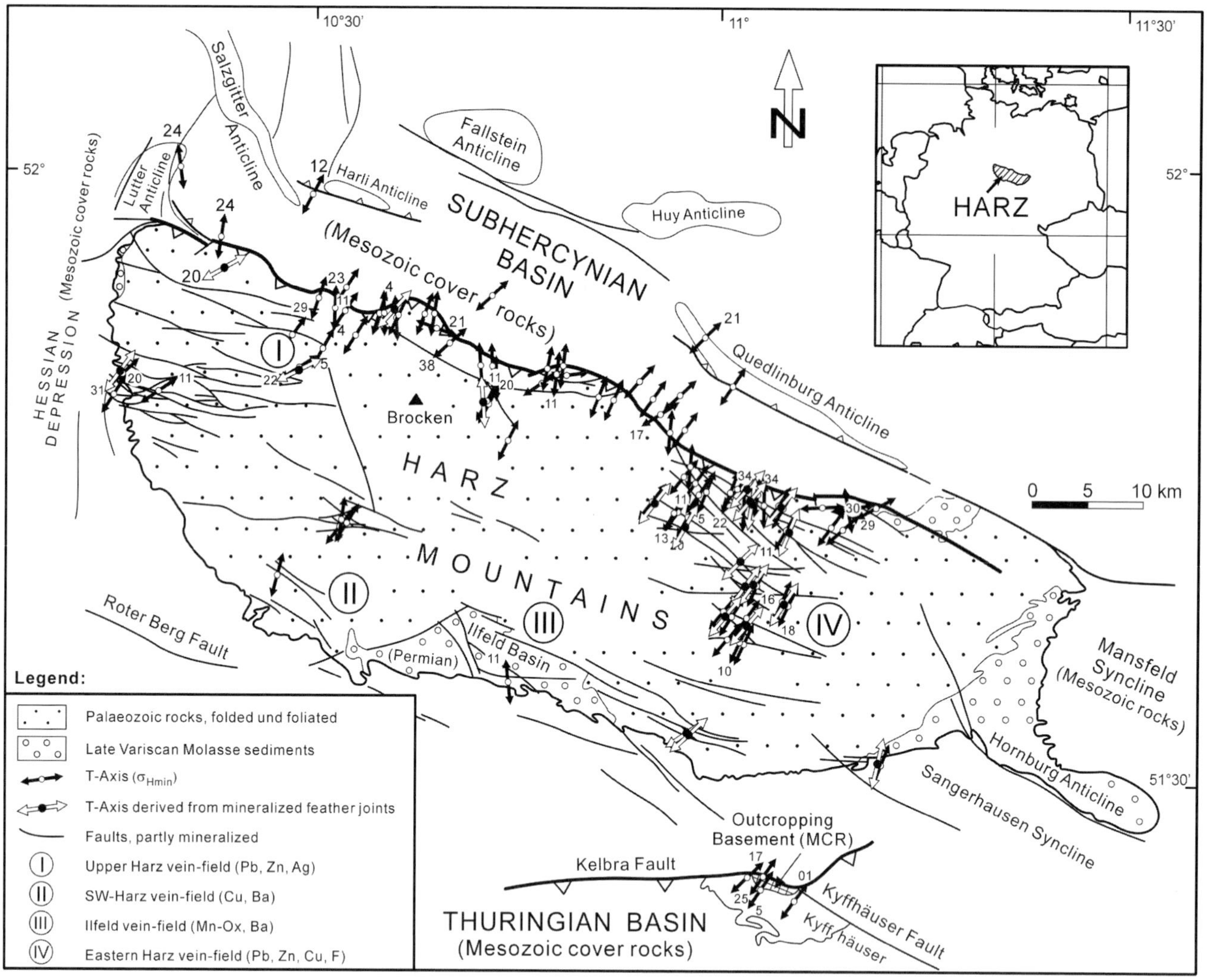


**Fig. 19.24.** Palaeostress map of the directions of the minimum principal stress axes of the Mesozoic dilatational period of the Harz (stage 4, see Fig. 19.26). Solid arrows represent stress axes from fault kinematics; open arrows represent stress axes from feather sets and mineral fibre growth. Numbers next to the arrows describe the inclinations of stress axes greater than 10°. Number of outcrops is 99.

Swell in the Upper Cretaceous chalk basin. Rare and isolated sandstone bodies of Campanian–Maastrichtian age are found to the east and SW of the Pomeranian segment of the Mid-Polish Swell and are associated with local tectonics and salt structures (Leszczyński 2002). The majority of the Upper Cretaceous sediments lack detritus definitively supplied from the Mid-Polish Swell (Połońska 1997). Thus, it can be suggested that this high was not significantly uplifted and eroded before the end of the Cretaceous. Lateral thickness changes of the Upper Cretaceous sediments do not, however, provide clear evidence for the timing and mechanism of uplift. According to reconstructions by Dadlez (1980), Krassowska (1997) and Leszczyński (2002), the thinning of sedimentary successions onto the Mid-Polish Swell could have started as early as the Turonian. This assumption has been questioned by Świdrowska & Hakenberg (1999), who claimed that the uplift of the Mid-Polish Swell could not have begun earlier than the Campanian–Maastrichtian (Kutek & Głazek 1972).

Along the margins of the Mid-Polish Swell, the Danian chalk-facies sediments overlie older strata, with the same erosional gap developed in the marginal troughs (Fig. 19.28A). This gap usually comprises only the upper part of Maastrichtian or the upper part of the Campanian to the Maastrichtian (Piwocki & Kramarska 2004). Locally, in the Baltic Sea region, the Danian chalk was deposited directly upon Jurassic sediments (Kramarska *et al.* 1999). This indicates a phase of significant uplift and erosion of the Mid-Polish Swell at the end of the Maastrichtian and beginning of the Danian. The Danian chalk contains a greater detrital clastic component than the Upper Cretaceous chalk, with the resultant development of glauconitic sandstones, mudstones and rare sandstones within the chalk marls (Połońska 1997). However, the provenance of the detritus is unclear, being from either the Mid-Polish Swell or an eastern source, i.e. the East European Platform.

A major erosion gap during the late Palaeocene and early Eocene (Piwocki 2001, 2004), with no deposition in the Polish Lowlands (Fig. 19.28B), represents another important stage of uplift and erosion of the Mid-Polish Swell. The geometry of the

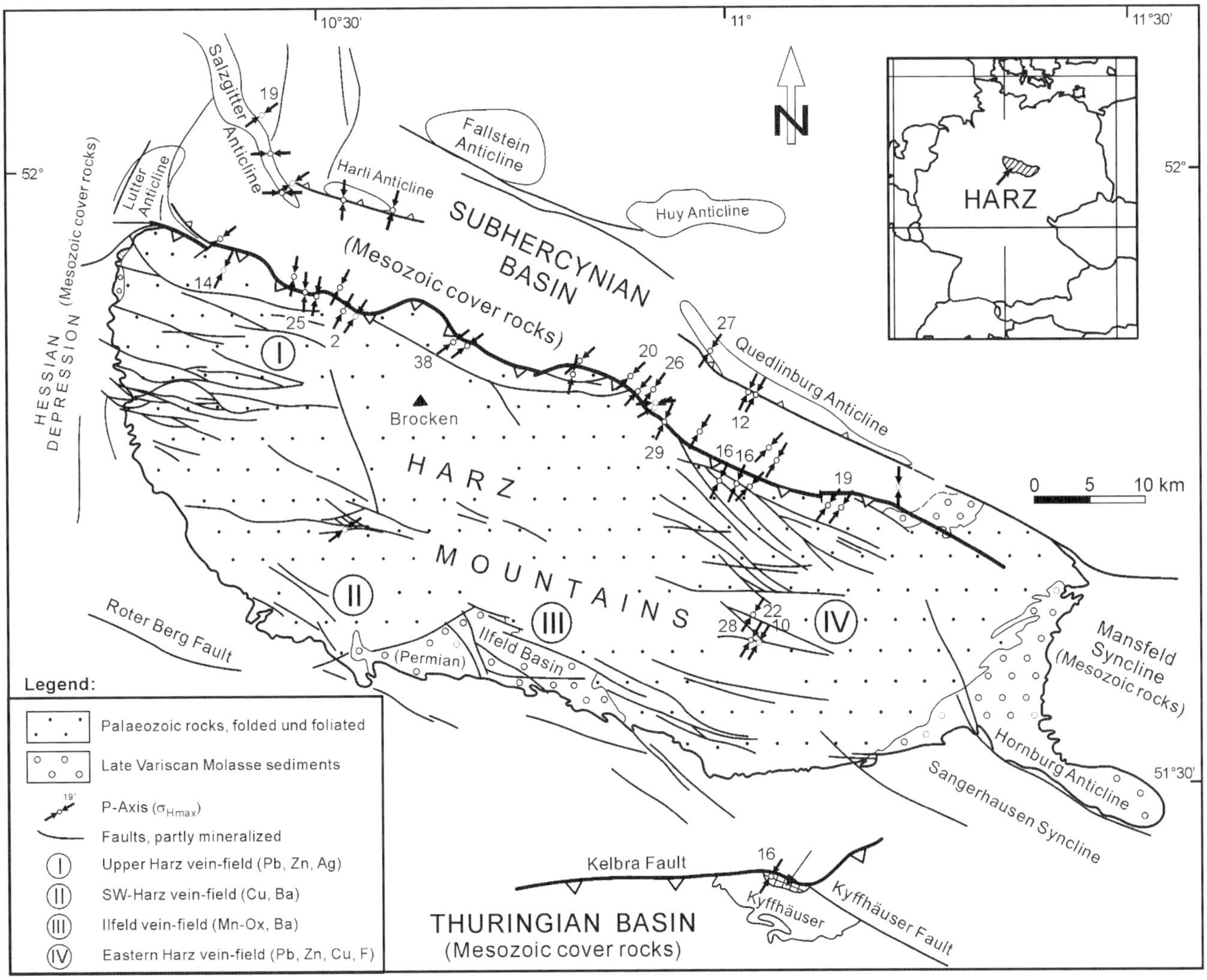


**Fig. 19.25.** Palaeostress map of the directions of the maximum horizontal principal stress axes of the Upper Cretaceous inversion period of the Harz (stage 5, see Fig. 19.26). Stress axes determined by kinematic indications of 41 outcrops, supported by measurements of H-stylolites in mineral veins.

Middle and Upper Eocene depocentres and biofacies suggests that at this time the high still existed as an elevated zone (Fig. 19.28C). In particular, the dominance of the Mediterranean and Boreal fauna documented to the SW and NE of the Mid-Polish Swell, respectively (Pożaryska & Odrzywolska-Bieńkowa 1977), indicates that there was a topographic barrier in between the two faunal zones. The periodic mixing of the two fauna types suggests a relatively low relief of the swell at this stage. Oligocene sediments unconformably overlie the eroded swell, providing an upper time limit for the end of inversion-related uplift and erosion. Since that time the subsidence pattern of the Polish Lowlands has no longer been related to the NW–SE trending structures of the Trans-European Suture Zone, but rather to the activity of the Carpathian forebulge and the depocentre which developed to the north (Fig. 19.28D).

The magnitude of tectonic uplift and the thickness of the section removed during inversion of the Polish Trough remain poorly constrained. Judging from analysis of thermal maturity profiles and maturity modelling (Poprawa & Grotek 2004), as well as from mechanical compaction studies (Stefaniuk *et al.* 1996; Dadlez *et al.* 1997), *c.* 2000–3000 m of sediments may have been eroded from the axis of the Mid-Polish Swell during inversion. In the Sudetes, the Late Cretaceous inversion along Variscan faults attained values of up to 1000 m in the Intra-Sudetic syncline and 2000 m in the Kaczawa Mountains (Oberc 1972).

## *Eocene–Miocene faulting and development of tectonic grabens*

### *Polish Lowlands*

The Tertiary sediments accumulated to the north of the Carpathian domain and the Sudetes in Poland have generally not undergone significant faulting or deformation. Exceptions, however, include narrow grabens and active salt structures in SW Poland (Fig. 19.29). These basins are *c.* 1–2 km wide, several kilometres long and several hundred metres deep and originated from the reactivation of older tectonic structures. The amount of extension was low. These grabens are, therefore, not an important factor of the overall foreland area deformation, but they do provide valuable

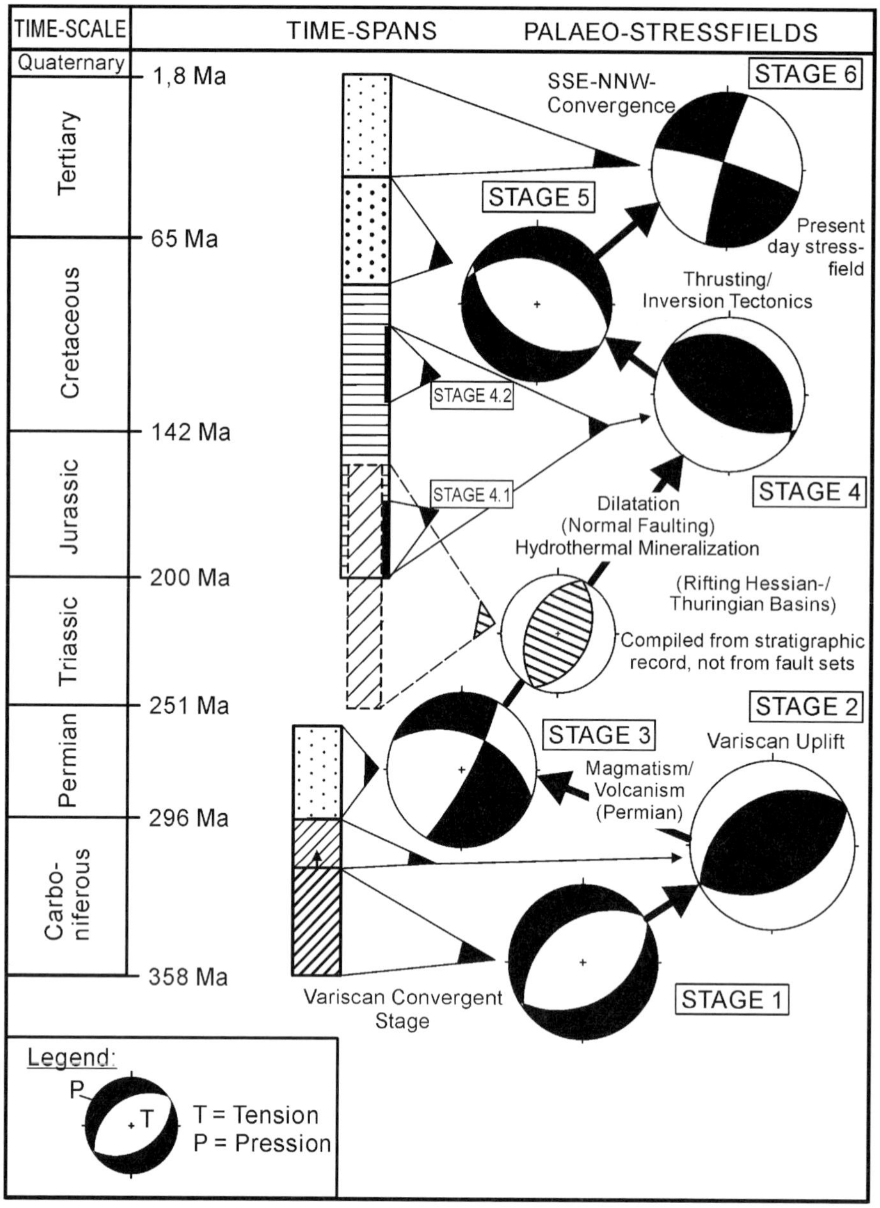


**Fig. 19.26.** Discrimination of six main stages of palaeostress fields in the Harz Mountains and surrounding areas based on investigations of synchronously activated fault sets in basement and cover rocks.

information on stress regime changes. However, information concerning the kinematics of their boundary faults is usually lacking, such that in most cases they are only interpreted from seismic profiles and constrained by borehole data. The oldest, Eocene, stage of graben development can be recognized in the western part of the Fore-Sudetic monocline (west of the Poznań-Oleśnica Lineament; Fig. 19.29) (Deczkowski & Gajewska 1980). Here, graben formation was coeval with the opening of the European Cenozoic Rift System (Prodehl *et al.* 1995) and coincided with a phase of increased tectonic subsidence within the Outer Carpathian sedimentary basins at the southern margin of the East European Platform (Poprawa *et al.* 2002). The grabens overprint the Late Triassic–Early Jurassic grabens and create a conjugate pattern of the ENE–WSW or north–south trending faults, suggesting a change from a transtensional to an extensional stress regime. During this early stage, subsidence in the grabens was of the order of several tens of metres. In the well-studied Krzywin Graben (Fig. 19.29), this stage of limited subsidence extended from the Late Eocene to the Oligocene (Kasiński 1984). The Eocene sediments were deposited in two sedimentary units and represent mainly lagoonal environments. The main subsidence phase took place during the Miocene, when lacustrine and fluvial sediments were accumulated (Kasiński 1984). Coal-bearing sediments are present in the entire Miocene succession, but the main seams occur in the Middle Miocene succession. Possible mechanical compaction of the Miocene coals and clays prohibits the calculation and differentiation of tectonic subsidence during the Pliocene.

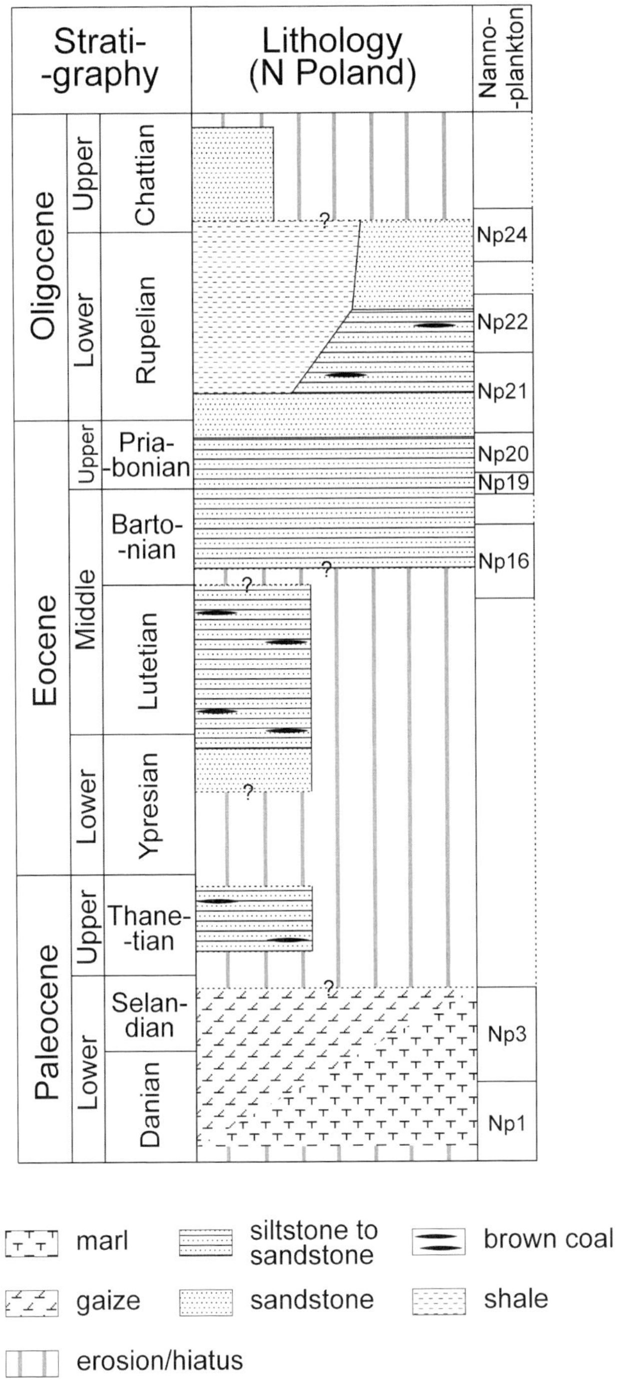


**Fig. 19.27.** Simplified lithostratigraphic column of the Palaeogene in the Polish Lowlands (after Piwocki 2001). Gaize: glauconitic or calcitic sandstone.

Eastwards of the Poznań-Oleśnica Lineament, similar grabens developed at the end of the Oligocene or in the earliest Miocene, and were coeval with the onset of the major subsidence event in the graben systems further west. This represents a phase of tectonic activity, which was almost synchronous with the development of the Inner Carpathian foredeep basin in the south (Oszczypko & Ślączka 1989). These grabens are found along the TESZ. One example is the Kleszczów Graben (Fig. 19.29) which developed on a complex structural junction within the TESZ. According to Gotowała & Hałuszczak (2002), Late Oligocene–Early Miocene sedimentation was triggered by oblique reactivation of two conjugate WSW–ENE and NW–SE trending faults due to WNW–ESE directed compression and SSW–NNE directed extension. During the Middle Miocene, secondary extensional sub-basins developed along the WSW–ENE trending faults in the Kleszczów Graben. Subsidence ceased in the Sarmatian when the basin fill was deformed and selectively inverted and eroded. Late Miocene and Pliocene deposits within the graben unconformably cover this complex. The final structure of the graben was shaped during a phase of Quaternary transpression (Gotowała & Hałuszczak 2002).

Subsidence in some of the grabens located at the top of Zechstein salt structures shows a similar evolution, and may thus also be related to tectonic activity. At the top of the Damasławek salt diapir (Fig. 19.29), a small oval-shaped basin was initiated in the Miocene (Krzywiec *et al.* 2000). Coal-bearing Miocene-age sediments, restricted to the area above the salt diapir, were accumulated in two stages. According to Jarosiński (1999*a*) the migration of depocentres and the fault pattern suggest dextral transtensional motion along a NW–SE orientated basement fault leading to a pull-apart mechanism of salt descent and a related increase in accumulation space. Prior to the Late Miocene, the diapir rose and the basin was uplifted by 50–100 m. Positive flower structures which developed along the boundaries of the basin suggest transpressive activity of inversion due to the strike-slip motion along the NW–SE trending basement fault (Jarosiński 1999*a*). Although the inversion of the basin has not been dated precisely, it can be correlated with the Middle Miocene inversion of the Kleszczów Graben. This phase of transpression may be related to the final paroxysm of collision in a northerly direction within the Western Outer Carpathians (e.g. Książkiewicz 1972).

*The Sudetes*

The Tertiary evolution of the Sudetes and the Fore-Sudetic Block is comparable to the rest of the Palaeozoic platform to the north. However, faulting was more intense and volcanism also played a role in this area. During the Palaeocene and Eocene the area was elevated and eroded. The subsequent Oligocene and Miocene marine ingressions came from the Central European Basin (Oberc 1972). During the Middle Miocene, the eastern Sudetic Basin was linked with the Carpathian Foredeep Basin.

Tertiary deposits in the Sudetes and the Fore-Sudetic Block filled narrow basins, frequently synsedimentary grabens (Dyjor 1993). In the latest Oligocene or the early Miocene, sedimentation commenced in the Paczków-Kędzierzyn and the Roztoka-Mokrzeszów grabens, located along the Sudetic Marginal Fault Zone (Fig. 19.29; Dyjor 1976, 1983). The initial stage of marine sedimentation, continuing until the Middle Miocene, was controlled by the west–east trending faults. Additionally, in Early Miocene times volcanic activity with basalt eruption took place. In the Late Miocene, reactivation of NW–SE trending faults can be observed. Another subsidence centre, the Zittau Depression (Fig. 19.29), developed at the intersection of NW–SE trending Sudetic faults and the SW–NE trending continuation of the Eger Graben (Kasiński 1984). The basin was filled with terrestrial coal-bearing sediments in two discrete phases of subsidence, associated with intense faulting: the Miocene–Early Pliocene and the Pliocene. Extension of the Eger Graben, triggering Quaternary volcanic activity, may also have resulted in a relatively young phase of subsidence in the region.

In the Late Miocene, the activated Sudetic Marginal Fault

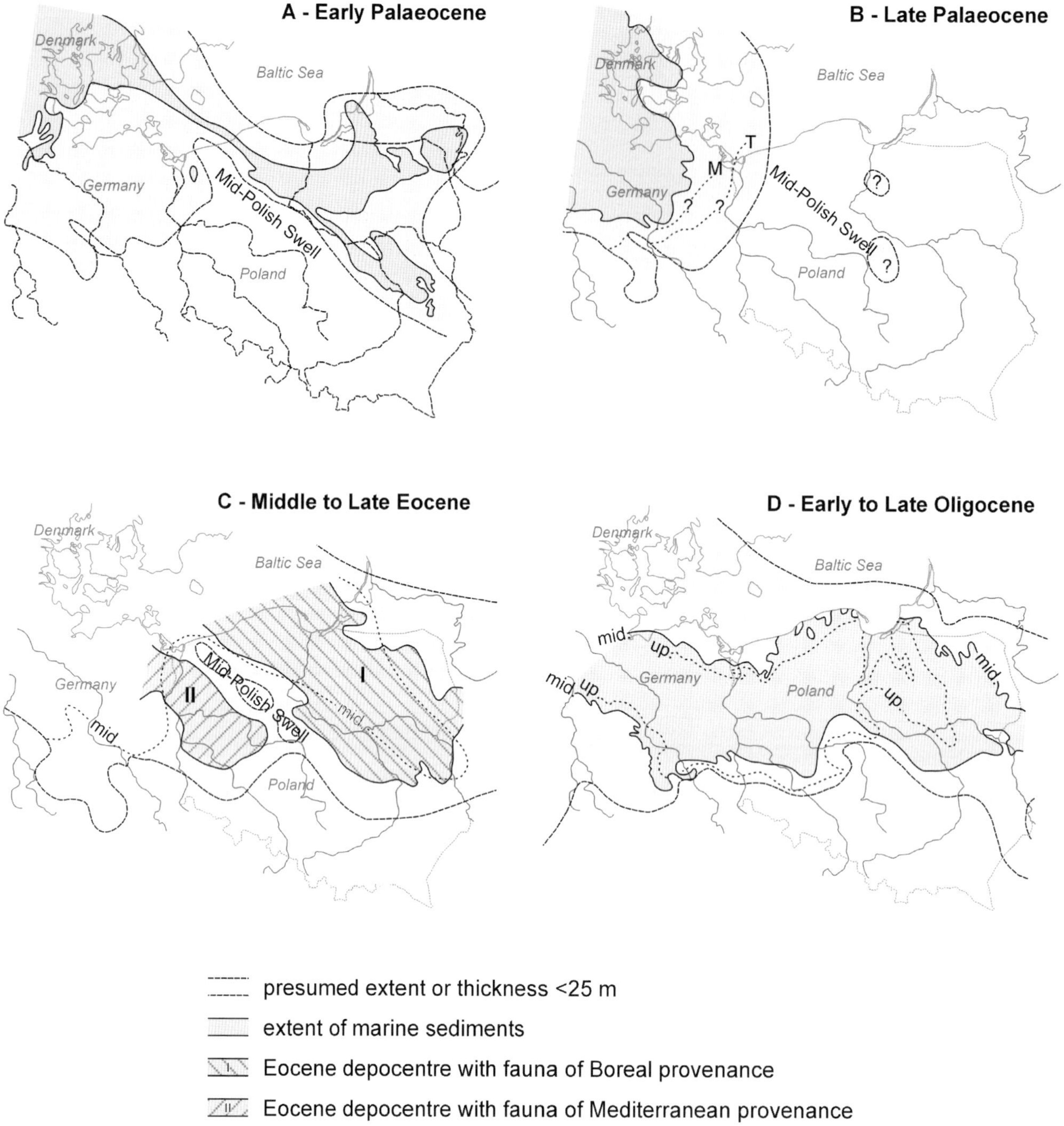


**Fig. 19.28.** Palaeogeographic evolution of the depocentres in the Polish Lowlands during the Palaeogene after Vinkena (1988), Stankowski (1996) and Peryt & Piwocki (2004). Note the presence of a NW–SE trending topographic barrier (Mid-Polish Swell) until the late Eocene, and a change to the east–west elongated depocentre in the Oligocene.

exerted control on the sedimentation pattern in the Sudetes and surrounding region. This represented the end of activity along the Carpathian forebulge in Lower Silesia. The Upper Miocene change in stress regime also ended tectonic subsidence within the Miocene grabens in the Polish Lowlands. In the Pliocene, uplift of the entire region occurred with relative elevation of the Sudetes versus the Fore-Sudetic block, where syntectonic coarse sediments of the Gozdnica beds were accumulated. The uplift of the Sudetes since Miocene times, with respect to the Fore-Sudetic block, is estimated at *c.* 1200–1500 m (Oberc 1972; Dyjor 1983).

From the Oligocene to the Pliocene, there was a major phase of basaltic volcanism in the Sudetes. Most of the basalts are found within the elevated areas and along their structural boundaries, such as the Sudetic Marginal Fault or the Middle-Odra Fault (Fig. 19.29). The initial, Oligocene, phase of

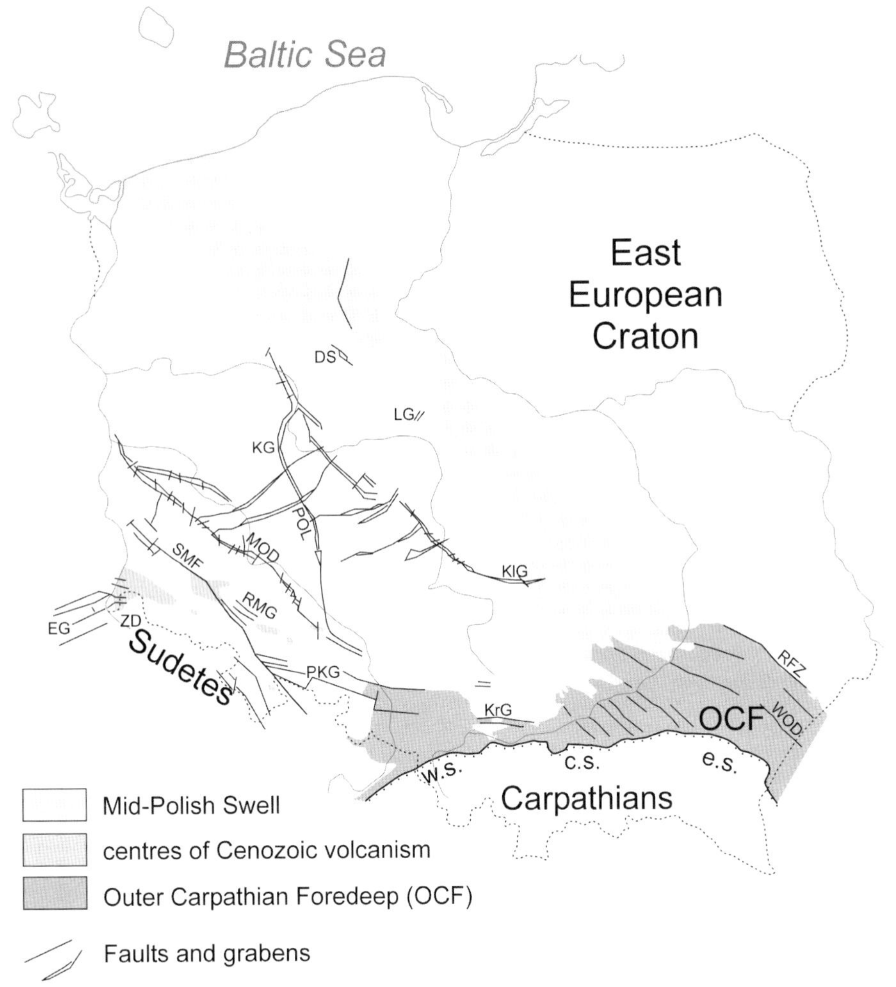


**Fig. 19.29.** Simplified Eocene to Miocene tectonic setting of the Carpathian foreland in Poland (after Kasiński 1984; Piwocki 2001; Jarosiński 1999*b*; Krysiak 2000). Abbreviations: DS, Damasł awek Salt Structure; EG, Eger Graben; KG, Krzywin Graben; KlG, Kleszczów Graben; KrG, Krzeszowice Graben; LG, Lubstów Graben; MOD, Mid-Odra Fault Zone; PKG, Paczków-Kędzierzyn Graben; POL, Poznań-Oleśnica Lineament; RFZ, Roztocze Fault Zone; RMG, Roztoka-Mokrzeszów Grabens; SMF, Sudetic Marginal Fault; WOD, Wielkie Oczy Fault; ZD, Zittau Depression; w.s., c.s., e.s., western, central, eastern segment of the Outer Carpathians and their foredeeps.

volcanism (30–26 Ma) was widespread in Lower Silesia (Birkenmajer *et al.* 2004). Basalts of the second, Oligocene–Early Miocene, phase (26–18 Ma) are more localized within the Sudetes and in the vicinity of the marginal faults. The location of the third stage of volcanism, dated at the Miocene–Pliocene boundary (5.5–3.8 Ma), shifted further to the south and was linked with the volcanic province of the Central Sudetes. In the Czech part of this province, the youngest lavas are Pleistocene in age (Birkenmajer *et al.* 2004). The origin of Cenozoic basaltic volcanism in the Sudetes is related to a mantle plume (Downes 2001).

## *Quaternary deformations and recent stress field*

*Neotectonic subdivision*

A new neotectonic–structural subdivision of Poland, proposed as a result of the IGCP Project 346 'Neogeodynamica Baltica' (Karabanov & Schwab 1997) for the Baltic countries, includes the following major units (Fig. 19.30): (1) the Baltic-Belarus Basin, including both the areas subsiding since the onset of the Oligocene (Mazovian and Gdansk depressions, middle and eastern Pomerania), and those that originally subsided and were then uplifted (Suwałki, Podlasie, Polesie Lubelskie regions); (2) the Central European Subsidence Zone, including the Odra Depression and the West Baltic Step (subsided since the Oligocene), as well as the Pomeranian Depression and the Mid-European High (which originally subsided and were then uplifted); (3) the Central European Uplift Zone, including the Lusatian-Sudetic and Holy Cross blocks, as well as South Polish–Podolian Uplift, uplifted since Oligocene times; (4) the Carpathian Foredeep, which originally subsided and was then uplifted; as well as (5) the Carpathians, showing variable uplift.

The most geodynamically active area, apart from the Carpathians, is the Central European Uplift Zone, and particularly the Lusatian-Sudetic Block (including the Sudetic Marginal Fault). Areas showing recent uplift tendencies, inferred from remote sensing data (Ostaficzuk 1999), are irregular in shape, but tend to cluster in east–west orientated belts (Fig. 19.31). Of particular importance is the pattern observed within the Central European Uplift Zone.

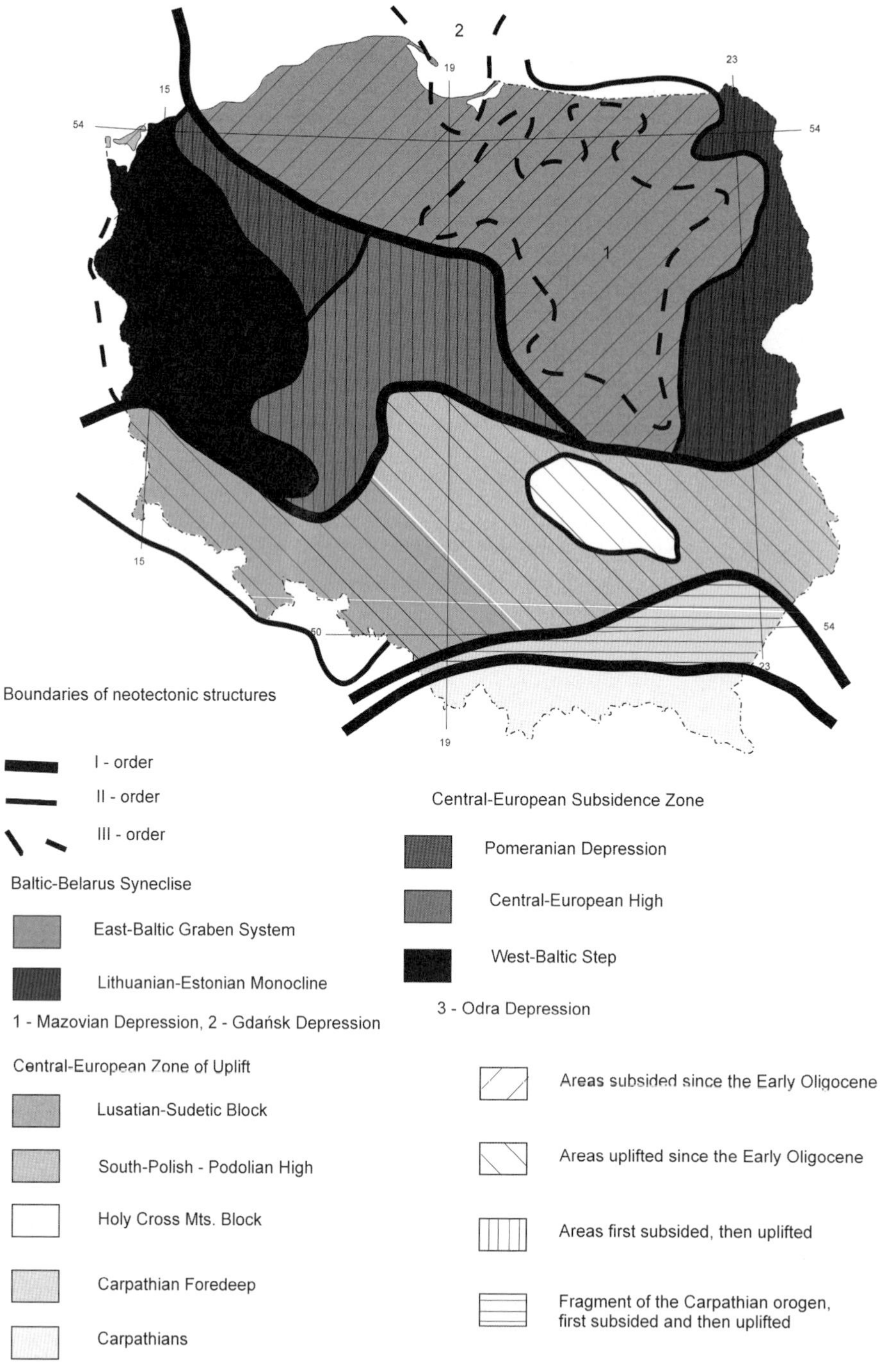


**Fig. 19.30.** Neotectonic–structural units of Poland (modified after Karabanov & Schwab 1997).

*Amplitudes and rates of vertical crustal movements*

The amplitudes and spatial distribution of zones showing Quaternary tectonic mobility have been treated differently by different authors, depending on the timescale considered (Zuchiewicz 1995, 2000). According to Rühle (1969, 1973), the amount of Quaternary uplift exceeded 100 m in the Baltic Basin, the Mazury-Suwałki Anticline, as well as in the southern Lublin Upland and the Roztocze region, while subsidence (−50 to <−100 m) was confined to the lower Vistula River valley and the Szczecin Lowland. Large thicknesses of Quaternary sediments (>200 m) within basins in the Kuyavian-Pomeranian High and in the East European Platform, however, indicate higher amplitudes of vertical movements (Rühle 1973; Baraniecka 1975, 1980). Therefore, the average rates of displacement calculated for the entire Quaternary are 0.04–0.08 mm/a. The Quaternary neotectonic amplitudes during individual episodes of increased activity ranged from 15–20 m (subsidence in the Kleszczów Graben during the Pilica/Drenthe-Warthe Interglacial stage; Brodzikowski 1987) and 20–30 m (uplift of the Roztocze region during the Mazovian/Holsteinian Interglacial; Harasimiuk & Henkiel 1980) to 30–40 m (uplift of the Wałbrzych Foothills, Sudetes Mountains, in the Mazovian/Holsteinian Interglacial;

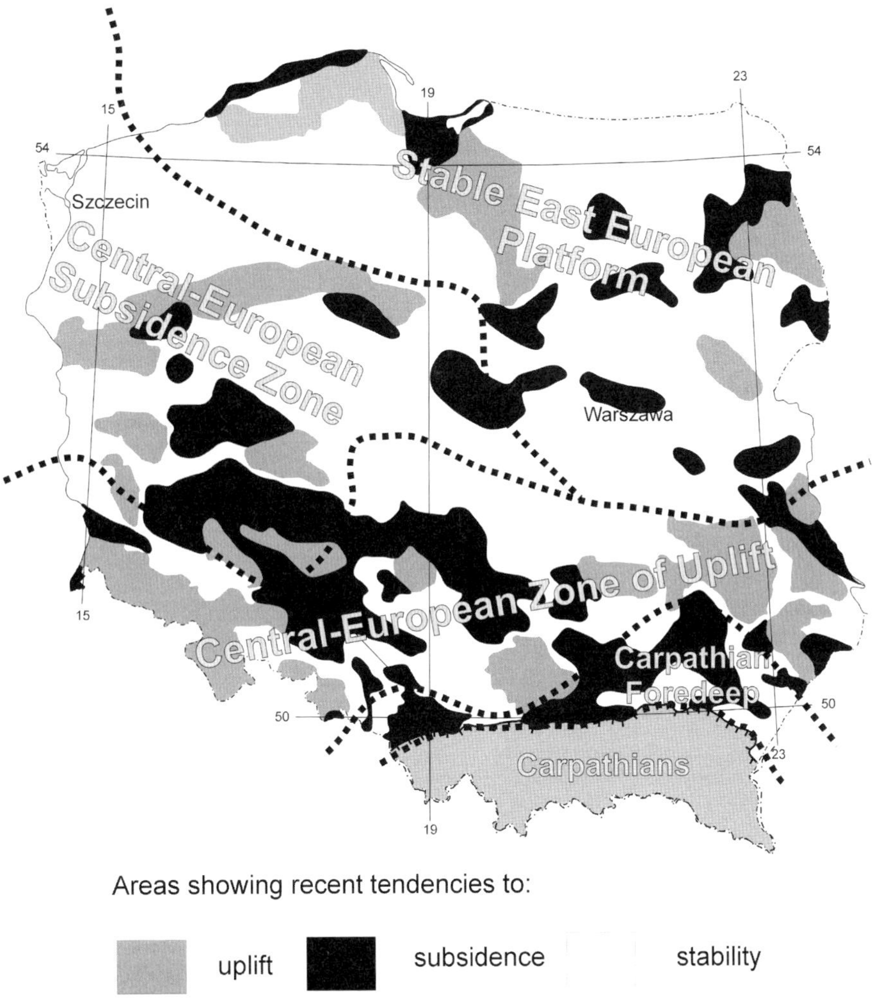


**Fig. 19.31.** Recent tectonic tendencies in Poland inferred from remote-sensing data (modified after Ostaficzuk 1999).

Krzyszkowski *et al.* 1995) and 70–100 m (early Pleistocene uplift of some structures of the West Carpathians; Zuchiewicz 1991). The rates of movement in the Polish Outer Carpathians range from 0.02 to 2 mm/a (Zuchiewicz 1991; Zuchiewicz *et al.* 2002), which are comparable to values recorded from the northern foreland of the Alps.

In the North Polish Lowland, episodes of increased neotectonic activity occurred at the end of the Pliocene, in early (1.45–1.35 Ma) middle (1.15–1.00 Ma) and late Pleistocene (0.60–0.45 Ma) times (Mojski 1991). The subsidence of the Mazovian Depression and the Baltic Basin was interrupted by a phase of glacio-isostatic uplift that followed every Scandinavian glaciation, and was combined with the reactivation of basement structures along the Kuyavian-Pomeranian Swell (Baraniecka 1975; Liszkowski 1993; Zuchiewicz 1995).

The most recent map of Recent vertical crustal movements in Poland (Wyrzykowski 1985) appears to indicate prevailing subsidence (usually between 0 and −3 mm/a) across the country, except for the more weakly uplifted parts of Pomerania and the SE portion of the Carpathians. The highest rates of subsidence (<−3.5 mm/a) are recorded in the Paczków Graben, Lower Silesia, the upper Odra River valley and the Płock Basin. The results of repeated GPS campaigns are available for selected areas of Lower Silesia only (Kontny 2003).

*Faults active in the Quaternary*

Seismotectonic faults in Poland developed in the Quaternary due to the reactivation of Neogene faults (Kowalski & Liszkowski 1972; Rühle 1973; Liszkowski 1982, 1993; Henkiel 1983, 1984, 1993; Dyjor 1983, 1993, 1995; Baraniecka 1995; Dyjor *et al.* 1995; Krzyszkowski *et al.* 1995; Jura 1995, 1999; Ostaficzuk 1995; Nitychoruk 1996; Brzezińska-Wójcik 1999; Kasiński & Piwocki 1999; Ber 1999; Zuchiewicz 2000). These include faults in the Lower Silesia (Wrocław-Ozimek, Przeworno-Węgliniec, Sudetic Marginal Fault, a fault along the northern margin of the Karkonosze Mountains; Dyjor 1983, 1993, 1995; Migoń 1991) and Upper Silesia regions (east–west trending faults showing recently downthrown northern blocks; Czarnecka 1988), the NW–SE, north–south, NE–SW, east–west, and ESE–WNW orientated faults of the Lublin Upland and Roztocze region (Harasimiuk & Henkiel 1984; Henkiel 1984; Buraczyński 1984), NNE–SSW and NE–SW orientated faults in the northern part of the Sandomierz Basin (Laskowska-Wysoczańska 1979, 1983), as well as several oblique-slip, strike-slip and thrusts faults in the Carpathians (Zuchiewicz 1995; Zuchiewicz *et al.* 2002).

Episodes of increased fault activity took place in the early Quaternary, in the Mazovian (Holsteinian) Interglacial and during or shortly after the Odranian (Drenthe) glacial stage. Some of the faults were also active in Holocene times (Karkonosze Mountains, Roztocze region, Beskid Sądecki Mountains, Jasło-Sanok Depression). In NW Poland (Kopczyńska-Lamparska 1979) and on the NW margin of the Holy Cross Mountains (Lindner 1978), Quaternary faulting continued in the Cromerian and Holsteinian interglacials. On the NE margin of the Holy Cross Mountains, faulting also took place in the Warthe and Eemian stages (Kosmowska-Suffczyńska 1986). In the central part of the Holy Cross Mountains reactivation of Palaeozoic faults was noticeable in the early and middle Quaternary (Kowalski 1995). During the Middle Polish (Saalian) glaciations and Eemian interglacial, marked subsidence in the Szeszupa Graben, NE Poland (Kociszewska-Musiał 1978), and the Lower Vistula River Graben (Ostaficzuk 1981) became apparent. Grabens with throws of up to 40–50 m formed in the Łódź Upland during Holsteinian times (Zuchiewicz 1995).

The Quaternary faulting is reflected in increased thicknesses of young deposits on downthrown blocks (including stacks of colluvial/solifluction wedges; Henkiel 1993), deformation of river terraces and alluvial fans, changes in drainage patterns, as well as in the formation of cracks within Pleistocene icesheets, controlling the preferred orientation of glaciofluvial structures (e.g. Klajnert 1984). The throw along Quaternary faults changed from 40–50 m to more than 100 m in the Sudetes, the Lublin Upland and the Inner Carpathians, and from several to several tens of metres in the Outer Carpathians. The average rate of faulting during Quaternary times was 0.02 to 0.05 mm/a, which is similar to recent values. A strike-slip component has been suggested for some Quaternary faults, including the Sudetic Marginal Fault (Mastalerz & Wojewoda 1990) or the Janowice Fault in the Lublin Upland (Henkiel 1984). Single faults in central Poland (Kleszczów Graben) represent Mid-Quaternary thrusts of displacements of up to 40–50 m (Hałuszczak 1999; Gotowała & Hałuszczak 2002).

Faults active in Quaternary times are frequently accompanied by lineaments, nearly 70% of which coincide with epicentres of historic and present-day seismicity (Graniczny 1991). Historical seismic activity is often related to strike-slip faults, which in the Carpathians trend ENE–WSW and NE–SW (Bażyński *et al.* 1984; Graniczny 1991), whereas outside the Carpathians they are orientated parallel to the margin of the East European Platform and the Sudetic Marginal Fault (Liszkowski 1982; Guterch & Lewandowska-Marciniak 2002).

*Case studies of Quaternary faulting*

In terms of Quaternary faulting the areas of Lower Silesia, the Kleszczów Graben, the Lublin Upland, and the Carpathian Foredeep represent the best-studied regions. The neotectonic map of **Lower Silesia**, SW Poland, by Badura & Przybylski (2000) is the only detailed neotectonic map of a large part of Poland that shows the distribution of faults either reactivated or formed in Neogene and Quaternary times (Fig. 19.32). This map also portrays the distribution of young Alpine folds and thrusts, exposures of young volcanics, distribution of hydrothermal and mineral waters, traces of young mineralization, and heat flow values.

Among faults reactivated in Quaternary times, the most important is the **Sudetic Marginal Fault** (SMF), nearly 300 km long, which marks the boundary between the uplifted Sudetes and the stable and/or subsided Fore-Sudetic Block (Dyjor 1995; Dyjor *et al.* 1995; Krzyszkowski *et al.* 1995; Badura *et al.* 2003; Kontny 2003). Its NW segment shows, apart from dip-slip, a minor sinistral component, while the SE segment is characterized by predominant dip-slip and, perhaps, an insignificant dextral component. Quaternary activity of the SMF has been a matter of debate. Some researchers have suggested uplift of the footwall ranging from 20–30 m to 60–80 m, and even 80–100 m, a large portion of it due to glacio-isostatic rebound after the Saalian glaciation (cf. Krzyszkowski *et al.* 1995). Faulting of Quaternary terraces, rectilinearity of the fault scarp, possible seismotectonic deformation within Pleistocene alluvial fans, as well as historical seismicity and contemporaneous, GPS-detected mobility, all testify to recent activity of this zone (cf. Badura *et al.* 2003, and references therein).

The southeastern portion of this fault (nearly 100 km long) between Złotoryja in the NW and Złoty Stok in the SE has been studied (Badura *et al.* 2003). This portion of the SMF has been subdivided into seven segments each showing slightly different strikes (N28°W to N55°W), geological settings, lengths (8.8–22.9 km), heights of the fault scarp and fault-line scarp (40 m to 300 m), as well as the values of morphometric parameters of small catchment areas of streams that dissect the scarp. The latter parameters, particularly those characterizing the elongation, relief and average slope of individual catchment areas, together with abnormally small values of the valley floor width to valley height ratios, and mountain front sinuosity indices (which are indicative of a nearly straight trace of the mountain front) allow conclusions to be drawn about Quaternary uplift tendencies of the SMF footwall in the Sowie Mountains segment (Badura *et al.* 2003).

The remaining faults reactivated in the Quaternary are clustered in the Sudetic Block, in the Karkonosze and Izera Mountains, as well as in the Upper Nysa Kłodzka Graben, whereas in the Fore-Sudetic Block they are found in the Niemcza, Strzelin and Ziębice zones, and on the northern margin of the Paczków Graben and within the Niemodlin Hills.

The **Kleszczów Graben**, central Poland, is 80 km long and 2–3 km wide, and originated in Late Oligocene–Early Miocene times (Gotowała & Hałuszczak 2002). The structure was quiescent from the Late Miocene until the South Polish/Elsterian glaciation, when intensive faulting occurred (Fig. 19.33), resulting in the formation of NW-striking faults and folding of Cenozoic strata (Krzyszkowski 1991, 1992; Hałuszczak 1994; Hałuszczak *et al.* 1995). It was probably at that time that the NW-striking Folwark thrust fault, showing top-to-the NE displacement, was formed (Hałuszczak *et al.* 1995; Hałuszczak 1999). This episode terminated at *c.* 260 ka, shortly before the Warthe stage. The recent development of the Kleszczów Graben consists in reactivation of some of the pre-existing faults, partly due to mining exploitation, and also owing to present-day seismicity with magnitudes up to 4.6 and epicentres aligned parallel to one of the regional basement faults. Focal mechanisms of these earthquakes indicate oblique-slip kinematics (Gotowała & Hałuszczak 2002).

Cenozoic faulting in the **Lublin Upland**, SE Poland, post-dating Late Sarmatian movements, continued in the Early Quaternary (Henkiel 1983, 1984; Harasimiuk & Henkiel 1984; Buraczyński 1997; Brzezińska-Wójcik 2002). The principal fault zones include (Fig. 19.34): the dextral Kock-Łęczna lineament (NW–SE); the Wieprz River valley fault zone (north–south), comprising alternating asymmetric grabens and half-grabens reactivated in Early Quaternary times; the Early Quaternary fault zone of the northern margin of the Lublin Upland (east–west), including the Mogielnica and Sobianowice grabens filled with more than 70 m of Quaternary alluvium; the usually pre-Quaternary Bystrzyca River valley fault zone (NE–SW), composed of normal faults bounding narrow grabens and horsts; the Włodawka River fault zone; and the pre-Quaternary Kaplonosy lineament (NNW–SSE).

The NW portion of the Lublin Upland includes the Janowice

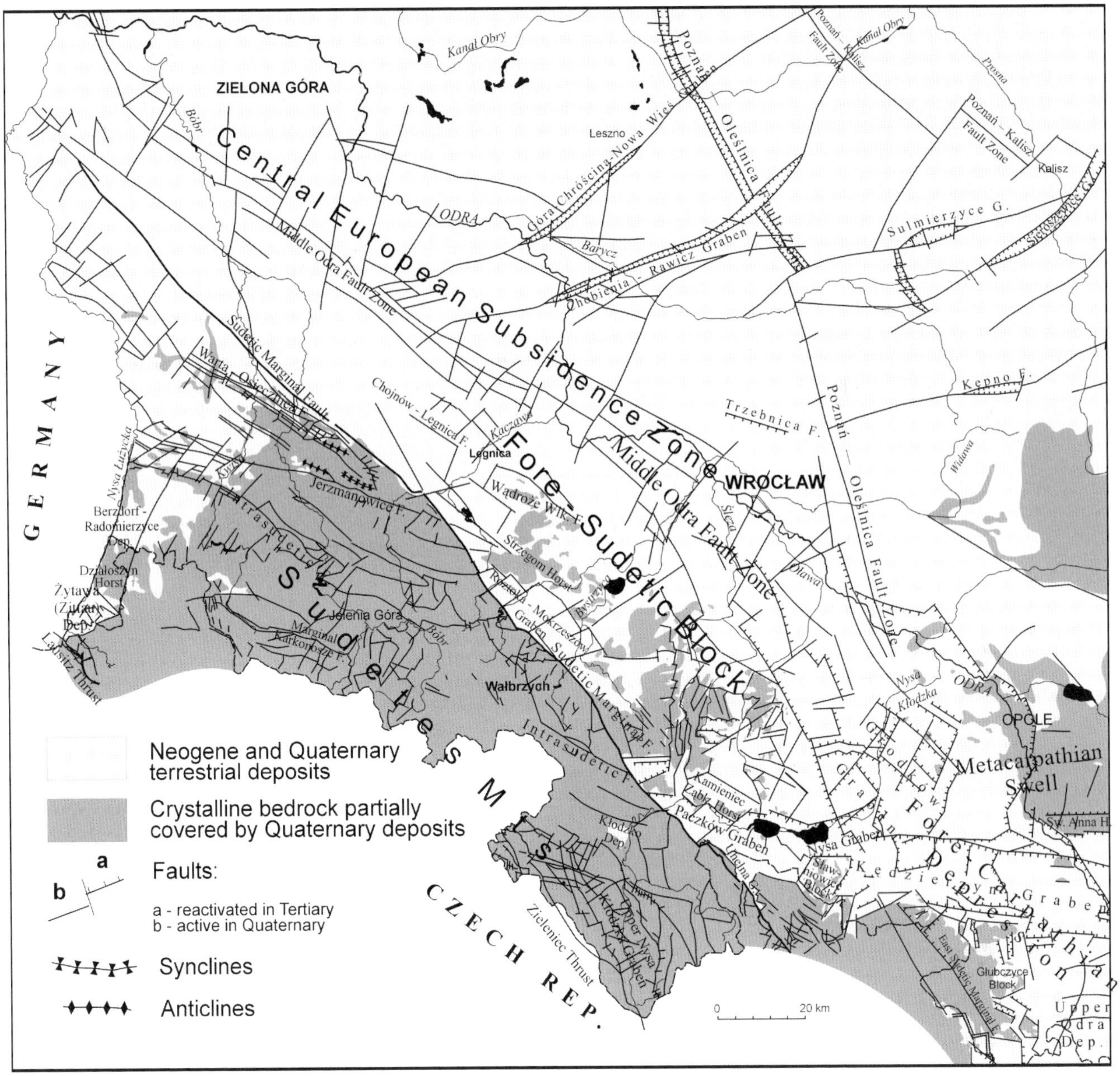


**Fig. 19.32.** Neotectonic map of Lower Silesia (after Badura & Przybylski 2000).

Fault (NE–SW), considered by some authors as a Quaternary sinistral fault zone with up to 1 km of offset (Henkiel 1983, 1984). The morphotectonic scarp at Dobre (NW–SE), Nałęczów Plateau, was interpreted as a seismotectonic normal fault associated with a series of superimposed colluvial wedges, probably formed due to repeated palaeoseismic events (Henkiel 1993). The escarpment zone (NW–SE) of the Roztocze region was uplifted by 20–30 m following the South Polish/Elsterian glaciations (e.g. Harasimiuk & Henkiel 1980; Laskowska-Wysoczańska 1984).

*The Recent stress field in Poland*

Neotectonic phenomena (e.g. Liszkowski 1982; Zuchiewicz 1995, 2000) are not sufficient to enable reconstruction of the recent stress field in the Carpathian foreland. More complete data sets are provided by borehole breakout analysis (Zoback 1992). Stress measurements (Fig. 19.35) indicate that the Carpathians were recently exposed to tectonic push from the hinterland, resulting in NNE–SSW orientated compression in the eastern part of the Outer Carpathian fold-and-thrust belt (i.e. the Małopolska Massif; Jarosiński 1998, 2005*a*). This so-called Carpathian push was transmitted further to the north along the marginal part of the East European Platform. Successive accommodation of this push is evidenced by the systematic distortion of tectonic compression from NNE–SSW in the southern segment to NNW–SSE in the Baltic portion of the East European Platform, where the Carpathian push is balanced the North Atlantic ridge push. Within the TESZ, frequent stress rotations from north–south to NW–SE in vertical borehole sections, and between boreholes, suggest discrete strike-slip accommodation of the Carpathian push (Jarosiński 2005*a*). Additionally, in the western segment of the Carpathians a

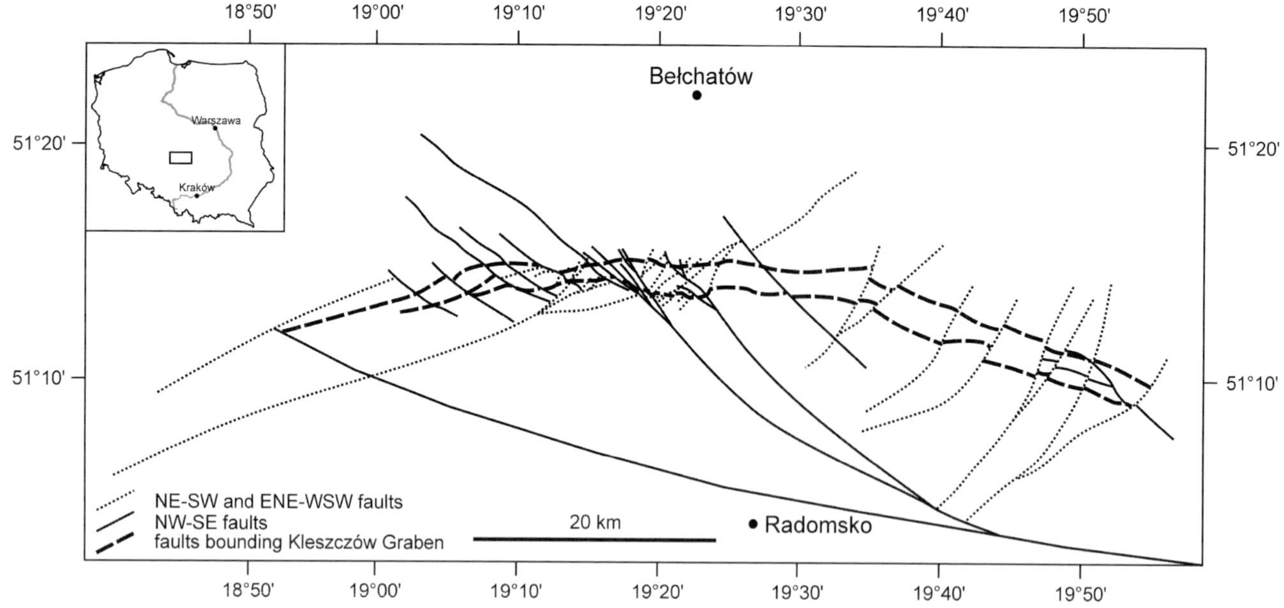


**Fig. 19.33.** Faults associated with the Kleszczów Graben (simplified after Gotowała & Hałuszczak 2002).

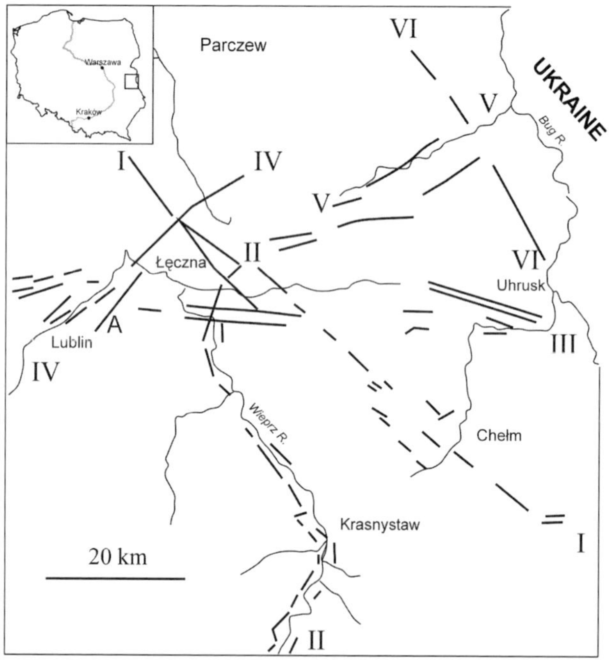


**Fig. 19.34.** Young fault zones in the Lublin Upland (modified after Henkiel 1983, 1984). Fault zones: I, Kock-Łęczna lineament; II, Wieprz River valley; III, northern margin of the Lublin Upland; IV, Bystrzyca River valley; V, Włodawka; VI, Kaplonosy lineament.

systematic shift in stress direction between the nappes and their basement indicates strain partitioning due to the Carpathian push compensation.

Complementary but rare data come from the survey of natural and mining-induced tremors which provide an additional source of information on recent geodynamics in the region (Guterch & Lewandowska-Marciniak 2002; see Fig. 19.35). For the inner part of the Outer Carpathians (i.e. vicinity of the Pieniny Klippen Belt) either strike-slip or thrust fault stress regimes may be inferred for the nappes (Wiejacz 1994). The strike-slip stress regime was also determined for isolated earthquakes in the Kleszczów Graben (Gibowicz *et al.* 1982; Gotowała & Hałuszczak 2002) and the Kaliningrad district near the Polish border (Wiejacz 2004). The dominance of a strike-slip fault stress regime was constrained by hydraulic fracturing tests in boreholes located in SE Poland (Jarosiński 2005*b*). In western Poland, an extensional stress regime with some degree of strike-slip activity predominates (Wiejacz & Gibowicz 1997; Jarosiński 2005*b*).

## The North German Basin (K.R., M.B.H., C.H., W.S.)

The North German Basin (NGB, Fig.19.1) is a sub-basin of the Southern Permian Basin (Ziegler 1990; Scheck & Bayer 1999) and is one of a series of related Permo-Carboniferous intracontinental sag basins extending from the southern North Sea to northern Poland (Kossow *et al.* 2000), and referred to as the Central European Basin System. The Ringkøbing-Fyn High is a chain of east–west striking basement highs extending across the North Sea and the Danish mainland (Clausen & Pedersen 1999) that form the northern boundary of the NGB (Fig. 19.1). The southern flank of the Ringkøbing-Fyn High is more or less coincident with the path of the Caledonian Deformation Front (Fig. 19.36). To the south, the NGB terminates at the Variscan Deformation Front (Fig. 19.36) and to the east at the Teisseyre-Tornquist Zone. Furthermore, two approximately east–west striking structural lineaments cross the NGB: the so-called Trans-European Fault and the Elbe Lineament further to the south, although the existence of the Trans-European Fault has been questioned by McCann & Krawczyk (2000).

The NGB developed on the Palaeozoic platform of Central Europe which was consolidated during the Caledonian and Variscan orogenies. During the Caledonian period, Avalonia and Baltica collided, and now form a complex suture zone of heterogeneous crustal and lithospheric structures (see also Krawczyk *et al.* 2008). Basin formation was initiated in the Late

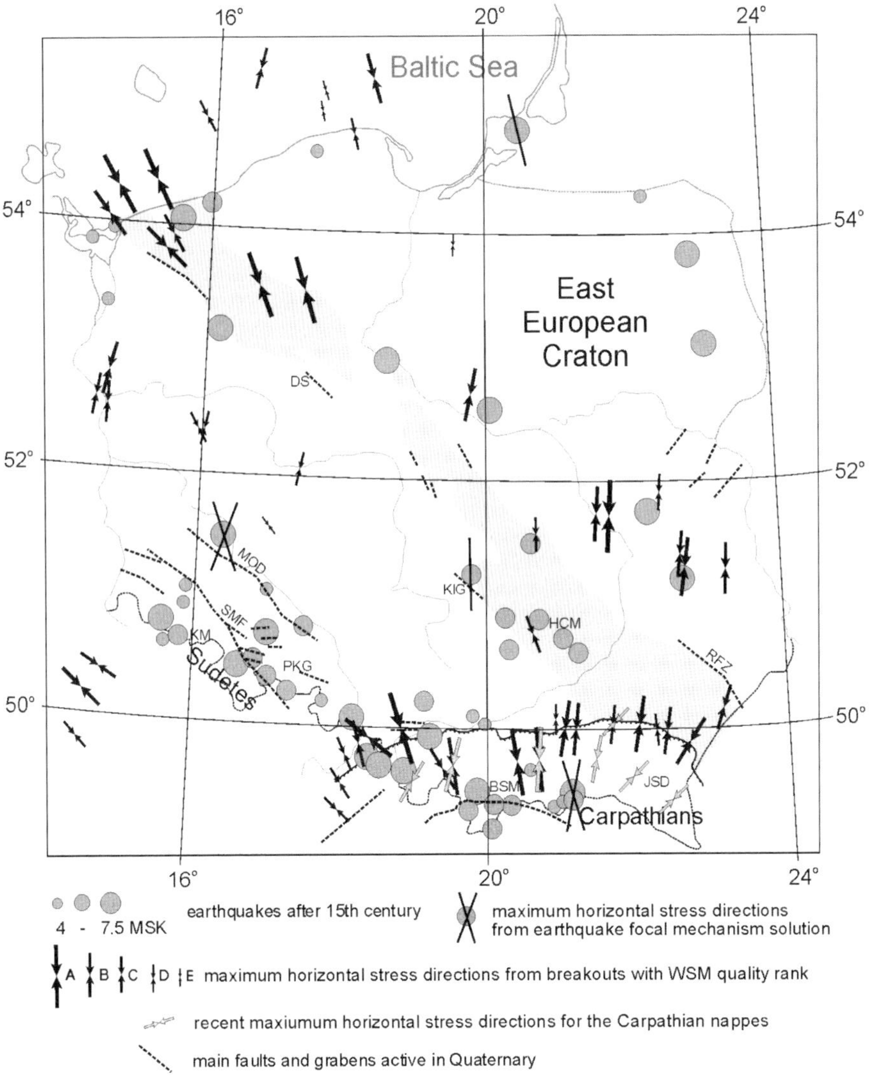


**Fig. 19.35.** Recent stresses (Reinecker *et al.* 2004; Jarosiński, 2005*a*) and earthquakes of Poland (Guterch & Lewandowska-Marciniak 2002). Abbreviations: DS, Damasł awek Salt Structure; KIG, Kleszczów Graben; MOD, Mid-Odra Fault Zone; PKG, Paczków-Kędzierzyn Graben,; POL, Poznań-Oleśnica Lineament; RFZ, Roztocze Fault Zone; SMF, Sudetic Marginal Fault.

Palaeozoic and was followed by several subsidence and inversion episodes (e.g. Ziegler 1990; McCann 1999; Petmecky *et al.* 1999, Scheck & Bayer 1999; van Wees *et al.* 2000). The initial main phase of thermal subsidence in the NGB began in the Early Permian and lasted until the Middle Triassic (van Wees *et al.* 2000). Permo-Carboniferous volcanics and aeolian, fluvial and lacustrine sediments are overlain by Upper Permian (Zechstein) evaporites (McCann 1999; Scheck & Bayer 1999). The Triassic succession is characterized by a Lower Triassic clastic sequence (Buntsandstein, Bunter), overlain by marine carbonates (Muschelkalk) and the continental Keuper facies (Fig. 19.37). The overlying Lower Jurassic sequence, consisting of interbedded marine mudstones and sandstones, was deposited under shallow-marine conditions (Kossow *et al.* 2000). The subsidence pattern of the NGB was interrupted by a period of uplift from the Middle Jurassic to Early Cretaceous (Ziegler 1990; Underhill 1998) with considerable erosion of the Lower Jurassic and Upper Triassic sedimentary sequences (Kossow *et al.* 2000). A thin succession of constant thickness, traceable in the Bay of Kiel area (Hansen *et al.* 2005), marks a major transgression of Albian age from non-deposition to shallow-marine conditions. The succession consists of calcareous sediments, primarily red marls of Early Cretaceous age (Fig. 19.37). The Upper Cretaceous succession consists of 400–500 m of chalky sediments deposited in a shallow-marine environment, which subsequently changed to more open-marine conditions.

During the Late Cretaceous and earliest Tertiary, initial indications of compression were related to the reorganization of the Iberian and African plates, culminating in the formation of the Pyrenees (Reicherter & Pletsch 2000; Voigt *et al.* 2004, 2006). Subsequently, during the Oligo-Miocene Alpine inversion affecting the intracratonic sag basin, the stresses of the mobile Alpine belt were transmitted into its distant foreland (Ziegler 1990). The Cenozoic succession displays a facies pattern of terrestrial and shallow-marine clastic sediments deposited under the influence of halokinesis during the Palaeocene and Eocene (Kossow *et al.* 2000). During the Tertiary, there were repeated alternating regressions (lower and middle Palaeocene) and

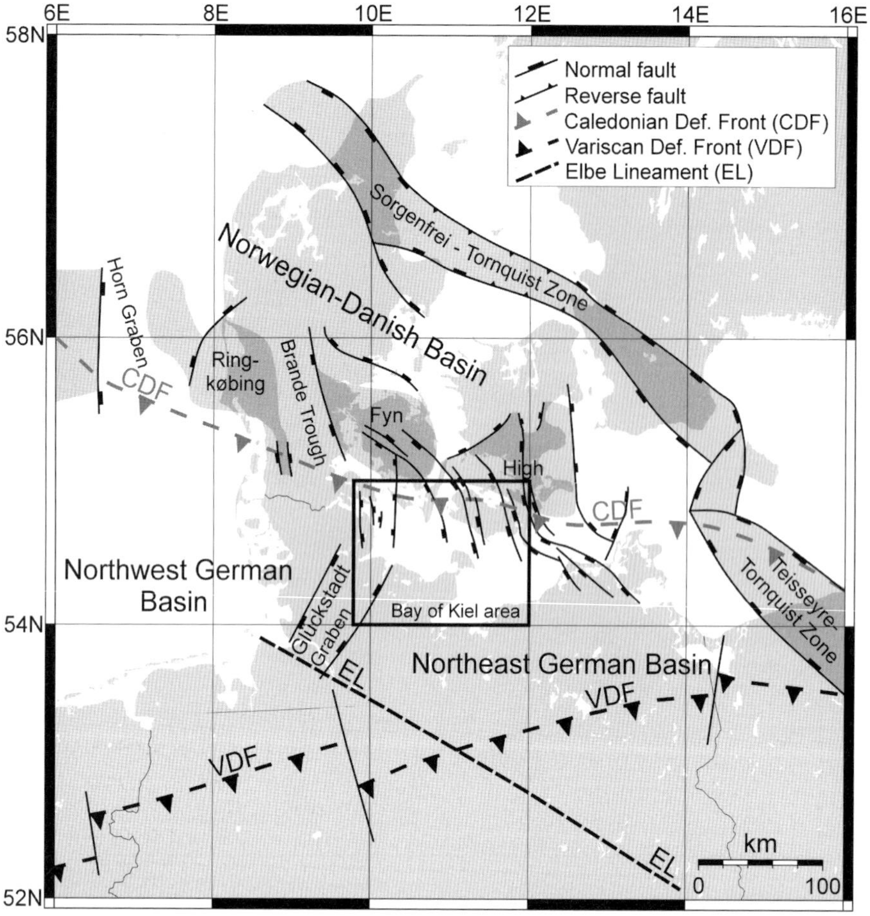


**Fig. 19.36.** Main structural elements of north Germany and Denmark (from Hansen *et al.* 2005; modified after Bayer *et al.* 1999; Clausen & Pedersen 1999).

transgressions (upper Palaeocene and Eocene). The most extensive transgression occurred during the Early Oligocene in the Rupelian. Marine deposits of Rupelian clays are widespread across the entire basin including the Hessian Depression and the Upper Rhine Graben. The Rupelian clays serve as a basin-wide marker horizon for the differential subsidence and uplift in the North German Basin (Fig. 19.38). The subsequent transgression in the Late Oligocene and the Early Miocene was not as extensive as that of Rupelian age; the marginal deposits are characterized by sands and lignite layers. The main lignite deposits of northern Germany are of Middle Miocene age; they were flooded due to a sea-level rise in the Cologne area inundating parts of the Upper Rhine Graben. The Pliocene marine transgression extended only as far east as Hamburg and the North Friesian Islands (Sylt); the remainder of the North German Basin area was characterized by fluvial or limnic sediments.

The transitional zone to the Central European uplift zone in NE Germany (Garetzky *et al.* 2001) is characterized by a set of normal faults (Mitteldeutsche Hauptabbrüche). In the Lausitz area, normal faulting with associated grabens affects Miocene brown coal deposits and the Raunoer Formation of the Mio-/Pliocene transition (Nowel *et al.* 1994). Repeated glaciation/deglaciation processes during the Pleistocene also impacted on the landscape of northern Germany. Glacio-isostatic models demonstrate that the recovery from Late Pleistocene glaciation is deep-rooted, involving elastic lithospheric flexing and viscous mantle flow that affect large areas.

### *Tectonics and salt tectonics of the Western Baltic Sea (Bay of Kiel)*

Extensive seismic reflection surveys of the Bay of Kiel indicate that post-Palaeozoic deposition took place during two different phases of generally continuous subsidence in the northern part of the NGB (Hansen *et al.* 2005). Subsidence periods were separated by pronounced uplift and erosion during Middle Jurassic to Early Cretaceous times. Deposition during subsidence phases was accompanied by halokinesis controlled by the regional stress field. During the Early and Middle Triassic no major tectonic activity is observed in the Bay of Kiel area, nor in adjacent regions of the Baltic Sea (e.g. Scheck & Bayer 1999; Kossow & Krawczyk 2002; Scheck *et al.* 2003*a*; Hübscher *et al.* 2004).

The onset of vertical salt movement between the Middle and Late Triassic created north–south stretching depositional centres, and salt structures correlate with the regional east–west directed extension. In the western Baltic Sea, Triassic extension is indicated by the evidence of accelerated subsidence and basement-affecting normal faulting in the north–south trending Central and Horn grabens in the North Sea area, the adjacent Glückstadt Graben as well as the development of the Rheinsberg

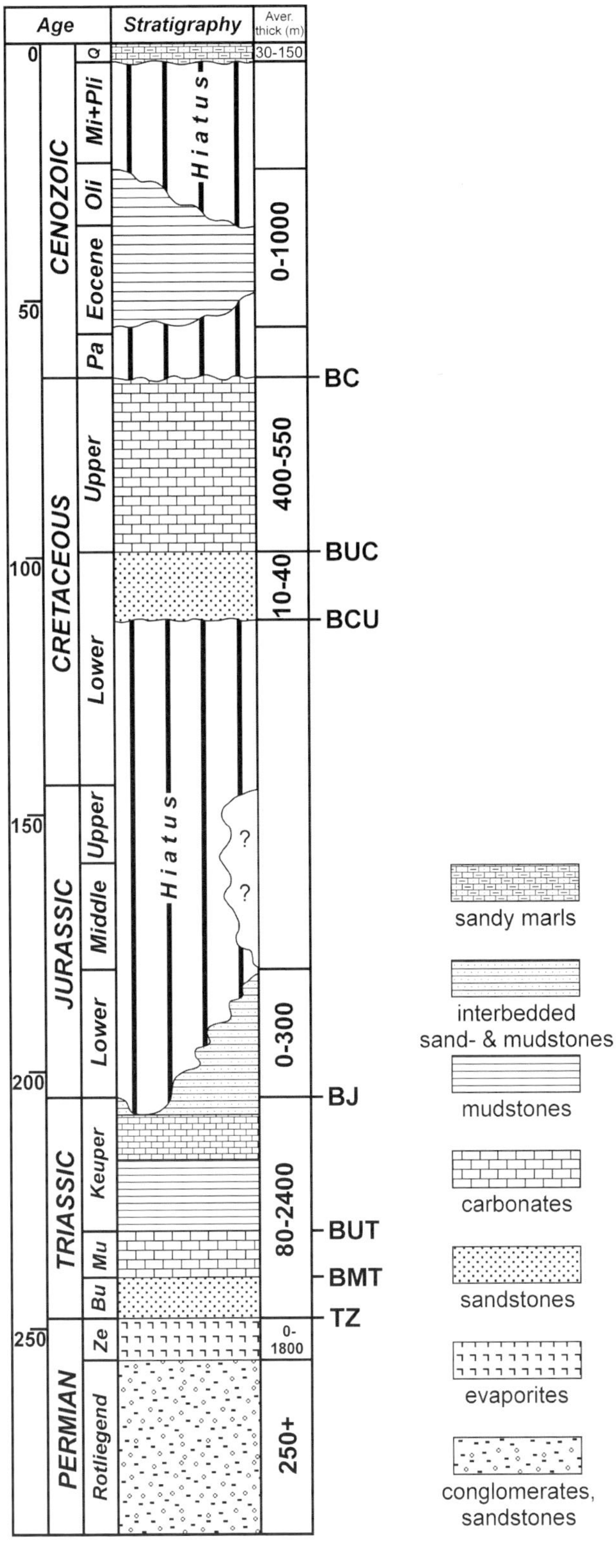


**Fig. 19.37.** Stratigraphic table showing the dominant lithologies, average thicknesses and the ages of the major horizons interpreted from seismic reflection data in the northern part of the North German Basin (from Hansen *et al.*, 2005). The thickness data are from Nielsen & Japsen (1991). Abbreviations (from bottom): TZ, top Zechstein; BMT, base Middle Triassic; BUT, base Upper Triassic; BJ, base Jurassic; MJU, Mid Jurassic Unconformity; BUC, base Upper Cretaceous; BC, base Cenozoic.

Trough to the SE of the Bay of Kiel (Fig. 19.36; Ziegler 1990; Fisher & Mudge 1998; Scheck *et al.* 2003*b*). East–west directed extension began between Middle and Late Triassic times and continued at least into the Early Jurassic. This was accompanied by the formation of major, basement-involving, north–south striking fault systems (Fig. 19.39A), and minor east–west striking fault systems. The latter developed on top of salt pillows, in a thin-skinned style as a result of vertical salt movement (Fig. 19.39B) (Hansen *et al.* 2005).

The Middle Jurassic to Early Cretaceous period of uplift was marked by significant erosion, removing parts of the Lower Jurassic and Upper Triassic successions within the Bay of Kiel area. The major, basin-wide unconformity which resulted can be correlated with the rise of the Central North Sea Dome as a result of plutonic activity (Ziegler 1990; Underhill 1998). The uplifted area was centred upon what later, as a result of the rising plume, formed the North Sea rift triple-junction (Underhill 1998). This explains the higher degree of erosion west of the Bay of Kiel towards the centre of the dome (Hansen *et al.* 2005). At the same time the adjacent NE German Basin region, including the Ringkøbing-Fyn High to the north (Ziegler 1990), was an area of non-deposition (Kossow *et al.* 2000; Kossow & Krawczyk 2002; Scheck *et al.* 2003*b*).

At the end of the Early Cretaceous sedimentation resumed, and continued subsidence without major tectonic activity extended into the Late Cretaceous. Vertical salt movements again occurred during the Late Cretaceous (*c.* 83–85 Ma; Coniacian–Santonian) and were initiated by a change in the regional stress field from extension to NE-directed compression due to a major phase of plate reorganization and the onset of the Alpine Orogeny (Gemmer *et al.* 2003). Large WNW–ESE striking synclines form depocentres between the salt structures during the deposition of the Cenozoic succession, while NW-striking large open folds are observed in the NE German Basin (Scheck *et al.* 2003*a*). Normal faults developed over salt pillows in a thin-skinned style as a result of halokinesis (Fig. 19.39). The north–south orientated faults evidence the decoupling of the suprasalt sequences from the regional NE–SW to NNE–SSW directed horizontal compressive stresses. However, a right-lateral strike-slip component along the north–south faults cannot be excluded. The distribution of the Cenozoic sediments shows an overall thickening trend towards the centre of the basin to the south and SW. Cenozoic strata are absent above the Fehmarn Pillow, suggesting that there was renewed vertical salt movement towards the end of the Late Cretaceous which continued into the Cenozoic. Abrupt thickness variations in the sedimentary succession are related to the activity of north–south striking fault systems crossing the salt pillows. Faulting took place up to the seafloor during the Cenozoic. The Cenozoic succession was deposited in WNW–ESE striking depocentres in the rim synclines between the salt structures. NW–SE orientated faulting in the Cenozoic succession has been described by Novak (2002) and Novak & Björck (2002). The maximum principal stress direction at this time was NNE–SSW, which is similar to the present-day stress field (Reicherter *et al.* 2005).

### *Recent stresses and seismicity*

The super-regional Central European stress field is complex due to varying plate boundary conditions and the different rheologic buffers (e.g. the Bohemian Massif; Grünthal & Stromeyer 1992). Major forces are generated by the Atlantic ridge push and the collision/convergence of the Eurasian and African plates in the Alps (Gölke & Coblentz 1996; Goes *et al.* 2000). Present-day

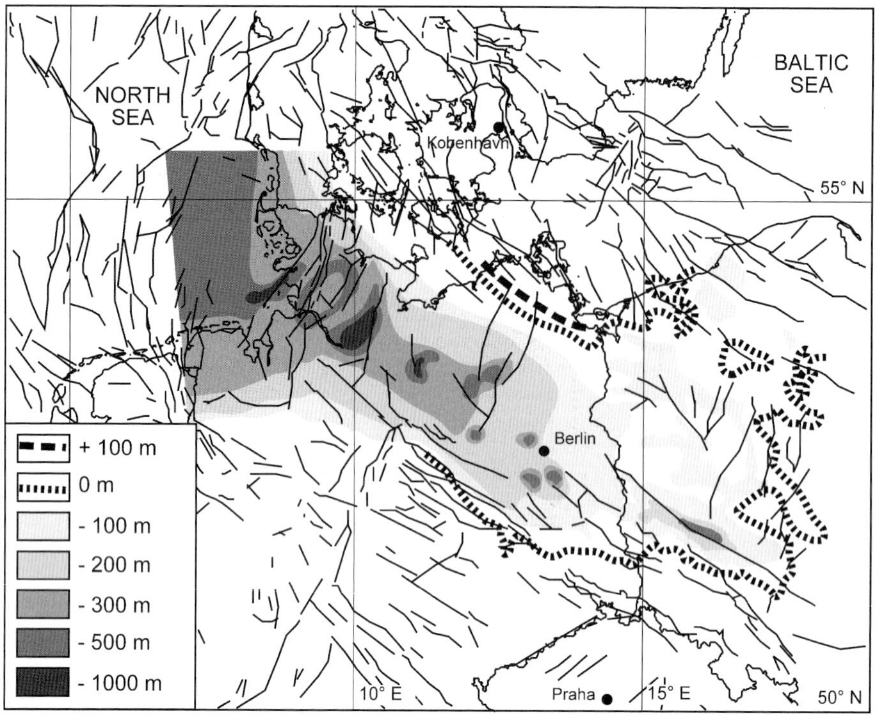


**Fig. 19.38.** Amplitude of uplift or subsidence since beginning of the Rupelian (Early Oligocene) in the North German Basin (from Stackebrandt 2004).

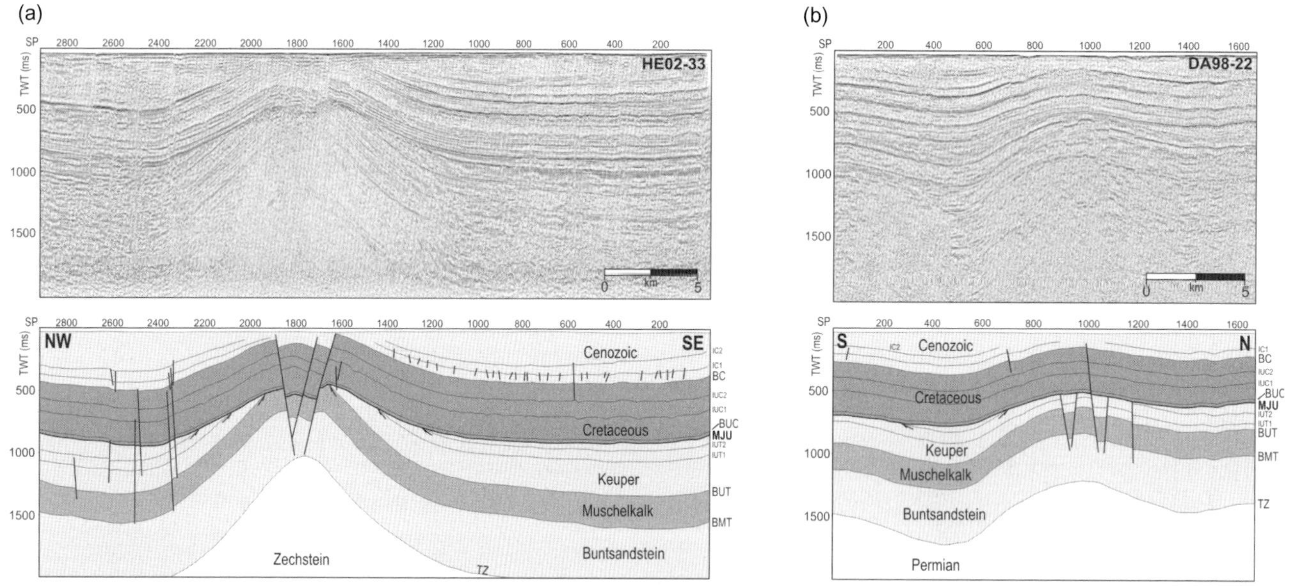


**Fig. 19.39.** (**A**) Time-migrated seismic section HE02–33 (from Hansen *et al.* 2005) and interpreted section crossing Salt Pillow B in the southwestern corner of the Bay of Kiel. The section shows that the fault system above the salt structure developed thin-skinned as a result of halokinesis. (**B**) Time-migrated seismic section DA98–22 (from Hansen *et al.*, 2005) and interpreted section crossing Salt Pillow C in the northern part of the Bay of Kiel. The section reveals how most of the individual faults of the fault system on top of the salt structure terminate at the Mid-Jurassic Unconformity. Abbreviations (from bottom): TZ, top Zechstein; BMT, base Middle Triassic; BUT, base Upper Triassic; IUT1 and 2,: internal Upper Triassic 1 and 2; MJU, Mid-Jurassic Unconformity; BUC, base Upper Cretaceous; IUC 1 and 2, internal Upper Cretaceous 1 and 2; BC, base Cenozoic; IC 1 and 2, internal Cenozoic 1 and 2.

horizontal stresses in the NGB have been described by Gregersen (1992) and Müller *et al.* (1992) and are also detailed in the world stress map (Reinecker *et al.* 2004). The stress field for the basin has been almost stable since the Miocene and the maximum compressive stress is orientated NW–SE (Fig. 19.40). Poorly constrained data from southern Sweden suggest clockwise rotation towards a NNE–SSW directed $S_{Hmax}$ (Reinecker *et al.* 2004). In the Danish Central Graben and the Ringkøbing-Fyn

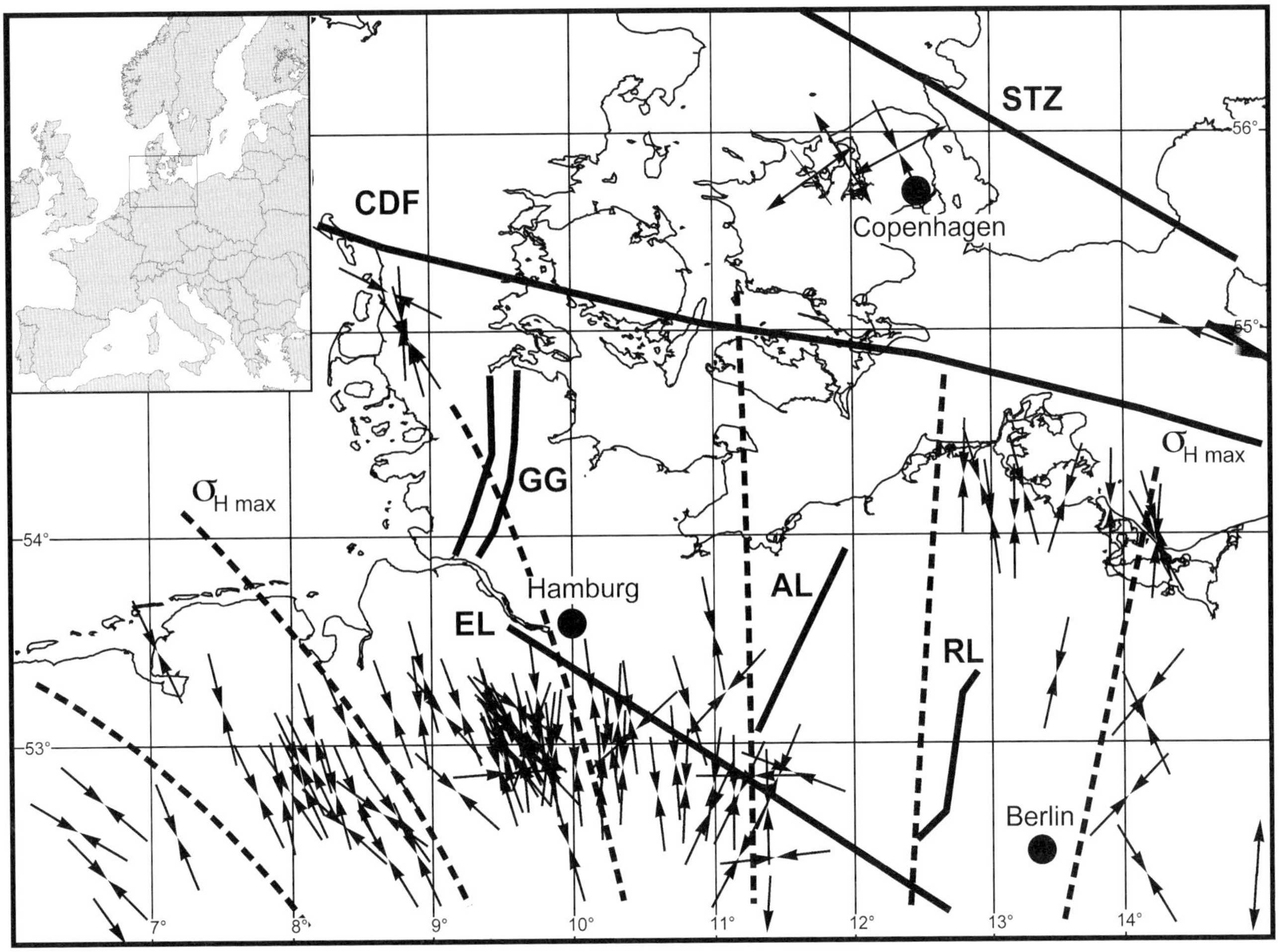


**Fig. 19.40.** Compilation of recent stress data obtained from subsalt formations (Röckel & Lempp 2003; Reinecker *et al.* 2004) including borehole break-out, hydro-frac and earthquake data. Inferred maximum horizontal stresses ($\sigma_{Hmax}$) fan and swing from NW direction in the west to NNE in the east of the study area. Major faults systems: AL, Arendsee Line; CDF, Caledonian Deformation Front; EL, Elbe Line; GA, Grimmen Anticline; GG, Glückstadt Graben; RL, Rheinsberg Line; STZ, Sorgenfrei-Tornquist Zone; TESZ, Trans-european Suture Zone. Inset shows study area. After Reicherter *et al.* (2005).

High, data are scattered between the NE and the SE (i.e. maximum horizontal compression direction) (Ask 1997); a certain residual stress can be assumed.

Presently, the isostatic rebound of the Fenno-Scandian Shield has the greatest influence on the stress field in northern Germany (Kaiser *et al.* 2005). The Scandinavian post-glacial rebound dome and glacial forebulge has resulted in the formation of a pattern of alternating regions of higher and lower seismicity with respect to the underlying tectonic stress field (Reicherter *et al.* 2005). The most dramatic evidence of active faulting and seismicity is reported from those areas where icesheets reached their maximum thickness, including the marginal regions of Scotland and the NGB (Wahlstrom 1989; Arvidsson 1996; Mörner 2003, 2004; Stewart *et al.* 2000). Early Holocene Swedish lake deposits provide evidence of major earthquakes which occurred there prior to 3000 years before present (Mörner 2003). Seismic shocks in the early, probably rapid, phase of the post-glacial isostatic rebound of the Scandinavian shield were caused by fault reactivation. Present-day crustal deformation is still the consequence of the mantle response to deglaciation (Scherneck *et al.* 1998), accompanied by decelerating seismic activity (e.g. earthquake catalogues of Sweden, and the German Bundesanstalt für Geowissenschaften und Rohstoffe (BGR), Hannover; see summary in Reicherter *et al.* 2005).

Seismicity in northern Germany is rather low and of low magnitude. The occurrence of earthquakes larger than intensity 5 on the European Macroseismic Scale (Grünthal & Mayer-Rosa 1998), as documented in the earthquake catalogue for the last 1000 years (Leydecker 1986), is also very low, and they have an expected recurrence interval of 10 000 years (Leydecker *et al.* 1999). Up until now there is no evidence for strong earthquakes during prehistoric times in the NGB (in contrast to larger deglaciation earthquakes in Sweden; e.g. Mörner 2003). During historical times only moderate earthquakes have occurred and seismological data suggest a relationship with the underlying basement faults. Due to the low seismic activity of the area, few data about the stress field are available from fault plane solutions. These indicate NNW directed maximum horizontal stress (Henderson 1991; Reicherter *et al.* 2005).

### *Neotectonics*

A broad zone of subsidence stretches from Hamburg via Berlin to Wroclaw (Poland) and is delineated by the elevation of the base of the Rupelian (Fig. 19.38; Early Oligocene, 33.9 Ma;

Garetzky *et al.* 2001). The amplitude of uplift and subsidence varies within the range of *c.* −1000 m in the North Sea area, Hamburg and the Rheinsberg Trough (Fig. 19.38) to +100 m in the Rügen area. This results in average subsidence rates in the deep depocentres of 0.03 mm/a. However, subsidence and uplift vary across the NGB, mainly as a result of the pre-existing fault zones (Schwab 1985; Franke & Hoffmann 1999; Bayer *et al.* 1999, 2002). The post-glacial faults and lineaments in the NGB (Fig. 19.41) clearly mark the distributed reactivation of favourably orientated basement structures at the receding margins of a decaying icesheet. Thus far, no seismogenic faults have been reported to be active during the Holocene in northern Germany (Reicherter *et al.* 2005). All historical and instrumental earthquake data point to magnitudes of M < 5. The hypocentral depth of the major portion of the observed earthquakes exceeds the Zechstein base; they are, hence, interpreted to be of tectonic origin. The most prominent geomorphological and satellite lineations are associated with basement faults and even with crustal or lithospheric discontinuities (Reicherter *et al.* 2005). The maximum is directed NW–SE; minor maxima are directed NE–SW and NNW–SSE (Fig. 19.41).

In contrast to the Polish Basin or the Carpathian Foredeep (see previous sections), there has been little systematic research on the neotectonics of the NGB. Prominent recent vertical crustal movements have been observed along NW–SE striking faults in eastern Germany (Ahrens *et al.* 1982; Ellenberg 1992). Most of these do not correspond to morphological features. Ihde *et al.* (1987) and Sirocko (1998) found evidence for active structures in northern Germany. Neotectonic deformation and faulting have also been observed in Denmark (Lykke-Andersen 1981). The Sorgenfrei-Tornquist Zone, situated onshore between the Skagerrak and Kattegat straits (roughly between the cities of Aalborg and Skagen in Denmark), is characterized by active crustal movements, earthquakes and neotectonic faulting (Gregersen *et al.* 1995; Lykke-Andersen & Borre 2000). The Danish Midlands (Jotland) are also affected by neotectonics, and significant normal faulting and strike-slip faulting has been observed there (Lykke-Andersen *et al.* 1996).

Recent uplift rates decrease to the south of the Scandinavian Shield, with subsidence predominating in the area of Hamburg (1–2 mm/a). In contrast, salt diapirs are rising (*c.* 1–1.2 mm/a (e.g. the Kalkberg, Bad Segeberg, Schleswig-Holstein, Lüneburg, Niedersachsen, Sperenberg, south of Berlin) accompanied by dissolution and subrosion processes and the formation of rim syncline lakes in the Holocene. NW–SE trending lineaments cut Saalian push moraines in the Brandenburg area (Stackebrandt 2004). Signals for a dynamic post-Pleistocene landscape modification are provided by asymmetric river channels, bifurcation (Stackebrandt 2004), migration of the meandering fluvial systems (e.g. the courses of the rivers Havel and Spree; Juschus 2001)

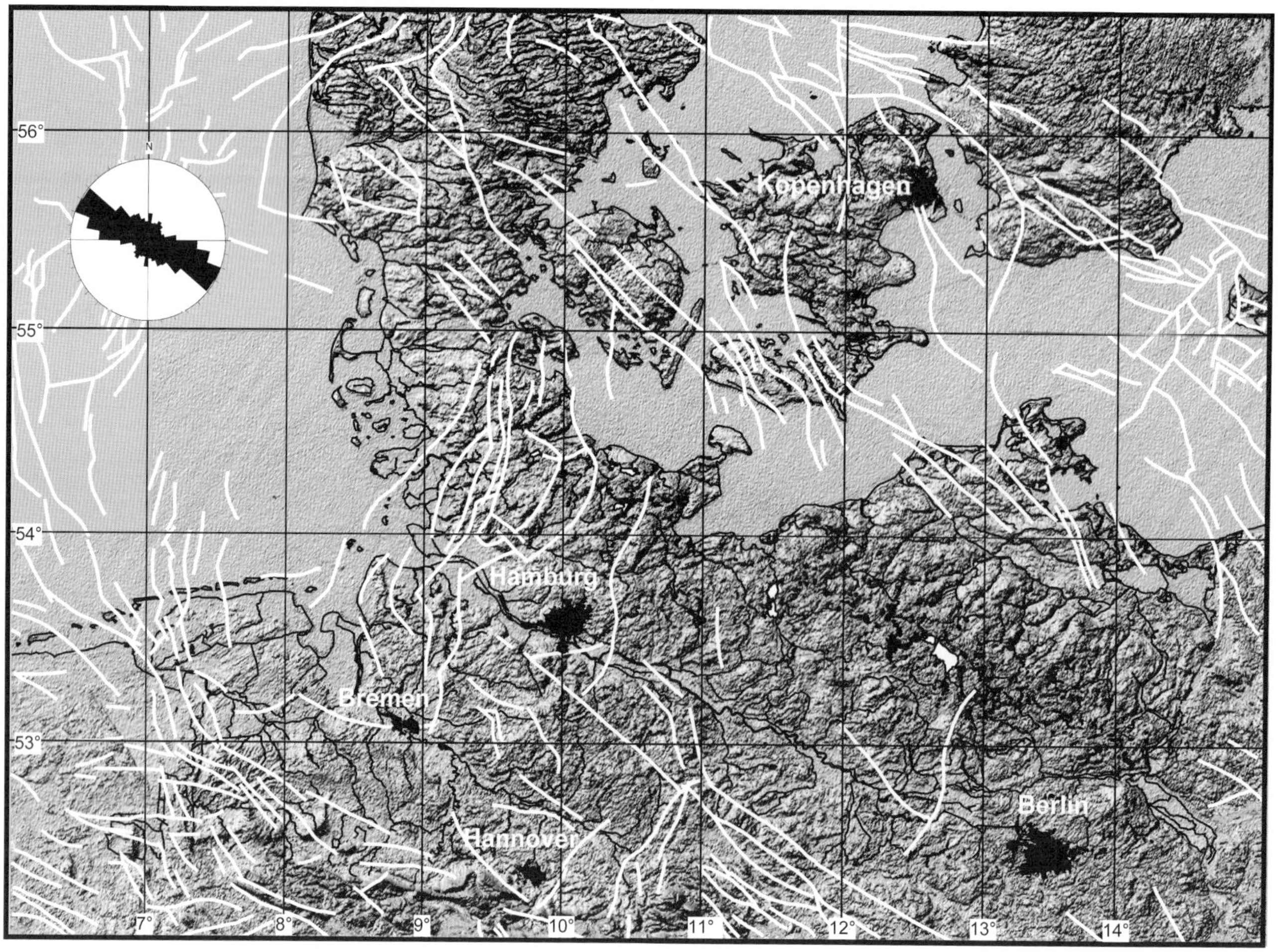


**Fig. 19.41.** Shaded relief of the North German Basin and its surroundings (generated from SRTM 2000); resolution 3 arc seconds with drainage pattern (black) and major faults (white). Inset: rose diagram of fault trends. Note NW–SE direction of the major rivers in northern Germany.

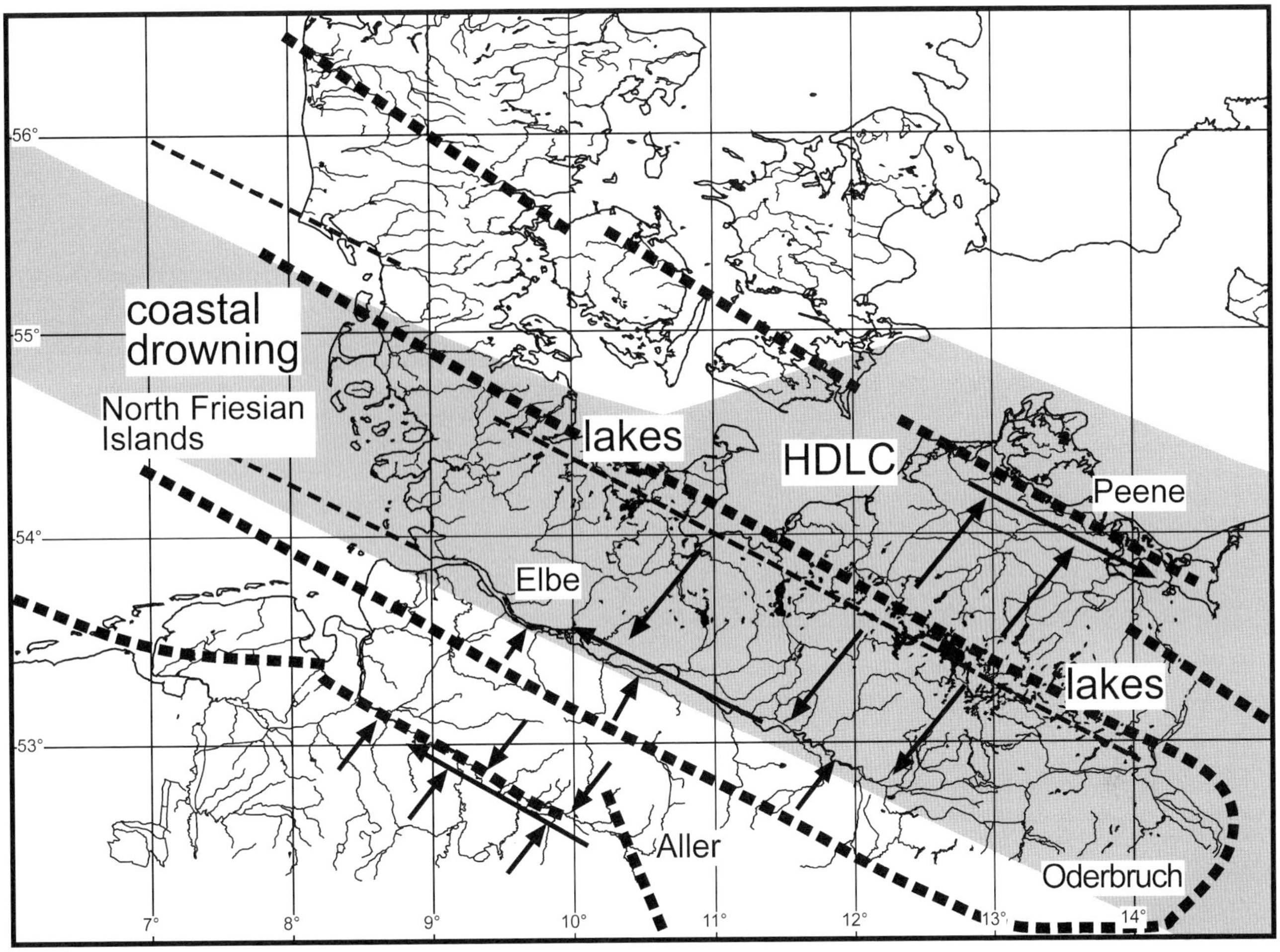


**Fig. 19.42.** Position of the high-density lower crust (HDLC; after Bayer *et al.* 2002). Note the trellis-like drainage pattern and downstream direction of rivers; rivers Aller and Elbe run NW into the North Sea, whereas in the area from the Oderbruch passing the lakes of Mecklenburg-Vorpommern and Schleswig-Holstein no preferred discharge direction is shown; lastly, the river Peene runs towards the SE. The zone of inferred coastal drowning is related to two NW–SE striking lineaments, hence forming the North Friesian Islands in the north German tidal flats. NW–SE lineaments are apparently parallel to each other and apparently equidistant. Note linear coastline along the northern border of the HDLC body. Stippled line marks the zone of subsidence of proposed future drowning (from Stackebrandt, 2004). After Reicherter *et al.* (2005).

and changes in discharge directions (e.g. the river Oder), mostly following basement faults. As a consequence, the north German coastal lines of both the Baltic and the North Sea have been subject to intense modifications (i.e. drowning; Fig. 19.42) over the last thousand years, affecting both humans and society (Behre 2003; Schwarzer *et al.* 2003; Meier 2004). Active tectonics above inherited deep structures and above salt structures have also been observed in NW Poland (Kurzawa 2003), resulting in vertical movements of 0.3 to 2.0 mm/a since the Pleistocene.

## References


Abel, T., Sauter, M. & Hinderer, M. 2000. Integrative Ansätze zur Bestimmung von Denudationsraten auf der Schwäbischen Alb. *Laichinger Höhlenfreund*, **35**, 65–90.

Ahorner, L. 1983. Historical seismicity and present-day microearthquake activity of the Rhenish massif, Central Europe. *In:* Fuchs, K., von Gehlen, K., Mälzer, H., Murawski, H. & Semmel, M. (eds) *Plateau Uplift. The Rhenish Shield – A Case History*. Springer, Berlin, 198–221.

Ahorner, L. 1994. Fault-plane solutions and source parameters of the 1992 Roermond, the Netherlands, mainshock and its stronger aftershocks from regional seismic data. *Geologie en Mijnbouw*, **73**, 199–214.

Ahorner, L., Baier, B. & Bonjer, K.-P. 1983. General pattern of seismotectonic dislocation and the earthquake-generating stress field in Central Europe between the Alps and the North Sea. *In:* Fuchs, K., von Gehlen, K., Mälzer, H., Murawski, H. & Semmel, M. (eds) *Plateau Uplift. The Rhenish Shield – A Case History*. Springer, Berlin, 187–197.

Ahrens, H., Lotsch, D. & Schwab, G. 1982. Präglaziale tektonische Aktivierung im Nordteil der DDR. *Zeitschrift für geologische Wissenschaften*, **10**, 671–678.

Arvidsson, R. 1996. Fennoscandian earthquakes: whole crustal rupturing related to postglacial rebound. *Science*, **274**, 744–746.

Ask, M. V. S. 1997. In situ stress from breakouts in the Danish Sector of the North Sea. *Marine and Petroleum Geology*, **14**, 231–243.

Aubert, D. 1958. Sur l'existence d'une ride de plissement oligocène dans le Jura Vaudois. *Bulletin de la Société neuchâteloise des sciences naturelles*, **81**, 47–53.

Bachmann, G. H., Müller, M. & Weggen, K. 1987. Evolution of the Molasse Basin (Germany, Switzerland). *Tectonophysics*, **137**, 77–92.

Badura, J. & Przybylski, B. 2000. *Mapa neotektoniczna Dolnego Śląska*. Archiwum Oddziału. Dolnośląskiego Państwowego Instytutu Geologicznego, Wrocław.

Badura, J., Zuchiewicz, W., Górecki, A., Sroka, W., Przybylski, B. & Żyszkowska M. 2003. Morphotectonic properties of the Sudetic

Marginal Fault, SW Poland. *Acta Montana IRSM AS CR, ser. A*, **24**(131), 21–49.

Baraniecka, M. D. 1975. The dependences of the development of Quaternary deposits upon the structure and dynamics of the basement in the central part of the Polish Lowlands. *Biuletyn Instytutu Geologicznego*, **288**, 5–97 [In Polish with English summary].

Baraniecka, M. D. 1980. The origin of concave elements of the basement of the Quaternary in the area of the Kujawy Swell and the Warsaw Basin. *Biuletyn Instytutu Geologicznego*, **322**, 31–64 [In Polish with English summary].

Baraniecka, M. D. 1995. Quaternary tectonic structures of the margins of the Kujavian Ridge, Polish Lowland. *Folia Quaternaria*, **66**, 39–49.

Baumann, H. 1984. Aufbau und Meßtechnik zweier Stationen zur Registrierung von Spannungsänderungen im Bereich des Hohenzollerngrabens – Erste Resultate. *Oberrheinische Geologische Abhandlungen*, **33**, 1–14.

Baumann, H. 1986. Der Hohenzollerngraben - Wirkung einer tiefreichenden Störung auf das regionale Spannungsfeld. Report 1984–1986, A, SFB 108, *Spannung und Spannungsumwandlung in der Lithosphäre*. University of Karlsruhe, Karlsruhe, 15–28.

Bayer, U., Scheck, M., *et al.* 1999. An integrated study of the NE-German Basin. *Tectonophysics*, **314**, 285–307.

Bayer, U., Grad, M., *et al.* 2002. The southern margin of the East European Craton: new results from seismic sounding and potential fields between the North Sea and Poland. *Tectonophysics*, **360**, 301–314.

Becker, A. 1993. An attempt to define a "neotectonic period" for Central and northern Europe. *Geologische Rundschau*, **82**, 67–83.

Becker, A. 2000. The Jura Mountains – an active foreland fold-and-thrust belt? *Tectonophysics*, **321**, 381–406.

Behre, K. E. 2003. Eine neue Meeresspiegelkurve für die südliche Nordsee. *Probleme der Küstenforschung im südlichen Nordseegebiet*, **28**, 9–63.

Ber, A. 1999. Glaciotectonics of the Suwałki-Augustów Lakeland in connection to neotectonic movements and tectonic structures of the crystalline basement (NE Poland). *Przegląd Geologiczny*, **47**, 831–839 [in Polish with English summary].

Berger, J.-P., Reichenbacher, B., *et al.* 2005. Paleogeography of the Upper Rhine Graben (URG) and the Swiss Molasse Basin (SMB) from Eocene to Pliocene. *International Journal of Earth Sciences*, **94**, 697–710.

Bergerat, F. 1983. Paléocontraintes et évolution tectonique paléogène du Fossé Rhenan. *Comptes Rendus de l'Académie des Sciences, II*, **297**, 77–80.

Bergerat, F. 1987. Stress fields in the European Platform at the time of the Africa-Eurasia collision. *Tectonics*, **6**, 99–132.

Bergerat, F. 1994. From inversion methods to paleostress field reconstructions in platforms, chains and basins: an overview. Some examples in Western and Central Europe. *In:* Roure, F. (ed.) *Peri-Tethyan Platforms*. Editions Technip, Paris, 159–178.

Bergerat, F. & Geyssant, J. 1983. Fracturation tertiaire et évolution des contraintes en Bavière orientale: le Jura franconien et al forêt bavaroise (R.F.A.). *Geologische Rundschau*, **72**, 935–954.

Birkenmajer, K., Pecskay, Z., Grabowski, J., Lorenc, M. W. & Zagożdżon, P. P. 2004. Radiometric dating of the tertiary volcanics in Lower Silesia, Poland. IV. Further K - Ar and paleomagnetic data from late oligocene to early miocene basaltic rocks of the Fore - Sudetic Block. *Annales Societatis Geologorum Poloniae*, **74**, 1–9.

Bitterli, T. 1990. The kinematic evolution of a classical Jura fold: a reinterpretation based on 3-dimensional balancing techniques (Weissenstein Anticline, Jura Mountains, Switzerland). *Eclogae geologicae Helvetiae*, **83**, 493–511.

Bonjer, K.-P. 1997. Seismicity pattern and style of seismic faulting at the eastern borderfault of the southern Rhine Graben. *Tectonophysics*, **275**, 41–69.

Brandmayr, M, Dallmeyer, R. D., Handler R. & Wallbrecher, E. 1995. Conjugate shear zones in the Southern Bohemian Massif (Austria): implications for Variscan and Alpine tectonothermal activity. *Tectonophysics*, **248**, 97–116.

Brinkmann, R. 1932. Morphogenie und jüngste Tektonik im Leinetalgrabengebiet. *Abhandlungen der preußischen Geologischen Landesanstalt, N.F.*, **139**, 101–135.

Brodzikowski, K. 1987. Charakterystyka oraz interpretacja paleogeograficzna osadów formacji "Chojny". *In:* Baraniecka, M. D., Brodzikowski, K. & Kasza, L. (eds) *Czwartorzęd rejonu Bełchatowa. II Symp. Państwowy Instytut Geologiczny*, Wrocław-Warszawa, 47–62.

Brun, J. P., Gutscher, M.-A. & DEKORP-ECORS teams 1992. Deep crustal structure of the Rhine Graben from DEKORP-ECORS seismic reflection data: a summary. *Tectonophysics*, **208**, 139–147.

Brunner, H. & Hinkelbein, K. 1987. Tektonische Untersuchungen im Bereich der alten Neckarschlinge bei Neckarwestheim. *Jahresberichte und Mitteilungen des Oberrheinischen Geologischen Vereins, N.F.*, **69**, 229–250.

Brunner, H., Hinkelbein, K. & Simon, T. 1988. Geologie und Tektonik im Gebiet von Ellenweiler (Gmde. Oppenweiler, Rems-Murr-Kreis). *Jahresheft des Geologischen Landesamtes Baden-Württemberg*, **30**, 167–200.

Brzezińska-Wójcik, T. 1999. Tectonic activity of the escarpment zone of Tomaszowskie Roztocze in the light of morphometric coefficients (eastern Poland). *Przegląd Geologiczny*, **47**(9), 840–845 [in Polish with English summary].

Brzezińska-Wójcik, T. 2002. The dependence of relief on tectonics in the South-West escarpment zone of Tomaszowskie Roztocze (SE Poland). *Landform Analysis*, **3**, 13–24.

Buchner, F. 1981. Rhinegraben: Horizontal stylolites indicating stress regimes of earlier stages of rifting. *Tectonophysics*, **73**, 113–118.

Buchner, E., Seyfried, H. & van den Boogard, P. 2003. $^{40}$Ar/$^{39}$Ar laser probe age determination confirms the Ries impact crater as the source of glass particles in Graupensand sediments (Grimmelfingen Formation, North Alpine Foreland Basin). *International Journal of Earth Sciences*, **92**, 1–6.

Buraczyński, J. 1984. The influence of neotectonics on development of the escarpment zone of Roztocze. *Annales Societatis Geologorum Poloniae*, **54**, 209–225 [In Polish with English summary].

Buraczyński, J. 1997. *Geology, Relief and Landscape of Roztocze Upland*. Wydawnictwo UMCS, Lublin [in Polish with English summary].

Burkhard, M. 1990. Aspects of the large-scale Miocene deformation in the most external part of the Swiss Alps (Subalpine Molasse to Jura fold belt). *Eclogae geologicae Helvetiae*, **83**, 559–583.

Buxtorf, A. 1907. *Geologische Beschreibung des Weissensteintunnels und seiner Umgebung*. Beiträge zur Geologischen Karte der Schweiz (N.F.), **21**.

Buxtorf, A. 1916. Prognosen und Befunde beim Hauensteinbasis- und Grenchenbergtunnel und die Bedeutung der letzteren für die Geologie des Juragebirges. *Verhandlungen der Naturforschenden Gesellschaft in Basel*, **27**, 184–254.

Camelbeeck, T. & van Eck, T. 1994. The Roer Valley Graben earthquake of 13 April 1992 and its seismotectonic setting. *Terra Nova*, **6**, 291–300.

Campbell, J., Kümpel, H. J., Fabian, M., Fischer, D., Görres, B., Keysers, C. J. & Lehmann, K. 2002. Recent movement pattern of the Lower Rhine embayment from tilt, gravity and GPS data. *Geologie en Mijnbouw - Netherlands Journal of Geosciences*, **81**, 223–230.

Carlé, W. 1950. Neue Beobachtungen zur Deckgebirgs-Tektonik von Südwest-Deutschland. *Jahresberichte und Mitteilungen des Oberrheinischen Geologischen Vereins, N.F.*, **32**, 11–33.

Carlé, W. 1955. *Bau und Entwicklung der Süddeutschen Großscholle*. Beihefte zum Geologischen Jahrbuch, **16**.

Chauve, P., Martin, J., Petitjean, E. & Sequeiros, F. 1988. Le chevauchement du Jura sur la Bresse. Données nouvelles et réinterprétation des sondages. *Bulletin de la Société géologique de France, 8, IV*, **5**, 861–870.

Clausen, O. R. & Pedersen, P. K. 1999. The Triassic structural evolution of the southern margin of the Ringkøbing-Fyn High, Denmark. *Marine and Petroleum Geology*, **16**, 653–665.

Cloetingh, S., Ziegler, P. A., *et al.* 2005. Lithospheric memory, state of stress and rheology: neotectonic controls on Europe's intraplate continental topography. *Quaternary Science Reviews*, **24**, 241–304.

Contini, D. & Théobald, N. 1974. Relations entre le Fossé rhénan et le Fossé de la Saône. Tectonique des régions sous-vosgiennes et préjurassiennes. *In:* Illies, J. H. & Fuchs, K. (eds) *Approaches to Taphrogenesis*. Schweizerbart, Stuttgart, 310–321.

Coubal, M. 1990. Compression along faults: example from the Bohemian Cretaceous Basin. *Mineralia Slovaca*, **22**, 139–144.

Coyle, D. A., Wagner, G. A., Hejl, E., Brown, R. & Van den Haute, P. 1997. The Cretaceous and younger thermal history of the KTB site (Germany): apatite fission-track data from the Vorbohrung. *Geologische Rundschau*, **86**, 203–209.

Czarnecka, K. 1988. Genesis of tectonic movements in Upper Silesia, Poland. *Journal of Geodynamics*, **10**, 301–307.

Dadlez, R. 1980. Tectonics of the Pomeranian Stell (NW Poland). *Geological Quarterly*, **24**, 741–767 [English summary].

Dadlez, R. 1995. Debates about pre-Variscan tectonics of Poland. *Studia geophysica et geodætica*, **39**, 227–234.

Dadlez, R., Jóźwiak, W. & Młynarski, S. 1997. Subsidence and inversion in the western part of the Polish Basin – data from seismic velocities. *Geological Quarterly*, **41**, 197–208.

Deczkowski, Z. & Gajewska, J. 1980. Mesozoic and Tertiary troughs in the Fore-Sudetic Monocline. *Przegląd Geologiczny*, **28**(3), 151–156 [in Polish with English summary].

Dèzes, P., Schmid, S. M. & Ziegler, P. A. 2004. Evolution of the European Cenozoic Rift System: interaction of the Alpine and Pyrenean orogens with their foreland lithosphere. *Tectonophysics*, **389**, 1–33.

Doebl, F. & Olbrecht, W. 1974. An isobath map of the Tertiary base in the Rhinegraben. *In:* Illies, J. H. & Fuchs, K. (eds) *Approaches to Taphrogenesis*. Schweizerbart, Stuttgart, 71–72.

Downes, H. 2001. Formation and modification of the shallow sub-continental lithospheric mantle: a review of geochemical evidence from ultramafic xenolith suites and tectonically emplaced ultramafic massifs of western and central Europe. *Journal of Petrology*, **42**, 233–250.

Dyjor, S. 1976. Late Tertiary Roztoki-Mokrzeszów tectonic graben. *Materiały I Krajowego Sympozjum "Współczesne i neotektoniczne ruchy skorupy ziemskiej w Polsce", II*. Wydawnictwa Geologiczne, Warszawa, 135–138 [in Polish with English summary].

Dyjor, S. 1983. Evolution of Tertiary grabens situated before Central and Eastern Sudetes. *Materiały III Krajowego Sympozjum* "Współczesne i neotektoniczne ruchy skorupy ziemskiej w Polsce", IV. Wydawnictwa Geologiczne, Warszawa, 155–181 [in Polish with English summary].

Dyjor, S. 1993. Stages of Neogene and Early Quaternary faulting in the Sudetes and their foreland. *Folia Quaternaria*, **64**, 25–41 [in Polish with English summary].

Dyjor, S. 1995. Young Quaternary and recent crustal movements in Lower Silesia, SW Poland. *Folia Quaternaria*, **66**, 51–58.

Dyjor, S., Mroczkowska, B. & Mroczkowski J. 1995. Hydrogeochemical indicators of current tectonic activity in Lower Silesia. *Acta Universitatis Wratislaviensis*, **1739**; *Prace Geologiczno-Mineralogiczne*, **50**, 109–115 [in Polish with English summary].

Dürr, R. 1982. *Strukturgeologische Untersuchungen im Bereich der Neckar-Jagst-Furche (Baden-Württemberg)*. Arbeiten aus dem Instituten für Geologie und Paläontologie der Universität Stuttgart, n.F., **77**.

Edel, J. B. & Weber, K. 1995. Cadomian terranes, wrench faulting and thrusting in the central Europe Variscides: geophysical and geological evidence. *Geologische Rundschau*, **84**, 412–432.

Ellenberg, J. 1992. Recent fault tectonics and their relationship to the seismicity of East Germany. *Tectonophysics*, **202**, 117–121.

Fisher, M. J. & Mudge, D. C. 1998. Triassic. *In:* Glennie, K. W. (ed.) *Petroleum Geology of the North Sea*. Blackwell, Oxford, 212–244.

Flick, H. 1986. The Hercynian Mountains – a postorogenic overthrusted massif? *Naturwissenschaften*, **73**, 670–671.

Franke, D. & Hoffmann, N. 1999. Das Elbe-Lineament – bedeutende Geofraktur oder Phantomgebilde? Teil 1: Die Referenzgebiete. *Zeitschift für geologische Wissenschaften*, **27**, 279–314.

Franzke, H. J., Voigt, T., v. Eynatten, H., Brix, M. R. & Burmester, G. 2004. Geometrie und Kinematik der Harznordrandstörung, erläutert an Profilen aus dem Gebiet von Blankenburg. *Geologische Mitteilungen von Thüringen*, **11**, 39–63.

Garetzky, R. G., Ludwig, A. O., Schwab, G. & Stackebrandt, W. 2001. *Neogeodynamics of the Baltic Sea depression and adjacent areas, results of IGCP project 346*. Brandenburgische Geowissenschaftliche Beiträge, **8**.

Geissler, W. H. Kämpf, H., *et al.* 2005. Seismic structure and location of a $CO_2$ source in the upper mantle of the western Eger (Ohře) Rift, central Europe. *Tectonics*, **24**(5), TC5001.

Gemmer, L., Nielsen, S. B. & Bayer, U. 2003. Late Cretaceous-Cenozoic evolution of the North German Basin – results from 3-D geodynamic modelling. *Tectonophysics*, **373**, 39–54.

Geyer, O. F. & Gwinner, M. P. 1986. *Geologie von Baden-Württemberg*, **3**. Aufl. E. Schweizerbart'sche Verlagsbuchhandlung, Stuttgart.

Giamboni, M., Ustaszewski, K., Schmid, S. M., Schumacher, M. E. & Wetzel, A. 2004. Plio-Pleistocene transpressional reactivation of Paleozoic and Paleogene structures in the Rhine-Bresse transform zone (northern Switzerland and eastern France). *International Journal of Earth Sciences*, **93**, 207–223.

Gibowicz, S. J., Guterch, B., Lewandowska-Marciniak H. & Wysokiński, L. 1982. Seismicity induced by surface mining of the Bełchatów, Poland, earthquake of 29 November 1980. *Acta Geophysica Polonica*, **30**, 193–219.

Goes, S., Loohuis, J. J. P., Wortel, M. J. R. & Govers, R. 2000. The effect of plate stresses and shallow mantle temperature on tectonics of northwestern Europe. *Global and Planetary Change*, **27**, 23–38.

Gölke, M. & Coblentz, D. 1996. Origins of the European regional stress field. *Tectonophysics*, **266**, 11–24.

Gorin, G. E., Signer, C. & Ambeger, G. 1993. Structural configuration of the western Swiss Molasse Basin as defined by reflection seismic data. *Eclogae geologicae Helvetiae*, **86**, 693–716.

Gotowała, R. & Hałuszczak, A. 2002. The Late Alpine structural development of the Kleszczów Graben (Central Poland) as a result of a reactivation of the pre-existing regional dislocations. *EGU Stephan Mueller Special Publication Series*. Copernicus, Northeim, **1**, 137–150.

Graniczny, M. 1991. Possibilities of the use of photolineaments in estimating seismic risk. *Biuletyn Państwowego Instytutu Geologicznego*, **365**, 5–46 [in Polish with English summary].

Gregersen, S. 1992. Crustal stress regime in Fennoscandia from focal mechanisms. *Journal of Geophysical Research*, **97**(B8), 11821–11827.

Gregersen, S., Lykke-Andersen, H., *et al.* 1995. Recent crustal movements and earthquakes in the area of the Tornquist zone. *Studia Geophysica Geodaetica*, **39**, 257–261.

Grünthal, G. & Mayer-Rosa, D. 1998. Einheitliche Erdbebengefährdungskarte für Deutschland, Österreich und die Schweiz (D-A-CH). *Schweizerischer Pool für Erdbebendeckung, Geschäftsbericht*, **1997**, 11- 24.

Grünthal, G. & Stromeyer, D. 1992. The recent crustal stress field in Central Europe: trajectories and finite element modeling. *Journal of Geophysical Research – Solid Earth*, **97**(B8), 11805–11820.

Guterch, B. & Lewandowska-Marciniak, H. 2002. Seismicity and seismic hazard in Poland. *Folia Quaternaria*, **73**, 85–99.

Guterch, A., Grad, M., *et al.* 1994. Crustal structure of the transition zone between Precambrian and Variscan Europe from new seismic data along LT-7 profile (NW Poland and eastern Germany). *Comptes rendus de l'Académie des sciences (Paris), série II*, **319**, 1489–1496.

Guterch, A., Grad, M., Thybo, H., Keller, G.R. & POLONAISE Working Group 1999. POLONAISE'97 – an international seismic experiment between Precambrian and Variscan Europe in Poland. *Tectonophysics*, **314**, 101–122.

Haase, K. M., Goldschmidt, B. & Garbe-Schönberg, C. D. 2004. Petrogenesis of Tertiary intra-plate lavas from the Westerwald region, Germany. *Journal of Petrology*, **45**, 883–905.

Hałuszczak, A. 1994. Clastic dikes in uppermost Tertiary sediments of the Kleszczów Graben and their significance to reconstruction of Quaternary diastrophism. *Kwartalnik Geologiczny*, **38**, 117–132.

Hałuszczak, A. 1999. Struktury deformacyjne o cechach kontrakcyjnych w utworach trzeciorzędowych zachodniej części odkrywki KWB Bełchatów i problem ich genezy. *In:* Hałuszczak, A. & Gotowała, R. (eds) *Młodoalpejski rów Kleszczowa: rozwój i uwarunkowania w tektonice regionu*. XX Konferencja terenowa Sekcji Tektonicznej Pol. Tow. Geol., Słok k. Bełchatowa, 15–16 October 1999, Wrocław, 39–57.

Hałuszczak, A., Gotowała, R. & Czarnecki, L. 1995. Manifestations of strike-slip tectonics in the western part of the Bełchatów open pit mine (Central Poland). *Przegląd Geologiczny*, **43**(5), 409–411 [in Polish with English summary].

Hansen, M. B., Lykke-Andersen, H., Dehghani, A., Gajewski, D., Hübscher, C., Oleson, M. & Reicherter, K. 2005. Mesozoic and Cenozoic geological evolution of the Bay of Kiel, western Baltic Sea. *International Journal of Earth Sciences*, **94**, 1070–1082.

Harasimiuk, M. & Henkiel A. 1980. The influence of neotectonics upon valley floor development: A case study from the Wieprz Valley, Lublin Upland. *Quaestiones Geographicae*, **6**, 35–53.

Harasimiuk, M. & Henkiel, A. 1984. Kenozoik Lubelskiego Zagłębia Węglowego. *Przewodnik 56 Zjazdu Polskie Towarzystwo Geologiczne*, Lublin 6–8 September 1984. Wydawnictwa Geologiczne, Warszawa, 56–70.

Henderson, J. R. 1991. An estimate of the stress tensor in Sweden using the earthquake fault-plane solution. *Tectonophysics*, **192**, 213–244.

Hennig, D. 1906. *Erdbebenkunde*. Johann Ambrosius Barth, Leipzig.

Henkiel, A. 1983. Tektonika. *In:* Henkiel, A. (ed.) *Kenozoik Lubelskiego Zagłębia Węglowego*, Sympozjum 9–11 września 1983, Lublin. Wydawnictwo UMCS, Lublin, 41–64.

Henkiel, A. 1984. Tectonics of Meso-Cainozoic cover of the northern slope of the Meta-Carpathian Swell. *Annales UMCS, Sec. B*, **39**, 15–38 [in Polish with English summary].

Henkiel, A. 1993. Selected sections of young fault-related deposits in north-western part of the Lublin Upland. *Folia Quaternaria*, **64**, 123–136 [in Polish with English summary].

Hiller, W. 1936. Das oberschwäbische Erdbeben am 27.Juni 1935. *Württembergisches Jahrbuch für Statistik und Landeskunde*, **1934/1935**, 209–226.

Hindle, D. & Burkhard, M. 1999. Strain, displacement and rotation associated with the formation of curvature in fold belts; the example of the Jura arc. *Journal of Structural Geology*, **21**, 1089–1101.

Hinzen, K.-G. 2003. Stress field in the Northern Rhine area, Central Europe, from earthquake fault plane solutions. *Tectonophysics*, **377**, 325–356.

Hoffers, B. 1974. Horizontalstylolithen, Abschiebungen, Klüfte und Harnische im Gebiet des Hohenzollerngrabens und ihre Altersverhältnisse. *Oberrheinische Geologische Abhandlungen*, **23**, 65–73.

Homberg, C., Bergerat, F., Philippe, Y., Lacombe, O. & Angelier, J. 2002. Structural inheritance and cenozoic stress fields in the Jura fold-and-thrust belt (France). *Tectonophysics*, **357**, 137–158.

Houtgast, R. F. & Van Balen, R. T. 2000. Neotetonics of the Roer Valley Rift System, the Netherlands. *Global and Planetary Change*, **27**, 131–146.

Hübscher, C., Lykke-Andersen, H., Hansen, M. B. & Reicherter, K. 2004. Investigating the structural evolution of the western Baltic. *EOS*, **85**(12), 115.

Ihde, J., Steinberg, J., Ellenberg, J. & Bankwitz, E. 1987. On recent vertical crustal movements derived from relevellings within the territory of the G.D.R. *Gerlands Beiträge Geophysik*, **96**(3/4), 206–217.

Illies, H. 1978. Neotektonik, geothermale Anomalie und Seismizität im Vorfeld der Alpen. *Oberrheinische Geologische Abhandlungen*, **27**, 11–31.

Illies, H. 1982. Der Hohenzollerngraben und Intraplattenseismizität infolge Vergitterung lamellärer Scherung mit einer Riftstruktur. *Oberrheinische Geologische Abhandlungen*, **31**, 47–78.

Illies, H. & Greiner, G. 1976. Regionales Stress-Feld und Neotektonik in Mitteleuropa. *Oberrheinische Geologische Abhandlungen*, **25**, 1–40.

Illies, J. H. 1975. Recent and paleo-intraplate tectonics in stable Europe and the Rhine-graben rift system. *Tectonophysics*, **29**, 251–264.

Illies, J. H., Baumann, H. & Hoffers, B. 1981. Stress pattern and strain release in the alpine foreland. *Tectonophysics*, **71**, 157–182.

Jamison, W. R. 1987. Geometric analysis of fold development in overthrust terranes. *Journal of Structural Geology*, **9**, 207–219.

Jarosiński, M. 1998. Contemporary stress field distortion in the Polish part of the Western Outer Carpathians and their basement. *Tectonophysics*, **297**, 91–119.

Jarosiński, M. 1999*a*. Zintegrowana interpretacja "geofizyczno-geologiczna. *In:* Krzywiec, P. (ed.). *Rozpoznanie budowy czapy gipsowo-anhydrytowej wysadu solnego "Damasławek" płytkimi badaniami sejsmicznymi*. Archive of Polish Geological Institute, Warsaw, 80–100.

Jarosiński, M. 1999*b*. *Analiza strukturalna deformacji tektonicznych w obrębie zapadliska przedkarpackiego na podstawie wyników interpretacji profili sejsmicznych*. Archive of Polish Geological Institute, Warsaw, 1–60.

Jarosiński, M. 2005*a*. Ongoing tectonic reactivation of the Outer Carpathians and its impact on the foreland: results of borehole breakout measurements in Poland. *Tectonophysics*, **410**, 189–216.

Jarosiński, M. 2005*b*. Recent tectonic stress regime in Poland based on analyses of hydraulic fracturing of borehole walls. *Przegląd Geologiczny*, **53**, 863–872 [English abstract].

Jordan, P. 1992. Evidence for large-scale decoupling in the Triassic evaporites of Northern Switzerland: An overview. *Eclogae geologicae Helvetiae*, **85**, 677–693.

Jung, K. 1953. *Kleine Erdbebenkunde*. Springer, Berlin.

Jura, D. 1995. The young-Alpine morphotectonics of the Silesian Carpathian Foredeep and the recent geodynamics of the Upper Silesian Coal Basin. *Technika Poszukiwań Geologicznych, Geosynoptyka i Geotermia*, **34**(3), 13–21.

Jura, D. 1999. Young-Alpine Kłodnica fault scarps of the Metacarpathian High in the Silesian Upland. *Technika Poszukiwań Geologicznych, Geosynoptyka i Geotermia*, **38**(1), 52–56.

Juschus, O. 2001. *Das Jungmoränenland südlich von Berlin – Untersuchungen zur jungquartären Landschaftsentwicklung zwischen Unterspreewald und Nuthe*. PhD thesis, Humboldt University, Berlin.

Kaiser, A., Reicherter, K., Hübscher, C. & Gajewski, D. 2005. Variation of the present-day stress field within the North German Basin – insights from thin shell FE-modelling. *Tectonophysics*, **397**, 55–72.

Kälin, D. 1997. Litho- und Biostratigraphie der mittel- bis obermiozänen Bois de Raube – Formation (Nordwestschweiz). *Eclogae geologicae Helvetiae*, **90**, 97–114.

Karabanov, A. K. & Schwab, G. 1997. *Neotectonic Structural Subdivision, 1:5,000,000*. IGCP Project 346 Neogeodynamica Baltica. Geological Survey of Brandenburg, Kleinmachnow.

Karnik, V. 1971. *Seismicity of the European Area, Part II*. Reidel, Dordrecht.

Kasiński, J. R. 1984. Tektonika Synsedymantacyjna jako czynnik warunkujący sedymentację formacji brunatnowęglowej w zapadliskach tektonicznych na obszarze zachodniej Polski. *Przegląd Geologiczny*, **373**, 260–268 [English summary].

Kasiński, J. R. & Piwocki, M. 1999. Tertiary tectonic troughs in the Polish Lowlands. *Technika Poszukiwań Geologicznych, Geosynoptyka i Geotermia*, **38**(1), 57.

Kazmierczak, M., Brunner, H. & Hinkelbein, K. 1999. Geologie und Tektonik im Bereich der Haslacher Störungszone (GK25: Blatt 7419 Herrenberg). *Jahreberichte und Mitteilungen des Oberrheinischen Geologischen Vereins, N.F.*, **81**, 365–390.

Keller, J., Kraml, M. & Henjes-Kunst, F. 2002. $^{40}Ar/^{39}Ar$ single crystal laser dating of early volcanism in the Upper Rhine Graben and tectonic implications. *Schweizerische Mineralogische und Petrographische Mitteilungen*, **82**, 121–130.

Kempf, O., Schlunegger, F., Strunck, P. & Matter, A. 1998. Palaeomagnetic evidence for late Miocene rotation of the Swiss Alps: results from the north Alpine foreland basin. *Terra Nova*, **10**, 6–10.

Keyser, M., Ritter, J. R. R. & Jordan, M. 2002. 3D shear-wave velocity structure of the Eifel plume, Germany. *Earth and Planetary Science Letters*, **203**, 59–82.

Klajnert, Z. 1984. Analysis of kames for paleogeographical reconstructions. *Boreas*, **13**, 95–109.

Knufinke, H.-U. & Kothen, H. 1997. Die Tektonik der Niederrheinischen Bucht vor, während und nach der Hauptflözbildung. *Braunkohle/Surface Mining*, **49**, 473–479.

Kociszewska-Musiał, G. 1978. Quaternary aggregates of the Suwałki region against its geological background. *Prace Muzeum Ziemi*, **29**, 3–79 [in Polish with English summary].

Kockel, F. 2003. Inversion structures in Central Europe – Expressions and reasons, an open discussion. *Netherlands Journal of Geosciences/Geologie en Mijnbouw*, **82**, 367–382.

König, W. & Blumenstengel, H. 2005. Neue Tertiäraufschlüsse im Mittelharz bei Elbingerode. *Exkursionsführer und Veröffentlichungen der DGG*, **227**, 18–23.

Kontny, B. 2003. Geodetic research of contemporary kinematics of the main tectonic structures of the Polish Sudetes and the Fore-Sudetic Block with the use of GPS measurements. *Zeszyty Naukowe Akademii Rolniczej we Wrocławiu*, **468**; *Wydział Inżynierii, Kształtowania Środowiska i Geodezji, Rozprawy*, **202**, 1–146 [in Polish with English summary].

Kopczyńska-Lamparska, K. 1979. The oldest glaciation, the origin of the Quaternary substratum and the age of the Warszewo Hills, based on the geological structure of the Szczecin area. *Biuletyn Geologiczny Uniwersytetu Warszawskiego*, **23**, 41–57 [in Polish with English summary].

Kosmowska-Suffczyńska, D. 1986. Relationship between relief and tectonics on the NE border of the Holy Cross Mountains. *Miscellanea Geographica*. Wydawnictwa Uniwersytetu Warszawskiego, Warszawa, 31–40.

Kossow, D. & Krawczyk, C. M. 2002. Structure and quantification of processes controlling the evolution of the inverted NE-German Basin. *Marine and Petroleum Geology*, **19**, 601–618.

Kossow, D., Krawczyk, C., McCann, T., Strecker, M. & Negendank, J. 2000. Style and evolution of salt pillows and related structures in the northern part of the Northeast German Basin. *International Journal of Earth Sciences*, **89**, 652–664.

Kowalski, B. J. 1995. Manifestations of young tectonic activity in Kielce - Łagów Valley (Holy Cross Mts., Central Poland) and their influence on the river system. *Przegląd Geologiczny*, **43**(4), 307–316 [in Polish with English summary].

Kowalski, W. C. & Liszkowski, J. 1972. The dependence between the recent vertical movements of the Earth's crust in Poland and its geological structure. *Biuletyn Geologiczny Uniwersytetu Warszawskiego*, **14**, 5–19 [in Polish with English summary].

Kramarska, R., Krzywiec, P. & Dadlez, R. 1999. *Geological Map of the Baltic Sea Bottom Without Quaternary Deposits*. Państwowy Instytut Geologiczny, Gdańsk-Warszawa.

Kraml, M., Keller, J. & Henjes-Kunst, F. 1999. Time constraints for the carbonatitic intrusions of the Kaiserstuhl volcanic complex, Upper Rhine Graben, Germany. *EUG 10, Journal of Conference Abstracts*, **4**, 322.

Krassowska, A. 1997. Upper Cretaceous (Upper Albian-Maastichtian) – sedimentation, palaeogeography and palaeotectonics. *In:* Marek, S. & Pajchlowa, M. (eds) *The Epicontinental Permian and Mesozoic in Poland*. Prace Państwowy Instytut Geologiczny, **153**, 386–402 [English summary].

Kriele, W. 1968. *Tektonische Untersuchungen auf der Hohenzollernalb*. Diploma thesis, University of Tübingen.

Krysiak, Z. 2000. Tectonic evolution of the Carpathian Foredeep and its influence on Miocene sedimentation. *Geological Quarterly*, **44**, 137–156.

Krzyszkowski, D. (ed.) 1991. The polyinterglacial Czyżów Formation in the Kleszczów Graben (Central Poland). *Folia Quaternaria*, **61–62**, 1–257.

Krzyszkowski, D. 1992. Quaternary tectonics in the Kleszczów Graben (Central Poland): a study based on sections from the "Bełchatów" outcrop. *Quaternary Studies in Poland*, **11**, 65–90.

Krzyszkowski, D., Migoń, P. & Sroka, W. 1995. Neotectonic Quaternary history of the Sudetic Marginal Fault, SW Poland. *Folia Quaternaria*, **66**, 73–98.

Krzywiec, P., Jarosiński, M., *et al.* 2000. Geofizyczno-geologiczne badania stropu i nadkładu wysadu solnego "Damasławek". *Przegląd Geologiczny*, **48**(11), 1005–1014 [English summary].

Książkiewicz, M. 1972. *Geology of Poland. Vol. 4, Tectonics. Part 3, Carpathians*. Wyd. Geol., Warszawa [in Polish].

Kunze, T. 1982. *Seismotektonische Bewegungen im Alpenbereich*. PhD thesis, Universität Stuttgart.

Kutek, J. & Głazek J. 1972. The Holy Cross area, Central Poland, in the Alpine cycle. *Acta Geologica Polonica*, **22**(4), 603–652.

Larroque, J. M. & Laurent, P. H. 1988. Evolution of the stress field pattern in the south of the Rhine Graben from Eocene to the present. *Tectonophysics*, **148**, 41–58.

Laskowska-Wysoczańska, W. 1979. Quaternary vertical movements of marginal zone of the Carpathian Foredeep in front of the Roztocze. *Przegląd Geologiczny*, **27**(6), 318–321 [in Polish with English summary].

Laskowska-Wysoczańska, W. 1983. The Quaternary vertical movements in middle and east part of the Sandomierz Depression. *Materiały III Krajowego Sympozjum*. Ossolineum, Wrocław, 207–221 [in Polish with English summary].

Laskowska-Wysoczańska, W. 1984. Czwartorzędowe i współczesne zjawiska tektoniczne oraz ich wpływ na przebieg procesów kształtujących rzeźbę Kotliny Sandomierskiej. *In:* Maruszczak, H. (ed.) *Przewodnik Ogólnopol. Zjazdu Polskie Towarzystwo Geographicznego*. Lublin 13–15 September 1984, cz. I. Wydawnictwo UMCS, Lublin, 79–83.

Laubscher, H. P. 1961. Die Fernschubhypothese der Jurafaltung. *Eclogae geologicae Helvetiae*, **54**, 221–281.

Laubscher, H. P. 1965. Ein kinematisches Modell der Jurafaltung. *Eclogae geologicae Helvetiae*, **58**, 231–318.

Laubscher, H. P. 1973. Jura Mountains. *In:* De Jong, K. A. & Scholten, R. (eds) *Gravity and Tectonics*. Wiley, New York, 217–227.

Laubscher, H. P. 1974. Basement uplift and decollement in the Molasse Basin. *Eclogae geologicae Helvetiae*, **67**, 531–537.

Laubscher, H. 1987. Die tektonische Entwicklung der Nordschweiz. *Eclogae geologicae Helvetiae*, **80**, 287–303.

Laubscher, H. 2001. Plate interactions at the southern end of the Rhine graben. *Tectonophysics*, **343**, 1–19.

Laubscher, H. 2003. Balanced sections and the propagation of décollement: A Jura perspective. *Tectonics*, **22**(6), article no. 1063.

Le Pichon, X., Bergerat, F. & Roulet, M.-J. 1988. Plate kinematics and tectonics leading to the Alpine belt formation; A new analysis. *Geological Society of America Special Papers*, **218**, 111–131.

Leszczyński, K. 2002. Late Cretaceous inversion and salt tectonics in the Koszalin-Chojnice and Drawno-Człopa-Szamotuły zones, Pomeranian sector of the Mid-Polish Trough. *Geological Quarterly*, **46**, 347–362.

Leydecker, G. 1986. Erdbebenkatalog für die Bundesrepublik Deutschland mit Randgebieten für die Jahre 1000–1981. *Geologisches Jahrbuch Reihe E*, **36**, 3–8.

Leydecker, G., Kopera, J. R. & Rudloff, A. 1999. Abschätzung der Erdbebengefährdung in Gebieten geringer Seismizität am Beispiel eines Standortes in Norddeutschland. *In:* Savidis, S. A. (ed.) *Entwicklungsstand in Forschung und Praxis auf den Gebieten des Erdbebeningenieurwesens, der Boden- und Baudynamik*. DGEB Berlin, Publikation **10**, 89–97.

Lindner, L. 1978. Palaeogeomorphologic evolution of the western part of the Holy Cross region in Pleistocene. *Annales Societatis Geologorum Poloniae*, **48**, 479–508 [in Polish with English summary].

Lippolt, H. J. & Hess, J. C. 1996. Numerische Stratigraphie permokarbonischer Vulkanite Zentraleuropas. Teil II: Westharz. *Zeitschrift der deutschen geologischen Gesellschaft*, **147**, 1–9.

Lippolt, H. J., Todt, W. & Horn, P. 1974. Apparent potassium-argon ages of Lower Tertiary Rhine Graben volcanics. *In:* Illies, J. H. & Fuchs, K. (eds) *Approaches to Taphrogenesis*. Schweizerbart, Stuttgart, 213–221.

Liszkowski, J. 1982. *The Origin of Recent Vertical Crustal Movements in Poland*. Rozprawy Uniwersytetu Warszawskiego, Warszawa [in Polish].

Liszkowski, J. 1993. The effects of Pleistocene ice-sheet loading-deloading cycles on the bedrock structure of Poland. *Folia Quaternaria*, **64**, 7–23.

Lopes Cardoso, C. G. O. & Granet, M. 2003. New insight in the tectonics of the southern Rhine Graben-Jura region using local earthquake seismology. *Tectonics*, **22**(6), article no. 1078.

Lopes Cardozo, G. G. O. & Granet, M. 2005. A multi-scale approach to study the lithospheric structure of the southern Upper Rhine Graben: from seismic tomography through reflection seismics to surface geology. *International Journal of Earth Sciences*, **94**, 615–620.

Lotze, F. 1937. Zur Methodik der Forschungen über saxonische Tektonik. *Geotektonische Forschungen*, **1**, 6–27.

Lykke-Andersen, H. 1981. Indications of neotectonic features in Denmark. *Zeitschrift für Geomorph. N. F.*, **40**, 43–54.

Lykke-Andersen, H. & Borre, K. 2000. Aktiv tektonik i Danmark - der er liv i Sorgenfrei-Tornquist Zonen. *Geologisk Nyt*, **6**, 12–13.

Lykke-Andersen, H., Madirazza, I. *et al.* 1996. Tektonik og landskabsdannelse i Midtjylland. *Geologisk Tidsskrift*, **3**, 1–32.

McCann, T. 1999. The tectono-sedimentary evolution of the northern margin of the Carboniferous foreland basin of NE-Germany. *Tectonophysics*, **313**, 119–144.

McCann, T. & Krawczyk, C. M. 2000. The Trans-European Fault – a critical reassessment. *Geological Magazine*, **138**, 19–29.

Malkovsky, M. 1987. The Mesozoic and Tertiary basins of the Bohemian Massif and their evolution. *Tectonophysics*, **137**, 31–42.

Mälzer, H. 1988. Regionale Höhenänderungen und seismische Aktivitäten in Südwestdeutschland. *Das Markscheidewesen*, **95**(1), 10–13.

Mälzer, H., Hein, G. & Zippelt, K. 1983. Height changes in the Rhenish Massif: Determination and analysis. *In:* Fuchs, K., von Gehlen, K., Mälzer, H., Murawski, H. & Semmel, M. (eds) *Plateau Uplift. The Rhenish Shield – A Case History.* Springer, Berlin, 164–176.

Marotta, A. M., Bayer, U., Scheck, M. & Thybo, H. 2001. The stress field below the NE German Basin: effects induced by the Alpine collision. *Geophysical Journal International*, **144**, F8–F12.

Marotta, A. M., Bayer, U., Thybo, H. & Scheck, M. 2002. Origin of the regional stress in the North German basin: results from numerical modelling. *Tectonophysics*, **360**, 245– 264.

Mastalerz, K. & Wojewoda, J. 1990. The Pre-Kaczawa alluvial fan – an example of sedimentation in an active wrench zone, Plio-Pleistocene age, Sudetes Mts. *Przegląd Geologiczny*, **38**(9), 363–370 [in Polish with English summary].

Maystrenko, Y., Bayer, U. & Scheck-Wenderoth, M. 2005. The Glueckstadt Graben, a sedimentary record between the North and Baltic Sea in north Central Europe. *Tectonophysics*, **397**, 113–126.

Meghraoui, M., Delouis, B., Ferry, M., Giardini, D., Huggenberger, P., Spottke, I. & Granet M. 2001. Active normal faulting in the upper Rhine graben and paleoseismic identification of the 1356 Basel earthquake. *Science*, **293**, 2070–2073.

Meier, D. 2004. Man and environment in the marsh area of Schleswig-Holstein from Roman until late Medieval times. *Quaternary International*, **112**, 55–69.

Merle, O. & Michon, L. 2001. The formation of the West European rift: A new model as exemplified by the Massif Central area. *Bulletin de la Societé Géologique de France*, **172**, 213–221.

Meyer, W. & Stets, J. 1998. Junge Tektonik im Rheinischen Schiefergebirge und ihre Quantifizierung. *Zeitschrift der deutschen geologischen Gesellschaft*, **149**, 359–379.

Meyer, W. & Stets, J. 2002. Pleistocene to Recent tectonics in the Rhenish Massif (Germany). *Netherlands Journal of Geosciences/ Geologie en Mijnbouw*, **81**, 217–221.

Meyer, W., Albers, H. J., *et al.* 1983. Pre-Quaternary uplift in the central part of the Rhenish massif. *In:* Fuchs, K., von Gehlen, K., Mälzer, H., Murawski, H. & Semmel, M. (eds) *Plateau Uplift. The Rhenish Shield – A Case History.* Springer, Berlin, 39–46.

Michon, L. & Merle, O. 2005. Discussion on "Evolution of the European Cenozoic Rift System: interaction of the Alpine and Pyrenean orogens with their foreland lithosphere" by P. Dèzes, S.M. Schmid and P.A. Ziegler, Tectonophysics 389 (2004) 1–33. *Tectonophysics*, **401**, 251–256.

Michon, L., Van Balen, R. T., Merle, O. & Pagnier, H. 2003. The Cenozoic evolution of the Roer Valley Rift System integrated at a European scale. *Tectonophysics*, **367**, 101–126.

Migoń, P. 1991. Quaternary faulting on the northern margin of the Karkonosze Mts. (SW Poland). *Bulletin of the INQUA Neotectonics Commission*, **14**, 54–55.

Mitra, S. 2003. A unified model for the evolution of detachment folds. *Journal of Structural Geology*, **25**, 1659–1673.

Mojski, J. E. 1991. Czwartorzędowy rytm zmian środowiska. *In:* Starkel, L. (ed.) *Geografia Polski.* Środowisko przyrodnicze. PWN, Warszawa, 67–80.

Mörner, N. A. 1979. The Fennoscandian uplift and Late Cenozoic geodynamics: geological evidence. *GeoJournal*, **3**, 287–318.

Mörner, N. A. 2003. *Paleoseismicity of Sweden – A Novel Paradigm.* A contribution to INQUA from sub-commission on Paleoseismology, University of Stockholm.

Mörner, N. A. 2004. Active faults and paleoseismicity in Fennoscandia, especially Sweden. Primary structures and secondary effects. *Tectonophysics*, **380**, 139–157.

Müller, B., Zoback, M. L., *et al.* 1992. Regional patterns of tectonic stress in Europe. *Journal of Geophysical Research – Solid Earth*, **97**(B8), 11783–11804.

Murawski, H. 1955. Das Ausmaß der Vertikal-Leistung jungtertiärer Tektonik im Gebiet des Leinetalgrabens. *Neues Jahrbuch für Paläontologie und Geologie – Monatshefte*, **1955**, 297–308.

Murawski, H. *et al.* 1983. Regional tectonic setting and geological structure of the Rhenish Massif. *In:* Fuchs, K., von Gehlen, K., Mälzer, H., Murawski, H. & Semmel, M. (eds) *Plateau Uplift. The Rhenish Shield – A Case History.* Springer, Berlin, 78–88.

Nachtmann, W. & Wagner, L. 1987. Mesozoic and Early Tertiary evolution of the Alpine foreland in Upper Austria and Salzburg, Austria. *Tectonophysics*, **137**, 61–76.

Negendank, J. 1983. Cenozoic deposits of the Eifel-Hunsrück area along the Mosel river and their tectonic implications. *In:* Fuchs, K., von Gehlen, K., Mälzer, H., Murawski, H. & Semmel, M. (eds) *Plateau Uplift. The Rhenish Shield – A Case History.* Springer, Berlin, 9–38.

Nielsen, L. H. & Japsen, P. 1991. *Deep wells in Denmark 1935–1990. Lithostratigraphic Subdivision.* Geological Survey of Denmark, DGU Series A, 31.

Nitychoruk J. 1996. Glacial deposits of Southern Podlasie. *In:* Marks, L. (ed.) *Stratygrafia plejstocenu Polski. Mater. II Konferencji Komisji Stratygrafii i Paleogeografii Plejstocenu Kom.* Bad. Czwart. PAN, Grabanów 18–20 września 1995. Państwowy Instytut Geologiczny, Warszawa, 7–16 [In Polish with English summary].

Nivière, B. & Winter, T. 2000. Pleistocene northwards fold propagation of the Jura within the southern Upper Rhine graben: seismotectonic implications. *Global and Planetary Change*, **27**, 263–288.

Novak, B. 2002. Early Holocene brackish and marine facies in the Fehmarn Belt, southwest Baltic Sea: depositional processes revealed by high-resolution seismics and core analysis. *Marine Geology*, **189**, 307–321.

Novak, B. & Björck, S. 2002. Late Pleistocene-early Holocene fluvial facies and depositional processes in the Fehmarn Belt, between Germany and Denmark, revealed by high-resolution seismic and lithofacies analysis. *Sedimentology*, **49**, 451–465.

Nowel, W., Bönisch, R., Schneider, W. & Schulze, H. 1994. *Geologie des Lausitzer Braunkohlenreviers.* Lausitz Braunkohle AG, Senftenberg.

Oberc, J. 1972. Tektonika, częśc 2. *In: Władysław Pożaryski, Budowa Geologiczna Polski t. IV.* Wydawnictwa Geologiczne, Warszawa, 1–307.

Olszewska, B., Odrzywolska-Bieńkowa, E., Giel, M. D., Pożaryska, K. & Szczechura, J. 1996. Fauna – bezkręgowce. Rząd Foraminiferida. *In:* Malinowska, L. & Piwocki, M. (eds) *Budowa geologiczna Polski, T. III, Atlas skamieniałości przewodnich i charakterystycznych, cz. 3a, Kenozoik, Trzeciorzęd.* Paleogen. Wyd. PAE Warszawa, 45–216.

Ostaficzuk, S. 1981. Lineaments as representation of tectonic phenomena against a background of some examples from Poland. *Biuletyn Geologiczny Uniwersytetu Warszawskiego*, **29**, 195–267 [in Polish with English summary].

Ostaficzuk, S. (ed.) 1995. Proceedings of the International Colloque Neogeodynamica Baltica, September 1994, Katowice, Poland. *Technika Poszukiwań Geologicznych, Geosynoptyka i Geotermia*, **34**(3), 1–107.

Ostaficzuk, S. 1999. Neogeotectonic features in the sub-Quaternary surface. *Technika Poszukiwań Geologicznych, Geosynoptyka i Geotermia*, **38**(1), 77–81.

Oszczypko, N. & Ślączka, A. 1989. The evolution of the Miocene basin in the Polish Outer Carpathians and their foreland. *Geologica Carpathica*, **40**(1), 23–36.

Paulus, E. 1866. *Begleitworte zur geognostischen Specialkarte von Württemberg.* Atlasblatt 30, Freudenstadt, Stuttgart.

Peryt, T. & Piwocki, M. (eds) 2004. *Budowa Geologiczna Polski:, Kenozoik, Paleogen, Neogen,* Vol. I 3a. Wydawnictwa Państwowego Inststutu Geologicznego, Warszawa.

Peters, G. & van Balen, R. T. 2007. Pleistocene tectonics inferred from fluvial terraces of the northern Upper Rhine Graben, Germany. *Tectonophysics*, **430**, 41–65.

Peters, G., Buchmann, T. J., Connolly, P., van Balen, R. T., Wenzel, F. & Cloetingh, S. A. P. L. 2005. Interplay between tectonic, fluvial and erosional processes along the Western Border Fault of the northern Upper Rhine Graben, Germany. *Tectonophysics*, **406**, 39–66.

Petmecky, S., Meier, L., Reiser, H. & Littke, R. 1999. High thermal maturity in the Lower Saxony Basin: intrusion or deep burial? *Tectonophysics*, **304**, 317–344.

Pfiffner, O. A., Erard, P.-F. & Stäuble, M. 1997. Two cross sections through the Swiss Molasse Basin (lines E4-E6, W1, W7-W10). *In:* Pfiffner, O. A., Lehner, P., Heitzmann, P., Mueller, S. & Steck, A. (eds) *Deep Structure of the Swiss Alps: Results of NRP 20.* Birkhäuser, Basel, 73–100.

PFLUG, R. 1982. *Bau und Entwicklung der Oberrheingrabens*. Wissenschaftliche Buchgesellschaft, Darmstadt.

PHARAOH, T. C. 1999. Palaeozoic terranes and their lithospheric boundaries within the Trans-European Suture Zone (TESZ): a review. *Tectonophyscis*, **314**, 17–41.

PHILIPPE, Y., COLLETTA, B., DEVILLE, E. & MASCLE, A. 1996. The Jura fold-and-thrust belt: a kinematic model based on map-balancing. *In:* ZIEGLER, P. A. & HORVATH, F. (eds) *Peri-Tethys Memoir 2: Structure and Prospects of Alpine Basins and Forelands*. Mémoires du Muséum National d'Histoire Naturelle, Paris, **170**, 235–261.

PIWOCKI, M. 2001. New ideas on litostratigraphy of the Paleogene in Poland. *Polskie Towarzystwo Geologiczne, Streszczenia Referatów*, **10**, 50–60 [in Polish].

PIWOCKI, M. 2004. Polish Lowlands and its southern rim. Stratigraphy – Paleogene. *In:* PERYT, T. & PIWOCKI, M. (eds) *Geology of Poland*, T. I, *Stratigraphy*, part 3a, *Cenozoic*, Państwowy Instytut Geologiczny, Warszawa, 22–71.

PIWOCKI, M. & KRAMARSKA, R. 2004. Polish Lowlands and its southern rim. Stratigraphy. *In:* PERYT, T. & PIWOCKI, M. (eds) *Geology of Poland*, T. I, *Stratigraphy*, part 3a, *Cenozoic*. 19–22.

PLENEFISCH, T. & BONJER, K.-P. 1997. The stress field in the Rhine Graben area inferred from earthquake focal mechanisms and estimations of frictional parameters. *Tectonophysics*, **275**, 71–97.

PLESSMANN, W. 1972. Horizontal-Stylolithen im französisch-schweizerischen Tafel- und Faltenjura und ihre Einpassung in den regionalen Rahmen. *Geologische Rundschau*, **61**, 332–347.

POŁOŃSKA, M. 1997. Upper Cretaceous (Upper Albian-Maastichtian) – petrographic characteristics. *In:* MAREK, S. & PAJCHLOWA, M. (eds) *The Epicontinental Permian and Mesozoic in Poland*. Prace Państwowy Instytut Geologiczny, Warszawa, **153**, 383–386 [English summary].

POPRAWA, P. & GROTEK, I. 2004. Thermal evolution of the Permian-Mesozoic Polish Basin – model predictions confronted with analytical data. *Bolletino di Geofisica teorica ed applicata*, **45**(1), 258–261.

POPRAWA, P., MALATA, T. & OSZCZYPKO, N. 2002. Tectonic evolution of the Polish part of Outer Carpathian's sedimentary basins – constraints from subsidence analysis. *Przegląd Geologiczny*, **50**(11), 1092–1108 [English summary].

PÖSCHL, W. & SCHWEIZER, V. 1977. Zur Tektonik am Nordende des Sindelfinger Grabens. *Jahresberichte und Mitteilungen des Oberrheinischen Geologischen Vereins, N.F.*, **59**, 99–103.

POŻARYSKA, K. & ODRZYWOLSKA-BIEŃKOWA, E. 1977. On the Upper Eocene in Poland. *Geological Quarterly*, **21**(1), 59–73 [in Polish].

PRODEHL, C., MUELLER, S. & HAAK, V. 1995. The European Cenozoic Rift System. *In:* OLSEN, K. H. (ed.) *Continental Rifts: Evolution, Structure, Tectonics*. Developments in Geotectonics, Elsevier, Amsterdam, 133–212.

REGELMANN, C. 1907. Erdbebenherde und Herdlinien in Südwestdeutschland. *Jahreshefte des Vereins für Vaterländische Naturkunde in Württemberg*, **63**, 110–176.

REICHERTER, K., WURM, F. & KLEINGOOR, I. 1994. Deformationsstrukturen der Sindelfinger Störungszone bei Magstadt (Baden-Württemberg). *Göttinger Arbeiten zur Geologie und Paläontologie*, **Sb1**, 194–196.

REICHERTER, K., KAISER, A. & STACKEBRANDT, W. 2005. The postglacial landscape evolution of the North German Basin: morphology, neotectonics and crustal deformation. *International Journal of Earth Sciences*, **94**, 1083–1093.

REINECKER, J. & SCHNEIDER, G. 2002. Zur Neotektonik der Zollernalb: Der Hohenzollerngraben und die Albstadt-Erdbeben. *Jahresberichte und Mitteilungen des Oberrheinischen Geologischen Vereins, N. F.*, **84**, 391–417.

REINECKER, J., HEIDBACH, O. & MÜLLER, B. 2004. *World Stress Map* (2004 release). World Wide Web address: www.world-stress-map.org

RICOUR, J. 1956. Le chevauchement de la bordure occidentale du Jura sur la Bresse dans la région de Lons-le-Saunier. *Bulletin der Schweizerischen Vereinigung der Petroleum-Geologen und -Ingenieure*, **23**, 67–70.

RITTER, J. R. R. JORDAN, M., CHRISTENSEN, U. R. & ACHAUER, U. 2001. A mantle plume below the Eifel volcanic fields, Germany. *Earth and Planetary Science Letters*, **186**, 7–14.

RÖCKEL, T. & LEMPP, C. 2003. Der Spannungszustand im norddeutschen Becken. *Erdöl Erdgas Kohle*, **119**, 73–80.

ROLL, A. 1979. Versuch einer Volumenbilanz des Oberrheingrabens und seiner Schultern. *Geologisches Jahrbuch, Reihe A*, **52**, 1–82.

ROTH, F. & FLECKENSTEIN, P. 2001. Stress orientations found in north-east Germany differ from the West European trend. *Terra Nova*, **13**, 289–296.

ROTSTEIN, Y. & SCHAMING, M. 2004. Seismic reflection evidence for thick-skinned tectonics in the northern Jura. *Terra Nova*, **16**, 250–256.

ROTSTEIN, Y., SCHAMING, M. & ROUSSE, S. 2005. Structure and Tertiary tectonic history of the Mulhouse High, Upper Rhine Graben: Block faulting modified by changes in the Alpine stress regime. *Tectonics*, **24**(1), TC1012.

RÜHLE, E. 1969. Sur les mouvements néotectoniques en Pologne. *Geographia Polonica*, **17**, 41–54.

RÜHLE, E. 1973. Ruchy neotektoniczne w Polsce. *In:* RÜHLE, E. (ed.) *Metodyka badań osadów czwartorzędowych*. Wydawnictwa Geologiczne, Warszawa, 13–31.

SCHÄFER, A. 1994. Die Niederrheinische Bucht im Tertiär – Ablagerungs- und Lebensraum. *In:* VON KOENIGSWALD, W. & MEYER, W. (eds) *Erdgeschichte im Rheinland*. Dr. Friedrich Pfeil, München, 155–164.

SCHÄFER, A., UTESCHER, T., KLETT, M. & VALDIVIA-MANCHEGO, M. 2005. The Cenozoic Lower Rhine Basin – rifting, sedimentation, and cyclic stratigraphy. *International Journal of Earth Sciences*, **94**, 621–639.

SCHECK, M. & BAYER, U. 1999. Evolution of the Northeast German Basin – inferences from a 3D structural model and subsidence analysis. *Tectonophysics*, **313**, 145–169.

SCHECK, M., BAYER, U. & LEWERENZ, B. 2003*a*. Salt movements in the Northeast German Basin and its relation to major post-Permian tectonic phases – results from 3D structural modelling, back-stripping and reflection seismic data. *Tectonophysics*, **361**, 277–299.

SCHECK, M., BAYER, U. & LEWERENZ, B. 2003*b*. Salt redistribution during extension and inversion inferred from 3D backstripping. *Tectonophysics*, **373**, 55–73.

SCHENK, E. 1974. Die Fortsetzung des Rheingrabens duch Hessen. Ein Beitrag zur tektonischen Analyse der Riftsysteme. *In:* ILLIES, J. H. & FUCHS, K. (eds) *Approaches to Taphrogenesis*. Schweizerbart, Stuttgart, 286–302.

SCHERNECK, H. G., JOHANSSON, J. M., MITROVICA, J. X. & DAVIS, J. L. 1998. The BIFROST project: GPS determined 3-D displacement rates in Fennoscandia from 800 days of continuous observations in the SWEPO network. *Tectonophysics*, **294**, 305–321.

SCHNEIDER, G. 1979. The earthquake in the Swabian Jura of 16 Nov. 1911 and present concepts of seismotectonics. *Tectonophysics*, **53**, 279–288.

SCHNEIDER, G. 1980. Das Beben vom 3. September 1978 auf der Schwäbischen Alb als Ausdruck der seismotektonischen Beweglichkeit Suedwestdeutschlands. *Jahresberichte und Mitteilungen des Oberrheinischen Geologischen Vereins, N. F.*, **62**, 143–166.

SCHNEIDER, G. 1993. Beziehungen zwischen Erdbeben und Strukturen der Süddeutschen Großscholle. *Neues Jahrbuch für Geologie und Paläontologie – Abhandlungen*, **189**, 275–288.

SCHRÖDER, B. 1987. Inversion tectonics along the western margin of the Bohemian Massif. *Tectonophysics*, **137**, 93–100.

SCHRÖDER, B. 1988. Outline of the Permo-Carboniferous basins at the western margin of the Bohemian massif. *Zeitschrift für geologische Wissenschaften*, **16**, 993–1001.

SCHRÖDER, B., AHRENDT, H., PETEREK, A. & WEMMER, K. 1997. Post-Variscan sedimentary record of the SW margin of the Bohemian massif: a review. *Geologische Rundschau*, **86**, 178–184.

SCHUMACHER, M. E. 2002. Upper Rhine Graben: Role of preexisting structures during rift evolution. *Tectonics*, **21**(1). DOI: 10.1029/2001TC900022.

SCHWAB, G. 1985. *Paläomobilität der Norddeutsch-Polnischen Senke*. Dissertation, Akademie der Wissenschaften der DDR, Potsdam.

SCHWARZER, K., DIESING, M., LARSON, M., NIEDERMEYER, R. O., SCHUMACHER, W. & FURMANCZYK, K. 2003. Coastline evolution at different time scales – examples from the Pomerian Bight, southern Baltic Sea. *Marine Geology*, **194**, 79–101.

SIEBEL, W., BLAHA, U., CHEN, F. & ROHRMÜLLER, J. 2005. Geochronology and geochemistry of a dyke-host rock association and implications for the formation of the Bavarian Pfahl shear zone, Bohemian Massif. *International Journal of Earth Sciences*, **94**, 8–23.

SIEBERG, A. & LAIS, R. 1925. *Das mitteleuropäische Erdbeben vom 16.11.1911, Bearbeitung der makroseismischen Beobachtungen.* Veröffentlichungen der Reichsanstalt für Erdbebenforschung Jena, H. 4, Jena.

SIROCKO, F. 1998. Die Entwicklung der nordostdeutschen Ströme unter dem Einfluß jüngster tektonischer Bewegungen. *Brandenburgische Geowissenschaftliche Beiträge*, **5**(1): 75–80.

SISSINGH, W. 1998. Comparative Tertiary stratigraphy of the Rhine Graben, Bresse Graben and Molasse Basin: correlation of Alpine foreland events. *Tectonophysics*, **300**, 249–284.

SISSINGH, W. 2003*a*. Tertiary paleogeographic and tectonostratigraphic evolution of the Rhenish Triple Junction. *Palaeogeography Palaeoclimatology Palaeoecology*, **196**, 229–263.

SISSINGH, W. 2003*b*. *Stratigraphic Framework of the European Cenozoic Rift System: A Visual Overview.* Geologica Ultraiectina, Special Publications, **2**.

ŠPIČÁKOVÁ, L., ULIČNÝ, D. & KOUDELKOVÁ, G. 2000. Tectonosedimentary evolution of the Cheb Basin (NW Bohemia, Czech Republic) between Late Oligocene and Pliocene: A preliminary note. *Studia geophysica et geodetica*, **44**, 556–580.

SRTM 2000. Shuttle Radar Topographic Mission data set. World Wide Web address: ftp://edcsgs9.cr.usgs.gov/pub/data/srtm

STACKEBRANDT, W. 2004. Zur Neotektonik in Norddeutschland. *Zeitschrift für geologische Wissenschaften*, **32**, 85–96.

STANKOWSKI, W. 1996. *Wstęp do geologii Kenozoiku.* Wydawnictwo Naukowe UAM, Poznań.

STEFANIUK, M., BARANOWSKI, P., CZOPEK, B. & MAĆKOWSKI, T. 1996. Study of compaction in the Pomeranian Anticlinorium Area. *Oil and Gas News From Poland*, **6**, 150–162.

STELLRECHT, R. & MOELLE, K. H. R. 1980. Bruchtektonisch-genetisches Modell des Hohenzollern- und Lauchertgrabens/Süddeutschland. *Jahresberichte und Mitteilungen des Oberrheinischen Geologischen Vereins, N. F.*, **62**, 229–250.

STEWART, I. S., SAUBER, J. & ROSE, J. 2000. Glacio-seismotectonics: ice sheets, crustal deformation and seismicity. *Quaternary Science Reviews*, **19**, 1367–1389.

STRÖBEL, W. 1953. Neue tektonische Aufschlüsse bei Sindelfingen (Württemberg). *Neues Jahrbuch für Geologie und Paläontologie – Abhandlungen*, **97**, 328–337.

ŚWIDROWSKA, J. & HAKENBERG, M. 1999. Subsidence and the problem of incipient inversion of the Mid-Polish Trough based on thickness maps and Cretaceous lithofacies analysis – discussion. *Przegląd Geologiczny*, **47**(1), 61–68 [in Polish with English summary].

TESAURO, M., HOLLENSTEIN, C., EGLI, R., GEIGER, A. & KAHLE, H.-G. 2005. Continuous GPS and broad-scale deformation across the Rhine Graben and the Alps. *International Journal of Earth Sciences*, **94**, 525–537.

THOMSON, S. N., BRIX, M. R. & CARTER, A. 1997. Late Cretaceous denudation of the Harz Massif assessed by apatite fission track analysis. *Schriftenreihe der Deutschen Geologischen Gesellschaft*, **2**, 115.

TIMAR-GENG, Z., FÜGENSCHUH, B., WETZEL, A. & DRESMANN, H. 2006. Low-temperature thermochronology of the flanks of the southern Upper Rhine Graben. *International Journal of Earth Sciences*, **95**, 685–702.

TRÜMPY, R. 1980. *Geology of Switzerland. A Guide-book. Part A: An Outline of the Geology of Switzerland.* Wepf, Basel, Switzerland.

TSCHANZ, X. 1990. Analyse de la déformation dans le Jura central entre Neuchâtel (Suisse) et Besançon (France). *Eclogae geologicae Helvetiae*, **83**, 543–558.

TURNOVSKY, J. 1981. *Herdmechanismen und Herdparameter der Erdbebenserie 1978 auf der Schwäbischen Alb.* PhD thesis, Universität Stuttgart.

ULRYCH, J., LLOYD, F. E. & BALOGH, K. 2003. Age relations and geochemical constraints of Cenozoic alkaline volcanic series in W Bohemia: a review. *Geolines*, **15**, 168–180.

UNDERHILL, J. R. 1998. Jurassic. *In:* GLENNIE, K. W. (ed.) *Petroleum Geology of the North Sea.* Blackwell, Oxford, 245–293.

USTASZEWSKI, K., SCHUMACHER, M. E. & SCHMID, S. M. 2005. Simultaneous normal faulting and extensional flexuring during rifting: an example from the southernmost Upper Rhine Graben. *International Journal of Earth Sciences*, **94**, 680–696.

VAN BALEN, R. T., VERWEIJ, J. M., VAN WEES, J. D., SIMMELINK, H., VAN BERGEN, F. & PAGNIER, H. 2002*a*. Deep subsurface temperatures in the Roer Valley Graben and Peel Block, the Netherlands – new results. *Netherlands Journal of Geosciences/Geologie en Mijnbouw*, **81**, 19–26.

VAN BALEN, R.T., HOUTGAST, R. F., VAN DER WATEREN, F. M. & VANDENBERGHE, J. 2002*b*. Neotectonic evolution and sediment budget of the Meuse catchment in the Ardennes and the Roer Valley Rift system. *Netherlands Journal of Geosciences/Geologie en Mijnbouw*, **81**, 211–215.

VAN DEN BERG, M. W. 1994. Neotectonics of the Roer Valley rift system. Style and rate of crustal deformation inferred from syntectonic sedimentation. *Geologie en Mijnbouw*, **73**, 143–156.

VAN MIERLO, J. & HARTMANN, P. 1989. *Kriechende Spannungsumwandlungen: Rezente vertikale und horizontale Bewegungen.* Report SFB 108 "Spannung und Spannungsumwandlung in der Lithosphäre", 1987–1989, Teil A, University of Karlsruhe, Karlsruhe, 17–63.

VAN MIERLO, J., OPPEN, S., RAUHUT, P. & VOGEL, M. 1992. *Kriechende Spannungsumwandlungen: Rezente vertikale und horizontale Bewegungen.* Report SFB 108 "Spannung und Spannungsumwandlung in der Lithosphäre", 1990–1992, Teil B, University of Karlsruhe, Karlsruhe, 657–723.

VAN WEES, J.-D., STEPHENSON, R. A., *et al.* 2000. On the origin of the Southern Permian Basin, Central Europe. *Marine and Petroleum Geology*, **17**, 43–59.

VILLEMIN, T. & BERGERAT, F. 1987. L'évolution structurale du fossé rhénan au cours du Cénozoique : un bilan de la déformation et des effets thermiques de l'extension. *Bulletin de la Société géologique de France, série 8*, **3**, 245–255.

VINKENA, R. 1988. *Results of the International Geological Correlation Programme, Project No. 124.* Geologisches Jarbich Reikr, A100, Hannover.

VOIGT, E. 1963. Über Randtröge vor Schollenrändern und ihre Bedeutung im Gebiet der Mitteleuropäischen Senke und angrenzender Gebiete. *Zeitschrift der deutschen geologischen Gesellschaft*, **113**, 378–418.

VOIGT, T., V. EYNATTEN, H. & FRANZKE, H. J. 2004. Late Cretaceous unconformities in the Subhercynian Cretaceous Basin (Germany). *Acta Geologica Polonica*, **54**, 673–694.

VOIGT, T., WIESE, F., V. EYNATTEN, H., FRANZKE, H. J. & GAUPP, R. 2006. Facies evolution of syntectonic Upper Cretaceous deposits in the Subhercynian Cretaceous Basin and adjoining areas (Germany). *Zeitschrift der deutschen Gesellschaft für Geowissenschaften*, **157**, 203–244.

WAGNER, G. 1961. *Raumbilder zur Erd- und Landschaftsgeschichte Südwestdeutschlands.* Spectrum Verlag, Stuttgart.

WAHLSTROM, R. 1989. Seismodynamics and postglacial faulting in the Baltic Shield. *In:* GREGERSEN, S. & BASHAM, P. W. (eds) *Earthquakes at the North Atlantic Passive Margins: Neotectonics and Postglacial Rebound.* Kluwer, Dordrecht, 467–482.

WEINLICH, F., BRÄUER, K., KÄMPF, H., STRAUCH, G., TESAR, J. & WEISE, S. M. 1999. An active subcontinental mantle volatile system in the western Eger rift, Central Europe: Gas flux, isotopic (He, C, and N) and compositional fingerprints. *Geochimica et Cosmochimica Acta*, **63**, 3653–3671.

WEINLICH, F. H., BRÄUER, K., KÄMPF, H., STRAUCH, G., TESAR, J. & WEISE, S. M. 2003. Gas flux and tectonic structure in the western Eger Rift, Karlovy Vary – Oberpfalz and Oberfranken, Bavaria. *Geolines*, **15**, 181–187.

WEINLICH, F. H., FABER, E., BOUSKOVA, A., HORALEK, J., TESCHNER, M. & POGGENBURG, J. 2006. Seismically induced variations in Marianske Lazne fault gas composition in the NW Bohemian swarm quake region, Czech Republic – A continuous gas monitoring. *Tectonophysics*, **421**, 89–110.

WERNER, W. & FRANZKE, H. J. 2001. Postvariszische bis neogene Bruchtektonik und Mineralisation im südlichen Zentralschwarzwald. *Zeitschrift der deutschen geologischen Gesellschaft*, **152**, 405–437.

WERNER, W., FRANZKE, H. J., WIRSING, G., JOCHUM, J. LÜDERS, V. & WITTENBRINK, J. 2002. *Die Erzlagerstätte Schauinsland bei Freiburg im Breisgau.* Aedificatio Verlag, Freiburg.

WETZEL, H.-U. & FRANZKE, H. J. 2003. Lassen sich über die Fernerkundung erweiterte Kenntnisse zur seismogenen Zone

Bodensee-Stuttgart (9°-Ost) gewinnen? *Publikationen der Deutschen Gesellschaft für Photogrammetrie und Fernerkundung*, **12**, 339–347.

WIEJACZ, P. 1994. An attempt to determine tectonic stress patterns in Poland. *Acta Geophysica Polonica*, **3**, 169–176.

WIEJACZ, P. 2004. Preliminary investigation of the September 21, 2004, earthquakes of Kaliningrad region, Russia. *Acta Geophysica Polonica*. **52**, 425–441.

WIEJACZ, P. & GIBOWICZ, J. 1997. Source mechanism determined by miment tensor inversion for seismic events at Rudna and Polkowice cooper mines in Poland. *Acta Geophysica Polonica*, **45**, 291–302.

WREDE, V. 1988. Der nördliche Harzrand – flache Abscherbahn oder wrench-fault-system? *Geologische Rundschau*, **77**, 101–114.

WURM, F. 1985. Einblick in die erdgeschichtliche Vergangenheit das geologische Fenster an der Pfarrwiesenallee in Sindelfingen. *Jahrbuch Sindelfingen*, 256–262.

WURM, F. 1992. Die Sindelfinger Störungszone - Entwicklung und Bau einer herzynischen Struktur im süddeutschen Schichtstufenland. *Frankfurter geowissenschaftliche Arbeiten, A*, **11**, 317–319.

WURSTER, P. 1986. Development of the South German Triangle: some geological remarks. *In:* FREEMAN, R., MUELLER, S. & GIESE, P. (eds) *Proceedings of the Third Workshop on the European Geotraverse (EGT) Project*, Strasbourg, 179–186.

WYRZYKOWSKI, T. 1985. *Mapa prędkości współczesnych pionowych ruchów powierzchni skorupy ziemskiej na obszarze Polski*. Instytut Geodezji i Kartografii, Warszawa.

ZIEGLER, P. A. 1990. *Geological Atlas of Western and Central Europe*, 2nd edn. Shell Internationale Petroleum Maatschappij B.V. (distributed by Geological Society, London).

ZIEGLER, P. A. 1994. Cenozoic rift system of western and central Europe: an overview. *Geologie en Mijnbouw*, **73**, 99–127.

ZIJERVELD, L., STEPHENSON, R., CLOETHING, S., DUIN, E. & VAN DEN BERG, M. W. 1992. Subsidence analysis and modelling of the Roer Valley Graben (SE Netherlands). *Tectonophysics*, **208**, 159–171.

ZOBACK, M. L. 1992. First- and second-order patterns of stress in the lithosphere: the World Stress Map Project. *Journal of Geophysical Research*, **97**(B8), 11703–11728.

ZUCHIEWICZ, W. 1991. On different approaches to neotectonics: A Polish Carpathians example. *Episodes*, **14**, 116–124.

ZUCHIEWICZ, W. 1995. Neotectonics of Poland: a state-of-the-art review. *Folia Quaternaria*, **66**, 7–37.

ZUCHIEWICZ, W. 2000. Mapy w skali 1: 5 000 000: Współczesne ruchy tektoniczne, Ruchy tektoniczne w czwartorzędzie I, II, Jednostki neotektoniczno-strukturalne. *In:* MAÇIEJOWSKI, W. & ULISZAK, R. (eds) *Encyklopedia Geograficzna Świata. Atlas Polski*. OPRES, Krakow, 29–30.

ZUCHIEWICZ, W., TOKARSKI, A. K., JAROSIŃSKI, M. & MÁRTON, E. 2002. Late Miocene to present day structural development of the Polish segment of the Outer Carpathians. *EGU Stephan Mueller Special Publication Series*. Copernicus, Northeim, **3**, 185–202.

ZULAUF, G. 1993. Brittle deformation events at the western border of the Bohemian Massif (Germany). *Geologische Rundschau*, **82**, 489–504.

ZULAUF, G. & DUYSTER, J. 1997. Faults and veins in the superdeep well KTB: constraints on the amount of Alpine intra-plate thrusting and stacking of Variscan basement (Bohemian Massif, Germany). *Geologische Rundschau*, **86**(suppl.), S28-S33.

# 20 Quaternary

THOMAS LITT (co-ordinator), HANS-ULRICH SCHMINCKE, MANFRED FRECHEN & CHRISTIAN SCHLÜCHTER

The Quaternary as a System is traditionally considered to be the Ice Age – an interval of oscillating climate extremes (glacials and interglacials) encompassing the Pleistocene and the Holocene as Series. The term was formally introduced by Desnoyers (1829). The basic principles used in subdividing the Quaternary into chronostratigraphic units are the same as for other Phanerozoic units which require boundary definitions and the designation of boundary stratotypes (Salvador 1994). However, in contrast to the rest of the Phanerozoic, the division of Quaternary sequences on the basis of climatic changes documented in the sedimentary record is fundamental and has a long tradition. Classifications based on climatostratigraphic units such as 'glacials' or 'interglacials' are reasonably well-established in different countries or areas of Central Europe, and are accepted as regional chronostratigraphic standards (Gibbard & West 2000; Gibbard & Kolfschoten 2004; Litt *et al.* 2005).

The climatostratigraphic terms 'interglacial' and 'interstadial' were first defined by Jessen & Milthers (1928) for periods with characteristic records of non-glacial climate, as indicated by palaeobotanical evidence for major vegetation changes. Following these suggestions, interglacials in Central Europe are classified as temperate periods with a climate optimum at least as strong as the present interglacial (Holocene) in the same region. Interstadials are assumed to have been either too short or too cold to reach the climate level of interglacial type in the same region.

In North America, the fundamental units of geological–climate classification have been defined as follows (American Commission on Stratigraphic Nomenclature 1961): 'A glaciation is a climatic episode during which extensive glaciers developed, attained a maximum extent, and receded. A stadial is a climatic episode, representing a subdivision of a glaciation, during which a secondary advance of glaciers took place. An interstadial is a climatic episode within a glaciation during which a secondary recession or standstill of glaciers took place. An interglacial is an episode during which the climate was incompatible with the wide extent of glaciers that characterize a glaciation' (see also Gibbard & Kolfschoten 2004). The glacially based terms, however, are very difficult to apply in regions which were not directly affected by ice activity. Furthermore, cold rather than glacial climates have often tended to characterize the periods between interglacial events. Therefore, the term 'cold stage' has been adopted instead of 'glacial' or 'glaciation' (Gibbard & West 2000).

The status of the Quaternary, long regarded as a geological period, has recently been questioned as a formal stratigraphic unit, with proposals for its abandonment or modification (Gradstein *et al.* 2004; Pillans 2004; Steininger 2002). Gibbard *et al.* (2005), however, argue that the Quaternary should be retained as a formal period of geological time following the Neogene which would be formally subdivided into the Pleistocene and Holocene epochs (see also Bowen & Gibbard 2006). A formal decision on its chronostratigraphic status is pending.

The precise definition of the base of the Pleistocene (and Quaternary) has also been the subject of discussion (Partridge 1997; Gibbard *et al.* 2005). The classification of this boundary in central Europe traditionally follows that used in the Netherlands. Thus, the Pliocene–Pleistocene boundary, and consequently the base of the entire Quaternary, is defined by the first unequivocal cooling (Praetiglian Stage) at the end of the Neogene. This climatic deterioration led to the extinction of typical Tertiary floral elements such as *Sequoia, Nyssa, Liquidambar* and *Sciadopitys* after the Reuverian Stage (Zagwijn 1960, 1963, 1974). This climatically induced floral change is convenient for the correlation of terrestrial records within Central Europe. Furthermore, it is easily reproducible due to its position slightly above the palaeomagnetically defined Gauss–Matuyama boundary (*c.* 2.6 Ma BP; see Partridge 1997). However, at the 27th International Geological Congress in Moscow (1984), the Vrica profile in Italy was established as a Global Stratotype Section and Point (GSSP) for the lower boundary of the Pleistocene (top of the Olduvai magnetic zone, *c.* 1.8 Ma BP; see Aguirre & Pasini 1985). This definition, however, has been criticized because it does not cover the first cold climatic event in the late Cenozoic (Zagwijn 1992, 1998; Partridge 1997; Suc *et al.* 1997; Mauz 1998). The Commission on Quaternary Stratigraphy of the International Union for Quaternary Reasearch (INQUA) thus suggested a new definition of the Pliocene–Pleistocene boundary that corresponds to the Gauss–Matuyama magnetic epoch boundary (2.6 Ma BP; see Partridge 1997). A joint vote of the International Subcommissions on Neogene and Quaternary Stratigraphy took place in 1998, but failed to achieve the required two-thirds majority. Consequently, the Vrica section is still considered to be the GSSP for the base of the Pleistocene (i.e. beginning of the Calabrium). Nevertheless, many scientists studying Quaternary sequences in Central Europe favour defining the Quaternary as beginning prior to the base of the Pleistocene GSSP at Vrica. Furthermore, they tend to consider the beginning of the Pleistocene to be coincident with the base of the Dutch terrestrial Praetiglian Stage (e.g. Heumann & Litt 2002; Gibbard & Kolfschoten 2004; Gibbard *et al.* 2005, Bowen & Gibbard 2006).

In terms of the subdivision of the Pleistocene, a quasi-formal tripartite classification into Lower, Middle and Upper is generally used. At the XIIth INQUA Congress in Ottawa (1987), the responsible stratigraphic commission also suggested using the palaeomagnetically defined Brunhes–Matuyama boundary (780 ka BP) as the boundary between the Lower and Middle Pleistocene (Richmond 1996). While there is broad international support for this proposal (e.g. Pillans 2003), a GSSP has not yet been formally defined. The boundary between the Middle and Upper Pleistocene is also not yet formally defined. The last glacial (Weichselian–Würmian) and the last interglacial (Eemian) are considered to be included in the Upper Pleistocene, at least in Europe, based on the milestone publications of Woldstedt (1955) and Zeuner (1959). Gibbard (2003) has proposed using the beginning of the last interglacial (126 ka years ago) as the Middle–Upper Pleistocene boundary. In addition, he has suggested using the newly processed cores from the Amsterdam Terminal (parastratotype for the Eemian; see van Leeuwen *et al.* 2000) as the boundary stratotype. This proposal is currently under examination by a working group of the International Subcommission on Quaternary Stratigraphy.

Whereas the basal chronostratigraphic units (stages/ages) have not yet been formally defined internationally, cold and warm intervals are used as chronstratigraphic units in terms of regional stages in both northern and central Europe (e.g. Elsterian Cold Stage, Weichselian Cold Stage or Würmian Cold Stage in the Alpine region, Holsteinian Warm Stage, Eemian Warm Stage; see Gibbard & Kolfschoten 2004; Litt *et al.* 2005). The chronostratigraphic units include several complex stages (e.g. Cromerian, Tiglian, Saalian).

This chapter is subdivided into four parts: (1) the Quaternary ice age in the glacially affected north-central Europe; (2) the Quaternary ice age in the Alps; (3) periglacial environments in north-central Europe, and (4) Quaternary volcanism of the East and West Eifel, Central Europe. The first two parts are clearly related to areas which were strongly affected by glaciations. Therefore, special emphasis is placed on the relationship between glacial and interglacial deposits in both regions, because in other parts of Central Europe, from which Quaternary successions are known (i.e. the periglacial area), relationships to particular glaciations are sometimes difficult to clarify. The north-central European lowland as well as the Alpine region provide good opportunities to establish regional chronostratigraphies of the Pleistocene. Tephrochronology can aid identification of particular volcanic events as golden spikes for correlation and synchronization of Quaternary sequences in Europe. In addition, the Quaternary Eifel volcanic fields are key areas for investigating the ongoing geodynamic processes beneath Central Europe.

## The ice age in north-central Europe (T.L.)

The north-central European lowland – affected by the Fenno-Scandinavian ice sheets – is a classic region for the study of Quaternary geology on a continental scale. Morlot (1844) suggested that a Scandinavian ice sheet might have reached the Erzgebirge (Ore Mountains) in Saxony (Eissmann *et al.* 1995). The recognition of glacial striae on the Triassic limestone rocks at Rüdersdorf near Berlin by Torell (1875) resulted in the general acceptance of the glacial theory in Germany and adjacent regions. It was assumed by Penck (1879) that northern Germany had been affected by three glaciations. The mapping of the Pleistocene ice margins by the Prussian Geological Survey, starting in 1910, was a milestone for the understanding of the Quaternary sequences, and the terms Elsterian, Saalian and Weichselian were introduced. Quaternary geologists from Saxony and Prussia such as L. Siegert, W. Weißermel, K. Keilhack, R. Grahmann and P. Woldstedt recognized the fundamental pattern of the glacial history of the north-central European lowlands and its correlation with fluvial processes during the first decades of the twentieth century. Additionally, the Quaternary geology of this region is well known because of the presence of closely spaced boreholes and open-cast lignite mines. Of particular importance is the detailed knowledge with regard to the inter-digitation of fluvial and glacial facies, i.e. the relationship between the terrace deposits, till sheets and interglacial sequences (Benda 1995; Ehlers 1994; Ehlers *et al.* 1995; Ehlers & Gibbard 2004; Eissmann & Litt 1994).

### *Lower Pleistocene*

The chronostratigraphic subdivision of the north-central European Lower Pleistocene was mainly influenced by biostratigraphic data from the Netherlands (stage names such as the Praetiglian, Tiglian, Eburonian, Waalian, Menapian and Bavelian; Zagwijn 1985; see Fig. 20.1). Pollen analysis in particular has been used to construct a climatic record that is as complete as possible. However, because the sedimentary basin in the Netherlands is largely fluvial, the pollen record had to be constructed using data from different sites. The climate pattern shows cool to warm temperate forests, alternating with an open vegetation, representing a colder climate. The Praetiglian Stage is the first remarkable cooling during the Upper Cenozoic and is characterized by a predominance of non-arboreal (herb) pollen. However, the palaeoclimatic variation during the Lower Pleistocene is more complicated and cannot be represented in a simple warm–cold classification scheme. For example, the Tiglian Stage was initially thought to be a warm stage. Later it became clear that it is a climatically complex interglacial stage with alternating cooler and warmer phases. Permafrost conditions may even have occurred during at least one of the cooler phases (Kasse 1993).

In northern Germany, the classification of the Lower Pleistocene, which was not glacially affected, is mainly based on a long continental profile at Lieth in Schleswig-Holstein (Menke 1975). The criteria for the palaeoclimatological classification into cold and warm stages are based on palynology. The Lieth succession is the most informative profile for almost the entire lower Pleistocene in north-central Europe (Fig. 20.2). It documents the timespan from the beginning of the Praetiglian (Kaltenhörn Cold Stage) up to the Bavelian Complex (Pinneberg Warm Stage) extremely well in a continuous section (Stephan & Menke 1993). In this respect, the Lieth sequence is more complete than the different type sections in the Netherlands. The lower Pleistocene in northern Germany lacks the typical Pliocene flora (with *Sequoia, Nyssa* etc.), though the presence of some Pliocene elements like *Tsuga, Carya* and *Eucommia* represents a significant difference from the Middle and Upper Pleistocene. In addition, the cold intervals are less severe than the glacial stages of the Middle and Upper Pleistocene.

The onset of a cold climate in the Praetiglian Stage led to a marked change in the depositional style of the NW European rivers, for example the Rhine and the Meuse, as reflected in the increased input of gravels and the development of a braided system (Gibbard 1988). The return to temperate conditions in the Tiglian led to the re-establishment of the meandering river form and the deposition of fine-grained sediments. The subsequent period of cold climate in the Eburonian and Menapian resulted in frost weathering and, therefore, the loading of rivers with freshly eroded detrital material. This significant increase in sediment load is reflected in the expansion of deltaic environments in the Netherlands.

In central Germany three Lower Pleistocene glacial terraces, assigned to the regionally defined Mulde, Whyra and Pleiße cold stages respectively, were described by Eissmann (1995). Intraformational frost phenomena such as ice-wedge casts, indicating permafrost conditions, are present in all of these gravel-dominated terrace deposits.

There is evidence that all of the major rivers in north-central Europe have repeatedly changed their course since the Lower Pleistocene as a result of the Middle Pleistocene glaciations (Fig. 20.3). However, considerable readjustments of river courses are also known from the preglacial part of the Pleistocene (Eissmann 1995). The destruction of the fluvial courses in the Baltic region

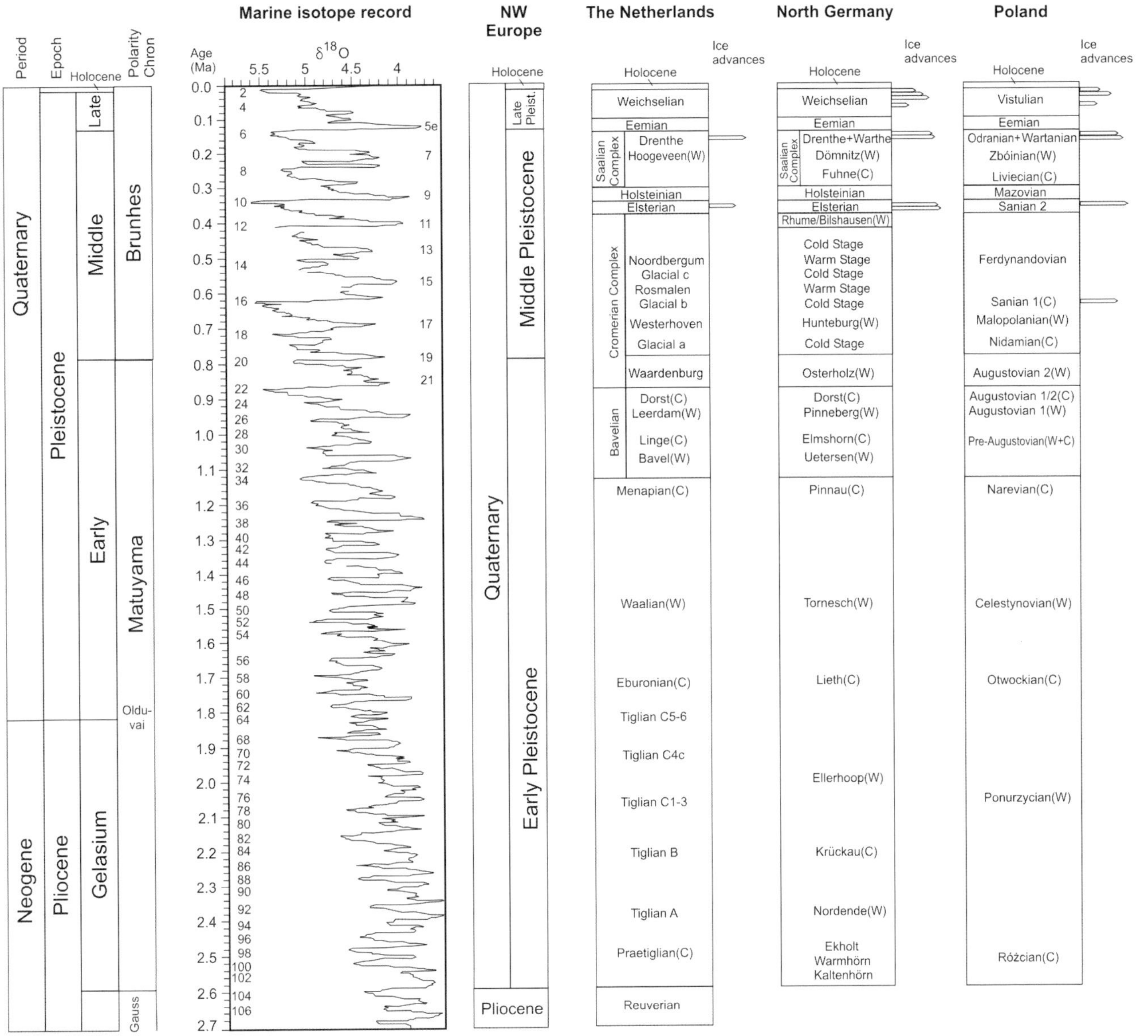


**Fig. 20.1.** Stratigraphic subdivision of the Quaternary in north-central Europe. Global chronostratigraphy and marine isotope record modified after Gibbard & Kolfschoten (2004); subdivision of the Quaternary sequences in the Netherlands after Zagwijn (1989), in northern Germany after Litt *et al.* (2005), in Poland after Lindner *et al.* (2004).

during the Menapian may have been the result of glaciation in Scandinavia which led to the formation of a proto-Baltic Basin as a result of glacial scour (Gibbard 1988). In addition, the so-called Hattem Beds in the Netherlands are characterized by major quantities of Scandinavian erratics (Zandstra 1993).

## *Middle Pleistocene*

### *Cromerian Complex Stage*

The 'Cromerian Complex' Stage of the Netherlands, that mainly corresponds to the early Middle Pleistocene, is subdivided into four warm temperate and three cold substages (Zagwijn 1985, 1996) indicating the climatic complexity of this particular time interval (Fig. 20.1). As previously noted, the Early–Middle Pleistocene boundary should be linked to the Brunhes–Matuyama palaeomagnetic boundary which is either within Interglacial I (Waardenburg) of the Cromerian Complex or a little later (780 ka, Marine Isotope Stage 19; see Turner 1996). The upper boundary of the Cromerian Complex is widely accepted in north-central Europe and is located at the point where major climate cooling heralds the onset of the Elsterial Glacial Stage.

In northern Germany, the warm stages of the lower Middle Pleistocene were palynostratigraphically defined based on a long continental record at Gorleben (Müller 1986, 1992). The Gorleben sequence encompasses five warm phases in a stratigraphic superposition above the Bavelian and below the Elsterian stages (Fig. 20.4). The oldest phase is that of the mainly reversely magnetized Osterholz interglacial (= Waardenburg). The youngest one, the Rhume (or Bilshausen) Interglacial immediately preceding the Elsterian ice advance, is the best studied Cromerian interglacial in northern Germany. The duration of this interglacial is estimated as about 27 000 years, based on the

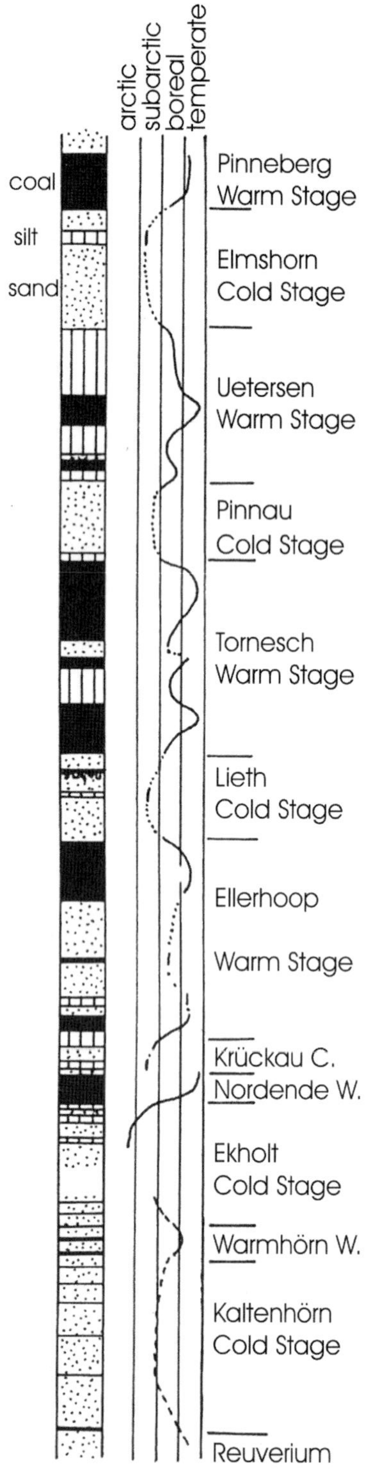


**Fig. 20.2.** Pliocene and Early Pleistocene sequence at Lieth, Schleswig-Holstein, northern Germany (after Stephan & Menke 1993). For correlation with equivalent stratigraphical units in the Netherlands see Figure 20.1.

varve counts of Müller (1992). The pollen sequence shows several oscillations and two distinct forest declines which may indicate rapid climate deteriorations. The youngest decline overlies a tephra layer derived from the Eifel Volcanic Field (probably the Rieden phase, see below). The pollen sequence of the Bilshausen Interglacial correlates well with the corresponding part of the Kärlich Interglacial in the Middle Rhine area (Bittmann & Müller 1996). The age of the so-called Brockentuff – a tephra layer related to the Kärlich Interglacial – is about 400 ka based on the $^{40}Ar/^{39}Ar$ laser method (P. Bogaard *et al.* 1989), which would correspond to Marine Isotope Stage (MIS) 11.

During the Cromerian Glacial A, glaciation in Scandinavia was more pronounced. There is evidence of a till bed in the central North Sea Basin which was deposited during that time (Sejrup *et al.* 1987). In Poland, the Ferdynandovian sequence suggests a possible early Middle Pleistocene glaciation. In accepting that the Ferdynandovian interglacial, which overlies a till, belongs to the Cromerian Complex (Zagwijn 1996), Rzechowski (1996) assumes that this glacial deposit (San I Till of the South Polish glaciation) must be of early Middle Pleistocene age (see also Mojski 1995). However, the correlation and synchronization of the early Middle Pleistocene records in Europe is still uncertain (Turner 1996).

*Elsterian Stage*

The term Elsterian (after the river Elster in central Germany) first appeared on 1:25 000 geological maps of the 'Königlich Preußische Geologische Landesanstalt' (i.e. Keilhack 1911). In the extraglacial areas, the onset of the Elsterian is characterized by a phase of intense gravel deposition. On hilly ground and along the lowland margin of central Germany, gravel units, up to 20 m thick, were deposited (Eissmann *et al.* 1995). Over 30% of the lowland area between the Elbe and Saale rivers was buried by the widespread Early Elsterian fluvial terrace. The gravels contain abundant frost structures such as cryoturbation, convolutions and frost wedges and these date from the period shortly before the main continental ice advance.

The oldest glaciation, represented by widespread till sheets throughout north-central Europe, is the Elsterian glaciation. Ice advance led to a complete reorganization of the fluvial drainage system across the region. Those rivers that previously had mostly drained into the Baltic Sea were dammed and forced to alter their courses (Eissmann *et al.* 1995; Ehlers *et al.* 2004). Glaciolacustrine deposits (varved clays) below and above the till beds are very common in the central German type region (i.e. Saxony). The river Elbe was dammed and formed a large lake up to 150 km long south of Dresden, with drainage to the west. Further to the east, rivers drained towards the river Danube and the Black Sea via the so-called Moravian Gate.

The Elsterian was the most extensive of all of the glaciations in the central German type region (Fig. 20.5). The maximum distribution of Nordic erratics, the so-called flint line, marks the extent of the Elsterian ice sheet. These sediments were not overridden by later ice sheets. During this stage, the continental ice advanced into the southern valleys of the Thuringian Basin up to an altitude of 300 m a.s.l., to 400 m a.s.l. at the foot of the Erzgebirge and to 450–500 m a.s.l. in the Oberlausitz area (Eissmann *et al.* 1995). However, the western extent of the ice sheet is uncertain. In the Wesergebirge, a flint line is found at an altitude of 200 m a.s.l., but this represents the upper limit of the Saalian ice sheet (Kaltwang 1992). The Elsterian limit was possibly lower (probably somewhere north of Osnabrück), and the deposits were subsequently overridden by the younger Saalian ice advance (Drenthe) not only in Lower Saxony (Niedersachsen), but also in Nordrhein-Westfalen and the Netherlands. At its maximum extent, the Elsterian ice sheet extended from the Dutch coast in a SW direction towards Ipswich in East Anglia (Laban & van der Meer 2004).

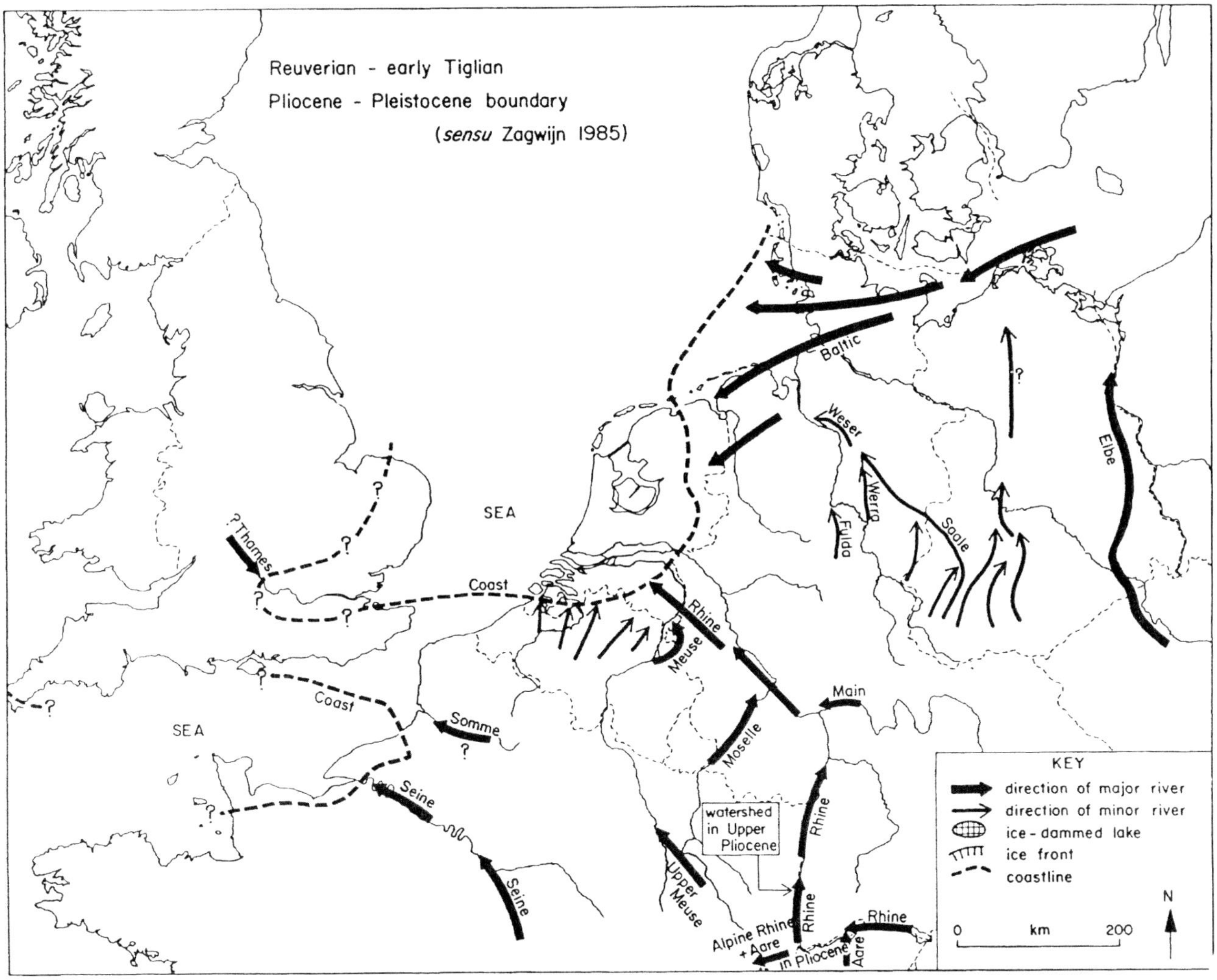


**Fig. 20.3.** Schematic palaeogeographical reconstruction of the major drainage lines during the Reuverian (Late Pliocene) and Early Tiglian (Early Pleistocene) Stages *sensu* Zagwijn (1985; from Gibbard 1988).

In most parts of Poland, the southernmost glacial limit is attributed to the South Polish Glaciations (Elsterian). Only in SW Poland this was locally overridden by the Odrian (Saalian 1) ice sheet (Marks 2004). The ice sheet of the Sanian 2 Glaciation (younger South Polish Glaciation) is the most extensive across much of Poland. It extended as far as the Carpathians and the Sudetian Mountain Zone in the south, and entered the Moravian Gate in the upper Oder drainage basin.

Two glacial cycles can be identified in the central German type region of the Elsterian Stage. In the older, the Zwickau Phase, the ice sheet reached its maximum extent. During the second, the Markranstädt Phase, it remained 20–50 km north of its earlier maximum (Eissmann *et al.* 1995). Both glacial cycles begin with the deposition of varved clays, followed by till and ending with various types of meltwater deposits (Fig. 20.6). A zone of ice decay, probably several hundred kilometres wide, can be recognized between both of these phases. This is termed the Miltitz Interval. However, no intra-Elsterian interglacial has been identified.

Both Elsterian Stage ice advances probably correlate with MIS 10 based on absolute dates of the preceding youngest Cromerian interglacial (MIS 11), as mentioned above, and the following Holsteinian interglacial (MIS 9, see below). The advances were associated with extensive erosion leading to the development of major erosional zones which were partly connected with the deeply incised valleys beneath the North German Lowlands (i.e. subglacial channels and basins). To the south of Berlin, channels are up to 250 m deep, while in NW Germany channels as deep as 400 m below sea level have been recognized (Ehlers *et al.* 1984; see also Fig. 20.7). They were gradually filled with glacial, glaciolacustrine and fluvial sediments. In the erosional zones, lakes formed which persisted through into the subsequent Holsteinian Stage.

*Holsteinian Stage*

The term Holsteinian originates from Geikie (1894), who described interglacial marine sediments as 'Holsteinian beds'. Hallik (1960) first defined the Holsteinian sediments palynostratigraphically and correlated them with continental/lacustrine interglacial records. The type sections of the Holsteinian are at Hamburg-Dockenhuden (marine deposits) and at Bossel to the west of Hamburg (lacustrine deposits) (see Jerz & Linke 1987; Linke & Hallik 1993). New Th–U dates based on peat deposits from the type section of Bossel near Hamburg indicate an age of

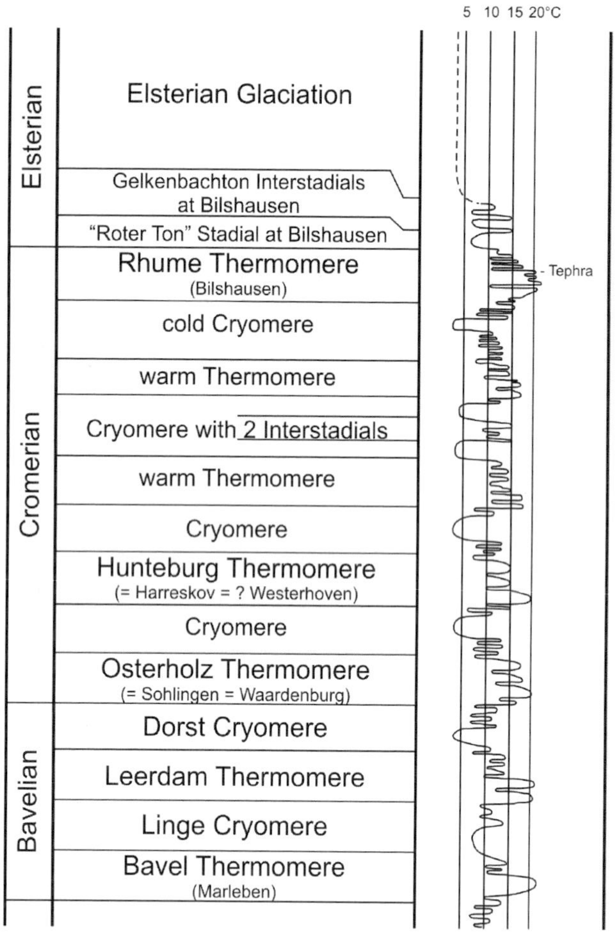


**Fig. 20.4.** Schematic diagram of the stratigraphy and reconstructed mean July temperature between Menapian and Elsterian in Lower Saxony, NW Germany (Gorleben sequence) (after Müller 1992).

about 310–330 ka BP (Geyh & Müller 2005). A sequence of consistent Th–U ages was also determined throughout the palynostratigraphically defined Hoxnian peat profile at Tottenhill (Norfolk) resulting in a mean age of around 320 ka (Rowe *et al.* 1997). The consequence of this is that the Holsteinian Interglacial in the type region as well as the equivalent Hoxnian Interglacial in England can be correlated with MIS 9 (for detailed geochronological discussion see Geyh & Müller 2005). This contradicts previous assumptions that MIS 11 should be correlated with the Holsteinian/Hoxnian stage (Sarnthein *et al.* 1986). However, absolute dates of the youngest interglacial of the Cromerian Complex immediately preceding the Elsterian correspond to MIS 11 (see above) and, thus, confirm the correlation between the Holsteinian and MIS 9. The duration of the Holsteinian is estimated as about 15 000 to 16 000 years, based on varve counts of Müller (1974*a*) at Munster-Breloh (lacustrine deposits).

The vegetation succession of the Holsteinian warm period has been described by several authors who recognized regionally differing pollen assemblage zones (Erd 1973 for eastern Germany; Müller 1974*a* for NW Germany; Krupinski 2000 for Poland where this interglacial stage is termed the Mazovian). The INQUA Subcommission on European Quaternary Stratigraphy defined the lower boundary of the Holsteinian as the transition from subarctic (late Elsterian) to boreal conditions, and the upper boundary as the transition from boreal to subarctic (Saalian) conditions (Jerz & Linke 1987).

The development of vegetation within this interglacial has been reconstructed by palynological data and is very similar throughout north-central Europe. The onset of the warm stage is generally marked by the establishment of a pine–birch (*Pinus–Betula*) forest (Fig. 20.8). The immigration of thermophilous trees including *Alnus, Quercus, Ulmus, Tilia, Fraxinus, Taxus* and *Corylus* occurred more or less simultaneously. The early expansion of *Picea* is remarkable, and *Carpinus* and *Abies* immigrated during the course of the interglacial. Particulary characteristic of the Holsteinian Stage in north-central Europe is the appearance of *Pterocarya* and *Azolla filiculuides,* both of which were extinct in Europe during the later Saalian Complex Stage.

The first half of the Holsteinian is characterized by temperatures somewhat lower than today. In the second half, the reconstructed mean temperatures are higher than today, in particular the July temperature (*c.* 1–2°C; see Kühl & Litt 2007). In addition, the Holsteinian would appear to be less stable than the present interglacial (Holocene) or the last interglacial (Eemian) with some intra-interglacial coolings. The magnitude of the main cooling in the Mid-Holsteinian is reconstructed as *c.* 5°C for January temperatures. No great change can be reconstructed for the July temperatures during this episode.

The Holsteinian Interglacial is characterized by a marine influence in northern Germany (Fig. 20.9). The transgression of the Holsteinian Sea reached not only the area of Hamburg, but also covered larger parts of the NE German lowland (Mecklenburg–Vorpommern).

*Saalian Complex Stage*

The term Saalian, named after the river Saale in central Germany, first appeared on the geological maps (1:25 000) of the Königlich Preußische Geologische Landesanstalt (i.e. Keilhack 1911). Based on the definition of the Subcommission on European Quaternary Stratigraphy (Litt & Turner 1993), the Saalian Complex Stage encompasses the period from the end of the Holsteinian Interglacial Stage (boundary between boreal and subarctic phase of the subsequent Fuhne cold phase) to the beginning of the Eemian Interglacial Stage (beginning of the birch zone). The Saalian was a complex period including several cold and warm fluctuations (Fig. 20.1).

The Lower Saalian Complex Stage, i.e. the period between the end of the Holsteinian Stage and the initial Saalian ice advance, is characterized by extensive widening of valleys and the accumulation of fluvial gravels. In the exposures (lignite open pits) of the type region in central Germany, a generally continuous, 5–20 m thick coarse sand and gravel terrace can be observed (Eissmann *et al.* 1995). This terrace sequence is an important lithostratigraphical marker horizon separating the Elsterian and Saalian glacigenic successions (Fig. 20.10). In many profiles several successive generations of ice wedge casts are found and silty intercalations are often disturbed by cryoturbation. However, this terrace complex also reflects changing climatic conditions during the Lower Saalian Substage. There is some evidence in north-central Europe of at least one pronounced warm event (Dömnitz warm Stage, NE Germany (Erd 1965), = Wacken warm Stage, NW Germany (Menke 1968)). Urban (1995) has even suggested the possibility of two warm periods (Reinsdorf and Schöningen interglacials). However, these warm phases are documented as incomplete pollen sequences. In no case are they separated by glacial sediments and stratigraphi-

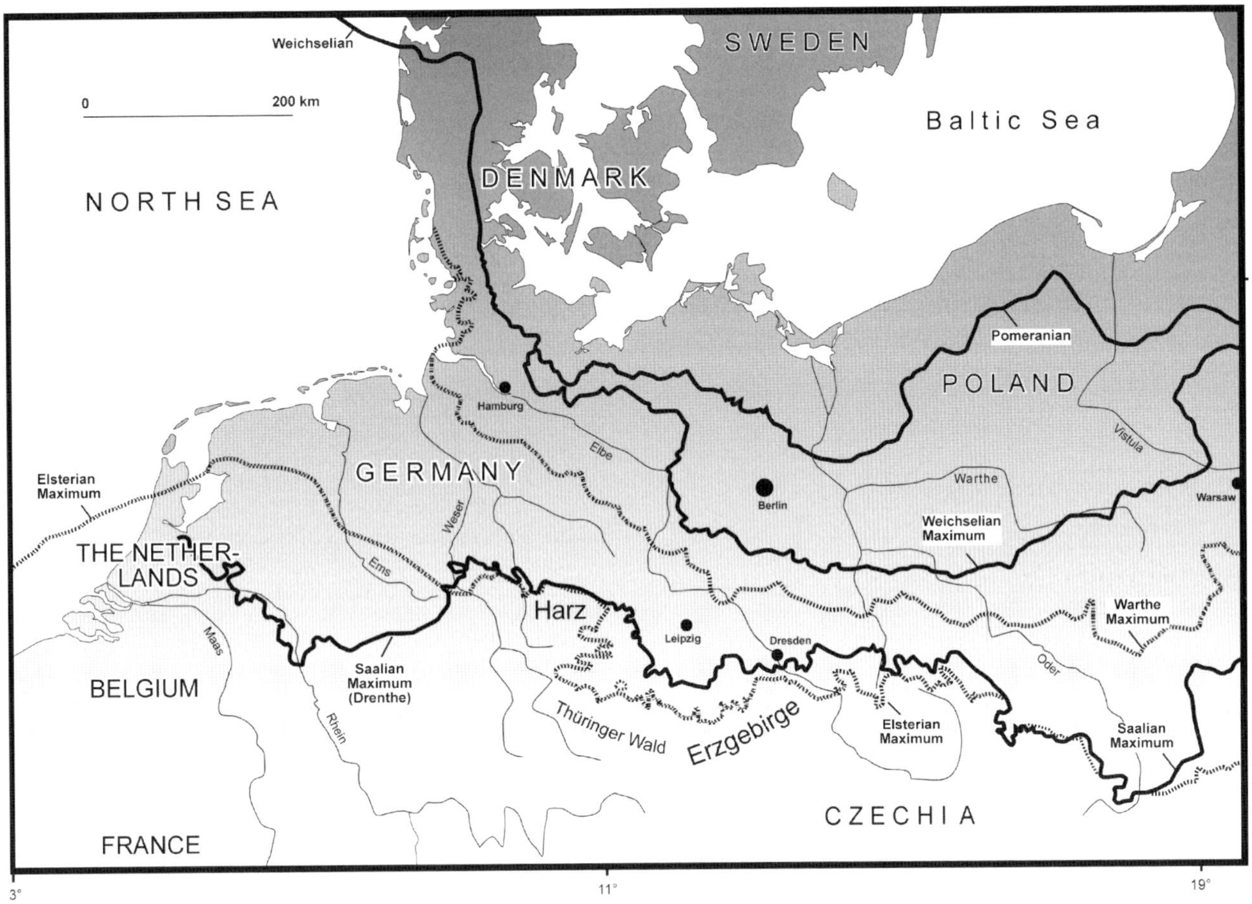


**Fig. 20.5.** Glacial limits and end moraines in north-central Europe (modified after Ehlers *et al.* 2004).

cally they are clearly positioned after the Holsteinian deposits and before the first Saalian ice advance (Fig. 20.6). For the Schöningen Interglacial (Urban 1995), which probably correlates with the Wacken/Dömnitz warm Stage, $^{230}$Th–$^{234}$U dates are available and these suggest that there is a correlation with MIS 7, whereas the Fuhne Cold Stage just after the Holsteinian, which is only documented by periglacial deposits, could be equivalent to MIS 8.

Comparable temperate conditions in between a period of periglacial climate have also been documented in the Netherlands (Zagwijn 1985; Vandenberghe 1995). This temperate interval (Hoogeveen) also preceded the advance of the Saalian land ice. Similar to the Wacken/Dömnitz warm stage, this is also decribed as an interstadial with interglacial character rather than a full interglacial based on the absence of *Abies* and thermophilous genera such as *Hedera* and *Buxus* which do occur in the underlying Holsteinian beds.

Several ice advances are known to have occurred in north-central Europe during the Upper Saalian Complex Stage. In northern Germany, the subdivision of the period into two major ice advances has been used since Woldstedt (1954). The older Saalian ice advance (i.e. Drenthe; Van der Vlerk & Florschütz 1950) marks the maximum extent of the Saalian ice sheet (Fig. 20.5). In the type region of the Saalian, between the Elbe and Saale rivers, two oscillations can be correlated to the Drenthe ice advance (Fig. 20.6). During the first one, the so-called Zeitz Phase, the Saalian ice sheet reached its southernmost extent at least as far south as the towns of Altenburg and Zeitz in Saxony and Thuringia (Eissmann *et al.* 1995). Further to the east, in the Elbe valley, it reached Meißen. Subsequently the ice margin retreated to the area north of Leipzig. The subsequent readvance extended to the area south of Leipzig (the so-called Leipzig Phase). The Polish Odra Glaciation (older Middle Polish Glaciation) is the equivalent of the older Saalian ice advance (Fig. 20.5). It reached the northern slopes of the Sudetes, the Polish Jura, the Holy Cross Mountains and the Lublin Upland (Mojski 1995; Marks 2004). It also overrode the so-called Moravian Gate, extending to the drainage divide between the Baltic and the Black seas. The glacial meltwaters flowed into the Danube drainage basin. The ice sheet blocked the river valleys in mid-eastern Poland, forming ice-dammed lakes. In the Netherlands, all Saalian glacial sediments are placed in one lithostratigraphic unit, the Drenthe Formation (Zagwijn 1961). This formation includes only one till sheet indicating a single ice advance (Laban & van der Meer 2004).

The younger Saalian ice advance is termed the Warthe Substage (Woldstedt 1954). The maximum extent of the ice sheet reached the area between the Weser and Elbe rivers to the west. Its maximum extent was more than 100 km behind the Drenthe maximum (Fig. 20.5). The so-called Aller-Weser Urstromtal served as the drainage pathway for the meltwaters. To the east, the ice sheet of the so-called Wartanian Glaciation in Poland (younger Middle Polish Glaciation) covered Wielkopolska, Mazovia and Podlasie (Marks 2004). The western part of the Polish region was drained by the sub-Sudetian ice-marginal streamway towards the Weser drainage system, and the eastern

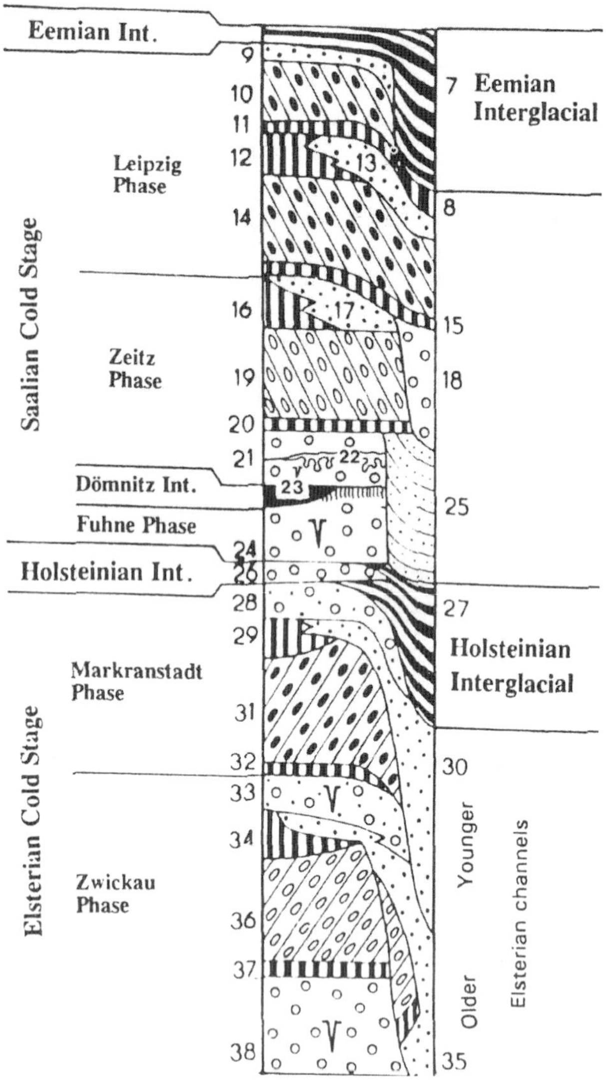


**Fig. 20.6.** Synopsis of the lithostratigraphy and facies of the glacially affected Middle Pleistocene in central Germany (Leipzig lowland and surrounding areas) (after Eissmann 1995). Key: 7, *Eemian* lacustrine sediments. *Saalian Complex Stage*: 8, glaciolacustrine varved clay and silt; 9, fluvial and glaciofluvial sand and gravel; 10, Upper Saalian Till, upper unit; 11, Upper Breitenfeld Varved Clay; 12, Lower Breitenfeld Varved Clay; 13, glaciofluvial sand and gravel; 14, Upper Saalian Till, lower unit; 15, Upper Bruckdorf Varved Clay; 16, Lower Bruckdorf Varved Clay; 17, glaciofluvial sand and gravel; 18, fluvial and glaciofluvial Pomßen Gravel; 19, Lower Saalian Till; 20, Böhlen and Lochau Varved Clay; 21–24, Main Terrace Complex (gravel); 21, upper gravel; 22, silt and fine sand, strongly cryoturbated Markkleeberg horizon; 23, mud, silt and fine sand; 24, lower gravel; 25, slope wash, solifluction and lacustrine sediments (fine sand and silt). *Holsteinian Stage*: 26, fine-grained gavel and sand; 27, lacustrine sediments. *Elsterian Stage*: 28, fluvial and glaciofluvial gravel and sand; 29, glaciolacustrine varved clay and silt; 30, glaciofluvial sand and gravel; 31, Upper Elsterian Till; 32, Miltitz Varved Clay; 33, fluvial and glaciofluvial gravel and sand; 34, Brösen Varved Clay; 35, glaciofluvial sand and gravel; 36, Lower Elsterian Till; 37, Dehlitz-Leipzig Varved Clay; 38, gravel and sand.

part drained into the Dnepr (Pilica-Piprat Urstromtal; Różycki 1965). Recently, Ehlers *et al.* (2004) argue that two ice advances may have occurred in northern Germany within the Warthe Substage *sensu* Woldstedt (1954). These have been termed the middle and younger Saalian glaciations. In the entire Nordic glaciation area, there is no evidence of interglacial deposits between any of the Saalian glacigenic deposits. Depressions in the land surface, either on the youngest Saalian glacial deposits or outside the area of the 'Warthe Line', are infilled only with Eemian lacustrine sediments (Fig. 20.11). In many cases these are glacial basins, which were already formed during the maximum advance of the Saalian glaciation. In these basins limnic sedimentation only began during the Saalian Late Glacial, heralding the Eemian Interglacial. In some cases it continued through the Early Weichselian. From this it can be concluded that between the maximum of the Saalian glaciation (i.e. the Drenthe phase) and the Eemian no true interglacial intervened, because otherwise it would have been documented in the sedimentary record. (Litt & Turner 1993; Eissmann & Litt 1995). Consequently, both the Drenthe and the Warthe are correlated with MIS 6.

## *Upper Pleistocene*

### *Eemian Stage*

The term Eemian (derived from a small creek near Amersfoort, the Netherlands) was proposed by Harting (1874), who used it to describe sediments deposited during a warm period. The term was first used for marine sediments of the last interglacial in Denmark, northern Germany and the Netherlands. Subsequently, it was expanded to include isochronous terrestrial sediments. The type section (Amersfoort Basin) has been palynostratigraphically defined by Zagwijn (1961). Recently, a borehole at Amsterdam Terminal has been suggested as a new parastratotype, because it is more complete (van Leeuwen *et al.* 2000). The U–Th age of the upper part of the interglacial deposits is $118.2 \pm 6.3$ ka BP (van Leeuwen *et al.* 2000). Currently, there is a consensus concerning the correlation and synchronization of the Eemian warm stage with MIS 5e. Consequently the onset of this warm stage is approximately 126 ka, with the termination at around 115 ka BP. Based on varve counts of Eemian lacustrine sediments from Bispingen/Niedersachsen, Müller (1974*b*) calculated the duration of the interglacial as being approximately 11 000 years.

In the area of the nordic glaciations, the Eemian Stage is by far the best-studied of the interglacials. In this northern area the sediments are located immediately above the glacial deposits of the Saalian Stage. Within the type area (Amersfoort Basin in the Netherlands, but also in the Amsterdam Basin as parastratotype) the classic Eemian sequences overlie the deposits of the Drenthe ice advance. In areas which were also affected by the younger Saalian ice advance (Warthe), Eemian deposits are found above the Warthe till (Eissmann & Litt 1995; see also Fig. 20.11).

At present, the definition of the Eemian pollen assemblage zones in Central Europe differs slightly according to the regional differences (see Aalbersberg & Litt 1998; Kühl & Litt 2003). The main characteristics of the vegetational succession are, however, unambiguously visible in most parts of Europe (Menke & Tynni 1984). The initial interglacial forest development is characterized by *Betula* woodland, followed by *Pinus* and mixed *Quercus* woodland (Fig. 20.12). Subsequently, a widespread *Corylus* colonization occurred. The interglacial climate optimum was reached in the early Eemian *Corylus–Taxus Tilia* zone and in the early *Carpinus* zone with temperatures of approximately 2°C higher than the average summer and winter temperatures today. A gradual climatic deterioration can be followed through the *Carpinus–Picea–Abies* zone to the boreal *Pinus* phase. The Eemian Stage was not interrupted by pronounced climatic oscillations as demonstrated by both isotope studies and quantita-

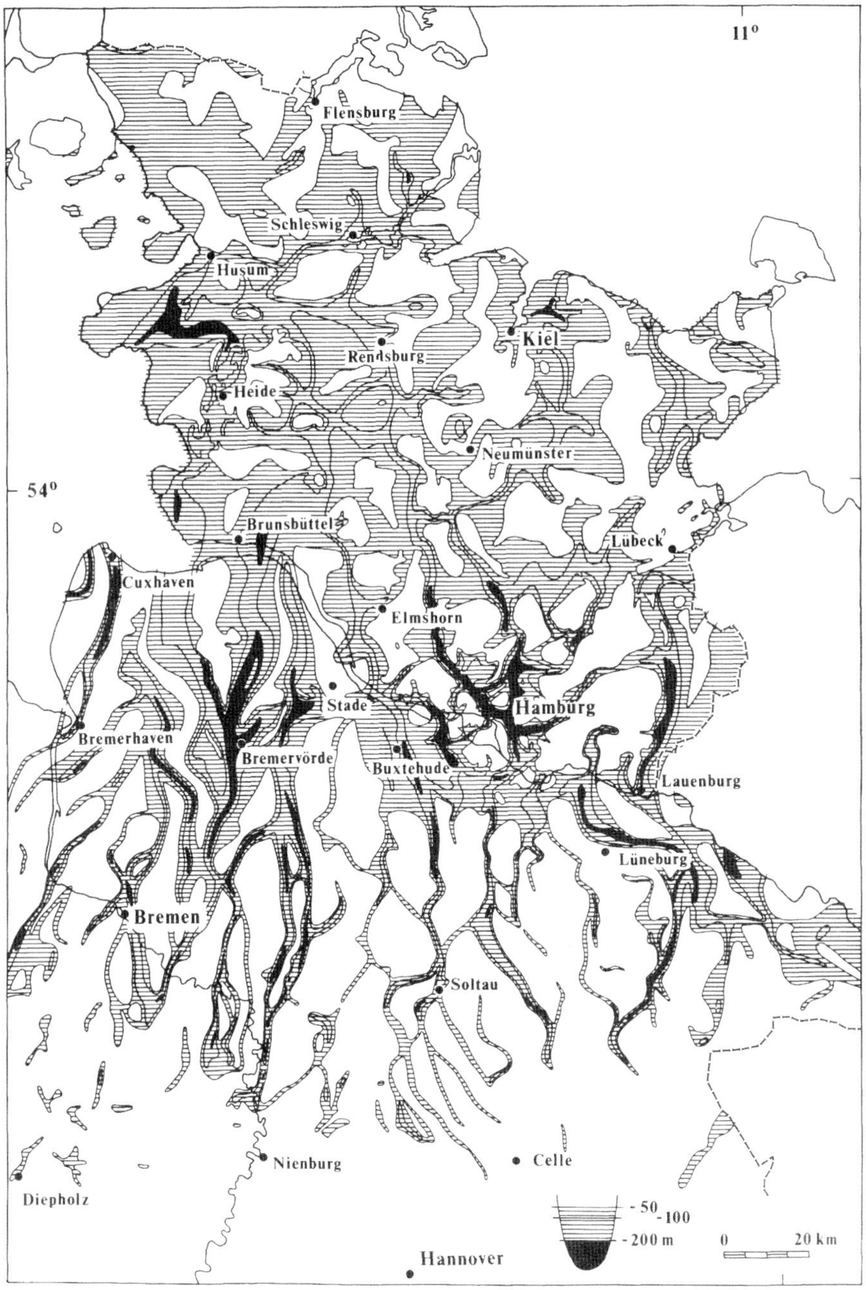


**Fig. 20.7.** Elsterian channel system in NW Germany (from Ehlers *et al.* 1984).

tive palaeoclimate reconstructions based on palaeobotanical data (Litt *et al.* 1996; Kühl & Litt 2003).

In contrast to the Hosteinian, the marine influence was not very marked in northern Germany during the Eemian (Ehlers 1994; see also Fig. 20.13). However, the extent of the Eemian Sea was much more pronounced in the eastern Baltic region and adjacent areas of Russia, and Scandinavia became an island (Grosfjeld *et al.* 2006).

*Weichselian Stage*

The term Weichselian was introduced by Keilhack (1899). The type region is in the upper valley of the river Weichsel (Vistula in Polish; Meyer 1981).

According to palynological data, the Weichselian Cold Stage begins with the transition from boreal forest vegetation at the end of the Eemian Warm Stage to subarctic tundra vegetation. The Early Weichselian is characterized by alternating subarctic stadials and two interstadials with boreal forest (Brörup and Odderade), whereas during the Middle Weichselian Pleniglacial interstadial, vegetation reached only the level of a shrub tundra (Behre 1989). Most probably, in Central Europe the onset of the main glaciations commenced at about 25 ka BP, though glaciers had possibly already advanced between 70 and 50 ka into the area of the western Baltic Sea/eastern Denmark (Houmark-Nielsen 1994; Stephan 1995). In northern Germany, the maximum extent of the Weichselian glaciation reached up to the

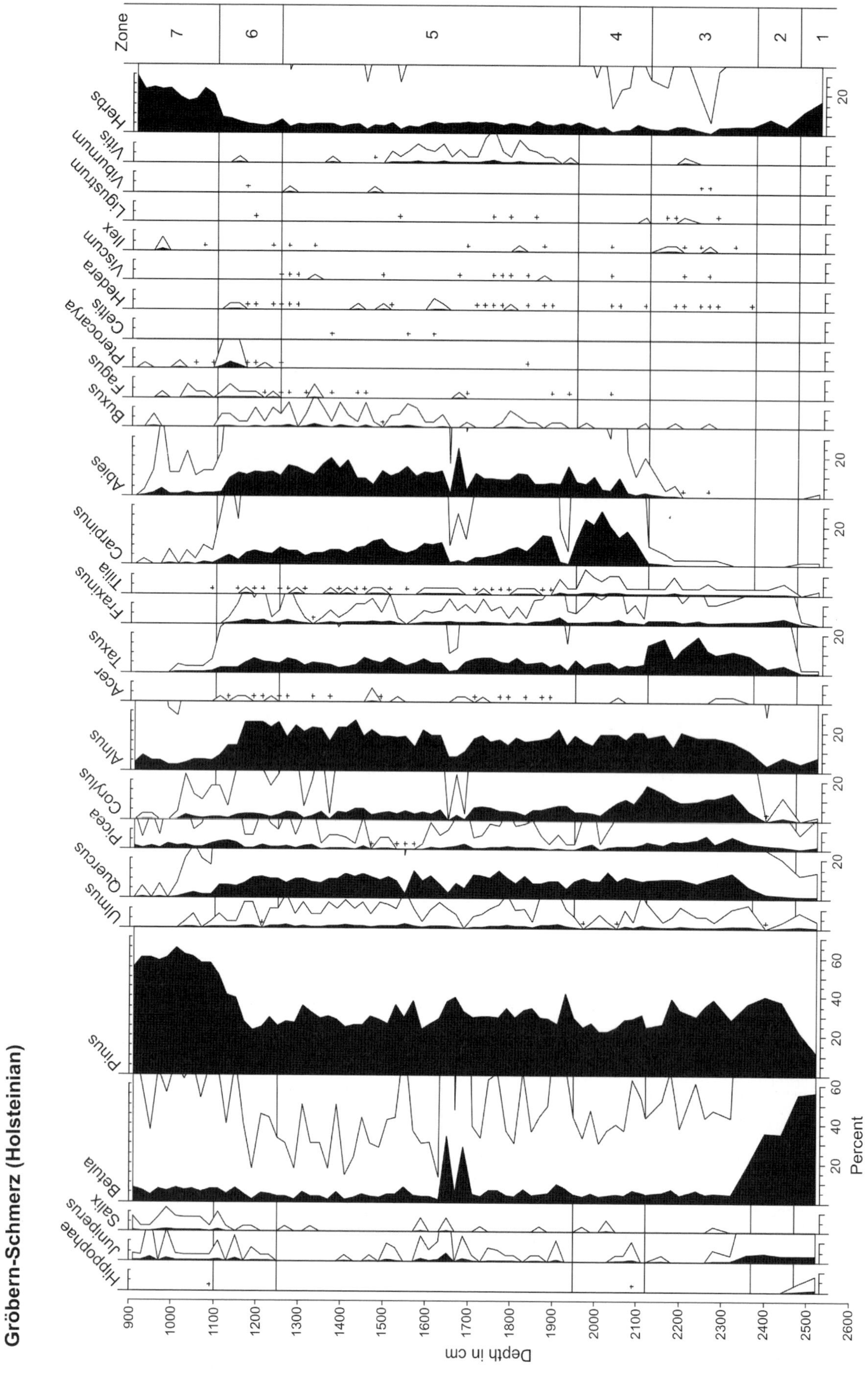


**Fig. 20.8.** Holsteinian Interglacial. Simplified pollen diagram from the Gröbern-Schmerz sequence, central Germany (modified after Eissmann *et al.* 1995).

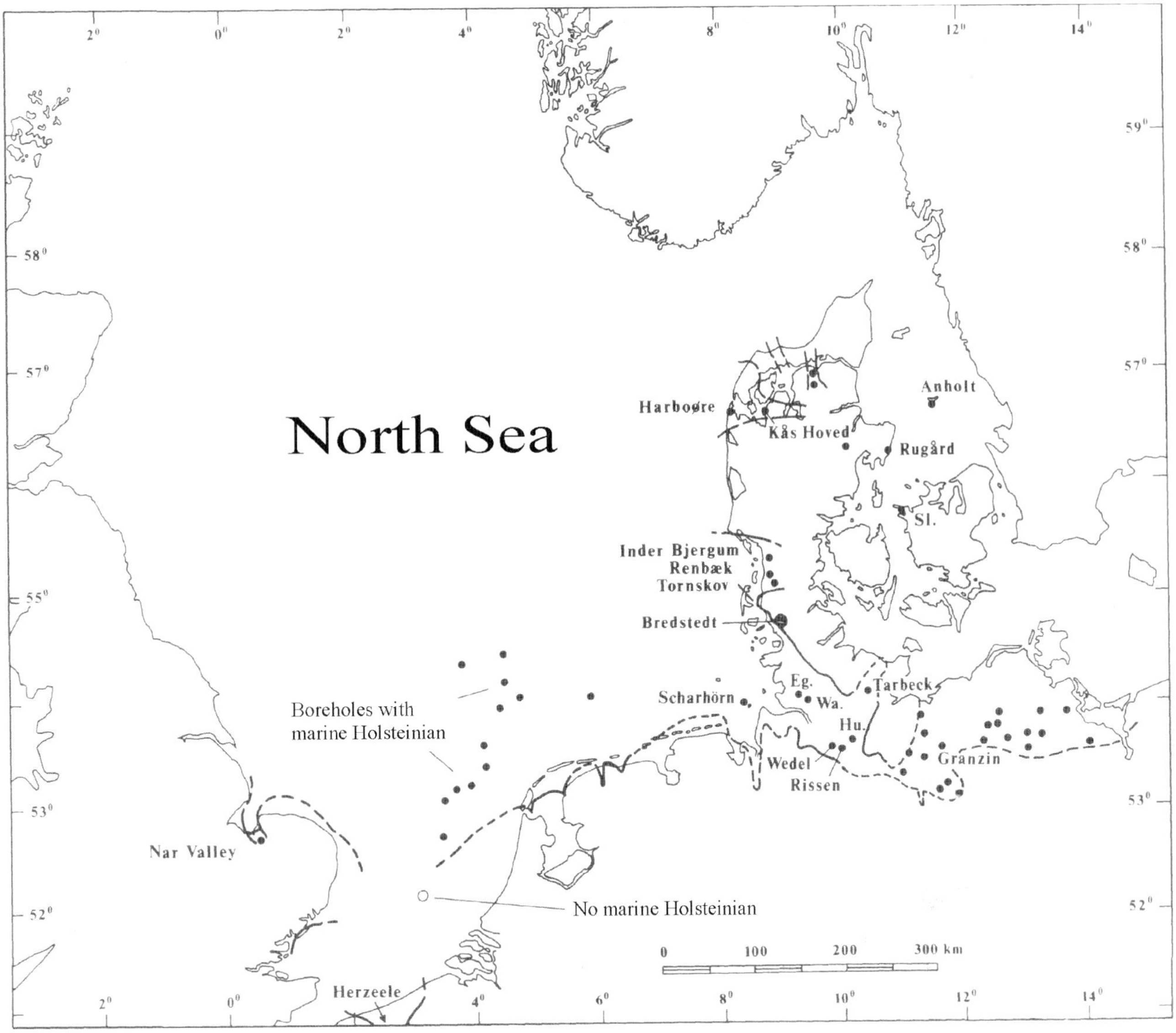


**Fig. 20.9.** Maximum extent of the Holsteinian Sea and location of Holsteinian sites in northern Germany (from Ehlers 1994).

Brandenburg area in the east; further west it extended as far as the northern parts of Hamburg and the eastern part of Schleswig-Holstein (Fig. 20.5). The classic morphostratigraphical subdivision of the Weichselian Glaciation into Brandenburg, Frankfurt and Pommeranian phases (Woldstedt 1925) was based on the ice-marginal positions in Mecklenburg-Vorpommern and Brandenburg. However, the morphological subdivision of the glaciation is not reflected in the stratigraphy of the glacial deposits. The three morphologically defined glaciation phases are documented by only two tills (Brandenburg and Pomeranian tills, see Fig. 20.11). The end moraines of the Frankfurt Phase represent only an oscillation of the maximum (Brandenburg) ice advance (Cepek 1965). In Mecklenburg, a third till unit can locally be distinguished from the two older Weichselian tills (Mecklenburg advance; Rühberg 1987; Müller *et al.* 1995).

In Poland, the ice sheet may already have reached the lower Vistula region during the Middle Vistulian (50–70 ka BP) (Mojski 1995). However, the precise extent of that ice advance is under debate. The youngest Scandinavian glaciation in Poland reached the areas of southern Wielkopolska, Pomerania, Kujawy and Mazury (Fig. 20.5). The maximum limit is represented by the Leszno (= Brandenburg) Phase in western Poland and by the younger lobes of the Poznan (= Frankfurt) Phase in central and eastern Poland (Marks 2004). The ice blocked the pre-existing drainage system and the so-called Warsaw-Berlin Urstromtal and Warsaw-Torun-Eberswalde Urstromtal were formed as ice-marginal streamways which channelled the glacial and extraglacial waters from the east to the river Elbe in the west.

The Weichselian Late Glacial in Central Europe, encompassing the timespan between the last deglaciation and the Holocene (*c.* 14.5 – 11.6 ka BP), is characterized by several large-scale high-amplitude and regional-scale low-amplitude climatic oscillations (Litt *et al.* 2001, 2003; see also Fig. 20.14) as well as by other significant events such as the volcanic eruption of the Laacher See Volcano at around 12.9 ka BP (see below). The last prominent cooling event prior to the Holocene is the so-called

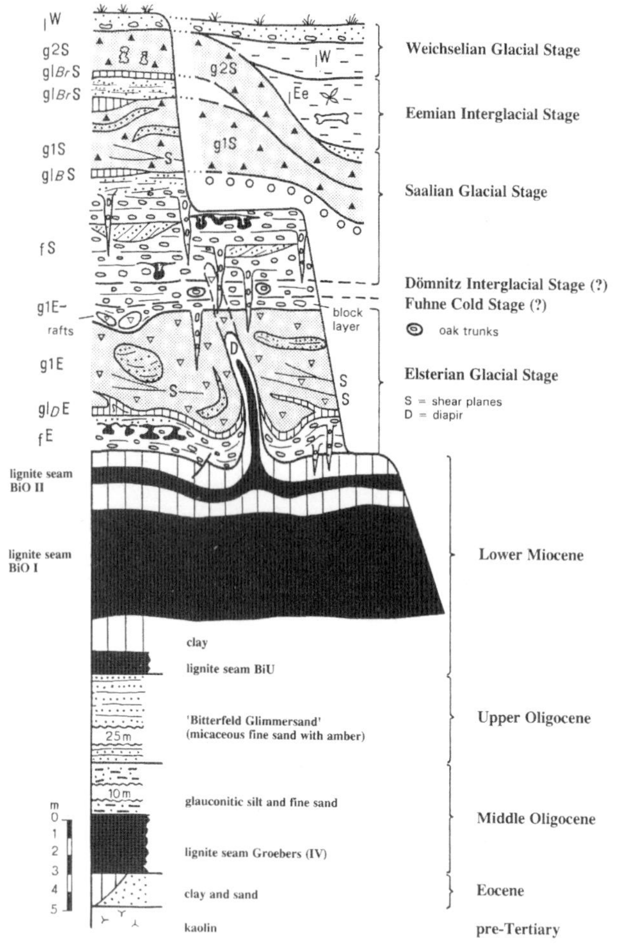


**Fig. 20.10.** The Cenozoic sequence of the Delitzsch-Südwest open-cast lignite mine, the type sequence of the Elsterian and Saalian stages (from Eissmann *et al.* 1995). Abbreviations: lW – Weichselian lacustrine sediments; lEe, Eemian lacustrine sediments (Grabschütz site, see Litt 1994); g2S, Saalian till (Leipzig phase); glS, glacio-limnic sediments (varved clay); g1S, Saalian till (Zeitz phase); fS, Saalian fluvial sediments (so-called Saalian Main Terrace with ice-wedge casts and cryoturbation structures); g1E, first Elsterian till; glE, Elsterian glaciolimnic sediments (varved clay); fE, Elsterian fluvial sediments (Early Elsterian Terrace with ice-wedge casts and cryoturbation structures).

Younger Dryas Stadial between 12.7 ka BP and 12.6 ka BP (based on varve countings in the Western Eifel Maar region; see Brauer *et al.* 1999*a*).

## *Holocene Epoch*

The Holocene is regarded as an independent Epoch encompassing the most recent interval of Earth history and extending to the present day. The lower boundary is palynologically defined at the beginning of the birch–pine afforestation after the Younger Dryas cold event of the Weichselian Late Glacial. According to varve counts, based on annually laminated lacustrine sediments, the boundary is located at 11 590 calendar years BP (Fig. 20.14) which is in good agreement with dendrochronological data (Litt *et al.* 2001). The term Flandrian (derived from marine transgression sediments of the Belgian coast) has been used as a synonym for the Holocene (Gibbard & Kolfschoten 2004), but this term has been losing ground. The most established zonation scheme of the Holocene in north-central Europe is based on vegetational development reflecting climatic changes. This comprises, in stratigraphic order: the Preboreal, Boreal, Atlantic, Subboreal and Subatlantic (terminology introduced by Blytt (1867) and Sernander (1894)). Although this terminology has been largely replaced by absolute chronology, it is still in use in north-central Europe.

During the last few years progress has been achieved in reconstructing the development of the Holocene vegetation of the Eifel region based on investigations of annually laminated sequences (Litt 2004). The great advantage of varved lacustrine sediments is the high time resolution and chronological precision of natural and anthropogenically influenced vegetation changes. The brief outline of the Holocene vegetation succession, presented here, is based on the palynological data obtained from the Holzmaar record (Fig. 20.15). The Ulmener Maar Tephra (11 ka BP) forms the base of this sequence. This period belongs palynostratigraphically to the Preboreal (zone IV, after Firbas 1953), represented by *Betula* and *Pinus* forests. *Quercus* and *Corylus* invaded the Eifel region at that time. The beginning of the Boreal (zone V) is characterized by an increase in *Corylus* at 10.8 ka BP. *Quercus* and *Ulmus* become abundant whereas birch and pine lost their competitive edge. *Tilia* immigrates at the end of the Boreal. The Atlantic (zones VI/VII) is the classical Mixed Oak Forest period (with an increase in *Quercus, Ulmus, Tilia,* and *Fraxinus*), representing the climatic optimum (occurrence of *Viscum* and *Hedera*). Immigration of *Alnus* commenced at the same time. The beginning of this zone is dated by varve chronology to about 8.5 ka BP. Around 6.2 ka BP (late Atlantic) minor vegetation changes resulted from Neolithic farming (cereal pollen and anthropogenic indicators such as *Plantago lanceolata* and *Plantago major*). The Subboreal (zone VIII) begins at around 5.6 ka BP and is marked by the arrival and spread of *Fagus*. Human colonization in the Eifel region during the early Neolithic and the Bronze Age is slight. The late Subatlantic (zone IX) started at about 2.8 ka BP with a significant decrease of *Fagus* pollen. As a result of pre-Roman Iron Age colonization, the vegetation changed drastically. The forest density decreased and herb pollen values (including anthropogenic indicators: cereals, Gramineae, *Artemisia, Rumex, Plantago lanceolata* etc.) increased. The extensive land use lasted more or less continuously through the Roman Period. During the Migration Period the forests became dense once again (increase in the *Fagus* and *Carpinus* curves, reduced values of anthropogenic indicators). The region was resettled in the younger Subatlantic (zone X, 1 ka BP). Subsequently, the marked human influence on the vegetation pattern continued and this has been ongoing as everywhere in Central Europe, until the present day.

## *Pleistocene turnovers in the mammalian fauna*

In the mammalian record of north-central Europe, no typical cold faunas are known thus far from the Early Pleistocene. This may be due to the very scarce fossil record, or to the fact that the mammalian fauna was not yet adapted to a cold environment (Koenigswald 2007). There are also no indications of faunal exchange as occurred in the Middle and Late Pleistocene, when the mammalian fauna in Central Europe was characterized by drastic turnovers induced by climatic changes (Koenigswald 2002). A continental fauna including *Mammuthus* and *Coelodonta* characterizes the cold periods. During the interglacials, a fauna dominated by *Elephas antiquus* was present. The *Mammuthus* assemblages immigrated from the NE (Siberia), whereas

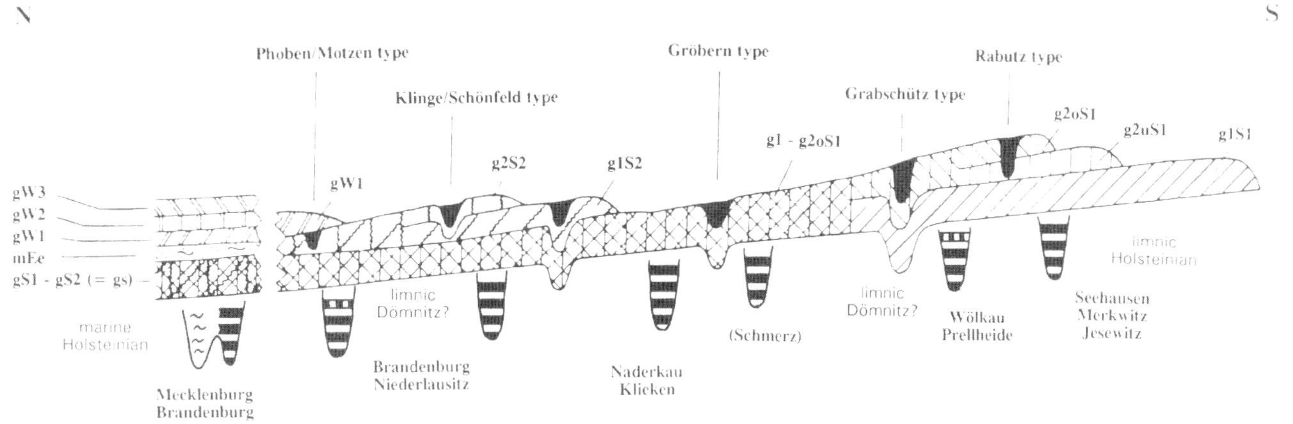


**Fig. 20.11.** Schematic north–south section (NE Germany: Mecklenburg–Brandenburg–Saxony) through the Saalian and Weichselian till sequence with the geological position of important sedimentary basins with Holsteinian and Eemian sediments (after Eissmann; from Eissmann & Litt 1995). Abbreviations: g1S1, Saalian (Drenthe) till (Zeitz phase); g2uS1, Saalian (Drenthe) till (Leipzig Phase, lower unit); g2S1, Saalian (Drenthe) till (Leipzig Phase, upper unit); g1S2, Saalian (Warthe) till, lower unit; g2S2, Saalian (Warthe) till, upper unit; gW1, Weichselian (Brandenburg) till; gW2, Weichselian (Pomeranian) till; gW3, Weichselian (Mecklenburg) till.

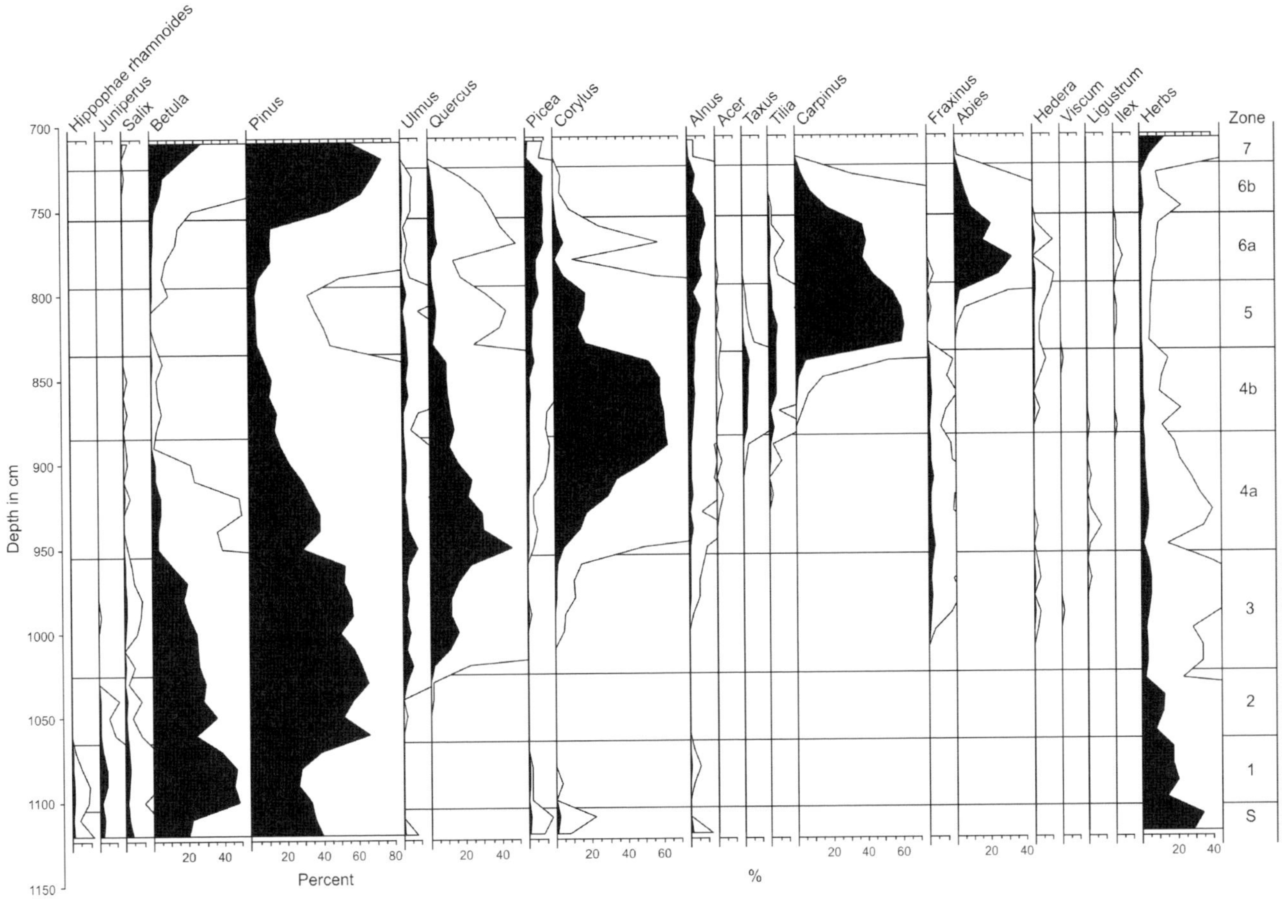


**Fig. 20.12.** Eemian Interglacial. Simplified pollen diagram from the Gröbern sequence, central Germany (after Litt 1994).

the *Elephas* assemblage expanded their area from the Mediterranean regions, indicating that Central Europe was an area of 'temporal occurrence' for most mammalian species (Koenigswald 2003). Thus the invasion of new fauna was coeval with the local extinciton of the previous one (Koenigswald 2007).

Very few herbivores are found in the glacial and interglacial faunal assemblages. Carnivores were generally not affected to the same degree by climate fluctuations (Fig. 20.16). Indeed, mammalian faunas can often be better attributed to a glacial or an interglacial environment than to a specific age, because the

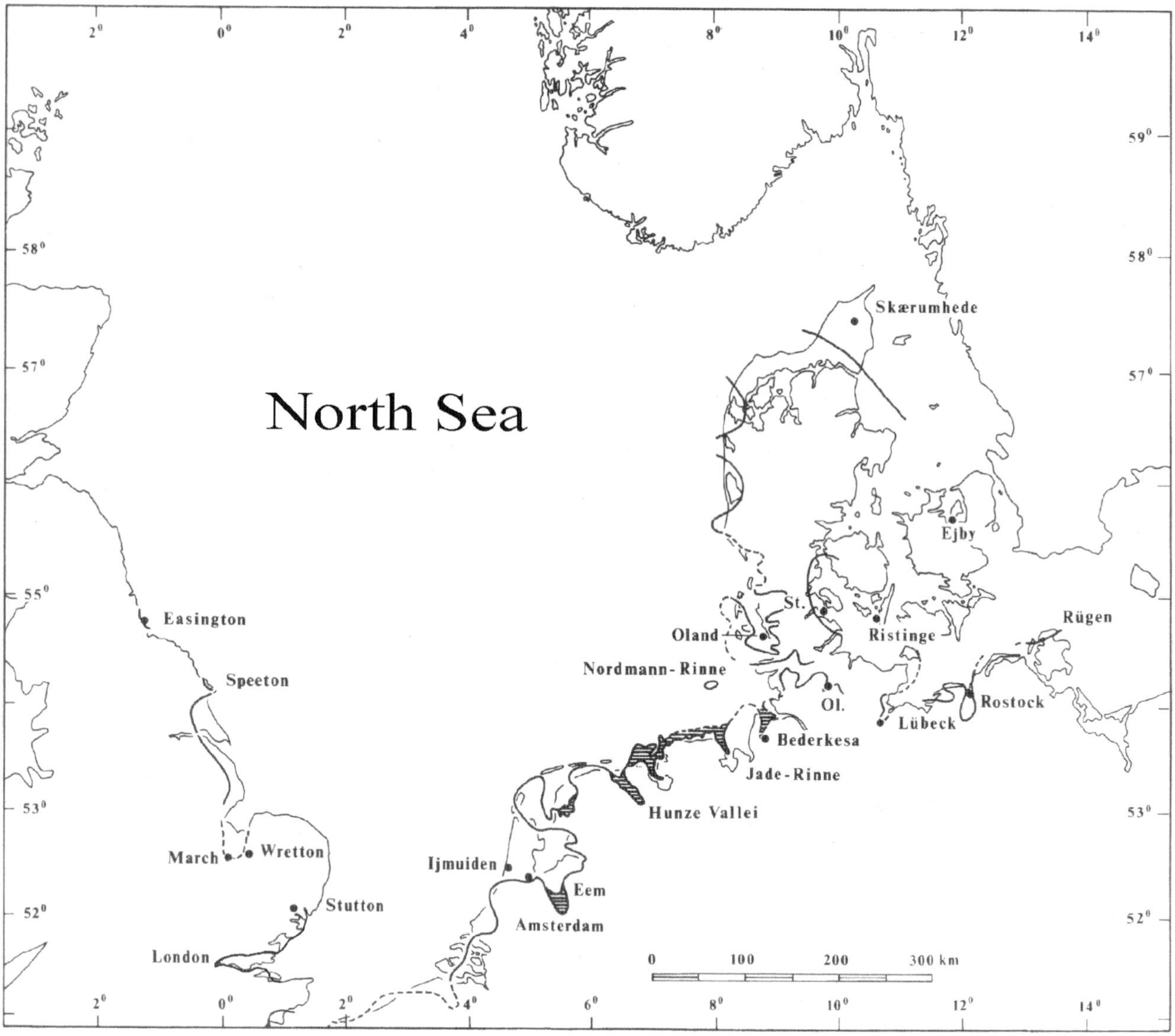


**Fig. 20.13.** Maximum extent of the Eemian Sea in northern Germany (from Ehlers 1994).

timespan of the Middle and Upper Pleistocene is generally too short for major evolutionary changes. One exception is the micromammalian genus of *Arvicola*, a vole, present in Central Europe throughout the various glacial–interglacial cycles from the Middle Pleistocene onwards, which shows evolutionary changes that can be used as suitable stratigraphic markers (Koenigswald & Heinrich 1999). During the Cromerian Complex, the ancestor vole species *Mimomys savini* was replaced by *Arvicola cantianus*. The so-called early *Arvicola cantianus* faunas antedate the Elsterian (Fig. 20.17). After the Elsterian, *Arvicola cantianus* remained an index fossil until the end of the Saalian Complex (so-called late *Arvicola cantianus* faunas). Faunas of the Eemian and the early Weichselian reflect a transition from *Arvicola cantianus* to *Arvicola terrestris*, although the large mammals of the Weichselian *Mammuthus* assemblage are very similar to those of the Saalian. In a similar manner, the *Elephas antiquus* assemblage of the last interglacial does not show any significant evolutionary changes comparable to the previous interglacials (Koenigswald 2007). In general, it is difficult to determine, based solely on the faunal record of Central Europe, whether two (or possibly more) different interglacial phases may have existed between the Elsterian and the Saalian. Furthermore, it remains open to what extent human populations were involved in the faunal exchange (Koenigswald 2006).

During the early Middle Pleistocene, humans occurred only during interglacial periods in north-central Europe (the Cromerian, Mauer near Heidelberg with *Homo heidelbergensis*; the Holsteinian, Bilzingsleben in Thuringia with *Homo erectus*). During the Saalian Complex, Pre-Neanderthals also coexisted with *Mammuthus* assemblages, indicating their ability to survive under cold climate conditions. The early humans hunted various large mammals. At the Eemian site Gröbern near Leipzig, a skeleton of *Elephant antiquus* was discovered together with stone artifacts which document the butchering of the carcass (Weber & Litt 1991). During the Weichselian, the classic Neanderthals coexisted once again alongside the *Mammuthus* assemblage. However, there is no indication of any significant changes in the

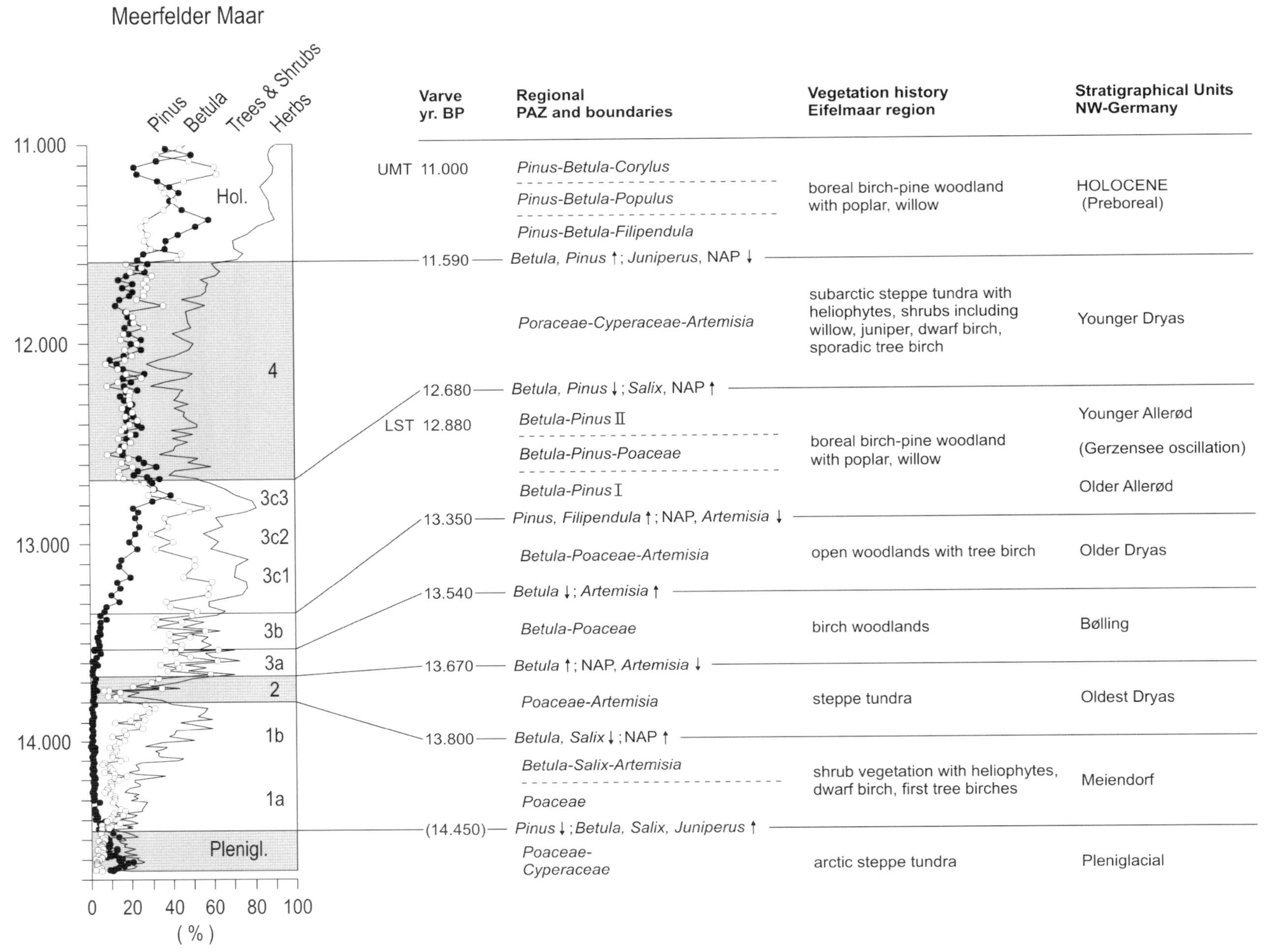


**Fig. 20.14.** Weichselian Late Glacial sequence from the Meerfelder Maar (Eifel, western Germany). Regional Pollen Assemblage Zones (PAZ) based on varve chronology, vegetation history in the western Eifel region and Late Glacial climatostratigraphic units of northern Germany. LST, Laacher See Tephra; UMT, Ulmener Maar Tephra (from Litt *et al.* 2003); NAP, Nonarboreal pollen (herbs).

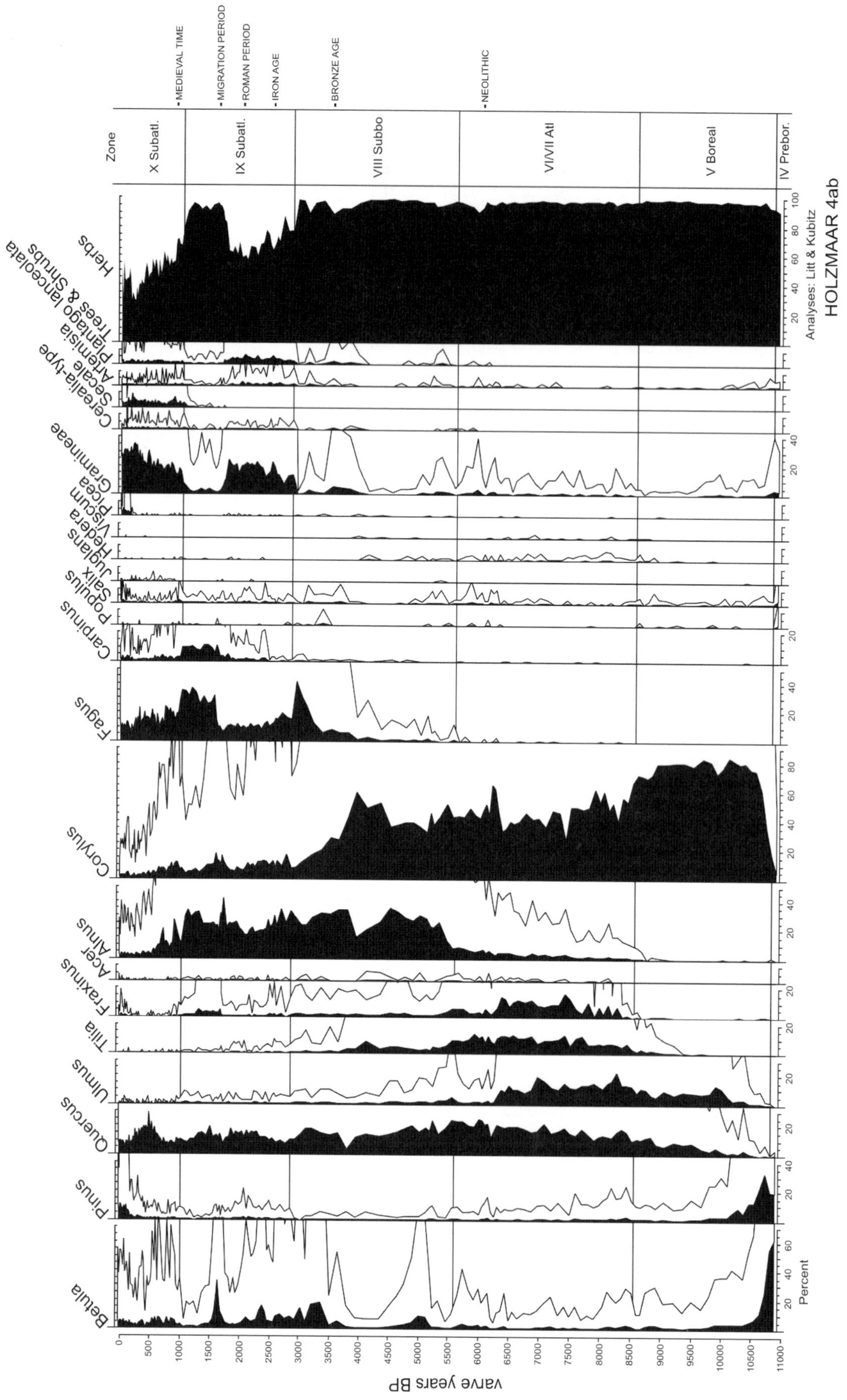


**Fig. 20.15.** Holocene. Simplified pollen diagram from the Holzmaar sequence (Western Eifel Volcanic Field, western Germany) above the Ulmener Maar Tephra (UMT, 11 ka BP). Pollen analyses by Litt & Kubitz, varve countings by Zolitzschka (from Litt 2004).

**Fig. 20.16.** The *Elephas* assemblage and the *Mammuthus* assemblage occurred alternatively in Central Europe during the Middle and Late Pleistocene. Only a few herbivores but several carnivores occurred during interglacial and glacial environments (from Koenigswald 2002).

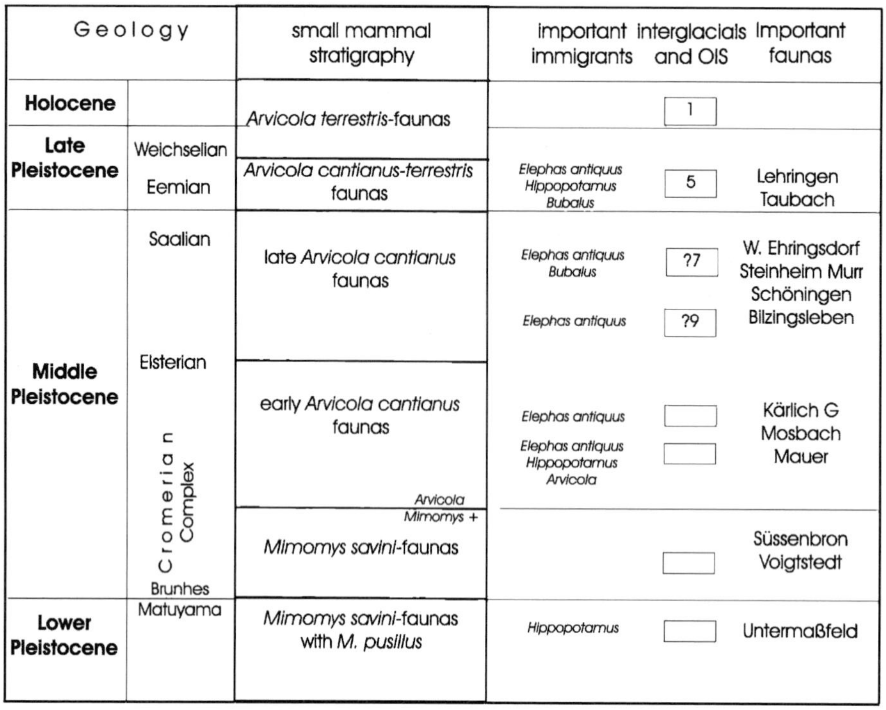

Geology
small mammal stratigraphy
important immigrants
interglacials and OIS
Important faunas
Holocene
Arvicola terrestris-faunas
1
Late Pleistocene
Weichselian
Eemian
Arvicola cantianus-terrestris faunas
Elephas antiquus
Hippopotamus
Bubalus
5
Lehringen
Taubach
Saalian
late Arvicola cantianus faunas
Elephas antiquus
Bubalus
?7
W. Ehringsdorf
Steinheim Murr
Schöningen
Elephas antiquus
?9
Bilzingsleben
Elsterian
Middle Pleistocene
early Arvicola cantianus faunas
Elephas antiquus
Elephas antiquus
Hippopotamus
Arvicola
Kärlich G
Mosbach
Mauer
Cromerian Complex
Arvicola
Mimomys +
Mimomys savini-faunas
Süssenbron
Voigtstedt
Brunhes
Matuyama
Lower Pleistocene
Mimomys savini-faunas with M. pusillus
Hippopotamus
Untermaßfeld


**Fig. 20.17.** Biostratigraphy of the Middle and Late Pleistocene in Central Europe (from Koenigswald 2007; after Koenigswald & Heinrich 1999).

faunas coincident with the arrival of modern humans (*Homo sapiens sapiens*) in Central Europe at 35 ka BP. Indeed, the *Mammuthus primigenius* fauna remained unaltered until the end of the last glacial period.

### *Summary*

(1) The Quaternary ice age as a system is subdivided into the Pleistocene and the Holocene series.
(2) The base of the Pleistocene in north-central Europe is traditionally defined by the first clear unequivocal (Praetiglian) at the end of the Neogene at around 2.6 Ma BP (Gauss–Matuyama palaeomagnetic boundary).
(3) The Lower Pleistocene (2.6–0.78 Ma BP) is characterized by alternating cold and warm stages. However, the north-central European lowland was not affected by inland ice, but permafrost conditions may have occurred in some of the cold phases.
(4) The Middle Pleistocene (780–126 ka BP) encompasses the Cromerian Complex Stage, the Elsterian Stage, the Holsteinian Stage and the Saalian Complex Stage.
(5) The oldest glaciation, represented by widespread till sheets throughout north-central Europe, is the Elsterian glaciation (MIS 10), whereas evidence of older (Cromerian) ice advances is still uncertain in this region.
(6) The Holsteinian Interglacial Stage corresponds to MIS 9 (absolute dates of about 310–330 ka BP). The duration of this warm stage is estimated as about 15–16 ka.
(7) The Saalian Complex Stage corresponds to MIS 8–MIS 6. The Lower Saalian, i.e. the period between the end of the Holsteinian Interglacial and the first Saalian ice advance, was not affected by Scandinavian ice sheets. Only periglacial processes took place during the Fuhne Cold Stage (MIS 8), whereas the warm phases of MIS 7 were interstadials with an interglacial character rather than fully developed interglacials. Two major glaciations (Drenthe and Warthe) occurred during the Upper Saalian (MIS 6). In the entire Nordic glaciation area there is no evidence of interglacial deposits between these Saalian ice advances.
(7) The Upper Pleistocene includes the Eemian and the Weichselian stages.
(8) The Eemian Interglacial correlates with MIS 5e (*c*. 126–115 ka BP).
(9) The Weichselian Stage (115–11.6 ka, MIS 5c to beginning of MIS 1) is characterized by several alternating stadials and interstadials. The main glaciation commenced at about 25 ka BP and reached its maximum extent at about 20 ka BP (Last Glacial Maximum, MIS 2).
(10) The Holocene (11.6 ka BP to present day), as an interglacial stage, is strongly influenced by human impact.
(11) The mammalian fauna in north-central Europe was characterized by drastic turnovers during the Middle and Upper Pleistocene caused by climatic changes.

## The ice age in the Alps (C.S.)

Environmental change in the Alps during the Quaternary Period is primarily the history of the multiple expansion and disappearance of glaciers and related Earth surface phenomena. There are two fundamental questions related to these processes: (a) what are the frequencies and amplitudes of the glacier advances beyond the border of the Alps; and in more detail, (b) what is the structure of the last glacial cycle. The classic answer to question (a) has been that the Last Glaciation was of limited extent with clearly mappable ice limits (= Würmian Glaciation) and that beyond these limits an older glaciation of substantially broader extent occurred (= Rissian Glaciation). This older event is now defined as the Most Extensive Glaciation (MEG) of the Central Alps. Prior to this glaciation, glacial activity is partially inferred and to some extent directly related to sediment aggradation (i.e. Deckenschotter) in the northern Alpine foreland, roughly between Zürich to the west and Linz to the east. This stratigraphic concept has been pursued over the last century to meet the requirements of the classic alpine ice-age stratigraphy as defined in southern Germany by Penck & Brückner (1909).

Along an east–west transect there is considerable debate on the age of the most extensive ice advance and there is good evidence that in the eastern Alps the most advanced position was reached by a glaciation prior to the Rissian, i.e. the Mindelian of the classic chronology (van Husen 2004). This east–west disharmony may be due either to a quantitative variation in moisture input to the Alps or to a change in moisture transport paths during different glacial cycles, or it may have been controlled by the different uplift histories of the respective hinterlands and the inner-alpine catchments. In addition, it should be noted that the largest northern piedmont glaciers of the Last Glaciation – the Rhône, the Rhine and the Inn glaciers – were all connected to high-altitude, south-central inner-alpine catchment areas.

With the most recent construction boom beginning in the 1970s, large outcrops and an important number of drillcores became available; this resulted in a change in the philosophy of analysing Quaternary archives, from an exclusively morphostratigraphic interpretation to multidisciplinary analytical efforts to reconstruct environmental change from stratigraphic sections. An early expert using this approach was Beck (1933).

Naturally, the structure of the last glacial cycle has been, and still is, of primary interest, since its archives are more directly accessible and less modified by later environmental change than older records. Early in the last century the question was raised of whether the Last Glaciation was a one- or a two-phase event (Beck 1933), and if it were a two-phase event which one of the two would have been the maximum: the earlier or the later advance. Based on geomorphic and soil-intensity mapping, it was concluded that the second ice advance had been more extensive than the first. However, Welten (1976) introduced the idea of a very early cold phase (with glaciers extending to the outer limit of the Alps) immediately following the last interglacial.

Apart from the question of glacial cycles and palaeoclimatic forcing mechanisms, the results of landscape evolution have been focused by Quaternary research. For instance, the alpine and the perialpine morphology is characterized by considerably overdeepened valleys and the question of valley formation has been on the research agenda since Rütimeyer (1869). In some sectors of the main valleys, e.g. the Rhône Valley, overdeepening reaches 800 to 1000 m below the present valley floor (Pfiffner *et al.* 1997) prompting the question of a genetic relationship between palaeoglaciations and valley formation. More specifically it is questioned whether the palaeoglaciers were erosive agent for the substantially overdeepened valleys and basins, both in the high mountain areas and in the northern and southern forelands.

To a certain degree, the Quaternary records of the Alps also reflect the climate pattern over the North Atlantic since the Alps are a downwind morphological obstacle for easterly airflow. However, another airflow path adds considerably to the moisture input: the northerly flowing Föhn (Florineth & Schlüchter 2000). Therefore, the Alps cannot be considered as a simple control area for airflow and moisture transport from the North Atlantic.

### *The Middle Pleistocene Event*

On a broad scale, inner and perialpine valleys are characterized by a two-phase Quaternary evolution: the initial period of primary erosion and the later (partial) infilling. The open valleys of today are not at maximum erosional depth with regard to bedrock surface. Earlier in the Quaternary, incision into the bedrock was much more substantial, both in depth and in width, and since that time a partial refilling of the valleys has taken place. This infilling was not a continuous process but was interrupted by many shorter erosional phases. However, a substantial event in switching from the erosional to the accumulative pattern in the drainage systems from the Alps to their forelands occurred in the past. Whether this was exclusively related to a change in the erosive capacity of the palaeoglaciers only, or whether a tectonic component was also involved has not yet been conclusively answered. To determine the age of this event is only possible through dating the base of the sedimentary infill. A number of interglacial deposits are known from sedimentary fillings of the overdeepened valleys. Unfortunately, none of them allows absolute dating. In some sections two or more different interglacials are recorded (Meikirch, Thalgut, Buchberg; Fig. 20.18). This suggests that the change pre-dates the second but last interglacial. Analysis of the palynostratigraphy at Thalgut and Buchberg suggests that maximum erosion was much earlier, and prior to the last four glacial cycles. Interestingly, at Thalgut the basal unit of a long Quaternary succession comprises a glacial sediment unit overlying bedrock. This would suggest that the deepest erosion may have been related to a glacial advance. In detail, however, the precise sequence of events is difficult to determine as the sediment overlying the bedrock is waterlain and not a lodgement till. In a fully infilled valley between Lake Zürich and Lake Zug five till units are recognized, and these are separated by palaeosols or compressed peat and characterized by distinct gravel petrographic compositions (Wyssling 2002).

With the Lake Zürich drilling project in 1987 the Quaternary succession in the modern lake was drilled down to the bedrock. Surprisingly, most of the Quaternary fill in the Lake Zürich basin is of Last Glacial age, and the complete sequence may be younger than the last interglacial except for the lowermost recovered unit of sandy gravel. Unfortunately, core quality was poor and the interpretation was difficult. For dating purposes, however, it does not matter if the basal core unit was a fluvioglacial gravel or a Tertiary conglomerate broken up by the drilling operation since the age of the basal deposit remains open.

In the insubric (= southern) Alps the valleys are deeply incised into bedrock (as deep as 600 m below the present level of the Adriatic Sea). In this southerly area, Upper Pliocene marine clays form part of the valley infill (or the full vertical excavation also) suggesting that the full valley width was only reached in Pliocene times. Most likely, the onset of deep valley erosion in the southern Alpine foreland was related to the Messinian event whereas in the northern foreland downcutting occurred later (Fig. 20.19). This later northern phase is defined as the Middle Pleistocene Event (MPE), and was most likely caused by a combination of tectonics and river dynamics. Of significance in this context is the relationship, in the area between Zürich and Linz in the northern Alpine foreland, between the older gravel aggradations of the Deckenschotter Complexes (now at higher elevations) pre-dating the deeply excavated valleys with their younger sedimentary infill. This relationship suggests that the MPE is an important hydrographic event that occurred between the accumulation of the older and younger Pleistocene units, most likely in combination with a substantial uplift component.

### *Pre-MPE glaciations*

To the north and NE of the Lägern (= the easternmost extension of the Jura Fold Belt) a pronounced landscape element occurs: the table mountains of the so-called Swiss Deckenschotter

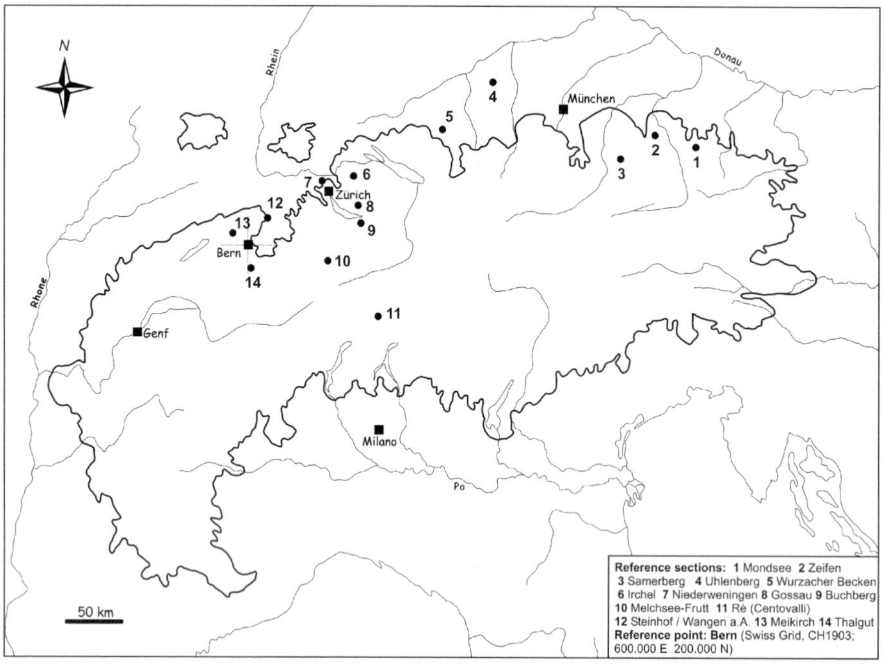


**Fig. 20.18.** Circumalpine glacier extension during the Last Glacial Maximum (LGM = Würmian of the classical chronology), 18 000 to 20 000 years ago, with the most important reference sections mentioned in the text: 1, Mondsee; 2, Zeifen; 3, Samerberg; 4, Uhlenberg; 5, Wurzacher Becken; 6, Irchel; 7, Niederweningen; 8, Gossau,; 9, Buchberg; 10, Melchsee-Frutt; 11, Rè (Centovalli); 12, Steinhof/Wangen a.A.; 13, Meikirch; 14, Thalgut.

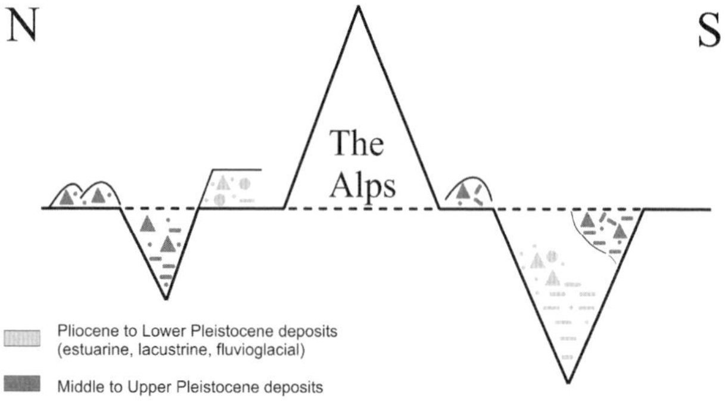


**Fig. 20.19.** Schematic north–south transalpine cross-section with overdeepened basins in the north and Messinian fjords in the south; vertically hatched units are pre-Middle Pleistocene Event sediments. This schema shows the north–south disharmony in Pliocene and Pleistocene valley morphogenesis. The modern valley floor to the north of the Alps is about 300 to 450 m higher in absolute elevation than in the south.

(= cover gravel). These coarse gravel aggradations are superimposed on Molasse (Tertiary) or Mesozoic bedrock with a well-developed unconformity. Early discussions considered these deposits to be part of the Tertiary accumulations. Graf (1993 and references therein) published a geological study of these units and concluded that they could be subdivided morphostratigraphically into Upper, Middle and Lower Deckenschotter and that they formed as a result of specific climatic and tectonic events. For the Upper Deckenschotter four glacial advances, for the Middle Deckenschotter at least three, and for the Lower Deckenschotter also at least three advances are recognized based on gravel petrography. The lithostratigraphic subdivision proposed by Graf (1993) demonstrates a dynamic palaeoglaciational regime in the northern Alpine foreland during the Lower Pleistocene. More precise dating, at that time, was not possible. Subsequently, Bolliger *et al.* (1996) produced a publication on a mammalian fauna from flood loam deposits at the top of the third oldest Deckenschotter unit. This *Arvicolidae* fauna with *Borsodia* sp., *Lagurodon* sp., *Pliomys* sp., *Mimomys pitymreidi* and *Mimomys pliocaenicus* belongs to the mammalian stage MN 17 of the Upper Pliocene. With this stratigraphic classification the oldest glacially induced aggradations of the north-central Alpine foreland are, therefore, of pre-Pleistocene age, following the stratigraphic scheme of the International Commission on Stratigraphy with the Pliocene–Pleistocene boundary at 1.8 Ma.

The 'Swiss' Deckenschotter landscape continues into southern Germany to its type area around Biberach (Penck & Brückner 1909). The morphostratigraphical setting in southern Germany along the rivers draining the Alpine foreland to the Danube continues as far east as Linz to the eastern limit of the South German Stable (tectonic) Block. This configuration favours a tectonic control, at least to a certain extent, of pre-MPE landscape evolution. The Deckenschotter in the western part (between the upper Rhine area of Switzerland and Biberach) have a more complex stratigraphy (Graf 1993) than in the eastern sector (van Husen 2004). There are two sites in the Deckenschotter area with substantially more complete lithostratigraphies than at other sites which represent a close to identical time window in the Upper Pliocene–Lower Pleistocene: the Irchel site in northern Switzerland (Bolliger *et al.* 1996) and Uhlenberg (near Augsburg) in Germany (Ellwanger *et al.* 1994).

Along the southern Alpine foreland the Upper Pliocene–Lower

**Fig. 20.20** Stratigraphic subdivision of the Quaternary in the Alps. Global chronostratigraphy and marine isotope record modified after Gibbard & Kolfschoten (2004). Abbreviations: Thalgut/F+P, interglacial site of Thalgut with *Fagus* and *Pterocarya*; MEG, Most Extensive Glaciation; MPE, Middle Pleistocene Event.

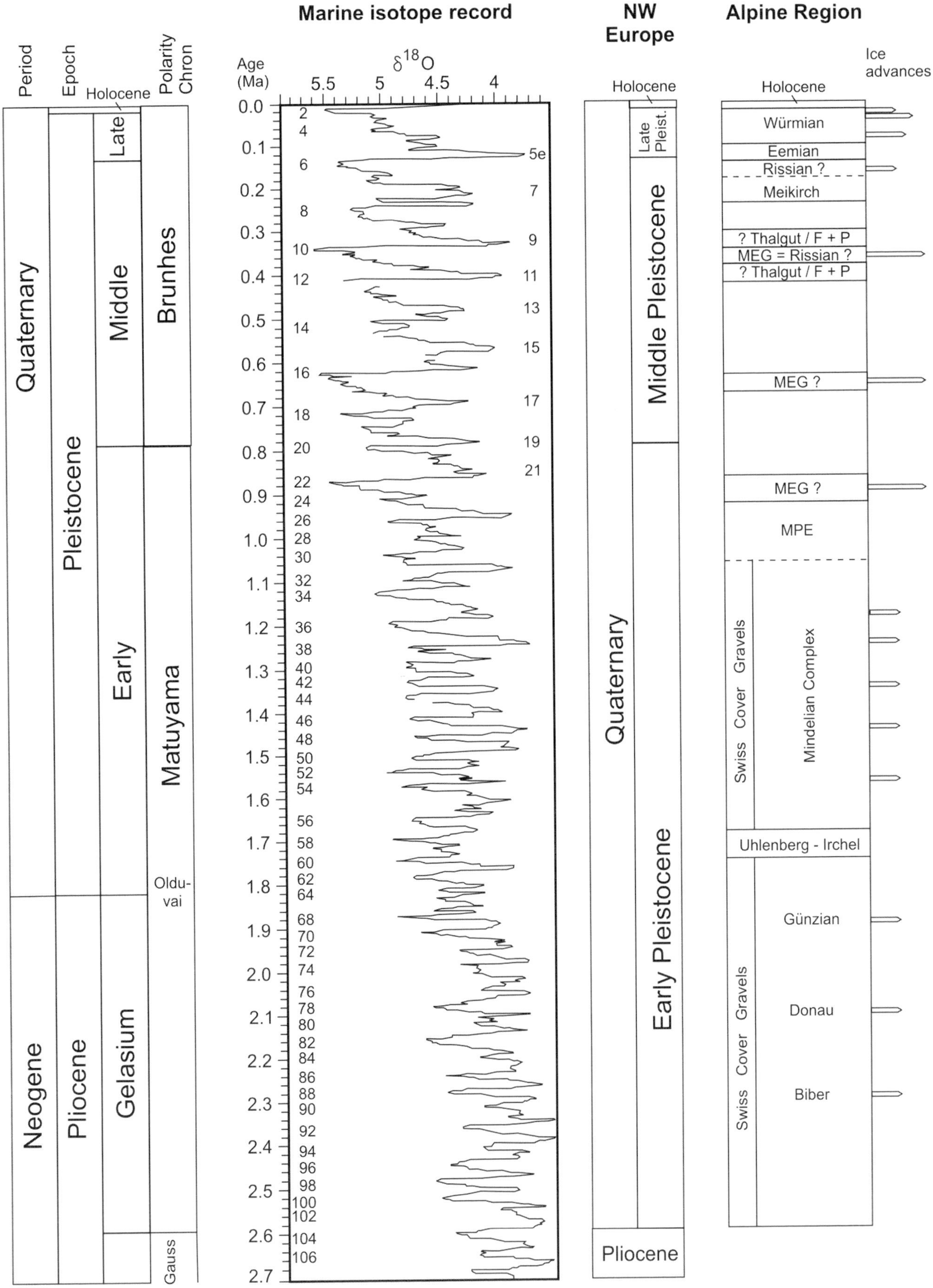
Marine isotope record
NW Europe
Alpine Region
Period
Epoch
Holocene
Polarity Chron
Age (Ma)
δ18O
5.5
5
4.5
4
Ice advances
Quaternary
Neogene
Pleistocene
Pliocene
Late
Middle
Early
Gelasium
Brunhes
Matuyama
Oldu-vai
Gauss
0.0
0.1
0.2
0.3
0.4
0.5
0.6
0.7
0.8
0.9
1.0
1.1
1.2
1.3
1.4
1.5
1.6
1.7
1.8
1.9
2.0
2.1
2.2
2.3
2.4
2.5
2.6
2.7
5e
Late Pleist.
Middle Pleistocene
Early Pleistocene
Würmian
Eemian
Rissian ?
Meikirch
? Thalgut / F + P
MEG = Rissian ?
? Thalgut / F + P
MEG ?
MEG ?
MPE
Swiss Cover Gravels
Mindelian Complex
Uhlenberg - Irchel
Günzian
Donau
Biber

Pleistocene accumulations are part of the Messinian fjord infill (Fig. 20.20). This configuration requires a different regional tectonic history in the south to that in the north (Felber & Bini 1997, and references there). The petrographic compositions of the Upper Pliocene–Lower Pleistocene coarse fluvioglacial aggradations differ significantly from recent fluvial gravels. This reflects the fact that the older deposits were formed from erosion of higher tectonic units in the Alps than the current younger ones.

## *Pre-Last Interglacial and post-MPE glaciations*

*The Most Extensive Glaciations*

The extent of the Most Extensive Glaciation (= classical Rissian) is based on the distribution pattern of erratic boulders throughout the Jura Mountains as far to the NE as the Upper Rhine Valley. *In situ* basal till is rarely found. The type locality for the MEG event in the Swiss Midlands is the Möhlin area, up-valley from Basel. From the only open section in the area a complex multiphase sequence has been described (Dick *et al.* 1996). The section is cut into a rolling hilly loess-covered landscape with two broad ridges which have traditionally been interpreted as the terminal moraines of the MEG. The regional continuation of the ridges is difficult to determine and so far the units are undated. However, the section displays depositional evidence of at least three glacial advances with intermediate soil-forming stages.

From this complex section it is evident that the MEG, in its terminal area, was a multiphase event. Without direct physical dating, these multiphase MEG glaciations cannot be considered to belong to the penultimate glaciation (as the classical concept would request). Instead, they might be much older and have occurred at the time of the Middle Pleistocene Event or immediately thereafter. An attempt to apply surface exposure dating on erratic boulders of the MEG is in progress in the Swiss Jura Mountains (Graf *et al.* 2007). Further to the east, in southern Germany, the MEG is mapped as the Rissian 'Altendmoräne' and only to the east of the Inn Glacier lobe is the MEG considered to be of 'pre-Rissian' age (van Husen 2004).

*Extensive Glaciations*

The area between the MEG terminal zone and the well-developed morainic landscape of the Last Glacial Maximum (LGM) is morphologically not well structured. However, it is lithostratigraphically complex. Again, the main problem is the absence of reliable absolute dates. Two lines of evidence are important here.

(1) At the base of the fluvioglacial aggradations of the last glaciation a pronounced erosional unconformity is developed. In some localities it is linked to a palaeosol on older gravel or till (Graf *et al.* 2007). In addition to these observations it has been noted that the aggradations and palaeosol developments in the Canton of Aargau and further into NE Switzerland result from multiphase glacial advances beyond the LGM position. In the central part of the Swiss Midlands, localities have been described which lie beyond the LGM and which show evidence of repeated aggradations and contain lag deposits of erratic boulders (Wohlfarth 1986). Such boulder beds just outside the LGM limit have also been interpreted as a 'Supermaximum Glaciation of the classical Würmian'.

(2) Surface soil evolution beyond the LGM provides evidence of a substantial time lag between the period of the pre-LGM and that of the LGM pedogenesis. Hildbrand (1990) has mapped the frontal part of the Rhône Glacier in the Central Midlands and has also logged a large number of pit sections in the area. Decalcification depths of >2 m are common and cannot, by any means, represent post-LGM soil development. This advanced and complex soil evolution is consistent for large areas of the Swiss Midlands as well as the alpine border area. It can be concluded that at least three glacial advances beyond the LGM and within the MEG ice limits reached the Swiss Midlands.

Similar complexities have been reported from the western and southern forelands areas (Mandier 1983; Felber & Bini 1997) and from the Pannonian loess areas in the east. Multiple glacial advances have also been reported from the south German foreland for this period (Schreiner 1989), indicating that the classic stratigraphic scheme needs to be extended.

## *The Last Glaciation and the Last Glacial Maximum*

The Last Glaciation is palaeoglaciologically and morphologically a well-defined mappable event. It can be litho- and climatostratigraphically subdivided into two main units. The second unit represents the most extensive glacier advance of the last glacial cycle.

Based on radiocarbon dating at Zürichberg (Schlüchter & Röthlisberger 1995) and Gossau (Schlüchter *et al.* 1987; Preusser 1999), the most recent advance to the Swiss Midlands cannot be older than 28 ka $^{14}$C BP. Based on surface exposure dates on erratic boulders from the terminal area of the Rhône Glacier at Steinhof, moraine stabilization occurred at 18 to 24 ka (Ivy-Ochs *et al.* 2004). It can safely be concluded that the LGM corresponds to a glacier buildup during MIS 2. Deglaciation from the maximum must have happened rapidly, as the last readvance to the youngest LGM stadial in the Swiss Midlands (Zürich Stadial) was reached shortly after 19 ka $^{14}$C BP (Schlüchter & Röthlisberger 1995). The retreat from that stadial was completed by 14.6 ka $^{14}$C BP (Lister 1988) and by that time the (northern) perialpine lakes were ice-free.

Prior to the most recent advance the Alpine forelands experienced an ice-free period of at least 20 to 30 ka. This inner-Würmian interstadial complex has been documented in the Gossau gravel pit to the east of Zürich. The lithostratigraphy of the interstadial complex commences with a delta foreset sequence grading into the final infilling of the lake followed by peat growth. This is followed by a periglacial coarse aggradation, which also grades into peat. This second peat is finally covered by the fluvioglacial gravels and basal tills of the LGM advance. The interstadial beds at Gossau have been extensively dated by radiocarbon isotopes, and subsequently verified by the U–Th series and more recently by optically stimulated luminescence (OSL) dates. The oldest part of the interstadial complex dates back to 52 ka $^{14}$C BP. The Gossau site is also important as it contains a collection of: fossil beetles which indicate, in agreement with the palynostratigraphy, an oscillating climate pattern with substantially more pronounced winter than summer temperature depressions compared to today. The site is at 800 m a.s.l., and from palynostratigraphy and the fossil beetles it would appear that the upper forest line was fluctuating around that elevation between 28 and 52 ka $^{14}$C (Schlüchter *et al.*1987; Jost-Stauffer *et al.* 2005; Preusser 1999; Geyh & Schlüchter 1998). Keller & Krayss (2005) have presented evidence for a fluctuating LGM glacier position for the Rhine Glacier between 28 and 24 ka $^{14}$C.

An ongoing problem is the location of the glaciers between >54 ka and 28 ka $^{14}$C. At 1250 m a.s.l. in the inner-Alpine border zone near Engelberg the bones of a brown bear have been found in a cave. The bones produced a radiocarbon age of 32 ka. At that time, this area must have been ice-free (Morel *et al.* 1997). This is evidence for a considerably reduced Alpine ice cover during MIS 3. Consequently, the glacier advance leading to the LGM was a genuine ice advance from inner-Alpine catchments.

By luminescence dating of pre-interstadial fluvioglacial aggradations at Gossau, Preusser (1999) produced evidence for an early last glacial ice advance during MIS 5d. Evidence is also available from the western Swiss Midlands where luminescence dating of a sequence at Finsterhennen supports an ice advance during MIS 4. The Finsterhennen OSL dates are confirmed for the upper part of the section by a radiocarbon date on a mammoth tusk of 25.4 ka. The rich mammoth finds at Niederweningen (Zürich) represent the Gossau interstadial complex beyond the LGM moraines. The deposits yielded radiocarbon dates of about 35 to 45 ka and belong to a complex peat–permafrost facies (Schlüchter 1988).

Based on palynostratigraphic evidence, Welten (1976) proposed a three-phase last glaciation with an early advance beyond the Alpine border lakes immediately after the interglacial. The new luminescence dates seem to confirm an initial advance phase during MIS 5d, followed by MIS 4 and MIS 2 advances, with substantial recessions in between. Such scenarios suggest that the Last Glaciation in the Alps was a highly dynamic palaeoclimatic period.

A stimulating discussion is currently ongoing on the correlation of data from the central part of the Alpine glacier system with records from the eastern and western Alps. The eastern Alpine record suggests a one-phase last glaciation (van Husen 1987), whereas the French perialpine record suggests multiple advances and a much earlier maximum extent of the ice (Preusser & Schlüchter 2004). This discrepancy may be due to dating problems or it may reflect a genuine palaeoglacial/palaeoclimatic west to east gradient.

### *The inner-Alpine LGM*

Some of the most fascinating aspects of the Alpine glaciations were revealed by mapping the geometry and thickness of the inner-Alpine LGM ice body. Florineth & Schlüchter (1998) produced a reconstruction for the central and SE Swiss Alps with three substantial ice-domes dominating the dynamics of the outflow glacier system. The ice-domes were situated in the Upper Engadine, in the headwaters of the river Rhine and river Rhône. These have been located at places where, today, broad and vast open valleys exist. These domes reached altitudes of >3000 m a.s.l. and caused substantial ice transfluence to the north across the main Alpine divide. A similar mapping and palaeo-ice surface reconstruction was undertaken by Kelly *et al.* (2004) for the SW part of the Swiss Alps. Here, no ice-domes accumulated but in the Zermatt valley a huge ice-field developed with ice flowing at >3010 m a.s.l. This enormous body of ice dominated ice flow in the main Rhône Valley and caused ice from the Aletsch and Upper Rhône catchments to flow across the Simplon Pass directly to the south. The reconstruction of the inner-Alpine ice is based on the mapping of glacial striae, rat-tails, roches moutonées and trimlines. There is, of course, an argument over whether or not the well-developed trimline, e.g. in the Grimsel area, really belongs to the LGM. However there is no evidence for any alternative explanations (Brack 2003). The inner-Alpine ice-domes to the south of the main Alpine divide coincide with a precipitation pattern dominated by northerly winds (Florineth & Schlüchter 2000).

### *Interglacial records*

Welten (1982, 1988) has summarized diverse palynostratigraphical records of interglacial character from the forelands. One key record is from peat in the LGM ice-free area in the central Swiss Midlands where the end of the interglacial is dated by a U–Th series (mean of six dates) at 115 ka (Wegmüller 1992). More of a challenge is the comparison of palynostratigraphical records containing either none or some *Fagus* or none or substantial amounts of *Pterocarya* pollen. In the Thalgut and Meikirch sections (Bern area) two interglacials (as defined by palynostratigraphy) are found in superposition. The upper interglacial at Thalgut is compared to the Eemian and its age is verified by OSL dating to 125 ka. The lower interglacial is dominated by *Pterocarya* and *Fagus* pollen and is clearly older, as at least one additional interglacial is represented by an unconformity in the sequence with a relict palaeosol. The *Pterocarya–Fagus* Interglacial cannot be younger than MIS 9 and is most likely of MIS 11 age (Schlüchter 1989, Preusser & Schlüchter 2004).

A similar sequence was found at Meikirch, where below a coarse fluvioglacial gravel–till complex a lacustrine unit was recovered from a drillcore. Welten (1988) found two different interglacial units in the lacustrine succession. He compared the upper one to the Eemian and the lower one to the Holsteinian stages. However, there are discrepancies between the Meikirch and the Thalgut sequences. *Fagus* is present to some extent in the upper parts at Meikirch only, and *Pterocarya* is present in the lower interglacial at Thalgut but not in Meikirch. Dating of the Meikirch core by OSL (Preusser *et al.* 2005) has produced evidence that the lacustrine unit at Meikirch represents MIS 7 with three distinct interglacial vegetation peaks. A new study of the palynostratigraphy supports that interpretation (Preusser *et al.* 2005).

The interglacial pollen records from the north-central Alpine foreland are supplemented by key interglacial records further to the east for the Eemian at Zeifen and at Lake Starnberg (Beug 1972, 1979). More complete records were found at Samerberg (near Rosenheim; Grüger 1979), in the Wurzacher Basin (Grüger & Schreiner 1993) and at Mondsee (Drescher-Schneider 2000) where the post-Eemian sedimentary record continues into early Würmian interstadial deposits. A last interglacial record has been published from Rè (Canton of Ticino; Hantke 1978–89) and a number of interglacial sites with pre-Eemian pollen sequences are under investigation in the broader area of the southern Alpine border.

### *Summary*

(1) The history of the Quaternary ice age in the Alps and their forelands is complex and multiphase.

(2) The Middle Pleistocene Event (MPE) divides an older from a younger set of ice advances and its age is at, or shortly after, the Brunhes–Matuyama magnetic reversal.

(3) The older glaciations are recorded in the cover gravel deposits (Deckenschotter). According to their mammalian faunal assemblages, the three oldest units are of Upper Pliocene age (in the current IUGS-ICS stratigraphic scheme, older than 1.7 Ma).

(4) The oldest event of the younger set of glaciations is the Most Extensive Glaciation (MEG), in itself a set of three oscillations. Between the MEG and the Last Glaciation at least three advances of intermediate extent, but beyond the LGM, are recorded.

(5) The Last Glaciation was initiated by an ice advance as early as MIS 5d, with two subsequent advances during MIS 4 and 2. The most recent advance is the LGM. During MIS 3 interstadial climate conditions produced complex lithostratigraphies, almost all of which contain peat.

(6) Physical dating techniques (radiocarbon, luminescence and surface-exposure dating) were applied for the time-calibration of the Last Glaciation. The reconstruction of the inner-alpine LGM ice geometry with several ice-domes to the south of the main Alpine divide allows an interpretation of the atmospheric circulation over the Alps and the western Mediterranean during the period of LGM ice buildup.

## Fluvial and aeolian archives of climate change in periglacial environments of north-central Europe (M.F.)

During the cold periods of the Pleistocene, large areas of the now temperate parts of the mid-latitudes of Europe were affected by periglacial conditions. Permafrost and the various frost action processes such as involution or cryoturbation, thermokarst and hillslope processes with stratified slope and solifluction deposits played a major role in shaping the landscape. During the Pleistocene, deep seasonal frost rather than permafrost characterized large parts of the ice-free areas of north-central Europe for a significant amount of time (Poser 1953–54; Vliet-Lanoë 1989; Vliet-Lanoë & Hallégouët 2001). As the periglacial conditions did not prevail in the area of interest, only relict periglacial features, sediments and structures can be studied.

Periglacial features, as described in detail in the textbook by French (1996), are recorded in fluvial and aeolian successions along the Lower Rhine (Boenigk 2001) and in the Middle Rhine (Brunnacker *et al.* 1969) from Lower Pleistocene times onward. During the cold periods of the Pleistocene, two types of large river systems drained the periglacial area. In the north adjacent to the ice margins, very well-developed wide and shallow meltwater channels and streams, termed pradolinas ('Urstromtäler' in German), flowed from east to west into the North Sea. In the south, large rivers such as the Rhine and the Danube flowed away from the Alpine ice margins through a tundra–steppe environment. The presence of thermal cracking pseudomorphs, cryoturbated grounds and faunal remains within the terrace sediments indicate that aggradation took place under cold climate conditions. During cold periods, the fluvial processes in the Rhine system were dominated to varying degrees by spring-snowmelt-induced peak discharge resulting in the development of an extensive braided-river system with significant transport of suspended and bedload sediments. An excellent modern analogue for fluvial activity under periglacial conditions is the northern part of the Mackenzie River in the western Canadian Arctic (French 1996; Murton *et al.* 2004, 2007). The Mackenzie River usually has flowing water beneath the uppermost frozen water surface during the winter, since the channels of the braided-river system are often deep. Breakup of the ice is usually rapid and often accompanied by considerable flooding (French 1996).

A detailed record of sediment successions along the River Rhine is available for the Upper Pleistocene. The close interaction between fluvial and aeolian deposition led to the formation of distinct fluvio-aeolian environments along the river, including fluvial terraces in river valleys related to periods of aggradation and erosion, and aeolian deposits including loess, sand sheets and dune sands.

The periglacial environment adjacent to large river systems such as those of the Rhine and the Maas were characterized by particularly intense wind action (Huissteden *et al.* 2000). Extensive and thick loess and sand sheet deposits formed along the valleys during the Late Glacial post-dating permafrost degradation related to climate warming after the Last Glacial Maximum (Högbom 1923; Maarleveld 1960; Seppälä 1995; Kasse 1997; Frechen *et al.* 2001*a*). The Upper Pleniglacial fluvial and fluvio-aeolian sand successions underlying the Late Glacial sand sheet deposits are characterized by large ice wedge-casts and cryoturbated grounds indicative of permafrost conditions. Periglacial dune fields and sand sheets are located south of the Pleistocene ice margin in Belgium, the Netherlands, northern Germany and Poland (Fig. 20.21). These sands were derived most likely from non-vegetated floodplains, glacial outwash plains or till plains. In the Netherlands and Belgium, the availability of sand is also related to the proximity of the Rhine delta and the extended continental shelf, which resulted from sea-level lowering.

Loess is a widespread aeolian sediment, which accumulated in a broad belt across the northern hemisphere (Fig. 20.21). It is an unstratified and well-sorted deposit formed as a result of wind blowing across desiccated alluvium and is typical for the periglacial environment (Lieberoth 1963; Frechen 2002). The loess of north-central Europe is slightly calcareous, homogeneous and weathers into characteristic polygonal shrinkage cracks. Loess–palaeosol sequences provide a relatively detailed and continuous terrestrial record of climate and environment change throughout the Pleniglacial.

This section presents the fluvial and aeolian record from periglacial areas in north-central Europe based upon the fluvial sediments along the Upper, Middle and Lower Rhine, and the loess deposits along the River Rhine. The Lower and Middle Pleistocene sedimentary succession will be described in more detail for the Lower Rhine area owing to its extensive exposures in the adjacent lignite open-cast mines.

### *Fluvial record along the River Rhine*

The River Rhine is one of the few major fluvial systems that connect the areas of the Alpine glaciers and the Scandinavian ice

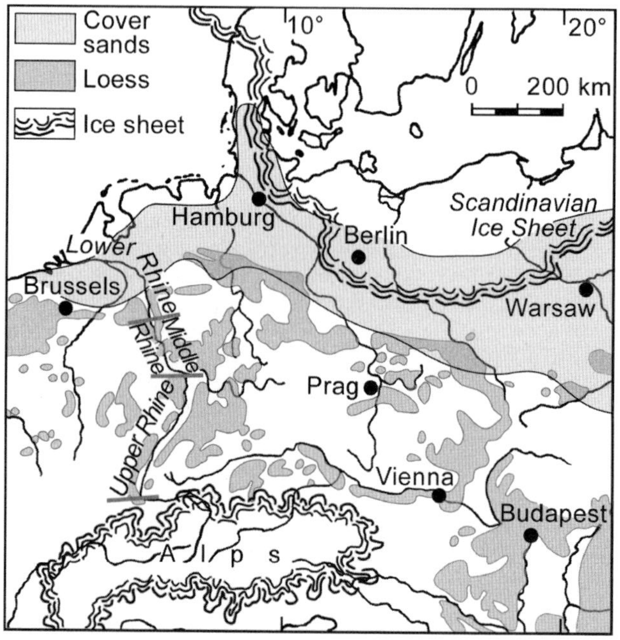


**Fig. 20.21.** Map showing the maximum ice extent during the last glaciation and the distribution of loess (dark grey) and cover sands (light grey) in north-central Europe including the Upper Rhine, the Middle Rhine and the Lower Rhine areas (modified from Frechen *et al.* 2003; Kasse 1997).

sheet and so provides a key for correlating the two glacial areas in northern and Central Europe (Boenigk & Frechen 2006). The fluvial sequences of the Rhine Valley include at least 12 Pleistocene terraces in the Lower Rhine area, two Pliocene and 13 Pleistocene terraces in the Middle Rhine area, resulting in 16 different Pliocene and Pleistocene terraces based on the correlation between the Lower and Middle Rhine (Boenigk & Frechen 2006). The formation of fluvial terraces was significantly influenced by climatic and tectonic processes. The terrace staircases are a result of uplift in the Middle Rhine area and the southern part of the Lower Rhine area, whereas subsidence in the northern part of the Lower Rhine area and the Upper Rhine Graben resulted in buried stacked sequences.

*Upper Rhine*

The Upper Rhine Graben (URG) has acted as a major sediment sink since its origin in the late Eocene (Ziegler 1990; Cloetingh *et al.* 2005). During the Quaternary, the URG has been affected by increased tectonic subsidence creating accommodation space, which has been subsequently filled by sediments from the Alpine source area and to a minor degree from the Vosges and Black Forest (Ellwanger *et al.* 2003). Increased aggradation in the southern URG post-dates the filling up of the Lake Constance Basin and occurred coevally with periods of major ice melting and the end of a glacial period.

A detailed summary of the stratigraphy of the Tertiary and Quaternary sediment successions of the URG is provided by Hagedorn (2004). The sediment successions consist of alternating fluvial and lacustrine environments (Ellwanger *et al.* 2003). In the Heidelberg Basin with its maximum subsidence, the Quaternary has a thickness of 300–400 m (Bartz 1974). Interglacial deposits are sparse because most of the results are related to drilling cores only. In the northern URG, more recent palaeobotanical investigations yielded pollen spectra correlating to the Tiglian A (core 'Schifferstadt BK 30c GM'), to the Waalian and Cromerian ('Schifferstadt Interglacial' and tentatively the 'Mannheim Interglacial', respectively) and to the Holsteinian or Early Rissian/Saalian interglacials (Knipping 2004; Frechen *et al.* 2007). As a comprehensive chronological framework for the Lower and Middle Pleistocene record is still required, the Upper Pleistocene record will be summarized in more detail.

In the southern part of the URG, Pleniglacial-age fan deposits have been partly reworked into a braided river system. Climate-induced changes in fluvial activity led to a distinct stepwise progradation of coarse sediments downstream, in the form of alluvial fans. OSL age estimates of intercalated sand lenses yielded Weichselian and Early Holocene depositional ages.

The Pleistocene sequence of the URG consists of sand and gravel units as well as dune sands and loess deposited as a result of fluvial and aeolian activity, respectively. The surface of the floodplain consists of reworked sand and gravel, often covered by alluvial clay and flood loam deposits of Holocene age. The floodplain has acted as a sediment source for deflation, evidenced by loess deposits, cover sands and dunes up to 20 m thick (Frechen 1999; Frechen *et al.* 2003, 2007; Lang *et al.* 2003; Zöller & Löscher 1999) although a finer fraction may have been derived from more distant sources. A coeval increase in fluvial and aeolian activity is likely.

In the southern part of the URG the sediments are coarser than in the northern part. Local rivers laterally supply sediments from the Vosges and Black Forest into the URG, where the sediments mix with Alpine material. A correlation of the Quaternary sediment successions from south to north is problematical owing to reduced subsidence in the area around the city of Karlsruhe resulting in a reduced thickness of Quaternary sediments. Furthermore, the petrography of the sediments changes from south to north owing to increased sorting and mixture with local material from the margins of the URG (Hagedorn 2004). In the southern part of the URG, the Quaternary sedimentary succession is subdivided lithologically into three units: from youngest to oldest, the Neuenburg Formation, the Breisgau Formation and the Iffezheim Formation (Ellwanger *et al.* 2003). In a chronological study, sedimentary records of the last glacial Stage were investigated by luminescence dating methods indicating several aggradation periods during the Middle Pleniglacial and the Late Glacial. The chronological framework of aggradation periods in the URG shows an excellent correlation with the record from the Swiss Midlands (Fig. 20.22).

*Middle Rhine*

Along the Middle Rhine, which is situated between the towns of Bingen and Bonn, a series of terraces may be correlated with alternating periods of incision and aggradation (Fig. 20.23). Towards the end of the Pliocene, the Rhine extended its catchment area to the Alps, as evidenced by the pebble spectrum of the Upper Terrace complex. There is a notable change to a more heterogeneous mixture of sand and gravel, and also the first appearance of garnet, epidote, green hornblende and alterite in the heavy-mineral spectrum (Boenigk 1970), as well as radiolarite in the gravel fraction (Schnütgen & Brunnacker 1976), and the decreasing content of quartz.

The Upper Terrace complex consists mainly of braided-river sediments deposited in a valley up to 8 km wide. The Upper Terrace sediments were deposited during a time interval between the Jaramillo event *c.* 1 Ma ago to *c.* 600 ka before present (BP). The Upper Terrace complex can be subdivided into four terraces (UT1–UT4), as summarized in detail by Boenigk & Frechen (2006).

The Middle Terraces (Lower Middle Terrace (LMT), Middle Middle Terrace (MMT), Upper Middle Terrace (UMT)) are present as narrow steps along the entrenched valley. The morphological change from the broad plateau valley to the entrenched valley was due to increased uplift of the Rhenish Massif. The most rapid uplift was between *c.* 600 and 350 ka BP, as evidenced by intercalated tephra from the reactivated volcanism in the east Eifel area (Bogaard & Schmincke 1990). The tectonic activity resulted in 150 m of downcutting into the Palaeozoic bedrock, forming steep valley sides with minor terrace relicts. Petrographically, the Middle Terrace deposits are characterized by pebbles with a high percentage of volcanic rocks and a heavy-mineral spectrum with a high percentage of minerals from the Eifel volcanism, neither of which are present in the Upper Terrace sediments.

The Middle Terraces are poorly preserved and consist mainly of rock-cut terraces with only rare exposures of terrace deposits. However, in contrast to the Upper Terraces, the Middle Terraces can be distinguished on the basis of their elevations, because there is less faulting than in the case of the Upper Terraces. The deposits from below the MMT are up to 30 m thick and are exposed in a gravel pit at Ariendorf. This terrace deposit correlates with the fifth from the last glaciation (Boenigk 1995) on the basis of the overlying loess/palaeosol sequence and tephra layers at the top of the terrace gravel and intercalated in the loess/palaeosol sequence (Boenigk & Frechen 1998). $^{40}Ar/^{39}Ar$ dating of the tephra at the top of the gravel yielded an age of $419 \pm 18$ ka (Fuhrmann 1983) and *c.* 490 ka (Bogaard & Schmincke 1990). The LMT correlates with the penultimate

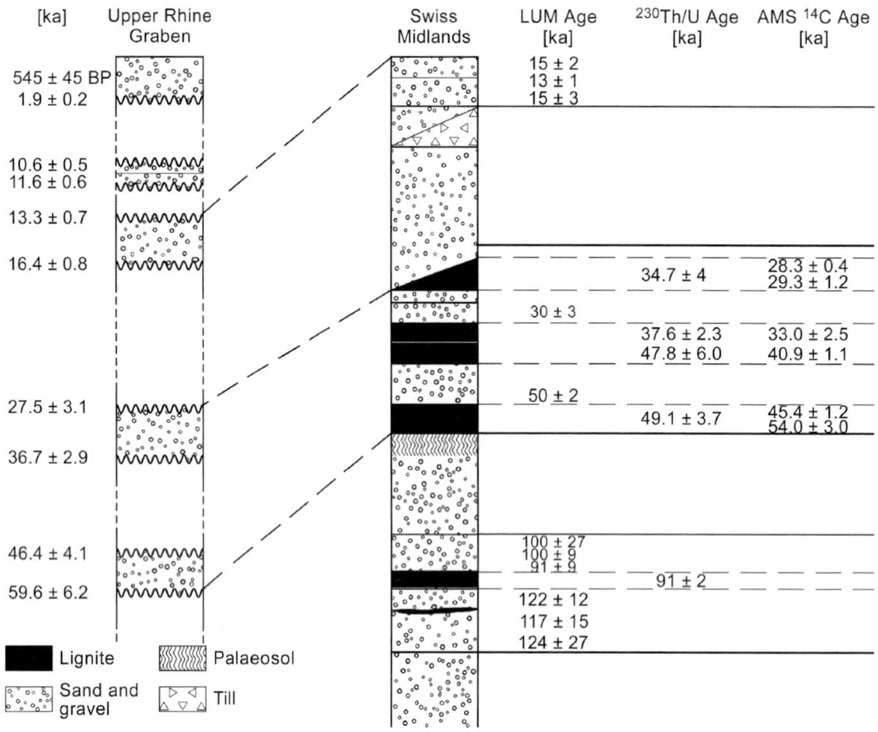


**Fig. 20.22.** Correlation between Swiss Midlands and Upper Rhine Graben. The OSL age estimates are given in thousands of years (ka), whereas the radiocarbon ages (545 ± 20 BP) are given in years. The chronological data of the idealized sediment succession from the Swiss Midlands were taken from Preusser *et al.* (2001, 2003) and Geyh & Schlüchter (1998).

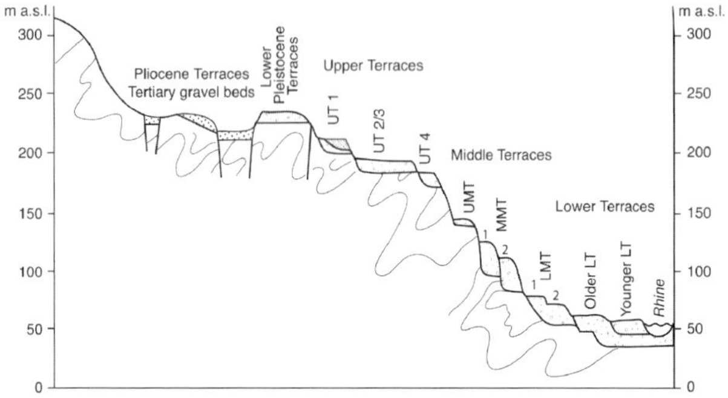


**Fig. 20.23.** Idealized sketch of the terrace staircase in the Middle Rhine area including Tertiary terraces and gravel beds, the Lower Pleistocene Terraces (LPT), the Upper Terraces (UT1–4), the Middle Terraces (UMT–LMT2) and the Lower Terraces (Older LT and Younger LT) (from Boenigk & Frechen 2006).

glaciation. The fluvial sediments of the LMT are overlain by Upper Pleistocene loess and intercalated with several palaeosols (Boenigk & Frechen 2001).

The youngest deposits in the Middle Rhine area are those of the Lower Terraces (LT) and the Holocene. The Older LT is of Pleniglacial age and is overlain by the Laacher See tephra, which provides a widespread tephrochronological marker horizon (see next section). The surface of the Younger LT – the terrace deposits correlate with the Younger Dryas – is *c.* 2 m lower than that of the Older LT in the area. The fluvial sediments of the Younger LT are, in general, underlain by those of the Older LT. Schirmer (1990) distinguishes a third lower terrace in the Neuwied Basin, which is considered to be older than the Older LT. The youngest terrace, including the floodplain deposits of the River Rhine, was formed during the Holocene. However, this terrace does not have the same significance as the LT because it is not as distinctly developed as a terrace.

During the Pleniglacial and Late Glacial periods, the sediments from below the Older LT were deposited in a braided-river system in the Middle and Lower Rhine areas, prior to the eruption of the Laacher See. This event is independently dated to *c.* 12.9 ka (see next section). The Older LT most likely overlies older terrace sediments in many cases but cannot be distinguished from the older deposits due to the lack of appropriate dating control. The Older LT is more likely to correlate with the last Pleniglacial and/or Late Glacial. The sediments from below the Younger LT were deposited following the cataclysmic eruption of the Laacher See, as evidenced by the presence of pumice in the gravel. The surface of the Younger LT is *c.* 2 m lower than the surface of the Older LT.

*Lower Rhine*

The Lower Rhine area (Lower Rhine Embayment) is an area of subsidence, block faulting and tilting within the Rhenish Massif, which opens towards the NW into the southern North Sea basin (Fig. 20.21). It forms part of the European rift system in western Europe. In the Erft Basin, located in the centre of the Lower Rhine Embayment, the Tertiary and Quaternary sediments have a combined thickness of 600 m. This succession is partly exposed in large lignite mines, thus providing detailed information about the fluvial regime of the Rhine system during the Tertiary and Quaternary (Boenigk 1978*a*, 1979). Fluvial sediments were deposited from Late Miocene to Middle Pleistocene times (Boenigk 1978*a*, 1979). The depositional history became more complex, owing to intensive block faulting after the Pliocene (Fig. 20.24). The western part of the Lower Rhine Embayment, especially the Rhine/Maas system in the Netherlands, has been studied in detail by van den Berg (1995) and Tebbens (1999). The Cenozoic sediments in this area attain a maximum thickness of 1200 m and provide an excellent terrestrial archive of climate change.

The fluvial record in the Lower Rhine Embayment is more complete than that in the Middle Rhine area owing to subsidence. The Early and Middle Miocene sediments were deposited by the pre-Rhine fluvial system. At that time the depositional environment of the Lower Rhine Embayment was marine in the north and lacustrine and fluvial in the south, which is where extensive lignite deposits also formed. During the Late Miocene and Pliocene, Kieseloolite gravel up to 280 m thick was deposited in large fans.

The Pliocene–Pleistocene boundary in the Lower Rhine Embayment is defined as being at the top of the Reuver Clay on the basis of the pollen spectra, with *Sequoia*, *Taxodium* and *Nyssa* as typical Tertiary genera. A palaeomagnetic boundary in the 'Reuverian C' correlates with the Gauss–Matuyama boundary (Boenigk *et al.* 1974; Brunnacker & Boenigk 1976; Urban 1979). This clay contains mammal bones and teeth, which provide a correlation with Mammal Zones NM16a and NM16b of the Neogene terrestrial mammal stratigraphy (Kolfschoten *et al.* 1998; Mörs *et al.* 1998). The Reuver Clay is characterized by a significant change in the petrographic content. The first appearance of Alpine material in Rhine sediment is observed in the Reuverian B sediments, as evidenced by the palynological remains present (Boenigk 1970, 1976, 1978*b*).

Pleistocene fluvial deposits overlie the Reuver Clay (Reuverian A–C). Although the upper part of this succession is referred to as 'Upper Terrace' (UT2 and 3), morphological terraces or terrace steps did not form. The Kieseloolite Formation is overlain by the Tegelen Formation (including the Oebel beds which correlate with the Pliocene; Boenigk & Frechen 2006). Palynological analysis of Clay B1 by Urban (1978*a*) yielded pollen spectra indicative of a boreal climate with permafrost ('Fortuna Oscillation'), most probably of Pretiglian age. Sedimentological and petrographic evidence indicates that the Clay B1 layer is most likely only part of unit 13 (*sensu* Schneider & Thiele 1965).

In the central part of the Lower Rhine Embayment on the Jackerath Horst, the Tegelen Formation is overlain by the Holzweiler Formation (Boenigk 2001). These sediments comprise coarse gravels intercalated with silt and sand horizons and were derived from the area of the River Maas (Boenigk 1978*a*, 2001). Due to the presence of numerous coarse blocks or boulders and cryoturbation features at the upper boundary of the unit, deposition of the gravel during a glacial stage is most likely. However, the intercalated clays have not been investigated palynologically or palaeomagnetically.

In the southern Lower Rhine Embayment, the equivalent of these deposits consists of alternating clay and gravel layers exposed in the Frechen open-cast mine. These clay and gravel beds are interpreted as having been deposited during interglacial and glacial intervals, respectively. The sediments deposited during the glacial intervals are denoted, from bottom to top, as Gravel b2, Gravel c and Gravel d (Fig. 20.25). Each of these gravel layers is overlain by a clay horizon, named Clay B2, Clay C and Clay D; i.e. Gravel b2 is overlain by Clay B2, etc. These clay horizons correlate with Lower Pleistocene interglacials, termed the Frechen Interglacials I to III (= Clay B2, Clay C and Clay D). The pollen spectra of the Frechen Interglacial I (= Clay B2) have been assigned to the Tiglian A (Urban 1978*a*, *b*). The chronostratigraphy of these Lower Pleistocene deposits is based on floral and palaeomagnetic evidence.

The heavy-mineral spectrum of the Upper Terrace sediments indicates that there was a complete restructuring of the drainage pattern in the Lower Rhine Embayment at this time. Initially the sediment supply was from SW to NE along the River Maas (Holzweiler Formation). Subsequently, the fluvial system changed to a SE to NW drainage direction with sediment supply only from the River Rhine in the whole of the Lower Rhine area (Boenigk 2001).

The fluvial deposits are termed Upper Terrace 1 (UT1) and consist of at least eight coarse-grained–fine-grained cycles rich in blocks and boulders near the base. The sequence is overlain by Clay E (Urban 1978*a*; Brunnacker & Boenigk 1983), which correlates with the Lower Pleistocene based on its pollen spectra.

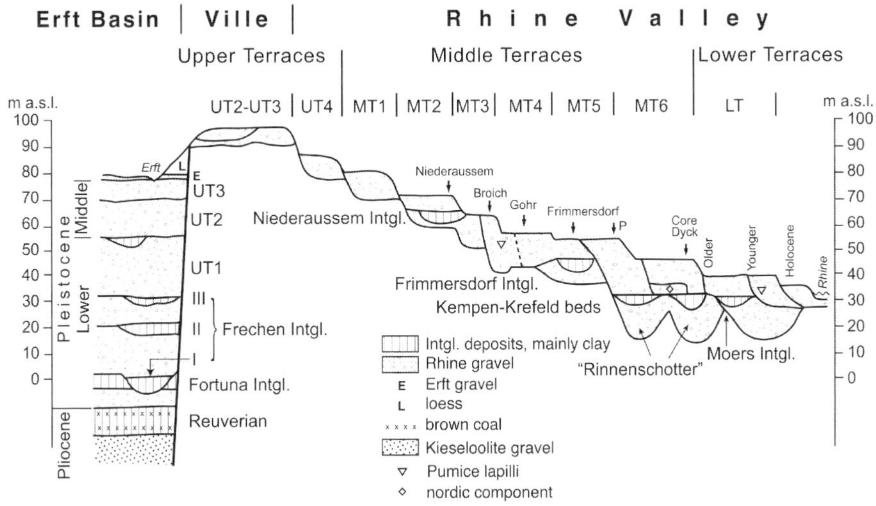


**Fig. 20.24.** Idealized sketch of the terrace staircase in the southern Lower Rhine Embayment around Cologne. The altitudes are related to the region of Grevenbroich, except the sequence at section P (Köln-Portz). The Lower Middle Terrace and the 'Rinnenschotter' from this section are altitude-corrected for the sequence of this figure (from Boenigk & Frechen 2006).

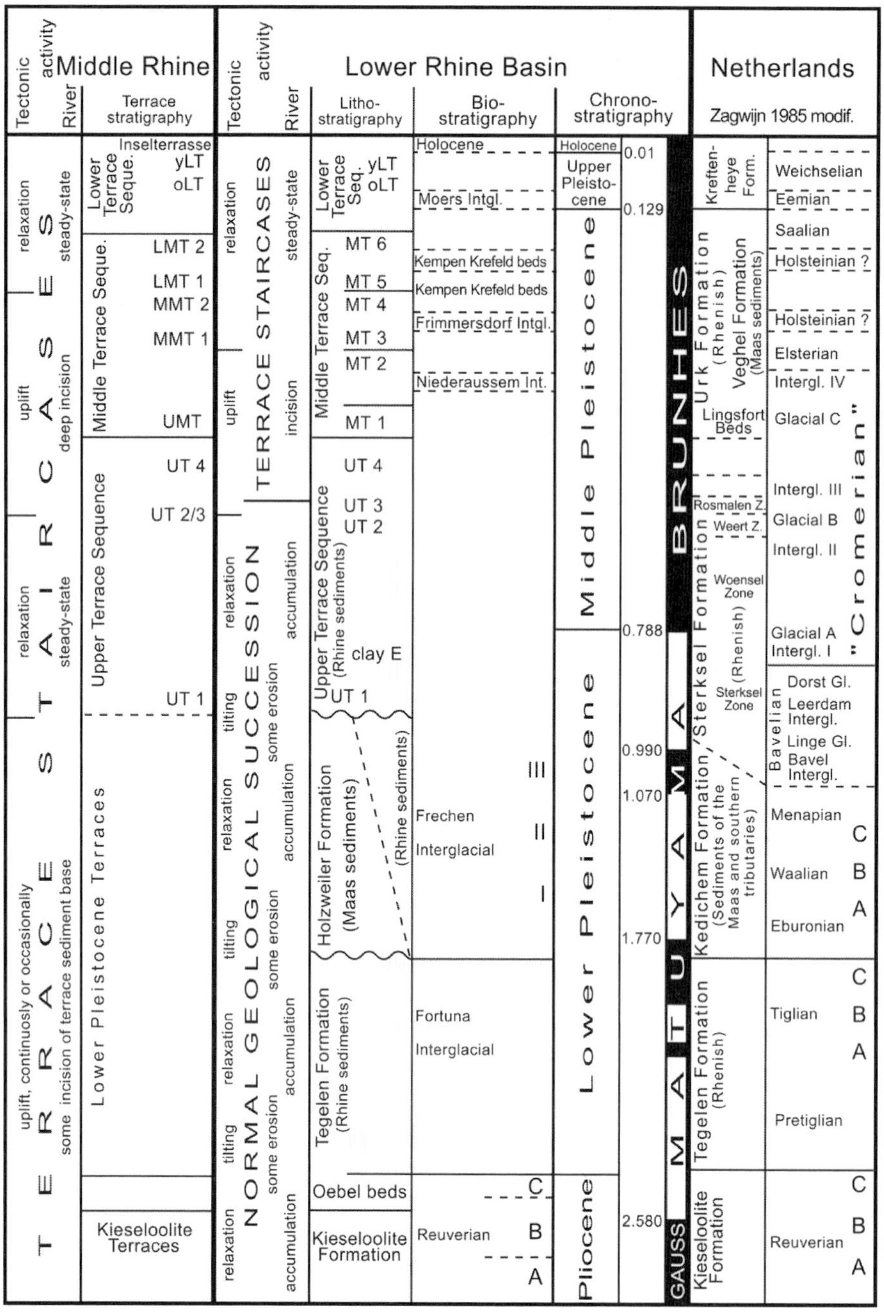


**Fig. 20.25.** Summary of the chronostratigraphic interpretation and correlation of terraces in the Middle Rhine and Lower Rhine areas with the Dutch stratigraphy (from Boenigk & Frechen 2006).

Additionally, the possibly reversed magnetic polarity (Boenigk 1979) may represent the uppermost part of the Matuyama chron. In the Frechen brown coal pit, the stratigraphic equivalent of Clay E is represented by a weathering horizon of interglacial origin (Boenigk 1978*a*).

Upper Terrace 2 (UT2) forms the first and laterally most extensive terrace in the Lower Rhine Basin. These terrace deposits can be correlated on morphological, sedimentary and petrographic (high content of alterite and saussurite) evidence with Glacial B of the Cromerian Complex (Boenigk 1978*b*; Zagwijn 1985). Although there is evidence for this correlation, it is likely that this interpretation applies to the terrace only. The gravel body from below UT2 forms a thick sedimentary unit. In the middle part of the Lower Rhine Embayment, these deposits, with an average thickness of 10 m, extend more than 60 km in an east–west direction. It is unlikely that this sediment body was deposited only during parts of Glacial B of the Cromerian complex; it is more likely that these sediments were deposited during an extended period of tectonic quiescence with active lateral erosion and redeposition of sediments.

Upper Terrace 3 (UT3) consists of well-bedded fluvial sediments, layers of large boulders, cryoturbation features and intraformational ice-wedge casts, indicating cold climatic conditions (Brunnacker *et al.* 1978). UT3 is exposed only in erosional channels within UT2 (Boenigk 1978*b*) and so evidences the reactivation of tectonic uplift in the Lower Rhine Basin followed by the incision of the Rhine into UT2. The first occurrence of rare, but typical, heavy minerals from the Eifel volcanism is found in the sediments from below UT3. The UT3 terrace deposits are overlain by an interglacial palaeosol (Schnütgen *et al.* 1975). Due to the increasing tectonic activity during the Middle Pleistocene, the Rhine changed its course to east of Ville Horst. Upper Terrace 4 (UT4) in the southern Lower Rhine represents a morphological transition to the Middle Terraces.

The Middle Terrace complex forms a terrace staircase in the southern Lower Rhine embayment in the area of Cologne, as described by Brunnacker *et al.* (1978). The most complete sequence of the Middle Terrace complex is exposed in the type area on the west side of the Rhine valley between Cologne and Grevenbroich near Düsseldorf, where the Middle Terraces can be subdivided into six units (Boenigk & Frechen 2006) (Fig. 20.24).

Middle Terrace 1 (MT1, *sensu* Boenigk & Frechen 2006) is both the oldest and the stratigraphically uppermost Middle Terrace in the southern Lower Rhine area. There are only rare relicts of the MT1. Cold-climate indicators are often found in the sediments from below MT1 (Brunnacker *et al.* 1978). The sediment from below MT2 can be subdivided into two gravel bodies, separated by a laterally discontinuous clay horizon of interglacial origin. This clay horizon is termed the 'Niederaussem Interglacial' and is exposed in the Fortuna open-cast mine (Brunnacker *et al.* 1978; Boenigk 1995). The gravel below the 'Niederaussem Interglacial' is characterized by its high content of brown hornblende, whereas the gravel on top of the clay has a predominance of clinopyroxene in its heavy-mineral spectrum. MT3 is exposed to the west of the city of Broich. Pumice is intercalated into the gravel deposits *c.* 8 m below the surface. The sediments from below MT5 can be subdivided into two gravel-rich units, separated by a younger Middle Pleistocene interglacial clay horizon termed the 'Frimmersdorf Interglacial' (Brelie *et al.* 1959), the upper part of which is rich in peat (Boenigk 1995; Brunnacker *et al.* 1978; Urban 1980*a*, *b*; Klostermann 1992). Gravels from below MT4 near Broich are intercalated with several thin layers of pumice as described by Paas (1961) and Brunnacker *et al.* (1978). Boenigk & Frechen (2006) reported similar fragments from *c.* 8 m below the surface. A more detailed investigation indicated that the pumice layers are exposed to *c.* 63.5 m a.s.l. and, therefore, are intercalated into sediments from below the MT3. The pumice thus enables the Eifel volcanism and the terrace stratigraphy from the Middle Rhine area to be correlated. MT4 overlaps older sediments owing to lateral erosion (Fig. 20.24). MT6 (*sensu* Boenigk & Frechen 2006) can be distinguished from the older terraces on account of its morphological position. It is the lowest of the Middle Terraces and its gravel deposits are found only in channels. The gravel from below MT6 is intercalated with several clay and peat layers of possibly varying ages of interglacial origin and exposed at similar elevations.

Between the late Elsterian and the Drenthe stadial of the Saalian glaciation, there were a number of warm-temperate periods (interstadials/interglacials), which are well-known from other parts of Central Europe, for example from the Schöningen site in Lower Saxony (Germany) (Thieme *et al.* 1995; Thieme 1997; Urban 1995, 2007). Glaciofluvial gravel including Nordic pebbles was deposited stratigraphically between the 'Rinnenschottern' or the Kempen-Krefeld beds and the gravel from below MT6. The age of the Kempen-Krefelds beds is controversial, ranging from youngest Cromerian to Early Saalian (Kempf 1966; Urban 1980*a*, *b*; Klostermann 1992; Boenigk & Frechen 2006).

The Lower Terraces (LT) can be subdivided into two terrace units, an Older LT and a Younger LT. In the southern part of the Lower Rhine Embayment, south of Cologne, the two terraces show a difference in elevation of *c.* 2 m (Thoste 1974). From Grevenbroich northwards, there is no difference in elevation between these two terrace levels. The terrace deposits of the Older LT are intercalated with fine-grained interglacial sediments and are, thus, subdivided into two gravel units. These interglacial deposits correlate with the Eemian and are termed the Moers (Bertsch & Steeger 1927) or Weeze beds or the Weeze Interglacial (Klostermann 1992) (Fig. 20.25).

The gravel from below the Older LT and on top of the interglacial sediments is considered to be of Weichselian Pleniglacial age. The terrace is not covered by loess, in contrast to the Middle Terraces. The Younger LT correlates with the Younger Dryas on the basis of cold-climate indicators and the presence of pumice lapilli from the Laacher See eruption.

The floodplain of the Rhine is slightly lower than the Lower Terraces owing to reworking and erosion. The terrace deposits are subdivided into island-like sand and gravel deposits from different Holocene periods, separated by oxbows.

### *Aeolian record*

During the Pleistocene glaciations, much of Europe was subjected to extensive and increased dust accumulation and loess formation. The area affected extended from NW France and Belgium, with a mainly oceanic-driven climate, via Central Europe to the Ukraine and the Russian Plain with a more continental climate (Frechen *et al.* 2003). In Europe, loess–palaeosol sequences have been intensively studied over the last century. These deposits display a wide variety of climate proxies for periglacial periods and, therefore, supply some major clues concerning the climate and environmental changes on land during the past 130 000 years.

Loess is a clastic, predominantly silt-sized sediment, which is formed by the accumulation and diagenesis of wind-blown dust. During the Pleistocene, loess and loess-like sediments were formed in periglacial environments in north-central Europe. Loess deposits include a variety of cold- and warm-climate indicators and provide a long-term record of climate change over the past 2 million years. Snail faunas, such as *Pupilla*, *Columella* and *Striata*, are designated to represent cold and dry climate (loess steppe), cold and humid subarctic climate and cold winter/warm summer (warm loess steppe), respectively (Lozek 1964, 1969). Skeletal remains of large mammals, such as mammoth, woolly rhino, musk ox and reindeer, are also cold-climate indicators. Periglacial features are common in loess from north-central Europe, and include ice wedges, solifluction, gelifluction, drop structures and periglacial slopewash deposits.

Loess deposits are often intercalated with palaeosol horizons displaying differing degrees of weathering intensity. Palaeosols represent periods of reduced dust accumulation and are characterized by their clay, carbonate and organic content, as well as their colour and structure. Different palaeosols reflect specific climatic conditions, for example deciduous forest (brown forest soil), forest steppe (chernozem) or tundra (cryosol or tundra gley).

The oldest loess deposits of the Middle Rhine area are exposed at the Kärlich section (Brunnacker *et al.* 1969, 1971) and most likely correlate with the time period between 600 and

650 ka BP (Boenigk & Frechen 1998, 2001). The Pleistocene successions from this section contain evidence of the prehistorically important Kärlich Interglacial (Bosinski *et al.* 1980; Urban 1983; Bittmann 1990; Gaudzinski *et al.* 1996). The Kärlich Interglacial I (Boenigk & Frechen 2001) has a maximum age of 400 ka, as determined by $^{40}Ar/^{39}Ar$ dating (Bogaard & Schmincke 1990).

The onset of the Upper Pleistocene loess deposition is related to the first cold stadial following the last interglacial optimum (i.e. the Eemian interglacial), at *c.* 115 ka. In north-central Europe, increased aridity, dust storms and a decline in thermophilous trees at the time of glacial inception were typical for the post-Eemian period. Remains of dust storm events and landscape alteration can be found in loess–palaeosol sequences (Boenigk & Frechen 2001) and sediment cores from maar lakes (Sirocko *et al.* 2005) in the Eifel area, Germany. Several cycles of slope erosion and sediment accumulation also occurred, as well as soil-forming processes. At the Tönchesberg section in the Eifel area, four A horizons are intercalated (Fig. 20.26): the lowermost chernozem-like palaeosol most likely correlates with the Early Weichselian (MIS 5c); the uppermost one, a chernozem-like palaeosol with strong clay illuviation, correlates to MIS 5a (Boenigk & Frechen 2001). Loess beds, up to 20 cm thick, accumulated at the early stage of the Middle Pleniglacial and correlate to the boundary between MIS 5a and MIS 4, in the Eifel. This loess most likely correlates to a Europe-wide dust storm which occurred at that time (see Boenigk & Frechen 2001; Frechen *et al.* 1999; Rousseau *et al.* 1998); the loess has many small frost cracks and ice-wedge pseudomorphs indicative of a cold and stadial environment following interstadial conditions. In Belgium, aeolian loess-like depositis were also found during the same period (Frechen *et al.* 2001*b*), thus autochthonous loess

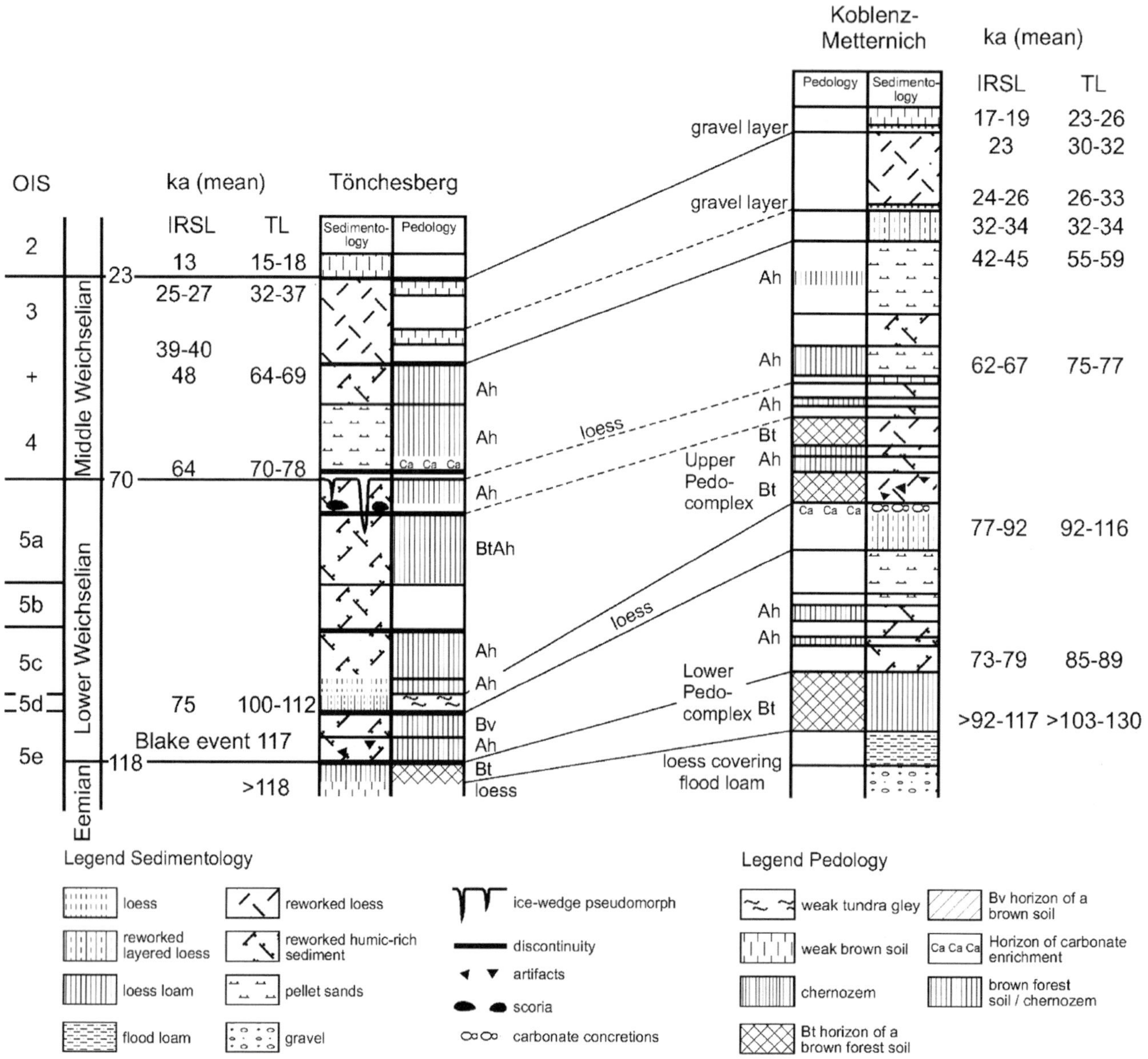


**Fig. 20.26.** Correlation of the last interglacial/glacial loess record from the Tönchesberg section and from the Koblenz-Metternich section (from Boenigk & Frechen 2001).

was deposited during MIS 4. Dust accumulation was followed by a period of erosion, as documented by the presence of a hiatus and/or pellet sands in many Central European loess regions. In the Rhine area, the pedosediments underwent at least two periods of soil formation, as documented by two weak A horizons (Fig. 20.26).

During the early part of MIS 3, between 65 and 55 ka BP, loess was deposited in NW France along the River Seine and was followed by several soil-forming periods; from the bottom to the top these are a brown arctic soil, a gelic cambisol, an arctic brown soil and a tundra gley, as exposed at the Villier-Adam section (e.g. Locht *et al.* 2003). These palaeosols formed most likely between 55 and 35 ka BP. The latter tundra gley is covered by reworked layered loess and a second brown arctic soil, which formed at the end of MIS 3. The top of the succession consists of calcareous loess intercalated with gelic gleysols (between 25 and 20 ka). Late Glacial loess was deposited between 18 and 13 ka.

In early MIS 3, weak soil formation also occurred in the Middle Rhine area, as evidenced by the presence of A horizons. The sediment successions documenting the period between 59 and *c.* 40 ka are poorly preserved and present in only a few sections due to a major phase of erosion prior to 40 ka BP. A period of loess accumulation between 40 and 25 ka BP was intercalated with two periods of soil formation at the Tönchesberg section. At the Remagen-Schwalbenberg section near the confluence of the rivers Rhine and Ahr, MIS 3 is characterized by the presence of loess and reworked loess intercalated with six weak soils within the time period ranging from 45 to 25 ka BP. The relatively high number of palaeosols was most likely due to increased slope dynamics.

The upper part of the Middle Pleniglacial is characterized by loess-like deposits with two intercalated weak brown soils indicating interstadial intervals; a correlation with the Hengelo (39–36 ka) and the Denekamp (32–28 ka) interstadials of the Middle Weichselian is likely. Two main periods of permafrost extension were recorded in the loess record from Belgium at *c.* 60 ka and at *c.* 28 ka BP (Vliet-Lanoë 1989; Frechen *et al.* 2001*b*). These two periods were triggered by low insolation rates in spring and summer and by a low precipitation rate. The first phase of permafrost thickening took place prior to the Hengelo-Denekamp interstadial, while the second phase occurred after this interstadial. Ice-wedge activity during the last glaciation was confirmed by luminescence dating of loess covering the ice-wedge horizon at the Harmignies section in Belgium (Frechen *et al.* 2001*b*).

During MIS 2, two main periods of loess accumulation occurred between 24 and 20 ka BP and between 17 and 13 ka (Frechen 1992; Frechen *et al.* 1995). A significant period of surface destabilization occurred at *c.* 17 ka, as evidenced in NW Europe and the Rhine area. The event decreased in intensity towards the more continental environment to the east.

The Upper Pleniglacial record has a thickness of 10–12 m at the Nußloch section (Lang *et al.* 2003; Zöller & Löscher 1999). Calcareous loess with no evidence of weathering is exposed. The

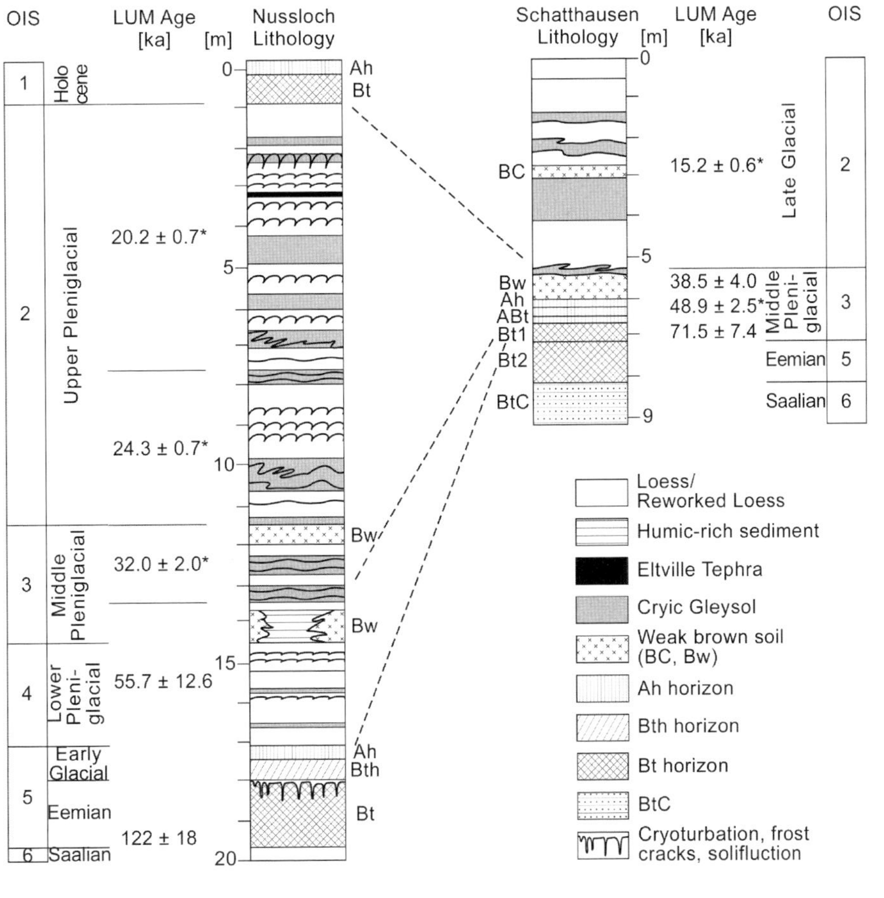


**Fig. 20.27.** Chronological interpretation and correlation of the last glacial loess records from the Nussloch section and the Schatthausen section (modified from Frechen *et al.* 2007).

loess units have a thickness of 0.5 to 2.0 m and are intercalated with tundra gleys (gelic gleysols) which are mostly cryoturbated or subjected to solifluction under periglacial conditions (Fig. 20.27). The tundra gleys resulted from hydromorphic conditions and show slight decalcification with the redistribution of carbonates at the base of the profile (carbonate concretions), reduction and redistribution of iron (oxidized patches and bands), as well as slight enrichment in organic carbon (more intense rooting and biological activity). The snail fauna is mainly represented by species typical of open habitats. Tundra gleys represent short periods of marked reduction or cessation of loess sedimentation and reflect very cold and locally relatively more humid environments with the development of permafrost (cryo-injections) and local cracks with ice-wedges. Pleniglacial and Late Glacial tundra gleys are present in the majority of the profiles in NW and Central Europe. The tundra gleys represent very short periods of decreased loess accumulation, whereas the loess represents periods of increased dust storms.

During the Pleniglacial and the Late Glacial period, cover sands were deposited along the River Maas in Belgium and the Netherlands (Frechen *et al.* 2001*a*; Frechen & Berg 2002) and loess intercalated with weak soil horizons accumulated in the Upper Rhine Graben (Zöller & Löscher 1999; Lang *et al.* 2003; Frechen *et al.* 2007).

High mass accumulation rates of dust most likely occurred in the transition between the Pleniglacial and the Late Glacial periods. Early summer floods were able to transport gravels, whereas the remainder of the year was characterized by aridity. The resulting dry surfaces and floodplains facilitated extensive deflation of silt- and sand-sized material. There would appear to be some correlation between increased accumulation rates in the loess record (silt and fine sand, dust) and periods of increased aggradation in the fluvial record (sand, gravel) of the Upper Rhine Graben (Fig. 20.28). In north-central Europe, the major period of dust accumulation took place during the Pleniglacial and the Late Glacial (Frechen *et al.* 2007), whereas the major fluvial accumulation periods of sand and gravel apparently occurred during the Late Glacial and the Middle Pleniglacial. However, due to highly dynamic transport processes during the Upper Pleniglacial, resulting in poorly sorted coarse components including Helvetic limestone up to block (car) size within a fine-grained matrix; this material is not suitable for dating.

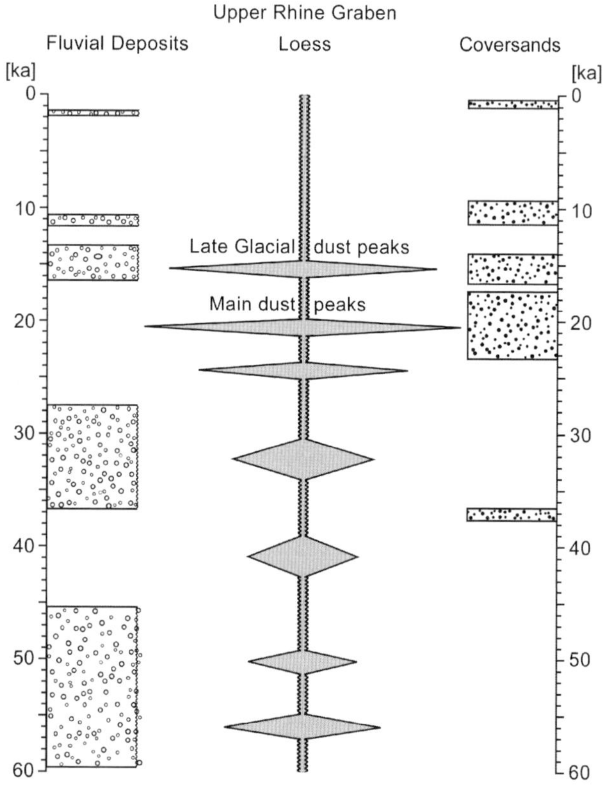


**Fig. 20.28.** Idealized sketch of periods of increased fluvial and aeolian sediment accumulations in the Upper Rhine Graben. The aeolian record is based on the loess record from Nussloch and Schatthausen, both near to the city of Heidelberg in the northern part of the Upper Rhine Graben and the cover sand record from the Netherlands (Kasse 1997).

### *Summary*

(1) Both the fluvial and the aeolian record are very sensitive archives of climate change in periglacial environments.
(2) The Rhine system was dominated to varying degrees by spring-snowmelt-induced peak discharge resulting in the development of an extended braided-river system under periglacial conditions.
(3) Loess sequences provide a relatively detailed and continuous terrestrial record of climate and environmental change throughout the Pleniglacial.
(4) The dust accumulation rates, as determined from the loess record, and periods of increased aggradation show some correlation.

## Volcanism of the East and West Eifel (H.U.S.)

The total volume of magma erupted in the Quaternary Eifel volcanic fields is small compared to that represented by the much more voluminous Tertiary volcanic fields in Central Europe. Yet, young volcanic areas such as the Eifel are not only morphologically attractive landmarks. Since volcanic eruptions in the very recent geological past are the most visible sign of ongoing dynamic processes beneath Central Europe. The Eifel volcanism was accompanied by a high degree of microseismicity in some areas (Ahorner 1983), vigorous lithosphere degassing and a still-rising major lithospheric block, the Rhenish Shield. All of this is apparently driven by a mantle anomaly delineated in great detail by seismic methods, probably an ascending plume of mantle peridotite (Ritter & Christensen 2007).

The stratigraphic importance of the Quaternary volcanism in Central Europe is based upon widespread and precisely dated fallout tephra layers. Those of evolved – dominantly phonolitic – composition form the major chronostratigraphic markers in Pleistocene continental deposits which are notoriously difficult to correlate and date. The Laacher See eruption 12.9 ka ago was a significant, non-climatic, sudden geological event during the Late Glacial in Central Europe. Some basaltic lapilli and ash layers can be traced for many kilometres and form excellent stratigraphic markers, especially in thick glacial and interglacial sedimentary successions in Eifel scoria cone craters. These craters also harbour evidence of human activity, dating at least as far back as *c.* 200 ka (Bosinski *et al.* 1986, 1995). Chemical and mineralogical data, as well as volcano structures and rock types, are discussed only briefly in this section but are described in detail in Schmincke (2007*a*, *b*), which also contain more extensive bibliographies, maps and photographic documentation.

Wilson & Downes (2007) provide a detailed up-to-date summary of Tertiary to Quaternary volcanism in continental Europe and the Mediterranean area.

### *General setting of the Eifel volcanic fields*

Most geologically young Central European Volcanic Fields (CEVF) developed in Tertiary times between c. 40 and 10 Ma with a peak in the Miocene (20–15 Ma) and minor volcanism in the Pliocene. Volcanic activity followed and accompanied Eocene to Miocene rifting of the Rhine graben and uplift of the Rhenish Shield and other Palaeozoic blocks (Figs 20.29 & 20.30). Significant Quaternary volcanism in Central Europe is restricted to the Eifel (West Eifel Volcanic Field (WEVF) and East Eifel Volcanic Field (EEVF)) in Germany, apart from two very localized small centres at Cheb (northern Bohemia, Czech Republic) (Fig. 20.29). The WEVF and EEVF resemble each other in their temporal, spatial and compositional evolution but also show significant differences. Quaternary volcanic fields and local centres also occur in western Europe (Auvergne) and southern France. The Eifel volcanic fields developed above the Rhenish Shield, a large lithospheric block that has undergone several periods of uplift over the last 40 million years and is still rising in some areas (Fuchs *et al.* 1983). Indeed, uplifted river terraces along the Rhine and its tributaries provide clear evidence that the process of uplift is continuing (Meyer & Stets 2007). Dominantly alkali basalts, basanites and, rarely, tholeiites erupted in the large-volume Tertiary volcanic fields, and contrast with the highly alkaline and silica-undersaturated magmas which erupted in the small-volume Quaternary volcanic fields in Central Europe.

The upper 4–6 km of the pre-Tertiary basement beneath both the WEVF and the EEVF comprise Lower Devonian sandstones, slates and greywackes (Siegen, Hunsrück and Ems formations) (Meyer 1986) (Fig. 20.31). Middle Devonian limestones and Buntsandstein occur in structural depressions in the eastern central part of the WEVF (Eifel North-South Zone), a structural lineament that is also reflected in the fissure directions and particular xenolith types. Few intraplate volcanic areas on Earth are better exposed than those in the Eifel. The level of exposure facilitates detailed studies of the internal structure and evolution of the scoria cones.

### *Criteria for correlating tephra layers erupted in Eifel volcanoes*

Widespread tephra layers are of singular importance in precisely dating Pleistocene continental (and marine) sedimentary units and correlating them over tens, sometimes hundreds, of kilometres. This is particularly relevant because of the inherent problems and limitations of all other methods of physical age determinations and also the regionally highly variable environmental conditions. The main macroscopic and microscopic lithological criteria include the type of pumice or glass shards, the qualitative mineral assemblage and the type of xenoliths. The chemical composition of many tephra layers is highly characteristic, even in strongly altered pumice, when the interpretation is based on relatively immobile high field strength trace elements such as Nb and Zr. In tephra layers with similar phenocryst mineralogy, contrasting mineral compositions are also very useful in fingerprinting specific layers. All of these diagnostic criteria suffice for correlating and determining the age of a widespread distal tephra when the layers contain little or no material for precise physical dating, provided the age and composition of a particular layer has been well analysed at a proximal locality. In general, tephra layers erupted in Eifel volcanoes are highly alkaline and are thus easy to distinguish compositionally from, for example, Icelandic tephra all of which are of subalkaline composition.

### *Age determinations of volcanic eruptions in the Eifel Volcanic Fields*

Methods employed to date the Quaternary Eifel volcanoes include $^{14}C$ (for deposits younger than c. 40 ka), whole-rock K–Ar and Ar/Ar, single-crystal laser fusion Ar/Ar, U–Th, palaeomagnetics, varve counting and thermoluminescence. Physical methods of dating Eifel volcanic deposits have been described in three pioneer publications: $^{14}C$ (Arnold & Libby 1951; Firbas 1953) and K–Ar whole-rock dating (Frechen & Lippolt 1965). Palaeoclimatic proxies such as soil horizons and vegetation as well as relative morphological relationships between volcanic deposits and river terraces have also proved very useful (e.g. Mertes & Schmincke 1983). All of the methods listed have their limitations. Calibrated $^{14}C$ ages are crucial to temporally define events and boundaries in the Weichselian and Late Glacial. The overall temporal evolution of volcanism in the Eifel fields is, however, fairly well established although increased resolution generates new questions requiring further improved precision in dating. Most physical age determinations during the 1970s and 1980s were carried out by Lippolt and co-workers (e.g. Fuhrmann & Lippolt 1987). Single-crystal laser fusion ages based mainly on sanidine, determined by Lippolt and co-workers but chiefly by Bogaard (see below) have been fundamental in establishing a fairly precise age framework for the EEVF, thus allowing unequivocal identification of more distant tephra layers. These are essential for the correlation and dating of glacial terrestrial deposits, a major example being the formerly controversial Ariendorf and Kärlich sections well-known middle/late Pleistocene sections in Central Europe (see below).

### *Composition of the magmas*

The Eifel volcanic fields (Figs 20.32 & 20.33) are dominated by scoria cones and maars and are typical intraplate volcanic fields except for their unusual K-rich, chiefly silica-undersaturated nephelinitic–leucititic–basanitic compositions. The presence of phenocrystic phlogopite and microlitic leucite are particularly diagnostic for the potassic nature of the magmas. Phenocrysts in the mafic lavas are dominated by clinopyroxene (Ti-augite) with generally <5% olivine, phlogopite and titanomagnetite. Amphibole, apatite, titanite and, in some rocks, haüyne appear as liquidus phases in the rare intermediate rocks, with phenocrystic plagioclase, sanidine, haüyne, nosean, leucite and phlogopite/biotite being restricted to the phonolitic and rare trachytic (Wehr) magmas, the latter lacking feldspathoids. Calcite occurs as phenocrysts in some pre-Rieden phonolites, in late Laacher See tephra, in the groundmass of melilite nephelinites and in some subvolcanic rocks (carbonatite) in both fields.

### *Differentiation of magmas*

Highly evolved magmas (<1.5 wt% MgO), dominantly phonolite, are characterized by low Mg, Cr, Ti, P, Fe and related trace elements and by an enrichment in Si, Al, Na and trace elements such as LREE, Zr, Nb, Rb, Ba, U and Th. Minor phonolite occurs locally in the WEVF but there are three or four large, highly differentiated phonolitic volcanic complexes in the EEVF

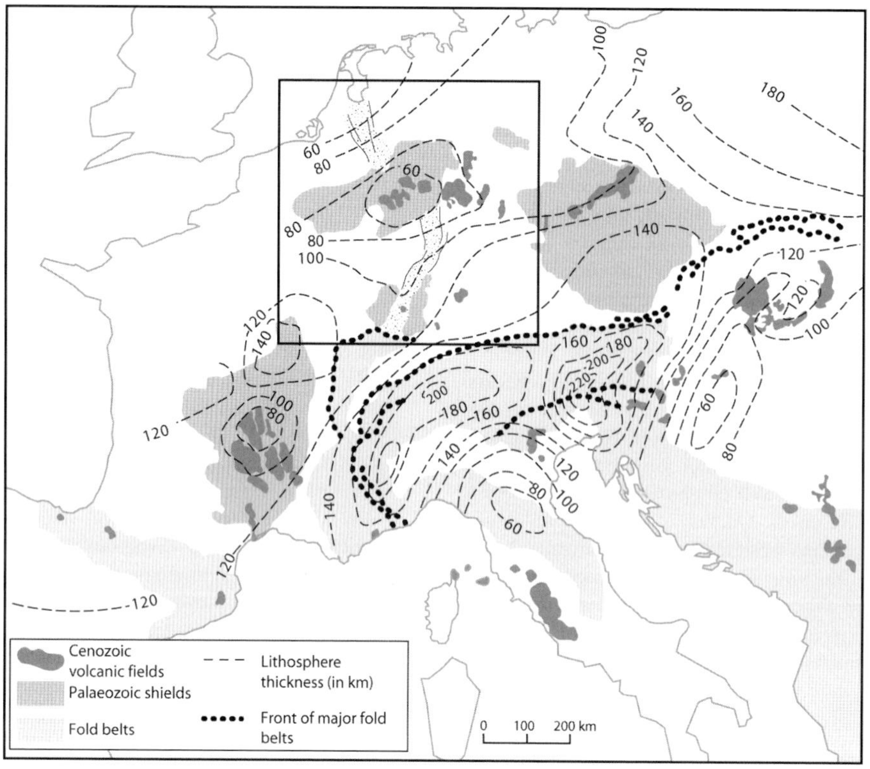


**Fig. 20.29** Cenozoic volcanic fields in the three major uplifted Palaeozoic blocks in Central Europe. Dashed line shows depth to lithosphere after Babuska & Plumerova (1992). Box shows enlarged portion (Fig. 20.30). Modified from Schmincke (1982).

(Kempenich(?), Rieden, Wehr, Laacher See) (Wörner & Schmincke 1984; Bogaard & Schmincke 1984, 1985; Viereck 1984; Wörner *et al.* 1988; Bourdon *et al.* 1994; Harms & Schmincke 2000; Harms *et al.* 2004; Schmitt 2006).

## *Type of volcanoes*

Scoria cones, the most common type of volcano in the Eifel, consist of several volcanic phases of pyroclastic, phreatic and phreatomagmatic origin, belying their simple external shape. These phases may be separated from one another by the presence of one or more soil zones, providing evidence of vegetation and other indications of major interruptions (warm stadials) lasting thousands to tens of thousands of years. Nearly all of the scoria cones begin with an initial hydroclastic stage, represented by an initial maar and/or tephra ring phase. The widespread occurrence of magma–water interaction in the Eifel volcanoes is probably largely due to the basement structure. The basement rocks in the Eifel (Devonian sandstones and slates) have almost no porosity and both water and magma move along crustal fractures that are also the sites of groundwater circulation (Lorenz 1973). Increasing rate of magma flux and/or dwindling water supply have commonly led to a later change to pyroclastic eruptions including the formation of agglutinate/scoria cones. Minor to moderate interactions of magma and water are common throughout much of the evolution of many of the cones in the area, as reflected in the presence of well-bedded lapilli deposits, the poor vesiculation of juvenile clasts and variable amounts of country-rock fragments (e.g. Herchenberg volcano; Bednarz & Schmincke 1990).

Widespread fallout deposits, up to several metres thick and commonly of more mafic composition compared to the bulk of a cone, are a characteristic late phase in many scoria cones. Some of these extend for many kilometres and are particularly useful in correlating volcanic complexes in the field. All of the scoria cones in the Eifel have been modified during several subsequent glacial and interglacial stages. Some clastic crater successions ('Deckschichten') comprise several hundred thousand years of volcanic and non-volcanic sedimentation and erosion (Fig. 20.34). In the East Eifel, the presence of bone fragments and tools records human activity in the area dating back at least 200 ka (Bosinski *et al.* 1986).

The Eifel maars are the type locality for a characteristic type of volcanic centre comprising a more or less circular crater in the basement surrounded by a low wall of tephra, dominated by fragments of country-rock. The traditional explanation for maars suggested that they were the products of gas explosion funnels resulting from $CO_2$-rich magmas. The highly alkaline, and therefore $CO_2$-rich, Eifel magmas were thought to provide suitable boundary conditions for gas explosions. More detailed studies during the past few decades have provided conclusive evidence that maars and the related tephra rings formed mainly as a result of the explosive contact of magma and external water (i.e. phreatomagmatic eruptions; Lorenz 1973; Schmincke 1977) as well as interacting with $CO_2$-driven eruptions of highly alkaline low-viscosity magmas (Schmincke 2007*a*, *b*).

## *Volcanic field analysis*

The term volcanic field was introduced for the Quaternary Eifel volcanic areas in order to call attention to the systematic zonation of several parameters which help us to understand the location and evolution of the melting areas in the mantle and

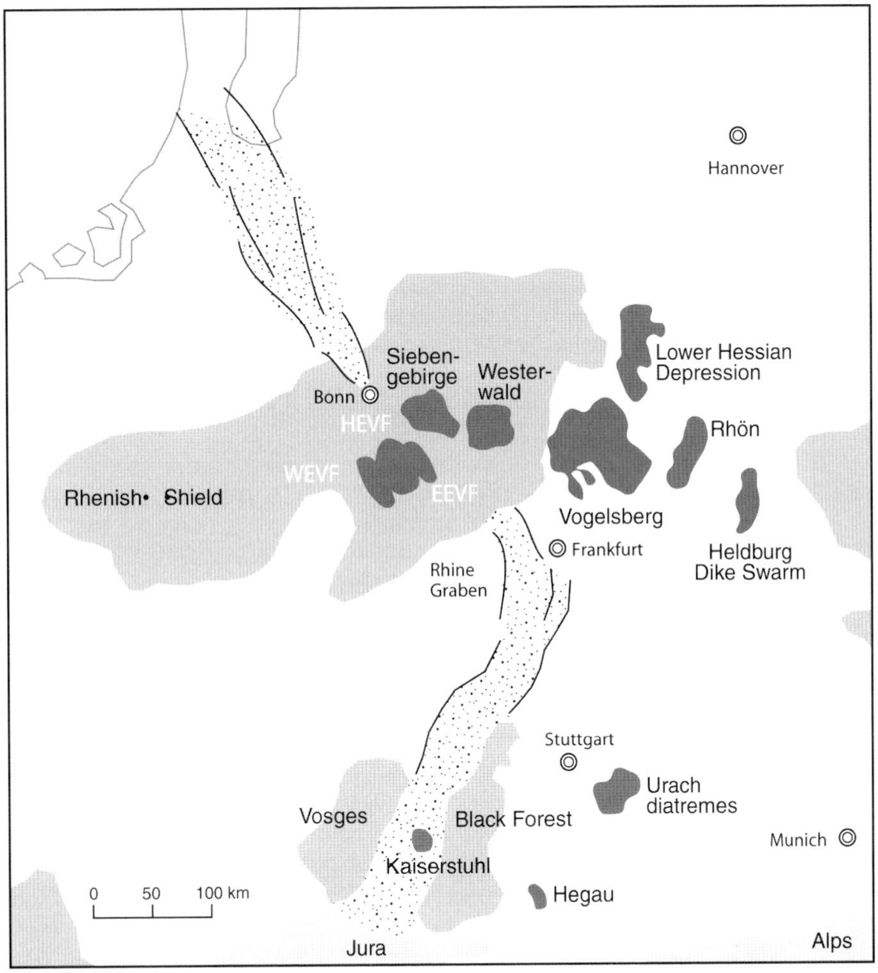


**Fig. 20.30.** Enlargement boxed arc of Figure 20.29, showing Cenozoic volcanic fields on the uplifted Rhenish shield, Rhine Graben and in adjacent areas. The area of the Eocene Hocheifel Volcanic Field (HEVF) overlaps that of the Quaternary East and West Eifel Volcanic Fields (WEVF and EEVF). Modified from Schmincke (1982).

magma detachment zones (Schmincke 1982). Volcanic field analysis indicates that magma mass eruption rates increased toward the centre of both Eifel volcanic fields and that this was coupled with an increasing degree of magma differentiation. The central parts of the fields also contain the greatest volumes of volcanic products and have the highest flux of magmatic gases. These and related parameters are interpreted as reflecting the central part of one or more magma collection zones in the upper mantle/Moho. These zones are at least 30 km (EEVF) to 50 km (WEVF) long and resulted in magma focusing in the centre of both areas. The Eifel volcanic fields are dominantly orientated NW–SE, reflecting lithosphere cracking in response to the present lithospheric SW–NE orientated tensional stress field north of the Alps that, however, was probably strongly enhanced by the similarly orientated Palaeozoic stress field.

### *The hypothetical Eifel plume*

The CEVF extending from central France to Silesia forms a peripheral belt roughly parallel to, and *c.* 300 km NNW of, the Alps. Volcanic activity broadly coincided in time with the major metamorphic, magmatic and deformational phases in the Alps, as well as with the uplift of some lithospheric blocks, rifting and subsidence (e.g. the Rhine Graben) (Fig. 20.35). Plate tectonic processes were ultimately driven by the collision of the Eurasian and African plates and were in some unknown way responsible for triggering both uplift and rift formation throughout central and western Europe. The local rise of fertile mantle was probably a dominantly passive process. Volcanic activity in western and central Europe appears to have been fed from a string of separate individual small melting anomalies, some of which were simultaneously active over a wide area. Lavas of different composition were produced at different times.

### *The West Eifel Volcanic Field*

The WEVF field (600 km$^2$) is *c.* 50 km long and comprises *c.* 240 volcanoes (*c.* 70% scoria and lapilli cones, half with lava flows, and 30% maars). The WEVF is of greater size than the EEVF and is dominated by more mafic and silica-undersaturated magmas, and a greater abundance of large peridotite xenoliths. Highly differentiated magmas are restricted to two small localities in the eastern centre of the field. Among the *c.* 10% maars, those of greatest volcanological and petrological interest are the Dauner maar group (Schalkenmehren Maar, Weinfelder Maar, and the Gemündener Maar) in the SE, the large Meerfelder Maar

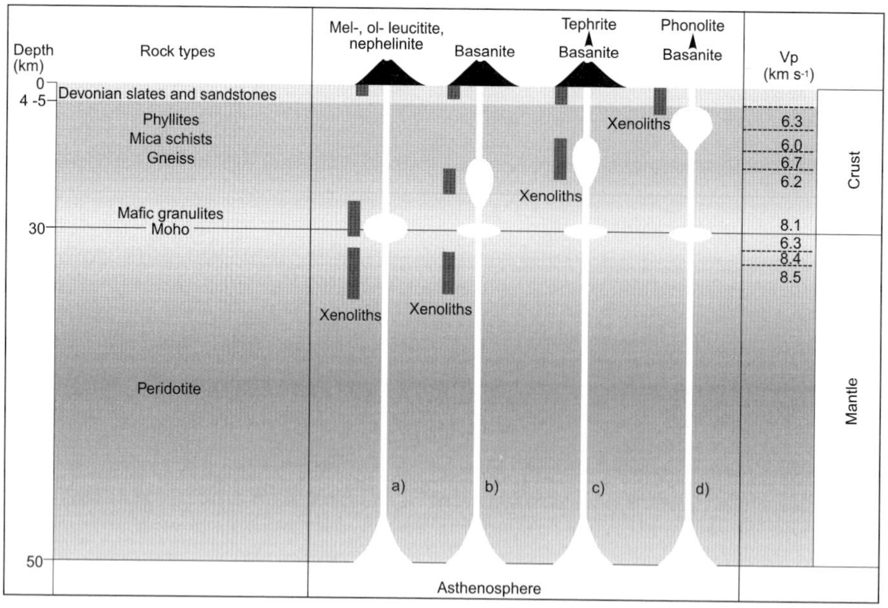


**Fig. 20.31.** Cartoon of crustal section beneath the Quaternary Eifel volcanic fields showing four different types of volcano–magma systems and hypothetical position of magma reservoirs at several levels. These positions have been inferred from different types of xenoliths, thermobarometry of phenocrysts, microthermometry of fluid inclusions in minerals and other criteria. (a) Volcanoes of primitive composition with magma reservoirs along the crust–mantle boundary and below. (b, c) Volcanoes with intermediate to mafic zoned magma reservoirs in the middle crust. (d) Highly evolved, mostly phonolitic volcanoes such as Laacher See Volcano. Seismic velocities from Mechie *et al.* (1983) and Prodehl *et al.* (1992). Modified from Schmincke (1982).

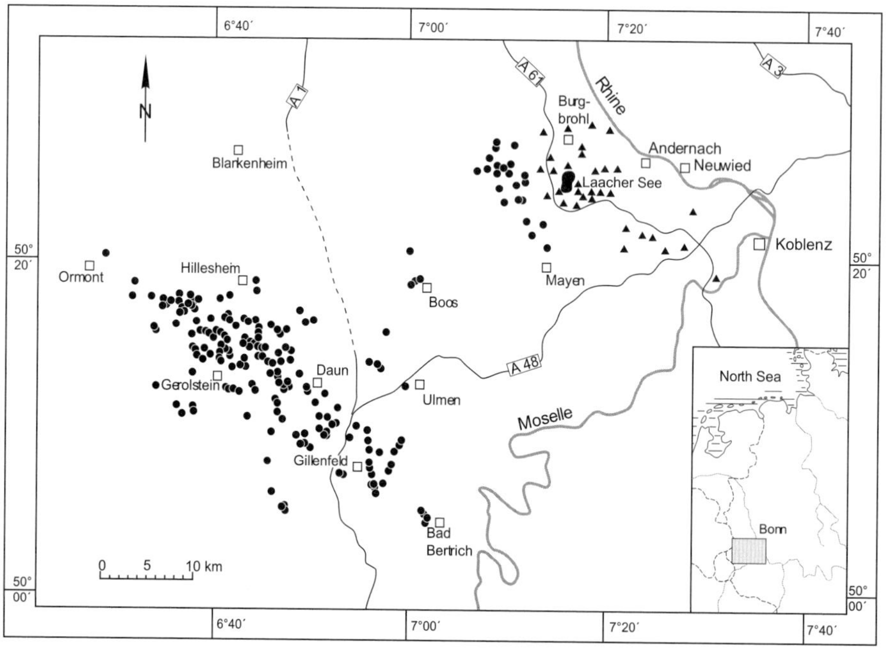


**Fig. 20.32.** Major eruptive centres of the Quaternary West and East Eifel Volcanic Fields. The younger centres of the EEVF (<0. 215 Ma) are shown by triangles (eastern subfield). Modified from Schmincke (1982).

in the west, and, in the southern part of the field, the especially well-preserved Pulvermaar.

Available age data and palaeoclimatic and geomorphologic criteria (Lippolt 1983; Büchel & Lorenz 1982; Mertes & Schmincke 1983; Fuhrmann & Lippolt 1987; Schnepp & Hradetzky 1994; Zolitschka *et al.* 1995) indicate that probably all of the volcanoes erupted within the Brunhes epoch (i.e. <0.78 Ma, subsequent to the phase of accelerated uplift of the Rhenish Shield. A possible major peak in volcano formation seems to have occurred between *c.* 550 and 450 ka especially in the central NW part of the field. Following a likely, but still poorly constrained, lull in activity between *c.* 450 and 100 ka, litho-

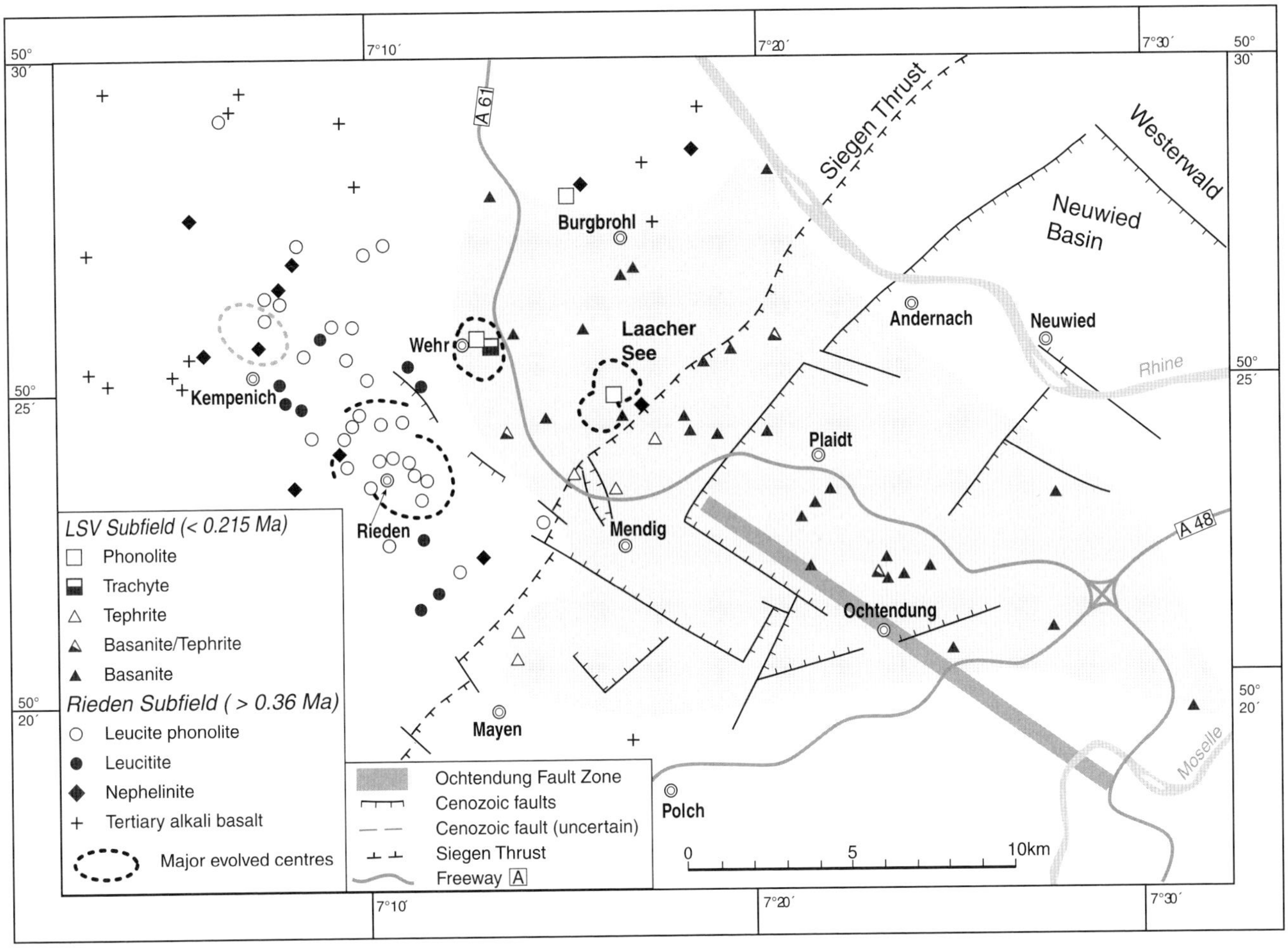


**Fig. 20.33.** Distribution of volcanoes and Cenozoic faults in the East Eifel Volcanic Field. The four main phonolitic evolved centres are Kempenich (tentative), Rieden, Wehr and Laacher See. The younger Laacher See Volcano (LSV) subfield is shaded but includes two older foiditic volcanoes NE of LSV. The main tectonic features are the Palaeozoic Siegen Thrust and the Cenozoic normal faults (after Meyer 1986; Ahorner 1983) bounding, and within, the Neuwied Basin. The seismically active Ochtendung Fault Zone (Ahorner 1983) is paralleled by a graben just NW of Mendig formed synvolcanically during the first phase (LLST) of eruption of the LSV. Modified from Duda & Schmincke (1978) and Bednarz *et al.* (1983).

spheric cracking extended to the SE as reflected in the migration of melt supply, surface volcanic activity and the frequency of volcano formation increasing over the past *c.* 100 ka (possibly <50 ka). Very mafic and much less silica-undersaturated sodic olivine nephelinites and relatively LILE-poor sodic basanites with groundmass plagioclase erupted in the SE WEVF over the past *c.* 50 ka. At about the same time, and closely associated in space, compositionally distinct mantle domains were activated beneath the SE WEVF. Many of the young maars, from Gemünden in the north to Pulvermaar in the south, erupted foiditic magmas rich in subvolcanic cumulates but almost lacking mantle peridotites. The outlying Meerfelder Maar, which is the largest of the Eifel maars and is dated at 45 ka (based on charcoal from the basal tephra deposits that are rich in tree moulds; unpublished data), compositionally also belongs to the foidite group but is famous for its mantle-derived xenoliths.

The rare juvenile lapilli of the youngest volcano in the Eifel, Ulmen Maar, are of extremely LILE-enriched, more evolved intermediate composition and erupted at the eastern edge of the WEVF *c.* 11 ka BP, which is 2000 years later than the Laacher See Volcano. Ulmen Maar is the youngest volcano in Germany, based on the correlation of Ulmen tephra layers in cores taken in Holzmaar and the Meerfelder and Weinfelder maars (Zolitschka *et al.* 1995).

### *East Eifel Volcanic Field*

The EEVF (*c.* 30–35 km in length, 10–20 km wide, 400 km$^2$) consists of *c.* 100 volcanoes (*c.* 80% scoria cones) (Fig. 20.33), rare maars, tephra rings and some lava flows as well as three larger phonolitic volcanic complexes (Rieden, Wehr, Laacher See). In the EEVF, the Neuwied Basin subsided by some 350 m, beginning in the Eocene and culminating during the Oligocene/Miocene. The steeply dipping, roughly NE–SW striking 120 km long Siegen Thrust crosses the EEVF just east of Laacher See (Meyer & Stets 1981). This thrust marks the approximate

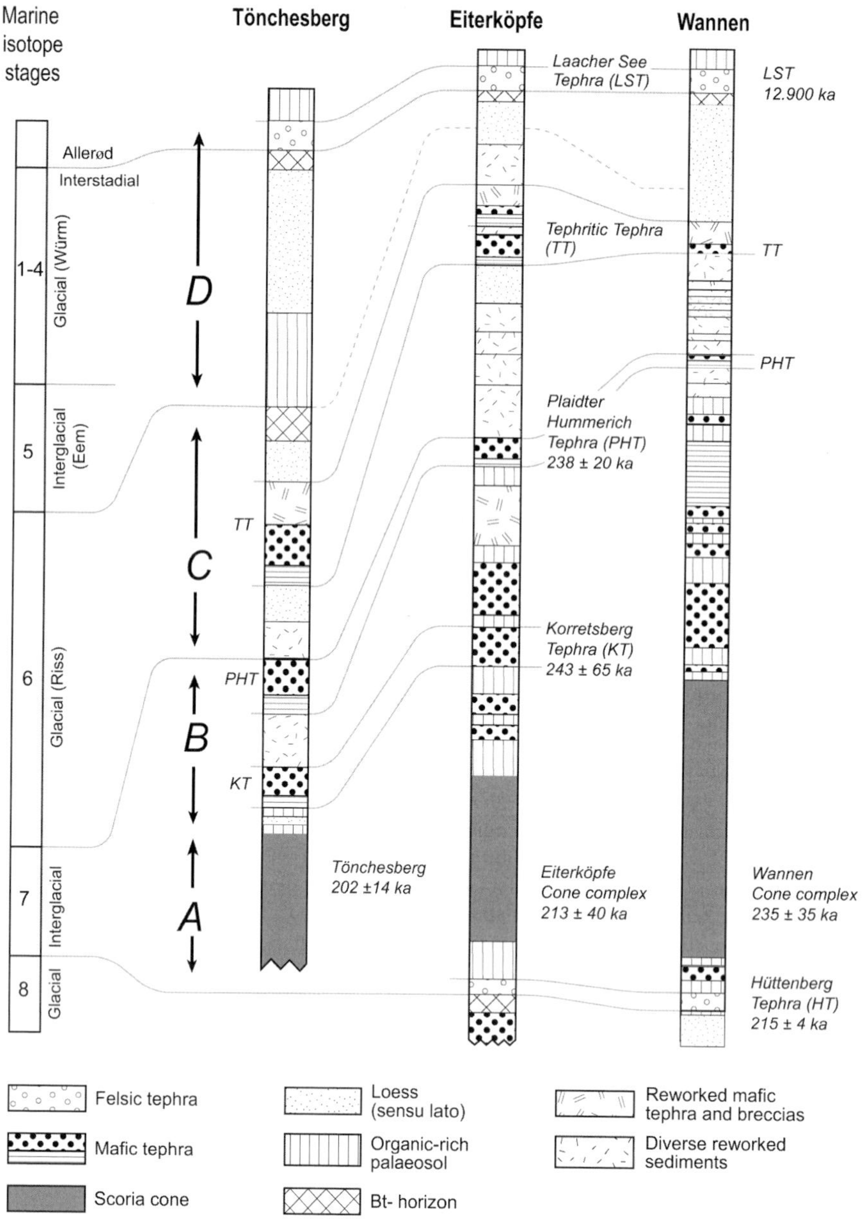


**Fig. 20.34.** Approximate age and stratigraphic correlation of prominent marker tephra layers within clastic crater deposits (CCDs) of basanite centres Tönchesberg, Eiterköpfe and Wannen scoria cone complexes in the EEVF. Modified from Bogaard & Schmincke (1990).

boundary between the older western and younger eastern subfields of the EEVF. The EEVF occupies the central part of the Neuwied Basin west of the Rhine, that subsided along several faults, some active after the Laacher See eruption. The age distribution of volcanic activity in the EEVF is well known due largely to the three major, highly evolved volcanic centres and the dominantly phonolitic tephras containing sanidine phenocrysts, which provide the best material for high-precision single-crystal laser dating (Fig. 20.36). Four eruptive periods, as outlined below, three of which can be spatially, temporally, compositionally, tectonically and morphologically relatively well defined, can be distinguished from each other in the EEVF (Schmincke *et al.* 1983, 1990; Viereck 1984; Bogaard & Schmincke 1988, 1990). These are preceded by one or more older fallout tephra layers (see below and Table 20.1).

*I. Pre-Rieden volcanic phase*

Volcanic activity in the EEVF began *c.* 460 ka ago or slightly earlier. The oldest poorly exposed and poorly defined peripheral Kempenich centre in the NW consists of (olivine) (melilite) nephelinite mafic volcanoes and several moderately to highly evolved leucite phonolite necks and flows (*c.* 450 to 500 ka). The lowermost tephra layers in the classic Quaternary section at Kärlich, tentatively dated as 0.6 Ma (C. Bogaard *et al.* 1989), have since been reanalysed by Bogaard as *c.* 480 ka (pers. comm.) and provisionally correlated to the small phreatomagmatic phonolitic centre Auf Dickel in the WEVF. The Kempenich volcanotectonic basin(?) is an alternative eruptive centre but exposures are poor. A conspicuous phonolite tephra layer (DT2) *c.* 450 ka old is a prominent marker at Kärlich (Fig. 20.37). The age of the melilite–nephelinitic Herchenberg volcano (*c.* 450 ka)

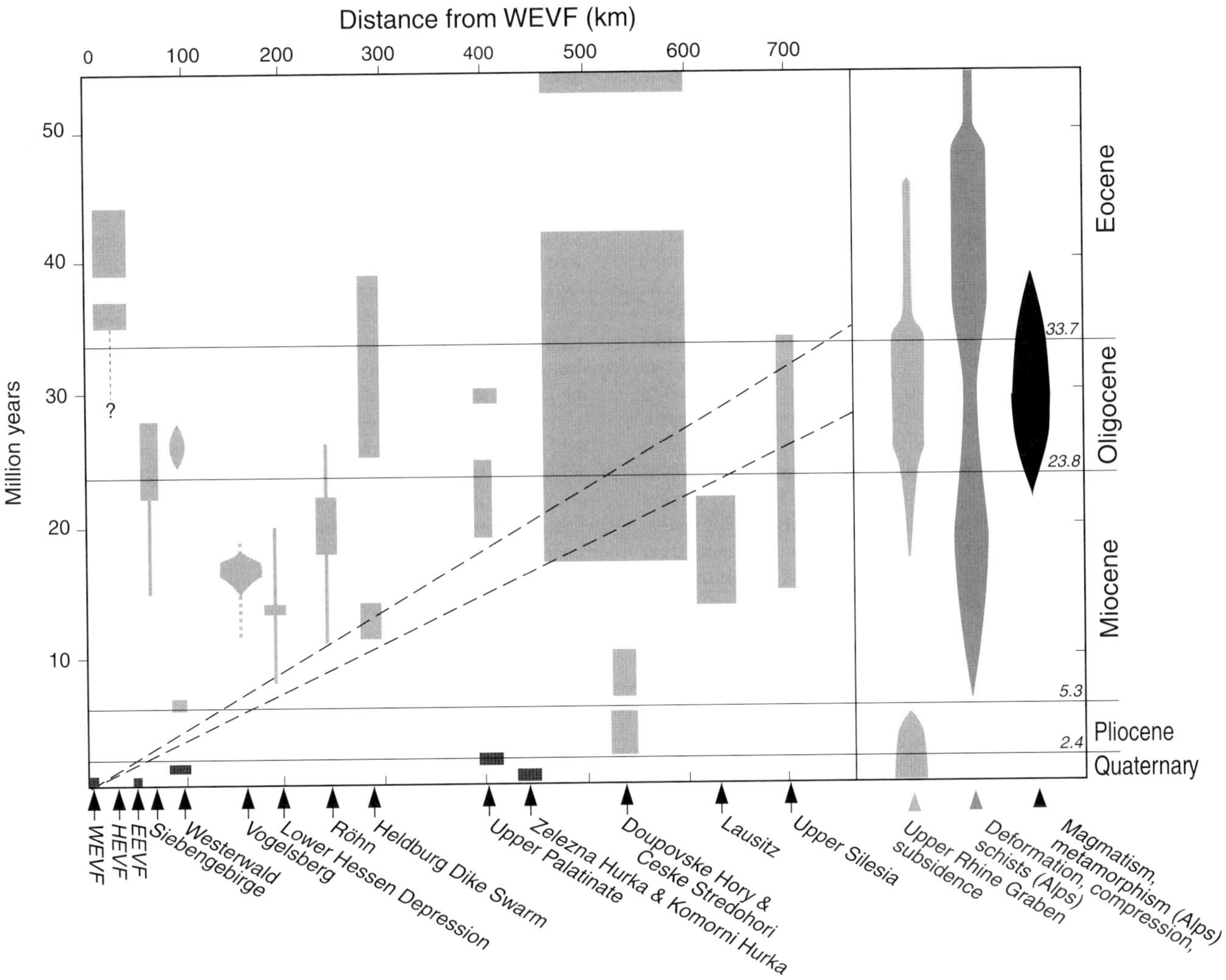


**Fig. 20.35.** Age and area occupied by Cenozoic volcanic fields in Central Europe. Dashed line = trace of age progression of the so-called Eifel plume postulated by Duncan *et al.* (1972). The main phases of subsidence of the Rhine Graben, and folding and emplacement ages of magmas in the Alps are given for comparison. Ages of HEVF lavas based on Fekiacova (2007), Westerwald lavas on Haase *et al.* (2004), Vogelsberg lavas on Bogaard & Wörner (2003) and Rhön lavas on Jung & Hoernes (2000). High-precision dating is lacking for most fields and the age distributions shown are very approximate. Modified from Schmincke (1982, 2004), with modifications based on Becker (1993).

is practically identical to pumice lapilli fallout DT2 that immediately overlies melilite–nephelinitic mafic tephra BT3 in the Kärlich section, suggesting that the mafic tephra may have been sourced from the Herchenberg volcano and that the source of the DT2 layer may have been located in the Kempenich basin (caldera?). Characteristically, these older phonolites contain calcite phenocrysts but lack plagioclase. Emphasis in the following discussion is on the presence of widespread felsic tephra layers of more clear-cut stratigraphic significance.

*II. Rieden system (Rieden Tephra)*

The better-exposed and well-documented older volcanic phase in the western subfield of the EEVF is the Rieden volcanic complex (*c.* 5 km$^3$ dense rock equivalent; *c.* 430 to 360 ka) in the topographically higher area around Rieden (Viereck 1984). Eruptions occurred during several phases from a number of overlapping centres beneath and around the town of Rieden, now the most deeply eroded part of the volcanic complex. The deposits include garnet-bearing leucite–phonolite ignimbrites, exogenous and endogenous domes, fallout tephra (some regionally widespread), and thick lake sediments and these fill a caldera basin up to 2.5 km in diameter. The peripheral mafic centres are mainly mafic to intermediate leucitite scoria cones and lava flows similar in age to the main complex. Characteristically, plagioclase is completely lacking in the Rieden volcanic rocks.

The dating of pumice tephra layers in the classic Pleistocene sections at Kärlich and Ariendorf by single-crystal $^{40}Ar/^{39}Ar$ laser methods has resulted in a major revision of the main tephra layers by several hundred thousands of years (e.g. Bogaard & Schmincke 1988; P. Bogaard *et al.* 1989; Lippolt 1983). Two *c.* 400 ka old tephra layers at Ariendorf can also be correlated to the Rieden centre based on both age and chemical/mineralogical compositions (Fig. 20.38).

The migration of volcanism in the EEVF from west to ESE

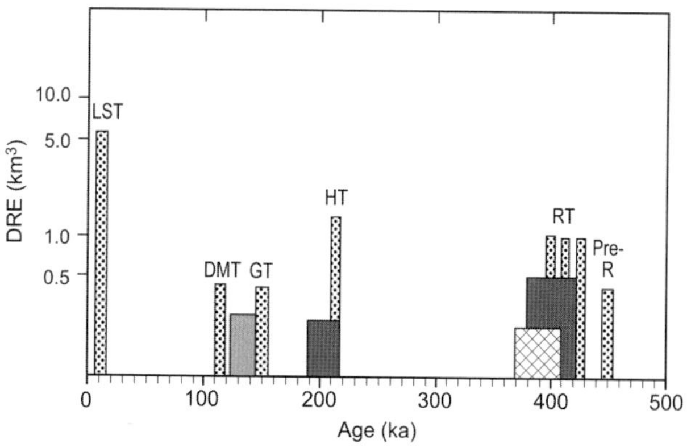


**Fig. 20.36.** Age distribution and approximate volumes of major volcanic phases in the EEVF. Modified from Bogaard & Schmincke (1990). Ages and durations of the three younger phases (Laacher See, Wehr and Rieden) are reasonably well constrained but those of the older (pre-Rieden, Pre-R) phase are still uncertain. Volumes of erupted magma (dense rock equivalent, DRE) are well constrained only for LST but entirely speculative for the older phases due to lack of medial and distal outcrops on which to base well-founded mass estimates. Abbreviations: DMT, Dümpel Maar Tephra; GT, Glees Tephra; HT, Hüttenberg Tephra; LST, Laacher See Tephra; RT, Reiden Tephra.

occurred during a pause in volcanic activity between *c.* 350 and 215 ka and was associated with the activation of a compositionally distinct melting domain in the mantle.

*III. Wehr Tephra*

The SE subfield of the EEVF (younger than *c.* 215 ka) is dominated by basanite–tephrite volcanic centres and two highly evolved complexes (Fig. 20.33). As a volcanic field, the Wehr, which includes the most prominent scoria cones in the Neuwied Basin, and the Laacher See systems are here grouped petrologically and volcanologically because the mafic (parent) magmas are compositionally similar (K-rich phlogopite-bearing basanites). Thus, they were probably fed from the same melting anomaly in the mantle. The Wehr volcano, located 3 km north of the Laacher See and 2 km east of the village of Rieden, forms a 160 m deep morphological depression. The plagioclase-bearing phonolitic to minor trachytic Wehr volcano, compositionally resembling the Laacher See magma, erupted twice, with its major (older) eruption being $^{40}Ar/^{39}Ar$ laser dated as 215 ± 4 ka BP (Hüttenberg Tephra (HT) or Wehr Tephra (WT)) (P. Bogaard *et al.* 1989) (Fig. 20.34). The Wehrer Kessel crater structure probably formed during the eruption of the WT, a term here preferred to HT. The WT comprises Plinian fallout pumice beds and pyroclastic flow deposits, as well as phreatomagmatic base

**Table 20.1** *Eight chemical analyses of widespread tephra layers. (1) Auf Dickel phonolite pumice (ADT) (WEVF); (2) Rieden phonolitic fallout pumice lapilli (RT) (Pit Riedener Berg); (3) Wehr Tephra (HT) (Hüttenberg); (4) Glees Tephra (GT) (Dachsbusch); (5) Dümpel Maar Tephra (DMT) (Herchenberg); (6, 7, 8) Lower, Middle and Upper Laacher See Tephra (LLST, MLST, ULST). All analyses by H.U.S. (unpublished except for HT (Wörner* et al. *1988)).*

| Name of tephra<br>Locality<br>Sample No. | ADT<br>Auf Dickel<br>2006-04-19-04c | RT<br>Rieden<br>2006-04-20-06 | HT<br>Hüttenberg<br>2017 | GT<br>Dachsbusch<br>2006-04-20-05 | DMT<br>Herchenberg<br>2006-04-20-02 | LLST base<br>Marienstätter<br>2001-06-23-02 | MLST base<br>Burgerhaus<br>2001-06-11-03 | ULST B10<br>Wingertsberg<br>98-07-18-21 |
|---|---|---|---|---|---|---|---|---|
| Major elements (wt%) | | | | | | | | |
| $SiO_2$ | 53.84 | 53.7 | 62.90 | 58.67 | 59 | 56.72 | 55.82 | 55.23 |
| $TiO_2$ | 0.25 | 0.27 | 0.24 | 0.14 | 0.23 | 0.13 | 0.24 | 1 |
| $AL_2O_3$ | 19.5 | 21.57 | 18.76 | 20.65 | 20.35 | 21.94 | 21.11 | 19.29 |
| $Fe_2O_3$ | 2.92 | 2.74 | 2.00 | 1.85 | 2.15 | 1.71 | 2.04 | 3.87 |
| MnO | 0.33 | 0.25 | 0.24 | 0.27 | 0.24 | 0.51 | 0.27 | 0.13 |
| MgO | 0.27 | 0.14 | 0.13 | 0.13 | 0.2 | <0.03< | <0.03< | 0.79 |
| CaO | 1.90 | 0.81 | 1.12 | 0.80 | 1.06 | 0.39 | 0.96 | 5.05 |
| $Na_2O$ | 4.86 | 7.02 | 7.29 | 8.99 | 7.36 | 11.75> | 8.88 | 4.99 |
| $K_2O$ | 7.21 | 8.45 | 5.90 | 5.61 | 5.79 | 4.87 | 5.77 | 6.6 |
| $P_2O_5$ | 0.17 | 0.04 | 0.03 | 0.03 | 0.04 | 0.03 | 0.04 | 0.22 |
| $H_2O$ | 6.35 | 4.94 | 1.40 | 2.63 | 3.69 | 0,93 | 3.30 | 0.83 |
| $CO_2$ | 0.23 | 0.06 | 0.08 | 0.04 | 0.04 | 0,02 | 0.05 | 0.92 |
| Trace elements (ppm) | | | | | | | | |
| Co | 5 | <4 | 26 | <4 | <4 | 6 | 7 | 12 |
| Cr | <18 | <18 | 13 | 28 | <18 | <18 | 26 | <18 |
| Ni | <2 | <2 | 8 | <2 | <2 | 7 | 6 | <2 |
| V | 150 | 94 | 15 | 12 | 21 | <12< | 20 | 88 |
| Zn | 179 | 147 | 128 | 168 | 137 | 273 | 131 | 61 |
| Ce | 178 | 125 | nd | 182 | 192 | 125 | 70 | 141 |
| La | 248 | 112 | nd | 101 | 141 | 202> | 135 | 99 |
| Nb | 1008 | 369 | 147 | 235 | 184 | 286 | 155 | 116 |
| Ga | 41 | 41 | nd | 56 | 40 | 58> | 35 | 15 |
| Pb | 26 | 36 | nd | 47 | 33 | 41 | 30 | 4 |
| Pr | 70 | 20 | nd | 11 | 28 | 9 | 8 | 9 |
| Rb | 163 | 192 | 297 | 407 | 317 | 587 | 328 | 115 |
| Ba | 2683 | 75 | 68 | 8 | 42 | <8< | 168 | 1714 |
| Sr | 1886 | 529 | 46 | 29 | 68 | <4 | 88 | 1360 |
| Th | 66 | 52 | nd | 73 | 48 | 101 | 38 | 10 |
| Y | 24 | 27 | 16 | 4 | 7 | <2< | 6 | 23 |
| Zr | 2194 | 892 | 769 | 1177 | 1023 | 2383 | 957 | 288 |
| Total | 98.71 | 100.25 | 100.04 | 100.07 | 100.37 | 99.27 | 98.71 | 99.33 |
| Zr/Nb | 2.18 | 2.42 | 5.23 | 5.00 | 5.56 | 8.33 | 6.17 | 2.48 |

**Fig. 20.37.** Dark melilite–nephelinitic mafic tephra (BT3, *c.* 10 cm thick) compositionally resembles Herchenberg melilite–nephelinite (*c.* 450 ka in age). The mafic tephra is overlain abruptly by light-coloured 1. 2 m thick compositionally zoned phonolitic pumice fallout lapilli layer, becoming grey (more mafic) at the top (Tephra DT2, pre-Rieden, *c.* 450 ka, practically identical in age to Herchenberg volcanic complex). The overlying 0.8 m loess (L) is weathered at the top. This soil is cut sharply by phreatomagmatic deposits of locally erupted leucititic Kärlich Brockentuff (BT, *c.* 400 ka). Locality: Kärlich clay pit. For ages see P. Bogaard *et al.* (1987), C. Bogaard *et al.* (1989), Schmincke *et al.* (1990) and Figure 20.10.

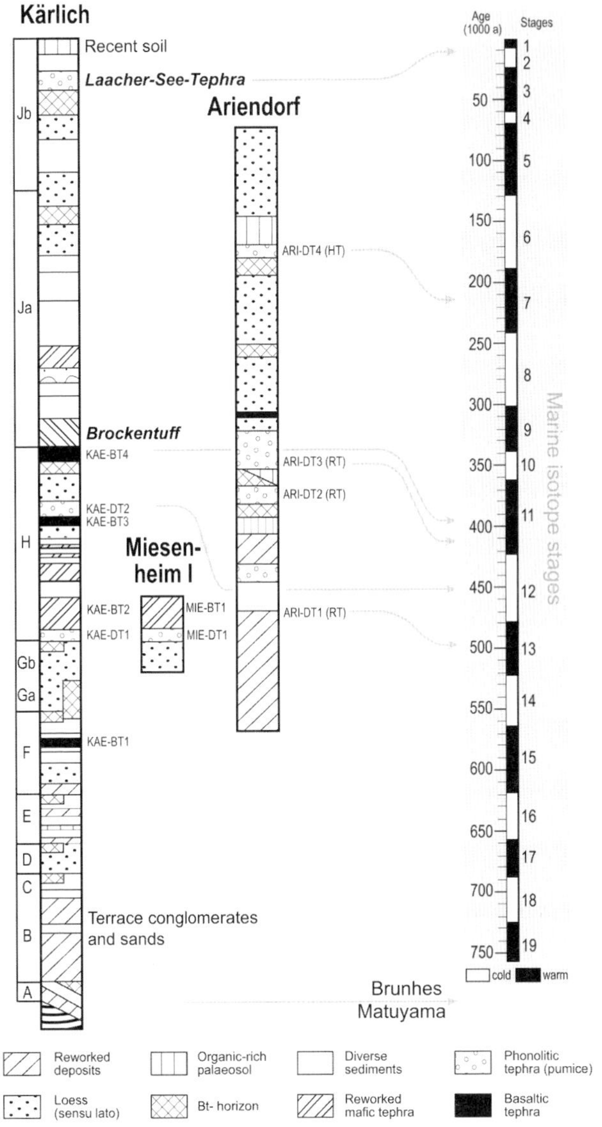


**Fig. 20.38.** Correlation of key Pleistocene sections Kärlich and Ariendorf. Modified from Bogaard & Schmincke (1990). The Kärlich section contains no phonolitic Rieden (RT) and Wehr (Hüttenberg) Tephra (HT) both of which have been encountered at Ariendorf. Modified from Bogaard & Schmincke (1990) and including more recent age determinations (P. Bogaard pers. comm.).

surge and fallout deposits. Its xenolith suite (abundant mica schists, lack of basanite xenoliths) is unique in the EEVF, the metamorphic xenolith suite from the Wehr volcanic field being famous (e.g. Wörner *et al.* 1982). The WT phenocryst assemblage includes K-feldspar (anorthoclase), plagioclase, clinopyroxene, amphibole and titanite. In contrast to the Laacher See phonolite, however, feldspathoids are totally absent. Compositionally zoned composite tephra sections (i.e. at Niederzissen and below the scoria cones of Kunkskopf and Bausenberg) demonstrate that the WT represents a strongly zoned eruption that commenced with highly evolved, silica-undersaturated phonolite magma but ended with mafic, silica-saturated trachyte magmas. This precisely dated event is a very critical one because the WT directly underlies many potassic basanitic and tephritic scoria cones of the EEVF. Most of these formed soon after WT eruption between *c.* 215 and 200 ka, and are located far to the east of the Wehrer Kessel in the central part of the Neuwied Basin. Volcanism extended as far east as the River Rhine and south to close to the Moselle river.

The WT of the Wehr volcano erupted during the brief time interval of transition from a cold (loess-forming) to a warm (soil-forming) climatic period that occurred *c.* 215 ka ago and is known as the Dömnitz- or Wacken-Warmzeit (Interstadial?). The WT is therefore considered an important chronostratigraphic marker for the beginning of the second-last interglacial climatic period (MIS 7) in Central Europe.

**Glees Tephra.** A haüyne phonolite eruption occurred at 151 ± 11 ka BP at Wehrer Kessel (Glees Tephra (GT); (P. Bogaard *et al.* 1989) (Fig. 20.39). Unfortunately, the GT has been definitely identified only at the type locality. Since it was erupted during a cold period, regional erosional removal may have been especially severe. Phonolitic tephra encountered at the base of a drillcore in a dry maar west of Hoher List (WEVF), some 40 km SW of Wehr, and dated as 132 ka (Schaber & Sirocko 2005) is here tentatively correlated with the GT. If this can be substantiated, the magnitude of the Glees eruption was much larger than hitherto documented.

**Dümpel Maar Tephra.** The melilite–nephelinite Herchenberg Volcanic Complex at the northern margin of the EEVF is capped by reworked tephra and an up to 1 m thick loess/soil bed. This is locally overlain by up to 6 m of poorly sorted phreatomagmatic deposits containing large clay lumps and Devonian-age mostly quartzitic blocks up to 1 m in diameter (Fig. 20.40). The juvenile, almost aphyric phonolite occurs both as almost non-vesicular (in clastic dykes) and as moderately vesicular pumice lapilli, compositionally resembling the Laacher See phonolite. The deposit is fining-upward like most maar deposits. Grain size changes, impact directions of ballistically emplaced blocks, and magnetic anomaly mapping (Bednarz 1982) all suggest an eruptive centre *c.* 0.5–1 km west of the centre of Herchenberg. Volcaniclastic dykes up to 60 cm wide and of the same lithology (Devonian rock fragments, clay and pebbles and less than 10%

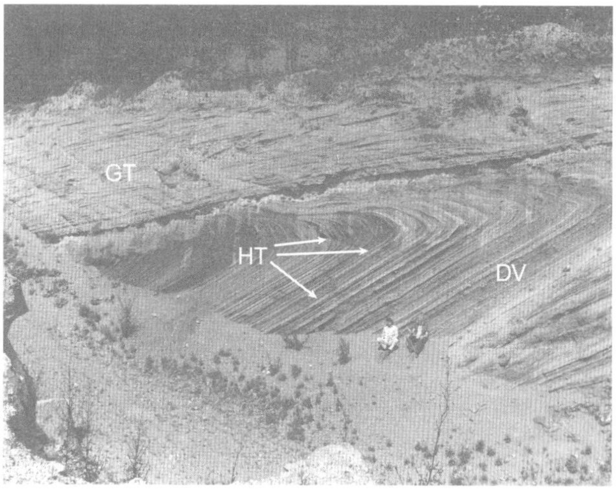


**Fig. 20.39.** Well-bedded phreatostrombolian to phreatomagmatic deposits of basanitic Dachsbusch Volcano (DV) including fragments of 215 ka old Hüttenberg Tephra (HT), the upper layers having moved downslope periglacially. This assembly is unconformably overlain by loess and *c.* 150 ka old phreatomagmatic phonolitic bedded Glees Tephra (GT).

**Fig. 20.40** Dümpel Maar Tephra (DMT, *c.* 110 ka) section near the top of Herchenberg Volcano. The DMT overlies Eem soil (a) and begins with 10 cm of fine-grained massive tuff. (b) A coarse-grained poorly sorted phreatomagmatic phase characterized by clay lumps up to 50 cm in diameter and, slightly higher, Devonian rocks, chiefly quartzite blocks up to 1 m in diameter, the blocks having impacted the soft substratum. (c) Better-sorted light-coloured pumice lapilli occur above the basal units. The top of the DMT (d) is partly reworked and capped by younger, mostly slope-wash deposits.

angular phonolite fragments) cutting though the Herchenberg cone are likely to have been emplaced by steam overpressure formed during the shallow emplacement of the local phonolite magma into Tertiary clays and gravels. Feldspar phenocrysts of this phonolite were dated at 116 000 ± 16 000 years (P. Bogaard *et al.* 1989). The Dümpel Maar Tephra (DMT) forms an excellent stratigraphic marker in several cores drilled in dry maar deposits in the WEVF (Schaber & Sirocko 2005) (Fig. 20.41). The DMT is now tuned to *c.* 105 ka, slightly younger than the Eem Interglacial, organic-rich sediments of which were found in several maar cores beneath the DMT in the WEVF (Sirocko *et al.* 2005). The occurrence of a significant thickness of DMT in several dry maar cores in the WEVF as far as *c.* 50 km to the WSW is remarkable since the older major evolved tephra layers

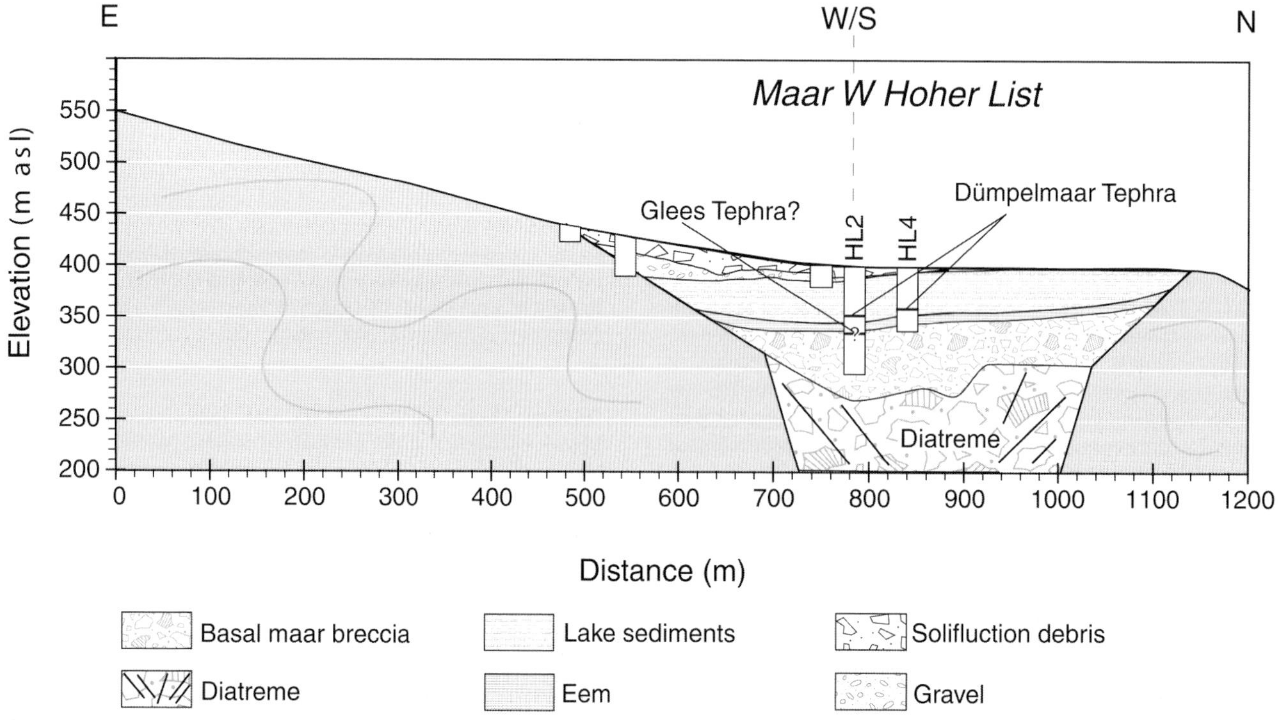


**Fig. 20.41.** Drillhole stratigraphy and cross-section through maar west of Hoher List (WEVF) with Dümpel Maar Tephra (DMT) being the significant marker horizon at the waning Eem Interglacial. Phonolitic tephra encountered at the base of the section is here tentatively correlated with Glees Tephra. Modified from Schaber & Sirocko (2005).

in the EEVF (Rieden, Wehr) as well as the younger Laacher See Tephra were mostly transported eastward. It is not known, however, how much of the DMT was transported to the east since it has not yet been found in eastern areas. Additionally, it has not yet been established whether the dominant wind direction was westward at the time of the DMT eruption. In any case, the mass of phonolite magma erupted at Dümpel Maar must have been much larger than previously documented as is the case for the GT (see above). Careful scrutiny of sediments deposited between *c.* 100 and 150 ka elsewhere in Central Europe may lead to the discovery of these widespread phonolitic tephra layers and thus aid in fine-tuning sediments and climate evolution for this time period.

At least one major tephrite centre (Niedermendig cone and lava flow connected to a dyke in Wingertsberg) and a few (as yet undated) tephritic eruptions, some producing widespread sub-plinian tephritic fallout lapilli layers, occurred around 100 ka ago, or later, but precise ages are lacking (Bogaard & Schmincke 1990). Volcanic activity was minor in the Eifel volcanic fields prior to *c.* 12.9 ka BP when the phonolitic Laacher See Volcano erupted. The exact source of the widespread so-called Eltviller Tuff (*c.* 20 ka BP) is unknown but was most likely located in the WEVF based on its mineral content.

*IV. Laacher See system*

The Laacher See Volcano (LSV) will be outlined in some detail because it is a significant Late Glacial stratigraphic marker bed in Central Europe and because it is unusually well dated by several different methods. In view of the general problem of precisely dating continental sediments, the documentation of the Laacher See Tephra, not only in lake sediments but also in terrestrial successions, continues to be important for correlating disparate sites across Central Europe.

The Laacher See eruption drastically impacted the environment close to the volcanic centre, predominantly in the low-lying Neuwied Basin traversed by the Rhine. Lakes were alternately dammed up and drained repeatedly during the eruption. Final collapse of the major dam resulted in catastrophic flooding of the Rhine valley for tens of kilometres downstream (Fig. 20.42). Moreover, the sudden generation of several cubic kilometres of solid matter provided a major source of sediment particles for many decades following the eruption. Finally, the eruption must have had a major impact on climate in the northern hemisphere on account of the high sulphur content of the magma.

The Laacher See is a water-filled crater *c.* 2.5 km in diameter and 65 m deep. The LSV is located 40 km south of Bonn on the western shoulder of the Neuwied Basin (Fig. 20.29). The terrain drops from 290–300 m a.s.l. in the vicinity of the LSV to *c.* 55 m a.s.l. within the basin. Much of the >6 km$^3$ magma erupted over only a few days, far exceeding the magma volume erupted from the more than 300 scoria cones, maars, and lava flows of the Eifel volcanic fields together. The generation of well-exposed tephra deposits erupted from the LSV was governed by the complex interplay of intrinsic and extrinsic factors. Characteristics include the following: (1) the Laacher See phonolite tephra deposits show strong compositional zoning, from initial extremely phenocryst-poor, highly evolved haüyne phonolite (*c.* 750°C) to hotter, very crystal-rich (up to 50 vol. %) mafic phonolite; (2) the high-level magma reservoir of the strongly evolved Laacher See phonolites developed largely within Devonian slates and sandstones at depths of 5–8 km; (3) several feedback cycles exist in which external forcing (influx of water, conduit collapse) became dominant when internal forcing mechanisms (e.g. magmatic volatile pressure) decreased; magma–groundwater interaction was especially powerful during initial and terminal stages.

The eruption of the LSV was likely triggered by the influx of hotter mafic magma into the resident cooler evolving magma reservoir. There was an opening blast phase, and an initial fine-grained lithic-dominated tuff was generated by the opening hydroclastic eruption. Repeated enlargement and deepening of the conduit and collapse of the unstable crater walls are reflected in the lithic component stratigraphy. Lateral migration of the crater about halfway through the eruption and temporary simultaneous eruption from both vents are indicated by the presence of two major overlapping depositional lobes. Characteristic fall deposits include well-sorted lapilli layers, which mimic the morphology, and whose thickness and grain size decrease with distance from source in a semi-logarithmic manner. Fallout lobes with contrasting directional axes reflect variable wind fields and the dependence of the height of the eruption column on the degree of magma–water interaction. Massive, poorly sorted, low to very low temperature pyroclastic flow deposits (ignimbrites) are restricted to valleys. There are also several types of surge deposits, and debris jet deposits. Flood wave deposits, resulting from the instantaneous emptying of a temporary tephra-dammed lake, formed during the eruption at the mouth of the Brohltal, which was the main supply channel for pyroclastic flows. The sulphur-rich magma and stratospheric injection had a major climatic impact.

The pumice and ash deposits of the Laacher See Tephra (LST) are subdivided into a Lower (LLST, I, A, B, C), a Middle (MLST, A, B, C) and an Upper (ULST, A, B, C) sequence (Fig. 20.42). These differ from each other in terms of lithology, chemical composition, eruptive and depositional mechanisms as well as areal extent (Bogaard & Schmincke 1984, 1985; Schmincke *et al.* 1990). The eruptive products are compositionally zoned (Wörner & Schmincke 1984) from highly evolved phonolitic, phenocryst-poor white pumice erupted during the LLST (assumed top of the magma chamber) to more mafic, crystal-rich, poorly vesiculated grey lapilli erupted at the end of the MLST-C and during the ULST. These stratigraphic subdivisions reflect the most significant changes in the eruptive mechanism, the position of the vent, the stability of the eruptive pipe and the composition of the erupted magma and of the country rock fragments (basement stratigraphy).

**Initial phase (LST-1).** The highly explosive opening phase of the LSV eruption was characterized by the interaction of rising magma and/or hot gases with groundwater. The initial deposits, therefore, consist almost exclusively of country-rock fragments, ground-up Tertiary clay and vegetation remains from downed, splintered and defoliated trees.

**Lower Laacher See Tephra (LLST).** The subsequent eruption column probably rose to a height of >20 km. Pumice lapilli and ash were transported by prevailing winds for >1000 km chiefly to the NE where they form thin layers in lake sediments, bogs and swamps. This first Plinian phase, subdivided into two subphases (Figs. 20.43 & 20.44) ended with an impressive marker bed extremely rich in Devonian slate fragments ('big bang layer', BBL) (LLST-C) and probably emplaced by a high-angle blast. The lithic fragments of the BBL were probably generated when the walls around the deeply reamed-out conduit became unstable and caved in, overpressure possibly being due to the collapsed and temporarily blocked conduit.

**Mud rain phase (MLST-A).** The dynamics of the eruption changed radically following the BBL explosion. A new crater

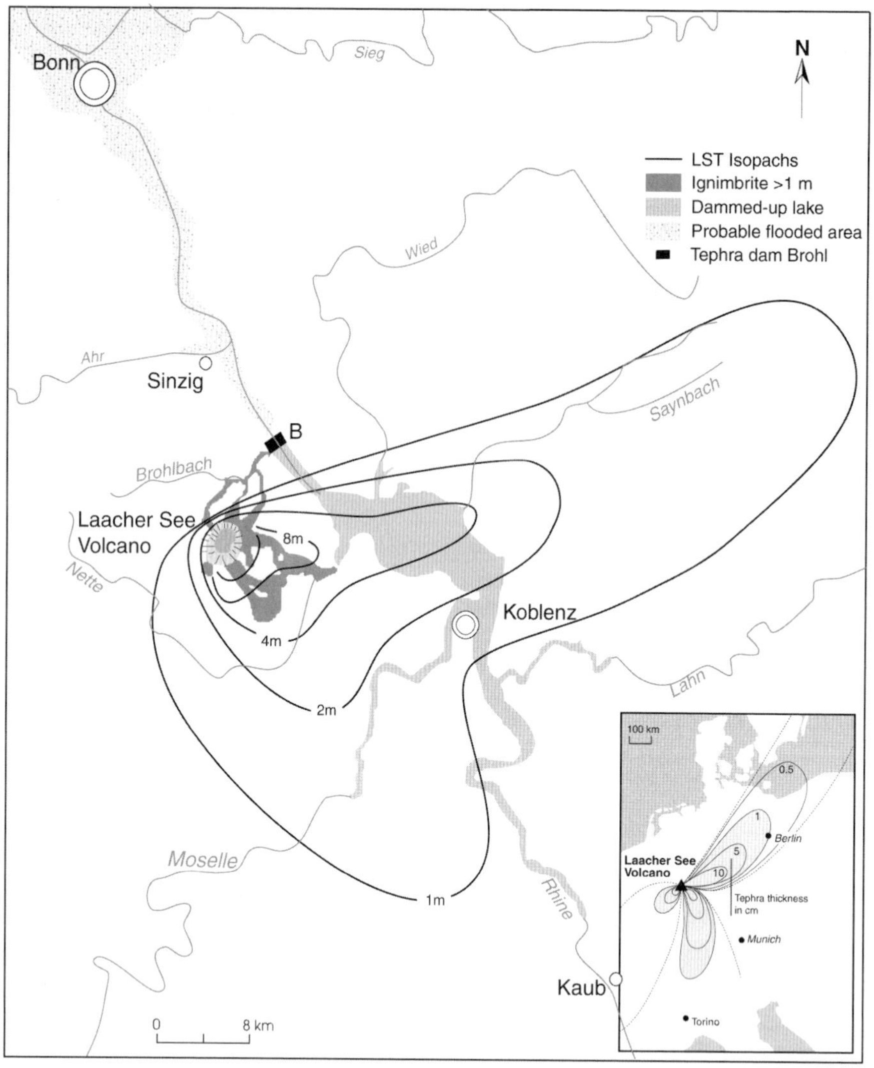


**Fig. 20.42** Distribution of Laacher See Tephra lobes in Central Europe (inset) and in the proximal area across the Rhine River (after Bogaard & Schmincke 1985). Ignimbrite deposits are shown in some radial valleys (Brohltal and Nettetal) (after Freundt and Schmincke 1986). Approximate extent of dammed-up lake generated during the late phase of the eruption (intermediate grey area; after Park & Schmincke 1997). Temporary tephra dam formed at the mouth of Brohlbach (B) where pyroclastic flows channelled within Brohltal valley entered the Rhine.

was established in the northern part of the basin. A drastic compositional hiatus in trace and major element concentrations across the LLST–MLST boundary suggests that the early erupted cupola magma may have been physically separated from the main volume which was subsequently erupted. A characteristic succession of fine-grained tuffs (the Hauptbritzbank) was deposited as mud rain; some layers are rich in small, concentrically structured ash balls (accretionary lapilli), and the succession includes minor Plinian pumice lapilli fallout layers (Schumacher & Schmincke 1991) (Fig. 20.44).

**Main ignimbrite and second major Plinian phase (MLST-B).** Several pyroclastic flows generated at the end of this transitional phase were funnelled through radial valleys and entered the Rhine (Freundt & Schmincke 1986). The second and major Plinian phase began with an oscillating eruption column and evolved into a sustained column generating the main pumice fallout beds with the largest proximal pumice bombs. The eruption column may have reached >30 km in height. This phase ended with a compositionally distinct partly phreatomagmatic phase (MLST-C) and minor ignimbrites.

**Late phreatomagmatic phase and third compositional hiatus (ULST).** The spectacular deposits of the terminal phreatomagmatic phase (ULST) comprise a rhythmic succession including (a) massive, very-low-T pyroclastic flows, (b) medium-grained, cross-bedded, high-energy dune deposits, and (c) coarse-grained breccia layers. The latter two were laid down by laterally moving base surges and debris jets. The lapilli are dense, cauliflower-shaped, and crystal-rich, and include many small chips of Devonian slate. The deposits are >30 m thick proximally but were deposited mainly within 5 km of the Laacher See except for widespread terminal volcanic silts (Fig. 20.45). All structural and textural criteria indicate phreatomagmatic eruptive processes, most probably caused by massive groundwater influx into the partially emptied and collapsed magma chamber.

**Synvolcanic formation of lakes.** Repeated damming up of the

Fig. 20.43. Proximal Laacher See Tephra (*c.* 20 m thick) at Wingertsberg *c.* 1 km SE of Laacher See. Grey duned phreatomagmatic Upper Laacher See Tephra (ULST) dominates in this proximal facies. Middle LST shown by light-coloured fallout pumice lapilli beds underlain by more poorly sorted ash flow, fallout and surge deposits. Lower part of section (LLST) hidden. Scale is 2 m.

Fig. 20.44. Medial facies of Laacher See Tephra *c.* 5 km east of Laacher See at western slope of Plaidter Hummerich. The deposit is typically subdivided into the Lower LLST-A separated from Upper LLST-B by widespread tuff band. LLST is capped by distinctive 'big bang layer' (BB) (LLST-C) rich in Devonian slate fragments. Fine-grained tuffs, mostly deposited wet, dominate the Hauptbritzbank (HBB) overlain by MLST fallout pumice lapilli. The top of the section has been eroded.

Rhine, probably initially at the confluence of Rhine and Moselle rivers, was followed by episodic draining, locally deep incision into abandoned river channels and massive reworking. A major temporary tephra dam formed during the eruption, probably at the mouth of the Brohlbach, a tributary of the Rhine, where huge masses of pumice and ash had accumulated, chiefly supplied by several pyroclastic flows (Fig. 20.42). A lake, at least 18 m deep,

Fig. 20.45. Complete section of *c.* 8 m thick primary Laacher See Tephra (LST) topped by massive fine ash (S) overlain by *c.* 15 m reworked LST (RLST). In the Neuwied Basin west of the River Rhine, this reworked facies consists basically of a thick, lower, relatively fine-grained, gritty, more massive facies deposited very fast (L-RLST), and an upper, more strongly layered facies (U-RLST) with common lahars and episodic sedimentation. Temporary tephra pit 500 m SW of Kruft.

formed behind this natural dam (Park & Schmincke 1997). A pumice raft had covered the lake and was left behind in marginal flooded shallow-water areas following drainage and the collapse of the dam between the eruption of ULST-A and -B. The catastrophic draining resulted in flood-wave deposits, some of which occur as far north as Bonn.

**Waning phase and instantaneous reworking.** An extended period of low-energy phreatomagmatic eruptions resulting in the deposition of widespread fine-grained, dominantly massive ash beds, some rich in accretionary lapilli, was interrupted by a brief phase of rapid and significant steep-sided erosional gullying. We speculate that the very heavy rains postulated as a consequence of the climatic impact of the eruption may have caused this extremely energetic and rapid gullying. Huge volumes of poorly sorted, horizontally bedded, dominantly coarse-grained, xenolith-rich reworked tephra deposits are up to 20 m thick between the Laacher See and the Rhine (Fig. 20.45). They are interbedded with local lake and lahar deposits.

Today, $CO_2$-dominated gases escape from vents throughout the Eifel volcanic field, where in many places they are of economic importance. A strong $CO_2$ flux is evident over a distance of *c.* 200 m along the eastern shore of the Laacher See (Giggenbach *et al.* 1991). The area around the Laacher See basin is characterized by elevated microseismic activity (Ahorner 1983).

**Age of the LST.** The first radiometric date of *c.* 11 ka $^{14}C$ BP was determined on plant material incorporated within the LST shortly after Libby developed the $^{14}C$ dating method (Arnold & Libby 1951; Firbas 1953). This date has been confirmed by many subsequent carbon dating studies (summarized in Bogaard & Schmincke 1985; Friedrich *et al.* 1999; see also summary in Litt *et al.* 2001, 2003) but increased to *c.* 13 ka BP due to recalibration of the $^{14}C$ timescale. Absolutely dated tree-ring chronologies (premier source establishing a $^{14}C$ calibration data set) are, however, still lacking for this time interval. The high-precision $^{14}C$ age for the eruption of the LSV is $11\,063 \pm 13$ years BP based on a sequence of decadal tree-ring samples, obtained from a poplar tree buried by the LST (Street *et al.* 1994). Single-crystal laser fusion dating ($^{40}Ar/^{39}Ar$) on sanidine phenocrysts indicate an age of 12 900 + 560 years BP (Bogaard 1995), practically identical to the results of recent varve studies of maar deposits west of the Laacher See (Brauer *et al.* 1999*a*, *b*; Negendank & Zolitschka 1993; Hajdas *et al.* 1995) and other lakes (Merkt, 1991). U–Th dating on sanidines (Bourdon *et al.* 1995) also gives an age of *c.* 13 ka BP. An age of *c.* 12.9 ka BP nearly 200 years prior to the Younger Dryas (Hämelsee, Meerfelder Maar) is now accepted by most workers.

**Season of the eruption.** The LSV erupted during the late spring/early summer as shown by several independent lines of evidence. Firstly, late spring is indicated by the seasonal development of plants directly overlain by the LST (Schweitzer 1958; F. Bittmann, pers. comm.). Secondly, the LST is found above the winter layer, but below the summer layer in several lakes in Germany (Brauer *et al.* 1999*a*; Hajdas *et al.* 1995; Merkt 1971, 1991). Thirdly, the presence of a summer carbonate layer overlying the LST in lake deposits of the Steislinger See (southern Germany) indicates Plinian tephra sedimentation prior to June (H. Schneider, pers. comm.). Finally, Laacher See ashes were deposited as two separate graded layers in the Black Forest lakes (Titisee and Mummelsee), further indicating that the LSV volcano erupted later than early spring (Merkt 1991). If the tephra had been deposited on a frozen lake surface it would subsequently have been redeposited as a massive mixed ash bed following melting of the ice.

Archaeological findings in the strata beneath the LST indicate that the Laacher See area was inhabited at the time of eruption (Bosinski *et al.* 1995). The eruption was most likely witnessed by humans. No unequivocal remains of victims of the eruption have, however, been detected thus far. Precursory phenomena such as more or less continuous seismic activity punctuated by strong earthquakes and/or increased gas emissions may have been so traumatic that any inhabitants left the immediate surroundings of the eruptive site (Schmincke *et al.* 1990). Tracks of ptarmigan, brown bear and deer were uncovered during pumice mining in a layer deposited prior to the uppermost tephra (ULST) (Baales & Berg 1997).

**Duration of Laacher See volcano eruption.** The extremely high mass eruption rate of $3–5 \times 10^8$ kg/s during the major Plinian fallout phases (LLST and MLST-B) suggested to Bogaard & Schmincke (1985) that the bulk of the magma volume was likely to have been erupted in *c.* 10 hours. Tree moulds of upright trees, common in the Neuwied Basin and locally extending for >5 m throughout the entire tephra sequence cannot, however, be used to postulate a short duration of the entire eruption as previously thought. For example, upright uncarbonized trees occur in >6 m thick pumice fallout deposits of the *c.* AD 960 Baitoushan eruption in North Korea (Horn & Schmincke 2000). Moreover, former estimates of the short duration of the main stages of the eruption does not take into account several breaks and changes in the mode of eruption. These include the presence of a widespread ash layer between the coarser-grained and more poorly sorted LLST-A and the layered, well-sorted LLST-B, the singular BBL phase (LLST-C), minor breaks during the deposition of the HBB, both prior to, and following, the eruption of the MLST-C and distinct changes in composition and/or modes of deposition between the MLST and the ULST-A, -B and -C units. Gully erosion and the deposition of locally more than one lahar in the proximal and medial facies indicate several breaks close to the end of the eruption between ULST-B and -C and within ULST-C, where eruption-triggered heavy rains are thought to have been responsible for both incision of deep channels and late-stage phreatic/phreatomagmatic eruptions ('green silts'). Finally, re-evaluation of the erosional channels and reworked tephra intercalated with the primary tephra in the LST deposits on the flood plain of the River Rhine indicate several stages of temporary damming both downstream and upstream (contrasting with one main stage of tephra dam formation; Park & Schmincke 1997) and rapid collapse and ensuing erosion; the first major stage having occurred directly after HBB deposition. Thus, the eruption could have lasted several weeks but most likely not more than a few months.

**Was there a second eruption of the Laacher See Volcano or another similar eruptive centre?** Eruptive phases preceding, and/or following, the climactic eruption of the Laacher See Volcano are occasionally postulated in the literature. For example, Schirmer (1995) and Waldmann (1996) suggested that a second eruption occurred *c.* 200 years later based on *c.* 50 cm thick plant-bearing tephra successions near the confluence of the rivers Ahr and Rhine (Goldene Meile locality). The deposit underlying this succession is, however, a non-volcanic pre-eruption floodplain deposit. The overlying LST deposits at this locality are interpreted as having formed as a result of flood waves triggered when the tephra dam collapsed. Traces of a second LSV eruption have not been found elsewhere, neither above nor below the well-documented LST sequence. The only younger volcanic eruption in the Eifel is that of 11 ka BP old mafic Ulmener Maar located *c.* 30 km SW of the Laacher See Volcano (Zolitschka *et al.* 1995).

**Stratigraphic importance of the LST.** The characteristic chemical (alkali-rich phonolite) and mineral (amphibole, clinopyroxene, sanidine, plagioclase, phlogopite, haüyne and titanite) composition of the LST are easily distinguished from subalkaline ashes of Late Glacial Icelandic tephra, which are common in bogs in northern Germany (Bogaard & Schmincke 2002). The LST is clearly the most important stratigraphic marker in distal Late Glacial deposits across Central Europe. To the NE, the LST can be traced as far as southern Sweden where it is limited by the Late Glacial ice boundary (1100 km). To the east, the LST can be traced as far as Poland, to the south as far as northern Italy and to the west as far as central France (Bogaard & Schmincke 1985). The LST has been cored in many lakes in Central Europe, the southernmost being Lake Geneva and the northernmost the Haemel See in northern Germany (Merkt & Müller 1999; Brauer *et al.* 1999*a*). The distribution to the east, e.g. in the area of the former German Democratic Republic where studies prior to 1990 were limited for political reasons, is even more extensive than shown on the maps of Bogaard & Schmincke (1985; e.g. Juvigne *et al.* 1995).

**Climatic impact of the LSV eruption.** The climatic impact of a Plinian eruption of the magnitude of the LSV is a function of the eruption column entering the stratosphere, the column height being a function of the mass eruption rate and thus of the amount of volatiles liberated, chiefly magmatic $H_2O$. The second factor is the amount of total sulphur injected into the stratosphere which is dependent on the mass of magma erupted for a given sulphur content and the longevity of the stratospheric layer of sulphate aerosols. The sulphur released is transformed into sulphuric acid droplets (aerosols) within weeks following an eruption. The aerosols usually migrate to the poles where they can influence the global circulation patterns. They may reside in the stratosphere for several years, reducing surface temperatures by absorbing and reflecting solar radiation.

A minimum of 2 Mt of total sulphur was calculated to have been released into the stratosphere during the LSV eruption by comparing pre- and post-eruptive volatile concentrations in glass inclusions and pumice matrix glasses (Harms & Schmincke 2000). Because a separate sulphur-bearing vapour phase was probably present in the magma prior to eruption, as indicated by the high melt-$H_2O$ contents close to saturation level, the actual amount of sulphur released during the eruption could have significantly exceeded 2 Mt. The sulphuric acid aerosol layer formed after the eruption probably had a significant impact on climate in the northern hemisphere and thus the environment, as suggested by modelling (Graf & Timmreck 2001) and several proxies. For example, the increased sediment supply into several lakes has been interpreted by Schmincke *et al.* (1999) as due to the increased precipitation in Central Europe which occurred for several years following the eruption. Such increased rainfall is likely to have accelerated reworking of tephra in the Neuwied Basin and may have been responsible for the drastic phase of cutting V-shaped, steep-sided channels prior to the end of the eruption (see above). Widespread destruction of vegetation by the tephra blanket may have been another factor leading to an increase in clastic supply to lakes. There was also a lasting impact on the vegetation of the region caused by sulphuric acid release from the sulphur-rich glass shards during diagenesis, a process documented for a much less sulphur-rich tephra layer in Patagonia by Kilian *et al.* (2006). The cool Younger Dryas Stadial was clearly not triggered by the LSV eruption, as formerly thought, since it commenced *c.* 200 years after the eruption (Brauer *et al.* 1999*a*; Merkt & Müller 1999).

## *Is volcanism in the Quaternary Eifel volcanic fields extinct?*

As late as the 1980s the prevalent opinion was that volcanism in the Eifel region of Germany is extinct (see review in Schmincke 2000). However, such an interpretation has never been based on convincing empirical data or on scientific logic. The question as to whether or not one can expect future volcanic eruptions in a volcanic field is obviously not only of scientific interest. There are several different parameters and criteria on which to base plausible arguments suggesting that volcanism in the Eifel is not extinct and might even increase in the future. Several of these arguments have been discussed elsewhere in detail (e.g. Schmincke 2007*a*, *b*). In summary, although volcanism in the Eifel is at present dormant, new volcanoes could form at any time. These new volcanoes are most likely to grow in the southern to eastern areas of both fields, and would be maars or scoria cones of mafic/intermediate composition in both fields but possibly strongly explosive and of highly evolved compositions in a future LSV eruption.

## *Conclusions*

(1) Volcanically active periods in the EEVF, and probably WEVF indicate pronounced episodicity; short eruptive intervals alternate with longer non-eruptive pauses. Whether this episodicity is caused by phases of enhanced melting and/or episodic stress changes, facilitating the rise of magma to the surface, is unknown. The correlation of some compositional jumps with eruptive episodes indicates a shift in compositionally distinct melting domains.

(2) The lifetime of distinct mantle domains, as expressed in compositional batches of erupted lavas unrelated to others by fractionation and/or differences in the degree of partial melting, is of the order of several hundred thousand years.

(3) Low degrees of magma leaking in the WEVF, as reflected in the more isolated volcano occurrences, contrasts with large-volume magma pooling in high level reservoirs in the EEVF which is also shown by a concomitant scarcity of very primitive (MgO $>$ 10 wt%), and an abundance of extremely evolved, phonolitic magmas in the EEVF. The Laacher See Volcano eruption involving the production of $>$6 $km^3$ of magma is most prominent.

(4) The stratigraphic importance of the Quaternary volcanism is based on the presence of widespread fallout tephra layers, some of evolved (phonolitic) composition, that form important chronostratigraphic markers. Classic Quaternary stratigraphic sections (e.g. Ariendorf and Kärlich) have been precisely dated by single-crystal laser fusion ages of tephra layers erupted in the Rieden (*c.* 400 ka) and Wehr (*c.* 215 ka) eruptive centres, facilitating the correlation of climate-controlled Quaternary continental sediments with marine oxygen isotope stages.

(5) The Laacher See eruption at 12.9 ka BP was the most important non-climatic sudden geological event during the Late Glacial in Central Europe. The eruption had a major impact on the near-field environment, including damming of the Rhine. Flood wave deposits resulting from dam collapse are found as far as 50 km north of the Laacher See. The highly evolved phonolitic magma was very sulphur-rich. This fact coupled with stratospheric eruption columns exceeding 30 km in height apparently impacted climate in the northern hemisphere.

(6) Some basaltic lapilli and ash layers can be traced for many kilometres and form excellent stratigraphic markers in thick glacial and interglacial sedimentary successions in Eifel scoria cone craters. These craters also contain abundant evidence for human activity dating as far back as 200 ka.

(7) The strong NW–SE orientation of lithosphere cracks along which magmas rose and erupted was probably related to the reactivation of Palaeozoic structural discontinuities by similarly orientated present-day lithospheric stress fields on a variety of scales.

(8) Volcanism in both Eifel fields is dormant at present, but not extinct.

B. Urban (Lüneburg) and B. van Vliet-Lanoë (Lille) are thanked for their valuable comments on an early version of the manuscript, and J. Herrmann (GGA-Institut) is thanked for the art work. The work summarized here is a group effort, carried out by students and colleagues between 1970 and 2005 and still ongoing. Some of the studies were supported by grants from the Deutsche Forschungsgemeinschaft, e.g. Schm 250/58 in the priority research programme 'Wandel der Geo-Biosphäre' which is gratefully acknowledged. Critical comments on the manuscript by P. Gibbard, F. Sirocko and T. McCann are very much appreciated. M. Sumita helped greatly in the final design of the figures.

## References

Aalbersberg, G. & Litt, T. 1998. Multi-proxy climate reconstructions for the Eemian and Early Weichselian. *Journal of Quaternary Science*, **13**, 367–390.

Aguirre, E. & Pasini, G. 1985. The Pliocene-Pleistocene boundary. *Episodes*, **8**, 116–120.

Ahorner, L. 1983. Historical seismicity and present-day micro-earthquake activity of the Rhenish Massif, Central Europe. *In:* Fuchs, K. *et al.* (eds) *Plateau Uplift*. Springer Heidelberg, 198–221.

American Commission on Stratigraphic Nomenclature 1961. Code of stratigraphic nomenclature. *Bulletin of the American Association of Petroleum Geologists*, **45**, 645–660.

Arnold, J. R. & Libby, W. F. 1951. Radiocarbon dates. *Science*, **113**, 111–120.

Baales, M. & Berg, A. V. 1997. Tierfährten in der allerödzeitlichen Vulkanasche des Laacher See-Vulkans bei Mertloch, Kreis Mayen-Koblenz. *Archäologisches Korrepondenzblatt*, **27**, 1–12.

Babuska, V. & Plomerova, J. 1992. The lithosphere in Central Europe – seismological and petrological aspects. Tectonophysics, **207**, 101–163

Bartz, J. 1974. Die Mächtigkeit des Quartärs im Oberrheingraben. *In:* Illies, J. H. & Fuchs, K. (eds) *Approaches to Taphrogenesis*. Inter-Union Commission on Geodynamics, Scientific Reports, **8**, 78–87.

Beck, P. 1933. Über das schweizerische und europäische Pliozän und Pleistozän. *Eclogae geologicae Helvetiae*, **26**(2), 335–437.

Becker, A. 1993. An attempt to define a "Neotectonic period" for central and northern Europe. *Geologische Rundschau*, **82**, 67–83

Bednarz, U. 1982. *Geologie und Petrologie der spätquartären Vulkane Herchenberg, Leilenkopf und Dümpelmaar (nördliches Laacher See-Gebiet)*. Diplomarbeit (Diploma thesis) Ruhr Universität Bochum, 1–298

Bednarz, U. & Schmincke, H.-U. 1990. Evolution of the Quaternary melilite-nephelinite Herchenberg volcano (East Eifel). *Bulletin of Volcanology*, **52**, 426–444

Bednarz, U., Freundt, A. & Schmincke, H.-U. 1983. *Die Eignung von Lokationen in der E- und W-Eifel für ein deutsches HOT-DRY-ROCK Geothermik Projekt*. BMFT Berichte, 1–100.

Behre, K.-E. 1989. Biostratigraphy of the Last Glacial Period in Europe. *Quaternary Science Reviews*, **8**, 25–44.

Benda, L. (ed.) 1995. *Das Quartär Deutschlands*. Gebrüder Bornträger, Berlin.

Berg, M. W. van den, 1995. *Fluvial sequences of the Maas – a 10 Ma record of neotectonics and climate change at various time-scales*. Thesis, University of Wageningen.

Bertsch, K. & Steeger, A. 1927. Jungdiluviale pflanzenführende Ablagerungen am nördlichen Niederrhein. *Berichte über die Versammlung des Niederrheinischen Geologischen Vereins für 1926*, 49–65.

Beug, H. J. 1972. Das Riss/Würm-Interglazial von Zeifen, Landkreis Laufen a.d. Salzach. *Bayerische Akademie der Wissenschaften, Mathematisch-Naturwissenschaftliche Klasse N.F.*, **151**, 46–75.

Beug, H. J. 1979. Vegetationsgeschichtlich-pollenanalytische Untersuchungen am Riss/Würm-Interglazial von Eurach am Starnberger See/obb. *Geologica Bavarica*, **80**, 91–106.

Bittmann, F. 1990. *Vegetationsgeschichtliche Untersuchungen an mittel- und jungpleistozänen Ablagerungen des Neuwieder Beckens (Mittelrhein)*. Dissertation, University of Göttingen.

Bittmann, F. & Müller, H. 1996. The Kärlich Interglacial site and its correlation with the Bilshausen sequence. *In:* Turner, C. (ed.) *The Early Middle Pleistocene in Europe*. Balkema, Rotterdam, 187–193.

Blytt, A. 1867. *Immigration of the Norwegian Flora*. Cammermeyer, Christiania.

Boenigk, W. 1970. Zur Kenntnis des Altquartärs bei Brüggen. Geologischen Institutes der Universität Köln, *Sonderveröffentlichungen des Geologischen Instituts der Universität zu Köln*, **17**, 1–138.

Boenigk, W. 1976. Schwermineraluntersuchungen zur Entwicklung des Rheinsystems. *Eiszeitalter und Gegenwart*, **27**, 202.

Boenigk, W. 1978*a*. Gliederung der altquartären Ablagerungen in der Niederrheinischen Bucht. *Fortschritte in der Geologie von Rheinland und Westfalen*, **28**, 135–212.

Boenigk, W. 1978*b*. Zur Ausbildung und Entstehung der jungtertiären Sedimente in der Niederrheinischen Bucht. *Kölner Geographische Arbeiten*, **36**, 59–68.

Boenigk, W. 1979. Die Gliederung der tertiären Braunkohleschichten in der Ville (Niederrheinische Bucht). *Fortschritte in der Geologie von Rheinland und Westfalen*, **29**, 193–263.

Boenigk, W. 1995. Terrassenstratigraphie des Mittelpleistozän am Niederrhein und Mittelrhein. *Mededelingen Rijks Geologische Dienst*, **52**, 71–81.

Boenigk, W. 2001. The Pleistocene drainage pattern in the Lower Rhine Basin. *Geologie en Mijnbouw*, **81**, 201–209.

Boenigk, W. & Frechen, M. 1998. Zur Geologie der Deckschichten von Kärlich im Rheinland. *Eiszeitalter und Gegenwart*, **48**, 38–49.

Boenigk, W. & Frechen, M. 2001. The loess record in sections at Koblenz-Metternich and Tönchesberg in the Middle Rhine Area. *Quaternary International*, **76/77**, 201–209.

Boenigk, W. & Frechen, M. 2006. The Pliocene and Quaternary fluvial archives of the Rhine system. *Quaternary Science Reviews*, **25**, 550–574.

Boenigk, W., Heye, D., Schirmer, W. & Brunnacker, K. 1974. Paläomagnetische Messungen an vielgliedrigen Quartär-Profilen (Kärlich/Mittelrhein und Bad Soden i. Taunus). *Mainzer Naturwissenschaftliche Archiv*, **12**, 159–168.

Bogaard, v. d. C. & Schmincke, H.-U. 2002. Linking the North Atlantic to Central Europe: A high-resolution Holocene tephrochronological record from Northern Germany. *Journal of Quaternary Science*, **17**, 3–20.

Bogaard, v. d. C., Bogaard, P. V. D. & Schmincke, H.-U. 1989. Quartärgeologisch-tephrostratigraphische Neuaufnahme und Interpretation des Pleistozänprofils Kärlich. *Eiszeitalter und Gegenwart*, **39**, 62–86

Bogaard, v. d. P. 1995. $^{40}Ar/^{39}Ar$ ages of sanidine phenocrysts from Laacher See Tephra (12,900 yr BP): Chronostratigraphic and petrological significance. *Earth and Planetary Science Letters*, **133**, 163–174.

Bogaard, v. d. P. & Schmincke, H.-U. 1984. The eruptive center of the late Quaternary Laacher See tephra. *Geologische Rundschau*, **73**, 935–982

Bogaard, v. d. P. & Schmincke, H.-U. 1985. Laacher See Tephra: a widespread isochronous late Quaternary ash layer in Central and Northern Europe. *Geological Society of America Bulletin*, **96**, 1554–1571.

Bogaard, v.d.P., Schmincke, H.-U. 1988. Aschenlagen als quartäre Zeitmarken in Mitteleuropa. *Geowissenschaften*, **6**, 75–84.

Bogaard, v. d. P. & Schmincke, H.-U. 1990. Die Entwicklungsgeschichte des Mittelrheinraumes und die Eruptionsgeschichte des Osteifel-Vulkanfeldes. *In:* Schirmer, W. (ed.) *Rheingeschichte zwischen Mosel und Maas*. Deuqua-Führer, **1**, Dusseldorf, 166–190.

Bogaard, v. d. P., Hall, C. M., Schmincke, H.-U. & York D. 1987. $^{40}Ar/^{39}Ar$ Laser dating of single grains: Ages of Quaternary tephra from the East Eifel Volcanic Field, FRG. *Geophysical Research Letters*, **14**, 1211–1214.

Bogaard, v. d. P., Hall Ch., Schmincke, H.-U., & York D. 1989. Precise single-grain $^{40}Ar/^{39}Ar$ dating of a cold to warm climate transition in Central Europe. *Nature*, **342**, 523–525.

Bogaard, P. J. F. & Wörner, G. 2003. Petrogenesis of basanitic to tholeiitic volcanic rocks from the Miocene Vogelsberg, Central Germany. *Journal of Petrolology*, **44**, 569–602.

Bolliger, T., Fejfar, O., Graf, H. & Kälin, D. W. 1996. Vorläufige Mitteilung über Funde von pliozänen Kleinsäugern aus den Höheren Deckenschottern des Irchels (Kt. Zürich). *Eclogae geologicae Helvetiae*, **89**(3), 1043–1048.

Bosinski, G., Brunnacker, K., Lanser, K. P., Stephan, S., Urban, B. & Würges, K. 1980. Altpaläolithische Funde von Kärlich, Kreis Mayen-Koblenz (Neuwieder Becken). *Archäologisches Korrespondenzblatt*, **10**, 295–314.

Bosinski, G., Kröger, K., Schäfer, J. & Turner, E. 1986. Altsteinzeitliche Siedlungsplätze auf den Osteifel-Vulkanen. *Jahrbuch des Römisch-germanischen Zentralmuseums*, **33**, 97–130

Bosinski, G., Street, M. & Baales, M. 1995. The Paleolithic and Mesolithic of the Rhineland. *In:* Schirmer, W. (ed) *Quaternary Field Trips in Central Europe*, **2**, Pfeil, München, 829–999.

Bourdon, B., Zindler, A. & Wörner, G. 1994. Evolution of the Laacher See magma chamber: Evidence from SIMS and TIMS measurements of *U-Th* disequilibria in minerals and glasses. *Earth and Planetary Science Letters*, **126**, 75–90.

Bowen, D. Q. & Gibbard, P. L. 2006. The Quaternary is here to stay. *Journal of Quaternary Science*, **22**, 3–8.

Brack, A. 2003. *Beispiele zur Glazialgeologie. Zeil (b) Bemerkungen zur Geologie der Schliffgrenze im Grimselgebiet (Oberhasli, Kt. Bern)*. Dissertation, Geologischen Institut der ETH, Zürich.

Brauer, A., Endres, Ch., Günter, Ch., Litt, T., Stebich, M. & Negendank, J. F. W. 1999*a*. High resolution sediment and vegetation responses to Younger Dryas climate change in varved lake sediments from Meerfelder Maar, Germany. *Quaternary Science Reviews*, **18**, 321–329.

Brauer, A., Endres, Ch. & Negendank, J. F. W. 1999*b*. Lateglacial calendar year chronology based on annually laminated sediments from lake Meerfelder Maar, Germany. *Quaternary International*, **61**, 17–25.

Brelie, von der, G., Kilpper, K. & Teichmüller, R. 1959. Das Pleistozän-Profil von Frimmersdorf an der Erft. Fortschritte der Geologie in Rheinland und Westfalen **4**, 179–196.

Brunnacker, K. & Boenigk, W. 1976. Über den Stand der paläomagnetischen Untersuchungen im Pliozän und Pleistozän der Bundesrepublik Deutschland. *Eiszeitalter und Gegenwart*, **27**, 1–17.

Brunnacker, K. & Boenigk, W. 1983. The Rhine Valley between the Neuwied Basin and the Lower Rhenish Embayment. *In:* Fuchs, K., Gehlen, K. v., Maelzer, H., Murawski, H. & Semmel, A. (eds) *Plateau Uplift – The Rhenish Shield – A Case History*, Springer, Berlin, 62–73.

Brunnacker, K., Streit, R. & Schirmer, W. 1969. Der Aufbau des Quartär-Profils von Kärlich/Neuwieder becken (Mittelrhein). *Mainzer naturwissenschaftliche Archiv*, **8**, 102–133.

Brunnacker, K., Heller, F. & Lozek, V. 1971. Beiträge zur Stratigraphie des Quartär-Profils von Kärlich am Mittelrhein. *Mainzer naturwissenschaftliche Archiv*, **10**, 77–100.

Brunnacker, K., Boenigk, W., *et al.* 1978. Die Mittelterrassen am Niederrhein zwischen Köln und Mönchengladbach. *Fortschritte in der Geologie von Rheinland und Westfalen*, **28**, 277–324.

Büchel, G. & Lorenz, V. 1982. Zum Alter des Maarvulkanismus der Westeifel. *Neues Jahrbuch Geologie Paläontologie Abhandlungen*, **163**, 1–22

Cepek, A. G. 1965. Stratigraphie der quartären Ablagerungen des norddeutschen Tieflandes. *In:* Gellert, J. F. (ed.) *Die Weichsel-Eiszeit im Gebiet der Deutschen Demokratischen Republik*. Akademie-Verlag, Berlin, 45–65.

Cloetingh, S., Ziegler, P. A., *et al.* 2005. Lithospheric memory, state of stress and rheology: neotectonic controls on Europe's intraplate continental topography. *Quaternary Science Reviews*, **24**, 241–304.

Desnoyers, J. 1829. Observations sur un ensemble de dépôts marins plus récents que les terrains tertiaires du Bassin de la Seine et constituant une formation géologique distincte: précédées d'un aperçu de la non-simultanéité des bassins tertiaires. *Annales scientific naturelles*, **16**, 171–214, 402–419.

Dick, K. A., Graf, H. R., Müller, B. U., Hartmann, P. & Schlüchter, C. 1996. Das nordalpine Wasserschloss und seine eiszeitgeologische Umgebung. *Eclogae geologicae Helvetiae*, **89**(1), 635–645.

Drescher-Schneider, R. 2000. Die Vegetations- und Klimaentwicklung im Riss/Würm-Interglazial und im Früh- und Mittelwürm in der Umgebung von Mondsee. Ergebnisse der pollenanalytischen Untersuchungen. *In:* van Husen, D. (ed.) *Klimaentwicklung im Riss/Würm Interglazial (Eem) und Frühwürm (Sauerstoffisotopenstufe 6 – 3) in den Ostalpen*. Mitteilungen der Kommission für Quartärforschung der Österreichischen Akademie der Wissenschaften, Wien, Bd. 12, 39–92.

Duda, A. & Schmincke, H.-U. 1978. Petrology of Quaternary basanites, nephelinites and tephrites from the Laacher See area (Eifel). *Neues Jahrbuch Mineralogie Abhandlungen*, **132**, 1–33.

Duncan, R. A., Petersen, N. & Hargraves, H. B. 1972. Mantle plumes, movement of the European plate and polar wandering. *Nature*, **239**, 82–86.

Ehlers, J. 1994. *Allgemeine und historische Quartärgeologie*. Enke, Stuttgart.

Ehlers, J. & Gibbard, P. L. (eds) 2004. Quaternary Glaciations – Extent and Chronology. Part I: Europe. Elsevier, Amsterdam.

Ehlers, J., Meyer, K.-D. & Stephan, J. 1984. Pre-Weichselian glaciations of North-West Europe. *Quaternary Science Reviews*, **3**, 1–40.

Ehlers, J., Kozarski, S. & Gibbard, P. L. (eds) 1995. *Glacial Deposits in North-East Europe*. Balkema, Rotterdam.

Ehlers, J., Eissmann, L., Lippstreu, L., Stephan, H.-J. & Wansa, S. 2004. Pleistocene glaciations in North Germany. *In:* Ehlers, J. & Gibbard, P. L. (eds) *Quaternary Glaciations – Extent and Chronology. Part I: Europe.* Elsevier, Amsterdam, 135–146.

Eissmann, L. 1995. The pre-Elsterian Quaternary deposits of central Germany. In: Ehlers, J., Kozarski, S. & Gibbard, P. L. (eds) *Glacial Deposits in North-East Europe*. Balkema, Rotterdam, 423–437.

Eissmann, L. & Litt, T. (eds) 1994. Das Quartär Mitteldeutschlands. Ein Leitfaden und Exkursionsführer. *Altenburger Naturwissenschaftliche Forschungen*, **7**, 1–458.

Eissmann, L. & Litt, T. 1995. Late Pleistocene deposits in central Germany. *In:* Ehlers, J., Kozarski, S. & Gibbard, P. L. (eds) *Glacial Deposits in North-East Europe*. Balkema, Rotterdam, 465–472.

Eissmann, L., Litt, T. & Wansa, S. 1995. Elsterian and Saalian deposits in their type area in central Germany. *In:* Ehlers, J., Kozarski, S. & Gibbard, P. L. (eds) *Glacial Deposits in North-East Europe*. Balkema, Rotterdam, 439–464.

Ellwanger, D., Fejfar, O. & von Koenigswald, W. 1994. Die biostratigraphische Aussage der Arvicolidenfauna vom Uhlenberg bei Dinkelscherben und ihre morpho- und lithostratigraphischen Konsequenzen. *Münchner Geowissenschaftliche Abhandlungen, A*, **26**, 173–191.

Ellwanger, D., Lämmermann-Barthel, J. & Neeb, I. 2003. Eine landschaftsübergreifende Lockergesteinsgliederung vom Alpenrand zum Oberrhein. *GeoArchaeoRhein*, **4**, 81–124.

Erd, K. 1965. Pollenanalytische Gliederung des mittelpleistozänen Richtprofils Pritzwalk-Prignitz. *Eiszeitalter u. Gegenwart*, **16**, 252–253.

Erd, K. 1973. Pollenanalytische Gliederung des Pleistozäns der Deutschen Demokratischen Republik. *Zeitschrift für geologische Wissenschaften*, **1**, 1087–1103.

Fekiacova, Z., Mertz, D. & Hofmann, A. W. 2006. Geodynamic setting of the Tertiary Hocheifel volcanism (Germany), Part II: Geochemistry and Sr, Nd and Pb isotopic compositions. *In:* Ritter, J. R. R. & Christensen, J. (eds) *Mantle Plumes – a Multidisciplinary Approach*. Springer, Heidelberg, 207–240.

Fekiacova, Z., Mertz, D. F. & Renne, P. R. 2007. Geodynamic setting of the Tertiary Hocheifel volcanism (Germany. Part I: $^{40}Ar/^{39}Ar$ geochronology). *In:* Ritter, R. & Christensen, U. (eds) *Mantle Plumes – a Multidisciplinary Approach*. Springer, Heidelberg, 185–206

Felber, M. & Bini, A. 1997. Seismic survey in alpine and prealpine valleys of Ticino (Switzerland). Evidence of a Late Tertiary fluvial origin. *Geologica Insubrica*, **2**(2), 46–67.

Firbas, F. 1953. Das absolute Alter der jüngsten vulkanischen Eruptionen im Bereich des Laacher Sees. *Naturwissenschaften*, **40**, 54–55.

Florineth, D. & Schlüchter, C. 1998. Reconstructing the Last Glacial Maximum (LGM) ice surface geometry and flowlines in the Central Swiss Alps. *Eclogae geologicae Helvetiae*, **91**, 391–407.

Florineth, D & Schlüchter, C. 2000. Past atmospheric circulation pattern in Europe: glacial geologic evidence from the Alps. *Quaternary Research*, **54**, 295–308.

Frechen, J. & Lippolt, H.-J. 1965. Kalium-Argon Daten zum Alter des Laacher Vulkanismus, der Rheinterrassen und der Eiszeiten. *Eiszeitalter und Gegenwart*, **16**, 5–30.

Frechen, M. 1992. Systematic thermoluminescence dating of two loess profiles from the Middle Rhine Area (F. R. G.). *Quaternary Science Reviews*, **11**, 93–101.

Frechen, M. 1999. Upper Pleistocene loess stratigraphy in Southern Germany. *Quaternary Science Reviews*, **18**, 243–269.

Frechen, M. 2002. Wind action. *In:* Cilek, V. (ed.) *Earth System: History and Natural Variability*. Encyclopaedia of Life Support Systems, EOLSS, Cambridge (World Wide Web address: www. eolss. com).

Frechen, M. & Berg, M. W. van den 2002. The coversands and the timing of Late Quaternary earthquake events along the Peel Boundary Fault in the Netherlands. *Netherlands Journal of Geosciences*, **81**, 61–70.

Frechen, M., Boenigk, W. & Weidenfeller, M. 1995. Chronostratigraphie des "Eiszeitlichen Lößprofils" in Koblenz-Metternich. *Mainzer geowissenschaftliche Mitteilungen*, **24**, 155–180.

Frechen, M., Zander, A., Cilek, V. & Lozek, V. 1999. Loess chronology of the last interglacial/glacial cycle in Bohemia and Moravia/Czech Republic. *Quaternary Science Reviews*, **18**, 1467–1493.

Frechen, M., Vanneste, K., Verbeeck, K., Paulissen, E. & Camelbeeck, T. 2001*a*. The deposition history of the coversands along the Bree Fault Escarpment, NE Belgium. *Netherlands Journal of Geosciences*, **80**, 171–185.

Frechen, M., Vliet-Lanoë, B. van & Vandenhaute, P. 2001*b*. The Upper Pleistocene loess record at Harmignies/Belgium – High resolution terrestrial archive of climate forcing. *Palaeogeography*

*Palaeoclimatology Palaeoecology*, **173**, 175–195.

Frechen, M., Oches, E. A. & Kohfeld, K. E. 2003. Loess in Europe – mass accumulation rates during the Last Glacial Period. *Quaternary Science Reviews*, **22**, 1835–1857.

Frechen, M., Sierralta, M., Oezen, D. & Urban, B. 2007. Uranium-series dating of peat from Central and Northern Europe. *In:* Sirocko, F., Claussen, M., Sanchez-Goni, M. F. & Litt, T. (eds.) *The Climate of Past Interglacials.* Elsevier, Amsterdam, Developments in Quaternary Science, **7**, 93–117.

Frechen, M., Terhorst, B. & Rähle, W. 2007. The Upper Pleistocene loess/palaeosol sequence from Schatthausen in the Upper Neckar valley. *Eiszeitalter und Gegenwart*, **56**, 221–227.

French, H. M. 1996. *The Periglacial Environment.* 2nd edn. Longman, Harlow.

Freundt, A. & Schmincke, H.-U. 1986. Emplacement of small-volume pyroclastic flows at Laacher See volcano (East Eifel, Germany). *Bulletin of Volcanology*, **48**, 39–60

Friedrich, M., Kromer, B., Spurk, M., Hofmann, J. & Kaiser, K. F. 1999. Paleao-environment and radiocarbon calibration as derived from Late Glacial/Early Holocene tree-ring chronologies. *Quaternary International*, **61**, 27–39.

Fuchs, K., von Gehlen, K., Mälzer, H., Murawski, H., & Semmel, A. (eds) 1983. *Plateau uplift, the Rhenish Shield – A Case History.* Springer, Heidelberg, 1–411.

Fuhrmann, U. 1983. *Kalium-Argon-Untersuchungen an neogenen Vulkaniten des Rheinischen Schilds.* Dissertation, Universität Heidelberg.

Fuhrmann, U. & Lippolt, H. J. 1987. Excess argon and dating of Quaternary Eifel volcanism: III. Alkalibasaltic rocks of the Central West Eifel/FR Germany. *Neues Jahrbuch Geologie Paläontologie Monatshefte*, 213–236.

Gaudzinski, S., Bittmann, F., Boenigk, W., Frechen, M. & Kolfschoten, Th. van 1996. Palaeoecology and Archaeology of the Kärlich-Seeufer open air site (Middle Pleistocene) in the Central Rhineland, Germany. *Quaternary Research*, **46**, 319–334.

Geikie, J. 1894. *The Great Ice Age, and its Relation to the Antiquity of Man.* Stanfort, London.

Geyh, M. A. & Müller, H. 2005. Numerical $^{230}$Th/U dating and a palynological review of the Holsteinian/Hoxnian Interglacial. *Quaternary Science Reviews*, **24**, 1861–1872.

Geyh, M. A. & Schlüchter, C. 1998. Zur Kalibration der $^{14}$C-Zeitskala vor 22.000 Jahren v. h. *GeoArchaeoRhein*, **2**, 139–149.

Gibbard, P. L. 1988. The history of the great northwest European rivers during the past three million years. *Philosophical Transactions of the Royal Society of London B*, **318**, 559–602.

Gibbard, P. L. 2003. Definition of the Middle–Upper Pleistocene boundary. *Global and Planetary Change*, **36**, 201–208.

Gibbard. P. L. & Kolfschoten, v. T. 2004. The Pleistocene and Holocene Epochs. *In:* Gradstein, F., Ogg, J. & Smith, A. (eds) *A Geologic Time Scale 2004.* Cambridge University Press, Cambridge, 441–452.

Gibbard P. L. & West, R. G. 2000. Quaternary chronostratigraphy: the nomenclature of terrestrial sequences. *Boreas*, **29**, 329–336.

Gibbard, P. L., Smith, A. G., *et al.* 2005. What status for the Quaternary? *Boreas*, **34**, 1–6.

Giggenbach, W., Sano, Y. & Schmincke, H.-U. 1991. $CO_2$ rich gases from lakes Nyos and Monoun (Cameroon), Laacher See (Germany), Dieng (Indonesia), and Mt. Gambier (Australia) – variations on a common theme. *Journal of Volcanology and Geothermal Research*, **45**, 311–323

Gradstein, F., Ogg, J. & Smith, A. (eds) 2004. *A Geologic Time Scale 2004.* Cambridge University Press, Cambridge.

Graf, A., Strasky, S., Ivy-Ochs, S., Akcar, N., Kubrik, P. W., Burkhard, M., & Schlüchter, C. 2007. First results of cosmogenis dated pre-Last Glaciation erratics from the Montoz area, Jura Mountains, Switzerland. *Quaternary International*, **164–165**, 43–52.

Graf, H. R. 1993. *Die Deckenschotter der zentralen Nordschweiz.* Dissertation, ETH-Zürich..

Graf, H.-F. & Timmreck, C. 2001. Aerosol radiative forcing of the Laacher See volcano eruption. *Journal of Geophysical Research*, **106**, 14747–14756.

Grosfjeld, K., Funder, S., Seidenkranz, M.-S. & Glaister, C. 2006. Last Interglacial marine environments in the White Sea region, northwestern Russia. *Boreas*, **35**, 493–520.

Grüger, E. 1979. Spätriss, Riss/Würm und Frühwürm am Samerberg in Oberbayern – ein vegetationsgeschichtlicher Beitrag zur Gliederung des Jungpleistozäns. *Geologica Bavarica*, **80**, 5–64.

Grüger, E. & Schreiner, A. 1993. Riss/Würm- und würmzeitliche Ablagerungen im Wurzacher Becken (Rheingletschergebiet). *Neues Jahrbuch für Geologie und Paläontologie, Abhandlungen*, **189**, 81–117.

Haase, K. M., Goldschmidt, B. & Garbe-Schönberg, C. D. 2004. Petrogenesis of Tertiary continental intra-plate lavas from the Westerwald region, Germany. *Journal of Petrology*, **45**, 883–905.

Hagedorn, E. M. 2004. Sedimentpetrographie und Lithofazies der jungtertiären und quartären Sedimente im Oberrheingebiet. Dissertation, Universität zu Köln.

Hajdas, I., Zolitschka, B., *et al.* 1995. AMS radiocarbon dating of annually laminated sediments form Holzmaar, Germany. *Quaternary Science Review*, **14**,137–143.

Hallik, R. 1960. Die Vegetationsentwicklung der Holstein-Warmzeit in Nordwestdeutschland und die Altersstellung der Kieselgurlager der südlichen Lüneburger Heide. *Zeitschrift der Deutschen Geologischen Gesellschaft*, **112**, 326–333.

Hantke, R. 1978–89. *Eiszeitalter. Die jüngste Erdgeschichte der Schweiz und ihrer Nachbargebiete*, 3 vols, Ott, Thun.

Harms, E. & Schmincke, H.-U. 2000. Volatile composition of the Laacher See phonolite magma (12,900 yr BP): Implications for syneruptive S, F, Cl and $H_2O$ decassing. *Contributions to Mineralogy and Petrology*, **138**, 84–98.

Harms, E., Gardner, J. E., & Schmincke, H.-U. 2004. Phase equilibria of the Lower Laacher See Tephra (East Eifel, Germany): constraints on pre-eruptive storage conditions of a phonolitic magma reservoir. *Journal of Volcanology and Geothermal Research*, **134**, 125–138.

Harting, P. 1874. De bodem van het Eemdal. *Verslagen en Verhandelingen Koninklijke Academie van Wetenschappen*, **II Deel VIII**, 282–290.

Heumann, G. & Litt, T. 2002. Stratigraphy and palaeoecology of the late Pliocene and early Pleistocene in the open-cast mine Hambach (Lower Rhine Basin). *Netherlands Journal of Geoscience/Geologie en Mijnbouw*, **81**, 193–199.

Hildbrand, K. 1990. *Das Endmoränengebiet des Rhônegletschers östlich von Wangen a.A.* Dissertation, Universität Zürich.

Högbom, I. 1923. Ancient inland dunes for northern and middle Europe. *Geografiska Annaler*, **5**, 113–243.

Horn, S. & Schmincke, H.-U. 2000. Volatile emission during the eruption of Baitoushan Volcano ca. 969 AD. *Bulletin of Volcanology*, **61**, 537–555.

Houmark-Nielsen, M. 1994. Late Pleistocene stratigraphy, glaciation chronology and Middle Weichselian environmental history from Klintholm, Møn, Denmark. *Bulletin of the Geological Society of Denmark*, **41**, 181–201.

Huissteden, K. van, Vandenberghe, J., Hammen, T. van der & Laan, W. 2000. Fluvial and aeolian interaction under permafrost conditions: Weichselian Late Pleniglacial, Twente, eastern Netherlands. *Catena*, **40**, 307–321.

Ivy-Ochs, S., Schäfer, J., Kubik, P. W., Synal, H.-A. & Schlüchter, C. 2004. Timing of deglaciation on the northern Alpine foreland (Switzerland). *Eclogae geologicae Helvetiae*, **97**, 47–55.

Jerz, H. & Linke, G. 1987. Arbeitsergebnisse der Subkommission für Europäische Quartärstratigraphie: Typusregion des Holstein-Interglazials (Berichte der SEQS 8). *Eiszeitalter und Gegenwart*, **37**, 145–148.

Jessen, K. & Milthers, V. 1928. *Stratigraphical and palaeontological studies of freshwater deposits in Jutland and north-west Germany.* Danmarks Geologiske Undersøgelse, II Ræække **48**.

Jost-Stauffer, M., Coope, G. R. & Schlüchter, C. 2005. Environmental and climatic reconstructions during Marine Isotope Stage 3 from Gossau, Swiss Midlands, based on coleopteran assemblages. *Boreas*, **34**, 35–60.

Jung, S. & Hoernes, S. 2000. The major and trace element and isotope (Sr, Nd, O) geochemistry of Cenozoic mafic volcanic rocks from the Rhön area (central Germany); constraints on the origin of continental alkaline and tholeiitic basalts and their mantle source. *Journal of Petrology*, **86**, 151–177.

Juvigne, E., Cosarski, S., Nowaczyk, B. 1995. The occurrence of Laacher See tephra in Pomerania, NW Poland. *Boreas*, **24**, 225–231.

Kaltwang, J. 1992. Die pleistozäne Vereisungsgrenze im südlichen Niedersachsen und im östlichen Westfalen. *Mitteilungen des Geologischen Instituts der Universität Hannover*, **33**, 1–161.

Kasse, C. 1993. Periglacial environments climatic development during the Early Pleistocene Tiglian Stage (Beerse Glacial) in northern Belgium. *Geologie en Mijnbouw*, **72,** 107–124.

Kasse, C. 1997. Cold-Climate aeolian sand-sheet formation in North-Western Europe (c. 14–12.4 ka); a response to permafrost degradation and increased aridity. *Permafrost and Periglacial Processes*, **8**, 295–311.

Keilhack, K. 1899. Die Stillstandslagen des letzten Inlandeises und die hydrographische Entwicklung des pommerschen Küstengebietes. *Jahrbuch der Preußischen Geologischen Landesanstalt*, **19**, 90–152.

Keilhack, K. 1911. *Geologische Karte von Preußen 1:25000*. Erläuterungen zu Blatt Teltow.

Keller, O. & Krayss, E. 2005. Der Rhein-Linth Gletscher im letzten Hochglzial ö 2 Teil: Datierung und Modelle der Rhein-Linth-Vergletscherung, Klimarekonstruktionen. *Vierteljahresschrift der Naturforschenden Gesellschaft in Zürich*, **150**, 69–85.

Kelly, M. A., Buoncristiani, J.-F. & Schlüchter, C. 2004. A reconstruction of the last glacial maximum (LGM) ice-surface geometry in the western Swiss Alps and contiguous Alpine region in Italy and France. *Eclogae geologicae Helvetiae*, **97**, 57–75.

Kempf, E. K. 1966. Das Holstein-Interglazial von Tönisberg im Rahmen des niederrheinischen Pleistozäns. *Eiszeitalter und Gegenwart*, **17**: 5–60.

Kilian, R., Biester, H., *et al.* 2006. Millennium-scale volcanic impact on a superhumid and pristine ecosystem. *Geology*, **34**, 609–612.

Klostermann, J. 1992. *Das Quartär der Niederrheinischen Bucht*. Geologisches Landesamt Nordrhein-Westfalen, Krefeld.

Knipping, M. 2004. Pollenanalytische Untersuchungen an einem mittelpleistozänen Interglazial bei Mannheim. *Tübinger geowissenschaftliche Arbeiten*, Reihe D, **10**, 199–217.

Koenigswald, W. v. 2002. Lebendige Eiszeit - Klima und Tierwelt im Wandel. Theiss, Stuttgart.

Koenigswald, W. v. 2003. Mode and cause for the Pleistocene turnovers in the mammalian fauna of Central Europe. *Deinsia,* **10**, 305–312.

Koenigswald, W. v. 2006. Climatic changes, faunal diversity and environment of the Neanderthals in Central and Western Europe during the Middle and Upper Pleistocene. *Terra Nostra,* **2006**(2), 35–40.

Koenigswald, W. v. 2007. Mammalian faunas from the interglacial periods in Central Europe and their stratigraphic correlation. *In:* Sirocko, F., Claussen, M., Sanchez Goñi, M. F. & Litt, T. (eds) *The Climate of Past Interglacials*, Elsevier, Amsterdam, 445–454.

Koenigswald, W. v. & Heinrich W. D. 1999. Mittelpleistozäne Säugetierfaunen aus Mitteleuropa - der Versuch einer biostratigraphischen Zuordnung. *Kaupia*, **9**, 53–112.

Kolfschoten, T. van, Meulen, A. J. van den & Boenigk, W. 1998. The late pliocene rodents (mammalia) from Frechen (Lower Rhine Basin, Germany). *Mededelingen Nederlands Instituut vorr toegepaste Geowetenschappen TNO*, **60**, 161–171.

Krupiński, K. M. 2000. *Palynostratigraphic correlation of deposits of the Mazovian interglacial of Poland.* Prace Państwowy Instytut Geologiczny, **169**, Warsaw.

Kühl, N. & Litt, T. 2003. Quantitative time series reconstruction of Eemian temperature at three European sites using pollen data. *Vegetation History and Archaeobotany,* **12**, 205–214.

Kühl, N. & Litt, T. 2007. Quantitative time series reconstructions of Holsteinian and Eemian temperatures using botanical data. *In:* Sirocko, F., Claussen, M., Sanchez Goñi, M. F. & Litt, T. (eds) *The Climate of Past Interglacials*, Elsevier, Amsterdam, 239–254.

Laban, C. & van der Meer, J. J. M. 2004. Pleistocene glaciation in The Netherlands. *In:* Ehlers, J. & Gibbard, P. L. (eds) *Quaternary Glaciations – Extent and Chronology. Part I: Europe*. Elsevier, Amsterdam, 251–260.

Lang, A., Hatté, C., Rousseau, D. D., Antoine, P., Fontugne, M., Zöller, L. & Hambach, U. 2003. High-resolution chronologies for loess: comparing AMS $^{14}C$ and optical dating results. *Quaternary Science Reviews*, **22**, 953–959.

Lieberoth, I. 1963. Löss-Sedimentation und Bodebildung während des Pleistozäns in Sachsen. *Geologie*, **12**, 149–187.

Lindner, L., Gozhik, P., Marciniak, B., Marks, L. & Yelovicheva, Y. 2004. Main climatic changes in the Quaternary of Poland, Belarus and Ukraine. *Geological Quarterly,* **48**, 97–114.

Linke, G. & Hallik, R. 1993. Die pollenanalytischen Ergebnisse der Bohrungen Hamburg-Dockenhuden (qho 4), Wedel (qho 2) und Hamburg-Billbrook. *Geologisches Jahrbuch A,* **138,** 169–184.

Lippolt, H. J. 1983. Distribution of volcanic activity in space and time. *In:* Fuchs, K. *et al.* (eds) *Plateau Uplift - The Rhenish Shield - A Case History*. Springer, Heidelberg, 112–120.

Lister, G. 1988. A 15,000-year isotopic record from Lake Zürich of deglaciation and climatic change in Switzerland. *Quaternary Research*, **29**, 129–141.

Litt, T. 1994. Paläoökologie, *Paläobotanik und Stratigraphie des Jungquartärs im nordmitteleuropäischen Tiefland*. Cramer, Berlin, Dissertationes Botanicae, **227**.

Litt, T. 2004. Eifelmaare als Archive für die Vegetations- und Klimageschichte der letzten 15000 Jahre. *Berichte der Reinhold-Tüxen-Gesellschaft*, **16**, 87–95.

Litt, T. & Turner, C. 1993. Arbeitsergebnisse der Subkommission für Europäische Quartärstratigraphie: Die Saalesequenz in der Typusregion. *Eiszeitalter und Gegenwart*, **43**, 125–128.

Litt, T., Junge, F. & Böttger, T. 1996. Climate during the Eemian in north-central Europe – a critical review of the palaeobotanical and stable isotope data from central Germany. *Vegetation History and Archaeobotany*, **5**, 247–256.

Litt, T., Brauer, A., *et al.* 2001. Correlation and synchronisation of Lateglacial continental sequences in northern central Europe based on annually-laminated lacustrine sediments. *Quaternary Science Reviews*, **20**, 67–83.

Litt, T., Schmincke, H.-U. & Kromer, B. 2003. Environmental response to climate and volcanic events in central Europe during the Weichselian Lateglacial. *Quaternary Science Reviews,* **22**, 7–32.

Litt, T., Ellwanger, D., Villinger, E. & Wansa, S. 2005. Das Quartär in der Stratigraphischen Tabelle von Deutschland 2002. *Newsletters on Stratigraphy*, **41**, 385–399.

Locht, J. L., Antoine, P., *et al.* 2003. Le gisement paléolithique moyen et les séquences pléistocènes de Villier-Adam (Val d'Oise, France): Chronostratigraphie, environnement et implantations humaines. *Gallia Préhistoire*, **45**, 1–111.

Lorenz, V. 1973. On the formation of maars. *Bulletin Volcanologique*, **37**, 183–204.

Lozek, V. 1964. Quartärmollusken der Tschechoslowakei. *Rozpravy Ustredniho ustravu geologickeho*, **31**, 1–376.

Lozek, V. 1969. Paläontologische Charakteristik der Löß-Serien in Periglazialzone, Löß und Paläolithikum der Tschechoslowakei. *Akademie d. Wissenschaften, Geographie*, 43–60.

Maarleveld, G. C. 1960. Wind directions and cover sands in the Netherlands. *Biuletyn Peryglacjalny*, **8**, 49–58.

Mandier, P. 1983. Pluralité des glaciations dans la region Lyonnaise et la Moyenne Vallée du Rhône. *In: IGCP-Project 73/1/24 "Quaternary Glaciations in the Northern Hemisphere"*, vol. 9. Geological Survey, Prague, 184–204.

Marks, L. 2004. Pleistocene glacial limits in Poland. *In:* Ehlers, J. & Gibbard, P. L. (eds) *Quaternary Glaciations – Extent and Chronology. Part I: Europe*. Elsevier, Amsterdam, 295–300.

Mauz, B. 1998. The onset of the Quaternary: A review of new findings in the Pliocene-Pleistocene chronostratigraphy. *Quaternary Science Reviews*, **17**, 357–364.

Mechie, J., Prodehl, C. & Fuchs, K. 1983. The long-range seismic refraction experiment in the Rhenish Massif. *In:* Fuchs, K. *et al.* (eds) *Plateau Uplift – The Rhenish Shield – A Case History.* Springer, Heidelberg, 260–275.

Menke, B. 1968. Beiträge zur Biostratigraphie des Mittelpleistozäns in Norddeutschland (pollenanalytische Untersuchungen aus Westholstein). *Meyniana*, **18**, 35–42.

Menke, B. 1975. Vegetationsgeschichte und Florenstratigraphie Nordwestdeutschlands im Pliozän und Frühquartär — Mit einem Beitrag zur Biostratigraphie des Weichsel-Frühglazials. *Geologisches Jahrbuch A*, **26**, 3–151.

Menke, B. & Tynni, R. 1984. Das Eemglazial und das Weichselfrühglazial von Rederstall/Dithmarschen und ihre Bedeutung für die mitteleuropäische Jungpleistozän-Gliederung. *Geologisches Jahrbuch A*, **76**, 3–120.

Merkt, J. 1971. Zuverlässige Auszählungen von Jahresschichten in

Seesedimenten mit Hilfe von Gross-Dünnschliffen. *Archiv Hydrobiologie*, **69**, 145–154.

MERKT, J. 1991. *Hochauflösende Zeitreihen aus jahreszeitlich geschichteten Seesedimenten*. Archiv des Niedersächsischen Landesamtes für Bodenforschung (NLfB), Archiv No. 108658.

MERKT, J. & MÜLLER, H. 1999. Varve chronology of Lateglacial in Northwest Germany from lacustrine sediments of the Hämelsee/ Lower Saxony. *Quaternary International*, **61**, 41–59.

MERTES, H., & SCHMINCKE, H.-U. 1983. Age distribution of volcanoes in the West-Eifel. *Neues Jahrbuch Geologie Paläontologie Abhandlungen*, **166,** 260–283.

MEYER, K.-D. 1981. Arbeitsergebnisse der Subkommission für Europäische Quartärstratigraphie: Stratotypen des Elster- und Weichsel-Glazials. *Eiszeitalter und Gegenwart*, **31**, 203–209.

MEYER, W. 1986. *Geologie der Eifel*. Schweizerbart'sche Verlagsbuchhandlung, Stuttgart, 1–615.

MEYER, W. & STETS, J. 1981. Die Siegener Hauptaufschiebung im Laacher-See-Gebiet (Rheinisches Schiefergebirge). *Zeitschrift deutsche geologische Gesellschaft*, **132**, 43–53.

MEYER, W. & STETS, J. 2007. Quaternary uplift in the Eifel area. *In:* RITTER, J. R. R. & CHRISTENSEN, J. (eds) *Mantle Plumes – a Multidisciplinary Approach*. Springer, Heidelberg, 369–378.

MOJSKI, J. E. 1995. Pleistocene glacial events in Poland. *In:* EHLERS, J., KOZARSKI, S. & GIBBARD, P. L. (eds) *Glacial Deposits in North-East Europe*. Balkema, Rotterdam, 287–292.

MOREL, P., GUBLER, T., SCHLÜCHTER, C. & TRÜSSEL, M. 1997. Entdeckung eines jungpleistozänen Braunbären auf 1800 m ü. M. in einer Höhle der Obwaldner Voralpen, Melchsee-Frutt, Kerns, OW. *Naturforschende Gesellschaft Ob- und Nidwalden*, **1**, 116–125.

MORLOT, A. VON 1844. *Ueber die Gletscher der Vorwelt und ihre Bedeutung*. Rätzer, Bern.

MÖRS, TH., KOENIGSWALD, W. V. & HOCHT, F. V. D. 1998. Rodents (Mammalia) from the late Pliocene Reuver Clay of Hambach (Lower Rhine Embayment, Germany). *Mededelingen Nederlands Instituut voor Toegepaste Geowetenschappen, TNO*, **60**, 135–159.

MÜLLER, H. 1974*a*. Pollenanalytische Untersuchungen und Jahresschichtenzählungen an der holsteinzeitlichen Kieselgur von Munster-Breloh. *Geologisches Jahrbuch A*, **21**, 107–140.

MÜLLER, H. 1974*b*. Pollenanalytische Untersuchungen und Jahresschichtenzählungen an der eemzeitlichen Kieselgur von Bispingen/Luhe. *Geologisches Jahrbuch A*, **21**, 149–169.

MÜLLER, H. 1986. Altquartäre Sedimente im Deckgebirge des Salzstockes Gorleben. *Zeitschrift der Deutschen Geologischen Gesellschaft*, **137**, 85–95.

MÜLLER, H. 1992. Climatic changes during and at the end of the interglacials of the Cromerian Complex. *In:* KUKLA, G. J. & WENT, E. (eds) *Start of a Glacial*. NATO ASI Series I (3), 51–69.

MÜLLER, U., RÜHBERG, N. & KRIENKE, H.-D. 1995. The Pleistocene sequence in Mecklenburg-Vorpommern. *In:* EHLERS, J., KOZARSKI, S. & GIBBARD, P. L. (eds) *Glacial Deposits in North-East Europe*. Balkema, Rotterdam, 501–514.

MURTON, J. B., WALLER, R. I., HART, J. K., WHITEMAN, C. A., POLLARD, W. H. & CLARK, I. D. 2004. Stratigraphy and glaciotectonic structures of permafrost deformed beneath the northwest margin of the Laurentide Ice Sheet, Tuktoyaktuk Coastlands, Canada. *Journal of Glaciology*, **49**, 399–412.

MURTON, J. B., FRECHEN, M. & MADDY, D. 2007. Luminescence dating of the last advance of the Laurentide Ice Sheet across the Beaufort Sea coast, NW Canada, during Marine Isotope Stage 2. *Canadian Journal of Earth Sciences*, **44**, 857–869.

NEGENDANK, J. F. W. & ZOLITSCHKA, B. 1993. Maars and maar lakes of the Westeifel volcanic field. *In:* NEGENDANK, J. F. W. & ZOLITSCHKA, B. (eds) *Paleolimnology of European Maar Lakes*. Lecture Notes in Earth Sciences, Springer-Verlag, Berlin, 61–80.

PAAS, W. 1961. Rezente und fossile Böden auf niederrheinischen Terrassen und deren Deckschichten. *Eiszeitalter und Gegenwart*, **12**, 165–230.

PARK, C. & SCHMINCKE, H.-U. 1997. Lake formation and catastrophic dam burst during the late Pleistocene Laacher See eruption (Germany). *Naturwissenschaften*, **84**, 521–525.

PARTRIDGE, T. C. 1997. Reassessment of the position of the Plio-Pleistocene boundary: Is there a case for lowering it to the Gauss-Matuyama palaeomagnetic reversal? *Quaternary International*, **40**, 5–10.

PENCK, A. 1879. Die Geschiebeformation Norddeutschlands. *Zeitschrift der Deutschen Geologischen Gesellschaft*, **31**, 117–203.

PENCK, A. & BRÜCKNER, E. 1909. *Die Alpen im Eiszeitalter*. Tauchnitz, Leipzig.

PFIFFNER, O. A., HEITZMANN, P., LEHNER, P., FREI, W., PUGIN, A. & FELBER, M. 1997. Dynamic Alps. Incision and backfilling of alpine valleys: Pliocene, Pleistocene and Holocene processes. *In:* PFIFFNER, O. A., LEHNER, P., HEITZMANN, P., MÜLLER, S. & STECK, A (eds) *Deep Structure of the Swiss Alps*. Birkhäuser, Berlin, 265–288.

PILLANS, B. 2003. Subdividing the Pleistocene using the Matuyama-Brunhes boundary (MBB): an Australasian perspective. *Quaternary Science Reviews*, **22**, 1569–1577.

PILLANS, B. 2004. Proposal to redefine the Quaternary. *Episodes*, **27**, 127.

POSER, H. (ed.) 1953–54. Studien über die Periglazialerscheinungen in Mitteleuropa. *Göttinger Geographische Abhandlungen*, **14–17**.

PREUSSER, F. 1999. Luminescence dating of fluvial sediments and overbank deposits from Gossau, Switzerland: fine grain dating. *Quaternary Geochronology (Quaternary Science Reviews)*, **18,** 217–222.

PREUSSER, F. & SCHLÜCHTER, C. 2004. Dates from an important early Late Pleistocene ice advance in the Aare valley, Switzerland. *Eclogae geologicae Helvetiae*, **97**, 245–253.

PREUSSER, F., MÜLLER, B. U. & SCHLÜCHTER, C. 2001. Luminescence dating of sediments from the Luthern Valley, Central Switzerland, and implications for the chronology of the last glacial cycle. *Quaternary Research*, **55**, 215–222.

PREUSSER, F., GEYH, M. A. & SCHLÜCHTER, C. 2003. Timing of Late Pleistocene climate change in lowland Switzerland. *Quaternary Science Reviews*, **22**, 1435–1445.

PREUSSER, F., DRESCHER-SCHNEIDER, R., FIEBGIG, M. & SCHLÜCHTER, C. 2005. Re-interpretation of the Meikirch pollen record, Swiss Alpine Foreland, and implications for Middle Pleistocene chronostratigraphy. *Journal of Quaternary Science*, **20,** 607–620.

PRODEHL, C., MÜLLER, ST., GLAHN, A., GUTSCHER, M., HAAK, V. 1992. Lithospheric cross-section of the European Cenozoic rift system. *In:* ZIEGLER, P. A. (ed.) Geodynamics of rifting, Vol I. Case history studies on rifts: Europe and Asia. *Tectonophysics*, **208**, 113–138.

RICHMOND, G. M. 1996. The INQUA-approved provisional Lower-Middle Pleistocene boundary. *In:* TURNER, C. (ed) *The Early Middle Pleistocene in Europe*. Balkema, Rotterdam, 319–326.

RITTER, J. R. R. & CHRISTENSEN, U. R. (eds) 2007. *Mantle Plumes – a Multidisciplinary Approach*. Springer, Heidelberg.

ROUSSEAU, D. D., KUKLA, G., ZÖLLER, L. & HRADILOVA, J. 1998. Early Weichselian dust storm layer at Achenheim in Alsace, France. *Boreas*, **27**, 200–208.

ROWE, P. J., RICHARDS, D. A., ATKINSON, T. C., BOTTRELL, S. H. & CLIFF, R. A. 1997. Geochemistry and radiometric dating of a Middle Pleistocene peat. *Geochimica et Cosmichimica Acta*, **61**, 4201–4211.

RÓŻYCKI, S. Z. 1965. Die stratigraphische Stellung des Warthe-Stadiums in Polen. *Eiszeitalter und Gegenwart*, **16**, 189–201.

RÜHBERG, N. 1987. Die Grundmoräne des jüngsten Weichsel-Vorstoßes im Gebiet der DDR. *Zeitschrift für Geologische Wissenschaften*, **15**, 759–767.

RÜTIMEYER, L. 1869. *Über Tal- und Seebildung. Beiträge zum Verständnis der Oberfläche der Schweiz*. Schweighausersche Verlagsbuchhandlung, Basel.

RZECHOWSKI, J. 1996. The Ferdynandovian Interglacial and ist stratigraphical position in the Middle Pleistocene of Europe. *In:* TURNER, C. (ed.) *The Early Middle Pleistocene in Europe*. Balkema, Rotterdam, 279–293.

SALVADOR, A. (ed.) 1994. *International Stratigraphic Guide: A Guide to Stratigraphic Classification, Terminology, and Procedure*, 2nd edn. IUGS, Trondheim.

SARNTHEIN, M., STREMME, H. E. & MANGINI, A. 1986. The Holsteinian Interglaciation: time-stratigraphic position and correlation to stable isotope stratigraphy of deep-sea sediments. *Quaternary Research*, **26**, 283–298.

SCHABER, K. & SIROCKO, F. 2005. Lithologie und Stratigraphie der spätpleistozänen Trockenmaare der Eifel. *Mainzer Geowissenschaftliche Mitteilungen*, **33**, 295–340.

SCHIRMER, W. 1990. Terrassentreppe am Ostrand von Neuwied. *In:* SCHIRMER, W. (ed.) *Rheingeschichte zwischen Mosel und Maas*. Deuqua-Führer, **1**, 99–104.

SCHIRMER, W. 1995. Pellenz- und Meile-Eruption des Laacher See Vulkanismus. *Erlanger Beiträge Petrologie Mineralogie*, **5**, 87–89.

SCHLÜCHTER, C. 1988. Neue geologische Beobachtungen bei der Mammutfundstelle in Niederweningen (Kt. Zürich). *Vierteljahrsschrift der Naturforschenden Gesellschaft Zürich*, **133**(2), 99–108.

SCHLÜCHTER, C. 1989. Thalgut. Ein umfassendes eiszeitstratigraphisches Referenzprofil im nördlichen Alpenvorland. *Eclogae geologicae Helvetiae*, **82**(1), 277–284.

SCHLÜCHTER, C. & RÖTHLISBERGER, C. 1995. *100,000 Jahre Gletschergeschichte – Gletscher im ständigen Wandel*. vdf-Hochschulverlag AG, Zürich, 47–63.

SCHLÜCHTER, C., MAISCH, M., SUTER, J., FITZE, P., KELLER, W. A., BURGA, C. A. & WYNISTORF, E. 1987. Das Schieferkohlenprofil von Gossau (Kt. Zürich) und seine stratigraphische Stellung innerhalb der letzten Eiszeit. *Vierteljahrsschrift der Naturforschenden Gesellschaft Zürich*, **132**(3),135–174.

SCHMINCKE, H.-U. 1977. Phreatomagmatische Phasen in quartären Vulkanen der Osteifel. *Geologisches Jahrbuch*, **39**, 3–45

SCHMINCKE, H.-U. 1982. Vulkane und ihre Wurzeln. *Rheinisch-Westfälische Akademie der Wissenschaften, Westdeutscher Verlag (Opladen), Vorträge*, **315**, 35–78.

SCHMINCKE, H.-U. 2000. *Vulkanismus*, 2nd edn. Wissenschaftliche Buchgesellschaft Darmstadt.

SCHMINCKE, H.-U. 2004. *Volcanism*. Springer, Heidelberg.

SCHMINCKE, H.-U. 2007*a*. *Die quartären Vulkanfelder der Eifel*. Görres Verlag, Koblenz.

SCHMINCKE, H.-U. 2007*b*. The Quaternary volcanic fields of the East and West Eifel (Germany). *In:* RITTER, R. & CHRISTENSEN, U. (eds) *Mantle Plumes – a Multidisciplinary Approach*. Springer, Heidelberg, 241–322.

SCHMINCKE, H.-U., LORENZ, V. & SECK, H. A. 1983. The Quaternary Eifel volcanic fields. *In:* FUCHS, K. *et al.* (eds) *Plateau Uplift – The Rhenish Shield – A Case History*. Springer, Heidelberg, 139–151.

SCHMINCKE, H.-U., BOGAARD, P. V. D. & FREUNDT, A. 1990. *Quaternary Eifel Volcanism*. Excursion guide, Workshop in explosive volcanism. IAVCEI International Volcanology Congress, Mainz, Germany. Pluto Press, Witten.

SCHMINCKE, H.-U., PARK, C. & HARMS, E. 1999. Evolution and environmental impacts of the eruption of Laacher See Volcano (Germany) 12,900 a BP. *Quaternary International*, **61**, 61–72.

SCHMITT, A. K. 2006. Laacher See revisited: High-spatial-resolution zircon dating indicates rapid formation of a zoned magma chamber. *Geology*, **34**, 597–600.

SCHNEIDER, H. & THIELE, S. 1965. *Geohydrologie des Erftgebietes*. Ministerium für Ernährung, Landwirtschaft und Forsten Land Nordrhein-Westfalen, Düsseldorf.

SCHNEPP, E. & HRADETZKY, H. 1994 Combined paleointensity and 40Ar/39Ar age spectrum data from volcanic rocks of the East Eifel field (Germany): Evidence for an early Brunhes geomagnetic excursion. *Journal of Geophysical Research*, **99**, 9061–9076.

SCHNÜTGEN, A. & BRUNNACKER, K. 1976. Zur Kieselschiefer –Führung in Schottern am Niederrhein. *Decheniana*, **130**, 293–298.

SCHNÜTGEN A., BOENIGK, W., BRUNNACKER, M., KOCI, A. & BRUNNACKER, K. 1975. Der Übergang von der Hauptterrasenfolge zur Mittelterrasenfolge am Niederrhein. *Decheniana*, **128**, 67–86.

SCHREINER, A. 1989. Zur Stratigraphie der Risseiszeit im östlichen Rheingletschergebiet (Baden-Württemberg). *Jahreshefte des Geologischen Landesamtes Baden-Württemberg*, **31**, 183–196.

SCHUMACHER, R. & SCHMINCKE, H.-U. 1991. Structure of accretionary lapilli and cluster sedimentation of fine-grained volcanic ashes. *Bulletin of Volcanology*, **53**, 612–634.

SCHWEITZER, H.-J. 1958. Entstehung und Flora des Trasses im nördlichen Laacher See-Gebiet. *Eiszeitalter und Gegenwart*, **9**, 28–48.

SEIJRUP, H. P., AARSETH, I., *et al.* 1987. Quaternary stratigraphy of the Fladen area, central North Sea: a multidisciplinary study. *Journal of Quaternary Science*, **2**, 35–58.

SEPPÄLÄ, M. 1995. Deflation and redeposition of sand dunes in Finnish Lappland. *Quaternary Science Reviews*, **14**, 799–809.

SERNANDER, R. 1894. *Studier öfver den Gotländska vegetationens utvecklingshistoria*. Dissertation, Uppsala.

SIROCKO, F., SEELOS, K., *et al.* 2005. A late Eemian aridity pulse in central Europe during the last glacial inception. *Nature*, **436**, 833–836.

STEININGER, F. F. 2002. Das Känozoische Ärathem – Versuch einer Revision der chronostratigraphischen Gliederung. *Courier Forschungs-Institut Senckenberg*, **237**, 39–45.

STEPHAN, H.-J. 1995. Schleswig-Holstein. *In:* BENDA, L. (ed.) *Das Quartär Deutschlands*. Verlag, Berlin, 1–13.

STEPHAN, H.-J. & MENKE, B. 1993. Das Pleistozän in Schleswig-Holstein. *Geologisches Landesamt Schleswig-Holstein*, **3**, 19–62.

STREET, M., BAALES, M. & WENINGER, B. 1994. Absolute Chronologie des späten Paläolithikums und des Frühmesolithikums im nördlichen Rheinland. *Archäologisches Korrespondenzblatt*, **24**, 1–28.

SUC, J.-P., BERTINI, A., LEROY, S. A. G. & SUBALLYOVA, D. 1997. Towards the lowering of the Pliocene/Pleistocene boundary to the Gauss-Matuyama Reversal. *Quaternary International*, **40**, 37–42.

TEBBENS, L. A. 1999. Late Quaternary evolution of the Meuse fluvial system and its sediment composition. Dissertation, Universal Press, Veenendaal.

THIEME, H. 1997. Lower Paleolithic hunting spears from Germany. *Nature*, **385**, 807–810.

THIEME, H., MANIA, D., URBAN, B. & KOLFSCHOTEN, TH. VAN 1995. Brown coal opencast mining E of Schöningen. *In:* SCHIRMER, W. (ed.) *Quaternary Field Trips in Central Europe*, Vol. 1. Pfeil Verlag, München, 593–594.

THOSTE, V. 1974. *Die Niederterrassen des Rheins vom Neuwieder Becken bis in die Niederrheinische Bucht*. Dissertation, Universität zu Köln.

TORELL, O. 1875. Schliff-Flächen und Schrammen auf der Oberfläche des Muschelkalkes von Rüdersdorf. *Zeitschrift der Deutschen Geologischen Gesellschaft*, **27**, 961.

TURNER, C. 1996. A brief survey of the early Middle Pleistocene in Europe. *In:* TURNER, C. (ed) *The Early Middle Pleistocene in Europe*. Balkema, Rotterdam, 295–317.

URBAN, B. 1978*a*. Vegetationsgeschichtliche Untersuchungen zur Gliederung des Altquartärs der Niederrheinischen Bucht. *Sonderveröffentlichung Geologisches Institut Universität Köln*, **34**, 1–165.

URBAN, B. 1978*b*. The Interglacial of Frechen I/Rheinland – A section of the Tiglian A-type. *Geologie en Mijnbouw*, **57**(3), 401–406.

URBAN, B. 1979. Bio- und Magnetostratigraphie Plio/Pleistozäner Ablagerungen in der Niederrheinischen Bucht. *Acta Geologica Academiae Scientarum Hungaricae*, **22**, 153–160.

URBAN, B. 1980*a*. Zur Stratigraphie des Frimmersdorf-Interglazials und Krefeld-Interglazials in der Niederrheinischen Bucht. *Decheniana*, **133**, 224–228.

URBAN, B. 1980*b*. Paläoökologische Untersuchungen zum Krefeld-Interglazial am Niederrhein. *Eiszeitalter und Gegenwart*, **30**, 73–88.

URBAN, B. 1983. Biostratigraphic correlation of the Kärlich Interglacial, Northwestern Germany. *Boreas*, **12**, 83–90.

URBAN, B. 1995. Palynological evidence of younger Middle Pleistocene Interglacials (Holsteinian, Reinsdorf and Schöningen) in the Schöningen open cast lignite mine (eastern Lower Saxony, Germany). *Mededelingen Rijks Geologische Dienst*, **52**, 175–186.

URBAN, B. 2007. Interglacial pollen records from Schöningen, north Germany. *In:* SIROCKO, F., CLAUSSEN, M., SANCHEZ-GONI, M. F. & LITT, T. (eds) *The Climate of Past Interglacials*. Developments in Quaternary Science **7**, Elsevier, Amsterdam, 417–444.

VANDENBERGHE, J. 1995. The Saalian Complex and the first traces of human activity in the Netherlands in a stratigraphic and ecologic context. *Mededelingen Rijks Geologische Dienst*, **52**, 187–194.

VAN DER VLERK, I. M. & FLORSCHÜTZ, F. 1950. *Nederland in het Ijstijdvak*. De Haan, Utrecht.

VAN HUSEN, D. 1987. Die Entwicklung des Traungletschers während des Würm-Glazials. *In:* VAN HUSEN, D. (ed.) *Das Gebiet des Traungletschers, O. Ö. Eine Typregion des Würm-Glazials*. Mitteilungen der Kommission für Quartärforschung der Österreichischen Akademie der Wissenschaften, **7**, 19–35.

VAN HUSEN, D. 2004. Quaternary glaciations in Austria. *In:* EHLERS, J. & GIBBARD, P. L. (eds) *Quaternary Glaciations - Extent and Chronology*. Elsevier, Amsterdam, 1–13.

VAN LEEUWEN, R. J. W., BEETS, D. J., *et al.* 2000. Stratigraphy and integrated facies analysis of the Saalian and Eemian sediments in the Amsterdam Terminal borehol, The Netherlands. *Netherlands Journal of Geoscience/Geologie en Mijnbouw*, **79**, 161–198.

VIERECK, L. 1984. Geologische und petrologische Entwicklung des pleistozänen Vulkankomplexes Rieden, Ost-Eifel. *Bochumer geologisch geotechnische Arbeiten*, **17**, 1–337.

VLIET-LANOË, B. VAN 1989. Dynamics and extent of the Weichselian Permafrost in Western Europe (Stages 5e to 1). *Quaternary International*, **3–4**, 109–114.

VLIET-LANOË, B. VAN & HALLÉGOUËT, B. 2001. European permafrost at the LGM and its maximal extent. *In:* PAEPE, R. & MELNIKOV, V. (eds) *Permafrost Response on Economic Development, Environmental Security and Natural Resources*. Kluwer, Dordrecht, 105–213.

WALDMANN, G. 1996. Vulkanfossilien im Laacher Bims. *Documenta naturae*, **108**, 1–329.

WEBER, T. & LITT, T. 1991. Der Waldelefantenfund von Gröbern, Kr. Gräfenhainichen. Jagdbefund oder Dekrophagie? *Archäologisches Korrespondenzblatt*, **21**, 17–32.

WEGMÜLLER, S. 1992. *Vegetationsgeschichtliche und stratigraphische Untersuchungen an Schieferkohlen des nördlichen Alpenvorlandes.* Denkschriften der Schweizerischen Akademie der Naturwissenschaften, **112**.

WELTEN, M. 1976. Das jüngere Quartär im nördlichen Alpenvorland der Schweiz auf Grund pollenanalytischer Untersuchungen. *In:* FRENZEL, B. (ed.) *Führer zur Exkursionstagung des IGCP-Projektes 73/1/24 "Quaternary Glaciations in the Northern Hemisphere"*, **5**(13). Deutsche Forschungsgemeinschaft, Stuttgart.

WELTEN, M. 1982. *Pollenanalytische Untersuchungen im Jüngeren Quartär des nördlichen Alpenvorlandes der Schweiz.* Beiträge zur Geologischen Karte der Schweiz, N. F, **156**.

WELTEN, M. 1988. *Neue pollenanalytische Ergebnisse über das Jüngere Quartär des nördlichen Alpenvorlandes der Schweiz (Mittel- und Jungpleistozän).* Beiträge zur Geologischen Karte der Schweiz, N.F., **162**.

WILSON, M. & DOWNES, H. 2006. Tertiary-Quaternary intra-plate magmatism in Europe and its relationship to mantle dynamics. *In:* STEPHENSON, R. & GEE, D. (eds) *European Lithosphere Dynamics*. Geological Society, London, Memoirs **32**, 147–166.

WOHLFARTH (MEYER), B. 1986. Das jüngere Quartär im westschweizer Seeland. *Revue de Paléobiologie*, **5**(2), 337–374.

WOLDSTEDT, P. 1925. Die großen Endmoränenzüge Norddeutschlands. *Zeitschrift der Deutschen Geologischen Gesellschaft*, **77**, 172–184.

WOLDSTEDT, P. 1954. Saaleeiszeit, Warthestadium und Weichseleiszeit in Norddeutschland. *Eiszeitalter und Gegenwart*, **4/5**, 34–48.

WOLDSTEDT, P. 1955. *Norddeutschland und angrenzende Gebiete im Eiszeitalter*, 2nd edn. Koehler, Stuttgart.

WÖRNER, G. & SCHMINCKE, H.-U. 1984. Mineralogical and chemical zonation of the Laacher See tephra sequence. *Journal of Petrology*, **25**, 805–835.

WÖRNER, G., SCHMINCKE, H.-U. & SCHREYER, W. 1982. Crustal xenoliths from the Quaternary Wehr volcano (East Eifel). *Neues Jahrbuch Mineralogie Abhandlungen*, **144**, 29–55.

WÖRNER, G., VIERECK, L. G., PLAUMANN, S., PUCHER, R., BOGAARD, P. VD, & SCHMINCKE H.-U. 1988. The Quaternary Wehr Volcano: A multiphase evolved eruption center in the East Eifel Volcanic field (FRG). *Neues Jahrbuch Mineralogie Abhandlungen*, **159**, 73–99.

WYSSLING, G. 2002. Die Ur-Sihl floss einst ins Reusstal. *Vereinigung Pro Sihltal, Jahresheft*, **52**, 1–14.

ZAGWIJN, W. H. 1960. Aspects of the Pliocene and Early Pleistocene Vegetation in the Netherlands. *Mededelingen van de Geologische Stichting, Serie C-III-1*, **5**, 1–78.

ZAGWIJN, W. H. 1961. Vegetation, climate and radiocarbon datings in the Late Pleistocene of the Netherlands, Part I: Eemian and Early Weichselian. *Mededelingen van de Geologische Stichting Nieuwe Series*, **14**, 15–45.

ZAGWIJN, W. H. 1963. Pollen-analytic investigations in the Tiglian of the Netherlands. *Mededelingen van de Geologische Stichting Nieuwe Series*, **16**, 49–71.

ZAGWIJN, W. H. 1974. The Pliocene-Pleistocene boundary in western and southern Europe. *Boreas*, **3**, 75–97.

ZAGWIJN, W. H. 1985. An outline of the Quaternary stratigraphy of the Netherlands. *Geologie en Mijnbouw*, **64**, 17–24.

ZAGWIJN, W. H. 1989. The Netherlands during the Tertiary and the Quaternary: A case history of Costal Lowland evolution. *Geologie en Mijnbouw*, **68**, 107–120.

ZAGWIJN, W. H. 1992. The beginning of the ice age in Europe and its major subdivisions. *Quaternary Science Reviews*, **11**, 583–591.

ZAGWIJN, W. H. 1996. The Cromerian Complex Stage of the Netherlands and correlation with other areas in Europe. *In:* TURNER. C. (ed.) *The Early Middle Pleistocene in Europe*. Balkema, Rotterdam, 145–172.

ZAGWIJN, W. H. 1998. Borders and boundaries: a century of stratigraphical research in the Tiglium (Tegelen) – Reuver area of Limburg (The Netherlands). *Mededelingen Nederlands Instituut voor Toegepaste Geowetenschappen TNO*, **60**, 19–34.

ZANDSTRA, J. G. 1993. Nördliche kristalline Leitgeschiebe und Kiese in der Westfälischen Bucht und angrenzenden Gebieten. *In:* SKUPIN, K., SPEEZEN, E. & ZANDSTRA, J. G. (eds) *Die Eiszeit in Nordwestdeutschland*, Verlag, Krefeld, 43–106.

ZEUNER, F. 1959. *The Pleistocene Period*. Royal Society, London.

ZIEGLER, P. A. 1990. *Geological Atlas of Western and Central Europe*, 2nd edn. Shell Internationale Petroleum Mij B V, Geological Society, London.

ZOLITSCHKA, B., NEGENDANK, J. F. W. & LOTTERMOSER, B. G. 1995. Sedimentological proof and dating of the early Holocene volcanic eruption of Ulmener Maar (Vulkaneifel, Germany). *Geologische Rundschau*, **84**, 213–219.

ZÖLLER, L. & LÖSCHER, M. 1999. The last glacial–interglacial cycle in the loess section at Nussloch and underlying upper Tertiary loams. *In:* WEIDENFELLER, M. & ZÖLLER, L. (eds) *Loess in the Middle and Upper Rhine area*. Field Guide Loessfest '99, Bonn, 37–50.

# 21 Fossil fuels, ore and industrial minerals

HARALD G. DILL, REINHARD F. SACHSENHOFER (co-ordinators), PAVOL GRECULA, TIBOR SASVÁRI, LADISLAV A. PALINKAŠ, SIBILA BOROJEVIĆ-ŠOŠTARIĆ, SABINA STRMIĆ-PALINKAŠ, WALTER PROCHASKA, GIORGIO GARUTI, FEDERICA ZACCARINI, DIDIER ARBOUILLE & HANS-MARTIN SCHULZ

The mining of metallic and non-metallic commodities in Central Europe has a history of more than 2000 years. Today mainly non-metallic commodities, fossil fuels and construction raw materials play a vital role for the people living in Central Europe. Construction raw materials, albeit the most significant raw material, are not considered further here; for details refer to thematic maps issued by local geological surveys and comprehensive studies such as the textbook by Prentice (1990).

Even if many deposits in Central Europe, especially metallic deposits, are no longer extensive by world standards, the huge number and variety of deposits in Central Europe is unique and allows the student of metallogenesis to reconstruct the geological history of Central Europe from the Late Precambrian to the Recent in a way best described as 'minerostratigraphy'.

The term 'deposit' is used in this review for sites which were either mined in the twentieth century or are still being operated. A few sites that underwent exploration or trial mining have also been included in order to clarify certain concentration processes. They are mentioned explicitly in the text to avoid confusion with real deposits. Tonnage and grade are reported in the text only for the most important deposits. Production data for the year 2005 are listed in Table 21.1 for the countries under consideration. Reserves and production data of hydrocarbons in Central European basins are given in Table 21.2.

In the present study, Central Europe covers the Variscan core zones in the extra-Alpine part of Central Europe stretching from eastern France (Massif Central) into Poland where the contact between the Variscan Orogen and the Baltic Shield is concealed by a thick pile of platform sediments. In a north–south direction, Central Europe stretches from central Denmark to the southern boundary of the Po Plain in Italy, making the entire Variscan Foreland Basin, the Alpine Mountain Range, the Western Carpathians and the North Dinarides part of the study area.

An outline of the geological and geographical settings is shown in Figure 21.1. The precise geographical position of mineral sites, wells of special interest, hydrocarbon provinces, oil shale deposits and coal fields may be deduced from Tables 21.3 to 21.11 and the map 'Mineral and energy resources of Central Europe', at a scale 1:2 500 000 (see CD inside back cover).

Many deposits were mined for different commodities during different time periods. In the text the various types of mineralization of each deposit are described to provide a complete picture of the concentration process through time. In the map (see CD inside back cover), however, each deposit is attributed to that group of commodities for which it was operated for the longest time or for which it is currently mined.

The history of the accumulation of ores, industrial minerals and fossil fuels in Central Europe can be subdivided into two principal phases: the first spans the time period from the Late Proterozoic to the Late Palaeozoic, and the second the epoch from the Late Palaeozoic to the Cenozoic. The first phase is considered as the Variscan cycle, although it includes some deposits of older orogenies, the second is representative of the Alpine cycle. Both cycles overlap slightly. The Variscan metallogenetic cycle fades out with collision-related deposits and the collapse of the Variscan craton during the Late Palaeozoic, while the Alpine cycle commences with coeval intracontinental rift-related deposits. Those Late Palaeozoic deposits with a great affinity to compressional tectonics are grouped under the heading of the Variscan cycle, whereas those largely related to extensional regimes belong to the Alpine cycle.

There are marked structural and geomorphological differences between the Alpine mountain belt in the southern part of Central Europe and its extra-Alpine northern part. In terms of metallogenesis these differences are minor (see also Froitzheim *et al.* 2008; Reicherter *et al.* 2008). Indeed, deposits of Variscan age form an integral part of the metallogenic evolution of the Alpine belt. Furthermore, deposits of Alpine age are found also in the Variscan basement of the extra-Alpine part of Central Europe (Petrascheck 1963; Bernard *et al.* 1976; Baumann 1979; Pouba & Ilavský 1986; Walther 1982; Jaffé 1986; Dill 1989; Walther & Dill 1995).

Metallogenesis in Central Europe has been studied by many researchers, particularly for the great variety of epigenetic deposits, which made the area a textbook example of vein-type ore mineralization (see Schneiderhöhn 1962, and references therein). In the early 1970s, a tremendous change in the conception of ore formation occurred. Many deposits, notably in the Alpine region, that were formerly interpreted as epigenetic, were re-interpreted as strata-bound and time-bound (Tufar 1972; Maucher 1974).

The classification of mineral and energy resources may be performed in different ways. The traditional classification scheme is based on mineral commodities, metal groups or mineral associations. This approach is suitable for stand-alone mineral resource maps, for papers satisfying the special demands of

**Table 21.1** *Production figures of Central European countries for 2005 (Weber & Zsak 2007). Last column shows the share of the world production. Note that only part of the French, Italian and Serbian and Montenegrinian production is from the area under consideration. All numbers are in metric tons, except where indicated.*

| | Austria | Belgium | Bosnia-Herzegovina | Croatia | Czech Republic | Denmark | France | Germany | Hungary | Italy | Netherlands | Poland | Serbia and Montenegro | Slovakia | Slovenia | % |
|---|---|---|---|---|---|---|---|---|---|---|---|---|---|---|---|---|
| Industrial Minerals | | | | | | | | | | | | | | | | |
| Asbestos | | | 500 | | | | | | | | | | 620 | | | 0.0 |
| Barite | | 30 000 | 2 100 | | | | 82 000 | 88 591 | | 15 800 | | 25 000 | | 4 200 | | 3.2 |
| Bentonite | | | 18 000 | 1 472 | 186 000 | | | 352 374 | 4 900 | 500 000 | | 2 200 | | 120 000 | 48 | 7.7 |
| Diatomite | | | | | 38 000 | (Moler) 231000m$^3$ | 75 000 | | | | | | | 910 | | 8.3 |
| Feldspar | | | | | 472 000 | | 650 000 | 3 309 134 | 33 000 | 2 500 000 | | 300 000 | 3 000 | | | 49.7 |
| Fluorite | | | | | | | 110 000 | 35 364 | | 66 000 | | | | | | 4.1 |
| Graphite | | | | | 3 000 | | | 2 638 | | | | | | | | 0.8 |
| Kaolin | 55 508 | 460 | 3 800 | | 854 040 | | 370 000 | 3 768 000 | 400 | | | 380 000 | 50 000 | 27 730 | | 20.6 |
| Magnesite | 693 754 | | 1 900 | | | | | | | | | 37 000 | 60 000 | 1 555 000 | | 17.2 |
| Perlite | | | | | | | | | 69 900 | | | | | 99 900 | | 7.3 |
| Sulphur (all types) | 8 458 | | | | | | 802 345 | 1 054 800 | | 650 000 | | 950 000 | 77 000 | | | 7.9 |
| Talc | 166 569 | | | | | | 330 000 | 5 000 | 650 | 180 000 | | | | 200 | | 8.6 |
| Metallic Ores | | | | | | | | | | | | | | | | |
| Copper | | | | | | | | | | | | 531 000 | 20 000 | 65 | | 3.8 |
| Lead | | | 1 000 | | | | | | | 3 600 | | 74 000 | 3 300 | | | 2.4 |
| Zinc | | | 400 | | | | | | | 9 000 | | 135 600 | 6 500 | | | 1.6 |
| Iron | 665 344 | | 120 000 | | | | | 37 796 | | | | | 70 000 | 258 500 | | 0.2 |
| Manganese | | | 500 | | | | | | 13 700 | 920 | | | | | | 0.1 |
| Tungsten | 2 365 | | | | | | | | | | | | | | | 4.2 |
| Gold (kg) | | | | | | | 5 200 | | | 680 | | 420 | 700 | 115 | | 0.3 |
| Silver (kg) | | | | | | | 1200 | | | 34 500 | | 1 262 400 | 1 000 | 60 | | 6.4 |
| Cadmium | | | | | | | 160 | | | 250 | | 130 | | | | 4.1 |
| Gallium | | | | | | | | | 6 | | | | | | | 18.2 |
| Bauxite | | | 460 000 | 500 | | | 175 000 | | 304 000 | | | | 210 000 | | | 0.8 |
| Uranium | | | | | 482 | | 18 | 74 | | | | | | | | 1.1 |
| Evaporites | | | | | | | | | | | | | | | | |
| Potash ($K_2O$) | | | | | | | 68 000 | 3 664 000 | | | | | | | | 12.6 |
| Salt (all types) | 1 024 090 | 200 000* | 86 000 | 17 100 | | 610 000 | 4 900 000 | 18 731 000 | | 3 600 000 | 6 155 651 | 1 500 000 | 10 500 | 105 100 | 4 200 | 16.4 |
| Gypsum. Anhydrite | 1 017 194 | 300 000* | 80 000 | 207 918 | 25 000 | | 3 500 000 | 1 644 000 | 35 000 | 1 200 000 | | 1 300 000 | | 107 500 | | 9.0 |
| Fossil Fuels | | | | | | | | | | | | | | | | |
| Hard Coal | | | 3 400 000 | 700 000 | 13 250 000 | | 780 000 | 28 018 000 | 240 000 | 90 000 | | 97 703 000 | 80 000 | | | 2.9 |
| Lignite | 6 168 | | 4 800 000 | 100 000 | 49 125 000 | | 180 000 | 177 907 000 | 9 602 000 | 200 000 | | 61 636 445 | 38 700 000 | 2 513 000 | 4 539 556 | 37.6 |
| Natural Gas (mio m$^3$) | 1 654 | | | 2 432 | 356 | 9 400 | 1 100 | 19 762 | 3 159 | 12 000 | 73 116 | 6 100 | 680 | 151 | 44 | 4.9 |
| Oil | 854 775 | | 120 000 | 745 589 | 306 000 | 18 719 900 | 1 200 000 | 3 572 462 | 948 000 | 6 100 000 | 2 137 440 | 800 000 | 820 000 | 33 150 | 470 | 0.9 |
| Oil Shale | | | | | | | 12 200 | 292 385 | | 24 000 | | | | | | 2.5 |

* Data from Switzerland

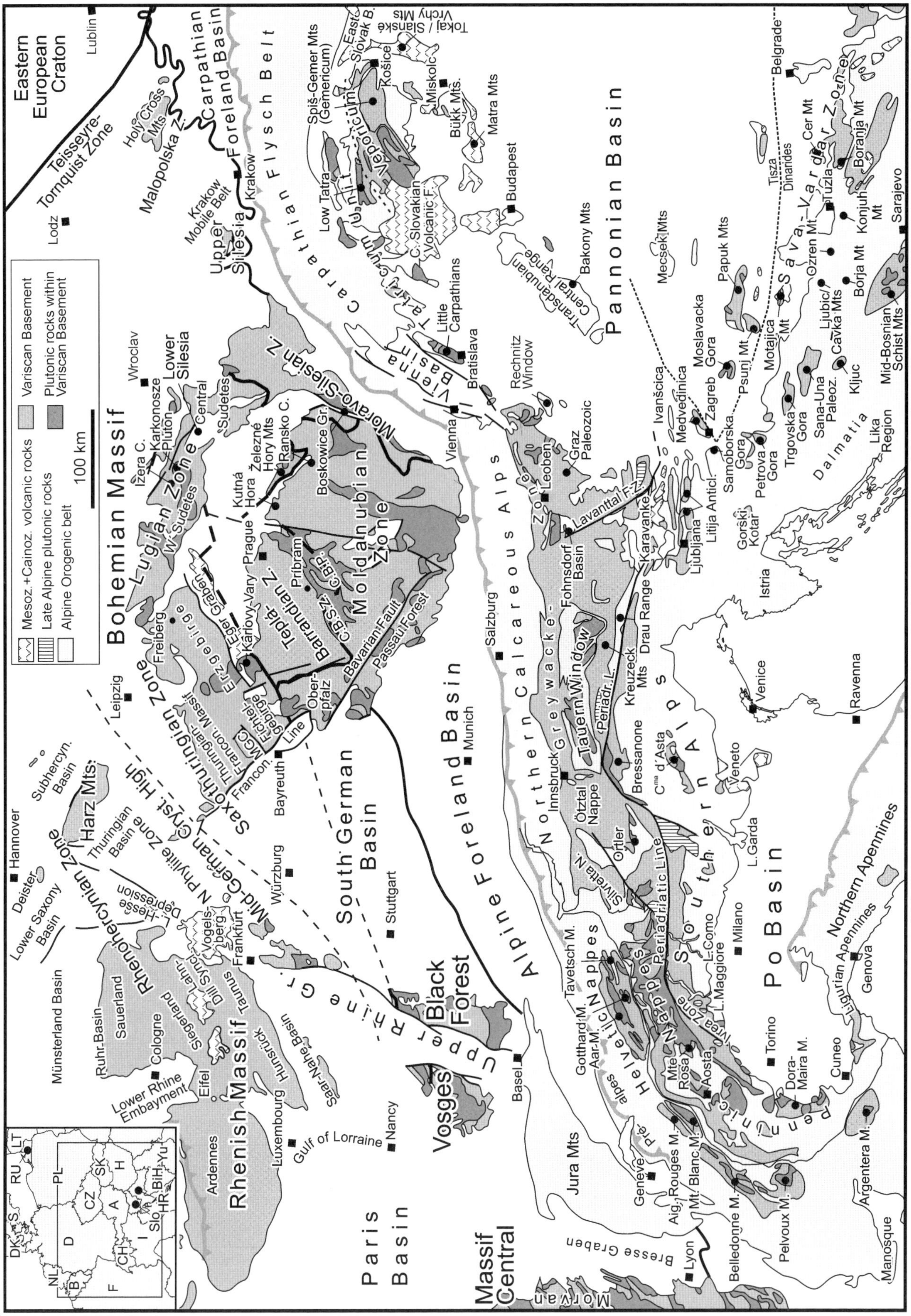


**Fig. 21.1.** Map showing some major geographical and geological units in Central Europe (the area north of Hannover–Warsaw is not shown). Abbreviations: C.B.P., Central Bohemian Pluton; C.B.S.Z., Central Bohemian Shear Zone; MCG, Münchberg Gneiss Complex.

**Table 21.2.** *Estimated reserves and cumulative production in Central European basins (according to IHS Energy 2004).*

| | Estimated total recoverable reserves | | Fields/ discoveries | Cumulative production | |
|---|---|---|---|---|---|
| | Oil (MMbl) | Gas (Bscf) | | Oil (MMbl) | Gas (Bscf) |
| Baltic Syneclise | 480 | 340 | 101 | 250 | 20 |
| Northwest European Basin | 5700 | 220 000 | >1000 | 3800 | 132 000 |
| Lower Saxony Basin | 1930 | 32 900 | 283 | 1750 | 12 600 |
| Paris Basin | 309 | 116 | 82(12) | 260 | 80 |
| Upper Rhine Graben | 110 | 50 | 56 | 80 | 40 |
| Alpine Foreland Basin | 150 | 2300 | 193 | 137 | 1700 |
| Carpathian Foreland | CZ: 70 | 372 | 43 | 17 | 70 |
| and Flysch Belt | PL: 140 | 6700 | 219 | 130 | 4000 |
| Vienna Basin | 980 | 4500 | 148 | 780 | 3000 |
| Pannonian Basin | 2500 | 15 500 | 550 | 1930 | 9000 |
| Po Basin Province | 460 | 24 700 | 329 | 300 | 16 000 |

Bscf, billion standard cubic feet; MMbl, million barrels.

**Table 21.3** *Iron–manganese deposits (see CD inside back cover)*

| Number | Deposit | Element association | Age of formation |
|---|---|---|---|
| 1 | Romanèche-Thorins (F) | Mn (F) | Jurassic ? |
| 2 | Change (F) | Fe | Jurassic |
| 3 | Ougney (F) | Fe | Jurassic |
| 4 | Délémont (CH) | Fe | Eocene |
| 5 | Herznach (CH) | Fe | Jurassic |
| 6a | Gutmadingen (D) | Fe | Jurassic |
| 6b | Geislingen (D) | Fe | Jurassic |
| 6c | Aalen (D) | Fe | Jurassic |
| 7 | Eisenbach (D) | Fe-(F-Ba) | Alpine |
| 8 | Saar District (D) | Fe | Carboniferous-Permian |
| 9 | Lorraine – Luxembourg (F/L) | Fe | Jurassic |
| 10 | Namur- Liege (B) | Fe | Devonian |
| 11 | Eifel (D) | Fe | Devonian |
| 12 | Waldalgesheim (D) | Mn-Fe | Tertiary |
| 13 | Bieber (D) | Fe-Mn-Bi-Co-Ni-(Ba) | Alpine |
| 14 | Lindener Mark (D) | Mn-Fe | Tertiary |
| 15 | Lahn-Dill area – Wald-Erbach- Mosel Syncline – Dollendorf Syncline (D) | Fe | Devonian |
| 16 | Siegerland-Wied (D) | Fe-(Mn-Pb-Cu-Zn-Bi-Sb) | Variscan |
| 17 | Laisa near Battenberg (D) | Mn-Fe | Carboniferous |
| 18 | Adorf (D) | Fe | Devonian |
| 19 | Ruhr (D) | Fe | Carboniferous |
| 20 | Hüggel (Massif of Bramsche, Vlotho, Uchte) (D) | Fe-Pb-Zn | Alpine |
| 21 | Damme (D) | Fe | Cretaceous |
| 22 | Nammen (D) | Fe | Jurassic |
| 23 | Staffhorst (D) | Fe | Jurassic |
| 24 | Achim (D) | Fe | Tertiary |
| 25 | Gifhorn (D) | Fe | Jurassic |
| 26 | Peine-Bülten-Lengede (D) | Fe | Cretaceous |
| 27 | Salzgitter (D) | Fe-(P) | Cretaceous |
| 28 | Elbingerode – Zorge (D) | Fe-(Fe sulphides) | Devonian |
| 29 | Zorge- St. Andreasberg (D) | Fe (with Se-bearing veins near Zorge and Tilkerode) | Variscan |
| 30 | Lerbach (D) | Fe | Devonian |
| 31 | Schmalkalden (D) | Fe-Ba-Cu-Bi-Co-Ni | Alpine |
| 32 | Kamsdorf-Saalfeld (D) | Fe-Ba-Cu-Bi-Co-Ni | Alpine |
| 33 | Schleiz (D) | Fe | Devonian |
| 34 | Schmiedefeld-Wittmannsgereuth (D) | Fe-(P) | Ordovician |
| 35 | Arzberg-Tröstau (D) | Fe | Cambrian |
| 36 | Gleißinger Fels, Rotenfels (D) | Fe (W) | Post-Permian |
| 37 | Pegnitz/Auerbach (D) | Fe-(P) | Jurassic/Cretaceous |
| 38 | Amberg-Sulzbach-Rosenberg (D) | Fe-(P) | Cretaceous |
| 39 | Bodenwöhr Embayment (D) | Fe | Jurassic |
| 40 | Ejpovice- Krušná Hora- Nučice- Zdice- Mníšek-Komárov (CZ) | Fe-(P) | Ordovician |

(*continued*)

**Table 21.3.** (*continued*)

| Number | Deposit | Element association | Age of formation |
|---|---|---|---|
| 41 | Moravský Krumlov (CZ) | Fe | Proterozoic |
| 42 | Jeseníky Mts. (CZ) | Fe | Devonian+Variscan |
| 43 | Šumperk (CZ) | Fe | Proterozoic |
| 44 | Kudowa (PL) | Fe | Post-Permian |
| 45 | Železný Brod (CZ) | Fe | Proterozoic - Early Palaeozoic |
| 46 | Kowary (PL) | Fe-(Bi-Co-Ni) | Proterozoic + Variscan |
| 47 | Męcinka (PL) | Fe-(Mn) | Variscan |
| 48 | Częstochowa – Zawiercie (PL) | Fe | Jurassic |
| 49 | Dąbrowa (PL) | Fe | Post-Devonian |
| 50 | Parczów-Białaczów-Konskie-Przytyk (PL) | Fe | Jurassic–Cretaceous |
| 51 | Łęczyca (PL) | Fe | Jurassic |
| 52 | Fyledalen (S) | Fe | Jurassic |
| 53 | Krzemianka (PL) | Fe-Ti | Precambrian |
| 54 | Stępina (PL) | Fe | Early Cretaceous |
| 55 | Gorlice - Cieklin - Jasło area (PL) | Mn-Fe-Mg | Early Eocene |
| 56 | Rajbrot (PL) | Fe | Early Cretaceous |
| 57 | Wiśniowa (PL) | Fe | Early Cretaceous |
| 58 | Rudňany - Poráč - Bindt - Ráztoky (SK) | Fe-Cu-Hg- Ba | Permian |
| 59 | Gelnica - Slovinky (SK) | Fe-Cu | Permian |
| 60 | Medzev-Jedl'ovec (SK) | Fe | Permian |
| 61 | Rožňava (SK) | Fe-Cu-Ag | Permian |
| 62 | Rudabánya (H) | Fe, Cu-Pb-Zn | Triassic |
| 63 | Šankovce - Licince (SK) | Fe | Early Triassic |
| 64 | Železník - Hrádok (SK) | Fe | Permian |
| 65 | Nižná Slaná - Kobeliarovo (SK) | Fe-(Hg) | Permian |
| 66 | Kišovce - Švábovce (SK) | Mn | Eocene |
| 67 | Kościelisko - Dolina Lejowa (PL) | Fe-Mn | Triassic–Early Jurassic |
| 68 | Zázrivá (SK) | Mn | Jurassic |
| 69 | Třinec - Cieszyn (CZ/PL) | Fe | Cretaceous–Early Eocene |
| 70 | Frenštat p.Radhoštem area (CZ) | Fe | Cretaceous–Early Eocene |
| 71 | Lednické Rovné (SK) | Mn | Jurassic |
| 72 | Borinka (SK) | Mn | Jurassic |
| 73 | Eplény (H) | Mn | Jurassic |
| 74 | Úrkút (H) | Mn | Jurassic |
| 75 | Čevljanovići (BiH) | Mn | Triassic |
| 76 | Vareš (BiH) | Fe- Ba-Pb-Zn | Triassic |
| 77 | Ključ (BiH) | Fe | Devonian (?) Variscan |
| 78 | Omarska (BiH) | Fe | Alpine (Permian ?) |
| 79 | Tomašica (BiH) | Fe | Alpine (Permian ?) |
| 80 | Ljubija- Adamuša-Brdo- Atlijina kosa (BiH) | Fe-(Ba-Pb-Zn±F) | Alpine (Permian ?) |
| 81 | Tomašica (HR) | Fe-(Cu- Pb- Ni-Co) | Alpine (Permian) |
| 82 | Gradski potok (HR) | Fe-Cu | Alpine (Permian) |
| 83 | Majdan (HR) | Fe-Pb | Alpine (Permian) |
| 84 | Gvozdansko (HR) | Fe | Alpine (Permian) |
| 85 | Žirovac (HR) | Fe | Alpine (Permian) |
| 86 | Bužim (BiH) | Mn | Triassic |
| 87 | Bukovica (HR) | Fe -Ba | Alpine (Permian–Triassic) |
| 88 | Medvednica Mt. (HR) | Fe-Mn-Ba | Variscan |
| 89 | Ivanščica Mt. (HR) | Mn-Fe | Triassic |
| 90 | Pitten (A) | Fe | pre-Alpine |
| 91 | Arzberg (A) | Fe | Permian |
| 92 | Grillenberg (A) | Fe | Permian |
| 93 | Schendleck-Hirschwang (A) | Fe | Permian |
| 94 | Kaskogel Großveitsch (A) | Mn | pre-Alpine |
| 95 | Gollrad (A) | Fe | pre-Alpine |
| 96 | Erzberg (A) | Fe | Permian |
| 97 | Radmer (A) | Fe | Permian |
| 98 | Waldenstein (A) | Fe | Tertiary |
| 99 | Wölch /St. Gertraud (A) | Fe | Tertiary |
| 100 | Kathal (A) | Fe | Tertiary |
| 101 | Hüttenberg (A) | Fe | Tertiary |
| 102 | St. Martin am Silberberg (A) | Fe | Tertiary |
| 103 | Olsa (A) | Fe | Tertiary |
| 104 | Einöd/Friesach (A) | Mn | pre-Alpine |
| 105 | Nußdorf (A) | Fe | Tertiary |
| 106 | St. Nikolai (A) | Fe | Tertiary |
| 107 | Innerkrems-Altenberg (A) | Fe | ? |
| 108 | Raggabach (A) | Fe | pre-Alpine |
| 109 | Strubberg (A) | Mn | Jurassic |

(*continued*)

**Table 21.3.** (*continued*)

| Number | Deposit | Element association | Age of formation |
|---|---|---|---|
| 110 | Hochkranz (A) | Mn | Jurassic |
| 111 | Teisenberg (D) | Fe | Eocene |
| 112 | Grünten (D) | Fe | Eocene |
| 113 | Gonzen (CH) | Mn-Fe | Jurassic |
| 114 | Oberhalbstein (CH) | Mn | Jurassic |
| 115 | Val Ferrera (CH) | Mn-Fe | Jurassic |
| 116 | Alfredo-S. Aloisio (I) | Fe | Lower Triassic |
| 117 | Erzegg (CH) | Fe | Jurassic |
| 118 | Chamoson (CH) | Fe | Jurassic |
| 119 | Mont Chemin (CH) | Fe | Variscan |
| 120 | Praborna (I) | Mn | Jurassic–Cretaceous |
| 121 | Cogne (I) | Fe | Jurassic–Cretaceous |
| 122 | St. Georges d'Hurtiéres (F) | Fe-Cu | Variscan |
| 123 | Gambatesa (I) | Mn | Jurassic–Cretaceous |

**Table 21.4.** *Bi–Co–Ni–Ti–Cr–PGE deposits (see CD inside back cover)*

| Number | Deposit | Element association | Age of formation |
|---|---|---|---|
| 1 | Wittichen (D) | Bi-Co-Ni-U-F-Ba | Variscan–Alpine |
| 2 | Freudenstadt (D) | Bi-Co-Ni-Ba | Alpine |
| 3 | Neubulach (D) | Bi-Co-Ni-Ba | Alpine |
| 4 | Weilburg-Odersbach (D) | Ni-Cu | Lower Carboniferous |
| 5 | Bad Liebenstein (D) | Bi-Co-Ni | Alpine |
| 6 | Harzburg (D) | Ni-Cu | Carboniferous |
| 7 | Midlum (D) | Ti -(Zr) | Pliocene |
| 8 | St. Egidien (D) | Ni | Cretaceous–Tertiary (Palaeogene) |
| 9 | Sohland-Šluknov (D, CZ) | Ni | Variscan |
| 10 | Křemže (CZ) | Ni | Tertiary |
| 11 | Staré Ransko (CZ) | Ni-Cu-Zn | Proterozoic (–Cambrian?) |
| 12 | Szklary (PL) | Ni | Tertiary (Miocene) |
| 13 | Tąpadła (PL) | Cr | Early Devonian |
| 14 | Dobšina (SK) | Ni-Co-Fe-Cu-(asbestos) | Variscan (Triassic) |
| 15 | Hodkovce (SK) | Ni-Co-Cr | Cretaceous–Tertiary |
| 16 | Szarvaskő (H) | Fe-Ti | Jurassic |
| 17 | Brezik, Tadići, Konjuh Mt. (BiH) | Ni-Co | Cretaceous–Tertiary |
| 18 | Ozren Mt. (BiH) | Cr-(magnesite) | Jurassic |
| 19 | Ozren Mt. (BiH) | Ni | Cretaceous |
| 20 | Borja Mt. (BiH) | Cr | Jurassic |
| 21 | Gornje Orešje, Medvednica Mt. (HR) | Ni | Cretaceous |
| 22 | Kraubath (A) | Cr | Pre-Variscan |
| 23 | Hochgrößen (A) | Cr | Variscan |
| 24 | Schladming (A) | Ni-Co-Zn | Pre-(?)Variscan |
| 25 | Leogang (A) | Ni-Co-Hg-Cu | Early Palaeozoic |
| 26 | Totalp (CH) | Ni | Jurassic |
| 27 | Poschavio (CH) | Ni | Jurassic |
| 28 | Palagnedra (CH) | Ni | Late Palaeozoic Permian |
| 29 | Kaltenberg (CH) | Ni-Co | Alpine |
| 30 | Campello Monti (I) | Ni | Late Palaeozoic Permian |
| 31 | Gula (I) | Ni | Late Palaeozoic Permian |
| 32 | Scopello (I) | Ni | Late Palaeozoic Permian |

economic geologists and mining engineers, and for monograph series such as 'The Iron Ore Deposits of Europe' (Zitzmann 1977). However, the mineral associations in Central Europe are highly variable in time and space and were used for different commodities during different time periods. Thus, a subdivision according to commodities (e.g. ores, industrial minerals, fossil fuels) would cause numerous repetitions. To avoid this and in view of the structure of this book, the geological timescale and the geodynamic setting are used as the principal classification criteria. This classification provides a direct link to the stratigraphy-orientated chapters of this book so that mineralogical and chemical concentration processes are embedded into the geodynamic evolution of the Central European crust. Further subdivision is based on the particular element or mineral assemblages present in the deposits.

In the following sections, the mineralization processes and the resultant deposits are subdivided into six first-order categories:

(1) strata-bound deposits;
(2) thrust-bound metamorphogenic and/or fold-related deposits;
(3) deposits controlled by collision-related granitic activity;

**Table 21.5.** *Sn–W–U–Nb–Ta–Li–Mo deposits (see CD inside back cover)*

| Number | Deposit | Element association | Age of formation |
|---|---|---|---|
| 1 | Chateau Lambert (F) | Mo | Variscan |
| 2 | St. Hippolyte (F) | U | Alpine |
| 3 | Breitenbach (F) | Mo | Variscan |
| 4 | Framont-Grandfontaine (F) | Fe-W | Variscan |
| 5 | Schelingen-Kaiserstuhl (D) | Nb | Tertiary |
| 6 | Menzenschwand (D) | U | Variscan |
| 7 | Wittichen (D) | U-Bi-Co-Ni | Variscan, Alpine |
| 8 | Müllenbach (D) | U | Alpine |
| 9 | Ellweiler (D) | U | Alpine |
| 10 | Burgsandstein-Stubensandstein area (D) | U | Triassic |
| 11 | Schwarzach Area (D) | U | Variscan |
| 12 | Hagendorf- Pleystein-Waidhaus (D) | Li-feldspar-quartz-phosphate | Variscan |
| 13 | Dylen (CZ) | U | Variscan |
| 14 | Mähring (D) | U | Variscan |
| 15 | Poppenreuth (D) | U | Variscan |
| 16 | Zadní Chodov (CZ) | U | Variscan |
| 17 | Vítkov (CZ) | U | Variscan |
| 18 | Falkenberg Granite (D) | U | Variscan, Alpine |
| 19 | Weißenstadt (D) | Sn-W | Variscan–Quaternary |
| 20 | Gräfenthal Horst (D) | U-(Fe /see "Ockerkalk") | Variscan (Silurian), Alpine |
| 21 | Grossschloppen (D) | U | Variscan |
| 22 | Hebanz (D) | U | Variscan |
| 23 | Möschwitz (D) | U | Variscan, Alpine |
| 24 | Gera-Ronneburg area (D) | U | Variscan, Alpine |
| 25 | Schneeberg (D) | U | Variscan |
| 26 | Hartenstein (D) | U-(Hg) | Variscan |
| 27 | Aue (D) | U | Variscan |
| 28 | Schwarzenberg (D) | U | Variscan |
| 29 | Jáchymov (CZ) | U-Ag-Bi-Co-Ni | Variscan |
| 30 | Horní Slavkov (CZ) | Sn-W-U | Variscan |
| 31 | Tipersdorf (D) | W | Variscan |
| 32 | Zobes (D) | W | Variscan |
| 33 | Pechtelsgrün (D) | W | Variscan |
| 34 | Zschorlau (D) | W | Variscan |
| 35 | Gottesberg-Mühlleiten (D) | W-Sn | Variscan |
| 36 | Rotava (CZ) | W | Variscan |
| 37 | Krasno (CZ) | Sn-W | Variscan |
| 38 | Breitenbrunn-Pöhla (D) | Sn-W | Variscan |
| 39 | Ehrenfriedersdorf (D) | Sn | Variscan |
| 40 | Veřneřov (CZ) | Sn-Li | Variscan |
| 41 | Sadisdorf (D) | Sn | Variscan |
| 42 | Altenberg (D) | Sn | Variscan |
| 43 | Zinnwald-Cínovec (D/CZ) | Sn-W-Li | Variscan |
| 44 | Krupka (CZ) | Sn | Variscan |
| 45 | Teplice (CZ) | U | Cretaceous |
| 46 | Pirna (D) | U | Cretaceous |
| 47 | Königsstein (D) | U | Cretaceous |
| 48 | Hamr (CZ) | U | Cretaceous |
| 49 | Nové Město pod Smrkem (CZ) | Sn-Co | Variscan |
| 50 | Giercyn - Krobica (PL) | Sn-Co | Variscan |
| 51 | Zólkiewka (PL) | Nb-Ta | Variscan |
| 52 | Obří Důl (CZ) | W | Variscan |
| 53 | Kowary (PL) | U | Variscan |
| 54 | Kletno (PL) | U | Variscan |
| 55 | Příbram (CZ) | U | Variscan |
| 56 | Okrouhlá Radouň (CZ) | U | Variscan |
| 57 | Dobrá Voda (CZ) | Li | Variscan |
| 58 | Jihlava (CZ) | Li | Variscan |
| 59 | Horní Babakoc (CZ) | W | Variscan |
| 60 | Rožná (CZ) | U-Li | Variscan |
| 61 | Olší (CZ) | U | Variscan |
| 62 | Scheibengraben (CZ) | Be-Nb-Ta | Variscan |
| 63 | Novoveská Huta (SK) | U-Mo-Cu | Permian |
| 64 | Hnilec-Medvedí potok - Dlhá Dolina (SK) | Sn(-REE) | Variscan–Alpine |
| 65 | Rochovce (SK) | Mo-W | Variscan–Alpine |
| 66 | Vikartovce-Spišský Štiavnik (SK) | U | Variscan |
| 67 | Jasenie-Kyslá (SK) | W-Au-As | Variscan |
| 68 | Kálnica (SK) | U | Variscan |
| 69 | Cer Mt. (SRB) | Nb-Ta-W-Sn-fluorite | Oligocene |

(*continued*)

**Table 21.5.** (*continued*)

| Number | Deposit | Element association | Age of formation |
|---|---|---|---|
| 70 | Ninkovača creek (HR) | U | Silurian–Devonian |
| 71 | Kővagószőlős – Bakonya (H) | U | Permian |
| 72 | Prinzenkogel (A) | U | Permian |
| 73 | Weinebene (A) | Li | Permian |
| 74 | Žirovski Vrh (SLO) | U | Permian |
| 75 | Pusterwald (A) | Li | Permian |
| 76 | Mallnock (A) | W | Alpine? |
| 77 | Forstau (A) | U | Permian |
| 78 | Mittersill (A) | W | Pre-Variscan (Cambrian) to Variscan (Carboniferous) |
| 79 | Novazza-Val Vedello (I) | U | Alpine |
| 80 | Mürtschenalp (CH) | U-Cu | Permian |
| 81 | Trun (CH) | U | Variscan |
| 82 | Naters (CH) | U | Variscan |
| 83 | Isérables (CH) | U | Permian |
| 84 | Le Chatelard (CH) | U | Variscan |
| 85 | Grange Serre Preit (I) | U | Permian |
| 86 | Rio Freddo Peveragno (I) | U | Permian |
| 87 | Bric Colme' Pamparato (I) | U | Permian |

**Table 21.6.** *Sb–Au–Hg–As deposits (see CD inside back cover)*

| Number | Deposit | Element association | Age of formation |
|---|---|---|---|
| 1 | Genf-Allondon (CH) | Au | Quaternary |
| 2 | Napf (CH) | Au | Tertiary–Quaternary |
| 3 | St. Ulrich-Sulzburg (D) | Sb (+Ag) | Variscan-(Alpine) |
| 4 | Silberwald (F) | Sb | Variscan |
| 5 | Charbes (F) | Sb | Variscan |
| 6 | Rheingold (D) | Au | Quaternary |
| 7 | Stahlberg (D) | Hg | Alpine |
| 8 | Landsberg – Obermoschel (D) | Hg | Alpine |
| 9 | Hohes Venn (D) | Au | Variscan |
| 10a | Brück a. d. Ahr (D) | Sb | Variscan |
| 10b | Goesdorf (L) | Sb | Variscan |
| 11 | Rauppach (Apollo Mine) (D) | Sb | Variscan |
| 12 | Arnsberg (D) | Sb | Variscan |
| 13 | Korbach-Goldhausen (D) | Au | Alpine |
| 14 | Eder (D) | Au | Quaternary |
| 15 | Wolfsberg (D) | Sb | Variscan |
| 16 | Schwarza (D) | Au | Quaternary |
| 17 | Schleiz-Greiz-Wolfersgrün (D) | Sb | Variscan |
| 18 | Brandholz-Goldkronach (D) | Au-Sb | Variscan |
| 19 | Luby (CZ) | Hg | Variscan |
| 20 | Kašperské Hory (CZ) | Au-Pb | Variscan |
| 21 | Kasejovice (CZ) | Au | Variscan |
| 22 | Nový Knín - Psí Hory – Mokrsko -Čelina (CZ) | Au | Variscan |
| 23 | Milešov Krásna Hora (CZ) | Au-Sb | Variscan |
| 24 | Jílové (CZ) | Au-Cu-Ag-Sb-As | Variscan |
| 25 | Roudny (CZ) | Au | Variscan |
| 26 | Wleń (PL) | Au-As | Variscan |
| 27 | Złoty Stok (PL) | Au-As | Variscan |
| 28 | Dubník-Merník (SK) | Hg | Neogene |
| 29 | Telkibánya (H) | Au-Ag | Miocene |
| 30 | Zlatá Idka (SK) | Sb-Au | Variscan |
| 31 | Dúbrava - Magurka (SK) | Sb-Au | Variscan |
| 32 | Medzibrod-Dolná Lehota (SK) | Sb-Au | Variscan |
| 33 | Klokoč - Kalinka (SK) | Au | Neogene |
| 34 | Malachov (SK) | Hg | Neogene |
| 35 | Kremnica (SK) | Au-Ag-Sb | Neogene |
| 36 | Vyhne (SK) | Au-Ag-Sb, Fe | Neogene |
| 37 | Nagybörzsöny (H) | Au-Ag-Pb-Cu | Miocene |
| 38 | Zlatníky (SK) | Au | Quaternary |
| 39 | Pezinok (SK) | Sb-Au-As/Fe suphides | Variscan |
| 40 | Klížska Nemá (SK) | Au | Quaternary |
| 41 | Zajača (SRB) | Sb- As- Pb- Cu-Zn | Oligocene |

(*continued*)

**Table 21.6.** (*continued*)

| Number | Deposit | Element association | Age of formation |
|---|---|---|---|
| 42 | Stolice (SRB) | Sb- As- Pb- Cu-Zn | Oligocene |
| 43 | Krupanj (SRB) | Sb- As- Pb- Cu-Zn | Oligocene |
| 44 | Draževići (BiH) | Hg | Triassic |
| 45 | Hrmza (BiH) | Hg-As-Ba | Permo-Carboniferous |
| 46 | Bakovići (BiH) | Au - Fe sulphide | Permo-Carboniferous |
| 47 | Fojnica(BiH) | Au-Fe-Sb-As-Ba-Pb-Cu | Permo-Carboniferous |
| 48 | Vrtlasce (BiH) | As-Fe-Zn-Pb-Sn-Mo-Cu-Bi | Permo-Carboniferous |
| 49 | Čemernica (BiH) | Sb-As-Hg-Fe- Zn-Cu | Permo-Carboniferous |
| 50 | Mid-Bosnian Schist Mts. (BiH) | Au-As-Sb-Hg-Fe- Ba-Cu | Permo-Carboniferous |
| 51 | Tršće, Gorski kotar region (HR) | Hg | Triassic |
| 52 | Idrija (SLO) | Hg | Triassic |
| 53 | Schlaining (A) | Sb | Miocene |
| 54 | Tallackkogel (A) | Hg | Alpine |
| 55 | Flatschach (A) | Au | Alpine |
| 56 | Kliening-Kothgraben (A) | Au- As | Alpine |
| 57 | Pusterwald (A) | Au | ? |
| 58 | Schellgaden (A) | Au-W | Pre-Alpine–Alpine |
| 59 | Rotgülden (A) | Au- As- Bi | Alpine |
| 60 | Gastein/Rauris (A) | Au | Alpine |
| 61 | Fusch (A) | Au | Alpine |
| 62 | Stockenboi (A) | Hg | Alpine |
| 63 | Siflitz (A) | Au | Alpine |
| 64 | Glatschach (A) | Hg | Alpine |
| 65 | Rabant (A) | Sb | Alpine |
| 66 | Calanda (CH) | Au | Late Alpine |
| 67 | Astano (CH) | Au-As-Sb | Variscan ? |
| 68 | Val Toppa (Pieve Vergonte) (I) | Au | Variscan ? |
| 69 | Maglioggio-Alfenza Crodo (I) | Au | Tertiary (Oligo-Miocene) |
| 70 | Gondo (CH) | Au-Ag | Tertiary (Oligo-Miocene) |
| 71 | Mottone (Antronapiana) (I) | Au | Tertiary (Oligo-Miocene) |
| 72 | Pestarena-Macugnana (I) | Au | Tertiary (Oligo-Miocene) |
| 73 | Kreas, Alagna (I) | Au | Tertiary (Oligo-Miocene) |
| 74 | Brusson (I) | Au | Tertiary (Oligo-Miocene) |
| 75 | Salanfe (CH) | Au | Variscan |
| 76 | La Gardette (F) | Au | Late Alpine |

**Table 21.7.** *Pb–Zn–Cu–Fe sulphide–Ba deposits (see CD inside back cover)*

| Number | Deposit | Element association | Age of formation |
|---|---|---|---|
| 1 | Sain Bel (F) | Cu-Fe sulphide | Devonian |
| 2 | Chessy (F) | Zn-Cu-Ba | Devonian |
| 3 | Giromagny (F) | Pb-Zn | Alpine |
| 4 | Sainte-Marie-aux-Mînes, La Croix aux Mines (F) | Pb-Zn-Bi-Co-Ni | Alpine |
| 5a | Schauinsland (D) (+vein-type deposits in the environs of St. Blasien, Münstertal) | Pb-Zn | Alpine |
| 5b | Badenweiler (D) | Pb-Zn | Alpine |
| 6 | Wiesloch (D) | Zn-(Pb) | Alpine |
| 7 | Fischbach (D) | Cu | Alpine (Permian) |
| 8 | Tellig - Altlay (D) | Pb-Zn | Variscan |
| 9 | Werlau (D) | Pb-Zn | Variscan |
| 10 | Lohrheim (D) | Fe sulphide-Ba | Devonian |
| 11 | Holzappel (D) | Pb-Zn | Variscan |
| 12 | Ems - Braubach (D) | Pb-Zn | Variscan |
| 13 | Mühlenbach (D) | Pb-Zn | Variscan |
| 14 | Rheinbreitbach (D) | Cu | Alpine |
| 15 | Bleialf - Rescheid (D) | Pb | Alpine |
| 16 | Maubach - Mechernich (D) | Pb-Zn | Alpine (Triassic) |
| 17 | Aachen - Moresnet (D, B) | Pb-Zn | Alpine |
| 18 | Erkelenz (D) | Pb-Zn | Alpine |
| 19 | Bensberg (D) | Pb-Zn | Variscan |
| 20 | Velbert Anticline (D) | Pb-Zn | Alpine |
| 21 | Ruhr-District (D) | Pb-Zn | Alpine |
| 22 | Iserlohn - Schwelm (D) | Zn | Alpine |
| 23 | Meggen (D) | Fe sulphide-Zn-Pb-Ba | Devonian |
| 24 | Ramsbeck (D) | Pb-Zn | Variscan |

(*continued*)

**Table 21.7.** (*continued*)

| Number | Deposit | Element association | Age of formation |
|---|---|---|---|
| 25 | Marsberg (D) | Cu | Permian–Alpine |
| 26 | Helgoland (D) | Cu | Triassic |
| 27 | Rammelsberg (D) | Zn-Pb-Cu- Fe sulphide Ba-(Ag-Au) | Devonian |
| 28 | Grund (D) (+ Oberharz vein-type deposits near Clausthal-Zellerfeld, Lautenthal, St. Andreasberg) | Pb-Zn | Alpine |
| 29 | Mansfeld-Sangerhausen (D) | Cu-(Ag) | Permian–Alpine |
| 30 | Richelsdorf (D) | Cu | Permian–Alpine |
| 31 | Wallenfels-Dürrenwaid-Remschlitz (D) | Pb-(Zn) | Alpine |
| 32 | Kupferberg-Wirsberg-Sparneck-Neufang (D) | Cu (Zn) Fe sulphides | Early Palaeozoic (Ordovician) |
| 33 | Waldsassen-Bayerland (D) | Fe sulphide-Zn | Cambrian |
| 34 | Weiden Embayment-Freihung (D) | Pb-(Mn) | Alpine (Triassic) |
| 35 | Erbendorf (D) | Pb-(Zn) | Alpine |
| 36 | Lam (D) | Fe sulphide | Precambrian–Cambrian |
| 37 | Bodenmais area (D) | Fe sulphide | Precambrian–Cambrian |
| 38 | Struhadlo-Klatovy (CZ) | Fe sulphide-(Cu-Zn) | Precambrian–Cambrian |
| 39 | Příbram(CZ) | Pb-Zn-U | Variscan-(Alpine) |
| 40 | Stříbro (CZ) | Pb-Zn | Variscan-(Alpine) |
| 41 | Oloví (CZ) | Pb-Zn | Alpine |
| 42 | Klingenthal (D) - Tisová (CZ) | Fe sulphide-Cu | Cambrian |
| 43 | Přísečnice - Měděněc (CZ) | Fe- Sn-Cu | (Proterozoic) Variscan |
| 44 | Annaberg - Marienberg (D) | Pb | Alpine |
| 45 | Hermsdorf - Elterlein - Lengefeld - Jahnsbach (D) | Pb-Zn | Cambrian |
| 46 | Mikulov (CZ) | Pb-Zn | Variscan |
| 47 | Freiberg-Halsbrücke (D) | Pb | (Proterozoic) Variscan |
| 48 | Kutná Hora (CZ) | Pb-Zn-Sb-Ag | Variscan |
| 49 | Chvaletice - Hromnice (CZ) | Fe sulphide-Mn | Precambrian–Cambrian |
| 50 | Nowa Ruda (PL)-Horní Verneřovice (CZ)-Okrzeszyn (PL) | Cu | Permian–Alpine |
| 51 | N Sudetic Basin, Konrad - Lena (PL) | Cu | Permian–Alpine |
| 52 | Fore Sudetic Monocline, Lubin – Sieroszowice (PL) | Cu | Permian–Alpine |
| 53 | Miedzianka - Stara Góra (PL) | Cu-Zn | Variscan |
| 54 | Wieściszowice (PL) | Fe sulphide | Precambrian |
| 55 | Zlaté Hory (CZ) | Zn-Pb-Cu-Au-Ag | Devonian |
| 56 | Horní Benešov, Horní Město, Oskava (CZ) | Fe sulphide-Pb-Zn | Devonian |
| 57 | Upper Silesia: Bytom-Tarnowskie Góry-Olkusz-Zawiercie (PL) | Zn-Pb | Triassic–Alpine |
| 58 | Zawiercie (PL) | Zn-Pb | Variscan |
| 59 | Pilica (PL) | Cu | Variscan |
| 60 | Dolina Bedkowska (PL) | Cu | Variscan |
| 61 | Karczówka-Kielce (PL) | Pb(-Zn) | Alpine |
| 62 | Łagów (PL) | Pb(-Zn) | Triassic–Alpine |
| 63 | Rudki (PL) | Fe sulphide | Variscan |
| 64 | Zlatá Baňa (SK) | Cu-Pb-Zn (Au-Ag) | Neogene |
| 65 | Brehov (SK) | Cu-Pb-Zn (Au-Ag) | Neogene |
| 66 | Smolník- Mníšek nad Hnilcom (SK) | Cu-Fe sulphides | Silurian-Devonian |
| 67 | Recsk (H) | Cu-Zn (Mo-Au) | Neogene |
| 68 | Gyöngyösoroszi (H) | Pb-Zn | Miocene |
| 69 | Ľubietová SK) | Cu | Variscan |
| 70 | Špania Dolina (SK) | Cu | Variscan |
| 71 | Banská Štiavnica-Hodruša-Pukanec (SK) | Cu-Pb-Zn (Au-Ag) | Neogene |
| 72 | Zlatno (SK) | Cu-Pb-Zn-Mo (Au) | Neogene |
| 73 | Pátka – Szüzvár (H) | Zn-Pb-Mo-fluorite | Eocene |
| 74 | Srebrenica (BiH) | Pb-Zn-Ag-Au-Cu-Cd-Sb-As | Oligocene |
| 75 | Olovo (BiH) | Pb-Zn | Triassic |
| 76 | Srednje (BiH) | Pb-Zn-Ba | Triassic |
| 77 | Veovača (BiH) | Pb-Zn-Ba | Triassic |
| 78 | Borovica (BiH) | Pb-Zn-Ba | Triassic |
| 79 | Rupice (BiH) | Pb-Zn-Ba | Triassic |
| 80 | Ribnica-Maglajac-Kamenac, Krivaja river valley (BiH) | Cu | Jurassic |
| 81 | Srb, Lika region (BiH) | Pb-Zn | Triassic |
| 82 | Čavka Mt. (BiH) | Cu | Jurassic |
| 83 | Svinica, Petrova gora Mt. (HR) | Pb-Zn | Triassic |
| 84 | Rude, Samoborska gora Mt. (HR) | Fe-(Ba-Cu- Pb-Zn- Ba) | Permian |
| 85 | Sv. Jakob, Medvednica Mt. (HR) | Pb-Zn | Triassic |
| 86 | Ivanščica Mt. (HR) | Pb-Zn | Triassic |
| 87 | Litija (SLO) | Cu-Pb-Zn- Sb-Hg- Ba-Fe | Permian |
| 88 | Škofje (SLO) | Cu | Permian |
| 89 | Mežice (SLO) | Pb-Zn | Triassic |

(*continued*)

**Table 21.7.** (*continued*)

| Number | Deposit | Element association | Age of formation |
|---|---|---|---|
| 90 | Topla (SLO) | Pb-Zn | Triassic |
| 91 | Arzberg-Graz Palaeozoic (A) | Pb-Zn | Palaeozoic |
| 92 | Oberzeiring (A) | Pb-Zn (Ag- Ba) | Late Alpine |
| 93 | Meiselding (A) | Pb-Zn | Palaeozoic |
| 94 | Walchen (A) | Cu | Alpine |
| 95 | Bleiberg (A) | Pb-Zn | Triassic |
| 96 | Raibl (I) | Pb-Zn | Triassic |
| 97 | Rauschberg (D) | Pb-Zn-(Fe sulphide) | Triassic |
| 98 | Königsberg (D) | Pb-Zn-(Fe sulphide) | Triassic |
| 99 | Mitterberg (A) | Cu, Ni | Alpine |
| 100 | Grossfragant (A) | Cu | Triassic |
| 101 | Salafossa (I) | Zn-Pb | Triassic |
| 102 | Kitzbühel (A) | Cu-Ba | Alpine |
| 103 | Schwaz (A) | Cu- Ag-Ba | Palaeozoic |
| 104 | Lafatsch (A) | Pb-Zn | Triassic |
| 105 | Höllental (D) | Pb-Zn-(Mo) | Triassic |
| 106 | Säuling (A) | Fe sulphide-Zn-Ba- limonite | Triassic |
| 107 | Monteneve (I) | Zn-Pb | Pre-Variscan |
| 108 | Montafon (A) | Cu-Fe-Au | Permian |
| 109 | Bleiberg (CH) | Pb-Zn | Triassic |
| 110 | Silberberg (CH) | Pb-Zn | Triassic |
| 111 | Bärenbühl (CH) | Pb-Zn | Triassic |
| 112 | Alp Taspin (CH) | Pb-Zn | Alpine |
| 113 | Alp Nadéls (CH) | Pb-Zn | Variscan ? |
| 114 | Bristenstock (CH) | Pb-Zn | Variscan |
| 115 | Val Seriana, Val Brembana (I) | Pb-Zn | Triassic |
| 116 | Agogna-Motto-Piombino (I) | Pb-Zn-(Ag) | Variscan |
| 117 | Migiandone-Ornavasso (I) | Cu | Pre-Variscan |
| 118 | Trachsellauenen (CH) | Pb-Zn-(Ba) | Alpine |
| 119 | Goppenstein (CH) | Pb-Zn-(Ba-F) | Alpine |
| 120 | Grimentz (CH) | Cu-Bi-Ag | Alpine |
| 121 | Praz Jean-St. Luc (CH) | Pb-Zn | Alpine |
| 122 | Promise La Thuile (I) | Pb-Zn | Alpine? |
| 123 | Peisey (F) | Pb-Ag | Lower Triassic |
| 124 | La Plagne (F) | Pb-Ag | Lower Triassic |
| 125 | L'Argentière-la-Bassée (F) | Pb-Ag | Lower Triassic |
| 126 | Menglon (F) | Zn-Pb | Alpine? |
| 127 | Saint Véran (F) | Cu | Jurassic–Cretaceous |
| 128 | Le Cerisier (F) | Cu | Lower Triassic |
| 129 | Valauria (F) | Pb-Zn | Alpine |
| 130 | Libiola (I) | Cu-Fe sulphide | Jurassic–Cretaceous |
| 131 | Vigonzano (I) | Cu-Fe | Jurassic–Cretaceous |
| 132 | Bisano (I) | Cu | Jurassic–Cretaceous |

**Table 21.8** *Industrial minerals deposits (see CD inside back cover)*

| Number | Deposit | Mineral association | Age of formation |
|---|---|---|---|
| 1 | Les Baux (F) | Bauxite | Cretaceous |
| 2 | Saint-Bauzile (F) | Diatomite | Neogene |
| 3 | Larnage (F) | Kaolin | Eocene (?) |
| 4 | Antully (F) | Fluorite | Liassic |
| 5 | Maine (F) | Fluorite | Liassic |
| 6 | Courcelles (F) | Fluorite-barite | Liassic |
| 7 | Faymont-Val d' Ajol (F) | Fluorite-barite | Alpine |
| 8 | Maxonchamp (F) | Fluorite | Alpine |
| 9 | Münstertal (D) | Fluorite-barite | Alpine |
| 10 | Oberwolfach-Clara (D) | Barite- fluorite-(Ag) | Alpine |
| 11 | Käfersteige (D) | Fluorite-(barite) | Alpine |
| 12 | Neuhütten (D) | Barite | Alpine |
| 13 | Vogelsberg (D) | Bauxite | Tertiary |
| 14 | Usingen (D) | Quartz | Alpine |
| 15 | Lahn (D) | Phosphorite | Tertiary |
| 16 | Geisenheim, Diez, Niederdresselndorf ("Westerwald Kaolin") (D) | Kaolin | Tertiary |
| 17 | Rohberg near Wiesbaden (D) | Barite | Devonian |

(*continued*)

**Table 21.8.** (*continued*)

| Number | Deposit | Mineral association | Age of formation |
|---|---|---|---|
| 18 | Baumholder-Wolfstein (D) | Barite | Alpine |
| 19 | Nohfelden (D) | Kaolin-(feldspar) | Permian |
| 20 | Eisen (D) | Barite | Devonian |
| 21 | Haut-Fays | Kaolin | Tertiary |
| 22 | Baudour (B) | Phosphorite | Cretaceous |
| 23 | Ciply (B) | Phosphorite | Cretaceous |
| 24 | Rocour (B) | Phosphorite | Cretaceous |
| 25a | Vierves-sur-Viron (B) | Barite | Alpine |
| 25b | Ava-et-Auffe (B) | Barite | Alpine |
| 25c | Fleurus (B) | Barite | Alpine |
| 25d | Chaudfontain (B) | Barite | Variscan (Devonian) (Alpine ?) |
| 26 | Cologne Basin (D) | Quartz | Tertiary |
| 27 | Oberwinter (D) | Kaolin | Tertiary |
| 28 | Dreislar (D) | Barite | Alpine (Post-Jurassic) |
| 29 | Brilon-Thülen (D) | Calcite | Alpine |
| 30 | Richelsdorf (D) | Barite (Co-Ni) | Alpine |
| 31 | Ruhla, Steinach, Trusetal (D) | Barite-fluorite | Alpine |
| 32 | Lauterberg (D) | Barite | Alpine |
| 33 | Rottleberode Mining District (Stolberg, Straßberg-Ilfeld mines) (D) | Barite-fluorite (Fe-Mn) | Alpine |
| 34 | Haltern (D) | Quartz | Cretaceous |
| 35 | Hemmelte (D) | Celestite | Jurassic |
| 36 | Weferlingen (D) | Quartz | Cretaceous |
| 37 | Hetendorf-Lüneburg (D) | Diatomite | Quaternary |
| 38 | Moler Jutland Peninsula (DK) | Diatomite-bentonite | Eocene |
| 39 | Friedland (D) | Bentonite | Tertiary |
| 40 | Rönne (DK) | Kaolin | Pre-Lower Cretaceous |
| 41 | Darlowo (PL) | Amber | Tertiary-Quaternary |
| 42 | Leba (PL) | Phosphorite | Cretaceous |
| 43 | Sztutowo (PL) | Amber | Tertiary |
| 44 | Jantarnj (RU) | Amber | Tertiary |
| 45 | Ilmenau (D) | Fluorite-barite | Alpine |
| 46 | Halle a.d. Saale (D) | Kaolin | Cretaceous–Tertiary |
| 47 | Merseburg (D) | Kaolin | Cretaceous–Tertiary |
| 48 | Kemmlitz (D) | Kaolin | Cretaceous–Tertiary |
| 49 | Meißen (D) | Kaolin | Cretaceous–Tertiary |
| 50 | Kamenz – Bautzen (D) | Kaolin | Cretaceous–Tertiary |
| 51 | Hohenbocka (D) | Quartz | Tertiary |
| 52 | Lichtenberg-Issigau-Lobenstein (D) | Fluorite | Alpine |
| 53 | Schönbrunn-Bösenbrunn-Wiedersberg (D) | Fluorite | Alpine |
| 54 | Brunndöbra (D) | Barite | Alpine |
| 55 | Schwarzenbach a.d. sächs. Saale (D) | Talc | Variscan |
| 56 | Münchberg Gneiss Complex (D) | Feldspar-quartz | Variscan |
| 57 | Kronach (D) | Kaolin | Triassic |
| 58 | Göpfersgrün (D) | Talc (soapstone) | Permian |
| 59 | Tirschenreuth (D) | Kaolin | Tertiary |
| 60 | Pegnitz (D) | Coloured clay | Tertiary |
| 61 | Püllersreuth (D) | Feldspar | Variscan |
| 62 | Neukirchen (D) | Coloured clay | Tertiary |
| 63 | Hirschau-Schnaittenbach (D) | Quartz-feldspar-kaolin | Triassic |
| 64 | Nabburg-Wölsendorf (D) | Fluorite-(barite) | Alpine |
| 65 | Nittenau (D) | Barite-(fluorite) | Alpine |
| 66 | Donaustauf (D) | Fluorite | Alpine |
| 67 | Pfahl (D) | Quartz | Variscan |
| 68 | Hoher Bogen (D) | Asbestos | Proterozoic |
| 69 | Plzeň Mining District with mines at Kaznějov, Horní Bříza and Chlumčany (CZ) | Kaolin | Carboniferous |
| 70 | Karlovy Vary - Podbořany (CZ) | Kaolin | Carboniferous |
| 71 | Rokle-Kadaň (CZ) | Bentonite | Tertiary |
| 72a | Hradište (CZ) - Niederschlag-Marienberg (D) | Fluorite-barite (Bi-Co-Ni) | Alpine |
| 72b | Moldava - Vrchoslav (CZ) | Fluorite-barite | Alpine |
| 72c | Jílové (CZ) | Fluorite-barite | Alpine |
| 73 | Neuburg a.d. Donau (D) | Tripolite | Cretaceous |
| 74 | Landshut (D) | Bentonite | Tertiary |
| 75 | Kropfmühl (D) | Graphite | Proterozoic |
| 76 | Černá (CZ) | Graphite | Proterozoic |
| 77 | Český Krumlov (CZ) | Graphite | Proterozoic |
| 78 | Mittergallsbach (A) | Phosphorite | Tertiary |

(*continued*)

**Table 21.8.** (*continued*)

| Number | Deposit | Mineral association | Age of formation |
|---|---|---|---|
| 79 | Linz-Plesching (A) | Phosphorite | Tertiary |
| 80 | Weinzierl-Kriechbaum (A) | Kaolin | Tertiary |
| 81 | Mühlberg (A) | Graphite | Proterozoic |
| 82 | Limberg-Oberdürnbach (A) | Diatomite | Tertiary |
| 83 | Retz – Znojmo (CZ) | Kaolin | Tertiary |
| 84 | Ivančice (CZ) | Bentonite | Miocene |
| 85 | Javorka (CZ) | Fluorite-barite | Alpine |
| 86 | Křišany (CZ) | Fluorite(-barite) | Alpine |
| 87 | Rozdroze Izerskie (PL) | Quartz | Variscan ? |
| 88 | Harrachov (CZ) | Fluorite-Pb | Variscan–Alpine |
| 89 | Berzdorf (D) | Bentonite | Tertiary |
| 90 | Czerwona Woda (PL) | Kaolin | Cretaceous |
| 91 | Zebrzydowa (PL) | Kaolin | Cretaceous |
| 92 | Stanisławów-Boguszów (PL) | Barite-fluorite | Alpine ? |
| 93 | Zarów (PL) | Kaolin | Cretaceous–Tertiary |
| 94 | Sobótka (PL) | Magnesite | Devonian |
| 95 | Wyszonowice (PL) | Kaolin | Tertiary |
| 96 | Szklary (PL) | Magnesite | Devonian |
| 97 | Braszowice (PL) | Magnesite | Devonian |
| 98 | Nowa Ruda (PL) | Bauxite | Carboniferous |
| 99 | Kletno (PL) | Fluorite | Alpine |
| 100 | Staré Město (CZ) | Graphite | Proterozoic |
| 101 | Radzionków (PL) | Bentonite | Upper Carboniferous |
| 102 | Burzenin (PL) | Phosphorite | Cretaceous |
| 103 | Chmielnik (PL) | Bentonite | Tertiary (Tortonian) |
| 104 | Staszów-Tarnobrzeg-Lubaczów-Swoszowice-Posądza-Czarkowy (PL) | Sulphur | Tertiary |
| 105 | Dąbrowa Tarnowska (PL) | Kaolin | Miocene |
| 106 | Mielec – Kolbuszowa (PL) | Kaolin | Miocene |
| 107 | Radom - Annopol (PL) | Phosphorite | Cretaceous |
| 108 | Michów – Branica (PL) | Phosphorite | Cretaceous |
| 109 | Leszczawka (PL) | Diatomite | Oligocene–Miocene |
| 110 | Miedzybrodzie (PL) | Bentonite | Palaeogene |
| 111 | Jaworze (PL) | Bentonite | Miocene |
| 112 | Polany (PL) | Bentonite | Palaeogene |
| 113 | Majerovce-Nižný Hrabovec (SK) | Zeolite | Neogene |
| 114 | Pozdišovce-Michalovce (SK) | Kaolin/halloysite | Pliocene |
| 115 | Lastovce-Kuzmice (SK) | Bentonite | Miocene |
| 116 | Füzérradvany (H) | Mica (illite) | Miocene |
| 117 | Pálháza (H) | Perlite | Miocene |
| 118 | Mád-Koldu (H) | Kaolin | Miocene |
| 119 | Mád-Királyhegy (H) | Bentonite-allevardite-alunite | Miocene |
| 120 | Bomboly (H) | Dickite | Miocene |
| 121 | Bodrogkeresztúr Kakas (H) | Zeolite | Miocene |
| 122 | Erdőbénye (H) | Diatomite | Miocene |
| 123 | Mád-Szegilong (H) | Kaolin-bentonite | Miocene |
| 124 | Košice (SK) | Magnesite | Permian |
| 125 | Paňovce (SK) | Asbestos | Triassic |
| 126 | Drienovec (SK) | Bauxite | Cretaceous |
| 127 | Švedlár (SK) | Quartz | Alpine |
| 128 | Drnava (SK) | Barite | Variscan |
| 129 | Gemerská Poloma (SK) | Talc | Alpine |
| 130 | Malužiná (SK) | Barite | Variscan |
| 131 | Jelšava (SK) | Magnesite | Permian |
| 132 | Hnúšt'a (SK) | Talc | Alpine |
| 133 | Breznička-Poltár(SK) | Kaolin | Pliocene |
| 134 | Tomášovce – Halič (SK) | Kaolin | Pliocene |
| 135 | Pinciná (SK) | Diatomite | Neogene |
| 136 | Močiar (SK) | Diatomite | Neogene |
| 137 | Stará Kremnička-Jelšový potok-Kopernica (SK) | Bentonite | Miocene |
| 138 | Bartošova Lehôtka (SK) | Kaolin | Pliocene |
| 139 | Mojtín (SK) | Bauxite | Late Cretaceous |
| 140 | Smolenice (SK) | Barite | Variscan |
| 141 | Poštorna (CZ) | Illite | Neogene |
| 142 | Istenmezeje (H) | Bentonite | Miocene |
| 143 | Nemti (H) | Zeolite | Neogene |
| 144 | Szurdokpüspöki (H) | Diatomite | Miocene |
| 145 | Romhány (H) | Kaolin | Oligocene |
| 146 | Felsőpetény-Bánk (H) | Kaolin | Oligocene |

(*continued*)

**Table 21.8.** (*continued*)

| Number | Deposit | Mineral association | Age of formation |
|---|---|---|---|
| 147 | Nagyegyháza (H) | Bauxite | Eocene |
| 148 | Gánt (H) | Bauxite | Eocene |
| 149 | Iszkaszentgyörgy (H) | Bauxite | Eocene |
| 150 | Fenyőfő (H) | Bauxite | Eocene |
| 151 | Dudar (H) | Bauxite | Eocene |
| 152 | Zirc – Alsóperepuszta (H) | Bauxite | Cretaceous |
| 153 | Halimba – Szőc (H) | Bauxite | Cretaceous–Eocene |
| 154 | Iharkút – Nyirád (H) | Bauxite | Cretaceous–Eocene |
| 155 | Sümeg (H) | Bauxite | Late Cretaceous |
| 156 | Cserszegtomaj (H) | Kaolin/coloured clay | Cretaceous |
| 157 | Zlatibor-Varda (BiH) | Magnesite | Jurassic |
| 158 | Vlasenica (BiH) | Bauxite | Cretaceous |
| 159 | Zvornik (BiH) | Bentonite | Miocene |
| 160 | Krivaja-Konjuh Mt. (BiH) | Magnesite | Jurassic |
| 161 | Mušići, Ozren Mt. (BiH) | Talc | Jurassic |
| 162 | Žarkovac, Ozren Mt. (BiH) | Talc | Jurassic |
| 163 | Bosansko Petrovo Selo, Ozren Mt. (BiH) | Asbestos (chrysotile) | Jurassic (Oligocene?) |
| 164 | Gračanica (BiH) | Bentonite | Miocene |
| 165 | Tešani (BiH) | Bentonite | Miocene |
| 166 | Jajce (BiH) | Bauxite | Cretaceous |
| 167 | Babići, Jajce (BiH) | Bentonite | Miocene |
| 168 | Barači (BiH) | Bauxite | Tertiary |
| 169 | Dalmatia, Herzegovina (HR; BiH) | Bauxite | Tertiary |
| 170 | Kijak, Dinara Mt., Dalmatia (HR) | Bauxite | Cretaceous |
| 171 | Gračac, Lika region (HR) | Barite | Carboniferous |
| 172 | Vrace, Lika region (HR) | Bauxite | Triassic |
| 173 | Obrovac, Dalmatia (HR) | Bauxite | Tertiary |
| 174 | Divoselo (HR) | Bentonite | Miocene |
| 175 | Grmeč Mt. (BiH) | Bauxite | Jurassic |
| 176 | Bosanska Krupa, Grmeč Mt. (BiH) | Bauxite | Cretaceous |
| 177 | Žune (Dolinac) (BiH) | Barite-fluorite | Permian |
| 178 | Vidrenjak (BiH) | Barite | Permian |
| 179 | Lješani- Bosanski Novi (BiH) | Bentonite | Miocene |
| 180 | Kozara-Pastirevo (BiH) | Magnesite | Jurassic |
| 181 | Banja Luka-Prnjavor (BiH) | Magnesite | Jurassic |
| 182 | Motajica Mt. (BiH) | Kaolin-feldspar-quartz | Eocene–Oligocene |
| 183 | Kaptol-Sivornica- Brusnik (HR) | Graphite | Ordovician–Silurian |
| 184 | Dukina Kosa (HR) | Feldspar-mica | Devonian–Carboniferous |
| 185 | G. Jelenska (HR) | Bentonite | Miocene |
| 186 | Kijak (HR) | Barite | Permian |
| 187 | Gejkovac (HR) | Barite | Permian |
| 188 | Kordun (HR) | Bauxite | Cretaceous |
| 189 | Lokve (HR) | Barite | Permo-Triassic |
| 190 | Mrzle vodice (HR) | Barite | Permo-Triassic |
| 191 | Školski Brijeg (HR) | Barite | Permo-Triassic |
| 192 | North Adriatic islands (HR) | Bauxite | Tertiary |
| 193 | Rovinj (HR) | Bauxite | Jurassic |
| 194 | Vrsar (HR) | Bauxite | Jurassic |
| 195 | Istria (HR) | Bauxite | Tertiary |
| 196 | Central and NW Slovenia deposits (SLO) | Bauxite | Tertiary |
| 197 | Hrušica (SLO) | Bauxite | Jurassic |
| 198 | Kamnik (SLO) | Bauxite | Triassic |
| 199 | Žužemberk (SLO) | Bauxite | Jurassic |
| 200 | Poljanska Luka (HR) | Bentonite | Miocene |
| 201 | Bednja-Šaša (HR) | Bentonite | Miocene |
| 202 | Stainz (A) | Bentonite | Miocene |
| 203 | Rutzendorf (A) | Bentonite | Miocene |
| 204 | Gossendorf (A) | Bentonite | Miocene |
| 205 | Schlaining (A) | Asbestos | Alpine |
| 206 | Aspang (A) | Mica | Cretaceous |
| 207 | Eichberg/Weißenbach (A) | Magnesite | Permian |
| 208 | Semmering (A) | Barite | Permian |
| 209 | St. Jakob (A) | Talc-chlorite | Cretaceous |
| 210 | Rabenwald (A) | Talc | Cretaceous |
| 211 | Steg/Anger (A) | Feldspar | Variscan |
| 212 | Großveitsch (A) | Magnesite | Permian |
| 213 | Breitenau (A) | Magnesite | Permian |
| 214 | Mixnitz (A) | Phosphorite | Pleistocene |
| 215 | Aflenz (A) | Diatomite | Miocene |

(*continued*)

**Table 21.8.** (*continued*)

| Number | Deposit | Mineral association | Age of formation |
|---|---|---|---|
| 216 | Oberdorf (A) | Magnesite | Permian |
| 217 | Gams (A) | Jet | Cretaceous |
| 218 | Gams (A) | Fluorite | Alpine |
| 219 | Unterlaussa (A) | Bauxite-jet | Cretaceous |
| 220 | Kaisersberg (A) | Graphite | Alpine |
| 221 | Mautern (A) | Talc | Cretaceous |
| 222 | Wald/Schober (A) | Magnesite | Permian |
| 223 | Trieben/Sunk (A) | Graphite | Alpine |
| 224 | Trieben (A) | Magnesite | Permian |
| 225 | Lassing (A) | Talc | Cretaceous |
| 226 | Weisskirchen (A) | Mica | Cretaceous |
| 227 | Fohnsdorf (A) | Bentonite | Miocene |
| 228 | Hirt (A) | Talc | Alpine? |
| 229 | Radenthein (A) | Magnesite | Permian |
| 230 | Edling/Spital (A) | Feldspar | Variscan |
| 231 | Hochfilzen (A) | Magnesite | Permian |
| 232 | Achselalm (A) | Fluorite-(Pb-Zn) | Alpine |
| 233 | Gösleswand (A) | Asbestos | Alpine |
| 234 | Hollenzen (A) | Asbestos | Alpine |
| 235 | Wolfendorn (A) | Kyanite | Alpine |
| 236 | Corvara (I) | Fluorite-(Pb-Zn) | Alpine (Permian?) |
| 237 | Case a Prato (I) | Fluorite-(barite-Pb) | Permian |
| 238 | Vallarsa (I) | Fluorite | Permian |
| 239 | Zumpanell (I) | Magnesite | Triassic |
| 240 | Vignola (I) | Fluorite-(Cu-Pb-Zn) | Alpine (Permian?) |
| 241 | Vegri-Campotamaso (I) | Bentonite | Cretaceous? |
| 242 | Marigole-Pice (I) | Barite | Alpine (Permian) |
| 243 | Torgola (I) | Fluorite | Alpine (Permian) |
| 244 | Pozzuolo (I) | Barite | Triassic |
| 245 | Valle di Meraldo, Gardena, Monte Elto (I) | Barite | Triassic |
| 246 | Laghetto di Polzone (I) | Fluorite | Triassic |
| 247 | Scortaseo (CH) | Talc | Jurassic–Cretaceous |
| 248 | Ruola (I) | Barite | Triassic |
| 249 | Val Brembana (I) | Fluorite | Triassic |
| 250 | Camissinone (I) | Fluorite | Triassic |
| 251 | Le Trappistes (CH) | Fluorite | Alpine |
| 252 | Baldissero (I) | Magnesite | Pleistocene |
| 253 | Balangero (I) | Asbestos | Alpine |
| 254 | Termignon (F) | Asbestos | Upper Jurassic–Cretaceous |
| 255 | Icla Brutta Comba (I) | Graphite | Carboniferous |
| 256 | Rocheray (=Bois Feuillet) (F) | Fluorite-(Pb) | Alpine |
| 257 | Rochefort-Samson (F) | Quartz-kaolin | Eocene |
| 258 | Hostun (F) | Kaolin-quartz | Eocene |
| 259 | Berbiéres (F) | Kaolin-quartz | Eocene |
| 260 | Condorcet (F) | Celestite-barite | Alpine |
| 261 | Mormoiron (F) | Bentonite-attapulgite | Oligocene |
| 262 | Apt (F) | Coloured clay | Cenomanian |
| 263 | Tapets (F) | Sulphur | Oligocene |
| 264 | Manosque (F) | Sulphur | Oligocene–Miocene |
| 265 | Perticara (I) | Sulphur | Miocene |

(4) unconformity-related fault-bound hypogene and supergene deposits of Early and Late Alpine age;
(5) deposits controlled by extension-related igneous activity along deep-seated fault zones;
(6) petroleum deposits.

This classification scheme is well-established for the extra-Alpine part of Central Europe (e.g. Dill 1988*a*, 1989, 1994; Dill & Nielsen 1987; Tischendorf *et al.* 1995) and is extended in the present review to the Alpine realm, where similar subdivisions have been applied by Pohl (1993), Pohl & Belocky (1999) and Rodeghiero *et al* (1996).

Categories 1 to 5 reflect extensional and compressional regimes and their resultant igneous activity, as well as uplift and erosion during the late stages of the Variscan and Alpine orogenies. The formation of petroleum deposits (6) requires a wide range of processes (e.g. deposition of source and reservoir rocks, trap formation, petroleum generation and migration) which may occur during different times and in different tectonic regimes, even within a single basin. Therefore, petroleum deposits do not fit into any of the first five categories and form a separate sixth category.

Cross-sections of typical deposits of categories 1 to 3 are shown in Figure 21.2. The complex geological setting of unconformity-related deposits is illustrated in a set of idealized cross-sections in Figure 21.3. Figure 21.4 presents the Kaiserstuhl Nb-bearing carbonatite in the Upper Rhine Graben as a representative of category 5. Cross-sections through petroliferous basins are portrayed in the relevant sections.

Modern radiometric age dating (e.g. Wernicke & Lippolt

**Table 21.9.** *Evaporite deposits (see CD inside back cover)*

| Number | Deposit | Element association | Age of formation |
|---|---|---|---|
| 1 | Hauterives (F) | Na | Eocene?–Oligocene |
| 2 | Etrez (F) | Na | Eocene–Oligocene |
| 3 | Perrigny (F) | Na | Upper Triassic |
| 4 | Poligny (F) | Na | Upper Triassic |
| 5 | Arc-et-Senans-Besancon (F) | Na | Upper Triassic–Neogene |
| 6 | Rheinfelden (CH) | Na | Middle Triassic |
| 7 | Zurzach (CH) | Na | Middle Triassic |
| 8 | Rheinheim (D) | Na | Triassic |
| 9 | Mulhouse (F) | K | Neogene |
| 10 | Buggingen (D) | K | Palaeogene |
| 11 | Stetten (D) | Na | Middle Triassic |
| 12a | Nancy - Dombasle (F) | Na | Upper Triassic |
| 12b | Dieuze (F) | Na | Upper Triassic |
| 13 | Jemeppe (B) | Na | Zechstein |
| 14 | Heilbronn (D) | Na | Middle Triassic |
| 15 | Bad Friedrichshall-Kochendorf (D) | Na | Middle Triassic |
| 16 | Philippshall - Bad Dürkheim (D) | Na | Neogene? |
| 17 | Bad Münster am Stein (D) | Na | Palaeogene |
| 18 | Bad Kreuznach (D) | Na | Palaeogene |
| 19 | Neuhof Ellers (D) | K-Mg | Zechstein |
| 20 | Merkers (D) | K-(Na-Br) | Zechstein |
| 21 | Unterbreizbach (D) | K | Zechstein |
| 22 | Hattorf - Unterbreizbach (D) | K-Na-Mg | Zechstein |
| 23 | Springen (D) | K-(Br) | Zechstein |
| 24 | Wintershall (D) | K Mg | Zechstein |
| 25 | Oberilm (D) | Na | Zechstein |
| 26 | Kassel-Wilhelmshöhe (D) | Na | Zechstein |
| 27 | Bad Karlshafen (D) | Na | Zechstein |
| 28 | Göttingen-Grone (D) | Na | Zechstein |
| 29 | Sollstedt (D) | K | Zechstein |
| 30 | Volkenroda-Päthess (D) | K | Zechstein |
| 31 | Sonderhausen (D) | K-(Br) | Zechstein |
| 32 | Bleicherode (D) | K | Zechstein |
| 33 | Bischofferode (D) | K | Zechstein |
| 34 | Roßleben- Georg-Unstrut (D) | K | Zechstein |
| 35 | Halle a.d. Saale (D) | Na | Zechstein |
| 36 | Bernburg-Gröhna (D) | Na | Zechstein |
| 37 | Staßfurt (D) | Na-K | Zechstein |
| 38 | Schönebeck-Salzelmen (D) | K-Na | Zechstein |
| 39 | Zielitz (D) | K-Na | Zechstein |
| 40 | Bartensleben-Marie (D) | Na | Zechstein |
| 41 | Braunschweig-Lüneburg (D) | Na | Zechstein |
| 42 | Hildesheimer Wald (D) | K-Mg-Br | Zechstein |
| 43 | Lehrte-Sehnde (D) | K-Mg | Zechstein |
| 44 | Wathlingen (D) | K-Na | Zechstein |
| 45 | Bokeloh (D) | K | Zechstein |
| 46 | Borth (D) | Na | Zechstein |
| 47 | Hengelo (NL) | Na | Lower Triassic |
| 48 | Epe (D) | Na | Zechstein |
| 49 | Weerselo Overijssel, NE Hengelo (NL) | Na | Zechstein |
| 50a | Zuidwending Groningen (NL) | Na | Zechstein |
| 50b | Veendam Groningen (NL) | Na-K-Mg | Zechstein |
| 51 | Harlingen (NL) | Na | Zechstein |
| 52 | Winschoten Groningen (NL) | Na | Zechstein |
| 53 | Harsefeld (D) | Na | Zechstein |
| 54 | Stade (D) | Na, | Zechstein |
| 55 | Hvornum (N of border of the map - DK) | Na-K | Zechstein |
| 56 | Lüneburg (D) | Na | Zechstein |
| 57 | Bad Sülze (D) | Na | Zechstein |
| 58 | Kolobrzeg (PL) | Na | Zechstein |
| 59 | Leba (PL) | Na-K | Zechstein |
| 60 | Nowa Sól (PL) | Na-K | Zechstein |
| 61 | Mogilno (PL) | Na | Zechstein |
| 62 | Inowrocław (PL) | Na | Zechstein |
| 63 | Kłodawa (PL) | Na | Zechstein |
| 64 | Barycz (PL) | Na | Miocene |
| 65 | Wieliczka (PL) | Na | Miocene |
| 66 | Łężkowice-Siedlec (PL) | Na | Miocene |
| 67 | Bochnia (PL) | Na | Miocene |

(*continued*)

**Table 21.9.** (*continued*)

| Number | Deposit | Element association | Age of formation |
|---|---|---|---|
| 68 | Tarnów-Sierakowice (PL) | Na | Miocene |
| 69 | Zbudza (SK) | Na | Miocene |
| 70 | Sol' (SK) | Na | Miocene |
| 71 | Prešov-Sol'ná Baňa (SK) | Na | Miocene |
| 72 | Tuzla (BiH) | Na | Miocene |
| 73 | Altaussee (A) | Na | Permian |
| 74 | Bad Ischl (A) | Na | Permian |
| 75 | Sulzbach (A) | Na | Permian |
| 76 | Hallstatt (A) | Na | Permian |
| 77 | Roßalm (A) | Na | Permian |
| 78 | Dürrnberg/Hallein (A) | Na | Permian |
| 79 | Berchtesgaden (D) | Na | Permian |
| 80 | Rosenheim (D) - Traunstein (D) | Na | Permian |
| 81 | Bad Reichenhall (D) | Na | Permian |
| 82 | Hall in Tirol (A) | Na | Permian |
| 83 | Bex (CH) | Na | Triassic |

**Table 21.10.** *Hydrocarbon provinces (see CD inside back cover)*

| Number | Hydrocarbon province |
|---|---|
| 1 | Northwest European Basin |
| 1a | Southern Permian Basin |
| 1a-1 | Thuringian Basin |
| 1a-2 | Mecklenburg District |
| 1a-3 | Pommerian District |
| 1a-4 | Lusatian - Fore-Sudetic District |
| 1a-5 | Zielona Góra Trough |
| 1a-6 | Poznan Trough |
| 1b | West Netherlands Basin |
| 1c | Broad Fourteens Basin |
| 1d | Southern Central Graben |
| 1e | Lower Saxony Basin |
| 1f | Gifhorn Trough |
| 1g | Hamburg Trough |
| 1h | Heide Trough |
| 1i | East Holstein Trough |
| 2 | Baltic Syneclise |
| 3 | Paris Basin |
| 4 | Upper Rhine Graben |
| 5 | Alpine Foreland Basin |
| 6 | Carpathian Foreland and Carpathian Flysch Belt |
| 7 | Vienna Basin |
| 8 | Po Basin |
| 9 | Pannonian Basin |
| 9a | Sava Depression |
| 9b | Drava Depression |
| 9c | Zala Basin |
| 9d | Danube Basin |
| 9e | Great Hungarian Plain |
| 9f | East Slovak Basin |

1997*a*) has allowed the Alpine unconformity-related deposits to be subdivided into two age groups. The older one encompasses Upper Carboniferous to Lower Jurassic vein mineralization immediately below the Variscan unconformity and epigenetic deposits in overlying sediments. These deposits are termed 'Early Alpine unconformity-related'. In contrast, 'Late Alpine unconformity-related' deposits include Upper Jurassic to Cenozoic epigenetic mineralization.

Each of the following sections begins with a brief discussion of the geodynamic setting providing a framework for the understanding of ore-forming processes. More detailed compilations are given in the relevant chapters of this book. The country of each mining site or mineralized area is given in parentheses, using the common international abbreviation: Austria (A), Belgium (B), Bosnia-Herzogovina (BiH), Croatia (HR), Czech Republic (CZ), Denmark (DK), France (F), Germany (D), Hungary (H), Italy (I), Lithuania (LT), Luxembourg (L), the Netherlands (NL), Poland (PL), Russia (RU), Serbia (SRB), Slovakia (SK), Slovenia (SLO), Spain (E), Switzerland (CH).

## Variscan cycle

### *Strata-bound deposits*

*Precambrian-Cambrian*

Several Palaeozoic plates, including Gondwana and Baltica, originated from the Late Proterozoic breakup of the Rodinia supercontinent. Apart from the Eastern European Craton (EEC) (East European Platform), which formed part of Baltica, the area of today's Central Europe was located at the active northern margin of Gondwana, where it became affected by the Neoproterozoic Cadomian Orogeny (e.g. Tait *et al.* 2000; Winchester *et al.* 2002; Krawczyk *et al.* 2008).

During Cambrian times, initial rift zones became apparent along the north Gondwana margin. However, only a few crustal blocks (e.g. Małopolska Terrane) rifted away from Gondwana and docked with the EEC. Thus, the majority of the pre-Variscan relicts in Central Europe remained near Gondwana and were characterized by the formation of oceanic crust, island arcs, and the deposition of carbonates and volcanosedimentary rocks in arc-related basins (Neubauer *et al.* 1999; von Raumer *et al.* 2002, 2003).

Evidence of Precambrian metallogenesis can be found mainly in the Bohemian Massif. In the Teplá-Barrandian Zone of the Bohemian Massif the Neoproterozoic/Cambrian boundary is marked by an angular unconformity between Neoproterozoic basement rocks and transgressively overlying Lower Palaeozoic sedimentary and volcanosedimentary sequences (Chlupáč *et al.* 1998). Irrespective of the unconformity, Precambrian and Cambrian strata-bound deposits are dealt with together, since the type of mineralization is similar. Moreover, due to the poor age data of the host rocks, a clear attribution to one or the other period is often impossible.

The Moldanubian Zone in the Bohemian Massif is subdivided from base to top into the Ostrong (= Monotonous), Drosendorf

**Table 21.11.** *Coal deposits (see CD inside back cover)*

| Carboniferous coal deposits | |
|---|---|
| C1a | Wallonian Basin (Hainault; B) |
| C1b | Wallonian Basin (Liege; B) |
| C2 | Aachen – South Limburg (D, NL) |
| C2a | Aachen – Erkelenz (D) |
| C3 | Campine Basin (B) |
| C4 | Ruhr (D) |
| C5 | Winterswijk (NL) |
| C6 | Ibbenbüren (D) |
| C7 | Saar-Lorraine (D, F) |
| C8 | Sincey (F) |
| C9 | Blanzy (F) |
| C10 | Autun (plus oil shales) (F) |
| C11 | St. Etienne (F) |
| C12 | La Mure (F) |
| C13 | La Thuile (I) |
| C14 | Lons-le-Saunier (F) |
| C15 | Ronchamp (F) |
| C16 | St. Hippolyte (F) |
| C17 | Baden-Baden (D) |
| C18 | Stockheim (D) |
| C19 | Manebach (D) |
| C20 | Ilfeld (D) |
| C21 | Wettin (D) |
| C22 | Zwickau-Ölsnitz (D) |
| C23 | Freital (D) |
| C24 | Doberlug (D) |
| C25a | Western Bohemian Basin (CZ) |
| C25b | Central Bohemian Basin (CZ) |
| C26 | Lower Silesian Basin (CZ, PL) |
| C27 | Rosice – Oslavany (CZ) |
| C28 | Upper Silesian Basin (CZ, PL) |
| C29 | Lublin (PL) |
| **Mesozoic coal deposits** | |
| M1 | Osnabrück (D) |
| M2 | Barsinghausen (D) |
| M3 | Zawiercie (PL) |
| M4 | Foreland of Łysa Góra (PL) |
| M5 | Gresten Coal District (A) |
| M6 | Lunz Coal District (A) |
| M7 | Grünbach (A) |
| M8 | Ajka (H) |
| M9 | Mecsek (H) |
| **Palaeogene coal deposits** | |
| P1 | Lower Hesse (Borken – Kassel) (D) |
| P2 | Sybhercynian Basin (D) |
| P3 | Middle Germany (Halle – Borna) (D) |
| P3a | Geiselthal (D) |
| P3b | Oberröblingen-Amsdorf (D) |
| P4 | Upper Bavaria (D) |
| P5 | Häring (A) |
| P6 | Herzogenburg – Krems (A) |
| P7a | Secovlje (SLO) |
| P7b | Vremski Britof (+latest Cretaceous coal) (SLO) |
| P7c | Rasa Valley (HR) |
| P8a | Zabukovica (SL) |
| P8b | Zasavje (Trbovlje – Hrastnik) (SLO) |
| P8c | Senovo (SL) |
| P8d | Pregrada – Radoboj (HR) |
| P9a | Oroszlány (H) |
| P9b | Tatabánya (H) |

*(continued)*

**Table 21.11.** (*continued*)

| Neogene coal deposits | |
|---|---|
| N1 | Lower Rhine Basin (D) |
| N2 | Wetterau (D) |
| N3 | Rhön (D) |
| N4 | Hoher Meißner (D) |
| N5 | Middle Germany (Leipzig –Bitterfeld) (plus amber) (D) |
| N6 | Lower Lusatia (D, PL) |
| N7 | Legnica (PL) |
| N8 | Poznan (PL) |
| N9 | Konin (PL) |
| N10 | Adamów (PL) |
| N11 | Łodz (PL) |
| N12 | Bełchatów (PL) |
| N13 | Radom (PL) |
| N14 | Eger [Ohře] Graben (D, CZ, PL) |
| N14a | Cheb (CZ) |
| N14b | Sokolov (CZ) |
| N14c | Most (CZ) |
| N14d | Zittau (D, PL) |
| N14e | Görlitz (D, PL) |
| N15 | Oberpfalz (Schwandorf - Wackersdorf) (D) |
| N16 | Käpfnach (CH) |
| N17 | Trimmelkam (A) |
| N18 | Hausruck (A) |
| N19 | Langau (A, CZ) |
| N20 | Noric Depression (A) |
| N20a | Fohnsdorf (A) |
| N20b | Leoben (A) |
| N21 | Lavanttal (A) |
| N22 | Velenje (SLO) |
| N23 | Wies – Eibiswald (A) |
| N24 | Köflach – Voitsberg (A) |
| N25 | Tauchen – Mariasdorf (A) |
| N26 | Torony (H) |
| N27 | Brennberg (H, A) |
| N28 | Zillingdorf – Sollenau (A) |
| N29 | Hodonin – Dubrany – Gbely (CZ, SK) |
| N30 | Upper Nitra Basin (Handlová, Novaký; SK) |
| N31 | Várpalota (H) |
| N32 | Nógrád - Modrý Kamen (HU, SK) |
| N33 | Borsod (H) |
| N34 | Visonta-Bükkábrány (H) |
| N34a | Visonta (H) |
| N34b | Bükkábrány (H) |
| N35 | Kocevje (SLO) |
| N36 | Globoko (SLO) |
| N37 | Konjscina (HR) |
| N38 | Ivanec-Varazdin (HR) |
| N39 | Pokupsko-Vukomer (HR) |
| N40 | Ludbreg-Koprivnica (HR) |
| N41 | Bilogora-Podravski Basin (HR) |
| N42 | Posavje Basin (HR) |
| N43 | Kamengrad (BiH) |
| N44 | Banja Luka (BiH) |
| N45 | Tesanj (BiH) |
| N46 | Stanari Basin (BiH) |
| N47 | Gracanica Basin (BiH) |
| N48 | Kreka – Tuzla (BiH) |
| N49 | Banovici (BiH) |
| N50 | Central Bosnia (Zenica-Kakanj-Breza; BiH) |
| N51 | Ugljevik (BiH) |
| N52 | Kolubara (SRB) |
| N53 | Kostolac (SRB) |

(= Variegated) and Gföhl units. The Ostrong Unit is derived from Late Proterozoic-age arenaceous and argillaceous clastic rocks deposited in a shallow-marine rift basin with local placer-like Au concentrations. In contrast an Early Palaeozoic age is likely for the sedimentary precursors of the Drosendorf Unit whose bimodal volcanic rocks may be assigned to within-plate volcanism (Kroner *et al.* 2008). The Gföhl Unit is mainly composed of high-pressure granulites.

Metallogenesis in Central Europe corresponds to the complex

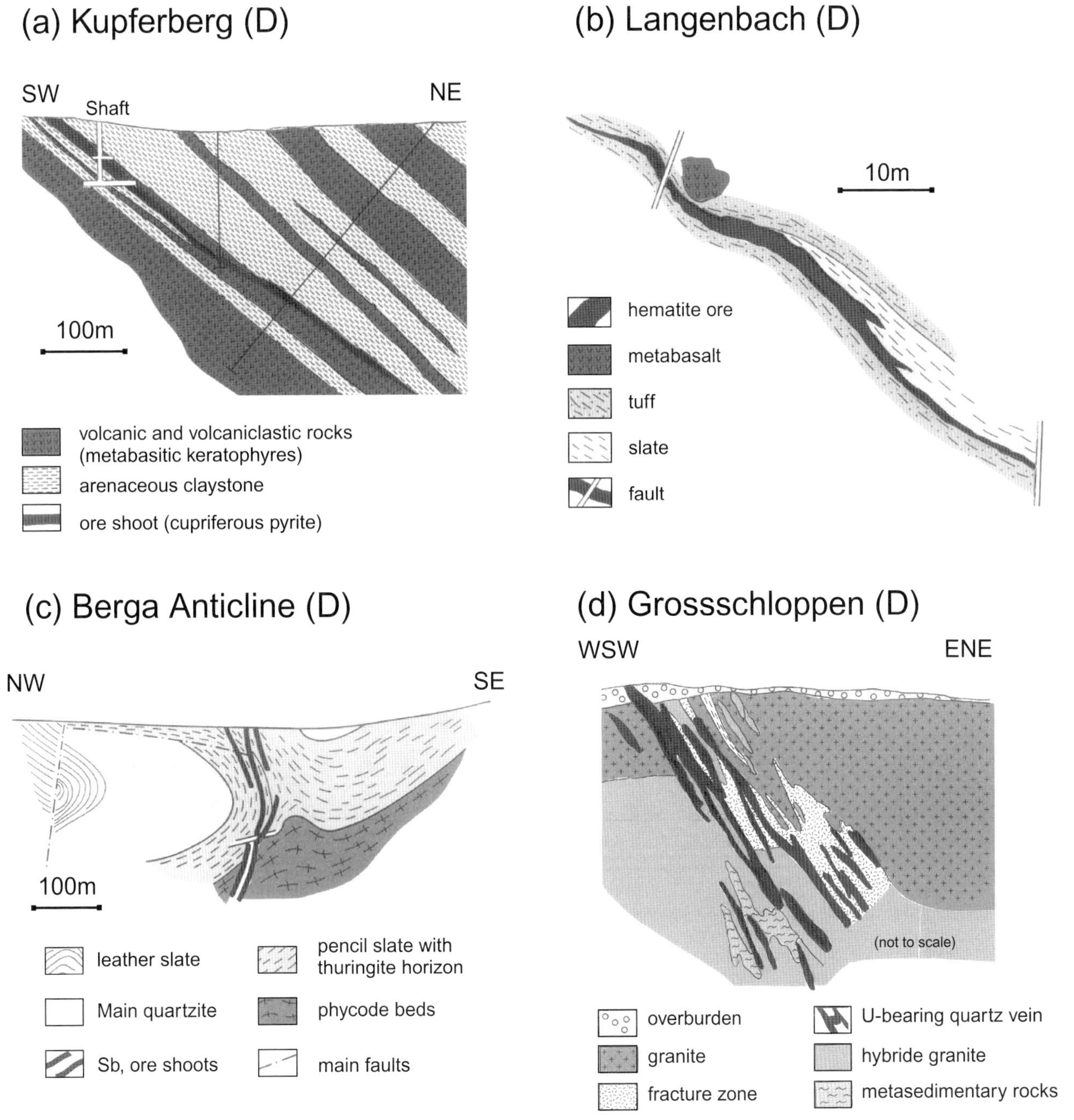


**Fig. 21.2.** Cross-sections of typical mineral deposits referrred to in the text: (**a**) strata-bound deposit, e.g. Kupferberg (D), Au-bearing Cu–Zn sulphide deposit (VMS type); (**b**) strata-bound–stratiform, e.g. Langenbach mining district (D), hematite deposit (Lahn Dill type/SEDEX type); (**c**) thrust-bound, e.g. Berga Anticline (D), stibnite–quartz veins (type: mesothermal Au–Sb–As vein); (**d**) granite-related, e.g. Grossschloppen (D), polymetallic U deposit (type: silicified mineralized structure zone and episyenite).

geodynamic evolution of the northern Gondwana margin during Neoproterozioc and Cambrian times. Deposits with graphite and Fe, Cu, Zn and Pb sulphides are widespread in the Bohemian Massif (Pouba & Křibek 1986). Bathymetric conditions led to the development of dysaerobic to anaerobic depositional environments. In calcareous rocks, base metal and sideritic Fe deposits developed under moderately reducing conditions. Moreover, active continental margin settings formed the basis for one of the most important scheelite deposits, and ophiolitic sequences host a suite of elements such as Cr, Ni and platinum-group elements (PGE) related to basic and ultrabasic igneous rocks.

**Graphite and semigraphite deposits.** At the southern margin of the Bohemian Massif (Moldanubian Zone; Drosendorf Unit), several graphite deposits occur in the Passau Forest at Kropfmühl-Pfaffenreuth (D), in Austria (e.g. Mühlberg; closed in 1988), at

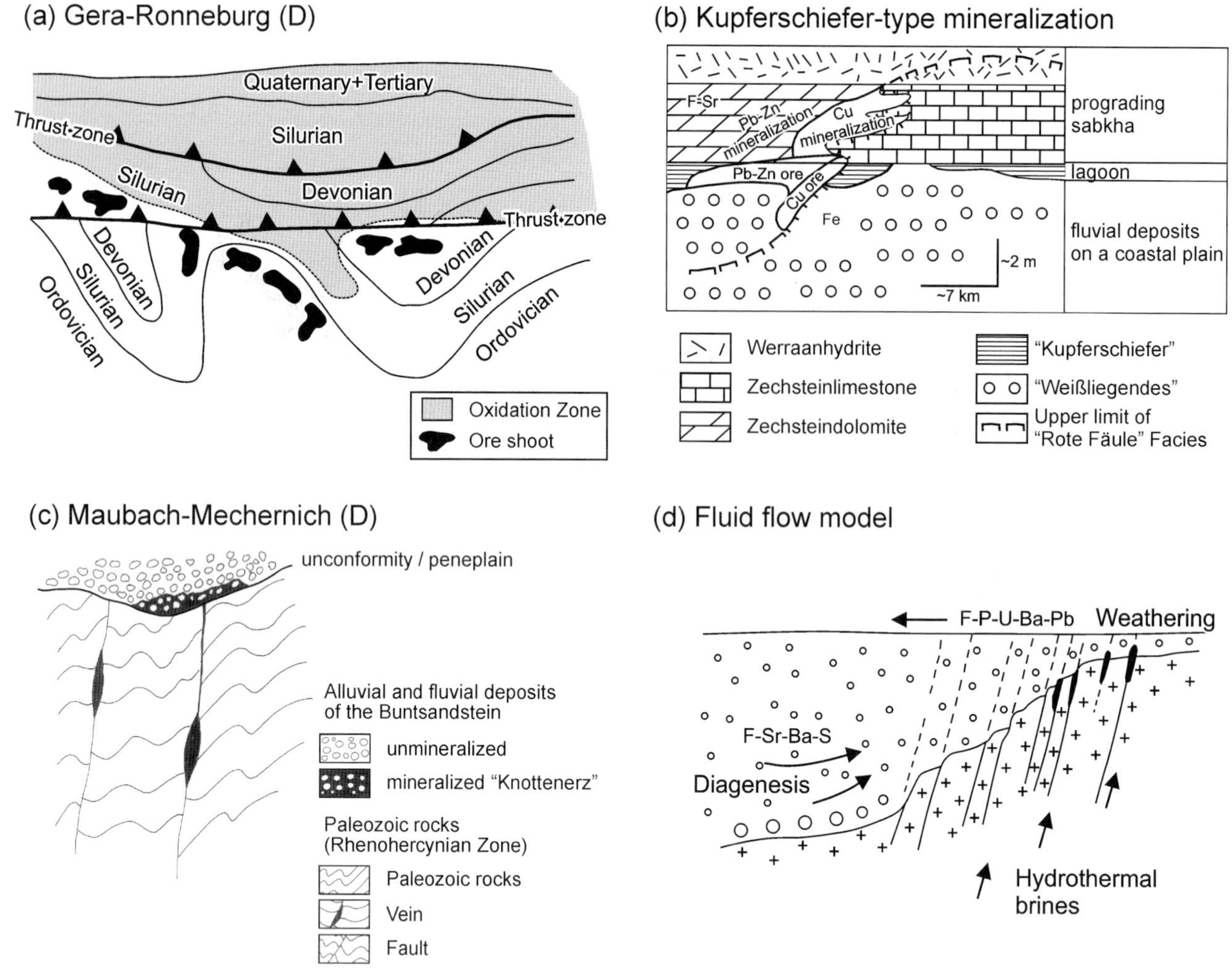


**Fig. 21.3.** Unconformity-related deposits. (**a**) Supergene unconformity-related U deposits in the Gera-Ronneburg mining district (D). Early Palaeozoic 'low-metal concentrations' were subject to chemical weathering from the Late Palaeozoic onward. (**b**) Kupferschiefer-type mineralization above and below the Early Alpine unconformity (model modified from Rentzsch 1974). (**c**) Schematic cross-section illustrating the genetic relation between post-Variscan vein-type deposits in the folded Variscan basement and arenaceous deposits of Triassic age (Maubach-Mechernich (D)). Lead mineralization forms cement ('Erzknotten') of siliciclastics spread across the unconformity/peneplain (model modified from Krahn 1988). (**d**) Model to show fluid movement and the direction of the sediment dispersal system above the unconformity near the basement edge (Dill & Carl 1987).

Černá (CZ), Krumlov (CZ), Koloděje nad Lužnicí (CZ) and Staré Město (CZ) (Houzar & Novák 2002). The sedimentary graphite deposits are, in places, abundant in metaphosphorites. Graphite with low crystallinity (amorphous graphite) and well-crystallized flaky graphite are exploited from lenses intercalated into paragneisses and marbles. Deposits of amorphous graphite have also been explored in the Moldanubian/Saxothuringian border zone near Tirschenreuth-Mähring (D) (Teuscher & Weinelt 1972).

**Silicate- (and carbonate-) hosted base metal–iron sulphide deposits (VMS, SMS, Kieslager type).** A compilation of deposits in the central parts of the Bohemian Massif was provided by Mrázek (1986) who also demonstrated that the Late Proterozoic metallogeny was related to volcanic and post-volcanic thermal activity. Pyrite and pyrrhotite mineralization with subordinate amounts of Cu and Zn sulphides occur in low-grade regionally metamorphosed basic and intermediate metavolcanic rocks. A representative of this type of ore deposit is located near Struhadlo/Klatovy (CZ) at the SW edge of the Teplá-Barrandian Zone. It is considered to be equivalent to the modern Cyprus-type ore deposits. Cu–Zn sulphide mineralization in basic and acidic metavolcanites of the Jílové Belt near the boundary between the Teplá-Barrandian and Moldanubian zones are considered to be genetically equivalent to mineralizations in Archean greenstone belts (Morávek & Pouba 1990).

A mineralization of Proterozoic age, unique for Central Europe, contains V-bearing garnet, roscoellite, coffinite and uraninite in silicites covering large areas in the SE and western parts of the Teplá-Barrandian Zone. Fe content is up to 35% while U and V contents are up to 0.2% (Mrázek & Pouba 1995). The role of organic matter in the formation of the metal-rich shales in the Late Precambrian Bohemian Massif has been noted by Pašava *et al.* (1996). This strata-bound mineralization is similar to that in Siluro-Devonian black shales (Graptolite Shales) elsewhere in Central Europe in terms of geochemistry and geodynamic setting.

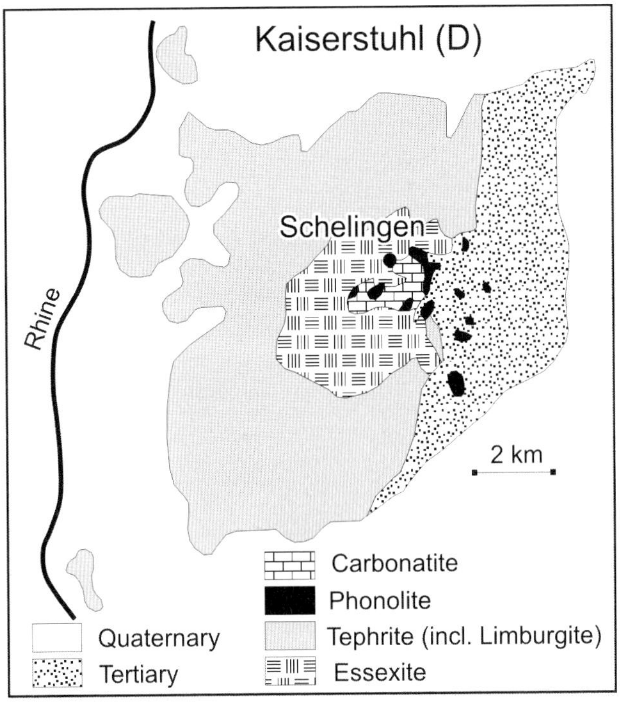


**Fig. 21.4.** Deposits controlled by extension-related igneous activity along deep-seated fault zones: the carbonatite-hosted Nb deposit in the Kaiserstuhl igneous complex at Schelingen (D) (modified after Keller 1984).

A pyrite-bearing mineralization in black shales was mined for Fe–Mn ore by open-pit operations at Chvaletice in the Železné Hory Mountains (CZ) and to produce sulphur for the chemical industry (Pouba & Ilavský 1986). The deposit also contains Mn-bearing silicates and carbonates together with Fe sulphides, but Mn could not be won economically. Mn carbonates are associated with coarse-grained clastic rocks attesting to some shallowing of the sea during the Late Precambrian in an otherwise deep-marine basin. Elevated organic matter contents in the Upper Precambrian sediments were decisive for the concentration of metals, while the metal source is related to submarine-exhalative vent systems associated with the aforementioned volcanism.

The Drosendorf Unit of the Moldanubian Zone hosts one of the most remarkable mineralizations, the Lam-Bodenmais Kies Belt (D) (Dill 1990*a*). The last mine was operated for raw materials used in the glass industry for polishing, and ceased production in 1953. These sediment-hosted Fe–Zn–Cu–Pb sulphides show a zonation into a proximal Fe–Zn–Cu association with Fe-enriched sphalerite, argentiferous galena, pyrite and pyrrhotite and a distal Pb–Ba mineralization. Zn concentration involved precipitation of the aforementioned sphalerite, Zn spinel/kreittonite, a black variety of gahnite containing ferrous Fe or ferric Fe, and Zn staurolite. In view of the significant amounts of Ba associated with these deposits and the Pb and S isotopes, these sediment-hosted deposits are classified as Sullivan-type/Meggen-type deposits *sensu* Krebs (1981), Jiang *et al.* (1998) and Taylor & Beaudoin (2000).

Within the Saxothuringian Zone, stratigraphically higher than the deposits of the Lam-Bodenmais Kies Belt (D), pyrrhotite- and pyrite ore bodies were found in the Fichtelgebirge within paragneisses and mica schists and were mined between 1923 and 1971 in the Bayerland Mine near Waldsassen (D). Magnetite-bearing layers are abundant in the vicinity and a silica zone was drilled in the footwall of these ore bodies (Wolf 1971; Dill 1989). The host rock sequence was subjected to low- to medium-grade regional metamorphism. Pyrite and pyrrhotite ore bodies are unrelated to the different degrees of metamorphism but are controlled palaeogeographically (Dill 1989). Pyrite is inferred to have been precipitated in a relatively shallow-marine environment, whereas pyrrhotite formed in deeper waters.

Restricted aeration and a high sulphur partial pressure in the basin were additional factors responsible for the preservation of organic matter and the concentration of Fe, Cu and Zn sulphides in metamorphosed clastic rocks in the Erzgebirge at Tisová (CZ), Klingenthal (D), Elterlein (D), and Jahnsbach (D) (Pertold *et al.* 1994; Tischendorf *et al.* 1995; Baumann *et al.* 2000). In addition to the siliciclastic-hosted Fe deposits, there are also some carbonate-hosted Fe–Zn–Cu–Pb deposits in the Erzgebirge, e.g. Lengefeld (D) and Hermsdorf (D) in the Cambrian Klinovec and Thum Groups. In comparison to the Irish-type or Mississippi-Valley type (MVT) Pb–Zn deposits, the Central European carbonate-hosted Zn–Cu–Pb deposits contain higher amounts of Ag and Sb (Sawkins 1984). These discrepancies between Early and Late Palaeozoic carbonate-hosted Fe–Zn–Cu–Pb deposits may be explained by the higher temperature regime during greenschist metamorphism, which the Central European base-metal deposits were subjected to.

In the Eastern Alps (Ötztal Nappe), the Monteneve/Schneeberg mine (I) forms part of a horizon mineralized with Zn–Pb minerals that extends over *c.* 20 km within paragneisses of pre-Silurian age (Förster & Schmitz 1972; Frizzo *et al.* 1982). The ore bodies contain Cd- and Mn-rich sphalerite and Ag-rich galena, with minor pyrrhotite, chalcopyrite, pyrite and stibnite. Gangue minerals include carbonates, quartz, garnet, amphibole, biotite, chlorite, muscovite, albite and tourmaline. The Monteneve deposit underwent strong metamorphism, that caused deformation, selective remobilization and recrystallization of a precursor sedimentary mineralization.

A number of 'Kieslager' deposits (Migiandone-Ornavasso (I), Cuzzago (I), Nibbio (I), Val di Mengo (I), Alpe Collio (I)) occur in the middle Val d'Ossola of Piedmont in the Kinzigitic Series of the Ivrea Zone. The ore deposits are associated with amphibolite–granulite facies metasediments and metavolcanics. Pyrrhotite, chalcopyrite, pyrite, sphalerite, ilmenite, titanite, and magnetite form either high-grade disseminated or massive ore bodies within the amphibolite, paragneiss and felsic granulites (Fagnani 1947). The ore mineralization originated from synsedimentary volcanic activity in an oceanic basin which is characterized by MORB-type basaltic magmatism.

**Carbonate-hosted iron deposits.** Fe deposits in the Saxothuringian Zone, closely related to the (Pre-)Cambrian Wunsiedel Marble, have been mined for many decades at various sites in the Fichtelgebirge (e.g. Arzberg (D), Tröstau (D)). The origin of the deposits and the age of the calcareous host rock have been much debated (e.g. Tischendorf 1986). Some authors suggest that the layered siderite ore bodies are part of the Variscan Fe skarn association, while others consider them to be related to Early Palaeozoic syngenetic siderite mineralization (Horstig & Teuscher 1979; Dill 1985*a*, 1989). Siderite, the most common mineral in these Lower Palaeozoic rocks, may be encountered either as massive bodies in metacarbonates, far from any granitic intrusion, or disseminated (even in metaclastic rocks) outside of the contact aureole of the granitic intrusions. Judging from the variegated lithology of the host sequence, the Fe-rich calcareous sediments formed on a shelf platform in a dysaerobic environment. As the Eh value was lowered, pyrite replaced siderite. Close to the surface, the sideritic Fe ore was altered into limonite which has been the target of mining. A total of 5 Mt of Fe ore containing 30–50% Fe were extracted until 1905. A re-evaluation of ore reserves during World War II yielded 4.3 Mt of ore.

During the Variscan Orogeny Fe, preconcentrated during the Early Palaeozoic, was remobilized from calcareous rocks. In the Železný Brod (CZ) area (West Sudetes), where an Arzberg-type ore exists, lenses of hematite and magnetite are conformably intercalated among Proterozoic or Lower Palaeozoic calcareous rocks exhibiting low-grade metamorphism (Mochnacka *et al.* 1995). The West Sudetes form part of the Lugian Zone (eastern part of the Saxothuringian Zone), which is characterized by many strata-bound magnetite, hematite and pyrite deposits related to submarine volcanic rocks. Subsequent regional metamorphism and the lack of reliable age data make any attempt at a minerostratigraphic correlation of these strata-bound ore mineralizations with the rest of the Bohemian Massif very difficult.

**Tin–tungsten–gold–lead–copper deposits (Freiberg Felsite Horizon and Mittersill type).** Pseudo-stratiform concentrations of cassiterite were discovered in the early 1960s in the Upper Proterozoic Freiberg Felsite Horizon (Erzgebirge; Saxothuringian Zone). A similar type of Sn accumulation was also found in the West Sudetes (Lugian Zone) at Nové Město pod Smrkem (CZ), Giercyn and Krobica (PL). The resources of the deposits at Giercyn and Krobica (PL) were estimated at about 2.9 Mt of ore with an average Sn content of about 0.48% (Polish Geological Institute 2004). Subeconomic cassiterite occurrences are hosted by mica–chlorite schists and accompanied by Fe, Cu, Bi, As, Co, Zn sulphides, scheelite and ferberite (Mochnacka *et al.* 1995). The rock suite passed through conditions of *c.* 520°C and 5–6 kbar at some stage during regional metamorphism, although a pre-metamorphic origin for at least some of the sulphides cannot be ruled out (Cook & Dudek 1994). Probably this sulphide-bearing Sn accumulation in Upper Proterozoic metamorphic rocks is the volcanosedimentary 'protore' of late Variscan granite-related Sn mineralizations (Baumann 1979). Collomorphous and needle-shaped cassiterite were precipitated late- to post-kinematically in mylonitic zones in the Erzgebirge, so that this Sn mineralization is categorized as thrust-bound rather than strata-bound. Some authors speculated that hydrothermal activity, associated with acid intrusives of the Variscan Karkonosze Pluton, introduced the mineralizing fluids along tectonic lineaments (Speczik & Wiszniewska 1984).

Significant W–Au–Cu–Pb mineralizations were formed in island-arc systems (Habach Terrane; Frisch & Neubauer 1989) now exposed in the Tauern Window of the Eastern Alps. Pb isotopes indicate mantle and crustal sources. The two ore fields in the Mittersill (Felbertal) scheelite deposit (A) were discovered in 1967 (Höll 1975; Höll & Eichhorn 2001). Since 1975 it has produced some 7 Mt of ore and still produces 400 000 t ore at a grade of 0.5% $WO_3$ annually. According to Eichhorn *et al.* (1999) the evolution of the Mittersill scheelite deposit commenced with the development of a volcanic arc at *c.* 550 Ma as indicated by the emplacement of volcanic-arc basalts. Approximately coeval crustal thinning occurred in a backarc region, accompanied by the emplacement of tholeiitic basalts and the intrusion of minor diorites. Subsequently (i.e. until 530 Ma), gabbroic and ultramafic melts intruded into the arc and backarc region followed by normal I-type granitoid melts with mantle signature. Highly differentiated, yet still mantle-dominated granitic melts were locally intruded between 530 Ma (Eastern Ore Zone) and 520 Ma (Western Ore Zone) into the Mittersill ore deposit.

**Chromium–titanium–nickel–PGE deposits.** Cr and Ni concentrations bound to basic and ultrabasic rocks occur in the Ransko Complex in eastern Bohemia (CZ). Ransko is a strongly differentiated intrusive body of peridotite, troctolites and gabbro undergoing liquid segregation which resulted in the formation of Ni–Cu and Zn–Cu sulphide concentrations (Pouba & Ilavský 1986; Van der Veen & Maaskant 1995; Pašava *et al.* 2003). An Early Cambrian age for the ultrabasic complex was suggested based on geological and palaeomagnetic studies (Marek 1970). The major minerals are pentlandite, pyrite and chalcopyrite associated with some mackinawite and magnetite, suggesting a Sudbury-type origin (Pouba & Ilavský 1986). Subeconomic Cr and PGE mineralizations occur in the Eastern Alps SW of Leoben at Kraubath (A) in a highly dismembered backarc ophiolite (Speik Terrane) (Malitch *et al.* 2003).

The Krzemianka ilmenite–magnetite deposit is located in NE Poland in the Mazury Complex (Baltic shield; East European Craton). The deposit is related to the Suwałki Anorthosite Massif and is liquid-magmatic in origin (Osika 1976; Wiszniewska 1998). It was discovered in 1962, but did not go into production for environmental reasons. Although it is completely obscured by Phanerozoic cover, the Suwałki intrusion has been drilled extensively. Isotope analyses were carried out using the Re–Os method for titanomagnetite and sulphide ores from Suwałki which yielded isochron ages of $1559 \pm 37$ and $1556 \pm 94$ Ma (Stein *et al.* 1998*a*; Wiszniewska 2000; Morgan *et al.* 2000).

*Ordovician–Silurian*

During Early Ordovician times Avalonia (i.e. Belgium, the Netherlands, parts of north Germany and Poland), including the Rhenohercynian Zone, began to rift away from Gondwana leading to opening of the Rheic Ocean. Subsequent collision with Baltica and Laurentia occurred during Ordovician/Silurian times (Krawczyk *et al.* 2008).

Drifting of the Armorican Terrane Assemblage and pre-Variscan relicts in the Alps, which were located in the eastern prolongation of Avalonia, was hampered by a (Proto-Tethyian) oceanic ridge. Instead of drifting, these detached terranes collided with Gondwana during an Ordovician orogeny (von Raumer *et al.* 2002, 2003). However, the resulting cordillera began to collapse during the Late Ordovician leading to the opening of the Palaeo-Tethys rift and the Late Silurian drift of the Hun-Superterrane comprising, amongst others, the Armorican Terrane Assemblage (including the Saxothuringian-Lugian, Teplá-Barrandian and Moldanubian zones) and most pre-Variscan relicts within the Alpine Mountain Range (Neubauer *et al.* 1999; Jurković & Pamić 2001; Stampfli & Borel 2002; von Raumer *et al.* 2003; see also Krawczyk *et al.* 2008). Evidence for Silurian rifting and volcanism is found in the Bohemian Massif, the Eastern Alps, the Western Carpathians and the Dinarides (e.g. Kukal 1985; Grecula *et al.* 1995; Jurković & Pamić 2001).

Within the Armorican Terrane Assemblage, a narrow 'Saxothuringian Ocean' separated the Saxothuringian and Bohemian (Teplá-Barrandian) terranes. The norhern margin of this ocean was characterized by shelf clastics (Thuringian facies exposed in the Thuringian-Franconian Massif) in the north and deeper water sediments interbedded with volcanic and volcaniclastic rocks, mainly of basaltic and spilitic composition (Vaavarian facies) in the South. Rocks of the Bavarian facies occur around the Münchberg Gneiss Complex in a sequence of tectonic klippen called the Randschiefer, Prasinit-Phyllit and Randamphibolit series, which underwent very low- to medium-grade regional metamorphism (Wirth 1978; Franke 1989). Oolithic Fe ore formed in a nearshore environment in the Thuringian facies, whereas the metallogenic inventory of the Bavarian facies (discussed below) is indicative of an active plate setting (Dill 1989) and has a metallogenetic equivalent in the Lower Austro-Alpine Nappe.

The Silurian was a period of worldwide anoxic events favouring the deposition of transgressive black shales (e.g. Cole 1994; Houseknecht *et al.* 1992; Paris *et al.* 1986; Xiao *et al.* 2000). Within Central Europe metalliferous black shales (Graptolite Shales) with a Silurian age are known from the Saxothuringian Zone, the Barrandian Zone, the Western Carpathians and the Tisza Unit basement of the south part of the Pannonian Basin. These black shales are enriched in base metals and rare earth elements all across Central Europe. Shallow-marine limestones interbedded with these black shales host syn- and epigenetic siderite ore.

**Ironstone deposits (Thuringite/Wabana type).** The worldwide deposition of Ordovician ironstones may be traced in the Lower Palaeozoic sedimentary rocks of the Bohemian Massif (Van Houten & Bhattacharyya 1982; Young 1989; Van Houten & Hou 1990).

In the Saxothuringian Zone, three seams of Ordovician-age oolithic Fe ores, containing siderite, thuringite, chamosite and magnetite, were formed during transgressions in a shallow-marine environment (Thuringian facies). The upper seam is up to 22 m thick (Bach *et al.* 1976) and formed the basis for mining operations near Gebersreuth (D), Schmiedefeld (D) and Wittmansgereuth (D). Related exploration was at Töpen, Bruck and Gräfenthal (D) (Reh & Schröder 1974; Dill 1985*a*). These massive beds of oolithic Fe ore are relatively high in P (*c.* 0.8 wt%) with Fe contents up to 50 wt% in magnetite-enriched beds.

Sedimentary Fe deposits of Ordovician age in the Teplá-Barrandian Zone were mined for hematite–siderite ore at Ejpovice and Krušná Hora (CZ), and for chamosite–siderite ore at Nučice and Zdice (CZ) until 1967 (Petránek 1975; Petránek & Van Houten 1977; Farshad 2001). The ironstones of the Czech deposits are grey-green in colour and contain ooids, pisoids and peloids. Chamosite is replaced by siderite almost completely at Nučice and Chrustinice. Relicts of chamosite may be admixed with high proportions of newly formed kaolinite and quartz (Zdice). At Nučice, pyrite framboids are strongly enriched together with magnetite, graphite, organic material, zircon, anatase and sulphides (galena, sphalerite, marcasite, chalcopyrite) (Farshad 2001).

Based on chemical composition, ore textures and lithofacies, these Ordovician-age Fe ores were attributed to the well-known Wabana type (Ranger 1979). The $\delta^{18}O$ values of mineral pairs from the Fe deposits yield calculated palaeotemperatures of *c.* 23°C. The epoch appears to have been characterized by atmospheric partial pressure of carbon dioxide ($P_{CO2}$) values which were 16–18 times higher than the present-day ones. The association of comparatively low tropical temperatures (and an icesheet at high palaeolatitude) with high atmospheric $P_{CO2}$ might have been the result of lower solar luminosity in the Late Ordovician (Yapp 1991, 1998).

**Gold-bearing copper–zinc–iron sulphide deposits (volcanic massive sulphide (VMS) type).** In Lower Palaeozoic rocks of the Bavarian facies (Fichtelgebirge; Saxothuringian Zone), stratiform ore bodies with pyrrhotite, pyrite, chalcopyrite, sphalerite and rare magnetite occur at Neufang and Sparneck (D) in the Prasinit-Phyllit Series and at Kupferberg (D) in the Randschiefer Series (Fig. 21.2a). The latter series is lithologically similar to the Prasinit-Phyllit Series, yet did not reach greenschist metamorphic conditions. The element composition of the ore includes Fe, Zn, and Cu, but no significant quantities of Pb. Au is present in amounts up to 2 ppm (Urban & Vache 1972). There is a striking difference between the S isotopes of the volcanic-hosted base-metal deposits of the Kupferberg-type and the sediment-hosted sulphide deposits at Waldsassen (D) previously discussed. Base-metal concentration is confined to bimodal volcanic and volcaniclastic host rocks of calc-alkaline affinity, so that the deposits of the Kupferberg–Neufang–Sparneck mineral belt are tentatively attributed to the Besshi-type deposits that reflect a subduction-related metallogenic setting (Hutchinson 1980; Fox 1984).

Within the Alpine region, some Austro-Alpine amphibolite/gneiss complexes (Ötztal, Kreuzeck Mountains (A)) contain stratiform polymetallic (Fe–Cu–Zn–Pb) mineralizations which were most probably formed in backarc settings (e.g. Raggabach (A)). The Pb isotope signatures are typical for continental environments (Ebner *et al.* 2000).

**Graphite/meta-anthracite and oil shale deposits.** In the Psunj Mountain (HR) (Tisza Unit) metasediments undergoing Barrovian-type metamorphism are interbedded with seams of graphite and (?)meta-anthracite (Šinkovec & Krkalo 1994). Several mines at Kaptol (HR), Sivornica (HR) and Brusnik (HR) were in operation. The total production was about 22 000 t of ore with 45–70% C. The reserves were estimated at 60 000 t (Šinkovec & Krkalo 1994).

**Uraniferous polymetallic deposits (black shale type).** Black shales in the Papuk Mountains (Tisza Unit) contain economic U concentrations. At Ninkovača creek (HR) the low-grade metamorphic Radlovac Series contains 0.04% $U_3O_8$ with reserves of 15 t $U_3O_8$. The U mineralization was discovered in the nearshore facies of a regressive marine series. The host environment has been interpreted in terms of a sabkha. 'Black ore' U mineralization with coffinite was replaced by U 'yellow ore' composed of autunite, uranospathite and uranosilite (Braun *et al.* 1983). The 'black ore' U mineralization is probably Devonian in age.

The oldest known strata-bound deposits in the Western Carpathians are subeconomic black-shale-hosted sulphide mineralizations. These include disseminated pyrite and a wide spectrum of elements such as V, Sb, Pb, Zn, Cu, As, Ag and Ni in rocks of the Tatricum (Little Carpathians) and the Gemericum (Spiš-Gemer Mountains) (SK) (Chovan *et al.* 1992).

In the extra-Alpine Variscides, polymetallic U concentration was at a maximum during the Silurian and Early Devonian. The palaeogeography, organic matter and metamorphism of Lower Silurian black shales from the Barrandian Zone (Liten and Kopanina formations) have been studied intensively (Suchý *et al.* 2002, 2004). During Silurian times, the Barrandian Zone occupied palaeolatitudes between 30 and 40°S and was probably a narrow rift that developed over thinned continental crust (Havlíček 1981). The Liten Formation was formed during a marine transgression following deposition of Upper Ordovician fluvioglacial deposits (Kosov Formation) (Brenchley & Štorch 1989). The organic-matter-rich shaly formations are laterally correlative to deeper-marine shelf and slope environments partially influenced by active submarine volcanism (Kukal 1985). The sedimentary environment was apparently quiet, hemipelagic, and completely, or at least partially, anoxic with only periodic influence of high-energy currents (Štorch & Pašava 1989). Based on sedimentological evidence, the water depth during deposition of the Graptolite Shales did not exceed 150–200 m. Changing upwelling regimes and sedimentary environments across the Silurian–Devonian boundary are attributed to short-term sea-level fluctuations (Porebska & Sawlowicz 1997).

The most promising mineralization in the Lower and Upper Graptolite Shales was deposited in the Saxothuringian Zone. Radiometric surveys carried out on black shales in the Thuringian-Franconian Massif yielded high readings due to the abnormally high U contents of the order of 60 ppm. The U contents of the black shales exceed significantly those of the over- and underlying Palaeozoic argillaceous rocks which average only 1–4 ppm U (Szurowski *et al.* 1991). High U contents together with elevated Cu (mean = 353 ppm), Zn (3144 ppm), Ba (1583 ppm), V (3817 ppm) and Sb (100 ppm) qualify the Graptolite Shale as a low-grade/large-tonnage deposit as is the case with the Cambro-Silurian Alum Shale in Sweden, the Jurassic Posidonia Shale in south Germany or the Upper Proterozoic Fe–V–U-bearing shales in the Železné Hory Mountains (CZ) (Dill 1986*a*). There are strata-bound fault-hosted mineralizations with Fe-, Zn-, Cu-, Pb-sulphides and sooty pitchblende at the Gräfenthal Horst (D). The relatively high U contents render these Lower Palaeozoic black shales a 'low-metal concentration' or 'protore' for the U deposits which have been mined near Gera-Ronneburg (D) and Möschwitz (D) (discussed in more detail in the section 'Post-Variscan/early Alpine unconformity').

**Carbonate-hosted manganiferous iron deposits.** During the Ludlow, euxinic conditions were briefly interrupted and the dominant black shale facies was replaced by a carbonate facies (Seidel 2003). The Ockerkalk (D) is a calcareous unit deposited on swell zones. It formed during a sea-level fall, when the basin changed from the euxinic $H_2S$ into the $CO_2$ zone. As a consequence of this change, Fe was no longer accommodated in pyrite and marcasite but in siderite. The primary Fe concentration in the Ockerkalk is not of economic grade. However, where supergene alterations increased the Fe content, short-term mining operations were possible (see unconformity-related 'Hunsrück-type' deposits). Siderite in the Ockerkalk is considered to be a younger analogue of the siderite found in the (?Pre-) Cambrian Wunsiedel Marble.

In the Western Carpathians black shales, stratigraphically equivalent to the Siluro-Devonian Graptolite Shales, are overlain by calcareous rocks. These carbonates form the parent material for large siderite (Nižná Slaná, Kobeliarovo (SK)), magnesite (Mníšek nad Hnilcom (SK)), ankerite (Hanková-Volovec-Holec belt (SK)), and rhodonite- and rhodochrosite-bearing Mn deposits (Čučma, Betliar, Bystrý potok (SK)), which formed at the beginning of the Late Palaeozoic as a result of metasomatism (Grecula *et al.* 1995) (see section on hypogene deposits related to the post-Variscan unconformity).

### *Devonian to (Lower) Carboniferous*

The Devonian to Early Carboniferous evolution of the Variscan Orogen was controlled by extensional and compressional events. Silurian(?)–Early Devonian ophiolites in the Central Sudetes probably represent a late stage of extension in the Saxothuringian Ocean (Franke & Zelazniewicz 2000). Contemporaneously, the Rheic Ocean located between Avalonia and the American Terrane Assemblage was closed, whereas the Saxothuringian Ocean was subducted to the south beneath the Teplá-Barrandian Zone during Early/Mid-Devonian time (Winchester *et al.* 2002).

Thereafter, an extensional rifting phase occurred along the Rheic suture and formed the Devonian Rhenohercynian Basin (Oncken *et al.* 2000; McCann *et al.* 2008*b*). This basin was dominated by thick clastic shelf sediments and rift-related volcanism. Further extension led to the opening of the Rhenohercynian Ocean. Sedimentary massive sulphide (SMS), (Rammelsberg-type), VMS and Lahn-Dill-type Fe–(Mn) deposits resulted from the rifting process. The volcanic-related mineralization began in the Middle Devonian with Fe deposits emplaced in the Rhenohercynian and Saxothuringian zones. The waning stages of this sedimentary exhalative (SEDEX) process lasted until the Lower Carboniferous when Mn-enriched analogues of the Lahn-Dill ores developed in the Rhenohercynian Zone. A chemical predisposition of the lithospheric crust in the Rhenohercynian Zone for base metals was responsible for the ubiquitous SMS and VMS deposits. The narrow Rhenohercynian Ocean was closed by SE-directed subduction during the Late Devonian–Early Carboniferous (Franke 2000). The lower Carboniferous successions in the extra-Alpine parts of Europe include a shallow-marine limestone (Kohlenkalk) grading to the south into the deeper-marine synorogenic clastic Culm facies.

Basement rocks in the Western Alps essentially form the direct continuation of the Moldanubian Zone in the French Massif Central. The situation in the Eastern Alps, Dinarides and the Carpathians is more complex. Penninic basement rocks, a part of the Austro-Alpine basement, and the Tatricum and Veporicum in the Western Carpathians record Silurian–Devonian metamorphism (Neubauer & von Raumer 1993; Neubauer *et al.* 1999). These units are considered to represent terranes, which were accreted along the active northern margin of the Rheic Ocean or an appendix of it (Frisch & Neubauer 1989). In contrast, the bulk of the basement rocks in the Eastern and Southern Alps and in the Dinarides belong to the Noric-Bosnian Zone, which separated from Gondwana during (Silurian to) Early Devonian rifting and drifted northward until its Carboniferous collision with the European margin (von Raumer 1998). During the drift stage passive continental margins with thick carbonate platforms evolved. The main period of Variscan deformation, during collision of Gondwana and Laurussia, continued into Namurian–Westphalian times (see also Kroner *et al.* 2008; McCann *et al.* 2008*b*).

The above situation is similar to that of the geodynamic setting in the Gemeric unit (Western Carpathians), where rifting with extensive bimodal volcanism (Lower and Upper Ore-Bearing Horizons) commenced in the Late Silurian and extended into the Middle Devonian. Oceanic crust was formed in the central part of the rift during Late Devonian times. Here, Early Carboniferous-age sediments rest unconformably on folded and metamorphosed Lower Palaeozoic basement rocks. Sedimentation ceased due to the onset of movement of the Variscan nappes. These horizontal movements transported most of the Early Palaeozoic basin fill over the northern continental plate. Subsequently, a basin formed in the area of the accretionary prism, filled with coarse siliciclastic material derived from the Lower Palaeozoic rocks. This sedimentary complex (i.e. Rudňany conglomerates) became metamorphosed when subduction continued during the Late Carboniferous (Grecula & Radvanec 2004).

**Chromium–nickel–PGE and magnesite deposits.** Ophiolites in the Central Sudetes are Silurian(?)–Early Devonian in age (Kroner *et al.* 2008). They contain Cr ore in the ultramafic massif of Tąpadła (PL), where lenticular ore bodies are associated with dunites and diallag peridotites which underwent strong listvenitization. Chromium occurs in Al-bearing chromite attaining contents of *c.* 40% $Cr_2O_3$ (Osika 1990). The Szklary

Deposit (PL), also hosted by serpentinites, is well known for its high-quality Ni ore (Piwocki & Przenioslo 2004)

Magnesite deposits in extra-Alpine Europe are generally rare, with the exception of the Central Sudetic ophiolites (South Wroclaw), e.g. Sobótka (PL), Szklary (PL) and Braszowice (PL) (Osika 1990). In the large Konstanty Deposit at Braszowice, serpentinites and Variscan gabbroic rocks are cross-cut by magnesite veins.

**Iron–manganese deposits (Lahn Dill type/SEDEX).** During the Middle and Late Devonian exhalative Fe ores of the Lahn-Dill type formed in the Rhenohercynian and Moravo-Silesian zones. The strata-bound Fe deposits contain hematite, magnetite, leptochlorite and rarely siderite and pyrite (Skácel 1966). The Lahn-Dill Fe-deposits are generally bound to basaltic (diabase) and Na-trachytic (keratophyres) submarine lavas or their pyroclastic equivalents (Bottke 1963, 1965). Mining in the Lahn-Dill area (D) ended in 1973 with a total of 97 Mt of Fe ore exploited. The estimated reserves are 10–20 Mt. A cross-section through the hematite-bearing ore bed of the Langenbach mine (D) is shown in Figure 21.2b. The Middle to Late Devonian transition is marked by strong crustal extension accompanied by bimodal submarine volcanism. Spreading and the resultant submarine volcanism continued in parts of the Rhenohercynian Basin until the Lower Carboniferous. At higher stratigraphic levels, hematite–magnetite ores became substituted by stratiform Mn ore mineralization which was mined at Laisa near Battenberg in Hessen (D) (Schaeffer 1998). This is a siliceous Mn ore made up mainly of rhodochrosite and braunite which were both produced by volcanic solutions.

West of the River Rhine, ferruginous sediments (chamosite, hematite and goethite) occur in several Lower and Middle Devonian horizons (Martin 1979; Simon 1979). The calcareous and oolithic iron ore was strongly deformed by Variscan activity. Ore texture and the abundance of bioclastic limestones interbedded with the Fe ore seams suggest ore formation in a high-energy regime. These Fe ores are transitional between volcano-sedimentary to true marine-sedimentary.

Manganese quartzites at Einöd/Friesach (A) in Austro-Alpine units east of the Tauern Window are interpreted as Devonian-age oceanic sediments (Ertl *et al.* 2005); they supported minor wartime mining activities.

Intensive bimodal volcanism of Devonian age also occurred in the Western Carpathians. Hematite–magnetite ore mineralization in Lower Palaeozoic rocks of the Gemericum is related in time and space with diabase–keratophyre volcanism resembling that of the Lahn-Dill Fe ore deposits in the extra-Alpine Variscides (Hnilec Formation, e.g. Trochanka, Hýľov, Gondarská, Švedlár (SK) (Grecula *et al.* 1995). Magnetite mineralization, in some places with associated pyrrhotite and chalcopyrite, occurs near Kokava nad Rimavicou (SK) in the Veporicum (Zoubek & Nemčok 1951). The primary oolitic Fe ore was metamorphosed at 550–580°C during Variscan metamorphism and converted into a magnetite–grunerite–garnet schist (Korikovskij *et al.* 1989). In the Low Tatra Mountains (Tatricum) a similar pyrrhotite mineralization occurs near Hel'pa and magnetite occurrences are found NW of Bacúch (SK) (Grecula *et al.* 1996; Slavkay & Chovan 1996).

Within the Dinarides SEDEX deposits with Fe, Mn and Ba occur in the Medvednica Mountains (Šinkovec *et al.* 1988), while stratiform occurrences of magnetite, chamosite and pyrite were encountered in the Palaeozoic rocks of the Ključ area, NW Bosnia (Jurković 1959).

**Base-metal–iron sulphide–barite deposits (Rammelsberg type/SMS type).** A belt of syndiagenetic to syngenetic sulphide ores which formed during the Eifelian and Late Givetian extends from the Rhenohercynian to the Moravo-Silesian zones. Pyrite–barite ores with Zn, Pb and Cu sulphides were concentrated at Meggen (D) and Rammelsberg (D) (Fig. 21.5). The latter is the most prominent representative of this type of ore deposit, with 27 Mt of ore containing 13.7% Zn, 5.9% Pb, 1.1% Cu, 100 ppm Ag and 22% $BaSO_4$ (Dornsiepen 1976; Sperling & Walcher 1990; Maynard & Okita 1991; Large & Walcher 1999).

*Rammelsberg deposit.* The Rammelsberg mine located in the north Harz Mountains has a history of more than 1000 years

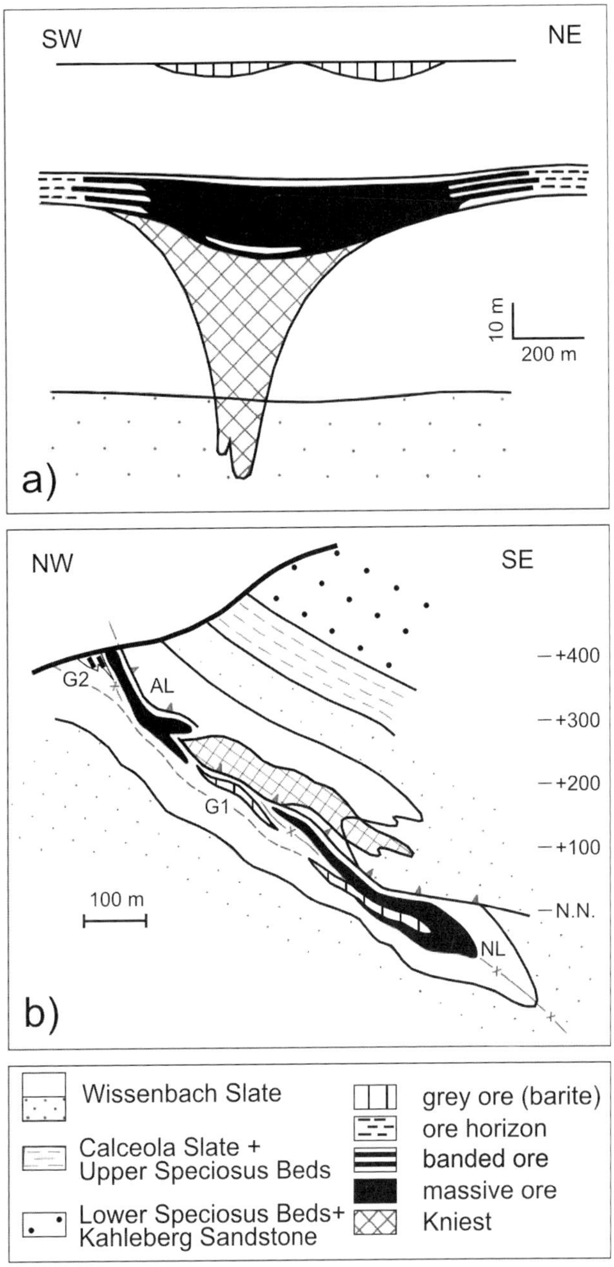


**Fig. 21.5.** Reconstruction of the Rammelsberg ore body (D) in its pre-deformational state (**a**) and after the Variscan folding shown in a cross-section through the Rammelsberg Deposit (**b**). Redrawn from Walther (1986).

(968 to 1988). In 1988 annual production was 55 000 t Pb+Zn, 3500 t Cu, 22 t Ag. Intensive investigations of ore and country-rock have made it a classic example of a submarine hydrothermal deposit and its name is used to describe a class of strata-bound deposits. The mineral association consists of sphalerite, pyrite, barite, galena, chalcopyrite, pyrrhotite, covellite, arsenopyrite and tetrahedrite. Ore mineralization proper followed a pre-stage of silica concentration termed 'Kniest'. The wedge-shaped ore body of the 'Kniest' marks the vent systems (Fig. 21.5a). The main ore stage commenced with pyritic ore succeeded by sphalerite ore with little chalcopyrite. In chronological order, a succession of barite–galena–sphalerite, barite–galena and barite evolved, terminating with the main ore stage. In the post-ore stage, fine-grained barite came up again and was mined from what is called the Grey Orebody (averaging 65 to 75% $BaSO_4$). The entire ore-bearing Devonian series was intensively folded and faulted during the Variscan Orogeny and the ore beds became an isoclinal syncline where the 'Kniest' eventually came to rest in the hanging wall (Fig. 21.5b).

At Meggen in the eastern part of the Rhenish Massif, 59.2 Mt of ore grading 8% Zn, 1% Pb and 9.5 Mt barite were mined until 1992 (Werner & Walther 1995). A similar mineralization was mined for barite at the SW margin of the Rhenish Massif in the Korb Mine near Eisen/Hunsrück (D) up until 1988 and in the Rohberg Mine near Wiesbaden (D). Massive sediment-hosted pyrite–barite deposits near Lohrheim (Taunus) and Elbingerode (Harz Mountains) are genetically related to keratophyres of Devonian age. The Einheit deposit in the Harz Mountains (D), which was mined for pyrite until 1989, is a VMS deposit (Werner & Walther 1995). It produced 15 Mt of ore with 15 to 20% pyrite. The westernmost Rammelsberg-type strata-bound barite deposit of Devonian age was found when drillholes encountered a Frasnian biostrome near Chaudfontaine (B) (Dejonghe 1998). The Rammelsberg-type deposits are considered to be a product of metalliferous basin-dewatering brines, conducing to SEDEX or SMS-type mineralization during the synrift phase of the Rhenohercynian Basin (Werner 1989; Maynard & Okita 1991).

In the Moravo-Silesian Zone (eastern Bohemian Massif), Fe-bearing base-metal deposits with subordinate amounts of Au formed in a geodynamic setting similar to that known from the Rhenohercynian Basin. The Devonian volcanosedimentary series (Vrbno Group), however, underwent regional metamorphism up to greenschist-facies conditions (Patočka & Vrba 1989; Kalenda & Vaněček 1989). Several districts were explored and exploited between 1959 and 1980 but all of them abandoned production by the beginning of 1994. The extensive mining was focused on the deposits in the northern part of the Moravo-Silesian Zone (Zlaté Hory (CZ), Horní Město (CZ), Oskava (CZ), Horní Benešov (CZ)). The total ore exploited from these deposits amounts to 100 Mt of mostly low-grade ore (Aichler *et al.* 1995). Due to Variscan metamorphism and deformation, the strata-bound ore was completely recrystallized and intersected by numerous Au-bearing quartz and sulphide veins. The S isotope ratios obtained from barites closely resemble those from Meggen and Rammelsberg, whereas the sulphide sulphur is isotopically much lighter (Hladíková *et al.* 1992). High radiogenic Pb contents of the galena-enriched ore show the significant contribution of upper crustal rocks to the metal-bearing hydrothermal or exhalative solutions creating the strata-bound mineralization in the Moravo-Silesian Zone (Vaněček *et al.* 1985).

In the Massif Central (F), Late Devonian-age base-metal deposits have been exploited for Cu and Zn from pyritic lenses associated with quartz–keratophyre rocks in the old Sain-Bel mine (F) and at Chessy (F), where chalcopyrite and sphalerite are associated with barite averaging 2.5 wt% Cu, 10 wt% Zn and 15 wt% Ba (Bril *et al.* 1994). The latter mineralization occurs in two effusive acid volcanic units (mainly submarine lava flows) characterized by their dacitic to rhyolitic composition (Lacomme *et al.* 1987; Milesi & Lescuyer 1993). The ore bodies comprise a central zone with alternating beds of pyrite, sphalerite and thin volcanic flows surrounded by a barite rim. The main ore body is rooted in quartz–pyrite–white mica stockworks. Similar stockworks occur at several volcanic levels, demonstrating the longevity of hydrothermal activity in the Chessy area (Lacomme *et al.* 1987).

In the Eastern Alps, ore mineralization of Cu, Fe, Pb and Zn occurs within the Lower and Upper Austro-Alpine nappes. The mineralization in the Lower Austro-Alpine nappe was pervasively deformed and subjected to several phases of regional metamorphism, e.g. Pitten (A). This is usually taken as proof of pre-Alpine syngenetic ore formation that took place under euxinic conditions in an active continental margin setting (Ebner *et al.* 2000). Ore formation within the Upper Austro-Alpine Nappe (Noric Composite Terrane) was controlled by extensional tectonics, alkaline basaltic intraplate volcanism and euxinic environments (Weber 1990). Strata-bound mineralization is predominantly of the SEDEX and VMS types, including Fe–Cu(Pb–Zn) (e.g. Meiselding (A)) and Pb–Zn–Ag(Ba) associations (e.g. Schwaz, Graz Palaeozoic Complex (A)). Generally the Pb isotopes of these ores suggest a crustal origin for the Pb. Of particular importance is the stratiform Pb–Zn mineralization of volcanosedimentary origin, which is widespread within the Silurian and Devonian (meta)sediments of the Graz Palaeozoic Complex (e.g. Arzberg (A)) (Weber 1990). These deposits resulted from hydrothermal activity at the seafloor which produced a warming of the seawater in semiclosed basins. The warming of the seawater together with poor water exchange with the open sea were responsible for the euxinic conditions in these basins.

In the Smolník Formation of the Gemericum (Western Carpathians), the origin of base-metal deposits, concentrated in an upper ore bed, and hematite and magnetite deposits in a lower ore bed are both linked to basalts and keratophyres with the type localities in the Jalovičí vrch and Hutná dolina deposits (SK), respectively (Grecula 1982; Grecula *et al.* 1995). Sulphur isotopes of sulphides (+2 to +15‰) (Žák *et al.* 1991; Radvanec *et al.* 1993) suggest a Lower Palaeozoic source of marine sulphate and inorganic or biogenic reduction in a closed system. In the Smolník Deposit massive pyritic ores in the central part of the ore horizon grade outwards into disseminated pyritic ores. During the most recent mining period, the element contents of the ore decreased to 0.2–0.6% Cu, while in the past it was much higher with 2–4% Cu, up to 0.33% Pb, up to 0.37% Zn and up to 8 g/t Ag. A total of *c.* 19 Mt of ore was exploited in the period 1326–1990 with the remaining resources of ore totalling about 6.2 Mt (Popreňák & Ilavský, in Bartalský 1993).

**Tungsten and magnesite deposits.** Ore formation within the Noric Composite Terrane (Eastern Alps) includes W mineralization and small magnesite bodies (e.g. Mallnock (A)) linked to black shales (Neinavaie *et al.* 1989).

**Copper–molybdenum–tungsten deposits (porphyry type).** The majority of porphyry Cu deposits are associated with Mesozoic and Cenozoic orogenic belts, island arcs and active continental margins (e.g. Mitchell 1996; Herrington 2000). A peculiar type of porphyry Cu deposits has been recorded from Central Europe by Haranczyk (1980, 1983). The mineralization does not show all of the features known from modern 'disseminated porphyry Cu deposits' and is also erratically distributed within the Variscan metallogenetic cycle in Central Europe. The polyorogenic Kraków and Moravian mobile belts, both deformed during the Caledonian and Variscan orogenies, include the western margin of the Małopolska Zone and parts of the Moravo-Silesian Zone. These are the locus of Early Carboniferous-age igneous activity with associated porphyry Cu mineralization. Late Palaeozoic Cu–Mo–W porphyry deposits formed at Mrzyglod–Zawiercie (PL), Pilica (PL), Dolina Bedkowska (PL) and Miedzianka–Stara Góra (PL) (Haranczyk 1980, 1983; Osika 1986; Chaffee *et al.* 1994).

*Upper Carboniferous*

Early Carboniferous thrust loading resulted in the formation of the large Variscan foreland basin, which extended to the north of the Variscan Front between Ireland and Poland. This asymmetric basin, which overlay marine sediments, was filled mainly with continental deposits during the Late Carboniferous. At the same time, intramontane basins, orientated subparallel to the Variscan core zone, formed within the Variscan Orogen. However, deposition in these latter basins continued into the Permian, and so they will be discussed in the Alpine section (see also McCann *et al.* 2008*a*, *b*). Coal is the most important resource in the Upper Carboniferous strata; however, ironstone also formed in the Variscan Foreland Basin.

**Coal deposits in the Variscan Foreland.** During Late Carboniferous times the Variscan Foreland Basin was filled with coal-bearing terrestrial sediments, several kilometres thick. Overlying the Lower Carboniferous carbonate platform and associated deep-marine sediments, the coal measures display a gradual shift from marine-influenced to continental settings. The internal architecture of these deposits is characterized by repeated successions (cyclothems) of siliciclastics, coal and carbonates controlled by sea-level variations (Izart *et al.* 1998). Coal formation during Late Palaeozoic times was promoted by a tropical climate and favourable palaeogeographic and tectonic conditions (McCann *et al.* 2008*b*). The stratigraphic range of the Palaeozoic coal measures is indicated in Figure 21.6.

Several major coal districts are located within the Variscan Foreland Basin and these show a number of common features including a very high number of relatively thin, but often extensive seams. Coal rank ranges widely from high volatile bituminous to anthracite. Coalification mainly occurred during deep burial and is mainly pre-deformational. Therefore, rank isolines generally dip parallel to bedding planes (e.g. Juch 1991; Nöth *et al.* 2001). The seams are strongly deformed, with the intensity of deformation decreasing with distance from the Variscan Front (e.g. Oncken *et al.* 2000). Marine bands and volcanic ash layers are frequent and form important lithostratigraphic marker horizons.

Coal mining commenced as early as the twelfth century in southern Belgium (Dinant Syncline). However, large-scale industrial coal mining only began in the nineteenth century. In total more than 20 Gt of hard coal have been produced in the Belgian, German, Czech and Polish sectors of the basin. Today mines are active in this area only in the Ruhr District (coal production in 2005 was 20 Mt) and in the Upper Silesian Basin (*c.* 110 Mt). About 4.5 Mt are produced annually by a coal mine in the Polish part of the Lublin Basin.

*Wallonian and Campine basins.* Extensive coal mining activities took place in the Nord-Pas-de-Calais Basin (F) and in the Namur Syncline (B), located on the southern flank of the Brabant Massif (Fig. 21.7a). Smaller depleted deposits also occur in the Dinant Syncline. The Namur and Dinant synclines (Wallonian Basin) extend eastwards into the Aachen coalfields, which are also connected with the South Limburg (NL) and Campine basins (B) to the north of the Brabant Massif. In the Campine Basin, the Upper Carboniferous coal measures are disconformably overlain by Permo-Mesozoic and Cenozoic sediments and were, thus, only detected in 1901.

The Westphalian succession, with a maximum preserved thickness of 3.5 km, reflects a change from lower delta plain to braid plain settings. Westphalian A lower delta plain coal is generally thin (<1 m) and often split. The Westphalian B hosts many seams up to 3 m thick and was the main coal-producing unit. The Westphalian C contains rather thick seams (up to 5 m), partly formed in raised mires. Only a few mineable seams are associated with the gravelly braid plain (Westphalian D; Dreesen *et al.* 1995; Langenaeler 2000).

Major differences exist in the tectonic style of the basins. The Wallonian Basin, located near the Variscan Front, was strongly affected by folding and thrusting. In contrast, Variscan deformation of the gently north-dipping Campine Basin was minor. Its structural style is dominated by NW–SE-striking normal faults causing a rapid deepening of the coal measures towards the NE. A western and an eastern mining district are separated by the north–south oriented Donderslag Fault Zone. The thickness of sediments and coalification are significantly higher in the eastern part of the Campine Basin (Dreesen *et al.* 1995; Van Keer *et al.* 1998).

Average seam thickness in the Wallonian and Campine basins is 0.6 m and 1.1 m, respectively. Ash and sulphur contents are low. Coal rank ranges from high volatile bituminous to anthracite. Coalification occurred mainly during deep Westphalian burial, but Jurassic subsidence and slightly elevated heat flows may have caused a second coalification event in the eastern Campine Basin (Langenaeker 2000; Van Keer *et al.* 1998).

Unfavourable geological factors led to the closure of the last mine in the Wallonian Basin in 1984. Coal mining in the Campine and Aachen areas continued until 1992 and 1997, respectively. Huge mineable coal reserves remained in the Campine Basin (van Tongeren *et al.* 2002). Van Bergen *et al.* (2003) have highlighted the coal-bed methane potential.

*Ruhr Basin (including Ibbenbüren).* Folded and thrusted Upper Carboniferous coal measures crop out along the River Ruhr (Fig. 21.7b). Here, coal mining began in the fourteenth century. Current mining activities are concentrated northwards below the Münsterland Basin down to a depth of 1500 m.

The Ruhr Basin (RB) covers an area of about 12 000 km$^2$. The erosional surface of the Carboniferous dips northwards beneath up to 2 km of Upper Cretaceous strata of the Münsterland Basin (Fig. 21.7c). The northern basin margin is formed by a prominent strike-slip fault (Osning Fault) separating the basin from the Lower Saxony uplift zone. Within the inversion zone, three NW–SE trending blocks with coal-bearing sediments are exposed (Fig. 21.7; Ibbenbüren District).

The coal measures (Namurian C–Westphalian D) in the RB thin northwards from about 5 km to less than 3 km (Drozdzewski 1993). A lower delta plain environment prevailed from Namurian C to Westphalian B times and was replaced by an upper delta plain during the Late Westphalian C. The marine influence decreased during the Westphalian B/C and a general regressive trend ended in the deposition of red-beds and the formation of palaeosols in the Westphalian D, mainly in the north of the RB (Drozdzewski 1993; Strehlau & David 1989).

More than 100 coal seams of variable thickness are present in

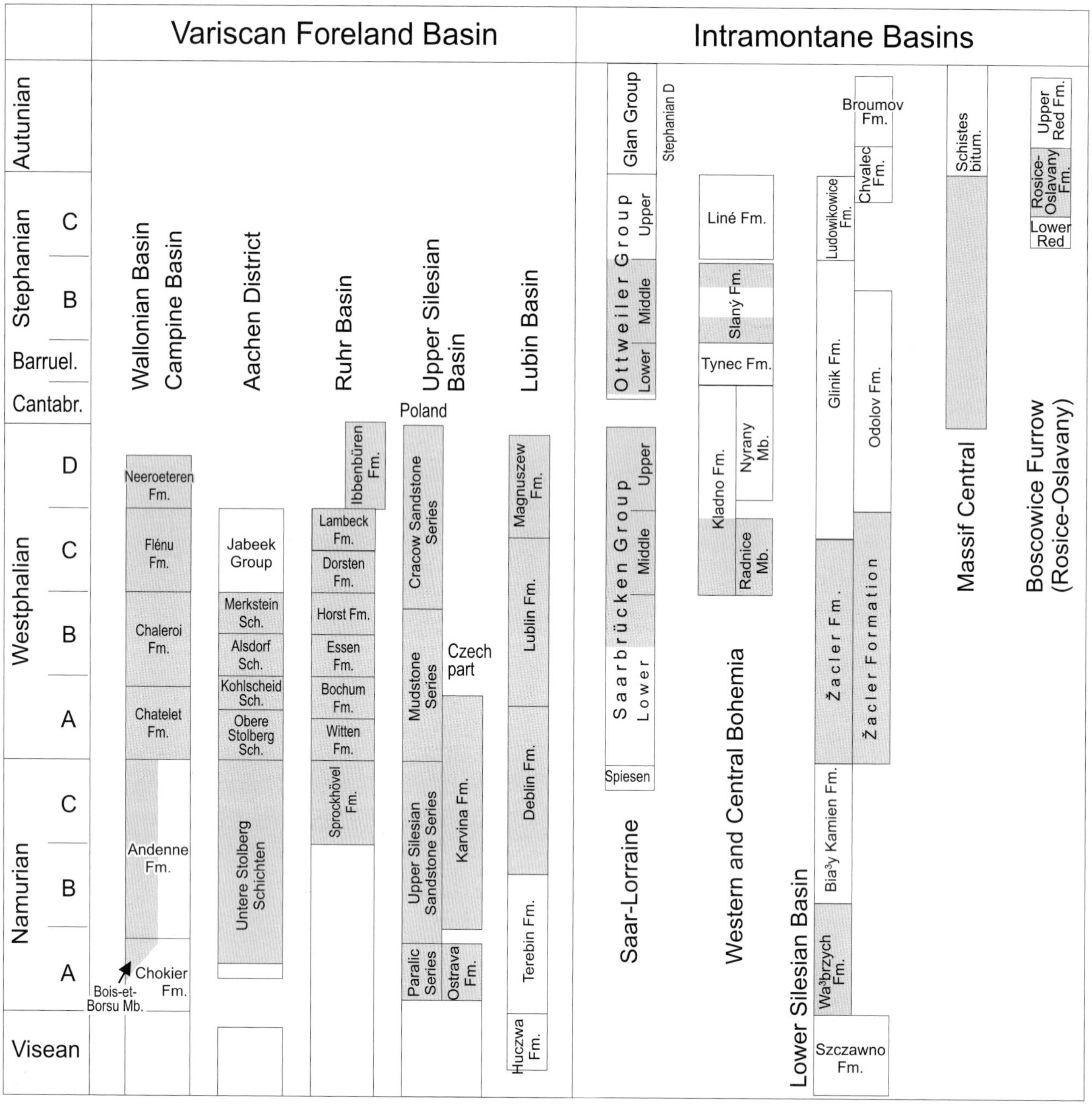


**Fig. 21.6.** Stratigraphic position of late Palaeozoic coal-bearing sediments. Series with economic seams are indicated by grey shading (after Zdanowski & Zakowa 1995; Izart *et al.* 1998; Oplustil & Pešek 1998).

the RB. The thickest seams are 2.8 m thick. The coal seam distribution shows two trends (Drozdzewski 1993): (1) from the Namurian C to the Westphalian the area with maximum coal content shifted towards the NW; and (2) within each formation the coal content decreases in the same direction. The maximum net coal thickness occurs in the lower Westphalian B (Gaschnitz 2001).

Extensive seams with low-ash, low-sulphur coals dominate in the upper Westphalian A to lower Westphalian C and were interpreted as former raised mires or as open mires with herbaceous vegetation ('densosporinite facies'; see Dehmer 2004). Upper Westphalian C coal formed in forest swamps ('vitrinite-fusinite facies') and is less clean. On average, the coal consists of about 70% vitrinite, 20% inertinite and 10% liptinite (Scheidt & Littke 1989).

The RB was affected by folding and thrusting during the Stephanian. The intensity of folding decreases towards the NW (Fig. 21.7). NW–SE trending faults affected the Carboniferous strata subsequent to folding and thrusting. These faults are generally extensional in nature, albeit with some evidence of lateral movement. The Blumenthal Fault (Fig. 21.7b) subdivides the RB into a western and an eastern part. The coal measures in the west are mostly flat-lying and covered by Permo-Triassic sediments. In contrast, the Carboniferous in the east is intensely folded and directly overlain by Cretaceous rocks. The NW–SE extensional structures were reactivated during Mesozoic and Cenozoic times.

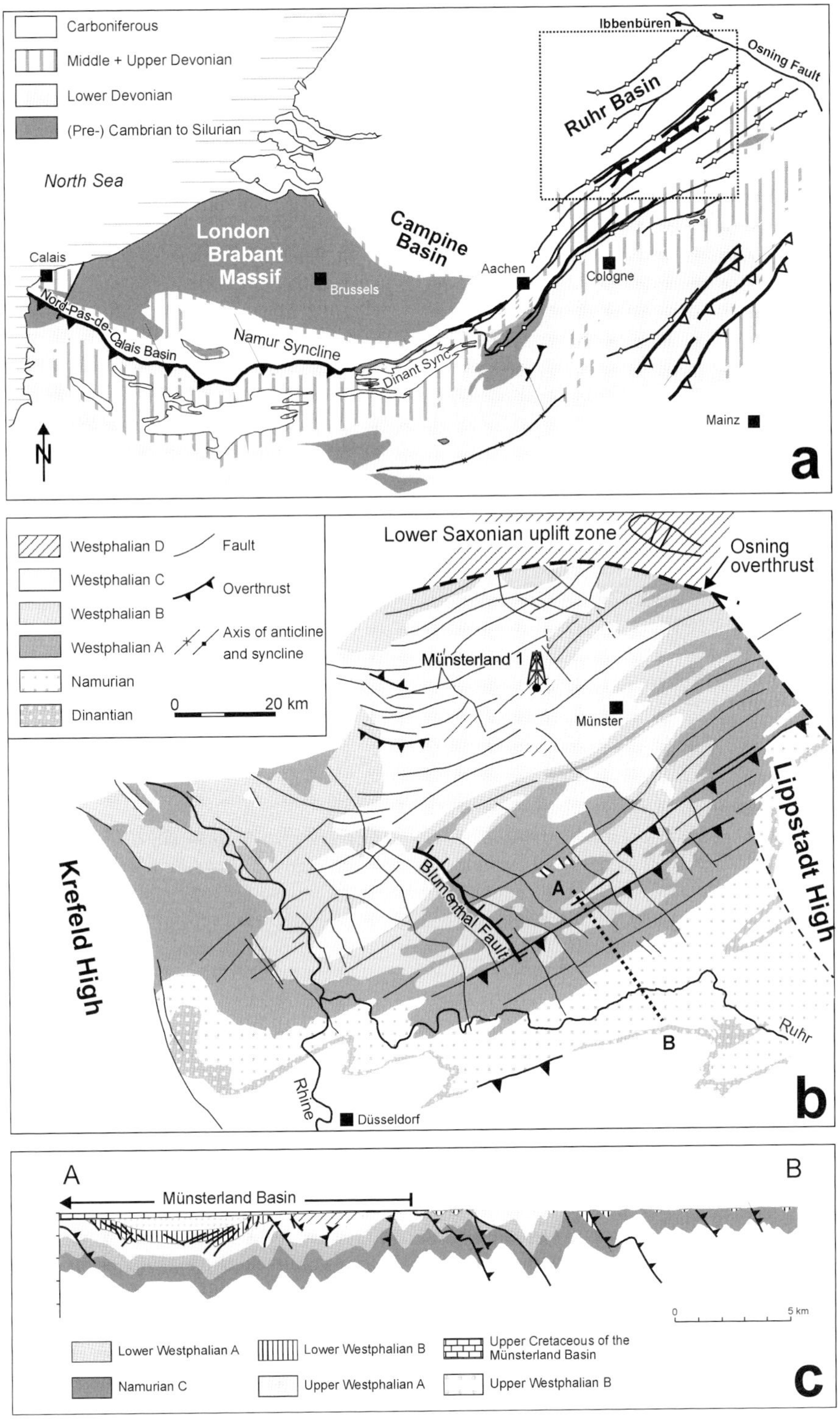


**Fig. 21.7.** (**a**) Structural subsurface map of the Variscan Front in Central Europe (modified after Drozdzewski 1993). (**b**) Geological map of the Ruhr Basin and northern areas (without Mesozoic cover). (**c**) Geological cross-section (see (b) for location; modified after Walter 1992).

During the Late Cretaceous basin inversion, the 'Lower Saxony uplift zone' overthrust the northern edge of the Münsterland Basin (Fig. 21.7). Uplift was perhaps accompanied by deep mafic intrusions. A post-Albian to pre-Late Campanian age for this magmatic event has been postulated based on a coalification anomaly. However, numeric basin models suggest that the high thermal maturity is a result of deep Cretaceous burial (Petmecky *et al.* 1999; Senglaub *et al.* 2006). Today, low-volatile bituminous coal and anthracite are exploited in the Ibbenbüren district.

Coal rank in the RB (*sensu stricto*) ranges from high-volatile bituminous coal to semi-anthracite. Carboniferous rocks, up to 2.8 km thick, were eroded during post-Stephanian uplift in the

Münster area, whereas up to 6 km were eroded at the southern basin rim (Büker *et al.* 1995). Renewed subsidence commenced during the Late Permian and was followed by Late Jurassic to Early Cretaceous uplift. Mesozoic subsidence did not influence coal rank in the main part of the RB (Littke *et al.* 1994, 2000).

Both coals and dispersed organic matter are sources for coal-bed methane (CBM). The two parts of the RB have different CBM contents. The western area is characterized by a gas-free section below the post-Carboniferous cover. In contrast, gas contents increase directly below the cover in the east. Gaschnitz (2001) has shown that gas distribution and gas composition are controlled by phases of exhumation and reburial causing complex adsorption–desorption cycles. Maximum CBM contents are related to anticlines or horst structures and reflect lateral gas migration and accumulations due to vertical differences in permeability (Kunz 1999). Today, CBM is produced in areas with active and abandoned coalfields in the southern RB (Thielemann 2001).

The *Upper Silesian Basin* (USB) straddles the border between Poland and the Czech Republic and covers an area of about 7250 $km^2$ (Dopita & Kumpera 1993; Jura *et al.* 2000) (Fig. 21.8). The USB formed within the eastern foreland of the Moravo-Silesian foldbelt. The thickness of the Upper Carboniferous terrestrial deposits increases dramatically towards the west (8.5 km). As in other Variscan foreland basins, the coal measures include a lower paralic (Namurian A) and an upper continental series (Namurian B to Westphalian D). However, in the USB continental conditions were established earlier than in other districts.

The overburden is formed by thin (<200 m) Permian to Jurassic sediments in the northern part and by Miocene rocks, including salt deposits, in the south (Fig. 21.8). In the basin centre, the Carboniferous is overlain by Quaternary sediments. The Variscan Orogeny led to the formation of two distinct tectonic zones: folds and thrusts predominate in the western part, whereas the eastern part is characterized by a flat syncline with roughly west–east trending faults. The southern part of the basin became overthrust by Carpathian nappes during Neogene times.

The *Paralic Series* (*Ostrava Fm.* in CZ; Namurian A) was deposited in coastal plains and vast deltaic systems. It contains numerous horizons with marine and brackish fauna and 114 economic coal seams with an average thickness of only 0.73 m. The percentage of coal within the Paralic Series is 2.6%.

The continental sediments (*Karviná Fm.* in CZ; Namurian B–Westphalian D) were deposited following a break in sedimentation. In Poland, they are subdivided into three series. The *Upper Silesian Sandstone Series* (Namurian B–C) is characterized by a predominance of coarse-grained sediments of braided river systems and has 23 thick seams. Seam thicknesses range from 4 to 8 m and may reach 24 m. The cumulative percentage of coal is 7.3%. Pelitic rocks deposited on the alluvial plain of meandering river systems predominate in the *Siltstone Series* (Westphalian A–B) and contain 71 economic, but relatively thin, seams (0.4–1.3 m). The percentage of coal in the Siltstone Series is 5.6%. The *Cracow Sandstone Series* (Westphalian B–D) formed on alluvial plains of a braided river system and has 26 economic seams; the thicker seams reaching 7 m. The percentage of coal is 2.9%. Barren Stephanian sediments complete the Carboniferous profile.

Coal rank (sub-bituminous C–anthracite) exhibits complex coalification patterns, because coalification during deep Carboniferous burial was overprinted during Mesozoic and Cenozoic times. Post-orogenic heating is perhaps related to deep igneous activity (e.g. Kotas & Hadro 2001). Ash yields are highly variable, while the average sulphur content is 1.1%$_{af}$. Continental coals are significantly thicker and contain more inertinite than paralic coals (Dopita & Kumpera 1993). Coal is used both as steam coal and for coke production.

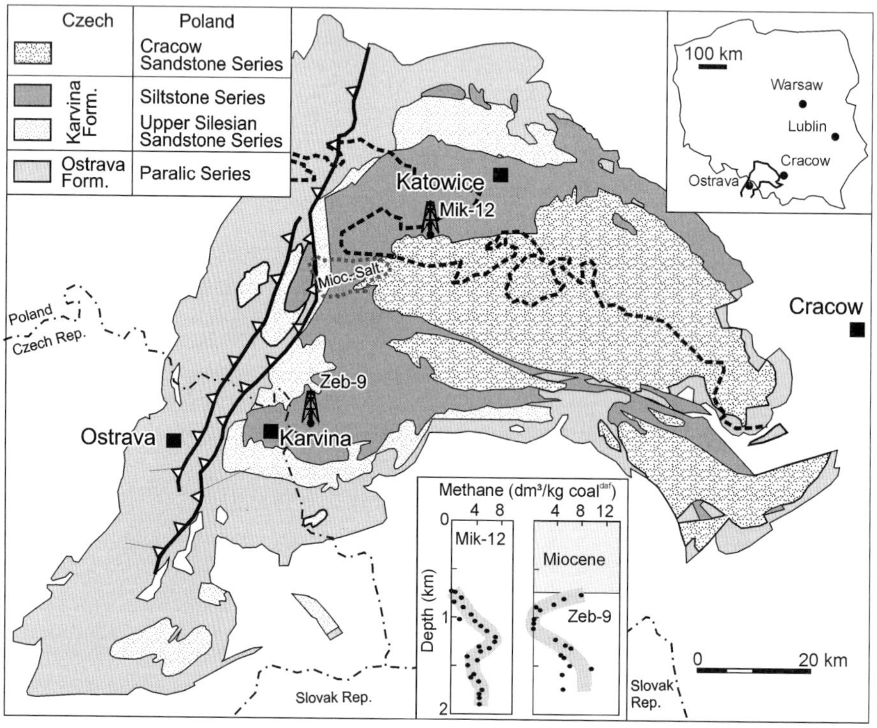


**Fig. 21.8.** Geological map of the Upper Silesian Basin (simplified after Jureczka & Krieger 2000). Methane contents in two drillholes are shown after Kotarba (2001).

In terms of CBM potential a southern area with thick impermeable Miocene overburden, and a northern area without sealing rocks can be distinguished (Jureczka 1995; Kotarba 2001). In the southern area two zones of high methane contents occur: an up to 300 m thick 'methane cap' beneath the top of the Carboniferous, and a primary methane zone at a depth of 1000 to 1500 m. In the northern area, only the primary zone is preserved, below a 500 to 1000 m thick degassing zone (Fig. 21.8). The USB has the potential to become one of the world's largest CBM producers. In addition, $CO_2$ sequestration in coal seams is currently being tested in the USB (e.g. Gale 2004).

Underground mine water in the USB is often highly mineralized, a consequence of the presence of a salt unit in the Miocene overburden. A major part of the resultant saline brines is discharged into the Vistula and Odra rivers causing serious ecological problems.

Only the NW edge of the *Lublin Basin* (Poland, Ukraine) is situated within the borders of the study area. The basin formed on the slope of the East European Craton. Its Upper Carboniferous succession, up to 3.5 km thick, comprises marine–paralic (Upper Viséan to Namurian A), paralic (Namurian B to Westphalian A) and continental (Westphalian B–D) deposits with a large number of coal seams (Porzycki & Zdanowski 1995). Late Variscan deformation resulted in uplift, erosion and the formation of a series of NW–SE striking folds. The coal measures are discordantly overlain by Mesozoic deposits.

The most important seams present are connected with the continental Lublin Formation. The average thickness of these seams is 1.4 to 3.5 m. The Lublin coalfield was discovered only relatively recently. Production of high- to medium-volatile bituminous coal (22 MJ/kg, 10% ash, 1.0–1.5% S) in the Polish part of the basin commenced in 1984 and production is from two seams at 800 to 1000 m depth (Philpott 2002). The coal is used mainly in power stations. Proven economic reserves are enormous.

**Graphite deposits in the Alpine belt.** Graphite occurs in Upper Carboniferous continental sediments and was produced in several mines in the Greywacke Zone of the Eastern Alps (e.g. Kaisersberg (A), Trieben (A)). Within the Western Alps, graphite-bearing rocks with a supposed Carboniferous age occur in the Dora-Maira Massif (Pinerolo Valley; Ridoni 1938). Graphite mineralization at Icla (I) and Brutta-Comba (I) occurs in a single horizon, variable in thickness from a few centimetres up to a few metres, within metamorphic rocks comprising paragneisses, garnet-bearing mica schists and minor quartzites. The average C content is about 60–80%.

**Ironstone deposits in the Variscan Foreland and in intramontane basins (claybands and blackbands).** Thin seams of Fe ores termed claybands and blackbands, formed during Late Carboniferous times in the Variscan Foreland. They are interbedded with coal seams and form part of the paralic facies in the coal measures (Walther & Dill 1995). Several seams of siderite-bearing ironstones were mined in the Ruhr Basin (D). Beds enriched in siderite are also found alternating with seams in the intramontane Saar-Nahe Basin where they were mined as Fe ores (even perhaps in pre-Roman times) from 1852–1912 and 1934–1942 with a total of 10 Mt of Fe ore extracted. The origin of these clayband and blackband Fe ores is related to the special palaeogeographic and climatic conditions which also favoured coal accumulation.

## *Thrust-bound and fold-related metamorphogenic deposits*

The Devonian to Carboniferous Variscan collision of Gondwana, the Armorican Terrane Assemblage and Laurussia led to intense deformation, metamorphism and igneous activity along deep-seated suture zones (Franke & Oncken 1990; see Kroner *et al.* 2008; McCann *et al.* 2008*b* for more details on the tectonic history).

As a result of crustal deformation, thrust-bound and fold-related metamorphogenic (cleavage-parallel) vein deposits were formed. These are markedly different from epigenetic vein-type deposits of post-Variscan age (Dill 1985*b*). The Variscan ore in the Rhenohercynian Zone, containing Sb, Pb, Zn, Cu sulphides, Au and siderite, shows pervasive textural distortion and strong mylonitization. Base metals, Sb, Au and siderite are related to shear zones and cleaved psammo-pelitic series, that developed along the fold axes of the Variscan anticlines.

### *Silver-bearing base-metal vein-type deposits*

Variscan-age base metal vein mineralization contrasts strikingly with Alpine-age vein mineralization. Silver-enriched tetrahedrite and Fe-enriched sphalerite are uncommon in the post-Variscan vein mineralization (Schaeffer 1984; Krahn 1988). The Pb-isotopic signature of the Variscan vein mineralization also differs from the post-Variscan (Upper Rotliegend) mineralization in that it is distinctly more radiogenic (Krahn & Baumann 1996). On the other hand, there is a striking similarity in the Pb-isotope signatures between the fold-related metamorphogenic vein-type deposits and strata-bound Devonian base-metal mineralization, suggesting that the source of metals for both types of deposits was within the Devonian synrift volcanosedimentary rock succession.

The Pb–Zn veins in the Rhenish Massif at Bensberg (D), Ramsbeck (D), the so-called 'schistosity or cleavage-parallel veins' near Holzappel (D), Werlau (D), Tellig (D) and Altlay (D), may be attributed to Variscan thrust-bound epigenetic mineralization (Podufal 1983; Fenchel *et al.* 1985; Werner & Walther 1995; Wagner & Boyce 2001). The veins in the Bensberg (D) Pb–Zn mining district have been worked since 1934 by Altenberg AG. Hesemann (1978) has estimated the Pb + Zn quantity in the Bensberg mining disctrict at 3 Mt. Mining operations were closed down in 1978 due to actions by citizens which stopped exploitation of a newly discovered ore body near Bensberg (D). From 1840 to 1974, the production in the largest deposit at Ramsbeck totalled about 16 Mt ore, averaging 4.4% Zn and 2.1% Pb. The syntectonic hydrothermal Pb–Zn veins of the Ramsbeck deposit have been extensively overprinted by late-stage fluids responsible for fissure vein mineralization. This has caused remobilization of vein components, notably of sphalerite and galena, as well as the formation of various Sb sulphosalt minerals, including boulangerite, semseyite, tetrahedrite and bournonite (Wagner & Boyce 2001; see also Siegerland-type vein deposits discussed below). Udubasa (1996) has compared syn- and epigenetic Pb–Zn deposits of the Ramsbeck mining district with Pb–Zn deposits in the Eastern Carpathians.

Silver, Pb, Zn and Cu accumulations in the Příbram ore district (CZ) (Bohemian Massif) were also attributed to the thrust-bound and fold-related metamorphogenic ore mineralization, although there are remarkable structural differences between the metamorphogenic veins in the Rhenohercynian and Teplá-Barrandian zones. In the Rhenohercynian Zone the structural deformation and metamorphic alteration of the Lower Palaeozoic rocks was less intense and occurred at shallower crustal levels than in the

Bohemian Massif. Several base-metal veins were emplaced around the Central Bohemian Pluton where underground mines reached an operational depth of more than 1500 m. The ore veins are feather structures accompanied by diabase dykes of similar shape (Pouba & Ilavsky 1986). Important Ag carriers, in addition to galena, are pyrargyrite, stephanite and diaphtorite.

*Copper-bearing iron oxide and selenium vein-type deposits*

Hydrothermal veins of probable Variscan age were the target of mining operation for Fe during the nineteenth and early twentieth centuries in the Harz Mountains near Zorge and St. Andreasberg (D) (Neumann-Redlin *et al.* 1977). The major ore mineral is hematite associated with chalcopyrite. In the same mining district selenides were discovered in veins near Tilkerode (D) and Zorge (D) (Tischendorf 1960; Ramdohr 1975). Investigations have revealed that this Se vein mineralization is of no economic, but of great mineralogical importance because of its rare minerals. The selenide mineralization occurs as aggregates in a carbonate matrix, and is composed of clausthalite, tiemannite, chrisstanleyite, stibiopalladinite and Au. Recently a new Pd–Hg selenide was discovered from the Eskeborn Adit at Tilkerode; i.e. Tischendorfite ($Pd_8Hg_3Se_9$) (Stanley *et al.* 2002). The origin of this mineralization is not yet fully understood. Palladium and Au associated with selenide minerals in these veins may have been derived either from the country-rocks or originated by downward movement of oxidizing solutions circulating in the Permian rocks and reacting with more reduced solutions below the unconformity. If the latter model proves to be correct, this unique Se vein mineralization will have to be categorized as unconformity-related.

At Mont Chemin (CH) magnetite-bearing lenses occur in tightly folded sericite gneisses and mica schists that form part of the metamorphic envelope around the Variscan Mont Blanc Massif (De Quervain & Zitzmann 1977; Beck & Serneels 2000). In addition to martitized magnetite, some pyrite and Co arsenides are present in the ore bodies. Subsequent metamorphism has altered the primary mineral assemblage and overprinted the texture to such an extent that the origin of this Fe deposit is still a matter of conjecture (Hugi *et al.* 1948). The attribution of the Mont Chemin Fe deposit (CH) in this chapter to the thrust-bound (transitional into granite-related (?)) deposits is mainly for textural reasons, reflecting the latest stages of remobilization of the Fe ore and its spatial relationship with the Mont Blanc Massif. A plausible alternative would be an attribution of the Fe deposit to the Early Alpine unconformity-related deposits (cf. fluorite veins in the country-rocks of the Mont Blanc Massif, as outlined below).

*Siderite–copper–lead–zinc vein-type deposits (Siegerland type)*

The Siegerland Fe district (D), located in the Rhenish Massif, was one of the major mining districts in Germany. After 2000 years of operation and the production of 175 Mt of Fe ore, the last mines were shut down in 1965. Hein (1993) suggested that the Siegerland siderite veins, which extend down to a depth of 1000 m, formed from low-salinity $CO_2$-undersaturated fluids at temperatures between 180 and 320°C following the peak of metamorphism and prior to the post-kinematic magmatism. The textural and paragenetic relationships of sulphide and sulphosalt minerals within the Fe–Cu–Pb–Sb–Bi hydrothermal veins show evidence of an earlier period of primary sulphide mineralization with pyrite, chalcopyrite, galena and sphalerite as the main components, and this was subsequently overprinted by Sb-, Bi- and Cu-rich fluids. This superposition resulted in the formation of new quartz–boulangerite–stibnite veins (Wagner & Cook 1997).

Detailed investigation of polysulphide mineralization, alteration and fluid characteristics of a high-strain zone in the Lower Palaeozoic rocks of the Brabant Massif (B) by Piessens *et al.* (2000) may offer a possible clue to unravel the history of thrust-bound mineralization in the NW part of the Variscides. Ore mineralization occurred synkinematically and was closely associated with the shear zone. Low saline $H_2O$–$CO_2$–(–$CH_4$)–NaCl fluids with temperatures of >260°C were involved in the hydrothermal circulation, which caused the alteration of the host rock. Isotope data and the general setting indicate a metamorphic-driven system, that may be attributed to the main Early to early Middle Devonian deformation event.

Metamorphogenic fold-related deposits are also widespread in the Carpathians where siderite–sulphide veins formed in low-grade rocks and quartz-Sb veins in higher-grade metamorphic rocks (Fig. 21.9). The siderite–sulphide veins extend from several hundreds of metres up to 15 km. A total of 80 Mt of siderite have been mined and 50 Mt of reserves have been calculated (Fenchel *et al.* 1985). Quartz-Sb veins are smaller in length but deserve mentioning due to their Au contents of up to 2 g/t (Chovan *et al.* 1995; Grecula *et al.* 1995; Dill 1998).

The mineral successions in the most important siderite–sulphide ore deposits at Rudňany (SK), Slovinky (SK) and Rožňava (SK) show marked differences, especially as far as siderite and barite distribution are concerned (Bernard 1961; Háber 1980; Rojkovič 1977; Chovan *et al.* 1994; Sasvári & Mat'o 1996). Barite was mainly concentrated in the Rudňany deposit where barite veins give way to stratiform barite lenses and layers (Grecula *et al.* 1995; Žák *et al.* 2005). Chalcopyrite, tetrahedrite, galena and sphalerite usually precipitated together with barite but do not form individual veins. Mercury is widespread in all of these mineral associations. There is common consensus that the cinnabar which is present is indicative of the youngest (?Alpine) stage of siderite–sulphide mineralization (Radvanec *et al.* 2004*a*).

The origin of siderite–sulphide veins in the area is highly controversial. Some authors suggest that they are related to Late Carboniferous or Permian-age basic intrusions (Ilavský *et al.* 1977), while others suggest that they are related to Alpine granite magmatism (Rozložník 1989), or to Alpine metamorphism (Schneiderhöhn 1962). The Rb–Sr isotopic ages of the granites in the Gemericum indicate a Permian intrusion age (290 ± 40 to 220 ± 32 Ma; Kovách *et al.* 1986) and form the basis for the metamorphic–hydrothermal model for the siderite–sulphide and pure sulphide veins in the Gemericum (Grecula 1982; Radvanec *et al.* 2004*a*).

The sulphur source has been constrained by isotope analyses. Positive $\delta^{34}S$ data between +3 and +10‰ for the sulphides are indicative of sulphur remobilized from stratiform sulphide accumulations in Lower Palaeozoic Gemericum sequences. Variable $\delta^{34}S$ values for barite (+5 to +18‰) are interpreted as resulting from the oxidation of sulphur accommodated in the lattice of sulphides.

The $\delta^{13}C$ data for siderite (−8 and −3.5‰) and $\delta^{18}O$ data (+14.5 and +21‰) yielded formation temperatures between 150 and 200°C (Žák *et al.* 1991). The $CO_2$ of fluids was derived from the mixing of organic-matter-derived, and carbonate-derived, $CO_2$. The $^{87}Sr/^{86}Sr$ isotope ratios (0.71042 to 0.71541) of barite suggest a crustal source related to the Variscan magmato-metamorphic M1 event (Radvanec *et al.* 1990). New $^{87}Sr/^{86}Sr$ data obtained from analyses of strontianite and celestite (sampling was carried out in veinlets cutting the siderite–sulphide

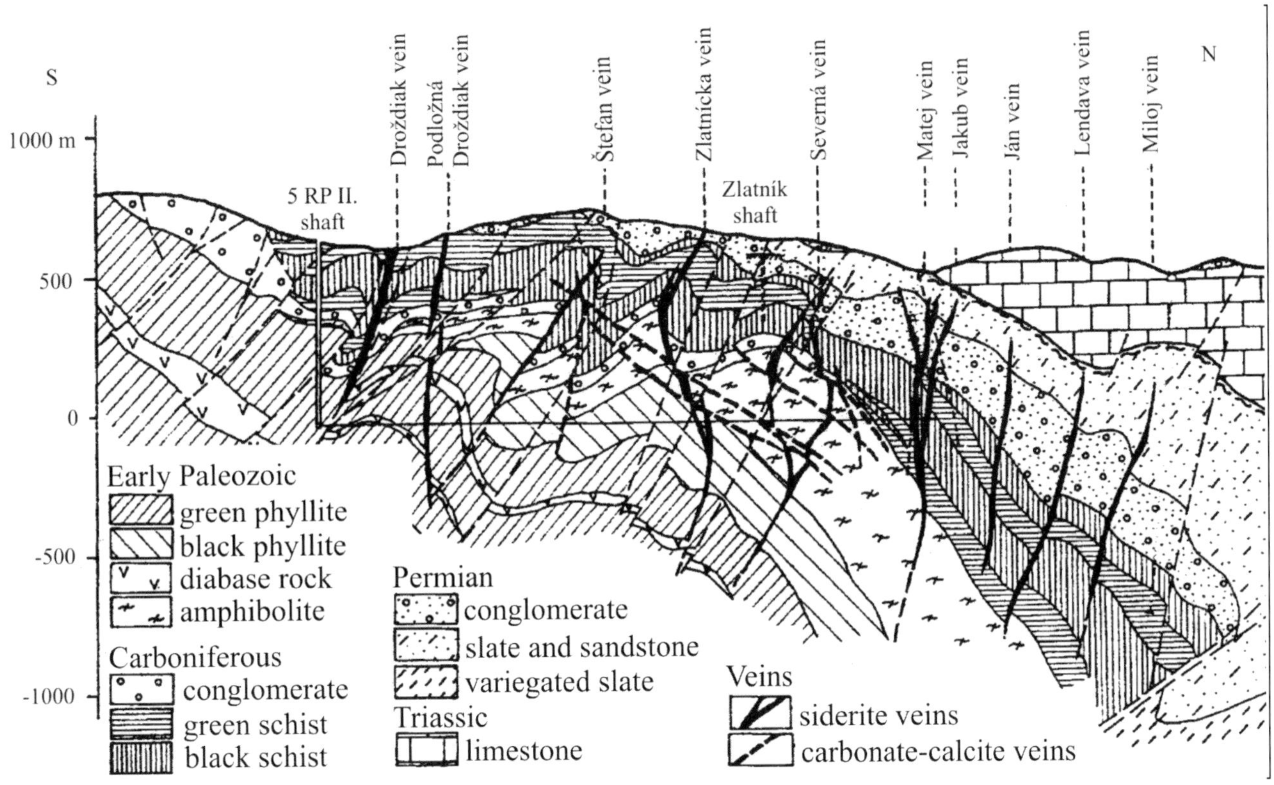


**Fig. 21.9** Transverse geological profile through the Rudňany siderite-sulphide deposit (Hudáček & Fabian, in Grecula *et al.* 1996).

veins) from the same mineral district are significantly higher than the $^{87}Sr/^{86}Sr$ range obtained by Radvanec *et al.* (1990) for the main-stage barite. The results suggest that a phase of hydrothermal activity contemporaneous with the Alpine metamorphism M2 was superimposed on the older Variscan mineralization (Radvanec *et al.* 2004*a*).

Petrological data suggest that metamorphic fluids released during the period of Variscan low-pressure/medium-temperature metamorphism contributed significantly both to the vein siderite–sulphide mineralization and to the replacement siderite deposits.

*Gold–antimony–arsenic vein-type deposits (mesothermal gold–antimony vein type)*

In the Rhenohercynian Zone, thrust-bound Sb mineralization is found in some deposits scattered across the Rhenish Massif, e.g. Ahrbrück (D), Wolfsberg (D), Nuttlar (D), Arnsberg (D), Raubach (D) and Goesdorf (L) (Wagner & Boyce 2003). It is a low diversity mineral assemblage dominated by stibnite and quartz with subordinate Pb sulphosalts such as jamesonite, zickenite and chalcostibite but without economic Au contents. Minor stibnite mineralization has also been recorded from the Siegerland-type siderite veins (see previous section).

In the Saxothuringian Zone thrust-bound Sb mineralization is very common in vein-type deposits, mainly along the Berga and Fichtelgebirge anticlines (Fig. 21.2c). This vein mineralization contains not only stibnite, arsenopyrite and Sb sulphosalts but also native Au (e.g. Brandholz (D)) and cinnabar (e.g. Horní Luby (CZ)) (Dill 1985*b*; Kvet 1994). Antimony was mined near Schleiz (D) and Greiz (D) until the 1950s and at Wolfersgrün (D) in the 1920s. At Brandholz (D) and Neualbenreuth (D) the old mining sites were revisited during the 1970s, but proved to be no longer feasible for Au mining. Following an Early Palaeozoic protore stage (see section on Ordovician–Silurian strata-bound deposits above), Au, Sb and Hg were redeposited along thrust zones parallel to the Schwarzburg, Berga and Fichtelgebirge-Erzgebirge anticlines (Dill 1993). Polymetallic Au-stibnite mineralization occurs in a proximal position relative to the anticlines cored by the Late Variscan granites, whereas the monotonous stibnite veins, lacking Au of economic grade, are located in a more distal position relative to these 'high-heat zones'.

The Złoty Stok (PL) As–Au deposit located in the Lugian Zone was the largest producer of primary Au in the Western Sudetes until its closure in 1961. Its origin is still under discussion (Mochnacka *et al.* 1995) with the most recent interpretation suggesting a hydrothermal/metasomatic origin. Gold is concentrated in loellingite with an average ore grade of between 3 and 5 ppm Au.

In the Moravo-Silesian Zone low-sulphide quartz veins and quartz mobilizates also have anomalously high Au contents. The ratio of free Au to Au accommodated in the sulphides is a function of metamorphic remobilization. Sulphide Au-quartz vein mineralization of the Andělská Hora District (CZ) is encountered along cleavage planes, foliation and fold-related joints in slates, tuffs and dolerites of the Devonian-age Vrbno Group. The thrusted and metamorphosed slates were favourable sites for ascending metamorphogenic/hydrothermal fluids (Ďurišová 1990).

Much effort has been invested in Au exploration in the central part of the Bohemian Massif (Central Bohemian Shear Zone; e.g. Koubová *et al.* 2001). Accumulations of Sb and Au were found at Jílové (CZ), Mokrsko (CZ), Čelina (CZ) and Roudny (CZ) (Mrázek 1986; Morávek & Pouba 1990; Morávek 1996*a*, *b*; Stein *et al.* 1997; Zachariáš *et al.* 2004). Metamorphic quartz lenses occur in the Kašperské Hory Au district (CZ) (Pertoldová *et al.* 1993; Ďurišova *et al.* 1995; Pertold & Puncochár 1995). The low-sulphide Au mineralization is hosted by paragneiss and migmatite with intercalated quartzite, calc-silicate rocks, felsic volcanic rocks, amphibolite and marble. The mineralization is bound to east–west trending zones containing native Au of high purity (>910), Au–Bi–Te minerals, and scheelite. The Mokrsko deposit (CZ) is one of the largest Au resources of Central Europe with Au reserves of more than 100 t proven during exploration between 1970 and 1990. In 1997 Au exploration and a mining project at Mokrsko (CZ) were cancelled owing to mounting public pressure. During the main ore stage (east–west compression) at Mokrsko, parallel and regularly spaced quartz veinlets formed and were filled by quartz, pyrite, pyrrhotite and arsenopyrite. Corresponding fluids belong to a fluid system enriched in C, N, O and H and probably resulted from fluid–rock interactions within the metamorphic series at high-pressue/high-temperature conditions (T = *c.* 450–550°C and P = *c.* 250–400 MPa) (Boiron *et al.* 2001). Arsenic contents of the ore material are up to 1%. Most of the veins are categorized as mesothermal Au veins (Zachariáš *et al.* 2004). Stein *et al.* (1998*b*) suggest that the emplacement of Au lodes in the Proterozoic and Lower Palaeozoic high-grade metamorphic rocks occurred at the Devonian–Carboniferous boundary. A porphyry-style model has been suggested to explain the Petrackova Au mineralization (CZ) (Zacharias *et al.* 2001).

In the Vosges-Black Forest basement a number of stibnite veins have been mined for several decades. Charbes (F), located near the Saxothuringian-Moldanubian border, is barren with respect to Au but strongly enriched in Pb (Coulombeau 1980). Quartz veins with pyrite, stibnite, tetrahedrite and arsenopyrite at Münstergrund (D), St. Ulrich (D) and Sulzburg (D) are bound to a graben which subsided into the basement gneisses of the Moldanubian Zone and was filled with sediments of Carboniferous age. These stibnite veins contain only minor amounts of Au (Gehlen 1989). These vein-type deposits evolved over the course of the structural segmentation of this Moldanubian basement during the Late Carboniferous and are definitely older than the Cenozoic Pb–Zn veins discussed later in the context of the post-Variscan unconformity.

In the Rhenohercynian Zone, at the NW edge of the Variscan orogen, thrust-bound metamorphogenic mineralization occurs at a very shallow structural level in the form of schistosity veins mainly containing Pb and Zn. In the Moldanubian Zone, the core zone of the Central European Variscan Orogen, mineralized linear structures bridge the gap between thrust-bound and granite-related deposits *sensu stricto*. Not surprisingly, W, Sn and U mineralization is locally associated with Sb, Hg and Au in vein mineralizations along the SE boundary of the Teplá-Barrandian Zone such as in the area of Přibram (CZ).

A large Sb–Au–As province also extends across the Western Carpathians and this is the Alpine metallogenic province closest to the Variscan Bohemian Massif. The most well-known deposits of this type are located in the Lesser Carpathians (Tatricum). In the Pezinok-Kolársky Vrch Deposit (north Bratislava) (SK) stibnite- and Au-bearing mineralization is confined to black shales (Chovan *et al.* 1992). The physicochemical parameters are: T = 150–320°C, P = 3.5 kbar (Chovan *et al.* 1995); sulphide $\delta^{34}S$ = −1 to −13‰; $\delta^{13}C$ = −11.8 to −9.7‰; and $\delta^{18}O$ = −17.5 to −13.6‰ (Andráš 1983).

The main Sb–Au–As ore fields in the Gemericum are in the Betliar–Čučma area (SK) where veins with 2–15% Sb, 0.2–2.2 g/t Au (in the Klement vein 10–20 g/t Au and 13–40 g/t Ag) occur. Additional ore-mining districts are located at Bystrý potok (SK) (18–24% Sb), Poproč (SK) (1.8–6.8% Sb, 3 g/t Au, 27–151 g/t Ag) and in the Zlatá Idka ore field (SK) which is transitional with the Siegerland-type siderite–sulphide-type mineralization (Grecula *et al.* 1995) as discussed previously.

In the Low Tatra Mountains Sb–Au veins and impregnations were mined at Dúbrava (SK), Magurka (SK), Medzibrod (SK), Lom (SK) and Dve Vody (SK) (1–3% Sb, 1 g/t Au). These deposits are aligned along deep-seated mylonite zones intersecting Variscan granitoids, metamorphic rocks and migmatites. Sulphur isotopes ($\delta^{34}S$ = 0.6–1.9‰) of pyrite suggest a mantle source for the sulphur. Molybdenite, scheelite and arsenopyrite, associated with the Sb mineralization, crystallized from solutions at temperatures of between 315 and 355°C and at a pressure of more than 2 kbar; such conditions are typical of the metamorphic conditions in that area (Chovan *et al.* 1995). High $CaCl_2$ contents found in fluid inclusions of barite are indicative of evaporite-derived solutions (Chovan *et al.* 1995). They probably originated from Permo-Triassic evaporites thus suggesting an upper limit to the age of formation of the Sb mineralization. The black schists in the country-rocks are likely to have been the source of elements which were mobilized during metamorphism to amphibolite-facies grade (Radvanec *et al.* 2004*a*). All stibnite veins are bound to mylonitic shear zones and considered to be synkinematic relative to the deformation of the country-rocks. Alpine-age fault zones found in the area are barren with respect to Sb mineralization and did not act as conduits for the ore-bearing fluids (Slavkay & Petro 1993).

Many of the shear-zone-hosted stibnite deposits can be attributed to the greywacke- or turbidite-hosted mesothermal Au (Sb) lodes in Upper Proterozoic and Palaeozoic sequences of backarc basins, which are sediment-dominated and lack thick volcanic sequences (Hutchinson 1987; Madu *et al.* 1990; Dill *et al.* 1997). This categorization is mainly based on vein mineralization and structural and textural features observed in these vein-type deposits. Recently, a model for the Au vein mineralization in Central Europe was proposed by Boiron *et al.* (2003), involving the mixing of metamorphic and surficial fluids in the upper crust and hydrocarbon migration.

*Gold–tungsten vein deposits*

Thrust-bound Au–W mineralization was recorded from the Carpathians, where vein-type scheelite and Au mineralizations are known from the Tatricum and Veporicum areas. At Jasenie-Kyslá (SK), Au and W mineralization is found mainly in quartz veins (Pecho 1980). Three types of ore mineralization have been distinguished: (1) hydrothermal veins and stockwork-type mineralization; (2) impregnation zones occurring along the main fault zone with intensive wall-rock silicification; and (3) disseminated scheelite most frequently in amphibolites (Molák & Pecho 1983; Pulec *et al.* 1983). The latter type is of subeconomic grade.

Two vein-type Au deposits in the Swiss Alps at Salanfe (CH) and Astano (CH) are grouped under this heading of thrust-bound Au–W deposits. At Salanfe sulphides and arsenides together with Au were found in a scheelite-bearing skarn of the Aiguilles Rouges Massif (Chiaradia 2003). Anatexis and leucogranite formation occurred at peak metamorphic conditions (P = 0.45 Gpa, T = *c.* 650–700°C). This metamorphic event, dated at 317 Ma in the adjacent Mont Blanc Massif, was related to dextral transpression following Variscan continental collision. Structural evidence indicates that the initial stages of skarn formation also occurred under the above-mentioned P-T conditions (Chiaradia

2003), suggesting a Variscan formation age. The Salanfe skarns were formed at deep crustal levels by fluids in equilibrium with an anatectic leucogranite, possibly channelled along permeable paragneiss during regional-scale transpression.

Astano (CH) is located east of Lago Maggiore in the Southern Alps and contains a typical Au–(Sb) vein-type mineralization with a variegated spectrum of Sb sulphides. Here, the complicated polyphase metamorphic history inducing several stages of high-temperature Alpine remobilization makes it difficult to derive any information on the genesis of the deposit. Köppel (1966) suggested that it is a mesothermal Au–Sb deposit with Au being accommodated in the arsenopyrite and pyrite lattices as 'invisible Au' and present as native Au or electrum. This element combination is similar to the Variscan thrust-bound Au–As–Sb vein-type deposits in the extra-Alpine parts of Central Europe. Therefore, a Variscan age for the Astano deposit seems plausible. However, the mineralogy of the vein-type deposits in the Alps is different from that in the extra-Alpine deposits. For example, Sb-bearing sulphosalts (e.g. jamesonite, boulangerite, zinkenite) are more common than stibnite in the Alps, and monotonous quartz–stibnite veins, very common to the Rhenohercynian and Saxothuringian zones, are absent. Therefore, the age of formation is still problematic.

*Thrust-bound talc and asbestos deposits in (ultra)basic igneous rocks*

Retrograde metamorphism was responsible for the talc mineralization in basic and ultrabasic rocks located along the margin of the Münchberg Gneiss Complex (e.g. Schwarzenbach/Saale (D), Wirsberg (D), Erbendorf (D)). The klippen of the Erbendorf-Vohenstrauß Zone and the Münchberg Gneiss Complex, a previously coherent eclogite-bearing nappe complex with medium-pressue metamorphics, were strongly deformed during emplacement. During the final (retrograde) stages of structural deformation thrust-bound metamorphogenic deposits (e.g. pegmatitic mobilizates) Au–(Te)-bearing veinlets and talc-bearing shear zones, developed along the southern edge, and within, the Münchberg Gneiss Complex (Dill 1979, 1981).

In some places in the Moldanubian Zone (e.g. Hoher Bogen near Neunkirchen (D)), late-stage hydrothermal alteration of Proterozoic (ultra)basic rocks was responsible for asbestos mineralization developing along the shear zones. Asbestos mineralization of this kind, however, was relatively moderate with respect to quantity, and was of inferior quality, so that its deposits have been mined only during wartime. This is also true for the chrysotile and actinolite mineralization in the Rhenish Massif (D) and the Frankonian Massif (D). These were emplaced during the later stages of diabase magmatic activity at the end of the Devonian.

*Feldspar–quartz pegmatoids and quartz lodes*

In the Variscan Orogen, heat production reached its climax during the Late Carboniferous and the concentration of rare elements reached a maximum in the highly differentiated granites and pegmatites. These coarse-grained pegmatitic mobilizates (discussed in the next section) have precursors of metamorphogenic origin. Unlike their granite-related successors, the metamorphogenic mobilizates lack both mineral zoning and rare elements. A simple mineralogy with garnet and tourmaline as the only 'rare element accessories' and little segregation of feldspar and quartz, can be observed in the metapegmatites of the Oberpfalz in the Klobenreuth and Wendersreuth mines (D) and the Rotgneis of the Erzgebirge (D) (Teuscher & Weinelt 1972). Pegmatoid schlieren and patches with up to 80% albite and 20% quartz have also been mined for abrasives at more than 30 locations over a period of several decades, by open-cast and underground mining in the Münchberg Gneiss Complex (Bauberger 1957; Dill 1979).

Investigations on metamorphogenic types of pegmatitic mobilizates and their metabasic country-rocks (banded amphibole gneisses) were carried out by Okrusch *et al.* (1991). Their studies suggested maximum formation temperatures of 620 ± 30°C for the banded amphibole gneisses. White mica, interstitial to the framework silicates of the pegmatites, suggested a formation temperature greater than 400°C for the quartz–feldspar association. The structural conformity of these mobilizates with the textures of the enclosing country-rocks suggests that pegmatitization was contemporaneous with country-rock deformation.

Further to the south in the Bohemian Massif, the Bavarian Fault (Bayrischer Pfahl or Great Bavarian Quartz Lode (D)) occurs together with some smaller, but structurally equivalent fault zones in the western part of the Czech Republic. The steeply dipping Bavarian Fault is one of the most prominent shear zones in the Varican Orogen, which was reactivated during the Permo-Carboniferous (Zulauf *et al.* 2002). Open-cast operations for quartz are found at various locations along this quartz lode.

Non-metallic deposits of this type are also found in the Dinarides, where numerous pegmatitic mobilizates evolved in the migmatites of the Papuk Mountain (HR), the most extensive of which is at Dukina Kosa; feldspars and muscovite are the major minerals. In addition, there are quartz lenses and veins of syn- and post-kinematic secretional origin (termed Alpine-type veins) (Jurković 1962).

## *Collision (granite)-related deposits*

The late stages of Variscan convergence in mid-Carboniferous times resulted in the emplacement of abundant synorogenic granites (Seltmann & Faragher 1994; Henk *et al.* 2000; Kroner *et al.* 2008). Petrological data suggest that this occurred at 600–850°C in upper- to mid-crustal levels. Radiogenic heating in the thickened continental crust is considered to have been the main heat source. Simultaneously, processes such as convective removal of the thermal boundary layer, delamination of part of the lithospheric mantle or subduction of mantle lithosphere must have prevented the thickening of the mantle (Henk *et al.* 2000; see Kroner *et al.* (2008) and Timmerman (2008) for more details on Variscan-age magmatic activity). Arc-related plutonism occurred during mid-Carboniferous times (340–325 Ma) along the Mid-German Crystalline High which was the active SE margin of the Rhenohercynian Zone (McCann *et al.* 2008*b*; Timmerman 2008).

Highly fractionated S- and I-type granites are the most fertile granites since they contain the essential fluids to create U, Sn, F, P, Li, Nb and Ta mineralizations. Mineralization of this set of elements can be traced from the Massif Central in France, through the Erzgebirge Mountains in Germany (Cuney *et al.* 1992; Štemprok & Seltmann 1994; Förster *et al.* 1998, 1999; Marinac & Cuney 1999). Small ore bodies containing Ni–Cu sulphides are bound to more basic predecessors of these granites (Walther & Dill 1995).

*Disseminated nickel–copper deposits*

Nickel and Cu mineralization evolved in the Harzburg Gabbro in the Harz Mountains (D). Pentlandite, pyrite and chalcopyrite constitute the major ore minerals in a partially anatectic hornfels with average contents of the disseminated and lense-shaped Ni–Cu ore bodies of 0.7% Ni and 0.3% Cu (Walther 1986; Walther

& Dill 1995). The geochemical characteristics of the magma are similar to those of an island-arc tholeiite, characterized by low $TiO_2$, alkalis and high $Al_2O_3$. Geochemical and Pb, Sr and Nd isotope data demonstrate that even the most primitive rocks have assimilated crustal material. Petrographic, geochemical and isotope evidence demonstrates that during a late stage of crystallization, hybrid rocks formed through the mechanical mixing of early cumulates and melts with strong crustal contamination from the upper levels of the magma chamber (Sano *et al.* 2002). The mode of formation of Ni–Cu ore in the Harzburg Gabbro is similar to that described as the Stillwater type. Intrusive diabases and picrites of Early Carboniferous age evolved in the Lahn-Dill area (D). In addition to partial serpentinization of these intrusive basic and ultrabasic igneous rocks, subeconomic-grade millerite, chalcopyrite and pyrite crystallized in these alteration zones.

*Tin–tungsten–molybdenum vein-type, greisen and skarn deposits*
Granite-related Sn-W mineralization occurs along the Czech–German border in the Erzgebirge Mountains leading to the formation of a large metallogenetic province matched in Europe only by the Cornwall Sn district (Breiter *et al.* 1999). The mining in the Erzgebirge dates back to the twelfth century and came to an end in 1991. The total Sn production from the Erzgebirge was 300 000 t, and the corresponding production figures for W are 21 400 t (Freels *et al.* 1995).

Particular attention should be drawn to the Poehla-Haemmerlein deposit at Gottesberg (D), which is a large, low-grade, refractory Sn skarn. Its reserves have been reported as 12.3 Mt, averaging 0.42% Sn (Buder *et al.* 1993). Scheelite is present in skarns which developed in Lower Palaeozoic limestones (e.g. Sparnberg-Pottiga (D), Göpfersgrün (D)). Locally, very complex mineralization developed (such as at Obří Důl (CZ)) with scheelite superimposed on a high-temperature mineral assemblage of cassiterite, stannite, malayaite, stockesite and Sn-bearing garnet (Mochnacka *et al.* 1995). Wolframite predominates in quartz veins (Krásno (CZ), Ehrenfriedersdorf (D), Altenberg (D), Zinnwald-Cínovec (D/CZ), Pechtelsgrün (D)) (Fig. 21.10). Cassiterite and wolframite in the Erzgebirge area are almost exclusively related to the younger granites (older granites, 330–310 Ma; younger granites, 305–290 Ma) (Baumann *et al.* 1986; Seltmann & Faragher 1994; Tischendorf *et al.* 1995; Breiter *et al.* 1999; Webster *et al.* 2004). However, there are obvious exceptions to the rule: for example, radiometric age dating by Kempe & Belyatsky (1997), using the $^{144}Nd/^{143}Nd$ and $^{147}Sm–^{144}Nd$ methods, yielded a Namurian formation age (321–326 Ma) for the Sadisdorf Sn–W mineralization (D). Tin–W mineralization occurs in the endo- and exocontact area of the Sn–F–Li granites and may locally extend into the pegmatitic bodies related to these Late Variscan granites (Thomas & Webster 2001). The Altenberg (D) and Zinnwald/Cínovec (D/CZ) deposits are among the best known Sn deposits in Europe (Baumann *et al.* 2000).

The **Altenberg Sn deposit** is located in the contact zone of the Altenberg granite porphyry and the Teplice quartz porphyry. The Altenberg granite forms a stock-shaped intrusion in the granite porphyry with extensive greisen zones measuring 300 to 400 m in diameter and 230 m in vertical extension. Greisen refers to pervasively altered lithium–albite granite in which feldspar and biotite are converted to a disseminated assemblage of quartz, topaz, muscovite, zinnwaldite and protolithionite (both Li-micas), cassiterite, sericite, fluorite, dickite, kaolinite, wolframite and scheelite. Pegmatitic parts altered to topaz (pycnite), zinnwaldite and quartz are called 'Stockscheider'. The main ore minerals are cassiterite, wolframite and molybdenite (Baumann *et al.* 1986). Mining commenced in 1620 with the opening up of the Great Pinge (Fig. 21.10).

The **Zinnwald/Cínovec Sn–W–Li deposit** consists of a system of regular veins in greisenized zones of a granite body, with quartz, wolframite, scheelite, cassiterite, zinnwaldite, topaz, fluorite, muscovite, Li-mica and feldspar forming the main mineral in the greisen zone.

The Saxothuringian and Moldanubian zones in the Vosges and the Black Forest contain no significant Sn deposits, although some Sn minerals may be found in the Triberg Granite (D). The Vosges contain W mineralizations in their northernmost part, near Framont Grandfontaine (F), where an Fe-bearing scheelite skarn was examined by the Bureau de recherches géologiques et minières (BRGM), and Mo accumulations near Breitenbach (F) (Bouladon 1989). The situation is similar in the Massif Central, where some W mineralization is known, but Sn deposits are absent. In contrast to the Saxothuringian and Moldanubian zones, the Rhenohercynian Zone contains neither W nor Sn deposits.

In the Variscan Aar Granite of the Swiss Alps, molybdenite- and scheelite-bearing quartz veins occur in the Baltschiedertal (CH) (Jaffé 1986). In the Mittersill W deposit (Eastern Alps) (A), Variscan-age magmatism (340 Ma) is considered to have

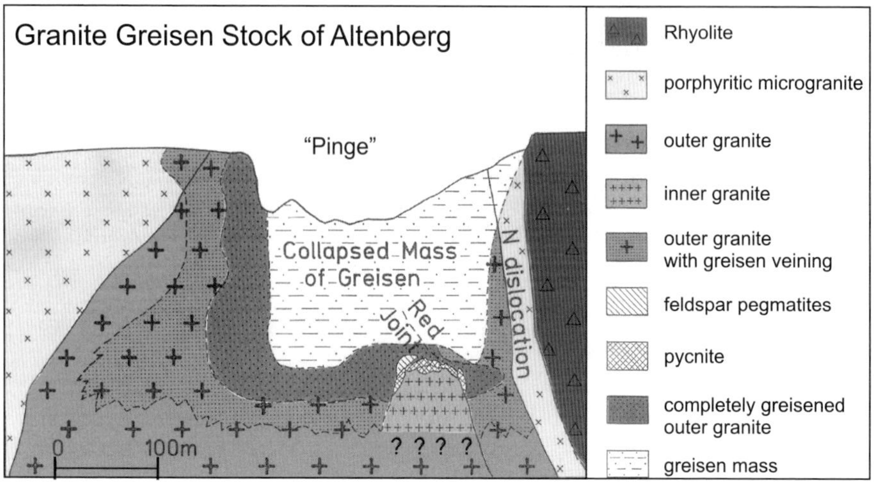


**Fig. 21.10.** The classic greisen stock at Altenberg (D) (Baumann 1965).

been responsible for a second phase of scheelite mineralization which was superimposed on the primary Early Palaeozoic phase (Eichhorn *et al.* 1999; see section on Precambrian–Cambrian strata-bound deposits above).

In the Carpathians (Gemericum) granite-related Sn–W–Mo deposits were encountered in the fine-grained two-mica granite near Hnilec (SK) and at Rochovce (SK). The apical parts of the granites are greisenized and rich in B, F, Li, Rb, Cs, Be, Mo and Sn (Broska & Uher 2001). Based upon high initial Sr isotope ratios ($I_{Sr}$ = 0.711–0.715) which are accompanied by higher $\varepsilon_{Nd(i)}$ of –4.6, elevated stable isotopes values of $\delta^{18}O$ (10‰) and $\delta^{34}S$ (4.48‰), a mature continental metasedimentary protolith can be assumed for these granites (Kohút & Recio 2002). A Late Variscan formation age may be concluded from the data obtained from radiometric age dating of monazite (276 ± 13 Ma and 263 ± 29 Ma; Finger & Broska 1999; Finger *et al.* 2003), single-grain U–Pb zircon dating (250 ± 18 Ma; Poller *et al.* 2002), and the Re–Os method on molybdenite (262.2 ± 0.9 and 263.8 ± 0.8 Ma; Kohút & Stein 2005).

*Lead–copper–zinc–silver vein deposits*

Lead, Cu, Zn sulphides and Ag-enriched tetrahedrite (= freibergite) and Sb sulphosalts as well as native Ag and argentite were emplaced in the Erzgebirge, e.g. at Freiberg (D) and Schneeberg (D) (Tischendorf *et al.* 1995; Baumann *et al.* 2000). Silver mining near Freiberg was described as early as 1168 and continued until 1968. During this time period, about 14 Mt of Pb and Zn with 5200 t of Ag metal were produced. The vein-type base-metal mineralizations are younger than the granite-related Sn-bearing mineralization described above. More than 1000 veins, cross-cutting and with a range of orientations, were mapped in the upper Proterozoic gneisses. These veins are famous for the presence of argyrodite ($Ag_8GeS_6$) which was used to extract the metal Ge. Argyrodite, as mined in Freiberg, contains 1.8 to 6.9% Ge. These veins have been considered to result from differentiation of magma with the development of a volatile fluid phase that escaped along faults to form the veins. More recently, researchers have preferred to invoke the mixing of cooler, upper-crustal hydrothermal or meteoric waters with rising fluids that could have been heated by an intrusion or expelled directly from a differentiating magma (Baumann *et al.* 2000).

Another representative of the Variscan polymetallic Ag-enriched Pb–Zn vein deposits is situated in the Moldanubian Zone of the Bohemian Massif where a set of parallel veins cuts through gneisses and migmatites of the Kutná Hora Crystalline Complex (CZ) (Pouba & Ilavský 1986). A conspicuous zonality may be recognized in the region around Kutná Hora, with Sb, Pb and Zn minerals being concentrated in the south, Pb, Ag and Zn in the central parts and Cu, As, Fe, Zn and Sn in the north. This is a classic example of how Sb-dominated thrust-bound mineralization gradually changes via Pb–Zn mineralization into Sn mineralization.

Small Pb–Zn vein-type deposits, with arsenopyrite, chalcopyrite, quartz and calcite, have been mined in the metamorphic envelope of the Gotthard (Bristenstock (CH)) and Aar massifs (Alp Nadèls (CH)) in the Swiss Alps (Jaffé 1986). Although they are mineralogically less variable than the Erzgebirge Pb–Zn deposits, the Swiss vein deposits have been correlated by Jaffé (1986) with the 'kiesige Bleiformation' at Freiberg. The Trachsellaunen (CH) and Groppenstein (CH) Pb–Zn vein-type deposits are also located in the Aar Massif. What distinguishes them from the adjacent Pb–Zn deposits is the presence of fluorite and barite. The ubiquity of F and Ba in these veins is taken as evidence for Alpidic mineralization being superimposed on Variscan Pb–Zn mineralization.

*Polymetallic and monotonous uranium vein-type deposits*

Much effort and money were spent on U exploration and exploitation in Germany, France and in the former Czechoslovakia over the last century. Based on mineral compositions, the fault-bounded Variscan U mineralization may be subdivided into a monotonous mineral association comprising pitchblende with coffinite, brannerite, U leucoxen, U-bearing carbonaceous matter and some molybdenite (e.g. Mähring (D) and Chateau-Lambert (F)) and a polymetallic mineral association with pitchblende associated with Pb, Bi, Cu selenides as diagnostic minerals (e.g. Erzgebirge U deposits). The polymetallic mineral association is genetically related to the intrusion of high-heat-production (HHP) granites. The metals involved in the mineralization and part of the aqueous solutions were mixed with meteoric waters percolating through these granitic bodies.

The best known U deposits in Central Europe are located in the Saxothuringian Zone. In the eastern part of the Saxothuringian Zone (i.e. Lugian Zone), polymetallic U deposits were discovered in the Kletno (PL) and Kowary (PL) areas (Piestrzynski 1997). Here, pitchblende and coffinite are accompanied by Co, Ni, As, Bi, Cu, Pb, Zn and Se minerals. A member of the 'monotonous U mineral association' is brannerite which was reported from quartz veins cutting through leucogranites near Kowary (PL) (Mochnacka *et al.* 1995). Uranium bearing fluorite veins are common in the Izera Gneiss Complex (Western Sudetes).

Several U vein-type deposits are located on both sides of the Czech–German border along the Erzgebirge area at Jáchymov (CZ), Hartenstein (D), Aue (D) and Oberschlema (D) (Tischendorf *et al.* 1995; Ondrus *et al.* 2003; Förster *et al.* 2004). The mineralogy of the U vein-type mineralization from the Erzgebirge was studied by Förster (1999). Based upon the occurrence of selenides (Förster *et al.* 2004), the mineralization can be attributed to the 'polymetallic U mineral association' (Banás 1991). Dating by U–Pb gives a formation age as early as 265 Ma (Mochnacka *et al.* 1995). Jáchymov (CZ) shows a wealth of minerals. About 180 mineralized veins in mica schists and phyllites around a granite massif contain Ag, U and minor amounts of Bi, Co, Ni, Zn, Pb, Cu, Sb and As. The veins also contain pitchblende, Ag-bearing sulphoarsenides and native Ag, along with other rare minerals and more common sulphides. Mining in the Jáchymov ore district began in 1516, and developed into one of the largest mining centres of Europe. The word 'dollar' originated from the German word 'Thaler' (Joachimsthal). At the end of the nineteenth century, the radioactivity of Jáchymov U ores was studied intensively and resulted in the discovery of radium.

Further to the west at Grossschloppen (D) and Hebanz (D) in the Fichtelgbirge area, silicified and episyenitic vein structures were investigated by drilling operations and test mining (Fig. 21.2d). In granites undergoing episyenitization, quartz is replaced either by dolomite or by calcite mineralized with U minerals. Another type of episyenite-bearing zeolite, mainly heulandite and stilbite, contains no U mineralization. Episyenitization is associated with Mg metasomatism of metacarbonate-bearing horizons subjacent to the U mineralization (Dill 1986*b*). Towards the south, test mining was carried out at Hoehensteinweg (D) and Mähring (D), where U mineralization is associated with fracture zones and quartz lodes. These extend across the border into the Czech Republic and were mined near Dyleň (CZ) and Zadní Chodov (CZ).

Hydrocarbon migration along faults is a major control on the precipitation of U minerals in vein mineralization. This has been shown by the various types of impsonite (epi- to kata-type) in the German U vein-type deposits as well as by results obtained during chemical investigations in the Přibram mining district (CZ) (Dill & Weiser 1981; Kříbek *et al.* 1999).

The origin of some U mineralization in the eastern part of the Bohemian Massif can also be associated with the infiltration of basinal brines which extracted U from U-bearing accessories in Upper Carboniferous to Lower Permian clastic rocks. The vein-type and disseminated-type U deposits of Rožná-Olši (CZ), containing minerals of the monotonous and polymetallic U mineral assemblages, are transitional from granite- to unconformity-related deposits and pertain to one of the mineralizations bridging the gap between the Variscan and Alpine metallogenetic cycles (Kříbek *et al.* 2005). Between 1954 and 2005 the total production from these deposits reached 20 000 t U.

Uranium vein mineralizations are associated with a variegated spectrum of metallic and non-metallic mineralizations such as at Nabburg-Wölsendorf (fluorite) (D), where a peculiar type of U mineralization was discovered at several sites in the Oberpfalz. The so-called Schwarzach U ores form part of the polymetallic U mineralization with pitchblende and Cu selenides (Dill 1983). What makes them distinct from their other counterparts in NE Bavaria is the massive yellow U ore mineralization with 'gummites' not discovered thus far anywhere else in Central Europe. In the Black Forest U vein mineralizations are associated with fluorite at Menzenschwand (D) and with Bi and Co sulphides at Wittichen (D) (Gehlen 1989).

The Variscan U belt also extends into France, where vein-type mineralization was extensively studied and operated until recently in the Vosges near Chateau-Lambert (F) (Bouladon 1989) and in the Massif Central, e.g. Magnac (F) and Funay (F) (Leroy 1978). Variscan-age U mineralization was also preserved during Alpine tectonic remobilization in the Tavetsch Massif near Trun (CH) in the Swiss Alps. Similar U showings were also discovered in the gneissic envelope of the Variscan Aar Massif (Naters (CH) and in the Aiguilles Rouge Massif at Le Chatelard (CH).

The oldest pitchblende in the vein-type deposits in northern Bavaria (Fichtelgebirge, Oberpfalz) (D) have yielded an upper intercept in the concordia plot at 295 ± 4 Ma (Carl *et al.* 1983). The post-tectonic granites from the Fichtelgebirge have been dated at 320 to 280 Ma (Wendt *et al.* 1988). These radiometric data show a genetic link between U mineralization and the Late Variscan igneous activity. Investigation of the pitchblende from the Menzenschwand area (Black Forest) by U–Pb indicates a Variscan formation age (310 ± 3.5 Ma) for the earliest mineralization at least. The pitchblende from Wittichen (D) yielded an age of 235 ± 5 Ma corresponding to a younger reshuffling of radioisotopes. Studies in the Massif Central suggest that the conduits for the U-bearing solution might have acted more than 20–30 Ma after trap formation as preferential channel ways. Radiometric age data indicate the longevity of hydrothermal circulation processes driven by exhumation (extension) and uplift in and around these granites. The initiation of regional uplift at *c.* 320 Ma triggered the circulation of in-situ derived low-density aqueous fluids at depth, that then reacted with the granite to form large vertical dissolution conduits (episyenites; Scaillet *et al.* 1996). The hydrothermal alteration was further enhanced during uplift by the structurally focused flow of large volumes of aqueous fluids along brittle faults cutting across the laccolith. Due to sustained hydrothermal circulation adjacent to terminal HHP injections, these conduits acted over a long period as preferential channels for the U-bearing fluids and resulted in the emplacement of U deposits along vertical fault zones and in the metasomatic columns.

The longevity of U-ore deposition is particularily remarkable, since it helps to bridge the gap between the Late Variscan granite-related deposits and some of the unconformity-related U-bearing deposits associated with the post-Variscan unconformity. It may also account for the precipitation of Late Palaeozoic U oxides during the early stages of vein formation in the Nabburg-Wölsendorf Fluorite District (D) and for the Late Variscan fetid fluorite or antozonite (German: Stinkspat) that was chronologically constrained by Sm–Nd isotope analyses to between 296.6 ± 23.2 and 281.2 ± 22.9 (Leipziger 1986).

*Feldspar–quartz and polymetallic lithium–niobium–tantalum pegmatites*

During the collisional stage of the Variscan Orogeny several pegmatites were emplaced in the Moldanubian Zone. Complex quartz–feldspar pegmatites, which have been the object of long-term mining operations and are still attractive for mineral collectors because of their mineral wealth, are situated at Hagendorf (D), Pleystein (D) and Waidhaus (D). The most prominent of these, at Hagendorf-South, shows well-developed zoning with an aplitic margin, a pegmatitic inner zone, a quartz core and a cone-shaped body with Li phosphates, Nb, Ta, U and numerous other rare element minerals (Mücke 1987, 2000; Mücke *et al.* 1990; Dill *et al.* 2008*a*, *b*). Between 1960 and 1972, 1000 t of Li ore were extracted, mainly from triphyline as a byproduct of the feldspar exploitation which was based on 8 Mt of feldspar–quartz ore. In 1983 the mining operation for feldspar and quartz proved to be no longer profitable.

This chain of pegmatites may also be extended through the Czech Republic into Poland with lepidolite pegmatite occurring near Rožná and Dobrá Voda (CZ) (Cerný *et al.* 1995; Novák & Cerný 2001), beryl columbite pegmatites near Scheibengraben (CZ) (Novák *et al.* 2003), and niobite–tantalite pegmatite at Zólkiewka (PL) (Janeczek 1996). The composition of microlite-type minerals and the textural relations indicate that the hydrothermal stage generating Nb–Ta ore in the pegmatite includes a broad range of P-T-X conditions (where X is the composition) from early subsolidus replacement at 500–350°C and 2.5–2.0 kbar at Dobrá Voda (CZ) to near-surface weathering at temperatures below 100°C (Novák & Cerny 1998). Rare-earth element minerals in addition to topaz may be found in the Late Variscan granites as shown by new data from the Karlovy Vary Pluton (CZ) (Kempe *et al.* 2001) and from the Třebíč Pluton (CZ) where thorium mineralization was discovered by Sulovský & Hlisnikovský (2001).

*Talc (soapstone) replacement deposits in carbonate rocks*

Soapstone/talc deposits associated with the (?Pre-)Cambrian-age Wunsiedel Marble have been worked at numerous sites in the Fichtelgebirge near Göpfersgrün (D) as a raw material for products ranging from electric insulators to powder in chewing gum production. Before the closure of the last open-cast mine in 1997, annual production was 10 000 t and reserves were estimated at 200 000 t of ore (Bayerisches Staatsministerium für Wirtschaft und Verkehr 1979). The talc deposit at Göpfersgrün was formed by hydrothermal alteration of the Wunsiedel Marble probably during Permian times. Hydrothermal talc mineralization occurred along a major fault zone and is associated with the formation of massive saddle dolomites. The main talc mineralization resulted from decarbonation at low $X_{CO_2}$ (where X = mole fraction; see Bucher & Frey 1994) and temperatures of between 250 and 400°C. Hydrothermal dolomitization, talc mineralization and vugs filled with carbonate during the waning stages of alteration are related to formation brines or crustal fluids that interacted with graphite-bearing metapelites under acidic conditions (Hecht *et al.* 1999).

### *Petroleum deposits*

Hydrocarbons, with the exception of coal-bed methane, are rare in pre-Permian rocks in Central Europe. However, a minor oil (and gas) province is located in the Baltic Basin (Syneclise). This basin, filled mainly with Lower Palaeozoic rocks, is situated on the western margin of the East European Craton. It forms an approximately oval-shaped interior basin with the SW part of the basin subsiding to 5 km near the Tornquist-Teisseyre Zone.

The **Baltic Basin** (Syneclise) is situated in the south Baltic Sea and the adjoining onshore areas of Latvia, Lithuania, Poland, and the Russian enclave of Kaliningrad. Exploration activity began in the 1960s and led to the discovery of 25 small- to medium-sized accumulations in Lithuania, two small oil discoveries in Latvia and 14 oil and/or gas discoveries in Poland. Exploration in the Russian sector of the basin has reaped the greatest rewards, including the largest onshore and offshore fields (Krasnoborskoye, Ushakovskoye, Kravtsovskoye), hosting about 60 million barrels each. Peak liquid production has not yet been reached but peak gas production was attained in 1988. In 2001, the daily production reached 30.8 million barrels per day. Small-scale oil production took also place on the Swedish island of Gotland.

Following a period of rifting in Late Vendian to Early Cambrian times (Poprawa *et al.* 1999), post-rift subsidence took place in the Middle Cambrian before being interrupted by uplift associated with arc–continent collision. Renewed subsidence in Early Ordovician times led to the deposition of a thin basal sandstone unit, which is overlain by a thick succession of Ordovician carbonates and marls. The early Caledonian Orogeny is represented by the closure of the Tornquist Sea. Reactivation of the Tornquist–Teisseyre Zone as a transpressive strike-slip fault during the Caledonian Orogeny led to a short period of deep-marine sedimentation followed by deformation and uplift. Mid-Devonian to Carboniferous sediments were laid down in a sag basin and were deformed in the Variscan Orogeny (Carboniferous to Permian). Diabase intrusions with a Late Palaeozoic age occur in the area of the Baltic Sea. The overlying sediments are generally thin and of minor importance for hydrocarbons.

Lower Silurian shales form the major source unit, but Cambrian and Ordovician sources also contributed to the accumulations (Zdanaviciute & Lazauskiene 2004). With increasing overburden, maturity varies from immature in the NE to post-mature in the SW.

The principal reservoir unit is the Middle Cambrian Deimena Formation. The shallow-marine sandstones are about 50 m thick and have a porosity of 3–15% (Sliaupa *et al.* 2004). Additional reservoir rocks are Ordovician to Devonian limestones and sandstones. Hydrocarbon accumulations also occur in fractured basement rocks. Seals include Middle Cambrian, Lower to Middle Ordovician and Silurian mudstones and muddy carbonates.

An early generation and migration phase occurred in Late Silurian to Devonian times (Zdanaviciute & Lazauskiene 2004). A major period of migration occurred in Late Jurassic to Cretaceous times into reservoirs in the SE and east of the basin. Structures in the basin are related to the major periods of structural activity, i.e. Vendian rifting, Cambrian to Silurian subsidence, Caledonian transpression, Variscan compression, and minor compressive events in Jurassic to Tertiary times.

## Alpine cycle

### *Supergene and hypogene deposits related to the post-Variscan/Early Alpine unconformity*

The Variscan Orogeny resulted in deformation, uplift of mountain ranges and significant erosion giving rise to the post-Variscan/Early Alpine unconformity (see Kroner *et al.* 2008). This unconformity is overlain by rocks ranging in age from Stephanian to Early Jurassic. The hiatus between the basement rocks and the overlying sediments, therefore, represents different time intervals in different areas. Peneplanation and etch planation (Twidale 2002) under semiarid to (sub)tropial climatic conditions occurred during these time intervals.

The distribution of the overlying Permo-Mesozoic rocks was controlled by eustacy and tectonic events related to the breakup of Gondwana. Major Permian to Jurassic tectonic events which influenced metallogenesis along the post-Variscan unconformity include: (1) Stephanian to Early Permian rifting accompanied by extensive magmatism; (2) Triassic to Jurassic opening of oceanic domains in the Alpine region; and (3) Mid-Triassic to Early Jurassic extension in the extra-Alpine region (see Scheck-Wenderoth *et al.* 2008). Isotope data increasingly show the significance of a thermal event at the Triassic–Jurassic boundary for ore formation in Central Europe (Wernicke & Lippolt 1997*a*).

One of the first discoveries of an ‘unconformity-related vein-type deposit’ was made in 1968 in Saskatchewan (Canada), when U was found in Upper Precambrian metasediments near Rabbit Lake. Since then unconformities have been recognized as major hydraulic planes for hypogene U deposits elsewhere in the world (Dahlkamp 1984).

Dill (1988*a*) recognized the post-Variscan unconformity as an important hydraulic plane in Central Europe and discussed its prominent role in relation to the numerous fluorite–barite vein deposits along the western edge of the Bohemian Massif and around the Vosges–Black Forest basement dome. Subsequently, the unconformity model was extended to the Central European Variscan basement and the overlying Meso-Cenozoic platform sediments (Dill 1994). This concept has also been applied to sulphide-, fluorite- and barite-bearing mineralizations elsewhere in Europe (Boni *et al.* 1992; Rodeghiero *et al.* 1996; Brigo *et al.* 2001).

The Late Variscan/Early Alpine unconformity was a geohydraulic plane for a great variety of epigenetic deposits which evolved where this unconformity was intersected by (sub)vertical fault zones (Fig. 21.3c, d). Hypogene (fluorite, barite, Hg, Ag, Cu, Pb, Zn, Sb, U, Mo) deposits related to the post-Variscan unconformities are found within Upper Carboniferous to Lower Jurassic igneous rocks and platform sediments, or immediately beneath the unconformity in Palaeozoic basement rocks. The transition from the Variscan to the Alpine cycle is more distinct in the extra-Alpine part than in the Alpine part of Central Europe, where sedimentation was continuous in some regions. Unconformity-related vein-type deposits grading upwards into strata-bound deposits are thus more widespread in the Alpine part, whereas strata-bound deposits developed quite separately from unconformity-related vein-type deposits in the extra-Alpine part of Europe.

In the Carpathians, Variscan movements continued into the Permian and the post-Variscan unconformity is overlain by

Lower Triassic rocks. Here, the complex interplay of *per ascensum* (metamorphogenic) and *per descensum* (hydrothermal–unconformity-related) fluids led to the precipitation of siderite and magnesite. Therefore, some researchers in the Western Carpathians consider this stage as part of the Variscan metallogenic cycle.

Supergene deposits with kaolin, Sn and U are related to peneplanation and etch planation processes (Twidale 2002). In an idealized cross-section from the basement to the lacustrine basin, unconformity-related and strata-bound ore deposits are plotted as a function of different host rock lithologies and depositional environments (Fig. 21.11).

*Supergene deposits*

**Kaolin saprolite associated with the Early Alpine unconformity.** Late Variscan uplift led to extensive erosion as a result of pervasive chemical weathering and denudation of the basement rocks under (sub)tropical climatic conditions. This is the current situation in central Africa, where a thick regolith of kaolin is being formed.

Kaolin quarried at Podbořany (CZ) (Central Bohemian Basin; west of Praha) immediately overlies the East Alpine unconformity in the form of a palaeoregolith/saprolite or is found redeposited within arkoses and conglomerates of Carboniferous age (Kužvart 1968). The kaolin from the Podbořany region occurs in the feldspathic sandstones of the Líně Formation. Climatic conditions favourable for the formation of kaolin prevailed in the Westphalian and Stephanian but also extended into the Mesozoic and even Early Cenozoic times. Kaolin from the Karlovy Vary deposits (CZ), which developed on granite, has few impurities and is of such high quality that it is used in the production of fine china.

Along the eastern margin of the South German Basin (west Nürnberg) kaolin is currently mined between Hirschau and Schnaittenbach (D) in several open pits, with a total production of about 400 000 t kaolin per year (Gilg 2000). The host rocks are Lower Triassic arkoses juxtaposed with the granites and gneisses of the Bohemian Massif. Based on stable isotope data, Gilg (2000) assumes an Early Cretaceous kaolinization age. Locally, these kaolinized arkoses contain elevated Pb contents (Köster 1980). The arenaceous sediments represent the proximal facies of what is later mentioned in relation to the Triassic-age strata-bound ore mineralization from the Bleiglanzbank (D) and the Freihung cerussite deposits (D). The Pb in both of these deposits was derived from the weathering of K feldspar in exposed crystalline rocks. In the kaolinitic arkoses, Pb is accommodated in the lattice of plumbogummite ($PbAl_3(PO_4)_2(OH)_5.H_2O$). This secondary mineral thus links the Pb source in the basement rocks with the more distal Pb deposits.

**Uranium vein-like deposits beneath the Early Alpine unconformity.** The most prominent representative of supergene deposits related to the post-Variscan unconformity was mined in the Gera-Ronneburg area (Fig. 21.3a) in the Thuringian-Franconian Massif. The Lower Palaeozoic carbonaceous 'protore' rocks or 'low-metal concentration' (see section on Ordovician–Silurian strata-bound U deposits) were folded, sheared and uplifted at the end of the Palaeozoic and subjected to chemical weathering from the Late Palaeozoic onward (Lange *et al*. 1991). The U mineralization is, in places, of 'yellow ore-type' consisting mainly of uraniferous Fe–Al phosphates (wavellite-type) that resulted from the decomposition of pyrite and apatite disseminated in the Silurian and Lower Devonian black shales (e.g. Gräfenthal Horst (D)) or of 'black ore-type' with sooty pitchblende and sulphides, such as in the Gera-Ronneburg mining district (D). Supergene U redeposition commenced around 240 Ma with the onset of the Late Palaeozoic peneplanation and ceased by the end of the Mesozoic. At that time another unconformity and another type of U deposits, related to the Late Alpine unconformity, evolved near Königsstein-Pirna (D).

*Hypogene deposits*

**Meso- to epithermal polymetallic mercury–precious metal vein-type deposits in volcanosedimentary series.** A complex polymetallic mineralization with Hg as the marker element was precipitated in the aftermath of the granite-related mineralization, as calc-alkaline volcanic and subvolcanic rocks were erupted in the Saar-Nahe Basin. The volcanites and their subvolcanic equivalents host Cu deposits near Imsbach (D) and Fischbach (D) and high-quality Hg ore near Obermoschel (D) and Stahlberg (D) (Dreyer 1973, 1975). Mineralization has produced some rather obscure Hg alloys such as belendorffite ($Cu_7Hg_6$), paraschachnerite ($Ag_3Hg_2$) and schachnerite ($Ag_{1.1}Hg_{0.9}$). Mining commenced in the early fifteenth century and has made this area one of the leading Hg producers in the world. In the twentieth century Hg mining sites were reopened in 1934 and closed in 1942 when the ore bodies became exhausted. Output during this period was *c*. 250 t of Hg. Almost all of the dacites and rhyolites in the Saar-Nahe Basin contain anomalously high U contents; this has led to extensive exploration which has proved some significant U discoveries (e.g. Bühlskopf/Ellweiler (D)).

Mercury is also a common element in some U vein-type deposits along the Erzgebirge Anticline (e.g. Hartenstein (D)). These bridge the gap between the true granite-related U deposits and those bound to the subvolcanic and volcanic calc-alkaline equivalents of the Late Variscan granites.

Along the SE margin of the Alps, in the area of Ljubljana (SLO), Permo-Carboniferous siliciclastic rocks contain concordant and discordant ore veins with a very variegated mineral assemblage. More than 40 deposits are known in the area of the Litija Anticline (SLO). Unlike their counterparts in extra-Alpine Central Europe, these deposits do not contain granitophile elements such as U. According to their major mineral assemblages, the deposits can be subdivided into different vein types, namely: (1) sphalerite, (2) galena–sphalerite, (3) galena–sphalerite–cinnabar, (4) cinnabar, and (5) stibnite veins.

The Litija deposit (SLO) is one of the biggest of its kind in the Sava Nappe and was interpreted by Drovenik *et al.* (1980) as a meso-epithermal Pb–Zn–Cu–Hg–Ba–Fe deposit. The ore reserves in Litija enabled production of 50 000 t of Pb, 1 t Ag, 42.5 t Hg and 30 000 t barite to take place. The major minerals are galena, sphalerite, chalcopyrite, tetrahedrite, cinnabar, barite and siderite. The $\delta^{34}S$ ratios of the sulphide fluctuate around 0.0‰, whereas those of barite are much heavier, at between +17 and +23‰. The veins were filled prior to the deposition of the Middle Permian sediments. The mineralization may be related to the Lower Permian quartz porphyries and keratophyres in the Eastern Alps (Drovenik *et al.* 1980). In Slovenia, however, volcanic units are absent, although reworked pebbles in the Permian-age Val Gardena Beds provide evidence of their former presence (Drovenik *et al.* 1980).

In the Dinarides, the spectrum of minerals is more varied than in any other Central European region and the quantity of Au increases. Indeed, the history of mining in this region is a long one. The ore deposits of the Durmitor Nappe in the Mid-Bosnian Schist Mountains (BiH) (west Sarajevo) were the major Au-mining district in the Roman Empire. Epithermal high- and low-sulphidation-type Au deposits with Hg, Fe, Ba, Cu, Sb and As

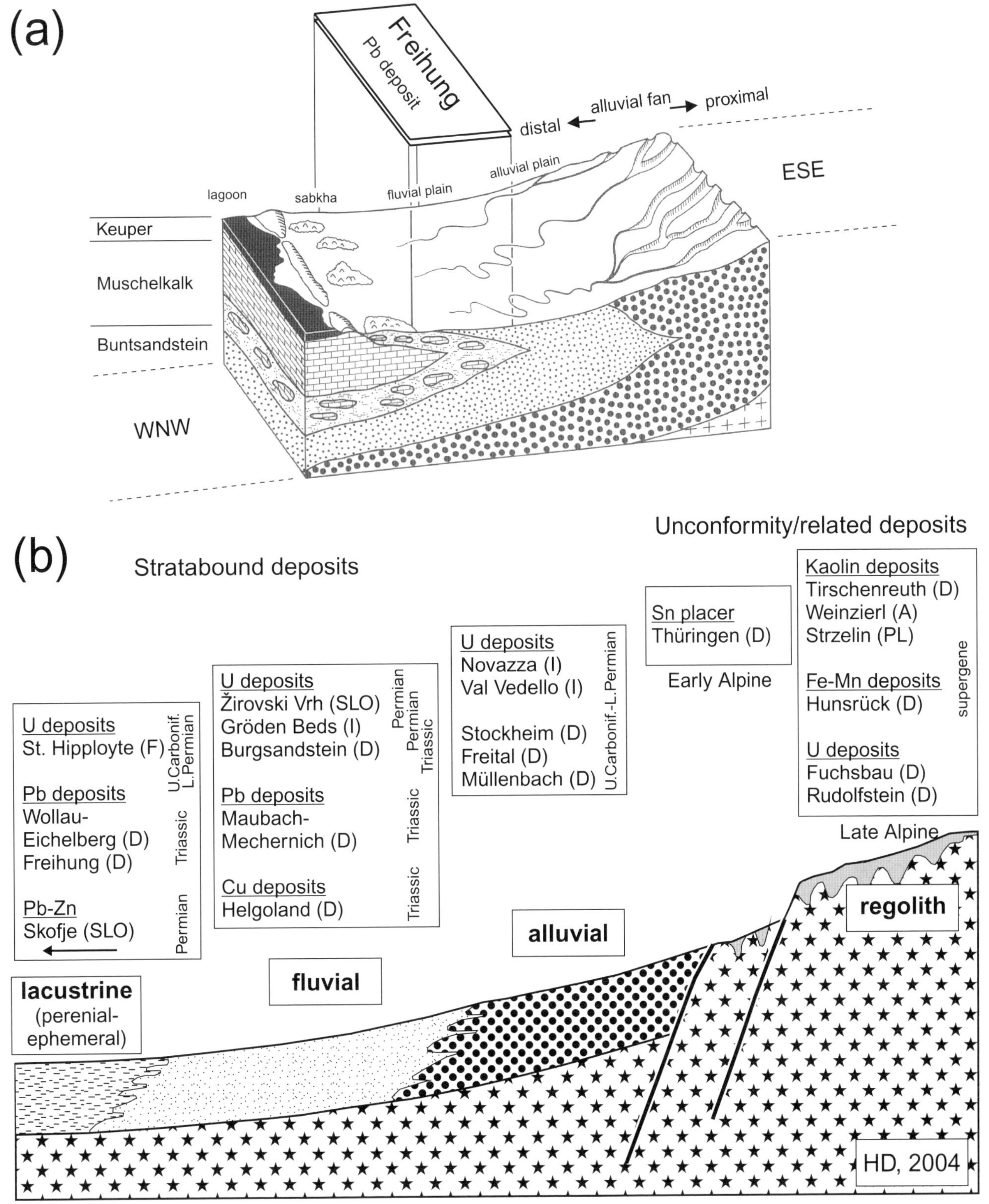


**Fig. 21.11.** Depositional environments and ore mineralization referred to in the text. (**a**) Block-diagram illustrating precipitation of cerrusite–galena ore in a sabkha environment, e.g. Freihung (D). (**b**) Metallogenetic 'catena' from the regolith through the lacustrine basin.

formed from a rhyolitic magma erupting or intruding during the Late Carboniferous to Early Permian (Jurković 1957). The overall mineral assemblage consists of pyrite, pyrrhotite, sphalerite, galena, siderite, cassiterite, molybdenite, arsenopyrite, chalcopyrite, stibnite, cinnabar, realgar, native Au (up to 20 g/t), barite, and traces of Pb–Sb- and Bi-sulphosalts. A conspicuous zonal distribution of mineral parageneses around the volcanic vent system can be recognized. High-temperature veins with tourmaline are located in the deepest part of the metarhyolite complex. The zonal distribution of the deposits is as follows: Vrtlasce (kata-to mesothermal) (BiH), Čemernica (mesothermal) (BiH), Fojnica deposit (mesothermal) (BiH), Hrmza, and Berberuša Mountain (epithermal) (BiH). The Hg mineralization is of epithermal type and evolved distal to the vent system. The major ore mineral is Hg-enriched tetrahedrite. Gold-bearing pyrite impregnation such as at Bakovići occurs at the contact of the dolostones with the metarhyolites. Mercury-enriched tetrahedrite has $\delta^{34}S$ values in the range of between −5.5‰ and −15.4‰. Barite has $\delta^{34}S$ values of between +6.3‰ and +17.2‰. These data suggest that Permian seawater sulphate or evaporites may have contributed to the sulphur budget of the ore-bearing solutions. Fluid inclusion studies on specimens of quartz, fluorite and barite have helped to constrain the physicochemical conditions which may be described as follows: $T_H$, 190–310°C; fluid system, $NaCl–CaCl_2–H_2O$; salinity, 24.2–26.3 wt% $NaCl_{equ}$ and the presence of halite daughter crystals (Jurković & Palinkaš 2002).

**Uranium–molybdenum–copper vein-type and stratiform deposits in volcanosedimentary series.** A low metal concentration with U–Mo–Cu in Permian volcaniclastic complexes in the Gemericum (Krompachy Group: Knola, Petrova hora, Novoveská Huta formations) formed the protore for deposits, which underwent strong remobilization and an increase of ore grade during the Alpine Orogeny (e.g. Novoveská Huta (SK), Jahodná (SK)). This complex type of epigenetic mineralization is genetically related to the large group of strata-bound U and Cu deposits discussed in the following section and to collision/granite-related deposits with a 'monotonous U mineralization'. This type of U mineralization is also found in the Tatricum and Veporicum (Kálnica, Vikartovce-Spišský Štiavnik (SK)) and in the Mecsek Mountains (Kővagószőlős-Bakonya) (H). Ore mineralization took place in depositional environments transitional between continental (e.g. Novoveská Huta, Muráň, Hnilčík, Stratená, Krompachy, Jahodná) (Novotný & Mihál' 1987) and marine (e.g. Gočaltovo) settings.

The **Novoveská Huta U–Mo deposit** is the best known deposit of this kind and is related to Permian dacites and andesites. Its mineral assemblage comprises uraninite, U–Ti minerals and molybdenite which are associated with accessory galena, hematite, chalcopyrite, ilmenite, leucoxene, magnetite, marcasite, pyrite, rutile, sphalerite, tennantite, arsenopyrite, goethite and tetrahedrite (Rojkovič 1981; Háber 1996). Isotopic analysis of $^{206}Pb$ and $^{207}Pb$ yielded a formation age of 240 ± 40 Ma for the low-grade and 130 ± 30 Ma for the high-grade ore (Archangelskij & Daniel 1981). Vertically, the Huta Complex grades upward into the Grúň Complex, a volcanosedimentary series with lens-shaped ore bodies quite similar to those from Novoveská Huta. In addition to the minerals reported from Novoveská Huta, pyrrhotite, montroseite, autunite, torbernite and tyuyamunite were also identified in the U ore mineralization (Rojkovič 1981). Archangelskij & Daniel (1981) determined the formation age of this U-mineralization as 200 ± 30 Ma.

**Uranium-bearing fluorite–barite–base metal vein-type and sandstone-hosted deposits.** Unconformity-related F–Ba–Pb–Zn–U vein-type deposits are known from all Variscan basement highs as well as from coarse-grained Permo-Triassic rocks overlying the Variscan peneplain *sensu* Summerfield (1999). However, their number decreases with increasing distance from the basement highs. Deep boreholes in the South German Basin revealed elevated U contents at the contact between basement rocks and the overlying Permo-Triassic platform sediments (Schmid & Weinelt 1978; Gudden *et al.* 1985). The age relations and genetic parameters of unconformity-related deposits are discussed below in more detail for a number of key deposits located either immediately beneath the Variscan unconformity or hosted by siliciclastic rocks deposited on the Variscan peneplain.

In basement uplifts of the Central European Variscides, such as the Vosges, Black Forest, Harz Mountains, Rhenish Massif and the Bohemian Massif, many F–Ba and Pb–Zn–Cu vein-type deposits were mined during the last decades. Based upon the available chemical and mineralogical data, many deposits may be attributed to unconformity-related mineralization, e.g. Val d' Ajol (F), Maxonchamp (F), Freudenstadt (D), Eisenbach (D), Oberwolfach (D), Neuenbürg (D), Bad Grund (D), Nabburg-Wölsendorf (D), Hranice (CZ), Vyškov (CZ) (Losert 1957; Endlicher 1982; Huck 1984; Bouladon 1989; Stedingk & Stoppel 1993).

The easternmost representatives of this fluorite–barite mineralization are located in the Lugian Zone at Křišany (CZ), Harrachov (CZ), Stanislawów (PL) and Boguszów (PL) (Paulo 1994; Mochnacka *et al.* 1995). The Stanislawów deposit (PL), with reserves of 10 Mt of $BaSO_4$ in epimetamorphic greenschists and diabases, is one of the largest barite concentrations in Europe. Barite is accompanied by siderite, quartz, Zn and Pb sulphides. Fluorite contents increase with depth (Mochnacka *et al.* 1995). Barite veins at Boguszów (PL) penetrate Upper Carboniferous sediments. The barite–fluorite vein mineralization is of multistage origin. Pre-Variscan and Variscan faults were rejuvenated during the Alpine period of deformation (Reichmann 1975). The mining of barite and fluorite ceased in the Harrachov district (CZ) in 1992 and in Poland in 1998.

*Fluorite–barite vein-type deposits in Germany.* Fluorite and barite veins in the Black Forest, the Saar-Nahe region and the Rhenish and Bohemian massifs played a vital role for the recovery of Germany in the post-World War II era with a maximum barite production of 0.5 M t achieved during 1960. Today only the Clara Mine at Oberwolfach (D) in the Black Forest is still in operation for fluorite and barite and together with the barite mines at Lauterberg (D) (closed in 2007) in the Harz Mountains accounts for the total amount of fluorite and barite exploited in Germany during 2005 (Table 21.1). The Dreislar barite mine (Rhenish Massif) was closed in 2002 (Bundesanstalt für Geowissenschaften und Rohstoffe 2005). Many of the barite–fluorite companies in west Germany ceased mining between the late 1960s and 1970s. Mines in the former German Democratic Republic (GDR) had to close their operations for economic reasons in 1990 when the planned economy was transformed into a free enterprise economy (the closures were not due to the lack of reserves). In 2005, due to a shortage of fluorite and a 'bottleneck' on import from China, a new shaft was sunk in the Ilmenau (D) fluorite–barite mining district by Phönix Fluss- und Schwerspat Bergwerk GmbH near Gehren in Thuringia (Dr. Bucholz pers. comm.). Even in the western part of Germany, the reopening of fluorite mines is currently envisaged in view of a shortage of high quality fluorite (e.g. Käfersteige near Pforzheim in the northern Black Forest).

*Bad Grund Pb–Zn deposit (D).* Numerous Pb–Zn veins were mined in the Harz Mountains near Clausthal-Zellerfeld, St. Andreasberg and Lautentahl. The Bad Grund mining district was the last one in the Harz Mountains to be exploited for Pb and Zn. It was one of the most productive mining districts in Germany focused on unconformity-related/post-orogenic vein-type deposits. The veins strike at 80 to 145°, dip steeply to the south and are in general within strike-slip faults with a variable vertical component of movement (Sperling & Stoppel 1981). Hydrothermal ore mineralization took place in four phases. Galena is the main Ag carrier and sphalerite is rich in Cd. Subordinate minerals include chalcopyrite, pyrite, marcasite, tetrahedrite (Ag-bearing), pyragyrite, bournonite, and boulangerite. Among the gangue minerals calcite, siderite, barite and quartz prevail. Various minerals of different ages are intimately intergrown with each other and dependent on the active tectonic processes (Sperling 1973). From 1831 to 1992 19 Mt ore with 1.1 Mt Pb and 0.7 Mt Zn were produced (Stedingk & Stoppel 1993). Detailed studies of the ore-bearing solutions by Möller & Lüders (1993) suggest that vein mineralization of this type in the Harz Mountains developed from highly saline and bicarbonate-enriched fluids in the temperature range of 250 to 300°C.

Radiometric age dating of pitchblende from the Nabburg-Wölsendorf area (D) (Oberpfalz) yielded ages as old as $295 \pm 14$ Ma, and from pitchblende mineralization cross-cutting $CaF_2$–$BaSO_4$ vein systems dates as old as $205.9 \pm 2.7$ (Dill 1988*a*). The U–Pb and Sm–Nd isotope data constrain the mineralization related to the post-Variscan unconformity to the interval from the Permian to the Late Jurassic (Leipziger 1986).

*Maubach-Mechernich Pb–Zn deposit (D).* Ascending metalliferous fluids did not only precipitate their elements within the Variscan basement rocks, but were also able to impregnate the coarse-grained porous clastic rocks resting immediately above the Palaeozoic rocks, e.g. the sandstone-hosted Pb–Zn ore deposits at Maubach-Mechernich (D) (south of Cologne), also considered to be a red-bed-hosted Pb–Zn deposit (Fig. 21.3c & 21.10b). About 3 Mt of Pb metal were mined from these Triassic sandstone-hosted deposits until their closure in 1969 (Werner & Walther 1995). At Maubach the average grade was 2.7% Pb and 0.9% Zn and at Mechernich 0.8% Pb and 1.1% Zn. The main ore minerals are galena, sphalerite, chalcopyrite, bravoite, pyrite, tetrahedrite, bournonite, marcasite and covellite (Friedrich *et al.* 1993; Schneider *et al.* 1999). Based on Rb–Sr dating, a Middle Jurassic (Dogger: $170 \pm 4$ Ma) ore age was assumed (Schneider *et al.* 1999). Lead isotopes of galena from sandstone-hosted deposits in the lower Triassic Buntsandstein and vein-type deposits in Late Variscan greywackes and slates of the Rhenish Massif display a similar trend and do not allow distinction between the two types of Pb deposits (Large *et al.* 1983; Krahn 1988) (Fig. 21.3c). Steep hydraulic and chemical gradients between the bedrock and the overburden are responsible for the emplacement of hypogene ore mineralization above and below the unconformity by means of the movement of intrastatal solutions and/or convectively circulating fluids.

A similar Pb deposit in Lower Triassic sandstones and Middle Triassic carbonates was mined at Largentiere (F) near the eastern border of the Cévennes (Bjørlykke & Sangster 1981; Warren 1999). Although not attaining economic grade, the 'Pingarten Porphyry' in the Passau Forest should also be mentioned in this context (Endlicher 1977). It is a Permo-Triassic arkose resting on top of Moldanubian basement rocks, pervasively impregnated with barite, fluorite, quartz and cerussite (Dill 1985*a*) (Fig. 21.3d). Support for the idea of the barite and fluorite mineralization being related to the post-Variscan unconformity is provided by Sr isotope studies on barites collected along transects from the basement to the Permo-Triassic platform sediments. These data showed an increase in radiogenic Sr in barite towards the crystalline basement (Dill & Carl 1987).

*Marsberg Cu deposit (D).* An example of a very complex argillaceous, arenaceous and calcareous host rock lithology of Permo-Carboniferous age is found in the Marsberg deposit (D) near the NE edge of the Rhenish Massif (Stribrny 1987). It contained 63 000 t of Cu. This mineralization, also containing sulphides and selenides of Cu, Zn, Pb and native Au, was attributed by Large (1993) to the group of deposits related to the post-Variscan unconformity. The temperature (250–200°C) and chemical composition of the post-Variscan F–Ba solutions (Na–Cl–Ca, salt > 100 g/l) are very similar over great distances and are likely to have been derived from the formation waters of the adjacent sedimentary rocks (Klemm 1994). Möller & Lüders (1993) and Krahn & Baumann (1996) claim that this post-Variscan mineralization originated from fluids which sourced the metals from the Variscan basement (Fig. 21.3c). Precipitation resulted from the mixing of S-bearing formation waters at low temperatures. In the area of Marsberg numerous abandoned mines working Kupferschiefer-type mineralizations are located along the eastern border of the Rhenish Massif, e.g. Korbach (D), Geismar (D), Leitmar (D) (Kulik *et al.* 1984). Some of these mines contain considerable amounts of Au (e.g. Korbach-Goldhausen (D)). The area may be considered as representative for the transition between unconformity-related deposits and strata-bound deposits that rest upon the Early Alpine unconformity, for example the Kupferschiefer-type Cu deposits, the Silesian-type Pb–Zn deposits, and the Sabkha-type Pb deposits (Fig. 21.3b) referred to in later sections. Underground mining at Marsberg ended in 1945.

The westernmost representatives of fluorite–barite vein deposits in and around Variscan basement highs are located in France. Among the French fluorite deposits, the mines at Morvan (F) are the most important ones in terms of both tonnage and size. Fluorite is found in veins in the basement (Voltennes, Maine) or as stratiform fluorite mineralization at the base of the Liassic cover (Courcelles, Antully) (Bouladon 1989; Thiery 2004). In addition to fluorite, the mineralization includes barite and traces of galena, sphalerite and chalcopyrite. Several fluorite–barite–quartz veins bearing Mn minerals cut across the 'Granite des Morvan' and impregnate its sedimentary cover of Triassic to Early Jurassic age near Romanèche-Thorins (F) (Lougnon 1956; Hauptmann & Lippolt 2000). Manganiferous siderite is the primary source of Mn in the 'chapeau oxidé', a term used to describe a concentration of tetravalent Mn oxides (romanechite, pyrolusite, todorokite) restricted to a deep oxidation zone which was the only object of previous mining operations. Age constraints may be deduced from some U deposits in the region. Primary U-oxide from the Bertholène uraniferous ore body (F) on the western margin of the Massif Central was found to be $173 \pm 9$ Ma old. This phase of U concentration (or remobilization) has also been encountered in deposits located in Limousin and Morvan (F). The thermal event which mobilized U in these deposits was related to the Liassic pre-rifting phase that preceded the Malmian opening of the Piedmont-Liguria Ocean (Lévêque *et al.* 1988).

In addition to the unconformity-related F–Ba–Pb–Zn–U vein-type deposits known from Variscan basement highs and coarse-grained Permo-Triassic rocks overlying the Variscan peneplain in the extra-Alpine region, there are similar deposits in the Western Alps. These are found along the margins of the Variscan External Massifs (Mont Blanc, Belledonne, Argentera) and in the (Middle Penninic) Briançonnais Terrane. The F–Pb–Zn–Ag deposits in both domains are quite similar in terms of mineralogy. Therefore, these base-metal mineralizations have been attributed to the same mineralization group. Due to intensive element remobilization during the Alpine Orogeny, the primary origin cannot be unravelled for each of the deposits discussed below.

The Les Trappistes fluorite deposit (CH) is located in the

Mont Blanc Massif. All of the veins, containing galena, sphalerite, pyrite, chalcopyrite, quartz and calcite in addition to fluorite, are hosted by two-mica granites and by quartz porphyries. This is also true for the fluorite veins at Tête des Econduits in the same area (Hubacher 1983). The fluorite veins are known to extend over a length of 1250 m and down to a depth of 800 m representing a significant fluorite potential of 44 000 t at an average grade of 14% $CaF_2$ (Jaffé 1986). The majority of the veins are conformable with the foliation of the gneissic country-rocks, although some of them cut through the metamorphic structures (Wutzler 1983). In the French Alps veins at Rocheray (= Bois Feullet) (F) (Belledonne Massif) and at Valauria (F) (Argentera Massif) occur in gneisses forming a stockwork mineralization in the uppermost 20 m of the basement, immediately beneath the Permian overburden which is scarcely mineralized. Apart from Zn (20 000 t) and Pb (3 000 t), the Valauria mine yielded 4 t of Ag (Bouladon 1989).

The Casanna Schists of the Middle Penninic Bernhard Nappe in Switzerland host polymetallic vein-type deposits at St. Luc (Pb–Zn) and Praz-Jean (Pb–Zn–Ag). At St. Luc (CH) the host rocks consist of metasediments of Permo-Triassic and Permo-Carboniferous age (Schmutz 1984). Galena, sphalerite, pyrite, chalcopyrite, pyrrhotite and Ag-rich fahlore are associated with barite, quartz and calcite. The Pb–Zn–Ag-bearing vein of Praz-Jean (CH) is hosted by metamorphic rocks of Palaeozoic age. Sphalerite, galena and sulphosalts (freibergite and boulangérite) are its main ore-forming minerals. Microprobe investigations indicate that the Ag is contained in freibergite and not in an argentian galena (Schmid *et al.* 1990). They obviously formed from Early Alpine hypogene processes related to the post-Variscan unconformity. Further to the SW, La Plagne (F), Peisey (F) and L'Argentière-la-Bessée (F) form part of a small Pb–Ag province in the Middle Penninic Nappe of the French Alps (Bouladon 1989). The mine at La Plagne produced *c.* 125 000 t of Pb and 360 t of Ag. The mineralization is stratiform and is within Lower Triassic quartzites and in underlying Permian volcanogenic schists. The mineral assemblage is dominated by Ag-rich galena, barite, and subordinate pyrite, ankerite, bournonite, tetrahedrite and sphalerite. The mineralization is interpreted as being syngenetic and of hydrothermal sedimentary origin (Bouladon 1989). In the Penninic Magna Nappe at Alp Taspin (CH) similar Pb–Zn veins occur.

In the Southern Alps of Italy, vein-type deposits at Corvara (I) and Vignola (I) are spatially related to the Variscan-age granites of Ivigna-Bressanone and Cima d'Asta (Di Cobertaldo 1965; Bakos *et al.* 1972). The Vignola deposit comprises four fluorite veins with a disseminated mineralization of galena, sphalerite, pyrite and chalcopyrite. The vein deposit at Corvara is situated in a tectonically disturbed contact zone between a granitic core and its surrounding metasediments. At Corvara the mineralization mainly consists of fluorite with sporadic sphalerite and galena. Veins are also abundant between Lake Garda and Lake Como: The veins of Torgola in Val Trompia, Lombardy (I) cut across granodiorite and Permian metasediments of the South Alpine basement and younger sandstones (Dal Bianco 1969). Here, fluorite is the main mineral accompanied by minor sphalerite, galena and chalcopyrite. The Marigole and Pice deposits in the Darzo area (I) occur in Permian tuffs and rhyolithic ignimbrites (Di Colbertaldo & Marzolo 1964). Barite is the main mineral, accompanied by some quartz, carbonates, rare pyrite and chalcopyrite. Barite deposits are also located in Lombardy (I) at Pozzuolo, Valle di Meraldo, Gardena, Monte Elto and Ruola. All of these show a set of cross-cutting veins and concordant layers in Permian and Lower Triassic metasediments (Servino and Verrucano-Lombardo formations). The veins generally represent the Triassic remobilization of former stratiform deposits (Gillieron 1959). Barite, the main mineral, is associated with some siderite, hematite and chalcopyrite.

**Iron–(barite) vein-type deposits.** Hematite-bearing quartz veins with or without barite were the target of previous mining activities in the Black Forest and along the Fichtelgebirge-Erzgebirge Anticline, e.g. Gleißinger Fels (D). Geochemical evidence for a Permo-Triassic age has been provided by Mankopf & Lippott (1997). For the quartz–hematite–barite veins near Obersexau (Middle Black Forest) (D) multiple hematite formation within a single vein was demonstrated, attesting to Late Alpine remobilization having taken place until *c.* 120 Ma. Helium retention in the various oxide minerals played an important role and will certainly provide more accurate new data sets in the future to enable the precise dating of this epigenetic mineralization.

**Iron–base metal–barite vein-type and replacement deposits.** Iron-base metal–barite vein-type and replacement deposits are confined to the Italian Southern Alps and to the Dinarides. Several Fe deposits (Alfredo, S. Aloisio, Manina, Barisella, Sopracroce-Fondi) in Lower Triassic sediments occur in Lombardy (I), between Lake Como and the Caffaro Valley (Gillieron 1959). Deposits are hosted by sedimentary successions composed of limestones intercalated with terrigenous siliciclastics. Siderite deposits contain about 35% Fe and 3–4% Mn with minor constituents such as barite, quartz, hematite, fluorite and rare sulphides. The mining operations ceased in the early 1980s, when the Alfredo and S. Aloisio mines were shut down.

In the Dinarides, similar deposits with a very varied element spectrum are constrained by two unconformities; the older is genetically related to Early Carboniferous deformation and the younger to the Saalian (Rotliegend) deformation. Deposits related to these unconformities are stratiform and vein-type containing siderite, barite, various sulphides and rare fluorite within limestones, dolostones, shales and silts of Carboniferous age.

Rude in the Samoborska gora Mountain (HR) (west Zagreb) is interpreted to be an epigenetic–mesothermal stratiform deposit with Fe, Cu, Pb, Zn and Ba emplaced in the Sava Nappe (Fig. 21.12). An epigenetic, hydrothermal vein-type mineralization evolved here in the footwall of a stratiform, SEDEX-type mineralization. The mesothermal, quartz–siderite veins with chalcopyrite, galena, sphalerite and barite beneath the SEDEX mineralization form a type of stockwork mineralization in Middle to Upper Permian clastics and represent the mineralized feeder channels for the stratiform ore. The latter formed in an evaporitic pond or lagoon filled with gypsum, anhydrite, hematite, siderite and barite. The stratiform gypsum–anhydrite mineralization has $\delta^{34}S$ ratios of between +9 and +12‰. Vein galena and cogenetic barite with $\delta^{34}S$ ratios of +3‰ and +11.6‰, respectively, suggest that the Permian seawater affected the ore-bearing brines and, thus, a Permian age for the deposit is most likely. Studies of fluid inclusions in quartz crystals within the feeder channels suggested that the enclosed fluids had a $NaCl–CaCl_2–H_2O$ composition, with a salinity of 6.7–18.9 wt% $NaCl_{equ.}$, and a formation temperature of 130–170°C (Palinkaš *et al.* 2000). Other related deposits are found at Žune (barite–fluorite deposit) and at Trgovska gora (mesothermal Fe–Cu–Zn–Pb–Ba deposit) (Palinkaš 1988). The country-rocks at Trgovska gora consist of Lower Devonian to Carboniferous siliciclastics

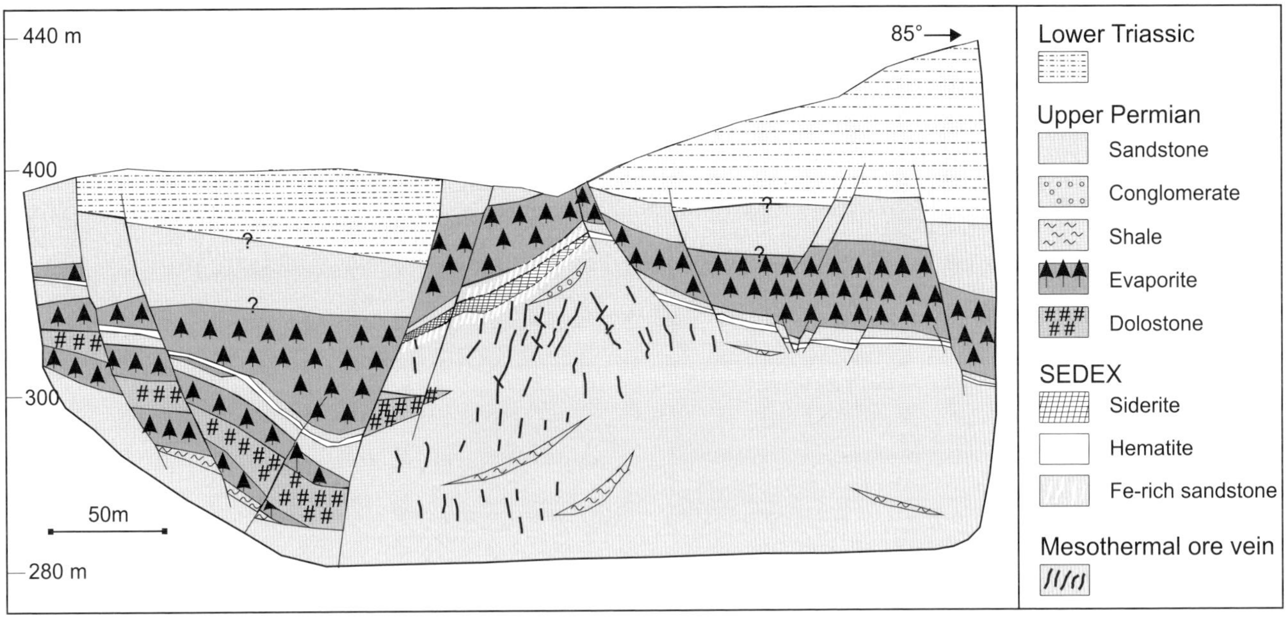


**Fig. 21.12.** Geological cross-section of the Rude deposit (HR) (modified after Šinkovec 1971).

intercalated with calcareous rocks. The uppermost transgressive part of the succession is formed by the Permian-age Val Gardena Sandstone (Jurković 1993).

A different deposit type from that of the composite mineralization described above are strata-bound mesothermal replacement bodies associated with veins and lenticular stocks in the Trgovska gora Mountains and the Sana-Una Palaeozoic. These are present in several mining districts, which differ from each other in terms of the major ore minerals present, for example ankerite (Žirovac), siderite (Gvozdansko), siderite with chalcopyrite (Gradski potok), siderite with galena (Majdan), and siderite, chalcopyrite, galena, pyrite, Ni–Co sulphides and barite (Tomašica) (Jurković 1962). Based on the study of fluid inclusions ($T_H$ = 90–250°C, 8–11 wt% $NaCl_{equ}$.) and the $\delta^{34}S$ values of barite (+8.7 and +10.2‰) and sulphides (−3.2 and +2.7‰), Permian-age seawater is considered to be the most likely source for the ore-bearing fluids (Palinkaš *et al.* 2003).

The best known deposits in the Sana-Una Palaeozoic are located in the Ljubija ore field. Ljubija Fe–Ba–Pb–Zn replacement deposits are located in non-metamorphosed Middle Carboniferous-age deep-marine sediments (Grubić *et al.* 2000) that form part of the Pannonian Nappe of the Internal Dinarides. Hydrothermal–metasomatic siderite–barite–polysulphide ore in the Ljubija ore field occurs at Adamuša, Brdo, Atlijina Kosa, Tomašica and Omarska (BiH). The largest barite–fluorite deposit is located at Žune (Dolinac), and the largest barite deposit is found at Vidrenjak. The replacement-type ore forms massive bodies of siderite and ankerite and sequences of alternating sparry siderite and dark fine-grained siderite exhibiting typical zebra textures (also called diagenetic compaction rhythmites). Microcaverns are partly filled with quartz, galena, sphalerite and cookeite. Fluid inclusion studies in quartz yielded $T_H$ data in the range of 100–275°C and fluids of low to high salinity (2–39 wt% $NaCl_{equ}$.) (Palinkaš *et al.* 2003; Borojević-Šoštarić 2004). The $\delta^{34}S$ values in barite are between +8.5 and +14.5‰.

In the Petrova gora Mountain, upper Palaeozoic continental clastic sediments host numerous mesothermal–epithermal Fe–Ba deposits with quartz–siderite and quartz–sulphide veins (Kijak, Gejkovac) (Jurković 1993). Fluid inclusion studies yielded homogenization temperatures of between 100 and 200°C and salinities ranging from 12 to 26 wt% $NaCl_{equ}$. The $\delta^{34}S$ in barite varies between +5.5 and +11.4 ‰ (Palinkaš *et al.* 2003).

**Polymetallic siderite and magnesite replacement deposits.** The close association of siderite and magnesite is unique for the Alpine–Carpathian Mountain chain and makes this range quite distinct from the extra-Alpine realm where siderite never occurs together with magnesite. The mode of formation in the Eastern Alps and the Western Carpathians, however, is slightly different.

Numerous siderite and magnesite mineralizations of various dimensions are found in the **Eastern Alps** where both mineralizations are closely associated in time and space. Today, the Erzberg siderite mine (A), located NW of Leoben in the Greywacke Zone, is the only active Fe mine, with a production of about 1.4 Mt of Fe ore per year. Sparry magnesite mineralizations of the Veitsch type have considerable economic importance. Presently, about 0.7 Mt of magnesite are produced in five mines (Breitenau (A), Oberdorf (A), Wald (A), Radenthein (A), Hochfilzen (A)).

The formation of epigenetic/metasomatic siderite (Fig. 21.13) and magnesite is related to Permo-Triassic rifting and the circulation of brine-derived fluids. The mineralizing event is interpreted as being post-Variscan and pre-Cretaceous based on the presence of mineralized post-Variscan conglomerates and the cessation of hydrothermal features at the Alpine nappe boundaries (Ebner *et al.* 2000). High salinity and the chemical composition of fluid inclusions in the siderites/magnesites indicate that the mineralizing fluids were originally oxidized evaporitic, bittern brines which were modified (reduced) by water–rock reactions (uptake of Fe) while percolating through the crust. The sharp contrast in fluid composition between the marine host-rock carbonates and the mineralizations characterized by evaporitic fluids is not compatible with a simple marine–sedimentary model. No indications of a synsedimentary concentration of Mg or Fe and stratabound/stratiform mineralizations can be observed. The structure of the mineralizations is actually hydrothermal–metasomatic. Ongoing Sm/Nd investigations on sparry magnesites of the Eastern Greywacke Zone show distinct

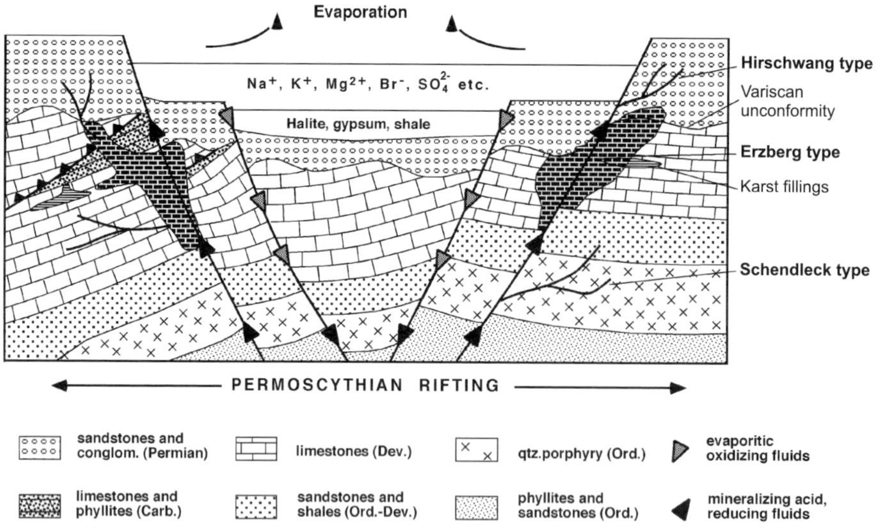


**Fig. 21.13.** Model of Permoscythian siderite formation in the Greywacke Zone (Eastern Alps; Ebner *et al.* 2000).

differences between the magnesites and the host rocks thus arguing for a hydrothermal origin. First isochrons reveal Triassic ages for the magnesite formation (Prochaska & Henjes-Kunst 2007).

In Permo-Triassic times evaporitic basins were ubiquitous in the Austro-Alpine realm. High degrees of evaporation produced residual bitterns with increased salinities and concentrations of Br, Mg, K and $SO_4$. The peculiar fluid composition of the siderites and magnesites is, in itself, a strong argument for the Permo-Triassic timing of the mineralization. High heat flow in the rift environment induced hydrothermal convection systems connected with the hydrosphere and the residual evaporitic brines. In higher, more oxidizing levels, Mg-enriched brines led to the formation of magnesites. Diagenetic reactions and host-rock alterations changed these brines at deeper levels into acid and reducing fluids with the capacity of leaching Fe from the country-rocks. Vein-type siderite–haematite–sulphide mineralizations were formed in the metapelitic and metavolcanic host-rocks in a reducing environment (e.g. Schendleck (A)). Within Devonian platform carbonates metasomatic siderite bodies were formed (e.g. Erzberg (A)). Metasomatism and mimetic crystallization of the marine host-rock carbonates often preserved primary sedimentary textures very well, which led earlier researchers to postulate syngenetic models.

In the western part of the Eastern Alps (Ortler Group), the magnesite deposit of Zumpanell (I), south of the village of Gomagoi, is of special interest. Here, lenses of sparry magnesite are concordant with Triassic Fe-rich dolomites. Magnesite is grey-black in colour due to the presence of organic matter dispersed within the carbonate. According to Andreatta (1957), the origin of the Zumpanell magnesite deposit is hydrothermal–metasomatic, in contrast to the ideas of Burckhardt (1966) who proposed a sedimentary origin.

In the **Western Carpathians** some deposits are currently mined for siderite and magnesite. The Nižná Slaná (SK) mining district in the Spiš-Gemer Mountains, encompassing Nižná Slaná - Kobeliarovo and smaller deposits at Železník, Rákoš, Hrádok, Gampel' and Ignác, has economic reserves of 60 Mt of siderite. The average grade of economic ores is 33.5% Fe, 2.18% Mn, 8.5% $SiO_2$, 0.001% As, the 0.5–1.5% S (according Boláček & Mihók, in Grecula *et al.* 1995).

Folding and thrusting had a strong impact on the shape of the siderite deposits (Sasvári *et al.* 1996). Early Permian metasomatic alteration of Silurian to Carboniferous limestones was the major process in creating these deposits. The siderite-forming fluids moved along tectonic discontinuities such as unconformities. There is no difference either in terms of source or in composition between the fluids forming the siderite veins and those causing replacement of calcite by ankerite and siderite in the Lower Palaeozoic and Carboniferous calcareous rocks. Both fluids were generated under the same geothermal regime during Early Permian M1 prograde metamorphic events (high temperature; low pressure). The main stage during which the ore veins and metasomatic siderite deposits were formed is Early Permian in age (only in the northern part of the Gemericum do the ore veins cross-cut the basal Permian formation, e.g. Rudňany ore field; Fig. 21.9). Those calcareous rocks, which did not undergo any Fe replacement, were uplifted following the Variscan collision during Middle–Late Permian times. Subsequently, those limestones still unaltered by any hydrothermal processes underwent alteration by $MgCO_2$-rich saline brines descending from Permian evaporites. The resultant dolomite–magnesite mineral association is the final product of the Late Permian (in the Carpathians attributed to the Variscan) mineralization. Carbon ($\delta^{13}C$ = −1 to +3.7‰) and oxygen ($\delta^{18}O$ = 12.5 to 17.5‰) isotopes of magnesite and of carbonates in ore shoots resulting from Fe replacement suggest a marine sedimentary origin for the carbonate. Initial $^{87}Sr/^{86}Sr$ ratios of magnesite (0.71124 to 0.71140) suggest different sources for the Sr. Fluids showing initial Sr ratios of Carboniferous and Permian seawaters were mixed with fluids from other local crustal Sr sources (Radvanec & Prochaska 2001; Koděra & Radvanec 2002; Radvanec *et al.* 2004*b*).

The metasomatic magnesite belt (Podrečaný–Jelšava–Ochtiná) is separated from the metasomatic siderite belt (Hanková–Nižná Slaná–Volovec–Holec). In contrast to siderite, magnesite deposits occur nearly exclusively in Carboniferous host rocks and only two occurrences of magnesite were encountered by drilling operations in rocks of Early Palaeozoic age.

In the Dobšiná–Mlynky area (Biengarten, Massörter, Altenberg, Zuzana) Carboniferous-age limestones were replaced by siderite, but not by magnesite. In the Gemerská Poloma deposit an older ankerite–siderite mineral association, related to metasomatic Fe replacement, may be distinguished from a younger mineral association composed of dolomite and Fe-bearing magnesite resulting from Mg metasomatism (Radvanec *et al.* 2004*b*). Magnesite and siderite mineralizations were separated from each other in time and space.

The Carboniferous calcareous series in the western and eastern parts of the Gemericum underwent metasomatic alteration during the Late Permian, resulting in the formation of magnesite replacement bodies (Abonyiová & Grecula in Grecula *et al.* 1995). Magnesite deposits are located in a belt extending from Podrečany (SK), Cinobaňa (SK), Ružín (SK) and Jelšava (SK) through Ochtiná (SK) into the mining areas east of Košice (SK).

The biggest deposit currently mined is situated at Jelšava in the Dúbrava Massif (Fig. 21.14). This deposit has an average content of 42.53% MgO with economic reserves of 536 Mt. The Košice deposit in the eastern part of Gemericum is the second largest magnesite deposit in Slovakia with confirmed reserves of 150 Mt and about 476 Mt of estimated reserves. The deposit is hosted by limestones and dolomitic limestones. The footwall of the deposit consists of black schists and the hanging wall rock of Upper Carboniferous chloritic schists and Neogene sediments (Grecula *et al.* 1995).

Slightly younger rocks are host to Fe mineralizations in the Folkmár region (SK) and in the Aggtelek-Rudabánya Mountains north of Miskolc (H). Numerous, but small, occurrences of hematite ore were discovered in Permian to (?) Lower Triassic-age strata, e.g. Folkmár area (SK) (Kamenický 1952). Some locations of sedimentary hematite ores are not only spatially, but also mineralogically and geochemically linked to vein mineralization containing siderite, e.g. Rudňany, Folkmár, Krompachy (SK) (Grecula *et al.* 1995; Radvanec *et al.* 2004*a*). In the Aggtelek-Rudabánya Mountains (H) metasomatic Fe ore is located in Upper Permian to Lower Triassic successions consisting of carbonates and evaporites (Perkupa Anhydrite) (Hofstra *et al.* 1999; Szakáll 2000). The principal Fe mineral of the Rudabánya deposit is siderite, which was formed by the partial metasomatism of the Gutenstein Dolomite as well as the Campilian Dolomite and Limestone. This siderite belt, including the Rudabánya (H), Martonyi (H) and Esztramos deposits (H), extends over 25 km along the eastern border of the Rudabánya Mountains and marks the zone where conduits were opened for hydrothermal solutions during early rifting. The current position of the ore shoots, however, resulted from collision during the Middle Jurassic to Early Cretaceous north-directed subduction. Many ore deposits have subsequently been altered by late hydrothermal processes and *per descensum* solutions, whereby spherosiderite was formed (Hofstra *et al.* 1999). In addition to that alteration, a monotonous mineral assemblage of siderite,

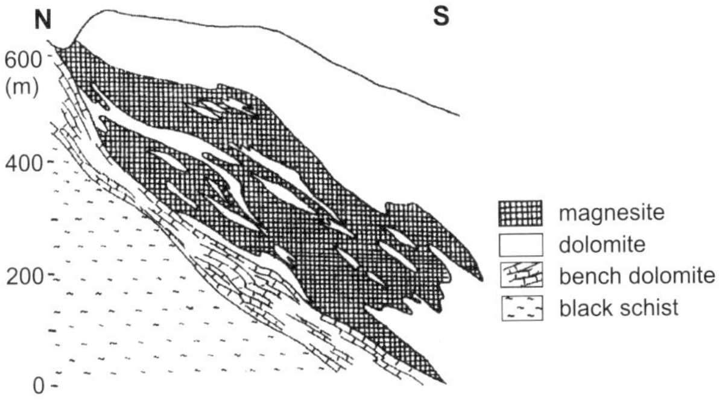


**Fig. 21.14.** Geological north–south profile through the magnesite deposit in the Jelšava-Dúbrava massif (SK) (Čapo, modified by Grecula *et al.* 1996).

ankerite and pyrite was transformed into one containing base-metal sulphides and barite. The secondary Fe minerals such as goethite, hematite, spherosiderite and marcasite are associated with accessory minerals of Mn, Cu, Ag, Pb and Hg. Isotope studies at Rudabánya and Nižná Slaná by Szakáll (2000) gave $\delta^{13}C$ in the range −6.7 to −4.4‰ and $\delta^{18}O$ in the range +14.3 to +17.3‰; these values resemble those obtained from vein siderite deposits of the Gemericum. This would suggest that similar processes were involved in the evolution of both types of siderite accumulations.

## *Strata-bound deposits*

*Upper Carboniferous–Lower Permian*

The post-Variscan evolution of Central Europe is characterized by wrench-dominated fragmentation of the Variscan orogen and the formation of numerous fault-controlled basins during Late Carboniferous (Stephanian) and Early Permian times (Falke 1971; Lützner 1987; Dill *et al.* 1991; McCann *et al.* 2008*b*; Scheck-Wenderoth *et al.* 2008) (Figs 21.6 & 21.10). Wrenching was accompanied by widespread magmatic activity. A contemporaneous northward shift of Europe from equatorial latitudes caused a change from coal-measure to red-bed deposition. Important raw materials include coal, Fe and U. Uranium is related to either organic-rich sediments or volcanic activity (Fig. 21.11).

**Coal deposits and oil shales in intramontane basins.** Two groups of non-marine ('limnic') coal-bearing intramontane basins formed within the Variscan Orogen. The first group comprises relatively large basins orientated subparallel to the Variscan belt. In these basins coal formation was coeval with that of the foreland, but continued into Stephanian times (e.g. Saar-Lorrain Basin, Western and Central Bohemian Basin, Lower Silesian Basin, Zone Houillère). The second group comprises significantly smaller basins, which developed during late orogenic extension (Stephanian–Early Permian) along major north–south, NE–SW or NW–SE trending strike-slip faults (e.g. Massif Central, Boskovice Graben).

Coal formation was controlled by tectonic activity in all intramontane basins, but the control is especially obvious in the Stephanian–Early Permian-age basins. Seam thickness is often high, but the lateral continuity of the seams is often restricted. Coal rank is variable, reflecting the varying burial depths, heat flows and hydrothermal activity. The economic significance of the intramontane basins was always less than that of the foreland. Currently mines are active only in the German part of the Saar-Lorraine Basin, producing 4.7 Mt of coal in 2005.

The NW–SE trending **Saar-Lorraine Basin** (SLB) has a half-graben geometry and is *c.* 250 km long and 75 km wide. It evolved as a strike-slip basin and is filled by Permo-Carboniferous sediments with a cumulative thickness of more than 10 km (Schäfer & Korsch 1998). The basin is bounded to the north by the major Hunsrück Boundary Fault. The south, west and east borders are largely covered disconformable by Triassic and Cenozoic successions.

The Palaeozoic evolution of the SLB commenced with the deposition of marine Devonian and Lower Carboniferous rocks. Synrift sedimentation began with the deposition of the Upper Namurian Spiesen conglomerate and fluvial, deltaic and lacustrine sediments of Westphalian to Stephanian age (Schäfer & Korsch 1998). Intense magmatic activity occurred during Early Permian times. Red alluvial and playa-lake sediments predominate in the Permian succession overlying the pyroclastic beds.

The depocentre of the basin shifted through time from the SW (Lorraine) to the NE (Saar). The internal architecture was controlled by strike-slip and normal faults, and also by several major anticlines parallel to the basin trend. Folding and overthrusting occurred at the Westphalian/Stephanian boundary and during the Permian, when up to 3 km of Permo-Carboniferous rocks were eroded (Hertle & Littke 2000).

Several hundred coal layers with a cumulative thickness of up to 150 m are known, but less than 50 are considered economic. The most important seams are located within the Westphalian C and D (Saarbrücken Group). The upper Westphalian C (Sulzbach Formation) is the most prolific unit with 10% coal. The number of seams decreases significantly in Stephanian and Lower Permian strata. Typical seam thicknesses are 1.5 to 2.5 m (maximum 7 m). Synsedimentary faults cause lateral thickness variations (Stollhofen 1998).

The coal is often high in ash, and cokable despite a relatively low rank (high-volatile bituminous). The cokability of coals is probably related to the high bitumen content. Cannel coals are also found. The methane content of the coal is generally high making the SLB a favourite site for coal-bed methane and coal-mine methane projects. Coalification was synkinematic. An influence of magmatic activity on regional coalification patterns cannot be observed (Hertle & Littke 2000).

Since 1668, an outgoing seam in the Sulzbach Formation (no. 13) has been burning in the subsurface (the so-called 'burning mountain' near Dudweiler, which impressed Goethe in 1770). The resulting heat burnt the overlying pyrite-rich mudstones forming green vitriol and potassium alum. These minerals were produced between 1691 and the 1840s.

The **Zwickau-Oelsnitz** mining districts (Ruder 1998) cover an area of about 35 $km^2$ and are located in the fault-controlled Erzgebirge Basin (south of Leipzig). Here, up to 15 coal seams occur in the *c*. 400 m thick Zwickau Formation (Westphalian D; Schneider *et al.* 2005). The Carboniferous strata are unconformably overlain by lower Permian red-beds. Mining began in 1348 and ended after the extraction of 375 Mt of bituminous coal in 1979.

Within the Bohemian Massif, the **Western and Central Bohemian Basin** (Plzen & Kladno basins) extends west of Prague in a WSW–ENE direction and covers an area of about 3500 $km^2$ (Pesek 1994). The coal-bearing succession (Westphalian C–Stephanian) overlies basement rocks and is partly covered by Cretaceous and Cenozoic deposits. The Carboniferous strata, up to 1.6 km thick, are divided into four formations. Economic seams occur in the lower part of the Kladno Formation (Radnice Member) and in the Slaný Formation (Fig. 21.6).

The Radnice Member (Westphalian C), up to 280 m thick, fills erosive or tectonically controlled river valleys (Oplustil *et al.* 1999; Oplustil 2005). The seams formed in topogenic mires and wedge out on the slopes of the palaeohighs. The wedging out of the seams, and post-depositional erosion, resulted in the formation of several isolated coalfields. Three groups of seams occur within the Radnice Member. In west Bohemia the Plzen seams are several metres thick, whereas in central Bohemia the Radnice seams predominate. The Lower Radnice seam is typically 0.5 to 2.0 m thick and overlies fluvial deposits. The seam is terminated by the volcanogenic Whetstone Horizon (3–7 m thick) which grades upwards into mudstones, the Upper Radnice seam and finally lake deposits. The Upper Radnice seam is up to 14 m thick and was the most valuable seam. The Upper Radnice Member continues above an erosional surface. It hosts the three mineable Lubná seams. The Lower Lubná seam is up to 5 m thick. Lubna coal is often rich in inertinite (20–30%). The Slaný Formation (Stephanian B) contains several economic seams including the Main Melnik (*c*. 2 m thick, occasionally up to 5 m) and the Main Kounov seams (0.7–1.0 m thick).

Numerous tuff layers in coal seams and intraseam sediments are indicative of intense volcanic activity and were partly altered into refractory clays. Coal rank (vitrinite reflectance, 0.5–0.7%Rr) and the percentage of coking coal are low. The last mine in the Kladno region was closed in 2002.

The **Lower Silesian Basin** (Bossowski 1995), located in the Czech Republic and Poland, forms part of the Intrasudetic Basin (Depression). It is filled with Carboniferous, Permian, Triassic and Upper Cretaceous deposits and forms a NW–SE trending synform. The coal-bearing Upper Carboniferous sediments overlie basement rocks or marine Lower Carboniferous-age deposits. Economic seams occur in the Wałbrzych Formation (Namurian A), the Žacleř Formation (Westphalian A–C) and partly in the Glinik Formation (Westphalian C–Stephanian B?) (Fig. 21.6).

The Wałbrzych and Žacleř formations represent fluvial systems and exhibit a marked cyclic structure. The Wałbrzych Formation is up to 300 m thick and contains more than 20 coal seams. Seam thickness is generally about 1 m (maximum 3 m). The cumulative thickness of the exploited coal is 9 m. The Žacleř Formation (up to 900 m thick) contains up to 50 seams with a maximum cumulative coal thickness of 20 m.

Coal accumulated in raised and low-lying mires (Mastalerz & Wilks 1992; Nowak & Górecka-Nowak 1999) and has highly variable ash yields. Sulphur contents are generally low (<1%). The coal is high-volatile bituminous to anthracite. Coal rank increases from the basin margins to the basin centre. Variscan magmatism locally influenced coalification trends and produced natural coke (Mastalerz & Jones 1988; Kwiecinska *et al.* 1992).

Methane contents are locally high (>20 $m^3$/t coal). Apart from methane, $CO_2$ constituted a major mining hazard. Significant rock and gas outbursts occurred in areas with large amounts of endogenic $CO_2$, which had migrated from the upper mantle and/or from magma chambers along deep faults and displaced the autochthonous thermogenic methane (Kotarba & Rice 2001). Economic and safety issues, together with the difficult mining conditions, resulted in a series of mine closures. The last mine was abandoned in 2000. However, there is still a considerable coal-bed methane potential.

The **Zone Houillère** represents a Namurian to Early Stephanian-age graben. Today it forms a more than 100 km long zone in the Western Alps (Desmons & Mercier 1993). The 2.5 km thick basin fill contains ash-rich anthracite, which was exploited in France, Italy (e.g. La Thuile) and Switzerland, mainly during times of economic crises. Today, these coals have no economic significance.

Many small Stephanian to Early Permian-age coal basins developed along major strike-slip faults within the **Massif Central** (e.g. Mattauer & Matte 1998). In the eastern Massif Central these faults are NE–SW trending and delimit the Sincey, Blanzy, Autun and St. Etienne basins. The basins are filled with alluvial fan, fluvial and lacustrine deposits, up to 3 km thick. Coal seams are Stephanian in age and can be as thick as 50 m. Coal rank ranges from high-volatile bituminous to anthracite, even within a single basin (e.g. Blanzy). This reflects the very high Late Palaeozoic heat flows resulting from volcanic and hydrothermal activity (e.g. Copard *et al.* 2000). Transpressional events resulted in extreme deformation of the coal, which was mined both by underground and open-cast methods. The last open pits were closed in 2001. Organic-rich 'boghead shale' is present in Lower Permian units and was mined as oil-shale as early as 1839.

Similar coals were mined at Ronchamp, St. Hippolyte (Vosges), Baden-Baden (Black Forest) and La Mure (Alps, south Grenoble). Anthracite seams, up to 10 m thick, were exploited at La Mure until 1997.

Northerly trending, rapidly subsiding basins formed during Stephanian C and Early Permian time within the Bohemian Massif. The **Boskovice Graben** is an 80 km long and 2.5 km deep half-graben. The basin fill comprises alluvial plain sediments interfingering with fault scarp conglomerates near the eastern marginal fault (Pesek *et al.* 1998). Three Stephanian seams occur in the lower part of the fluvial sequence. One or two seams were mined until the 1990s in the Rosice-Oslavany district down to a depth of >1300 m. Seam thickness is generally 3–5 m, but may reach 15 m. Most of the high-ash, high-sulphur coal is crushed to dust, probably as a result of later Permian transpression. The coal is medium- to low-volatile bituminous.

**Uranium deposits in intermontane basins in the extra-Alpine realm (coal- and oil-shale type).** Extensive carbonaceous sediments deposited in swamp and marsh environments evolved during Late Carboniferous and Permian times in intramontane basins (see previous section). The organic-matter-rich sediments concentrated U derived from metalliferous solutions drained from U-bearing granites and acidic volcanic/volcaniclastic source rocks.

The U-rich carbonaceous rocks were either explored or exploited in the Lower Silesian Basin (PL), the Western and Central Bohemian Basin (Plzen & Kladno-Rakovnik basins) (CZ), the Döhlen (Freital), Stockheim, Weiden, Oos-Saale and Saar-Lorraine basins (D) and near St. Hippolyte (F) (Pironon 1981; Barthel & Hahn 1985; Pagel & Pironon 1986; Dill 1987) (Fig. 21.11b). Uranium mineralization such as that at St. Hippolyte (Vosges) (F) is of the stratiform type. It is present in carbonaceous host rocks, with high V and Mo contents, overlying granites. Similar sapropelic facies have also been described from Proterozoic and Silurian black shales. Uranium mineralization is mainly of ‘monotonous’ and to a lesser extent the ‘polymetallic’ type (Fig. 21.11b). The latter has been recognized in the Müllenbach deposit (D) (Brockamp *et al.* 1987).

**Uranium deposits in intermontane basins in the Alpine realm (volcanic type).** The Novazza and Val Vedello U deposits were discovered in the Lombardy region (I) in the 1950s (Cadel *et al.* 1987). Disseminated pitchblende was found together with sphalerite and pyrite in Carboniferous to Lower Permian volcanosedimentary sequences, acidic tuffs and rhyolithic ignimbrites (Fig. 21.11b). The Novazza mine has never come into production and is presently in a stand-by condition. Uranium shows in SW Piedmont, in the province of Cuneo at Lurisia (I), Grange Serre Preit (I), Rio Freddo Peveragno (I) and Bric Colme’ Pamparato (I) are spatially related to porphyries and pyroclastic rocks of Permo-Carboniferous age that were subject to low-grade regional metamorphism (Cevales 1954). The most important U mineral is pitchblende accompanied by pyrite, chalcopyrite, sphalerite, galena, arsenopyrite and tetrahedrite, all of which show textural evidence of remobilization.

**Tin–gold–PGE/PGM palaeoplacers.** During the Permian, cassiterite palaeoplacer deposits were formed when erosion cut into the apical parts of highly differentiated Sn granites which were intruded in the Saxothuringian Zone during the Late Palaeozoic (Fig. 21.11b). By present standards, these palaeoplacers are of subeconomic grade.

More important than the aforementioned sites, alluvial palaeoplacers were recorded from the basal Carboniferous and Permian sedimentary sequences in the Lugian Zone. Gold placers with up to 10 wt% Pd accommodated in native Au, together with some rare Pd minerals such as potasite and stibiopalladinite, have provoked much interest among mineralogists but not yet among exploration geologists (Malec & Veselovsky 1985).

*Middle–Upper Permian*

In the Alpine region Permian transtension and intracratonic rifting resulted in basin subsidence which was accompanied by an extensive bimodal tholeiitic–rhyolitic volcanism and the intrusion of anorogenic igneous rocks. Evaporites, locally in contact with ultrabasic/basic magmatic rocks, are an additional argument for Permo-Triassic rifting.

Following a moderate rifting phase in the Early Permian, thermal relaxation and subsidence prevailed in the northern part of Central Europe and led to the formation of the South Permian Basin, a prominent depression extending between England and Poland (Ziegler 1990; McCann *et al.* 2008*a*; Scheck-Wenderoth *et al.* 2008). Subsidence and marine transgressions from the north resulted in the formation of the Zechstein Sea.

Arid climatic conditions favoured the formation of red-bed- (e.g. Cu, U) and Kupferschiefer-type deposits as well as the precipitation of evaporites in the Alpine and extra-Alpine parts of Central Europe under coastal sabkha conditions closely resembling those along the present-day Trucial Coast of the Arabian Gulf. Rift-related (Fe–Ni–Cu) and SEDEX-type deposits are restricted to the mobile Alpine part.

**Polymetallic copper deposits in epicontinental and Alpine domains (red-bed type).** Compared to Late Carboniferous depositional environments, Early Permian marshy (paludal) environments contain higher concentrations of Cu. In the Lower Silesian Basin, chalcocite, bornite, covellite, azurite and malachite, grading basinward into mineralizations of galena and sphalerite, were mined near Horní Vernéřovice (CZ), Nowa Ruda (PL) and Okrzeszyn (PL) (Čadková 1971; Osika 1986). In the Okrzeszyn deposit (PL) anomalously high amounts of U in the range 0.001 to 0.1 wt% U, were analysed but no discrete U minerals have yet been discovered. Uranium is present in the coalified matter in what might be called ‘carburan’ or ‘thucholite’. The polymetallic Cu occurrences are considered to be syndiagenetic.

A very variable mineralization with Cu, U, Ag, As, PGE, Au, Se, Pb, Zn, Ni and Co was recorded from coeval series, with a similar facies in Switzerland by Hofmann (1989). Although subeconomic, these metalliferous beds help to unravel the nature of these sandstone-hosted deposits. Sulphur isotope values from the sulphides of the Upper Palaeozoic red-beds rule out any hydrothermal involvement in their origin and suggest diagenetic formation.

Disseminated Cu mineralization was also encountered in Lower Triassic sandstones and in underlying Permian pelites east of the Argentera Massif at Le Cerisier (F) (Bouladon 1989). The mineralization, which is characterized by anomalously high contents of As, contains chalcocite, bornite and chalcopyrite. This mineral suite is quite similar to that reported from Switzerland. The source for the Cu is probably in ancient veins in the nearby basement.

The sandstone of the Val Gardena Formation (‘red and grey beds’) west of Ljubljana hosts Cu mineralization at Škofje (SLO) (Fig. 21.11b). The position of the mineralization along the boundary between the dark grey Val Gardena Formation and the overlying Late Permian-age, transgressive dolostones and limestones of the Žažar Formation suggests an early diagenetic to epigenetic origin. Bornite, chalcopyrite, chalcocite and pyrite act as cement minerals for the sandstones. The $\delta^{34}S$ values show a remarkable depletion in $^{34}S$ resulting in S isotope ratios of as low as −38‰. These isotope values indicate a bacteriogenic origin for the sulphur in the sandstone-hosted ore deposits (Drovenik *et al.* 1980). Two Cu deposits related to the Permian Verrucano were mined in the Western Carpathians at Špania dolina (SK) and at L'ubietová (SK). The latter mineralization also contains Pb, Ni, Co and Sb minerals in addition to Cu sulphides (Slávik 1967).

The metal content of these sediment-hosted mineral deposits may be attributed to the release of trace metals from continental sediments during leaching by oxidized, low-temperature pore fluids. The common labile rock-forming minerals pyroxene, amphibole and biotite contain significant trace amounts of Cu that is soluble in oxidizing solutions as an aqueous metal complex (Brown 2003). This process may be responsible for some other ore deposits (see the following sections).

**Uranium deposits in the Alpine domain (red-bed type).** The Forstau (A) U mineralization in the Eastern Alps occurs in a quartzitic series of Permo-Triassic age. Similar mineralizations, mainly with U, are also known from several locations of Upper Permian continental conglomerates and coarse sandstones (Val Gardena Formation) in the Southern Alps (South Tyrol (I)). Uranium mineralization occurs as irregular lenses and thin layers of variable size that are characterized by their close association with organic matter. These U deposits are believed to have been derived by the erosion and leaching of Permo-Carboniferous volcanics, and the redeposition of U in chemical traps under reducing conditions (D'Agnolo 1966).

The most important deposit of this type was worked west of Ljubljana near Žirovski Vrh (SLO) (Fig. 21.11b). The **Žirovski Vrh red-bed U deposit** is situated in the 1750 m thick Middle Permian Val Gardena Formation in the Sava Nappe. The succession lies uncomformably on Permo-Carboniferous beds and underlies Upper Permian-age dolostones and limestones of the Žažar Formation (Skaberne 2002). It consists of grey, grey-green and red clastics deposited in fluvial, floodplain and tidal-flat environments. The peneconcordant, lenticular U ore bodies are situated within the grey-green clastics, with intercalations of red varieties. The major U minerals are pitchblende and coffinite. These are associated with pyrite, and accessory galena, sphalerite, chalcopyrite, arsenopyrite and tennantite (Drovenik *et al.* 1980). The deposit was formed within braided-river sediments by precipitation from oxidizing bicarbonate sulphate groundwaters. Precipitation took place at an organic-rich hydrogen sulphate geochemical barrier by the activity of desulphurizing bacteria (Palinkaš 1988). The $\delta^{34}S$ value of the sulphides is almost −37‰. The deposit was discovered in 1960 and closed in 1992, producing 100 t of U per year during its period of operation.

**Uranium–copper deposits in the Alpine domain (red-bed type).** The origin of U and Cu deposits forming concordant lenses in the red-beds ('Verrucano') of the Helvetic Glarner Nappe at Mürtschenalp (CH) and some sites in eastern Switzerland, where U and Cu were discovered in volcaniclastic rocks at a subeconomic level, is still controversial (Bächtiger 1963; Burkhard *et al.* 1985). Uranium mineralization is 'monotonous' with pitchblende, melnikovite-pyrite and bravoite, whereas the Cu-bearing lenses contain some bornite, chalcopyrite and tetrahedrite. Copper was subject to intensive redeposition and its primary minerals were subsequently replaced by supergene minerals (Woodtli & Disch 1996). At Isérables (CH) in the Penninic Bernhard Nappe, a syndiagenetic mineral association similar to that at Mürtschenalp consists of pitchblende associated with chalcopyrite and tetrahedrite. The U mineralization in the Permian Casanna Schists underwent strong Alpine remobilization (Hügi *et al.* 1967). Although the Permian age of the Mürtschenalp (CH) and Isérables (CH) Cu–U deposits is well constrained, the origin of both ore mineralizations is not yet clear.

**Polymetallic copper deposits in epicontinental basins (Kupferschiefer type).** By the beginning of the Late Permian the Southern Permian Basin was flooded by the Zechstein Sea and the Kupferschiefer of the Werra Cycle was emplaced as the first transgressional unit. The sedimentary environment during Kupferschiefer deposition can be characterized as a tide-dominated nearshore–marine environment with flats and lagoons (see also McCann *et al.* 2008*b*).

Copper, Pb, Zn and several other minor elements were concentrated under anaerobic to dysaerobic conditions in a shallow-marine environment similar to that of the Silurian Graptolite Shales. Non-economic base-metal mineralizations can be found everywhere in the Kupferschiefer-age basin, but ore deposits developed in only a few locations such as Richelsdorf (D), Mansfeld-Sangerhausen (D) and Spremberg-Weisswasser (D), the North Sudetic Basin (Konrad-Lena) (PL) and the Fore Sudetic Monocline (Lubin-Sieroszowice) (PL). The last mine in the Mansfeld area closed in 1990, but active mines are located in SW Poland. Cu deposits are currently exploited in 650–1150 m deep mines in the Lubin-Polkowice-Rudna-Sieroszowice area (Suchan 2003). Annual production (2003) was 569 000 t Cu, 17.750 t Pb, 1.561 t Ag, 1.955 t Ni sulphate, 296 kg Au, 34 kg Pt+Pd slime, and 68 t Se. Economic reserves were estimated at 2.369 Mt ores with 47 Mt of Cu content and 135 000 t of Ag (Oszczepalski & Blundell 2005). These figures show that the Kupferschiefer deposits are among the most important base metal deposits in Europe and the world.

Metals in the Kupferschiefer are zonally arranged relative to basin highs characterized by the oxidized facies of the Kupferschiefer (Rote Fäule) (Rentzsch 1974; Sawlowicz & Wedepohl 1992; Oszczepalski 1999). PGE mineralization has been reported from the Polish Kupferschiefer strata (Kucha 1982; Oszczepalski *et al.* 2002). Precious metals were preferentially concentrated in the carbonaceous rocks and organic matter (Kucha & Przylowicz 1999) at the transitional zone between the reducing and the oxidized facies of the Kupferschiefer.

The mode of ore formation has been much discussed and numerous models have been put forward to explain the concentration of the broad spectrum of metals. These models range from purely syndiagenetic to epigenetic (Rentzsch 1974; Kucha & Pawlikowski 1986; Vaughan *et al.* 1989; Dill & Botz 1989; Wodzicki & Piestrzynski 1994; Speczik 1995; Blundell *et al.* 2003). It is, however, clear that the interaction of oxidizing brines from the underlying red-beds with hydrocarbons in the Kupferschiefer played a significant role during base-metal precipitation (Bechtel *et al.* 2001). In samples of the Kupferschiefer, Weissliegend sandstone and overlying Zechstein Limestone at varying distances from the Rote Fäule zones (characterized by the replacement of pyrite by hematite) in the Lubin-Sieroszowice Cu-mining district, differences in base and precious metal contents were found to be associated with variations in the molecular composition of the hydrocarbons. These results provide evidence for the oxidative alteration of organic matter in the Kupferschiefer samples, within and adjacent to, the Rote Fäule zones.

A clue to the origin of the Kupferschiefer mineralization is also provided by the mineralogy, and K–Ar dating of illites (Bechtel *et al.* 1999). The K–Ar ages of clay mineral size fractions, a mixture of $2M_1$, 1M, and/or $1M_d$ illites, indirectly date the time of base-metal mineralization within the Kupferschiefer in the Polish Zechstein Basin. The K–Ar ages of the <2 μm fraction of the Kupferschiefer from the mineralized zone fall within a narrow range around 250 Ma while those from the non-mineralized zone are greater, ranging from 277 to 348 Ma. The ages of diagenetic illites are in the range of 190 to 216 Ma, and increase with increasing distance to the areas of base-metal mineralization in the vicinity of Rote Fäule zones. These data indicate that Cu-mineralization occurred after the deposition of the Kupferschiefer (258 Ma) because the differences in crystallinity, the ratios of $2M_1/(1M + 1M_d)$, and the K–Ar ages of illite with regard to distance to the Cu-mineralized zones cannot be exclusively explained by the respective burial depth of the Kupferschiefer in the Polish Zechstein Basin. The results suggest that the formation of diagenetic illite was induced by the mineralizing event. However, bacterial sulphate reduction and diagenetic reactions are proven to have been involved in metal sulphide precipitation by sulphur isotope studies.

Irrespective of the genetic models considered, the Cu–Pb–Zn mineralized districts of the Kupferschiefer are located above or close to suture zones in the Carboniferous basement of Central Europe (separating the Saxothuringian from the Rhenohercynian zones). The occurrence of Lower Permian volcaniclastic rocks in the Rotliegend basins is obviously a prerequisite for Cu-mineralization in the overlying Kupferschiefer deposits.

**Sodium-, potassium- and bitter salt-bearing evaporite deposits in epicontinental and Alpine domains (Zechstein and Haselgebirge type).** Following the cessation of Kupferschiefer deposition, thick Zechstein salts accumulated in the Southern Permian Basin (McCann *et al.* 2008*a*). The basin fill comprises a series of depositional units with lowstand evaporites (K–Na–Mg–Cl–$SO_4$) onlapping highstand carbonate (dolomite) platform edges and overlapping onto the platform tops. Potassium and Na chlorides are the target of both underground and solution mining at many sites in the Netherlands, Germany and Poland. Some underground mines work undisturbed Zechstein salina beds, e.g. in Hesse, Thuringia (D) and near Gdanzk (PL). However, the majority of salt-mining operations are focused on salt plugs and domes that offer much better access to the valuable K- and Na-chlorides and sulphates, e.g. in Lower Saxony (D).

Salt diapirism was provoked by several tectonic phases during Mesozoic and Cenozoic times (Scheck-Wenderoth *et al.* 2008). The present-day distribution of salt domes and plugs is mainly controlled by Late Triassic–Jurassic extension and Late Cretaceous to Early Cenozoic inversion (Scheck & Bayer 1999; Scheck *et al.* 2003).

The Zechstein succession, with a primary thickness of 1500 to 2000 m in basinal areas (Olsen 1987), is subdivided in north Germany into up to seven cycles (Best 1989; McCann *et al.* 2008*a*). Potash salt seams with halite, sylvite, kieserite and carnallite occur in the Z1 cycle. Zechstein cycles Z2 and Z3 contain the major potash salt deposits. Kieserite, halite and carnallite-bearing layers are also present, but are not mined for potash. Two potash cycles in the Z1 are exploited in the Werra-Fulda area SE of Kassel. Two potash beds in the Z2 and Z3 are mined near Hannover, while potash is extracted from the Z4 in the Netherlands (Warren 1999). The total, potash extracted from the Zechstein evaporites provide *c.* 20% of the world's potash (Warren 1999). Germany is the leading producer of rock salt in the European Union contributing one-third of the total production in Europe (Bundesanstalt für Geowissenschaften und Rohstoffe 2005). Europe's leader in salt production is ESCO (European Salt Company) which operates the mines at Bernburg (D), Borth (D), Jemeppe (B) and a site used for underground solution at Harlingen (NL).

In the Northern Calcareous Alps (A, D) halite was precipitated during Permian and early Triassic times in an aborted rift arm of the NW Tethys. The marine precipitates were deposited in a marine basin surrounded by alluvial fans and mudflats. Due to various deformational processes (halokinesis, gravitational sliding, Alpine thrust tectonics), the evaporites occur in a chaotic mélange, termed the Haselgebirge (Spötl 1989*a*). The Haselgebirge comprises shales, silts, sandstones, anhydrites, carbonates and rare magmatites embedded in a clayey halite matrix. Mining has been carried out for many centuries at Berchtesgaden (D) (Ambatiello & Ney 1983) and Hall in Tyrol (A) (Spötl 1989*b*). However, the most important mines are located near Salzburg (e.g. Hallstatt, Hallein (A)), where rock salt has been mined since the Hallstatt period (800–400 BC) (Schauberger 1986). Several anhydrite and gypsum deposits are found in the eastern part of the Northern Calcareous Alps. The latter transfer to coeval anhydrite and gypsum deposits in the Western Carpathians.

Evaporite beds in the southern Gemericum (e.g. Bohúňovo, Šankovce, Meliata (SK)) attain a thickness of between 200 and 1000 m, whereas in the northern part the evaporites are only 50–200 m thick (e.g. Novoveská Huta, Grétla, Biele Vody-Mlynky (SK)). Locally, these evaporite beds were affected by halokinetic deformation. Reserve calculations in the Carpathians have yielded several hundred megatonnes of proven reserves (Antaš *et al.*, in Grecula *et al.* 1995; Zuberec *et al.* 2005). The Šankovce deposit deserves particular discussion in this section since its evaporite layers are associated with chalcopyrite, pyrite, tetrahedrite, stibnite, magnetite, arsenopyrite, chalcostibnite and siderite. Ore mineralization was coeval with the basic igneous magmatic activity related to rifting in the Meliata Ocean during the Triassic.

**Barite deposits in the Alpine domain (sabkha type).** Barite mineralization in the Gorski Kotar area (HR) (Dinarides) is strata-bound and the contact between Permian clastics and Lower Triassic occurs along dolostones. Cryptalgal fabrics in the ore-bearing horizon are indicative of a tidal-flat depositional environment. Dolomitization resulted from strong evaporation. The early-diagenetic, sabkha-type mineralization extends for tens of kilometres along the Permo-Triassic boundary. Pyrite mineralization is confined to the siliciclastics, whereas barite is abundant in the dolostones. The Fe sulphides formed as a result of early diagenetic, bacteriogenic sulphate reduction in peritidal, organic-rich siliciclastic mud. Disseminated barite in the mud was dissolved under reducing conditions, and was subsequently reprecipitated by seawater in the overlying, calcareous-mud layer. The $\delta^{34}S$ values for pyrite vary between −15.5 and +20.2‰, and for barite between +17 and +30‰. The chemical composition of fluid inclusions in barite is close to that of seawater (Palinkaš *et al.* 1993). The largest deposits are found at Lokve (HR) (Fig. 21.15), Mrzle Vodice (HR) and Školski Brijeg (HR) (Šušnjara & Šinkovic 1973).

**Polymetallic barite deposits in the Alpine domain (initial rift–SEDEX type).** The Gračac strata-bound barite deposits are located in the Lika Region of the Dinarides and occur in the Upper Carboniferous Auernig Beds. The monotonous ore paragenesis, with barite, pyrite, galena and sphalerite, is considered to be of diagenetic–epigenetic origin. A single model Pb age (264 Ma, single stage growth model; Doe & Stacey 1974) is probably too young (Palinkaš 1985). Production has yielded close to 450 000 t in total.

**Nickel–copper–PGE and iron sulphide deposits in the Alpine domain (rift-related type).** Several Fe–Ni–Cu sulphide deposits associated with layered peridotite, pyroxenite and gabbros in the basic complex of the Ivrea Zone (Southern Alps; Garuti *et al.* 1986) occur in the valleys of the Strona, Sesia and Mastallone rivers (I) and at Palagnedra (CH). The Campello Monti (I), Gula (I) and Scopello (I) deposits consist of high-grade to massive ore bodies of pyrrhotite, pentlandite and chalcopyrite with minor cubanite, mackinawite and platinum-group minerals (Garuti & Rinaldi 1986). These are believed to have been formed at an early magmatic stage by segregation of an immiscible sulphide liquid from the mafic silicate magma. The Fe–Ni–Cu sulphide ore deposits of the Ivrea Zone are among the most important in Europe and they have been economically viable for Ni at various times (e.g. 1855–1874 and 1937–1943). Mining activities were closed in 1948.

*Triassic*

In the extra-Alpine domain of Central Europe, thermal subsidence and a general rise in sea level controlled sedimentation during the Early Triassic. Subsequently, an overall east–west extensional regime during Mid- and Late Triassic times led to the subsidence of deep north–south trending grabens in the northern part of Central Europe (see Scheck-Wenderoth *et al.* 2008). Continental and marine successions made up of clastic rocks alternating with calcareous and evaporitic beds were deposited within the extra-Alpine domain (Germanic Facies Province) until the end of the Triassic when the (Rhaetian-) Jurassic transgression established fully marine conditions across Central Europe (see Feist-Burkhardt *et al.* 2008).

Within the Alpine region rifting, which commenced during Permian times, culminated in the opening of the Meliata (?back-arc) Ocean, an embayment of the Tethys Ocean (e.g. Stampfli & Borel 2002). The Carpathian–Alpine–Dinaridic domain overlying Variscan basement formed the passive continental margin of Europe. Extensive carbonate platforms evolved along the shelf and were the sites of continuous sedimentation except for a regressive phase in the Carnian, when clastic beds with minor coal (e.g. Lunz (A)) and evaporites were deposited within the Northern Calcareous Alps. Significant alkaline volcanism occurred in the South Alpine and Dinaridic domains during Middle and Late Triassic times.

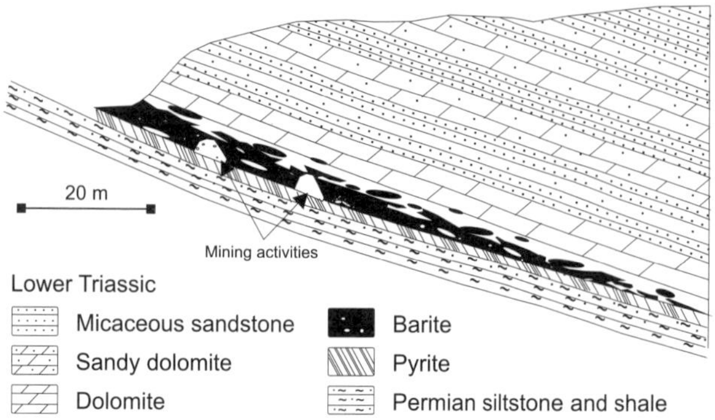


**Fig. 21.15.** Geological cross-section of the barite ore body at Lokve village, Homer locality (HR) (modified after Šušnjara & Šinkovec 1973).

Triassic mineral deposits are very varied and are found in a range of geodynamic settings and depositional environments of the Tethys Ocean and the epicontinental sea of the Germanic Province. Red-bed U–Cu deposits and evaporites were emplaced at the edge of the Alpine ocean and in the extra-Alpine epicontinental seas. Carbonate-hosted Pb–Zn (MVT) deposits occur in the extra-Alpine realm (Silesian type) and in thick shelf carbonates along the Tethyan shelf (Alpine type). Deposits of Fe–Mn–Cu as well as various SEDEX deposits containing Ba, Hg, Fe and Mn are exclusive to rifts in the Alpine realm, where they were caused by intensive volcanic activity. The Cu–Ni mineralizations are related to the remnants of the Meliata Ocean.

**Polymetallic copper deposits in epicontinental and Alpine domains (red-bed type).** The base-metal mineralization in the Lower Triassic Buntsandstein Beds has not received much attention among modern mining engineers, but was mined in the Bronze Age and during the Middle Ages (Lorenzen 1965). The most famous example is disseminated mineralization with cuprite, native Cu and malachite in arenaceous and argillaceous red-beds of the Middle Buntsandstein on the island of Helgoland (D) (Fig. 21.11b). The type and size of base-metal mineralization in these red-beds is strongly dependent on changes in the fluvial palaeodrainage system which were mainly braided and meandering settings, e.g. Twiste, Wallerfangen and Wrexen (D) (Meisl 1965; Walther 1986).

**Uranium deposits in epicontinental and Alpine domains (red-bed type).** In the Upper Triassic Sandsteinkeuper Beds in the South German Basin unidirectional fluid flow from the Variscan basement towards the basin resulted in the formation of U concentrations in the fluvial environment of the Burgsandstein and Stubensandstein units (Ballhorn & Wollenberg 1979; Elrod 1982; Dill 1988*b*). In terms of geometry, the various sandstone-hosted U ore bodies can be described as conformable, peneconformable tabular, channel-like or roll-type (Fig. 21.11b). Poorly crystallized U oxides ('sooty pitchblende') and rare coffinite are found together with pyrite, marcasite and chalcopyrite at the contact between highly permeable sand bodies (channels) in a back-swamp delta-related environment and argillaceous floodplain deposits containing humic matter. In some places U was concentrated in calcretes and silcretes without any well-crystallized U ore minerals. Uranium, in the form of apicretes and francolite-bearing arkoses, was exclusively found in stacked channel fills ('Aktivarkosen'), with braid-bar and channel sands. Uraniferous silcretes are found in both active and abandoned channels of these fluvial systems. Throughout phosphatization and silicification U was concentrated under oxidizing conditions and occurs in the hexavalent state. Pitchblende or coffinite representative of U in the tetravalent state were not observed. Subsequent oxidizing conditions formed the rare V–U minerals tyuyamunite and carnotite, disseminated among uraniferous apatite. Because of the element association characterized by U and V, these red-bed deposits are considered to be Colorado-Plateau-type U deposits. During the Triassic, the source of U in the red-bed deposits in the Burgsandstein were rocks of the Vindelician High, a projection of the Bohemian Massif towards the SW into the South German Basin.

**Sodium- and alkaline-earth-elements-bearing evaporite and lead deposits in epicontinental and Alpine domains (sabkha type).** During the Middle (Muschelkalk) and Late Triassic

(Keuper) the epicontinental basin in Germany was temporarily cut off from the open sea giving rise to sabkha-like environmental conditions. As a result of this isolation in the Middle Muschelkalk, and extensive evapotranspiration, strontianite, celestite and fluorite forming lenses, pods and layers were precipitated near Eschwege (D) and Göschwitz-Jena (D). These mineralizations are not economic. Coeval halite seams, up to 40 m thick, developed in the South German Basin so that underground and solution mining operations became feasible near Bad Friedrichshall (D), Heilbronn (D) and Haigerloch-Stetten (D). In northern Switzerland these Triassic halite seams are exploited by solution mining at Rheinfelden (CH) and Zurzach (CH) (Hauber 1971). Rock salt is used for both industrial and curative purposes (e.g. Rheinfelden spa (CH)). Because the rate of evaporation was not so intensive as in the Zechstein Sea basin, potassium and bitter salt-bearing evaporites did not develop.

In the Swiss Alps near Bex (CH), Triassic salt is contained within a brecciated horizon ('brèche salifère') together with anhydrite and gypsum in the Utrahelvetic Nappe. Intensive tectonic deformation has made underground working of this salt extremely difficult. Therefore, exploitation is currently carried out by solution mining (Badoux 1966). In neighbouring France, salt of Late Triassic (Norian) age occurs in the Jura Mountains near Lons-le-Saunier (= Perrigny) (F).

The 'Gipskeuper' is another Triassic unit where evaporites were precipitated and mined for halite near Nancy at Dombasle (F) and Dieuze (F). The Dombasle salt mine is currently mined by the European Salt Company (ESCO). In the South German Basin these evaporitic units pass into varicoloured mudstones, marls and gypsum-bearing seams and form the basis for a flourishing gypsum industry at Ipfhofen near Würzburg (D). The areal extension is not shown on the map. Middle Triassic (Muschelkalk) anhydrite seams are exploited near Trier (D) and were exploited in an underground mine near Bayreuth (D). At Bayreuth, rehydration of anhydrite to gypsum was impeded by the uplift of Triassic beds along the Franconian Line, a deep-seated boundary fault of the Bohemian Massif.

The formation of Late Triassic evaporites in the Eastern Alps and the Western Carpathians resulted from the Carnian regression. Gypsum and anhydrite are mined at many locations in the Northern Calcareous Alps (A). Within the Lower Austro-Alpine unit (A) gypsum is known from sediments which are also widely distributed in Tatro-Veporic cover sediments (SK) (Carpathian Keuper).

Strata-bound Pb mineralizations are found at different locations in the South German Basin in the Gipskeuper and in a landward arenaceous facies of the Muschelkalk. The Gipskeuper is a coastal sabkha deposit that includes a continuous, but very thin galena bed (Bleiglanzbank) that can be traced across the basin centre. Another Pb mineralization, stratigraphially equivalent to the Muschelkalk, was mined SE of Bayreuth at Freihung (D), Wollau (D) and Eichelberg (D) (Fig. 21.11). The mineralization consists of syndiagenetic to epigenetic galena, cerussite, with subordinate amounts of chalcopyrite, sphalerite, bravoite, covellite and barite, filling the pore space of arenites and locally replacing detrital K feldspar (Schwarzenberg 1975; Gudden 1975; Schmid 1981; Dill 1990*b*). The isotopic composition is relatively homogeneous and resembles isotopically average basement Pb (Schweizer 1979; Lippolt *et al.* 1983). This Pb mineralization is facies-bound to the marginal calcareous–siliciclastic beds of the Middle to Upper Triassic and may well be explained by a brine-mixing model under arid climatic conditions. Basinward-flowing solutions contained Pb that was derived from the decomposition of K feldspar in gneisses and granites of the Moldanubian basement. In contrast, significant evaporation provoked a landward reflux of sulphate- and carbonate-enriched brines. Mixing of both brines in the arenaceous Middle Triassic sediments in the area of Freihung resulted in the formation of $PbCO_3$ subsequently replaced by PbS (see also sections on kaolin saprolite associated with the Early Alpine unconformity and on manganiferous Pb deposits associated with the Late Alpine unconformity).

**Iron–manganese–copper polymetallic deposits in the Alpine domain (rift-related – Red Sea stage).** The Vareš metallogenic province (BiH) is located in the Dinarides, north of Sarajevo and within the Durmitor Nappe. During the advanced rifting stage of Tethys, magmatism led to the eruption of spilites, basalts, keratophyres and diabases which were interbedded with Ladinian-age sedimentary rocks (Pamić 1984). The Vareš deposits at Smreka and Droškovac are taken as the *locus typicus* mineralization of the Mid-Triassic, advanced Tethyan rifting (Red Sea stage; Fig. 21.16).

The deposits at Smreka and Droškovac contain hydrothermal, stratiform siderite–hematite–chert beds. The ore mineralization is intercalated with rocks of Anisian and Ladinian-age. A distinct vertical zonation reflects the gradual changes of redox conditions in the depositional environment. The succession commences with bituminous, thinly bedded black shales with pyrite and base-metal sulphides, overlain by barite and siderite, all of which were deposited under reducing conditions. Clastic rocks and oolitic limestones rest upon this metalliferous series and are succeeded by another metalliferous series with hematitic shales and siliceous hematite beds. In contrast with the footwall rocks, these were deposited under oxidizing conditions. The overall mineralization consists of siderite, Mn-enriched hematite, barite, pyrite, marcasite, chalcopyrite, galena, sphalerite, tetrahedrite and Pb-sulphosalts.

The $\delta^{34}S$ values of barite vary from +21 to +29‰. The $\delta^{34}S$ mean for Triassic seawater is +23‰. These data obtained for the

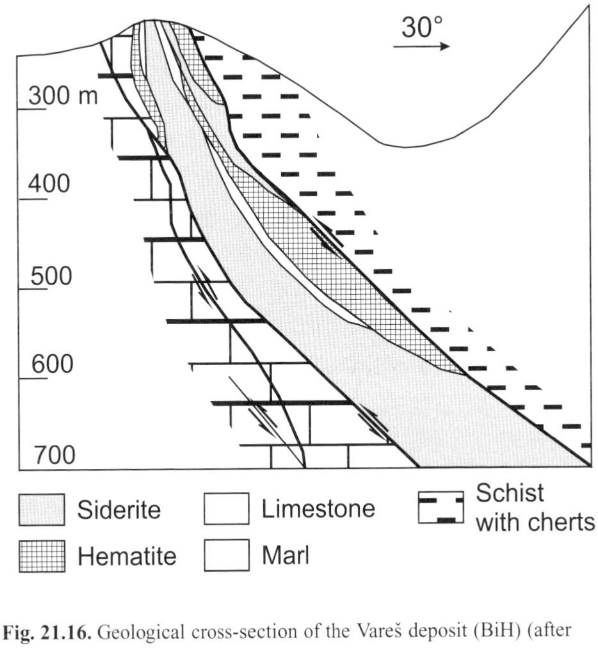


**Fig. 21.16.** Geological cross-section of the Vareš deposit (BiH) (after Janković 1967).

Red Sea type phase of rifting are in marked contrast with the much lower values of around +10‰, that were obtained for barite from the Permian-age siderite–barite–polysulphide deposits that formed during the early intracontinental phase of Tethyan rifting. The $\delta^{34}S$ value for pyrite is −11‰ (Šiftar 1988). The chemical composition of fluids in the inclusions in sphalerite and barite may be described as a $CaCl_2$–NaCl–$H_2O$ system which evolved under moderately high temperatures ($T_H$ = 110–230°C). Salinity ranges from 2 to 4 wt% $NaCl_{equ}$. In view of the Cl/Br ratios the fluids are assumed to have been derived from modified seawater (Strmić *et al.* 2001).

**Polymetallic barite deposits in the Alpine domain (advanced rift–SEDEX type).** Polymetallic barite deposits occur in the Dinarides north of Sarajevo. The Srednje (BiH) and Borovica (BiH) deposits comprise mineralized dolostones and dolomitized limestones, 60 to 120 m thick, with rare intercalations of chert and shale. This sedimentary complex was formed on the flanks of a graben–horst structure. Slope instability initiated gravitational sliding, intraformational slumping and brecciation, which created massive, irregularly shaped ore bodies, and ore breccias. The major minerals present include barite, galena and sphalerite accompanied by minor melnikovite–pyrite and marcasite. Other accessory minerals are arsenopyrite, chalcopyrite, bournonite, tetrahedrite, stibnite and cinnabar. Some of the ore bodies contain 5–10 wt% Pb+Zn, and 1–20 wt% barite. The massive ore bodies in the Rupice (BiH) deposit are between 1 and 20 m thick and comprise Fe sulphides with 10–30 wt% barite. There are also massive (Rammelsberg type) barite bodies with 60–90 wt% barite and 1–4 wt% Zn. In the Veovača Pb–Zn–Ba deposit (BiH), ore breccias are common, with clasts cemented by microcrystalline barite and Pb–Zn sulphides. The breccia units are up to 1 m thick. The $\delta^{34}S$ value of barite from the Borovica and Veovača deposits (+21‰) is typical of Triassic-age SEDEX deposits elsewhere in the Dinarides (Šiftar 1988).

**Mercury deposits in the Alpine domain (composite SEDEX type).** Mercury is the only element which is more common in Europe than in the rest of the world. The composite SEDEX epithermal **Hg deposit at Idrija** (SLO) is the second largest Hg deposit in the world, surpassed only by Almaden in Spain. In Idrija 145 000 t Hg have been produced since 1490 (Mlakar 1974). The average grade of ore has decreased since these times from 17.0 to the present-day value of 0.3 wt% Hg. The Idrija mine ceased production in 1988.

The Idrija deposit (Fig. 21.17) is located near Ljubljana in the Trnovo Nappe, which forms part of the Sava Nappe. It is composed of two types of ore: concordant and discordant. The former is associated with fault zones in Permo-Carboniferous to Upper Ladinian-age beds. It occurs as veins, open-space fillings, and as the replacement of carbonate cement in clastic rocks. The epigenetic mineralization is interpreted as a feeder zone of the overlying syngenetic, stratiform cinnabar–pyrite beds in the Upper Ladinian organic-rich Skonca Beds, which are overlain by tuffs (Fig. 21.17). The ore beds are up to 100 m long and 0.5 m thick with the richest ore being up to 79 wt% Hg. Ore minerals include cinnabar, metacinnabar, native Hg, pyrite and rare barite.

The genesis of the Idrija deposit is linked to Ladinian-age rifting, which induced effusive and explosive bimodal volcanism (tuff, tuffites, diabases, pillow lavas, quartz porphyries). The Idrija failed rift was active from the Early Scythian to the Early Carnian and became an isolated basin with lacustrine and swamp environments (Placer 1982). Ascending Hg-bearing hydrothermal fluids mineralized the sediment infill along subvertical faults and

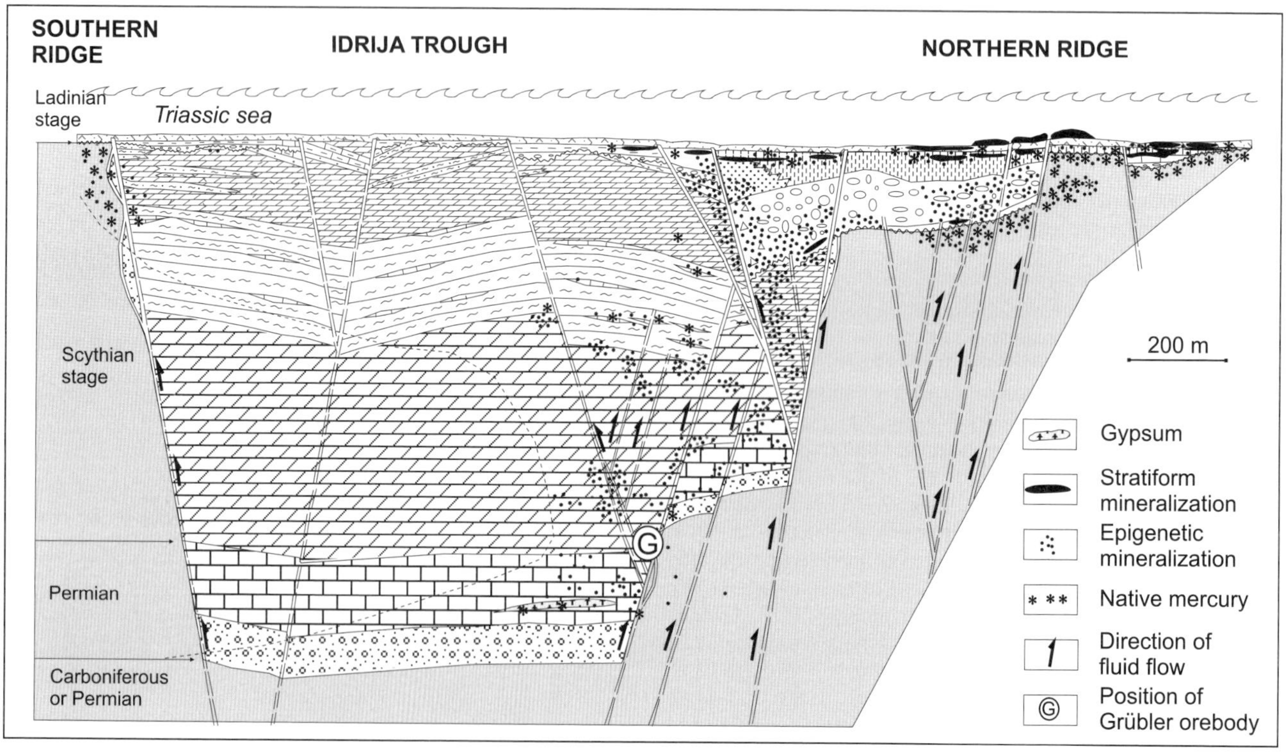


**Fig. 21.17.** Schematic reconstruction of the Middle Triassic Idrija Trough (SLO) during deposition of the Langobardian sediments (modified after Placer & Čar 1977).

poured out at the base of the lacustrine and swampy basins where strongly reducing conditions occurred.

Fluid inclusion data, obtained from analyses of cinnabar, quartz and barite from the Gruebler ore body, indicate mineralization temperatures of between 160 and 220°C at depths of *c.* 750 m. Salinities were low to moderate (2.1–5.8 wt% $NaCl_{equ.}$). The fluids had a $CaCl_2$–NaCl–$H_2O$ composition, and a NaCl/$CaCl_2$ ratio of between 0.6 to 1.5 (Palinkaš *et al.* 2004). The $\delta^{13}C$ and $\delta^{18}O$ data of carbonates indicates a fracture-controlled hydrothermal system. The large $\delta^{34}S$ variations in cinnabar are attributed to the different mixing ratios between the magmatic and other sulphur sources such as seawater, evaporites, pyrite and organic sulphur (Lavrič & Spangenberg 2003).

The Middle Triassic-age Tršće, Gorski Kotar Hg deposit (HR) is monomineralic in composition and epithermal with respect to the formation temperatures. It is hosted by Permian sandstones, conglomerates and shales, and Lower Triassic dolostones (Šinkovec 1961). The monotonous ore paragenesis comprises cinnabarite with minor pyrite, accessory sphalerite and calcite. Cinnabarite replaces calcite cements or fills interstices between clasts in the sandstones. Mercury concentrations rarely exceed 0.02 wt%. The mode of deposition during advanced rifting is similar to that of the Idrija Hg deposit.

Cinnabar occurs as impregnations and as vein infill in the Triassic-age Werfen Beds at Draževići (BiH) near Sarajevo. Cinnabar is the main mineral in this epithermal mineralization, whereas pyrite, calcite and marcasite are rare (Ramović *et al.* 1979).

**Iron–manganese deposits in the Alpine domain (SEDEX type).** The Čevljanovići Mn deposit (BiH) is located near Sarajevo and contains psilomelane, pyrolusite, braunite, rhodochrosite and hausmannite. The primary ore has a rather low Mn content of 10–20 wt%, but the primary content is significantly upgraded as a result of weathering to *c.* 45 wt%. The stratiform Bužim Mn deposit (NW BiH), in the Pannonian Nappe, is interbedded within a Middle Triassic-age volcanosedimentary series. Ore minerals include pyrolusite, psilomelane, manganite, haematite, goethite, braunite, pyrite and marcasite. The Ivanščica SEDEX Mn deposit (HR) within the Zagorje–Mid-Transdanubian Zone consists of small ore beds within Middle Triassic-age cherts and shales, and includes mainly psilomelane and pyrolusite (Jurković 1962). These SEDEX Mn deposits mark the incipient phase of a much more intensive Jurassic-age Mn concentration in the Tethyan Basin.

**Copper–nickel deposits in the Alpine domain (embryonic ophiolite type).** In the Bükk Mountains (Szarvaskö (H)) bodies of titanomagnetite with a poor Cu–Ni sulphide paragenesis contained within Middle Triassic gabbroic and peridotitic magmatic rocks represent remnants of the oceanic crust that was produced during the opening of the Meliata Ocean. These deposits represent an embryonic ophiolite-type Cu–Ni mineralization which, due to the failed development of this oceanic basin, did not reach its full extent (like the lithologically equivalent ophiolite units during the Jurassic spreading phase in the Penninic Ocean (Alpine Tethys) in the Alps) (Balla *et al.* 1983).

**Carbonate-hosted lead–zinc deposits in the epicontinental domain (Silesian type/MVT).** In the calcareous lithofacies of the Middle Triassic Muschelkalk, subeconomic base-metal mineralization, mainly with Zn, was encountered at many Muschelkalk-age locations in north (Hofmeister *et al.* 1972) and south Germany (Fluck *et al.* 1975). A mineralization in the Upper Muschelkalk at Wiesloch (D) (NW Stuttgart) became economic only as a result of major Neogene redeposition and is therefore discussed below.

Economic-grade base-metal mineralization in the Muschelkalk is mined near Cracow in the world class **Upper Silesia Zn-Pb mining district** (PL) (Sass-Gustkiewicz *et al.* 1982). Mining for Pb, Ag and Fe began in Upper Silesia (NW Krakow) in the twelfth century. Currently two underground mines are active in the Olkusz (PL) and Chrzanow (PL) area and work three out of 21 known Pb–Zn deposits. The Olkusz-Pomorzany mine extracts 2.5 Mt annually of ore grading 4.2% Zn and 1.4% Pb. The Trzebionka mine extracts 2.3 Mt of ore (3.4% Zn, 1.5% Pb) (Kulczycka 2004). Current resources include 183 Mt of sulphide ore (3.8% Zn, 1.6% Pb) and 57 Mt of oxide ore (5.6% Zn and 1.4% Pb) (Sass-Gustkiewicz & Kucha 2005).

Ore occurs in Middle Triassic carbonates converted by the mineralizing process into Fe–Zn-dolomites. Zn–Pb ore bodies are located close to the dolomite–limestone contact. The main ore types are stratiform layers of semi-massive ZnS and dolomite breccias cemented by sulphides (Szuwarzynski 1996). Haloes have been observed around ore bodies composed of Fe- and Zn-dolomites and Zn–Fe-smithsonite. The mineral assemblages of the Silesian Muschelkalk deposits may be subdivided according to their textural features into four types: (a) strata-bound; (b) karstiform caves and collapse breccias; (c) columnar-nest type; and (d) vein type. Emplacement of the sulphides began in the Middle Triassic, but probably continued until Middle Tertiary times. This interpretation is supported by palaeomagnetic and geochemical information suggesting an emplacement of at least part of the Pb–Zn minerals during the Cenozoic formation of the Carpathian foldbelt (Leach *et al.* 1996).

A hydrothermal karst model was proposed for the Polish Pb–Zn deposits by Sass-Gustkiewicz *et al.* (1982). According to Haranczyk (1989) hydrothermal activity was intermittent in two different karst systems and the fluids originated from the mixing of meteoric and intrastratal solutions. As previously discussed for various vein and strata-bound deposits in Central Europe, the availability of organic matter had an impact on the primary accumulation of Pb–Zn ore minerals in this MVT deposit (Sass-Gustkiewicz & Kwiecinska 1999). Non-sulphidic Zn ore mineralization was produced by supergene oxidation of primary carbonate-hosted Zn sulphides during the complex interplay of uplift and karstification, fluctuation of the water table and weathering (Boni & Large 2003). The host rock lithology, the regional geological setting and the ore mineralization are typical of MVT deposits. The main ore minerals are sphalerite, pyrite, marcasite, galena, Fe- and Zn-dolomites, oxysulphides of base metals, As and Tl.

**Carbonate–hosted lead–zinc deposits in the Alpine domain (Alpine type/MVT).** Carbonate-hosted, low-temperature, Pb–Zn deposits formed during the Middle Triassic rifting stage in the Eastern Alps (e.g. Bleiberg-Kreuth (A), Mežica (SLO), Topla (SLO)) and the Southern Alps (e.g. Raibl (I), Salafossa (I)). These deposits have thus far provided more than 10 Mt of Pb–Zn metal.

The carbonate-hosted mineralization is generally strata-bound in carbonates of Ladinian and Carnian age. Traditionally this Alpine Triassic-age carbonate-hosted Pb–Zn mineralization was considered under the term 'Bleiberg type' and has often been compared with MVT deposits (e.g. Schroll 1996). The ores have a simple mineralogy containing galena, crystalline and colloform sphalerite, pyrite and marcasite and typically lacking Ag and Cu. Wurtzite, arsenopyrite and molybdenite are rarely present. Zinc ores, particularly at Raibl (I) and Bleiberg-Kreuth (A), have significant Ge contents. In the oxidation zones of Bleiberg-Kreuth and Mežica Mo mineralization occurs as wulfenite and jordesite. These deposits are characterized by anomalous Pb model ages (300–490 Ma) and dolomitization as an alteration phenomenon. Fluid inclusion studies reveal the dominance of $Ca^{2+}$ in ore-bearing fluids, biogenic sulphur in sulphides and the low temperatures of formation ($T_H = 100–200°C$) (e.g. Cerny 1989; Kuhlemann 1995; Schroll 1996).

Strata-bound ores occur in the Carnian Raibl Formation in Bleiberg-Kreuth and Mezica (Drovenik *et al.* 1980; Cerny 1989). In Bleiberg-Kreuth (A), located in the Drau Range, more than 3 Mt of Pb–Zn metal have been mined over the last 700 years. In addition to strata-bound and pipe-shaped ore bodies, which continue for 400 to 800 m along strike, there are also vein-type ore shoots as well as breccias that contain bodies of between 0.5 to 1 Mt of ore. Mežica is located in the Northern Karavanke Mountains and was active for *c.* 300 years. The $\delta^{34}S$ value in Pb–Zn sulphides at Mežica vary between −1.7 and −21‰ (mean −12‰). The host rocks are Ladinian-age Wetterstein Limestones deposited in a lagoonal environment passing laterally into reef limestones, and Wetterstein Dolostones.

In contrast to the deposits of Bleiberg-Kreuth and Mežica, the Topla Pb–Zn deposit is situated in the central part of the Anisian carbonate rocks (Northern Karavanke Mountains). The ore is characterized by abundant synsedimentary structures and textures, such as the rhythmic alternation of ore and gangue minerals. Framboidal pyrite, marcasite and sphalerite were formed during an early diagenetic stage. The $\delta^{34}S$ values in base-metal sulphides from Topla vary between +8 and −24‰ and thus comparable with biogenically reduced sulphates (Drovenik *et al.* 1980).

The Raibl and Salafossa deposits are located in the Southern Alps (I). At Raibl the ore body is hosted within dolomites of the Ladinian/Lower Carnian-age Cassian Formation and mainly consists of tectonically controlled veins accompanied by minor stratiform mineralization (Romagnoli 1966). The Raibl deposit has been known since Roman times and was active until 1971. The Salafossa deposit was discovered in 1957 and closed in 1986. The mineralized Salafossa body is *c.* 500 m long, 200 m wide and *c.* 50 cm thick. It occurs in brecciated Ladinian-age dolomites in a strongly tectonized zone. The origin of the Salafossa ore deposits is considered to be epigenetic by Di Colbertaldo & Franceschetti (1960). Other Pb–Zn mineralizations of lesser importance are also present in the Triassic dolomites of the Seriana and Brembana valleys (I).

The origin of the Pb–Zn ores has sparked some discussion. There is general agreement that these Pb–Zn mineralizations are syngenetic and linked to low-temperature Pb- and Zn-bearing fluids (Kucha *et al.* 2004; Schroll & Prochaska 2004). However, Leach *et al.* (2003) have assumed a Late Triassic/Early Jurassic age of ore formation. The Pb model ages, which are older than the Triassic host rock, are interpreted to have been caused by fluids percolating through Palaeozoic sediments beneath the ore-bearing Triassic strata. However, the mechanisms of concentration of Pb–Zn metals for these deposits are not yet fully understood. The above-mentioned authors invoke models including the supply of metals by deep-seated hydrothermal basinal and connate brines, expelled during Middle Triassic advanced rifting. Other mechanisms discussed include metal derivation from the sediments as a consequence of diagenesis and dolomitization, the formation of residual sediments during intense evaporation phases, and metal supply by weathering of former continental regions.

Apart from the above-noted deposits, there are more than 200 similar Pb–Zn occurrences recorded from the External Dinarides, and the Southern and Eastern Alps. Some of these are briefly reviewed below.

The Sv. Jakob (HR) Pb–Zn deposit, hosted by non-metamorphosed dolostones, is situated in the Medvednica Mountains (east of Zagreb) and is probably of Triassic age. The vein-type mineralization has a simple association of galena, minor sphalerite and pyrite with quartz and calcite as the only gangue minerals (Šinkovec *et al.* 1988). Isotope studies of galena gave an isotopic composition of common Pb typical of the B-type/Bleiberg type and a resultant model age of 490 Ma (Palinkaš 1985). Fluid inclusion studies on quartz suggested a $NaCl–CaCl_2–H_2O$ composition and salinities in the range 6–19 wt% $NaCl_{equ.}$. Homogenization temperatures vary over a wide range ($T_H = 80–230°C$, mean 130°C). The $\delta^{34}S$ values of galena and sphalerite vary between +7 and +10‰ (Borojević-Šoštarić 2004).

Deposits of Pb–Zn in Middle Triassic carbonates also occur in the Ivanšćica Mountain (HR) (Šinkovec 2000), on the eastern slopes of the Petrova gora Mountains (Svinica mine) (HR), and in the Srb deposit of the Lika region (BiH). All of these are within units which can be correlated with the Mesozoic carbonate platform of the External Dinarides.

The Olovo Pb–Zn MVT deposit in central Bosnia (north of Sarajevo) is located within the Durmitor Nappe and is hosted by Middle Triassic-age dolomitic and calcitic limestones which were deposited in a reef environment. The major ore minerals are Pb and Zn carbonates, mainly cerussite and to a lesser extent smithsonite. The cerussite–smithsonite ore mineralization is found in various ore traps such as karstic cavities, brecciated carbonate rocks and thin fissures cutting the calcareous host rocks. Disseminated galena is also found, together with sporadic traces of pyrite and sphalerite.

Small-scale mines were active until the 1920s in the Northern Calcareous Alps at Lafatsch (A), Rauschberg (D) and Königsberg (D) where strata-bound Pb–Zn–(Fe) deposits occur in carbonate sequences of Ladinian to Carnian age. Some of these deposits contain considerable amounts of Mo accommodated in wulfenite, e.g. Höllental (D). Descloizite and ilsemannite may also be found to contain Mo. During the initial stages of base-metal exploitation in the Northern Calcareous Alps mainly limonitic galmei ore, with smithsonite, hemimorphite, cerussite and hydrozincite, was mined. The anomalously high Cd contents of the original Zn ore are reflected by the yellow coatings of greenockite.

The mining district around Silberberg (CH), Bleiberg (CH) and Bärenbühl (CH) has become known for its strata-bound Pb–Zn deposits in Anisian and Ladinian-age dolomites. These are located within the Austro-Alpine Silvretta Nappe (Jaffé 1986). The Swiss deposits are similar to the 'Bleiberg type' carbonate-hosted deposits.

**Oil shales.** Triassic bituminous shales are located in the Monte San Giorgio (CH) area near Lake Lugano. These oil shales, intercalated between Anisan dolomites, were exploited and processed to produce a medical ointment (named Saurol). This trademark was coined because of the numerous finds of saurians in these oil shales (Russel 1990). Another deposit in host rocks of the same stratigraphic age is situated at Besaro (I). However, the most well-known deposits in the Alpine Mountain Range occur in the Norian Hauptdolomite NW of Innsbruck near Seefeld (A). Here, the bituminous strata are up to 140 m thick and have a total organic carbon (TOC) content of 7–25% (maximum 52%; Weber 1997).

*Jurassic–Lower Cretaceous*
In the Germanic Facies Province a major Rhaetian–Early Jurassic transgression resulted in the establishment of shallow-marine conditions across much of the region. During Middle Jurassic to Early Cretaceous times, large parts of the extra-Alpine region of Central Europe became erosional domains, whereas NW–SE trending depocentres evolved in its northern part during Late Jurassic–Early Cretaceous times (Scheck-Wenderoth *et al.* 2008; see also Voigt *et al.* 2008). Sedimentation in the South German Basin was influenced by processes within the Alpine region, which was affected by a very different tectonic evolution.

In the Alpine realm, the Middle Jurassic opening of the South Penninic Piedmont-Liguria Ocean (Alpine Tethys) caused the separation of the Apulian Plate (South Alpine-Dinaridic-Austro-Alpine-Carpathian-(?)Tisza units) from Europe (e.g. Schmid *et al.* 2004). Subsequently, the Early Cretaceous opening of the North Penninic Valais Ocean led to the detachment of the Briançonnais Terrane from the south European margin. Thus, the Helvetic domain became the new southern margin of Europe. An initial, Late Jurassic pulse of the Alpine Orogeny (closure of the Meliata Ocean, obduction of parts of the Jurassic Vardar Ocean) affected the Austro-Alpine and Dinaridic domains (Gawlick *et al.* 1999).

The distribution of mineral deposits in Central Europe highlights the different facies in the extra-Alpine and Alpine areas. Evaporites, (minor) coal and shallow-marine Fe ores developed in the Germanic Facies Province, whereas deep-water Mn deposits and deposits related to ophiolites (Cr, Cu, magnesite) are widespread in Alpine Europe.

**Sodium- and alkaline-earth-element-bearing evaporite deposits in epicontinental domains.** In northern Germany the presence of a silled basin led to the establishment of hypersaline conditions and resulted in the precipitation of various carbonate–evaporite cycles during the Portlandian (latest Malmian) in a stratigraphic unit termed the 'Münder Mergel' (Deister Hills (D)). Celestite alternating with anhydrite was concentrated to extractable grades at Hemmelte-West and Hemmelte-East (D) (Müller 1962). In the Münsterland Basin around 100 000 t of strontianite were won until 1910 (Walther 1986). Strontium- and S-isotopes are compatible with those of Late Jurassic seawater. A detailed investigation of these sabkha-type Sr deposits has been performed by Salter & West (1965) for the stratigraphically equivalent Purbeck Beds in England, and by Dill *et al.* (2005) for modern environments along the coast of Qatar.

Celestite, gypsum and microbial mats (stromatolites) are very widespread in these Mesozoic and Cenozoic sabkha sediments, indicating a close genetic link between the growth of microbial domes and gypsum precipitation. The marine calcareous sediments were deposited in a microtidal wave-dominated environment.

**Coal deposits and oil shales.** The Early Jurassic transgression of the sea from the Penninic realm towards the north established conditions favouring coal formation along the southern margin of Europe (e.g. Gresten coal near the Alpine front (A), Mecsek Basin (H), Zawiercze (PL)). Most coal seams were mined for local use only, but coal mines in the Mecsek Basin were active until 2004.

The **Mecsek Basin**, located in southern Hungary, covers an area of *c.* 350 to 400 km$^2$. The Upper Triassic and Lower Jurassic Mecsek Coal Formation increases in thickness towards the SW to 1200 m and comprises clastic sediments and coal. Coal seams are mainly Jurassic in age and are arranged in three groups. The lower and upper groups represent paralic environments, while the middle one was deposited in a limnic environment. Up to 38 seams, each with a thickness of more than 0.5 m, are found, but only five to ten are considered to be economically viable. The thickness of the latter ranges from 1.5 to 3 m (maximum 10 m). The high ash, high sulphur coal ranges from high volatile bituminous to semi-anthracite, some of which is suitable as coking coal. Cretaceous and Miocene igneous dykes intruded the coal and formed natural coke. As noted above mining activities in the Mecsek Basin ceased in 2004. The remaining economically extractable resources are estimated at 197 Mt. Very high methane contents (50 m$^3$/t coal) indicate a high coal-bed methane potential (Landis *et al.* 2003).

Many Liassic-age beds contain elevated contents of organic carbon. Some of these were mined as oil shales, especially during times of energy shortage, e.g. Schandelah (D), Mt. Terri (CH) and Bächental (A). Near Schöningen-Dotternhausen (D) (SW of Stuttgart) Liassic-age bituminous Posidonia Shale is currently mined as an energy source for a local cement factory. The 9 m thick oil shale is Toarcian in age. Organic material occurs in some beds in concentrations of up to 16% together with pyrite, indicating anoxic conditions, persistent stagnation and slow sedimentation in this part of the Jurassic basin.

**Ironstone deposits in the epicontinental domain (Minette Type).** The Lower and Middle Jurassic sea encroached upon the deeply weathered Variscan basement of the Rhenish Massif, the Vindelician High and the Bohemian Massif. In the nearshore high-energy zone of a shallow-marine environment oolitic ironstones termed 'Minette' developed from the Aalenian to the Callovian in the Gulf of Lorraine (Luxembourg and eastern France), and between the Vindelician High and the Black Forest areas, both of which are part of the basement highs of the Moldanubian Region in Germany and Switzerland. The Fe-bearing Jurassic series includes as many as 12 ore seams which formed in a similar fashion to the Ordovician-age Clinton-type ironstones. Deposition of oolitic ironstones with chamosite, leptochlorites, some thuringite and berthierine occurred at the top of a coarsening- and shallowing-upward regressional megasequence (Teyssen 1989). Silica-rich ferric oxides may be converted during diagenesis in a reducing environment into siderite and berthierine (Siehl & Thein 1989). Microbial activity probably also played a key role during Fe accumulation in the nearshore environments (Burkhalter 1995).

The Gulf of Lorraine (F, L) is the type locality for the Minette ironstones. The maximum annual production of about 62 Mt in France and 6 Mt in Luxembourg was reached in 1960 (Bouladon 1989). The ore comprises 32% Fe and 0.7% P (Bubenicek 1968). The last mine was closed in 1981 in the Luxembourg part of the Minette mining district (Differdingen) and in 1997 in the French part (Montrouge Audun-le-Tiche). According to Horon (1976), 7.33 Mt of Fe ore (25–28% Fe, 0.15% Mn, 0.45% P, 0.15% S) were mined from slightly older Hettangian-age rocks at Change (Mazeney) (F) and Ougney (F) up until 1921.

Studies of Aalenian and lower Bajocian-age minette Fe ore from the Swiss Jura Mountains show a close mineralogical and micromorphological resemblance to ferruginous microbiolites and ooids, suggesting a common biogenic origin. Structural rearrangement of a biologically accreted gel-like precursor, consisting of various amorphous hydroxides, is considered to be a probable mode for the formation of the ferruginous ooids (Burkhalter 1995). Apatite, present in the Fe ore, is detrital and the siderite is of diagenetic origin. Magnetite and pyrite are very rare as are barite and Pb–Zn sulphides which fill veins cross-cutting the Fe ore seam. Many of the ferruginous series are cross-bedded and burrowed, and some are interbedded with a ferruginized or phosphatized hardground. In addition, the recurring development of chamositic ooids is commonly coincident with repeated regional transgressions. Silica-rich ferric oxides may be converted, during diagenesis in a reducing environment, into siderite, berthierine, and some pyrite (Siehl & Thein 1989). Palaeocurrent data suggest that the material was derived from the NE (i.e. the Rhenish Massif) and transported into various basins and embayments along the eastern edge of the Paris Basin, e.g. Differdange (L), Rumelange (L), Landres-Ottange (F) and Nancy (F) basins.

The Chamoson oolitic Fe ore deposit (CH) in the Swiss Alps (east of Geneva) is Late Dogger in age and belongs to the group of minette ironstones. This location deserves particular attention since it is the type locality of the mineral chamosite ($(Fe^{2+}, Mg, Fe^{3+})_5(Al(Si_3Al)O_{10}(OH,O)_8$, an Fe ore mineral synonymous with the Jurassic-age sedimentary ore deposits. Unlike the Jurassic ironstones, the Chamoson deposit was deformed and hosted by the Helvetic Morcles Nappe (De Quervain & Zitzmann 1977). The Erzegg deposit (CH) is similar to the Chamoson ironstone deposit (CH) in terms of its tectonic position, tonnage and grade (*c.* 1.5 Mt of 30% Fe).

The Middle and Upper Oxfordian Coral Oolite in north Germany (e.g. Nammen (D), Gifhorn (D)) marks the waning stages of Jurassic ironstone deposition. This area is the only mining district in Germany still working this metalliferous series, albeit no longer for the Fe ore but rather for the Fe-bearing calcareous rocks which alternate with the ore seams. Here, sandy oolitic Fe ores containing goethite, berthierine and some siderite (e.g. Gifhorn) were deposited in rim synclines associated with salt domes which were derived from the underlying Zechstein evaporites.

**Manganese deposits in the Alpine domain.** Stratiform Mn ore deposits, in places containing considerable amounts of Fe, are common in the Alpine regions of Central Europe. These deposits are mainly found in Mn carbonates in Jurassic (often Lower Toarcian) pelagic deposits in the Western Carpathians (SK), the Bakony Mountains (H), and the Eastern and Western Alps (D, A, SLO, CH, I) (Jenkyns *et al.* 1991). Palaeogeographically these deposits belong to the rifted continental margin of the Meliatta-Hallstatt (Tethys) and Piedmont-Liguria Ocean (Alpine Tethys).

In the Western Carpathians Mn ore is found in Liassic calcareous units between Dolina Chochołowska (PL), Kościelisko (PL) and Dolina Lejowa (PL). The ore is composed of ooids made up of pyrolusite, and braunerite and biogenic detrius such as crinoid fragments. The primary ore contains 13–52 wt% MnO, 2–5 wt% Fe, 3–6 wt% $SiO_2$ and 20–40 wt% CaO (Osika 1990). A similar type of Mn ore developed in strongly folded Middle Jurassic calcareous marls, e.g. Zázrivá and Borinka (SK). In the Lednické Rovné deposit (SK) the primary ore in the 1–5 m thick Mn ore beds typically has contents of 13–25% MnO, 4.7–10.5% Fe and 0.1–21% $SiO_2$. However, some parts of the deposits are very rich in Mn with contents of as much as 40 wt% Mn. Deformation of the primary ore beds caused uplift and weathering in near-surface positions, where pyrolusite and manganite were formed. The oxidized zone contains around 26% MnO, 15% Fe, 22% $SiO_2$ and 5% CaO (Slávik 1967).

The Mn deposits in the Bakony Mountains (Úrkút, Eplény (H)) are associated with laminated organic-rich shales. The Úrkút Manganese Ore Formation, a Toarcian black shale, is *c.* 27 m thick. The Toarcian shales are underlain by calcareous marls and overlain by a chert layer several tens of centimetres thick. The ore is developed in two layers: a lower high-grade ore bed (24% MnO, Mn/Fe ratio of 2.25) and an upper low-grade ore bed (15% MnO, Mn/Fe ratio of 0.9). Rhodochrosite and goethite predominate in the Mn-carbonate ore, while Mn-rich calcite and pyrite are most common in the marls. Volcanic–hydrothermal activity is regarded as the main source for the metals, although some Mn may have been derived from a continental source (Polgári *et al.* 2000). Negative carbonate $\delta^{13}C$ values of the ore and a negative correlation of carbonate $\delta^{13}C$ with Mn content indicates early diagenetic bacterial oxidation of the sedimentary organic matter coupled with Mn precipitation (Polgári *et al.* 1991). Furthermore, bottom-water currents, perhaps involving upwelling, resulted in the concentration of organic matter and Mn.

In the Northern Calcareous Alps there is evidence for at least three distinct mineralized levels. In the Lofer area SW of Salzburg (e.g. Hochkranz (A)), Krainer *et al.* (1994) distinguished a Lower Toarcian and an Aalenian to Bajocian ore-bearing series. The Toarcian-age shales (Sachrang Formation) contain up to 20% MnO (Mn/Fe ratio of 1.8). Mn minerals found in these deposits include rhodochrosite, and Mn-rich siderite with subordinate amounts of pyrolusite. Middle to Upper Jurassic Mn-rich sediments from the Tennengebirge (e.g. Strubberg (A)) and Berchtesgaden Ranges (D)) were deposited within the deep-water trench (Lammer Basin) of an active continental margin. In the Lammer Basin, upper Middle to lower Upper Jurassic deep-water sediments (Strubberg Formation), more than 1.5 km thick, overlie Upper Triassic platform carbonates and Lower to Middle Jurassic pelagic carbonates (Gawlick 2000). The Lower Callovian to Oxfordian part of the Strubberg Formation is composed of cherty limestones, radiolarites, marlstones, and Mn-rich shales with up to 20% MnO and a Mn/Fe ratio of 2.3 (Beran *et al.* 1983). The primary Mn minerals are Mn-carbonates (Ca-rich rhodochrosite, kutnahorite, Mn-rich calcite). Pyrolusite ($MnO_2$) and manganite ($MnO(OH)$) are the secondary Mn minerals. Rantitsch *et al.* (2003) proposed a hydrogenous precipitation of Mn by strongly varying redox conditions at the sediment–water interface of a slope basin to explain the origin of these deposits.

In the Gonzen Mn–Fe deposit (CH) the ore-bearing beds are located in the Malmian-age Quintenkalk and the overlying Plattenkalk of the Helvetic Nappe. Here, hematite is gradually replaced by rhodochrosite and hausmannite. The presence of Fe–Mn ores in calcareous rocks adjacent to volcanic rocks in the Penninic nappes was considered to be indicative of an exhalative–sedimentary derivation of the ore-bearing fluids (Epprecht 1946). The Fe/Mn ratio in the Gonzen deposit is about at 3:1. About 2.55 Mt of ore were mined between 1921 and 1967.

Stratiform Fe–Mn deposits, related to the Piedmont-Liguria Ocean, are widespread in the Penninic Nappes of the Western Alps. Deposits were encountered at Val Ferrera (CH) in Jurassic quartzites, dolomites and marbles of the Suretta and Schams nappes (Briançonnais Terrane) and at Oberhalbstein/Falotta (CH) closely associated with the ophiolitic sequence of the Penninic Platta Nappe. The main ore minerals in these epimetamorphic and strongly folded Jurassic host rocks are hematite and braunite. Siliceous host rocks containing radiolaria are frequently found next to the Mn ore beds, suggesting that deposition occurred in a deep-marine setting. It would appear to be an analogue of the Carboniferous SEDEX-type Mn deposit at Laisa (D). Unlike their Carboniferous counterparts in the Rhenish Massif, the Alpine Mn ores underwent strong remobilization during Alpine metamorphism with a variety of very rare Mn minerals concentrated along fissures and fractures. Tinzenite a Mn borosilicate which is widespread in veins in Mn deposits (Cortesogno *et al.* 1979; Fuchs & Oyman 2000) and parsettensite were described for the first time from these mining sites in Switzerland. The historical Praborna Mn deposit (I) is located close to the town of Aosta. The initial stage at Praborna was related to volcanosedimentary processes in the Piedmont Ocean. Subsequently the Mn ore underwent high pressure/low temperature metamorphism.

Gambatesa (I) is the largest of a number of chert-hosted Mn deposits that are found in the Jurassic–Cretaceous ophiolites of the Ligurian Apennines (Bonatti *et al.* 1976). Mn was originally discharged at the seafloor as fluids expelled from hydrothermal vent systems. The Mn ore is rhythmically interbedded with silica-rich sediments (cherts) giving rise to metalliferous series, more than several tens of metres thick, and overlying pillow basalts. Massive ore bodies at Gambatesa are the result of syntectonic remobilization and reconcentration of Mn oxides along axial planes and fold hinges. The main ore mineral is braunite.

**Chromium–copper–iron and nickel deposits in the Alpine domain (ophiolite type).** The most important deposits related to the formation of Jurassic and Cretaceous ophiolite complexes are located in the Dinarides and include Cr, Cu and magnesite deposits. Some deposits also occur in the Alps (Fe, Cu, Ni) and the Northern Apennines (Cu).

The common view of the ophiolite sequences in the Dinarides was that a lherzolite belt occurs in the Dinarides, *sensu stricto*, and a harzburgite–dunite belt is present within the Vardar Zone. Recent interpretations have distinguished two dismembered ophiolite belts: the Dinaride Ophiolite Zone related to the open-ocean Tethys, and the Vardar Ophiolite Zone linked with a backarc basin (Pamić *et al.* 2002). In this chapter, the Dinaridic ophiolites are treated as one unit formed by seafloor spreading during Jurassic to Early Cretaceous times.

The Dinaridic ophiolites are partially preserved as blocks of basalts, diabases, gabbros, serpentinites and peridotites. The peridotitic bodies cover an area of between 200 and 500 $km^2$. They are sheeted into slices, a few hundred metres to two kilometres thick. These bodies are thrust onto an olistostrome mélange. The Konjuh Ultramafic Massif is underlain by amphibolites and eclogites. Gabbros, sheeted diabases, basalt flows and basalt (spilites) pillows are accompanied, in the mélange, by greywackes, shales and radiolarites. Amphibolites intercalated with peridotites were dated and yielded K–Ar ages of 160–170 Ma, whereas the dating of lherzolites gave an apparent Sm–Nd isochron age of 136 Ma (Lanphere *et al.* 1975; Lugović *et al.* 1991). The ophiolites in the Ozren, Čavka, Ljubić and Borja mountains consist of a series of dunites, feldspathic peridotites, harzburgites, lherzolites, olivine gabbros, amphibolites, dolerites, diabases, spilites and younger Tertiary dacites.

Podiform chromite bodies are linked with dunites in the Ozren Mountain. The ore contains between 17 and 37 wt% $Cr_2O_3$. There are fewer podiform chromite bodies in the Borja Mountains.

Cyprus-type Cu vein mineralization and massive sulphide-type mineralization are another facet of the Dinaridic ultramafic massifs. An elongated Cu ore belt extends along the Krivaja River over a length of 80 km from the Konjuh Mountains to the Čavka Mountains. Within this ore belt, Cu deposits occur at Ribnica, Maglajac and Kamenac. More than 30 additional localities in the Čavka Mountains are known to contain significant amounts of Cu. Cu ore shoots are related to gabbro and diabase dykes cross-cutting ultramafic igneous rocks. In detail, it can be seen that the ore is predominantly concentrated along the contact between serpentinites, amphibolites and gabbros where it is dissected by diabase dykes. Two types can be distinguished and these contrast strongly with respect to mineralization and geometry. Type I is described as dykes with lenticular bodies of pyrrhotite (95–97% of the ore mass) and pentlandite. They are surrounded by a variegated mineralization, disseminated and stockwork-like in shape, and with chalcopyrite, cubanite, ilmenite, hematite, bravoite and millerite (crude ore contains 0.6% Cu, 0.2% Ni, 0.003% Co). Type II encompasses quartz–chalcopyrite veins and stockwork mineralization with pyrite, chalcopyrite, arsenopyrite, pyrrhotite and calcite. Supergene alteration has converted the primary minerals into malachite, azurite, chrysocolla, cuprite, native Cu, chalcocite and psilomelane (Durić & Kubat 1962). Another vein mineralization between 0.1 and 0.3 m thick with pyrite and chalcopyrite occurs within the ophiolitic complexes of the Kozara and Konjuh mountains.

The occurrence of nickel, Fe, and Cu ore in the Central and Western Alps is related to the presence of Jurassic to Cretaceous-age (South Penninic) ophiolites of the Piedmont-Liguria Ocean. Nickel deposits with pentlandite, awaruite and heazlewoodite have been reported from Totalp (CH) and Poschavio (CH) in eastern Switzerland. An ore body consisting of pods of massive magnetite was worked in the Cogne Mine (Aosta Valley Region; I) until the 1970s. Here, the ore developed at the base of a large serpentinite lens. Magnetite was formed during magmatic segregation with enrichment of Fe to about 45–50% (Di Cobertaldo *et al.* 1967). In addition to magnetite, minor hematite, pyrite, pyrrhotite and chalcopyrite are also found within the Fe ore. The gangue is a mixture of serpentine, brucite, olivine, calcite and dolomite. A small but high-grade (5–6% Cu) stratiform sulphide concentration was mined at St. Véran (F) in the French Alps (Bouladon 1989).

The Cu deposits of the Northern Apennines (I) are also related to Jurassic to Cretaceous-age ophiolites. The mineralization occurs within volcanosedimentary breccias and, in places, stockwork-like veins. The ore bodies are very variable both in terms of their shape and mineral assemblage. In addition to the massive ore bodies, there are also high-grade disseminated Cu mineralizations. The main ore minerals are pyrite and chalcopyrite with minor sphalerite (Ferrario & Garuti 1980). The biggest mines, at Libiola (east Liguria) (I) and Vigonzano (I), were shut down in the early 1970s for economic reasons.

*Cretaceous*

Major changes, from spreading and passive continental margin settings to subduction and collision, occurred during Cretaceous times within the Alpine realm (see Voigt *et al.* 2008). Intraplate stresses related to the (Early Alpine) collision led to the inversion of the Jurassic–Early Cretaceous rifts and major uplift within the northern parts of Central Europe (Ziegler 1990; Froitzheim *et al.* 2008; Scheck-Wenderoth *et al.* 2008).

There are relatively few strata-bound deposits of Cretaceous age in Central Europe. Apart from Fe ores and phosphorus, some economically significant deposits of coal and jet can also be found.

**Iron–phosphorus deposits in the epicontinental domain (pebble iron ore and Black River type).** Ironstone formation occurred in a shallow-marine high-energy zone during the Early Cretaceous in present-day Lower Saxony. Ore conglomerates of goethite formed at Salzgitter (D) (Kolbe 1962). Concretionary Fe ores were derived from Liassic and Dogger-age ironstones exposed to erosion on the adjacent mainland and were concentrated in local sinks. These depressions (= Kolke) subsided mainly as a result of intensive subsurface leaching of Permian salt. Sorting, which is generally poor, and Fe concentration in the nearshore environment, are both a function of the transport distance and the palaeoslope gradient. Thus, palaeomorphology was a major control on the occurrence of the shoreline Fe deposits (i.e. marine Fe placers or pebble Fe ore). During the Late Cretaceous, deposition of Fe placers continued north of the Central European mainland in an offshore environment, e.g. at Peine (D). In 1982 the last mine at Haverlahwiese was shut down in the Peine-Salzgitter mining district after an overall extraction of 165 Mt and 140 Mt of Fe ore from Lower Cretaceous and Upper Cretaceous ore beds, respectively.

In the South German Basin an embayment, termed the Regensburg Strait, developed during the Cretaceous. At its northern margin Fe was precipitated in a fluviolacustrine environment during Cenomanian times near Amberg-Sulzbach-Rosenberg (D) (Gudden 1984) The Fe deposits of the Amberg Erz-Formation were also derived from the reworking of the Dogger-age Minette ironstones. It was, however, not mechanical reworking that gave rise to these Fe ore bodies but rather chemical redeposition. Fluids draining from the hinterland were crucial in the formation of the Fe deposits.

The **Amberg-Sulzbach-Rosenberg area** (D) (east of Nürnberg) was one of the largest mining districts in southern Germany, accounting for 17% of Fe mined in Germany during 1971 (Gudden 1972). In 1982, 580 000 t of Fe ore were mined underground by 350 miners from the Leonie Mine. In 1987 the mine was forced to shut down.

Siderite ('white ore', reducing facies *c.* 39% Fe) and goethite ('brown ore', oxidizing facies *c.* 46% Fe) were, together with F apatite, enriched in a karstic depression up to 4 km long and 5 km wide that evolved in uplifted Malm-age limestones. In the nearby arenaceous to argillaceous lignite-bearing clastic rocks, Fe was diagenetically concentrated in nodules and cleats of pyrite and marcasite. The alternating beds have been interpreted in terms of an anastomosing fluvial/paludal environment. Humate-complexed Fe was transported and precipitated as goethite, siderite or Fe-bisulphide in the various host environments depending on the predominant Eh values. Phosphate was precipitated prior to the concentration of siderite, thereby lowering the Ca content of the intrastratal and meteoric solutions down to a level favourable for the accumulation of Fe carbonate. Siderite associated with some rhodochrosite, chamosite and pyrite formed in a stagnant freshwater lake. In contrast, during the initial evolutionary phase, characterized by the concentration of phosphate, the 'ore trough' was connected with the open sea. The primary phosphorite mineralization underwent some late-stage alteration during which REE phosphates such as weinschenkite (Y,Er) $PO_4.2H_2O$ and rare Al- and Fe phosphates such as wavellite, crandallite, strengite, beraunite and vivianite formed (Andritzky 1963, 1964). The evolution of these basins was controlled by displacements along the deep-seated Bavarian Fault in basement that evolved to a flexural bulge in the Upper Jurassic limestones and through which Dogger-age ironstones were exposed by weathering. Continuous displacements along this fault resulted in landslides which covered the Fe ore with sand, clay and boulders of Jurassic limestones, thereby protecting the Fe ore from later erosion.

During the Cretaceous, phosphorite was concentrated to economic grade in a nearshore marine environment and was exploited near Radom-Annopol (PL), Leba (PL) and Lengede (D). Its mode of deposition was similar to that of the Amberg deposit (see above). The Cretaceous phase of phosphorite accumulation extended in part until the Oligocene (e.g. Emsland (D), Semba peninsula (RU), and southern Lithuania).

**Strontium deposits in epicontinental domain.** Strontianites are known from various deposits in the Münsterland area (D). They have an extremely uniform Sr isotopic composition, identical with that of the Campanian-age host limestones, and reflecting the prevalent seawater composition (Kramm 1985). The precipitation of Sr minerals, especially celestite, is favoured by intense evaporation in a restricted basin under arid climatic conditions. However, this process alone cannot account for the presence of strontianite instead of celestite (Grobe & Machel 2002). The derivation of saline groundwater from subsurface coal mines, wells and artesian springs in the area of the halite-free Münsterland Cretaceous Basin is considered to be of great importance. Grobe & Machel (2002) suggest a six-stage model for the evolution of the saline groundwater, commencing with (1) halite dissolution, followed by (2) the water–rock interaction of highly saline fluids with siliciclastic sediments, and (3) the mixing of highly saline fluids with less saline waters of marine isotopic composition. Subsequently, (4) the fault-controlled upward movement of warm saline $^{87}Sr$-enriched groundwater from the Palaeozoic bedrock into the overlying Upper Cretaceous limestone aquifer, was followed by (5) water–rock interaction of ascending saline groundwater with the limestone aquifer, and finally (6) dilution by meteoric waters. The results of this study are important in terms of the problems related to the timing and origin of Pb–Zn vein-type deposits, as discussed in the context of deposits controlled by igneous activity along deep-seated faults.

**Coal and jet deposits and oil shales.** Wealden Coal (D) accumulated in the Lower Saxony Basin during Early Cretaceous times. Several adits and galleries in the area of Barsinghausen (D) near Hannover mark the outcrop of the coal seam. Following Early Alpine nappe stacking, Upper Cretaceous Gosau Coal formed in separate pull-apart basins (e.g. Grünbach (A), Ajka (H)).

Upper Cretaceous (Santonian–Campanian) brown coal was mined until 2004 in the Ajka Basin Bakony Mountains (H). The coal forms part of the Ajka Coal Formation which accumulated in SE–NW orientated basins which overlie Mesozoic carbonates (Haas *et al.* 1992). Locally, up to 6 m of bauxite underlies the 100 m thick coal-bearing rocks. The Ajka Coal Formation consists of alternations of clastic rocks, limestones, and five to seven commercial seams with a total thickness of 15 m. Abundant molluscs indicate a gradual change upward from freshwater to fully marine conditions. Laterally the Ajka Coal Formation interfingers with fluvial clastic rocks. The coal is high in ash and sulphur (11.1 MJ/kg, 32% ash, 3–4% S) reflecting deposition in a low-lying mire with marine influence. Additionally, the Ajka Coal Formation has very high U contents (Tomschey 1995).

Jet was mined from shallow marine sediments with a Turonian age in the Gosau Basin in the Northern Calcareous Alps (e.g. Gams, Unterlaussa (A)) from the fifteenth to the eighteenth century. Oil shales occur in the Wealden Beds at Bentheim (D) and are intercalated with calcareous rocks of the Cenomanian-age Urgon Facies at Vagnas (F).

### *Cenozoic*

The main phases of the Alpine Orogeny occurred during Cenozoic time. Foreland basins filled with deep-marine and continental sediments formed along the Alps, Carpathians, Dinarides and Apennines (see also Froitzheim *et al.* 2008; Reicherter *et al.* 2008). Final compression was accommodated by thrusting of the orogens onto the foredeep sediments and the lateral extrusion of crustal wedges in the Eastern Alps towards the Pannonian Realm (e.g. Ratschbacher *et al.* 1991; see also Rasser *et al.* 2008). The main lateral movements occurred along normal and strike-slip faults. The evolution of pull-apart basins in the region (e.g. Fohnsdorf and Vienna basins) is related to these fault zones (Decker & Peresson 1996).

A retreating subduction zone along the Carpathians caused extensive east–west extension and subsidence in the Pannonian Basin. Thrusting along the Carpathians and extension in the Pannonian Basin were accompanied by a major phase of magmatic activity. Initial andesitic volcanism is related to the subduction of an ocean during the Early Miocene, and the final phase of calc-alkaline volcanism was associated with slab detachment during accelerated roll-back (Popescu 1994; Teleki *et al.* 1994; Neubauer e*t al.* 2005).

The compressional deformation within the Alpine system was paralleled by the development of Cenozoic rift systems in the extra-Alpine realm (e.g. Ziegler 1990; Reicherter *et al.* 2008). A wide variety of economic deposits were formed in strata-bound deposits during Cenozoic times. These include Ti–Zr placers, amber, diatomite, Fe–Mn deposits, evaporites including sulphur, various clay minerals, and quartz. Epithermal ore deposits (including Au–Ag–Cu–Mo) related to Cenozoic magmatic activity were of great importance during medieval times. At the present time Cenozoic lignite deposits are of prime importance for the energy supply of Central Europe.

**Titanium–zirconium placer deposits in the epicontinental domain.** A Pliocene-age ilmenite placer deposit, with subordinate amounts of zircon and rutile, was discovered recently at Midlum (west of Hamburg) (D) (Ludwig & Figge 1979). These placers cover some coastal areas of the Palaeo-North Sea. The proven reserves amount to 110 Mt of placer sand with 9% heavy minerals. Further placer deposits, some of which contain monazite and garnet, have been discovered at several localities on the Frisian barrier island belt extending from the Netherlands to the Danish border. These marine placers have been explored but mining is not currently economically viable.

**Amber deposits in the epicontinental domain.** Baltic amber originates from the resin of a pinaceous conifer similar to *Pseudolarix* (Anderson & LePage 1995). Amber beds formed from the Eocene to the Early Oligocene in a nearshore marine environment along the eastern Baltic Sea coast. The Baltic Sea region has been one of the main amber sources from prehistoric times onward, and Baltic amber has been found along ancient barter and trade routes across Europe and north Africa. The best known deposits are still operated at Jantarnyj (RU) and Svetlogorsk (RU) on the Semba Peninsula, while another site is located near Darłovo (PL) (Kharin *et al.* 2004). The amber units were redeposited during the Quaternary and accumulations are now also found along the Polish coast (Kosmowska-Cevanowicz 2004). On the Semba Peninsula, Quaternary-age arenaceous–argillaceous beds form the overburden on top of the 'blue earth' of the Eocene-age Prussia Formation. This overlies glauconitic sands and siltstones which are well exposed in the various open-cast mines of the region which occupy an area of *c.* 700 $km^2$ (Paškevićius 1997). The thickness of the productive amber beds ranges from 1 to 17.45 m. Outside of the areas currently operated, amber is also found near Zelenogradsk (RU), Shatrovskoye (RU) and Bagrationovsk (RU). The amber reserves are estimated at 42 000 t in this region.

Holocene amber deposits are found along the coast of the Baltic Sea up as far as the Kuršių Marios lagoon. They were derived from the Prussia Formation during post-glacial times. Although the amber content is lower than in the Prussia Formation, these beds were also mined before World War II.

**Iron–manganese deposits in the foreland and deep-marine (flysch) basins (pelosiderite type).** In the eighteenth and nineteenth centuries Fe was mined at various sites of the Carpathian Flysch Belt (e.g. Cieszyn area (PL), Třinec (CZ), Frenštat pod Radhoštem area (CZ)). Iron formation occurred in a marine environment and was continuous from the Cretaceous to the Early Eocene (Wiśniowa, Rajbrot, Stępina, Jasło, Nowy Sącz (PL)) (Osika 1976). Similar deposits were also formed along the northern boundary of the Alps from Switzerland (Delemont (CH)) to Germany (Grünten (D), Teisenberg (D)) (De Quervain & Zitzmann 1977; Ziegler 1983). The Fe ore consists of pelosiderite (clay siderite) and ooids of goethite, locally with subordinate amounts of Mn. In places the Mn contents may reach ore grade of up to 30 wt% Mn, e.g. Gorlice-Cieklin-Jasło area (PL). The ore seams are generally thin, varying from several to several tens of centimetres.

In a similar marine environment, Fe ore was also deposited during the Early Tertiary in north Germany. Here, however, the mineral assemblage is different, comprising glauconite, goethite and siderite pebbles (e.g. Achim (SW of Hamburg) (D)).

**Alkaline- and alkaline-earth-element-bearing evaporite deposits in rift, foreland and intramontane basins.** During the Palaeogene, northward-directed marine ingressions reached the Upper Rhine Graben (Pechelbronn Beds) (D/F) (see also Rasser *et al.* 2008). These, together with Middle Miocene ingressions in the Carpathian Foreland (PL) were responsible for another phase of evaporite formation in Central Europe namely the precipitation of K-enriched salt near Muehlhausen (Alsace, F) and at Buggingen (Baden-Württemberg, D) as well as Na-enriched salt in Upper Silesia (e.g. Wieliczka, PL). The potash mine at Buggingen stopped its underground working in 1973 with 0.12 Mt of $K_2O$ produced during the final year (at that time 4.5% of K production in Germany).

The evaporite deposits in the Upper Rhine Graben formed as a result of the arid climate, the low rate of sedimentation within the graben, and the rare communication between the rift basin and the open sea to the south (Courtot *et al.* 1972). The evaporitic succession contains sylvite, halite, Fe oxides, anhydrite and clay minerals. Unlike the Zechstein-age beds, carnallite is almost totally absent. The potash beds may be disrupted by some salt domes which formed within the underlying halite beds during the Oligocene (Bouladon 1989).

In the Polish Carpathians two deposits were discovered during the 1960s and 1970s namely, Łężkowice-Siedlec-Moszczenica (1960/61) and Wójnicz near Tarnów (1970) (Garlicki 1971). Rock-salt deposits in the East Slovak Basin are of Miocene age (Prešov-Sol'ná Baňa, Zbudza (SK)) (Slávik 1967). The Sol'-Poša (SK) deposit was recently discovered in the same geological formation as the Zbudza deposit. Proven reserves are 454 Mt of salt, containing 75% NaCl.

The only rock-salt deposit in the Dinarides is found at Tuzla (BiH). This more or less stratified salt body of Early Miocene age (Karpatian) is the largest of its kind on the Balkan Peninsula. It comprises banded halite, anhydrite, dolomite and marls. In addition to the major components (halite and thenardite–mirabilite) a suite of accessory minerals including northupite ($Na_3Mg\ [Cl/(CO_3)_4]$ and searlesite ($NaB[Si_2O_6].H_2O$ are also found (Kniewald *et al.* 1986; Bermanec *et al.* 1987). Of particular interest is the presence of the boron mineral tuzlaite

($NaCaB_5O_8(OH)_2{\cdot}3(H_2O)$) which was first discovered in the Tuzla mine (Bermanec *et al.* 1994).

**Sulphur deposits in foreland basins.** Sulphur is produced during the desulphurization of natural gas and the roasting of pyrite which was mined in Kieslager-type deposits. In addition, native sulphur occurs in Central Europe in Cenozoic foreland basins. Here, native sulphur formed by the early diagenetic reduction of Oligo-Miocene gypsum mediated by anaerobic bacteria.

In the Carpathian Foreland Basin, recovery of Badenian-age sulphur lasted until 1959 near Staszów (PL). The discovery of S deposits between the rivers San and Vistula has been described by Kubica (1994).

In SE France sulphur is found at Tapets (F) and Manosque (F) within an Oligo-Miocene succession of organic-rich, lignite-bearing, gypsiferous marls. Sulphur appears to be of synsedimentary origin, since native sulphur also occurs as inclusions in flints. Sodium chloride brines, enriched in hydrocarbons (and $H_2S$), have been derived from the decomposition of organic material (Bouladon 1989). Sulphur later precipitated out when the sulphur-bearing solutions came into contact with oxidizing surface waters.

Along the margin of the Po Plain (I) sulphur deposits are associated with Upper Miocene evaporites, which crop out discontinuously along the northern margin of the Apennines. In the main sulphur mining district, extending over more than 15 km between the Ronco and Savio rivers, about ten mines were operated until the 1960s. Massive lenses of sulphur ore, varying in thickness from a few centimetres to more than 10 m, may be traced along-strike over several tens of metres. Sulphur is concentrated at the boundary between the limestones and the overlying gypsum beds (Scicli 1972).

**Smectite–attapulgite deposits in foreland and deep-marine basins.** Bentonites and bentonitic shales are known from many Palaeogene-age units of the Carpathian Flysch Belt (Outer Carpathians), the Podhale Flysch (Central Carpathian Flysch), and the Southern Alps (Veneto area), and from Neogene series in the Alpine/Carpathian Foreland Basin.

In the Carpathian Flysch Belt the formation of the bentonitic clay shales began in the Late Cretaceous and lasted until the Eocene. The Polany deposit (PL) contains bentonized tuffs, between 0.3 and 0.7 m thick, alternating with clay shales and shaly sandstones.

In the Carpathian Foredeep bentonite beds occur at Jaworze (PL) and Ivančice (CZ) in argillaceous units of Miocene age. In the Alpine Foreland Basin, bentonite is common in the Miocene Upper Freshwater Molasse where it may be traced along the northern edge of the Alps from SE Bavaria to SW Switzerland. Although widespread and of utmost importance for the industry, the origin of the bentonite in this region is enigmatic. Recent research suggests that the bentonites were derived from airfall tuffs sourced from volcanoes located in the Carpathians. However, this is certainly not the only explanation for the origin of the widespread occurrences of smectite and mixed-layer illite–montmorillonite. Weathering, pedogenesis and peculiar hydrological conditions in freshwater lakes are possible alternatives (Refai 1993; Kallis & Bleich 1994).

At Mormoiron (F), bentonite and attapulgite are mined from Oligocene rocks in the Vaucluse area (Bouladon 1989). In Italy, bentonite deposits occur in the Southern Alps (Veneto region), where montmorillonite of Eocene age is found in argillaceous series. These bentonites originated from the alteration of Triassic volcanic rocks (Peco 1953).

**Arc-related gold–silver–copper–molybdenum–lead–zinc–antimony–mercury porphyry and epithermal deposits.** The Carpatho-Pannonian region and the Spiš-Gemer Mountains host one of the most complex and varied mineralizations in Central Europe. Numerous base and precious metals and Fe deposits are found in central Slovakia and northern Hungary. The mines in these regions have been the principal European metal suppliers since prehistoric times. The concentrated nature of the deposits sparked a 'rush' during medieval times, when many people flocked into the area resulting in the growth of sprawling mining towns. Presently, the mines are mostly exhausted and closed, but are still of great interest for mineralogists.

Many deposits in the region are genetically bound to Neogene (and sometimes Eocene) (sub)volcanic activity. The age range of mineralization, however, is much narrower (10.7–12.5 Ma; Neubauer *et al.* 2005). Stratovolcanic edifices, calderas, and horst-and-graben structures are the most prominent structural and geomorphological features. Epithermal deposits close to the surface indicate the presence of skarn- and porphyry-type deposits at depth. A general tectonic model investigating the structural traps and preferred locations for stock emplacement was suggested by Drew (2003). This model concentrates on the origin of the porphyry- and vein-type deposits in the Central Slovakian Volcanic Field and the Matra Mountains in Hungary. Based on a comprehensive study by Konečný *et al.* (1995), who investigated the Cenozoic igneous activity, Lexa (1999) and Lexa *et al.* (1999) have described the genetic relationship between the volcanic-hosted and sediment-hosted mineralization in the region. The various deposits may be classified into three types: (1) porphyry-type Cu–Mo–Au deposits related to subvolcanic stocks of andesitic and dioritic composition, e.g. Kalinka (SK); (2) skarn-type Cu–Mo–Au deposits related to diorite or granodiorite porphyry subvolcanic stocks and dykes intruded into Triassic calcareous rocks, e.g. Zlatno (SK), Pukanec (SK), Recsk (H) (Fig. 21.18); and (3) magnetite skarns located at the contact of diorites and granodiorites and their cogenetic porphyry subvolcanic rocks with calcareous rocks of Mesozoic age, e.g. Vyhne-Klokoč (SK) and Tisovec (SK). Intrusion-related base-metal stockworks are transitional between the porphyry–skarn and the epithermal mineralizations. These (intrusion-related) stockworks are closely associated in space and time with the emplacement of subvolcanic stocks, e.g. Hodruša-Rozália (SK), Pukanec (SK), Brehov (SK), Zlatá Baňa (SK) and Nagybörzsöny (H).

The epithermal deposits were subdivided into four metallogenetic–hydrothermal systems (Lexa 1999; Lexa *et al.* 1999). These are: (1) high-sulphidation epithermal Au-(Cu) deposits, e.g. Klokoč-Podpolom (SK) and Lahóc (H) which are very similar to the low-sulphidation epithermal deposits with regard to their geological setting; (2) barren high-sulphidation alteration systems possibly representing the topmost parts of porphyry-type hydrothermal systems; (3) intrusion-related low-sulphidation epithermal Au ($\pm$ base metal) deposits commonly occurring vein clusters, stockworks and mineralized breccia pipes in the apical parts of subvolcanic andesites and porphyritic diorite stocks or close to their contacts, e.g. Hodruša-Rozália (SK) and Nagybörzsöny (H); and (4) volcanic-related low-sulphidation epithermal deposits with veins and stockworks which are related in space and time to rhyolites. These deposits are structurally controlled by extensional faults, especially by faults bounding horsts and characterized by a pervasive wall rock alteration including silicification, adularization and sericitization.

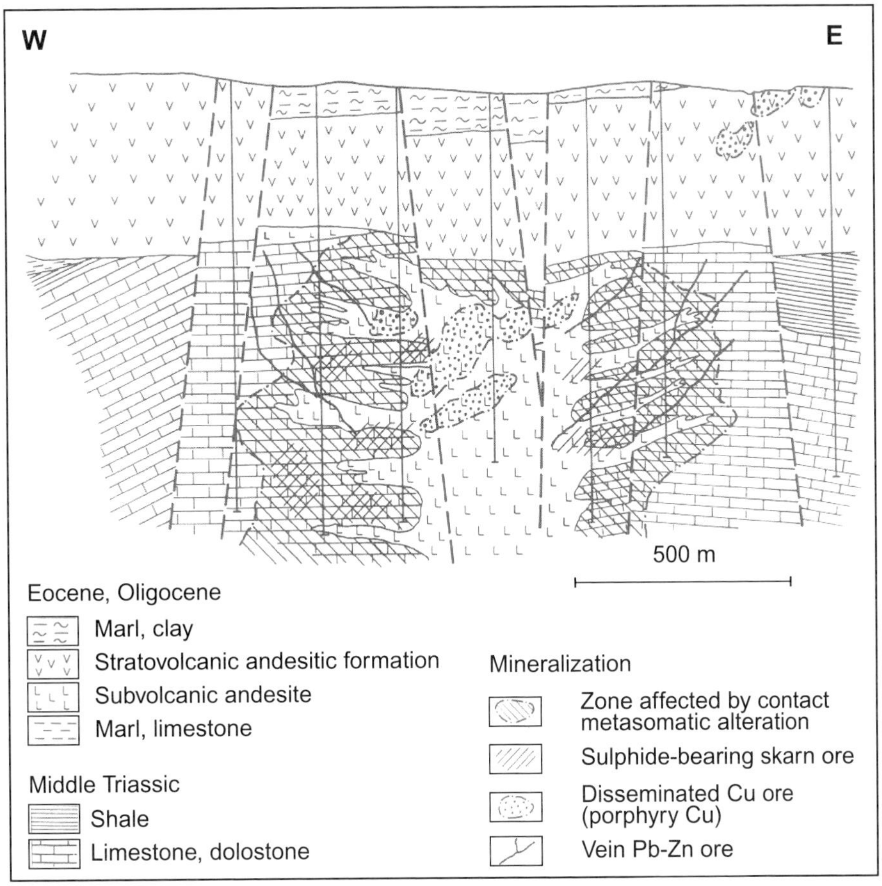


**Fig. 21.18.** Schematic geological section through the Recsk-Lahóca polymetallic deposit (H) (after Gatter *et al.* 1999).

With regard to the sulphide content and the depth of the hydrothermal system, three different subtypes of mineralization may be distinguished within the volcanic-related low-sulphidation-type deposits (Lexa 1999): (a) base-metal veins abundant in pyrite, chalcopyrite, sphalerite and galena are marker for the lowest level of the epithermal system, e.g. Banská Štiavnica (SK), Gyöngyösorosi (H), Bányabérc (H) and Mátrasentimré (H); (b) silver–base-metal veins are representative of the intermediate level of the epithermal system, e.g. Hodruša (SK), Pukanec (SK), Gyöngyösorosi (H), Bányabérc (H) and Mátrasentimré (H); (c) gold–Ag ± Sb, base-metal veins and stockworks enriched in electrum, Ag sulphosalts and stibnite represent the topmost near-surface level of the epithermal system with deposits at Kremnica (SK), Vyhne-Trojkrál'ová (SK), Banská Belá (SK), Zlatá Baňa (SK), Telkibánya (H) Rudabányacska (H), Komlóska (H) and Füzérradvány (H).

Of the epithermal mineralization related to the Neogene volcanism, Hg is of particular importance because of the great variety of types of Hg deposits present (including almost only Hg). Steam-heated (hot spring) systems represent the upper part of the epithermal system. In addition to cinnabar, minerals such as barite and Au have been recorded from these deposits, e.g. Dekýš (SK), Sárospatak (H), Mád (H), Komlóska (H) and Füzérradvány (H). Disseminated Hg mineralization is superimposed on an advanced argillic alteration in the apical part of andesitic stratovolcanoes or found in the outermost zones of low-sulphidation-type epithermal deposits subject to moderate erosion, e.g. Dolná Ves (SK), Čertov kopec (SK), Dubník (SK) and Vihorlat-Morské Oko (SK). Sediment-hosted cinnabar mineralization predominates in sandstones and dolomites immediately overlying basement. This type of Hg mineralization is interpreted in terms of remobilization as a result of the intrusion of small subvolcanic bodies into sedimentary deposits, or the mineralization may be related to distal off-shoots of deep-seated igneous bodies, e.g. Malachov (SK), Merník (SK) and Ladomirov (SK).

The Vel'ká Studňa (SK) deposit is the most important in the Malachov Ore Field (Knésl & Linkešová 1971). The stockwork-like oligomineralic impregnation with accessory pyrite, marcasite and arsenopyrite is located beneath a Badenian-age stratovolcanic complex within a Palaeogene-age mixed calcareous–clastic unit. The Hg mineralization belongs to a hydrothermal system driven by volcanic activity of rhyolitic composition. Reserves were estimated at 282 kt, grading 0.21% Hg (Knésl 1979).

The cinnabar ore bodies in the Dubník deposit (SK) are rimmed by a zone of As ore that gives way to an outer zone abundant in Sb minerals. Ore reserves are calculated at 2426 kt averaging 0.16 wt% Hg. The Merník Hg deposit (SK) is contained within Miocene sediments. Here the cinnabar–metacinnabar mineralization developed from Late Badenian to Early Sarmatian times, coeval with the intrusion of rhyodacites into the sandstones (Burian *et al.* 1985).

Sediment-hosted Au deposits are also common in the Carpathian region. These are similar to the well-known Carlin-type Au deposits. Gold was concentrated in calcareous rocks immediately overlying basement, and adjacent to deep-seated extensional faults. The metalliferous fluids used these fault zones as channels. The heat necessary to keep this hydrothermal system operative was provided by a large volcanoplutonic system, examples of which are found at Vel'ké Pole-Sokolec (SK), Sklené Teplice (SK) and Remata (SK).

To characterize these Neogene, arc-related mineralizations better, one example of each, epithermal and porphyry-type ore deposits is discussed below.

*Zlatno porphyry-skarn Cu deposit (SK).* The Zlatno porphyry Cu deposit is located in the western part of the Central Slovakian Volcanic Field. Within the deposit, an extensive network of veinlets developed in a granodiorite porphyry stock at a depth of between 700 and 1000 m in the lower part of the stratovolcanic edifice, near to the SW margin of the Štiavnica stratovolcano (Fig. 21.19). Close to the surface, the igneous rocks were pervasively altered hosting considerable amounts of pyrite, and to a lesser extent pyrrhotite, chalcopyrite, galena and sphalerite. In the nearby Triassic calcareous wall rocks, the Neogene volcanic activity led to the development of skarns which contain the highest concentration of Cu in the district. Subsequent to ore mineralization, quartz-diorite porphyry dykes dissected the entire Cu deposit (Burian *et al.* 1985).

*Kremnica epithermal Au–Ag deposit (SK).* The Kremnica deposits, located in the northern part of the Central Slovakian Volcanic Field, were among the most important Au producers in medieval Europe. According to the mining records of the fourteenth century, there was an average annual production of 120 kg Au and *c.* 1200 kg of Ag. In the fifteenth century the output gradually decreased to less than 100 kg per year and in 1970 the Kremnica mines finally closed.

The epithermal vein-type deposits at Kremnica originated from an extensional setting during Late Sarmatian to Pannonian times. Coeval with this tectonic deformation, andesitic stratovolcanoes were erupted at the surface and subvolcanic diorite–gabbrodiorite stock intruded at depth (Štohl *et al.* 1994; Konečný *et al.* 1995). Gold forms visible aggregates, wires and feather-like sheets (bonanza-type Au) in cavernous quartz–carbonate gangue. The ore grade decreases with depth from 1–5 ppm Au down to 0.5 ppm Au (Bartalský & Finka 1999).

The Ardovo (SK) and Poniky-Drienok Pb–Zn deposits (SK) are located in Middle Triassic limestones and dolomites. Vein-type mineralization and disseminated Pb–Zn ore are typical of these deposits. The ore grades range between 11 and 20% Pb, and up to 30% Zn and 24 g/t Ag, with galena, sphalerite, boulangerite, tetrahedrite, chalcopyrite and pyrite as the main ore minerals. The age of mineralization is not yet proven, but is assumed to be contemporaneous with the Neogene volcanism (Slavkay & Petro 1993).

Epithermal mineralization of Cenozoic age, and containing Pb, Zn, Cu, Ag and Te minerals, was also recorded from outside the Carpathians, e.g. from the Roztoky volcanic centre in the Eger [Ohře] Graben (CZ) (Pivec *et al.* 1998). These deposits are of subeconomic grade.

**Kaolinite–illite–smectite–mixed layer–alunite–silica deposits in intra-arc backarc and rift basins.** Neogene volcanic activity in the Carpathian region not only resulted in the development of a great variety of metallic deposits but was also responsible for a wide spectrum of argillaceous deposits containing kaolinite at Mád-Koldu, (H), dickite at Bomboly (H), bentonite at Pétervására and Istenmezeje (H), bentonite and allevardite at Mád-Királyhegy (H), and illite at Füzérradvány (H). The Füzérradvány deposit, unique in Europe, is a concentration of almost pure

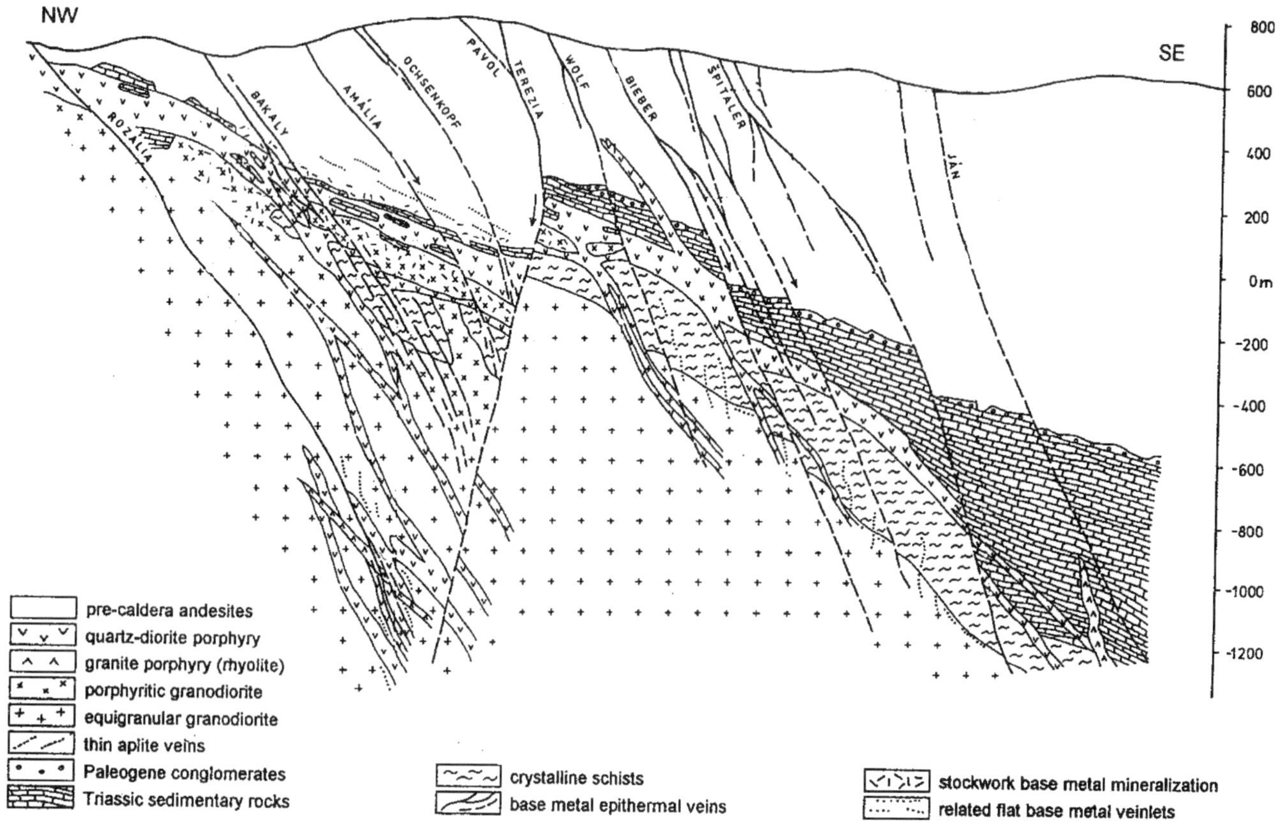


**Fig. 21.19.** Section of the stockwork-disseminated base-metal ore deposit of the Banská Štiavnica ore district (SK) (Štohl *et al.* 1990).

illite. Reserves are 800 kt and resources were estimated at 1700 kt (Molnár *et al.* 1999).

There are very close genetic links between the formation of phyllosilicates, alunite-group minerals and silica alteration, and the Neogene igneous activity which was the driving force behind these mineralizations. Moreover, the intimate relationship between the various non-metallic raw materials is also highlightened by the cluster of mining operations in the area. Many of the argillaceous raw materials originated from halmyrolithic processes. Hydrothermal brines were vented into freshwater lakes within volcanic depressions which subsided subsequent to the rhyolite–andesite eruptions (Molnár *et al.* 1999). In addition to the above-mentioned phyllosilicates, alunite developed in some deposits in the Tokaj Mountains near Regéc (H) and Mogyoróska (H). At Mád-Királyhegy (H) fluctuating physicochemical conditions resulted in the narrowly spaced zonation of sheet silicate and sulphate deposits around the vent systems (Gyarmati 1977; Gyarmati & Pentelényi 1973; Molnár *et al.* 1999).

A marked increase in silica during volcanic activity led, in some places, to the formation of geyserites (e.g. Sárospatak Bothö (H)). These geyserites contain cumulates of $\alpha$-quartz. An additional, and widespread, source of silica in this region are the limnoquartzites that closely interfinger with argillaceous deposits (e.g. Mád-Koldu (H)) (Morvai 1986). The hydrothermally altered rocks provided excellent building material and the silicified tuffs were used as millstones, with their first usage dating back as far as the sixteenth century. During the twentieth century the deposit was exploited up into the 1960s (Gyarmati & Pentelényi 1973).

In the Lastovce deposit (SK) (Slanské Vrchy Mountains) Upper Sarmatian to Pannonian rhyolite lavas and tuffs are intercalated with beds of clay, diatomite, bentonite and horizons containing concretions of opal and opalized tuffs. Several other deposits occur at this same lithostratigraphic level, for example at Kuzmice (SK), Nižný Žipov (SK), Vel'aty (SK) and Tŕňa (SK). These deposits have a total of 2 Mt of proven reserves.

At Stará Kremnička (Jelšový potok) (SK), Bartošova Lehôtka (SK) and Kopernica (SK), smectite was derived from the alteration of vitric tuffs in a shallow-lacustrine environment. A conspicuous vertical zonation is recognized within the deposits. The bentonitic beds are at the base of a limnoquartzite unit of Upper Miocene to Pliocene age. In the bentonitic clay beds, smectite is mixed with cristobalite and clinoptilolite, whereas the overlying limnoquartzites contain only smectite. Other localities in the region are devoid of silica concentrations but rich in argillaceous raw materials (e.g. Žiarska kotlina Basin (SK)). In the Bartošová Lehôtka and Kopernica deposits, reserves of illite with minor kaolinite exceed 5 Mt each (Zuberec *et al.* 2005). The Pliocene Pozdišovce deposit (SK) contains mainly illite and smectite (Slávik 1967). The raw material in the Michalovce (Biela hora) deposit (SK) is composed of halloysite and kaolinite. Here the phyllosilicates occur in Upper Miocene-age calcareous clays beneath rhyolites and rhyolitic tuffs. The argillaceous raw material was derived from rhyolites undergoing supergene alteration during a Late Sarmatian to Pontian hiatus. Halloysite was formed as meteoric waters, with a pH of between 6 and 7, percolated through the rhyolitic complex and leached its alkaline elements and silica (Slávik 1962). Proven reserves of more than 5 Mt are available in the Michalovce deposit (SK) (Zuberec *et al.* 2005). A deposit, similar in size and grade is located close to Poruba pod Vihorlatom (SK).

The bentonite deposits in the Dinarides and south Tisza are all related to Middle Miocene pyroclastic units which contain up to 95% of smectite in addition to quartz, calcite, feldspar, muscovite and biotite. The pyroclastic deposits underwent devitrification and chemical alteration by seawater. More than 22 deposits in Bosnia-Herzegovina, and four in Croatia are related to this devitrification. The deposits in Bosnia are clustered around Bosanski Novi (Lješani deposit), Jajce (Babići deposit), Tešani (Radeša, Žabljak, Trepče deposits), Gračanica (Džombe, Kulić, Stražbe deposits) and Zvornik (Zvornik deposits). The deposits in Croatia are found at Poljanska Luka, Bednja-Šaša, Gornja Jelenska (Moslavačka gora Mountain) and Divoselo.

The Miocene-age Fohnsdorf Basin (A) is the largest intramontane basin within the Eastern Alps. The basin fill comprises more than 3 km of sediments with some tuffaceous and bentonitic layers that were mined together with coal (Sachsenhofer *et al.* 2000; Strauss *et al.* 2001).

The Rokle deposit, located in the Eger Graben, is the largest bentonite deposit in the Czech Republic. Here, the bentonites include a 25-m-thick unit of basal pyroclastics, forming the margin of the Tertiary alkaline volcanic rocks of the Doupov Mountains (Franče 1992). A detailed mineralogical study of the sorption capacity of the Czech smectites has been published by Vejsada *et al.* (2005).

**Zeolite deposits in intra-arc and backarc basins.** Zeolitization in the Carpathian region is related to the Neogene volcanic activity coeval with the subsidence of the intravolcanic depressions. Occasionally, zeolite may also be dispersed in argillaceous raw materials. A prerequisite for high-silica zeolites, such as mordenite and clinoptilolite is volcanic glass enriched in silica. Both of these zeolites crystallized from solutions oversaturated in $SiO_2$ with regard to quartz (Kraus *et al.* 1994). During diagenesis volcanic glass is altered to clinoptilolite and subsequently to mordenite (K–Ca–Na variety). The conversion of clinoptilolite into mordenite is related to a change in the geothermal gradient (Šamajová *et al.* 1992).

Zeolite deposits occur across the Neogene volcanic regions of Slovakia (e.g. near Nižný Hrabovec, Majerovce, Kučín, Bartošová Lehôtka, Jastrabá) and Hungary (near Nemti, Bodrogkeresztúr Kakas). In the lower Sarmatian-age welded rhyolithic tuffs at Bodrogkeresztúr Kakas (H), the presence of clinoptilolite and desmine is related to auto-pneumatolytic processes. As a result of their high insulating capacity, these industrial minerals are quarried as raw material for construction purposes.

**Perlite deposits in intra-arc backarc basins.** Perlite deposits are economically very significant and typical of the Neogene volcanics in the Carpathian region. Perlite is often bound to acid vitreous volcanic rocks of rhyolitic composition. The quantity of volcanic glass in the perlitic rock may reach as much as 75% and the $H_2O$ content is within the range of 2.5–3.5%. The density of the exploited raw material is between 980 and 1230 kg/m$^3$, whereas the expanded end-product has a density in the range of 60–150 kg/m$^3$ (time of expansion is 2–15 s at temperatures of 900–1000°C).

Deposits of perlite are common within the Central Slovakian Volcanic Field (Lehôtka pod Brehy, Jastrabá (SK)) and in the Slanské Vrchy (Byšta (SK)) and Tokaj mountains (Pálháza (H). The largest perlite deposit is currently being worked at Gyöngyköhegy, near Pálháza (H). Rhyolitic lava spread across semiconsolidated argillaceous sediments of Middle Miocene age in a brackish lagoon. The Lehôtka pod Brehy (SK) deposit is located in the marginal part of a large rhyolite stock which is covered by rhyolitic pyroclastics (up to 50 m thick) and underlain by Badenian–Sarmatian-age sedimentary rocks. Exploration in the Lehôtka pod Brehy area resulted in the recognition of an ore body with reserves of several megatonnes of perlite (Slávik 1971).

**Diatomite deposits in intra-arc backarc, foreland and epicontinental basins.** Diatoms may bloom in lacustrine and marine ecosystems, provided there is an ample reservoir of silica. In nature this is usually supplied by volcanic processes. Therefore, diatomite occurs in Central Europe in areas with volcanic activity, notably in the Carpathian/Pannonian realm (PL, SK, H), close to the Massif Central (F), but deposits are also found in Denmark.

Diatomite in the Central Carpathians occurs in three different depositional environments: (1) small intravolcanic depressions (e.g. Močiar, Dúbravica, Bory deposits (SK)); (2) maars (e.g. Pinciná, Jelšovec deposits (SK)); and (3) local basins close to Neogene stratovolcanoes. The content of diatomaceous debris in the sediments ranges from 40 to 95%. The Upper Miocene sediment filling the maar near Pinciná and Jelšovec consists of tuffs, sandstones, tuffaceous clay, diatomite and diatomaceous clay (Vass *et al.* 1997). The uppermost part of the succession comprises 40 m of dark bituminous shale ('alginite'). The presence of algae suggest a warm temperate climate during the Late Miocene (Pontian).

In Hungary, volcanosedimentary deposits of Badenian age hosting diatomaceous earth are found at Erdöbénye (H) in the Tokaj Mountains and at Szurdokpüspöki (H) in the SW Mátra Mountains (Hajós 1993). Here, the diatoms bloomed under a great variety of hydrological conditions ranging from freshwater through limnobrackish to marine conditions. The deposits contain very pure diatomite with little quartz, smectite, pyrite, calcite or gypsum. The highly porous siliceous raw material has a specific internal surface ranging from 2800 to 6900 $cm^2/g$ (Morvai 1986).

Diatomaceous rocks also occur in the lower Oligocene-age Menilite Shales (SK, PL) of the Carpathian Flysch Belt. Here, the sediments comprise siliceous claystones, cherts and marls intercalated with thinly laminated siltstones. The thickness of the Menilite Shales ranges from 800 m to 1000 m, but the thickness of the workable diatomite beds is only 1 to 80 cm (Leszczawka, Krzywe (PL)).

A large diatomite deposit related to the Miocene volcanism occurs in the Rhone Valley at Saint-Bauzile (F) (Demarco *et al.* 1989). However, the most important producer of diatomaceous earths in Central Europe is located on the west coast of the Jutland Peninsula (DK). A mixture of diatomite, with up to 30% of bentonitic clays, is termed Moler in Denmark and is worked in open-cast mines (Antonides 1998). Source rocks for silica facilitating such a diatom bloom are volcanic ash layers within the Palaeogene sediments of the Danish Basin. The ash layers are completely altered and only recognizable as varicoloured stripes in the clay. In NW Denmark, the ash-bearing succession consists of diatomite (Mo clay) that formed in a local embayment (Pedersen & Surlyk 1983).

**Quartz sand deposits (glass sand) in epicontinental basins.** During the Late Cretaceous and Tertiary, high-quality quartz sands formed in the Northwest European Cenozoic Basin at Haltern (D), Frechen (D), Weferlingen (D) and Hohenbocka (D). *Per descensum* fluids rich in organic acids leaked from Tertiary lignite seams (see below) into the underlying rocks and improved the quality of Tertiary sand deposits in the Lower Rhine Basin (D). Leaching of the labile constituents, such as Fe minerals (<0.024 wt% $Fe_2O_3$) and feldspar, from the arkoses resulted in almost pure quartz sand deposits with $SiO_2$ contents exceeding 98% and with reserves exceeding 3000 Mt at Haltern (D).

**Coal deposits and oil shales.** Most Cenozoic coal basins host lignite, but only a few basins containing coal of higher rank. The bulk of the coal is utilized as fuel for power plants. The resources of some of these basins are amongst the largest in the world. Coal-bearing Cenozoic basins formed in very different tectonic settings and various processes acted as the main controls on peat deposition. Figure 21.20 provides an overview of the stratigraphic position of the coal-bearing sediments in Central Europe.

The **Northwest European Cenozoic Basin** (NWECB) is the world's largest lignite producer with major discrete deposits located across north Germany and Poland (Klett *et al.* 2002; Präger *et al.* 2003; Standke *et al.* 1993; Kasiński & Piwocki 2002). About 195 Mt of lignite, representing more than 20% of the world's lignite production, were mined in the NWECB in 2003.

Peat accumulation in the region was mainly controlled by Palaeocene to Miocene transgressions and regressions of the North Sea. The Belchatów district, which formed a branch of the NWECB, was mainly controlled by rifting and is discussed below. (Note that production from the Belchatów district is not included in the above production figure.)

Palaeocene and Eocene coal deposits occur in the Lower Hesse Depression (e.g. Borken), the Subhercynian Basin and the Leipzig area. In the *Subhercynian Basin* (e.g. Helmstedt-Egeln) several Palaeocene to Middle Oligocene seams, totalling more than 100 m occur. The coal fills long, but narrow, rim synclines bordering salt structures. Halokinesis also played a role in the preservation of the coal measures. Indeed, the high ash coal is typically rich in salt.

The accumulation of coal in the *Leipzig area* occurred in estuaries and coastal plains and was controlled by sea-level variations, the underground solution of Zechstein salt (e.g. Geiselthal), and horizontal salt movement (e.g. Oberröblingen-Amsdorf). Therefore, the typically uniform seams, 10–15 m thick, are locally up to 120 m thick (e.g. Geiselthal). Bitumen-rich lithotypes from the Amsdorf deposit are used for the production of montan wax, while those from the Weißelster area (south of Leipzig) were used for the production of tar. About 408 t of amber were produced as a byproduct from Upper Oligocene beds in the Bitterfeld area at Goitsche (north of Leipzig) (Wimmer *et al.* 2004).

Oligocene seams are of some economic importance in the Leipzig area and in the Lower Hesse Depression. In north Hesse weathered Oligo-Miocene lignite was used as raw material for the production of colour pigments (Kassel Brown).

Miocene coals constitute the main lignite reserves in the NWECB. Located in the western part of the NWECB, the *Lower Rhine Basin* is Europe's largest lignite producer (Hager 1993). It forms a NW–SE trending asymmetrical graben, about 100 km long and 50 km wide. The basin fill, which is up to 600 m thick, comprises shallow-marine Oligocene to Lower Miocene rocks with minor coal (e.g. Bergisch-Gladbach Formation, Köln Formation), and the coal-bearing Ville (uppermost Lower to Upper Miocene) and Inden formations (Upper Miocene). Plio-Pleistocene fluvial sediments cap the sedimentary sequence.

The Ville and the Inden formations include the Main Seam (up to 100 m thick) and the Inden Seam (up to 35 m). A sequence stratigraphic model suggests that the Main Seam formed during an early sea-level highstand on a vast coastal plain (Klett *et al.* 2002). It interdigitates to the north with marine

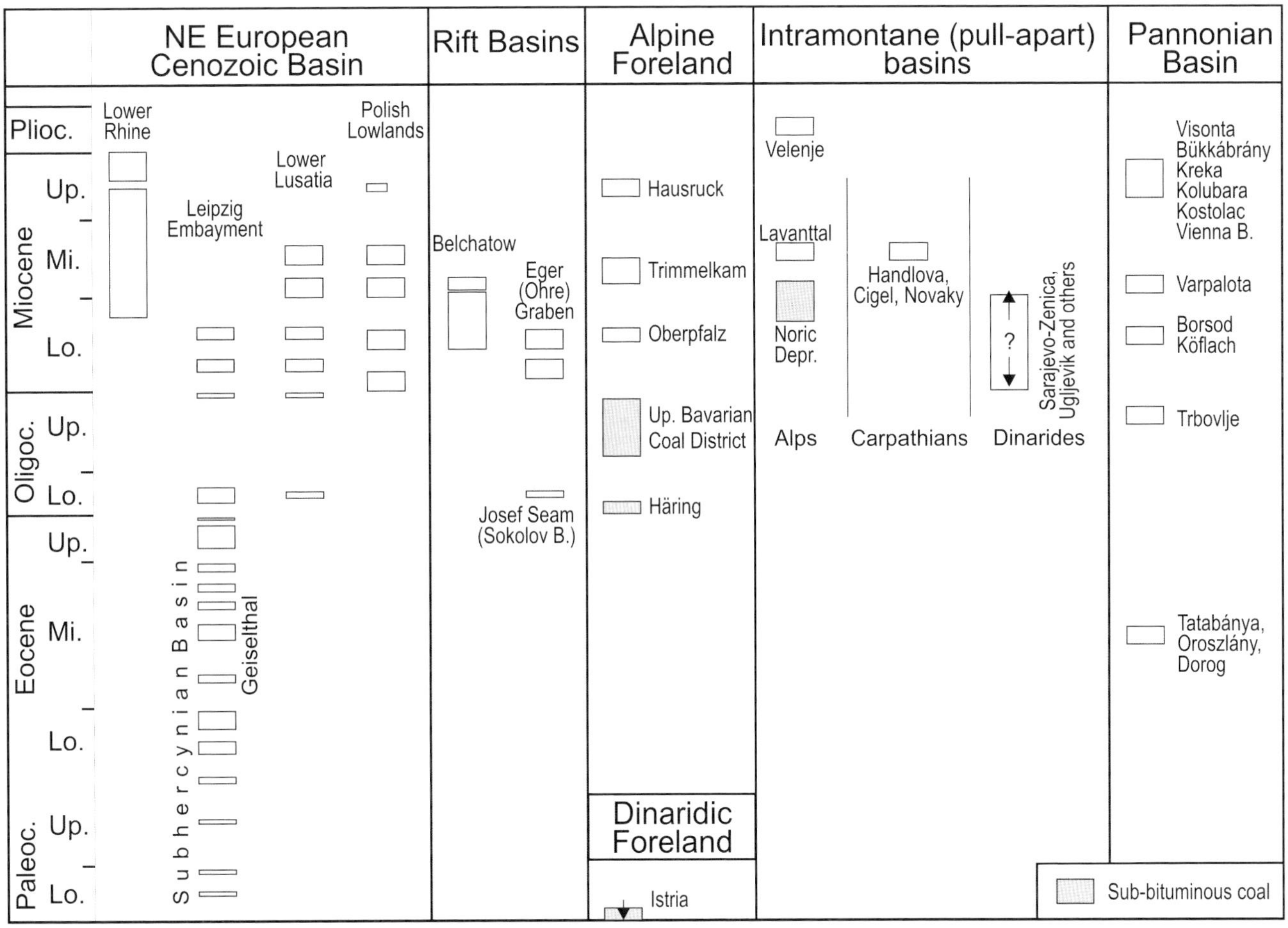


**Fig. 21.20.** Stratigraphic position of Cenozoic coal seams (Hager 1993; Präger *et al.* 2003; Standke *et al.* 1993; Kasiński & Piwocki 2002; Kasiński 2000; Sachsenhofer 2000; Hamrla 1959).

deposits and subdivides into the Morken, Frimmersdorf and Garzweiler seams.

NW–SE trending faults displace the basin fill and define several tilted blocks. Open-pit mines excavate the lignite within uplifted blocks. The largest open-pit mine is at Hambach with a scheduled final depth of 470 m. Annual production from this mine is about 40 Mt. In 2005 a total of 97.3 Mt of lignite (7.8–10.5 MJ/kg; 50–60% $H_2O$) was produced from the Lower Rhine Basin. In terms of macropetrography, xylitic, fusitic and detritic coals are the most common forms present. The detritic coal is either stratified or compact. Ash yields (1.5–8.0%$_{db}$) and sulphur contents (<0.5%$_{daf}$) are very low. Geological resources are 55 Bt, and 35 Bt of this are considered mineable.

Outside the Lower Rhine Basin, Miocene successions are generally thin (e.g. Leipzig area, Lower Lusatia, Polish Lowlands: 150–250 m) and seam thicknesses range typically from 10 to 40 m.

In the NWECB the distribution of the coal seams and facies architecture are mainly controlled by sea-level variations. A wealth of pioneer papers using petrological, palaeobotanical, organic geochemical and isotope techniques reconstructed Miocene peat facies in the NWECB (for a review see Dehmer 2004). These papers showed that subtle changes in the height of the water table are recorded in cyclic changes from low-lying swamps to raised mires. Additionally, block faulting influenced the Lower Lusatian Basin (Seifert *et al.* 1993). Locally the coal seams are cut by Pleistocene channels or dislocated by forces associated with Quaternary ice movement (Kasiński & Piwocki 2002).

*(Oligo-)Miocene rift basins.* High subsidence rates in relatively small rift basins resulted in the formation of very thick lignite seams restricted lateral continuity. Typical examples include the Bełchatów Basin and the Eger [Ohře] Graben. Annual production consists of about 35 Mt of lignite at Bełchatów and about 60 Mt in the Eger Graben. This basin type, therefore, accounts for more than 10% of the world's lignite production. Typically the deposits contain high-ash lignites, which accumulated in low-lying mires. This is probably because the high subsidence rates prevented the formation of raised mires.

The **Bełchatów** lignite region in central Poland (south of Łodz) includes nine major deposits (Kasiński *et al.* 2000). The largest of these deposits are located within the west–east trending Kleszczów Trough (Szczerców, Bełchatów, Kamieńsk). Other deposits are located within neighbouring en-echelon depressions. The western segment of the Kleszczów Trough is separated from the eastern one by the Debina salt dome.

The lignite occurs within a thick Miocene sequence, which is subdivided into three units: (1) the *sub-coal complex* (fluvial and limnic clastic deposits with intercalations of freshwater limestone); (2) the Lower Miocene *coal complex* (the Main Seam, up to 250 m thick, and two minor seams); and (3) the overlying *clay-coal complex* with an additional seam. The overburden is formed by Upper Miocene and/or Pliocene and Pleistocene sediments up to several hundred metres thick.

The Main Seam is generally monotonous, but interdigitates with sandy sediments along the basin margins and is split by several thin tonstein layers. Limestone layers represent fossil bog-lime. Lignite sulphur contents are low to moderate (55% $H_2O$; 7.6–8.1 MJ/kg; 20%$_{db}$ ash), but higher in the Szczerców deposit (2.5%$_{db}$).

The maximum mining depth is 280 m. Dewatering wells pump 190 $Mm^3$ of water every year. Some of the water is used for the production of mineral water and soft drinks. Other important byproducts include building material, pits and fertilizers (lacustrine chalk).

The WSW–ENE trending **Eger Graben** is located mainly in the Czech Republic, but continues northeastwards into Germany and Poland (Fig. 21.21). This rift basin consists of several fault-controlled sub-basins with slightly different geological histories (i.e. Cheb, Sokolov, Most, Zittau, Berzdorf basins). The sub-basins are a few hundred metres deep and are separated from one another by Oligo-Miocene volcanic rocks. The oldest Cenozoic sediments present are Eocene in age, although the main phase of basin subsidence commenced during the Late Oligocene. The sub-basins are filled with alluvial, fluvial and lacustrine deposits. Tuffs and basalts record several magmatic phases.

Lignite seams formed mainly during Early Miocene times and are up to 70 m thick (e.g. Most, Berzdorf). Two major seams occur in the Zittau Basin (Kasiński 2000). Coal rank varies considerably between the different sub-basins (9–19 MJ/kg, 20–55% $H_2O$), probably as a result of volcanic activity. Ash yields in the coal range from 20 to 45%$_{db}$. Sulphur contents in the freshwater coal vary significantly and reach high values (>4%$_{db}$) in some parts of the Most Basin (Bouska & Pesek 1999). Bitumen-rich lithotypes occur in the western Eger Graben. At present coal is mined in large open-pits in the Sokolov, Most and Zittau basins. The coal is mainly used in power plants. Some (0.3 Mt) is also used for briquetting and to produce synthetic fuels and gas.

*Cenozoic foreland basins.* Coal formation in the Cenozoic foreland basins of Central Europe was controlled by the interplay of sea-level variations, foreland subsidence, and the uplift of the orogen, which controlled the input of clastic material into the basin (e.g. Steininger 1988/89). Unlike the Variscan Foreland, relatively little coal accumulated in the Cenozoic foreland basins and no mines are active today.

Lower Palaeogene (and uppermost Cretaceous) coal accumulated in the **Dinaric Foreland**. The coal seams (up to 1.5 m thick) are intercalated with marine and non-marine limestones, and contain sub-bituminous to medium volatile bituminous coal with very high sulphur (*c.* 10%) bitumen (>10%) and U contents. The high sulphur contents are a result of relatively high pH values fostering bacterial activity. The coal was mined near Vremsky Britof, Secovlje and in the Rasa Valley (Istria; SLO, HR; Hamrla 1959).

Relatively important coal districts in the **Alpine Foreland** are located near Häring (A) (Lower Oligocene), in Upper Bavaria (D) (Upper Oligocene; Geissler 1975), near Trimmelkam (A) (Middle Miocene) and in the Hausruck hills (A) (Upper Miocene; Bechtel *et al.* 2003). Coal also formed during Early Miocene transgressions of the southern margin along the Bohemian Massif (e.g. Oberpfalz (D), Langau (A)).

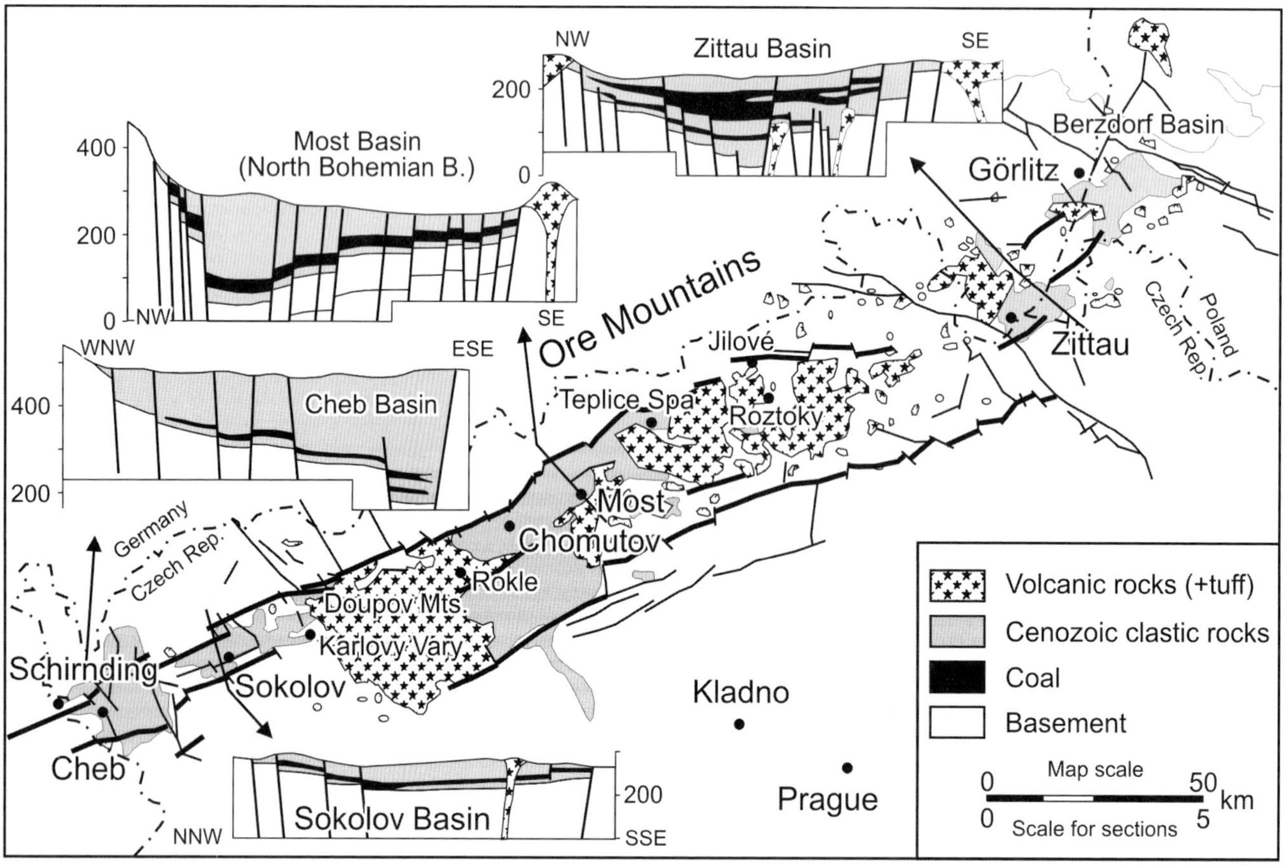


**Fig. 21.21.** Geological sketch of the Eger (Ohre) Graben (D, CZ, PL) (after Kasiński 2000).

*Pull-apart basins and half-grabens within the Alpine foldbelts.* Pull-apart basins and half-grabens filled with non-marine sediments were formed during the late stages of the Alpine Orogeny within the Alps (e.g. Noric Depression, Lavanttal, Velenje), the Carpathians (e.g. Upper Nitra Basin) and the Dinarides (BiH). Some of these basins host very thick Miocene or Pliocene seams of considerable economic significance.

In the Alpine realm, basins are typically filled from bottom to top by fluvial sediments, a single thick coal seam, a sapropelite, and lacustrine deposits. This sequence reflects the drowning of the peat due to high subsidence rates and is typical for pull-apart basins (Sachsenhofer 2000; Sachsenhofer *et al.* 2003). Depending on the depositional environment, the coal properties vary significantly. High-ash, high-sulphur coal in the Fohnsdorf Basin formed in swamps influenced by a brackish lake. In contrast, Leoben coal accumulated in a raised bog and is very clean (Gruber & Sachsenhofer 2001). The Pliocene Velenje Basin is surrounded by Mesozoic carbonates. Here, relatively high sulphur contents in the 160 m thick seam result from the Ca-rich palaeo-environment (Markic & Sachsenhofer 1997). Because of deep burial and elevated heat flows, the rank of Miocene coals reaches the subbituminous stage (Sachsenhofer 2001).

Today, the Velenje (SLO), Handlová, Cigel and Novaky (Upper Nitra B., SK) underground mines, as well as underground and surface mines in several areas in Bosnia, are active. The annual production in the Velenje mine is 4.2 Mt of lignite (9.7 MJ/kg, 45% $H_2O$, 10–35% ash, 1.8% S). The Novaky mine works a 10 m thick seam, while the Handlová mine exploits two seams totalling 5 to 10 m. The Handlová deposit has been buried by a thick pile of Miocene volcanics and thus, the coal quality differs between Novaky (11.3 MJ/kg, 35% $H_2O$, 37.5% ash, 3.5% S) and Handlová (15.4 MJ/kg, 24.4% $H_2O$, 23% ash, 1.6% S). Natural coke occurs at the contact with the magmatic feeder channels. Production in the Upper Nitra Basin in 2003 was 2.5 Mt. The chief mining district in Bosnia is that of Sarajevo-Zenica (central Bosnia). It is located in a 77 km long NW-trending half-graben. The basin fill, which is up to 3 km thick, includes a basal conglomerate, sandstones, pelites, freshwater (bituminous) limestones, and up to nine coal seams. Maximum seam thickness is 8 to 20 m. The brown coal (17.5–23 MJ/t, *c.* 20% $H_2O$, 15–25% ash, 1.5–2.5% S) is currently mined at Zenica, Kakanj and Breza. Coal in similar settings, but partly with a lower rank, is also mined near Kamengrad, Tesanj, Banja Luka, Banovici, Ugljevik and Livno. Current output is very low (*c.* 1 Mt), an effect of the Yugoslav war in the 1990s.

*Pannonian Basin System.* Coal deposits in the Pannonian Basin occur in different stratigraphic positions. Most of them are related to changes in sea/lake level. Because of the brackish or marine influence, the sulphur content is often high. Eocene to Middle Miocene brown coal (10–13 MJ/kg, 25–30% ash, 2.5–3.5% S) is mainly mined underground (total production in 2003 was 4.8 Mt), whereas Upper Miocene lignite (*c.* 45% $H_2O$, 6–8 MJ/kg, 15–25% ash, 0.6–1.9% S) is mainly produced from large open-cast pits. The latter account for about 5% of the world's lignite production.

An Eocene transgression in the Hungarian Palaeogene Basin resulted in the deposition of upper Lutetian coal seams, several metres thick (Oroszlány, Tatabánya, Dorog (H); Vörös 1989). Production in 2003 was 2.3 Mt. A subsequent Late Oligocene transgression resulted in coal formation along the eastern margin of the Pannonian Basin. The strongly deformed seams, up to 30 m thick, have been mined in Slovenia and Croatia for more than 200 years. Present mining activity is limited to the Trbovlje region (SLO). Production in 2004 was 0.6 Mt of hard brown coal.

Early Miocene (Ottnangian) coal in the Brennberg area (H), was excavated mainly in the early twentieth century. Up to 90 m thick seams, filling small isolated (half-)grabens, were mined until 2004 in the Köflach-Voitsberg district (A) (Steininger 1998). Currently, Ottnangian coal (several metres thick) is exploited in the NE Pannonian Basin (Borsod, Nógrád (H), Modrý Kamen (SK)). Production in 2003 was 1.8 Mt.

Middle Miocene brown coal, related to Badenian rises in sea level, is found in Hungary (Várpalota, Herend, Hidas) and Austria (Tauchen, Wies), but is no longer mined. Oil shale occurs together with coal in the Várpalota area (Solti 1980).

Late Miocene lignite seams formed almost everywhere in the shallow lacustrine, delta plain, fluvial plain environments, which became increasingly widespread as Lake Pannon was filled during the Late Miocene (e.g. Magyar *et al.* 1999). Economically the most important deposits are the paralic coals along the north (Visonta, Bükkábrány (H)) and southern margins of former Lake Pannon. The latter include the Kreka (BiH), Kolubara and Kostolac deposits (SRB; Ercegovac *et al.* 2006). Annual production in Visonta and Bükkábrány (east of Budapest) is 8.6 Mt (2003). In Kreka (Tuzla) four lignite seams, each 12–20 m thick, occur in two NW–SE trending synclines. Pre-war (i.e. pre-1992) production was 5.7 Mt of high-quality lignite (9.1–11.5 MJ/kg, 30–50% $H_2O$, 10–25% ash, *c.* 0.5% S). In Kolubara a single seam (up to 50 m thick) is mined, whereas three seams, each up to 17 m thick, are present in the Kostolac district. A total of 32.8 Mt of lignite were produced in 2003 in Kolubara and Kostolac (near Belgrade). In addition to lignite, diatomite, kaolinite and glass sand are also exploited in the Kolubara area. Natural outcrops of these lignites have been related to Balkan endemic nephropathy (BEN), an irreversible kidney disease (Finkelman *et al.* 2002).

Late Miocene lignite also occurs within the Vienna Basin. Coal in Zillingdorf (A) is no longer mined, but lignite in the North Vienna Basin (45% $H_2O$, 9.3 MJ/kg, 7–22% ash, 2.9% S) supports limited underground mining (Hodonín (CZ); Gbely (SK); 0.3 Mt). Late Miocene Torony lignite (H) located at the western margin of the Pannonian Basin constitutes a major reserve for the future.

Volcanic craters and maar structures evolved in the Pannonian Basin (NW Hungary) as a result of Pliocene and Quaternary volcanic activity. Some of these contain up to 40 m of oil shale (e.g. Pula, Gérce, Varkeszo, Egyházaskeszö). The oil shale was formed by *Botryococcus* algae and is therefore termed alginite. Alginite is sold as fertilizer or blended with bentonite to yield a high-quality Fuller's earth (Solti 1985).

The **Messel Basin** (D) is located south of Frankfurt. It formed as a result of a volcanic eruption when basaltic magma, at *c.* 1000°C, came into contact with groundwater. The resulting maar structure was infilled with Eocene organic-rich sediments. Oil shale and lignite were operated by the Messel Mineraloel and Paraffin Works. Some smaller maars, also with organic-matter-rich deposits, evolved in the nearby surroundings. The Messel oil shale is well-known for the numerous fossils found in the open pit. Due to its wealth in insects and mammals this site has obtained the status of a UNESCO World Cultural Heritage Site.

*Quaternary*

Sedimentological and geomorphological processes effective under cold glacial and warm interglacial/post-glacial climatic conditions modified the landscape in the Alpine and extra-Alpine regions. Alluvial, fluvial and aeolian depositional environments developed across Central Europe while the North Sea and the Baltic Sea shaped the northern coastline of NW and Central Europe. Uplift in the Alps and alkaline extrusive magmatic activity in the Eifel region (D) are the only evidence for endogeneous geological processes during the Quaternary. The volcanic activity during the Allerød stage (10 000 BC) resulted in the deposition of extensive pyroclastic beds and lavas covering the Rhenohercynian basement rocks (see also Litt *et al.* 2008). These volcanogenic rocks form the basis for a flourishing quarrying industry focused on dimension stones and construction materials ('trass'). Additionally, the widespread exploitation of sand and gravel from the present-day drainage systems is used for construction purposes. However, to avoid overloading the map, these ubiquitous quarrying activities are not shown on the map (see CD inside back cover). Apart from diatomaceous earths and redeposited amber, placer and peat deposits are considered as typical of the Quaternary.

**Tin–gold–titanium and gemstone placer deposits (type: modern placers).** Alluvial and fluvial Au and Sn placer deposits formed clastic aprons around the primary deposits in the Variscan and Alpine mountain ranges (Au: Napf (CH), Rhine (D), Eder (D), Schwarza (D); Sn: Erzgebirge-Fichtelgebirge (D/CZ)). Along the River Danube there are several sand and gravel beds known for their high contents of Au (Klížská Nemá (SK)). In the Western Carpathians, alluvial Au deposits are common in regions with Au-bearing Neogene volcanic rocks (e.g. Zlatníky (SK), Magurka (SK), Zlatá Idka (SK); Hvožd'ara 1999).

Some Au placers in the Alps were already being exploited in pre-Roman times. However, none of these alluvial and fluvial heavy mineral accumulations have been the focus of long-term exploitation, even if some of these modern placers could be 'harvested' on an episodic basis due to the redeposition of Au mediated by bacterial activity.

Placers containing Ti and Nb minerals and native Au are known from sites near Staré Město (CZ) in the Lugian Zone, and sapphires were identified in stream sediments (Mochnacka *et al.* 1995). None of these localities are of more than mineralogical or historical importance.

**Diatomite deposits.** High-quality diatomite was exploited south of Hamburg near Hetendorf (D) (Benda & Paschen 1993). These diatomites are intercalated with fluvioglacial sediments of Quaternary age. For economic reasons, the last open-cast mine was closed down in 1994 with reserves of 2.5 Mt of final kieselgur still in place.

**Peat deposits.** Large areas of north Central Europe, extending from the Netherlands, Denmark and Germany into Poland as well as in the Alpine Foreland from Switzerland into Austria, are covered by various types of peatland. The widespread occurrence of mires in Central Europe could not be shown on the map (see CD inside back cover) for the sake of clarity. A more detailed treatment of climatic changes during the post-glacial era, the economic use of peat and the distribution of different mire complex types is given by Lappalainen (1996), who also provides the most recent overview of this organic resource.

As the climate became increasingly wet following the ice retreat during the Würm/Weichsel glacial period in Central Europe, swamps with different varieties of deciduous trees developed on the exposed glacial till. The wet ground, composed of decomposing vegetation and with poor drainage, was unfit for cultivation and so was cut and dried to be used for fuel. In the twentieth and twenty-first centuries, peat has been exploited on an industrial scale. Peat is used as a soil medium for gardens, although the exploitation of this raw material is criticized by environmentalists as unsustainable. Therefore, many former sites in northern Germany, the Netherlands and along the Alpine Mountain Range have been abandoned and much peat is now imported from the Baltic countries.

## *Thrust-bound and fold-related metamorphogenic deposits*

The Late Jurassic to Palaeogene history of the southern part of Central Europe is related to the successive closure of oceanic basins in the Tethyan domain (Meliata–Vardar Ocean; Alpine Tethys) and continental collision between Africa and Eurasia (Schmid *et al.* 2004; Scheck-Wenderoth *et al.* 2008). Subduction and continental collision induced several stages of deformation, nappe stacking and metamorphism. Obduction of ophiolite complexes played a major role in the Dinarides. Synorogenic magmatism is generally of subordinate importance.

The Oligocene to Miocene (Late Alpine) evolution of the Alps was controlled by sinistral wrenching along ENE-trending faults within the Eastern Alps and the subsequent eastward lateral escape of crustal wedges towards the Pannonian realm (Ratschbacher *et al.* 1991; see also Froitzheim *et al.* 2008). Orogen-parallel extension and tectonic denudation of metamorphic core complexes (Tauern and Rechnitz windows), with exhumation rates up to several millimetres per year, resulted from this lateral extrusion (Neubauer *et al.* 1999).

In the Eastern Alps metamorphism in deeper structural units and the transition of the tectonic style from compression to extension were important for the generation and migration of fluids. Two groups of mineralizing fluids have been recognized within these syn- to late-orogenic regimes (Pohl 1993; Prochaska 1993; Pohl & Belocky 1994). (1) Deposits which were formed immediately following Alpine events in the Cretaceous (e.g. Cu-veins at Mitterberg (A), talc at Rabenwald (A)) were produced at high pressures by metamorphic fluids of very high salinity. These fluids were formed by the devolatilization of subducted South Penninic rocks. (2) In contrast, the deposits that formed after the Alpine events in the Palaeogene originated at relatively low pressures from $CO_2$-rich fluids of low to moderate salinities (e.g. Fe-deposits at Hüttenberg-Waldenstein (A), Au at Gastein (A), Sb at Schlaining (A)). Isotopic data indicate a deep crustal or even mantle source for $CO_2$, while the water may have mixed sources (both surficial and metamorphic). Tectonic control of these Oligo-Miocene mineralizations was exerted by transtensional faulting, which exposed hot metamorphic rocks to fluid convection along brittle structures. These deposits conform best to the model of metamorphogenic metallogenesis by retrograde leaching.

### *Polymetallic copper deposits*

Alpine-age polymetallic Cu deposits occur mainly in the Greywacke Zone of the Eastern Alps, but may also be found also in the Western Alps. In the Palaeozoic series of the Greywacke Zone (e.g. Mitterberg, Kitzbühel (A)), several vein-type Cu-mineralizations with Ni, Co and Au are found. The most prominent example of these mineralizations is the abandoned Cu mine of Mitterberg, where mining began during the Bronze Age. There is no unanimous opinion about the age and nature of the mineralizations and age data are rarely available. At Mitterberg a U–Pb age of $90 \pm 5$ Ma was reported from a cogenetic uraninite (Petrascheck 1978).

The Promise Pb–Zn mine (I) is located in the La Thuile Valley, in the Aosta Valley. Hydrothermal quartz veins and some concordant lenses, up to 2 m thick, in Carboniferous metasediments of the Gran San Bernardo Formation (schists, metapelites, sandstones) have been worked for base metals. The most important ore minerals are sphalerite and galena, with subordinate pyrite, arsenopyrite, pyrrhotite, chalcopyrite and rare tetrahedrite. Dessau (1936) concluded that the epigenetic Promise deposit was formed during the final stage of Alpine metamorphism.

*Thrust-bound talc–nephrite–asbestos–leucophyllite deposits in (ultra)basic igneous and carbonate rocks*

Asbestos deposits in the Alps are related to obducted ophiolite complexes. The asbestos deposit at Termignon (F) is related to Jurassic/Cretaceous ophiolites (Bouladon 1989). The largest asbestos mine in Europe is situated near Balangero (I), NW of Torino (Peretti 1966; Prete 1995). Here, zones rich in asbestos were discovered in a strongly deformed serpentinite belonging to the Lanzo Ultramafic Massif in the Jurassic-age ophiolites of the Piedmont Basin. The highest concentration of asbestos occurs along a major shear-zone striking east–west, and dipping *c.* 45° towards the north. This shear zone, which is *c.* 250 m wide, has been traced along strike for more than one kilometre. The maximum asbestos content is 6 vol%. It is thought that the asbestos evolved from the hydrothermal remobilization of elements from the serpentinite in the wall rock. The true nature of the fluids, however, is still not known, but the timing of emplacement is without doubt synkinematic with the main phases of Alpine deformation. Asbestos mining began in 1918 with the maximum output after World War II. During that time more than 150 000 t of asbestos were produced annually. In 1991, the mine was forced to close, not because of exhaustion of the deposits, but as a consequence of the awareness of the dangers of asbestos fibres to health.

Several chrysotile deposits in the Gemericum near Dobšiná, Paňovce, Jaklovce, Jasov, and Kalinovo (SK) are hosted by Lower Triassic lherzolite–harzburgites and peridotites (Kamenický 1957; Zlocha & Hovorka 1971). These were formed during Jurassic to Cretaceous times.

The largest asbestos deposit in the Dinarides is located in the Ozren Peridotite Massif near Bosanko Petrovo Selo (BiH) with 40 Mt of ore (2.5 wt% asbestos fibre). Here, the asbestos is concentrated in veins and stringers.

Talc deposits are present on the north flanks of the Ozren Mountain, and mined at Mušići and Žarkovac (BiH). A large talc zone several hundred to one thousand metres in length and several hundred metres in width, is intercalated with talc-bearing, silicified and carbonitized serpentinites. Talc is accompanied by 30–40 vol% breunnerite (5–7 wt% FeO). In addition to breunnerite, the talc ore body also contains subordinate siderite, chlorite (5%), and pyrite (3–5%). The talc deposits are surrounded by magnesite–talc and quartz–magnesite rocks. The total reserves are estimated at 7 Mt of ore. Based on the proximity of granite–porphyry and syenite dykes, Pamić & Olujić (1974) proposed a hydrothermal/metasomatic origin for the talc.

Several carbonate-hosted talc deposits were formed in the Alps and the Western Carpathians during the Alpine Orogeny due to alteration by metamorphic fluids along shear and fault zones. The Rabenwald talc mine (A), located in the easternmost part of the Alps, is a big open-pit mine and the largest talc producer in Central Europe (*c.* 140 000 t per year). The **Rabenwald talc deposit** is located in metamorphic rocks of the Lower Austro-Alpine Nappe system (Grobgneis complex) and is linked to a distinct shear-zone (Fig. 21.22). A strongly altered rock (leucophyllite) typically surrounds the talc schists. The age of metamorphism of the gneissic host rocks is Variscan. Retrograde metamorphic overprinting during the Late Cretaceous is ubiquitous. Leucophyllitization and talc formation are contemporaneous with this Cretaceous-age metamorphism. The genetic model for the talc formation includes thrusting of Upper Austro-Alpine sedimentary magnesites into the underlying Lower Austro-Alpine gneisses during Cretaceous nappe stacking. Hydrothermal fluids produced during the Alpine tectonometamorphic event mobilized Si from the adjacent host rocks during leucophyllitization and the magnesite reacted in the shear zone with the Si component of the fluid. Mg was only locally transported in the fault (Prochaska 1984).

Another cluster of talc deposits can be found in the Greywacke Zone of the Eastern Alps. The most important, the **Lassing talc deposit** (A), ceased production in July 1998 following a tragic mine collapse. The talc deposit is situated in the Carboniferous (Veitsch Nappe) of the Greywacke Zone along the northern flank of an east–west striking anticline. The deposit is bordered to the north and south by fault zones. Talc occurs only in dolomitic protoliths in the intensely deformed block between these two fault zones. No talc formation occurred in the undeformed carbonates. Fractures in the fault zone acted as channels for Si-bearing hydrothermal fluids, which reacted with the dolomitic component of the carbonate rocks to form talc. Talc formation includes the removal of $Ca^{2+}$ and thus only newly formed talc and residual (but recrystallized) dolomite can be found in the talc-bearing area. Tectonic movement during talc formation compensated for the drastic decrease in volume as a consequence of the total removal of calcite. Talc formation ceased with the

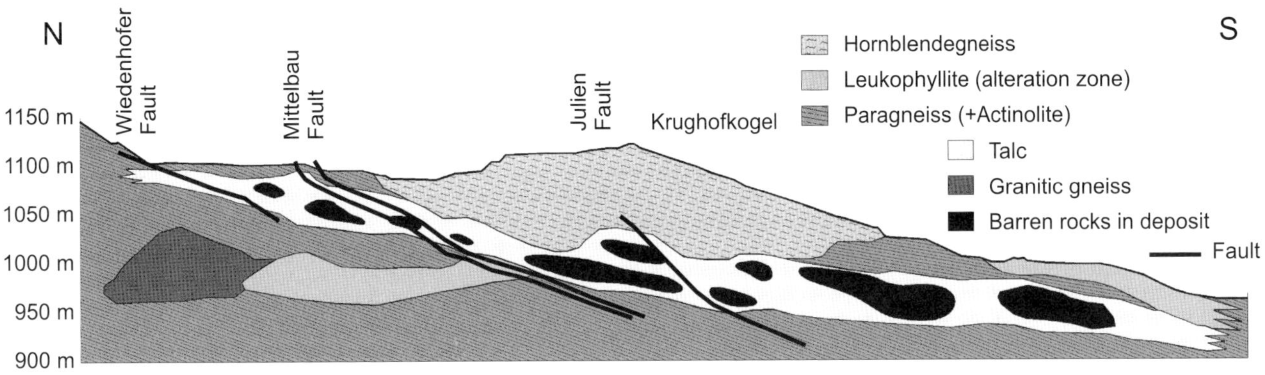


**Fig. 21.22.** Schematic cross-section through the Rabenwald talc deposit (A).

end of hydrothermal activity and Si supply; dolomite was not completely consumed by the reaction. Continuous availability of $H_2O$ and the removal of $CO_2$ from the system along fractures are basic requirements for talc formation of this type (Prochaska 1989). Annual production before the mine disaster was 35 000 t. Reserves were estimated at 1 Mt.

In the Western Alps nephrite and talc were mined at Scortaseo (CH) in a 'Schuppenzone' partly assigned to the Upper Penninic Margna Nappe (Jaffé 1986). The mineralization here is located within dolomitic marbles or along the contact between the marble and muscovite–chlorite gneisses. Iron- and Al-free grammatite nephrite formed together with the talc as a result of the metasomatism of marble. The fluids responsible for this metasomatism are supposed to be genetically related to the nearby Malenco serpentinite. While the talc was used as a filler in the nearby Italian paper industry, the nephrite was, in places, of sufficient quality to be used in the jewellery industry.

In the Carpathians numerous talc deposits are bound to magnesite deposits, mainly in the western part of the 'magnesite belt' of the Gemericum (see section on deposits related to the post-Variscan unconformity). The parent rocks of the magnesite–talc deposits were Lower Palaeozoic (Gemerská Poloma (SK)) and Carboniferous (Hnúšt'a area (SK)) calcareous rocks. Small talc occurrences along shear zones are spatially related to the basic and ultrabasic rocks at Hačava and Muráňska Dlhá Lúka (SK). The timing of mineralization and the origin of the fluids responsible for the formation of talc are still a matter of speculation. Despite all of these uncertainties, textural and mineralogical data suggest that there was a relationship with a metamorphic event (termed M-2) of Alpine age (Radvanec *et al.* 2004*b*). The reserves of the Gemerská Poloma deposits (SK) comprise 29 Mt of high-quality talc (Tréger & Baláž 2001).

A hydrothermal quartz-mica product (with similar industrial applications as talc or kaolin) called 'leucophyllite' has been mined in Austria since 1850. Today it is produced in two mines at Aspang (A) and Weißkirchen (A) under various brands (*Leukophyllit, Kaolin, Weißerde*, etc.). This non-metallic commodity is derived from alteration zones associated with shear belts intersecting the Austro-Alpine metamorphic terranes (Prochaska *et al.* 1992). Generally the term 'leucophyllite' is used for white, micaceous, hydrothermally altered phyllonitic rocks (in most cases gneisses), which mainly consist of quartz, muscovite, variable amounts of Mg-chlorite and subordinate kyanite, apatite, zircon, rutile and ilmenite. Leucophyllite in the Eastern Alps resulted from compressional deformation, accompanying metamorphism and subsequent exhumation during the Cretaceous. The mineralization is the result of a chemical wall rock alteration caused by hydrothermal fluids at temperatures of between 400 and 500°C. The fluids ascended along deep-seated shear zones, most of which are found in the eastern parts of the Eastern Alps. Heavy $\partial$D-values indicate the influence of seawater (or formation water similar to seawater) expelled from deeper tectonic units after nappe stacking. The K–Ar cooling ages of the micas in the phyllonites are identical to the regional cooling ages, and Ar/Ar ages (*c.* 90 Ma) indicate complete recrystallization and rejuvenation of the mineral assemblage in these shear zones.

*Quartz vein-type deposits (Alpine-type quartz veins)*

Deposits of vein quartz, which has a metamorphic/hydrothermal origin, are worked mainly for the high-quality quartz glass industry. Several sites occur in the Western Carpathians at Švedlár, Stará Voda, Závadka, Smolník, Budiná, Mýtna and Grapa (SK). Despite their proximity to Variscan-age vein mineralization, the quartz veins are genetically related to the strike-slip movements along fault zones of Alpine age. Total reserves are 430 kt in the Gemericum and 120 kt in the Veporicum (Grecula 1971).

*Gold deposits (Alpine-type/mesothermal gold veins)*

Gold mineralization at Uderiná (SK), Mladzovo (SK) and České Brezovo (SK) is closely associated with Alpine-age shear zones along the southern margin of the Veporicum. The mineral association comprises quartz, carbonates, pyrite, arsenopyrite, pyrrhotite, galena, sphalerite, chalcopyrite, tetrahedrite, bornite and native Au. The metamorphogenic fluids may have been derived from the deeper parts of the crystalline complex of the Veporicum (Mat'o & Mat'ová 1993).

Mesothermal Au veins in the Eastern (Tauern District; Paar 1997) and Western Alps (Monte Rosa District; Curti 1987; Pettke *et al.* 1999) have been worked since Roman times. The Au veins formed during rapid Oligo-Miocene exhumation of high-grade metamorphic domes and, thus, are classified as metamorphogenic deposits. Vein mineralization formed from fluids in a hydrothermal convection system along deep-seated structures during retrograde leaching of favourable host rocks such as metabasites. Small-scale Au–As mineralizations also occur in the Eastern Alps east of the Tauern Window (e.g. Kliening (A)).

*Gold veins of the Tauern District (A).* In the Tauern area, Oligo-Miocene uplift and decompression resulted in the development of a series of NE–SW to NNE–SSW trending faults and fractures. The fractures facilitated the circulation of metamorphogenic residual fluids, which were mixed with supergene-derived waters, and formed the mineralization.

Epigenetic Au (and Ag) mineralization is confined to some districts within the Tauern area. The largest accumulations occur in the Gastein and Rauris valleys (A), where Au veins cut through Variscan granitoids and even intersect the overlying Permo-Mesozoic carbonate-bearing metasediments (Paar 1997). Structurally controlled Au mineralization has also been mined in the Fusch area (A) and the Rotgülden (A) district in an area underlain by metasedimentary rocks (Paar 1997). Bonanza-grade Au occurs in Mesozoic serpentinites and Upper Precambrian magmatites. The mineralized structures in the Gastein and Rauris districts can be traced up to 7 km along strike and extend more than 1000 m along dip. Pinch-and-swell structures are quite common. The most economically workable ore can be found in the 'swells', which are very irregularly shaped, show very steeply plunging axes and vary considerably in size. Hypogene wall rock alteration is moderate and can be recognized only over a distance of little more than one metre on both sides of the veins. K–Ar age dating on sericite samples taken from the zone of wall rock alteration at Siglitz (Gastein/Rauris district) yielded a crystallization age of 27 Ma. Using fluid inclusion data combined with arsenopyrite geothermometry, a formation temperature of between 370 and 420°C and between 200 and 260°C was deduced for the Au-rich and Ag-rich mineral associations, respectively. The ore-forming fluids contained abundant $CO_2$ and salinities in the range of 2 to 11 wt% $NaCl_{equ}$.

*Gold veins of the Monte Rosa District (I, CH).* Numerous epigenetic Au-bearing quartz veins are scattered in the Monte Rosa District, extending over 140 km between Maglioggio-Alfenza Crodo (I) and Brusson (I) (Curti 1987). Here, the Au mineralization is mainly associated with extensional faults and fractures that cross-cut the wall rock. The vein mineralization consists of quartz, carbonate minerals, muscovite and sulphides such as pyrite, arsenopyrite and minor amounts of sphalerite, galena, pyrrhotite, chalcopyrite, tetrahedrite and bismuthinite. Gold occurs as 'invisible Au' forming a solid solution in pyrite and arsenopyrite and as native Au included in quartz. The formation temperatures are in the range 240 to 300°C at Brusson. Elsewhere in the district they may be up to 300–350°C and, locally, as much as 400–450°C. Based on fluid inclusion data, the metalliferous solutions had $CO_2$ contents of between 6 and 11 mol% $CO_2$ and salinities in the range 2–10 wt% $NaCl_{equ}$. Dependent on the rate of uplift of the Western Alps, ore formation continued over a period of at least 20 million years from 31 to 10 Ma (Pettke *et al.* 1999).

Late Alpine Au mineralization has been reported by Bächtiger *et al.* (1972) from the root zone of the Helvetic nappes at Calanda (eastern Switzerland), where native Au was concentrated together with scheelite, fluorite and arsenopyrite in calcitic gangue. The veins at Calanda (CH) cut through Lower Dogger-age shales. Gold veins in the Mont Blanc Massif formed during the Late Miocene (*c.* 10 Ma) at Mont Chemin (CH) and were discovered only recently (Marshall *et al.* 1998). The number of occurrences of Au in the French Alps is small. Gold is found in quartz veins associated with Alpine metamorphism ('Alpine fissures') together with epidote, zoisite and prehnite (Bouladon 1989). The best-known example is at La Gardette (F).

Although it is a polymetallic sulphide mineralization, the Lengenbach/Binntal mineralization (CH) is herein discussed in terms of Alpine element mobilization. It has been exploited for mineral collections or to investigate certain aspects of Pb–Cu–Ag–As–Tl sulphosalts, almost exclusively encountered in this mineralization (Cannon 2000; Baumgärtl & Burow 2005). The protore mineralization consisted of pyrite, galena and sphalerite which were deposited in Triassic dolomites. Sulphosalts containing predominantly As and Tl formed in a closed system with temperatures of up to 450°C during regional metamorphism at around $18.5 \pm 0.5$ Ma. Thus, the minerals underwent significant changes and the complexity of the mineral assemblage may be used to measure the degree of Alpine remobilization (Hofmann 1994). The element budget may, however, still reflect the parent material and is thus used for 'minero-stratigraphic correlations' between deposits of the Alpine and extra-Alpine realms.

*Iron deposits*

Numerous vein mineralizations are found in polymetamorphic Austro-Alpine units to the east of the Tauern Window in the Hüttenberg-Waldenstein (A) Iron Ore District (Ebner *et al.* 2000). They formed from deep-seated (metamorphogenic?) fluids, possibly being expelled from overthrust tectonic units, which mixed with supergene, meteoric or marine fluids that were incorporated into shallow hydrothermal systems along faults operating during Cenozoic escape tectonics. The Hüttenberg-Waldenstein District comprises a number of siderite mineralizations within calcite marble. The largest is the Hüttenberg Deposit which was worked from Roman times until 1979 (Clar & Meixner 1981). A few mineralizations are associated with hematite. Currently the Waldenstein Deposit is producing specularite for industrial mineral applications.

The geological setting of all of the deposits in the Hüttenberg-Waldenstein Iron Ore District is very similar. The dominant lithologies present include muscovite–garnet schists, biotite gneisses, calc-silicate schists, and quartzites with interbedded bands and lenses of amphibolite and possibly Devonian-age calcitic marble. Several phases of ductile deformation and metamorphism have been distinguished in the area. The youngest (Cretaceous) metamorphic event is best developed in the deeper parts of country-rocks in the Hüttenberg-Waldenstein District.

The Hüttenberg-Waldenstein District is spatially and genetically associated with a transtensional fault system, which formed during a late stage of the Alpine Orogeny. The NNW–SSE trending Lavanttal Fault Zone occurs *c.* 5 km west of Waldenstein (Prochaska *et al.* 1995). This zone, which is marked by several Miocene-age basins, is downthrown to the west and has a dextral component of movement. To the west, the Hüttenberg Deposit is associated with a comparable fault system, which was initiated in the Palaeogene. Minor movements along these faults still occur, as demonstrated by the local earthquakes and the presence of hot springs.

It is generally accepted that the mineralizations in the Hüttenberg-Waldenstein District formed during a single metallogenetic event. All of the mineralizations are surrounded by a wide halo caused by hydrothermal wall rock alteration and are younger than metamorphism and orogenic deformation of the country-rocks. These observations, together with data from microthermometry, fluid analysis and isotope age determinations, indicate that the mineralizations are the result of epigenetic, hydrothermal metasomatism of the hosting calcitic marbles.

During the Cretaceous the crystalline country-rocks in the Hüttenberg-Waldenstein District were subjected to regional metamorphism attaining amphibolite- to eclogite-grades at deep crustal levels (metamorphic $\partial D$ signature in the unaltered host rocks of the deposits). During the Tertiary, transtensional faulting and uplift of metamorphic domes resulted in positive temperature anomalies at higher crustal levels. This rapid uplift induced large hydrothermal convection cells where the faults acted as pathways for the percolating fluids. Fluids of deep-seated origin rose through the cooler rocks at the onset of faulting (Middle Eocene) thereby precipitating early ilmenite and magnetite under more reducing conditions, and later hematite and chlorite during the main phase of ore formation.

The fluid chemistry in the Hüttenberg-Waldenstein Iron Ore District (A) is heterogeneous suggesting an influence from seawater (i.e. decrease of $\delta^{18}O$ values and the relatively heavy $\delta D$ values) and/or meteoric or river water (i.e. decrease of Br with respect to Na and Cl compared to seawater). Thus the hydrothermal regime in the Hüttenberg-Waldenstein District was evidently dominated by surface fluids in a shallow crustal environment depending on the corresponding morphologic situation. Hematite formation at Waldenstein probably took place at a depth of only *c.* 700 m and at temperatures of 300°C.

*Antimony deposits*

The epithermal stibnite deposit at Schlaining (A) was one of the largest Sb mines in Europe. It is located in the Penninic Rechnitz Window at the eastern end of the Alps. The deposit formed during rapid Miocene uplift, which resulted in very high surface heat flow and led to the development of a hydrothermal convection system. The mineralizations were precipitated from aqueous solutions of low salinity at shallow depths and at temperatures of between 210 and 280°C (Belocky *et al.* 1991). The Sb was leached either from a deep (Penninic?) source or from Lower Austro-Alpine rocks (Grum *et al.* 1992). Any relation to magmatic activity can be ruled out. Antimony concentration may most plausibly be accounted for by a retrograde metamorphic process (Grum *et al.* 1992).

## Collision (granite)-related deposits

Collision-related granites formed in the Western Carpathians in Mesozoic times and in the Alps/Dinarides in Palaeogene times. Following the closure of the Meliata Ocean, continental collision resulted in igneous intrusion in the inner zones of the Carpathians during Late Jurassic and Cretaceous times (Plašienka *et al.* 1997; Hraško *et al.* 1999; Poller *et al.* 2001). Crustal thickening together with heat produced by the mantle, triggered partial melting and was responsible for some of the granites generated in the lower crust. The granites were intruded into Upper Palaeozoic metapelites and metasandstones. Together with crustal shortening in the Veporicum, the Cretaceous Rochovce Granite was emplaced along a shear zone associated with W–Mo mineralization.

Within the Alps, granitoids including tonalities were intruded during the Oligocene along the Periadriatic Line, which separates the Western and Eastern Alps from the Southern Alps. This magmatic belt continues along the Sava-Vardar Zone into the Dinarides, where the intrusion of granitoids commenced slightly earlier. Marked dextral strike-slip faulting, caused by the Apulian indentation occurred contemporaneously along the Periadriatic-Sava-Vardar Zone (Pamić & Palinkaš 2000; Palinkaš & Pamić 2001). In the Dinarides, Eocene syncollisional granites were followed by granitoids, shoshonites and, to a lesser extent, high-K calc-alkaline volcanic rocks that formed between 30.4 and 28.5 Ma (Pamić 2002). Magmatic activity post-dated the subduction of oceanic crust and was interpreted as a result of slab break-off (Blankenburg & Davis 1995). The intrusives in the Dinarides belong to the S-type granites transitional into S-I-type granites (Pamić & Balen 2001). The intrusion of monzogranites through quartz-diorites was post-dated by the formation of greisen, pegmatites and aplites abundant in Be, B, Li, F, Mo, W, Sn, Bi, Cs, Rb, U and Th, and low in P.

*Tungsten–molybdenum–niobium–tantalum–lead and fluorite vein and greisen deposits*

The Mo–W mineralization in the Rochovce Granite (SK), a member of the magnetite series, was encountered by drilling at a depth of about 700 m. This mineralization consists of two events. The stockwork Mo mineralization attains its greatest thickness (230–380 m) in the central part with an average grade of 0.1 to 0.7% Mo. The minerals of economic interest include molybdenite, scheelite and, to a lesser extent, wolframite. The W-zone overlies the Mo-zone and contains scheelite and to a lesser extent wolframite, which is confined to thin quartz–carbonate–pyrite veinlets. A characteristic feature of the W-zone is the presence of pyrite disseminated in the W stockwork (Határ 1989).

The greisenization belt in the granites of the Motajica Mountains (BiH) is 2 km long and several hundreds of metres wide. Greisenization affected different types of igneous rocks ranging from granite to leucogranite and aplitic granite. A wide spectrum of pneumatolitic metasomatism is also recognized in the area, including intensive silicification, muscovitization and the sericitization of feldspars. Greisen zones generally have a simple mineralogy with quartz, muscovite and sericite being the major minerals, while zircon, apatite, microcline and biotite are rare. The only ore minerals of interest which are present are wolframite, scheelite, fluorite and molybdenite. Hydrothermal ore mineralization also extends into the surrounding metasediments where veins with galena, tetrahedrite, hematite, cerussite, covellite and goethite occur.

*Polymetallic feldspar quartz pegmatite and greisen deposits*

The pegmatites and aplites of the Motajica Mountains (BiH) were classified on the basis of their geochemical signature and geological setting as LCT (i.e. Li, Ce, Ta) pegmatites using the classification scheme of Cerný (1991). The pegmatites pertaining to the LCT family are marked by the presence of lithophile elements such as Be, B, Li, F, Mo, W, Sn, Bi, Cs, Rb, Sr, U and Th. They occur in a low-pressure metamorphic environment classified as Abukuma-type, and were emplaced within granites. The major mineral present is quartz, with lesser microcline, orthoclase, albite, muscovite, beryl and tourmaline. Beryl varies greatly in terms of crystal size and quantity. Locally, vein mineralization is composed of between 10 and 50% beryl and, hence, termed beryllites. Accessory minerals include scheelite, pyrrhotite, zircon, apatite, magnetite, ilmenite, titanite, molybdenite, epidote, garnet and rutile. Minerals of economic value are feldspar and quartz (Jurković 2004).

The granitoid complex in the Cer Mountains in western Serbia covers 70 km$^2$. The pegmatite deposits are located within biotite- and biotite–amphibolite granodiorites emplaced at 22 to 33 Ma (Knežević *et al.* 1994). Erosion exposed the pegmatites and greisen zones of the granitoid complex. The mineral content of the pegmatites is rather monotonous containing quartz, microcline, albite, and plagioclase, with rarer muscovite, biotite, beryl, tourmaline, zircon and apatite. Accessory minerals include epidote, cassiterite, scheelite, columbite, rutile, uraninite, monazite, sphalerite and chalcopyrite. The Li content (45 ppm) is comparatively low for highly differentiated granitoids. Greisen zones of the Cer Mountains are categorized as quartz–muscovite and quartz–muscovite–tourmaline–fluorite types. The main ore minerals are cassiterite, tantalo-niobates, bismuthinite, fluorite and scheelite (Janković 1990).

*Polymetallic lead–zinc–copper deposits*

Mesothermal polymetallic Pb–Zn deposits related to Oligocene magmatic activity occur in the Srebrenica area east of Sarajevo (BiH). They are found in Lower and Middle Carboniferous metasediments and limestones, surrounded by Triassic, Jurassic and Cretaceous strata and large amounts of dacitic to andesitic tuffs and propylitized dacites. The ore-bearing zone is several kilometres long. The high-grade ore occurs in fault breccias and forms open-space fillings in veins. Replacement ores and impregnation types are less frequent. The thickness of the veins and ore stringers ranges from centimetres to decametres (maximum 20–25 m). Based on the mineral assemblages present, different types of ore bodies can be distinguished including: (1) tourmaline veins and stockworks; (2) quartz–pyrrhotite–chalcopyrite veins; (3) quartz–pyrrhotite–galena–sphalerite veins with accessory stibnite, cubanite, proustite etc.; (4) siderite–marcasite–galena–sphalerite veins; (5) quartz–stibnite veins; and (6) pyrite–marcasite–loellingite veins. The polymetallic ore averages 6.2% Pb, 8% Zn, 80–100 g/t Ag, 1 g/t Au, 0.01–0.03% Cd, 0.04–0.1% Cu, 0.06–0.46% As, and 0.5–0.7% Sb. Production during the period between World Wars I and II reached 400 000 t ore. The latest calculation suggested reserves of 15 Mt (Ramović *et al.* 1979). The history of mining activity in this district shows that there were several epochs during which these veins were operated by Illyrian, Roman, Slavic, Saxon, Turkish and Austrian miners. With the disbanding of the former Republic of Yugoslavia, mining has ceased in the Srebrenica mining distict.

*Iron–copper–arsenic–antimony–mercury–gold skarn and vein deposits*

Some subeconomic Fe–Cu skarns and As-, Sb-, Hg-, Au-mineralizations in the Eastern Alps are linked to Oligocene igneous activity along the Periadriatic Line. For many of these mineralizations located within polymetamorphic complexes south of the Tauern Window (e.g. Siflitz (A), Stockenboi (A), Rabant (A)) the heat flow created by Oligocene intrusions is considered to have been the driving force.

*Antimony replacement and vein-type deposits*

Antimony deposits in the Boranja Mountains in western Serbia (SRB) are hosted by granitoids of Early Oligocene (33.7–29.6 Ma) age (Pamić 2002). Carboniferous, Permian and Triassic successions with granodiorite intrusions, dacitic–andesitic volcanic rocks and their equivalent pyroclastics, provide the lithological setting in the Sb-bearing area of Podrinje (SRB). The Sb deposits are concentrated along the outer edge of the contact aureole of the granodioritic massif. Where the granitoids came into contact with calcareous rocks, magnetite–chalcopyrite skarns developed. In more distal locations, galena–sphalerite mineralizations formed. These are surrounded by a wide zone of stibnite deposits. Antimony contents attain a maximum where silicified Upper Carboniferous limestones are subjacent to impermeable Upper Carboniferous schists thus favouring the formation of replacement ore bodies. Vein-type deposits with well-developed salbands and fault breccias, whose fragments are cemented by stibnite and calcite, were also worked for Sb. These deposits are among the most significant Sb producers in Europe. The outermost zone of this granite-related metallogenic province contains fluorite. The largest deposits of these mesothermal Sb mineralizations are found at Zajača, Stolice (Fig. 21.23) and Krupanj. Here, the mineral associations are rather monotonous, containing stibnite, some Sb oxides, galena, sphalerite, pyrite, quartz and calcite. The Stolice ore contains 30.8% Sb, 0.13% As, 0.005% Pb, 0.007% Cu and 0.001% Zn (Janković 1990).

In the Carpathians, Hg deposits of Alpine age were found in the Spiš-Gemer Mountains at Rákoš, Nižná Slaná-Svätá Tojica, Čuntava and Zenderling (SK). Irregularly shaped veinlets, vugs and pockets are filled with siderite, ankerite, pyrite, hematite, tetrahedrite, schwatzite, chalcopyrite and barite. The main mineralization, with cinnabar and native Hg, was superimposed on the aforementioned mineralization (Drnzíková & Mandáková, in Slávik 1967). The overal Hg content averages *c.* 0.2%.

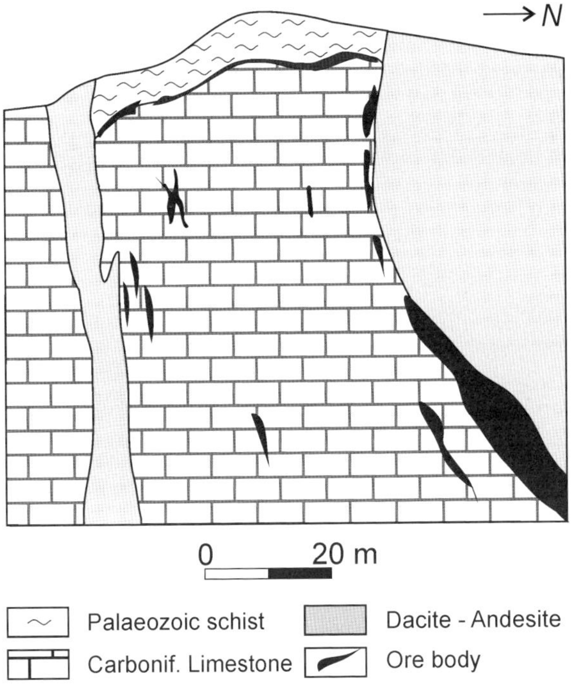


**Fig. 21.23.** Geological cross-section of the Stolice Sb deposit (SRB) (after Janković 1967).

## *Late Alpine supergene and hypogene deposits related to the Subhercynian and Laramide unconformity*

In the extra-Alpine realm, Late Cretaceous to Palaeogene (Subhercynian and Laramide) deformations led to widespread faulting and uplift of basement blocks. (Sub)tropical climates during the Late Mesozoic and Cenozoic resulted in pervasive chemical weathering and extensive erosion which affected both, the older Variscan basement rocks and the Permian to Cenozoic cover.

Only a few deposits contain minerals suitable for radiometric dating, and reliable age data exist only for some epigenetic mineralizations in Central Europe. Methods used include U–Pb, U–Xe, and Xe/Xe dating of hydrothermal pitchblende, U–He dating of hematite, and K–Ar dating of K-bearing Mn minerals (Hofmann & Eikenberg 1991; Segev *et al.* 1991; Wernicke & Lippolt 1993, 1997*a*, *b*; Meshik *et al.* 2000). The problems involved in trying to date deposits is a major reason for using a structural element, such as an unconformity which is easily traceable in the field, as a key element for metallogenetic classification, rather than the age of mineralization. In contrast to the deposits associated with the Early Alpine unconformity, which are mostly Permo-Triassic in age, the host rocks of deposits overlying the Late Alpine unconformity are much younger (Cretaceous and Cenozoic). Hypogene deposits related to the Late Alpine unconformity are similar in composition (Ca, F, Ba, Pb, Zn, Cu, U) to their Early Alpine counterparts. In contrast, supergene deposits are of greater variety than their Early Alpine counterparts and frequently of greater size (clay, amber, silica, Ni, Cr, P, Mn, Al, Mg).

*Supergene deposits*

**Kaolinite saprolite on the Variscan basement and in Mesozoic to Cenozoic rocks.** A tropical to subtropical climate, persisting throughout Late Cretaceous and Tertiary times, caused pervasive chemical weathering on the uplifted basement blocks across Central Europe. The most conspicuous sign for supergene *in-situ* alteration is a thick regolith of kaolin, measuring locally up to several tens of metres, particularly on granitic parent material. In some areas, the quality of clays underlying Cenozoic lignite seams was improved by humic acids leaking out of the peat bogs. The humic acids decomposed labile constituents such as feldspar and lithoclasts in the underlying argillaceous rocks, thereby upgrading the quality of kaolin to such an extent that it is still exploited near Halle, Oschatz and Meißen (D) for high-quality products.

In the Westerwald mining district (D) (Rhenish Massif), numerous open-cast mining operations have targeted fluviolacustrine deposits overlying Devonian psammo-pelitic parent material. Here, the mined kaolin and kaolinitic clays are used for red- and white-firing ceramic products. In the Westerwald area Tertiary basalts, overlying the kaolinitic clays, have protected them from erosion. Open-cast operations are also active near Tirschenreuth (D) and Görlitz (D), and at Czerwona Woda (PL), Zebrzydowa (PL), Strzegom (PL) and Strzelin (PL) (Fig. 21.11). Granitic wash or reworked kaolin is exploited near Bolesławice (PL) from deltaic deposits. The kaolin belt in Moravia (SE margin of the Bohemian Massif), e.g., Znojmo (CZ) extends southwestwards across the border into Austria, where kaolin is exploited from the regolith of the Schwertberg Granite at Weinzierl-Kriechbaum (A) (Fig. 21.11).

The thicknesses of sedimentary kaolin deposits in the Carpathian Foredeep in Poland (e.g. Dąbrowa Tarnowska, Mielec, Kolbuszowa (PL)) range from several centimetres to a few metres (rarely tens of metres). Resource calculations of the Tertiary kaolin yielded 116 Mt of clay (Osika 1990).

Within the Carpathians, kaolin developed under alternating dry and humid conditions (pollen indicates an annual precipitation in the range of 500–1000 mm and an annual temperature of 16–18°C) in the northern part of the Lučenská and Ipel'ská kotlina basins (SK) and in the NW part of the Košická kotlina Basin (SK). The weathering of crystalline rocks began during the Late Cretaceous when the Veporic Block was uplifted. This uplift phase continued until the Late Miocene. The kaolinitic regolith preserved in the Lučenská kotlina Basin is more than 50 m thick (Vass & Kraus 1985). Proven reserves are 10 Mt in the Poltár deposit, 5 Mt in the Hrabovo deposit, and about 3 Mt in the Kalinovo, Mládzovo and Breznička deposits (SK) (Zuberec *et al.* 2005).

Numerous kaolin deposits are located around granitic plutons in Bosnia-Herzegovina, e.g. Brusnik, Ciganluk, Grebski potok, Kameni potok, Didovi, Filipovića Kosa and Babin grob (BiH). These deposits are autochthonous, some having a hydrothermal origin, while others may have been formed by kaolinitization of the Motajica granitoid in Neogene–Pleistocene times. The major mineral present is kaolinite and minor illite, associated with residues of quartz, orthoclase, albite, sericite, magnetite and zircon. Total reserves are estimated at 1.57 Mt.

In France, near Rochefort-Samson (F), Hostun (F) and Berbières (F), kaolin sands of Eocene age are exploited along the Alpine margin.

**Bauxite deposits on Late Alpine unconformities.** In the SW corner of Central Europe the type locality for bauxite is located at Les Baux (F). In the Dinarides bauxite developed from the Middle Triassic to the Miocene within a variety of lithologies. Ten stratigraphic horizons with bauxite deposits have been recognized (Sokač & Šinkovec 1991), including Upper Triassic (Lika region (HR)), Malm (Istria (HR), Vrsar (HR), Rovinj (HR), Hrušica (SLO), Žužemberk (SLO)), Lower Cretaceous (Dalmatia (HR)), upper Lower Cretaceous (Vlasenica (BiH)), lower Upper Cretaceous (Nikšić deposits), Senonian (Bosanska Krupa (BiH)), Lower Palaeogene (North Adriatic islands (HR)), Upper Palaeogene (Dalmatia, Obrovac (HR)), Oligocene (central and NW Slovenia (SLO)), and Miocene (Dalmatia, Sinj (HR)).

Bauxite deposits are also found in the Transdanubian Central Range in Hungary. Here, they occur in Cretaceous- to Eocene-age beds, including Halimba–Szőc (H) (Fig. 21.24), Iharkút–Nyirád (H), Sümeg (H) and Fenyőfő (H). Their formation is linked to Alpine epeirogenic phases and a peculiar karst topography which reached a mature stage at the Mesozoic–Cenozoic boundary in the region (Bárdossy 1969).

Outside of the Alpine mountains bauxite deposits are rare (e.g. Nowa Ruda) (PL). Today, bauxite covering the Vogelsberg basalt stock (D) is purely of scientific interest, although small-scale mining operations at Vogelsberg continued until 1976.

**Tripoli deposits on Late Alpine unconformities.** Tripoli (rottenstone) is often used to describe weathered and decomposed siliceous (Antonides 1998). In the present study the term 'tripoli' is used to refer to the siliceous residues produced as a result of the pervasive chemical weathering of calcareous rocks. Open-cast mining is currently practiced in the South German Basin near Neuburg/Donau (D) where the siliceous material was concentrated in pockets, cavities and shallow depressions on the Upper Jurassic denudation surface during Turonian times (Streit 1987). Kaolinite, quartz and siliceous sponge spiculae predominate in the fine-grained raw material that is used for extender, functional filler and abrasives. The annual production in 1990 stood at 100 000 t (Walther & Dill 1995). Similar deposits formed in calcareous rocks of the Middle Triassic Muschelkalk and were mined at Kraichgau/Bauland (D) until 1966.

**Iron–manganese phosphate deposits on the Variscan basement (Hunsrück and Lahn type).** The Fe–(Mn) deposits of the Hunsrück type were derived from the products of extensive chemical weathering of basalts, greywackes and shales in the Variscan basement complexes of the Rhenish Massif (Waldalgesheim (D)), the Thuringian-Franconian Massif and the Black Forest (Fig. 21.11b) (Bottke 1969). Oxide hydroxides of Al, Fe-bearing silcretes, goethite, poorly hydrated Mn oxides and manganomelan are the main components of these supergene deposits that can be subdivided into five principal types: (1) ferricretes *sensu stricto*; (2) pebble Fe ores; (3) ferruginous conglomerates and breccias (Fe–Mn cement); (4) Fe–Mn replacement ores; and (5) limonitic gossans (Dill 1985*d*). The Fe–Mn enrichments, irrespective of their host rocks, are interpreted as being remnants of hydromorphic soils of non-lateritic origin (Plio-Pleistocene). Ferruginous silcretes are considered to be the precursors of the concentrations which were exploited until 1971 at Waldalgesheim. Some are occasionally quarried as coloured clay in the foreland of the Variscan basement, south of Bayreuth, near Pegnitz (D).

Hydrothermal siderite-rich vein-type deposits can also become parent material for Hunsrück-type deposits. In this case, there is

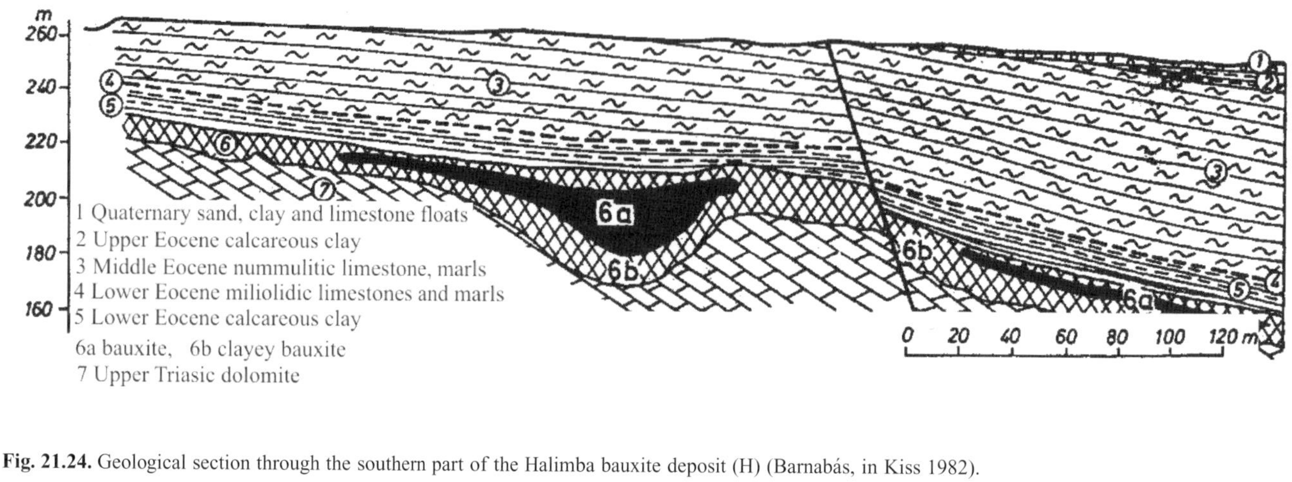


**Fig. 21.24.** Geological section through the southern part of the Halimba bauxite deposit (H) (Barnabás, in Kiss 1982).

no sharp mineralogical boundary between the supergene Fe–Mn deposits and the limonitic gossans underlain by manganiferous siderite deposits (e.g. Romanèche-Thorins (F) in the Massif Central).

Among the limonitic Fe–Mn minerals, K-bearing Mn minerals can be used for isotopic dating of ore-forming events. The Ar/Ar ages of Mn oxides are between 25 and 1 Ma, indicating intense chemical weathering during Neogene times (Hauptmann & Lippolt 2000). Formation of supergene Mn oxides may result from the combination of climatic and tectonic factors. Local uplift, exhumation, and associated fracturing of rocks provided fresh mineral surfaces for percolating meteoric fluids that acted under warm-temperate to subtropical conditions.

Vein-like deposits of Ca- and Al-sulphate-phosphates (APS) were accumulated during Tertiary times in karst pockets which developed on limestones (e.g. Lahn-Phosphorite (D)) and in clay deposits (e.g. Lohrheim Kaolin Deposit) on the Devonian rocks of the Rhenish Massif (German *et al.* 1981; Dill *et al.* 1995; Dill 2001). The phosphate production from the Lahn and Dill region in Germany amounted to some 750 000 t at the end of the twentieth century, and these deposits are the most important domestic source. The phosphorite deposits overlie the karstic surface of a Middle Devonian reef limestone (Massenkalk). The microphosphoritic ores are characterized by repeated cracking and cementation by fibrous crusts of apatite. The prevailing apatite phase of the ores is a carbonate–fluorapatite (francolite), the $CO_2$ and F contents of which average 3.2 and 1.45% respectively. With their extremely low Sr values and anomalously high iodine contents (mean value 0.044%), the Lahn phosphorites can be distinguished from marine phosphorites. There are different types of APS minerals including those dominant in gorceixite $BaAl_3(PO_4)_2(OH)_5{\cdot}H_2O$, florencite-(Ce) $CeAl_3(PO_4)_2(OH)_6$ and goyazite $SrAl_3(PO_4)_2(OH)_5{\cdot}H_2O$. Mineral production resulted from the weathering of pyritiferous parent material, which led to a lowering of the pH of the meteoric water. The Ba in gorceixite was provided by supergene alteration of barite-bearing Eifelian shales and volcanics which locally underlie the kaolinitic saprolite, whereas the rare earth elements are likely to have been derived from the Devonian keratophyres and basalts which form the direct substrate of the loam of the weathering zone.

**Manganiferous lead deposits associated with the Late Alpine unconformity.** Sandstone-hosted Pb deposits of Triassic age, with Pb carbonate as the major ore mineral (as well as some galena) were mined at Freihung (D). Their depositional environment was described in a previous section. During the Cenozoic these Pb carbonates underwent extensive supergene alteration resulting in the formation of large duricrusts which were explored in the early 1970s. Coronadite ($Pb(Mn^{2+}, Mn^{4+})_8O_{16}$), which is isostructural with hollandite and cryptomelane formed in a poorly drained swampy environment. It is a hardpan or continental manganiferous nodules that formed during the Quaternary, mainly in the environs of Weiden (D), where the primary cerussite ore mineralization came into contact with meteoric waters (Schwarzenberg 1975).

**Nickel–chromium–cobalt laterites on ultrabasic rocks.** Ultrabasic igneous rocks in the Bohemian Massif form the parent material for garnierites present at St. Egidien (D), Křemže (CZ), Szklary (PL) and Ząbkowice Śląskie (PL). Garnierite is a comprehensive term to descibe the weathering products above ultrabasic rocks, which in places is abundant in Co. Garnierite was mined until 1983 in Ząbkowice Śląskie. The garnierites developed on a Cretaceous to Palaeogene peneplain during pervasive chemical weathering under subtropical conditions. Some of these supergene Ni–(Co)–(Cr) concentrations in the Central Sudetes are underlain by ultrabasic deposits containing primary Cr minerals (e.g. Tąpadła (PL), Góra Sleża (PL)). Others developed from nickeliferous serpentinites devoid of any primary mineralization. The Mg–Ni hydrosilicate-bearing regolith with garnierite, nepouite, schuchartite, pimelite and, locally, opaline and chalcedony, belong to the New Caledonia-type mineralization which occurs in present-day (sub)tropical climates in the West Pacific area. Gemstone-quality chrysoprase was found in the Szklary deposit (PL), in the nickeliferous part of the regolith (Ostrowicki 1965).

In the Carpathians, garnierites (average thickness 10 m; 0.4 wt% Ni, 0.01 wt% Co, 0.8 wt% $Cr_2O_3$) evolved from the Late Cretaceous to the Late Neogene as a result of supergene alteration of serpentinized ultrabasic bodies at Hodkovce (SK) (Zlocha 1975). The laterites are composed of nontronite, Ni hydrosilicates, goethite, chlorite, talc and subordinate amounts of amorphic magnesite.

In the Gornje Orešje deposit (HR) in the Medvednica Mountains Ni-laterites developed from Alpine-type peridotites (Lugović & Slovenec 2004). Upper Cretaceous rudist limestones cover the Ni-lateritic crust with 0.8% Ni and provide an age constraint on the formation of the residual Ni enrichment.

A 0.3 and 2 m thick crust, abundant in Ni hydrosilicates, developed in the Ozren Massif (BiH). The residual ore contains 9–34% Fe, 1–4% MnO, 0.42–0.61% NiO and 0.05–0.15% Co. The serpentinites of the adjacent Konjuh Massif underwent pervasive weathering during the Lower Cretaceous. Subsequently, the Ni laterites were redeposited, taking on oolitic and pseudo-oolitic textures. The Brazik-Tadići (BiH) Ni–Co ore body is lens-shaped and up to 12 m thick with 0.1 wt% Co and 0.5 wt% Ni. It is a Cretaceous-age Ni–Co-bearing lateritic encrustation which was redeposited during the Cenozoic.

**Amorphous magnesite deposits.** Amorphous magnesite is found in Central Europe in many areas and results from the supergene alteration of ultramafic rocks. The minor Kraubath deposit (A) in the Eastern Alps, related to the Kraubath Ultramafic Complex (SW Leoben), was used as a reference locality for cryptocrystalline magnesite related to ultramafics (Kraubath type) (Redlich 1909).

The Baldissero peridotite (I) is the southernmost of three mantle massifs exposed at the base of the lower crust in the Ivrea Zone (Southern Alps). The peridotite is partly serpentinized and contains stockwork mineralizations of white and microcrystalline magnesite (Micheletti 1964). Amorphous magnesite occurs in veinlets and is rarely thicker than 60 cm. Despite its high quality (44–46 wt% MgO), it was not mined because of the presence of more extensive deposits with sparry magnesite (see section on magnesite replacement deposits).

In the Carpathians, amorphous magnesite with 44–46% MgO was mined in Hodkovce (SK) (Zlocha 1972). Moderate production in Poland (Table 21.1) exploits massive and amorphous magnesites which are found in ultrabasic rocks in Lower Silesia (Central Sudetes) (Osika 1990).

The origin of amorphous magnesite in the Dinarides has not yet been clarified. For some of these deposits hydrothermal activity related to Tertiary magmatism is taken as a probable model. Magnesite along the margin of the Ozren Massif has been mined at Rječica, Paklenica, Brusnica, Velika and Mala Prenja (BiH). Sites with magnesite of economic grade were also discovered within several other ultramafic complexes in Bosnia such as (from SE to NW) Zlatibor-Varda, Krivaja-Konjuh, Banja Luka-Prnjavor and Kozara-Pastirevo (BiH).

*Hypogene deposits*

**Lead–zinc–iron and fluorite–barite–calcite–quartz vein-type deposits.** Vein-type deposits are found in sediments overlying the Late Alpine unconformity and in rocks beneath the unconformity. These veins mainly contain base metals, fluorite and barite. Calcite veins in the Rhenish Massif (up to 45 m thick) have been worked near Brilon (D) as a raw material for construction purposes. Quartz veins at Usingen (D) are selectively worked so as to attain a grade of almost 100 wt% $SiO_2$.

In the Sauerland (D) (NE Rhenish Massif), Cretaceous to Tertiary sandstones and marls as well as karst cavities in Palaeozoic reef limestones were mineralized with base-metal sulphides (Schaeffer 1984). Pb is thought to have been derived by the lateral secretion from Palaeozoic pelitic rocks; a view supported by Pb isotope studies (Schaeffer 1984). The Fe/Mn ratios in carbonate minerals indicate that oxidizing conditions were dominant during mineral precipitation. Fluids descending from platform sediments, overlying the Late Alpine unconformity mixed with hydrothermal brines circulating in the basement rocks. Homogenization temperatures, derived from fluid inclusions in barite, fluorite and carbonate minerals yielded moderate formation temperatures in the range of 70–250°C for the mineral deposits in the Rhenish Massif (Schaeffer 1984).

Barite deposits in the Ardennes (western Rhenish Massif) in the environs of Fleurus (B) contain 1.5 Mt of barite together with some galena and pyrite in karstified Frasnian limestones; however, these were reopened in 1979 (Walther & Dill 1995). Their origin is still open to discussion (Dejonghe & Fuchs 2002). Sulphur isotope data of the Fleurus barite suggest leaching of Givetian and/or Visean evaporitic rocks by underground waters. The mineralization also shares features common to the carbonate-hosted Pb–Zn deposits discussed in the following section, as well as numerous small Pb–Zn veins and fluorite vein-like deposits located at the northern rim of the Ardennes (Dejonghe 1986). The Cretaceous unconformity is considered as the geohydraulic plane most significant to the emplacement of the vein- and replacement-type deposits lined up along the northern rim of the uplifted basement block of the Rhenish Massif.

The carbonate- and barite-bearing Pb–Zn veins in the Ruhr Basin are hosted in Upper Carboniferous-age sediments. The veins are related in space to NW–SE-striking extensional faults which are predominantly enriched in galena and sphalerite at their intersections with the anticlinal axis (see also Fig. 21.7). Based on the Stephanian to Permian age of these structures (see also section on coal in the Ruhr Basin), an initial Late Palaeozoic mineralization phase may be assumed. Towards the top, the position of these veins is controlled by the major unconformity between the Carboniferous and Upper Cretaecous sediments. The largest mine is the Auguste Victoria, which produced 5 Mt of ore with an average of 7 wt% Zn, 3.9 wt% Pb and 65 ppm Ag. Another 5 Mt of ore are still present at the Klara and Auguste Victoria mines.

Close to the northern margin of the Eger Graben at Jilové and Teplice Spa (CZ; for location see Fig. 21.21) fluorite deposits occur in Cenomanian and Lower Turonian sandstones at the contact between permeable and impermeable rocks and in the crystalline basement rocks. The deposit, which was mined until 1989, contains a fluorite content in the range 30 to 50% (Reichmann 1983). These deposits were formed during the last 500 000 years by hot springs which are still active in this region (Cadek & Malkovsky 1986). The homogenization temperatures of fluid inclusions fall in the range of 90 to 100°C (Reichmann 1983).

Single- to multiple-stage remobilization is a general characteristic of most base metals, fluorite- and barite-bearing veins in the Black Forest area. The veins generally run subparallel to the Upper Rhine Graben. The emplacement of some veins parallel to have been Upper Rhine Graben is believed to have been related to graben subsidence from Cretaceous to Tertiary times (Werner & Franzke 2001). The bounding surface for the vein mineralization is the post-Variscan unconformity truncating the uplifted Vosges-Black Forest dome and gently dipping away from the basement towards the west and east beneath the platform sediments.

Investigations by Cathelineau *et al.* (1999) may help to understand the emplacement of these unconformity-related deposits. Mineralogical and fluid inclusion data of carbonate minerals from veins intersecting plutonites at Charroux–Civray (SW France), and overlain by Jurassic sediments, have shown that these carbonate minerals crystallized from brines at rather low temperatures (Cathelineau *et al.* 1999). According to these authors, fluids underwent mixing after the deposition of the Jurassic sediments. Examples include the base-metal mineralization on both sides of the Upper Rhine Graben, where both present-day fluids and fluid inclusions found in fracture fillings provide evidence for the presence of brines in Triassic formations and of the recharge of meteoric waters involved in deep convective systems (Pauwels *et al.* 1993; Dubois *et al.* 1996).

**Carbonate-hosted lead–zinc deposits.** Calcareous rocks can host unconformity-related base-metal deposits. If the metalliferous fluids come in contact with the highly reactive country-rocks near the unconformity, replacement deposits with Pb, Zn and barite may form. This occurred in the Palaeozoic limestones of the Rhenish Massif near Aachen-Stolberg (D), Iserlohn-Schwelm (D) and in the reef complex at Brilon (D) (Werner 1990).

Some limestone-hosted base-metal deposits contain non-sulphidic Zn minerals such as smithsonite, willemite and hemimorphite in palaeokarstic cavities and replacement pockets (Dejonghe 1998). The best known representative of this type of deposit is the La Calamine (Kelmis-Moresnet) mining district (B), for which a Jurassic to Cretaceous (?) age has been postulated (Dejonghe 1998). In an overview of non-sulphidic Zn mineralization in Europe, Boni & Large (2003) discussed the possible mode of formation of the La Calamine ore body as being related either to palaeoweathering or to hydrothermal processes (see also Brugger *et al.* 2003; Hitzmann *et al.* 2003); both being largely active around unconformities. High-grade calamine ore (grading 33–47% Zn) was extracted until the closure of the La Calamine mine in 1879 (Dejonghe 1998). Homogenization temperatures of fluid inclusions in the willemite crystals range from 70 to 190°C and $T_m$ data suggest a salinity close to 0 wt% $NaCl_{equ}$. This type of carbonate-hosted base-metal mineralization closely resembles the Pb–Zn mineralization recorded from the waning mineralizing stages in the MVT or Silesian-type Pb–Zn deposits in Germany and Poland.

**Uranium deposits.** The Königsstein (D) and Hamr (CZ) U deposits located in the northern part of the Bohemian Massif are hosted in clastic rocks deposited by alluvial fans (Křibek 1989; Lange *et al.* 1991). Epigenetic U mineralization is confined to Cenomanian host rocks (Hamr; Křibek 1989) or is located in rocks extending from the basal Cenomanian to the Turonian (Königsstein; Lange *et al.* 1991). Uranium was sourced from the Late Variscan granites of the Saxothuringian Zone that were subject to renewed denudation during the Cretaceous and

Cenozoic. The process of U transport and fixation in black ore minerals at a redox barrier has already been described from the Triassic Burgsandstein in the South German Basin.

Marked supergene redeposition and pervasive chemical weathering under tropical to subtropical conditions also affected many of the previously noted Late Variscan to Mesozoic U deposits, giving rise to the so-called 'yellow ores' with predominantly uranyl phosphates, arsenates, silicates and 'gummite', a mixture of several U oxide–hydroxide minerals. Only in the Fichtelgebirge at Rudolphstein (D) and Fuchsbau (D) did vein-like deposits, unrelated to any Variscan protore, develop (Fig. 21.11b). Following some trial mining during World War II, exploitation of these U yellow ores resumed between 1950 and 1957. Here, uranyl phosphates, silicates and gummites formed during Neogene times on a peneplain beneath a blanket of kaolinitic saprolite. Uranium yellow ores in fault zones intersecting the granites may be traced down to a depth of 100 m; its ultimate depth is controlled by an ancient aquifer (Dill 1985*c*). This palaeogroundwater table in the crystalline basement rocks may be correlated with a groundwater table present at the same topographic level in siliciclastic sediments covering an alluvial plain in front of the escarpment. U–Pb age dating indicates that the Late Miocene–Early Pliocene was the most important period for this supergene U concentration (Carl & Dill 1985). Uraniferous Fe–Al phosphates (wavellite type) resulted from the decomposition of pyrite and apatite disseminated in underlying Silurian and Lower Devonian black shales.

## *Petroleum deposits*

Petroleum has been used in Europe since the fifteenth century, but major hydrocarbon exploration first began in the middle of the twentieth century. Today, oil and gas play a significant role in the economy of Central Europe. However, with shares of about 1% and 5% for oil and gas, respectively, production is small on a global scale (Table 21.1).

The most prominent European petroleum province is the Northwest European Basin (NWEB) (Table 21.2). This is a complex basin system including several sub-basins. Within Central Europe, both the largest oil producer (Denmark, 36th in the world) and the largest gas producer (the Netherlands, tenth in the world) are located within the NWEB. Petroleum is also produced from Alpine fold- and thrust- belts and related foreland basins (Vienna Basin, Carpathian Flysch Belt, Alpine-Carpathian Foreland Basin, Po Basin), and from the intramontane Pannonian Basin. The Paris Basin and the Upper Rhine Graben are minor petroleum provinces. The hydrocarbon habitat of these basins is outlined in the following sections.

Most of the basins are currently in a mature state of exploration. However, smaller discoveries continue to be made, particularly due to the increased use of 3D seismics. Mature oil and gas fields are also surveyed for their use as underground storage for gas and oil as well as for the storage of the greenhouse gas $CO_2$.

### *Northwest European Basin*

The structural evolution of the NWEB began during the final phase of the Variscan Orogeny. In terms of basin development, the investigated area comprises Palaeozoic elements of the Southern Permian Basin (see McCann *et al.* 2008*a*) and is superimposed by Mesozoic elements (e.g. Central Graben, Lower Saxony Basin; Fig. 21.25a). In terms of petroleum systems, two different stratigraphic petroleum systems occur: a Palaeozoic gas system (including Lower Triassic reservoirs) and a Mesozoic oil and gas system. Acccording to IHS Energy (2008) over 800 fields and/or discoveries have been made in the NWEB.

**Palaeozoic gas system.** The *Southern Permian Basin* (SPB) extends from the UK in the west to Poland in the east. It hosts Europe's most prolific gas province, containing the super-giant Groningen gas field. This major discovery was made in 1959 and triggered the main phase of natural gas exploration in the Netherlands. The SPB is also a major gas province in Germany and Poland.

The SPB overlies thick Upper Carboniferous coal measures. Following an early Rotliegend phase of extensive volcanism and basin subsidence, the surface of the basin was probably several hundred metres below global sea level at the beginning of the Late Rotliegend (McCann 1998; van Wees *et al.* 2000). A playa lake developed in the central basin during Late Rotliegend times (Verdier 1999; Karnkowski 1999). Erosional products from the surrounding uplands were carried into the basin by ephemeral streams or wadis. Deflation of these sediments led to the formation of a concentric dune belt along the western basin margin (Fig. 21.25b). This clastic continental phase of the Rotliegend was abruptly terminated when the North Sea High partly subsided and the basin was flooded from the north. During Zechstein times, the restricted supply of marine water together with the hot dry climate led to the precipitation of six carbonate–evaporite cycles. Both carbonates and anhydrites formed swells and ramparts paralleling the rims of the basin and of local highs. The earliest Triassic sedimentation took place in an inland sea or playa lake setting. The mud-dominated rocks are overlain by fluvial sandstones (Buntsandstein) capped by a largely fine-grained clastic and evaporitic sequence (Muschelkalk and Keuper).

Upper Carboniferous coal seams are the predominant source rocks and generated methane-rich gas during the Late Palaeozoic and Mesozoic. Deep burial during the latest Cenozoic led to high maturity of coal favouring the generation of nitrogen-rich gas. Gas compositions with locally up to 100 vol% N in the eastern part of the basin have stopped further gas exploration in this area (Littke *et al.* 1995; Gras & Clayton 1998). Namurian shales and coals and basinal Zechstein carbonates are additional sources for gas (Hoffmann *et al.* 2001). The latter are also the source for some oil in east Germany and Poland (e.g. Thuringian Basin; Karnin *et al.* 1996).

Reservoirs occur in Upper Rotliegend aeolian and wadi sandstones, in Zechstein platform and slope carbonates, and in fluvial Lower Triassic sandstones. Furthermore, Cenozoic subsidence resulted in migration into Cretaceous and Palaeogene reservoirs. Gas accumulations also occur in Upper Carboniferous sandstones, but many of these are classified as tight gas reservoirs (permeability $k < 0.1$ mD). The Upper Rotliegend is economically by far the most prominent reservoir.

A belt of proven viability (mature Carboniferous source rocks, Rotliegend in reservoir facies, thick sealing Zechstein evaporites; Fig. 21.25b) extends from the east English coast through the northern Netherlands and the south Lower Saxony Basin to Poland. The Groningen super-giant gas field, just crossing the Dutch–German onshore border, is one of the largest gas fields in the world. It contains *c.* $100 \times 10^{12}$ cubic feet of original natural gas within Rotliegend aeolian sandstones (porosity $\Phi$ up to 30%; k up to 3D) at a depth of 2.8 km, from which about half was produced by the end of 1998. Gas from Permian reservoirs is mainly produced from *c.* 2–5 km depth. Structurally, large flat anticlines predominate. Compartmentalization of the gas fields due to fault sealing is widespread.

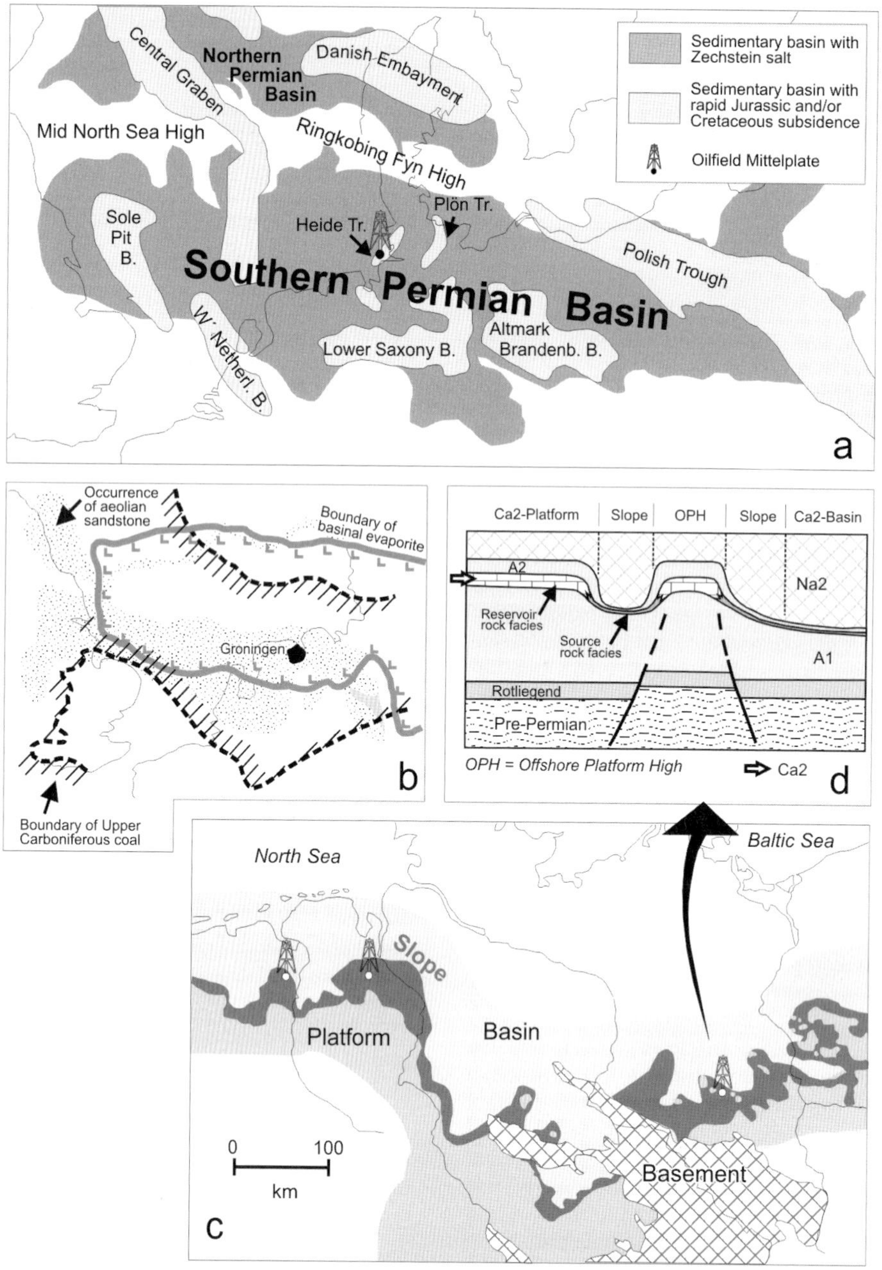


**Fig. 21.25.** (**a**) Sedimentary basins in northwestern Europe (modified after Ziegler 1990). (**b**) Occurrence of source rock, carrier rock and cap rock in the Southern Permian Basin (modified after Perrodon 1985). (**c**) Basin configuration during deposition of Stassfurt Carbonate Ca2 along the southern margin of the Southern Permian Basin (after Strohmenger *et al.* 1996). (**d**) Geological cross-section across the southern margin of the Southern Permian Basin with petroleum relevant elements (after Piske & Rasch 1998).

Platform and slope carbonates, mainly of the second Zechstein cycle, form the gas reservoirs along the southern margin of the Southern Permian Basin (Fig. 21.25c,d; Strohmenger *et al.* 1996; Piske & Rasch 1998). The carbonate (Main Dolomite, or Ca2) overlies anhydrite banks (A1) of the first Zechstein cycle and encompasses both transgressive and regressive features. The Ca2 thickness ranges from 20 to 80 m along the platform and is less than 10 m in basinal settings. The maximum thickness (up to 250 m) is attained where the Ca2 overlies the A1-slope. Ca2 reservoir characteristics are best in dolomitized slope deposits, but very poor in dedolomitized intervals. The Ca2 is sealed by the anhydrite (A2) and halite (Na2) of the second Zechstein cycle. Gas from Zechstein reservoirs occasionally contains high $H_2S$ contents (>5 vol%) as a result of the thermochemical sulphate reduction of methane with capping anhydrite.

**Mesozoic oil and gas system.** Mesozoic oil and gas systems occur in various sub-basins of the NWEB which experienced strong Jurassic–Cretaceous subsidence (cf. Fig. 21.25a). Halokinesis, the formation of Zechstein diapirs and Cretaceous/Cenozoic basin inversion also play a major role. Petroleum habitats in the Southern Central Graben and in the Lower Saxony Basin are briefly reviewed below.

The roughly north–south trending *South Central Graben* is a very rich oil province. Although only a small southern segment is located within Central Europe (DK, NL), more than 50% of the current oil production is from this small area. The Central Graben is mainly a Jurassic rift system. The main subsidence phase was from Late Triassic to Middle Jurassic times. A complex evolution including rifting, wrenching and halokinesis resulted in block uplift and erosion. Lower Cretaceous sediments are dominated by marine sandstones and marls, whereas chalk deposits dominate the Upper Cretaceous units. Wrench faulting and a later inversion phase occurred at the Cretaceous–Palaeogene boundary. Jurassic deposits were preserved along the graben flanks in the rim synclines of Zechstein diapirs.

The most important source rocks are the Lower Toarcian Posidonia Shale and the Upper Jurassic (Kimmeridgian) Farsund Formation containing type II kerogen. Middle Jurassic coal is an additional source (Petersen *et al.* 1996).

The most prominent reservoir rocks are Upper Cretaceous and Danian chalks, while structural and stratigraphic traps as well as the seals are Cenozoic in age. There is evidence that some traps are dynamic (e.g. Halfdan Field; Hemmet 2005), a consequence of the low permeability of chalk (0.1–1.0 mD). Therefore, hydrocarbon migration is extremely slow and it takes millions of years for the hydrocarbons to migrate out of the area. Jurassic sandstones deposited in different environments, ranging from fluvial to deep-marine, constitute additional reservoirs. Until now all of the Jurassic deposits have been found in structural traps sealed by shales.

The *Lower Saxony Basin* (LSB) is a highly differentiated graben filled with Upper Jurassic and Lower Cretaceous sediments (Fig. 21.25a; Kockel *et al.* 1994). Basin inversion occurred during Late Cretaceous times. Oil production in the LSB is derived from a Jurassic and an Early Cretaceous petroleum system. Several oil seeps and asphalt deposits have been recognized in the LSB beginning in the Middle Ages. The first drilled hole was successful and led to the Wietze discovery of (19 million barrels of oil equivalent — MMboe) in 1859 which was followed by the first oil boom in the 1880s and 1890s. The largest oil discovery, Ruehle (228 million barrels of oil — MMbo), was found in 1949. It is estimated that more than 10 000 wells have been drilled in the basin.

The source rocks within the LSB are of Lower Toarcian (Posidonia Shale: 8% TOC, type II kerogen) and Berriasian age (Wealden paper shale: 4–7% TOC, type I–II). Oils generated from these source rocks may occur as single phases or as mixtures, the last exclusively in Valanginian sandstones. Reservoir rocks are mainly sandstones of Middle Jurassic and Early Cretaceous age, and occur either as facies and unconformity traps (pre-Turonian age) or as structural traps which were formed during the Late Cretaceous basin inversion. The economically most important reservoir rocks are Valanginian sandstones. Seal rocks are shales and evaporites of Jurassic and Early Cretaceous age.

Today, recoverable oil accumulations are concentrated along the northern margins where Late Cretaceous inversion was at a minimum, and the maturity range is 0.5–0.9% $R_r$. Oil generation began during the Albian to Turonian period. Inversion movements and overmaturation of source rocks led to the destruction of these oil accumulations in the central basin (Kockel *et al.* 1994; Petmecky *et al.* 1999).

The Heide Trough has a setting similar to that of the LSB. The Mittelplate Oil Field, within the Heide Trough, is an example of an offshore field sourced from the Posidonia Shale (Fig. 21.25). The field is located in Middle Jurassic reservoir sandstones beneath the North Sea tidelands. In order not to destroy the ecosystem, the reservoir is exploited by extended reach drilling from onshore about 8 km distant (Langhans *et al.* 2003).

*Paris Basin*

The Paris Basin is a Mesozoic and Palaeogene intracratonic basin (Perrodon & Zabeck 1991). It is a crudely oval feature of about 140 000 km$^2$ and with a maximum depth of more than 3 km. However, only the easternmost part of the Paris Basin is located within the area shown in the attached map. In this part, the Mesozoic partly overlies Permo-Carboniferous-age coal measures of the Saar-Lorraine Basin (Mascle *et al.* 1994).

The Paris Basin is a minor oil and gas province (Lamiraux & Mascle 1998). Over 1000 exploratory wells have been drilled in the basin since the early 1950s. Exploration efforts peaked during the 1960s and 1980s and resulted in the discovery of 83 oil and/or gas fields. The first oil field in the Paris Basin started production in 1954. The first oil field in the area shown on the map (see CD inside back cover) came on-stream shortly afterwards (Grandville Field; 1959).

The Paris Basin is characterized by a relatively simple petroleum system. The main source rocks are marine Lower Jurassic mudstones with the most prolific being the 10 to 60 m thick Lower Toarcian 'paper shale' (6.2% TOC, type II kerogen). The source rocks reach the oil window at 2 km depth within a relatively small area in the central part of the basin. This fact limits the prospectivity of the basin. The slightly less organic-rich Lotharingian and Domerian marls also possibly played an important role in hydrocarbon generation because of their deeper burial. With regard to the location of the oil kitchen, significant lateral (10–15 km) and vertical (2.5 km) movements of hydrocarbons have to be assumed. The most important reservoir rocks are Upper Triassic sandstones and Doggerian oolitic limestones. Hettangian limestones and Neocomian sandstones provide additional reservoirs. Traps are mainly (faulted) anticlines formed during latest Cretaceous–Eocene shortening, but stratigraphic (diagenetic) traps also exist. The small Trois-Fontaines gas field west of Nancy (105 billion standard cubic feet gas — Bscfg), producing from Middle Triassic sandstones, and the tiny Forcelles oil field (south of Nancy) were sourced by Stephanian coal seams (Kettel 1989).

*Upper Rhine Graben*

The north–south trending Upper Rhine Graben is the oldest known oil province in western Europe (Boigk 1981). It extends from Frankfurt to Basel (D, F, CH). The graben is about 300 km long, and has an average width of 35 to 45 km (Fig. 21.26a). More than 300 new field wildcats have been drilled, resulting in 56 discoveries in the German and French sectors. Despite the large number of discoveries, the majority of the fields and the recoverable reserves are small (Table 21.2). This is probably due to the small drainage areas, tectonic blocking, rapid facies changes, non-sealing faults, hydrothermal activity and biodegradation (Lampe *et al.* 2001; Plein 1993).

The largest field in the French sector is Pechelbronn (23 MMboe). The tar sands at Pechelbronn are known to have been exploited on a small scale by local farmers since 1498, and on a larger scale since the seventeenth century. It is thought that approximately 4850 wells were drilled in Pechelbronn between 1888 and 1953. The largest discovery in Germany, Landau (35 MMboe), was made in 1956 (Plein 1994; Fig. 21.26a). With the exception of Landau, Pechelbronn and Stockstadt (12 MMboe), all of the discoveries have been small to very small. Since the 1980s, there have been very few discoveries and the remaining recoverable reserves are being rapidly depleted.

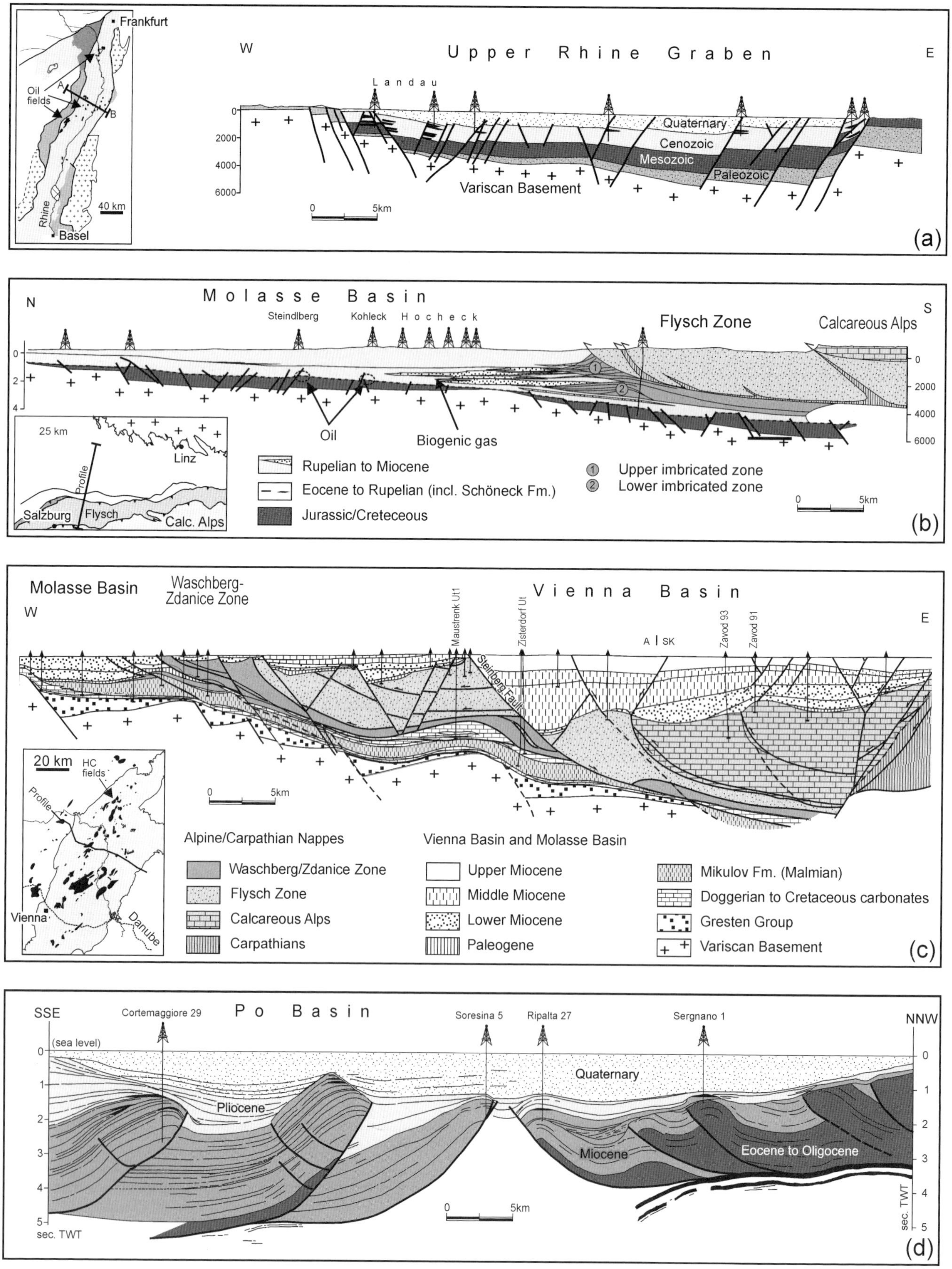


**Fig. 21.26.** Cross-sections through petroleum basins. Scale is the same for all profiles, but vertical scale in (d) is two-way travel time (TWT). (**a**) Upper Rhine Graben (Boigk 1981). (**b**) Alpine Foreland Basin (Hamilton *et al.* 2000). (**c**) Vienna Basin (Arzmüller *et al.* 2006). (**d**) Po Basin (Casero 2004).

The Upper Rhine Graben is a crustal-scale rift with a northward-dipping and thickening graben fill (Behrmann *et al.* 2003). Graben subsidence and synrift sedimentation began in the Late Eocene with the main phase of subsidence being the Oligocene to Miocene. Cenozoic siliciclastics, cyclic, mainly marine and up to 4 km thick, were deposited locally (Berger *et al.* 2005). In the southern part of the basin, these deposits also contain Oligocene evaporites. The cycles represent initial marine ingressions and fluvial–evaporitic end-members. Post-Miocene subsidence in the north was counter-balanced by uplift of the southern graben segment and its rift shoulders (Black Forest, Vosges). Volcanic activity 18–16 Ma ago occurred in the southern Upper Rhine Graben which is still seismically active (Illies & Fuchs 1974).

The hydrocarbon system of the Upper Rhine Graben comprises multiple source rocks. The greater part of the hydrocarbons was derived from two marine source rocks; the Grey Beds of Rupelian (Early Oligocene) age and the Liassic Shales. The Grey Beds comprise marls and shales alternating with limestone and dolomite. The sequence has high sulphur contents and contains humic organic matter. The Rupelian shales are mature for oil only in the northern part of the basin, where the Oligocene to Pliocene cover is sufficiently thick and where geothermal gradients are up to 8°C/100 m. The Rupelian source rock is responsible for the oil accumulations in Germany and two significant fields in France.

Hydrocarbon migration began during the Neogene and is locally still active (Rückheim 1993). Oil fields on the western graben margin are the result of westward migration due to local prism-shaped graben fill, the result of asymmetric rifting (Fig. 21.26a). Gas deposits are probably biogenic in origin.

The main reservoirs in the Upper Rhine Graben are in the Cenozoic succession with subordinate reservoirs in the Keuper sandstones and the Doggerian Grand Oolithe. The Cenozoic sandstone reservoirs were deposited under fluviatile or deltaic conditions and are typically of limited lateral extent (maximum 1 km wide, 5 km long). Pay zone thicknesses and porosities are moderate. At Pechelbronn, a gross pay thickness of 800 m contains numerous productive intervals with pay zones of between 2 m and 20 m, and 25% porosity. The Keuper reservoirs are productive in the northern part of the French sector and in the adjacent German sector. The reservoirs consist of shallow-marine sandstones and dolomites, predominantly with fracture permeability. Dogger reservoirs consist of heterogeneous oolitic limestones, sometimes tight and with localized high porosity zones. Typical reservoirs have some 50 m of oolith limestone and a 15% porosity. The permeability is low, except in fractured zones where it reaches 1 D. The reservoirs typically occur in fault or stratigraphic traps sealed by salt or shale.

Geothermal power plants are planned in parts of the Upper Rhine Graben where local geothermal temperatures are up to 150°C at a depth of 2500 m (Kreuter *et al.* 2003).

*Alpine Foreland Basin*

The Alpine Foreland Basin extends along the northern margin of the Alps from Geneva to Vienna and reaches a depth of 6 km near the Alpine front in Bavaria (Roeder & Bachmann 1996; Wagner 1998). The southern part of the basin was overthrust by the Alpine nappes (Fig. 21.26b).

The Alpine Foreland Basin is a minor oil and moderate gas province (Table 21.2). While over 1200 exploratory wells have been documented, only 198 fields were discovered, 56 of which are still producing. With the exception of the Swiss Entlebuch gas field, all of the deposits are located in Germany and Austria. The majority of the fields have less than 1 MMboe of recoverable reserves. Over 1400 development wells have been drilled to date. Peak liquid production was reached in the late 1960s. Peak gas production was reached in 1973 with an annual production of 82 354 million standard cubic feet gas (MMscfg). Given the large number of fields discovered in Austria and Germany, and the decades of exploration activity, the basin must be considered mature in terms of hydrocarbon exploration. However, the most recent gas discoveries in the basin were made in 2006.

Within the Alpine Foreland Basin, the sedimentary history can be characterized into three stages separated by unconformities: Permo-Carboniferous graben sedimentation; Mesozoic mixed carbonate–siliciclastic shelf sedimentation; and Cenozoic Molasse sedimentation. The latter stage began in Late Eocene time with deposition of fluvial and shallow-marine sandstones, shales and carbonates. Several hundred metres of Oligocene and Miocene deep-marine turbiditic and contouritic deposits derived from the Central Alps were deposited in the eastern part, whereas the western basin was dominated by a prograding–retrograding delta system.

The Cenozoic sediments are divided structurally into the Autochthonous Molasse and the Allochthonous Molasse. The Autochthonous Molasse rests relatively undisturbed on the European basement. The Allochthonous Molasse is composed of the south Molasse sediments, which are included in the Alpine thrusts and which were moved tectonically into and across the south Autochthonous Molasse.

Two fault systems can be distinguished within the Autochthonous Molasse: (1) NW- and NE-trending Palaeozoic faults, which were reactivated as strike-slip faults during Mesozoic and Cenozoic times; and (2) a dense network of west–east trending, antithetic and synthetic extensional faults caused by Eocene/Oligocene bending of the European crust in front of the Alpine nappes.

The main source rock for oil and thermal gas is the *c.* 10 m thick lower Oligocene Schöneck Formation (2–10% TOC, type II kerogen; Schulz *et al.* 2002; Sachsenhofer & Schulz 2006). Other Oligocene pelites and Jurassic rocks in the western Molasse Basin (e.g. Posidonia Shale) may provide additional hydrocarbons. The rocks are immature where the oil fields are located and only enter the oil window (4–6 km depth) beneath the Alpine nappes, indicating long-distance migration. Generation of oil and thermal gas commenced in Miocene times and may still be ongoing. The source for thermal gas in the Entlebuch well are Permo-Carboniferous coals (Kettel 1989). Gas in Oligocene and Miocene reservoirs is of bacterial origin.

Reservoirs of oil and thermal gas are fluvial and shallow-marine sandstones and carbonates of Mesozoic, Eocene and Oligocene age, with Upper Eocene basal sandstones being most important. The oil is trapped in fault, stratigraphic, combined-stratigraphic/fault structures, anticlines and imbrication structures. Most of the fields are on the upthrown side of the west–east trending antithetic normal faults.

Reservoirs of biogenic gas are Upper Oligocene and Lower Miocene deep-marine clastics (Puchkirchen Formation, Hall Formation; De Ruig & Hubbard 2006) and shallow-marine to brackish sands. Seals are provided by intraformational shales. The gas is trapped mainly in stratigraphic and compaction structures or in a combination of both types and with imbrication structures. Strike-slip faulting influenced, and delineated, the distribution of the reservoirs.

Mesozoic strata underlying the Molasse sediments are exposed north of the Alpine Foreland Basin. In the Jura Fold Belt near Neuchâtel (CH) these strata host asphalt within Barrèmian carbonates. This asphalt was produced in the Val-de-Travers mine between 1711 and 1986.

Untested deep-gas potential exists in footwall imbrications near the Alpine front. Thus, additional exploration is inferred in the Allochthonous Molasse and in the subthrust zone beneath the Alpine nappes.

*Carpathian Foreland and Carpathian Flysch Belt*

The Carpathian Foreland and the Carpathian Flysch Belt extend from the Czech Republic to Romania and contain a large number of oil and gas fields, especially in Poland, Ukraine and Romania. Only the western part of the Carpathian Foreland and the Carpathian Flysch (CZ, PL) is within the area of interest (Ciprys *et al.* 1995; Bessereau *et al.* 1996; Klecker *et al.* 2001).

The first oil discovery in the Polish Carpathians dates back to 1853 (Bobrka-Rowne-Rogi, 12 MMboe) but natural petroleum seeps have been recorded in the Carpathian Flysch Belt since pre-historic times. Petroleum exploration in the Carpathian Foreland began at the end of the nineteenth century. To date, 229 fields and discoveries had been made in the Carpathian Foreland and Carpathian Flysch Belt of Poland and 44 fields in the Czech part.

The Carpathian Foreland reaches a depth of 3.5 km in eastern Poland. It comprises mainly Middle Miocene terrestrial and shallow-marine sediments, which rest unconformably on thick Palaeozoic and Mesozoic rocks, or on Precambrian basement. Organic-rich Palaeogene rocks, up to 1500 m thick, fill two palaeovalleys/submarine canyons in the Czech part of the basin. These rocks, which remained in their autochthonous position, are marginal equivalents of the organic-rich Menilite Formation in the Carpathian Flysch Belt (Picha & Peters 1998). Miocene rocks predominantly consist of shallow-marine, prodeltaic shales and marls with intercalated fine-grained sands. The sands were mainly shed towards the north. A Middle Badenian evaporitic layer up to 50 m thick occurs near the base of the sequence.

The southern part of the basin is overridden by north-verging thrust-fold nappes of the Carpathian Flysch Belt. The Lower Cretaceous to Lower Miocene sandy–shaly deep-marine sediments were deposited in a complex system of troughs and foredeeps.

**Carpathian Foreland.** The main source rocks for oil and thermogenic gas are found in Devonian, Upper Carboniferous (including coal), Jurassic (1–3% TOC, type II–III kerogen), and Palaeogene (1–9% TOC, type III–II) rocks. Miocene deposits (0.7% TOC; type III) are the source for bacterial gas in the Miocene reservoirs.

Pre-Miocene reservoir rocks include fractured basement and Palaeozoic rocks as well as Mesozoic sandstones and limestones. Traps consist of flat buried hills, sealed by Miocene pelites. Most of the deposits contain oil; only two contain thermogenic gas. Miocene reservoir sandstones ($\Phi = 20–30\%$) are often stacked and are typically fine-grained. The Miocene reservoirs form flat anticlines and are frequently offset by faults or pinch out laterally. Production depths vary from 500 to 3000 m. In the Czech part of the foreland, gas is mainly produced from Neogene sandstones (350–1500 m) in the subthrust of nappes. Some fields (e.g. Zdanice (CZ)) produce from the pre-Miocene basement.

**Carpathian Flysch Belt.** Lower Oligocene shales (Menilite Formation; 3–10% TOC; type II kerogen) are the most important source rock. There is evidence for two phases of generation: an early phase of generation due to deep sedimentary burial, and a late phase subsequent to nappe emplacement. Lower Cretaceous and Lower Palaeocene black shales have a limited generative potential.

The Carpathian Flysch Belt contains many oil fields, but only a few gas fields. The best reservoir sandstones ($\Phi = 10–25\%$) are related to Upper Cretaceous and Lower Eocene basin floor fans (Klecker *et al.* 2001). Typical traps are complexly folded, asymmetric anticlines developed in the hanging walls of large thrust faults. The aerial closure of the fields is small, but the vertical closure can be high.

*Vienna Basin*

The rhomb-shaped, 200 km long and up to 60 km wide Vienna Basin is located on the outer allochthonous nappes of the Alpine-Carpathian thrust belt (Fig. 21.26c; Arzmüller *et al.* 2006). The basin remains one of the major gas producers in Central Europe (Table 21.2). With over 6000 wells drilled to date, it is one of the most intensively explored basins in the study area. Exploration in the basin commenced in the early 1900s, with 125 oil and gas accumulations discovered since then, the majority of them being in the Austrian part of the basin. The largest oil and gas discovery, Matzen (525 MMbo and 1385 Bscfg), was made in Austria in 1949. Production in the basin began in 1914 in Slovakia (Gbely-Staré Pole field, 5 MMboe). Peak liquid production was reached in 1955–56, when over 70 000 barrels per day (b/d) were produced. During the 1980s and 1990s, production remained at 18–20 million barrels per day (Mb/d). Peak gas production was reached in the early 1960s at approximately 250 000 MMscf per day and has declined since then.

Three stages are recognized during the development of the Vienna Basin. (1) *Pre-Vienna Basin*: the area of today's Vienna Basin evolved from a Doggerian rift zone to a passive margin (Malmian to Cretaceous) and became part of the Molasse Basin during the Oligocene. The foreland sediments were finally overthrusted by the Alpine-Carpathian thrust complex. (2) *Proto-Vienna Basin*: tensional forces, which were active during Early Miocene thrusting, led to the development of a piggyback basin filled by open-marine clastic deposits. (3) The *Neo-Vienna Basin* is a Middle to Late Miocene pull-apart basin superimposed on the older piggyback basin. It formed after the termination of thrust movements, as a result of easterly directed extrusion of Central Alpine blocks. The basin is bordered by major faults and is filled by more than 5 km of pelites, sandstones, and some gravel.

Traditionally, three 'levels' are distinguished in the Vienna Basin area. The first level consists of the Neogene basin fill and overlies the allochthonous second level, which is represented by the Alpine thrust complex including the Calcareous Alps (Permoscythian–Palaeocene) and the Flysch Zone (Cretaceous–Eocene). The allochthonous nappes overthrust the autochthonous third level, which consists of Variscan basement, Mesozoic cover, and Cenozoic Molasse deposits.

The Mesozoic succession commenced with deltaic rocks of Doggerian age deposited in rift-related half-grabens. These are overlain by Upper Doggerian sandy carbonates (reservoir of gas-condensate in the Höflein Field) and Malmian platform carbonates, which interfinger towards the east with basinal marls (Mikulov Formation). These organic-rich marls, more than 1 km thick (1.5–2.0% TOC; type II–III kerogen; Ladwein *et al.* 1991) are the main source rocks for hydrocarbons in the Vienna Basin. Autochthonous Palaeogene rocks are additional sources in the north Vienna Basin (Francu *et al.* 1996), whereas coal-bearing Doggerian strata are probably the source rocks for gas in the Höflein Field (Sachsenhofer *et al.* 2006). As a result of overthrusting, the source rocks entered the oil window at 4–6 km depth in Early Miocene times, and are overmature in areas with strong Miocene subsidence. The generated hydrocarbons migrated from the authochthonous Malmian, along faults through the Alpine thrust complex, into the Miocene basin fill. Small gas fields in the south and SE Vienna Basin contain biogenic gas generated in the Neogene succession.

Most of the hydrocarbon production originates from shallow depths (<2000 m) within the Neogene basin fill. Nearly all of the oil and gas is found in clastic reservoirs. Only a few gas fields are related to Middle Miocene patch reefs. The architecture of the reservoirs is controlled by a major Middle Miocene transgression and the subsequent progradation of delta lobes into the basin. The reservoir sands can be classified into delta-plain, delta-front, delta-slope, pro-delta and marine transgressive sands.

Lower Miocene reservoir sands are usually elongated lens-shaped bodies of basinal or delta-plain origin isolated by shale. The reservoirs of Middle and Late Miocene age are stacked sand sequences. Most of today's hydrocarbon-bearing sand horizons were deposited during Middle Miocene transgressive–regressive cycles in a delta-front and delta-slope environment. Upper Miocene reservoir sands were mainly deposited as delta-plain and delta-front environments.

Most of the oil and gas is found in structural traps. The most prominent feature is the giant Matzen Field (Fuchs *et al.* 2001), which is located in a compactional anticline over a basement high. In addition, the anticline is cut by a series of faults. This combined anticline/fault structure is typical of fields in the basin centre (e.g. Aderklaa, Zwerndorf). A second type of trap is associated with large synsedimentary faults. The Steinberg Fault with a maximum displacement of 6 km (Fig. 21.26c) creates a classic roll-over structure. Many oil fields are aligned along these deep-seated faults (e.g. Bernhardsthal, Pirawarth). Stratigraphic traps are dominant in the Lower Miocene section. Combined traps also appear.

Oil and gas deposits in the allochthonous nappes, beneath the Neogene basin fill, have been found at depth ranges of between 2600 and 6100 m, mainly along central highs. They are mainly bound to fractured Triassic carbonates (e.g. Hauptdolomit) of the Calcareous Alps. The dolomitic reservoirs are sealed either by Neogene marls (e.g. Schönkirchen Tief oil field; Aderklaa, Závod, Borský Jur gas fields) or by impermeable units within the Calcareous Alps (e.g. Schönkirchen Übertief, and Aderklaa Tief gas fields). The Schönkirchen Tief and Übertief fields are of particular importance because they contain the second largest oil and gas deposits, respectively. Reservoirs within the Flysch Zone are restricted to Palaeogene turbiditic sandstones of the Steinberg area, which exhibit good production when fractured.

Four wells, including the 8533 m deep Zistersdorf ÜT2a well, drilled allochthonous sediments beneath the Alpine Nappes (Milan & Sauer 1996; Fig. 21.26c). No commercial success has been achieved, but good petroleum shows have been found. Moreover, relatively high porosities (up to 7% in the Malmian Mikulov Marl, a result of late gas generation within this thick source rock) suggest the presence of a non-conventional gas reservoir. However, at the present time there is no economic justification for this ultra-deep exploration.

*Po Basin Province*

The Po Basin Province includes the Po Plain (I) and the north Adriatic Sea (I, HR; Anelli *et al.* 1996; Casero 2004). In the subsurface of the Po Basin, the older South Alpine/Dinaric and the younger North Apennine thrust fronts delimit their common foreland. (Fig. 21.26d).

The Po Basin Province is a major gas and oil producer (Table 21.2). The first discovery was made in 1923 but the major fields were discovered between 1951 and 1971 in the Adriatic Homocline (e.g. Porto Garibaldi-Agostino: 3500 Bscfg) and in the Ferrara-Romagna Arc (e.g. Porto Corsini Mare Est: 1750 Bscfg) and contain nearly 50% of the basin's gas reserves. The Villafortuna-Trecate Field, discovered in 1984 in the Pedealpine Homocline, is the largest oil field (265 MMbl, 155 Bscfg) in the province.

Onshore, peak gas production attained maximum values in the 1960s when nearly 700 MMscf/d were produced. Offshore gas production reached maximum values in the late 1990s (*c.* 1200 MMscf per day). Peak liquid production was reached in the late 1990s with nearly 70 Mb/d.

In a simple model of the formation of the Po Basin Province, a Mesozoic to Early Palaeogene pre-flexural stage can be distinguished from a younger flexural stage. Sediments of the pre-flexural stage are dominated by epicontinental carbonates. Thick terrigenous sediments were deposited during the flexural stage (e.g. Casero 2004). The Neogene to Quaternary fill of the Po Basin comprises clastic series as much as 8 km thick. Most recoverable hydrocarbon reserves consist of bacterial gas. However, thermal oil and gas are also present (e.g. Lindquist 1999).

Very thick Cenozoic shaly distal basin plain deposits with moderate organic carbon contents (0.7%) are the source for the bacterial gas. Some thermal hydrocarbons are sourced from the Marnoso Arenacea Formation (0.68% TOC), a Miocene deep-marine sequence. The most important source rocks for thermogenic hydrocarbons are Middle Triassic carbonate–black shale successions (Besano Formation, Meride Formation), which formed in intrashelf euxinic basins. The Besano Formation, up to 16 m thick, is an excellent source rock (12% TOC; type II kerogen) and was mined as oil shale in the Swiss Alps (Monte San Giorgio). The overlying 300 m thick Meride Formation consists of limestones with shaly interbeds. The latter contain an average of 2.4% TOC and type III kerogen. The Upper Triassic Riva di Solto Shale and the upper Zu Limestone (*c.* 0.5% TOC) generated gas and condensate.

Based on stratigraphic age, a subordinate Miocene biogenic gas system can be distinguished from a major Plio-Pleistocene one. Reservoirs are located in thrust-top, shallow-marine sands, turbiditic multilayer sands, and foreland basin marine sands. The main traps are provided by synsedimentary thrust anticlines (e.g. Ravenna Field) and by gentle anticlines adjacent to the thrust-front (e.g. Porto Garibaldi-Agostino Field). In the NW Po Plain, structural, stratigraphic and combination traps are associated with the Messinian unconformity (e.g. Sergano and Caviaga fields). In the same area, up-dip shale-outs of sands provide stratigraphic traps (e.g. Settala Field). The large Barbara Field in the north Adriatic Sea (1400 Bscfg) is contained within a gentle drape fold. Low geothermal gradients allowed the formation of bacterial gas to a depth of 4500 m.

Minor thermal gas, condensate and oil sourced from Miocene rocks are found onshore within the Apennine Foreland and fold front where the geothermal gradient is highest. Reservoirs are found both in Mesozoic (e.g. heavy oil in the Cortemaggiore field) and in Cenozoic sediments.

Thermal Triassic-sourced hydrocarbons (mainly oil) have been discovered in very deep (4.6–6.2 km) carbonate reservoirs in the western Po Plain (e.g. Malossa; Villafortuna; Gaggiano). Most Mesozoic fields are in faulted, Mesozoic-age palaeohighs that have been modified into basement-involved, thrusted anticlines. Although some traps existed in Mesozoic times, the Neogene Alpine and Apennine orogenies were the critical events for trap formation and hydrocarbon generation/migration. Hydrocarbon generation occurred at a depth of 7 km or more.

*Pannonian Basin*

The Pannonian Basin is one of the major hydrocarbon-producing provinces in Central Europe with large discovered reserves (Table 21.2) in more than 580 hydrocarbon accumulations. Nearly 9000 exploratory wells have been drilled and the basin is considered as very mature.

Exploration of the basin has a long history that dates back to the 1850s, when the first well was drilled near seeps in northern Croatia. Production began in 1923 in the Bujavica Field (HR). However, exploration only took off in the 1950s in Hungary. In the early 1960s over 100 km were drilled annually. Key discoveries include the Nagylengyel Field (151 MMbo, 23 Bscfg; discovered in 1951) and the giant Algyó Gas Field (3000 Bscf; 1965) in Hungary and the large Benicanci Field (115 MMbo, 50 Bscfg; 1969) and the Molve Sour Gas Field (1200 Bsfcg, 18 MMbl; 1974) in Croatia. Peak liquid production took place during two periods (1977–80; 1989–92) and reached 120 000 b/d. During the 1990s, production decreased and is now about 53 000 b/d. Peak gas production was reached during 1986–87, when approximately 820 000 MMscf were produced daily. The production has declined since then and is now over 260 000 MMscf per day. Production from the Algyó Field (H) constitutes roughly 25% of the total output in the basin (Magyar *et al.* 2005). The Pannonian Basin will remain prospective for production in the coming years, although about 11 000 producing wells have been drilled to date. Oil production was the main target, but with the development of the Molve and Algyó fields, gas production has increased in importance.

The Pannonian Basin developed during the Miocene as a result of extensional tectonics behind the Alpine–Carpathian Orogenic Front. High geothermal gradients (4–8°C/100 m) are a result of lithospheric thinning. Basement highs define several sub-basins including sub-basins within the Great Hungarian Plain (east Hungary), the Zala Basin (west Hungary; Horváth & Tari 1999), and the Sava and Drava basins in Croatia (e.g. Lucic *et al.* 2001; Baric *et al.* 2001).

The structurally complex basement is formed by Palaeozoic and Mesozoic rocks. The Cenozoic sediments are subdivided into two megasequences. The *Palaeogene megasequence* in the central part of the basin formed as a result of a retro-arc flexural stage of basin evolution (Tari *et al.* 1993) and is distinctly different from the Neogene one which represents an extensional stage. The *Neogene megasequence* is subdivided into a Lower/Middle Miocene synrift (19–13.5 Ma) and an Upper Miocene to Recent post-rift unit. At the end of the Middle Miocene the Pannonian Lake was isolated. The Late Miocene infill of the Pannonian Lake (which was more than 1000 m deep) resulted from a single cycle of deltaic sedimentation. The depositional environment changed from open-marine conditions to shallow lacustrine, fluvial and marsh conditions. Major strike-slip faulting occurred during basin evolution. Compressional events occurred subsequent to the rifting stage and during the Quaternary.

Source rocks with relatively low TOC contents (typically *c.* 1%; type III–II) occur within the Neogene basin fill. Upper Oligocene pelites with a type III kerogen sourced the large gas-condensate fields in the Drava Basin (e.g. Molve). The Upper Triassic (Rhaetian) Kössen Formation (*c.* 10% TOC, type II–S) is the proven source for most oil in the Zala Basin (e.g. Nagylengyel; Clayton & Koncz 1994). Additional potential source rocks are found in Mesozoic (Veszprem Marl, Toarcien Shale) and Palaeogene units (e.g. Tard Clay: 0.5–5.0% TOC; type II and III kerogen; Brukner-Wein *et al.* 1990). The oil window is generally located at depths of 2.1 to 4 km. In most areas, hydrocarbon generation began late and is still ongoing. However, very high Early/Middle Miocene heat flow due to magmatic activity (?) resulted in early generation phases in some western sub-basins (Styrian Basin, Mura Depression), and this has had a negative effect on the petroleum potential (Hasenhüttl *et al.* 2001).

Reservoirs are located in weathered and faulted metamorphic rocks, Triassic (Dachstein limestone, Main Dolomite), Cretaceous (Ugod) and Eocene limestones, Lower Oligocene sands of the Kiscell Formation, Neogene pro-delta turbidites, and various delta sands. Delta-plain sandstones are amongst the best reservoirs (up to 29% porosity in the Algyó Field). $CO_2$ is present in many gas deposits, and contents may be very high (e.g. 80 vol% in the Budafa Field).

The most common traps are structural but stratigraphic and combined traps have also been recognized. Drape anticlines occur above basement highs and host the Algyó Field, among others. Onlap structures and fractured basement rocks sealed by Neogene pelites provide additional traps in the Algyó Field. Anticlines, inverted former normal faults and flower structures (e.g. Budafa field) related to late-stage basin inversion are also prospective. Traps in tilted fault blocks host the second largest field (Nagylengyel). Growth faults and related rollover structures contain fields in the Dévaványa area. Some deposits are related to palaeotopography (e.g. buried hills).

## *Deposits controlled by remobilization and igneous activity along deep-seated faults*

Faults are the prime conduits for metalliferous solutions and many of the previously discussed primary deposits owe their occurrence to metalliferous fluids ascending along deep-seated lineaments. Some of these structures were active only for a short period coeval with the emplacement of the primary deposit, e.g. Lahn-Dill Fe ores or some of the Variscan-age thrust-bound Sb–Au deposits. In these cases, the hydrothermal system became extinct, because the fault systems were not reactivated after ore formation. Other fault systems such as the Franconian Line (D) at the western edge of the Bohemian Massif, or the Eger (Ohře) Graben (CZ) have been reactivated several times since Late Palaeozoic times.

Many deposits and mineralizations in Central Europe show evidence of remobilization during the Late Triassic–Jurassic. Near Bayreuth, palygorskite associated with U minerals was identified in Upper Permian-age beds (D) (Salger 1982). The K–Ar age dating of the palygorskite yielded a Jurassic age, attesting to a late diagenetic origin. Illite–bearing hydrothermally altered sedimentary rocks, associated with epithermal vein mineralization in the Harz Mountains, yielded model ages of 226 ± 1 Ma and 209 ± 2 Ma (Schneider *et al.* 2003). In pitchblende mineralizations cross-cutting $CaF_2$–$BaSO_4$ veins in the Wölsendorf (D) (Dill 1994) and Müllenbach (D) deposits (Brockamp *et al.* 1994) at the margins of the Bohemian Massif and the Black Forest, respectively, a coeval thermal event has been determined. A statistical treatment of all chronological data available from ore mineralizations and related wall alterations, mainly from the SW part of Central Europe, would give a positively skewed age curve with a maximum at the Early–Middle Jurassic boundary (Bonhomme 1983; Zuther & Brockamp 1988; Brockamp *et al.* 1994; Hagedorn & Lippolt 1994; Lancelot *et al.* 1995; Schaltegger *et al.* 1995; Wernicke & Lippolt 1993, 1997*a*, *b*; Brander & Lippolt 1999).

Hydrothermal remobilization in the unconformity-related vein-type deposits during the Jurassic coincides with a pronounced phase of subsidence in the Central European epicontinental basins and with a maximum in the formation of strata-bound ironstone deposits at the margin of the uplifted Variscan basement blocks. Remobilization took place during an era of little vertical displacement in the area under study, but at a time of considerable tectonic extension in the nearby Tethyan realm, particularly in western Switzerland and France (Lemoine *et al.* 1986; Borel 1995).

*Bismuth–cobalt–nickel deposits*

Areas of Bi–Co–Ni mineralization in the Erzgebirge (D/CZ) and in the Black Forest (D) at Wittichen were targets of short-term mining activities when Co was among the sought-after elements for glazing chinaware and Ag could be economically won as a byproduct. The 'five-element association' (Bi–Co–Ni–Ag–U) is one of the most enigmatic among the various hydrothermal element associations in Central Europe and its origin and source are still much discussed (Baumann 1958, 1965; Dill 1982; Behr *et al.* 1987; Wagner & Cook 1999).

The Bi–Co–Ni mineral assemblage consists of scattered rammelsbergite, safflorite, skutterudite-chloantite, linneite *sensu stricto*, gersdorffite, niccolite, bismuthinite, native bismuth and complex Cu–Bi sulphides (e.g. emplectite). The Bi–Co–Ni mineralization is encountered at shallow levels in some Variscan-age veins. In the Freiberg (D) district the Bi–Co–Ni–Ag formation predominantly occurs near vein intersections (Baumann 1958). The term 'Kobaltrücken' was coined by German miners who were interested in the strata-bound Kupferschiefer mineralizations at Richelsdorf (D) and Bieber (D) but were confronted with the strange vein mineralization of Ni–Co arsenides in areas where faults intersected with the Kupferschiefer seam. However, these Ni–Co minerals only attain ore grade in the area of the Kupferschiefer. The Ni–Co arsenides can also be found in unconformity-related vein-type deposits such as in the Nabburg-Wölsendorf (D) or Lichtenberg-Issigau fluorite districts in the western part of the Bohemian Massif (D). In the Rhenish Massif Ni–Co arsenides were encountered as the miners reached the shallow mining levels of the thrust-bound deposits in the siderite veins of the Siegerland (D) and the Pb–Zn veins at Ramsbeck (D) and Bensberg (D). In some mining areas of the Rhenish Massif, as well as in the Bergisches Land and the Lower Rhine Embayment, the age of Bi–Co–Ni mineralization can be confined to the Tertiary on structural and stratigraphic grounds. These vein-type deposits are without doubt of Alpine age and indicative of stages of strong remobilization along deep-seated structures.

The driving force for this Alpine remobilization in the extra-Alpine Region has not yet been fully understood. Initial phases of extension in the Proto-Atlantic Ocean and mantle processes in the Penninic Ocean (Alpine Tethys) are possible candidates for this remobilization.

The Cu–Co–Ni–Bi–Ag mineralization at Grimentz (CH) in the Permo-Carboniferous Casanna Schists of the Middle Penninic Bernhard Nappe (Briançonnais) may possibly bridge the gap between the extra-Alpine Ag–Bi–Co–Ni formation and the geodynamic–metallogenic evolution in the Alps (Halm 1945). Chalcopyrite, tetrahedrite, pyrite and bismuthinite in a gangue composed of ankerite, barite, quartz and albite were mined near Grimentz in the Anniviers Valley (CH). Possible genetic models range from classic hydrothermal to volcanosedimentary origins (Jaffé 1986). The mineralization at Kaltenberg (CH) occurs in the same geological setting. It more closely resembles the extra-Alpine Bi–Co–Ni formation with smaltite, chloanthite, safflorite, rammelsbergite, arsenopyrite, cobaltite, niccolite, maucherite and bismuth contained within ankerite, siderite and dolomite. Based on this example, Jurassic-age mantle processes in the Penninic Ocean (Alpine Tethys) are probably accountable for the Bi–Co–Ni mineralizations observed in Central Europe (see also section on Jurassic-age Ni deposits).

*Iron–lead–zinc and barite–fluorite deposits*

As indicated above, there are mineralizations and deposits in Mesozoic platform sediments with no direct link to any unconformity. In the Lower Saxony Basin, vein-type and metasomatic mineralization is found in Late Palaeozoic to Campanian-age sediments. Siderite occurs in metasomatic ore shoots in Upper Permian calcareous rocks at Hügel (D) (Stadler 1971). Carbon and O isotope studies by Stahl (1971) indicated that the carbonates infilling the veins are of hydrothermal origin, with the carbon having been derived from Lower Cretaceous Wealden coals. The veins are related to basic magmas which ascended along zones of crustal weakness (so-called Bramsche, Uchte and Vlotho massifs). A Late Cretaceous intrusion at about 6 km depth has been postulated based on seismic and magnetic surveys and this is considered to be made responsible for the coalification anomaly. However, numeric models of the temperature history do not show any thermal influence of the postulated magmatic intrusion (Senglaub *et al.* 2006).

A peculiar form of base-metal and sulphate deposits in the French Pre-Alps is related to deep-seated fault zones that were also used during halokinetic processes. Deposition of Pb, Zn, Sr, Ba near Menglon (F) and Condorcet (F) is related to major north–south directed fractures, coincident with Triassic salt domes. At Menglon the calamine-bearing ore body is within Tithonian breccias deposited on the flanks of vast submarine canyons. Menglon produced 22 000 t Zn and 400 t Pb. At Condorcet four ore bodies with celestite and barite have been found at the contact with a salt dome. The mineralization, accompanied by a little galena and sphalerite, replaces a brecciated dolomitic limestone of possible Bathonian age at the contact with Triassic cargneules (Bouladon 1989).

More than 90% of the workable Pb–Zn ore (150 000 t of Zn+Pb) in the Wiesloch deposit (D) was extracted up until 1953 from joint-controlled karst cavity fillings formed by Late Tertiary redeposition. Isotopically very heavy S, analysed from barite (+93‰), is due to hydrocarbon migration from Tertiary source rocks in the adjacent Upper Rhine Graben (Gehlen 1966). This mode of redeposition may also be observed in parts of the Upper Silesian Muschelkalk Pb–Zn deposits (PL).

*Polymetallic niobium deposits*

During the Tertiary, basic magmas were vented along the Upper Rhine Graben and gave rise to a small carbonatite-hosted Nb deposit in the Kaiserstuhl igneous complex at Schelingen (D) (Keller 1984; Fig. 21.4). Lava and pyroclastic rocks of essexitic and leucite–tephritic composition contain pyrochlor and Nb-perowskite. Before 1952 Nb-perowskite ore grading 0.078 wt% Nb was mined in the central parts of the Kaiserstuhl. Another carbonatite in the ultramafic Delitzsch (D) complex, of Upper Cretaceous age (Seifert *et al.* 2000), is located about 25 km NW of Leipzig and was drilled for its Pb–Zn–Cu (Ag,Te) mineralization.

## Summary and conclusions

The geodynamic evolution in Central Europe over the last 600 million years has provided economic geologists with a varied spectrum of mineral deposits and energy resources (see map on CD inside back cover). A wide variety of deposits was emplaced in tectonic settings ranging from extensional through to compressional regimes. Equivalent deposits may be encountered, albeit often much larger, outside Central Europe in modern foldbelts such as the Andes, and rift-related deposits quite similar to their Variscan counterparts are thought to have developed in older Precambrian series such as in the Scandinavian basement terrains. Although many of the deposits, especially in the metal sector, are mined out or no longer considered deposits by world standard, it is worth investigating old mine workings and mineralizations in Central Europe in order to develop new metallogenic models or refine existing ones to aid prospecting for mineral commodities and energy raw materials elsewhere in the world. Two thousand years of mining have provided an excellent coverage of the region and sparked numerous scientific investigations (see references and tables).

Rifting, continental breakup, crustal melting collision and updoming in Central Europe took place in two different metallotects, the Variscan and the Alpine. The sequence of metallogenetic events shows a high degree of cyclicity, closely resembling the scenario of the metallogenetic Wilson cycle, with stratabound deposits at the beginning and deposits related to continental collision being emplaced during the waning stages of the cycle. Not all of the events in the Variscan and Alpine metallotects find a direct match in the Wilson cycle, due to the particular geodynamic settings at the interface of two metallotects. Thrust-bound and unconformity-related deposits have been paid little attention in terms of the application of global tectonics models to metallogenetic terrain analyses (Sawkins 1984; Zentilli & Maksaev 1995; Laznicka 1999; Kay *et al.* 1999; Kay & Mpodozis 2001; Oyarzún 2000; Lips 2002). This chapter does not set out to create a new Alpine-type or Variscan-type model for metallogenic sequences but rather to update and refine well-established models.

The Variscan and Alpine metallotects, including non-metallic energy resources such as coal and petroleum are significantly different with respect to their composition but texturally resemble each other like the bottom (Variscan) and top (Alpine) of the same box (i.e. the Central European crustal lithosphere). Key elements used to describe the position of the various deposits are (sub)vertical structural elements and (sub)horizontal bounding surfaces and the principal processes to account for the origin of these Central European deposits are crustal specialization, element recycling and heat produced by intracrustal thrusting or delivered by subcrustal/mantle heat sources. The latter play a more significant role in the younger Alpine metallogenesis; frictional heat production is considered to be a major driving force for the Variscan metallogenesis.

## *Crustal specialization and subcrustal source*

In the course of the Variscan Orogeny, over short periods of time the crust was attenuated or even torn apart to give rise to what might called a 'mature' oceanic crust. Ophiolite sequences, as recorded from the Alpine foldbelts or even dismembered remnants of ophiolite sequences containing a peculiar suite of elements such Cr, PGE or Cyprus-type sulphide, magnesite and asbestos deposits, are very rare or can no longer be identified in the Variscan Orogen. In the Alpine realm, the formation of oceanic crust and ophiolite sequences played a much greater role in metallogenesis than in its Variscan predecessor, especially during Triassic and Jurassic times.

It is therefore not surprising that those elements typical of the upper mantle are more widespread in the Alpine metallotect than in the Variscan one. Mercury is a first-order marker element in the Alpine Orogen, while Sb, Mn, Cr and Ni, which represent the (ultra)basic igneous or subcrustal rocks, are second-order markers. Magnesite is characteristic for the Alpine metallogenesis and almost absent in the record of the Variscides. In contrast, Sn is almost exclusive to the Variscan metallotect and thus becomes a first-order marker element for the extra-Alpine realm. Tungsten and U deposits are widespread in the Variscan Orogen. Although not restricted to the Variscan Orogen, they may be considered as second-order marker elements. Granitophile elements such as Sn, U and Li characterize the Variscan metallogenesis.

The two metallotects also differ with respect to the budget and source of elements. The Variscan metallogenesis in Central Europe outside the Alps is an 'ensialic metallogenesis', acting under more or less closed-system conditions on a thick lithospheric crust, whereas the Alpine successor shows all the hallmarks of an 'ensimatic metallogenesis', since for certain periods of time the system was open for elements to be introduced from subcrustal sources (Dill 1985*a*). The Variscan metallogenesis may be taken largely as a metallogenetic 'continuum' with little interruption by large-scale seafloor spreading, whereas the Alpine metallogenesis in the Tethyan basin was either indirectly or directly affected by the formation of oceanic crust in the Penninic, Meliata and Vardar zones.

The elements of the five-element association (Ag–Bi–Co–Ni–U), representatives of which are found in deposits within the uplifted Variscan basement block as well as in platform sediments covering the Variscan basement in the extra-Alpine region, were at least in part derived from a subcrustal source and as such leave a basic or ensimatic imprint on an otherwise ensialic metallogenesis in extra-Alpine Europe. The emplacement of the five-element association (Ag–Bi–Co–Ni–U) in extra-Alpine Europe is discussed in the context of extensive seafloor spreading at the Triassic–Jurassic boundary in the Alpine domain. Thus the five-element association (Ag–Bi–Co–Ni–U) may be the missing link between an ensimatic Alpine and ensialic extra-Alpine metallogenesis.

## *Element recycling*

In the ensimatic Alpine Orogen, elements typical of (ultra)basic rocks are widespread but not homogeneously distributed across the Alpine metallotect. Chromium, Ni, Hg and Sb tend to be concentrated in the Dinarides, the Carpathians and the Apennines. The same elements are rather scarce in the Alps. Deposits with Sb and Au are abundant in the Carpathians. Is this compositional pattern a heritage of the Variscan metallogenesis?

Towards the NW, in the Swiss Alps, Alpine metallogenetic reactivation gradually fades out into what might be called a Moldanubian metallotect overprinted by Alpine metallogenic processes (Fig. 21.27). In the Western Alps in Switzerland and France the older Variscan mineralization was superimposed by Alpine processes. Element assemblages (Cu, Pb, Zn, U, F), particularly at the NW edge of the Western Alps, are very similar to those of the supposed Variscan 'parent' materials (Fig. 21.27).

A similar but less pronounced effect may be recognized at the SE edge of the Bohemian Massif, where the Variscan core zone was brought into contact with the Carpathians. Both the Moldanubian Zone and the adjacent Western Carpathians have abundant Sb and Au deposits.

There is a marked contrast between the SE and the SW extremities of the Variscides. With the aid of chemical fingerprinting, a rough correlation between mineral assemblages altered by Alpine thermometamorphic processes and the overall

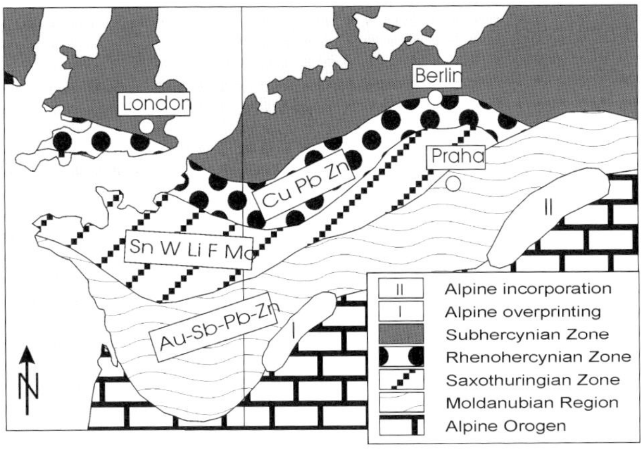


**Fig. 21.27.** Geodynamic setting of the European Variscides and element assemblages typical of the different geodynamic zones. Overprinting and incorporation of predecessor mineralization from the Moldanubian region are shown by Roman numerals. The area to the east of the vertical line denotes the area under consideration in the text and covered by the map (see CD inside back cover).

Variscan mineralization in the Central European core region can be achieved in the outermost Western Alps. In the SE, the Variscan mineralization can no longer be detected as such, since it was incorporated by plate tectonic processes into the present-day Carpathians (Dill 1998).

In the central parts of the Alps, large-scale north-directed nappe movements have blurred and concealed the contact between Alpine and Variscan Europe. Thus neither superimposition nor incorporation can be invoked to explain the Variscan mineralization.

### *Element preconcentration and closed-system conditions in the Variscan metallotect*

A closer look at the element composition of strata-bound, thrust-bound and collision-related deposits in the Central European Variscides (endogenous cycle) reveals that there is a close link between the element composition of the mineral deposits and the geodynamic position of the host rocks (Fig. 21.27). A careful examination of the sediment-hosted deposits in Mesozoic to Cenozoic platform sediments suggests a link between element composition of the deposit and the level of erosion in the source area (exogenous cycle).

In the Moldanubian Zone of the Variscan Orogen, deposits with Au, Sb, U and some Pb and Zn occur. This area constitutes a 'core' Variscan region. To the north and east, the Saxothuringian Zone, forms almost a geodynamic 'onion skin' around the Moldanubian core, U, W, Li, F, Mo and Sn deposits have been mined in this area for more than a century. Moving further away from the 'core' area, the NW 'onion skin', the Rhenohercynian Zone, does not host deposits containing any of these granitophile elements, but instead contains abundant deposits of Pb, Zn, Cu and barite.

A similar pattern may also be seen for the barite–fluorite mineral association, which shows significant changes from the Moldanubian to the Rhenoherynian zones. In the Moldanubian Zone fluorite is more common than barite in F–Ba vein-type deposits. This may be due to the granites which are often enriched in F during the waning stages of granite formation. In contrast, $Ba^{2+}$ may substitute for $K^{+}$ in the unit cell of K-feldspar which is a common rock-forming mineral of greywackes in the Rhenohercynian Zone. This mineral trend can be traced as far south as the SW Swiss Alps (Les Trappistes deposit (CH)). Towards the north the barite/fluorite ratio is reversed and fluorite is totally absent from veins in the Harz Mountains.

These mineral and element variations, discussed as a function of the geodynamic position, suggest that there was a preconcentration of elements in the various lithospheric plates of the Variscan basement. Independent support is furnished by Pb, Sr, and Sm–Nd isotope analyses of galena, fluorite and barite from various mineral deposits which were compared with the isotope ratios of potential source rocks in the various geodynamic realms. The metallogenetic system of the Central European Variscides is supposed to have been more or less 'closed' or 'self-sufficient' as far as the element budget of Late Palaeozoic strata-bound, thrust-bound and collision-related deposits are concerned.

The post-Variscan metallogenesis in the intermontane Permo-Carboniferous rift basins and in the Mesozoic and Cenozoic epicontinental basins also shows almost 'closed-system' conditions as far as metal redeposition is concerned. Debris and metalliferous solutions were delivered by the uplifted basement rocks bounding the epicontinental basins and grabens. As far as the accumulation of organic matter/energy resources is concerned, climatic conditions played a similar significant role to basin subsidence and uplift in the hinterland. The interplay of basin subsidence and the provision of accommodation space were decisive for the formation of the coal deposits.

The variation of the lithology of the Variscan basement with depth has been revealed by uplift and denudation and is also reflected in the element spectrum of Mesozoic strata-bound deposits, commencing with Cu–Pb–Zn deposits (gneisses) and leading to U deposits (granites) (Dill 1994). Five metallogenetic sequences may be delineated in the Mesozoic–Cenozoic basin fill in the extra-Alpine realm, four of which begin with base-metal mineralization in fluvial environments and terminate with the precipitation of Sr- and F-bearing mineralization in a mixed clastic–carbonate marine shelf environment (sabkha). Metallogenetic sequences in these basins in the Germanic Province reflect marine transgressions and regression, which are correlative with rifting and spreading events outside of the stable European craton, e.g. in the Tethyan or Atlantic oceans.

### *Vertical structure zones versus horizontal bounding surfaces*

Horizontal bounding surfaces called (para-)sequence boundaries, transgressive surfaces and maximum flooding surfaces are key elements in sequence stratigraphy (Van Wagoner *et al.* 1990). The methodology of sequence stratigraphy is well established in hydrocarbon exploration and has been successfully applied to coal resource evaluation. However, it can also be used for mineral commodities (Holz *et al.* 2002; Dill *et al.* 2003).

Metallic and non-metallic commodities are concentrated in seams, lenses, plugs and veins. (Sub)vertical structure zones of various dimensions act as conduits for the metalliferous solutions and provide the space for mineralization. Horizontal bounding surfaces may be described as transgressive surfaces (e.g. Kupferschiefer deposits). Unconformities control the distribution of vein-type deposits and strata-bound Pb–Zn–F–Ba deposits in space and are equivalent to a type-one sequence boundary in terms of sequence stratigraphy. As with hydrocarbon exploration, locating the oil or gas trap is the prime goal; the reconstruction of the age of filling is secondary. Since the majority of metallic or non-metallic deposits have been formed from metal-bearing solutions, it is pertinent to apply methods that have proved valuable in the petroleum industry to mineral commodities.

The Mid-German Crystalline High, a NE–SW striking suture zone, and the Tornquist-Teyssere Zone were both zones of considerable crustal weakness. Both acted as hosts to porphyry-type and subvolcanic Cu–Mo–Hg–W–Au mineralizations during the waning stages of crustal accretion. Within the Kupferschiefer Basin, these sutures were crucial since they controlled the emplacement of the 'genuine' base-metal deposits in an otherwise euxinic environment with 'low-metal concentration' related to a shallow-marine transgression onto the Variscan basement or underlying Permo-Carboniferous red-beds. The intersection of a horizontal transgression surface with vertical deep-seated lineaments may, thus, guide the exploration geologist to the metal deposit.

Other subvertical structures of metallogenic significance include the Upper Rhine Graben or the Eger (Ohre) Graben. Such (sub)vertical structures are key elements in the understanding of the position of vein-type deposits. Another is provided by horizontal bounding surfaces (sequence boundaries or unconformities). Two sets of the latter have been identified as significant for the Central European metallogenesis: (1) Late Variscan/Early Alpine; and (2) Late Alpine.

### *Structural facies variation*

Vertical structural zones and horizontal bounding or erosional surfaces were discussed in the previous section to delineate supergene and near-surface hypogene strata-bound and vein-type deposits. Between thrust-bound, fold-bound and hydrothermal metamorphogenic deposits and unconformity-related deposits there are only quantitative rather than qualitative differences (measured by time and depth). In the following paragraphs some examples are selected to highlight this 'telescoping' of metallogenetic processes and illustrate these gradual changes.

Hydrothermal–metamorphogenic siderite mineralization in the Alpine metallotect was caused by *per ascensum* fluids while subsequently in the Permian magnesite mineralization developed as a result of *per descensum* fluids at the southern edge of the Variscan craton beneath the Early Alpine unconformity. During the Late Carboniferous, in the Variscan Foreland Basin an unconformity truncated coal-bearing series along the NW margin of the rising Variscan craton. Veins of Pb–Zn intersecting the coal measures are terminated by this unconformity and covered by Cretaceous platform sediments. The unconformity-related Pb–Zn deposits of the Ruhr Basin at the edge of the rising basement are strikingly different from vein-type deposits of Variscan age in the inner zones of the Rhenish Massif. True thrust-bound and fold-related cleavage veins with siderite, Pb, Zn and Sb developed in the Rhenish Massif. This occurred when the Rhenohercynian crust was consumed during Devonian and Early Carboniferous times by southward subduction. At the same time Sb-, Au-, Pb- and Zn-bearing veins developed in the Vosges, Black Forest and Bohemian Massif areas. These are similar in terms of the element compositions, but totally different in terms of the style of their host structures. Deformation took place at a much deeper level and regional metamorphism attained a higher grade in the Saxothuringian and Moldanubian zones than in the Rhenohercynian Zone. The textural differences in these vein-type deposits are a function of time and depth.

Along a transect from the NW to the SE in the Variscides, thrust-bound Sb veins were emplaced at rather shallow levels in Upper Palaeozoic country-rocks and these give way to thrust-bound Au–Sb veins along the Fichtelgebirge-Erzgebirge Anticline in the Saxothuringian Zone. These Au–Sb veins in the Saxothuringian Zone are located next to collision-related Sn–W and Ag–Pb–Zn veins of granitic origin (e.g. Freiberg). The Fichtelgebirge-Erzgebirge Anticline marks a zone of crustal weakness at depth in the Earth's crust (where the heat flow was anomalously high). Thrust-bound and collision-related ore deposits are genetically related to these structures, suggesting a similar mode of emplacement along thrust planes. They differ, however, in terms of their distance from the heat source or the depth of formation.

In the allochthonous tectonic units (Erbendorf-Vohenstrauß Zone) pegmatitic mobilizates that represent metamorphogenic deposits *par excellence* gradually merge with true pegmatites resulting from the Late Variscan collision of lithospheric plates. In the Moldanubian region U, Ag, Pb, Zn and Au veins associated with deep-seated linear structures occur within or next to the Variscan granites.

Radiometric age dating has provided evidence that while granite-related U mineralization was still evolving at depth in the Saxothuringian Zone, hypogene vein mineralization with fluorite commenced at shallow depths beneath the Early Alpine unconformity. At the same time tropical climatic conditions promoted kaolinitization and pervasive supergene alteration of the basement rocks on the post-Variscan/Early Alpine peneplain, thus truncating the uplifted Variscan basement blocks.

## Economic geology and ecology in Central Europe, past and present

Non-metallic deposits and energy resources (excluding U) still play a vital role in the economy of Central Europe. Industrial minerals and coal will be of importance for the domestic market in the European Union in the near future. In contrast, mining of metallic raw materials declined rapidly in Central Europe and at the present time, is a stable product only in the economy of Poland. Geological and political reasons caused the decline of metal mining in Central Europe.

During the twentieth centrury, many of the metal deposits in Central Europe became more and more sidelined as increasing number of giant ore deposits came on-stream elsewhere in the world. Limited resources, and the complicated structures of the host rocks and ore bodies rendered mining very difficult in many Central European ore deposits. There is a huge number of 'large-tonnage/low-grade' deposits outside of Europe providing the market with all kinds of commodities, especially Cu and Au. Many of the classic vein-type and small strata-bound deposits in Central Europe cannot compete successfully with these deposits.

Exploitation of ore deposits in Central Europe was in full swing in the first half of the twentieth century, which may be called the 'Century of the World Wars'. A saying by miners from the 'Kleine Johannes' (Little John) Fe mine at Pegnitz (south Bayreuth) tells a lot about the political impact on mining and the size of the deposits: 'When the wheel in the head-frame of the "Kleine Johannes" is spinning again, we are heading for war'. Many of the mines were only profitable before, during and after the two World Wars, when imports were hampered and an insatiable need for metals existed to build weapons or to rebuild what was left afterwards.

There is a geological border between extra-Alpine and Alpine Europe running almost east–west (Fig. 21.1) and there was a political border ('the Iron Curtain') running north–south. It separated the Warsaw Pact countries to the east from the NATO countries to the west. Both had very different views with regard to deposits and resources. The Warsaw Pact collapsed in 1991 causing the disbandment of the economic treaty of the COMECON. During the change from planned to free-market economy, many deposits in east Central Europe were downgraded to some level of mineralization.

Another severe blow was dealt to mining, particularly of U, in Central Europe by the 'ecological reorientation' of the late twentieth century. Costly reclamation of open-cast mines and mine spoil heaps and stringent mining regulations minimize the likelihood of a company venturing into exploration or exploitation in a densely populated area like Central Europe. The 'demonizing' of radioactivity added to the slump in mining. Unbalanced handling of economic/extractive geology versus environmental geology, simply called the 'E & E issue' or the 'conflict of use', has confronted many engineers, geologists and entrepreneurs with a host of problems which are difficult to resolve. The situation is comparable with an example from Greek mythology: working in the field of extractive geology in Central Europe is often like navigating a ship between Scylla (economy) and Charibdis (ecology) (Dill 1995).

For valuable comments on the paper and for directing our thoughts to some papers, we would like to extend our gratitude to our colleagues: F. Ebner (University of Leoben, Austria), M. Geluk (Shell, Netherlands), B. Kříbek (Czech Geological Survey, Prague, Czech Republic), P. Steffens (Geological Survey of Lower Saxony, Hannover, Germany) and H. Wagner (Federal Institute for Geosciences and Natural, Hannover, Germany). We also thank numerous unnamed colleagues, from both industry and academia, for providing help in the preparation of the manuscript. Further credit and appreciation is extended to IHS Energy for providing access to some of the petroleum-related data. We acknowledge with thanks the comments made by R. Littke (RWTH Aachen), R. Schaeffer (University of Applied Sciences, Bochum) and D. Rickard (Cardiff) during their reviews of the text and map.

## References

AICHLER, J., FOJT, B. & VANĚČEK, M. 1995. Metallogenesis. *In:* DALLMEYER, R. D., FRANKE, W. & WEBER, K. (eds) *Pre-Permian Geology of Central and Eastern Europe.* Springer, Berlin, 512–517.

AMBATIELLO, P. & NEY, P. 1983. The Berchtesgaden salt mine. *Proceedings of IV. ISMIDA (International Symposium of Mineral Deposits of the Alps)*, Berchtesgaden. Special Publications, Society of Geology and Applied Mineralogy, Springer, New York, **3**, 146–154.

ANDERSON, K. B. & LEPAGE, B. A. 1995. Analysis of fossil resins from Axel Heiberg Island, Canadian Arctic. *In*: ANDERSON, K. G. & CRELLING, J. C. (eds) *Amber, Resinite and Fossil Resins.* American Chemical Society, Washington, DC, Symposium Series, **617**, 170–192.

ANDRÁŠ, P. 1983. *Genetic problems of Sb- and Au-bearing ore mineralizatiom at the Pezinok deposit.* Open file report, Geofond Bratislava [in Slovak].

ANDREATTA, C. 1957. Un contributo alla conoscenza dell'origine dei giacimenti di magnesite: giacimenti metasomatici di Zumpanell (Ortles). *Rendiconti Società Mineralogica Italiana*, **13**, 71–106.

ANDRITZKY, G. 1963. Über Markasit, Kryptomelan, Lithiophorit und Kaolinit aus den Eisenerzlagerstätten von Sulzbach-Rosenberg/Opf. und Auerbach/Opf. *Neues Jahrbuch für Mineralogie Monatsheft*, **1963**, 180 -186.

ANDRITZKY, G. 1964. Über einige Kluft- und Drusenmineralien aus den kretazischen Eisenerzlagerstätten der Oberpfalz: Lithiophorit, Todorokit und Dufrenit. *Geologische Blätter Nordostbayern*, **14**, 14–20.

ANELLI, L., MATTAVELLI, L. & PIERI, M. 1996. Structural-stratigraphic evolution of Italy and its petroleum systems. *In*: ZIEGLER, P. A. & HORVATH, F. (eds) *Peri-Tethys Memoir 2, Structure and Prospects of Alpine Basins and Forelands.* Mémoires du Muséum National d' Histoire Naturelle, **170**, 455–483.

ANTONIDES, L. E. 1998. Diatomite. *In: Mineral Commodity Summary 1998.* USGS, Reston, 56–57

ARCHANGELSKIJ, S. A. & DANIEL, J. 1981. *Report about Pb isotopic results and the replacement of the concurrent elements in the U-bearing Permian sediments.* Open file report, Geofond Bratislava.

ARZMÜLLER, G., BUCHTA, S., RALBOVSKY, E., WESSELY, G. 2006. The Vienna Basin. *In:* GOLONKA, J. & PICHA, F. J. (eds) *The Carpathians and Their Foreland: Geology and Hydrocarbon Resources,* American Association Petroleum Geologists, Memoirs, **84**.

BACH, D., BORSDORF, K.-H., HETZER, H., LÄCHELT, S., METTCHEN, H.-J. & NÖLDEKE, W. 1976. The iron ore deposits in the German Democratic Republic. *Iron Ore Deposits of Europe*, Vol. 1. BGR, Hannover, 161–164.

BÄCHTIGER, K. 1963. Die Kupfer- und Uranimeralisationen der Mürtschenalp (Kt. Glarus, Schweiz). *Beiträge zur Geologie der Schweiz: Geotechnische Serie*, **38**, 1–113.

BÄCHTIGER, K., RÜDLINGER, G. & CABALZAR, W. 1972. Scheelit in Quarz- und Fluorit-Gängen am Calanda (Kt. Graubünden). *Schweizerische Mineralogische und Petrogrographische Mitteilungen*, **52**, 561–563.

BADOUX, H. 1966. Description gèologique des mines et salines de Bex et leurs environs. *Beiträge zur Geologie der Schweiz: Geotechnische Serie*, **41**, 1–56.

BAKOS, F., BRONDI, A. & PERNA, G. 1972. The age of mineral deposits in the Permian volcanites of Trentino Alto Adige (Northern Italy). *Proceeding 2nd International Symposium on Mineral Deposits in the Alps*, Ljubljana, 181–194.

BALLA, Z., HOVORKA, D., KUZMIN, M. & VINOGRADOV, V. 1983. Mesozoic ophiolites of the Bükk Mountains (North Hungary). *Ofioliti*, **8**, 1, 5–46.

BALLHORN, R. & WOLLENBERG, P. 1979. Uranvererzungen im mittleren Keuper von Baden-Württemberg. *Zeitschrift der Deutschen Geologischen Gesellschaft*, **130**, 527–534.

BANÁS, M. 1991. Pitchblende in Ag-Bi-Se paragenesis from Kletno deposit, Sudety Mts. SW Poland. *In:* CUNEY, M., VON PECHMANN, E., RIMSAITE, J., SIMOVA, F., SOERENSEN, H. & AUGUSTITHIS, S. S. (eds) *Primary Radioactive Minerals.* Theophrastus Publications, Athens, 269–285.

BÁRDOSSY, GY. 1969. Bauxite deposits of Hungary. *In: Bauxite–alumina–aluminium: Proceedings of the Second International Symposium of ICSOBA*, Budapest, 1969, Budapest Research Institute for Non-Ferrous Metals, 9–20.

BARIĆ, G., TARI, V. & IVKOVIĆ, Z. 2001. *Petroleum systems in the southern part of the Pannonian Basin, Croatia.* AAPG European Region Conference, Prague, Abstract Book, 106.

BARTALSKÝ, J. 1993. *Smolník – Stadt des Kupfererzbergbaues.* Mineralia Slovaca Monograph.

BARTALSKÝ, B. & FINKA, O. 1999. Up-to-date results of to the geological exploration of the 1th vein system of the Kremnica precious metal veins. *Mineralia Slovaca*, **31**, 291–296.

BARTHEL, F. & HAHN, L. 1985. Sedimentray uranium occurrences in eastern Europe with special reference to sandstone formations. *IAEA Tec Doc*, **328**, 51–67.

BAUBERGER, W. 1957. Über die "Albit-Pegmatite" der Münchberger Gneismasse und ihre Nebengesteine. *Geologica Bavarica*, **36**, 1–77.

BAUMANN, L. 1958. Tektonik und Genesis der Erzlagerstätte von Freiberg (Zentralteil). *Freiberger Forschungshefte*, **C 46**, 1–208.

BAUMANN, L. 1965. Die Erzlagerstätten der Freiberger Randgebiete. *Freiberger Forschungshefte*, **C 188**, 1–268.

BAUMANN, L. 1979. Some aspects of mineral deposits formation and the metallogeny of Central Europe. *Verhandlungen der Geologischen Bundesanstalt*, **3**, 205–220.

BAUMANN, L., KÖLBEL, B., KRAFT, S., LÄCHELT, J., RENTZSCH, J. & SCHMIDT, K. 1986. German Democratic Republic. *In*: DUNNING, F. W. & EVANS, A. M. (eds) *Mineral Deposits of Europe*, Vol. 3, *Central Europe*. Institution of Mining and Metallurgy, and Mineralogical Society, London, 303–329.

BAUMANN, L., KUSCHKA, E. & SEIFERT, TH. 2000. *Lagerstätten des Erzgebirges*. Enke im Thieme Verlag, Stuttgart.

BAUMGÄRTL, U. & BUROW, J. 2005. Die Grube Lengenbach im Binntal/Wallis Schweiz. *Aufschluss*, **56**, 261–374.

BAYERISCHES STAATSMINISTERIUM FÜR WIRTSCHAFT UND VERKEHR 1979. *Rohstoffprogramm für Bayern*. München.

BECHTEL, A., ELLIOTT, W. C., WAMPLER, J. M. & OSZCZEPALSKI, S.

1999. Clay mineralogy, crystallinity, and K-Ar ages of illites within the Polish Zechstein Basin; implications for the age of Kupferschiefer mineralization. *Economic Geology*, **94**, 261–272.

BECHTEL, A., GRATZER, R., PÜTTMANN, W. & OSZCZEPALSKI, S. 2001. Variable alteration of organic matter in relation to metal zoning at the Rote Fäule Front (Lubin-Sieroszowice mining district, SW Poland.). *Organic Geochemistry*, **32**, 377–395.

BECHTEL, A., GRUBER, W., SACHSENHOFER, R. F., GRATZER, R. & PÜTTMANN, W. 2003. Depositional environment of the Late Miocene Hausruck lignite (Alpine Foreland Basin): Insights from petrography, organic geochemistry, and stable carbon isotopes. *International Journal of Coal Geology*, **53**, 153–180.

BECK, B. & SERNEELS, V. 2000. The Mont Chemin iron mines and the ancient iron production in Wallis, Switzerland. *In:* CUCINI TIZZONI, C. & TIZZONI, M. (eds) *Il ferro nelle Alpi, Atti del convengo*, Bienno Italia, 2–4 Octobre 1998, Breno I, 167.

BEHR, H.-J., HORN, E. E., FRENTZEL-BEYME, K. & REUTEL, C. 1987. Fluid inclusion characteristics of the variscan and post-variscan mineralizing fluids in the Federal Republic of Germany. *Chemical Geology*, **61**, 273–285.

BEHRMANN, J. H., HERMANN, O., HORSTMANN, M., TANNER, D. C. & BERTRAND, G. 2003. Anatomy and kinematics of oblique continental rifting revealed: A three-dimensional case study of the southeast Upper Rhine graben (Germany). *American Association of Petroleum Geologists Bulletin*, **87**, 1105–1121.

BELOCKY, R., SACHSENHOFER, R. F. & POHL, W. 1991. Neue Argumente für eine miozäne epithermale Gemese der Antimonerzlagerstätte Schlaining (Burgenland/Österreich): Flüssigkeitseinschlußuntersuchungen und das Inkohlungsbild der benachbarten Tertiärbecken. *Berg- und hüttenmännische Monatshefte*, **136**, 209–213.

BENDA, L. & PASCHEN, S. 1993. Kieselgur (Diatomit)-ein vielseitig genutzter Rohstoff. *Geologisches Jahrbuch*, **A142**, 383–398.

BERAN, A., FAUPL, P. & HAMILTON, W. 1983. Die Manganschiefer der Strubbergschichten (Nördliche Kalkalpen, Österreich) – eine diagenetisch geprägte Mangankarbonatvererzung. *Tschermaks Mineralogische und Petrographische Mitteilungen*, **31**, 175–192.

BERGER, J.-P., REICHENBACHER, B., *et al.* 2005. Paleogeography of the Upper Rhine Graben (URG) and the Swiss Molasse Basin (SMB) from Eocene to Pliocene. *International Journal of Earth Sciences*, 94, 697–710.

BERMANEC, V., ZEBEC, V. & BRAJKOVIĆ, Z. 1987. Searlesite from the Salt mine Tušanj, Tuzla, Yugoslavia. *Geološki vjesnik*, **40**, 75–80.

BERMANEC, V., AMBRUSTER, T., TIBLJAŠ, D., STURMAN, D. & KNIEWALD, B. 1994. Tuzlaite, $NaCa[B_5O_8(OH)_2]\cdot 3H_2O$, a new mineral with pentaborate sheet structure from the Tuzla salt mine, Bosnia and Hercegovina. *American Mineralogist*, **79**, 562–569.

BERNARD, J. H., 1961. Regional primary zoning of ore vein fillings in the metallogenetic region of Spišsko-gemerské rudohoří (Czechoslovakia). *Acta Universitatis Carolinae, Geologica*, **1**, 9–20.

BERNARD, J. H., CADEK, J. & KLOMINSKY, J. 1976. Genetic problems of the Mesozoic fluorite-barite mineralization of the Bohemian Massif. *Geological Institute Warsaw*, **1976**, 217–226.

BESSEREAU, G., ROURE, F., KOTARBA, M., KUSMIEREK, J. & STRZETELSKI, W. 1996. Structure and habitat of the Polish Carpathians. *In:* ZIEGLER, P. A. & HORVATH, F. (eds) *Peri-Tethys Memoir 2, Structure and Prospects of Alpine Basins and Forelands.* Mémoires du Muséum National d' Histoire Naturelle, **170**, 343–373.

BEST, G. 1989. Die Grenze Zechstein/Buntsandstein in Nordwest-Deutschland nach Borhmessungen. *Zeitschrift der deutschen geologischen Gesellschaft*, **140**, 73–85.

BJØRLYKKE, A. & SANGSTER, D. F. 1981. An overview of sandstone lead deposits and their relation to red-bed copper and carbonate-hosted lead-zinc deposits. *Economic Geology* (75th Anniversary volume), 178–213.

BLANKENBURG VON, F. & DAVIS, J. H. 1995. Slab break off: a model for syncollisional magmatism and tectonics in the Alps. *Tectonics*, **14**, 120–131.

BLUNDELL, D. J., KARNKOWSKI, P. H., ALDERTON, D. H. M., OSZCZEPALSKI, S. & KUCHA, H. 2003. Copper mineralization of the Polish Kupferschiefer: a proposed basement fault-fracture system of fluid flow. *Economic Geology*, **98**, 1487–1495.

BOIGK, H. 1981. Oberrheingraben. *In:* BOIGK, H. (ed.) *Erdöl und Erdölgas in der Bundesrepublik Deutschland.* Enke, Stuttgart, 194–234.

BOIRON, M. C., BARAKAT, A., CATHELINEAU, M., BANKS, D. A., DURISOVÁ, J. & MORÁVEK, P. 2001. Geometry and P–V–T–X conditions of microfissural ore fluid migration: the Mokrsko gold deposit (Bohemia). *Chemical Geology*, **173**, 207–225.

BOIRON, M.-CH., CATHELINEAU, M., BANKS, D. A., FOURCADE, S. & VALLANCE, J. 2003. Mixing of metamorphic and surficial fluids during the uplift of the Hercynian upper crust: consequences for gold deposition. *Chemical Geology*, **194**, 119–141.

BONATTI, E., ZERBI, M., KAY, R. & RYDDELL, H. 1976. Metalliferous deposits from the Apennine ophiolites: Mesozoic equivalents of the modern deposits from oceanic spreading centers. *Geological Society of America Bulletin*, **87**, 83–94.

BONHOMME, M. G., BÜHMANN, D. & BESNUS, Y. 1983. Reliability of K/Ar-dating of clays and silifications associated with vein mineralizations in western Europe. *Geologische Rundschau*, **72**, 105–117.

BONI, M. & LARGE, D. 2003. Nonsulphide zinc mineralization in Europe; an overview. *Economic Geology*, **98**, 715–729.

BONI, M., ALT, J., BALASSONE, G. & RUSSO, A. 1992. A reappraisal of the stratabound ores at the Mid-Ordovician unconformity in SW Sardinia. *In*: CAMIGNANI, L. & SASSI, F. P. (eds) *Contribution to the Geology of Italy with Special Regard to the Paleozoic Basements IGCP N. 276, Newsletter* **5**, Siena, 57–60.

BOREL, G. 1995. Préalpes médianes romandes: courbes de subsidence et implications géodynamiques. *Bulletin de Société de Vaudois de Science Naturelle*, **83**, 293–315.

BOROJEVIĆ-ŠOŠTARIĆ, S. 2004. *Genesis of siderite-barite-polysulphide ore deposits within Paleozoic of Internal Dinarides.* Master thesis, University of Zagreb [In Croatian with English summary].

BOSSOWSKI, A. 1995. Lower Silesian Coal Basin. *In:* ZDANOWSKI, A., ZAKOWA, H. (eds) *The Carboniferous System in Poland.* Polish Geological Institute, **CXLVIII,** 173–175.

BOTTKE, H. 1963. Zur Kenntnis der dichten Roteisenerz aus Eisenerzlagerstätten des Lahn-Dill-Typs und deren Bildungsbedingungen. *Erzmetall*, **16**, 437–443.

BOTTKE, H. 1965. Die exhalativ-sedimentären devonischen Roteisensteinlagerstätten des Ostsauerlandes. *Beiheft Geologisches Jahrbuch*, **63**, 1–147.

BOTTKE, H. 1969. Die Eisen-Manganerze der Grube Dr. Geier bei Bingen (Rhein) als Verwitterungsbildungen des Mangans vom Typ Lindener Mark. *Mineralium Deposita*, **4**, 355–367.

BOULADON, J. 1989. France and Luxembourg. *In:* DUNNING, F. W. *et al.* (eds) *Mineral Deposits of Europe*, Vol. 4/5, *Southwest and Eastern Europe, with Iceland.* Institution of Mining and Metallurgy and Mineralogical Society, London, Alden Press, Oxford, 37–104.

BOUSKA, V. & PESEK, J. 1999. Quality parameters of lignite of the North Bohemian Basin in the Czech Republic in comparison with the world average lignite. *International Journal of Coal Geology*, **40**, 211–235.

BRANDER, T. & LIPPOLT, H.-J. 1999. Das Alter der Roteisenerze in der Verkieselungszone bei Rammelsbach (Münstertal, Südschwarzwald) nach (U+Th)/4. He-Untersuchungen *Jahreshefte des Landesamts für Geologie, Rohstoffe und Bergbau Baden-Württemberg*, **38**, 7–42.

BRAUN, K., DRAVEC, J., SLOVIĆ, V., CRNOGAJ, S., VALKOVIĆ, V. & MAKLJANIĆ, J. 1983. Uranium ore occurrences from Mts. Papuk and Krndija (in Croatian). *Geološki vjesnik*, **36**, 111–115.

BREITER, K., FÖRSTER, H.-J. & SELTMANN, R. 1999. Variscan silicic magmatism and related tin-tungsten mineralization in the Erzgebirge-Slavkovsky les metallogenic province. *Mineralium deposita*, **34**, 505–531.

BRENCHLEY, P. J. & ŠTORCH, P. 1989. Environmental changes in the Hirnantian (upper Ordovician) of the Prague Basin, Czechoslovakia. *Geological Journal*, **24**, 165–181.

BRIGO, L., CAMANA, G., RODEGHIERO, F. & POTENZA, R. 2001. Carbonate-hosted siliceous crust type mineralization of Carnic Alps (Italy-Austria). *Ore Geology Reviews*, **17**, 199–214.

BRIL, H., MARIGNAC, CH., CATHELINEAU, M., TOLLON, F., CUNEY, M. & BOIRON, M. C. 1994. Metallogenesis of the French Massif Central: Time-space relationships between ore deposition and tectono-magmatic events. *In:* KEPPIE, J. D. (ed.) *Pre-Mesozoic Geology in France and Related Areas.* Springer, Berlin, 379–402.

BROCKAMP, O., ZUTHER, M. & CLAUER, N. 1987. Epigenetic-hydrothermal origin of the sediment-hostet Müllenbach uranium deposit, Baden-Baden, W-Germany. *Monograph Series on Mineral Depostis*, **27**, 87–89.

BROCKAMP, O., CLAUER, N. & ZUTHER, M. 1994. K–Ar dating of episodic Mesozoic fluid migrations along the fault system of Gernsbach between the Moldanubian and Saxothuringian (northern Black Forest). *Geologische Rundschau*, **83**, 180–185.

BROSKA, I. & UHER, P. 2001. Whole-rock chemistry and genetic typology of the West Carpathian Variscan granites. *Geoogica Carpathica*, **52**, 79–90.

BROWN, A. C. 2003. Redbeds: sources of metals for sediment-hosted stratiform copper, sandstone copper, sandstones lead, and sandstone uranium-vanadium deposits. *Geotext* **4**, 121–133.

BUCHER, K. & FREY, M. 1994. *Petrogenesis of Metamorphic Rocks*. Springer, Berlin.

BUDER, W., SCHUPPAN, W., SELTMANN, R. & WOLF, M. 1993. The Poehla Haemmerlein deposit. *In:* SELTMANN, R., REIMAR & BREITER, K. (eds) *Hercynian tin granites and associated mineralisation from the Saxonian and Bohemian parts of the Erzgebirge*. Excursion Guide, IAGOD Working Group on Tin and Tungsten, GeoForschungs Zentrum, Potsdam, 67–71.

BRUGGER, J., MCPHAIL, D. C., WALLACE, M. & WATERS, J. 2003. Formation of willemite in hydrothermal environments. *Economic Geology*, **98**, 819–835.

BRUKNER-WEIN, A., HETÉNYI, M. & VETÖ, I. 1990. Organic geochemistry of an anoxic cycle: A case history from the Oligocene section, Hungary. *Organic Geochemistry*, **15**, 123–130.

BUBENICEK, L. 1968. Géologie des minerais de fer oolithique. *Mineralium Deposita*, **3**, 89–108.

BÜKER, C., LITTKE, R. & WELTE, D. H. 1995. 2D-modelling of the thermal evolution of Carboniferous and Devonian sedimentary rocks of the eastern Ruhr basin and northern Rhenish Massif, Germany. *Zeitschrift der Deutschen Geologischen Gesellschaft*, **146**, 321–339.

BUNDESANSTALT FÜR GEOWISSENSCHAFTEN UND ROHSTOFFE 2005. *Rohstoffsituation 2004 Bundesrepublik Deutschland*. Rohstoffwirtschaftliche Länderstudien, **23.**

BURCKHARDT, C. E. 1966. Il giacimento di Magnesite dello Zumpanell (Ortles-Alto Adige). *Atti Symposium Internazionale Giacimenti Minerari Alpi*, Trento, **2**, 529–544.

BURIAN, J., SLAVKAY, M., ŠTOHL, J. & TÖZSÉR, J. 1985. *Metallogenesis of Neovulcanites in Slovakia*. Mineralia Slovaca Monograph.

BURKHALTER, R. M. 1995. Ooidal ironstones and ferruginous microbialites: origin and relation to sequence stratigraphy (Aalenian and Bajocian, Swiss Jura mountains). *Sedimentology*, **42**, 57–74.

BURKHARD, D. J. M., RYBACH, L. & BAECHTIGER, K. 1985. Uranium and copper ore minerals in a lower Permian lapilli-agglomerate tuff in eastern Switzerland (Weisstannental, Kanton St. Gallen). *Schweizerische mineralogische und petrographische Mitteilungen*, **65**, 335–352.

CADEK, I. & MALKOVSKY, M. 1986. Fluorite in the vicinity of Teplice Spa, Bohemia-A newtype of fluorite deposit. *Terra Cognita*, **6**, 514.

CADEL, G., MENEGHEL, L. & FUCHS, Y. 1987. Uranium mineralization associated with the evolution of a Permo-Carboniferous volcanic field: examples from Novazza and Val Vedello (Northern Italy). *Uranium*, **3**, 407–421.

CADKOVÁ, Z. 1971. Genesis of the Permian stratiform Cu- deposit at Horni Vernérovice. *Sbornik geologických Vĕdrada Ložisková geologie*, **15**, 65–88.

CANNON, R. 2000. Bibliography on the mineralogy and geology of Lengenbach quarry in the Binn Valley, Valais, Switzerland. *Jahrbuch des Naturhistorischen Museums Bern* **13**, 63–90.

CARL, C. & DILL, H. G. 1985. Dating of secondary uranium minerals from the NE Bavarian Basement. *Chemical Geology*, **52**, 295–316.

CARL, C., DILL, H. G., KREUZER, H. & WENDT, I. 1983. U-Pb dating of ores in NE Bavaria. *Terra Cognita*, **3**, 195–196.

CASERO, P. 2004. Structural setting of petroleum exploration plays in Italy. *In:* CRESCENTI *et al.* (eds) *Geology of Italy*. Special volume for ICG 32 Florence 2004, Societá Geologica Italiana, Rome, 189–199.

CATHELINEAU, M., CUNEY, M., BOIRON, M. C., COULIBALY, Y. & AYT OUGOUGDAL, M. 1999. Paléopercolations et paléointeractions fluides/roches dans les plutonites de Charroux–Civray—Etude du Massif de Charroux–Civray. *In*: *Actes des Journées Scientifiques CNRS/ANDRA*. EDP Sciences, Poitiers, 159–179.

CERNY, I. 1989. Die karbonatgebundenen Blei-Zink Lagerstätten des alpinen und außeralpinen Mesozoikums. *Archiv für Lagerstättenforschung der Geologischen Bundesanstalt*, **11**, 5–125.

CERNÝ, P. 1991. Rare-element granitic pegmatites. Part I: anatomy and internal evolution of pegmatite deposits. *Geoscience Canada*, **18**, 49–67.

CERNÝ, P., STANEK, J., *et al.* 1995. Geochemical and structural evolution of micas in the Rozná and Dobrá Voda pegmatites, Czech Republic. *Mineralogy and Petrology*, **55**, 177–201.

CEVALES, G. 1954. Il giacimento a pechblenda e solfuri di Rio Freddo-Peveragno. *Bollettino Società Geologica Italiana*, **73**, 51–92.

CHAFFEE, M. A., EPPINGER, R. G., LASON, K., SLÓSARZ, J. & PODEMSKI, M. 1994. The Mysków porphyry copper –molybdenum deposit, Poland. *International Geology Review*, **36**, 947–960.

CHIARADIA, M. 2003. Formation and evolution processes of the Salanfe W-Au-As-skarns (Aiguilles Rouges Massif, western Swiss Alps). *Mineralium Deposita*, **38**, 154–168.

CHLUPÁČ, V., HAVLÍČEK, J., KŘÍŽ, Z., KUKAL, & ŠTORCH, P. 1998. *Palaeozoic of the Barrandian (Cambrian–Devonian)*. Geological Survey, Prague.

CHOVAN, M., ROJKOVIČ, I., ANDRÁŠ, P. & HANAS, P. 1992. Ore mineralization of the Malé Karpaty Mts. (Western Carpathians). *Geologica Carpathica*, **43**, 275–286.

CHOVAN, M., HÁBER, M., JELEŇ, S. & ROJKOVIČ, I. 1994. *Ore Textures in the Western Carpathians*. Slovak Academic Press, Bratislava.

CHOVAN, M., HURAI, V., SACHAN, H. K. & KANTOR, J. 1995. Origin of the fluids associated with granodiorite-hosted, Sb-As-Au-W mineralization at Dúbrava (Nízké Tatry Mts., Western Carpathians). *Mineralium Deposita*, **30**, 48–54.

CIPRYS, V., ADÁMEK, J. & BENADA, S. 1995. Petroleum geology of the Carpathian Foredeep and overthrust zones in the Czech Republic. *Petroleum Geoscience*, **1**, 89–96.

CLAR, E. & MEIXNER, H. 1981. Die grundlegenden Beobachtungen zur Entstehung der Eisenspatlagerstätte von Hüttenberg. *Carinthia II*, **171**, 55–92.

CLAYTON, J. L. & KONCZ, I. 1994. Petroleum geochemistry of the Zala Basin, Hungary. *American Association of Petroleum Geologists Bulletin*, **78**, 1–22.

COLE, G. A. 1994. Graptolite–Chitinozoan reflectance and its relationship to other geochemical maturity indicators in the Silurian Qusaiba Shale, Saudi Arabia. *Energy Fuels*, **8**, 1443–1459.

COOK, N. J. & DUDEK, K. 1994. Petrography and geothermobarometry of rocks associated with Sn- and Co-Ni-As-Bi-Ag mineralization at Przecznica Gierczyn-Krobica in the Izera Mountains, SW Poland. *In*: SELTMANN, R., KÄMPF, H. & MÖLLER, P. (eds) *Metallogeny of Collision Orogen*. Czech Geological Survey, Prague, 247–254.

COPARD, Y., DISNAR, J. R. & BECQ-GIRAUDON, J.-F. 2000. Evidence and effects of fluid circulation on organic matter in intramontane coalfields (Massif Central, France). *International Journal of Coal Geology*, **44**, 49–68.

CORTESOGNO, L., LUCCHETTI, G. & PENCO, A. M. 1979. The manganese mineralization in the jasper of the Ligurian ophiolites: mineralogy and genesis. *Rendiconti Societad Italiana Mineralogia Petrologia*, **35**, 151–197.

COULOMBEAU, C. 1980. Prospection et reconnaissance par sondages carottés des indices antimonifères du Rain des Allemands et de la mine de Wagenbach (champ antimonifère de Charbes - Bas-Rhin). *Rapport BRGM*, **80**, RDM 015 FE.

COURTOT, C., GANNAT, E. & WENDLING, E. 1972. Le basin potassique de Mulhouse et ses environs. *Bulletin Scientifique Géologique Strasbourg*, **25**, 69–92.

CUNEY, M., MARIGNAC, C. & WEISBROD, A. 1992. The beauvoir topaz-lepidolite-albite granite (Massif Central, France): the disseminated magmatic Sn-Li-Ta-Nb-Be mineralization. *Economic Geology*, **87**, 1766–1794.

CURTI, E. 1987. Lead and oxygen isotope evidence for the origin of the Monte Rosa gold lode deposits (Western Alps, Italy): A comparison with Archean lode deposits. *Economic Geology*, **82**, 2115–2140.

D'AGNOLO, M. 1966. Manifestazioni uraninifere nell'arco alpino occidentale. *Atti Symposium Internazionale Giacimenti Minerari Alpi, Trento*, **2**, 279–288.

DAHLKAMP, F. J. 1984. Charcteristics and problematics of the metallogenesis of Proterozoic vein-like type uranium eposits. *In*: WASCHKUHN, A., KLUTH, C. & ZIMMERMANN, R. A. (eds) *Syngenesis and Epigenesis in the Formation of Mineral Deposits*. Springer, Berlin, 183–192.

DAL BIANCO, F. 1969. Il filone Ester a fluorite, blenda e galena nel comprensorio di Torgola in Val Trompia. *Atti Società Italiana*

*Scienze Naturali Museo Civico Storia Naturale Milano*, **109**, 291–328.

Decker, K. & Peresson, H. 1996. Miocene tectonics at the Alpine-Carpathian-Pannonian system: links between thrusting, transform faulting and crustal extension. *In*: Wessely, G. & Liebl, W. (eds) *Oil and Gas in Alpidic Thrustbelts and Basins of Central and Eastern Europe*. Geological Society, London, EAGE Special Publication, **5**, 69–77.

Dehmer, J. 2004. A short report of the investigations made on the facies of German coal deposits. *International Journal of Coal Geology*, **58**, 41–51.

Dejonghe, L. 1986. Belgium. *In*: Dunning, F. W. & Evans, A. M. (eds) *Mineral Deposits of Europe*, Vol. 3, *Central Europe*. Institution of Mining and Metallurgy, and Mineralogical Society, London, 99–112.

Dejonghe, L. 1998. Zinc-lead deposits of Belgium. *Ore Geology Review*, **12**, 329–354.

Dejonghe, L. & Fuchs, Y. 2002. Geochimie isotopique du soufre du gisement de barite de Fleurus (Belgique). *Geologica Belgica*, **5**.

Demarco, G., Mein, P., Ballesio, R. & Romaggi, J.-P. 1989. Le gisment'Andance (Coiron, Ardéche, France) dans le Miocène superieur de la Valleè du Rhône: Un essai de corrélations marine-continental. *Bulletin de Société géologique de France*, **8**, 797–806.

De Quervain, F. & Zitzmann, A. 1977. The iron ores of Switzerland. *In*: Walther, H. W. & Zitzmann, A. (eds) *The Iron Ore Deposits of Europe and Adjacent Areas*. Bundesanstalt für Geowissenschaften und Rohstoffe, **1**, 295–297.

De Ruig, M. J. & Hubbard, S. M. 2006. Seismic facies and reservoir characteristics of a deep marine axial channel belt in the Molasse Basin, Puchkirchen Formation, Upper Austria. *American Association of Petroleum Geologists Bulletin*, **90**, 735–752.

Desmons, J. & Mercier, D. 1993. Passing through the Briancon Zone (Brianconnais, France). *In*: von Raumer, J. F. & Neubauer, F. (eds) *Pre-Mesozoic Geology in the Alps*. Springer, Berlin, 279–295.

Dessau, G. 1936. La miniera di "La Promise" (La Thuile, Aosta). *Atti Reale Accademia Scienze Torino*, **71**, 85–96.

Di Cobertaldo, D. 1965. Il giacimento di a fluorite, blenda e galena di Vignola in Valsugana. *Industria mineraria nel Trentino Alto Adige, Economia Trentina*, **14**, 135–145.

Di Cobertaldo, D. & Franceschetti, G. 1960. Il giacimento piombo-zincifero di Salafossa nelle Alpi Orientali Italiane. *International Geological Congress, 21ª Session, Copenhagen*, **16**, 126–137.

Di Cobertaldo, D. & Marzolo, G. 1964. Il giacimento a baritina di Marigole (Darzo). *Industria mineraria nel Trentino Alto Adige, Economia Trentina*, **13**, 248–259.

Di Cobertaldo, D., Di Furia, E. & Rossi, F. 1967. Il giacimento a magnetite di Cogne in Val d'Aosta. *Rendiconti Istituto Lombardo Accademia Scienze Lettere*, **101**, 361–394.

Dill, H. G. 1979. Der Feldspatbergbau in der Münchberger Gneismasse. *Bergbau*, **30**, 301–304.

Dill, H. G. 1981. Der Schieferbergbau im Frankenwald - Alaunschiefer - Dachschiefer - Mahlschiefer. *Bergbau*, **3**, 591–600.

Dill, H. G. 1982. Kobaltminerale aus den Nailaer Eisenspatgängen. *Zeitschrift der Deutschen Geologischen Gesellschaft*, **133**, 643–647.

Dill, H. G. 1983. On the Formation of the Vein-type Uranium "Yellow Ores" from the Schwarzach-Area (NE-Bavaria, Germany) and on the Behaviour of P, As, V, and Se during Supergene Processes. *Geologische Rundschau*, **72**, 955–980.

Dill, H. G. 1985*a*. Die Vererzung am Westrand der Böhmischen Masse. - Metallogenese in einer ensialischen Orogenzone. *Geologisches Jahrbuch*, **D 73**, 3–461.

Dill, H. G. 1985*b*. Antimoniferous Mineralization from the Mid-European Saxothuringian Zone; Mineralogy, Geology, Geochemistry and ensialic Origin. *Geologische Rundschau*, **74**, 447–466.

Dill, H. G. 1985*c*. Genesis and mining of secondary uranium mineralization in Northern Bavaria (F. R. of Germany), with special reference to geomorphology. *Uranium*, **2**, 1–16.

Dill, H. G. 1985*d*. Terrestrial ferromanganese ore concentrations from Mid-European Basement Blocks and their implication concerning the environment of formation during Late Cenozoic (N Bavaria/F. R. Germany). *Sedimentary Geology*, **45**, 77–96.

Dill, H. G. 1986*a*. Metallogenesis of the Early Paleozoic Graptolite Shales from the Graefenthal Horst. *Economic Geology*, **81**, 889–903.

Dill, H. G. 1986*b*. Fault-controlled uranium black ore mineralization from the western edge of the Bohemian Massif (NE Bavaria/F. R. Germany). *In*: Fuchs, H. D. (ed.) *Uranium Vein-Type Deposits*. International Atomic Energy Agency, Vienna, 303–323.

Dill, H. G. 1987. Environmental and diagenetic analyses of Lower Permian epiclastic and pyroclastic fan deposits. Their role for coal formation and uranium metallogeny in the Stockheim trough (FRG). *Sedimentary Geology*, **52**, 1–26.

Dill, H. G. 1988*a*. Geologic setting and age relationship of fluorite – barite mineralization in Southern Germany – with special reference to the Late Paleozoic unconformity. *Mineralium Deposita*, **23**, 16–23.

Dill, H. G. 1988*b*. Diagenetic and epigenetic U, Ba and base metal mineralization in the arenaceous upper Triassic "Burgsandstein", Southern Germany. *Mineralogy and Petrology*, **39**, 93–105.

Dill, H. G. 1989. Metallogenetic and geodynamic evolution in the Central European Variscides – a pre-well site study for the German Continental Deep Drilling Programme. *Ore Geology Review*, **4**, 279–304.

Dill, H. G. 1990*a*. Chemical basin analysis of the metalliferous "Variegated Metamorphics" of the Bodenmais ore district (F. R. of Germany). *Ore Geology Review*, **5**, 151–173.

Dill, H. G. 1990*b*. Die Schwermineralführung in den Trias zwischen Weiden und Pressath mit besonderer Berücksichtigung der Buntmetallmineralizationen. *Erlanger Geologische Abhandlungen*, **118**, 61–73.

Dill, H. G. 1993. Die Antimonvorkommen der mitteleuropäischen Alpiden und Varisziden. *Zeitschrift der Deutschen Geologischen Gesellschaft*, **144**, 434–450.

Dill, H. G. 1994. Facies variation and mineralization in Central Europe from the late Paleozoic through the Cenozoic. *Economic Geology*, **89**, 42–61.

Dill, H. G. 1995. Preface. *In*: Dill, H. G. (ed.) *Past and Present in Geoadministriation and Geoindustry in the former COMECON countries*. Federal Institute for Geosciences and Natural Resources, Hannover, 9–12.

Dill, H. G. 1998. Evolution of Sb mineralisation in modern fold belts: Comparison of the Sb mineralisation in the Central Andes (Bolivia) and the Western Carpathians (Slovakia). *Mineralium Deposita*, **33**, 359–378.

Dill, H. G. 2001. The geology of aluminium phosphates and sulphates of the alunite supergoup: A review. *Earth Science Reviews*, **53**, 25–93.

Dill, H. G. & Botz, R. 1989. Lithofacies variation and unconformities in the Metalliferous Rocks Underlying the Permian Kupferschiefer of the Stockheim Basin/F. R. of Germany. *Economic Geology*, **84**, 1028–1046.

Dill, H. G. & Carl, C. 1987. Sr isotope variation in vein barites from the NE Bavarian Basement. Relevance for the source of elements and genesis of unconformity-related barite deposits. *Mineralogy and Petrology*, **36**, 27–39.

Dill, H. G. & Nielsen, H. 1987. Chemical and geological constraints on the formation of unconformity-related vein barite deposits of Central Europe. *Journal of the Geological Society of London*, **144**, 97–105.

Dill, H. G. & Weiser, T. 1981. Eine Molybdänsulfid-Impsonit Mineralisation aus dem Uranvorkommen Wäldel/Mähring (Oberpfalz). *Neues Jahrbuch Mineralogie Monatshefte*, **1981**, 452–458.

Dill, H. G., Teschner, M. & Wehner, H. 1991. Geochemistry and lithofacies of Permo-Carboniferous carbonaceous rocks from the southwestern edge of the Bohemian Massif (Germany). A contribution to facies analysis of continental anoxic environments. *International Journal of Coal Geology*, **18**, 251–291.

Dill, H. G., Fricke, A. & Henning, K.-H 1995. The origin of Ba-and REE-bearing aluminium-phosphate-sulphate minerals from the Lohrheim kaolinitic clay deposit (Rheinisches Schiefergebirge, Germany). *Applied Clay Science*, **10**, 231–245.

Dill, H. G., Pertold, Z. & Riera Kilibarda, C. 1997. Sediment-hosted and volcanic-hosted Sb vein mineralization in the Potosi region (Central Bolivia). *Economic Geology*, **92**, 623–632.

Dill, H. G., Nasir, S. & Al-Saad, H. 2003. Lithological and structural evolution of the northern sector of the Dukhan Anticline, Qatar, during the early Tertiary: With special reference to bounding surfaces of sequence stratigraphical relevance. *GeoArabia*, **8**, 201–226.

DILL, H. G., BOTZ, R., BERNER, Z., STÜBEN, D., NASIR, S. & AL-SAAD, H. 2005. Sedimentary facies, mineralogy and geochemistry of the sulphate -bearing Miocene Dam Formation in Qatar. *Sedimentary Geology* **174**, 63–96.

DILL, H. G., GERDES, A., MELCHER, F., WEBER, B., TECHMER, A. & FÜSSL, M. 2008*a*. Die Hagendorfer Pegmatitprovinz (Oberpfalz/Deutschland) aus sedimentologisch-geomorphologischer und mineralogisch-lagerstättenkundlicher Sicht. *Mitteilungen der Österreichischen Mineralogischen Gesellschaft* (in press) (with a summary in English).

DILL, H. G., TECHMER, A., WEBER, B. & FÜSSL, M. 2008*b*. Mineralogical and chemical distribution patterns of placers and ferricretes in Quaternary sediments in SE Germany: The impact of nature and man on the unroofing of pegmatites. *Journal of Geochemical Exploration*, **96**, 1–24.

DOE, B. R. & STACEY, J. S. 1974. The application of lead isotopes to the problems of ore genesis and ore prospect evaluation. A review. *Economic Geology*, **69**, 757–776.

DOPITA, M. & KUMPERA, O. 1993. Geology of the Ostrava-Karviná coalfield, Upper Silesian Basin, Czech Republic, and its influence on mining. *International Journal of Coal Geology*, **23**, 291–321.

DORNSIEPEN, U. 1976. *Zum geologischen und petrofaziellen Rahmen der hangenden Schichten des Schwefelkies-Zinkblende-Schwerspat-Lagers von Meggen/Westfalen*. PhD Thesis, TU Braunschweig.

DREESEN, R., BOSSIROY, D., DUSAR, M., FLORES, R. M. & VERKAEREN, P. 1995. Overview of the influence of syn-sedimentary tectonics and paleo-fluvial systems on coal seam and sand body characteristics in the Westphalian C strata, Campine Basin, Belgium. *In*: WHATELEY, M. K. G. & SPEARS, D. A. (eds) *European Coal Geology*. Geological Society, London, Special Publications, **82**, 215–232.

DREW, L. J. 2003. Model of the porphyry copper and polymetallic vein family of deposits; applications in Slovakia, Hungary, and Romania. *International Geology Review*, **45**, 143–156.

DREYER, G. 1973. Neue Mineralien der Rheinpfalz II. *Mitteilungen der Pollichia III R.*, **20**, 113–136.

DREYER, G. 1975. Neue Mineralien der Rheinpfalz II. *Mitteilungen der Pollichia III R.*, **63**, 5–9.

DROVENIK, M., PLENIČAR, M. & DROVENIK, F. 1980. The origin of Slovenian ore deposits. *Geologija*, **23**, 1- 157.

DROZDZEWSKI, G. 1993. The Ruhr coal basin (Germany): structural evolution of an autochthonous foreland basin. *International Journal of Coal Geology*, **23**, 231–250.

DUBOIS, M., AYT OUGOUGDAL, M., MEERE, P., ROYER, J. J., BOIRON, M. C. & CATHELINEAU, M. 1996. Temperature of paleo-to modern self-sealing within a continental rift basin: the fluid inclusion data (Soultz sous Forets, Rhine graben, France). *European Journal of Mineralogy*, **8**, 1065–1080.

DURIĆ, S. & KUBAT, I. 1962. Occurrences of copper ore in the Čavka Mt. (in Bosnian). *Geoloski Glasnik*, **6**, 131–143.

ĎURIŠOVA, J. 1990. Fluid inclusion study in the Jeseníky ore district (Czechoslovakia). *Sborník geologických ved, rada Ložisková geologie*, **29**, 167–186.

ĎURIŠOVA, J., STRNAD, L., PERTOLD, Z., PUDILOVÁ, M. & BOIRON, M. C. 1995. Gold-bearing quartz veins in a regional shear zone: Kašperské Hory gold deposit (Bohemian Massif). *In*: PASAVA, J., KRÍBEK, B. & ZÁK, K. (eds) *Mineral Deposits: From Their Origin to Their Environmental Impacts*, Balkema, Rotterdam, 109–112.

EBNER, F., CERNY, I., EICHHORN, R., GÖTZINGER, M. A., PAAR, W. H., PROCHASKA, W. & WEBER, L. 2000. Mineral resources in the Eastern Alps and adjoining areas. *In*: NEUBAUER, F. & HÖCK, V. (eds) Aspects of Geology in Austria. *Mitteilungen der Österreichischen Geologischen Gesellschaft*, **92**, 157–184.

EICHHORN, R., HÖLL, R., LOTH G. & KENNEDY, A. 1999. Implications of U-Pb SHRIMP zircon data on the age and evolution of the Felbertal tungsten deposit (Tauern Window, Austria). *Geologische Rundschau*, **88**, 496–512.

ELROD, I. 1982. *Uranium Project Middle Franconia*. Final report, 1981, British Petrol Gelsenberg, Hamburg.

ENDLICHER, G. 1977. Die Erzhäuser Arkosen von Pingarten ("Pingartener Porphyr") sedimentpetrographische Merkmale und tektonische Lagerungsverhältnisse. *Geologische Blätter von Nordost-Bayern*, **27**, 36–49.

ENDLICHER, G. 1982. Occurrences and geochemical-genetical aspects of the $CaF_2$-$BaSO_4$ mineralization from the SW part of the Bavarian Forest, W. Germany. *Bulletin de Bureau de recherches géologiques et minières*, **2**, 87.

EPPRECHT, W. 1946. Die Eisen- und Manganerze des Gonzen. *Beiträge der Geologie der Schweiz, Geotechnische Serie*, **24**, 1–128.

ERCEGOVAC, M., ŽIVOTIĆ, D. & KOSTIĆ, A. 2006. Genetic-industrial classification of brown coals in Serbia. *International Journal of Coal Geology*, **68**, 39–56.

ERTL, A., PERTLIK, F., PREM, M., POST, J. E., KIM, S. J., BRANDSTÄTTER, F. & SCHUSTER, R. 2005. Ranciéite crystals from Friesach, Carinthia, Austria. *European Journal of Mineralogy*, **17**, 163–172.

FAGNANI, G. 1947. Nota petrografica sulle rocce di Nibbio e Migiandone (Val d'Ossola). *Bollettino Società Ticinese Scienze Naturali*, **42**, 125–133.

FALKE, H. 1971. Zur Paläogeographie des kontinentalen Perms in Süddeutschland. *Abhandlungen des hessischen Landesantes für Bodenforschung*, **60**, 223–234.

FARSHAD, F. 2001. *Vergleichende Untersuchungen an oolitischen Eisensteinen von Nordwales/England, Thüringen/Deutschland und der Prager Mulde /Tschechische Republik sowie des Clinton-Typs (Red Mountain Formation) von Alabama/USA*. PhD thesis, Georg-August-University, Göttingen.

FEIST-BURKHARDT, S., GÖTZ, A. E. *et al.* 2008. Triassic. *In*: MCCANN, T. (ed.) *The Geology of Central Europe. Volume 2: Mesozoic and Cenozoic*. Geological Society, London, 749–821.

FENCHEL, W., GIES, H., *et al.* 1985. Die Sideritgänge im Siegerland-Wied-Distrikt. *Geologisches Jahrbuch*, **D77**, 3–517.

FERRARIO, A. & GARUTI, G. 1980. Copper deposits in the basal breccias and volcano-sedimentary sequences of the Eastern Ligurian ophiolites (Italy). *Mineralium Deposita*, **15**, 291–303.

FINGER, F. & BROSKA, I. 1999. The Gemeric S-type granites in southeastern Slovakia: Late Palaezoic or Alpine intrusions; Evidence from electron-microprobe dating of monazite. *Schweizerische Mineralogische und Petrogrographische Mitteilungen*, **79**, 439–443.

FINGER, F., BROSKA, I., *et al.* 2003. Electromicroprobe dating of manazite from Western Carpathian basement granitoids: plutonic evidence for an important Permian rifting event subsequent to Variscan crustal anatexis. *International Journal Earth Sciences (Geologische Rundschau)*, **92**, 86–98.

FINKELMAN, R. B., OREM, W., *et al.* 2002. Health impacts of coal and coal use: possible solutions. *International Journal of Coal Geology*, **50**, 425–443.

FLUCK, P., WEIL, P. & WIMMENAUER, W. 1975. Geologie des gites minéraux des Vosges et des régions limitrophes. *In*: AGARD, I. (ed.) *Gites mineraux de la France*, 2. Mémoires du BRGM, **87**, Orleans.

FÖRSTER, G. & SCHMITZ, N. 1972. Die Blei-Zinklagerstätte Pflersch in Südtirol. Ein Mittelalterlicher Bergbau im Wiederaufschluss. *Erzmetall*, **25**, 57–64.

FÖRSTER, H.-J. 1999. The chemical composition of uraninite in Variscan granites of the Erzgebirge, Germany. *Mineralogical Magazine*, **63**, 239–252.

FÖRSTER, H.-J., TISCHENDORF, G., SELTMANN, R. & GOTTESMANN, B. 1998. Die variszischen Granite des Erzgebirges: neue Aspekte aus stofflicher Sicht. *Zeitschrift für Geologische Wissenschaften* **26**, 31–60.

FÖRSTER, H.-J., TISCHENDORF, G., GOTTESMANN, B. & TRUMBULL, R. B. 1999. Late-collisional granites in the Variscan Erzgebirge, Germany. *Journal of Petrology*, **40**, 1613–1645.

FÖRSTER, H.-J., RHEDE, D. & TISCHENDORF, G. 2004. Mineralogy of the Niederschlema – Alberoda U–Se-polymetallic deposit, Erzgebirge, Germany. I. Jolliffeite, NiAsSe, the rare Se analogue of gersdorffite. *Canadian Mineralogist*, **42**, 841–849.

FOX, J. S. 1984. Besshi-type volcanogenic sulphide deposits – a review. *Canadian Institute of Mining and Metallurgy, Bulletin*, **77**, 57–68.

FRANČE, J. 1992. Bentonites in the eastern part of the Doupovské hory Mts. *Sborník geologických ved, rada Ložisková geologie*, **30**, 43–90 [in Czech, with English summary].

FRANCU, J., RADKE, M., SCHAEFER, R. G., POELCHAU, H. S., CASLAVSKY, J. & BOHACEK, Z. 1996. Oil–oil and oil–source rock correlations in the northern Vienna Basin and adjacent Carpathian Flysch Zone (Czech and Slovak area). *In*: WESSELY. G. & LIEBL, W. (eds) *Oil and Gas in Alpidic Thrustbelts and Basins of Central and Eastern Europe*. Geological Society, London, EAGE Special Publications, **5**, 343–353.

FRANKE, W. 1989. The geological framework of the KTB drill site, Oberpfalz. *In:* EMMERMANN, R. & WOHLENBERG, J. (eds) *The German Continental Deep Drilling Program (KTB).* Springer, Heidelberg, 37–54

FRANKE, W. 2000. The mid-European segment of the Variscides: tectonostratigraphic units, terrane boundaries and plate tectonic evolution. *In*: FRANKE, W., HAAK, V., ONCKEN, O. & TANNER, D. (eds) *Orogenic Processes: Quantification and modelling in the Variscan Belt.* Geological Society, London, Special Publications, **179**, 35–62.

FRANKE, W. & ONCKEN, O. 1990. Geodynamic evolution of the North-Central Variscides – a comic strip. *In*: FREEMAN, R., GIESE, P. & MUELLER, S. (eds) *The European Geotraverse: Integrative Studies.* European Science Foundation, Strasbourg, 187–194.

FRANKE, W. & ZELAZNIEWICZ, A. 2000. The eastern termination of the Variscides: terrane correlation and kinematic evolution. *In:* FRANKE, W., HAAK, V., ONCKEN, O. & TANNER, D. (eds) *Orogenic Processes: Quantification and Modelling in the Variscan Belt.* Geological Society, London, Special Publications, **179**, 63–86.

FREELS, D., STEMPROK, M., HÖSEL, G., TISCHENDORF, G., WASTERNACK, J. & BREITER, K. 1995. *Mineral resources in Erzgebirge-Vogtland/Krusné Hory. Explanatory Notes to Map 2: Metals, Fluorite/Barite, Occurrences and Environmental Impact.* Cesk'y geologick'y ústav, Prague, Sächsisches Landesamt für Umwelt und Geologie, Bereich Boden und Geologie, Freiberg.

FRIEDRICH, G., GERMANN, A. & JOCHUM, J. 1993. Schichtgebundene Pb-Zn-Vorkommen in klastischenSedimenten vom Typ Maubach - Mechernich. Lagerstättenbildung durch intraformationale Prozesse. *Mitteilungen der Österreichischen Mineralogischen Gesellschaft,* **138**, 93–105.

FRISCH, W. & NEUBAUER, F. 1989. Pre-Alpine terranes and tectonic zoning in the eastern Alps. *In*: DALLMEYER, R. D. (ed.) *Terranes in the Circum-Atlantic Paleozoic Orogens.* Geological Society of America, Special Publications, **230**, 91–100.

FRIZZO, P., MILLS, J. & VISONÁ, D. 1982. Ore petrology and metamorphic history of Zn-Pb ores, Monteneve, Tyrol, N. Italy. *Mineralium Deposita*, **17**, 333–347.

FROITZHEIM, N., PLAŠIENKA, D. & SCHUSTER, R. 2008. Alpine tectonics of the Alps and Western Carpathians. *In*: MCCANN, T. (ed.) *The Geology of Central Europe. Volume 2: Mesozoic and Cenozoic.* Geological Society, London, 1141–1232.

FUCHS, Y. & OYMAN, T. 2000. Hydrothermal synthesis of axinite and equilibrium conditions with Ca-tourmaline. *In: Eighth International Symposium on Experimental Mineralogy, Petrology and Geochemistry,* Abstracts. Cambridge Publications, Cambridge, 38.

FUCHS, R., RAMBERGER, R. & VEIT, Ch. 2001. Das Matzen Projekt - Renaissance des größten Öl- und Gasfeldes in Österreich (Wiener Becken). *Erdöl Erdgas Kohle*, **117**, 528–540.

GALE, J. J. 2004. Using coal seams for $CO_2$ sequestration. *Geologica Belgica*, **7**, 99–103.

GARLICKI, A. 1971. Facial map of the Tortonian evaporite horizon in Poland. *Acta Geologica Academiae Scientiarum Hungaricae*, **15**, 24–38.

GARUTI, G. & RINALDI, R. 1986. Melonite-Group and other Tellurides from the Ivrea-Verbano Basic Complex, Western Italian Alps. *Economic Geology,* **81**, 1213–1217.

GARUTI, G., FIANDRI, P. & ROSSI, A. 1986. Sulphide composition and phase relations in the Fe-Ni-Cu ore deposits of the Ivrea-Verbano basic complex (Western Alps, Italy). *Mineralium Deposita*, **21**, 22–34.

GASCHNITZ, R. 2001. *Gasgenese und Gasspeicherung im flözführenden Oberkarbon des Ruhr-Beckens.* Berichte des Forschungszentrums Jülich, **3859**.

GATTER, I., MOLNÁR, F., FÖLDESSY, J., ZELENKA, T., KISS, J. & SZEBÉNYI, G. 1999. High- and low-sulfidation epithermal mineralization of the Mátra Moutains, northeast Hungary. *In:* MOLNÁR, F., LEXA, J. & HEDENQUIST, J. W. (eds) *Epithermal Mineralization of the Western Carpathians.* Society Economic Geologists, Guidebook Series, **31**, 155–179.

GAWLICK, H.-J. 2000. Die Radiolaritbecken in den Nördlichen Kalkalpen (hoher Mittel-Jura, Ober-Jura). *Mitteilungen der Geologie- und Bergbaustudenten Österreichs*, **44**, 97–156.

GAWLICK, H.-J., FRISCH, W., VECSEI, A., STEIGER, T. & BÖHM, F. 1999. The change from rifting to thrusting in the Northern Calcareous Alps as recorded in Jurassic sediments. *Geologische Rundschau,* **87**, 644–657.

GEHLEN VON, K. 1966. Schwefel-Isotope und die Genese von Erzlagerstätten. *Geologische Rundschau*, **55**, 178–197.

GEHLEN VON, K. 1989. Ore and mineral deposits of the Schwarzwald. *In:* EMMERMANN, R. & WOHLENBERG, J. (eds), *The German Continental Deep Drilling Program (KTB).* Springer, Heidelberg, 277–295.

GEISSLER, P. 1975. Räumliche Veränderung und Zusammensetzung der Flöze in den Kohlenbergwerken Hausham und Penzberg. *Geologica Bavarica*, **73**, 61–106.

GERMANN, K., PAGEL, J.-M. & PAREKH, P. P. 1981. Eigenschaften und Entstehung der "Lahn-Phosphorite". *Zeitschrift der Deutschen Geologischen Gesellschaft,* **132**, 305–323.

GILG, H. A. 2000. D-H evidence for the timing of kaolinization in Northeast Bavaria, Germany. *Chemical Geology*, **170**, 5–18.

GILLIERON, F. 1959. Sulla geologia dei giacimenti di siderite delle Valli Lombarde. *Industria Mineraria*, **10**, 725–733.

GRAS, R. & CLAYTON, C. J. 1998. Non-hydrocarbon components of Carboniferous-sourced gas in the Southern Permian Basin, northwest Europe. *Petroleum Geoscience,* **4**, 147–156.

GRECULA, P. 1971. Vein Quartz Deposits in Slovakia. *Mineralia Slovaca*, **3**, 349–370.

GRECULA, P. 1982. *Gemericum – Segment of the Paleotethyan Riftogenous Basin.* Mineralia Slovaca Monograph [in Slovak with English abstract].

GRECULA, P. & RADVANEC, M. 2004. Geotectonic evolution of the Gemeric unit. *In:* GRECULA, P. & KOBULSKÝ, J. (eds) *Facial and Geotectonic Background of the Gemeric Paleozoic Rock-Complexes.* Open file report, Geofond Bratislava [in Slovak].

GRECULA, P., ABONYI, A., *et al.* 1995. *Mineral Deposit of the Slovak Ore Mountains.* Mineralia Slovaca Monograph, **1**.

GRECULA, P., CHOVAN, M., ROJKOVIČ, I. & SLAVKAY, M. 1996. The Variscan metallogeny of the Western Carpathians. *In:* GRECULA, P. & NÉMETH, Z. (eds) *Variscan Metallogeny in the Alpine Orogenic Belt.* Mineralia Slovaca Monograph, 191–238.

GROBE, M. & MACHEL, H. G. 2002. Saline groundwater in the Münsterland Cretaceous Basin, Germany: clues to its origin and evolution. *Marine and Petroleum Geology*, **19**, 307–322.

GRUBER, W. & SACHSENHOFER, R. F. 2001. Coal deposition in the Noric Depression (Eastern Alps): raised and low-lying mires in Miocene pull-apart basins. *International Journal of Coal Geology*, **48**, 89–114.

GRUBIĆ, A., PROTIĆ, LJ., FILIPOVIĆ, I. & JOVANOVIĆ, D. 2000. New data on the Paleozoic of the Sana-Una area. *In: Proceedings of the International Symposium Geology and Metallogeny of the Dinarides and the Vardar zone.* ANURS, Banja Luka, 49–54.

GRUM, W., FRIMMEL, H. E. & KOLLER, F. 1992. Sr-Isotopendaten zur Genese der Antimonit-Lagerstätte Schlaining (Burgenland). *Mitteilungen der Geologie- und Bergbaustudenten Österreichs*, **38**, 73–92.

GUDDEN, H. 1972. Die Bildung und Erhaltung der Oberpfälzer Kreide-Eisenerlagerstätten in Abhängigkeit von Biegungs- und Bruchtektonik. *Geologica Bavarica,* **65**, 107–125.

GUDDEN, H. 1975. Zur Bleiführung in Trias-Sedimenten der nördlichen Oberpfalz. *Geologica Bavarica*, **74**, 33–55.

GUDDEN, H. 1984. Zur Entstehung der nordostbayerischen Kreide-Eisenerz-Lagerstätten. *Geologisches Jahrbuch*, **D 66**, 3–49.

GUDDEN, H., SCHMID, H., *et al.* 1985. Die Forschungsbohrung Obernsees (westlich von Bayreuth). *Geologica Bavarica*, **88**, 1–161.

GYARMATI, P. 1977. A Tokaji-hegység intermdier vulkanizmusa. *Annals of the Hungarian Geological Institute*, **58**, 1–195.

GYARMATI, P. & PENTELÉNYI, L. 1973. *Explanation to the geological map of the Tokaj Mts., 1 : 25 000, Makkoshotyka – Sátoralyaúlyhely.* Geological Institute of Hungary [in Hungarian].

HAAS, J., JOCHA-EDELÉNYI, E. & CSÁSZÁR, G. 1992. Upper Cretaceous coal deposits in Hungary. *In:* MCCABE, P. J. & PARRISH, J. T. (eds) *Controls on the Distribution and Quality of Cretaceous Coals.* Geological Society of America, Boulder, Colorado, Special Papers, **267**, 245–262.

HÁBER, M. 1980. Mineralogisch-geochemische und paragenetische Erforschung hydrothermaler Gänge im Gebiet zwischen Prakovce und Kojšov (Spišsko-gemerské rudohorie). *Západné Karpaty, séria Mineralógia, Petrografia,Geochémia, Metalogenéza*, **7**, 7–131.

HÁBER, M. 1996. Vein Cu-mineralization in the Permian formation near the Novoveská Huta area. *In:* GRECULA, P. & NÉMETH, Z. (eds)

*Variscan Metallogeny of the Alpine Orogenic Belt.* Mineralia Slovaca Monograph, 283–292.

HAGEDORN, B. & LIPPOLT, H. J. 1994. Isotopische Alter von Zerrüttungszonen als Altersschranken der Freiamt-Sexau-Mineralisation (Mittlerer Schwarzwald). *Geologisches Landesamt Baden-Württemberg Abhandlungen,* **14**, 205–219.

HAGER, H. 1993. The origin of the Tertiary lignite deposits in the Lower Rhine region, Germany. *International Journal of Coal Geology,* **23**, 251–262.

HAJÓS, M. 1993. Szurdokpüspöki, diatomite quarry. 8th MID-European Geological Surveys, Budapest, 35–39.

HALM, E. 1945. Die Kupfer-Wismut-Lagerstätten im oberen Val d'Anniviers (Wallis). *Beiträge zur Geologie der Schweiz: Geotechnische Serie*, **22**, 1–89.

HAMILTON, W., WAGNER, L. & WESSELY, G. 2000. Oil and gas in Austria. *Mitteilungen der Österreichischen Geologischen Gesellschaft,* **92**, 235–262.

HAMRLA, M. 1959. On the conditions of origin of the coal beds in the Karst region. *Geologija*, **1959**, 180–264 [in Slovenian].

HARANCZYK, C. 1980. Development of the Variscan mineral paragenesis in Poland. *Freiberger Forschungshefte*, **C 354**, 7–17.

HARANCZYK, C. 1983. Mineral parageneses of the Cracovides and their cover, Southern Poland. *Annales de la Société Géologique de Polonaise*, **53**, 91–126.

HARANCZYK, C. 1989. Two solutions-multipulsations model of genesis of the Silesian- Cracovian Zn-Pb-ore deposits. *Rudarsko-geološknaftni*, **1**, 11–16.

HASENHÜTTL, C., KRALJIC, M., SACHSENHOFER, R. F., JELEN, B. & RIEGER, R. 2001. Source rocks and hydrocarbon generation in Slovenia (Mura Depression, Pannonian Basin). *Marine and Petroleum Geology,* **18**, 115–132.

HATÁR, J. 1989. *Mineralogical Study of the Jasenie Deposit. Open file report. Geofond Bratislava* [in Slovak].

HAUPTMANN, S. & LIPPOLT, H. J. 2000. $^{40}Ar/^{39}Ar$ dating of central European K-Mn oxides – a chronological framework of supergene alteration processes during the Neogene. *Chemical Geology,* **170**, 37–80.

HAVLÍČEK V. 1981. Development of a linear sedimentary depression exemplified by the Prague Basin (Ordovician–Middle Devonian; Barrandian area—central Bohemia). *Sborník geologických ved, rada Geologie,* **35**, 7–48.

HECHT, L., FREIBERGER, R., GILG, H. A., GRUNDMANN, G. & KOSTITSYN, Y. A. 1999. Rare earth element and isotope (C, O, Sr) characteristics of hydrothermal carbonates: genetic implications for dolomite-hosted talc mineralization at Göpfersgrün (Fichtelgebirge, Germany). *Chemical Geology,* **155**, 115–130.

HEIN, U. F. 1993. Synmetamorphic Variscan siderite mineralization of the Rhenish massif, central Europe. *Mineralogical Magazine*, **57**, 451–467.

HEMMET, M. 2005. The hydrocarbon potential of the Danish Continental Shelf. *In:* DORÉ, A. G. & VINING, B. A. (eds) *Petroleum Geology: North-west Europe and Global Perspectives*. Proceedings of the 6th conference. Geological Society, London, 85.

HENK, A., V. BLANCKENBURG, F., FINGER, F., SCHALTEGGER, U. & ZULAUF, G. 2000. Syn-convergent high-temperature metamorphism and magmatism in the Variscides - a discussion of potential heat sources. *In*: FRANKE, W., HAAK, V., ONCKEN, O. & TANNER, D. (eds) *Orogenic Processes: Quantification and Modeling in the Variscan Belt of Central Europe*. Geological Society, London, Special Publication, **179**, 387–399.

HERRINGTON, R. 2000. Copper porphyry deposits of Serbia, Macedonia, Romania and Bulgaria. *In*: *Abstracts – Europe's Major Base Metal Deposits*, Galway, Ireland, 11–14 May 2000.

HERTLE, M. & LITTKE, R. 2000. Coalification pattern and thermal modelling of the Permo-Carboniferous Saar Basin (SW-Germany). *International Journal of Coal Geology,* **42**, 273–296.

HESEMANN, J. 1978. Der Blei-Zink-Erzbezirk des Bergischen Landes (Rheinisches Schiefergebirge) als Prototyp einer frühorogenen und palingenen Vererzung. *Decheniana*, **131**, 292–299.

HITZMANN, M. W., REYNOLDS, N. A., SANGSTER, D. F., ALLEN, C. R. & CARMAN, C. 2003. Classification, genesis, and exploration guides for nonsulphide zinc deposits. *Economic Geology*, **98**, 685–714.

HLADÍKOVÁ, J., AICHLER, J. & MIXA, P. 1992. Source of sulfur of base metal sulphide deposits at the NE margin of the Bohemian Massif (Czechoslovakia). *Abstracts, 29th International Geological Congress, Kyoto*, **3**, 757.

HOFFMANN, N., JÖDICKE, H. & GERLING, P. 2001. The distribution of Pre-Westphalian source rocks in the North German Basin-Evidence from magnetotelluric and geochemical data. *Netherlands Journal of Geosciences*, **80**, 71–84.

HOFMANN, B. A. 1989. Erzmineralien in paläozoischen, mesozoischen und tertiären Sedimenten der Nordschweiz und Südwestdeutschland. *Schweizerische Mineralogische und Petrogrographische Mitteilungen*, **69**, 345–357.

HOFMANN, B. A. 1994. Formation of a sulphide melt during Alpine metamorphism of the Lengenbach polymetallic sulphide mineralization, Binntal, Switzerland. *Mineralium Deposita*, **29**, 439–442.

HOFMANN B. & EIKENBERG J. 1991. The Krunkelbach uranium deposit, Schwarzwald, Germany. Correlation of radiometric ages, U–Pb, U–Xe–Kr, K–Ar, Th–U with mineralogical stages and fluid inclusions, *Economic Geology,* **86**, 1031–1049.

HOFMEISTER, E., SIMON, P. & STEIN, V. 1972. Blei und Zink im Trochitenkalk (Trias, Oberen Muschelkalk 1) Nordwestdeutschlands. *Geologisches Jahrbuch*, **D 1**, 1–103.

HOFSTRA, A. H., KORPAS, L., CSALAGOVITS, I., JOHNSON, C. A. & CHRISTIANSEN, W. D. 1999. Stable isotopic study of the Rudabánya iron mine. A carbonate-hosted siderite, barite, base metal sulphide replacement deposit. *Geologica Hungarica Series Geologica*, **21**, 295–302.

HÖLL, R. 1975. *Die Scheelitlagerstätte Felbertal und der Vergleich mit anderen Scheelitlagerstätten in den Ostalpen.* Abhandlungen Bayerischen Akademie der Wissenschaften N. F., **157A.**

HÖLL, R. & EICHHORN, R. 2001. Tungsten mineralization and metamorphic remobilization on the Felbertal Scheelite Deposit, Central Alps, Austria. *Reviews in Economic Geology*, **11**, 233—264.

HOLZ, M., KALKREUTH, W. & BANERJEE, I. 2002 Sequence stratigraphy of paralic coal-bearing strata: an overview international. *Journal of Coal Geology*, **48**, 147–179.

HORON, O. 1976. Les gisement de fer de la France. *In*: WALTHER, H. W. & ZITZMANN, A. (eds) *The Iron Ore Deposits of Europe and Adjacent Areas*. International Geological Congress, BGR, Schweizerbart, Hannover, 143–159.

HORSTIG VON, G. & TEUSCHER, E. O. 1979. Die Eisenerze im Alten Gebirge NE-Bayerns. *Geologisches Jahrbuch*, **D 31**, 7–47.

HORVÁTH, F. & TARI, G. 1999. IBS Pannonian Basin project: a review of the main results and their bearings on hydrocarbon exploration. *In:* DURAND, B. *et al.* (eds) *The Mediterranean Basins: Tertiary Extension within the Alpine Orogen*. Geological Society, London, Special Publications, **156**, 195–213.

HOUSEKNECHT, D. W., HATHON, L. A. & MCGILVERTY, T. A. 1992. Thermal maturity of Paleozoic strata in the Arkoma Basin. *Oklahoma Geological Survey Circular,* **93**, 122–132.

HOUZAR, S. & NOVÁK, M. 2002. Marbles with carbonatite-like geochemical signeture from variegated units of the Bohemian Massif, Czech Republic, and their geological significance. *Journal of the Czech Geological Society,* **47**, 103–113.

HRAŠKO, L., HATÁR, J., HUHMA, H., MÄNTÄRI, I., MICHALKO, J. & VAASJOKI, M. 1999. U/Pb zircon dating of the Upper Cretaceous granite (Rochovce type) in the Western Carpathians. *Krystalinikum*, **25**, 163–171.

HUBACHER, W. 1983. L'exploration, de 1971 à 1976, de fluorine à la Tête des Econduits. *Minaria Helvetica, Schweizerische Gesellschaft historische Bergbauforschung*, **1983**, 9–20.

HUCK, K. H. 1984. *Die Beziehung zwischen Tektonik und Paragenese unter Berücksichtigung geochemischer Kriterien in der Flussspat und Schwerspatlagerstätte Clara bei Oberwolfach, Schwarzwald.* PhD Thesis, University of Heidelberg.

HUGI, E., HUTTENLOCHER, H. F., GASSMANN, F. & FEHLMANNN, H. 1948. Die Magnetitlagerstätten. *Beiträge Geologie Schweiz, geotechnische Serie*, **13**, 1–16.

HÜGI, TH., KÖPPLE, V., DE QUERVAIN, F. & RICKENBACH, E. 1967. Die Uranvererzungen bei Isérables (Wallis). *Beiträge zur Geologie der Schweiz: Geotechnische Serie,* **42**, 1–88.

HUTCHINSON, R. W. 1980. Massive base metal sulphide deposits as guides to tectonic evolution. *In*: STRANGWAY, D. W. (ed.) *The Continental Crust and its Mineral Deposits*, Geological Association of Canada, Special Papers, **20**, 659–684.

HUTCHINSON, R. W. 1987. Metallogeny of Precambrian gold deposits: Space and time relationships. *Economic Geology*, **82**, 1993–2007.

HVOŽD'ARA, P. 1999. Gold placers in the Western Carpathian area. *Mineralia Slovaca*, **31**, 241–248.

IHS ENERGY 2008. Exploration and Production Database. http://energy.ihs.com.

ILAVSKÝ, J., MALKOVSKÝ, M. & ODEHNAL, L. 1977. The iron ore deposits in the Czechoslovak Socialist Republic. *In*: ZITZMANN, A. (ed.) *The Iron Ore Deposits of Europe and Adjacent Areas, Explanatory notes to the international map of the iron ore deposits of Europe 1 : 2 500 000*. Bundesanstalt für Geowissenschaften und Rohstoffe, Hannover, **1**, 111–124.

ILLIES, H. & FUCHS, K. (eds) 1974. *Approaches to Taphrogenesis*. Schweizerbart, Stuttgart.

IZART, A. & *et al.* 1998. Stratigraphic correlations between the continental and marine Tathyan and Peri-Tethyan basins during the Late Carboniferous and the Early Permian. *Geodiversitas*, **20**, 521–593.

JAFFÉ, F. C. 1986. Switzerland. *In*: DUNNING, F. W. & EVANS, A. M. (eds) *Mineral Deposits of Europe, Vol. 3, Central Europe*. Institution of Mining and Metallurgy, and Mineralogical Society, London, 41–55.

JANECZEK, J. 1996. Nb-, Ta- and Sn-rich titanite and its alteration in pegmatites from Zólkiewka, Poland. *Neues Jahrbuch für Mineralogie Monatshefte*, **1996**, 459–469.

JANKOVIĆ, S. 1967. *Metallogenic Epochs and Ore-bearing Areas of Yugoslavia*. Faculty of Mining and Geology Belgrade, Belgrade.

JANKOVIĆ, S. 1990. *The Ore Deposits of Serbia (Yugoslavia), Regional Metallogenic Settings, Environments of Deposition, and Types (in Serbian)*. Faculty of Mining and Geology Belgrade, Belgrade.

JENKYNS, H. C., GÉCZY, B. & MARSHALL, J. D. 1991. Jurassic manganese carbonates of Central Europe and the early Toarcian anoxic event. *Journal of Geology*, **99**, 137–149.

JIANG, S.-Y., PALMER, M. R., SLACK, J. F. & SHAW, D. R. 1998. Paragenesis and chemistry of multistage tourmaline formation in the Sullivan Pb–Zn–Ag deposit, British Columbia. *Economic Geology*, **93**, 47–67.

JUCH, D. 1991. Das Inkohlungsbild des Ruhrkarbons - Ergebnisse einer Übersichtsauswertung. *Glückauf-Forschungshefte*, **52**, 37–47.

JURA, D., JURECKA, J. KRIEGER, W., KUZAK, R., LESNIK, D. & PERSKI, Z. 2000. Conditions of hard coal exploitation and its environmental impact in the western part of the Upper Silesian Coal Basin. *Guide to Field Trips, 4th European Coal Conference*, Ustron, Poland. Polish Geological Institute, Warsaw, 5–39.

JURECZKA, J. 1995. Upper Silesian Coal Basin. *In:* ZDANOWSKI, A. & ZAKOWA, H. (eds) *The Carboniferous System in Poland*. Polish Geological Institute, **CXLVIII**, 177–178.

JURECZKA, J. & KRIEGER, W. 2000. Outline of the coal deposits, geology and environmental impact of hard coal exploitation in the Upper Silesian Coal Basin. *In: Guide to Field Trips, 4th European Coal Conference*, Ustron, Poland. Polish Geological Institute, Warsaw, 7–15.

JURKOVIĆ, I. 1957. The basic characteristics of the metallogenic region of the Mid Bosnian Ore Mountains. *Proceedings, II Congress Geology Jugoslavia*, Sarajevo, 504–519.

JURKOVIĆ, I. 1959. Magnetite deposits at Muhamedbegova Priseka nearby Ključ in Bosnia. *Geološki vjesnik*, **12**, 115–124 [in Croatian].

JURKOVIĆ, I. 1962. Resultate der wissenschaftlichen Untersuchungen der Erzlagerstätten in V. R. Croatien (in Croatian with German abstract). *Geološki vjesnik*, **15**, 249–294.

JURKOVIĆ, I. 1993. Mineral resources of the Sisak region, Croatia. (in Croatian). *Rudarsko-Geološko-Naftni Zbornik*, **5**, 39–58.

JURKOVIĆ, I. 2004. Metallogeny of Eocene syncollisional granites of Motajica and Prosara Mountains. *Rudarsko-Geološko-Naftni Zbornik*, **16**, 1–17.

JURKOVIĆ, I. & PALINKAŠ, A. L. 2002. Discrimination criteria for assigning ore deposits located in the Dinaridic Palaeozoic-Triassic formations to Variscan or Alpidic metallogeny. *In:* BLUNDELL, D. J., NEUBAUER, F. & VON QUADT, A. (eds) *The Timing and Locations of Major Ore Deposition in an Evolving Orogen*. Geological Society, London, Special Publications, **206**, 229–245.

JURKOVIĆ, I. & PAMIĆ, J. 2001. Geodynamics and metallogeny of variscan complexes of the dinarides and south tisia as related to plate tectonics. *NAFTA*, **52**, 267–284.

KALENDA, F. & VANĚČEK, M. 1989. Base metal deposits of the Zlaté Hory District. *Excursion Guide 5A, Gold Districts of the Bohemian Massif, Gold 89 in Europe*, 39–43.

KALLIS, P. & BLEICH, K. E. 1994. Bodenentwicklung im Jungtertiär am Rande des Molassebeckens (Heidenheim-Mergelstetten/Ostalb). *Mitteilungen der Deutschen Bodenkundlichen Gesellschaft*, **74**, 379–382.

KAMENICKÝ, J. 1952. Hematite deposit near the Velký Folkmár. *Geologický sborník Slovenskej akadémie vied*, **4**, 279–274.

KAMENICKÝ, J. 1957. Serpentinite, diabase and glaucophanic rocks of the Triassic complexes in the Spiš-Gemer Ore Mts. *Geologické práce, Zošity*, **45**, 5–111 [in Slovak with English abstract].

KARNIN, W.-D., IDIZ, E., MERKEL, D. & RUPRECHT, E. 1996. The Zechstein Stassfurt carbonate system of the Thuringian Basin, Germany. *Petroleum Gesoscience*, **2**, 53–58.

KARNKOWSKI, P. H. 1999. *Origin and Evolution of the Polish Rotliegend Basin*. Polish Geological Institute, Special Publications, **3**.

KASIŃSKI, J. R. 2000. *Geological atlas of the Tertiary lignite-bearing association in the Polish part of the Zittau Basin. 1:50 000*. Polish Geological Institute, Warsaw.

KASIŃSKI, J. R. & PIWOCKI, M. 2002. Low-rank coals in Poland: Prospection – Mining – Progress. *In*: JURECZKA, J. & PODEMSKI, M. (eds) *Proceedings of the IV European Coal Conference*. Polish Geological Institute, Special Papers, **7**, 17–30.

KASIŃSKI, J. R., CZARNECKI, L., FRANKOWSKI, R. & PIWOCKI, M. 2000. Geology of the Bełchatów Lignite Deposit and environmental impact of exploration. *In: Guide to Field Trips, 4th European Coal Conference*, Ustron, Poland. Polish Geological Institute, Warsaw, 40–65.

KAY, S. M. & MPODOZIS, C. 2001. Central Andean ore deposits linked to evolving shallow subduction systems and thickening crust. *GSA Today* (March) 5–9.

KAY, S. M., MPODOZIS, C. & COIRA, B. 1999. Neogene magmatism, tectonism, and mineral deposits of the Central Andes (22°–33°S Latitude). *In*: SKINNER, B. J. (ed.) *Geology and Ore Deposits of the Central Andes*. Society of Economic Geologists, Special Publication, **7**, 27–59.

KELLER J. 1984. Der jungtertiäre Vulkanismus Südwestdeutschlands; Exkursion im Kaiserstuhl und Hegau. *Fortschritte der Mineralogie*, **62**(2), 2–35.

KEMPE, U. & BELYATSKY, B. V. 1997. An attempt at direct dating of the Sadisdorf Sn-W mineralization, Eastern Erzgebirge (Germany). *Journal of the Czech Geological Society*, **42**, 21.

KEMPE, U., RENÉ, M. & WOLF, D. 2001. Distribution of REE and REE-minerals in topaz-bearing granites of the Karlovy Vary pluton (Czech Republic). *Mitteilungen der Österreichischen Mineralogischen Gesellschaft*, **146**, 126–127.

KETTEL, D. 1989. Upper Carboniferous source rocks north and south of the Variscan Front (NW and Central Europe). *Marine and Petroleum Geology*, **6**, 170–181.

KHARIN, G., EMELYANOV, E. M. & ZAGORODNICH, A. V. 2004. Paleogene Mineral Resources of the SE Baltic Sea and Sambian Peninsula. *Zeitschrift für Angewandte Geologie*, Sonderheft **2**, 64–71.

KISS, J. 1982. *About Deposits in Detail*. Tankönyv, Alföldi Nyomda [in Hungarian].

KLECKER, R., BENTHAM, P., PALMER-KOLEMAN, S. & JAMINSKI, J. 2001. A recent petroleum-geologic evaluation of the Central Carpathian Depression, Southeastern Poland. *Marine and Petroleum Geology*, **18**, 65–85.

KLEMM, W. 1994. Chemical evolution of hydrothermal solutions during Variscan and post-Variscan mineralization in the Erzgebirge, Germany. *In*: SELTMANN, R., KÄMPF, H. & MÖLLER, P. (eds) *Metallogeny of Collision Orogen*. Czech Geological Survey, Prague, 150–158.

KLETT, M., EICHHORST, F. & SCHÄFER, A. 2002. Facies interpretation from well-logs applied to the Tertiary Lower Rhine Basin fill. *Netherlands Journal of Geosciences/Geologie en Mijnbouw*, **81**, 167–176.

KNÉSL, J. 1979. Geology of the Vel'ká studňa Hg deposit. *Mineralia Slovaca*, **11**, 327–384 [in Slovak with English abstract].

KNÉSL, J. & LINKEŠOVÁ, M. 1971. Up-to-date results from Hg-ore exploration in the Kremnické vrchy Mts. *Geologický pruzkum*, **5**, 135–137 [in Slovak].

KNEŽEVIĆ, V., KARAMATA, S. & CVETKOVIĆ, V. 1994. Tertiary granitic rocks along the southern margin of the Pannonian Basin. *Acta Mineralogica Petrographica,* **35**, 71–80.

KNIEWALD, G., BERMANEC, V. & TIBLJAŠ, D. 1986. *On the origin and type of the Tuzla salt deposit in Yugoslavia.* Commission Internationale pour l' Exploration Scientifique de la Mer Méditerrane, Monaco, Reports, **30/2.**

KOCKEL, F., WEHNER, H., GERLING, P. 1994. Petroleum systems of the Lower Saxony Basin, Germany. *In:* MAGOON, L. B. & DOW, W. G. (eds) *The Petroleum System – From Source to Trap.* American Association Petroleum Geologists, Memoirs, **60**, 573–586.

KODĚRA, P. & RADVANEC, M. 2002. Fluid inclusion and mineralogical data from the Hnúšt'a–Mútnik talc-magnesite and Miková–Jedl'ovec magnesite deposit (Western Carpathians, Slovakia). *Boletin Paranaense de Geociências*, **50**, 131–150.

KOHÚT, M. & RECIO, C. 2002. Sulfur Isotope study of selected Hercynian granitic and surrounding rocks from Western Carpathians (Slovakia). *Geologica Carpathica*, **53**, 3–13.

KOHÚT, M. & STEIN, H. 2005. Re–Os molybdenite dating of granite-related Sn–W–Mo mineralisation at Hnilec, Gemeric Superunit, Slovakia. *Mineralogy and Petrology*, **85**, 117–129.

KOLBE, H. 1962. Die Eisenerzkolke im Neokom-Eisenerzgebiet Salzgitter. Beispiele zur Bedeutung synsedimentärer Tektonik für die Lagerstättenbildung. *Mitteilungen des geologischen Staatsinstituts Hamburg*, **31**, 276–308.

KONEČNÝ, V., LEXA, J. & HOJSTRIČOVÁ, V. 1995. The Central Slovakia Neogene volcanic field: a review. *Acta Vulcanologica*, **7**, 2, 63–78.

KÖPPEL, V. 1966. Die Vererzungen im insubrischen Kristallin des Malcantone (Tessin). *Beiträgeder Geologie der Schweiz: Geotechnische Serie*, **40**, 1–123.

KORIKOVSKIJ, S. P., DUPEJ, J. & BORONICHIN, V. A. 1989. High-Fe metasediments from Kokava nad Rimavicou (Veporicum, Central Slovakia). *Mineralia Slovaca*, **21**, 251–258.

KOSMOSWSKA-CEVANOWICZ, B. 2004. Quaternary amber bearing deposits on the Polish Coast. *Zeitschrift für Angewandte Geologie*, Sonderheft **2**, 73–84.

KÖSTER, H. M. 1980. Kaolin deposits of eastern Bavaria and the Rheinische Schiefergebirge (Rhenish Slate Mountains). *Geologisches Jahrbuch, ser. D*, **39**, 7–23.

KOTARBA, M. J. 2001. Composition and origin of coalbed gases in the Upper Silesian and Lublin basins, Poland. *Organic Geochemistry,* **32**, 163–180.

KOTARBA, M. J. & RICE, D. D. 2001. Composition and origin of coalbed gases in the Lower Silesian basin, southwest Poland. *Applied Geochemistry,* **16**, 895–910.

KOTAS, A. & HADRO, J. 2001. Thermal maturity evolution of coal-bearing formations as a background for coalbed methane generation hypothesis – case study from the central part of the Upper Silesian Coal Basin, Poland. *In: 4th European Coal Conference*, Ustron, Poland. Polish Geological Institute, Warsaw, 42.

KOVÁCH, Á., SVINGOR, É. & GRECULA, P. 1986. Rb/Sr isotopic ages of granitoide rocks from the Spiš-Gemer metalliferous Mts., West Carpathians, Eastern Slovakia. *Mineralia Slovaca*, **18**, 1–14.

KOUBOVÁ, M., LOSOS, Z. & MALEC, J. 2001. Ore-Mineralogy of the Au-deposit near Voltyrov at Milevsko, Czech Republic. *Mitteilungen der Österreichischen Mineralogischen Gesellschaft,* **146**, 153–154.

KRAHN, L. 1988. *Buntmetall-Verzungen und Blei-Isotopie im linksrheinischen Schiefergebirge und in angrenzenden Gebieten.* PhD thesis, RWTH Aachen.

KRAHN, L. & BAUMANN, A. 1996. Lead isotope systematics of epigenetic lead-zinc mineralization in the western part of the Rheinisches Schiefergebirge, Germany. *Mineralium Deposita*, **31**, 225–237.

KRAINER, K., MOSTLER, H. & HADITSCH, J. G. 1994. Jurassische Beckenbildung in den Nördlichen Kalkalpen bei Lofer (Salzburg) unter besonderer Berücksichtigung der Manganerz Genese. *Abhandlungen der Geolischen Bundesanstalt,* **50**, 257–293.

KRAMM, U. 1985. Sr-Isotopenuntersuchungen zur Genese der Strontianitlagerstätte Münsterland/Westfalen. *Fortschritte der Mineralogie*, **63**, 124.

KRAUS, I., ŠAMAJOVÁ, E., ŠUCHA, V., LEXA, J. & HRONCOVÁ, Z. 1994. Diagenetic and hydrothermal alterations of volcanic rocks into clay minerals and zeolites (Kremnické vrchy Mts., the Western Slovakia). *Geologica Carpathica*, **45**, 151–158.

KRAWCZYK, C. M., MCCANN, T., COCKS, L. R. M., ENGLAND, R., MCBRIDE, J. & WYBRANIEC, S. 2008. Caledonian Tectonics. *In:* MCCANN, T. (ed.) *The Geology of Central Europe. Volume 1: Precambrian and Palaeozoic.* Geological Society, London, 303–381.

KREBS, W. 1981. The geology of the Meggen ore deposit. *In:* WOLF, K. H. (ed.) *Handbook of Strata-Bound and Stratiform Ore Deposits*, Vol. 9, *Regional Studies and Specific Deposits.* Elsevier, Amsterdam, 509–549.

KREUTER, H., HARTHILL, N., JUDT, M. & LEHMANN, B. 2003. Geothermal power generation in the Upper Rhine Valley – The Project Offenbach/Pfalz. *International Geothermal Conference*, Reykjavík, September 2003. S01 Paper 062, 20–26.

KŘÍBEK, B. 1989. The role of organic matter in the metallogeny of the Bohemian Massif. *Economic Geology*, **84**, 1525–1540.

KŘÍBEK, B., ZAK, K., SPANGENBERG, J. E., JEHLICKA, J., PROKES, S. & KOMINEK, J. 1999. Bitumens in the late Variscan hydrothermal vein-type uranium deposit of Pribram, Czech Republic; sources, radiation-induced alteration, and relation to mineralization. *Economic Geology*, **94**, 1093–1114.

KŘÍBEK, B., HAJEK, A., *et al.* 2005. *Uranové Ložisko Rožná-Model pozdně variskch a po variskch mineralizaci.* Česká geologická služba, Prague.

KRONER, U., MANSY, J.-L. *et al.* 2008. Variscan tectonics. *In:* MCCANN, T. (ed.) *The Geology of Central Europe. Volume 1: Precambrian and Palaeozoic.* Geological Society, London, 599–664.

KUBICA, B. 1994. The discovery of a new sulphur deposit between the Vistula and San rives (the Carpathian Foredeep, southern Poland) – a historic review. *Geological Quaterly*, **38**, 341–352.

KUCHA, H. 1982. Platinum-group metals in the Zechstein Copper Deposits, Poland. *Economic Geology*, **77**, 1578–1591.

KUCHA, H. & PAWLIKOWSKI, M. 1986. Two-brine model of the genesis of stratabound Zechstein. *Mineralium Deposita*, **21**, 70–80.

KUCHA, H. & PRZYLOWICZ, W. 1999. Noble metals in organic matter and clay-organic matrices, Kupferschiefer, Poland. *Economic Geology,* **94**, 1137–1162.

KUCHA, H., SCHROLL, E. & STUMPFL, E. F. 2004. Bacteriogenic zinc-lead mineralisation in the Bleiberg Deposit, Austria. *32nd International Geological Congress*, Florence, Italy, 20–28 August 2004. Abstrtacts, G15. 09.

KUHLEMANN, J. 1995. Zur Diagenese des Karanwanken-Nordstammes (Österreich/Slowenien): Spättriassische, epigenetische Blei-Zink-Vererzung und mitteltertiäre, hydrothermale Karbonatzementation. *Archiv für Lagerstättenforschung der Geologischen Bundesanstalt,* **18**, 57–116.

KUKAL, Z. 1985. *The Evolution of Sediments of the Bohemian Massif.* Czech Geological Survey, Prague [in Czech].

KULCZYCKA, J. 2004. EU new members: Implications for the Mining Industry. *Minerals & Energy - Raw Materials Report*, **19**, 34–44.

KULIK, J., LEIFELD, D., *et al.* 1984. Petrofazielle und chemische Erkundung des Kupferschiefers der Hessichen Senke und des Harz-Westrandes. *Geologisches Jahrbuch*, **68**, 1–223.

KUNZ, E. 1999. Die Gasführung des Ruhrkarbons in ihrer räumlichen Verteilung und Entstehung zur Prognose der Ausgasung. *Glückauf-Forschungshefte,* **60**, 40–44.

KUŽVART, M. 1968. Kaolin deposits of Czechoslovakia. *Proceedings of 23rd International Geological Congress*, Prague, **15**, 47–73.

KVET, R. 1994. Mineral mining on the bohemian side of the Krušné Hory Mountains/Erzgebirge up to the time of Agricola. *GeoJournal*, **32**, 101–102.

KWIECINSKA, B. K., HAMBURG, G., VLEESKENS, J. M. 1992. Formation temperatures of natural coke in the lower Silesian coal basin, Poland. Evidence from pyrite and clays by SEM-EDX. *International Journal of Coal Geology*, **21**, 217–235.

LACOMME, A., MILESI, J. P. & GROS, Y. 1987. L'amas sulfuré à Cu-Zn de Chessy (Rhone), évolution historique des recherches, état actuel des connaissances sur le gisement et son environment. *Chronique de la Recherche Minière*, **489**, 3–20.

LADWEIN, H. W., SCHMIDT, F., SEIFERT, P., WESSELY, G. 1991. Geodynamics and generation of hydrocarbons in the region of the Vienna Basin, Austria. *In*: SPENCER, A. M. (ed.) *Generation, Accumulation and Production of Europe's Hydrocarbons.* EAPG Oxford, Special Publications, **1**, 289–305.

LAMIRAUX, CH. & MASCLE, A. 1998. Petroleum exploration and production in France. *First Break,* **16**, 109–117.

LAMPE, C., PERSON, M., NÖTH, S. & RICKEN, W. 2001. Episodic fluid flow within continental rift basins: some insights from field data and mathematical models of the Rhinegraben. *Geofluids,* **1**, 42–52.

LANCELOT, J. L. BRIQUE, J.-P., RESPAUT & CLAUER, N. 1995. Géochimie isotopique des systèmes U–Pb/Pb–Pb et évolution polyphasée des gîtes d'uranium du Lodévois et du sud du Massif central. *Chronique de la Recherche Minière,* **521**, 3–18.

LANDIS, E. R., ROHRBACHER, J. R., BARKER, CH. E., FODOR, B. & GOMBAR, G. 2003. Coalbed gas in the Mecsek Basin, Hungary. *International Journal of Coal Geology,* **54**, 41–55.

LANGE, G., MÜHLSTEDT, F., FREYKOFF, G. & SCHRÖDER, B. 1991. Der Uranerzbergbau im Thüringen und Sachsen-ein geologisch-bergmännischer Überblick. *Erzmetall,* **44**, 162–171.

LANGENAEKER, V. 2000. The Campine Basin. Stratigraphy, structural geology, coalification and hydrocarbon potential of the Devonian to Jurassic. *Aardkundige Mededelingen* **10**, 1–142.

LANGHANS, G., BEUTHAN, H.-C. & WESSEL, F. 2003. Development of Mittelplate Oilfield. *Oil Gas European Magazine,* **3**, OG118-OG125.

LANPHERE, M. A., COLEMAN, R. G., KARAMATA, S. & PAMIĆ, J. 1975. Age of amphibolites associated with alpine peridotites in the Dinaride Ophiolite zone, Yugoslavia. *Earth and Planetary Science Letter,* **26**, 271–276.

LAPPALAINEN, E. (ed.) 1996. *Global Peat Resources*. International Peat Society, Geological Survey of Finland, Helsinki.

LARGE, D. E. 1993. Precious and base-metal mineralization at the Post-Variscan unconformity of Central Europe – a reconsideration. *In:* HACH-ALI *et al.* (eds) *Current Research In Geology Applied to Ore Deposits*, Geological Society of Ireland, Dublin, 495–497.

LARGE, D. E. & WALCHER, E. 1999. The Rammelsberg massive sulphide Cu-Zn-Pb-Ba, Germany: An example of sediment-hosted massive sulphide mineralization. *Mineralium Deposita*, **34**, 522–538.

LARGE, D. E., SCHAEFFER, R. & HÖHNDORF, A. 1983. Lead isotope data from selected galena occurrences in the north Eifel and north Sauerland, Germany. *Mineralium Deposita*, **18**, 235–243.

LAVRIČ, J. V. & SPANGENBERG, J. E. 2003. Stable isotope (C, O, S) systematics of the mercury mineralization at Idrija, Slovenia: constraints on fluid source and alteration processes. *Mineralium Deposita*, **38**, 886–889.

LAZNICKA, P. 1999. Quantitative relationships among giant deposits of metals. *Economic Geology,* **94**, 455–473.

LEACH, D. L., VIETS, J. B., KOSLOWSKI, A. & KIBITLEWSKI, S. 1996. Geology, geochemistry and genesis of the Silesia-Cracow zinc-lead district, southern Poland. *In*: SANGSTER, D. F. (ed.) *Carbonate-Hosted Lead-Zinc Deposits,* Society of Economic Geologists, Special Publications, **4**, 144–170.

LEACH, D., BECHSTÄDT, T., BONI, M. & ZEEH, S. 2003. Triassic-hosted MVT Zn-Pb ores of Poland, Austria, Slovenia and Italy. *In:* KELLY, J. G. *et al.* (eds) *Europe's Major Base Metal Deposits,* Irish Association of Economic Geologists, Dublin, 169–213.

LEIPZIGER, K. 1986. *Untersuchungen zur Raumschaffung der Fluoritmineralisation im Wölsendorfer Flußspatrevier.* PhD thesis, University of Mainz.

LEMOINE, M., BAS, T., *et al.* 1986. The continental margin of the Mesozoic Tethys of the western Alps. *Marine and Petroleum Geology,* **3**, 179–199.

LEROY, J. 1978. The Magnac and Funay uranium deposits of the La Crouzille District (Western Massif Central, France): geologic and fluid inclusion studies. *Economic Geology,* **73**, 1611–1634.

LÉVÊQUE, M. H., LANCELOT, J. R. & GEORGE, E. 1988. The Bertholène uranium deposit - Mineralogical characteristics and U-Pb dating of the primary U mineralization and its subsequent remobilization: Consequences upon the evolution of the U deposits of the Massif Central, France. *Chemical Geology,* **69**, 147–163.

LEXA, J. 1999. Outline of the Alpine geology and Metallogeny of the Carpatho-Pannonian region. *In:* MOLNÁR, F., LEXA, J. & HEDENQUIST, J. W. *Epithermal Mineralization ot the Western Carpathians.* Society of Economic Geologists, Guidebook Series, **31**, 65–108.

LEXA, J., ŠTOHL, J. & KONEČNÝ, V. 1999. The Banská Štiavnica ore district: relationship between metallogenetic processes and the geological evolution of the stratovolcano. *Mineralium Deposita,* **34**, 417–654.

LINDQUIST, S. J. 1999. *Petroleum Systems of the Po Basin Province of Northern Italy and the Northern Adriatic Sea: Porto Garibaldi (biogenic), Merida/Riva Di Solto (Thermal), and Marnoso-Arenacea (Thermal).* US Department of the Interior, US Geological Survey.

LIPPOLT, H. J., SCHORN, U. & PIDGEOM, R. T. 1983. Genetic implications of new lead isotope measurements on Schwarzwald vein and Upper Triassic sediment galenas. *Geologische Rundschau,* **72**, 77–104.

LIPS, A. L. W. 2002. Cross-correlating geodynamic processes and magmatic-hydrothermal ore deposit formation over time; a review on southeast Europe. *In:* BLUNDELL, D. J., NEUBAUER, F. & VON QUADT, A. (eds) *The Timing and Location Of Major Ore Deposits in an Evolving Orogen.* Geological Society, London, Special Publications, **204**, 69–79.

LITT, T., SCHMINCKE, H.-U., FRECHEN, M. & SCHLÜCHTER, C. 2008. Quaternary. *In*: MCCANN, T. (ed.) *The Geology of Central Europe. Volume 2: Mesozoic and Cenozoic.* Geological Society, London, 1284–1340.

LITTKE, R., BÜKER, C., LÜCKGE, A., SACHSENHOFER, R. F. & WELTE, D. H. 1994. A new evaluation of paleo-heat flows and eroded thicknesses for the Carboniferous Ruhr basin, Western Germany. *International Journal of Coal Geology,* **26**, 155–183.

LITTKE, R., KROOSS, B., IDIZ, E. F. & FRIELINGSDORF, J. 1995. Molecular nitrogen in natural gas accumulations: generation from sedimentary organic matter at high temperatures. *American Association of Petroleum Geologists Bulletin,* **79**, 410–430.

LITTKE, R., BÜKER, C., HERTLE, M., KARG, H., STROETMANN-HEINEN, V. & ONCKEN, O. 2000. Heat flow evolution, subsidence and erosion in the Rheno-Hercynian orogenic wedge of central Europe. *In:* FRANKE, W., HAAK, V., ONCKEN, O. & TANNER, D. (eds) *Orogenic Processes: Quantification and Modelling in the Variscan Belt.* Geological Society, London, Special Publications, **179**, 231–255.

LORENZEN, W. 1965. *Helgoland und das früheste Kupfer des Nordens.* Niederelbeverlag, Otterndorf.

LOSERT, J. 1957. Lead-zinc deposits and occurrences of Pb-Zn ores in Odra Hills (North Moravia). *Rozpravy Ceskoslovenské akademie ved,* **67**, 1–61.

LOUGNON, J. 1956. Rapport general sur les gisement de manganese en France. *20th International Geological Congress. Symposium Sobre Yacimientos de Manganeso*, Mexico, **5**, 63–171.

LUCIC, D., SAFTIC, B., KRIZMANIC, K., PRELOGOVIC, E., BRITVIC, V., MESIC, I. & TADEJ, J. 2001. The Neogene evolution and hydrocarbon potential of the Pannonian Basin in Croatia, *Marine and Petroleum Geology,* **18**, 133–147.

LUDWIG, G. & FIGGE, K. 1979. Schwermineralvorkommen und Sandverteilung in der Deutschen Bucht. *Geologisches Jahrbuch,* **D 32**, 23–68.

LUGOVIĆ, B. & SLOVENEC, D. 2004. Mantle harzburgite (serpentinites) from Gornje Orešje (Medvednica Mt., Croatia). *In*: HALAMIĆ, J. (ed.) *Excursion Guide, Geology of the Zagorje-Mid-Transdanubian Zone,* Joint meeting of Croatian and Hungarian Geological Societies, Zagreb.

LUGOVIĆ, B., ALTHERR, R. & RACZEK, J. 1991. Geochemistry of peridotites and mafic igneous rocks from the Central Dinaric Ophiolite Belt, Yugoslavia. *Contributions to Mineralogy and Petrology,* **106**, 201–216.

LÜTZNER, H. 1987. *Sedimentary and Volcanic Rotliegendes of Saale Depression.* Symposium on Rotliegendes in Central Europe (Erfurt), Excursion Guidebook. Academy of Science GDR, Potsdam.

MCCANN, T. 1998. Rotliegend prospectivity in the NE German Basin. *Petroleum Geoscience*, **4**, 17–27.

MCCANN, T., KIERSNOWSKI, H., *et al.* 2008*a*. Permian. *In:* MCCANN, T. (ed.) *The Geology of Central Europe. Volume 1: Precambrian and Palaeozoic.* Geological Society, London, 531–597.

MCCANN, T., SKOMPSKI, S., *et al.* 2008*b*. Carboniferous. *In:* MCCANN, T. (ed.) *The Geology of Central Europe. Volume 1: Precambrian and Palaeozoic.* Geological Society, London, 411–529.

MADU, B. E., NESBITT, B. E. & MUEHLENBACHS, K. 1990. A mesothermal gold stibnite-quartz vein occurrence in the Canadian Cordillera. *Economic Geology,* **85**, 1260–1268.

MAGYAR, I., GEARY, D. H. & MÜLLER, P. 1999. Paleogeographic evolution of the Late Miocene Lake Pannon in Central Europe. *Paleogeography, Palaeoclimatology, Palaeoecology,* **147**, 151–167.

MAGYAR, I., FOGARASI, A., VAKARES, G., BUKO, L. & TARI, G. 2005. The largest hydrocarbon field discovered to date in Hungary. Algyo. *In:* GOLONKA, J. & PICHA, F. (eds) *The Carpathians and their*

*Foreland; Geology and Hydrocarbon Resources,* American Association of Petroleum Geologists, Memoirs, **84**, 479.

MALEC, L. & VESELOVSKY, F. 1985. Gold mining in the neighbourhood of Svoboda nad Upou. *Rozpr Natural Technic Muzeum* **99**, 149–160 [in Czech].

MALITCH, K. N., THALHAMMER, O. A. R., KNAUF, V. V. & MELCHER, F. 2003. Diversity of platinum-group mineral assemblages in banded and podiform chromatite from the Kraubath ultramafic massif, Austria: evidence for an ophiolitic transition zone? *Mineralium Deposita*, **38**, 282–297.

MANKOPF, N. R. & LIPPOLT, H.-J. 1997. He-geochemische Belege für ein permotriassisches Alter des Roteisenerzes des Quarz-Hämatit-Baryt-Ganges westlich Obersexau im Brettental, Mittlerer Schwarzwald. *Jahreshefte des Landesamts für Geologie, Rohstoffe und Bergbau Baden-Württemberg,* **37**, 25–48.

MAREK, F. 1970. Estimated age of the Ransko basic massif based on palaeomagnetic data. *Věstník Ústředního Ústavu Geologického,* **45**, 99–102 [English summary].

MARINAC, C. & CUNEY, M. 1999. Ore deposits of the French Massif Central: Insight into the metallogenesis of the Variscan collision belt. *Mineralium Deposita*, **34**, 472–507.

MARKIC, M. & SACHSENHOFER, R. F. 1997. Petrographic composition and depositional environments of the Pliocene Velenje lignite seam (Slovenia). *International Journal of Coal Geology,* **33**, 229–254.

MARSHALL, D., MEISSER, N. & TAYLOR, R. P. 1998. Fluid inclusion, stable isotope, and Ar–Ar evidence for the age and origin of gold-bearing quartz veins at Mont Chemin, Switzerland. *Mineralogy and Petrology,* **62** 147–165.

MARTIN, G. 1979. Die marin-sedimentären Eisenerzelager der westlichen Mosel-Mulde (Grubenfeld Schweicher Morgenstern). *Geologisches Jahrbuch* **D 31**, 123–131.

MASCLE, A., BERTRAND, G. & LAMIRAUX, CH. 1994. Exploration for and production of oil and gas in France: A review of the habitat, present activity, and expected developments. *In:* MASCLE, A. (ed.) *Hydrocarbon and Petroleum Geology in France.* EAPG Special Publication, **4**, Springer, Berlin, 3–27.

MASTALERZ, M. & JONES, J. M. 1988. Coal rank variation in the Intrasudetic Basin, SW Poland. *International Journal of Coal Geology,* **10**, 79–97.

MASTALERZ, M. & WILKS, K. R. 1992. Coal seams of the Walbrzych formation, Intrasudetic Basin, Poland: inferences on changing depositional environment. *International Journal of Coal Geology,* **20**, 243–261.

MAŤO, L. & MAŤOVÁ, V. 1993. Gold mineralization of shear zones of the Uderiná prospect, southwestern part of the Veporicum crystalline complex, Central Slovakia. *Mineralia Slovaca*, **25**, 327–340.

MATTAUER, M. & MATTE, P. 1998. Le bassin Stéphanien de St-Etienne ne résulte pas d'une extension tardi-hercynienne généralisée: c'est un bassin pull-apart en relation avec un décrochement dextre. *Geodinamica Acta*, **11**, 23–31.

MAUCHER, A. 1974. Zeitgebundene Erzlägerstätten. *Geologische Rundschau*, **63**, 263–275.

MAYNARD, J. B. & OKITA, P. M. 1991. Bedded barite deposits of the U.S., Canada, Germany, and China: Two major types based on tectonic setting. *Economic Geology* **86**, 364–376.

MEISL, S. 1965. Metazeunerit in uranführenden vererzten Pflanzenresten im Oberen Buntsandstein bei Wrexen, Waldeck (Nordhessen). *Notizblatt des hessischen Landesamtes für Bodenforschung*, **93**, 266–280.

MESHIK A. P., LIPPOLT, H. J. & DYMKOV, Y. M. 2000. Xenon geochronology of Schwarzwald pitchblendes, *Mineralium Deposita,* **35**, 190–205.

MICHELETTI, T. 1964. Il Piemonte minerario. *Bollettino Associazione Mineralogica Subalpina*, **1**, 19–48.

MILAN, G. & SAUER, R. 1996. Ultra deep drilling in the Vienna Basin -a review of geological results. *In*: WESSELY, G. & LIEBL, W. (eds) *Oil and Gas in Alpidic Thrustbelts and Basins of Central and Eastern Europe.* EAGE Special Publication, **5**, Geological Society, London, 109–117.

MILESI, J.-P. & LESCUYER, J.-L. 1993. *The Chessy Zn-Cu-Pa massive sulphide deposit and the Devonian Brevenne volcano-sedimentary belt (Eastern Massif Central, France).* Documents du BRGM, **224**.

MITCHELL, A. H. G. 1996. Distribution and genesis of some epizonal Zn-Pb and Au provinces in the Carpathian–Balkan region. *Transactions of the Institution of Mining and Metallurgy (Sect. B: Applied Earth Science),* **105**, 127–138.

MLAKAR, I. 1974. An outline of production of the Idrija mercury mine through the centuries, *Idrijska razgledi*, **3–4**, 1–40

MOCHNACKA, K., BANAŚ, M., KRAMER, W. & POŠMOURNÝ, K. 1995. Metallogenesis. *In:* DALLMEYER, R. D., FRANKE, W. & WEBER, K. (eds) *Pre-Permian Geology of Central and Eastern Europe*, Springer, Berlin, 360–372.

MÖLLER, P. & LÜDERS, V. 1993. Synopsis. *Monograph Series on Mineral Deposits*, **30**, 285–291.

MOLÁK, B. & PECHO, J. 1983. Geological characteristic of the sheelite-Au-bearing mineralization in the region of Jasenie. *In: Scheelitovo-zlatonosné zrudnenie v Nízkych Tatrách.* Geological Survey of the Slovak Republic, 61–70 [in Slovak].

MOLNÁR, F., ZELENKA, T., MÁTYÁS, E., PÉCSKAY, Z., BAJNÓCZI, B., KISS, J. & HORVÁTH, I. 1999. Epithermal mineralization of the Tokaj Mountains, northeast Hungary: shallow levels of low-sulfidation type system. *In:* MOLNÁR, F., LEXA, J. & HEDENQUIST, J. W. 1999. *Epithermal Mineralization ot the Western Carpathians.* Society of Economic Geologists, Guidebook Series, **31**, 109–153.

MORÁVEK, P. 1996*a*. Gold in metallogeny of the Central and Western European units of the Peri-Alpine Variscan belt. *Global Tectonic Metallogenesis*, **5**(3–4), 145–163.

MORÁVEK, P. 1996*b*. *Gold Deposits in Bohemia.* Czech Geological Survey, Prague.

MORÁVEK, P. & POUBA, Z. 1990. L ór dans la métallogénie du massif de Bohème. *Mineralium Deposita (Suppl),* **25**, 90–98.

MORGAN, J. W., STEIN, H. J., HANNAH, J. L., MARKEY, R. J. & WISZNIEWSKA, J. 2000. Re–Os study of Fe–Ti–V oxide and Fe–Cu–Ni sulphide deposits, Suwalki Anorthosite Massif, Northeast Poland. *Mineralium Deposita,* **35**, 391–401.

MORVAI, G. 1986. Hungary. *In:* DUNNING, F. W. & EVANS, A. M. (eds) *Mineral Deposits of Europe*, Vol. 3, *Central Europe*. Institution of Mining and Metallurgy, and Minerlogical Society, London, 13–53.

MRÁZEK, P. 1986. Metallogeny of the West Bohemian Upper Proterozoic. *In: Proceedings of Conference on Metallogeny of the Precambrian.* IGCP, Project 91, 49–53.

MRÁZEK, P. & POUBA, Z. 1995. Metallogenesis. *In*: DALLMEYER, R. D., FRANKE, W. & WEBER, K. (eds) *Tectono-Stratigraphic Evolution of the Central and East European Orogens.* Springer, Heidelberg, 411–414.

MÜCKE, A. 1987. Sekundäre Phosphatmineralien (Perloffit, Brasilianit, Mineralien der Kingsmountit-Gruppe) sowie Brochantit und die Zwieselit-Muschketoffit-Stipnomelan-Pyrosmalith-Paragenese der 115-m-Sohle des Hagendorfer Pegmatits. *Aufschluss*, **38**, 5–28.

MÜCKE, A. 2000. Die Erzmineralien und deren Paragenesen im Pegmatit von Hagendorf-Süd, Oberpfalz. *Aufschluss*, **51**, 11–24.

MÜCKE, A., KECK, E. & HAASE, J. 1990. Die genetische Entwicklung des Pegmatits von Hagendorf-Süd /Oberpfalz. *Aufschluss*, **41**, 33–51.

MÜLLER, G. 1962. Zur Geochemie des Strontiums in Ozeanen Evaporiten unter besonderer Berücksichtigung der sedimentären Coelestin-Lagerstätte von Hemmelte-Westerfeld (Südoldenburg). *Beiheft des geologischen Jahrbuchs*, **35**, 1–90.

NEINAVAIE, H., THALMANN, F., ATAIE, B. & BERAN, A. 1989. Wolframite- and scheelite-bearing carbonate rocks of the Nock Mountains, Austria; a new type of tungsten mineralization in the Eastern Alps. *Mineralium Deposita*, **24**, 14–18.

NEUBAUER, F. & VON RAUMER, J. F. 1993. The alpine Basement – Linkage between Variscides and East-Mediterranean Mountain Belts. *In*: VON RAUMER, J. F. & NEUBAUER, F. (eds) *Pre-Mesozoic Geology in the Alps*. Springer, Berlin, 641–663.

NEUBAUER, F., HOINKES, G., SASSI, F. P., HANDLER, R., HÖCK, V., KOLLER, F. & FRANK, W. 1999. Pre-Alpine metamorphism of the Eastern Alps. *Schweizerische Mineralogische und Petrogrographische Mitteilungen*, **79**, 41–62.

NEUBAUER, F., LIPS, A., KOUZMANOV, K., LEXA, J. & IVASCANU, P. 2005. Subduction, slab detachment and mineralization: The Neogene in the Apuseni Mountains and Carpathians. *Ore Geology Reviews*, **27**, 13–44.

NEUMANN-REDLIN, C., WALTHER, H. W. & ZITZMANN, A. 1977. *The Iron Ore Deposits of the Federal Republic of Germany.* Bundesanstalt für Geowissenschaften und Rohstoffe, Hannover, 165–186

NÖTH, S., KARG, H. & LITTKE, R. 2001. Reconstruction of Late

Paleozoic heat flows and burial histories at the Rhenohercynian-Subvariscan boundary, Germany. *International Journal of Earth Sciences*, **90**, 234–256.

Novák, M. & Cerný, P. 1998. Niobium-tantalum oxide minerals from complex granitic pegmatites in the Moldanubicum, Czech Republic; primary versus secondary compositional trends. *Canadian Mineralogist*, **36**, 659–672.

Novák, M. & Cerný, P. 2001. Distinctive compositional trends in columbite-tantalite from two segments of the lepidolite pegmatite at Rozná, western Moravia, Czech Republic. *Journal of the Czech Geological Society*, **46**, 1–8.

Novák, M., Cerný, P. & Uher, P. 2003. Extreme variation and apparent reversal of Nb-Ta fractionation in columbite-group minerals from the Scheibengraben beryl-columbite granite pegmatite, Marsikov, Czech Republic. *European Journal of Mineralogy*, **15**, 565–574.

Novotný, L. & Mihál', F. 1987. New lithostratigraphical units in the Krompachy group (Eastern Slovakia). *Mineralia Slovaka*, **19**, 97–113 [in Slovak with English abstract].

Nowak, G. J. & Górecka-Nowak, A. 1999. Peat-forming environments of Westphalian A coal seams from the Lower Silesian Coal Basin of SW Poland based on petrographic and palynologic data. *International Journal of Coal Geology*, **40**, 327–351.

Okrusch, M., Matthes, S., Klemd, R., O'Brien, P. J. & Schmidt, K. 1991. Eclogites at the northwestern margin of the Bohemian Massif: A review. *European Journal of Mineralogy*, **3**, 707–730.

Olsen, J. C. 1987. Tectonic evolution of the North Sea region. *In*: Brooks, J. & Glennie, K. W. (eds) *Petroleum Geology of Northwest Europe*. Graham & Trotman, London, Vol. **1**, 389–403.

Oncken, O., Plesch, A., Weber, J., Ricken, W. & Schrader, S. 2000. Passive margin detachment during arc-continent collision (Central European Variscides). *In:* Franke, W., Haak, V., Oncken, O. & Tanner, D. (eds) *Orogenic Processes: Quantification and Modelling in the Variscan Belt.* Geological Society, London, Special Publications, **179**, 199–234.

Ondrus, P., Veselovský, F., Gabasová, A., Hlousek, J. & Srein, V. 2003. Geology and hydrothermal vein system of the Jáchymov (Joachimsthal) ore district. *Journal of the Czech Geological Society*, **48**, 3–18.

Oplustil, S. 2005. The effect of paleotopography, tectonics and sediment supply on quality of coal seams in continental basins of central and western Bohemia (Westphalian), Czech Republic. *International Journal of Coal Geology*, **64**, 173–203.

Oplustil, S. & Pesek, J. 1998. Stratigraphy, palaeoclimatology and palaeogeography of the Late Paleozoic continental deposits in the Czech Republic. *Geodiversitas*, **20**, 597–620.

Oplustil, S., Sýkorová, I. & Bek, J. 1999. Sedimentology, coal petrology and palynology of the Radnice Member in the S-E part of the Kladno-Rakovnik Basin, Central Bohemia (Bolsovian). *Acta Universitatis Carolinae, Geologica*, **43**, 599–623.

Osika, R. 1976. Les gisements de minerais de fer en Pologne. *In: Iron Ore Deposits of Europe* Vol. 1 BGR, Hannover, 245–253.

Osika, R. 1986. Poland. *In:* Dunning, F. W. & Evans, A. M. (eds) *Mineral Deposits of Europe*, Vol. 3, *Central Europe*. Institution of Mining and Metallurgy, and Mineraological Society, London, 55–97.

Osika, R. 1990. *Geology of Poland: Mineral Deposits*. Geological Institute, Warsaw.

Ostrowicki, B. 1965. Nickel minerals of the weathering zone of serpentinites at Sklary (Lower Silesia). *Prace Mineralogiczne*, **1**, 92 [in Polish].

Oszczepalski, S. 1999. Origin of the Kupferschiefer polymetallic mineralization in Poland. *Mineralium Deposita*, **34**, 599–613.

Oszczepalski, S. & Blundell, D. 2005. 7-4: Kupferschiefer copper deposits of SW Poland: Lubin-Sieroszowice District: Lat. 51°35' N, Long. 16°6' E. *Ore Geology Reviews*, **27**, 271.

Oszczepalski, S., Nowak, G., Bechetel, A. & Zák, K. 2002. Evidence of oxidation of the Kupferschiefer in the Lubin–Sieroszowice deposit, Poland: implications for Cu–Ag and Au–Pt–Pd mineralisation. *Geological Quarterly*, **46**, 1–23.

Oyarzún, J. 2000. Andean metallogenesis. A synoptical review and interpretation. *In*: Cordani, U. G., Milani, E. J., Thomaz Filho, A. & Campos, D. A. (eds) *Tectonic Evolution of South America. 31st International Geological Congress.* Folio Produção Rio de Janeiro, Brazil, 6–17 August, 725–753.

Paar, W. H. 1997. Edelmetalle. *In*: Weber, L. (ed) *Handbuch der Lagerstätten der Erze und Energierohstoffe Österreichs.* Archiv für Lagerstättenforschung der Geologischen Bundesanstalt, **19**, 276–287.

Pagel, M. & Pironon, J. 1986. Un modele de formation de gisements d'uranium dans les shales noirs continentaux. *Sciences géologiques Bulletin*, **39**, 277–292.

Palinkaš, A. L. 1985. Lead isotope patterns in galenas from some selected ore deposits in Croatia and NW Bosnia. *Geološki vjesnik*, **38**, 175–189.

Palinkaš, A. L. 1988. *Geochemical characteristics of Paleozoic metallogenic regions: Samoborska gora, Gorski Kotar, Lika, Kordun and Banija.* PhD thesis, University of Zagreb [In Croatian with English summary].

Palinkaš, A. L. & Pamić, J. 2001. Geochemical evolution of Oligocene and Miocene magmatism across the Easternmost Periadriatic Lineament. *Acta Volcanologica,* **13**(1–2), 41–56.

Palinkaš, A. L., Pezdić, J. & Šinkovec, B. 1993. the Lokve barite deposit, Croatia: an example of the early diagenetic sedimentary ore deposit. *Geologia Croatica,* **46**(1), 97–106.

Palinkaš, A. L., Borojević, S., Prochaska, W., Šinkovec, B. & Šiftar, D. 2000. Rude, Samobor, siderite-haematite-polysulphide-barite mineral deposit within the Zagorje-Mid-Transdanubian Zone, NW Croatia. *Geološke vijesti,* **37**(3), 96–97.

Palinkaš, A. L., Borojević, S., Strmić, S., Prochaska, W. & Spangenberg, J. 2003. Siderite-haematite-barite-polysulphide mineral deposits, related to the early intra-continental Tethyan rifting, Inner Dinarides. *In*: Eliopoulos, D. G. (ed.) *Mineral Exploration and Sustainable Development.* Millpress, Rotterdam, 1225–1228.

Palinkaš, L. A., Strmić, S., Spangenberg, J. E., Prochaska, W. & Herlec, U. 2004. Ore-forming fluids in the Grübler orebody, Idrija mercury deposit, Slovenia. *Swiss Bulletin of Mineralogy and Petrology*, **84**(1–2), 173–188.

Pamić, J. 1984. Triassic magmatism of the Dinarides in Yugoslavia. *Tectonophysics,* **226**, 503–518.

Pamić, J. 2002. The Sava-Vardar zone of the Dinarides and Hellenides versus the Vardar ocean. *Eclogae Geologicae Helvetiae,* **95**, 99–113.

Pamić, J. & Balen, D. 2001. Tertiary magmatism of the adjoining South Pannonian Basin. *Acta Volcanologica*, **13**, 9–24.

Pamić, J. & Olujić, J. 1974. Hydrothermal-metasomatic rocks (listvenite) form the northern border of the Ozren ultramafic massif (Yugoslavia). *Acta geologica, JAZU*, **7**, 239–255.

Pamić, J. & Palinkaš, A. L. 2000. Petrology and geochemistry of Paleogene tonalities from the easternmost parts of the Periadriatic Zone. *Mineralogy and Petrology,* **70**, 121–141.

Pamić, J., Tomljenović, B. & Balen, D. 2002. Geodynamic and petrogenetic evolution of Alpine ophiolites from the central and NW Dinarides: an overview. *Lithos*, **65**, 113–142.

Paris, F., Robardet, M. & Dabard, M.-P. 1986. Les milieux noirs du Paleozoique inferieur Armoricain dans leur contexte Nord-Gondwanien. *In*: Bréhèret, J. G. (ed.) *Les Couches Riches en Matière Organique et Leurs Conditions de Dépot*. Documents du BRGM, **110**, 259–275.

Pašava, J., Hladíková, J. & Dobeš, P. 1996. Origin of metal-rich black shales from the Bohemian Massif, Czech Republic. *Economic Geology,* **91**, 63–79.

Pašava, J., Vavrín, I., Fryda, J., Janousek, V. & Jelínek, E. 2003. Geochemistry and mineralogy of Platinum-group elements in the Ransko gabbro-peridotite massif, Bohemian Massif (Czech Republic). *Mineralium Deposita*, **38**, 298–311.

Paškevićius, J. 1997. *The Geology of the Baltic Republics. Vilnius.* Geological Survey and University of Lithuania.

Patočka, F. & Vrba, J. 1989. The comparison of stratabound massive sulphides deposits unsing the fuzzy-linguistic diagnosis of the Zlaté Hory deposits, Czechoslovakia, as an example. *Mineralium Deposita*, **4**, 192–198.

Paulo, A. 1994. Geology of barite veins in the Polish Sudetes. The metallogeny of the Erzgebirge (Krušné Hory). *In:* Seltmann, R., Kämpf, H. & Möller, P. (eds) *Metallogeny of Collision Orogen.* Czech Geological Survey, Prague, 383–390.

PAUWELS H., FOUILLAC, C. & FOUILLAC, A. M. 1993. Chemistry and isotopes of deep geothermal saline fluids in the upper Rhine Graben: origin of compounds and water–rock interactions. *Geochimica et Cosmochimica Acta*, **57**, 2737–2749.

PECHO, J. 1980. *Geology, mineral deposits and prognostic assessment of the W-mineralization in the Jasenie vicinity*. Open file report, Geofond Bratislava [in Slovak].

PECO, G. 1953. *Ricerche sulle argille del Tretto (Schio) e di Laghi (Arsiero)*. Memorie Istituto Geologia Mineralogia Università Padova, **17**.

PEDERSEN, G. K. & SURLYK, F. 1983. The Fur Formation, a late Paleocene ash-bearing diatomite from northern Denmark. *Bulletin of the Geological Society of Denmark*, **32**, 43–65.

PERETTI, L. 1966. Valorizzazione del giacimento asbestifero di Balangero (Torino) mediante il recupero degli sterili come sottoprodotti qualificati. *Atti Symposium Internazionale Giacimenti Minerari Alpi, Trento*, **2**, 1149–1165.

PERRODON, A. 1985. *Histoire des grandes découvertes pétrolières*. Elf ep-Editions, Paris.

PERRODON, A. & ZABECK, J. 1991. Paris Basin. *In:* LEIGHTON, M. *et al.* (eds) *Interior Cratonic Basins*. American Association of Petroleum Geologists, Memoirs, **51**, 633–680.

PERTOLD, Z., CHRT, J., *et al.* 1994. The Tisova Cu- deposit: a Besshi-type mineralization in the Krusné Hory Mts., Bohemian massif, Czech Republic. *Monograph Series on Mineral Deposits*, **31**, 71–95.

PERTOLD, Z. & PUNCOCHÁR, M. 1995. *Kašperské Hory ore district. Gold deposits of the central and SW part of the Bohemian Massif. Excursion Guide*. Czech Geological Survey, Prague, 87–104.

PERTOLDOVÁ, J., FIALA, J., PUDILOVÁ, M., PUNCOCHÁR, M., SCHARMOVÁ, M. & SZTACHO, P. 1993. Au-W mineralization of the Kašperské Hory ore district, SW Bohemia, Czechoslovakia. *In*: MAURICE, Y. T. (ed.) *Proceedings of the Eighth Quadrennial IAGOD Symposium*, Schweizerbart, Stuttgart, 627–636.

PESEK, J. 1994. *Carboniferous of Central and Western Bohemia (Czech Republic)*. Czech Geological Survey, Prague.

PESEK, J., OPLUSTIL, O., KUMPERA, O., HOLUB, V. & SKOCEK, V. (eds) 1998. *Paleogeographic Atlas – Late Paleozoic and Triassic Formations – Czech Republik*. Czech Geological Survey, Prague.

PETERSEN, H. I., ROSENBERG, P. & ANDSBJERG, J. 1996. Organic geochemistry in relation to the depositional environments of Middle Jurassic coal seams, Danish Central Graben, and implications for hydrocarbon generative potential. *American Association of Petroleum Geologists Bulletin*, **80**, 47–62.

PETMECKY, S., MEIER, L., REISER, H. & LITTKE, R. 1999. High thermal maturity in the Lower Saxony Basin: intrusion or deep burial? *Tectonophysics*, **304**, 317–344.

PETRANEK, J. 1975. Sedimentary iron ore deposit near Mnišek and Komárov. *Studie ČSAV*, **6**, 1–82 [English summary].

PETRÁNEK, J. & VAN HOUTEN, F. B. 1977. *Phanerozoic ooidal ironstones*, Czech Geological Survey, Special Papers, **7**.

PETRASCHECK, W. E. 1963. Die alpin-mediterrane Metallogenese. *Geologische Rundschau*, **53**, 376–389.

PETRASCHECK, W. E. 1978. Zur Altersbestimmung einiger ostalpiner Lagerstätten. *Mitteilungen der Österreichischen Geologischen Gesellschaft*, **68**, 79–87.

PETTKE, T., DIAMOND, L. W. & VILLA, I. M. 1999. Mesothermal gold veins and metamorphic devolatilization in the NW Alps: The temporal link. *Geology*, **27**, 641–644.

PHILPOTT, K. D. 2002. Evaluation of the Bogdanka mine, Poland. *In*: JURECZKA, J. & PODEMSKI, M. (eds) *Poceedings of the IV European Coal Conference*. Polish Geological Institute, Special Publications, **7**, 199–206.

PICHA, F. J. & PETERS, K. E. 1998. Biomarker oil-to-source rock correlation in the Western Carpathians and their foreland, Czech Republic. *Petroleum Geoscience*, **4**, 289–302.

PIESSENS, K., MUCHEZ, P., VIAENE, W., BOYCE, A. J., DE VOS, W., SINTUBIN, M. & DEBCKER, T. 2000. Alteration and fluid characteristics of a mineralised shear zone in the lower Palaeozoic of the Anglo-Brabant Belt, Belgium. *Journal of Geochemical Exploration*, **69–70**, 317–321.

PIESTRZYNSKI, A. 1997. Effects of uranium mining on the contamination of some areas in Poland. *Fuel and Energy Abstracts*, **38**, 321.

PIRONON, I. 1981. *Zonalités géochimiques et mineralogiques dans les bassins continentaux uranifères – exemples de St. Hippolyte (Massif Vosgien), Müllenbach (Forét Noire, RFA), Salamanièce (massif Central Français)*. Geologie, Geochemie Uranium Memoires de Nancy, **13**.

PISKE, J. & RASCH, H.-J. 1998. Die Paleogeographie des Staßfurt-Karbonats (Ca2) im östlichen Thüringer Becken. *In:* KARNIN, W. D, MERKEL, D., PISKE, J. & SCHRETZENMAYER, S. (eds) Geowissenschaftliche Ergebnisse der Kohlenwasserstoff-Exploration im Land Brandenburg und im Thüringer Becken in den Jahren 1991–1996 (Zechstein und Rotliegend). *Geologisches Jahrbuch*, **A 149**, 129–144.

PIVEC, E., ULRYCH, J., SREIN, V., BENDL, J., DOBES, P. & ZÁK, K. 1998. Epithermal Tertiary Pb-Zn-Cu (Ag, Te) mineralization in the Roztoky volcanic centre, Ceske Stredohori Mts., Czech Republic. *Geologica Carpathica*, **49**, 139–146.

PIWOCKI, M. & PRZENIOSLO, S. 2004 Mineral raw materials and commodities of Poland. *Przeglad Geologiczny*, **52**, 744–752.

PLACER, L. 1982. Tektonski razvoj idrijskega rudišča. *Geologija*, **25**, 7–94

PLACER, L. & ČAR, J. 1977. Middle Triassic structure of the Idrija region (in Slovene). *Geologija*, **20**, 141–166.

PLAŠIENKA, D., GRECULA, P., PUTIS, M., HOVORKA, D. & KOVÁČ, M. 1997. Evolution and structure of the Western Carpathians: an overview. *In*: GRECULA, P., HOVORKA, D. & PUTIŠ, M. (eds) *Geological Evolution of the Western Carpathians*. Mineralia Slovaca Monograph, 1–24.

PLEIN, E. 1993. Voraussetzungen und Grenzen der Bildung von Kohlenwasserstoff-Lagerstätten im Oberrheingraben. *Jahrbuch Mitteilungen des Oberrheinischen Geologischen Vereins Nachfahren*, **NF 75**, 227–253.

PLEIN, E. 1994. Deutschland/Germany. *In*: KULKE, H. (ed.) *Regional Petroleum Geology of the World. Part I: Europe and Asia*. Beiträge zur regionalen Geologie der Erde, **21**, 139–192.

PODUFAL, P. 1983. Die Blei-Zink-Erzlagerstätte von Ramsbeck. *In*: WALTER H. W. (ed.) *Field Guide to GDMB meeting 1983*. Warstein, Clausthal-Zellerfeld, 128–136.

POHL, W. 1993. Metamorphogene Lagerstätten in den Ostalpen. *Geowissenschaften*, **11**, 86–91.

POHL, W. & BELOCKY, R. 1994. Alpidic metamorphic fluids and metallogenesis in the Eastern Alps. *Mitteilungen der Österreichischen Geologischen Gesellschaft*, **86**, 141–152.

POHL, W. & BELOCKY, R. 1999. Metamorphism and metallogeny in the Eastern Alps. *Mineralium Deposita*, **34**, 614–629.

POLGÁRI, M., OKITA, P. M. & HEIN, J. R. 1991. Stable isotope evidence for the origin of the Úrkút manganese ore deposit, Hungary. *Journal of Sedimentary Petrology*, **61**, 384–393.

POLGÁRI, M., SZABÓ, Z. & SZENDERKÉNYI, T. 2000. *Manganese Ores in Hungary*. Juhász Nyomda Kft., Szeged.

POLISH GEOLOGICAL INSTITUTE 2004. http://www.pgi.gov.pl/mineral_resources/tin.htm

POLLER, U., UHER, P., JANÁK, M., PLAŠIENKA, D. & KOHÚT, M. 2001. Late Cretaceous age of the Rochovce granite, Western Carpathians, constrained by U-Pb single-zircon dating in combination with cathodoluminiscence imaging. *Geologica Carpathica*, **52**, 41–47.

POLLER, U., UHER, P., BROSKA, I., PLAŠIENKA, D. & JANÁK, M. 2002. First Permian – Early Triassic ages for tin-bearing granites from the Gemeric unit (Western Carpathians, Slovakia): connection to the post-collisional extension of the Variscan orogen and S-type granite magmatism. *Terra Nova*, **14**, 41–48.

POPESCU, B. M. 1994. *Hydrocarbons of Central Eastern Europe*. Springer, Heidelberg.

POPRAWA, P., SLIAUPA, S., STEPHENSON, R. & LAZAUSKIENE, J. 1999. Late Vendian-Early Paleozoic tectonic evolution of the Baltic Basin: regional tectonic implications from subsidence anaylsis. *Tectonophysics*, **314**, 219–239.

POREBSKA, E. & SAWLOWICZ, Z. 1997. Palaeoceanographic linkage of geochemical and graptolite events across the Silurian–Devonian boundary in Bardzkie Mountains (Southwest Poland). *Palaeogeography, Palaeoclimatology, Palaeoecology*, **132**, 343–354.

PORZYCKI, J. & ZDANOWSKI, A. 1995. Southeastern Poland (Lublin Carboniferous Coal Basin). *In:* ZDANOWSKI, A. & ZAKOWA, H. (eds) *The Carboniferous System in Poland*. Polish Geological Institute, **CXLVIII**, 102–109.

Pouba, Z. & Ilavsky, J. 1986. Czechoslovakia. *In:* Dunning, F. W. & Evans, A. M. (eds) *Mineral Deposits of Europe*, Vol. 3, *Central Europe*. Institution of Mining and Metallurgy, and Mineralogical Society, London, 117–173.

Pouba, Z. & Kříbek, B. 1986. Organic matter and the concentration of metals in Precambrian stratiform Deposits of the Bohemian Massif. *Precambrian Research*, **33**, 225–237.

Präger, R., Stedingk, K., Hartmann, O., Karpe, P., Model, E. & Koglin, N. 2003. *Übersichtskarte Tiefliegende Rohstoffe und Energierohstoffe in Sachsen-Anhalt 1:400000*. Blatt 1: Energierohstoffe, Halle (Saale).

Prentice, J. E. 1990. *Geology of Construction Raw Materials*. Chapman and Hall, London.

Prete, R. 1995. L'amiantifera di S. Vittore, Balangero, Torino. *Rivista Mineralogica Italiana*, **1995**, 313–333.

Prochaska, W. 1984. Neue geochemische Aspekte zur Genese der Talklagerstätte Rabenwald, Stmk. *Berg- und hüttenmännische Monatshefte*, **129**, 457–462.

Prochaska, W. 1989. Geologische und geochemische Untersuchungen an der Talklagerstätte Lassing. *Archiv für Lagerstättenforschung der Geologischen Bundesanstalt*, **10**, 99–114.

Prochaska, W. 1993. Untersuchung stabiler Isotope an alpidischen Ganglagerstätten in den Ostalpen. *Berg- und hüttenmännische Monatshefte*, **138**, 138–143.

Prochaska, W., Bechtel, A. & Kloetzli, U. 1992. Phyllonite formation and alteration of gneisses in shear zones (Gleinalmkristallin, Eastern Alps). *Mineralogy and Petrology*, **45**, 195–216.

Prochaska, W. & Henjes-Kunst, F. 2007. The origin of sparry magnesite in the Eastern Alps (Austria): evidence from inclusion fluid and Sr–Nd isotope chemistry. *In*: Andrew, C. J. *et al.* (ed.) *Proceedings of the 9th Biennial Meeting of the Society for Geology Applied to Mineral Deposits*, Dublin, IAEG, Vol. II, 823–826.

Prochaska, W., Pohl, W., Belocky, R. & Kucha, H. 1995. Tertiary metallogenesis in the Eastern Alps – the Waldenstein haematite deposit. *Geologische Rundschau*, **84**, 831–842.

Pulec, M., Klinec, A. & Bezák, V. 1983. Geology and W-Au mineralization in the Jasenie-Kyslá area. *In:* Pecho, J. (ed.) *W-Au mineralization in the Nízke Tatry Mts. Confererence and Symposium Seminar GÚDŠ*, 11–37 [in Slovak].

Radvanec, M. & Prochaska, W. 2001. Successive replacement of Upper Carboniferous calcite to dolomite and magnesite in Dúbrava deposit (Western Carpathians, Slovakia). *Mineralia Slovaca*, **33**, 517–525.

Radvanec, M., Žák, K. & Grecula, P. 1990. Isotope ratio 87Sr/86Sr in baryte of Gemericum. *Mineralia Slovaca*, **22**, 219–224 [in Slovak with English abstract].

Radvanec, M., Grecula, P., Návesňák, D. & Kobulsky, J. 1993. Zonality of submarine-exhalative mineralization in the Mníšek nad Hnilcom-Prakovce area, Lower Paleozoic of Gemericum. *Mineralia Slovaca*, **25**, 249–262 [in Slovak].

Radvanec, M., Grecula, P. & Žák, K. 2004*a*. Siderite mineralization of the Gemericum Superunit (Western Carpathians, Slovakia): review and a revised genetic model. *Ore Geology Review*, **24**, 267–298.

Radvanec, M., Kodéra & Prochaska, W. 2004*b*. Mg replacement at the Gemerská Poloma talc deposit, Western Carpathians, Slovakia. *Acta Petrolica Sinica*, **20**, 773–790.

Ramdohr, P. 1975. *Die Erzminerale und ihre Verwachsungen*. Akadmie-Verlag, Berlin.

Ramović, M., Kubat, I., Veljković, D., Kulenović, E. & Durić, S. 1979. Base-metal deposits. *In:* Čičić, S. (ed.) *Mineral Raw Materials of Bosnia and Herzegovina*, II. Geoinžinjering, Sarajevo, 3–122 [In Bosnian].

Ranger, M. R. 1979. *The sedimentology of a Lower Paleozoic peritidal sequence and associated iron formations, Bell Island, Conception Bay, Newfoundland.* MSc thesis, University of Newfoundland.

Rasser, M. W., Harzhauser, M. *et al.* 2008. Palaeogene and Neogene. *In*: McCann, T. (ed.) *The Geology of Central Europe. Volume 2: Mesozoic and Cenozoic*. Geological Society, London, 1031–1139.

Rantitsch, G., Melcher, F., Meisel, Th. & Rainer, Th. 2003. Rare earth, major and minor elements in Jurassic manganese shales of the Northern Calcareous Aps: hydrothermal versus hydrogenous origin of stratiform manganese deposits. *Mineralogy and Petrology*, **77**, 109–127.

Ratschbacher, L., Frisch, W., Linzer, H.-G. & Merle, O. 1991. Lateral extrusion in the Eastern Alps, 2. Structural analysis. *Tectonics*, **10**, 257–271.

Redlich, K. A. 1909. Die Typen der Magnesitlagerstätten. *Zeitschrift für praktische Geologie*, **17**, 300–310.

Reicherter, K., Froitzheim, N. *et al.* 2008. Alpine tectonics north of the Alps. *In*: McCann, T. (ed.) *The Geology of Central Europe. Volume 2: Mesozoic and Cenozoic*. Geological Society, London, 1233–1285.

Refai, T. R. 1993. *Mineralogical, geochemical and petrophysical investigations of limestone-marl alterations from the Upper Jurassic profiles in the Swabian and Franconian Alb (South Germany)*. PhD thesis, University of Erlangen, Germany.

Reh, H. & Schröder, N. 1974. Erze. *In*: Hoppe, W. & Seidel, G. (eds) *Geologie von Thüringen*. Haack, Gotha, 867–997.

Reichmann, F. 1975. Geology of the exploited fluorite deposits in the Bohemian Massif. *Sborník geologických ved, rada Ložisková geologie*, **17**, 39–58 [in Czech].

Reichmann, F. 1983. Fluorite and barite. *In:* Kuzvart M. (ed.) *Industrial Minerals and Rocks of the Czech Republic*. Geological Survey, Prague, 88–109 [in Czech].

Rentzsch, I. 1974. The Kupferschiefer in comparison with the deposits of the Zambian Copper Belt. *In*: Bartholomé, P. (ed) *Gisements stratiformes et provinces cupriferés*. Sociéte Géologique de Belge, Liège, 395–418.

Ridoni, E. 1938. Il talco e la grafite delle Alpi Cozie. *Industria Mineraria Italiana Oltremare*, **6**, 195–203.

Rodeghiero, F., Fanlo, I., Subias, I., Yuste, A., Fernandez Nieto, C. & Brigo, L. 1996. Sulphide-, fluorite-, barite-bearing siliceous "crusts" related to unconformity surfaces of different ages in Pyrenees and Alps. A new model in carbonate-hosted deposits? *Acta Geologica Hispannica*, **30**, 69–81.

Roeder, D. & Bachmann, G. 1996. Evolution, structure and petroleum geology of the German Molasse Basin. *In:* Ziegler, P. A. & Horvath, F. (eds) *Peri-Tethys Memoir 2, Structure and Prospects of Alpine Basins and Forelands*. Mémoires du Muséum National d' Histoire Naturelle, **170**, 263–284.

Rojkovič, I. 1977. *Mineralogical and geochemical study of opaque minerals at the Rudňany deposit*. Open file report, Comenius University [in Slovak].

Rojkovič, I. 1981. *Mineralogical and geochemical study U-mineralization of the second ore horizon of the north Gemeric Permian rocks in the Novoveská Huta*. Open file report, Geofond Bratislava.

Romagnoli, P. L. 1966. Contributo sulla conoscenza del giacimento di Raibl. *Atti Symposium Internazionale Giacimenti Minerari Alpi*, Trento, **2**, 135–145.

Rozložník, L. 1989. Questions of age and sources of siderite mineralization of Western Carpathians. *Geologický pruzkum*, **31**, 67–72 [in Slovak].

Rückheim, J. 1993. Migrations- und Akkumulationsgeschichte der Erdöle des Nördlichen Oberrheingrabens und deren Beziehung zur Speichergesteinsdiagenese. *Erdöl Erdgas Kohle*, **109**, 498–503.

Ruder, J. 1998. Ein geologisch-bergbaugeschichtlicher Überblick über die ehemaligen Steinkohlenbergbaureviere von Zwickau und Lungau-Oelsnitz. *Bergbau*, **49**, 367–380.

Russel, P. L. 1990. *Oil Shales of the World, their Origin, Occurrence and Exploitation*. Pergamon Press, Oxford.

Sachsenhofer, R. F. 2000. Geodynamic controls on deposition and maturation of coal in the Eastern Alps. *In*: Neubauer, F. & Höck, V. (eds) Aspects of Geology in Austria. *Mitteilungen der Österreichischen Geologischen Gesellschaft*, **92**, 185–194.

Sachsenhofer, R. F. 2001. Syn- and post-collisional heat flow in the Tertiary Eastern Alps. *International Journal Earth Sciences*, **90**, 579–592.

Sachsenhofer, R. F. & Schulz, H.-M. 2006. Architecture of Lower Oligocene source rocks in the Alpine Foreland Basin: a model for syn- and post-depositional source-rock features in the Paratethyan realm. *Petroleum Geoscience*, **12**, 363–377.

Sachsenhofer, R. F., Bechtel, A. *et al.* 2003. Evolution of lacustrine systems along the Miocene Mur-Mürz fault system (Eastern Alps, Austria) and implications on source rocks in pull-apart basins. *Marine and Petroleum Geology*, **20**, 83–110.

SACHSENHOFER, R. F., BECHTEL, A. *et al.* 2006. Depositional environment and source potential of Jurassic coal-bearing sediments (Gresten Formation, Höflein gas/condensate field, Austria). *Petroleum Geoscience*, **12**, 99–114.

SACHSENHOFER, R. F., STRAUSS, P., *et al.* 2000. Das miozäne Fohnsdorfer Becken - Eine Übersicht. *Mitteilungen der Geologie- und Bergbaustudenten Österreichs,* **44**, 173–190.

SALGER, M. 1982. Mineralogie des Bohrprofils Bindlach 1980. *Geologica Bavarica*, **83**, 217–219.

SALTER, D. L. & WEST, I. M. 1965. Calciostrontianite in the basal Purbeck Beds of Durlston Head, Dorset. *Mineralogical Magazine,* **35**, 146–150.

ŠAMAJOVÁ, E., KRAUS, I. & LAJČÁKOVÁ, A. 1992. Diagenetic alteration of Miocene acidic vitric tuffs of the Jastrabá Formation (Kremnické vrchy Mts., Western Slovakia). *Geologica Carpathica, Series Clays,* **1**, 27–30.

SANO, S., OBERHÄNSLI, R., ROMER, R. L. & VINX, R. 2002. Petrological, Geochemical and Isotopic Constraints on the Origin of the Harzburg Intrusion, Germany. *Journal of Petrology*, **43**, 1529–1549.

SASS-GUSTKIEWICZ, M. & KUCHA, H. 2005. 7–2: Zinc-Lead deposits, Upper Silesia, Poland. *Ore Geology Review*, **27**, 269.

SASS-GUSTKIEWICZ, M. & KWIECINSKA, B. 1999. Organic matter in the Upper Silesian (Mississippi Valley-Type) deposits, Poland. *Economic Geology*, **94**, 981–992.

SASS-GUSTKIEWICZ, M., DZULYNSKI, S. & RIDGE, I. D. 1982. The emplacement of zinc-lead sulphide ores in the Upper Silesian district - A contribution to the understanding of Mississippi Valley-type deposits. *Economic Geology*, **77**, 392–412.

SASVÁRI, T. & MAŤO, L. 1996. Chronology of tectonic events and mineralization on the epigenetic Strieborna-vein, Rožňava ore district, Slovakia. *In:* GRECULA, P. & NÉMETH, Z. (eds) *Variscan Metallogeny of the Alpine Orogenic Belt.* Mineralia Slovaca Monograph, 251–282.

SASVÁRI, T., MAŤO, L. & MIHÓK, J. 1996. Structural and mineralogical evaluation of the northern part of the Nižná Slaná ore field, the knowledge to initions on deep-seated continuation of siderite bodies of the exploitated deposits Ignác and Gampel'. *Acta Montanistica Slovaca*, **1**, 261–280.

SAWKINS, F. J. 1984. *Metal Deposits in Relation to Plate Tectonics*. Springer, New York.

SAWLOWICZ, Z. & WEDEPOHL, K. H. 1992. The origin of rhythmic sulphide bands from the Permian Sandstones (Weissliegendes) in the footwall of the Fore-Sudetic Kupferschiefer (Poland). *Mineralium Deposita*, **27**, 242–248.

SCAILLET, S., CUNEY, M., LE CARLIER DE VESLUD, C., CHEILLETZ, A. & ROYER, J. J. 1996. Cooling pattern and mineralization history of the Saint Sylvestre and western Marche leucogranite pluton, French Massif Central: II. Thermal modelling and implications for the mechanisms of uranium mineralization. *Geochimica et Cosmochimica Acta*, **60**, 4673–4688.

SCHAEFFER, R. 1984. Die postvariszische Mineralisationen im nordöstlichen Rheinischen Schiefergebirge. *Braunschweiger Geologisch Paläontologische Dissertationen*, **3**, 1–206.

SCHAEFFER, R. 1998. Stratiforme Manganerze. *Jahrbücher des Nassauischen Vereins für Naturkunde, Sonderband*, **1**, 131–136.

SCHÄFER, A. & KORSCH, R. J. 1998. Formation and sediment fill of the Saar-Nahe Basin (Permo-Carboniferous, Germany). *Zeitschrift der Deutschen Geologischen Gesellschaft*, **149**, 233–269.

SCHALTEGGER U., ZWINGMANN, H., CLAUER, N., LARQUE, P. & STILLE, P. 1995. K–Ar dating of a Mesozoic hydrothermal activity in Carboniferous to Triassic clay minerals of northern Switzerland. *Schweizerische Mineralogische und Petrographische Mitteilungen*, **75**, 163–176.

SCHAUBERGER, O. 1986. Bau und Bildung der Salzlagerstätten des ostalpinen Salinars. *Archiv für Lagerstättenforschung der Geologischen Bundesanstalt,* **7**, 217–254.

SCHECK, M. & BAYER, U. 1999. Evolution of the Northeast German Basin—inferences from a 3D structural model and subsidence analysis. *Tectonophysics*, **313**, 145–169.

SCHECK, M., BAYER, U. & LEWERENZ, B. 2003. Salt redistribution during extension and inversion inferred from 3D backstripping. *Tectonophysics*, **373**, 55–73.

SCHECK-WENDEROTH, M., KRZYWIEC, P., ZÜHLKE, R., MAYSTRENKO, Y. & FROITZHEIM, N. 2008. Permian to Cretaceous tectonics. *In:* MCCANN, T. (ed.) *The Geology of Central Europe. Volume 2: Mesozoic and Cenozoic.* Geological Society, London, 999–1030.

SCHEIDT, G. & LITTKE, R. 1989. Comparative organic petrology of interlayered sandstones, siltstones, mudstones and coals in the Upper Carboniferus Ruhr basin, Northwest Germany, and their thermal history and methane generation. *Geologische Rundschau*, **78**, 375–390.

SCHMID, H. 1981. Zur Bleiführung in der mittleren Trias der Oberpfalz - Ergebnisse neuer Bohrungen. *Erzmetall*, **34**, 652–658.

SCHMID, H. & WEINELT, W. 1978. Lagerstätten in Bayern Erze, Industrieminerale, Salze und Brennstoffe; mit einer Lagerstättenkarte 1:500000. *Geologica Bavarica,* **77**, 1–160.

SCHMID, E. A., JAFFE, F. C. & BURRI, M. 1990. La freibergite du gisement de plomb-zinc de Praz-Jean (Valais, Suisse). *Mineralium Deposita,* **25**, 198–204.

SCHMID, S. M., FÜGENSCHUH, B., KISSLING, E., SCHUSTER, R. 2004. Tectonic map and overall architecture of the Alpine orogen. *Eclogae Geologiae Helvetiae*, **97**, 93–117.

SCHMUTZ, L. 1984. *Mineralbildende Prozesse an einer Erzlagerstätte in Val d'Anniviers (Wallis, Schweiz)*. PhD thesis, University of Basel.

SCHNEIDER, J., HAACK, U., HEIN, U. F. & GERMANN, A. 1999. Direct Rb-Sr dating of sandstone-hosted sphalerites from strata-bound Pb-Zn deposits in the northern Eifel, NW Rhenish Massif, Germany. *In*: STANLEY, C. J. (ed.) *Mineral Deposits: Processes to Processing*, Proceedings of 5th Biennial SGA Meeting and 10th Quadrennial IAGOD Symposium, London, 22–25 August 1999, 1287–1290.

SCHNEIDER, J., HAACK, U. & STEDINGK, K. 2003. Rb-Sr dating of epithermal vein mineralization stages in the eastern Harz Mountains (Germany) paleomixing lines. *Geochimica et Cosmochimica Acta*, **67**, 1803–1819.

SCHNEIDER, J. W., HOTZ, K., GAITZSCH, B. G., BERGER, H. J., STEINBORN, H., WALTER, H. & ZEIDLER, M. K. 2005. Carboniferous stratigraphy and development of the Erzgebirge Basin, East Germany. *Zeitschrift der deutschen Geologischen Gesellschaft*, **156**, 431–466.

SCHNEIDERHÖHN, H. 1962. *Erzlagerstetten*. Fischer, Stuttgart.

SCHROLL, E. 1996. *The Triassic Carbonate-hosted Pb-Zn Mineralization in the Alps (Europe): The Genetic Position of Bleiberg Type Deposits.* Society of Economic Geologists, Special Publication, **4**, 182–194.

SCHROLL, E. & PROCHASKA, W. 2004. Contribution to ore fluid chemistry of Bleiberg Pb-Zn deposit (Austria) and affiliated deposits. *Goldschmidt Geochemistry*, Copenhagen, Denmark, 5–11 June 2004, Abstract volume, A306.

SCHULZ, H.-M., SACHSENHOFER, R. F., BECHTEL, A., POLESNY, H. & WAGNER, L. 2002. The origin of hydrocarbon source rocks in the Austrian Molasse Basin (Eocene-Oligocene transition). *Marine and Petroleum Geology*, **19**, 683–709.

SCHWARZENBERG VON, T. 1975. *Lagerstättenkundliche Untersuchungen an sedimentären Bleivererzungen der Oberpfalz.* PhD thesis, University of Munich.

SCHWEIZER, V. 1979. Geochemische Untersuchungen zur Erzanreicherung in der Bleiglanzbank des süddeutschen Gipskeupers (km 1, Karn). *Abhandlungen des Oberrheinischen Geologischen Vereins*, **28**, 55–71.

SCICLI, A. 1972. *L'attivita' estrattiva e le risorse minerarie della Regione Emilia Romagna.* Poligrafico Artioli, Modena.

SEGEV, A., HALICZ, L., LANG, B. & STEINITZ, G. 1991. K–Ar dating of manganese minerals from the Eisenbach region, Black Forest, southwest Germany. *Schweizerische Mineralogische und Petrographische Mitteilungen*, **71**, 101–114.

SEIDEL, G. 2003. *Geologie von Thüringen*. Schweizerbart, Stuttgart.

SEIFERT, A., BRAUSE, H. & RASCHER, J. 1993. Geology of the Niederlausitz Lignite district, Germany. *International Journal of Coal Geology*, **23**, 263–289.

SEIFERT, W., KÄMPF, H. & WASTERNACK, J. 2000. Compositional variation in apatite, phlogopite and other accessory minerals of the ultramafic Delitzsch complex, Germany: implication for cooling history of carbonatites, *Lithos*, **53**, 81–100.

SELTMANN, R. & FARAGHER, A. E. 1994. Collisional orogens and their related metallogeney-A preface. *In*: SELTMANN, R., KÄMPF, H. & MÖLLER, P. (eds) *Metallogeny of Collision Orogen*. Czech Geological Survey, Prague, 7–19.

Senglaub, Y., Littke, R. & Brix, M. R. 2006. Numerical modelling of burial and temperature history as an approach for an alternative interpretation of the Bramsche anomaly, Lower Saxony Basin. *International Journal of Earth Sciences*, **95**, 204–224.

Siehl, A. & Thein, J. 1989. Minette-type ironstones. *In*: Young, T. P. & Taylor, W. E. G. (eds) *Phanerozoic Ironstones*. British Geological Society Special Publications, **46**, 175–193.

Šiftar, D. 1988. Chemical characteristics of barite from some deposits in Bosnia. *Rudarsko-metalurški zbornik*, **35**, 75–89 [In Croatian].

Simon, P. 1979 Die marin-sedimentären Eisenerze in der Eifel. *Geologisches Jahrbuch* **D 31**, 133–151.

Šinkovec, B. 1961. Cinnabar occurrences at Tršće, Gorski Kotar. *Geološki vjesnik*, **14**, 120–140 [in Croatian].

Šinkovec, B. 1971. Geology of the iron and copper deposit at Rude near Samobor. *Geološki vjesnik*, **24**, 165–181 [in Croatian].

Šinkovec, B. 2000. Occurrence of Pb-Zn ore in the Ivanšćica Mt. near Ivanec (Croatia). *Rudarsko–geološki-naftni zbornik*, **12**, 11–14 [in Croatian].

Šinkovec, B. & Krkalo, E. 1994. Graphite deposits from Mt. Psunj in Slavonia. *Geološki vjesnik*, **24**, 165–181 [in Croatian].

Šinkovec, B., Palinkaš, L. & Durn, G. 1988. Ore deposits of Medvednica Mt. *Geološki vjesnik*, **41**, 395–405 [in Croatian].

Skaberne, D. 2002. Sedimentary facies, evolution and interpretation of the Brebivniški Member in the Gröden Formation on the Žirovski Vrh area. *Geologija*, **45**(1), 163–188 [in Slovene].

Skácel, J. 1966. Iron ore deposits of the Moravo-Silesian Devonian. *Rozpravy Ceskoslovenské akademie ved, rada Matematických a prirodních ved*, **76**, 1–59 [in Czech].

Slávik, J. 1962. Geology and genesis of the Neogene clay deposits in the Eastern Slovakia. *Geologické práce, Zošity*, **63**, 221–232 [in Slovak].

Slávik, J. 1967. *Mineral deposits of Slovakia. Aktuality Geologickeco Prieskumu*, **5**, 1–511 [in Slovak].

Slávik, J. 1971. Perlite. *In*: Grecula. P. (ed.) *Non-metallic Raw Material of Slovakia*. Mineralia Slovaca, 501–511.

Slavkay, M. & Chovan, M. 1996. A review of metallic ore mineralization of the Nízke Tatry Mts. *In*: Grecula, P. & Németh, Z. (eds) *Variscan Metallogeny in the Alpine Orogenic Belt*. Mineralia Slovaca Monograph, 239–250.

Slavkay, M. & Petro, M. 1993. Metallogenesis and ore formation of the Veporicum. *Mineralia Slovaca*, **25**, 313–317.

Sliaupa, S., Piske, J., Bleschert, K.-H. & Hoth, P. 2004. The Lower Palaeozoic petroleum system of the Baltic basin. *AAPG European Region Conference Abstract Book*, Prague, 106.

Sokač, K. & Šinkovec, B. 1991. The bauxite of the Dinarides. *Travaux*, **20–21**, 1–13.

Solti, G. 1980. The oil shale deposit of Várpalota. *Acta Mineralogica-Petrographica, Szeged*, **24**, 289–300.

Solti, G. 1985. Prospection and utilization of alginate and oil shale in Hungary. *In: Neogene Mineral Resource in the Carpathian Basin*, VIII[th] RCMNS Congress, Budapest, 503–517.

Speczik, S. 1995. The Kupferschiefer mineralization of Central Europe: new aspects and major areas of future research. *Ore Geology Review*, **9**, 411–426.

Speczik, S. & Wiszniewska, J. 1984. Some comments about stratiform tin deposits in the Stara Kamienica Chain (southwestern Poland). *Mineralium Deposita*, **19**, 171–175.

Sperling, H. 1973. Die Erzgänge des Erzbergwerkes Grund (Silbernaaler Gangzug, Bergwerksglücker Gang und Laubhütter Gang. *Geologisches Jahrbuch*, **D2**, 2–205.

Sperling, H. & Stoppel, D. 1981. Monographie der deutschen Blei-Zink-Erzlagerstätten. 3 Die Blei-Zink-Erzgänge des Oberharzes. *Geologisches Jahrbuch*, **D 46**, 1–90.

Sperling, H. & Walcher, E. 1990. Die Blei-Zink-Erzlagerstätte Rammelsberg. *Geologisches Jahrbuch*, **D 91**, 3–153.

Spötl, Ch. 1989*a*. The Alpine Haselgebirge Formation, Northern Calcareous Alps (Austria): Permo-Scythian evaporites in an alpine thrust system. *Sedimentary Geology*, **65**, 113–125.

Spötl, Ch. 1989*b*. Die Dalzlagerstätte von Hall in Tirol – Ein Überblick über den Stand der geologischen Erforschung des 700jährigen Bergbaubetriebes. *Veröffentlichungen Museum Ferdinandeum*, **69**, 137–167.

Stadler, G. 1971. Die Vererzung im Bereich des Bramscher Massivs und seiner Umgebung. *Fortschritte Geologie Rheinland Westfalen*, **18**, 439–500.

Stahl, W. 1971. Isotopen-Analysen an Carbonaten und Kohlendioxid-Proben aus dem Einflußbereich und der weiteren Umgebung des Bramscher Intrusivs und hydrothermalen Carbonaten aus dem Siegerland. *Fortschritte Geologie Rheinland Westfalen*, **18**, 429–438.

Stampfli, G. M. & Borel, G. D. 2002. A plate tectonic model for the Paleozoic and Mesozoic constrained by dynamic palte boundaries and restored synthetic oceanic isochrones. *Earth and Planetary Science Letters*, **196**, 17–33.

Standke, G., Rascher, J. & Strauss, C. 1993. Relative sea-level fluctuations and brown coal formation around the Early-Middle Miocene boundary in the Lusatian Brown Coal District. *Geologische Rundschau*, **82**, 295–305.

Stanley, C. J., Criddle, A. J., Förster, H.-J. & Roberts, A. C. 2002. Tischendorfite, $Pd_8Hg_3Se_9$, a new mineral from Tilkerode, Harz Mountains, Germany. *Canadian Mineralogist*, **40**, 739–745.

Stedingk, K. & Stoppel, D. 1993. History of mining operations and economic significance of the Harz vein deposits. *Monogaph Series Mineralium Deposita*, **30**, 1–3.

Stein, H. J., Markey, R. J., Morgan, J. W., Hannah, J. L. & Zák, K. 1997. Re–Os dating of shear-hosted Au deposits using molybdenite. *In*: Papunen, H. (ed.) *Mineral Deposits: Research and Exploration—Where Do They Meet?*, Balkema, Rotterdam, 313–317.

Stein, H. J., Morgan, J. W., Markey, R. J. & Wiszniewska, J. 1998*a*. A Re–Os study of the Suwalki anorthosite massif, North-east Poland. EUROBRIDGE 1998. *Journal of Geophysics*, **20**, 111–113.

Stein, H. J., Morgan, J. W., Markey, R. J. & Hannah, J. L. 1998*b*. An introduction to Re–Os—what's in it for the mineral industry. *Society of Economic Geology Newsletter*, **321**, 8–15.

Steininger, F. F. (ed.) 1998. The Early Miocene lignite deposit of Oberdorf N Voitsberg (Styria, Austria). *Jahrbuch der Geologischen Bundesanstalt*, **140**, 395–655.

Steininger, F. F., Rögl, F., Hochuli, P. & Müller, C. 1988/89. Lignite deposition and marine cycles. The Austrian Tertiary lignite deposits - A case history. Sitzber. *Österreichischen Akademie der Wissenschaften, mathematisch-naturwissenschaftliche Klasse, Abteilung I*, **197**, 309–332.

Štemprok, M. & Seltmann, R. 1994. The metallogeny of the Erzgebirge (Krušné Hory). *In*: Seltmann, R., Kämpf, H. & Möller, P. (eds) *Metallogeny of Collision Orogen*. Czech Geological Survey, Prague, 61–69.

Štohl, J., Hojstričová, V. & Rojkovičová, L. 1990. *Evaluation of the borehole B-1 Rovná Roveň*. Open file report, Geological Survey Slovak Republic, Bratislava.

Štohl, J., Lexa, J., Kaličiak, M. & Bacsó, Z. 1994. Genesis of stockwork base metal mineralization in the Neogene volcanics of Western Carpathians. *Mineralia Slovaca*, **26**, 75–117.

Stollhofen, H. 1998. Facies variations and seismogenic structures in the Carboniferous-Permian Saar-Nahe Basin (SW Germany): evidence for extension-related transfer fault activity. *Sedimentary Geology*, **119**, 47–83.

Štorch, P. & Pašava, J. 1989. Stratigraphy, chemistry and origin of the Lower Silurian black graptolitic shales of the Prague Basin (Barrandian, Bohemia). *Bulletin of the Geological Survey, Prague*, **64**, 143–162.

Strauss, P. H., Wagreich, M., Decker, K. & Sachsenhofer, R. F. 2001. Tectonics and sedimentation in the Fohnsdorf–Seckau Basin (Miocene, Austria): from a pull-apart basin to a half-graben. *International Journal of Earth Sciences*, **90**, 549–559.

Strehlau, K. & David, F. 1989. Sedimentologie und Flözfazies im Westfal C des nördlichen Ruhrkarbons. *Zeitschrift der Deutschen Geologischen Gesellschaft*, **140**, 231–247.

Streit, R. 1987. Neuburger Kieselerde (Kieselkreide). *Geologica Bavarica*, **91**, 153–158.

Stribrny, B. 1987. Die Kupfererzlagerstätte Marsberg im Rheinischen Schiefergebirge- Rückblick und Stand der Forschung. *Erzmetall*, **40**, 423–427.

Strmić, S., Palinkaš, A. L. & Prochaska, W. 2001. Ore forming fluids in Triassic, rifting related SEDEX deposits, Vareš and Veovača, Central Bosnia. *In:* Adam *et al.* (eds) *PANCARDI 2001, Abstracts*, Sopron, 5–6.

Strohmenger, C., Antonini, M., Jäger, G., Rockenbauch, K. &

STRAUSS, C. 1996. Zechstein 2 Carbonate reservoir facies distribution in relation to Zechstein sequence stratigraphy (Upper Permian, Germany): an integrated approach. *Bulletin des Centres de Recherches Exploration-Production Elf-Aquitaine,* **20**, 1–35.

SUCHAN, J. 2003. The stratabound Cu-Ag deposits of the Lubin-Glogow district, Fore Sudetic Monocline. *In:* KELLY, J. G. *et al.* (eds) Europe's Major Base Metal Deposits, Irish Association of Economic Geologists, Dublin, 239–252.

SUCHÝ, V., SÝKOROVÁ, I., STEJSKAL, M., ŠAFANDA, J., MACHOVIČ, V. & NOVOTNÁ, M. 2002. Dispersed organic matter from Silurian shales of the Barrandian Basin, Czech Republic: Optical properties, chemical composition and thermal maturity. *International Journal of Coal Geology,* **53**, 1–25.

SUCHÝ, V., ŠAFANDA, J., SÝKOROVÁ, I., STEJSKAL, M., MACHOVIČ, V. & MELKA, K. 2004. The contact metamorphism of a Silurian black shales by a basalt sill: geological evidence and thermal modelling in the Barrandian Basin. *Bulletin of Geosciences,* **79**, 133–145.

SULOVSKÝ, P. & HLISNIKOVSKÝ, K. 2001. Thorium mineralization in alkali feldspar syenite of the nordmarkite-type dyke in the Trebic pluton (Czech Republic). *Mitteilungen der Österreichischen Mineralogischen Gesellschaft,* **146**, 280–282.

SUMMERFIELD, M. A. 1999. *Global Geomorphology,* (2nd edn). Longman, Harlow.

SZAKÁLL, S. 2000. *Comparison of the Rudabánya (Hungary) and Nižná Slaná (Slovakia) metasomatic iron and hydrothermal sulphide ore deposits – with special references to the mineral paragenesis of Rudabánya.* PhD thesis, Technical University, Košice.

SZUROWSKI, H., RÜGER, F. & WEISE, W. 1991. Zu den Bildungsbedingungen und der Mineralisation der Uranlagerstätte. *Mineralien, Geologie und Bergbau in Ostthüringen, Museum Naturkunde Gera,* 25–43.

SZUWARZYNSKI, M. 1996. Ore bodies in the Silesian-Cracov Zn-Pb ore district, Poland. *In*: GORECKA, E., LEACH, D. & KOZLOWSKI, A. (eds) *Carbonate-hosted Zinc-Lead Deposits in the Silesian-Cracov Area, Poland.* Transactions of the Polish Geological Institute, **154**, PGI, Warsaw.

TAIT, J., SCHÄTZ, M., BACHTADSE, V. & SOFFEL, H. 2000. Paleomagnetism and Paleozoic paleogeography of Gondwana and European terranes. *In:* FRANKE, W., HAAK, V., ONCKEN, O. & TANNER, D. (eds) *Orogenic Processes: Quantification and Modelling in the Variscan Belt.* Geological Society, London, Special Publications, **179**, 21–34.

TARI, G., BÁLDI, T. & BÁLDI-BEKE, M. 1993. Paleogene retroarc flexural basin beneath the Neogene Pannonian Basin: A geodynamic model. *Tectonophysics*, **226**, 433–455.

TAYLOR, B. E. & BEAUDOIN, G. 2000. Sulphur stratigraphy of the Sullivan Pb–Zn–Ag deposit, B. C: evidence for hydrothermal sulphur, and bacterial and thermochemical sulphate reduction. *In*: LYDON, J. W., HÖY, T., SLACK, J. F. & KNAPP, M. (eds) *The Sullivan Deposit and its Geological Environment.* Mineral Deposits Division of the Geological Association of Canada, St. John's, Newfoundland, Special Publication, **1**, 696–719.

TELEKI, P. G., MATTICK, R. E. & KÓKAI, J. 1994. Basin Analysis in Petroleum Exploration; A Case Study from the Békés Basin, Hungary. Kluwer, Dordrecht.

TEUSCHER, E. O. & WEINELT, W. 1972. Die Metallogenese im Raum Spessart – Fichtelgebirge-Oberpfälzer Wald-Bayerischer Wald. *Geologica Bavarica*, **65**, 5–73.

TEYSSEN, T. A. L. 1989. Sedimentology of the Minette oolitic ironstones of Luxembourg and Lorraine: a Jurassic subtidal sandwave complex. *Sedimentology,* **31**, 195–211.

THIELEMANN, T. 2001. Induziert der Steinkohlenbergbau im Ruhrbecken Methanemissionen? *Zeitschrift der Deutschen Geologischen Gesellschaft*, **152**, 61–76.

THIERY, V. 2004. Les mines de fluorine de Voltenne. *Minéraux et Fossiles,* **329**, 5–11.

THOMAS, R. & WEBSTER, J. D. 2001 Strong tin enrichment in a pegmatite-forming melt. *Mineralium Deposita*, **35**, 570–582.

TISCHENDORF, G. 1960. Über Eskebornit von Tilkerode im Harz. *Neues Jahrbuch für Mineralogie Abhandlungen,* **94**, 1169–1182.

TISCHENDORF, G. 1986. Variscan ensialic magmatism and metallogenesis in the Ore Mountains – modelling of the process. *Chemie der Erde*, **45**, 75–104.

TISCHENDORF, G., DILL, H. G. & FÖRSTER, H.-J. 1995. Metallogenesis of the Saxothuringian Basins. *In:* DALLMEYER, R. D., FRANKE, W. & WEBER, K., (eds) *Tectono-Stratigraphic Evolution of the Central and East European Orogens*. Springer, Heidelberg, 266–273.

TOMSCHEY, O. 1995. Unusual enrichment of U, Mo and V in an Upper Cretaceous coal seam, Hungary. *In*: WHATELEY, M. K. G. & SPEARS, D. A. (eds) *European Coal Geology.* Geological Society, London, Special Publications, **82**, 299–305.

TRÉGER, M. & BALÁŽ, P. 2001. Economic assessment of magnesite and talc deposits in the Slovak Republic. *Mineralia Slovaca*, **33**, 527–534.

TUFAR, W. 1972. Neue Aspekte zum Problem der ostalpinen Spatlagerstätten am Beispiel einiger Paragenesen vom Ostrand der Alpen. *Geologija*, **15**, 141–153.

TWIDALE, C. R. 2002. The two-stage concept of landform and landscape development involving etching: origin, development and implications of an idea. *Earth-Science Reviews,* **57**, 37–74.

UDUBASA, G. 1996. Syngenese und Epigenese in metamorphen und nicht-metamorphen Pb-Zn- Erzlagerstätten, aufgezeigt an den Beispielen Blazna-Tal (Ostkarpaten, Rumänien) und Ramsbeck (Westfalen, BRD). *Heidelberger geowissenschaftliche Abhandlungen* **87**, 1–145.

URBAN, H. & VACHE, R. 1972. Die Kupfererzlagerstätten von Wirsberg (Oberfranken) im Lichte neuer Aufschluesse. *Geologica Bavarica*, **65**, 74–106.

VAN BERGEN, F., PAGNIER, H. J. M., DAMEN, K., FAAIJ, A. P. C. & RIBBERINK, J. S. 2003. *Feasibility study on $CO_2$ sequestration and enhanced CBM production in Zuid-Limburg.* NITG 03–150-B.

VAN BERGEN, F., PAGNIER, H.J.M., DAMEN, K., FAAIJ, A.P.C., RIBBERINK, J.S. 2003. Feasibility study on $CO_2$ sequestration and enhanced CBM production in Zuid-Limburg. Report commissioned by NOVEM (Netherlands Agency for Energy and the Environment) and by Netherlands Institute of Applied GeoScience (TNO) (NWS-E-2003-51). Copernicus Institute, Department of Science, Technology and Society, Utrecht University, Utrecht.

VAN DER VEEN, A. H. & MAASKANT, P. 1995. Chromian spinel mineralogy of the Stare Ransko gabbro-peridotite, Czech Republic, and its implications for sulphide mineralization, *Mineralium Deposita,* **30**, 397–407.

VAN HOUTEN, F. B. & BHATTACHARYYA, D. P. 1982. Phanerozoic oolitic ironstones - geologic record and facies model. *Annual Review of Earth and Planetary Science,* **10**, 441–457.

VAN HOUTEN, F. B. & HOU, H. F. 1990. Stratigraphic and palaeogeographic distribution of Palaeozoic oolitic ironstones. *In:* MCKERROW, W. S. & SCOTESE, C. R. (eds) *Palaeozoic Palaeogeography and Biogeography.* Geological Society, London, Memoirs, **12**, 87–93.

VAN KEER, I, ONDRAK, R., MUCHEZ, PH., BAYER, U., DUSAR, M. & VIAENE, W. 1998. Burial history and thermal evolution of Westphalian coal-bearing strata in the Campine Basin (NE Belgium). *Geologie en Mijnbouw - Netherlands Journal of Geosciences,* **76**, 301–311.

VAN TONGEREN, P., DREESEN, R., LAENEN, B. & DUSAR, M. 2002. Influence of geological and economic parameters on the (E)CBM-development in the Campin Basin (Belgium). *In*: JURECZKA, J. & PODEMSKI, M. (eds) *Poceedings of the IV European Coal Conference*, Polish Geological Institute, Special Papers, **7**, 271–280.

VAN WAGONER, J. C., POSAMENTIER, H. W., MITCHUM, R. M., JR., VAIL, R., SARG, J. F., LOUTIT, T. S. & HARDENBOL, J. 1990. An overview of the fundamentals of sequence stratigraphy and key definitions, *In*: WILGUS *et al.* (eds) *Sea Level Changes – An Integrated Approach,* Society of Palaeontology and Mineralogy, Special Publications, **42**, 39–46.

VAN WEES, J.-D., STEPHENSON, R. A., *et al.* 2000. On the origin of the Southern Permian Basin, Central Europe. *Marine and Petroleum Geology,* **17**, 43–59.

VANĚČEK, M., PATOČKA, F., POŠMOURN, K. & RAJLICH, P. 1985. The use of the isotope composition of ore lead in metallogenic analysis of the Bohemian Massif. *Rozpravy Ceskoslovenské akademie ved, rada Matematických a prírodních ved,* **95**, 1–114.

VASS, D. & KRAUS, I. 1985. Two basalts of different age in Southern Slovakia and their relation to the Poltár Formation. *Mineralia Slovaca*, **17**, 435–440 [in Slovak with English abstract].

VASS, D., KONEČNÝ, V., ELEČKO, M., FORDINAL, K., HALÁSOVÁ, E., ZLINSKÁ, A. & HOJSTRIČOVÁ, V. 1997. *Upper Miocene sediments and Middle Miocene volcanics at the Šahy elevation slopes and in the Vel'ký Lom depresion*. Open file report, Geological Survey of the Slovak Republic [in Slovak].

Vaughn, D. J., Sweeney, M., Friedrich, G., Diedel, R. & Haranczyk, C. 1989. The Kupferschiefer: An Overview with an appraisal of different types of mineralization. *Economic Geology*, **84**, 1003–1027.

Vejsada, J., Hradil, D., Randa, Z., Jelinek, E. & Stulik, K. 2005. Adsorption of cesium on Czech smectite-rich clays – A comparative study. *Applied Clay Science*, **30**, 53–66.

Verdier, J. P. 1999. The Rotliegend sedimentation history of the southern North Sea and adjacent countries. *In:* Rondeel *et al.* (eds) *Geology of Gas and Oil Under the Netherlands*. Kluwer, Dordrecht, 45–56.

Voigt, S., Wagreich, M. *et al.* 2008. Cretaceous. *In*: McCann, T. (ed.) *The Geology of Central Europe. Volume 2: Mesozoic and Cenozoic*. Geological Society, London, 923–997.

von Raumer, J. F. 1998. The Palaeozoic evolution in the Alps: from Gondwana to Pangea. *Geologische Rundschau*, **87**, 407–435.

von Raumer, J. F., Stampfli, G. M., Borel, G. & Bussy, F. 2002. Organisation of pre-Variscan basement areas at the north-Gondwanan margin. *International Journal of Earth Sciences*, **91**, 35–52.

von Raumer, J. F., Stampfli, G. M. & Bussy, F. 2003. Gondwana-derived microcontinents - the constituents of the Variscan and alpine collision orogens. *Tectonophysics*, **365**, 7–22.

Vörös, A. 1989. Middle Eocene transgression and basin evolution in the Transdanubian Central Range, Hungary: sedimentological contribution. *Fragmenta Mineralogica et Paleontologica,* **14**, 63–72.

Wagner, L. R. 1998. Tectono-stratigraphy and hydrocarbons in the Molasse Foredeep of Salzburg, Upper and Lower Austria. *In:* Mascle, A., Puigdefàbregas, C. & Luterbacher, H. P. (eds) *Cenozoic Foreland Basins of Western Europe*. Geological Society, London, Special Publications, **134**, 339–369.

Wagner, T. & Boyce, A. J. 2001. Sulphur isotope characteristics of recrystallisation, remobilisation and reaction processes: a case study from the Ramsbeck Pb-Zn deposit, Germany. *Mineralium Deposita,* **36**, 670–679.

Wagner, T. & Boyce, A. J. 2003. Sulphur isotope geochemistry of black shale-hosted antimony mineralization, Arnsberg, northern Rhenish Massif, Germany: Implications for late-stage fluid flow during the Variscan orogeny. *Journal of the Geological Society of London,* **160**, 299–308.

Wagner, T. & Cook, N. J. 1997. Mineral reactions in sulphide systems as indicators of evolving fluid geochemistry – a case study from the Apollo mine, Siegerland, FRG. *Mineralogical Magazine*, **61**, 573–590.

Wagner, T. & Cook, N. J. 1999. Carrollite and related minerals of the linnaeite group; solid solutions and nomenclature in the light of new data from the Siegerland District, Germany. *Canadian Mineralogist,* **37**, 545–558.

Walter, R. 1992. *Die Geologie von Mitteleuropa*, 5th edn. Schweizerbart, Stuttgart.

Walther, H. W. 1982. On the Alpidic mineralization in the western Central Europe outside the Alps. *In*: Schneider, H. J. (ed.) *Mineral Deposits of the Alps and of the Alpine Epoch in Europe*. Proceedings of the IV. Ismida, Berchtesgaden, October 4–10, 1981 (Special Publication) Geology Applied to Mineral Deposits, No. 3., Springer, New York, 598–606. Mineralium Deposita, Special Publications, **2**, 598–606.

Walther, H. W. 1986. Federal Republic of Germany. *In*: Dunning, F. W. & Evans, A. M. (eds) *Mineral Deposits of Europe*, Vol. 3, *Central Europe.* Institution of Mining and Metallurgy, and Mineralogical Society, London, 175–301.

Walther, H. W. & Dill, H. G. 1995. Die Bodenschätze Mitteleuropas - Ein Überblick. *In*: Walter, R. (ed.) *Die Geologie von Mitteleuropa.* Schweizerbart, Stuttgart, 526–542.

Warren, J. K. 1999. *Evaporites - Their Evolution and Economics.* Blackwell Science, Oxford.

Weber, L. 1990. Die Blei-Zinklagerstätten des Grazer Paläozoikums und ihr geologischer Rahmen. *Archiv für Lagerstättenforschung der Geologischen Bundesanstalt,* **12**, 1–289.

Weber, L. (ed.) 1997. Handbuch der Lagerstätten der Erze, Industrieminerale und Energierohstoffe Österreichs. *Archiv für Lagerstättenforschung der Geologischen Bundesanstalt,* **19**, 1–607.

Weber, L. & Zsak, G. 2007. *World-Mining-Data*, Vol. 22, Federal Ministry for Economy and Labour of the Republic of Austria, Vienna.

Webster, J., Thomas, R., Förster, H.-J., Seltmann, R. & Tappen, C. 2004. Geochemical evolution of halogen-enriched granite magmas and mineralizing fluids of the Zinnwald tin-tungsten mining district, Erzgebirge, Germany. *Mineralium Deposita*, **39**, 452–472

Wendt, I., Höhndorf, A., Kreuzer, H., Müller, D. & Stettner, G. 1988. Gesamtgesteins- und Mineraldatierungen der Steinwaldgranite (NE-Bayern). *Geologisches Jahrbuch*, **E 42**, 167–194.

Werner, W. 1989. Contribution to the genesis of SEDEX-type mineralization of the Rhenish Massif (Germany) – implications for future Pn-Zn exploration. *Geologische Rundschau*, **78**, 571–598

Werner, W. 1990. Die epigenetische Markasit –Schwerspat-Zinkblendevererzung "Altenbüren" (nordöstliches Rheinisches Schiefergebirge). *Geologisches Jahrbuch*, **D 95**, 139–176.

Werner, W. & Franzke, H. J. 2001. Postvariszische bis neogene Bruchtektonik und Mineralisation im südlichen Zentralschwarzwald. *Zeitschrift der Deutschen Geologischen Gesellschaft,* **152**, 405–437.

Werner, W. & Walther, H.-J. 1995. Metallogenesis. *In*: Dallmeyer, R. D., Franke, W. & Weber, K. (eds) *Pre-Permian Geology of Central and Eastern Europe*. Springer, Berlin, 87–95.

Wernicke, R. S. & Lippolt, H. J. 1993. Botryoidal haematite from the Schwarzwald (Germany): heterogeneous uranium distributions and their bearing on the helium dating method. *Earth and Planetary Science Letters*, **114**, 287–300.

Wernicke, R. S. & Lippolt, H. J. 1997*a*. Evidence of Mesozoic multiple hydrothermal activity in the basement at Nonnenmattweiher (southern Schwarzwald) Germany. *Mineralium Deposita*, **32**, 197–200.

Wernicke, R. S. & Lippolt, H. J. 1997*b*. (U+Th)–He evidence of Jurassic continuous hydrothermal activity in the Schwarzwald basement, Germany. *Chemical Geology*, **138**, 273–285.

Wimmer, R., Holz, U. & Rascher, J. 2004. Exkursionsführer und Veröffentlichung. *GGW Berlin*, **224**.

Winchester, J. A. & The PACE TMR Network Team 2002. Palaeozoic amalgamation of Central Europe: new results from recent geological and geophysical investigations. *Tectonophysics*, **360**, 5–21.

Wirth, R. 1978. *Geochemie und Petrographie der paläozoischen Magmatite des Frankenwaldes. Diabase-Keratophyre-Pikrite*. PhD thesis, University of Würzburg.

Wiszniewska, J. 1998. Mineralogy of Fe–Ti–V ores of the Suwalki Anorthosite Massif (SAM), northeast Poland. *In*: Ryka, W. & Podemski, M. (eds) *Geology of the Suwalki Massif – NE Poland*, Geological Institute, Warsaw, 137–150.

Wiszniewska, J. 2000. Strontium isotope ratios and REE geochemistry in the Suwalki anorthosites, NE Poland. *Geological Quarterly,* **44**, 183–186.

Wodzicki, A. & Piestrzynski, A. 1994. An ore genetic model for the Lubin-Sieroszowice mining district, Poland. *Mineralium Deposita*, **29**, 30–43.

Wolf, H. 1971. Die Schwefelkieslagerstätte"Bayerland" bei Waldsassen in der Oberpfalz und ihr geologischer Rahmen. *Acta Albertina Ratisbonentia*, **31**, 57–100.

Woodtli, W. & Disch, H. 1996. Sekundäre Mineralien von der Mürtschenalp. *Mineralienfreund*, **43**, 7–14.

Wutzler, B. 1983. Geologisch lagerstättenkundliche Untersuchungen am Mt. Chemin. *Clausthaler Geologische Abhandlungen*, **42**, 1–111.

Xiao, X. M, Wilkins, R. W. T., Liu, D. H., Liu, Z. F. & Fu, J. M. 2000. Investigation of thermal maturity of Lower Palaeozoic hydrocarbon source rocks by means of vitrinite-like maceral reflectance – a Tarim Basin case study. *Organic Geochemistry*, **31**, 1052–1941.

Yapp, C. J. 1991. Oxygen isotopes in an oolitic ironstone and the determination of goethite $\delta^{18}O$ values by selective dissolution of impurities: The 5 M NaOH method. *Geochimica et Cosmochimica Acta*, **55**, 2627–2634.

Yapp, C. J. 1998. Paleoenvironmental interpretations of oxygen isotope ratios in oolitic ironstones. *Geochimica et Cosmochimica Acta*, **62**, 2409–2420.

Young, T. P. 1989. Eustatically controlled ooidal ironstone deposition: facies relationships of the Ordovician open-shelf ironstones of Western Europe. *In*: Young, T. P. & Taylor, W. E. G. (eds)

*Phanerozoic Ironstones*. Geological Society, London, Special Publications, **46**, 51–64.

ZACHARIÁŠ, J., PERTOLD, Z., PUDILOVA, M., ZAK, K., PERTOLDOVA, J., STEIN, H. & MARKEY, R. 2001. Geology and genesis of Variscan porphyry-style gold mineralization, Petrackova hora deposit, Bohemian Massif, Czech Republic. *Mineralium Deposita,* **36**, 517–541.

ZACHARIÁŠ, J., FRÝDA, J., PATEROVÁ, B. & MIHALJEVIČ, M. 2004. Arsenopyrite and As-bearing pyrite from the Roudný deposit, Bohemian Massif. *Mineralogical Magazine*, **68,** 31–46.

ŽÁK, K., RADVANEC, M., GRECULA, P. & BARTALSKÝ, B. 1991. S, C, O, Sr isotopes and a metamorphic-hydrotermal model of vein mineralization, Gemeric unit, Western Carpathians. *Mineralia Slovaca*, **23**, 95–108 [in Slovak with English abstract].

ŽÁK, K., RADVANEC, M., & GRECULA, P. 2005. Siderite mineralization of the Gemericum Superunit (Western Carpathians, Slovakia): review and revised genetic model (Ore Geology Reviews 24, 267–298) – a reply. *Ore Geology Reviews*, **26**, 173–180.

ZDANAVICIUTE, O. & LAZAUSKIENE, J. 2004. Hydrocarbon migration and entrapment in the Baltic Syneclise. *Organic Geochemistry* **35**, 517–527.

ZDANOWSKI, A. & ZAKOWA, H. (eds) 1995. *The Carboniferous System in Poland*. Polish Geological Institute, Warszawa.

ZENTILLI, M. & MAKSAEV, V. 1995. Metallogenetic model for the late Eocene–early Oligocene supergiant porphyry event, northern Chile. *In: Proceedings of the Second Giant Ore Deposits Workshop*, 22–27 April, Queen's University, Kingston, Ontario, 52–165.

ZIEGLER, J.H. 1983. Eocene iron ore deposits at the northern welt of the Bavarian Alps. *In*: SCHNEIDER, H. J. (ed.) *Mineral Deposits of the Alps and of the Alpine Epoch in Europe*. Proceedings of IV. ISMIDA (International Symposium of Mineral Deposits of the Alps), Berchtesgaden. *Special Publication Society Geology Applied Mineralogy Deposits*, Springer, New York, **3**, 136-145.

ZIEGLER, P. A. 1990. *Geological Atlas of Western and Central Europe*, 2nd edn. Shell International Petroleum Maatschappij B. V.

ZITZMANN, A. (ed.) 1977. *The iron ore deposits of Europe and adjacent areas*. Bundesanstalt für Geowissenschaften und Rohstoffe, Hannover.

ZLOCHA, J. 1972. *Hodkovce – amorphous magnesite*. Open file report, Geofond Bratislava [in Slovak].

ZLOCHA, J. 1975. *Hodkovce Ni-ores*. Open file report, Geofond Bratislava [in Slovak].

ZLOCHA, J. & HOVORKA, D. 1971. Asbestos occurrences in the Western Carpathians. *Mineralia Slovaca*, **3**, 295–317.

ZOUBEK, V. & NEMČOK, A. 1951. *Report on magnetite deposit near the Kokava nad Rimavicou*. Open file report, Slovak Technical Universisty [in Slovak].

ZUBEREC, J., TRÉGER, M., LEXA, J. & BALÁŽ, P. 2005. *Mineral Deposits of Slovakia*. Geological Survey Slovak Republic [in Slovak with English abstract].

ZULAUF, G., BUES, C., DÖRR, W. & VEJNAR, Z. 2002. 10 km minimum throw along the West Bohmeian shear zone: Evidence for dramatic crustal thickening and high topography in the Bohemian Massif (European Variscides). *International Journal Earth Sciences (Geol. Rundschau)*, **91**, 850–864.

ZUTHER, M. & BROCKAMP, O. 1988. The fossil geothermal system of the Baden–Baden trough (Northern Black Forest, F. R. Germany). *Chemical Geology*, **71**, 337–353.

# Index

Page numbers in *italic* denote figures. Page numbers in **bold** denote tables.


Aalburg Formation 837
Aalenian
  northern Germany 844–845, *844*
  Poland 852, *853*
  southeast France 877
  southern Germany *866*, 867
  Swiss Jura *883*, 884
Aare Massif 488, *491*, 1145–1146, *1147*, 1148, *1149*, 1175, *1236*, 1237
Abbaye de Villiers Formation 208
Ablakoskővölgy Formation 802
Acadian Orogeny 599–600, 637
Acceglio Zone 1157
accommodation curves, Paris Basin 858–859
Achterhoek area, Jurassic 837, *838*, 839
Ackerl Nappe 1165
acritarchs
  Caledonides 307
  Cambrian 190, 191–192
    Ardennes 158
    Brabant Massif 161
    Brunovistulian Terrane 171, 173, 174
    Lublin-Podlasie Basin 186
  Cambrian–Ordovician boundary 204, 220, 222
  Ordovician
    Alps 237
    Ardennes inliers 213–214
    Bohemian Massif 226, 227, 228
    Brabant Massif 208–209
    Condroz Inlier 210, 211, 212
    Germany 215, 217, 218
    Poland 233, 234
    Saxothuringian Zone 224
  Silurian *252*
    Austria 276, 279
    Condroz Inlier 287
    Ireviken Event 251, *252*
    Montagne Noire 284
    Proto-Alps Terrane 259
  Triassic, German Basin 771
Adamello Pluton 1165, 1166, 1167, 1172, 1178, 1180
Aderklaa Formation 1062
Adnet Formation *893*, 894–895
Adria 1035
Adriatic Carbonate Platform 1106–1111
Adriatic coast
  Cenozoic 1106–1111
Adriatic Platform 1093
Adriaticum 1093, 1094
Adula Nappe 1150, 1152, 1173
Aegir Marine Band 434
aeolian sediment, Pleistocene 1310, 1315–1318
Agatharchides (181–146 BC) 3
Aggetelek Nappe 804
Aggtelek-Rudabánya Unit, Triassic basin evolution 802–805
Agly Massif 59
Agnatha, Devonian, southeastern Poland 395
agnostoids, Middle Cambrian 190
Agricola, Georgius (1494–1555) 4
Aiguilles d'Arves Unit 1148, *1149*, 1150
Aiguilles Rouges Massif 486, *488*, 1145–1146, *1147*
Aken Formation 949, *949*, *950*
Albertus Magnus (*c.* 1200–1280) 4
Albian
  Helvetic basin 970
  Lower Saxony Basin 936
  Mid-Polish Trough *933*, 934
  North German Basin 942, *943*
  sea-level change 924
Albstadt Shear Zone 1250–1251
  seismicity 1245–1246
Alcsútdoboz Limestone 800
Alderney *110*
Alemannic landmass 881
Alföld Phase 1215
algae, coccolithophorid
  Cretaceous 923, 925, 937
    *see also* chalk
  Ediacaran, Teplá-Barrandian Unit 74
  Jurassic, Moravian Karst 890
Alleghanian Orogeny 600–601
Aller cycle 572, 573, *574*, *575*, 580
Aller-Weser Urstromtal 1293
Allgäu Formation *893*, 894, 895, 1162
Alpine basins
  Cenozoic coal seams 1409
  Triassic tectonics 756–757
Alpine Foreland
  coal 1408
  Eastern *see* Helvetic Units
Alpine Foreland Basin *see* North Alpine Foreland Basin
Alpine Haselgebirge 580
Alpine Orogeny 14
  Alps 1141–1181
  north of Alps 1233–1277
  Bohemian Massif 1253–1255
  Carpathian Foreland 1258–1270
  Central Germany 1255–1258
  North German Basin 1270–1275
  South German Triangle 1243–1253
  Western Central Europe 1234–1243
  Western Carpathians 1181–1217
Alpine Terranes *2*
Alpine Verrucano 551
Alpone-Chiampo Graben 1088, 1089
Alps
  basement units
    Italy 237
    Precambrian 79–83
    tectonic evolution 82–83
  Cambrian 187
  Cenozoic 1051–1064
  central *1144*
    Middle Penninic Nappes 1156–1157
    tectonics *1142*, *1147*
      Tertiary 1173–1176
    Valaisian Nappes 1155
  Cretaceous 964–978
  Devonian 403–406
  eastern *1186*
    Jurassic 891–896
    Middle Penninic Nappes 1156–1157
    Penninic nappes 1159–1160
    Silurian 255
    tectonics *1142*, *1153*, *1154*
      Tertiary 1176–1180
  eastern and southern
    Carboniferous sedimentation 474–480, *506*
    Permian basins 550–555
    Zechstein cycles 580–581
  External Massifs 187, 1145–1148
  gold resources 1374–1375
  graphite 1371
  ice age 1304–1310
  minerals 1361, 1363
  northern, Carboniferous sedimentation 484–488, *506*
  Ordovician 236–237
  palaeogeography 1143–1145
  Permian–Triassic boundary 749–751
  polymetallic vein-type deposits 1383–1384
  Precambrian, sedimentary sequences 80–81
  Silurian 276–283
  siderite and magnesite deposits 1385–6
  southern
    Palaeogene, Italy 1087–1093
    Permian 553–554
    tectonics *1142*, *1154*, 1165–1167

Tertiary 1180–1181
Triassic basins 790–798
stratigraphy *792–793*
Triassic–Jurassic boundary 826
Zechstein cycles 581
subdivision 1141, 1143
sulphide ores 1366
tectonics 1141–1181, *1142*
Cretaceous 1170–1173
Jurassic 1168–1170
Permian–Triassic 1168
Tertiary–present 1173–1181
western *1144*
Middle Penninic Nappes 1157
tectonics *1142*, *1147*
Tertiary 1181
*see also* Austro-Alpine Domain; Carnic Alps; Northern Calcareous Alps; Proto-Alps
Altdorf Sandstone 1055
Altena Group 837, *838*, 839, 841
Altenberg tin deposit 1376
Altenberg-Teplice Caldera, Namurian–Westphalian magmatism 721–723
Altenfeld Formation, backarc basin 125–127, *128*, 129, 133
Altenstadt Formation 545
Alticola Limestone Formation 278, 279
Altlengbach Formation 1054
Altmark-Fläming Basin 930, *934*
Cretaceous 936, 948
Altopiano de Asiago 1089, 1090
Alzenau Formation 162, 449, 630, *631*
Åmål Formation 33
Åmål-Horred Belt *30*, 32–33
Amaltheenton Formation 865, *866*
Amazonia 10, *11*, 26, 145
amber
Baltic 1401
Blue Earths 1040
Amberg-Sulzbach-Rosenberg iron mining district 1400
Amden Formation 975
Ammonite Zones
Cretaceous 924
Mid-Polish Trough 932
Jurassic 823, *830*
Paris Basin 859, 861
Poland and Baltic Basin 849, 854–857
southeast France 875–880
Swiss Jura 881–888, *882, 883*
Triassic–Jurassic boundary 826
ammonites
Cretaceous
Danish Basin 937, 940
Mid-Polish Trough *933*
Jurassic
biostratigraphy 823, 829, *830*, 843
Bohemian Massif 889–890
Paris Basin 860, 864
southern Germany 865, 867, 868, 869, 870–871, 872
Ammonitico Rosso 973
ammonoids
Permian 531
Triassic, German Basin 760, 764
amphibolite
Erbendorf Vohenstrauss Zone 680
Hoher Bogen 676
Mariánské-Lázně Complex 672–4
Staré Město Belt 692
anatexis
Caledonian granite 323
Saint-Malo Terrane 115
Saxo-Thuringian Zone 136, 146
Variscan 424
Ancepsoolith Member *866*, 868
Anchamps Formation 158, *159*
Andrusov Ridge 1196
Anglo-Brabant Deformation Belt 207, 256, 285, 313, 316, 325
magnetic and gravimetric modelling 348
Anglo-Brabant Massif 431–433, 637
Angulatenton Formation 865, *866*
anhydrite
resources 1393
Zechstein 572, 573, *574*, *575*, 576–577
Anhydrite Breccia 577
Anhydritgruppe 785, 786
anoxia
Cretaceous 923–924
Helvetic basins 975
Lower Saxony Basin 936
North German Basin 944
Northern Calcareous Alps 974
Western Carpathians 970
Silurian 249
mineralization 1363–1364
Toarcian Ocean Anoxic Event 828, 867
Anthering Formation 1054
antimony
resources **1348–1349**
arc-related 1402–1404
granite-related 1414–1415
metamorphogenic 1413
vein-type 1373–1374
Antrona Ophiolites 1155, 1173
Antwerp Campine sub-basin 437
Antwerp Sands 1041
Aptian
Helvetic basin 970
Lower Saxony Basin 936
Mid-Polish Trough 932, *933*
sea-level change 924
Apulia Terrane, Silurian 255, 258, 276–283
Apulian Plate 1093
Apuseni Mountains 1033, 1035
Aquitanian, Upper Rhine Graben 1048
Arab scientific thought 3–4
Archaean 21, *23*
archaeocyaths, Lower Cambrian 164, 188
Arche Member buildups 390
Arctica supercontinent 23
Ardenne Allochthon 432, 637
Ardennes inliers 158, *159*, *189*, 206–207, 212–214, 315
Ardennes
Devonian, depositional environments 388–391, 637
Jurassic 860
Variscan tectonics 636–639
Ardon Nappe 1148, *1149*
Arenig
Brabant Massif 208, 209
Franconia 225
Holy Cross Mountains 233–234
Northern Phyllite Zone 218
Schwarzburg Anticline 223
Arfon Group *44*, 45, 46, *47*
Argentera Massif 1145, *1147*
Argiles de Levallois Formation 860
Argovian Realm 883, *887*
aridity, Jurassic 828
Arietenkalk Formation 865, *866*
Aristotle of Stagira (384–322 BC) 1, 3, 4
Arkona Schwarzschiefer Formation 218
Armorica microplate 121, 123, 218, 645
evolution 317–318
nomenclature 317
*see also* Armorican Terrane Assemblage
Armorican Massif 55–59
*see also* North Armorican Massif
Armorican Terrane Assemblage 13, 157, 206, 317, 667, 669
Devonian 383–384, *385*
depositional environments 399–403
Rheic suture 418, 420
Silurian 255
subduction 645–646
*see also* Cadomia
Arnager Greensand Formation 936, *938*, 940
Arnager Limestone Formation *938*, 940
Arosa Zone 1158
arsenic
resources **1348–1349**
granite-related 1414
vein-type 1373–1374
arthropods
Carboniferous 505
Devonian, eastern Rhenish Massif 393
Lower Cambrian, Pasecky Shales 176, 188
Artinskian, palaeogeography *536*
Arvernensis Gravel 1048
Arzberg Formation *866*, 870
asbestos, resources **1342**, 1375, 1411
Ashgill
Brabant Massif 209, 210

Holy Cross Mountains 234, 236
Schwarzburg Anticline 223
Asturian unconformity 433
Aszófő Dolomite 800
Atlantic, Triassic rifting 1016, *1018*
Atlantica supercontinent 23
atmosphere, Precambrian *22*, 23
attapulgite, resources, Cenozoic foreland basins 1402
Auerbach-Groß-Bieberau Schist Zone *631*, 632
Auernig cyclothems 479, *480*
Auernig Group 554
Auk Formation 550, *551*
Austria
Cenozoic, North Alpine Foreland Basin 1056–1058
Ordovician 236–237
Palaeogene Helvetic Unit *1046*, 1050–1051
Permian 550–551, *552*, 553
Silurian 276–283
*see also* Austro-Alpine Domain
Austro-Alpine basins
Cretaceous 967–968, 975–978
Palaeogene 1058–1060
Austro-Alpine Domain, 81, 82, 1143
Jurassic 891–896
nappes 893–894, 1160–1165
Cretaceous tectonics 1170–1172
Jurassic tectonics 1169–1170
Lower 1160
Upper 1160–1165
Precambrian 79–80
Autun Basin 556–557
Avalonia 10, 25, *44*, 45, 46, 123, 157, 316, 667, 668–669
Caledonian magmatism 324
East 43, *44*, 45–46, *47*, 123, 157
evolution 43–54
Far East 46–54, 144, 145, 315
Silurian 253–254, 255, 287
palaeogeography 256–257
magmatism 46
Ordovician 205–206, *214*, 218
palaeogeography 312–313, *318*, *361*, 362–367
reconstruction *11, 12*
Rheic suture 418
Silurian 253, 255, 284–287
palaeogeography 256
subduction 46, *47*
tectonic phases *314*
Avalonia–Baltica suture
magnetic-gravimetric modelling 348
seismic surveys **332**, 345, 351
Avalonia-related terranes 157, 316–317
Avalonian Terrane Assemblage 315
Avalonian–Cadomian magmatism 26
Averroes (1126–1198) 3
Avers Bündnerschiefer Nappe 1158
Avesnois sedimentation area 435–436
Avicenna (980–1037) 3, 4
Axen Nappe 1148, *1149*

BABEL seismic project **332**, 337, 338, 340, 343, *346*, *347*, 351, 358
Bacon, Roger (1214–1294) 4
Bad Grund lead–zinc deposit 1382–1383
Baden Group 1062
Baden-Baden Zone 472, *607*
Late Devonian–Early Carboniferous magmatism 711, 712
Variscan tectonics 606
Baden-Württemberg, Jurassic 865–873
Badenian, Paratethys basins 1101
Badenweiler-Lenzkirch Zone 216, 472–473, *607*
Late Devonian–Early Carboniferous magmatism 711–712
Variscan tectonics 608, 609, *610*
Badstub Formation 476
Bagå Formation 835
Bahre Series 700
Bajocian
northern Germany *844*, 845
Poland 852, *853*
southeast France 877–878
southern Germany *866*, 867–868
Swiss Jura *883*, 885–886
Western Carpathian basins 898–899
Bajuvaric Nappe System *1154*, 1160, *1161*, 1162, 1170
Bajuvaric unit 892, *893*
Bakony Mountains, Palaeogene 1068, *1069*
Balaton Lineament 570, *571*
Balatonfelvidék Sandstone Formation 570–572, 582
Baltic, eastern, Devonian 387–388
Baltic Basin 157, 847, 849
Cambrian 182–184
biostratigraphy 182–184
palaeontology 192
hydrocarbon deposits 1379
Jurassic 847, 849, 851, 854, 857–858
Silurian 256, 260–263
Baltic Sea
Precambrian 43
seismic surveys 342, *346*, *347*
Western
halokinesis 1272–1273
tectonics 1272–1273
Baltic Shield, growth 28–32, 34
Baltic-Belarus Granulite Belt *34*
Baltica 10, 25, *30*, 34, 307–309
fossils *308*, 309, 311
gravity model 347
magnetic-gravimetric modelling 348
margin, Cambrian 181–187
palaeogeography 186–187
palaeogeography 26–28, *310, 318*
reconstruction *11*, *12*, 157, *318*, 358–360, *361*, 363–367
Silurian 253, 255, 259–268
Bornholm 267–268
Germany 268
Lithuania 261–263
palaeogeography 256
Poland 263–267
upside-down model 27
Baltica-Laurentia collision structures 356
Baltica-peri-Gondwana suture 157
Baltica-related terranes 309–312, 364
Bamberg Formation 865
banded iron formations 23–24
Bannewitz Formation 563
Banovići Basin *1106*
Baranov Formation 1045
Bardo Basin 499
Bardo Beds 266
Bardo Hills 230, 289, *290*
barite, resources **1342**, **1346**, **1349–1351**
advanced rift-SEDEX 1394
Rammelsberg type 1365–1366
sabka type 1391
SEDEX type 1391–1392
vein-type 1380, 1382–1384, 1418
Barmstein Formation 896
Barrande, Joachim (1799–1883), *Silurian System in Central Bohemia* (1852) 276
Barrandian 138, 180
Cambrian–Early Ordovician magmatism *189*, 676–679
Devonian 399–402
Variscan tectonics 614, 616, 617
*see also* Teplá-Barrandian Unit
Barremian
Helvetic basin 970
Lower Saxony Basin 935–936
Mid-Polish Trough 932, *933*
sea-level change 924
Bärschwil Formation 886
Basal Anydrite 577
basalt
continental flood, Precambrian 37–38
Basbek Formation 1036
Base Cretaceous Unconformity 1003
BASIN seismic project **332**, 340–342, *346*
Bassano Thrust 1180
Basse-aux-Canes Formation 212
batholiths
Variscan 425
Bohemian Massif 469–470
*see also* plutons
Bathonian
northern Germany *844*, 845
Poland *853*, 854
southeast France 878
southern Germany *866*, 868
Swiss Jura *883*, 886
Baumgarten Formation 548–549

bauxite resources **1342**, 1416
Bavaria
  Jurassic 865–873
  Palaeogene Helvetic Unit 1050–1051
Bavarian Facies 220, 257, 403, *464*, 465
Bavarian Forest 180, **193**
  Late Devonian–Early Carboniferous magmatism 716–718
Bavnodde Greensand Formation *938*, 940
Bay of Kiel, tectonics and halokinesis 1272–1273
Bayerische Wald *see* Bavarian Forest
Bayreuth Formation 865
Beggingen Member 881, *882*
Belarus, Jurassic 846, 851, 854, 857
Belarus-Masurian High 260
Belarus-Podlasie Granulite Belt *see* Podlasie-Belarus Granulite Belt
Bełchatów Basin, lignite 1407–1408
BELCORP seismic project **332**, 340
belemnites
  Cretaceous 924–925
    Danish Basin 937, 940
    Lower Saxony Basin 936
  Jurassic
    Paris Basin 861, 864
    southern Germany 865, 870–1
Belgian Lorraine, Permian 549
Belgium
  Carboniferous, sedimentation and magmatism 431–438, *506*
  Devonian, depositional environments 388–391
  Ordovician 206–214
  Permian 549–550
  Silurian 284–287, *288*
  Thanetian transgression 1036
  Variscides 636–639
Belice Unit 1198
Belledonne Massif 1145–1146, *1147*
Bellerophon Formation 553–554, 581, 1167
Belleveaux Formation 158, *159*
Benkovo Phase 1215
Berga Anticline 123, *141*, 165–166, *1359*
  Ordovician *221*, 223
Bergleshof Formation 168
  palaeontology 188
Bergsträsser Odenwald 447–449, 630, 632
  Late Devonian–Early Carboniferous magmatism 708–709
Beringen-Rauw fault system 437
Berriasian
  Central Western Carpathians 974
  Helvetic basin 968
  Lower Saxony Basin 935
  Mid-Polish Trough 931–932, *933*
  Northern Calcareous Alps 970–971
  sea-level change 924, 931
Besançon Limestone 879
Beskydy Phase 1215
Betliar Phase 1213
Betlis Formation 968, *969*
Beutenaken Member *949*, 951
Białagóra Formation 183
Biebrza Complex 35
Biele Karpaty Unit 1191
Bielsko-Biała-Andrychów High 49, 51–52
Biely Váh succession 1207
Bierkowice Unit 691
Bihain Formation 213
Bílá Hora Formation *954*, 958
Bilshausen interglacial 1289–1290
Binic Formation 57
biostratigraphy
  Cambrian 172–174
  Carboniferous 416–417
  Cretaceous 924–925
  Jurassic
    northern Germany 843
    Poland 849–850, 854
  Neogene *1037*, 1042
  North Sea Basin 1036, *1037*
  Palaeocene, Polish Lowland Basin 1042, 1044
  Palaeogene *1037*
  Permian 535
  Triassic, German Basin 760–766
  Triassic–Jurassic boundary 826
BIRPS seismic project 331, **332**, 334, 335, 356, 357
Bischofalm facies 277, 279, 281–282
Biševo Island 1111
bismuth, resources **1346**, 1427
Bittesch Gneiss 144, 693
bivalves
  Cambrian 188
  Carboniferous 416
  Cretaceous, Danish Basin 937, 940
  Devonian 387
    Barrandian area 400
    eastern Rhenish Massif 393
    Saxo-Thuringian Zone 402, 403
  Jurassic
    Poland 850, 851
    southern Germany 865, 867, 868
  Ordovician, Bohemian Massif 227, 228
  Silurian
    Austria 276, 277, 279, 282
    Montagne Noire 284
    Perunica 258
    Prague Basin 272, 274, 276
    Proto-Alps Terrane 259
  Triassic 807
    Bundsandstein 775
    German Basin 771
Black Band Bed 938
Black Forest *459*, *607*, 1238, *1239*
  Cambrian 180
  Late Devonian–Early Carboniferous magmatism 711–712
  Ordovician 216
  Silurian, Saxo-Thuringian Zone 271
  Variscan batholith 425, 469–470
  Variscan orogeny 472–473
  Variscan tectonic evolution 606–611
black shale
  Carboniferous 411, 438
  Cretaceous 945
  Devonian 394, 403
  Jurassic, Posidonia 828, 837
  mineralization 1363–1364
  Ordovician 227
  Silurian 271, 274–275, 279, 284
  Zechstein 573
Blanice Graben 473, *475*
  Permian 562
Blankenburg Zone 634, *635*
Blanmont Formation *159*, 161
Blanowice Formation 849
Blansko Graben 890, 955
Blanzy-le Creusot Basin 556
Blatná Suite 715
Blattengrat Flysch 1150
Blätterton clays *934*, 936
Bleichenbach Formation 545
Blødoks Formation 937–938
Blovice Formation 73, 74, 138, 139
Blumenau Shear Zone 129
Boda Event 205
Boda Siltstone Formation *571*, 572
Bódva Nappe 804
Bódvaszilas Sandstone 803
Bohdalec Formation 228
Bohdasín Formation 581
Bohemia
  central and western
    basins 467–469
      Namurian–Westphalian magmatism 721
  Middle Cambrian, palaeontology 188, 190
  north, Jurassic 889–890
  north and east, Tournaisian sedimentation 473
  southwest Border Zone 1254
Bohemian Basin, Western and Central, coal 1388
  Cretaceous 953–959, 1254–1255
Bohemian Massif 121–146, *452*, *475*
  Cadomian basement 70, 121, *122*, 123–144, 146
  Cambrian 176–180
    biostratigraphy 176, 177
  Cambrian–Early Ordovician magmatism 674–675
  Cenozoic tectonism 1253–1255
  Cretaceous basins 930, 931, 953–964
  east, Precambrian 52–54
  faults 1254, 1255
  Jurassic 889–890
  magmatism 713–720

mineral deposits 1360–1361
northern margin, Cambrian 168–170
northern and western, Late Devonian–Early Carboniferous magmatism 716–718
Ordovician 206, 225–229
volcanism 228–229
Permian basins 559–563
Precambrian 60–79
Silurian 272–276
sulphide ores 1366
tectonomagmatic events **126**
uranium resources 1378
Variscan orogeny 121, 123, *615*
granitoids 469–470
volcanism 179–180
western margin, Cambrian 180
zircon dating 145
Bohemian Plateau, collapse 616, 617, 646–647
Bohemian Shear Zone 467
Variscan tectonics 614, 616
Bohemicum *see* Teplá-Barrandian Unit
Bohnertze 1244
Bohuslavice Formation 581
Bois Grand-Père Formation 286
Bolca, Palaeogene 1089
Bolków Unit 688
Bolland borehole 315
Böllstein Odenwald 161–162, 447, *448*, 630, 632
Late Ordovician–Silurian magmatism 697–698
Bolzano Volcanic Complex 553, 554–555, *555*
Bombaso Formation 479
Boreal Domain *see* Central European Basin System
Boreal Sea 573
Børglum Formation 836
Borinka Unit 1202
Bôrka Nappe 569–570
Bormes orthogneiss 60
Bornholm
Cretaceous 936, *938*, 939, 940
Jurassic 833, 835
Silurian, Baltica 267–268
Bornival Formation 209
Borucice Formation 849
Borzęta Formation 170
Boskovice Graben 473, *474*, *475*
Carboniferous–Permian, coal 1389
Permian 562–563, *562*
Bosmoreau Basin 484
Bosnia and Herzogovina, Cenozoic, Dinarides 1102–1106, 1111–1112
Boulonnais, Carboniferous sedimentation 436–437
boundaries, terrane and subterrane 357
Brabant Massif 313
Caledonian magmatism 324–5
Cambrian *159*, *160*, 161
Ordovician 207–210, *211*, *214*
seismic surveys 340
Silurian 284–287, *288*
Brabant Parautochthon 432, 637
brachiopods
Caledonides 307
Cambrian 188, 190, 192
Baltic Basin 182, 183, 184
Bohemian Massif 179
Brunovistulian Terrane 173
Franconian-Thuringian Slate Mountains 168
Saxo-Thuringian Zone 165
Carboniferous 416
Cretaceous 924–925
Danish Basin 937, 940
Devonian 386, 387, 388, 389, 390, 391
Barrandian area 400, 401
eastern Rhenish Massif 393
Saxo-Thuringian Zone 402, 403
southeastern Poland 396, 397
Jurassic
Bohemian Massif 890
Paris Basin 864
southern Germany 865, 867, 868, 869, 870
Ordovician *308*
Bohemian Massif 226–228
Condroz Inlier 212
Holy Cross Mountains 229, 233–234
Saxo-Thuringian Zone 219, 222, 223, 224, 225
Silurian *308*
Austria 276, 277, 279, 282
Franconian Terrane 269
Montagne Noire 284
Prague Basin 272
Triassic 807
German Basin 764
bradoriids, Middle Cambrian 188
Brandenburg, Weichselian Stage 1297, *1299*
Brandenburg-Wolsztyn-Pogorzela highs 542, *544*, 562
Branisko Mountains 1200
Branná Unit 501
Braszowice Gabbro, Cambrian–Early Ordovician magmatism 690
Braunau-Regensburg Basin, Cretaceous 963–964
Bray-Bouchy Fault 858, *859*
Breccia Nappe 1156–1157
Breeviertien Formation *838*, 839
oil 841
Breitenmatt Member *882*, 883
Bresse Graben *see* Rhône-Bresse Graben
Březno Formation *954*, 958
Briançonnais fragment 1143, 1145, 1155, 1156
Cretaceous, subduction 1172
nappes 1156–1157, 1158
Briançonnais High 873
Briançonnais terrane *1144*
Brioverian Supergroup 104–121
stratigraphy 117–118
Brisi Member *969*, 970
Bristol Channel-Bray Fault 627
Britain, Precambrian, East Avalonia 43, *44*, 45–46, *47*
British Caledonides 319, *320*, *321*
seismic surveys 333–337
Brittany, Armorican Massif 58, 114–116
Brno, Jurassic 890
Brno Batholith 144–145
Brno Massif 49, 54
Broad Fourteens Basin 837, *838*, 839, 841
Brocken Granite 47–48
Brodno Formation 970, *972*
Brökelschiefer cycle *575*, 580
Brongniart, Alexandre (1770–1847) 8
Brothers of Purity 3–4
Brotterode Formation 449–450, 710
Brotterode Group 629–630
Brtníky Formation 889
Bruche Unit 633
Brüggli Member *883*, 884
Brunhes-Matuyama palaeomagnetic boundary 1287, *1289*
Bruno-Silesia 311
Brunovistulian Terrane 123
Avalonia-type unit 145, 157, 311
Cadomian basement *143*, 144–145
Cambrian 170–172
tectonostratigraphy 171–172
isostopic data **124**
Peri-Gondwana 157, 258
Precambrian 49, 52, *53*, 54
Silurian 255
Brunovistulicum *see* Brunovistulian Terrane
Brusno Formation 567, 581
Brussel Sands 1040
Brûtia Formation 210, 286
Bryne Formation 835
bryozoans
Cretaceous, Danish Basin 940
Devonian 387
Ordovician
Bohemian Massif 226, 228
Saxothuringian Zone 223
Brzeziny-Zbrza area 231, *232*
Buchenstein Formation 797, 802
Bučina Formation 570
Bückeberg Formation *934*, 935
Buda Basin 1068, 1069, 1212, 1213
Budějovice Basin, Cretaceous 959
Buffon, Georges-Louis Leclerc, Compte de (1707–1788) 6
Bug Basin 260
Silurian 265

Bugliv Formation 1045
Bükk Mountains *571*, 572, 582–583, 802
Permian–Triassic boundary 751
Bükk Parautochthonous Unit 1211
Triassic basin evolution 802
Bükk Superunit 1211
Bükkfennsík Limestone 802
Bukówa Sandstone Formation 233–234
Bündnerschiefer 1173
Bunte Series 480
Buntsandstein Formation
Alpine 788, *789*
Denmark 784
German Basin 751, 761–763, 769–776
basin evolution 769–776
magnetostratigraphy 759
Netherlands 782
Switzerland 785
tectonism 753–754, 1013–1014
Upper Austro-Alpine tectonic units 580
Burgenland, Silurian 283
Burghorn Formation *887*, 888
Burgundy Gate 775, 776, 777, 1014
Burgundy Platform 885
Buridan, Jean (*c*.1328–1358) 4
Bystrica subunit 1191

Cabrières Klippes 283–284
Cadomia 25, 103, *106*, 123, 145
evolution 55
Cadomian
magmatic arc 62, 64, *65*, 68, 75, 125–137, 146, 668, 674
back-arc basin 125–127, *132*, 133, 135, *139*
passive margin shelf basin 131, 132–137, *134*
retro-arc basin 129, *132*, 133, 135, *140*
Cadomian basement, Bohemian Massif 70, 123–144, *132*
Cadomian Belt 55–60
Cadomian Orogeny 10, 49, 55, 58, 60, 103–147
definition 103
Cadomian unconformity 103, *105*, 123
Cahore Group 46
Calcaire à gryphées Formation 860
Calcareniti di Castelgomberto 1090
calcimicrobes, Lower Cambrian 188
Caldecote volcanics *44*, 45, 46
Caledonian deformation complex 342
Caledonian Deformation Front 28, 305, 316, 348, 352
seismic surveys 338–340, 342–343
Caledonian Orogeny 10, 13, 303–369, 667, 668
geodynamics 358–368
geophysical evidence 329–350, **332**
modelling 367–368
phases **306**
Caledonides 304–369
Belgian and Dutch, seismic surveys 340
evolution 304–329
granite 319–329
fossils 305, 307
potential field data 346–350
*see also* British Caledonides; North German Caledonides; Scandinavian Caledonides
Callovian
Bohemian Massif 889
Northern Calcareous Alps 895–896
northern Germany *844*, 845–846
Poland *853*, 854
southern Germany *866*, 868
southeast France 878–879
Swiss Jura *883*, 886
Western Carpathian basins 899
Cambrian 155–192
Alpine realm 187
Baltica margin 181–187
Black Forest 180
Bohemian Massif 168–170, 176–180
Brunovistulian Terrane 170–172
geochronology 192, **193**
Holy Cross Mountains 172–175
lithostratigraphic correlation *189*
Lublin-Podlasie Basin 185
magmatism 669–694
Mid-German Crystalline High 161–162
palaeogeography 155–158
palaeontology 187–192
Saxo-Thuringian Zone 162–170
sedimentation, Saxo-Thuringian Zone 136–137
stratigraphic division 155
tectonic evolution 155–158
Vosges 181
West–Central Europe 158–161
Cambrian–Ordovician boundary 155, 203–204, 234
Campanian
Danish Basin 938
Liège-Limburg Basin 949, 951
North German Basin *943*
inversion tectonics 946–948
sea-level change 924
Western Carpathians 978
Campine Basin 431–434
Carboniferous sedimentation 437
coal 1367
Permian 549–550
Canaveilles Group 59
Canavese Zone *1151*, 1158, 1165–1166
Canigou Massif 59
Caradoc
Brabant Massif 209
Condroz Inlier 212
East European Platform 236
Germany 215, 217, 218
Poland 231, 236
Schwarzberg Anticline 223
carbon cycle, global, Silurian 251
carbon dioxide
atmospheric
Carboniferous 412
Cretaceous 923
Jurassic 827–828
Permian 532
Silurian 249
Ohře Graben 1255
carbon isotopes, Silurian *250*, 251
carbonate compensation depth 1079
carbonate deposition
Carboniferous
Belgium and France 434–438
Kohlenkalk 421, 437, 438
Poland 441–442, *443*, *444*, 503–504
Rhenish Massif 438–441
Cenozoic, Adriatic carbonate platform 1106–1111
Devonian
Ardennes 388–391
Barrandian area 400–401
eastern Baltic 388
eastern Rhenish Massif 393–394
Eifel Mountains 393
Moravia 399
North Sea 386
Pomerania 387
southeastern Poland 396–397
Dolomites 1167
Jurassic
Austro-Alpine unit 894–896
Poland 848–849, 857
southeast France 876–879
Triassic
German Basin 772
Hungary 800–807
Netherlands 782
Northern Calcareous Alps 788–790
Southern Alps 796–798
Western Carpathians 799
Zechstein 576–583
Carboniferous 411–508
biostratigraphy 416–417
cyclothems 417, *444*
glaciation 412, 414, 416
magmatism 703–704, 707–720
magnetostratigraphy 417
mineralization 1367–1371
palaeoclimate 412, 414–416
palaeocontinental reconstruction *12*
palaeogeography 412, 420–424
palaeomagnetism 420
palaeontology 504–505
sea-level change 415–416
stratigraphic correlation *433*
stratigraphic division *414*
Central Europe *506*, *507*
terminology 416

tectonic setting 417–419
Upper–Lower Permian, mineralization 1387–1389
volcanism 427–428
*see also* Devonian–Carboniferous boundary
Carboniferous–Permian boundary 531
glaciation 532
magmatism 539, 1005
tectonism 1003, 1005–1011
Cardioceratidae 825
Cardiola Formation 277, 278, 279
Carnic Alps
alpine tectonics 1167
Carboniferous sedimentation 478–480, *506*
Devonian 405
Ordovician 236
Permian *552*, 553–554
Silurian 255, 258–259, 276, 277–282
Zechstein cycles 581
Carpathian Flysch Belt 1182–1183, 1189, 1190–1191
oil and gas 1424
Carpathian Foredeep 1189–1190
Cenozoic *1043*, 1064
Jurassic 851
Neogene
Czech Republic 1081–1083
Poland 1083–1084, *1085*
Western Ukraine 1086
Carpathian Foreland
Cenozoic, Poland, tectonic evolution 1258–1270
oil and gas 1424
Silurian 288
Carpathian Orogen 1189, 1190, 1198
Carpathian seaway 935
Carpathians
Cretaceous 964–967
Neogene basins *1061*, 1064–1078
Outer, Poland, Palaeogene 1078–1081
Western Ukraine, Neogene 1084–1086
*see also* Central Carpathian Palaeogene Basin; Western Carpathian Crystalline Zone;Western Carpathians
Cassian Dolomite 797–798
Catastrophism 7–9
Cejkov Formation 567
CELEBRATION seismic project 331, **332**, 345
Cellon section 276–279, *280*
Celtic Realm 883, *887*
Cenomanian
Bohemian Cretaceous Basin 955–957
Danish Basin 937, *938*, 940
Helvetic basins 974–975
Mid-Polish Trough 941–942
North German Basin 942, *943*, 944–945
North Sea 937
Outer Western Carpathians 974
sea-level change 924, *939*
Cenomanian–Turonian boundary event 956–957
Cenozoic 1031–1114
climate change 1031–1033
Dinarides 1102–1112
mineral resources 1400–1409
palaeocontinental reconstruction *15*
palaeogeography *1032*, 1033–1035
palaeomagnetism 1033, *1034*, 1035
*see also* Tertiary
Central Alpine Zone, Palaeogene 1058–1060
Central Atlantic Magmatic Province, volcanism 826, 828
Central Baltoscandian Confacies Belt 260
Central Basic Belt 144–145
Central Belarus Belt *34, 39*
Central Black Forest Gneiss Complex 472–473, *607*
Variscan tectonics 606–608, 609, *610*, 611
Central Bohemian Batholith 70, 72, 73, 74, 76, 425, 469–470, 713–715
Central Bohemian Shear Zone *613*, 616
Central Brittany Domain 58
Central Carpathian Palaeogene Basin 1208
Central European Basin System 999–1003
Carboniferous–Permian tectonics 1005–1011
Jurassic 825–826, *830*, 831, 832–890
Late Cretaceous 1023–1024
Central Gneiss Unit 449–450, 629, 630, 710
Late Devonian–Early Carboniferous magmatism 711, 712
Central Graben *1000*, 1001, 1002, 1003, 1016
Danish, Jurassic 836
sequence stratigraphy 829, *830*, 831
Dutch
Jurassic 837, *838*, 839, 841
oil and gas 841, 1420–1421
Permian 550, 782, *784*
Central Lithuanian Suture Zone 39, 40, 42
Central Moravian Block 54
Central Netherlands Basin *838*, 839
Central North Sea Dome 837, 840
Central Pangaean Mountain Range 538
Central Scandinavian Dolerite Group 34
Central Sudetes 499, 501
Variscan tectonics 624, 626
Central Sudetic Ophiolite 499, 624, 625
cephalopods
Devonian
Barrandian area 401
eastern Rhenish Massif 393, 394
Saxo-Thuringian Zone 403
southeastern Poland 397
Jurassic, southern Germany 867, 868, 869, 870
Ordovician, Bohemian Massif 227–228
Silurian, Prague Basin 272, 274
Triassic 807
Bundsandstein 775
ceratites, Triassic 760, *762*
Čerhov Formation 495
Cernochov Formation 581–582
Čertovica Fault 1200, 1204
Čertovo břemeno Suite 715
Cervinia terrane 1143, *1144*, 1169, 1172
České Středohoří Fault 1255
Cetic granitoids 425
Cévennes High 873
chalk 923
Danish Basin 937
North German Basin 948–949
Chalk Group, Danish Basin 937–940, *938*
chancelloriids, Lower Cambrian 188
Channel Islands 55–56
Charnian Supergroup *44*, 45, 46, *47*
charnockite, Lithuania 40
Cheb-Domažlice Graben 1255
Chemnitz, Petrified Forest 564
Chesselbach Flysch 1053
Chevlipont Formation 208, 210
Chiavenna ophiolite 1155, 1172
chitinozoans
Caledonides 307
Ordovician
Alps 236
Bohemian Massif 226, 227, 228
Brabant Massif 208, 209, 210
Condroz Inlier 211, 212
Germany 215, 217, 218
Silurian 251, *252*, 253
Austria 276, 279
Brabant Massif 285, 286
Condroz Inlier 287
Montagne Noire 284
Prague Basin 276
Proto-Alps Terrane 259
Chmielowa Formation 970, *972*
Chotěvice Formation 559–560
Christianity
age of Earth 4–5
early doctrine 3
chromium
resources **1346**, 1362, 1364–1365
Alpine domain ophiolite type 1399
Chumava-Baština Formation 177
Chvaletice Group 72
Ciechanow Complex 35
Ciechocinek Formation 849
Čierna Hora Mountains 1200
Čierny Váh succession 1207
Cimes-Blanches Nappe *1152*, 1157–1159
Cimmerian Orogeny 1005, 1014

Cimmerian terranes, Permian–Triassic 1012, 1014
Cimmerian unconformity 433, 877
Cínovec granite 722–723
Cipit Boulders 797
circulation, oceanic
Carboniferous 414
Devonian 385
North Atlantic 17
Ordovician 204
Silurian 251
Circum-Fennosarmatian Caledonides 186
Clanzschwitz Group 62, 131, 133
clay, Eocene, North Sea Basin 1036, 1039
Clay Deep Member *838*, 840, 841
clay minerals, resources 1402, 1404–1405
climate change
anthropogenic 15–17
Cenozoic 1031–1033
forecasting 17
Jurassic 827–829
Lower Pleistocene 1288
Middle Pleistocene 1292–1293
north–central Europe, Pleistocene, fluvial record 1310–1315
Palaeogene 14
Upper Pleistocene 1294–1295, 1297
coal 412
Boskovice Graben 1389
Campine Basin 1367
Döhlen Basin 563
Erzgebirge Basin 466
Intra-Sudetic Basin 499
Lower Silesian Basin 1388
Lublin Basin 1371
Massif Central 1388
mining 1367
Northwest European Cenozoic Basin 1406–1407
paralic
Mecsek Basin 1397
Variscan Belt 421, 429, 431, 433–434
Campine Basin 437
Lublin-Lvov Basin 442
Ruhr Basin 438–439
Upper Silesian Basin 503–504
Wallonian Basin 437–438
production **1342**
Radnice Group 468
resources **1358**, 1367–1371
Carboniferous 1387–1389
Cenozoic basins 1406–1409
Cretaceous 1400
Jurassic 1397
Ruhr Basin 1367–1370
Saar-Lorraine Basin 1387–1388
Slaný Formation 469
Tŕňa Formation 495
Upper Silesian Basin 1370–1371
Variscan Foreland 1367–1371
Wallonian Basin 1367
Western and Central Bohemian Basin 1388
Zone Houillère 1388
Zwickau-Oelsnitz district 1388
Coal Measures Group 433–434, 438
cobalt, resources **1346**, 1427
coccoliths, Jurassic, southern Germany 867
Coedana Complex 46, *47*
Coevorden Formation *838*, 840, 841
petroleum 841
Col di Foglia Formation 237
Colibeau Formation 287
collapse, orogenic 616, 617, 646–647, 721
Collio Basin 1166
Columbia supercontinent *22*, 23
compression
Austro-Alpine units 1169–70
Late Cretaceous 1024–1025
Precambrian, southern Sweden 33–34
Conchodon Dolomite 798, 826
conchostracans, Devonian 388
Condroz Group 391
Condroz Inlier 207, 210–212, *214*, 313, 315
Silurian 285, 287, *288*
Condroz sedimentation area 434
confacies belts 260
Coniacian
Bohemian Cretaceous Basin 958
GSSP 924–925
Mid-Polish Trough 942
North German Basin *943*
inversion tectonics 946–948
sea-level change 924
Western Carpathians 978
conodonts
Caledonides 307
Cambrian, Baltic Basin 184
Cambrian–Ordovician boundary 204
Carboniferous 411, 416
Devonian 383, 387, 388, 389
Saxo-Thuringian Zone 402, 403
South European terranes 404
southeastern Poland 396, 397
Ordovician
Alps 236
Ardennes inliers 213
Bohemian Massif 226
Poland 230, 231, 233–234, 236, *235*
Saxothuringian Zone 219, 223
Permian 531, 535
Silurian 251, *252*, 253
Austria 276, 277–278, 279, *280*, 282–283
Montagne Noire 284, *285*
Poland *264*
Prague Basin 276
Triassic
German Basin 760, 764
Northern Calcareous Alps 788, 790
continental crust, formation, Precambrian 21, *22*
continents, early assemblages, Proterozoic *22*, 23, 26
conulariids, Ordovician, Bohemian Massif 227–228
COOLE seismic survey 337
copper
production **1342**
resources
Alpine domain metamorphogenic 1410–1411
Alpine domain ophiolite type 1399
arc-related 1402–1404
disseminated 1375–1376
embryonic ophiolite type 1395
granite-related 1414
polymetallic Kupferschiefer type 1390–1391
polymetallic red-bed type 1389–1390, 1392
porphyry type 1366–1367, 1402–1404
red-bed type 1390
rift-related 1392, 1393–1394
vein-type 1371–1372, 1377, 1382, 1383
copper sulphide, resources **1346**, **1349–1351**, *1359*, 1362
Rammelsberg type 1365–1366
VMS type 1363
VMS, SMS, Kieslager type 1360
corals
Carboniferous 416
Devonian 386, 387, 389, 390, 391
Barrandian area 400
eastern Rhenish Massif 393, 394
Moravia 399
Saxo-Thuringian Zone 402, 403
southeastern Poland 396, 397
Jurassic
Paris Basin 864
Poland 857
southern Germany 867, 868, 869, 871, 872
Ordovician, Saxo-Thuringian Zone 223
Silurian 251
Austria 277, 282
Proto-Alps Terrane 259
Triassic 807
Triassic–Jurassic boundary 894
Coronaten Bench 845
Corroy Formation 286
Corsica 60
Cossato-Mergozzo-Brissago Shear Zone 1166
Costatenkalk Member 865, *866*
Courtemautruy Bed 881, *882*
Couvin Formation 390
Creationism 4

Cressim antiform 1175
Cretaceous 923–980, *926*
  Alps 964–978
  Base Cretaceous Unconformity 1003
  biostratigraphy 924–925
  Bohemian Massif basins 930, 931, 953–964
  Carpathians 964–967
  Danish Basin 928, 937–940
  Early, tectonism 1019–1021
  Late, tectonism 1021–1025
  Liège-Limburg Basin 930, 949–953
  Lower Saxony Basin 929, 934–936
  Mid-Polish Anticlinorium 927–928
  Mid-Polish Trough 927, 931–934, 940–942
  mineral resources 1399–1400
  North German Basin 929–930, 942–949
    inversion tectonics 946–949
  palaeoceanography 923–924
  palaeoclimate 923–924
  palaeogeography *924*, 930–931, *941*
  sea-level change 923, 924, 935–936, *1022*
    Bohemian Cretaceous Basin 953, 955–958
  sequence stratigraphy 925
  tectonics 925–927, 1019–1025
    Alps 1170–1173
    Western Carpathians 1214–1215
Cretaceous–Palaeogene boundary 1040, 1092
  Gosau Group 978
  north Dinarides 1103
  Slovenian Tethys basins 1094, 1097
crinoids
  Devonian 386, 387, 388, 391
    Barrandian area 400, 402
    eastern Rhenish Massif 393, 394
    southeastern Poland 397
  Jurassic
    Paris Basin 864
    southern Germany 865
  Silurian
    Austria 277, 282
    Bohemia 272, 274, 276
    Montagne Noire 284
  Triassic 807
    Bundsandstein 775
Črmel' Formation 494, 495
Črmel' Unit 1204
Croatia, Cenozoic
  Dinarides 1102–1106
  volcanism 1105–1106
Cromerian Complex Stage 1289–1290
  mammals 1300
crustaceans, Jurassic, Paris Basin 864
Cserd Conglomerate Formation *571*, 572, 583
Csővár Limestone 802
Csukma Dolomite 805, *806*
Culm facies 421, 442, 473
  Moravo-Silesian Fold-and-Thrust Belt 640–641, *642*
Culm Basin *500*, *502*, 705
Cuvier, Georges (1769–1832) 8
cyanobacteria, Lower Cambrian 164, 188
cyclicity
  Carboniferous 416–417
  Cretaceous 925
  Jurassic 823, 829, 832, 876–879
  Zechstein 532, 535, 572–580
cyclostratigraphy
  Jurassic, Western Carpathian Basins 898–900
  Permian 535, 554
  Triassic 752–753, 760, 766–767, 769, 772
    Switzerland 786–788
cyclothems 417, 433, *444*
  Auernig Group 479, *480*
  Třňa Formation 495
  Zechstein 572–580
*Cyrtograptus* Shales Formation 267–268
Czech Republic
  Carboniferous sedimentary basins 473
  Carpathian Foredeep, Neogene 1081–1083
  Jurassic 889–890
  Ordovician 225–229
  Permian basins 559–563
  Zechstein 581
Czempin Formation 1044
Czertezik succession 1193
Czorsztyn Ridge 898, 970, 978, *1194*, *1195*, 1198
Czorsztyn Succession 898
Czorsztyn Unit 1193

Dachsbusch volcano *1328*
Dachstein Formation 1162
  Triassic *789*, 790, 798, 799
  Triassic–Jurassic boundary 826, 827, 894
Dachstein Nappe 1169
dacryoconarids, Devonian
  Barrandian area 400
  eastern Rhenish Massif 393
  Moravia 398
  southeastern Poland 396
Dalmatia
  central and southern 1110–1111
  northern, Cenozoic 1110
Damasławek salt diapir 1263
Danish Basin
  Cretaceous 928, 937–940
  Jurassic 833, 835–836
    sequence stratigraphy 829, *830*, 832
Danube Basin, Neogene 1065–1066, 1213
Danube Fault 1254
Dauphiné Basin 873, 878
Dauphiné High 873
Dauphinois Zone 1146, *1147*
Dava Fault 1111
Dave Formation 287
Davle Formation 72, 74, 138, 139
Dębki Formation 183
Deckenschotter 1305–1306
Deerlijk Formation 285
DEKORP-BASIN seismic project 331, **332**, 340, 342, 343, 347, 356, 357, *1007*
Delfland Subgroup 839
Delitsch-Torgau-Doberlug Syncline 162, 163–165, *166*
  Lower Cambrian, palaeontology 188
  Middle Cambrian, palaeontology 190
Delitzsch Formation 165
Deluc, Jean-André (1727–1817) 8
Denmark
  Jurassic 832–836
    palaeogeography 832
    rifting 836
    sea-level change 832, 833–836
    sequence stratigraphy 829, *830*, 831–832
    uplift 835
  Rotliegend 550
  southern, Triassic, basin evolution 784
  *see also* Danish Basin
Dent Blanche Nappe *1151*, 1157–1159, 1173
Dentalienton Formation *866*, 868
Descartes, René (1596–1650) 5
Desná Dome 501
Dessau area, Late Devonian–Early Carboniferous 710–711
Detfurth Sandstone 772, 782
Dethlingen Formation *542*, 545, *546*
Deutenhausen Formation 1056
Deville Group 158, *159*
Devín Phase 1214
Devonian 383–406
  depositional environments 388–406
  magmatism 699–720
  ocean circulation 385
  palaeocontinental reconstruction *12*
  palaeogeography 383–384
  sea-level change 384–385
  stratigraphical subdivision 383
  timescale *384*
  *see also* Silurian–Devonian boundary
Devonian–Carboniferous, mineralization 1364–1367
Devonian–Carboniferous boundary 411–412, 438, 496
Diablerets Nappe 1148, *1149*
diamictite, Saxo-Thuringian Zone 62
diamond, Erzgebirge 121
Dianric Thrust 1093
diapirism, salt 572, 937, *1002*, 1003, 1016, 1391

diatomite
  resources
    Cenozoic basins 1406
    Quaternary 1410
Dietfurt Formation *866*, 870
Dill Basin, Carboniferous magmatism 703, *705*
Dill Syncline, Silurian, Franconian Terrane 269
Dimon Formation 478
Dinant Synclinorium
  Carboniferous sedimentation 434
  Devonian 389, 390–391
Dinantian 416, 505, 508
  sedimentation
    Belgium 431–437
    Boulonnais 437
Dinaric Foreland, coal 1408
Dinaric Platform 1093
Dinaric Thrust 1106–1111
Dinaricum 1093, 1094
Dinarides
  Cenozoic 1093, 1102–1112
    Bosnia and Herzogovina 1111–1112
    Croatia and north Bosnia 1102–1105
    eastern Adriatic coast 1106–1111
    Neogene, intramontane basins 1105, *1106*, 1112
    volcanism 1105–1106
  Inner, Cenozoic, Palaeogene 1112
  Outer, Cenozoic 1106–1111
    Palaeogene 1111–1112
    palaeomagnetism 1108
    sedimentation and stratigraphy 1108–1111
Dinnyés Dolomite Formation *571*, 582
dinoflagellate cysts
  Cretaceous 925
  Jurassic
    Netherlands 841
    Paris Basin 864
    Poland 849, 851, 856
dinosaur footprints
  Cretaceous, Lower Saxony Basin 935
  Jurassic
    Germany 846
    Poland 850
Diodorus Siculus (*c.* 44 BC) 3
Diphyoides Formation 968, *969*
Döbra Formation 225
Dobra orthogneiss 78, 144, 145, 693
  age 612
Dobříš conglomerates 74–75
Dobromierz Unit 688
Dobrotivá Formation 227
Dobrudza Foredeep 852, 854
Dogger Group 842
Döhlen Basin 563, *564*
  Stephanian–Early Permian magmatism 730
Döhlen Formation 563
Dolomia Principale *see* Hauptdolomit Formation
Dolomit-Kieselschiefer-Komplex 282
dolomite
  Hungary 800, 802, 805
  Keuper 766–767
Dolomites
  Permian 554–555
    Zechstein 581
  tectonics 1167, 1180
  Triassic 794–798
Dolsk Formation 540
Dölzschen Formation *954*, 956
Domažlice crystalline complex 143, 180, 614, 675
doming, thermal, North Sea 1017
Dömnitz warm stage 1292–1293
Donderslag Fault 437
Donovaly Phase 1215
Dora-Maira Nappe 1150, *1151*, 1152, 1157
Dorog Basin *1069*
Doubice Formation 889–90
Dowsing-South Hewett Fault Zone *352*
  as terrane boundary 357
Drahany Basin 502
Drahany Uplands *500*, 502
Drau Range, Permian 551, *552*, 553
Drauzug-Gurktal Nappe System *1161*, 1165, 1170
Drava Basin 1072–1073
Drenthe Formation 1293
Drietoma Unit 1196, 1206
Drosendorf Assemblage 470
  mineral resources 1358, 1359, 1360
Drusberg Formation *969*, 970
Drzewica Formation 849
Dubrau Formation 224
Düdelsheim Formation 545
Dukla Basin, Palaeogene 1078–1081
Dukla Unit 1191
Dult Formation 476
Dümpel Maar Tephra 1327–1329
dykes
  lamprophyre, Variscan Orogeny 424
  mafic, Fennoscandia 29, 33, 34
  porphyritic, Altenberg-Teplice Caldera 722

Earth
  age of, early ideas 4–5
  formation 21
  history, early ideas 5–6
earthquakes
  Lower Rhine Basin 1241
  North German Basin 1275
  Ohře Graben 1255
  Poland *1271*
  Rhenish Massif 1243
  South German Triangle 1245–1246, *1247*, *1248*
  Upper Rhine Graben 1240
East Antarctic Icesheet 1033
East Brandenburg High 936
East Carpathian Gate 771, 772, 775–776, 777, 847, 1014
East Eifel volcanic field 1323–1327
East European Craton 34–38, *34*
  gravity modelling 347
  magnetic field data 347, *351*
  seismic surveys 343, 345–346
  Silurian 256, 259
East European Platform *2*, 9, 1258, 1262
  Cambrian *186*
  Jurassic 855, 856, 857–858
  Ordovician *229*, *232*, 236
  Silurian 259, 266, 267
East Karkonosze Complex, Cambrian–Early Ordovician magmatism 685–687
East Lithuanian Domain *34*, 36, 38–43, *39*
East Slovak Basin
  Neogene 1066–1068
    sedimentation and stratigraphy 1067
    tectonics 1066–1067
    volcanism 1068
East Sudetes 496, 501–504, 624
East Sudetic Nappe Complex 626
East Thuringia, Devonian 403
Eastern Avalonia Terranes *2*
Eastern Carpathian Flysch Belt 1182–1183
Eastern Fore-Sudetic Basin 562
Eastern Gneiss Region *30*, 32, 33
Eau Noire Formation 389–390
Ebbe Anticline *214*, 215, 315
Eberstadt-Roßdorf Schist Zone *631*, 632
Ebtalschiefergebirge *134*
Eburnian Orogeny *see* West Africa Craton
echinoderms
  Cambrian
    Bohemian Massif 179
    Brunovistulian Zone 173
  Jurassic
    Bohemian Massif 890
    southern Germany 865, 868, 869
  Lower Cambrian 188
  Middle Cambrian 190
  Ordovician, Bohemian Massif 227–228
  Silurian 282
  Triassic, German Basin 764
echinoids
  Jurassic
    Bohemian Massif 890
    Paris Basin 864
Eckergneiss Complex 46–48, *49*, 633
eclogite
  Eo-Alpine 1170–1171
  Erzgebirge Crystalline Complex 451, 454, 669

Massif Central 483
Moldanubicum 75, 78
Münchberg Complex 671–672
Sub-Penninic nappes 1150, 1152, 1154
Eclogite Zone 1154, 1176
economic geology 1430–1431
Edegem Sands 1041
Ediacaran
Armorican Massif 58
biota 24, 46, 74, 81
Poland 52, 182, 184
reconstruction *11*
Saxo-Thuringian Zone 62, *64*, *65*, 129, 131, *137*
Teplá-Barrandian Unit 70–75
Ediacaran–Cambrian boundary 25
edrioasteroids, Middle Cambrian 190
Eemian Interglacial Stage 1294–1295, *1298*, *1299*, *1300*
Effingen Formation 886
Eger Graben *see* Ohře Graben
Egerian, Paratethys basins 1100
Eggenburnian, Paratethys basins 1100
Eggenfeld section 282
EGT seismic project **332**, 340
Eichberg Formation 224, *866*, 867
Eifel, Holocene 1298, *1302*
Eifel Mountains, Devonian 391, 393
Eifel plume 1243, 1321, *1325*
Eifel volcanic fields 1318–1333
East 1323–1327
West 1321–1323
Eifelian
Barrandian area 401
Belgium 389–390
eastern Rhenish Massif 393
Eifel Mountains 393
Moravia 399
Saxo-Thuringian Zone 403
southeastern Poland 396
Eisenach Basin 547, *548*
Eisenstadt-Sopron (Sub-)Basin 1063
Ekofisk Formation 937, *938*
Elbe Fault Zone 131, 133, *141*, 357, 496, *1002*, 1003
Cambrian 169–170, **193**
Devonian magmatism 699–700
isotopic data **125**
Ordovician 219, 224
Elbe Line 305, 316, 340, 341, 352
as terrane boundary 357, 343
Elbe Subgroup 545
Elbe Valley
Devonian 403
Elsterian glaciation 1290
Elbe Valley Slate Belt 699
Elbtalschiefergebirge *see* Elbe Valley Slate Belt
elevator tectonics, Teplá-Barrandian Unit 614, 616
Elsterian Glacial Stage 1290–1291, *1292*, *1295*, *1298*
Elterhof Formation 162, 449, 630, *631*
Ems Low 550, 782
Emscher Formation 947
Emsian
Barrandian area 401
eastern Rhenish Massif 393
Harz Mountains 394
Moravia 398–399
southeastern Poland 395
Engadine Fault 1175, 1176
Engadine Window 1143, *1144*, 1155, 1156, 1176
Lower 893
Engestieg Fault 450, 547
Entlebuch Basin 485–486
Eo-Alpine tectonics 968, 975, 1160, 1163, 1165, 1170–1171
Eocene
Central Alpine Zone 1060
climate 1031–1032
North Sea Basin 1036, *1037*, 1039–1040
palaeogeography *1032*
Upper Rhine Graben 1045, 1047
eocrinoids, Middle Cambrian 190
Epi-Palaeozoic Platform 1258
Epiadriaticum 1093, 1094
epithermal mineral deposits 1402–1404
Eratosthenes (*c*.276–194 BC) 3
Erbendorf-Vohenstrauss Zone 180
Cambrian–Early Ordovician magmatism 679–681
Ercall Granophyre 45, 46, *47*
Eridanos river system 1041
Erlachgraben Formation 476
Erlimoos Bed *882*, 883
Erquy Mafic Volcanic Formation 57, 113
Err Nappe 1166
Erzgebirge 62, *63*, 65–66, *141*
Cambrian 169, **193**, *331*
Cambrian–Early Ordovician magmatism 669–670
Late Devonian–Early Carboniferous magmatism 716–718, *719*
magmatism 328–329
metamorphism *330*, *331*
Ordovician 219, *331*
Silurian 270
uranium resources 1377
Erzgebirge Basin
Carboniferous sedimentation 465–466, *506*
Permian 564, *565*
Erzgebirge Block
isotopic data **125**
Variscan nappe pile 137
Erzgebirge Crystalline Complex 451, *452*, 453–455, 621–622
Erzgebirge granites 718
Erzgebirge granitoids 454–455
Esino Formation 796, 797
Estherienschiefer 787
EUGEMI seismic project **332**, 337, 339, 350, 358
EUGENO-S seismic project **332**, 337, 339, 350, *355*, 358
Euramerica *see* Laurussia
European Cenozoic Rift System 1262
European Geotraverse, geothermal modelling 349, *354*
European margin, Cretaceous tectonics 1172–1173
European Plate, Cenozoic 1035
eurypterids
Devonian
eastern Rhenish Massif 393
southeastern Poland 395
evaporites
Northeast German Basin 545
production **1342**
resources **1356–1357**
alkaline 1401–1402
sabkha-type 1392–1393
Zechstein 1391
Triassic
German Basin 775–776, 777, 778, 1016
Hungary 805
Netherlands 782–783
Switzerland 786, 787
Zechstein 572–580, 582, 999, 1001, *1002*
extension
Precambrian, southern Sweden 33–34
Tertiary, Central Alps 1173–1175
Exter Formation 766
External Domain 482
External Massifs 187, 1145–1148
External Thrust Belt 33
Externides, Variscan 602–603, 633–636, 639–644
extinction
Devonian–Carboniferous boundary 411–412
Frasnian 383
Permian–Triassic boundary 583, 749, 751, 807
Pliocene–Pleistocene boundary 1287
Silurian 251, 289
Triassic–Jurassic boundary 826–827
*see also* Cretaceous–Palaeogene boundary

Fackelgraben Member 1051
Falgairas Formation 284
Falknis Nappe 1156
Fallais Formation 286
Fammenian
Belgium 391
eastern Rhenish Massif 394

Moravia 399
Saxo-Thuringian Zone 402, 403
southeastern Poland 396–397
Farsund Formation 836
Fasiswald Member 881, *882*
FAST seismic profile 337
Fatra Formation 827
Fatric Superunit 1199
tectonics 1204–1206
Fatric Zone, Cretaceous 974
Fatricum *568*, 897, *1186*
faults
Bohemian Massif 1254, 1255
and Caledonian granite emplacement 321, 323
Eocene–Miocene, Polish Carpathian Foreland 1261–1265
Quaternary, Poland 1267–1270
South German Triangle 1246–1249
Variscan Orogeny 419
fauna
Carboniferous 505
Jurassic 833
Fauquez Formation 209
Fayaux Flysch 1053
Feldberg Nappe 606–608
feldspar, resources, pegmatites **1342**, 1375, 1378, 1414
Felsenkalk Formation *866*, 870–871
Felsőtárkány Limestone 802
FENNOLORA seismic project 337, 358
Fennoscandia
geochronology 29–30
Precambrian
southern
Baltic Sea 43
Lithuania 38–43
northeast Poland 34–38
southwestern 28–34
tectonic provinces *30*
Fennoscandian Border Zone 358
Fernschub hypothesis 1235, 1237
Ferdynandovian interglacial 1290
Ferques Unit 437
Fichtelgebirge *63*
Cambrian 168–169
magmatism *325*, 326
Cambrian–Ordovician 669- 670, *671*
Devonian–Carboniferous 716–718, *719*
Ordovician 219, 224
uranium resources 1377, 1378
Fichtelgebirge Crystalline Complex 455–456, *457*
Fil'akovo-Pétervášára Basin 1068, 1069–1070
Findenig facies 277, 279
Finefrau Nebenbank 434
Fischschiefer *934*, 936
fish
Devonian 388, 389
eastern Rhenish Massif 393
southeastern Poland 395
Jurassic, southern Germany 867
Triassic 807–808
Fjerritslev Formation 835
Flammenmergel 945
Flandrian *see* Holocene
Flannan Fault, reflector 335, 336
Flasergranitoid Zone 447–448
Flechtingen High 936
Flechtingen Horst 441
Flechtingen Volcanic Complex *724*, 726
flint line, Elsterian 1290
flora *see* plants
fluorite, resources **1342**, 1382–1384
granite-related 1414
vein-type 1418
fluvial sediment, Pleistocene 1310–1315
flysch
Austria *1046*
definition 1052–1053
Switzerland *1046*, *1049*, 1051–1053
Szolnok Basin 1074–1075
flysch nappes, Piedmont–Ligurian 1158
Flysch Zone, Dalmatia 1111
Flyvbjerg Formation 836
Fődolomit Formation 802
Foederata Unit 1203
Fohnsdorf Basin, Neogene 1064
Folded Jura 880, 881, *882*, 883, 886, 888, 1176
Triassic sediments 785
Folded Molasse 1178
foraminifera
Carboniferous 416
Cretaceous 925, 935
Danish Basin 940
Gosau Group 978
Helvetic basins 975
Devonian, Saxo-Thuringian Zone 402
Jurassic
Bohemian Massif 890
northern Germany 843
Paris Basin 861
Poland 850
southern Germany 867, 868, 869, 870–1
Middle Cambrian 190
Neogene, Istria 1108–1109
Silurian 276, 282
Triassic 807
German Basin 771, 772
Forcola Fault 1175, 1176
Foreland Molasse 1176, 1178
Fosses Formation 212
Fougères Unit *56*, 57, 115, *117*
France
northern, Carboniferous, sedimentation and magmatism 431–438, *506*
Permian basins 555–557
Precambrian 55–59
southeast basin and Jura
Jurassic 873–880, *874*, *875*
palaeogeography 880
Jurassic–Cretaceous boundary 876
Franconia
Ordovician 224–225
Silurian 254, 257, 268–269
Franconian Alb 864, 865, *866*, 870
Franconian Fault 1254
Franconian Fault System 547
Franconian Forest
Cambrian 167–168, *189*
Middle Cambrian, palaeontology 188, 190
Ordovician 219, 224
Frankenberg, Ordovician *221*, 224
Frankenberg nappes 457, 463
Devonian 403
Frankenberg Zwischengebirge nappes 62, 66
Frankenstein Gabbro Complex 447–448, 632
Late Devonian–Early Carboniferous magmatism 708, 709
Frankenwald *see* Franconian Forest
Frasnian
Belgium 390
biodiversity crisis 383
eastern Rhenish Massif 394
Eifel Mountains 393
Moravia 399
Saxo-Thuringian Zone 403
southeastern Poland 396–397
Frauenbach Group 220, 222
Frauengrube Member 1051
Frederikshavn Formation 836
Freiberg anticline *453*
Freiberg Felsite Horizon 1362
Fresnaye Shear Zone *107*, 115, 116, 121
Freudenstadt Graben 1248, 1249, *1250*
seismicity 1246
Frick Member 881, *882*
Friese Front Formation *838*, 839, 840, 841
Friesland cycle 572, *575*
Friuli Carbonate Platform 1092–1093
Friuli-Venezia-Giulia, Palaeogene 1092–1093
Frohnberg Formation 127, *128*, 129, 131, *132*, 135–136
Fuchsberg Formation 548
Füchsel, Georg Christian (1722–1773) 6
Fuhne Cold Stage 1293
Fur Formation 1036
Füred Limestone 802
Furongian
Ardennes 158, 161
Baltic Basin 182, 184, 192
Brunovistulian Terrane 170
Holy Cross Mountains 172, *173*, 174, *175*
palaeontology 191, 192

Rügen 186
volcanic complexes, Bohemian Massif 179–180
fusilinids, Permian 531

gabbro, corona 689
Gächlingen Bed 881, *882*
Gackowa Formation 688
Galgeløkke Member 834
Galgenberg Formation 168
Gänserndorf Formation 1062
Gansingen Dolomite 788
Gardelegen Fault, seismic surveys 340–341
garnet, Moldanubicum 75, 78
garnierite 1417
gas
Alpine Foreland Basin *1422*, 1423–1424
Carpathian Flysch Belt 1424
Carpathian Foreland 1424
Netherlands 841
Pannonian Basin 1426
Po Basin *1422*, 1425
production **1342, 1344**
resources **1344**
Southern Permian Basin 1419–1420
Vienna Basin *1422*, 1424–1425
gas hydrate
Jurassic 828, 835
Palaeogene 14
gas reservoirs
Campine Basin 437
Zechstein 573
Gassum Formation 833, 835
gastropods
Cretaceous, Danish Basin 940
Devonian 387
Barrandian area 400
Jurassic
Paris Basin 864
southern Germany 865, 867, 868, 869
Ordovician, Bohemian Massif 228
Silurian, Austria 277
Triassic 775, 807
gateways, marine
Tethys 771, 775–776, 777, 936, 1014
migration pathways 807
Gaudernbach Beds 634
Gauss-Matuyama palaeomagnetic chron 1287, *1289*
Gehren Subgroup 547, *548*
Geier Series *893*, 894
Geiselbach Formation 630
Geiseltal Lignite District 1040
Gemer Sub-belt 1201
Gemeric Superunit 1201
tectonics 1204, *1209*
Gemericum 897
northern *see* Northern Gemeric Unit
southern *see* Southern Gemeric Unit
sulphide ores 1366
Gemsmättli Bed 968, *969*
gemstones, resources, placer deposits 1410
Génicot Formation 212
geochemistry, Jurassic, Paris Basin 864
geochronology
Cambrian 192, **193**
Fennoscandia 29–30
Ordovician, Saxothuringian Zone 219
geophysics
potential field data
Caledonian terranes 346–350
northern Variscides 603–606
geothermal data, Europe 348–350, *353*, *354*
German Basin
Buntsandstein Formation, basin evolution 769–781
Zechstein *574*
Germanic Basin
Permian–Triassic boundary 751
Triassic
palynomorphs 760, *761*
stratigraphy/biostratigraphy 760–769
tectonics 753–756
Germany
Central
Pleistocene 1291–1293, *1294, 1299*
tectonics 1255–1258
fluorite–barite deposits 1382
northern
Jurassic 842–846
Middle Pleistocene 1289–1294, *1295*, *1297*
Upper Pleistocene 1295, 1297
*see also* North German Basin
Ordovician 214–225
Permian basins 563–564
Silurian, Baltica 268
South German Triangle, Cenozoic tectonics 1243–1253
southern, Jurassic 864–873
Zechstein *574*, *575*
Gesner, Conrad (1516–1565) 4
Gföhl Unit 75, 77–78, 426, 470, 480, 612, 693, 1358
Gielniów Formation 849
Gieselbach Formation 449, *631*
Giessen Nappes 316, *441*, 704, *705*
Giessen-Harz Nappe 439, *440*, *441*, *442*, 633, 635–6
Giessener Grauwacke 215, 704
Gießhübl Sycline 1058–1059
Gifhorn Trough 1256
Jurassic 842–843, 845
Gigaskalk Formation 846
Gipf Bed *882*, 883
Gipskeuper Formation 754, *755*, 778–780, 787
evaporites 1393
Giudicarie Fault 1172, 1180
Givetian
Belgium 390
eastern Rhenish Massif 393
Eifel Mountains 393
Harz Mountains 394
Moravia 399
Saxo-Thuringian Zone 403
southeastern Poland 396
glaciation
Alps 1304–1310
Carboniferous 412, 414, 416, 532
Elsterian 1290
Eocene–Oligocene 1032
Gaskiers 24
Hirnantian 249, 262, 289
Last Glacial Maximum 1304–1305, *1306*, 1308–1309
Last Glaciation 1304–1305, 1308
Marinoan 24
Miocene 1033
Most Extensive Glaciation 1308
Odra 1291, 1293
Ordovician 204, 249, 599
Plio-Pleistocene 14, 1033, 1042, 1287–1310
Precambrian *22*, 24
Proterozoic 24
Quaternary 1287–1310
Saalian 1291, 1292–1294
Sanian 1291
Sturtian 24
Weichselian 1295, 1297–1298
Glarner Verrucano Basin 487
Glarus Nappe 1148, *1149*
Glarus Permo-Carboniferous Basin *491*
Glarus Thrust 1148, *1149*, 1150, 1175
Glauconitsandmergel Member *866*, 868, 869
Glees Tephra *1326*, 1327, *1328*
Glemmtal Unit 282
Devonian 403
Glockner Nappe System 1155
Tauern Window *1153*, 1159
Glückstadt Graben 782, *784*, *1000*, 1001, 1003, *1009*, 1013, 1016
gneiss
Central Black Forest Gneiss Complex 472–473
East Sudetes 501
Erzgebirge Crystalline Complex 451, 453–454, 669–670
Fichtelgebirge Crystalline Complex 455–456, 669
Góry Sowie Complex 689
granite, Icart 106, *108*, *109, 112,* 120
Massif Central 483
Mid-German Crystalline Zone 67, 449, 450, 627–630
Moldanubian Zone 144, 611–614

Moldanubicum 78, 79
Tauern Window 481–482
Goczałkowice Formation 170, *171*
gold
production **1342**
resources **1348–1349**, 1362, 1363
Alpine type mesothermal veins 1412–1413
arc-related 1402–1404
granite-related 1414
palaeoplacer deposits 1389
placer deposits 1410
vein-type 1373 1375, 1380
Goldisthal Formation 220
Goldlauter Formation 547, *548*
Göller Nappe 1168
Gondwana 10, 14, *22*, 23, 307
apparent polar wander path 420
Cadomian Orogeny 103, *104*
Cambrian 155–156
Carboniferous 411, 419
palaeogeography 420–424
convergence with Laurussia *412*, 420–424, 536, 538, 599, *600*, 645
Devonian 383
fossils 307, *308*
northern, Silurian 254–255, 257, 258
Ordovician 204–206
palaeogeography *11*, *12*, 26, *27*, *30*, *318*
separation from Laurussia 1016
Silurian, palaeogeography 256
goniatites, Carboniferous 416
Gorleben sequence *1292*
Middle Pleistocene palynology 1289–1290
Görlitz Slate Belt 498, 625
Görlitz Syncline 162
Lower Cambrian, palaeontology 188
Görlitz-Kaczawa Unit 402
Görlitzer Schiefergebirge 271
Góry Sowie Complex, Cambrian–Early Ordovician magmatism 689–690
Góry Sowie Massif 326–328, 499, 625–626
Gorzów Block 854, 855, 856
Gosau Group
Cretaceous 975–978, *979*, 1162, 1171
Palaeogene 1058–1060, 1163, 1178
Gösmes Formation 225
Gotthard Nappe 1146, 1148, *1149*, 1150
Gozdnica Formation 1044
Gräfenthal Group 222–223
Gräfenwarth Group 271
Grajcarek Succession 898
Grajcarek Unit 1191
Grampian Orogeny *322*, *323*, 324, 337, 362
Gran Paradiso Nappe 1150, *1151*, 1152, 1157
granite
Altenberg-Teplice Caldera 722–723
Caledonian 319–329
collision-related minerals 1375–1379, 1413–1415
Dinarides 1112
Erzgebirge Crystalline Complex 454–455, 718
Mazury Complex 36–37
granitoids
Cambrian, Alps 187
Erzgebirge Crystalline Complex 454–455, 466, 670
Fichtelgebirge 670
Northern Oberpfalz 455
Moldanubian Zone 470
Odenwald Crystalline Complex 447–448
Periadriatic Fault 1178
Precambrian
Armorican Massif 55–56
Brunovistulian Block 54
northeastern Poland 35–36
southern Sweden 32–33
Saxo-Thuringian Zone 64–65, 131
Sudetes 496–497, *498*, 627
Variscan 424–427
Bohemian Massif 469–470
Massif Central 484
Tauern Window 480–482
granulite, Saxonian 456–457
Granulite Nappe *607*, 608
Granulitengebirge *see* Saxonian Granulite Massif
graphite
resources **1342**, 1359–1360, 1363
Alps 1371
graptolites
Caledonides 307
Cambrian–Ordovician boundary 204
Devonian 403
East European Platform 236
Ordovician
Alps 236–7
Ardennes inliers 213, *214*
Bohemian Massif 226, 227–228
Brabant Massif 161, 208–209, 210, *214*
Condroz Inlier 210, 212, *214*
Germany 215, 217, 218
Poland 231, 233, 234
Saxo-Thuringian Zone 219, *221*, 222, 224
Silurian *252*, 253
Austria 276, 278–279, 281, 282–283
Bohemia 272, *273*, 274, 276
Bornholm 267–268
Brabant Massif 285–286
Condroz Inlier 287
Franconian Terrane 268–269
Germany 268
*ludgreni* Event 251, *252*
Montagne Noire 284
Poland 263, *264*, 265, 266, 289, *290*
Proto-Alps 259
Saxo-Thuringian Terrane 271
Grauwacke Zone *see* Greywacke Zone
Grauwackenschiefer, (Rahlenberger) 215
gravel
Elsterian 1290
Saalian 1292
*see also* Rhine Valley, Quaternary sediment
gravity, map of Europe 346–347
gravity anomalies, northern Variscides 604–605
Graz area, Silurian 282–283
Graz Palaeozoic
Carboniferous 476
Devonian 404
Graz Thrust Complex 282
Great Glen Fault
seismic surveys 336–337
strike-slip motion 337
Great Hungarian Plain *1071*
Neogene 1073–1074
palaeogeography 1073
Great Superficial Massif 438
Greeks, geological writings 1, 3
Green-Point Formation, Cambrian–Ordovician boundary 204
greenhouse climate, Cretaceous 923
greenhouse effect, Jurassic 828
greenhouse gas, anthropogenic 17
Greifenstein Formation 1054
greisen, mineral deposits 1376, 1414
Grenville metamorphism 33
Grenville orogenic belts 10, 26, 358–359
Grenzdolomit Formation *755*, 763–764, 778
Grenzland Formation 554
Grenzmergel 826
Grès de Luxembourg 860
Grès d'Hettange 860
Gressony Shear Zone 1173
Gresten Klippen Zone 975
Grey Pelite *575*, 579
greywacke
Lausitz-Leipzig Greywacke Complex 64, 68, 129
Teplá-Barrandian Unit 74, 75
Greywacke Zone 276, 282
Devonian 403–404
nappe System *1161*, 1163, 1170
Ordovician 206
siderite 1385–1386
Griffelschiefer Formation 222–223, 224
Gröbern-Schmerz sequence *1296*, *1299*
Gröden Formation 553, 555, 580–581, 1167
Groningen gas field 1419
Gross Wolf Member *882*, 883
Großenhain Gneiss Complex 133

Grünscholz Member *882*, 883
Grünten Nappe 1150
Gryphaeensandstein 865, *866*
Guernsey, Precambrian basement 106–109
Guingamp migmatites 115
Guingamp Unit *56*, 57
Gulf of Lorraine, Minette ironstone 1397
Gulpen Formation *949*, *950*, 951
Gurktal Nappe 276, *552*, 1165
  Carboniferous sedimentation 477–478, *506*
  Devonian 404–405
  Permian 551, 553
  Silurian 283
Gurnigel Nappe 1053, 1158
Gutenstein Limestone 799, 803
gypsum, resources 1393, 1393, 1397
Gyürüfü Rhyolite Formation *571*, 572

Habay Formation 549
Haibach Gneiss 630, *631*, 698–699
Hainaut
  coal mining 438
  sedimentation area 434, *436*
Hainichen Subgroup 465
Halberstadt Formation 948
Haldanger Sand Formation 835, 836
Haldensleben Fault, seismic surveys 341
Haligovce Unit 1197
halite
  Dinarides 1401
  resources 1391
    sabkha-type 1393
  Swiss Jura 786
  Upper Austro-Alpine tectonic units 580
  Zechstein 572–573, *574*, *575*, 576, 577–580
Halle Laccolith Complex 728–729
Halle Lignite District 1040
Hallstatt Limestone 788, *789*, 804–805, 1162
Hallstatt-Meliata-Ocean 892
halokinesis
  Bay of Kiel 1274–1275
  Cretaceous 937
  Jurassic 836, 840, 842, 848
  Triassic 1016
  Western Baltic Sea 1272–1273
  Zechstein Salt 831, 999, 1001, 1003
Hamitenton Formation *866*, 867
Hámor Dolomite 802
Hámor Formation 495
Haná Fault Zone 54, 144
Hangenberg Event 411
Hangenberg Schiefer 412
Hangenden Bankkalk Formation *866*, 871–872, 1244
Hannover Formation *542*, 545, *546*
Hanonet Formation 390
Hardegsen Sandstone 772
Hardegsen Unconformity 773, 782, 1013
Härtensdorf Formation 564
Harz Block, Cretaceous uplift 948, 1257, *1261*
Harz Boundary Fault, seismic surveys 341
Harz Mountains *635*, *706*
  allochthonous units 633–636
  Carboniferous 438, 440–441
  Devonian 391–392, 394
    magmatism 704
  Eckergneiss Complex 46–48, *49*, 633
  Lower Rotliegend magmatism 539
  nickel-copper deposits 1375–1376
  Ordovician 218
  Silurian, Franconian Terrane 268–269
  tectonics 1255–1258, *1259*, *1260*, *1261*, *1262*
  Variscan tectonics 633–636
Harzburg Gabbro 47–48, 724
Harzgerod Zone 633, 634, *635*
Harznordrand Thrust 948
Haselgebirge, evaporite resources 1391
Hasle Formation 834
Hauenstein Member *883*, 884
Hauenstein-Murgtal Gneiss *607*, 608
Hauptdolomit Formation *789*, 790, 798, 799
Hauptmuschelkalk 785, 786–787
Hauptquarzit Formation 223
Hauptrogenstein Formation *866*, 868, *883*, 885–886
Haute-Chaîne High 879
Hauterivian
  Helvetic Basin 968
  Lower Saxony Basin 935
  Mid-Polish Trough 932, *933*
  sea-level change 924
Havel Subgroup 545
Havel-Müritz Basin *546*
heat-flow, Europe 348–350, *353*, *354*
Heersum Formation 846
Heide Trough, oil 1421
Heidelberg Formation 948
Heidelberg pluton *448*
Helchteren Formation 549–550
helcionellids, Middle Cambrian 190
Heldburg Gips sulphate complex 778–779
Helgoland-Pomerania Deformation Belt 218, 256, 387
Helle Formation 1036
Helminthoid Flysch Nappe 1158
Helmstedt Formation 1040
Helvetic Domain 79, *80*, 81
Helvetic nappes 1146, 1148–1150
  Cretaceous 965, 968–970, *973*, 974–975
Helvetic Units 1143
  Palaeogene 1036, 1049–1051
    sedimentation and stratigraphy *1046*, 1049, 1050–1051
  Tertiary tectonics 1174–1176
hematite, resources *1359*, 1372, 1384
Hemmoor transgression 1041
Henneberg Granite 539
Heppenheim Schist Zone *631*, 632
Herchenberg Volcanic Complex 1327–1328
Herodotus of Halicarnassus (*c*. 484–425 BC) 1, 3
Herscheid Group 287
Herscheider Schichten 215, 315
Herzegovina *see* Bosnia and Herzegovina
Herznach Formation *883*, 886
Hessen, Ordovician 215–216
Hessian Basin
  Rotliegend 545, *547*
  Zechstein *575*
Hessian Depression 777, 1240
  Leine Graben 1240, 1255, 1256
Hessian Seaway 865, 868
Hessische Schieferserie 634
Hettangian
  climate 827–828
  northern Germany 843, *844*
  Poland 849
  southeast France 876
  southern Germany 865, *866*
  Swiss Jura 880–881
  Western Carpathian basins 900
Hetvehely Dolomite 805, *806*
Hidegkút Formation 800
Hidra Formation 937, *938*
Hierlatz Formation *893*, 894, 1162
Highland Boundary Fault, seismic surveys 336, 337
Hindelang Nappe 1150
Hirnantian glaciation 205, 249, 262, 289
Hirnichopf Member *883*, 884
history, Central European geology 1–9
Hlboč Formation 974
Hluk Formation 970, *972*
Höchst Flysch 1053
Hochwipfel Formation 478
Hod Formation 938
Hohenems Nappe 1150
Hohenzollern Graben 1250, *1251*
  seismicity 1245–1246, *1248*
Hoher Bogen, Cambrian–Early Ordovician magmatism 676, *677*
Hoher Bogen Shear Zone *613*, 616
Hohleborn Formation 450
holmiids, Lower Cambrian 188
Holocene 1298, *1302*
Holšiny-Hořice Formation 176
Holsteinian Interglacial Stage 1291–1292, *1296*, *1297*
Holy Cross Fault Zone 49, *50*, 158
Holy Cross Mountains 157–158, *644*
  Baltica affinity 309, 311, 312
  Cambrian 172–174, *175*, *189*, *233*
    biostratigraphy 172–174, *175*
    palaeontology 188, 190

Carboniferous 643–644
Devonian 395–397, 643–644
Furongian, palaeontology 191, 192
Jurassic 857–858
Ordovician 229, 231, 233–236
Silurian *264*, 265
Holzweiler Formation 1313
Hoogstraten Fault 437
Hooke, Robert (1635–1703) 5
Horn Graben 550, 782, *784*, *1000*, 1001, 1003, 1016
Hörre-Gommern Unit 439–440, *441*, 633–634
Horred Formation 33
Hörstein-Huckelheim Formation 630, *631*
Hosdin Formation 286
Houthem Formation *949*
Hoxnian interglacial 1292
Hradiště Formation 970, *972*
Hrádok Formation 494
Hronic Nappe Unit 495–496
Hronic Superunit 1199
tectonics 1206–1207
Hronicum 567, *568*, *570*, 582, 799, 897, *1186*
Hrvatsko Zagorje Basin 1103, *1104*, 1105, 1106
Huet Formation 209
Hulsberg High 949, 951, 952
humans, Pleistocene 14–15, 1300
Humphriesioolith Formation *866*, 867
Hun Superterrane 123, 187, 645–646
Hungarian Central Range 1070–1072
Hungary
Cenozoic1068–1070
Permian 570–572
Triassic basin evolution 800–807
Zechstein 582–583
Hunsrück area, Late Ordovician–Silurian magmatism 696–697
Hunsrück Boundary Fault 458, 557, 727
Hüttenberg-Waldenstein district, iron ore deposit 1413
Hutton, James (1726–1797) 7
Huy Formation 210–211
hydrocarbons
resources **1344**, **1357**, 1379, 1419–1426
*see also* gas; oil; oil shale; petroleum
hyoliths
Cambrian 188, 190, 192
Ordovician, Bohemian Massif 227, 228
hypogene deposits 1380–1387, 1418–1419

Iapetus Ocean 10, 312, *445*
British Caledonides *320*, 321
formation 26, 28, 34
island arcs 309
palaeogeographic reconstruction *11*, 358–359, 362–363, 364, *365*
Silurian 255
Iapetus Suture 305
Caledonian granite 319, 323, 324
seismic surveys **332**, 337, 354, 356
Icart granite gneiss 106, *108*, *109*, *112*, 120
ice age, Quaternary 1287
Alps 1304–1310
north–central Europe
Lower Pleistocene 1288–1289
Middle Pleistocene 1289–1294
Upper Pleistocene 1294–1298
ichnofossils
Cambrian 173
Jurassic
Poland 850
southern Germany 865
Ordovician, Bohemian Massif 226, 227, 228
Permian 535
ichthyosaurs, Jurassic, southern Germany 867
Idrija mercury deposit 1394–1395
Ieper Clay Formation 1039
Il'anovo succession 1205
Ilfeld Basin 547–549
Stephanian–Early Permian magmatism 729
illite, resources, Cenozoic back-arc and rift basins 1404–1405
Ilmenau Formation 547, *548*
Impressamergel Formation *866*, 869, 870
Iňačovce-Krichevo Unit 1198
Indo-Pacific Ocean 1031
Industrial Revolution, natural resources 411
Infra-Tatric units 1202
inliers
Cambrian, Ardennes 158, *159*
Precambrian
Avalonia 43, *44*, 45–46
Sudetes 67–68
*see also* Bohemian Massif
Inner Western Carpathian Crystalline Zone 493
Innsbrucker Quartzphyllit Group 237
Inovec Nappe 1202
insects, oldest flying insect 460
Insubric Fault 1173, 1174, *1175*, 1176
Internides, Variscan 483–496, *507*, 602–603, 606–627
'Intra-Alpine' terrane 481–482
Intra-Sudetic Basin 499, 501, *506*, 560–561, 625
Cretaceous 959, *960*
Stephanian–Early Permian magmatism 730–732
Zechstein 581
Intra-Sudetic Fault 496, 497, 623, 626
interglacial 1287
interstadial 1287
inversion
Lower Rhine Basin 1241–1242
tectonic
Cretaceous 926–930, 940–941, 1024–1025
Liège-Limburg Basin 949
North German Basin 946–949, *1006*
Vienna Basin 1060
Ireland
Grampian Orogeny *322*
Precambrian, East Avalonia 43, 45–46
Ireviken Event 251, *252*
iron
banded 23–24
carbonate-hosted 1361–1362
production **1342**
resources
Alpine domain ophiolite type 1399
Black River type 1399–1400
granite-related 1414
hydrothermal 1427
metamorphogenic 1413
pelosiderite type 1401
rift-related 1393–1394
SEDEX type 1395
Variscan basement 1416–1417
vein-type 1384–1385, 1418
iron ore
Cretaceous, Lower Saxony Basin 936
Lahn-Dill/SEDEX type 1365
pebble 1399–1400
iron oxide, resources 1372
iron sulphide, resources **1349–1351**,
Rammelsberg type 1365–1366
rift-related 1392
VMS, SMS, Kieslager type 1360–1361
VMS type 1363
iron-manganese resources **1344–1346**, 1365, *1381*
ironstone
Minette type 1397–1398
South Germany 867–868
Swiss Jura 884
Thuringite/Wabana type1363
Variscan Foreland Basin 1371
island arcs, Cambrian 156
Islet Zone 138
Cambrian 176
Devonian 402
Silurian 272, 274
isotope analysis
Ordovician 205
Silurian *250*, 251
Işrutis Formation 852, 854
Istria, Cenozoic 1108–1110
Iszkahegy Limestone 800
Italia Terrane *see* Apulia Terrane
Italy
Ordovician, Alps 237
Palaeogene, Southern Alps 1087–1093

Ittre Formation 209
Ivrea Zone 1166, 1168
Izera-Karkonosze Block *see* Karkonosze-Izera Massif

Jakabhegy Sandstone 805, *806*
Jalhay Formation 213
Jarczów Formation 857
Jarmuta Phase 1215
Jasov Formation 570
Jaszczurowa Formation 171
Jászkunság Group 1074
Javoriv Formation 854
Jelar breccia 1110
Jeleniów Shale Formation 234
Jersey 113–114, *114*, 116
Jerzmanowice Formation 1044
Jeseníky Basin 502–503
Jeseníky Mountains, Devonian magmatism 704–707
jet, resources 1400
Jince Formation 177, *179*
palaeontology 188, 190
Jítrava-Hradec Basin 616
Jizera Formation *954*, 958
Jizera-Krkonose Complex *see* Karkonosze-Izera Massif
Johnston Complex *44*, 45, 46, *47*
Jonquoi Formation 287
Jospinet pluton 112
Julian Basin 1092, 1093
Jura Mountains
Cenozoic tectonics 1176, 1235–1238
French
Jurassic 873–880, *874*, *875*
Jurassic–Cretaceous boundary 876
structure 1235
Swiss, Jurassic 880–889
Swiss Jura Molasse, Cenozoic 1056
Triassic sediments 785–788
Jurassic 823–901, *824*
biostratigraphy, northern Germany 843
Bohemian Massif 889–890
Central European Basin System 825–826, 832–889
climate change 827–829
Early, tectonism 1014–1017
eastern Paris Basin 858–864
GSSPs 823, 876
Late, tectonism 1019, 1021
Mid, tectonic uplift 1017–1019
Milankovich cycles 823, 829
Netherlands 836–842
North Germany 842–846, *842*
palaeogeography *825*
Southeast France Basin 880
Swiss Jura *887*
palaeontology, Poland 849–850
Paris Basin
palaeogeography *861*
palaeontology 861
Poland 846–858
palaeogeography *847*
tectonic development 846–849
sea-level change 829, 831–832
Denmark 832, 833–836
Polish Basin 850–851, 854–858
southeast France 876–879
Western Carpathian basins 898–900
sedimentation 840–841, 848–858
sequence stratigraphy 829, *830*, 831–832, 840–841, 850–851
Paris Basin 861
southern Germany 865–873
southeast France and French Jura 873–880, *874*, *875*
southern Germany 864–873
subdivision 823
Swiss Jura Mountains 880–889
tectonics
Alps 1168–1170
Western Carpathians 1214
Tethyan Domain 825–826, 890–900
Jurassic–Cretaceous boundary 876, 923
Jurassic–Lower Cretaceous, mineral resources 1397–1399
Jurensismergel Formation *866*, 867
Juvavic Nappe System *1154*, 1160, *1161*, 1162, 1168, 1169, 1170
Juvavic unit 892, *893*
Jydegård Formation 936
Jylland, Cretaceous 939

K-bentonite 366
Carnic Alps 281
Kabeliai Complex 36–37
Kaczawa Complex 498
Cambrian–Early Ordovician magmatism 687–689
Kaczawa Hills 230, 289
Kaczawa Nappe Pile 625, 626, 627
Kadlubek Unit 973
Kahlenberg Nappe 970, *973*
Kaiserstuhl igneous complex, niobium deposit *1361*
Kaiserstuhl volcanism 1047, 1240, *1246*, 1249
Kaliningrad, Jurassic *847*, 851, 852, 854
Kališčo Formation 974
Kalkbank 223
Kalkknollenbank 945
Kallo Complex 1040
Kamenica Phase 1215
Kamieniec Formation 174
Kamieniec Metamorphic Belt 501
Kamienna Group 849
Kampinos Complex 35, 36
Kandern Formation *866*, 868, 869
Kantavár Calcareous Marl 805, *806*
kaolin
resources **1342**
Alpine unconformities 1380, *1381*, 1415–1416
Cenozoic back-arc and rift basins 1404–1405
Kaplonosy Formation 184
Karawanken Alps 276, 277
alpine tectonics 1167
Carboniferous sedimentation 478–480
Devonian 405–406
Permian 553–554
Zechstein cycles 581
Karawanken Pluton 1178
Kardosrét Formation 827
Karelian Orogeny 36
Karkonosze Complex *see* East Karkonosze Complex ; South Karkonosze Complex
Karkonosze Granite Pluton 498, 627
Karkonosze-Izera Massif *130*, 137, *141*, 498–499, 625, 626
Cambrian–Early Ordovician magmatism 683–684
Karkonosze Piedmont Basin 581
Stephanian–Early Permian magmatism 732
Karl Formation 550, *551*
Kärlich interglacial 1290
Kärlich section 1315, 1324, 1325, *1327*
Karolina Formation 857
Karpatian, Paratethys basins 1100–1101
karst, Palaeogene
Italian Southern Alps 1092–1093
Slovenia 1093, 1097
*see also* Moravian Karst; Slovak Karst Mountains
karstification
Devonian 399
Palaeogene 1110
Visean 436, 437
Kašov Formatioin 495
Kaszuby Complex 35
Kattegat, Cretaceous 939
Kcynia Formation 858
Kellerwald, Silurian, Franconian Terrane 269
Kellwasser horizon 393, 394, 399, 403
Kempenich volcanic centre 1324
Keprník Gneiss 144
Keprník Nappe 501
Kernzone Complex 127, *128*, 129
Keuper Formation 756, 777–781
Carpathians 799
Denmark 784
magnetostratigraphy 759–760
Netherlands 782–784
stratigraphy 765–769, *768*
Switzerland 787–788
Kiaman Superchron 13
Kiel Sands 1041
Kielce Zone 49, 172, *173*, 174, *644*
Devonian–Carboniferous 643–644

Ordovician *232*, 233–234
palaeontology 190
Silurian 266
Kieselkalk Formation 968, *969*
Kieslager ore deposits 1361
Kimmeridge Clay Formation *838*, 839, 840–841
Kimmeridgian
Northern Calcareous Alps 895–896
northern Germany *844*, 846
southeast France 879
southern Germany *866*, *868*, 869, 870–871
Swiss Jura *887*, 888
Western Carpathian basins 899
Kiskunhalas Sub-basin 1072, 1073
Kitzbühel Alps 282
Klabava Formation 226
Kladno Formation 468
Klagenfurt Basin 1180
Klape Unit 1196–1197, 1206
Klátov Unit 1204
Klaus Formation *893*, 895
Kleszczów Graben 1263, 1268, *1270*
Klikov Formation 959
Klingnau Formation 885, 886
klippen, Saxothuringian Basin 457, 463
Klippen Nappe 1156
Klitten Formation 224
Klitzschmar Formation 460
Kłodawa salt diapir 1016
Kłodzko Metamorphic Massif 68, 138, *141*, 499, 625–626
Cambrian–Early Ordovician magmatism 691
isotopic data **125**
Klonk, Silurian–Devonian boundary type section 400
Klonówka Shale Formation 174, 234
Klouček-Čenkov Formation 177
Kluki Formation 182
Kniest silica concentration 1366
Knola Formation 569
Knollenmergel Member 788
Köbbinghausen Formation 287
Kohanivska Formation 852, 854
Kohlenkalk 421, 428, 437, 438
Kohút Phase 1215
Kok Formation 278
Komagnes dyke 27
Komárov Volcanic Complex 227, 228
Komorowo Formation 849
Koňhora Formation 970, *972*
Kopanina Formation 275
Kopienec Formation 827
Korallenkalk Formation 869
Korallenoolith Formation 846
Koralpe-Wölz Nappe System *1161*, 1163, 1165, 1170, 1171
Korneuburg (Sub-)Basin 1062–1063
Korpád Sandstone Formation *571*, 572
Korycany Member *954*, 956
Kościeliska Formation 974
Kościelisko Beds 852
Kosov Formation 228
Kössen Formation *789*, 790, 802, 826
Kossmat, Franz (1871–1938), classification of Variscan Belt 123, 418, 601–602
Kostolec Unit 1196
Kostrzyń Formation 186
Koszalin-Chojnice Zone, Silurian 263
Kővágószőlős Sandstone Formation *571*, 583, *806*
Köveskál Dolomite 800
Kozár Limestone 805
Kozara Flysch 1112
Kozina-type limestone 1110
Kraichgau-Saale Basin, Rotliegend 545–547
Kraków-Lubliniec Fault Zone 49, *50*, 51, 229, 311
as terrane boundary 357
Kraków-Upper Silesia Basin 563
Královdvor Formation 228
Král'ovohol'ské Nízke Tatry mountains 1200
Kralupy-Zbraslav Group 71, 72, 73–74, 75, 138, 143
Krasín Phase 1214
Krefeld High 315
Kreideschiefer Basin 974
Kremnica epithermal gold-silver deposit 1404
Kressenberg Formation 1050–1051
Kreuzgraben Formation 978
Křivoklát-Rokycany Volcanic Complex 179–180
Krížna Unit 1205, 1206
Krk 1110
Krkonoše *see* Karkonosze
Kroisbach Member 1050–1051
Krosno Basin 1081
Krško Basin 1101, 1102
Krušné Hory Fault 1255
Krušné Hory Mountains 454
*see also* Erzgebirge
Krynica subunit 1191
Kryta Turbidite Member 974
Kryvtche Formation 1045
Krzywin Graben 1262
Ksiaż Wielkopolski Formation 540–541
Kuchyňa Unit 973
Kühberg unit 224
Kuhfeld Beds *934*, 935
Kujavian Basin, Cretaceous 931, 932, 940, 942
Kumburk Formation 499
Kupferberg mineral deposits *1359*, 1363
Kupferschiefer 573, *574*, *575*, 576
copper mineralization 1390–1391
Küre Ocean 1016
Kurovice Formation 970, *972*
Kutná Hora Crystalline Unit 75
Kutno Depression *847*, 848
Kyffhäuser Crystalline Complex 67, 628, *629*
Late Devonian–Early Carboniferous 710
Kysuca succession 1196

La Gleize Formation 158, *159*
La Hague, Precambrian basement 106–109, *110*
La Roche Derrien Formation 57
La Venne Formation 158, *159*
Laab Nappe 975, 1054
Laacher See volcano 1297, 1312, 1318, *1323*, 1329–1333
Tephra *1326*, 1329–1333
Lacunosamergel Formation *866*, 870
Łączna Unit 691
Lagów Region 231, *232*, 233
Lahn Syncline 440, *441*
Lahn-Dill area 393, 394, 431, 702, 703, *705*
iron ore 1365
Lake Pannon 1062, 1063, 1064, 1066, 1072
Lam-Bodenmais Kies Belt, sulphide minerals 1361
Lammer Basin 895
Lanaye Member *949*, *950*, 952
Landen Group 1036
Lanvollen Formation 57
Lapis Limestone 805, *806*
Laško back-bulge basin 1100
Lassing talc deposit 1411
Last Glacial Maximum 1304–1305, *1306*, 1308–1309
Last Glaciation 1304–1305, 1308
Late Palaeocene Thermal Maximum 1036
Latemar platform 797
laterite 1417
Latinne Formation 286
Latvia, Jurassic 846–847, 857, 858
Lau Event *252*, 263
Lauchert Graben 1248
Laurentia 10, 26, 28, 34
fossils 307
reconstruction *11*, *12*, *27*, *28*, *29*, *30*, *318*, 358–360, *361*, 362–367
Silurian 255
Laurussia 14, 26, 43
Carboniferous 411, 419, 420–424
convergence with Gondwana *412*, 420–424, 536, 538, 599, *600*, 645
Devonian 383–384
depositional environments 388–399
reconstruction *12*
separation from Gondwana 1016
Silurian 259

Lausitz Block 62, *65*, 68, *130*, *141*, 498, 625
isotopic data **125**
*see also* Lusatia
Lausitz Fault 1255
Lausitz Granitoid Complex 68, *130*, 131, *132*, 136
Lausitz Group 129, *130*, *132*, 133
Lausitz-Izera Unit, Devonian 402–403
Lausitz-Izera sub-basin, Cretaceous *954*, *955*, 957, 958
Lausitz-Leipzig Greywacke Complex 64, 68, 129, *130*, 133–134
Lava Formation 851
Lavanttal Basin, Neogene 1064
lead
production **1342**
resources **1349–1351**, 1361, 1362, *1381*, 1393
Alpine type/MVT 1395–1396
arc-related 1402–1404
carbonate-hosted 1418
fault zones 1427
granite-related 1414
Late Alpine unconformity 1417
Rammelsberg type 1365–1366
Silesian type/MVT 1395
vein-type 1371–1372, 1377, 1380, 1382–1384, 1418
Łebsko Formation 182
Lederschiefer Formation 223
Lehmann, Johann (1719–1776) 5–6
Leimitz Formation 224
Leine cycle 572, *574*, *575*, 579–580
Leine Graben 1255, *1256*, *1257*
Leipzig Group 64, 129
Leipzig Lignite District 1040, 1406
Leipzig Phase 1293
Leitha Mountains 1063
Leonardo da Vinci (1452–1519) 4, 5
Lepontine Dome 1150, 1152, 1155, 1173, 1176
Les Quatre Fils Aymon Formation 158, *159*
Les Trappistes fluorite deposit 1383
Lessini Shelf 1088, 1091
Leszczyniec Volcanic Formation 686, 687
Letná Formation 227
Letovice Complex, Cambrian–Early Ordovician magmatism 692–694
Letovice Formation 563
Lettenkeuper 778
Lettenkohle Formation 787
leucogranite, Variscan 427
leucophyllite, resources 1411–1412
Leukersdorf Formation 564
Lhotka Formation 970, *972*
Lias
southeast France 876–877
Swiss Jura 881
Lias Group, North Germany 842
Libeň Formation 227
Liburnian Formation 1111, 1112
Lichtenberg Horizon 952
Lidernen Bed *969*, 970
Liebenstein Formation 450
Liebenstein Nappe 1150, 1178
Liège-Limburg Basin
Cretaceous 930, 949–953
biostratigraphy 949
tectonic inversion 949
Liegende Bankkalk Formation *866*, 871
Liepona Formation 854
Lieth, Lower Pleistocene palynology 1288, *1290*
lignite
Cenozoic basins 1406–1409
Eocene 1039, 1040
Neogene 1041
production **1342**
Ligurian Cycle 829, *830*, 832
Ligurian-Penninic Ocean 899
Ligurian-Piedmontese Ocean 873, 878
Limbourg Campine sub-basin 437
Lindener Mark 635
Líně Formation 469
lingulids, Devonian, southeastern Poland 395
Lion Member buildups 390
Liplas-Tarnawa Graben 563
Lippertsgrün Formation 168
LISPB seismic project 335, 338, 357
lithium, resources **1347–1348**, 1378
lithostratigraphy
Permian 535
Triassic, German Basin 764–765
Lithuania
Jurassic 846–847, 851, 854, 857, 858
lithospheric structure 38–42
Precambrian 38–43
tectonic evolution 42–43
Silurian, Baltica 261–263
Lithuanian Confacies Belt 260
Litija mineral deposit 1380
Litohlavy Formation 274–275
Litošice conglomerates 72
Little Hungarian Plain Basin, Neogene 1070, *1071*
Livno-Duvno Basin 1105, *1106*
Lixhe Member *949*, *950*, 952
Lizard Ophiolite 356, 707
Llandovery 251, *252*
Austria 277–279
Belgium 212, 286, 287
Bornholm 267–268
Carnic Alps 281, *281*
Franconian Terrane 268
Germany 268
Holy Cross Mountains 234
Lithuania 260, 261
Montagne Noire 284
Poland 263, 265–266
Prague Basin 272, *273*, 276
sea-level change 250, 262
Llanvirn
Brabant Massif 208
Condroz Inlier 210–211
Germany 215, 217, 218
Poland 231, 234
Schwarzburg Anticline 223
Łobez Formation 849
Lochen Formation *866*, 869
Lochkovian
Barrandian area 400
eastern Rhenish Massif 393
Moravia 398–399
Saxo-Thuringian Zone 403
southeastern Poland 395
Lodève Basin *556*, 557
loess
Pleistocene 1310, 1315
Rhine Valley 1315–1318
Loibersdorf Formation 1057
Loire Fault 858, *859*
Lombardic-Giudicaric fold and thrust belt 1165–1167, 1172, 1180
Longmyndian Supergroup *44*, 45–46, *47*
Lorraine, Jurassic 858–864
Losenstein Formation 974, 1162
Lower Coloured Molasse 1057
Lower Freshwater Molasse 1055, 1056, 1057
Lower Gneiss Unit 483
Lower Graben Formation *838*, 839, 840
Lower Marine Molasse 1053, 1055, 1056
Lower Pseudoschwagerina Limestone 479–480
Lower Rhine Basin
deformation 1241–1242
evolution 1241–1242
inversion 1241–1242
lignite 1406–1407
Quaternary fluvial sediment 1312–1315
seismicity 1241
Lower Rhine Embayment 1040, 1041, 1042, 1241
Quaternary sediment 1312–1315
Lower Saxony Basin
Cretaceous 929, 934–936, 945
Jurassic *838*, 840, 842–843
oil 1421
Lower Saxony rift system *541*, 545
Lower Silesia, neotectonics 1268, *1269*
Lower Silesian Basin, coal 1388
LT seismic project 331, **332**, 338, 345, 358
Lubeník Formation 494
Lubeník-Margecany Fault 1201, 1203, 1207
Lublin Basin, coal 1371
Lublin Upland
Jurassic 857

neotectonics 1268–1269, *1270*
Lublin-Lvov Basin,
Carboniferous sedimentation 442, *444*
Devonian 395–397
Lublin-Podlasie Basin 37, 157
Cambrian 184, *185*, 186
palaeontology 192
Lúčkovská Formation 974
*ludgreni* Event 251, *252*
Ludlow *252*, 253
Austria 277–279, 282
Belgium 286, 287
Carnic Alps 281, *281*
Franconian Terrane 268
Lithuania 261–263
Montagne Noire 284
Poland 263, 265–267
Prague Basin 272, *273*, 276
sea-level change 250–251
Ludwigsdorf Member 162–163, *164*
Lugicum 496, 497
Lugodanubian Fault 52
Luhyna Formation 495
Lulu Formation 835
Lusatia
Cambrian 162–165, *189*, **193**
magmatism 326
Ordovician 219, *221*, 224
*see also* Lausitz Block
Lusatian Lignite District 1041
*Lusatiops* Member 162–163
Lust Formation 285
Lužice Formation 1060, 1062
Lvov Depression, Jurassic 851–852, 858
*see also* Lublin-Lvov Basin
Lydit-Kieselkalk-Komplex 282
Lyell, Charles (1797–1875) 8–9
Łyna Formation 184
Łysogóry Zone 172, *173*, 234, 236, *644*
Baltica affinity 310, 311–312
Devonian 395–397, 643–644
Silurian 265–266

maars, Eifel volcanic fields 1320, 1321–1323, 1327–1329
Maastricht Formation *949*, 952–953
Maastrichtian
Danish Basin 938–939
Liège-Limburg Basin 949, 951–953
Mid-Polish Trough 942
North German Basin *943*
inversion tectonics 946–949
sea-level change 924
Western Carpathians 978
Macrocephalenoolith Member *866*, 868
Madot Formation 209–210
Maggia Nappe 1150,1152
magma, Eifel volcanic fields 1319–1320
magmatism
Caledonian
Avalonia 324–325
central European terranes 325–329
Cambrian–Early Ordovician 669–694
Alps 81–82
Carboniferous 703–704
Tauern Window 480–482
Devonian 699–707
Fichtelgebirge Crystalline Complex 455–456
Jurassic, Netherlands 841–842
Late Devonian–Early Carboniferous 707–720
Namurian–Westphalian 720–723
Northern Oberpfalz 455
Ordovician 328–329
–Late Silurian 694–699
Palaeozoic 665–733
Periadriatic 1178
Permian
Alps 1168
Saar-Nahe Basin 559
post-Cadomian 116
Precambrian
Avalonia 46
northeastern Poland 36–37
southern Sweden 32, 33, 34
Stephanian–Early Permian 723–733
Stephanian–Lower Rotliegend 539
Thuringian Forest Basin 547
Variscan
Erzgebirge Crystalline Complex 453
Massif Central 483–484
Sudetes 498
Variscan Belt 424–428
magnesite
amorphous 1417–1418
resources **1342**, 1364–1365, 1366
replacement deposits 1385–1387
magnetic field, map of Europe 347–348, *351*
magnetic field anomalies, northern Variscides 603–606
magnetite, resources 1363, 1372
magnetostratigraphy
Carboniferous 417
Cretaceous 925
Triassic 757, 759–760
magnetotelluric surveys, North German Basin 352, *355*
Magura Basin 897, 898, *1194*, *1195*, 1198
Palaeogene 1078–1081
Magura Superunit 1183, 1191
Magyarürög Anhydrite 805
Maillet, Benoit de (1656–1738) 5
Main Anhydrite *575*, 580
Main Dolomite 577
Mainz Basin, Neogene 1048
Majevica Mountains 1112
Malá Fatra Mountains 1199, *1200*
Malé Karpaty Mountains 1199, 1200
Maliac Ocean 1014, 1016
Malm Group 842–843, 879
Malmédy Graben, Permian 549
Małopolska Massif 49, *50*, 51–52
Baltica affinity 310–312
Devonian 395, 396
Ordovician 206, *229*, 231, *232*
Silurian 267
Małopolska Region, Carboniferous sedimentation 441–442
Małopolski Basin, Lower Cretaceous 931
Malužiná Formation 567, 569, 582
Malverns Complex *44*, 45, 46, *47*
Mały Bozków Unit 691
mammals
Deckenschotter 1306
Last Glacial Maximum 1308–1309
Pleistocene 1298–1300, *1303*, 1304
Rhine sediment terraces 1313
Mancellian Batholith *56*, 57, 58, 115, 119
Mancellian Terrane **112**, 115, 118–120, **119**, 121
Manebach Formation 547
manganese
production **1342**
resources **1344–1346**, 1364, 1365
Alpine domaine 1398–1399
Late Alpine unconformity 1417
pelosiderite type 1401
rift-related 1393–1394
SEDEX type 1395
Variscan basement 1416–1417
Manín Unit 974, 1196, 1206
Mansfeld Group 461–462
mantle plumes 21, 453
Margna Nappe 1158–1159
Mariánské Lázně Complex 143, 614
Cambrian–Early Ordovician magmatism 672–674
Mariánské Lázně Fault 1255
Markranstädt Phase 1291
Marmorea Crust 895
Marnheim Bay 1048
Marsberg copper deposit 1383
Massenkalk Formation *866*, 869, 870–871
Massif Central 59–60
coal 1388
Permian basins 555–557
sulphide ores 1366
Variscan basins 484, *485*
Variscan granitoids 484
Variscan Internides 483–484
Matrei Zone, Tauern Window 1159
Matuyama palaeomagnetic chron 1314
*see also* Brunhes-Matayama palaeomagnetic chron; Gauss-Matayama palaeomagnetic chron
Maubach-Mechernich lead–zinc deposit 1383
Mauges Domain *56*, 58
Maures Massif 60
Silurian 255
Mazowsze Formation 184

Mazowsze Massif 36
Mazowsze-Lublin Graben 236
Mazurian High 157
Mazurian way, Jurassic 847, 857
Mazury Granitoid Complex *34*, 35
  magmatism 36–37
Mecklenburg, Weichselian Stage 1297, *1299*
Mecsek Basin, coal 1397
Mecsek Mountains *571*, 572, *806*, 1072
  Triassic basin evolution 805–807
  Triassic–Jurassic boundary 827
Medianes Nappes 1053
Medienicka series 851
Mediterranean Province 307
Megaerella Limestone 278, 279
megamonsoon, Pangaean 766
megaspores, Jurassic, Poland 849
Meggen, sulphide ores 394, 1366
Megyehegy Dolomite 800
Meilleret Flysch 1053
Meissen Formation, Cretaceous *954*, 955
Meissen monzonite-diorite 718–720
Melanien Limestone 1047
Meliata Ocean 799, 897, 898, 1016, 1143, 1167–1168, 1169
  Western Carpathians 1185, 1187, 1206, 1207, 1208
Meliatic Superunit, tectonics 1208, *1209*, 1210
Meliaticum *568*, *570*, 1167, 1168
Menai Strait Line *44*, 45, 46, *47*
Merboltice Formation *954*, 958
mercury
  resources **1348–1349**
    arc-related 1402–1404
    granite-related 1414
    SEDEX type 1394–1395
    vein type 1380–1382
Mergelkeuper Formation, Switzerland 787–788
Mergelstetten Formation *866*, 871
Mesozoic
  development of Europe 13–14
  palaeocontinental reconstruction *15*
Messel Basin, oil shale 1409
Messel Formation 1048
meta-anthracite 1363
Metabasite Belt 52, *53*, 54
metallogenesis 1341
  Precambrian–Cambrian 1357–1359
metamorphism
  Alpine 1163, *1164*, 1166, 1167, 1170–1173
  Eckergneiss Complex 47–48
  and mineralogenesis 1371–1375
  Permian, Alps 1168
  Ordovician, Alps 82
  Precambrian
    Brunovistulian Block 52, *53*, 54
    Lithuania 39–40
    northeast Poland 34–36
    southeast Poland 49, *50*, 51–52
  Sudetes 68, 498–499, 501
  Variscan 424, 446, 602, 1167
    Ardennes Brabant areas 637–638
    Erzgebirge Crystalline Complex 451, 453–454
    Massif Central 483–484
    Mid-German Crystalline High 627–633
    Moldanubian Zone 611–614
    Odenwald Crystalline Complex 447
    Saxothuringian Zone 621–622
    Sudetes 625–627
    Teplá-Barrandian Unit 616–617
    Western Carpathians 491
metasomatism, Lithuania 41
methane, coal-bed 1388
Metz Fault 858, *859*
Mid-German Crystalline High 26, 48, 55, *63*, 67, *122*, 601
  Cambrian 161–162
  development 446–447
  Late Devonian–Early Carboniferous magmatism 708–711
  Late Ordovician–Silurian magmatism 694–699
  tectonic setting 418–419
  Variscan tectonic evolution 627–633
Mid-Netherlands-Krefeld High 391
Mid-Polish Anticlinorium, Cretaceous 927–928
Mid-Polish Swell 1259–1261
Mid-Polish Trough 540, *542*, 543, 769, 778
  Buntsandstein 1014
  Cretaceous 927, 931–934, 940–942
    uplift 1259–1261
  Jurassic 846–848, 851, 854–855, 857–858
  Triassic 1016
Mid-Transdanubian Zone, Neogene basin 1072
Middle Ages, scientific thought 4
Middle Graben Formation *838*, 839, 840
Middle Lithuanian Suture Zone 36
Middle Miocene Climate Transition 1032–1033
Middle Odra Fault Zone 496, 627
Middle Penninic Nappes 1156–1157
Middle Pleistocene Event 1305
Midi Fault 437
Midi Thrust Zone 639
Midi-Eifel faults 433
Midland Microcraton 334
Miechów Depression, Cretaceous 941, 942
Międzygórz Formation 233–234
migmatite
  Lithuania 40
  Massif Central 483
  Saint-Malo Terrane 115
migration, faunal
  Jurassic 825, 829, 832–833, 851
  Triassic 807
Milankovitch cycles
  Cretaceous 925
  Jurassic 823, 829
  Triassic 753, 766, 767, 769, 772, 782
Mílina Formation 226
Militz Interval 1291
mineral resources 1341–1431
  Alpine cycle 1379–1427
  collision (granite)-related *1359*, 1375–1379, 1413–1415
  remobilization and igneous activity related 1426–1427
  strata-bound 1357–1371, *1359*, 1387–1410
  thrust-bound *1359*, 1371–1375, 1410–1413
  unconformity-related *1360*, 1379–1387, 1415–1419
  Variscan cycle 1357–1379
mineralization
  crustal specialization 1428
  element composition 1429
  element recycling 1428–1429
  Kupferschiefer-type *1360*
  structural facies variation 1430
  vertical structure zones 1429–1430
minerals, industrial,
  production **1342**
  resources **1351–1355**
mining 1341
Miocene
  climate 1032–1033
  Dinarides 1105
    freshwater basins 1112
  Eastern Alps, tectonics 1178–1180
  North Sea Basin 1041
  palaeogeography *1032*
  Polish Lowland Basin 1044
  Transylvanian Basin 1076
  Vienna Basin 1060, 1062–1063
Mirow Formation *542*, 545, *546*
Misarai impact crater 41–42
Misox Zone *1148*, 1155, 1156
Mississippian 416
Mittersill scheelite deposit 1362
Młynary Formation 184
Mnichovo Hradi Basin 559
MOBIL seismic profile **332**, 356, 357
Mobschatz Formation *954*
Moesia Terrane
  Silurian 255
    palaeogeography 259
Moho
  dome
    Ohře Graben 1255
    Upper Rhine Graben 1240
  Lithuania 38, *40*

Moine Thrust 335–336
North German Caledonides 340, 342
Scandinavian Caledonides 337, *338*, 340
Trans-European Suture Zone 346
Variscan basement 603
Möhrenbach Formation 539
Moine Thrust Zone 323
seismic surveys 334–336
Mójcza Limestone Formation 233, 234, *235*
Molasse Basin *see* North Alpine Foreland Basin
Moldanubia
Silurian 255, 258
Moldanubian Plutonic Complex 715–716
Moldanubian Zone 13, 52, *53*, 60, *61*, 68, 70–79, *122*, 602, *611*
Cadomian basement *143*, 144, 145
Cambrian 180, *181*
Carboniferous sedimentation 466–467, 469–482, *507*
isostopic data **124**
Late Devonian–Early Carboniferous 711–713
Silurian 272–276
tectonic setting 419
Variscan tectonic evolution 611–617
western, Cambrian–Early Ordovician magmatism 180, 679
Moldanubicum *see* Moldanubian Zone
Moldova, Jurassic 852, 854
Mölln cycle 572, *575*
molluscs
Devonian 387
Jurassic, Paris Basin 864
Middle Cambrian 190
molybdenum
resources **1347**
arc-related 1402–1404
granite-related 1376, 1382, 1414
porphyry type 1366–1367
Mömbris Formation 449, 630, *631*
Møn, Cretaceous 939
MONA LISA seismic project **332**, 337–340, 350–351, 357
Money Window 1157
Monian Supergroup *45*, 46
Monian-Rosslare Terrane *44*, 45, 46
Mónosbél Unit 1211
Monotone Series 480
Monotonous Unit 76–77, 78, 79, 612
Møns Klint 939
monsoon
Permian 531–532
Triassic 752, 766
Mont Blanc Massif 1145–1146, *1147*, 1148, *1149*
Mont Terri Member 881, *882*
Montagne Noire 59
Carboniferous sedimentation 484
Silurian 255, 258, 283–284, *285*
Monte Baldo 1088–1089, 1090
Monte Rosa district, gold 1412–1413
Monte Rosa Nappe 1150, *1151*, 1152, 1155
Tertiary shear 1173
Montello Thrust 1180–1181
Monti Berici 1088, 1089, 1090
Monti Lessini 1088–1089
Monto Grona Fault 1166
Moranci Formation 857
Moravia
Cambrian 172
Devonian 397–399
Moravian Gate 1014, 1290, 1291, 1293
Moravian Karst 890
Moravian Line 312
Moravo-Silesian Fold-Thrust Belt *500*, 501–504, *642*
Variscan tectonics 640–643
Moravo-Silesian Zone 49, 52, *53*, 54, 60, *61*, *122*
Cadomian basement 144–145
Culm Basin 473, *500*, 705
Devonian magmatism 704–707
Moray Firth, Jurassic sequence stratigraphy *830*, 831
Morcles Nappe 1148, *1149*
Mörnsheim Formation *866*, 872
Moro, Abbé Anton Lazzaro (1687–1764) 5
Morvan fluorite deposit 1383
Mosina Formation 1044
Most Extensive Glaciation 1308
Mostar Basin *1106*, 1112
Mosty Complex 36
Mousty Formation *159*, *160*, 161, 208
Mt Ślęża Complex, Cambrian–Early Ordovician magmatism 689, 690
Mulhouse High 1238
Mulhouse Horst 1047
Münchberg Complex 62, 67, 621–622
Cambrian 169, **193**, 670–672
nappes 457, 463
Devonian 403
Ordovician 219, *221*, 224–225
Münder Formation 846
Münsterland Cretaceous Basin 929–930, 945, 947
Münstertal Nappe *607*, 608
Mura-Zala Basin 1101, 1102
Muráň Formation 974
Murau Nappe 1165
Murchisonaeoolith Formation *866*, 867
Müritz Subgroup 545
Mürtschen Nappe 1148, *1149*
Muschelkalk Formation *755*, *775*
biostratigraphy 760, 763–764
Denmark 784
German Basin 776–777
magnetostratigraphy 759
Netherlands 782
Switzerland 785–787
tectonism 754, 1014
Müsenegg Member *882*, 883
Mykolayiv Formation 1045
Mylonite Zone *30*, 32, 33
Myszków area 231

Nagoryany beds 1045
Nagygörbő Basin 1071
Nagyvisnyó Formation *571*, 582–583
Permian–Triassic boundary 751
Namur sedimentation area 434
Namur Synclinorium 390, 432
Namur–Dinant Basin 431–432, 434–436
Namurian 508
magmatism 720–723
sedimentation
Belgium 434
North German Basin 428–429
Naninne Formation 287
nappes
Austro-Alpine 893–894, 1160–1165, 1171–1172
Black Forest 606, *607*, 608, *610*, 611
East Sudetes 501, 626
Engadine Window 1155, 1156
Erzgebirge *66*, 137
Helvetic 965, *966*, 1148–1150
Cretaceous 968–970
Inner Western Carpathian Crystalline Zone 495
metamorphic 457, 463, 475, 477–478
Middle Penninic 1156–1157
Pre-Piedmontais 1157
Rehberg and Letovice complexes 693
Saxo-Thuringian Zone *66*
Sub-Penninic 1150, 1152, 1154–1155
Tauern Window 481, 1152, 1154–5, 1159
Ultrahelvetic, Palaeogene 1053, 1150
Upper Penninic 1157–1159, 1172
Valaisian 1155–1156
Narayiv Formation 1045
Narva Group 388
nautiloids
Ordovician, Poland 234
Silurian
Austria 276, 277, 279, 282
Montagne Noire 284
Proto-Alps Terrane 259
NEC seismic profile **332**, 336, 356
Neckar-Jagst Fault 1248
Neeroeteren Sandstones 434
Nena supercontinent 23
Neogene 14
biostratigraphy *1037*, 1042
Carpathian Foredeep
Czech Republic 1081–1083
Poland 1083–1084, *1085*

Carpathians, Western Ukraine 1084–1086
Croatia and north Bosnia 1103
Danube Basin 1065–1066
Dinarides 1103, 1105–1106
East Slovak Basin 1066–1068
lithostratigraphy *1038*
North Sea Basin 1040–1042
Pannonian Basins System *1061*, 1070–1072
Slovenia *1095*
Styrian Basin 1063–1064
Vienna Basin 1060, 1062–1063
Neoproterozoic 10
Avalonian subduction *47*
palaeocontinental reconstruction *11*
tectonics 26
neotectonics
North German Basin 1275–1277
Poland 1265–1270, *1266*
Western Carpathians 1216–1217
Neotethys, opening 1012, 1016
nephrite, resources 1412
Nerineenkalk *866*, 869
Neringa Formation 851
Netherlands
Jurassic 836–842
magmatism 841–842
petroleum geology 841
tectonic setting 836–837
uplift 837
Permian 550
Triassic, basin evolution 781–784
Netzkater Formation 548
Neuburg Formation *866*, 872
Neukirchen-Kdyně Massif 143, 180
Cambrian–Early Ordovician magmatism 675–676, *677*
Neunkirchen Magmatic Suite 632
Neustadt Formation 548
Neuwied Basin 1323, 1324, 1329
Newer Granite 319, 321, 323–324
nickel
resources **1346**, 1362, 1364–1365
Alpine domain ophiolite type 1399
disseminated 1375–1376
embryonic ophiolite type 1395
hydrothermal 1427
rift-related 1392
Niederhäslich formation 563
Niedersachsen Group *838*, 840
Niederschöna Formation *954*, 955
Niedźwiedź Amphibolite Massif 501
Niemcza shear zone 501, 689, 690
Niesen Nappe 1053
Nieuwerkerk Formation *838*, 839
Niewachlów Beds 266
niobium
resources **1347**, *1361*, 1378, 1427
granite-related 1414
Niremont Flysch 1053
Nízke Tatry mountains 1199, 1200
Nizký Jesenik Mountains *500*, 502
Nižná Boca Formation 496
Nižná succession 1196
Nobbin-Grauwacken Formation 218
Nördliche Phyllitzone *see* Northern Phyllite Zone
Nordrahmenzone 1159, 1160
Nordsächsisches Schiefergebirge *see* Northern Saxonian Slate Mountains
Noric Composite Terrane 187
Noric Nappe 475, 1162, 1163, 1168, 1170
Noric Terrane 474
Noric-Bosnian Terrane, Silurian 255, 259
North Alpine Foreland Basin
Cenozoic *1046*, *1052*, 1054–1058, 1176, 1178
sedimentation and stratigraphy *1046*, 1055–1058
Cenozoic tectonics 1237
oil and gas *1422*, 1423–1424
North Armorican Massif 104, 106–121
palaeogeography 116–117
structural evolution 115–116
tectonic model 120–121
tectonomagmatic events **119**
terranes 118–120
North Armorican Shear Zone *56*, 58, 104, *107*
North Bohemian Cretaceous Basin, Devonian basement 402
North Bohemian Shear Zone *613*, 616
North Estonian Belt *34*
North German Basin *1000*, 1001
Buntsandstein 1013
Carboniferous sedimentation and magmatism 428–429
Cretaceous 929–930, 942–949, *1007*
inversion tectonics 946–949, 1003, *1006*, *1007*
Jurassic 842–846, *842*
magmatism 539
magnetotelluric surveys 352, *355*
neotectonics 1275–1277
Permian 534
seismic surveys 340–342, *344*, *345*
Stephanian–Early Permian magmatism 724–726
tectonics 1270–1275
North German Caledonides, seismic surveys 340–343
North Hungary Palaeogene Basin *see* Buda Basin
North Mecklenburg High 936, 942
North Saxon Anticline *64*, *65*, 131, *141*, **193**
isotopic data **125**
North Sea
Chalk Group 937, *938*
Devonian 385–386
thermal dome, Jurassic 1017
North Sea Basin
biostratigraphy *1037*
Cenozoic 1035
palaeogeography *1039*
volcanism 1042
Eocene
climate 1039
sea-level change 1039–1040
Neogene 1040–1042
sedimentation and stratigraphy 1041–1042
transgression 1041–1042
Palaeogene 1036–1040
sedimentation and stratigraphy 1036–1040
tectonics 1036, 1040–1041
volcanism 1040, 1042
North Sea Cycle 829, *830*
North Sudetic Basin 561–562
Cretaceous 959–960, *961*
North Swiss Permo-Carboniferous Basin 484–485, 565, *566*, 567
North Trégor Batholith 106, 113
North Variscan Foreland Basin, Carboniferous 428–430, *507*
Northeast German Basin, Rotliegend 545
Northern Calcareous Alps 1160, *1186*
Cretaceous 968, 970–971, *973*, 1171
Gosau Group 975–978
synorogenic 974
Jurassic 892–893, 894
radiolarite basin formation 895
Meliata Ocean 1168
Palaeogene, Gosau Group 1058–1060
Permian 551, *552*, 553, 580
Triassic 788, *789*, 790, 1162
Triassic–Jurassic boundary 826
Northern Gemeric Unit 491, 493, 494–495
Permian *568*, 569, *570*, 582
Northern German Dogger Group 842
Northern German Jurassic Supergroup 843
Northern German Lias Group 842
Northern German Malm Group 842–843
Northern Greywacke Zone 237
Northern Moravian Block 54
Northern Oberpfalz 455
Northern Permian Basin 14, 550, *551*, 1008, *1011*, *1012*
Northern Phyllite Zone 218, 601, 636
Carboniferous 430, 442–446
Late Ordovician–Silurian magmatism 695–697
tectonic setting 418
Northern Saxonian Slate Mountains 165, 224
Northwest European Basin
coal 1406–1407
petroleum 1419, 1420
Northwest Saxony 162

Northwest Saxony Volcanic Complex 729
Norway, North Sea, Chalk Group 938
Nossen-Wilsdruff Slate Belt 699, 700
Nötsch, Carboniferous sedimentation 475–476
Nové Město Belt 501, 625–626
Novohrad-Nógrád Basin 1068, 1070
Novoveská Huta U–Mo deposit 1382
Nowa Ruda Complex 689
Nowęcin Formation 182
Nowolesie Gneiss 68
NSDP seismic profile **332**, 336, 356
Numismalismergel Formation 865, *866*
Nýřany Member 468
Nysa Graben, Cretaceous 958, 959, *960*

Oberalm Formation 896, 970–971, 1162
Oberer Graptolithenschiefer Formation 271
Oberer (Solinger) Tonschiefer 215
Oberhäslich Formation *954*, 956
Oberhof Basin 547, *548*
Oberhof Formation 547, *548*
Oberpfalz, Late Devonian–Early Carboniferous magmatism 716–718
Oberpfalz Batholith 425, 469–470
Oberpfälzer Wald 180
Obtususton Formation 865, *866*
ocean closures 366–367
oceanography, *see* palaeoceanography
Ochtiná Unit 1204
Ociesęki Formation 174
  Lower Cambrian, palaeontology 188
Ockerkalk Formation 271, 276
Odenwald Crystalline Complex 67, 161–162, 447–449, *448*, *631*
  Late Devonian–Early Carboniferous magmatism 708–709
  Late Ordovician–Silurian magmatism 697–698
  Variscan metamorphism 630, 632
  *see also* Bergsträsser Odenwald; Böllstein Odenwald
Odenwald granitoids 425
Odolov Formation 499
Odra Fault Zone 52
Odra Formation 1042
Odra glaciation 1291, 1293
Oehrli Formation 968, *969*
Oelsnitz subbasin 465–466
Ohrazenice Formation 178
Ohře cycle 572, *575*, 580
Ohře Graben 1255
  lignite 1408
Ohře ramp *955*, 958
oil
  Alpine Foreland Basin *1422*, 1423–1424
  Carpathian Flysch Belt 1424
  Carpathian Foreland 1424
  Central Graben 1420–1421
  Lower Saxony Basin 1421
  Netherlands 841
  Pannonian Basin 1426
  Paris Basin 1421
  Po Basin *1422*, 1425
  production **1342**
  resources **1344**
  Upper Rhine Graben 1421, *1422*, 1423
  Vienna Basin *1422*, 1424–1425
  *see also* petroleum
oil shale
  Cenozoic basins 1409
  Cretaceous 1400
  Jurassic 841, 1397
  Messel Basin 1409
  production **1342**
  Triassic 1396
  *see also* Posidonia Shale Formation
Oisquercq Formation *159*, 161
Olching Formation 1050
Old Red Sandstone 385–386, 393
Older Granite 319, 716–718
Older Halite 577–579
olenids, Furongian 191
Oligocene
  climate 1032
  Eastern Alps, tectonics 1178, *1179*
  North Sea Basin *1037*, 1040
  palaeogeography *1032*
  Polish Lowland Basin 1044
  Upper Rhine Graben 1045
  Veneto 1090
Ølst Formation 1036
Olsztyn Formation 849, 851
Ombret Formation 212
oncolites, Jurassic
  southern Germany 868
  Swiss Jura 885, 886–887
oolites
  German Basin 772, 777
  Hungary 802
  Jurassic, northern Germany 846
  Swiss Jura 884–887
Opalinuston Formation *866*, 867, *883*, 884
ophiolites
  Grampian Orogeny 362
  mineralization 1395, 1399
  Mt Ślęża Complex 690
  Piedmont-Ligurian nappes 1158
  Valais Ocean 1155
  Variscan suture zones 417, *445*
ophiurids, Jurassic, Paris Basin 864
Opole Basin, Cretaceous 960–962
Orava succession 1196
Oravic Superunit 1185, 1193, 1196
Oravice Event 974
Oravicum 897
Ordovician 203–238
  glaciation 204
  magmatism 324, 328–329, 669–699
  Massif Central 59
  palaeoceanography 204, 205
  palaeoclimate 204–205
  palaeocontinental reconstruction *11*
  palaeogeography 205–206, 362
  palaeomagnetism 205
  Pyrenees 59
  sea-level change 205
  stratigraphical correlation *221, 226*
  stratigraphical subdivisions 203, *204*, *211*, *214*
  tectonic setting 205
  *see also* Cambrian–Ordovician boundary
Ordovician–Silurian, mineralization 1362–1364
Ordovician–Silurian boundary 249, 278
Ore-bearing Clay Formation 852
Origen (*c*.185-*c*.254AD) 3
Orla-Gołogłowy Unit 691
Orlica-Śnieżnik Massif *142*, 501, 625–626
  Cambrian–Early Ordovician magmatism 691–692
Orlice Graben, Permian *562*, 563
Orlice-Sneznik Complex *see* Orlica-Śnieżnik Massif
Orlice-Žd'ár sub-basin *954*, *955*, 956, 958
Ornatenton Formation 845–846, *866*, 868, 869
Orobic Basement 1166
orogenic collapse 616, 617, 646–647, 721
Orsha-Volhyn aulacogen 37, 184
Osięki Formation 183
Oskarshamn-Jönköping Belt 32
Oslo Graben, Carboniferous magmatism 428
Osning Sandstone *934*, 935
Osnitsk-Mikashevichi Igneous Belt *34*, *39*
Osterholz interglacial 1289
Östfold-Marstrand Belt *30*, 32–33
ostracods
  Caledonides 307
  Carboniferous 416
  Devonian 386, 387
    eastern Rhenish Massif 393
    Saxo-Thuringian Zone 403
  Jurassic
    Bohemian Massif 890
    northern Germany 843
    Paris Basin 860
  Ordovician
    Bohemian Massif 227–228
    Holy Cross Mountains *235*
    Saxo-Thuringian Zone 223
  Silurian
    Austria 282
    Franconian Terrane 269
    Montagne Noire 284
    Prague Basin 276
  Triassic 807
ostracods, Cretaceous 925, 935

Ostreenkalk Formation *866*, 867
Ostrong Unit 1357–1358
Ostrowiec Formation 849
Ottré Formation 213
Otzberg Shear Zone 447, *448*, 449, 630
Ötztal-Bundschuh Nappe System 1161, 1165, 1170
Ötztal-Stubai Crystalline Basement 187
Outer Carpathians, Polish, Palaeogene
palaeogeography 1078
palaeomagnetism 1078
sedimentation and stratigraphy 1078–1081
Overturned Thrust Sheets 637, 639
Ovid (43 BC-AD 17) 1
Oxfordian
Bohemian Massif 889–890
Northern Calcareous Alps 895–896
northern Germany *844*, 846
Polish Basin 857–858
southeast France 878–879
southern Germany *866*, 869–870
Swiss Jura 886–888, *887*
Western Carpathian basins 899, 900
Oxhe Formation 212
oxygen
atmospheric
Jurassic 829
Silurian 249
isotopes, Silurian *250*, 251
oysters
Cretaceous, Danish Basin 940
Jurassic, southern Germany 865, 867

PACE (Palaeozoic Amalgamation of Central Europe) 205
Paczyn Gneisses 686–687
Pag 1110
Paimpol Formation 56–57
Palaeo-Pacific Ocean 10
palaeoceanography
Cretaceous 923–924
Ordovician 204
Palaeocene
climate 1031–1032
North Sea Basin 1036, *1037*
sea-level change 1036
Palaeocene–Eocene boundary, Slovenian Tethys basins 1094, 1098
Palaeocene–Eocene thermal maximum 14, 1031, 1098
palaeoclimate
Carboniferous 412, 414–416
Cretaceous 923–924
Ordovician 204–205
Permian 531–533
Silurian 249
Triassic, Tethys Ocean 751–752, 766–767
palaeoclimatology 16–17
palaeocontinents, Silurian 253–255
Palaeogene 14
Alps 1051
biostratigraphy *1037,* 1042, 1044
Croatia and north Bosnia 1103
Helvetic Units 1049–1051
Inner Dinarides 1112
North Sea Basin 1036–1040
Outer Carpathians, Poland 1078–1081
Outer Dinarides 1111–1112
Slovenia *1095*, *1096*
Paratethys 1098–1100
Tethys 1098
Southern Alps, Italy 1087–1093
palaeogeography
Alps 1143–1145
Cambrian 155–158, 186–187
Caledonian terranes 358–368
Carboniferous 412, 420–424
Cenozoic *1032*, 1033–1035
Dinarides, Bosnia and Herzogovina 1111
North Alpine Foreland Basin 1054–1055
North Sea Basin *1039*
Upper Rhine Graben 1045, 1047
Cretaceous *924*, 930–931, *941*
Devonian 383–384
Jurassic *825*, *847*
Denmark 832
Paris Basin *861*
Southeast France Basin 880
Swiss Jura *887*
Neogene
Great Hungarian Plain 1073
Polish Carpathian Foredeep 1083
Ordovician 205–206
Palaeogene, Polish Outer Carpathians 1078
Permian *536*, *537*, 538
Rhenodanubian Flysch Zone 1054
Silurian 256
Slovenian Paratethys basins 1098
Triassic 751, *752*, 757–760, *768*
Variscan Orogeny 420–424
Western Carpathians 1185, 1187, *1188*, 1189
palaeohydrothermal activity 880
palaeomagnetic poles, Baltica *355*
palaeomagnetism
Carboniferous 420
Cenozoic 1033, *1034*, 1035
Outer Dinarides 1108
Ordovician 205
Palaeogene, Polish Outer Carpathians 1078
Permian 538
Precambrian 26, 27
Silurian 255–256
Tethys basins, Slovenia 1094
Triassic 757–760
palaeontology
Cambrian 187–192
Carboniferous 504–505
Jurassic 849–850, 854
Paris Basin 861
Permian 535, 583
Triassic 807–808
Palaeoproterozoic *22*, 23
Palaeotethys *12*
subduction 1012, 1014
Palaeozoic
Late, development of Europe 13–14
magmatism 665–733
palaeocontinental reconstruction *12*
Palaeozoic Amalgamation of Central Europe *see* PACE
Palaeozoic Platform
gravity modelling 347
magnetic field data 347
seismic surveys 345
Palatinate-Stockstadt Ridge 1048
Palfris Formation 968, *969*
Pałuki Formation 858
palynomorphs
Carboniferous 416
Cretaceous 925, 935
Devonian 386
Ordovician
Black Forest 216
Bohemian Massif 227
Brabant Massif 208
Saxothuringian Zone 219, 220, 223
Permian 535
Triassic, German Basin 760, *761*, 762–763, 764, 766
Pangaea *12*, 13, 14, 26
assemblage 415, 416, 420, 536, 599
megamonsoon 766
palaeomagnetic reconstruction 538
Permian 531–532
Triassic 1014
Pangaean Rim 538
Pannonian Basin *571*, 800, *801*, 1101–1102, 1113
Cenozoic coal seams 1409
Miocene 1189
Neogene *1061*, 1070–1072, 1103, *1104*, 1212–1213
oil and gas 1426
south, Bosnia and Herzogovina 1111–1112
Pannotia *see* Vendia Supercontinent
Panthalassa Ocean 531, 532, 536, 538
Paratethys basins
Slovenia 1098–1102
palaeogeography and tectonics 1098
sedimentation and stratigraphy 1098–1102
volcanism 1102
Paratethys Sea 1031
Parchim Formation *542*, 545, *546*

Paris Basin
  Jurassic 858–864
    geochemistry 864
    palaeogeography *861*
    palaeontology 861
    sequence stratigraphy 861
  Magnetic Anomaly 606
  oil 1421
  Triassic 1016–1017
Paseky Shales 176
  Lower Cambrian, palaeontology 188
Passwang Formation *883*, 884
Patacs Siltstone 805, *806*
Pavlovsko Formation 178
peat 1410
Pebidian Supergroup *44*, 45, 46, *47*
Pechelbronn beds 1047, 1048
pegmatites
  feldspar–quartz 1375, 1378
  LTC 1414
  Precambrian, southern Sweden 34
Pelso Megaunit 1185, 1187, 1210
Pelvoux Massif 1145–1146, *1147*
Penninic Basins, Cretaceous 966–967, 970, 975
Penninic Domain 79, *80*, 81–82, 891–896, 1143
  Palaeogene 1051–1053, 1173
    nappes 1155–1160, 1172
    Central Alps, Tertiary shear 1173–1174
    eastern Alps 1159–1160
    *see also* Sub-Penninic Nappes
  Permian 551, *552*, *553*
Penninic Ocean 891–892, 895, 967, 975
  Alpine tectonics 1143–1145, 1171, 1176, 1178
Pennsylvanian 416
Penthièvre Complex 109, 113, 120
Peri-Gondwana 25, *30*, *104*, 123, 667–668
  fragments 319
  palaeogeography 145, 157
  Silurian 254–255, 257, 258–259, 268–283
Peri-Gondwana-Baltica suture 157
Peri-Klippen Zone 1193, 1196
Peri-Pieniny Zone 49
Peri-Pieniny Lineament 1192
Peri-Tethys
  Triassic, tectonic setting 753–756
  Triassic palaeoclimate 751–752
Periadriatic Fault 276, *277*, 1166
  magmatism 1178
peridotite, Mt Ślęża Complex 690
Peripatetic philosophy 3
Perkupa Formation 582
perlite, resources 1405
Permian 531–586
  basin modelling 537–538
  Early, magmatism 723–733
  Early–Middle, basins 539–572, 1008
  intramontane basins 550–572, 1008
  Late, basins 572–583
  Late–Mid Triassic, tectonics 1012–1013
  mineralization 1387–1392
  palaeoclimate 531–533
  palaeocontinental reconstruction *12*
  palaeogeography *536*, *537*, 538
  palaeomagnetism 538
  palaeontology 583
  sea-level change 532–533
  stratigraphy 533–536, *533*, *584–585*
  tectonics 536–538, 1005, 1008
    Alps 1168
Permian–Triassic boundary 749–751
  extinctions 583, 749, 751, 807
  stratotype section 759
Peruc Member *954*, 955
Perunica microcontinent 206
  Silurian 254–255, 257, 258
    biostratigraphy 276
    Moldanubian Zone 272–276
Petit Commune Formation 158, *159*
Petit-Mont Member, stromatactis mounds 390
Petites Tailles Formation 213
petroleum, resources 1379, 1419–1426
  *see also* oil
petroleum geology, Netherlands 841
Petrova gora Mountain, mineral deposit 1385
Petrová Hora Formation 569
Pfahl Fault 1254
Phanerozoic
  collision and rift history *13*
  tectonic units *2*
phosphate, resources, Variscan basement 1416–1417
phosphorus, resources 1400
*Phycodes* Group 220, *221*, 222
phyllite
  Erzgebirge Crystalline Complex 451, 669
  *see also* Northern Phyllite Zone
Phylloceratidae 825
Piaśnica Formation 184
Piedmont-Ligurian Ocean 1143, *1144*, 1145, 1156, 1168–1169
  Upper Penninic nappes 1157–1159
Pieniny Basin 897, 898
Pieniny Klippen Belt 896–897, 1185, 1191–1193, *1195*, 1196–1198
  Cretaceous 970, 978
  tectonic evolution *1194*, *1195*, 1198
Pieniny Limestone Formation 970, *972*
Pieniny succession 1196
Pieniny Unit 1196
Pieprzowe Formation 174
Piesenkopf Formation 975
Pilbara Craton *22*, 23
Pindos Ocean 1014, 1016
Pinerolo Unit 1152, 1157
Pingarten Porphyry 1383
Pisznice Formation 827
Plaňava Formation 970, *972*
Planitz Formation 564
Plankogel Complex 1163, 1165
plants
  Carboniferous 504–505
  Devonian
    eastern Rhenish Massif 393
    southeastern Poland 395, 396
  forest
    Eemian Interglacial Stage 1294–1295
    Holsteinian interglacial 1292, *1296*
    Weichselian Cold Stage *1301*
  halophytic, Cenomanian 956
  Holocene 1298, *1302*
  Jurassic
    Denmark 833
    Poland 850
  Permian 583
Plassen Formation 896
plate tectonics, Precambrian 21, 23
platinum group elements, resources 1362, 1364–5, 1389, 1392
Plato (*c*.428-*c*.348BC) 3
Platta Nappe 1158–1159
Plattenkalk 786–787
Platy Dolomite 579–580
playa deposits
  Buntsandstein 772, 782
  Jurassic, Poland and Ukraine 857
  Keuper 766–767, *768*, 778
Pleising Nappe 693
Pleistocene
  GSSP, Vrica section 1287
  Lower, ice age 1288–1289
  mammals 1298–1300, *1303*, 1304
  Middle, north–central Europe, ice age 1289–1294
  Middle Pleistocene Event 1305
  north–central Europe
    aeolian sediments 1310, 1315–1318
    fluvial record 1310–1315
  subdivision 1287–1288, *1289*
  Upper, north–central Europe, ice age 1294–1298
Plenus Marl Formation 938
Plettenberger Bänderschiefer 215
Pliensbachian
  northern Germany 843, *844*
  Poland 849
  southeast France 876–877
  southern Germany 865, *866*
  Swiss Jura 881, 883
Pliny the Elder (AD 23–79) 3
Pliocene
  climate 1033, 1042
  Dinarides 1105

North Sea Basin 1042
Paratethys basins 1102
Polish Lowland Basin 1044
Pliocene–Pleistocene boundary 1287
north–central Europe, drainage patterns *1291*
pollen, Rhine sediment terraces 1313
Pliocene-Pleistocene, glaciation 14
Plöcken facies 277, 278–279
Plöcken Formation 278, 279
Plouer-Cancale Shear Zone *107*, 115, 116
plutonism
North Armorican Massif 106, 109, 112, 115
Stephanian–Early Permian 723–724
plutons
Bohemian Massif 179–180, 716
Caledonian granite 321, 323
Cambrian, Bohemian Massif 179–180
Central Bohemian Plutonic Complex 713–715
Erzgebirge Crystalline Complex 453, 454, 716–718
Fichtelgebirge Crystalline Complex 456, 716–718
Lithuania 40–41
Moldanubian Plutonic Complex 715–716
Odenwald Crystalline Complex 447–448
Saxo-Thuringian Zone 64, 136
Variscan granitoid 424–427
Po Basin
formation 14
oil and gas *1422*, 1425
Podgórki Volcanic Complex 688
Podlasie Basin 260
Podlasie Basin Silurian 265
Podlasie Complex 35
Podlasie-Belarus Granulite Belt 36, 38, *39*
Podmiedznik Formation 970, *972*
Podolecka series 851
Pogallo Shear Zone 1166
Pohorje Pluton 1178
Pohorje Trough, Devonian 405
Poland
Baltic Basin, Cambrian 182–184
Baltica, Silurian 263–267
Bundsandstein Formation, basin evolution 769–781
Carboniferous sedimentation 441–442, *443*
Carpathian Foredeep, Neogene 1083–1084, *1085*
Carpathian Foreland, tectonic evolution 1258–1270
Cretaceous 927–928
Jurassic 846–858
sequence stratigraphy 829, *830*, 831, 850–851
tectonic development 846–849
neotectonics 1265–1270, *1266*
north and northeastern, Cambrian 184
northeast, Precambrian 34–38
northwestern, Cambrian 182–184
Ordovician 229–236
Outer Carpathians, Palaeogene 1078–1081
Permian basins 563
Pomerania, Ordovician 218
Precambrian
northeastern 34–38
southeastern 48–52
Quaternary
glaciation 1291, 1293, 1297, *1299*
tectonism 1265–1270
southeastern, Devonian 394–397
southwest, Variscan tectonics 622–627, 639–640
Sudetes magmatism 326–328, 622–627, 1264–1265
Zechstein *574*, *575*
Polesie Formation 38
Polish Basin 999, *1000*, 1001, *1004*
Buntsandstein 1013
Jurassic 846–858, *1004*
Permian 540–543, *544*
sequence stratigraphy 535
Jurassic 829, *830*, 831, 850
Zechstein *574*, *1004*
Polish Jura Chain 851, 852, 854, 855
Polish Lowlands Basin
Cenozoic 1042–1044, *1264*
faulting and graben development 1261–1263
palaeogeography and tectonics 1042
sedimentation and stratigraphy 1042–1044
volcanism 1044
Polish Trough *784*
pollen
Holocene 1298, *1302*
Jurassic
Paris Basin 860
Poland 849–850
Last Glacial Maximum 1309
Lower Pleistocene 1288
Middle Pleistocene 1289–1290, 1292, 1293
Plio-Pleistocene, Rhine sediment terraces 1313
Upper Pleistocene 1294, *1296*, *1299*, *1301*
POLONAISE seismic project 331, **332**, 340, 345, *348*, 357–358
polymeroids, Middle Cambrian 190
Pomerania
Devonian 387
Jurassic 849, 850, *853*, 854
Ordovician 218
Silurian 263
Triassic–Jurassic boundary 827
Western
Carboniferous sedimentation 429–430
Cretaceous 948–949
Pomerania Formation 1044
Pomeranian Basin, Lower Cretaceous 931
Pomeranian-Rügen Caledonides 186, 315–316
Pomorska Formation 772
Pompeckj High 935, 936, 942, 944, *946*, 947
Ponikev Formation 502
Poniklá/Czarnów Formation 686, 687
Ponte Gardena Conglomerate 554–555
poriferids, Lower Cambrian 188
porphyry mineral deposits 1402–1404
Port Morvan pluton 112
Poruba Formation 1205, 1206
Posidonia Shale Formation 828, 837, *838*, 841, 865, *866*, 867
Post Collisional Deposits, Massif Central 484
potash
evaporite resources 1391, 1401
Zechstein 573, *574*, 1391
Potrójna Formation 171
Pötschen Limestone 804–805
Pouzdřany Unit 1190
Považsky Inovec Mountains 1199
Požáry Formation 275
Poznań Basin 562
Poznań Formation 1044
PQ2 seismic project **332**, 340, 342
Prabuty Formation 184
Praetiglian, climate change 1288
Pragian
Barrandian area 400
Moravia 398–399
Saxo-Thuringian Zone 403
southeastern Poland 395
Pragowiec Beds 266
Prague Basin, Silurian 255, 258, 272–276
Prague Basin facies 257, 272
Prasinite-Phyllite Series 671
Pre-Piedmontais nappes 1157
Préalpes Médianes Nappe *see* Klippen Nappe
Precambrian 21–84, *23*
atmosphere *22*, 23
continental crust formation 21, *22*
life 24
palaeogeography 26–28, *29*, *30*
subdivision 21, *23*
tectonic units *2*
Precambrian–Cambrian, metallogenesis 1357–1359
Predajná Formation 581
Preisselberg granite 722–723
Preremarton Supergroup 1072, 1073
Presumed Autochthonous Complexes, Massif Central 483–484

Pretzsch-Prettin area, Late Devonian-Early Carboniferous 710–711
Příbram-Jince Basin 176–178, *179*, 677
  palaeontology 188, 190
Přídolí *252*, 253
  Austria 277–279
  Belgium 286, 287
  Franconian Terrane 269
  Lithuania 260, 261, *262*, 263
  Montagne Noire 284, *285*
  Poland 263, 266–267
  Prague Basin 272, *273*, 276
Prignitz Basin, Cretaceous 936
Pripyat-Dneper Basin, Jurassic 856
Proman antiform 1166
Promina Beds 1110, 1111, 1112
Promise lead–zinc mine 1410–1411
Prosečné Formation 559
Proterozoic 21, *23*
Proto-Alps Terrane 645
  palaeogeography 258–259
Protogine Zone *30*, *31*, 32
  dolerites 34
Provence Platform 877, 878, 879
Provence White Limestone 879
Pruské succession 1193
Przysucha Ore-bearing Formation 849
Pseudoschwagerina Limestone 554
Psilonotenton Formation 865, *866*
Purpurberg Quartzite 131, *132*, *134*
Puzzle Hole Formation *838*, 839
Pyrenees, Precambrian 59
pyrite 1361, 1362, 1363
pyrrhotite 1361, 1363

quartz, resources 1375, 1378
  pegmatites 1414
  sand, Cenozoic basins 1406
  vein-type 1412
Quartzdiorite-Granodiorite-Complex 630, *631*
quartzophyllades 213
Quaternary 1287–1333
  faults, Poland 1267–1270
  ice-ages 1287–1310
    *see also* Pleistocene
  mineral resources 1409–1410
  stratigraphic subdivision *1289*, *1307*
  volcanism, Eifel volcanic fields 1318–1333
Quinten Formation 968, *969*

Raabs Unit 693
Raabs-Meisling Unit 612
Rab 1110
Rabenwald talc deposit 1411
Rača subunit 1191
radiolarians
  basin formation, Northern Calcareous Alps 895
  Devonian, Moravia 399
  Jurassic, southern Germany 870
  Silurian 282
Radków Bluff Sandstone 959
Radnice Group coal 468
Radom region
  Devonian 396
  Silurian 266–267
Radzimowice Slate 230
Radzomowice Unit 688
Radzyń Formation 186
Rahlenberger Grauwackenschiefer 215
Raibl Formation 798
Rakovec Unit 1204
Rammelsberg, sulphide ores 1365–1366
Ran Ocean 364
Rand Granite 473
  Variscan tectonics *607*, 608, 609, *610*, 611
Randamonys Complex 40
Randamphibolit Unit 671
Randschiefer Formation *see* Gösmes Formation
Rannach Nappe 276, 282
Ransko Complex, mineral deposits 1362
rapakivi
  Mazury Complex *34*, 35, 36–37
  Ryga Batholith 41
Rastenberg Pluton 716
Rastrites Shales Formation 267, 268
Rattendorf Group 553–554
Rauchkofel Boden 277–278, *279*
Rawa Ruska Formation 857
Rázdiel Unit 1205
Recent
  North German Basin, stresses and seismicity 1273–1275
  Poland, stress fields 1269–1270, *1271*
Rechnitz Window Group 893, 894, 1180
  Penninic nappes 1159
Reckner Complex 1159
reconstruction, palaeocontinental
    Cenozoic *15*
    Mesozoic *15*
    Neoproterozoic *11*, 358–359
    Palaeozoic *12*
    Precambrian *27–30*
redwitzite 716–717
reefs
  Devonian
    Barrandian area 400
    eastern Rhenish Massif 393–394
    Moravia 399
  Jurassic, southern Germany *866*, 869–871
  Triassic 807, 826
  Triassic–Jurassic boundary 894
  Zechstein 576
regression
  Devonian 389–391, 396
  Neogene, North Alpine Foreland Basin 1056
  Oligocene, Polish Lowland Basin 1044
  *see also* transgression–regression
Rehberg Complex, Cambrian–Early Ordovician magmatism 692–694
Reichenhall Formation 788, *789*
Reinbek transgression 1041
Reiselsberg Formation 975
remobilization, hydrothermal 1426–1427
Remscheid anticline 215, 315
Renggeriton Member *866*, 868, 869
Rennertshofen Formation *866*, 872
Rensen Pluton 1178
Répáshuta Limestone 802
reptiles
  Jurassic, southern Germany 867
  Triassic 760, 808
reservoirs, oil and gas, Zechstein 573
Reuchenette Formation *887*, 888
Reuver Clay 1313
Reuverian Stage *1291*
Revin Group 158, *159*
Řevnice Quartzite 227
Rhaetian 781, 790
rhax, Jurassic, Bohemian Massif 890
Rheic Ocean 10, *11*, *12*, 25–26, 205, 313, *445*
  closure 363, 418, 420, 474
  suture 55, 121, 123, 305, 317, 356–357, 418, 420, 599, *600*, 602, 645
    *see also* Mid-German Crystalline High
Rhein Graben, Late Devonian–Early Carboniferous magmatism 708
Rheinisches Schiefergebirge *see* Rhenish Massif
Rheinsberg Lineament *1010*
Rheinsberg Trough *1000*, 1001, 1003, *1009*, 1016
Rhenish Massif 315
  Carboniferous sedimentation 438–441, 636
  Cenozoic tectonics 1242–1243
  Devonian 391–394
    magmatism 701–704, *705*
  seismicity 1243
  Silurian 287
  uplift 1243
  Variscan tectonics 633–636
Rhenodanubian Flysch Zone
  Cretaceous 967, 970, *973*, 975
  Palaeogene *1046*, 1050, 1053–1054
  Penninic nappes 1150, 1159
Rhenohercynian Basin 418, 419, 420–421
  Carboniferous 430–431
Rhenohercynian Ocean 13, 384, 420, 646, 700
  closure 418, 707
Rhenohercynian Zone 13, 46–48, *61*, *63*, *122*, 601

Carboniferous
sedimentation and magmatism 430–442, *507*, 636
Belgium and France 431–438
Devonian 388–399
magmatism 700–701
Germany 316
tectonic setting 418
Rhine Valley
Quaternary sediment 1310–1315
Rhineland-Palatinate, Variscan evolution 632
Rhodanian Basin 880–881
Rhône Glacier 1308
Rhône-Bresse Graben 1235, *1236*, 1240
Rhume interglacial 1289–1290
Říčany Suite 715
Rickenbach Member *882*, 883
Rieden volcanic complex *1323*, 1325–1326
Ries meteorite impact crater 865, *1246*, 1248, 1056
Rieserferner Pluton 1178
Rietheim Member *882*, 883
Rifgronden Member 840
rifting
Cretaceous 1019, *1020*
Jurassic 1017, *1018*, 1019
Alps 1168–1169
Denmark 836
Lower Saxony rift system *541*, 545
Permian, Early 1005, 1008
Triassic 1016
Triassic–Jurassic, southern Alps 1167
Upper Rhine Graben 1240–1241
Variscan 614
Rigenée Formation 208–209
Rijeka hinterland 1110
Ringkøbing-Fyn High *551*, 928, *1000*, 1001
Jurassic 832, 835, 836
Zechstein 1013
Rissian Glaciation *see* Most Extensive Glaciation
rivers
Quaternary sediment terraces 1288, 1290, 1292, 1310–1315
*see also* individual river names
Robbedale Formation 936
Roches à Sept Heures Formation 158, *159*
Rocroi Massif 158, *159*, *189*, 213, 315
Variscan tectonics 637
Rodinia 10, *22*, 23, 358, *359*, 360
reconstruction *11*, 26, *27*
Roer Valley Graben 433, 437, 782, *784*, 1241, *1242*
Cretaceous inversion 949, *950*, 952, 1241
Jurassic 837, *838*, 839, 841
Rögling Formation *866*, 871, 872
Rohatce Member *954*, 958
Roitzsch Formation 461
Rókahegy Dolomite 805, *806*
Rokytná Conglomerate 562–563
Romans, geological writings 1, 3
Rønne Formation 833–834
Rønne Graben 833–834
subsidence 936
Rønne-Hasle Fault 834
Ronquières Formation 286
Roquemaillère Black Shale 284
Rossfeld Basin, Cretaceous 971
Rosslare Complex 46, *47*
Rostotchya Formation 1045
Röt Formation 763–764, 774–776, 782
Denmark 784
Hungary 805
Rote Wand-Modereck Nappe 1154
Rotgneiss Complex 449, 630, *631*, 698–699
Rothenfluh Member *883*, 884
Rothstein Formation, backarc basin 125–127, *132*, 133
Rotliegend 533–535, 583, 586
Bohemian Massif 559–563
Denmark 550
Döhlen Basin 563
Hessian Basin 545
Kraichgau-Saale Basin 545–547
magmatism 539
Netherlands 550
Northeast German Basin 545
Polish Basin 540–543, *544*
Saale Basin 546–547
southeastern Variscides 563
tectonics 1005, 1008–1009, *1011*
Thuringian Forest Basin 547, *548*
rottenstone *see* tripoli
Rotterode Formation 547, *548*
Rožňava Formation 569
Rožňava Suture 1210
Ruda Lubycka Formation 857
Rude mineral deposit 1384, *1385*
Rudawy Janowickie Complex *see* East Karkonosze Complex
Rudina Formation 970, *972*
Rudňany Formation 495
Rügen 315–316
affinity 309, 317
boreholes 216–217
Cambrian 186
Devonian 386–387
Ordovician *214*, 216–218, 365–366
Precambrian 43
Tournaisian sedimentation 428, *506*
Rügen-Usedom, Cretaceous 948–949
Ruhla Crystalline Complex 67, 162, 449–450, *462*, 547, 628–630
Late Devonian–Early Carboniferous magmatism 709–710
Ruhla Group 628, *629*
Ruhr Basin 438–439, *506*
coal 1367–1370
Rumunic Ridge 1170, 1171
Rupelian, Upper Rhine Graben 1048
Rüsselsheim Basin 1048
Rüssingen Formation 1048
Rya Formation 835
Ryga Batholith 40–41
Rzepin Beds 266, 267
Rzeszotary Horst 49, 51
Rzeszówek-Jakuszowa Unit 688

Saale Basin 460–462, *506*
Rotliegend 546–547
Stephanian–Early Permian magmatism 728–729
Saalian, mammals 1300
Saalian Complex Stage 1291, 1292–1294, *1298*
Saalian Unconformity 535
Saar-Lorraine Basin, coal resources 1387–1388
Saar-Nahe Basin 458–460, *461*, *506*, 632
Rotliegend 545, *547*, 557–559
Stephanian–Early Permian magmatism 726–727
Sächsisches Granulitgebirge *see* Saxonian Granulite Massif
Sádek Formation 176
St Bernard Nappe 1157
St Brieuc Unit 55, *56*
St Helens gabbro 46
St Malo Unit *56*, 57
St Marein-Freischling Formation 1056, 1057
St Martin de Bossenay Fault 858, *859*
Saint-Brieuc Terrane 109, **111**, 112–114, 116, 118–119, **119**, 120, 121
Saint-Malo Terrane **111–112**, 114–115, 116, 118–120, **119**, 121
Sakmarian, palaeogeography *536*
salt *see* diapirism; evaporites; halokinesis
Salvan-Dorénaz Basin 486–487, *488*, *489*, *490*
Salzberg Formation 948
San Giovanni Bianco Formation 798
San Salvatore Formation 796
Sana-Una Palaeozoic mineral deposit 1385
Sandersdorf Formation 460
Sándorhegy Formation 802
Sandsteinkeuper subgroup 766
Sanian glaciation 1291
Sankt Pankraz Member 1051
Säntis-Drusberg Nappe 1148, *1149*, 1150
Santonian
Bohemian Cretaceous Basin 958
Danish Basin 938, 340
Gosau Group 978
Liège-Limburg Basin 949
Mid-Polish Trough 942
North German Basin *943*

inversion tectonics 947–948
Western Carpathians 978
Sanzenkogel Formation 476
Sarajevo-Zenica Basin 1105, *1106*, 1112
Sarbsko Formation 183
Sardona Flysch 1150
Sark, Precambrian basement 106–109
Šárka Formation 227
Sarmatia *34*, 37
Sarmatian, Paratethys basins 1101
Sarn Complex *44*, 45, 46, *47*
Sart-Bernard Formation 212
Saualpe-Koralpe-Pohorje Complex 1163, 1171
Sava Fault 1111
Saxo-Thuringian Basin 462–465
Saxo-Thuringian Terrane, Silurian 270–271
Saxo-Thuringian Zone 13, 60, *61*, 601, *618*
allochthonous domain 621–622
autochthonous domain 619, *620*
back-arc basin 125–127, *132*, 133, 135, *139*, 146
Cadomian basement *122*, 123–137, *141*, 145, 146
Cambrian 157, 162–170, *620*, 669
Carboniferous sedimentation 446–466, *507*
Devonian depositional environments 402–403, 619, *620*
isotopic data **125**
Ordovician 218–225, *620*
passive margin shelf basin 131, 132–137, *134*, 146
plutons 64, 136
Precambrian 66–67
retro-arc basin 129, *132*, 133, 135, *140*, 146
Silurian 254, 257–258, *620*
tectonic setting 419
uranium resources 1377
Variscan tectonic evolution 617–622
wrench-and-thrust zone 619, *620*, 621
Saxonian Granulite Massif *63*, 66–67, 456–457, *459*, 621–622
Cambrian 169
Ordovician 219
Saxony
northern, Ordovician 224
Northwest 162
Saxony-Anhalt
Cretaceous 945
Mid-German Crystalline Zone 628
Sázava Pluton 714–715
Scaglia rossa 1089
Scaliger, Joseph (1540–1609) 4
Scandian Orogeny 309
Scandinavian Caledonides 309
seismic surveys **332**, 337–340
Scanian Confacies Belt 260, 268
Schambelen Member 881, *882*
Schams Nappe *1148*, 1156
Schaumburg Sandstone 845
Schellenbrücke Bed 886
Schellerhau granite 722–723
Schieferhülle 630, *631*, 632
Schieferzüge, Odenwald Crystalline Complex 447
Schieland Group, Jurassic *838*, 839
Schilfsandstein 754, 756, 778, *779*, 787
Schill Grund Member *838*, 840, 841
Schin op Geul Fault 951, 952
Schiste carton 864
Schleitheim Bed 881
Schleswig-Holstein, Ordovician 218
Schlieren Flysch 1053
Nappe 1158
Schmalwasserstein-Rennweg gneiss 450
Schmiedefeld Erzhorizont 223
Schmiedefeld Formation 223
Schneeberg Nappe 1168
Schnöll Formation *893*, 895
Schöneck Formation 545
Schönfeld Unit 721, 722
Schöningen Interglacial 1293
Schoonebeek oil field 841
Schrattenkalk Formation *969*, 970
Schwarzburg Anticline *330*, 621
Cambrian 166–167
Cambrian–Early Ordovician magmatism 681–682
Ordovician 219, 220–223, *221*
Schwarzburg Unit 62, *64*, 123, *128*, *141*
backarc basin 125–127
Cadomian retro-arc basin 129, 131
isotopic data **125**
Kernzone Complex 127, 129
passive margin basin 135–136
Schwarzeck Formation *893*, 894
Schwarzwald *see* Black Forest
Schweinheim Formation 449, 630, *631*
Schlern Formation 796, 797
Sciliar Formation *see* Schlern Formation
Ścinawka Unit 691
scoria cones, Eifel volcanic fields 1320, *1324*
Scotland, Grampian Orogeny *322*
Scruff Greensand Formation *838*, 840, 841
Scruff Group *838*, 839–840
sea-level change
Cenozoic, Transylvanian Basin 1076, 1078
Cretaceous 923, 924, 935–936, 1021, *1022*
Bohemian Cretaceous Basin 953, 955–958
Devonian 384–385, 399
Eocene, North Sea Basin 1039–1040
Jurassic 829, 831–832
Denmark 832, 833–836
Polish Basin 850–851, 854–858
southeast France 876–879
Western Carpathian basins 898–900
Miocene, North Sea Basin 1041
Neogene
Croatia 1105
Styrian Basin 1064
Vienna Basin 1062
Ordovician 205
Palaeocene 1036
Palaeogene, Helvetic Units 1051
Permian 532–533
Silurian 249–251, 277–278, 279, 284
Triassic 752–753, 1014
*see also* transgression–regression
seaways *see* gateways, marine
Sebesvíz Conglomerate 802
SEDEX mineralization 1365, 1384, *1385*, 1394–1395
sediment
aeolian *see* loess
fluvial *see* rivers, Pleistocene sediment terraces
sedimentation
Cambrian
Baltic Basin 182–184
Saxo-Thuringian Zone 136–137
Carboniferous, and magmatism 428–482
Cenozoic
Polish Lowlands 1042–1044
Upper Rhine Graben 1047–1049
Cretaceous 925–930
Early, epicontinental basins 931–936
Late, epicontinental basins 937–953
Lower Jurassic 849–851, 861, 864, 876–877, 880–881, 883
Western Carpathian basins 898–899, 900
Middle Jurassic 851–857, 864, 877–878, 883–886
Western Carpathian basins 899, 900
Neogene, North Sea 1041–1042
Ordovician, Brabant Massif 207–210
Palaeogene, Helvetic Units 1049
post-Cadomian 116
Quaternary 1310–1318
Upper Jurassic 840–841, 857–858, 864, 878–879, 886–889
Western Carpathian basins 899, 900
Seewen Formation 975
Seidlwinkl Nappe 1154
seismic data
Caledonian Orogeny 329, 331, **332**
British Caledonides 333–337
seismicity *see* earthquakes
Selb Granitic Gneiss 456
Selec Phase 1215
selenium, resources 1372
Seneca, Lucius Annaeus, the younger (*c.* 3 BC–AD 65) 3
Sengenthal Formation *866*, 868

Senice Shales 179
Sennely Fault 858, *859*
Senovo Basin 1101
Sequanian platform 879
sequence stratigraphy, Jurassic, Paris Basin 861
serpulids, Triassic 807
Sesia Nappe *1151*, 1157–1159, 1173
shale, black *see* black shale; oil shale
shear, Tertiary, Central Alps 1173–1174
shelly fauna facies 257, 272, 274, 275
Shetland Group 937
siderite
  resources 1361–1362, 1363, 1364, 1365
    replacement 1385–1387
    vein-type 1372
Siegen Thrust 1323
Siemień Formation 1044
Silbersberg Nappe 1163
Silesian 416
  sedimentation 433–434
Silesian Basin
  Carboniferous, coal 1388
  Jurassic 898
  Palaeogene 1078–1081
Silesian Unit 1190
Silesian-Krosno units 1190
Silesian-Moravian Gate 775–776, 777, 782
Silesicum *see* East Sudetes
silica, resources, Cenozoic back-arc and rift basins 1404–1405
Silica Nappe 495, 1201
Silicic Superunit 1201
  tectonics 1207–1208, *1209*
Silicicum *568*, *570*, 582, 897
Sillenkopf Basin 895
Silurian 249–291
  magmatism 694–699
  palaeoclimate 249
  palaeocontinents 253–255, *12*
  palaeogeography 256
  palaeomagnetism 255–256
  sea-level change 249–251
  stratigraphical subdivisions 249, *250*, 251, *252*, 253
  tectonic setting 253
  volcanism, Prague Basin 272
  *see also* Ordovician–Silurian boundary
Silurian–Devonian boundary 400
silver
  production **1342**
  resources
    arc-related 1402–1404
    vein-type 1371–1372, 1377
Silvretta Nappe 187
Silvretta-Seckau Nappe System *1161*, 1163, 1170
Simplon Fault 1175–1176
Sindelfingen Graben 1248, 1249–1250
Sinemurian
  northern Germany 843, *844*
  Poland 849
  southeast France 876
  southern Germany 865, *866*
  Swiss Jura 881, 883
  Western Carpathian basins 898–900
Sissach Member *883*, 884
Sjaelland, Cretaceous 939
Skagerrak-Kattegat Platform, Jurassic 835, 836
Skalka Quartzite 227
Skalniak-Szczeliniec Sandstone 959
Skåne, Cretaceous 940
skarn mineral deposits 1376, 1402–1404, 1414
Skłoby Formation 849
Skole Basin, Palaeogene 1078–1081
Skole Unit 1190
Skryje Shale, palaeontology 190
Skryje-Týřovice Basin 178–179, 677
  palaeontology 190
Skrznka shear zone 501
Slaný Formation 468–469
Slatviná Formation 495
Slavkov Terrane 52, *53*, 54, 144–145
Slavkov Unit, isostopic data **124**
Slawatycze series 37–38
Sleen Formation 837
Slovak Basin, south Cenozoic 1068–1070
Slovak Karst Mountains 1208, *1209*, 1210
Slovak Ore Mountains 1200, 1201
Slovakia
  Permian 567, *568*, 569–570
  Western Carpathians Carboniferous basins 488, 490–496, *506*
Slovako-Carpathian tectonic system 1201–1208
Slovenia
  Neogene *1095*
  Palaeogene *1095*, *1096*
  Paratethys basins 1098–1102
  Tethys basins 1093–1098
Słowiec Formation 174
Słowińska Formation 183
Småland-Värmland Granite-Porphyry Belt *see* Trans-Scandinavian Igneous Belt
smectite, resources
  Cenozoic back-arc and rift basins 1404–1405
  Cenozoic foreland basins 1402
Smolnik Formation, sulphide ores 1366
Smrekovica Unit 1205
Śnieżnik Massif 68, 691–692
Snowball Earth hypothesis 24
sodium, evaporite resources 1391, 1392–1393, 1397
Sokal Formation 857
Solingen Shale Formation 287
Solírov Phase 1214
Solling Formation 782
Solnhofen Formation *866*, 872
Somogy-Mecsek-Kiskunhalas Basin 1072
Sorgenfrei-Tornquist Zone 28, 343, 352, 357–8, 1001, *1002*, 1003, 1005
  Cretaceous 928, 940
  Jurassic 832, 835, 836
Sorthat Formation 834, 835
Sose Bugt Member 833–834
Sosnowiec Formation 170–171
South Alpine Domain 79, *80*, 81, 1143
  tectonics 1165–1167, 1172
South Armorican Shear Zone 104, *107*
South Bohemian Basins, Cretaceous 959
South Bohemian Main Thrust 612
South Brandenburg, Mid-German Crystalline Zone 628
South European terranes 383
  Devonian, depositional environments 403–406
South German Triangle 1243–1253
  Cenozoic tectonics 1245–1253
  faults and stresses 1246–1249, *1252*, *1253*
  seismicity 1245–1246, *1247*, *1248*
South Hunsrück Unit 443, 444
South Karkonosze Complex, Cambrian–Early Ordovician magmatism 684–685
South Slovak basins 1068–1070
South Taunus Unit 443, 444, 445
Southern Alpine basins, Cretaceous 968
Southern Black Forest Gneiss Complex 473, *607*
  Variscan tectonics 608, 609, *610*, 611
Southern Bohemian Batholith 425, 426, 469–470
Southern Gemeric Unit *568*, 569–570, 582
Southern Gneiss Unit, Late Devonian–Early Carboniferous magmatism 712
Southern Palaeozoic Nappe Complexes, Massif Central 484
Southern Permian Basin 14, *532*, 535, 538, 539–550, 1008, *1011*, *1012*
  gas 1419–1420
  grabens 540, *541*
  modelling 537
Southern Phyllite Zone, Cambrian–Early Ordovician magmatism 681–682
Southern Steep Belt 1175
Southern Veporic Unit 495
Southern Vosges Basin 470–472, 713
Søvind marls 1040
Sovolusky Group 72
Spessart Crystalline Complex 67, 449, 630, *631*
  Cambrian 162
  Late Devonian–Early Carboniferous magmatism 709
  Late Ordovician–Silurian magmatism 698–699
  Silurian, Saxo-Thuringian Zone 271
Spießnägel section 282

spilites 138
Spitz Gneiss 693
sponges
  Cretaceous, Danish Basin 940
  Jurassic
    Bohemian Massif 890
    southern Germany 869, 870–1, 872
  Triassic 807
spores
  Devonian 389
  Jurassic, Poland 849–850, 857, 858
  Silurian 251, *252*
Sprendlinger Horst 545
St-Julien High 873, 878
Stachów Complex 501, 689
Staffelegg Formation 881, *882*
Stangnock Formation 477–478, 551
Stanner-Hanter Complex *44*, 45, 46, *47*
Staré Hlavy Formation 974
Staré Hory Unit 1205
Staré Město Belt 501, 626
  Cambrian–Early Ordovician magmatism 692
Starlera Nappe 1156
Stassfurt cycle 572, *574*, *575*, 577
Stavelot-Venn Anticline 214
Stavelot-Venn Massif 158, *159*, *211*, 213, 315, 1243
Štěchovice Group 71, 73, 74, 75, 138–139
Steige Unit 258, 633
Steinach Nappe 478, 1165
Steinalm Limestone 788, *789*, 803
Steinmergelkeuper 756, 766, 780–781
Steinplatte reef 826, 894
Steno, Nicolaus (1638–1686) 5
Stephanian
  sedimentation 508
    North German Basin 429
Stephanian–Early Permian, magmatism 723–733
Stephanian–Lower Rotliegend, magmatism 539
Stevns Klint 939–940, 1040
Štítnik Formation 582
Stod Granite 616
Stoic philosophy 3
Stolzalpen Nappe 1165
Štós Unit 1204
Strabo (*c*.63 BC–after AD 21) 3
Strašice Complex 179
stratigraphy, early ideas 5–6
Stráž orthogneiss 78
Strážovské vrchy mountains 1199
Strehlen Formation *954*, 958
strike-slip tectonics
  British Caledonides 337
  Oligocene, Dinarides 1111
  Variscan Orogen 647
stromatactis mounds
  Devonian
    Ardennes 390, 391
    Barrandian area 400
stromatolites 1397
  Buntsandstein 772
  and gypsum precipitation 1397
  Hungary 802, 803
  Jurassic, Polish Basin 854
  Precambrian *22*, 24
  Triassic 807
stromatoporoids
  Devonian 387, 390, 391
    Barrandian area 400
    eastern Rhenish Massif 393, 394
    Moravia 399
    Saxo-Thuringian Zone 403
    southeastern Poland 396, 397
Strona-Ceneri Zone 1166
Stronie Formation 692
strontium, resources 1400
strontium isotopes
  Cretaceous 925
  Silurian *250*, 251
Strzelin Complex 68, *142*, 501, 689
Strzelin Gneiss 68, 145
Stubensandstein Member 788
Stuttgart Formation 766
Styrian Basin, Neogene 1063–1064
Styrian Unconformity 1101
Sub-Alpine Molasse 1053, 1055, 1176
Sub-Penninic Nappes 1150, 1152
  Tauern Window 1152, 1154–1155
Sub-Silesian Unit 1190
  Palaeogene 1078–1081
subduction
  Avalonia 46, *47*
  Cadomian 121, 136, 146
  Cambrian 156
  Cretaceous
    Briançonnais fragment 1172–1173
    Penninic oceans 1145, 1171, 1176, 1178
    Valais Ocean 1172–1173
  Late Devonian–Early Carboniferous, Rhenohercynian Ocean 707
  Magura Ocean 1189
  Meliata Ocean 1187
  Neoproterozoic, Metabasite Belt 54
  Palaeotethys 1012, 1014
  Pangaean Rim 538
  Tertiary, Penninic Ocean 1176, 1178
  Variscan 424, 645–646
    Massif Central 483
    Rhenohercynian Basin 421
    Saxo-Thuringian Zone 447, 622
    Sudetes 626
    Teplá-Barrandian Unit 614
Subhercynian Cretaceous Basin 930, 945, 947–948
  coal 1406
subsidence
  Early Triassic 1013
  Late Jurassic–Early Cretaceous 1019, 1021
  Neogene, Great Hungarian Plain 1073
  North German Basin *1007*, 1008
  Paris Basin 858–859, 1013
Süddeutsche Großscholle *see* South German Triangle
Sudetes 60, *61*, *63*, 67–68, *69*, *70*, *122*, 496, *497*, *623*
  Cadomian basement 137–138, *142*
  Carboniferous volcanosedimentation 496–504
  Cenozoic
    faulting and graben development 1263–1265
    volcanism 1264–1265
  isotopic data **125**
  lithostratigraphy 624–625
  magmatism 326–328
  Ordovician *229*, 230–231
  Permian basins 559–560
  Silurian 288–289
  Variscan tectonic evolution 622–627
SUDETES seismic project 345
Sudetic Boundary Fault 622
Sudetic Marginal Fault 1263–1264, 1268
Sudetic Ophiolite, Devonian 402
Sudmerberg Formation 948
Šugov Phase 1214
Súl'ov Phase 1215
sulphate, Zechstein 572–573
sulphide minerals 1360–1361, 1363–1364
sulphur, resources, Cenozoic foreland basins 1402
Sulzfluh Limestone *893*, 894
Sulzfluh Nappe 1156
Sülzhayn Formation 549
Sundgau Gravel 1048
Süntel Formation 846
supergene deposits 1380, 1415–1418
superposition 6, 8
Suretta Nappe 1156
sutures
  Caledonian 331, 341, 342, 343, 345–346, 350–352, 354–358
  Variscan 417, 419, *445*
Suwałki Anorthosite Massif *34*, *35*, 36, 37, 1362
Suwałki Formation 184
Svatý Jan Volcanic Centre 272
Svecofennian crust 29, 31–32
Svecofennian Orogeny 36
Svecofenno-Karelian domain 35
Svecokarelian 29
Sveconorwegian Deformation Front *30*, 32, 33, 34
Sveconorwegian Orogeny 32, 33, 34, 342
Sveconorwegian Province 32–33
Světlík orthogneiss 78, 144, 145, 612
  age 612
Svratka Crystalline Unit 75

Swabian Alb 864–873, 1244
Swabian Basin 880, 881
Swabian Lineament 1248
Swabian Marl Basin 869
Swabian Realm *887*
SWAT seismic profile 356
Sweden, southern, Precambrian 28–34
Świebodzice Basin 402, 499, 625
Świerzawa Unit 688
Swiss Jura Molasse, Cenozoic 1056
Swiss Molasse Basin 1235, *1236*, 1237
Swiss Plateau Molasse 1055–1056
Switzerland
  Cenozoic, North Alpine Foreland Basin 1055
  Cretaceous 965, *966*, 967, 968–970, *971*, 975
  flysch *1046*, *1049*, 1051–1053
  Jura Mountains, Jurassic 880–889
  Permian 564–567
  Triassic, basin evolution 785–788
Syrenov Formation 499
Szarvaskő ophiolites 1187
Szarvaskő Unit 1211
Szczecin Depression, Palaeocene 1042
Szczecin Formation 1044
Szczecin Trough 855, 856
Szentlélek Formation *571*, 572, 582
Szinpetri Limestone 803
Szolnok Flysch Basin 1074–1075

Tabajd Anhydrite Formation *571*, 582
Tabular Jura 880, 881, *882*, 883, 886, 888
  Triassic sediments 785, 788
Tagyon Formation 800
talc
  production **1342**
  resources 1375, 1378–1379, 1411–1412
Tambach Formation 547, *548*
Tambo Nappe 1156
Tanne Zone 634, *635*
Tannheim Formation 974
Tannheim-Losenstein Basin 974, 1162, 1170
Tanowo Formation 1044
tantalum
  resources **1347**, 1378
    granite-related 1414
Tarntal Formation *893*, 894
Tartarian, palaeogeography *537*
Tarvis Breccia 553, 554, 581
Tasna Nappe 1156, 1172, 1173
Tatra mountains 1199
Tatra-Fatra Belt 1185, 1199–1200, 1206
Tatric High, Cretaceous 973–974
Tatric Superunit 1199
  tectonics 1201–1202
Tatricum 567, *568*, *570*, 581, 799, 897, *1186*
Tauern district, gold 1412
Tauern Window 79, *80*, 81
  Cambrian 187
  Carboniferous 480–482
  Glockner Nappe System 1159
  Jurassic 893, 894
  Matrei Zone 1159
  Miocene 1180
  Penninic nappes 1159
  Sub-Penninic nappes 1152, 1154–1155
Tauglboden Basin 895
Taunus
  Devonian 392, 393
  Late Ordovician–Silurian magmatism 695–697
  *see also* South Taunus Unit
Tavetsch Massif 1148, *1149*
Taveyannaz Formation 1053, 1055, 1146
tectonics, salt *see* halokinesis
tectonism
  Alpine
    Alps 1141–1181
    north of Alps 1233–1277
    Western Carpathians 1182–1217
  Cretaceous, Alps 1170–1173
  Jurassic
    Alps 1168–1170
    Poland 846–849
  North Armorican Massif 120–121
  North German Basin 1270–1275
  Permian, Alps 1168
  Permian–Cretaceous 999–1026
  Precambrian, Lithuania 42–43
  Quaternary, Poland 1265–1270
  Tertiary–present, Alps 1173–1181
  Triassic, Alps 1168
  Variscan 599–649
  Western Baltic Sea 1272–1273
Tegelen Formation 1313
tentaculitids, Devonian 388, 403
tephra, Eifel Volcanic Fields 1318–1333
Teplá Crystalline Complex 614, 675, *676*
Teplá Unit 674
Teplá-Barrandian Unit 60, *61*, 68, 70–75, *122*, *613*
  Cadomian basement 138–140, 142–144
  Cambrian 176–180, *189*, **193**
  Cambrian–Early Ordovician magmatism 674–675
  Carboniferous sedimentation 466–469, *507*
  Devonian 399–402, 614
  isostopic data **124**
  Ordovician 225–229
  Variscan tectonics 612–617
Teplice Formation *954*, 958
Teplice Rhyolites 721–722
Ternopil beds 1045
Terres Noires Formation 878, 880
Terschelling Basin 837, 839, 840, 841
Tertiary
  tectonics, Alps 1173–1181
  *see also* Cenozoic; Neogene; Palaeogene
Těšsín Formation 970, *972*
Tête des Econduits fluorite deposit 1384
Tethyan Domain, Jurassic 825–826, *830*, 890–900
Tethyan realm
  faunal migration, Triassic 807
  Triassic, stratigraphy and basin development 788–807
Tethys basins
  Slovenia 1093–1098
    Palaeogene 1098
    palaeomagnetism 1094
    sedimentation and stratigraphy 1094–1097
Tethys Ocean 14, 531, 536
  Cretaceous 926
  Triassic
    climate evolution 751–752
    sea-level change 752–753
    tectonic setting 756–757
tetrapods, Triassic 808
Thales of Miletus (*c.* 624–548/545 BC) 1
Thanetian transgression 1036
Tharandt Volcanic Complex 730
Thaya Nappe 693
Thaya Terrane 52, *53*, 144–145
  isostopic data **124**
Theophilus of Antioch (AD 115–181) 4
Therasburg Formation 52
Thimensart Formation 287
tholeiite
  Cambrian, Bohemian Massif 179
  Precambrian, Slawatycze series 38
  Teplá-Barrandian Unit 74
Thor-Tornquist Suture 25
Thule landbridge 1036, 1041
Thule volcanism 1036, 1040
Thuringia, Saxo-Thuringian Terrane, Silurian 270–271
Thuringian Basin, Cretaceous 946
Thuringian Facies 220, 257, 274, 464–465
Thuringian Forest Basin 460–462, *506*, 545, 547
  Rotliegend 547, *548*
  Stephanian–Early Permian magmatism 727–728
Thuringian Main Granite 450, 710
Thuringian Trough 1256
Thuringian–Franconian Slate Mountains 165–168, 959
Tiefenbach Formation 167–168
Tier d'Olne Formation 212
Tiglian Stage *1291*
  climate change 1288
tin, resources **1347**, 1362
  granite-related 1376
  placer deposits *1381*, 1389, 1410

Tinée High 873, 878
Tirolic Nappe System *1154*, 1160, *1161*, 1162–1163, 1169
Tirolic unit 892, *893*
Tisza Mega-unit *571*, 572, 583, 805–807
Triassic basin evolution 805–807
titanium, resources **1346**, 1362
placer deposits 1401, 1410
Tithonian
northern Germany *844*, 846
southeast France 879
southern Germany *866*, 871–872
Swiss Jura *887*, 888–889
Western Carpathian basins 899, 900
Tlumačov Formation 970, *972*
Toarcian
northern Germany 843–844, *844*
Poland 849
southeast France 877
southern Germany 865, *866*, 867
Swiss Jura 881, *882*, 883
Western Carpathian basins 900
Toarcian Ocean Anoxic Event 828, 831, 849, 850
Todtmoos Gneiss *607*, 608
Tommarp Mudstone Formation 267
Tor Formation 938–939
TOR seismic project **332**, 340, 343
Torgau-Doberlug Basin 466
Torgau-Doberlug Syncline 62, *64*, *129*, *141*, 625
backarc basin 125–127
Cambrian–Early Ordovician magmatism 682–683
*see also* Delitsch-Torgau-Doberlug Syncline
Tornaic Superunit 1210
Tornquist Fan 358
Tornquist Ocean 10, 155, 229, 305, 326–328, 352, *445*
closure 365, 366–367
Ordovician 365
reconstruction *11*
Silurian 256
Tornquist Suture, geophysical identification 350–352, 354
Tornquist Zone
heat-flow 350
seismic surveys **332**, 340, 342, 343, 358
Tornquist-Teisseyre Fault Zone 28, 309, 352, 357, 537, 1001, 1008, 1016
seismic surveys 346
Tornquist-Teisseyre Lineament 25, *229*, 537
Tournaisian
sedimentation
Namur-Dinant Basin 435–436
north and east Bohemia 473
North German Basin 428
Western Pomerania 429, *430*
Traischbachschiefer Formation 216
Trans-European Suture Zone 9, *34*, 37, 48, 265, *306*, 1258
seismic surveys **332**, 343, 345–346, 357–358
*see also* Tornquist Suture; Tornquist-Teisseyre Lineament
Trans-Scandinavian Igneous Belt *30*, *31*, 32, *34*
Transcarpathian Basin
Neogene 1066, 1067, 1084–1085, 1213
volcanism 1086, 1213
Transcarpathian Depression, Cenozoic *1043*
Transdanubian Range *1186*
Cretaceous 976–977
Permian 570–572, 582
Triassic 800–802
Triassic–Jurassic boundary 827
Transdanubian Superunit 1211–1212
transgression
Cenozoic
Harz Mountains 1257
Transylvanian Basin 1076, 1078
Cretaceous
Bohemian Cretaceous Basin 955, 956
North German Basin 947
Jurassic
Denmark 833–835
Netherlands 840–841
Polish Basin 850, 854–857
Western Carpathian basins 898–900
Neogene
Danube Basin 1065
Little Hungarian Plain 1070
North Sea Basin 1041–1042
Swiss Plateau Molasse 1056
Palaeogene
North Sea Basin 1036, 1039
Polish Lowland Basin 1042, 1044
Upper Rhine Graben 1045, 1047, 1048
Venetia 1089–1090
Permian–Triassic, Alps 1168
Silurian, Alps 277
Thanetian 1036
Triassic
Alps 1168
German Basin 771–772, 775–776, 777
Netherlands 782
Zechstein 573–580, 1013–1014
transgression–regression
Carboniferous, Auernig cyclothems 479, *480*
Cretaceous 924, 931–932, 935–937
Devonian 384–385, 387, 388, 389–391, 393, 396
Eocene–Oligocene, North Sea Basin 1040
Jurassic 829, 831
southeast France 876–879
Namurian and Westphalian 429
Neogene, Vienna Basin 1060, 1062
Silurian, Lithuania 262–263
Triassic, Swiss Jura 786–787
Transitional Beds, Dalmatia 1109, 1110, 1111
Transylvanian Basin 1075–1078
palaeogeography and tectonics 1075–1076
sedimentation and stratigraphy 1076, *1077*, 1078
volcanism 1078
Trasadingen Bed *882*, 883
Travenazes Formation *see* Raibl Formation
Třeboň Basin, Cretaceous 959
Trebovac Mountains 1112
Tregiovo Basin 555
Trégor-La Hague Terrane 106, 108–109, **111**, 116, 118–119, **119**, 120, 121
Trégor-North Cotentin Domain 55, 56, 57
Tremadocian
Alps 237
Ardennes Inliers 213
Bohemian Massif 228
Brabant Massif 208
Condroz Inlier 210
East European Platform 236
Franconia 224
Holy Cross Mountains 233, 234
northern Germany 217
Třenice Formation 226
Trento Platform 1087–1088
Tressenstein Formation 896
Treutlingen Formation *866*, 870
Triassic 749–808
basin evolution
Denmark 784
Germany and Poland 769–781
Hungary 800–807
Netherlands 781–784
Northern Calcareous Alps 788, *789*, 790
Southern Alps 790–798
Switzerland 785–788
Western Carpathians 798–799
biostratigraphy 760–766
mineralization 1392–1396
palaeoclimate, Tethys Ocean 751–752, 766–767
palaeogeography 757–760
palaeomagnetism 757–760
palaeontology 807–808
sea-level change 752–753
sequence stratigraphy 749, 767
tectonism 1012–1017
Alps 1168
Tethyan realm, stratigraphy and basin development 788–807

Triassic–Jurassic boundary 826–827
  platform drowning 894
Tribeč Mountains 1199, 1200
Tribotte Formation 208
Triebenreuth Formation 168
Trigonodusdolomit 786–787
trilobites
  Caledonides 307
  Cambrian 155
    Baltic Basin 182, 183, 184, 192
    Bohemia 176, 178–179, 188, 190
    Brunovistulian Terrane 170
    Franconian Forest 168, 188, 190
    Holy Cross Mountains 172–173, 174, 188, 190, 191, 192
    Lower 188
    Lublin-Podlaise Basin *185*, 186, 192
    Lusatia 163–165, 188
  Carboniferous 411
  Devonian 388
    Barrandian area 400, 401
    Moravia 398
  Ordovician *308*
    Alps 236
    Bohemian Massif 226, 227–228
    Brabant Massif 210
    Condroz Inlier 212
    Holy Cross Mountains 233, 234
    Saxothuringian Zone *221*, 222, 223, 224
    western Germany 215
  Silurian
    Austria 276, 277, 279, 282
    Montagne Noire 284
    Poland 265
    Proto-Alps Terrane 259
tripoli, resources, Late Alpine unconformities 1416
Třňa Formation 495
Tröbitz Formation 165
Trochitenkalk 786
Trogkofel Group 553–554
Tromm pluton *448*
trondhjemite
  Rand Granite 609
  Teplá-Barrandian Unit 675
Truse Formation 450, 710
Trusetal Group 628–629
Tsaté Nappe *1151*, 1157–1159, 1173
TTZ seismic project 345
Tubize Formation *159*, *160*, 161
Tuhár Phase 1214
Tüllinger Kalk 1048
tundra, Weichselian Cold Stage 1295
tungsten
  production **1342**
  resources **1347–1348**, 1362
    granite-related 1376, 1414
    porphyry type 1366
    vein-type 1374–1375
Turba Normal Fault *1148*, 1156, 1158, 1173–1174
turbidites, Carboniferous, Rhenish Massif 438, 439, *440*
Türkenkogel Formation *893*, 894
Turnaic Unit 495, *568*, *570*, 582
Turnaicum *see* Turnaic Unit
Turonian
  Austro-Alpine domain 975
  Bohemian Cretaceous Basin 957–958
  Danish Basin 937–938, *938*
  Gosau Group 978
  Helvetic basins 975
  Mid-Polish Trough 942
  North German Basin *943*, 944–945
Turonian–Coniacian boundary 925
Tuzla Basin, Neogene 1105, 1112–1113
Twannback Formation *887*, 889
Týnec Formation 468
Týřovice Conglomerate 178
Tyszowce Formation 857

Uebernthal-Gommern Unit 634, *635*
Uggwakalk Formation 236
Uggwaschiefer Formation 236
Ukraine
  Jurassic 846, 851, 852, 854, *855*, 857–858
  Western, Carpathians, Neogene 1084–1086
Ulmen Maar volcano 1323
  Tephra 1298, *1302*
Ultra-Helvetic Nappes 1150, 1178
  Cretaceous 966, 968, 970, 975
  Palaeogene 1036, 1049, 1050, 1053
Uniformitarianism 8–9
Unkersdorf Formation 563
Unterer Graptolithenschiefer Formation 271
Unterer (Kiesberter) Tonschiefer 215
uplift
  Cenozoic, Rhenish Massif 1242–1243
  Cretaceous
    Harz Block 948, 1257
    Mid-Polish Trough 1259–1261
  Jurassic
    Denmark 835
    Netherlands 837
  Mid-Jurassic 1017–1019
Upohlav conglomerates 1196
Upper Austro-Alpine tectonic units
  Permian 551–553
    Zechstein 580–581
Upper Brioverian Group 57, 58
Upper Coloured Molasse 1057
Upper Elbe fault zone 626
Upper Epizonal Units 483
Upper Freshwater Molasse 1055, 1056
Upper Gneiss Unit 483
Upper Graben Formation *838*, 839
Upper Marine Molasse 1055, 1056, 1057, 1176
Upper Penninic nappes 1157–1159
Upper Rhine Graben 1235
  Cenozoic 1045–1049
    palaeogeography and tectonics 1045, 1047
    sedimentation and stratigraphy *1046*, 1047–1049
    tectonics 1238–1241
  deformation 1240–1241
  graben formation 1240–1241
  Jurassic *866*, 869
  oil 1421, *1422*, 1423
  Quaternary sediment 1311, *1318*
  seismicity 1240
  structure 1238
  volcanism 1240
Upper Silesian Basin 473, 503–504, 852–854
  coal 1370–1371
Upper Silesian Massif 48–49, *50*, 51–52, 311
  Devonian 395–397
  Silurian 267
Upper Silesian zinc–lead mining district 1395
Ur supercontinent *22*, 23
uranium
  production **1342**
  resources **1347–1348**, *1359*, *1381*
    black shale type 1363–1364
    intermontane basins 1389
    red-bed type deposits 1390, 1392
    unconformity-related 1418–1419
    vein-like 1380
    vein-type 1377–1378, 1382–1383
Urgonian limestones 974
Uriconian Group *44*, 45, 46, *47*
urstromtal 1293, 1297, 1310
Usarzów Formation 174
Usseltal Formation *866*, 872
Ussher, Archbishop James (1581–1656) 4

Vaals Formation *949*, *950*, 951
Vahic Ocean 1198
Vahic Superunit *1186*, 1197–1198
Vahicum *see* Vahic Superunit
Val Colla Zone 1166
Val d'Illiez Formation 1053, 1055
Val Visdende Formation 237
Valais Ocean 1143, 1145, 1155, 1156, 1172–1173
Valaisian Nappes 1155
Valanginian
  Helvetic Basin 968
  Lower Saxony Basin 935
  Mid-Polish Trough 932, *933*
  sea-level change 924
Valsugana Thrust 1180
Vanzone antiform 1175

Vardar Ocean 1143
Vareš metallogenic province 1393
Variansmergel Formation *866*, 868
Varied Unit 77, 78, 79, 612
Variscan basement *330*
  geophysics 603
  seismic surveys **332**
Variscan Deformation Front 417, 858, *859*
Variscan Foreland Basin 639–640, *641*, 720
  coal 1367–1371
  ironstone 1371
  Permian basins 539–550
  sedimentation and magmatism 430 442, 720
Variscan Gondwana Terranes *2*
Variscan Orogen 75, *412*, *413*, 417–419, *666*, 667–669
  architecture 601
  basin evolution 417, 420, 484
  evolution *422*
  Externides 602–603, 633–636, 639–644
  Internides 483–496, *507*, 602–603, 606–627
  intramontane Permian basins 550–572
  Kossmat's classification 418, 601–602
  magmatism 424–428
  orogenic collapse 616, 617, 646–647
  strike-slip tectonics 647
Variscan Orogeny 13, 60, 66, 70, 411, 420, 599, 600
  Bohemian Massif 121, 123, 469–470
  Moldanubian Zone 469–482
  palaeogeography 420–424
Variscan tectonics 599–649
  generic model 648–649
  lithospheric plates 645
  orogenic collapse 616, 617, 646–647
  subduction 645–646
    *see also* subduction, Variscan
Variscides 46, *48*, *53*
  geodynamic model 648–649
  southeastern, Permian basins 563
  *see also* Variscan Orogen; Variscan tectonics
VARNET seismic project **332**, 337
Varnkevitz-Sandstein Formation 217
Várpalota Basin 1071
Vászoly Formation 802
Vaulruz Formation 1055
Vbrno Group 706
Veitsch Nappe 475, 1163
Vel'ká Fatra mountains 1199, *1200*
Velké Vbrno Nappe 501
Vel'ký Bok Unit 1202, 1206
Vendia supercontinent 10, *11*, *22*, 23, 26
Venediger Nappe System 1154–1155
Venetian Pre-Alps
  Palaeogene 1087–1092, *1094*
    palaeogeography 1087
    sedimentation and stratigraphy 1087–1091, *1094*
    tectonics 1087
    volcanism 1091–1092
Veneto Volcanic Province 1092
Veneto, western, Cenozoic 1087–1090
Vepor Sub-belt 1201
Vepor-Gemer Belt 1200–1201
Veporic Superunit 567, *568*, *570*, 581, 897, *1186*, 1201, 1206
  tectonics 1202–1204
Veporicum *see* Veporic Superunit
Vermenton Fault 858, *859*
Verona Hills 1088
Veřovice Formation 970, *972*
Versoyen Complex 1155
vertebrates
  Jurassic, Paris Basin 864
  Silurian 251, *252*
  Triassic 760, 807–808
Vesser Complex, Cambrian–Early Ordovician magmatism 681–682
Vesser Zone 162
Vestervik-Gotland block 38, *39*
Veszprém Marl 802
Veverská Bítiška Formation 563
Vichenet Formation 286
Vienna Basin 1212–1213
  Neogene 1060, 1062–1063
  oil and gas *1422*, 1424–1425
Vieux-Moulins de Thilay Formation 213–214
Viganvár Limestone 805, *806*
Vijlen Member *949*, *950*, 951
Viking Graben 1017
Villé Unit 633
Villingen Formation *887*, 888
Vindelician landmass 865, 867
Vinice Formation 227–228
Vinodol 1110
Virgloria Formation 788, *789*
Visé-Maastricht sedimentation area 434–435
Visean
  Black Forest, tectonic evolution *610*, 611
  cyclothems 417
  magmatism 428
  palaeogeography 421
  sedimentation
    Campine Basin 437
    Namur-Dinant Basin 435–436
    North German Basin 428
    Rhenish Massif 438
    Western Pomerania 429
Vissoul Formation 286
Vitebsk Granulite Domain *34*
Vitrival-Bruyère Formation 212
Vittel Fault 858, *859*
Vitznau Formation 968, *969*
Vlieland Basin 839, 840
Vlieland Sandstone Formation 841
Vogelsberg, volcanism 1047, 1255, *1256*
Vogtendorf Formation 224
Vogtland
  Cambrian 169, *189*
  Devonian 403
  Ordovician *221*, 223
Voirons Flysch 1053
volcanic field analysis 1320–1321
volcanism
  Caledonian 324–325
  Cambrian
    Bohemian Massif 179–180
    Mid-German Crystalline High 161
  Carboniferous 427–428
  Cenozoic
    Croatia and north Bosnia 1105–1106
    North Sea Basin 1040, 1042
    Polish Lowlands Basin 1044
    Slovenian Paratethys basins 1102
    Sudetes 1264–1265
  Central Atlantic Magmatic Province 826, 828
  Devonian
    Moravia 399
    Rhenish Massif 702–703
      Eastern, 393–394
    Saxo-Thuringian Zone 403, 619
  Devonian-Carboniferous, Rhenohercynian 431, 703–704
  Jurassic
    Denmark 832, 835
    Netherlands 840, 842
  Kaiserstuhl, Upper Rhine Graben 1240, 1244
  Late Precambrian, eastern Poland 37–38
  Neogene
    East Slovak Basin 1068
    metallogenesis 1402–1405
    Pannonian Basin System 1213
    Transcarpathian Basin 1086
    Transylvanian Basin 1078
  Neoproterozoic, Saxo-Thuringian Zone *64*
  Ordovician, Bohemian Massif 228–229
  Palaeogene, Venetian Pre-Alps 1091–1092
  Polish Basin 540, 1044
  Precambrian, Armorican Massif 56–57, 58
  Quaternary, Eifel volcanic fields 1318–1333
  Rotliegend
    Northern Germany 539
    Thuringian Forest Basin 547
  Saint-Brieuc Terrane 113–114
  Silurian
    Graz area 282–283
    Prague Basin 272

South German Triangle *1246*, 1249
Stephanian–Early Permian 723–732
Teplá-Barrandian Unit 74–75
Thule 1036, 1040
Triassic 752
Hungary 802
Southern Alps 797
Upper Rhine Graben 1240
Variscan, northern Alps 484
Vogelsberg 1255, *1256*
Vosges Basin 471–472
Westphalian, Altenberg-Teplice Caldera 721–722
Volhynian Series 37, 38
Volhyno-Podolian Plate, Cenozoic *1043*, 1044–1045
Volovec Unit 1204
Volpriehausen Sandstone 772, 782
Vosges Mountains 216, *459*, *631*, 1238, *1239*
Cambrian 181, *182*
Late Devonian–Early Carboniferous magmatism 712–713
Northern, Carboniferous sedimentation 457
southern 470–472
Variscan evolution 633
Vosník Conglomerate 179
Vöstenhof-Kaintaleck Nappe 1163
Vrchlabí Formation 559
Vrica section, Pleistocene GSSP 1287
Vysoká succession 1205–1206

Wacken-Dömnitz warm stage 1292–1293
Wägital Flysch Nappe 1053, 1158
Waldenburg Member *883*, 884
Waldershof Gneiss 456
Walentowa Phase 1214
Wallonian Basin 437–438
coal 1367
Wang Formation 975
Wanne Formation 158, *159*
Warren House Formation 46, *47*
Warsaw-Berlin Urstromtal 1297
Warsaw-Torun-Eberswalde Urstromtal 1297
Wartanian Glaciation 1293
Wartenstein Gneiss 443, 633
Warthe substage 1293–1294
Waschberg-Ždánice Zone 1190
Cretaceous 964, *973*
Wasserburg Basin, Cretaceous 963–964
Waulsortian reefs *431*, 435, 436, 637
Wealden facies
Lower Saxony Basin 935
Prignitz and Altmark-Fläming basins 936
Wedelsandstein Formation *866*, 867
Weesenstein Group 62, 131, *132*, 133, *134*, 700
Wehr volcanic complex *1323*, 1326–1327
Weichselian Cold Stage 1295, 1297–1298, *1299*, *1301*
mammals 1300
Weichselian icesheet 14
Weinheim-Waldmichelbach Schist Zone *631*, 632
Weinsberg Pluton 716
Weissenstein Member 881, *882*
Weissliegend 573, 575
Weiteveen Formation *838*, 840, 841
Weitwies Member 1051
Wellengebirge 785–786
Wenlock *252*, 253
Austria 277–279
Bornholm 267–268
Brabant Massif 286
Carnic Alps 281
Franconian Terrane 268, 269
Lithuania 261–263
Montagne Noire 284
Poland 263, 266–267
Prague Basin 272, *273*, 276
sea-level change 250
Werfen Formation 581, 788, *789*, 791, 794, 1167
Werkendam Formation 837, *838*
Werna Formation 549
Werner, Abraham Gottlieb (1749–1817) 6–7
Werra Anhydrite *574*, 576–577
Werra cycle 572, 573, *574*, *575*, 576
Weschnitz Pluton *448*
Weschnitz-Heidelberg-Tromm Intrusive Complex 632
West African Craton 103, 117, 120, 133, 145
West Bohemian Shear Zone *613*, 616
West Eifel volcanic field 1321–1323
West Lithuanian Granulite Domain 38–43, *39*
West Mecklenburg Basin 545, *546*
West Netherlands Basin, Jurassic 837, *838*, 839, 841
West Orkney Basin, seismic survey 335–336
West Pomerania, Cretaceous 948–949
West Sudetes 498–499, 624
West Sudetic Island 956, 957
West Thuringian Fault 450, 547
Western Asian Mountain Range 538
Western Bohemian Basin, coal 1388
Western Carpathian Crystalline Zone
central 490–491, 567, 581–582
Inner 569–570, 582
Western Carpathians
Carboniferous basins 488, 490–496
Central 1183, *1184*, 1198–1201
Cretaceous 973–974
Gosau Group 978, *979*
synorogenic 974
Jurassic 897–898
tectonic evolution 1208–1210
crust 1216
evolution 1185–1189
External 1182–1183, *1184*
Internal *1184*, 1185, 1210–1212
tectonic evolution 1212
Jurassic 897–900
lithosphere 1215–1216
neotectonics 1216
Outer
Cretaceous 966, 970, *972*, 978
Jurassic 896–897
palaeogeography 1185, 1187, *1188*, 1189
Permian 581
siderite and magnesite deposits 1386–1387
subdivision 1181–1185
tectonics *1142*, 1182–1217
Cretaceous 1214–1215
Jurassic 1214
Permian–Triassic 1213–1214
Tertiary–present 1215
Triassic 798–799, *800*
Triassic–Jurassic boundary 827
Western Gate *see* Burgundy Gate
Western Moldanubian Terrane, Cambrian–Early Ordovician magmatism 679
Westphalian 508
magmatism 720–723
sedimentation
Belgium 434
Erzgebirge Basin 466
North German Basin 429
Poland 442
Saale Basin 461
Sudetes 499, 503
Western Pomerania 429
Wetterstein Complex 799, 803
Wetzldorf Group 271
Wielkopolska Ridge 848, 855
Wielkopolska Subgroup 540
Wiesbachtal Mylonite 443
Wiesbaden Formation 1048
Wiese-Wehra diatexites *607*, 608
Wiese-Wehra Nappe, Late Devonian–Early Carboniferous magmatism 712
Wildenfels Complex 457, 463
Devonian 403
Ordovician *221*, 224
Wildenstein Formation 168
wildflysch 1053, 1196
Wildhorn nappe 1148, *1149*
Wildseeloder Unit 282
WINCH seismic profile **332**, 336, 356
Wippra Unit 443–444
Late Ordovician–Silurian magmatism 696, 697
WIRE seismic profile **332**, 336, 356
Wiśniówka Formation 174
Wissenbach Shale 393, 394

Włodawa Formation 184
Wohlgeschichtete Kalk Formation *866*, 870
Wojcieszów Limestone 230
Wolayer facies 277–278
Wolayerkalk Formation 236, 277
Wolfendorn Nappe 1154
wood, fossil
  Cretaceous, Liège-Limburg Basin 923
  Jurassic, Paris Basin 864
Wordian, palaeogeography *537*
Wronine Formation 970, *972*
Wuerttemburgica Sandstone 845
Wunsiedel Gneiss 456
Wutach Formation *866*, 868
Wydryszów Beds 266
Wyrzeka Formation 540

Xanthus of Lydia (*c*. 480 BC) 1
Xenophanes of Colophon (540–510 BC) 1

Ybbsitz Klippen Zone 970, *973*, 1159
Younger Clay Halite *575*, 580
Younger Dryas Stadial 1298
Younger Granites 717, 718
Younger Halite *575*, 580
Younger Intrusive Complex 722
Ypresian, Belgium *1038*, 1039–1040

Žacléř Formation 499
Zagaje Formation 849
Zahořany Formation 228
Zala Basin 1068, *1069*, 1072–1073
Zalesie Formation 233, 234, *235*
Žarnov Phase 1214
Żarnowiec Formation 182
Zbrza Anticline 266
Ždánice Unit 1190
Zechstein 535, 538, 586
  Belgium 549
  evaporite 999, 1001, *1002*
    cyclicity 532, 572–580, 1013
    resources 1391
    seismic survey 340–341
  halokinesis 831, 832, 999, 1001
  Netherlands 550
  Polish Basin *1004*
  sequence stratigraphy 573–575, *574*, *575*
  southeastern Variscides 563
  transgression 573–580
  Variscan intermontane basins 580–583
Zechstein Basin 572–580, 1013
Zechstein Limestone 573, 574, 576
Zechstein Sea 572, 573, 1013
Zechstein–Buntsandstein boundary 751
Zeitz Phase 1293
Železné Hory Mountains 72
  Cambrian 179
  Devonian 402
Zellerndorf Formation 1057
Zementmergel Formation *866*, 871, 975
Zementstein Formation 968, *969*
Zemplín Unit 1212
Zemplinic Unit 495, 567, *568*, *570*, 581–582
Zemplinicum *see* Zemplinic Unit
Zeno (*c*. 336–264 BC) 3
zeolite 1405
Zermatt-Saas Zone *1151*, 1157–1159, 1173
Zeven Wegen Member *949*, *950*, 951
Žiar mountains 1199
zinc
  production **1342**
  resources **1346**, **1349–1351**,
    Alpine type/MVT 1395–1396
    arc-related 1402–1404
    carbonate-hosted 1418
    fault zones 1427
    granite-related 1414
    Rammelsberg type 1365–1366
    Silesian type/MVT 1395
    vein-type, 1371–1372, 1377, 1382–1384, 1418
    VMS, SMS, Kieslager type 1360–1361
    VMS type 1363
Zinnwald Granite 722–723
Zinnwald tin deposit 1376
zirconium, resources, placer deposits 1401
Žitec-Hluboš Formation 176
Zlambach Marl Formation 827
Zlatna Unit 898
Zlatno porphyry-skarn copper deposit 1404
Zliechov Basin 974, 1206
Zliechov Phase 1214
Zliechov succession 1205
Zone Houillère 1157
  coal 1388
Zu Limestone 798, 826
Zuhánya Limestone 805, *806*
Zuidwal volcanic dome 840, 842, 864
Zulová granite 706
Zurich Formation *838*, 839
Zurich Stadial 1308
Zwethau Formation 164, *166*
  palaeontology 188
Zwickau Phase 1291
Zwickau subbasin 465–466
Zwickau-Oelsnitz, coal mining 1388